Small Business Sourcebook

ISSN 0883-3397

Small Business Sourcebook

The Entrepreneur's Resource

FORTY-SECOND EDITION

Volume 5

General Small Business Resources
(Includes State Sections)

(Entries 36040-44620)

Holly M. Selden
Project Editor

Small Business Sourcebook, 42nd edition

Project Editor: Holly M. Selden

Editorial Support Services: Pranav Kokate

Composition and Electronic Prepress: Carolyn Roney

Manufacturing: Rita Wimberley

© 2025 Gale, a Cengage Company

ALL RIGHTS RESERVED. No part of this work covered by the copyright herein may be reproduced, transmitted, stored, or used in any form or by any means graphic, electronic, or mechanical, including but not limited to photocopying, recording, scanning, digitizing, taping, Web distribution, information networks, or information storage and retrieval systems, except as permitted under Section 107 or 108 of the 1976 United States Copyright Act, without the prior written permission of the publisher.

This publication is a creative work fully protected by all applicable copyright laws, as well as by misappropriation, trade secret, unfair competition, and other applicable laws. The authors and editors of this work have added value to the underlying factual material herein through one or more of the following: unique and original selection, coordination, expression, arrangement, and classification of the information.

> For product information and technology assistance, contact us at
> **Gale Customer Support, 1-800-877-4253.**
> For permission to use material from this text or product,
> submit all requests online at **www.cengage.com/permissions**.
> Further permissions questions can be emailed to
> **permissionrequest@cengage.com**.

While every effort has been made to ensure the reliability of the information presented in this publication, Gale, part of Cengage Group, does not guarantee the accuracy of the data contained herein. Gale accepts no payment for listing and inclusion in the publication of any organization, agency, institution, publication, service, or individual does not imply endorsement of the editors or publisher. Errors brought to the attention of the publisher and verified to the satisfaction of the publisher will be corrected in future editions.

Gale, part of Cengage Group
5191 Natorp Blvd.
Mason, OH 45040

978-1-5358-7663-6 (set)
978-1-5358-7664-3 (vol. 1)
978-1-5358-7665-0 (vol. 2)
978-1-5358-7666-7 (vol. 3)
978-1-5358-7667-4 (vol. 4)
978-1-5358-7668-1 (vol. 5)
978-1-5358-7669-8 (vol. 6)

ISSN 0883-3397

This title is also available as an e-book.
978-1-5358-7670-4
Contact your Gale sales representative for ordering information.

Contents

Volume 1
Introduction vii
User's Guide. ix
List of Small Business Profiles xv
Standard Industrial Classification (SIC) Codes for
 Profiled Small Businesses xix
Licensing Assistance Programs xxxiii
Guide to Publishers xxxvii
Glossary lxxxix

Small Business Profiles 1

Provides start-up information, associations and other organizations, educational programs, directories of educational programs, reference works, sources of supply, statistical sources, trade periodicals, video/audio media, trade shows and conventions, consultants, franchises and business opportunities, computerized databases, computer systems/software, libraries, and research centers.

Volume 2
Introduction vii
User's Guide ix
List of Small Business Profiles xv
Standard Industrial Classification (SIC) Codes for
 Profiled Small Businesses xix

Small Business Profiles 623

Volume 3
Introduction vii
User's Guide ix
List of General Small Business Topics xv

General Small Business Topics. 1253

Includes associations and other organizations, educational programs, directories of educational programs, reference works, sources of supply, statistical sources, trade periodicals, video/audio media, trade shows and conventions, consultants, computerized databases, computer systems/software, libraries, and research centers.

Volume 4
Introduction vii
User's Guide ix
List of General Small Business Topics xv

General Small Business Topics. 1827

Volume 5
Introduction vii
User's Guide ix

State Listings. 2393

Offers sources of small business assistance by state, territory, and Canadian province, including small business development centers, small business assistance programs, SCORE offices, better business bureaus, chambers of commerce, minority business assistance programs, financing and loan programs, procurement assistance programs, incubators/research and technology parks, educational programs, legislative assistance, small business development consultants, and publications.

Volume 6
Introduction vii
User's Guide ix

State Listings. 2951

Federal Government Assistance 3111

Lists U.S. federal government agencies and offices, including regional, branch, and district offices, which focus on small business issues, programs, assistance, and policy.

Master Index 3167

Introduction

The appeal of small business ownership remains perpetually entrenched in American culture as one of the most viable avenues for achieving the American Dream. To many entrepreneurs, going into business for themselves represents financial independence, an increased sense of identity and self-worth, and the fulfillment of personal goals. Small business owners strive to make their mark in today's competitive marketplace by establishing healthy businesses that can, over time, become legacies handed down from one generation to the next. Entrepreneurs from each generation tackle the obstacles and adversities of the current business and economic climate to test their business savvy and generate opportunities. Today's entrepreneurs face many of the problems of their predecessors, as well as some distinctly new challenges.

With the rightsizing, downsizing, and reorganization of corporate America, many individuals have decided to confront the risks of developing and operating their own businesses. Small business ownership is rapidly becoming a viable alternative to what is perceived as an equally unstable corporate environment. These entrepreneurs, many of whom have firsthand experience with the problems and inefficiencies inherent in today's large corporations, seek to improve upon an archaic business model and to capitalize on their own ingenuity and strengths. Led by their zeal, many would-be entrepreneurs let their desire, drive, and determination overshadow the need for business knowledge and skill. Ironically, aids in obtaining these components of entrepreneurial success are widely available, easily accessible, and often free of charge.

Small Business Sourcebook (*SBS*) is a six-volume annotated guide to nearly 17,000 listings of live and print sources of information designed to facilitate the start-up, development, and growth of specific small businesses, as well as more than 19,500 similar listings on general small business topics. An additional 12,500 state-specific listings and nearly 1,100 U.S. federal government agencies and offices specializing in small business issues, programs, and assistance are also included. *SBS* covers more than 300 specific small business profiles more than 100 general small business topics.

Features of This Edition

This edition of *Small Business Sourcebook* has been revised and updated, incorporating thousands of changes to names, addresses, contacts, and descriptions of listings from the previous edition. We have also added several hundred podcasts that will help users better understand topics on entrepreneurship and small business ownership.

Contents and Arrangement

The geographical scope of *SBS* encompasses the United States and Canada, with expanded coverage for resources pertaining to international trade and for resources that have a U.S. or Canadian distributor or contact. Internet sites that are maintained outside of the U.S. and Canada are also included if they contain relevant information for North American small businesses. Resources that do not relate specifically to small businesses are generally not included.

The information presented in *SBS* is grouped within four sections: Specific Small Business Profiles, General Small Business Topics, State Listings, and Federal Government Assistance. Detailed outlines of these sections may be found in the Users' Guide following this Introduction. Also included is a Master Index to Volumes 1 through 6.

Specific Small Business Profiles This section includes the following types of resources: start-up information, associations and other organizations, educational programs, directories of educational programs, reference works, sources of supply, statistical sources, trade periodicals, videos and podcasts, trade shows and conventions, consultants, franchises, and business opportunities, computerized databases, computer systems/software, Internet databases, libraries, and research centers. All resources are arranged by business type. Entries range from Accounting Service to Word Processing Service, and include such businesses as Cannabis Dispensaries, Computer Consulting, Food Trucks, and Web Site Design.

General Small Business Topics This section offers such resources as associations, books, periodicals, articles, pamphlets, educational programs, directories of educational

INTRODUCTION

programs, trade shows and conventions, consultants, computerized databases, Internet databases, software, libraries, and research centers. All resources in this section are arranged alphabetically by business topic.

State Listings Entries include government, academic, and commercial agencies and organizations, as well as select coverage of relevant state-specific publications. Listings are arranged alphabetically by state, territory, and Canadian province. Some examples include small business development consultants, SCORE offices, financing and loan programs, better business bureaus, and chambers of commerce.

Federal Government Assistance Listings Entries include federal organizations and agencies specializing in small business issues, programs, assistance, and policy. Listings are arranged alphabetically by U.S. government agency or office; regional or branch offices are listed alphabetically by state.

Master Index All entries in Volumes 1 through 6 are arranged in one alphabetic index for convenience.

Entries in SBS include (as appropriate and available):

- Organization, institution, or product name
- Contact information, including contact name, address and phone, toll-free, and fax numbers
- Author/editor, date(s), and frequency
- Availability, including price
- Brief description of purpose, services, or content
- Company and/or personal E-mail addresses
- Web site addresses

SBS also features the following:

Guide to Publishers—An alphabetic listing of nearly 1,000 companies, associations, institutions, and individuals that publish the periodicals, directories, guidebooks, and other publications noted in the Small Business Profiles and General Topics sections. Users are provided with full contact information, including address, phone, fax, and e-mail and URL when available. The Guide to Publishers facilitates contact with publishers and provides a one-stop resource for valuable information.

Method of Compilation

SBS was compiled by consulting small business experts and entrepreneurs, as well as a variety of resources, including direct contact with the associations, organizations, and agencies through Internet research or materials provided by those listees; government resources; and data obtained from other relevant Gale directories. SBS was reviewed by a team of small business advisors, all of whom have numerous years of expertise in small business counseling and identification of small business information resources. The last and perhaps most important resource we utilize is direct contact with our readers, who provide valuable comments and suggestions to improve our publication. SBS relies on these comprehensive market contacts to provide today's entrepreneurs with relevant, current, and accurate information on all aspects of small business.

Available in Electronic Formats

Licensing. Small Business Sourcebook is available for licensing. The complete database is provided in a fielded format and is deliverable on various forms of media. For more information, contact Gale's Business Development Group at 1-800-877-GALE, or visit our website at www.gale.com.

Comments and Suggestions Welcome

Associations, agencies, business firms, publishers, and other organizations that provide assistance and information to the small business community are encouraged to submit material about their programs, activities, services, or products. Comments and suggestions from users of this directory are also welcomed and appreciated. Please contact:

Project Editor
Small Business Sourcebook
27555 Executive Dr., Ste. 270
Farmington Hills, MI 48331
Gale, part of Cengage Group
URL: www.gale.com

User's Guide

Small Business Sourcebook (*SBS*) provides information in a variety of forms and presentations for comprehensive coverage and ease of use. The directory contains four parts within six volumes:

- Specific Small Business Profiles
- General Small Business Topics
- State Listings
- Federal Government Assistance

Information on specific businesses is arranged by type of business; the many general topics that are of interest to the owners, operators, or managers of all small businesses are grouped in a separate section for added convenience. Users should consult the various sections to benefit fully from the information *SBS* offers. For example, an entrepreneur with a talent or interest in the culinary arts could peruse a number of specific small business profiles, such as Restaurant, Catering Service, Cooking School, Specialty/Gourmet Food/Wine Shop, Food Truck, Healthy Restaurant, or Candy/Chocolate Shop. Secondly, the General Small Business Topics section could be consulted for any applicable subjects, such as Service Industry, Retailing, Franchising, and other relevant topics. Then, the appropriate state within the State Listings section would offer area programs and offices providing information and support to small businesses, including venture capital firms and small business development consultants. Finally, the Federal Government Assistance section could supply relevant government offices, such as procurement contacts.

Features Included in Volumes 1 and 2

List of Small Business Profiles. This list provides an alphabetic outline of the small businesses profiled. The page number for the beginning of each profile is indicated.

Standard Industrial Classification (SIC) Codes for Profiled Small Businesses. This section lists four-digit SIC codes and corresponding classification descriptions for the small businesses profiled in this edition. The SIC system, which organizes businesses by type, is a product of the Statistical Policy Division of the U.S. Office of Management and Budget. Statistical data produced by government, public, and private organizations is usually categorized according to SIC codes, thereby facilitating the collection, comparison, and analysis of data as well as providing a uniform method for presenting statistical information. Hence, knowing the SIC code for a particular small business increases access and the use of a variety of statistical data from many sources.

Guide to Publishers. This resource lists alphabetically the companies, associations, institutions, and individuals that publish the periodicals, directories, guidebooks, and other publications noted in the "Small Business Profiles" and "General Topics" sections. Users are provided with full contact information, including address, phone, fax, and e-mail and URL when available. The "Guide" facilitates contact with publishers and provides a one-stop resource for valuable information.

Glossary of Small Business Terms. This glossary defines nearly 400 small business terms, including financial, governmental, insurance, procurement, technical, and general business definitions. Cross-references and acronyms are also provided.

Small Business Profiles A-Z. More than 300 small business profiles are represented in volumes 1 and 2. Profiles are listed alphabetically by business type. Each profile may contain up to sixteen subheadings that correlate to a resource type; entries within are listed alphabetically. These resource types are detailed below:

- *Start-up Information*—Includes periodical articles, books, manuals, book excerpts, kits, and other sources of information. Entries offer title; publisher; address; phone, fax, toll-free numbers; company e-mail and URL addresses; and a description. Bibliographic data is provided for cited periodical articles whenever possible.

- *Associations and Other Organizations*—Includes trade and professional associations whose members gather and disseminate information of interest to small business owners. Entries offer the association's

Small Business Sourcebook • 42nd Edition

USER'S GUIDE

name; address; phone, toll-free and fax numbers; company e-mail address; contact name; purpose and objective; a description of membership; telecommunication services; and a listing of its publications, including publishing frequency.

- **Educational Programs**—Includes university and college programs, schools, training opportunities, association seminars, correspondence courses, and other educational programs. Entries offer name of program or institution, sponsor name, address, phone, toll-free and fax numbers, e-mail and URL addresses; and description of program.

- **Directories of Educational Programs**—Includes directories and other publications that list educational programs. Entries offer name of publication; publisher name, address, and phone, toll-free and fax numbers; editor; frequency or date of publication; price; and description of contents, including directory arrangement and indexes.

- **Reference Works**—Includes handbooks, manuals, textbooks, guides, directories, dictionaries, encyclopedias, and other published reference materials. Entries offer name of publication; publisher name, address, and phone, toll-free and fax numbers; e-mail and URL addresses; and, when available, name of author or editor, publication year or frequency, and price. A brief description is often featured.

- **Sources of Supply**—Includes buyer's guides, directories, special issues of periodicals, and other publications that list sources of equipment, supplies, and services related to the operation of the profiled small business. Entries offer publication name; publisher name, address, and phone, toll-free and fax numbers; e-mail and URL addresses; and, when available, editor's name, frequency or publication year, and price. A brief description of the publication, including directory arrangement and indexes, is often provided.

- **Statistical Sources**—Includes books, reports, pamphlets, and other sources of statistical data of interest to an owner, operator or manager of the profiled small business, such as wage, salary, and compensation data; financial and operating ratios; prices and costs; demographics; and other statistical information. Entries offer publication/data source name; publisher (if applicable); address; phone, toll-free and fax numbers of data source; publication date or frequency; and price. A brief description of the publication/data source is often provided.

- **Trade Periodicals**—Includes trade journals, newsletters, magazines, and other serials that offer information about the management and operation of the profiled small business. Such periodicals often contain industry news; trends and developments; reviews; articles about new equipment and supplies; and other information related to business operations. Entries offer publication name; publisher name, address, phone, toll-free and fax numbers, and e-mail and URL addresses; editor name; publication frequency; and price. A brief description of the publication's content is also included, when known.

- **Video/Audio Media**—Includes videos, podcasts, and other audiovisual media offering information on the profiled small business. Entries offer program title; creator or distributor name, address, phone, toll-free and fax numbers, and e-mail and URL addresses; description of program; price; and format(s).

- **Trade Shows and Conventions**—Includes tradeshows, exhibitions, expositions, conventions, and other industry meetings that provide prospective and existing business owners with the opportunity to meet and exchange information with their peers, review commercial exhibits, establish business or sales contacts, and attend educational programs. Entries offer event name; sponsor or management company name, address, phone, toll-free and fax numbers, and e-mail and URL addresses; a description of the event, including audience, frequency, principal exhibits, and dates and locations of event for as many years ahead as provided by the event's sponsor.

- **Consultants**—Includes consultants and consulting organizations that provide services specifically related to the profiled small business. Entries offer individual consultant or consulting organization name, address, and phone, toll-free and fax numbers; company and individual e-mail addresses; and a brief description of consulting services. (For e-mail and URL addresses, see the Small Business Development Consultants subheadings in the State Listings section in Volume 2.)

- **Franchises and Business Opportunities**—Includes companies granting franchise licenses for enterprises falling within the scope of the profiled small business, as well as other non-franchised business opportunities that operate within a given network or system. Entries offer franchise name, address, phone, toll-free and fax numbers, and e-mail and URL addresses, as well as a description of the franchise or business opportunity, which has been expanded whenever possible to include the number of existing franchises, the founding date of the franchise, franchise fees, equity capital requirements, royalty fees, any managerial assistance offered, and available training.

- **Computerized Databases**—Includes diskettes, magnetic tapes, CD-ROMs, online systems, and other computer-readable databases. Entries offer database name; producer name, address, phone, toll-free and fax numbers, e-mail and URL addresses; description; and available format(s), including vendor name.

(Many university and public libraries offer online information retrieval services that provide searches of databases, including those listed in this category.)

- *Computer Systems/Software*—Includes software and computerized business systems designed to assist in the operation of the profiled small business. Entries offer name of the software or system; publisher name, address, phone, toll-free and fax numbers; price; and description.

- *Libraries*—Includes libraries and special collections that contain material especially applicable to the profiled small business. Entries offer library or collection name; parent organization (where applicable); address; phone, toll-free and fax numbers; e-mail and URL addresses; contact name and title; scope of collection; and description of holdings, subscriptions, and services.

- *Research Centers*—Includes university-related and independently operated research institutes and information centers that generate, through their research programs, data related to the operation of the profiled small business. Also listed are associations and other business-related organizations that conduct research programs. Entries offer name of organization; address; phone, toll-free and fax numbers; company web site address; contact name and personal e-mail; a description of principal fields of research or services; publications, including title and frequency; and related conferences.

Features Included in Volumes 3 and 4

General Small Business Topics. This section offers chapters on different topics in the operation of any small business, for example, venture capital and other funding, or compensation. Chapters are listed alphabetically by small business topic; entries within each chapter are arranged alphabetically, within up to 14 subheadings, by resource type:

- *Associations and Other Organizations*—Includes trade and professional associations that gather and disseminate information of interest to small business owners. Entries offer the association's name; address; phone, toll-free and fax numbers; organization e-mail and URL addresses; contact name; purpose and objectives; a description of membership; telecommunication services; and a listing of its publications, including publishing frequency.

- *Educational Programs*—Includes university and college programs, schools, training opportunities, association seminars, correspondence courses, and other educational programs. Entries offer name of program or institution, sponsor name, address, phone, toll-free and fax numbers, e-mail and URL addresses, and description of program.

- *Directories of Educational Programs*—Includes directories and other publications that list educational programs. Entries offer name of publication; publisher name, address, phone, toll-free and fax numbers, and e-mail and URL addresses; editor; frequency or date of publication; price; and description of contents, including arrangement and indexes.

- *Reference Works*—Includes articles, handbooks, manuals, textbooks, guides, directories, dictionaries, encyclopedias, and other published reference materials. Entries offer title of article, including bibliographic information; name of publication; publisher name, address, phone, toll-free and fax numbers, and e-mail and URL addresses; and, when available, name of author or editor, publication year or frequency, and price. A brief description is often featured.

- *Sources of Supply*—Includes buyer's guides, directories, special issues of periodicals, and other publications that list sources of equipment, supplies, and services. Entries offer publication name; publisher name, address, phone, toll-free and fax numbers, and e-mail and URL addresses; editor's name, frequency or publication year, price, and a brief description of the publication, when available.

- *Statistical Sources*—Includes books, reports, pamphlets, and other sources of statistical data of interest to an owner, operator, or manager of a small business, such as wage, salary, and compensation data; financial and operating ratios; prices and costs; demographics; and other statistical information. Entries offer publication/data source name; publisher (if applicable); address; phone, toll-free and fax numbers of data source; publication date or frequency; and price. A brief description is often provided.

- *Trade Periodicals*—Includes journals, newsletters, magazines, and other serials. Entries offer name of publication; publisher name, address, phone, toll-free and fax numbers, and e-mail and URL addresses; and name of editor, frequency, and price. A brief description of the periodical's content is included when known.

- *Video/Audio Media*—Includes videos, podcasts, and other audiovisual media. Entries offer program title; distributor name, address, phone, toll-free and fax numbers, and e-mail and URL addresses; price; description of program; and format(s).

- *Trade Shows and Conventions*—Includes tradeshows, exhibitions, expositions, seminars, and conventions. Entries offer event name; sponsor or management company name, address, phone, toll-free and fax numbers, and e-mail and URL addresses; frequency of event; and dates and locations of the event for as many years ahead as known.

USER'S GUIDE

- **Consultants**—Includes consultants and consulting organizations. Entries offer individual consultant or consulting organization name, address, and phone, toll-free and fax numbers; company and individual e-mail addresses; and a brief description of consulting services. (See also Consultants in the State Listings section.)
- **Computerized Databases**—Includes diskettes, CD-ROMs, magnetic tape, online systems and other computer-readable databases. Entries offer database name; producer, address, phone, toll-free and fax numbers, and e-mail and URL addresses; description; and available format(s), including vendor name. (Many university and public libraries offer online information retrieval services that provide searches of databases, including those listed in this category.)
- **Computer Systems/Software**—Includes software and computerized business systems. Entries offer name of the software or system; publisher name, address, phone, toll-free and fax numbers, and e-mail and URL addresses; price; and description.
- **Libraries**—Includes libraries and special collections that contain material applicable to the small business topic. Entries offer library or collection name, parent organization (where applicable), address, phone and fax numbers, e-mail and URL addresses, scope of collection, and description of holdings and services.
- **Research Centers**— Includes university-related and independently operated research institutes and information centers that generate, through their research programs, data related to specific small business topics. Entries offer name of organization, address, phone, toll-free and fax numbers, e-mail and URL addresses, a description of principal fields of research or services, and related conferences.

Features Included in Volumes 5 and 6

State Listings. This section lists various sources of information and assistance available within given states, territories, and Canadian provinces; entries include governmental, academic, and commercial agencies, and are arranged alphabetically within up to 15 subheadings by resource type:

- **Small Business Development Center Lead Office**— Includes the lead small business development center (SBDC) for each state.
- **Small Business Development Centers**—Includes any additional small business development centers (SBDC) in the state, territory, or province. SBDCs provide support services to small businesses, including individual counseling, seminars, conferences, and learning center activities.
- **Small Business Assistance Programs**—Includes state small business development offices and other programs offering assistance to small businesses.
- **SCORE Offices**—Includes SCORE office(s) for each state. The Service Corps of Retired Executives Association (SCORE), a volunteer program sponsored by the Small Business Administration, offers counseling, workshops, and seminars across the U.S. for small business entrepreneurs.
- **Better Business Bureaus**—Includes various better business bureaus within each state. By becoming a member of the local Better Business Bureau, a small business owner can increase the prestige and credibility of his or her business within the community, as well as make valuable business contacts.
- **Chambers of Commerce**—Includes various chambers of commerce within each state. Chambers of Commerce are valuable sources of small business advice and information; often, local chambers sponsor SCORE counseling several times per month for a small fee, seminars, conferences, and other workshops to its members. Also, by becoming a member of the local Chamber of Commerce, a small business owner can increase the prestige and credibility of his or her business within the community, as well as make valuable business contacts.
- **Minority Business Assistance Programs**—Includes minority business development centers and other sources of assistance for minority-owned business.
- **Financing and Loan Programs**—Includes venture capital firms, small business investment companies (SBIC), minority enterprise small business investment companies (MESBIC), and other programs that provide funding to qualified small businesses.
- **Procurement Assistance Programs**—Includes state services such as counseling, set-asides, and sheltered-market bidding, which are designed to aid small businesses in bidding on government contracts.
- **Incubators/Research and Technology Parks**— Includes small business incubators, which provide newly established small business owners with work sites, business services, training, and consultation; also includes research and technology parks, which sponsor research and facilitate commercialization of new technologies.
- **Educational Programs**—Includes university and college programs, as well as those sponsored by other organizations that offer degree, nondegree, certificate, and correspondence programs in entrepreneurship and in small business development.
- **Legislative Assistance**—Includes committees, subcommittees, and joint committees of each state's

senate and house of representatives that are concerned with small business issues and regulations.

- *Consultants*—Includes consultants and consulting firms offering expertise in small business development.
- *Publications*—Includes publications related to small business operations within the profiled state.
- *Publishers*—Includes publishers operating in or for the small business arena within the profiled state.
- *Early Stage Financing*—Includes organizations offering early-stage capital needed to launch and grow new businesses.
- *Venture Capital Firm*—Includes organizations offering financial support to small, early-stage and emerging firms.

Federal Government Assistance. This section lists federal government agencies and offices, many with additional listings for specific offices, as well as regional or district branches. Main agencies or offices are listed alphabetically; regional, branch, or district offices are listed after each main office or agency.

Master Index. This index provides an alphabetic listing of all entries contained in Volumes 1 through 6. Citations are referenced by their entry numbers. Publication titles are rendered in italics.

Alabama

ASSOCIATIONS AND OTHER ORGANIZATIONS

36040 ■ Alabama Microenterprise Network (AMEN)
PO Box 1882
Birmingham, AL 35203
Co. E-mail: info@microenterprisealabama.org
URL: http://microenterprisealabama.org
Contact: Gaynell Adams Jackson, Co-President
E-mail: gjackson@microenterprisealabama.org
Facebook: www.facebook.com/alamicroenterprise

Description: Works to create opportunities and better environment for microenterprise development in Alabama. Aims to speak with one voice to serve, educate and empower the microenterprise service providers in Alabama and the entrepreneurs they represent. **Founded:** 2002. **Geographic Preference:** State.

36041 ■ Association of Fundraising Professionals Alabama Chapter
1600 7TH Ave. S
Birmingham, AL 35233
Co. E-mail: afpalabama1@gmail.com
URL: http://community.afpglobal.org/afpalalabamachapter/home
Contact: Morgan Hargrove Emahiser, President
Facebook: www.facebook.com/AfpAlabama
Linkedin: www.linkedin.com/company/afpal

Description: Seeks to empower individuals and organizations to practice ethical fundraising through professional education, networking, research and advocacy. **Geographic Preference:** State.

36042 ■ Business Network International Central Alabama and Southwest Georgia
3636 Haven View Cir.
Hoover, AL 35216
Ph: (205)461-4676
Co. E-mail: info@bnicalswga.com
URL: http://bnicalswga.com
Contact: William Keene, Executive Director
Facebook: www.facebook.com/BNICALSWGA

Description: Provides both men and women a structured environment for the development and exchange of quality business referrals. Offers members the opportunity to share ideas and contacts. **Geographic Preference:** Regional.

36043 ■ Business Network International Northern Alabama [BNI Northern Alabama]
3408 Wall Triana Hwy. No. 6941
Huntsville, AL 35813
URL: http://northern.bnialabama.com/en-US/index
Contact: Meaghan Chitwood, Executive Director
Facebook: www.facebook.com/BNIAlabama
Linkedin: www.linkedin.com/company/bni-alabama
X (Twitter): x.com/BNIAlabama
Instagram: www.instagram.com/bnialabama

Description: Provides both men and women a structured environment for the development and exchange of quality business referrals. Offers members the opportunity to share ideas and contacts. **Founded:** 1997. **Geographic Preference:** Local.

36044 ■ Business Network International - Southern Alabama
900 Hillcrest Rd., Ste. A2
Mobile, AL 36695
Ph: (251)639-5030
Fax: (251)639-5006
URL: http://southern.bnialabama.com
Contact: David Carpenter, President
E-mail: gchris@bnialabama.com
Facebook: www.facebook.com/BNISouthAlabama

Description: Provides both men and women a structured environment for the development and exchange of quality business referrals. Offers members the opportunity to share ideas and contacts. **Geographic Preference:** Local.

36045 ■ Entrepreneurs' Organization - Birmingham Chapter (EO)
Birmingham, AL
Co. E-mail: eobham@gmail.com
URL: http://www.eonetwork.org/birmingham
Founded: 2014.

36046 ■ National Federation of Independent Business Alabama
7550 Halcyon Summit Dr., Ste. 115
Montgomery, AL 36117
Ph: (334)264-2261
Fax: (334)262-7451
Co. E-mail: rosemary.elebash@nfib.org
URL: http://www.nfib.com/alabama
Contact: Rosemary Elebash, Director
E-mail: rosemary.elebash@nfib.org
X (Twitter): x.com/nfib_al

Description: Represents small and independent businesses. Aims to promote and protect the rights of members to own, operate and grow their businesses. **Geographic Preference:** State.

36047 ■ Young Business Leaders of Birmingham (YBL)
2310 Briarwood Trace
Birmingham, AL 35243
Ph: (205)776-5450
Fax: (205)933-5001
Co. E-mail: info@ybl.org
URL: http://ybl.org/birmingham
Contact: Phil Reddick, Director
E-mail: preddick@ybl.org
X (Twitter): x.com/YBLBirmingham
Instagram: www.instagram.com/yblbirmingham

Description: Aims to reach out businessmen and professionals and offer the tools and environment that facilitate holistic growth. **Founded:** 1981. **Geographic Preference:** Local.

SMALL BUSINESS DEVELOPMENT CENTERS

36048 ■ Alabama Small Business Development Consortium, Lead Office (ASBDC)
621 Greensboro Ave.
Tuscaloosa, AL 35401
Ph: (205)348-1582
Free: 877-825-7232
URL: http://www.asbdc.org
Contact: Michael Brooks, Associate Director

Description: Represents and promotes the small business sector. Provides management assistance to current and prospective small business owners. Helps to improve management skills and expand the products and services of members. **Geographic Preference:** State.

36049 ■ Alabama State University Small Business Development Center (ASU SBDC)
c/o Percy J. Vaughn, Jr
915 S Jackson St., 1st Fl., Rm. 101/102
Montgomery, AL 36104
Ph: (334)229-4138
Co. E-mail: arprice@alasu.edu
URL: http://www.alasu.edu/_qa/alabama-sbdc-asu.php
Contact: Percy J. Vaughn, Jr., Contact
Facebook: www.facebook.com/ALASUSBDC

Description: Represents and promotes the small business sector. Provides management assistance to current and prospective small business owners. Helps to improve management skills and expand the products and services of members. **Geographic Preference:** Local.

36050 ■ Auburn University Small Business Development Center
540 Devall Dr., Ste. 101
Auburn, AL 36832
Free: 877-825-7232
Co. E-mail: sbdc@auburn.edu
URL: http://harbert.auburn.edu/research-faculty/centers/small-business-development-center.html
Contact: Lindsay Bridges, Director
URL(s): asbdc.org/office-locations

Description: Represents and promotes the small business sector. Provides management assistance to current and prospective small business owners. Helps to improve management skills and expand the products and services of members. **Founded:** 1980. **Geographic Preference:** Local.

36051 ■ Decatur-Morgan County Entrepreneurial Center [The E-Center]
1629 4th Ave. SE
Decatur, AL 35601
Ph: (256)686-2999
Co. E-mail: info@alabamaincubator.com
URL: http://the-ecenter.org
Contact: Dr. Karockas Watkins, President
Facebook: www.facebook.com/alabamaincubator

Linkedin: www.linkedin.com/company/decatur-morgan-county-entrepreneurial-center
X (Twitter): x.com/alincubator

Description: Encourages new and small businesses as tenants and non-tenants of the E-Center facility and ensures successful start-up and continued business growth. **Founded:** 2010.

36052 ■ Huntsville Association of Small Businesses in Advanced Technology (HASBAT)
University Dr. NW
Huntsville, AL 35814
Ph: (256)203-6772
Co. E-mail: admin@hasbat.org
URL: http://www.hasbat.org
Contact: Allison Rhen, President
E-mail: arhen@hasbat.org
Facebook: www.facebook.com/HASBAT.ORG
Linkedin: www.linkedin.com/company/hasbat

Description: A nonprofit organization founded to increase business opportunities for high-technology small businesses in the Huntsville area. **Founded:** 1993. **Geographic Preference:** Local.

36053 ■ Small Business Development Center (JSU SBDC)
700 Pelham Rd. N
Jacksonville, AL 36265
Ph: (256)782-5271
Co. E-mail: sbdc@jsu.edu
URL: http://www.jsusbdc.com
Contact: Ken Grissom, Specialist
E-mail: kgrissom@jsu.edu

Description: Provides management assistance to current and prospective small business owners in Jacksonville. **Founded:** 1981. **Geographic Preference:** Local.

36054 ■ Small Business Development Center at the University of North Alabama (SBDC UNA)
541 W College St.
Florence, AL 35632-0001
Ph: (256)765-4629
Fax: (256)765-4813
URL: http://sbdc.una.edu
Contact: Kimberly Hughston, Director
E-mail: khughston@una.edu

Description: Provides management assistance to current and prospective small business owners in North Alabama. **Founded:** 1980. **Geographic Preference:** Local.

36055 ■ The Small Business Resource Center
600 S Court St.
Montgomery, AL 36104
Ph: (334)834-5200
Fax: (334)265-4745
URL: http://www.montgomerychamber.com/list/member/small-business-resource-center-montgomery-1365
Contact: Anna B. Buckalew, President

Description: Offers valuable services to prospective and new business owners, including mentoring in important areas such as financial planning, marketing, and future growth strategies.

36056 ■ Troy University Small Business Development Center (SBDC)
63 S Ct., Sq.
Troy, AL 36081
Ph: (334)770-2620
Co. E-mail: sbdc@troy.edu
URL: http://www.troy.edu/about-us/strategic-approach/small-business-center.html
Contact: Juliana Bolivar, Director
E-mail: jbolivar@troy.edu

Description: Represents and promotes the small business sector. Provides management assistance to current and prospective small business owners. Helps to improve management skills and expand the products and services of members. **Geographic Preference:** Local.

36057 ■ University of Alabama in Huntsville - Northeast Alabama Regional Small Business Development Center (NEAR SBDC)
301 Sparkman Dr.
Huntsville, AL 35899
URL: http://www.uah.edu/ovpr/service-and-outreach

Description: Provides assistance to small businesses and aspiring entrepreneurs. Provides business management counseling, startup counseling, training and workshops, and a resource library. **Scope:** Small business operations, entrepreneurship, and the success and failure of small businesses.

36058 ■ University of Alabama in Huntsville Small Business Development Center (UAH)
225 Church St., Ste. 319
Huntsville, AL 35801
Ph: (256)824-6422
Co. E-mail: sbdc@uah.edu
URL: http://www.uah.edu/sbdc
Contact: Hilary Claybourne, Regional Director
E-mail: hilary.claybourne@uah.edu
Facebook: www.facebook.com/UAHuntsvilleSBDC
X (Twitter): x.com/UAHSBDC

Description: Represents and promotes the small business sector. Provides management assistance to current and prospective small business owners. Helps to improve management skills and expand the products and services of members. **Geographic Preference:** Local.

36059 ■ University of Alabama Small Business Development Center
621 Greensboro Ave.
Tuscaloosa, AL 35401
Ph: (205)348-1582
Free: 877-825-7232
URL: http://asbdc.org
Contact: Michael Brooks, Associate Director

Description: Represents and promotes the small business sector. Provides management assistance to current and prospective small business owners. Helps to improve management skills and expand the products and services of members. **Geographic Preference:** Local.

36060 ■ University of Alabama - Small Business Development Center (SBDC)
621 Greensboro Ave.
Tuscaloosa, AL 35401
Ph: (205)348-1582
Free: 877-825-7232
URL: http://sbdc.ua.edu
Facebook: www.facebook.com/AlabamaSBDC
Linkedin: www.linkedin.com/company/alabama-small-business-development-center-network

Description: A statewide, inter-institutional program to enhance economic growth in Alabama by providing management and technical assistance to small businesses. **Scope:** Management assistance to the small business community. **Founded:** 1980. **Publications:** *West Alabama Small Business Handbook.* **Educational Activities:** Small Business Development Center Short courses, Offer exemplary teaching and training programs.

36061 ■ University of South Alabama Small Business Development Center (USA SBDC)
5811 USA Dr., South, MCOB Rm., 123
Mobile, AL 36688
URL: http://www.southalabama.edu/colleges/mcob/mcei/mbd.html

Description: Provides management assistance to current and prospective small business owners in South Alabama. **Geographic Preference:** Local.

36062 ■ University of West Alabama Small Business Development Center (UWA SBDC)
UWA SSS Station 17
Livingston, AL 35470
Ph: (205)652-3627
Fax: (205)652-3401
URL: http://www.uwa.edu/academics/collegeofbusinessandtechnology/aboutthecollege/smallbusinessdevelopmentcenter
Contact: Donald Mills, Director
E-mail: dmills@uwa.edu

Description: Represents and promotes the small business sector. Provides management assistance to current and prospective small business owners. Helps to improve management skills and expand the products and services of members. **Geographic Preference:** Local.

SMALL BUSINESS ASSISTANCE PROGRAMS

36063 ■ Alabama Department of Economic and Community Affairs (ADECA) - Community and Economic Development Programs
401 Adams Ave.
Montgomery, AL 36104
Ph: (334)242-5370
Fax: (334)242-5099
Co. E-mail: contact@adeca.alabama.gov
URL: http://adeca.alabama.gov/ced
Contact: Kenneth W. Boswell, Director

Description: Provides consultation services to small and developing businesses; provides information on federal grants and projects; and helps businesses to develop export contacts and markets. **Founded:** 1983.

36064 ■ Alabama International Trade Center (AITC)
621 Greensboro Ave.
Tuscaloosa, AL 35401
Ph: (205)348-7621
Co. E-mail: aitc@ua.edu
URL: http://aitc.ua.edu
Contact: Brian K. Davis, Director
Facebook: www.facebook.com/TheAITC

Description: Offers consulting services and seminars to help businesses develop international activities. Compiles information on foreign business climates. Services provided free of charge to smaller businesses; others must pay a fee. **Scope:** A university-based non-profit organization assisting regional companies with international trade with international market research. **Founded:** 1979. **Publications:** *Research Reports Series.*

36065 ■ Alabama Launchpad
1320 1st Ave. S
Birmingham, AL 35233
Ph: (205)943-4700
Co. E-mail: launchpad@edpa.org
URL: http://alabamalaunchpad.com
Facebook: www.facebook.com/AlabamaLaunchpad
Linkedin: www.linkedin.com/company/alabama-launchpad
X (Twitter): x.com/alalaunchpad
Instagram: www.instagram.com/alabamalaunchpad
YouTube: www.youtube.com/channel/UCpAkugvtbuzVNQwmVosjWww

Description: Supports, advocates, and recognized entrepreneurship in Alabama.

36066 ■ Alabama Technology Network (ATN)
135 S Union St., Ste. 441
Montgomery, AL 36104
Ph: (334)293-4671
Co. E-mail: atninfo@atn.org
URL: http://www.atn.org
Contact: Keith Phillips, Director
E-mail: kphillips@atn.org
Facebook: www.facebook.com/ALTechNetwork
Linkedin: www.linkedin.com/company/alabama-technology-network
X (Twitter): x.com/ALTechNetwork

Description: Offers technical assistance and training to Alabama businesses. **Founded:** 1987.

36067 ■ Women's Business Center of South Alabama
1350 Concourse Ave., Ste. 434
Mobile, AL 36693
X (Twitter): twitter.com/wbcsouth

Description: Offers management consulting and business support services.

STATE LISTINGS

Alabama ■ 36084

SCORE OFFICES

36068 ■ Anniston SCORE
1400 Commerce Blvd
NE Alabama Entrepreneurial Sys., Ste. 20
Anniston, AL 36207
URL: http://www.score.org/alabama

36069 ■ SCORE - Alabama Capitol
600 S Court St.
Montgomery, AL 36104
URL: http://www.score.org/alabama/score-alabama-capitol-branch
Description: Connects entrepreneurs with local mentors to help you build your business with free business advice. **Geographic Preference:** State.

36070 ■ SCORE - Anniston
1400 Commerce Blvd. NE, Alabama Entrepreneurial Sys
Anniston, AL 36207
URL: http://www.score.org/alabama
Description: Offers free business mentoring, low-cost or no-cost business training, and tools and templates for growing businesses.

36071 ■ SCORE - Birmingham
2 20th St. N
Birmingham, AL 35203
Co. E-mail: scorechapter84@gmail.com
URL: http://www.score.org/alabama
Description: Provides professional guidance and information to maximize the success of existing and emerging small businesses. Offers business counseling and workshops. **Geographic Preference:** Local.

36072 ■ SCORE - Huntsville
515 Spakrman Dr., NW
Huntsville, AL 35816
Co. E-mail: help@score.org
URL: http://www.score.org/find-location
Description: Dedicated to educating entrepreneurs and encouraging the formation, growth and success of small businesses by providing free counseling and no-cost or low-cost educational workshops.

36073 ■ SCORE - South Alabama
327 Fairhope Ave.
Fairhope, AL 36532
Ph: (251)928-6387
Fax: (251)928-6389
Co. E-mail: southalscore@gmail.com
URL: http://southalabama.score.org
Description: Provides free and confidential business advice and counseling tailored to meet the needs of your small business and your personal objectives. **Founded:** 1998. **Geographic Preference:** Local.

BETTER BUSINESS BUREAUS

36074 ■ Better Business Bureau of North Alabama
210 Exchange Pl., Ste. A
Huntsville, AL 35806
Ph: (256)533-1640
Fax: (256)533-1177
Co. E-mail: info@northalabama.bbb.org
URL: http://www.bbb.org/local-bbb/bbb-serving-north-alabama
Contact: Karen Reeves, President
Facebook: www.facebook.com/BBBservingNorthAlabama
Linkedin: www.linkedin.com/company/better-business-bureau-of-north-alabama
X (Twitter): x.com/BBBNorthAlabama
Instagram: www.instagram.com/bbbnorthalabama
Description: Fosters ethical relationship between businesses and the community through voluntary self-regulation, consumer and business education and service excellence. **Founded:** 1965. **Geographic Preference:** Local.

36075 ■ Better Business Bureau Serving Central & South Alabama - Birmingham Office
2101 Highland Ave., Ste. 410
Birmingham, AL 35205-4030
Ph: (205)558-2222
Fax: (205)558-2239
Co. E-mail: info@csal.bbb.org
URL: http://www.bbb.org/local-bbb/bbb-serving-central-and-south-alabama
Facebook: www.facebook.com/bbbcsal
Linkedin: www.linkedin.com/company/better-business-bureau-serving-central-&-south-alabama
X (Twitter): x.com/BBBcsal
Instagram: www.instagram.com/bbbcsal
YouTube: www.youtube.com/channel/UC7mMISP3EQE0BSo4ziz6t6Q
Description: Seeks to promote and foster the highest ethical relationship between businesses and the public through voluntary self-regulation, consumer and business education, and service excellence. Provides information to help consumers and businesses make informed purchasing decisions and avoid costly scams and frauds; settles consumer complaints through arbitration and other means. **Geographic Preference:** Local.

36076 ■ Better Business Bureau Serving Central and South Alabama - Mobile Office
150 Government St., Ste. 1004
Mobile, AL 36602
URL: http://www.bbb.org/local-bbb/bbb-serving-central-and-south-alabama
Description: Seeks to promote and foster the highest ethical relationship between businesses and the public through voluntary self-regulation, consumer and business education, and service excellence. Provides information to help consumers and businesses make informed purchasing decisions and avoid costly scams and frauds; settles consumer complaints through arbitration and other means. **Founded:** 1954. **Geographic Preference:** Local.

CHAMBERS OF COMMERCE

36077 ■ Alabama State Black Chamber of Commerce (ASBCC)
PO Box 550022
Birmingham, AL 35255
Ph: (205)895-1157
Co. E-mail: wehelp@alblackcc.org
URL: http://alblackcc.org
Contact: Jerry Mitchell, Contact
Facebook: www.facebook.com/AlabamaSBCC
Description: Advances the social, economic and intellectual condition of its affiliates and members in Alabama.

36078 ■ Alexander City Chamber of Commerce (ACCC)
175 Aliant Pky.
Alexander City, AL 35010
Ph: (256)234-3461
Co. E-mail: info@alexandercitychamber.com
URL: http://www.alexcitychamber.com
Contact: Ed Collari, Co-President Co-Chief Executive Officer
E-mail: ed.collari@alexandercitychamber.com
Description: Promotes business and community development in Alexander City, Lake Martin Area. **Founded:** 1910. **Publications:** *Chamber Currents* (Quarterly). **Geographic Preference:** Local.

36079 ■ Aliceville Area Chamber of Commerce (AACC)
419 Memorial Pky. E
Aliceville, AL 35442
Ph: (205)373-2820
Fax: (205)373-3165
URL: http://www.thecityofaliceville.com/chamber/chamber-information
Description: Promotes business and community development in the Aliceville, AL area. **Founded:** 1924. **Publications:** *Connecting Point* (Quarterly). **Geographic Preference:** Local.

36080 ■ Arab Chamber of Commerce
1157 N Main St.
Arab, AL 35016-1071
Ph: (256)586-3138
Co. E-mail: info@arab-chamber.org
URL: http://www.arab-chamber.org
Contact: Jynnah Mooney, President
E-mail: jmooney@arab-chamber.org
Facebook: www.facebook.com/arabchamberofcommerce
X (Twitter): x.com/arabalchamber
Instagram: www.instagram.com/arabchamberofcommerce
Description: Seeks to promote and perpetuate business growth, economic development, civic interest, general welfare and prosperity of the Arab area. Aims to stimulate public interest to these ends. **Founded:** 1965. **Geographic Preference:** Local.

36081 ■ Atmore Area Chamber of Commerce (AACC)
137 N Main St.
Atmore, AL 36502
Ph: (251)368-3305
Fax: (251)368-0800
Co. E-mail: info@atmorechamber.com
URL: http://www.atmorechamber.com
Contact: Erin Hankins, President
Facebook: www.facebook.com/AtmoreChamber
Description: Promotes business and community development in the Atmore, AL area. **Founded:** 1946. **Geographic Preference:** Local.

36082 ■ Bayou La Batre Area Chamber of Commerce
12701 Padgett Switch Rd.
Irvington, AL 36544
Ph: (251)824-1043
Co. E-mail: info@bayoulabatreareachamber.org
URL: http://www.bayoulabatreareachamber.org
Contact: Debra Jones, President
Facebook: www.facebook.com/BayouLaBatreAreaChamber
X (Twitter): x.com/blbareachamber
Description: Promotes business and community development in Bayou La Batre, AL. Conducts taste of the Bayou festival. **Founded:** 1940. **Geographic Preference:** Local.

36083 ■ Bessemer Area Chamber of Commerce (BACC)
321 18th St. N
Bessemer, AL 35020
Ph: (205)425-3253
Free: 888-423-7736
Fax: (205)425-4979
URL: http://www.bessemerchamber.com
Contact: Latasha Cook-Williams, President
E-mail: lacook1@bellsouth.net
Facebook: www.facebook.com/pages/Bessemer-Area-Chamber-of-Commerce/329259302610
Description: Promotes business and community development in the Bessemer and Southwest Metro area. **Founded:** 1922. **Publications:** *Communique* (Monthly). **Geographic Preference:** Local.

36084 ■ Birmingham Business Alliance (BBA)
505 20th St. N, Ste. 200
Birmingham, AL 35203
Ph: (205)324-2100
URL: http://www.birminghambusinessalliance.com
Contact: Fred McCallum, President (Acting)
E-mail: william.bryant@scouting.org
Facebook: www.facebook.com/bhmbizalliance
Linkedin: www.linkedin.com/company/bhmbizalliance
X (Twitter): x.com/BHMBizAlliance
Instagram: www.instagram.com/bhmbizalliance
YouTube: www.youtube.com/channel/UCt0PFXyIrtnnjila5rH1Lmg
Description: Promotes business and community development. Provides individual and group assistance. Issues publications. **Founded:** 1887. **Publications:** *Alliance Magazine*; *Birmingham Regional International Business Directory*; *Birminghamchamber.com Newsletter* (Monthly); *Major Employers*

Small Business Sourcebook • 42nd Edition

Directory (Annual); *Small Business Guide/Business Start-up Checklist*; *NTDRA Dealer News--Who's Who Directory Issue* (Annual). **Geographic Preference:** Local.

36085 ■ Blount-Oneonta Chamber of Commerce (BO)
110 1st Ave. E
Oneonta, AL 35121
Ph: (205)274-2153
Co. E-mail: barbara@blountoneontachamber.org
URL: http://blountoneontachamber.org
Contact: Bekah Phillips, Executive Director
E-mail: bekah@blountoneontachamber.org
Facebook: www.facebook.com/BlountOneontaChamberOfCommerce
Description: Individuals interested in preserving the history of Blount County, AL. **Founded:** 1987. **Publications:** *Chamber Connection* (Monthly). **Geographic Preference:** Local.

36086 ■ Boaz Chamber of Commerce (BCC)
100 E Bartlett St.
Boaz, AL 35957
Ph: (256)593-8154
Co. E-mail: boazchamberassist@gmail.com
URL: http://www.boazareachamberofcommerce.org
Contact: Jill Johnson, Executive Director
Facebook: www.facebook.com/BoazALChamber
Instagram: www.instagram.com/boazchamber
Description: Promotes business and community development in Boaz, Alabama. **Founded:** 1947. **Publications:** *Boaz Vision* (Monthly). **Awards:** Boaz Chamber of Commerce Citizen of the Year (Annual); Boaz Chamber of Commerce Educator of the Year. **Geographic Preference:** Local.

36087 ■ *Business View*
451 Government St.
Mobile, AL 36602
Ph: (251)433-6951
Free: 800-422-6951
Fax: (251)432-1143
Co. E-mail: info@mobilechamber.com
URL: http://mobilechamber.com
Contact: Bill Sisson, President
E-mail: bsisson@mobilechamber.com
URL(s): mobilechamber.com/news/blog
Released: Monthly **Description:** Contains news about the Mobile area's business community. **Availability:** Print.

36088 ■ Calhoun County Chamber of Commerce (CCCOC)
1330 Quintard Ave.
Anniston, AL 36201
Ph: (256)237-3536
Co. E-mail: info@calhounchamber.com
URL: http://www.calhounchamber.com
Contact: Linda Hearn, Executive Director
E-mail: lindah@calhounchamber.com
Facebook: www.facebook.com/calhouncountychamber
Linkedin: www.linkedin.com/company/calhoun-county-chamber-of-commerce
Instagram: www.instagram.com/calhounchamber
Description: Promotes business growth and development in the area. **Awards:** Calhoun County's Citizen of the Year (Annual). **Geographic Preference:** Local.

36089 ■ Central Baldwin Chamber of Commerce (CBCC)
23150 Hwy. 59
Robertsdale, AL 36567
Ph: (251)947-2626
Fax: (251)947-4809
Co. E-mail: bbutler@centralbaldwin.com
URL: http://www.centralbaldwin.com
Contact: Gail Quezada, President
Facebook: www.facebook.com/centralbaldwinchamber
Instagram: www.instagram.com/centralbaldwinchamber
Description: Promotes business and community development in the Robertsdale, AL area. **Founded:** 1975. **Geographic Preference:** Local.

36090 ■ Chamber of Commerce of Huntsville/Madison County
225 Church St. NW
Huntsville, AL 35801
Ph: (256)535-2000
Fax: (256)535-2015
Co. E-mail: info@hsvchamber.org
URL: http://hsvchamber.org
Contact: Chip Cherry, President
E-mail: ccherry@hsvchamber.org
Facebook: www.facebook.com/HuntsvilleAlabama
Linkedin: www.linkedin.com/company/huntsvillealchamber
X (Twitter): x.com/huntsvillealcoc
Instagram: www.instagram.com/hsvchamber
YouTube: www.youtube.com/user/huntsvillealabamausa
Description: Promotes business and community development in Madison County, AL. **Founded:** 1894. **Publications:** *Community Organizations Directory*; *Chamber of Commerce of Huntsville/Madison County--Industrial Directory*; *Membership Directory and Business Guide for Huntsville and Madison County*; *ChamberLink* (Monthly); *Initiatives Review* (Bimonthly). **Geographic Preference:** Local.

36091 ■ The Chamber of Commerce of Walker County
204 19th St. E, Ste. 101
Jasper, AL 35501
Ph: (205)384-4571
Co. E-mail: linda@walkerchamber.us
URL: http://www.walkerchamber.us
Contact: Linda Lewis, President
E-mail: linda@walkerchamber.us
Facebook: www.facebook.com/The-Chamber-of-Commerce-of-Walker-County-351670871839339
X (Twitter): x.com/hwnt
Description: Promotes business and community development in the Jasper, AL area. Conducts annual Heritage Day festival. **Founded:** 1938. **Geographic Preference:** Local.

36092 ■ Chamber of Commerce of West Alabama
2222 9th St.
Tuscaloosa, AL 35401
Ph: (205)758-7588
URL: http://westalabamachamber.com
Contact: Donny Jones, Vice President
E-mail: donny@tuscaloosachamber.com
Facebook: www.facebook.com/westalchamber
Linkedin: www.linkedin.com/company/the-chamber-of-commerce-of-west-alabama
X (Twitter): x.com/westalchamber
Instagram: www.instagram.com/westalchamber
Description: Promotes business and community development in western Alabama. Sponsors cable television channel. **Publications:** *The Commerce* (Monthly); *Perspectives*. **Awards:** The H. Pettus Randall III Entrepreneur of the Year Award (Annual). **Geographic Preference:** Local.

36093 ■ The Chamber of Gadsden/Etowah County
1 Commerce Sq.
Gadsden, AL 35901
Ph: (256)543-3472
Co. E-mail: info@etowahchamber.org
URL: http://www.etowahchamber.org
Description: Promotes business and community development in Etowah County, AL. **Founded:** 1866. **Geographic Preference:** Local.

36094 ■ *Chamber Newsletter*
101 S Beaty St.
Athens, AL 35611
Ph: (256)232-2600
Free: 866-953-6565
Fax: (256)232-2609
Co. E-mail: info@tourathens.com
URL: http://tourathens.com
Contact: Ray Neese, Chairman
URL(s): alcchamber.org/membership
Availability: Print.

36095 ■ Cherokee County Chamber of Commerce (CCCoC)
Bldg. A
801 Cedar Buff Rd.
Centre, AL 35960
Ph: (256)927-8455
Co. E-mail: info@cherokee-chamber.org
URL: http://cherokee-chamber.org
Contact: Craig Gilley, Treasurer
Facebook: www.facebook.com/cherokee.chamber.5
X (Twitter): x.com/WeissCCCOC
Instagram: www.instagram.com/cherokeechamberal
Description: Promotes business and community development in, and tourism the Cherokee County, AL area. **Founded:** 1946. **Publications:** *Vision* (Monthly). **Geographic Preference:** Local.

36096 ■ Chilton County Chamber of Commerce
205 6th St., N
Clanton, AL 35046
Ph: (205)755-2400
Co. E-mail: info@chiltonchamber.org
URL: http://www.chiltonchamber.org
Contact: Connie Bainbridge, President
Facebook: www.facebook.com/thechiltonchamber
X (Twitter): x.com/chiltonchamber
Description: Promotes business and community development in Chilton County, AL. **Publications:** *Chamber Newsletter* (Monthly). **Awards:** Chilton County Chamber of Commerce Youth Citizen of the Year (Annual). **Geographic Preference:** Local.

36097 ■ Clay County Chamber of Commerce - Alabama
88855 Hwy. 9
Ashland, AL 36251
Ph: (256)396-2828
Co. E-mail: claychamber@centurytel.net
URL: http://alabamaclaycounty.com
Contact: Patsy Sullivan, President
Description: Promotes business and community development in Clay County, AL. **Founded:** 1866. **Geographic Preference:** Local.

36098 ■ Coastal Alabama Business Chamber
3150 Gulf Shores Pky.
Gulf Shores, AL 36542
Ph: (251)968-7200
Co. E-mail: info@mygulfcoastchamber.com
URL: http://www.mygulfcoastchamber.com
Contact: Greg Alexander, President
Facebook: www.facebook.com/MyGulfCoastChamber
Linkedin: www.linkedin.com/company/alabama-gulf-coast-chamber-of-commerce
X (Twitter): x.com/BizChamberAL
Instagram: www.instagram.com/mygulfcoastchamber
YouTube: www.youtube.com/user/alagulfcoastchamber
Description: Promotes business and community development in Gulf Shores, AL. **Founded:** 1981. **Publications:** *Coast Connections*. **Educational Activities:** Business After Hours. **Awards:** Coastal Alabama Business Chamber Island Spirit Award (Monthly). **Geographic Preference:** Local.

36099 ■ *Communique*
321 18th St. N
Bessemer, AL 35020
Ph: (205)425-3253
Free: 888-423-7736
Fax: (205)425-4979
URL: http://www.bessemerchamber.com
Contact: Latasha Cook-Williams, President
E-mail: lacook1@bellsouth.net
URL(s): www.bessemerchamber.com/newsletter
Released: Monthly **Availability:** Online; PDF.

36100 ■ Cullman Area Chamber of Commerce (CACC)
301 2nd Ave., SW
Cullman, AL 35055
Ph: (256)734-0454
Co. E-mail: info@cullmanchamber.org
URL: http://www.cullmanchamber.org
Contact: Peggy Smith, President

E-mail: psmith@cullmanchamber.org
Facebook: www.facebook.com/cullmanareachamber
X (Twitter): x.com/cullmanchamber
Instagram: www.instagram.com/cullmanareachamber
Description: Promotes business and community development in Cullman County, AL. **Founded:** 1943. **Publications:** *Dateline Cullman* (Monthly). **Geographic Preference:** Local.

36101 ■ Dadeville Area Chamber of Commerce - Dadeville Public Library
345 E LaFayette St., Ste. 102
Dadeville, AL 36853
Ph: (256)825-4019
Co. E-mail: chamber@dadeville.com
URL: http://dadevillechamber.com
Contact: William S. Farrington, Contact
Facebook: www.facebook.com/Lake-Martin-Dadeville-Area-Chamber-100957114821341
X (Twitter): x.com/Dadeville
Pinterest: www.pinterest.com/dadevillec
Description: Promotes business and community development in Tallapoosa County, AL. Sponsors annual Chamber Day and annual Christmas pageant. **Scope:** Genealogy. **Services:** Interlibrary loan. **Founded:** 1950. **Holdings:** 10,000 Books; audiobooks; DVD. **Geographic Preference:** Local.

36102 ■ Decatur-Morgan County Chamber of Commerce (DCC)
515 6th Ave., NE
Decatur, AL 35602-2003
Ph: (256)353-5312
Fax: (256)353-2384
Co. E-mail: mandy@dcc.org
URL: http://www.dcc.org
Contact: John Seymour, Chief Executive Officer
E-mail: john@dcc.org
Facebook: www.facebook.com/decaturmorganchamber
X (Twitter): x.com/DMCChamber
Instagram: www.instagram.com/decaturmorganchamber
Description: Promotes business and community development in Decatur, AL. **Founded:** 1931. **Geographic Preference:** Local.

36103 ■ Demopolis Area Chamber of Commerce (DACC)
102 E Washington St.
Demopolis, AL 36732-2132
Ph: (334)289-0270
Co. E-mail: director@demopolischamber.com
URL: http://www.demopolisareachamber.com
Contact: Amy B. White, Co-President
X (Twitter): x.com/demopchamber
Description: Promotes business and community development in the Demopolis, AL area. Encourages integrity, good faith, and just and equitable practices in business. Sponsors Fourth of July fireworks, Arts in the Park, and Christmas on the River. **Founded:** 1915. **Geographic Preference:** Local.

36104 ■ Dothan Area Chamber of Commerce (DACC)
102 Jamestown Blvd.
Dothan, AL 36302
Ph: (334)792-5138
Free: 800-221-1027
Fax: (334)794-4796
URL: http://www.dothan.com
Contact: Matt Parker, President
Facebook: www.facebook.com/DothanAreaChamberofCommerce
Linkedin: www.linkedin.com/company/dothan-area-chamber-of-commerce
X (Twitter): x.com/DothanAreaChamb
Instagram: www.instagram.com/dothanareachamber
YouTube: www.youtube.com/channel/UC-N_TrPZfyjZVudTQXOe8zg
Description: Promotes business, industry, and community development in the Dothan, AL area. Sponsors trade shows. **Founded:** 1919. **Publications:** *Chamber Connections* (Monthly). **Geographic Preference:** Local.

36105 ■ East Alabama Chamber of Commerce
1107 Broad St.
Phenix City, AL 36867
Ph: (334)298-3639
Co. E-mail: info@ealcc.com
URL: http://www.ealcc.com
Contact: Dennis Beson, President
Facebook: www.facebook.com/EastAlabamaChamber
Description: Promotes business and community development in Russell County, AL. Seeks to attract commercial developments. **Publications:** *Quality of Life* (Periodic); *Quality of Life* (Annual). **Geographic Preference:** Local.

36106 ■ Eastern Shore Chamber of Commerce (ESCC)
327 Fairhope Ave.
Fairhope, AL 36532
Ph: (251)928-6387
Co. E-mail: officeadmin@eschamber.com
URL: http://www.eschamber.com
Contact: Casey Williams, President
E-mail: cgwilliams@eschamber.com
Facebook: www.facebook.com/easternshorechamber
X (Twitter): x.com/ESChamber
YouTube: www.youtube.com/user/ALEasternShore
Pinterest: www.pinterest.com/eschamber
Description: Promotes business and community development in Daphne, Fairhope, Montrose, Point Clear, and Spanish Fort, AL. Provides assistance to new businesses and industry. Sponsors Jubilee Festival, Arts and Crafts Festival, Mayors' Prayer Breakfast, Polo Tournament, Christmas Open House, Christmas Parades, Community Expo and Seminars. **Founded:** 1924. **Publications:** *Chamber Connections* (Monthly). **Geographic Preference:** Local.

36107 ■ Enterprise Chamber of Commerce
553 Glover Ave.
Enterprise, AL 36330
Ph: (334)347-0581
Co. E-mail: info@enterprisealabama.com
URL: http://www.enterprisealabama.com
Contact: Lisa Fenner, Director
X (Twitter): x.com/enterprisechmbr
YouTube: www.youtube.com/channel/UCEgJkiD3hf7jCbeLSSkBv8g/featured
Description: Promotes business and community development in Enterprise, AL area. **Founded:** 1941. **Geographic Preference:** Local.

36108 ■ Eutaw Area Chamber of Commerce
110 Main St.
Eutaw, AL 35462
Co. E-mail: eutawchamber@bellsouth.net
URL: http://alabamachambers.org/members/eutaw-area-chamber-of-commerce
Contact: Caitlin Holland, President
Description: Promotes business and community development in Eutaw, AL area. **Geographic Preference:** Local.

36109 ■ Evergreen/Conecuh Chamber of Commerce
100 Depot Sq.
Evergreen, AL 36401
Ph: (251)578-1707
Fax: (251)578-1044
URL: http://www.evergreenareachamber.com
Contact: Susan Brewton Coleman, Director
E-mail: scoleman@evergreenal.org
Facebook: www.facebook.com/evergreenconecuhchamberofcommerce
Description: Promotes business and community development in Evergreen/Conecuh area. **Founded:** 1950. **Geographic Preference:** Local.

36110 ■ Fayette Area Chamber of Commerce
102 2nd Ave.
Fayette, AL 35555
Ph: (205)932-4587
Co. E-mail: fcoc@cyberjoes.com
URL: http://www.fayetteareachamber.org
Contact: Daniel White, Contact
Facebook: www.facebook.com/FayetteAreaChamberOfCommerce
Description: Provides leadership and coordination for the advancement of economic growth and quality of life in Fayette and its surrounding area. **Founded:** 1960. **Geographic Preference:** Local.

36111 ■ Fort Payne Chamber of Commerce
300 Gault Ave., N
Fort Payne, AL 35967
Ph: (256)845-2741
Co. E-mail: info@fortpaynechamber.com
URL: http://www.fortpaynechamber.com
Contact: Angie McCurdy, President
Facebook: www.facebook.com/fortpaynechamber
Linkedin: www.linkedin.com/company/fort-payne-chamber-of-commerce
X (Twitter): x.com/FtPayneChamber
Instagram: www.instagram.com/fortpaynechamber1
Description: Promotes business and community development in Fort Payne, AL. **Founded:** 1947. **Geographic Preference:** Local.

36112 ■ Franklin County Chamber of Commerce
103 N Jackson Ave.
Russellville, AL 35653
Ph: (256)332-1760
Fax: (256)332-1740
URL: http://franklincountychamber.org
Contact: Cassie Medley, Executive Director
Facebook: www.facebook.com/VisitFranklinCoAL
X (Twitter): x.com/seefranklinco
Instagram: www.instagram.com/franklincountychamber
Pinterest: www.pinterest.com/seefranklinco
Description: Promotes business and community development in Franklin County, AL. **Founded:** 1840. **Publications:** *Franklin Findings* (Bimonthly). **Geographic Preference:** Local.

36113 ■ Greater Brewton Area Chamber of Commerce (GBACC)
1010-B Douglas Ave.
Brewton, AL 36426
Ph: (251)867-3224
Co. E-mail: info@brewtonchamber.com
URL: http://www.brewtonchamber.com
Contact: Judy Crane, Executive Director
E-mail: jcrane@brewtonchamber.com
Facebook: www.facebook.com/Greater-Brewton-Area-Chamber-of-Commerce-118180838196486
Description: Promotes business and community development in the Brewton, AL area. **Geographic Preference:** Local.

36114 ■ Greater Coosa Valley Chamber of Commerce (CCC)
805 Third St., SW
Childersburg, AL 35044
Ph: (256)278-3507
Co. E-mail: jfreeman@gcvchamber.com
URL: http://www.gcvchamber.com
Contact: Henry Moody, Contact
Facebook: www.facebook.com/GreaterCoosaValleyChamberofCommerce
Description: Promotes business and community development in Childersburg, AL. **Publications:** *Chamber Voice* (Monthly). **Educational Activities:** Chamber Coffees (Monthly). **Geographic Preference:** Local.

36115 ■ Greater Gardendale Chamber of Commerce
925 Main St.
Gardendale, AL 35071
Ph: (205)631-9195
Co. E-mail: info@gardendalechamber.com
URL: http://gardendalechamber.com
Contact: Nolita Williams, Co-President
Instagram: www.instagram.com/gardendalechamber
Description: Businesses, clubs and individual members. Promotes business and community development in Gardendale, AL. **Founded:** 1987. **Publications:** *Chamber Notes* (Monthly). **Educational Activities:** Gardendale Chamber of Commerce Banquet (Annual). **Geographic Preference:** Local.

36116 ■ Greater Shelby County Chamber of Commerce
1301 County Services Dr.
 Pelham, AL 35124
Ph: (334)269-1515
Free: 800-354-6154
Co. E-mail: info@shelbychamber.org
URL: http://www.shelbychamber.org
Contact: Kirk Mancer, President
E-mail: kirk@shelbychamber.org
X (Twitter): x.com/TheShelbyCC

Description: Promotes business and community development in the North Shelby area. **Founded:** 1979. **Publications:** *Viewpoint* (Monthly); *Cities on the Move: Alabaster/Pelham/Helena* (Annual). **Geographic Preference:** Local.

36117 ■ Greater Talladega Area and Lincoln Chamber of Commerce
Ph: (256)362-9075
Fax: (256)362-9093
Co. E-mail: info@talladegachamber.com
URL: http://www.talladegachamber.com

Description: Promotes business, community, and tourism development in the Talladega, AL area. Seeks to attract new business and promote the expansion of existing industry. Sponsors local programs and events which recognize the accomplishments of chamber members. **Founded:** 1909. **Publications:** *Greater Talladega and Lincoln Area Chamber of Commerce Newsletter* (Monthly). **Geographic Preference:** Local.

36118 ■ *Greater Talladega and Lincoln Area Chamber of Commerce Newsletter*
Ph: (256)362-9075
Fax: (256)362-9093
Co. E-mail: info@talladegachamber.com
URL: http://www.talladegachamber.com

Released: Monthly **Price:** Free. **Description:** Describes chamber activities and programs. **Availability:** Print.

36119 ■ Greater Tallassee Area Chamber of Commerce (TCC)
303 Barnett Blvd.
 Tallassee, AL 36078
Ph: (334)283-5151
Co. E-mail: chamber@tallasseechamber.com
URL: http://tallasseechamber.com
Contact: Melinda Emfinger, President
Facebook: www.facebook.com/tallasseechamber

Description: Promotes business and community development in Tallassee, AL. Sponsors festival. **Founded:** 1948. **Geographic Preference:** Local.

36120 ■ Greater Valley Area Chamber of Commerce (GVACC)
2918 20th Ave.
 Valley, AL 36854
Ph: (334)642-1411
Co. E-mail: chamber@greatervalleyarea.com
URL: http://www.greatervalleyarea.com
Contact: Carrie Royster, Executive Director
Facebook: www.facebook.com/
 GVAchamberofcommerce

Description: Promotes business and community development in Chambers County, AL and West Point, GA. **Founded:** 1963. **Geographic Preference:** Regional.

36121 ■ Haleyville Area Chamber of Commerce
PO Box 634
 Haleyville, AL 35565
Ph: (205)486-4611
Fax: (205)486-3170
Co. E-mail: haleyvillechamberofcommerce@gmail.com
URL: http://haleyvillechamber.org/Haleyville-Area-Chamber-of-Commerce
Contact: Bret Knight, Vice President Co-President
E-mail: bret@kithkitchens.com
Facebook: www.facebook.com/
 HaleyvilleAreaChamberOfCommerce

Description: Promotes business and community development in Haleyville, AL. **Founded:** 1988. **Geographic Preference:** Local.

36122 ■ Hartselle Area Chamber of Commerce
110 Railroad St.
 Hartselle, AL 35640
Ph: (256)773-4370
Fax: (256)773-4379
Co. E-mail: admin@hartsellechamber.com
URL: http://www.hartsellechamber.com
Contact: Missy Evans, President
E-mail: missy@hartsellechamber.com
X (Twitter): x.com/HartselleChambr
Pinterest: www.pinterest.com/hartselleareach

Description: Promotes business and community development in Hartselle, AL. **Founded:** 1870. **Publications:** *City/County Maps*. **Geographic Preference:** Local.

36123 ■ Headland Area Chamber of Commerce (HCC)
25 Grove St.
 Headland, AL 36345-1749
Ph: (334)693-3303
Fax: (334)785-5020
Co. E-mail: headlandalchamber@gmail.com
URL: http://headlandal.org
Contact: Pete Crews, President
Facebook: www.facebook.com/headlandchamber

Description: Promotes business and community development in Headland, AL. Sponsors various activities throughout promoting the Headland area and quality of life for its residents. **Founded:** 1980. **Educational Activities:** Daylily Art & Garden Festival. **Geographic Preference:** Local.

36124 ■ Homewood Area Chamber of Commerce (HACC)
7 Hollywood Blvd.
 Homewood, AL 35209
Ph: (205)871-5631
URL: http://www.homewoodchamber.org
Contact: Jodi Newton, Co-President
E-mail: parrish.hbat@gmail.com
Facebook: www.facebook.com/Homewoo
 dAreaChamberCommerce
X (Twitter): x.com/HomewoodChamber
Instagram: www.instagram.com/homewoodchamber

Description: Promotes business and community development in the area. Sponsors Fine Art Fair; conducts charitable activities. **Founded:** 1962. **Geographic Preference:** Local.

36125 ■ Homewood Chamber of Commerce (HCC)
7 Hollywood Blvd.
 Homewood, AL 35209
Ph: (205)871-5631
Fax: (205)871-5632
URL: http://www.homewoodchamber.org
Contact: Jim Harris, President
Facebook: www.facebook.com/Homewoo
 dChamberofCommerce
X (Twitter): x.com/HomewoodChamber
Instagram: www.instagram.com/homewoodchamber

Description: Promotes business and community development in the Homewood, AL area. **Founded:** 1940. **Publications:** *Homewood Magazine* (Annual). **Geographic Preference:** Local.

36126 ■ Hoover Area Chamber of Commerce
3000 Riverchase Galleria, Ste. 375
 Hoover, AL 35244
Ph: (205)988-5672
Co. E-mail: hooverchamber@gmail.com
URL: http://hooverchamber.org
Contact: Toni Herrera-Bast, Chief Executive Officer
Facebook: www.facebook.com/Hooverchamber
Linkedin: www.linkedin.com/company/hoover-chamber-of-commerce
Instagram: www.instagram.com/
 hooverchamberofcommerce

Description: Promotes business and community development in Hoover, AL area. **Founded:** 1978. **Awards:** Hoover Chamber of Commerce Freedom Award (Annual). **Geographic Preference:** Local.

36127 ■ Hueytown Chamber of Commerce
1320 Hueytown Rd.
 Hueytown, AL 35023
Ph: (205)491-8039
Co. E-mail: hueytownchamber@gmail.com
URL: http://hueytownchamber.com
Contact: Lisa Kriegel, President
Facebook: www.facebook.com/HueytownChamber
X (Twitter): x.com/hueytownchamber

Description: Promotes business and community development in the Hueytown, AL area. **Founded:** 1960. **Geographic Preference:** Local.

36128 ■ Huntsville Madison County Chamber
225 Church St., NW
 Huntsville, AL 35801
Ph: (256)535-2000
Fax: (256)535-2015
Co. E-mail: info@hsvchamber.org
URL: http://hsvchamber.org
Contact: Chip Cherry, President
E-mail: jkmanning@alz.org
Facebook: www.facebook.com/HuntsvilleAlabama
Linkedin: www.linkedin.com/company/hun
 tsvillealchamber
X (Twitter): x.com/huntsvillealcoc
Instagram: www.instagram.com/hsvchamber
YouTube: www.youtube.com/user/hun
 tsvillealabamausa

Description: Promotes business and community development in the area. **Founded:** 1894. **Geographic Preference:** Local.

36129 ■ *Initiatives Review*
225 Church St. NW
 Huntsville, AL 35801
Ph: (256)535-2000
Fax: (256)535-2015
Co. E-mail: info@hsvchamber.org
URL: http://hsvchamber.org
Contact: Chip Cherry, President
E-mail: ccherry@hsvchamber.org
URL(s): hsvchamber.org/news/publications

Released: Bimonthly **Availability:** Print; Download; PDF; Online.

36130 ■ Lake Guntersville Chamber of Commerce (LGCC)
200 Gunter Ave.
 Guntersville, AL 35976-1112
Ph: (256)582-3612
Co. E-mail: gcc@lakeguntersville.org
URL: http://www.lakeguntersville.org
Contact: Morri Yancy, President
Facebook: www.facebook.com/LakeGuntersvilleCC
X (Twitter): x.com/GuntersvilleCC
Instagram: www.instagram.com/lakegun
 tersvillechamber

Description: Promotes business and community development in Guntersville, AL. Conducts annual fishing tournament. **Founded:** 1847. **Publications:** *Lake Views* (Monthly). **Geographic Preference:** Local.

36131 ■ Lawrence County Chamber of Commerce
15379 AL HWY. 24, Ste. 4
 Moulton, AL 35650
Ph: (256)974-1658
Fax: (256)974-2400
Co. E-mail: contact@lawrencealabama.com
URL: http://www.lawrencealabama.com
Contact: Amy H. Thrasher, Owner
Facebook: www.facebook.com/lawcochamber2016

Description: Works with non-profit organizations, for-profit businesses, the church community, and residents to improve the quality of life for everyone in Lawrence County, Alabama. **Publications:** *Living in Lawrence* (Annual). **Geographic Preference:** Local.

STATE LISTINGS

36132 ■ Leeds Area Chamber of Commerce
7901 Pky. Dr.
Leeds, AL 35094
Ph: (205)699-5001
Fax: (205)699-1777
Co. E-mail: sandra@leedsareachamber.com
URL: http://leedsareachamber.com
Contact: Bill Morris, President
X (Twitter): x.com/leedsareachamb

Description: Promotes business and community development in the Greater Leeds, AL area. **Awards:** Leeds Area Chamber of Commerce Business of the Year (Annual); Leeds Area Chamber of Commerce Non-Profit Organization/Club of the Year (Annual); Leeds Area Chamber of Commerce Citizen of the Year (Annual); Leeds Area Chamber of Commerce Teacher of the Year (Annual). **Geographic Preference:** Local.

36133 ■ Limestone County Chamber of Commerce
101 S Beaty St.
Athens, AL 35611
Ph: (256)232-2600
Free: 866-953-6565
Fax: (256)232-2609
Co. E-mail: info@tourathens.com
URL: http://tourathens.com
Contact: Ray Neese, Chairman
Facebook: www.facebook.com/greaterlimestonecountychamberofcommerce

Description: Works to create an environment which promotes the general welfare and prosperity of its membership, the Athens-Limestone County Area and the municipalities and citizens within that area. Sponsors the Tennessee Valley Old Time Fiddler's Convention, Walk Through the Past, Business on Display, the Dogwood Festival and tours. **Founded:** 1938. **Publications:** Chamber Newsletter. **Geographic Preference:** Local.

36134 ■ Mobile Area Chamber of Commerce (MACC)
451 Government St.
Mobile, AL 36602
Ph: (251)433-6951
Free: 800-422-6951
Fax: (251)432-1143
Co. E-mail: info@mobilechamber.com
URL: http://mobilechamber.com
Contact: Bill Sisson, President
E-mail: bsisson@mobilechamber.com
Facebook: www.facebook.com/MobileChamber
X (Twitter): x.com/MobileChamber
YouTube: www.youtube.com/user/MobileChamber

Description: Promotes business and community development in the Mobile, AL area. Serves as a progressive advocate for business needs to promote the Mobile Alabama area's economic well-being. **Founded:** 1836. **Publications:** Who's Who in the Mobile Area (Annual); Business View (Monthly); The Weekly Business View (Weekly). **Geographic Preference:** Local.

36135 ■ Monroeville/Monroe County Chamber of Commerce
86 N Alabama Ave.
Monroeville, AL 36460
Ph: (251)743-2879
Co. E-mail: info@monroecountyal.com
URL: http://www.monroecountyal.com
Contact: Ricky Powell, President
E-mail: director@monroecountyal.com
Facebook: www.facebook.com/MonroevilleMonroeCountyChamberOfCommerce
X (Twitter): x.com/MvilleALChamber
YouTube: www.youtube.com/channel/UCH-6bEaitFiEGN6v28U0JXw

Description: Promotes business and community development in Monroe County, AL. Sponsors festivals and annual Christmas Parade; conducts seminars. **Founded:** 1936. **Geographic Preference:** Local.

36136 ■ Montevallo Chamber of Commerce (MCC)
PO Box 270
Montevallo, AL 35115
Ph: (205)665-1519
Co. E-mail: montevallochamber@gmail.com
URL: http://montevallocc.com
Contact: Adele Nelson, Executive Director
Facebook: www.facebook.com/montevallochamberofcommerce
X (Twitter): x.com/montevallocc

Description: Aims to advance the commercial, industrial, professional and civic interests of Montevallo. Provides support and assistance to existing businesses and industries. **Founded:** 1984. **Publications:** Chamber Chatter (Monthly). **Geographic Preference:** Local.

36137 ■ Montgomery Area Chamber of Commerce (MACOC)
600 S Ct. St.
Montgomery, AL 36101
Ph: (334)834-5200
Fax: (334)265-4745
URL: http://www.montgomerychamber.com
Contact: Anna B. Buckalew, President
Facebook: www.facebook.com/montgomerychamber
X (Twitter): x.com/mgmchamber
Instagram: www.instagram.com/mgmchamber
YouTube: www.youtube.com/c/Montgomerychamber

Description: Organization engages in creating jobs and better lives for Montgomery area residents. **Founded:** 1873. **Publications:** M (Bimonthly); ChamberLink (Monthly). **Geographic Preference:** Local.

36138 ■ *Monthly Newsletter*
19812 Underwood Rd.
Foley, AL 36536
Ph: (251)943-3291
Free: 877-461-3712
Co. E-mail: jeanette@southbaldwinchamber.com
URL: http://www.southbaldwinchamber.com
Contact: Donna Watts, President
E-mail: donna@mylocalchamber.net
URL(s): www.southbaldwinchamber.com/monthly-newsletter

Released: Bimonthly **Availability:** PDF; Online.

36139 ■ Mountain Lakes Chamber of Commerce
407 E Willow St.
Scottsboro, AL 35768
Ph: (256)259-5500
Fax: (256)259-4447
Co. E-mail: roden@scottsboro.org
URL: http://mountainlakeschamberofcommerce.com
Contact: Rick Roden, President
E-mail: roden@scottsboro.org
Facebook: www.facebook.com/MtLakesChamber
Linkedin: www.linkedin.com/company/the-mountain-lakes-chamber-of-commerce
X (Twitter): x.com/MTLakesChamber
Instagram: www.instagram.com/mtlakeschamber
YouTube: www.youtube.com/channel/UCq4PJdrETOA20s_hvTcy7uA

Description: Promotes business and community development in Jackson County, AL. Conducts charitable programs; sponsors festival. **Founded:** 1959. **Publications:** Action Bulletin (Monthly). **Geographic Preference:** Local.

36140 ■ *News and Views*
1975 Merryvale Rd.
Vestavia Hills, AL 35216
Ph: (205)823-5011
Fax: (205)823-8974
Co. E-mail: chamber@vestaviahills.org
URL: http://www.vestaviahills.org
Contact: Karen Odle, Co-Chief Executive Officer Co-President
URL(s): www.vestaviahills.org/news-views

Released: Monthly **Availability:** Download; PDF; Online.

36141 ■ North Baldwin Chamber of Commerce (NBCC)
301 McMeans Ave.
Bay Minette, AL 36507
Ph: (251)937-5665
Fax: (251)937-5670
Co. E-mail: ashley@northbaldwinchamber.com
URL: http://www.northbaldwinchamber.com
Contact: Ashley Jones Davis, Executive Director
E-mail: ashley@northbaldwinchamber.com
Facebook: www.facebook.com/NorthBaldwinChamberOfCommerce
Pinterest: www.pinterest.com/northbaldwincha

Description: Promotes and enhances economic growth and community development. **Geographic Preference:** Local.

36142 ■ *North Mobile Business*
939 Saraland Blvd. S
Saraland, AL 36571
Ph: (251)675-4444
Fax: (251)675-2307
Co. E-mail: shilo@saralandchamber.com
URL: http://www.saralandchamber.com
Contact: Jamie Warren, Assistant Vice President
URL(s): business.saralandchamber.com/list

Description: Covers businesses in Saraland/North Mobile, AL. **Availability:** Print; Online.

36143 ■ Northwest Alabama Junior Chamber of Commerce
2808 Jackson Hwy.
Sheffield, AL 35660
Ph: (256)740-0255
Co. E-mail: nwajcc@mail.com
URL: http://nwajcc.tripod.com
Contact: Martin Dean, President

Description: Works with businesses and local governments to provide training, events and services in the area. **Geographic Preference:** State.

36144 ■ Opelika Chamber of Commerce
601 Ave. A
Opelika, AL 36803-2366
Ph: (334)745-4861
Co. E-mail: coc@opelikachamber.com
URL: http://www.opelikachamber.com
Contact: Jay Jones, Chairman
Linkedin: www.linkedin.com/company/opelika-chamber-of-commerce
X (Twitter): x.com/opelikachamber
Instagram: www.instagram.com/opelikachamber
YouTube: www.youtube.com/channel/UC8wz3rGT3EVbuPLRjAj1rEw

Description: Promotes business and community development in Opelika, AL. **Founded:** 1941. **Publications:** Chamber Update (Bimonthly); Return on Investment. **Geographic Preference:** Local.

36145 ■ Opp and Covington County Area Chamber of Commerce
200 S Main St.
Opp, AL 36467
Ph: (334)493-3070
Fax: (334)493-1060
Co. E-mail: oppchamber@gmail.com
URL: http://www.oppcoc.net

Description: Promotes business and community development in Covington County, AL. Sponsors Old Home Folks Day festival; maintains Opp Hall of Fame and administers United Fund. **Founded:** 1947. **Geographic Preference:** Local.

36146 ■ Ozark Area Chamber of Commerce
285 E Broad St.
Ozark, AL 36360
Ph: (334)774-9321
Free: 800-582-8497
Fax: (344)774-8736
Co. E-mail: info@ozarkchamber.com
URL: http://www.ozarkchamber.com
Contact: Fred S. Watson, Contact
Facebook: www.facebook.com/OzarkChamberOfCommerce
X (Twitter): x.com/OzarkMOChamber

Description: Promotes business and community development in the area. **Founded:** 1835. **Publications:** Ozark Area Chamber of Commerce-- Professional Directory and Community Information (Annual). **Geographic Preference:** Local.

36147 ■ Prattville Area Chamber of Commerce
131 N Ct., St.
Prattville, AL 36067
Ph: (334)365-7392
Free: 800-588-2796
Fax: (334)361-1314
Co. E-mail: info@prattvillechamber.com
URL: http://www.prattvillechamber.com
Contact: Patty VanderWal, President
Linkedin: www.linkedin.com/company/prattville-area-chamber-of-commerce/about
X (Twitter): x.com/Prattvillec
YouTube: www.youtube.com/channel/UCSaXIw0gCPQ_1MPMTMcXf1A/about
Description: Promotes business and community development in Autauga County, AL. **Founded:** 1973. **Publications:** Focus (Monthly). **Geographic Preference:** Local.

36148 ■ Quality of Life
20 Hightower Pl.
Florence, AL 35630-4102
Ph: (256)764-4661
Fax: (256)766-9017
Co. E-mail: shoals@shoalschamber.com
URL: http://www.shoalschamber.com
Contact: Rebecca Moon, Director
E-mail: rmoon@shoalschamber.com
URL(s): www.shoalschamber.com/priorities-initiatives
Availability: Print.

36149 ■ Rainsville Chamber of Commerce
115 Main St. W
Rainsville, AL 35986
Ph: (256)638-7800
Co. E-mail: chamber@farmerstel.com
URL: http://www.rainsville.info
Contact: Sandy Goff, Executive Director
Description: Promotes business and community development in Rainsville, AL. Seeks to attract tourism business. Sponsors activities. **Founded:** 1965. **Geographic Preference:** Local.

36150 ■ Saraland Area Chamber of Commerce
939 Saraland Blvd. S
Saraland, AL 36571
Ph: (251)675-4444
Fax: (251)675-2307
Co. E-mail: shilo@saralandchamber.com
URL: http://www.saralandchamber.com
Contact: Jamie Warren, Assistant Vice President
X (Twitter): x.com/saralandchamber
Description: Promotes business and community development in Saraland, AL. **Founded:** 1984. **Publications:** Communigator; Insight; North Mobile Business. **Educational Activities:** Saraland Area Chamber of Commerce Board meeting (Monthly). **Geographic Preference:** Local.

36151 ■ Shoals Chamber of Commerce (SCC)
20 Hightower Pl.
Florence, AL 35630-4102
Ph: (256)764-4661
Fax: (256)766-9017
Co. E-mail: shoals@shoalschamber.com
URL: http://www.shoalschamber.com
Contact: Rebecca Moon, Director
E-mail: rmoon@shoalschamber.com
Description: Promotes business and community development in Colbert and Lauderdale counties, AL. Provides information to newcomers and tourists. Sponsors Leadership Shoals, a 9-month program for business people. Conducts small business week. **Publications:** Shoals Chamber of Commerce-- Membership Directory (Annual); Guide to the Shoals (Annual); Industrial List (Periodic); Quality of Life. **Educational Activities:** Business After Hours (Annual). **Geographic Preference:** Local.

36152 ■ South Baldwin Chamber of Commerce (SBCC)
19812 Underwood Rd.
Foley, AL 36536
Ph: (251)943-3291
Free: 877-461-3712
Co. E-mail: jeanette@southbaldwinchamber.com
URL: http://www.southbaldwinchamber.com
Contact: Donna Watts, President
E-mail: donna@mylocalchamber.net
Facebook: www.facebook.com/SouthBaldwinChamberofCommerce
Linkedin: www.linkedin.com/company/south-baldwin-chamber-of-commerce
X (Twitter): x.com/SBaldwinChamber
Instagram: www.instagram.com/southbaldwinchamber
YouTube: www.youtube.com/channel/UC9SrN76JaZCEQix6nrMKwww
Description: Seeks to promote business and community development by providing information, services, and leadership for economic development. **Founded:** 1944. **Publications:** Monthly Newsletter (Bimonthly). **Awards:** Walton M. Vines Free Enterprise Person of the Year (Annual). **Geographic Preference:** Regional.

36153 ■ Sylacauga Chamber of Commerce
17 W Ft. Williams
Sylacauga, AL 35150
Ph: (256)249-0308
Fax: (256)249-0315
Co. E-mail: chamber@sylacauga.net
URL: http://www.sylacaugachamber.com
Contact: Laura Strickland, Executive Director
Description: Promotes business and community development in Talladega County, AL. **Publications:** Sylacauga Chamber of Commerce News (Monthly); Sylacauga. **Geographic Preference:** Local.

36154 ■ Trussville Area Chamber of Commerce (TACC)
400 Main St.
Trussville, AL 35173
Ph: (205)655-7535
Co. E-mail: june.mathews@trussvillechamber.com
URL: http://trussvillechamber.com
Contact: Donna Lowery, President
Facebook: www.facebook.com/trussvillechamber
X (Twitter): x.com/TrussChamber
Description: Promotes business and community development in Trussville, AL. Sponsors activities, promotions, and special projects. **Founded:** 1946. **Publications:** Quality of Life Magazine (Periodic); Trussville Community Directory (Annual). **Geographic Preference:** Local.

36155 ■ Union Springs/Bullock County Chamber of Commerce
c/o Aimee Ryan-Ulver, Executive Director
212 N Prairie St., No. Union
Union Springs, AL 36089-5006
Ph: (334)738-2424
Co. E-mail: usacoc@ustcoline.net
URL: http://alabamachambers.org/members/union-springsbullock-county-chamber-of-commerce
Contact: Aimee Ryan-Ulver, Executive Director
Facebook: www.facebook.com/UnionSpringsBullockCountyChamberOfCommerce
Description: Promotes business and community development in Bullock County, AL. Sponsors civic activities and supports local schools. **Founded:** 1965. **Geographic Preference:** Local.

36156 ■ Vestavia Hills Chamber of Commerce (VHCC)
1975 Merryvale Rd.
Vestavia Hills, AL 35216
Ph: (205)823-5011
Fax: (205)823-8974
Co. E-mail: chamber@vestaviahills.org
URL: http://www.vestaviahills.org
Contact: Karen Odle, Co-Chief Executive Officer Co-President
Facebook: www.facebook.com/vhchamberofcommerce
Linkedin: www.linkedin.com/company/vestavia-hills-chamber-of-commerce
Instagram: www.instagram.com/vhchamber
YouTube: www.youtube.com/user/vhchamber
Description: Promotes business and community development in Vestavia Hills, AL. **Founded:** 1981. **Publications:** News and Views (Monthly). **Educational Activities:** I Love America Night (Annual). **Geographic Preference:** Local.

36157 ■ The Weekly Business View
451 Government St.
Mobile, AL 36602
Ph: (251)433-6951
Free: 800-422-6951
Fax: (251)432-1143
Co. E-mail: info@mobilechamber.com
URL: http://mobilechamber.com
Contact: Bill Sisson, President
E-mail: bsisson@mobilechamber.com
URL(s): mobilechamber.com/2023/01/mobile-chamber-online-benefits-user-guide
Released: Weekly **Description:** Provides important information about the Mobile area and the region's business community. **Availability:** Online.

MINORITY BUSINESS ASSISTANCE PROGRAMS

36158 ■ Birmingham Business Resource Center (BBRC)
1500 1st Ave. N, Unit 12
Birmingham, AL 35203
Ph: (205)250-6380
Fax: (205)250-6384
Co. E-mail: info@bbrc.biz
URL: http://mybbrc.biz
Contact: Bob Dickerson, Executive Director
E-mail: bdickerson@bbrc.biz
Facebook: www.facebook.com/mybbrcbiz
X (Twitter): x.com/mybbrcbiz
Description: Firm provides small business finance and related technical assistance. **Founded:** 1996.

36159 ■ Women's Business Alliance (WBA)
700 Lanier St.
Chickasaw, AL 36611
Ph: (251)660-2825
Fax: (251)660-8954
URL: http://womensbusinessalliance.org
Contact: Karen Edmonds, Executive Director
X (Twitter): x.com/WBAofAL
Description: Works to assist and empower women in starting or growing small businesses. **Founded:** 1993.

FINANCING AND LOAN PROGRAMS

36160 ■ Bonaventure Capital (BC)
820 Shades Creek Pky., Ste. 1200
Birmingham, AL 35209
URL: http://bonaventurecapital.net
Contact: Billy Reiser, Officer
E-mail: breiser@bonaventurecapital.net
Description: Venture capital firm investing in mid-stage to emerging growth businesses. **Founded:** 1998. **Preferred Investment Size:** $500,000 to $1,500,000. **Investment Policies:** Investment Policies. **Industry Preferences:** Computer software, industrial and energy, financial services and utilities.

36161 ■ Eastside Partners
207 Eastside Sq., 2nd Fl.
Huntsville, AL 35801
Ph: (256)327-8777
Co. E-mail: intro@eastsidepartners.com
URL: http://www.eastsidepartners.com
Contact: Benjamin Cobb, Partner
Description: Growth-equity investment firm. Also operates out of Atlanta. **Founded:** 1998. **Industry Preferences:** Vertical SaaS; healthcare; tech-enabled services.

STATE LISTINGS

36162 ■ FHL Capital Corp.
1823 27th Ave. S
  Birmingham, AL 35209
Ph: (205)328-3098
URL: http://www.fhlcapital.com
Contact: Edwin W. Finch, III, President
E-mail: efinch@fhlcapital.com
Linkedin: www.linkedin.com/company/fhl-capital-cor
  poration
Description: Provider of investment-banking and financial advisory services. **Founded:** 1984. **Preferred Investment Size:** $1,000,000 to $75,000,000.

36163 ■ Harbert Management Corp. (HMC)
2100 3rd Ave. N, Ste. 600
  Birmingham, AL 35203
Ph: (205)987-5500
URL: http://www.harbert.net
Contact: Travis J. Pritchett, President
Linkedin: www.linkedin.com/company/harber
  t-management-corporation
X (Twitter): x.com/harbertmgmtcorp
Description: Equity firm provides investment services. **Founded:** 1993. **Preferred Investment Size:** $1,000,000 to $4,000,000. **Industry Preferences:** Technology, semiconductors and other electronics, medical and health, biotechnology, communications, software and services.

PROCUREMENT ASSISTANCE PROGRAMS

36164 ■ Alabama Department of Finance - Division of Purchasing
RSA Union Bldg.
  100 N Union St., Ste. 192
  Montgomery, AL 36104
Ph: (334)242-7250
URL: http://purchasing.alabama.gov
Contact: Tina Barber, Executive Secretary
E-mail: tina.barber@purchasing.alabama.gov
Description: Contact for the state's list of bidders for government purchasing contracts. A small business representative is available.

36165 ■ Alabama Small Business Development Center Network (ASBDC)
621 Greensboro Ave.
  Tuscaloosa, AL 35401
Ph: (205)348-1582
Free: 877-825-7232
Co. E-mail: asbdc@ua.edu
URL: http://www.asbdc.org
Contact: Brian K. Davis, Director
Facebook: www.facebook.com/AlabamaSBDC
Linkedin: www.linkedin.com/company/alabama-small
  -business-development-center-network
Description: Providing management and technical assistance to small businesses. **Founded:** 1985.

36166 ■ APEX Accelerator of Alabama (PTAC) [Procurement Technical Assistance Center]
621 Greensboro Ave.
  Tuscaloosa, AL 35401
URL: http://ptac.ua.edu
Description: Identifies and implements innovative procurement practices in support of the efforts of our customers, and assists the University with its mission of teaching, research and public service by safeguarding the integrity of the purchasing and payables process.

36167 ■ U.S. Small Business Administration - Office of Government Contracting, Area III - Procurement Center Representative - Alabama
c/o Vick Peltier
  Bldg. 5303, Ste. 3135
  Redstone Arsenal, AL 35898-5000
Co. E-mail: vick.peltier@sba.gov
URL: http://www.sba.gov/contracting/resources-small
  -businesses/pcr-directory/pcr-directory-area-3
Contact: Vick Peltier, Contact
E-mail: vick.peltier@sba.gov

Description: Covers activities for Army Aviation and Missile Command, Huntsville, AL.

INCUBATORS/RESEARCH AND TECHNOLOGY PARKS

36168 ■ Alabama Department of Commerce - Enterprise Business Incubator
102 Commerce Dr.
  Enterprise, AL 36330
Ph: (334)393-4769
Free: 800-611-4769
URL: http://www.wiregrassedc.com/#!business
  -incubator/c1nc1
URL(s): www.madeinalabama.com/business
  -development/small-business/incubator-programs
Description: Business incubator that is part of a continual effort to help new and expanding business develop and grow in the region.

36169 ■ Auburn Business Incubator (ABI)
570 Devall Dr., Ste. 101
  Auburn, AL 36832
Ph: (334)844-7480
Co. E-mail: info@auburnrtf.org
URL: http://www.auburnrtf.org
Contact: Bill Dean, Executive Director
E-mail: billdean@auburn.edu
Facebook: www.facebook.com/auburnresearchpark
X (Twitter): x.com/AuburnRTF
Description: Provider of services like assistance, infrastructure and more.

36170 ■ Auburn Research and Technologoy Foundation (ARTF)
570 Devall Dr., Ste. 101
  Auburn, AL 36832
Ph: (334)844-7480
Co. E-mail: info@auburnrtf.org
URL: http://thepark.auburn.edu
Contact: Bill Dean, Executive Director
E-mail: billdean@auburn.edu
Facebook: www.facebook.com/auburnresearchpark
X (Twitter): x.com/AuburnRTF
Instagram: www.instagram.com/auburnresearchpark
YouTube: www.youtube.com/channel/UCmZ8sikl9LF
  _SPyL0OhY-vA
Description: Supports the entrepreneurial and economic development initiative to grow the knowledge-based economy and create a mixed-use research and business campus.

36171 ■ Baldwin County Business Incubator
PO Box 1340
  Robertsdale, AL 36567
Co. E-mail: helpdesk@auburn.edu
URL: http://auburn.edu
Description: A small business incubator that offers qualifying start-up companies a structured two-to-three-year program of advice and professional assistance to help ensure success. **Founded:** 1856.

36172 ■ Bessemer Business Incubation System (BBIS)
c/o Bessemer Business Center1020 Ninth Ave., SW
  Bessemer, AL 35022
Ph: (205)481-2000
Fax: (205)481-2100
Co. E-mail: bessemerincubator@yahoo.com
URL: http://www.bessemerincubator.net
Contact: Devron A. Veasley, Director
Description: A division of the Bessemer Development Board that provides in-house services for businesses with revenues up to $5,000,000. It serves not only startup operations, but challenged, former home-based, geographically-expanding and those operations still in the research/feasibility phase. Businesses can remain in the incubator for up to 5 years. **Founded:** 1996.

36173 ■ Bevill State Business Incubator Center
3512 Industrial Dr.
  Jasper, AL 35501
Ph: (205)648-3271

URL: http://www.bscc.edu/workforce/business-incuba
  tor.php
Contact: Tim Holt, Contact
Description: Business incubator providing hands-on assistance and business support services to startup companies. Access is provided to warehouse space, delivery bays and additional resources. **Founded:** 1990.

36174 ■ Chef's Workshop
3439 Lorna Ln.
  Birmingham, AL 35216
Ph: (205)637-1055
Co. E-mail: info@chefsworkshop.com
URL: http://www.chefsworkshop.com
Facebook: www.facebook.com/
  ChefsWorkshopBirmingham
Description: Firm is a commercial kitchen provider.

36175 ■ Chilton Food Innovation Center (CFIC)
500 Fifth Ave. N
  Clanton, AL 35045
Ph: (205)280-6268
URL: http://www.chiltonfoodinnovationcenter.com
Contact: Pennie Broussard, Contact
Facebook: www.facebook.com/ChiltonFoodInnova
  tionCenter
Description: Firm is a non-profit food-processing facility for small fruit and vegetable producers and small food businesses.

36176 ■ Covington County Economic Development Center (CCEDC)
21754 Bill Benton Ln.
  Andalusia, AL 36421
Ph: (334)222-7040
Fax: (334)222-0897
Co. E-mail: rick.clifton@covingtoncountyedc.com
URL: http://www.covingtoncountyedc.com
Contact: Rick Clifton, President
E-mail: rick.clifton@covingtoncountyedc.com
Facebook: www.facebook.com/Covingtoncountyedc
Description: Covington's small business development incubator assists home grown businesses in Covington county. Assists in all aspects of business startup.

36177 ■ Decatur-Morgan County Entrepreneurial Center [The E-Center]
1629 4th Ave. SE
  Decatur, AL 35601
Ph: (256)686-2999
Co. E-mail: info@alabamaincubator.com
URL: http://the-ecenter.org
Contact: Dr. Karockas Watkins, President
Facebook: www.facebook.com/alabamaincubator
Linkedin: www.linkedin.com/company/decatur-mor
  gan-county-entrepreneurial-center
X (Twitter): x.com/alincubator
Description: Encourages new and small businesses as tenants and non-tenants of the E-Center facility and ensures successful start-up and continued business growth. **Founded:** 2010.

36178 ■ The EDGE
2627 10th Ave.
  Tuscaloosa, AL 35401
Ph: (205)348-3343
Co. E-mail: edge@culverhouse.ua.edu
URL: http://edge.culverhouse.ua.edu
Contact: Dr. Theresa Welbourne, Executive Director
Description: Offers an incubation program for new and developing businesses. Through the program, resident businesses can take advantage of affordable office space and shared resources such as administrative support, audiovisual equipment, copying equipment, meeting rooms, and low-cost phone, fax, and internet services. **Founded:** 2012.

36179 ■ The Edge Entrepreneurship Center
2627 10th Ave.
  Tuscaloosa, AL 35401
Ph: (205)348-3343
Co. E-mail: edge@culverhouse.ua.edu
URL: http://edge.culverhouse.ua.edu
Contact: Dr. Theresa Welbourne, Executive Director

36180 ■ Alabama

Description: Business incubator that aids emerging businesses with the development of management, financial, and technical skills in a maturing environment so that they can thrive in the local business community. **Founded:** 2012.

36180 ■ EDGE Incubator and Accelerator
2627 10th Ave.
 Tuscaloosa, AL 35401
Ph: (205)348-3343
Co. E-mail: edge@culverhouse.ua.edu
URL: http://edge.culverhouse.ua.edu
Contact: Dr. Theresa Welbourne, Executive Director
Facebook: www.facebook.com/BamaEn
 trepreneurship
X (Twitter): x.com/TheEdgeCEI
Description: Incubator and accelerator focused on growing and supporting entrepreneurs. Partnership with the University of Alabama, the West Alabama Chamber of Commerce, and the city of Tuscaloosa. **Founded:** 2012.

36181 ■ EDGE Labs
720 2nd St.
 Tuscaloosa, AL 35401
URL: http://aei.culverhouse.ua.edu/edge-labs
Description: Technology incubator who helps high-growth, high-tech businesses grow into profitable industry leaders.

36182 ■ Fayette Center for Manufacturing and Innovation
203 Temple Ave. N
 Fayette, AL 35555
Ph: (205)932-5367
Fax: (205)932-8788
URL: http://fayetteal.org/about-2/about
Description: Business incubator providing support to startups in all aspects of starting a business. **Founded:** 1972.

36183 ■ Innovation Depot
1500 1st Ave. N
 Birmingham, AL 35203
Ph: (205)250-8000
Co. E-mail: info@innovationdepot.org
URL: http://innovationdepot.org
Contact: Drew Honeycutt, Chief Executive Officer
Facebook: www.facebook.com/InnovationDepot
Linkedin: www.linkedin.com/company/innovation
 -depot
X (Twitter): x.com/innovationdepot
Instagram: www.instagram.com/innovationdepot
YouTube: www.youtube.com/channel/UC7jt6gQVhP
 _hpbZclvQDKww
Description: Innovation Depot is a business incubator housing 70 start-up businesses. The Depot is a non-profit partnership formed by the combination of the Entrepreneurial Center and the University of Alabama at Birmingham's Office for the Advancement of Developing Industries. **Founded:** 1987.

36184 ■ Marengo County Economic Development Authority
2400 E Coats Ave.
 Linden, AL 36748
Ph: (334)295-4417
Co. E-mail: eda@marengoeda.com
URL: http://marengoeda.com
Contact: Jo Ellen Martin, Executive Director
Facebook: www.facebook.com/MarengoEconDev
X (Twitter): x.com/MarengoEDA
Description: Business incubator who aids business startups.

36185 ■ Mixson Business Center (MBC)
545 W Main St., Ste. 100
 Dothan, AL 36301
Ph: (334)836-0217
Co. E-mail: fscpropertymgt@aol.com
URL: http://mixsonbusinesscenter.org
Facebook: www.facebook.com/
 MixsonBusinessCenter
Description: Business incubator whose offerings include private offices, virtual offices, meeting rooms, and workshops.

36186 ■ Montgomery Area Chamber of Commerce (MACOC)
600 S Ct. St.
 Montgomery, AL 36101
Ph: (334)834-5200
Fax: (334)265-4745
URL: http://www.montgomerychamber.com
Contact: Anna B. Buckalew, President
Facebook: www.facebook.com/montgomerychamber
X (Twitter): x.com/mgmchamber
Instagram: www.instagram.com/mgmchamber
YouTube: www.youtube.com/c/Montgomerychamber
Description: Organization engages in creating jobs and better lives for Montgomery area residents. **Founded:** 1873. **Publications:** *M* (Bimonthly); *ChamberLink* (Monthly). **Geographic Preference:** Local.

36187 ■ Montgomery Area Chamber of Commerce Incubation Program
600 S Ct. St.
 Montgomery, AL 36101
URL: http://www.montgomerychamber.com/small
 -business-development
Description: A non-profit small business incubator program for new service and light manufacturing businesses in the Montgomery area.

36188 ■ Northeast Alabama Entrepreneurial Center (NEAES)
1400 Commerce Blvd., Ste. 1
 Anniston, AL 36207
Ph: (256)831-5215
URL: http://www.neaes.org
Description: A business incubator for start-up service companies and light manufacturing businesses. **Founded:** 1998.

36189 ■ Northeast Alabama Entrepreneurial System (NEAES)
1400 Commerce Blvd., Ste. 1
 Anniston, AL 36207
Ph: (256)831-5215
URL: http://www.neaes.org
Description: A business incubator in which start-up companies locate during their initial growth phase which can range from one to five years. **Founded:** 1998.

36190 ■ Ozark Technology Center (OTC)
3269 US Hwy. 231 S
 Ozark, AL 36360
URL: http://www.ozarkal.gov/economic-development
Contact: Tara Morris, Manager
E-mail: tara@odedc.com
Description: Business incubator with an environment that is conducive to the success and growth of new and expanding businesses, create regional job opportunities and expand the regional economy. Services include office space, business planning and financing assistance, and access to a small business resource library.

36191 ■ Shoals Business Incubator (SEI)
3115 Northington Ct.
 Florence, AL 35630
Ph: (256)760-9014
URL: http://www.shoalsbusinessincubator.com
Contact: Giles McDaniel, Executive Director
E-mail: giles@shoalsbusinessincubator.com
Facebook: www.facebook.com/ShoalsBusiness
Linkedin: www.linkedin.com/company/4687841
X (Twitter): x.com/ShoalsBusiness
Description: Firm provides cluster of commercial space, business counseling and technical assistance. **Founded:** 1992.

36192 ■ Shoals Commercial Culinary Center
3115 Northington Crt.
 Florence, AL 35630
Ph: (256)760-9014
URL: http://www.shoalsbusinessincubator.com
Contact: Giles McDaniel, Executive Director
E-mail: giles@shoalsbusinessincubator.com
URL(s): business.shoalschamber.com/list/member/
 shoals-commercial-culinary-center-3417.htm
Facebook: www.facebook.com/ShoalsBusiness
Linkedin: www.linkedin.com/company/shoals-en
 trepreneurial-center
X (Twitter): x.com/ShoalsBusiness
Description: Unique incubation concept offering assistance to specialty food producers in getting their product to market, a shared commercial kitchen allows small entrepreneurs in the food-related industry to share the equipment and facilities of a professionally-equipped kitchen and the expertise of food processing professionals in all aspects of the production and sales of their individual products.

LEGISLATIVE ASSISTANCE

36193 ■ Alabama Legislature House of Representatives - House Commerce and Small Business Committee
c/o Mary Ruth Davis, Clerk
 Rm. 418
 Montgomery, AL 36130
Ph: (334)261-0478
Co. E-mail: maryruth.davis@alhouse.gov
URL: http://alison.legislature.state.al.us/committees
 -house-standing-current
Contact: Mary Ruth Davis, Clerk
E-mail: maryruth.davis@alhouse.gov

REFERENCE WORKS

36194 ■ *Air Conditioning, Heating & Refrigeration News--HVACR Directory and Source Guide*
Pub: BNP Media
Contact: Harper Henderson, Owner Co-Chief Executive Officer
URL(s): www.bnpmedia.com/who-we-are
Released: Annual **Description:** Publication includes lists of about 2,086 manufacturers, 4,383 wholesalers and factory outlets, 1,667 HVACR products, exporters specializing in the industry; related trade organizations; manufacturers representatives, consultants, services; videos and software. **Entries include:** For manufacturers--Company Name, address, phone, fax, e-mail, URL, names of key personnel, brand names, list of products; similar information for other categories. **Arrangement:** Manufacturers and exporters are alphabetical; wholesalers and representatives are geographical. **Indexes:** Product, trade name. **Availability:** Online.

CONSULTANTS

36195 ■ The Catalyst Center for Business & Entrepreneurship
515 Sparkman Dr.
 Huntsville, AL 35816
Ph: (256)428-8190
Co. E-mail: info@catalystcenter.org
URL: http://catalystcenter.org
Contact: Lisa Davis Mays, Chief Executive Officer
E-mail: lisa.mays@catalystcenter.org
Facebook: www.facebook.com/thecatalystcenter
X (Twitter): x.com/thecatalysthsv
YouTube: www.youtube.com/channel/
 UChuJZMugZn8TWgTGrQmElgQ
Description: Serves as a driver for economic growth and job creation in Huntsville and surrounding areas by providing support for entrepreneurs and business owners in every stage of growth.

PUBLICATIONS

36196 ■ *Alabama Business*
1500 Greensboro Ave., Ste. 1
 Tuscaloosa, AL 35401
Ph: (205)348-6191
Fax: (205)348-2951
Co. E-mail: uacber@cba.ua.edu
URL: http://cber.culverhouse.ua.edu
Contact: Ahmad Ijaz, Executive Director
E-mail: aijaz@culverhouse.ua.edu
URL(s): cber.culverhouse.ua.edu/alabama-business

STATE LISTINGS

Released: Quarterly **Price:** Free. **Description:** Journal covering business in the state of Alabama. **Availability:** PDF.

36197 ■ *Alabama Business Confidence Index*
1500 Greensboro Ave., Ste. 1
Tuscaloosa, AL 35401
Ph: (205)348-6191
Fax: (205)348-2951
Co. E-mail: uacber@cba.ua.edu
URL: http://cber.culverhouse.ua.edu
Contact: Ahmad Ijaz, Executive Director
E-mail: aijaz@culverhouse.ua.edu
URL(s): cber.culverhouse.ua.edu/2024/04/16/mildly-confident-expansionary-forecast-for-q2-2024
Released: Quarterly **Availability:** Online.

36198 ■ Birmingham Business Journal Inc. (BBJ)
2140 11th Ave. S, Ste. 205
Birmingham, AL 35205
Ph: (205)443-5600
Fax: (205)322-0040
Co. E-mail: birmingham@bizjournals.com
URL: http://www.bizjournals.com
Contact: Joel Welker, President
E-mail: jwelker@bizjournals.com
Facebook: www.facebook.com/birminghambusinessjournal
Linkedin: www.linkedin.com/company/birmingham-business-journal
X (Twitter): x.com/bhambizjrnl

Description: Publisher of newspapers. **Founded:** 1983.

36199 ■ *Business Alabama*
3263 Cottage Hill Rd.
Mobile, AL 36606
URL: http://pmtpublishing.com
URL(s): businessalabama.com
Facebook: www.facebook.com/BusinessAlabamaMagazine
Linkedin: www.linkedin.com/company/business-alabama
X (Twitter): x.com/BusinessAlabama
Ed: Erica West. **Released:** Monthly **Price:** $4.95, for monthly; $29.95, for 1 year. **Description:** Magazine for owners, managers, and presidents of companies covering issues and people in business in Alabama. **Availability:** Print.

RESEARCH CENTERS

36200 ■ University of Alabama - Capstone International Center (CIC)
135 BB Comer Hall
Tuscaloosa, AL 35487-0134
Ph: (205)348-5256
Co. E-mail: cic@ua.edu
URL: http://international.ua.edu
Contact: Dr. Carolina Robinson, Director
E-mail: carolir@ua.edu

Description: Integral unit of University of Alabama. **Scope:** Developments in Latin America, Asia, and Mediterranean Europe through projects conducted by faculty members of the University and supported by international opportunity program travel grants. Also conducts market studies for small businesses in Alabama. **Founded:** 1966. **Publications:** *Capstone International Newsletter*.

36201 ■ University of Alabama - Culverhouse College of Commerce and Business Administration - Center for Business and Economic Research - Alabama State Data Center (ASDC)
1500 Greensboro Ave., Ste. 1
Tuscaloosa, AL 35401
Ph: (205)348-6191
Fax: (205)348-2951
URL: http://cber.culverhouse.ua.edu/alabama-state-data-center
Contact: Susannah Robichaux, Contact
E-mail: scrobichaux@culverhouse.ua.edu

Description: Integral unit of Center for Business and Economic Research in College of Commerce and Business Administration, University of Alabama. Offers consultation and telephone reference assistance (daily). **Scope:** Makes census data (1980-) available for research and other uses at the University and throughout the state. Maintains both census and other varied technical documentation. **Founded:** 1978. **Educational Activities:** Statewide workshops.

Alaska

ASSOCIATIONS AND OTHER ORGANIZATIONS

36202 ■ Business Network International Alaska
1601 E 84th St., No. 203
Anchorage, AK 99507
Ph: (517)449-1788
Fax: (866)274-3093
URL: http://bnialaska.com/en-US/index
Contact: Michelle Campbell, Executive Director
E-mail: michelle@bnialaska.com
Description: Provides both men and women a structured environment for the development and exchange of quality business referrals. Offers members the opportunity to share ideas and contacts. **Geographic Preference:** State.

36203 ■ International Association of Women Anchorage Chapter
Anchorage, AK
URL: http://www.iawomen.com/chapters/anchorage-chapter
Description: Serves as network of accomplished women united to achieve professional goals. Provides a forum for sharing ideas and experiences of professional women regarding career success. Promotes an active business and networking community from all industries. **Geographic Preference:** Local.

36204 ■ National Federation of Independent Business Alaska
PO Box 211231
Juneau, AK 99821
Ph: (907)723-1494
URL: http://www.nfib.com/alaska
Contact: Thor Stacey, Director
E-mail: thorstacey@gmail.com
X (Twitter): x.com/nfib_ak
Description: Represents small and independent businesses. Aims to promote and protect the rights of members to own, operate and grow their businesses. **Founded:** 1992. **Geographic Preference:** State.

SMALL BUSINESS DEVELOPMENT CENTERS

36205 ■ Alaska Small Business Development Center Fairbanks (ASBDC)
330 Wendell Ave., Ste. C
Fairbanks, AK 99701
Ph: (907)456-7232
Co. E-mail: info@aksbdc.org
URL: http://aksbdc.org
Contact: Jade Greene, Director
E-mail: jade.greene@aksbdc.org
Geographic Preference: Local.

36206 ■ Alaska Small Business Development Center Homer
1901 Bragaw St., Rm. 199
Anchorage, AK 99508
Ph: (907)786-7201
Co. E-mail: info@aksbdc.org
URL: http://aksbdc.org
Contact: Jon Bittner, Executive Director
E-mail: jon.bittner@aksbdc.org
Facebook: www.facebook.com/alaskasbdc
X (Twitter): x.com/AlaskaSBDC
YouTube: www.youtube.com/c/AlaskaSmallBusinessDevelopmentCenterAnchorage
Description: Provides no-cost, one-on-one business coaching and low-cost workshops throughout Alaska. **Founded:** 1986.

36207 ■ Alaska Small Business Development Center Juneau (ASBDC)
3030 Vintage Blvd.Ste. 100
Juneau, AK 99801
Ph: (907)463-3789
Co. E-mail: juneau@aksbdc.org
URL: http://aksbdc.org
Contact: Ian Grant, Director
E-mail: ian.grant@aksbdc.org
Geographic Preference: Local.

36208 ■ Alaska Small Business Development Center Ketchikan (SBDC)
3030 Vintage Blvd., Ste. 100
Juneau, AK 99801-9380
Ph: (907)463-3789
Co. E-mail: info@aksbdc.org
URL: http://aksbdc.org
Contact: Sandy Hussain, Director
E-mail: sandy.hussain@aksbdc.org
X (Twitter): x.com/AlaskaSBDC
Description: Provides business coaching for the members in Alaska. **Founded:** 1986.

36209 ■ Alaska Small Business Development Center Soldotna (ASBDC)
43335 Kalifornsky Beach Rd., Ste. 12
Soldotna, AK 99669
Ph: (907)260-5643
Co. E-mail: info@aksbdc.org
URL: http://aksbdc.org
Contact: Cliff Cochran, Director
E-mail: cliff.cochran@aksbdc.org
X (Twitter): x.com/AlaskaSBDC
Instagram: www.instagram.com/alaskasbdc
Geographic Preference: Local.

36210 ■ Alaska Small Business Development Center State Office (ASBDC) [Alaska Small Business Development Center Anchorage]
1901 Bragaw St., Rm. 199
Anchorage, AK 99508
Ph: (907)786-7201
Co. E-mail: info@aksbdc.org
URL: http://aksbdc.org
Contact: Jon Bittner, Executive Director
E-mail: jon.bittner@aksbdc.org
Facebook: www.facebook.com/alaskasbdc
Linkedin: www.linkedin.com/company/alaska-small-business-development-center
X (Twitter): x.com/alaskasbdc
Instagram: www.instagram.com/alaskasbdc
YouTube: www.youtube.com/channel/UCNm9OQt9HqLyj-g0-vorcig
Founded: 1986. **Publications:** *Alaska Manufacturer's Directory* (Semiannual). **Geographic Preference:** Local; State.

36211 ■ Alaska Small Business Development Center Wasilla (ASBDC)
201 N Lucille St., Ste. 2A
Wasilla, AK 99654-7010
Ph: (907)373-7232
Co. E-mail: info@aksbdc.org
URL: http://aksbdc.org
Contact: Jon Bittner, Executive Director
E-mail: jon.bittner@aksbdc.org
Facebook: www.facebook.com/alaskasbdc
Linkedin: www.linkedin.com/company/alaska-small-business-development-center
X (Twitter): x.com/alaskasbdc
Instagram: www.instagram.com/alaskasbdc
YouTube: www.youtube.com/c/AlaskaSmallBusinessDevelopmentCenterAnchorage
Founded: 1986. **Geographic Preference:** Local.

SMALL BUSINESS ASSISTANCE PROGRAMS

36212 ■ Alaska Department of Commerce, Community, and Economic Development (DCCED)
333 Willoughby Ave., 9th Fl.
State Office Building
Juneau, AK 99801
Ph: (907)465-2500
Fax: (907)465-5442
Co. E-mail: bsc@commerce.state.ak.us
URL: http://www.commerce.alaska.gov/web
Contact: Lori Wing-Heier, Director
Description: Assists entrepreneurs in starting new businesses or expanding existing businesses. Helps prepare applications for economic development programs. Holds seminars and workshops on various aspects of business management. **Publications:** *Alaska Community Database Online*; *Alaska Community Funding Database*; *Alaska Capital Projects Database*; *Alaskan Directory of Products & Services* (Annual); *Corporate Directory State of Alaska* (Annual).

SCORE OFFICES

36213 ■ SCORE - Alaska
12001 Business Blvd., Ste. 108
Eagle River, AK 99577
Ph: (206)553-7320
Co. E-mail: help@score.org
URL: http://alaska.score.org
Facebook: www.facebook.com/SCOREAlaska
Linkedin: www.linkedin.com/company/score-alaska

STATE LISTINGS

Description: Provides professional guidance and information to maximize the success of existing and emerging small businesses. Offers business counseling and workshops. **Founded:** 1964. **Geographic Preference:** Local.

36214 ■ SCORE - Anchorage
510 L St. Ste. 301
Anchorage, AK 99501
Ph: (360)685-4259
URL: http://www.score.org/alaska/content/contact-score-alaska
Description: Provides professional guidance and information to maximize the success of existing and emerging small businesses. Offers business counseling and workshops. **Founded:** 1964.

36215 ■ SCORE - Eagle
420 L St., Ste. 300
Anchorage, AK 99501
Ph: (360)685-4259
URL: http://www.score.org/alaska/about
Description: Provides professional guidance and information to maximize the success of existing and emerging small businesses. Offers business counseling and workshops.

36216 ■ SCORE - Fairbanks
330 Wendell Ave., Ste. E
Fairbanks, AK 99707
Ph: (907)452-2185
URL: http://alaska.score.org
Description: Provides professional guidance and information to maximize the success of existing and emerging small businesses. Offers business counseling and workshops.

BETTER BUSINESS BUREAUS

36217 ■ Better Business Bureau Great West + Pacific [BBB Great West + Pacific]
PO Box 191279
Boise, ID 83719
Ph: (208)342-4649
URL: http://www.bbb.org/local-bbb/bbb-great-west-pacific
Linkedin: www.linkedin.com/company/bbbgwp
Instagram: www.instagram.com/bbbgwp
YouTube: www.youtube.com/bbbgwp
Description: Seeks to promote and foster the highest ethical relationship between businesses and the public through voluntary self-regulation, consumer and business education, and service excellence. Provides information to help consumers and businesses make informed purchasing decisions and avoid costly scams and frauds; settles consumer complaints through arbitration and other means. **Geographic Preference:** State.

CHAMBERS OF COMMERCE

36218 ■ Alaska State Chamber of Commerce
471 W 36th Ave., Ste. 200
Anchorage, AK 99503
Ph: (907)278-2722
Co. E-mail: info@alaskachamber.com
URL: http://www.alaskachamber.com
Contact: Kati Capozzi, President
E-mail: kati@alaskachamber.com
Facebook: www.facebook.com/alaskachamber
X (Twitter): x.com/AlaskaChamber
Instagram: www.instagram.com/alaskachamber
Description: Promotes business and community development in Alaska. **Founded:** 1953. **Publications:** *The Chamber* (Quarterly); *Alaska State Chamber of Commerce--Membership Directory*. **Awards:** William A. Egan Outstanding Alaskan of the Year (Annual); Local Alaska Chamber of Commerce of the Year (Annual); Bill Bivin Small Business of the Year (Annual). **Geographic Preference:** State.

36219 ■ Anchor Point Chamber of Commerce
34175 Sterling Hwy.
Anchor Point, AK 99556
Ph: (907)235-2600
Co. E-mail: info@anchorpointchamber.org

URL: http://anchorpointchamber.org
Contact: Dawson Slaughter, Contact
E-mail: slaughterdawson1@gmail.com
Description: Seeks to promote and perpetuate business; to promote the general welfare of the Anchor Point area; and to stimulate public interest to these ends. **Publications:** *Anchor Point Brochure/Visitor Guide* (Periodic); *Business Directory*; *The Resolution* (Monthly). **Geographic Preference:** Local.

36220 ■ Anchorage Chamber of Commerce
1016 W 6th Ave., Ste. 303
Anchorage, AK 99501
Ph: (907)272-2401
Fax: (907)272-4117
Co. E-mail: info@anchoragechamber.org
URL: http://anchoragechamber.org
Contact: Bruce Bustamante, President
Facebook: www.facebook.com/QuadCountySnowmobileClub
Linkedin: www.linkedin.com/company/anchoragechamber
X (Twitter): x.com/AnchChamber
Instagram: www.instagram.com/anchoragechamber
YouTube: www.youtube.com/user/Anchchamber
Description: Promotes business and community development in Anchorage, AK. **Founded:** 1915. **Publications:** *News and Views* (Quarterly). **Awards:** Anchorage Chamber Gold Pan (Annual). **Geographic Preference:** Local.

36221 ■ *Chamber News*
PO Box 987
Delta Junction, AK 99737
Ph: (907)895-5068
Fax: (907)895-5141
Co. E-mail: deltacc@deltachamber.org
URL: http://www.deltachamber.org
Contact: Debbie Joslin, President
URL(s): www.deltachamber.org/chambernews.html
Released: Last Edition July 2016. **Availability:** PDF.

36222 ■ *Chugiak-Eagle River Business & Service Directory*
12001 Business Blvd., Ste. 108
Eagle River, AK 99577-0353
Ph: (907)694-4702
Co. E-mail: info@cer.org
URL: http://www.cer.org
Contact: Kelsie Sullivan, Co-President
URL(s): www.cer.org/list
Availability: Online.

36223 ■ Chugiak-Eagle River Chamber of Commerce
12001 Business Blvd., Ste. 108
Eagle River, AK 99577-0353
Ph: (907)694-4702
Co. E-mail: info@cer.org
URL: http://www.cer.org
Contact: Kelsie Sullivan, Co-President
Facebook: www.facebook.com/CERChamber
Description: Seeks to promote and perpetuate economic development, civic interest, general welfare and prosperity of the Chugiak-Eagle River area. Aims to stimulate public interest to these ends. **Founded:** 1970. **Publications:** *Chugiak-Eagle River Business & Service Directory*. **Educational Activities:** Chugiak-Eagle River Chamber of Commerce Board meeting (Monthly). **Geographic Preference:** Local.

36224 ■ Cordova Chamber of Commerce
404 1st St.
Cordova, AK 99574
Ph: (907)424-7260
URL: http://www.cordovachamber.com
Contact: Osa Schultz, Treasurer
Facebook: www.facebook.com/cordovachamber
Linkedin: www.linkedin.com/company/cordova-chamber-of-commerce
X (Twitter): x.com/cordovachamber
Description: Promotes business, community development, and tourism in Cordova, Alaska. **Geographic Preference:** Local.

36225 ■ *Delta Junction Chamber of Commerce*
PO Box 987
Delta Junction, AK 99737
Ph: (907)895-5068
Fax: (907)895-5141
Co. E-mail: deltacc@deltachamber.org
URL: http://www.deltachamber.org
Contact: Debbie Joslin, President
URL(s): www.deltachamber.org/memberdirectory.html
Released: Annual; last edition 2016. **Availability:** PDF.

36226 ■ Delta Junction Chamber of Commerce
PO Box 987
Delta Junction, AK 99737
Ph: (907)895-5068
Fax: (907)895-5141
Co. E-mail: deltacc@deltachamber.org
URL: http://www.deltachamber.org
Contact: Debbie Joslin, President
Description: Promotes business and community development in Delta Junction, Alaska. **Founded:** 1977. **Publications:** *Chamber News*; *Delta Junction Chamber of Commerce* (Annual); *Delta Junction Visitor Guide* (Annual). **Geographic Preference:** Local.

36227 ■ Denali Chamber of Commerce
Mile 4 Healy Spur Rd.
Healy, AK 99743
Ph: (907)683-4636
Co. E-mail: info@denalichamber.com
URL: http://denalichamber.com
Contact: Vanessa Jusczak, Executive Director
E-mail: director@denalichamber.com
Facebook: www.facebook.com/denalichamber
Description: Aims to promote and perpetuate the business, commercial, manufacturing and civic interest; to promote and perpetuate the general welfare and prosperity of Healy/Denali and its environs, and to stimulate public interest in these ends. **Founded:** 1991. **Geographic Preference:** Local.

36228 ■ Greater Copper Valley Chamber of Commerce
MP 115.5 Richardson Hwy.
Glennallen, AK 99588
Contact: Bruce Cain, Secretary
Description: Maintains a visitor center to promote and advertise businesses in the Copper Valley area. Seeks to promote economic growth. **Geographic Preference:** Local.

36229 ■ Greater Fairbanks Chamber of Commerce (GFCC)
100 Cushman St., Ste. 102
Fairbanks, AK 99701
Ph: (907)452-1105
Co. E-mail: info@fairbankschamber.org
URL: http://www.fairbankschamber.org
Contact: Jeremy Johnson, Co-President Co-Chief Executive Officer
Facebook: www.facebook.com/GreaterFairbanksChamberofCommerce
Linkedin: www.linkedin.com/company/greater-fairbanks-chamber-of-commerce
YouTube: www.youtube.com/channel/UCc172QKXzTn0AYMJqrgl0ig
Description: Promotes business and community development in the Greater Fairbanks, AK area. **Founded:** 1952. **Publications:** *Greater Fairbanks Chamber of Commerce--Membership Directory & Buyer's Guide* (Annual); *Membership Directory*. **Geographic Preference:** Local.

36230 ■ Greater Ketchikan Chamber of Commerce (GKCC)
2417 Tongass Ave., Ste. 111-337
Ketchikan, AK 99901
Ph: (907)225-3184
Fax: (907)225-3187
Co. E-mail: info@ketchikanchamber.com
URL: http://www.ketchikanchamber.com
Contact: Ben Edwards, President
Facebook: www.facebook.com/Ketchikan-Chamber-of-Commerce-127861255265

Description: Seeks to encourage leadership by business and professional individuals to improve business relations, economic well-being and the quality of living in Ketchikan. Monitors legislation and local, state, and federal issues. Sponsors Fourth of July parade, sales promotions, Salmon Derby, and local trade show. **Founded:** 1967. **Publications:** *Chamber Focus* (Monthly). **Awards:** Greater Ketchikan Chamber of Commerce Citizen of the Year (Annual); Greater Ketchikan Chamber of Commerce Outstanding Youth Leader (Annual); Greater Ketchikan Chamber of Commerce Business of the Year (Annual). **Geographic Preference:** Local.

36231 ▪ Greater Palmer Chamber of Commerce (GPCC)
550 S Alaska St., Ste. 101
Palmer, AK 99645
Ph: (907)745-2880
Co. E-mail: info@palmerchamber.org
URL: http://www.palmerchamber.org
Contact: Dusty Silva, President
Facebook: www.facebook.com/palmerchamber
Instagram: www.instagram.com/palmerchamber
Description: Promotes business and community development in the Palmer, AK area. **Founded:** 1971. **Publications:** *Matanuska Tradewinds*. **Geographic Preference:** Local.

36232 ▪ Greater Sitka Chamber of Commerce (GSCC)
104 Lake St.
Sitka, AK 99835-7573
Ph: (907)747-8604
Co. E-mail: sitkachamber.membership@gmail.com
URL: http://sitkachamber.com
Contact: Rachel Roy, Executive Director
E-mail: ed@sitkachamber.com
Facebook: www.facebook.com/SitkaChamber
Description: Promotes business and community development in Sitka, AK. **Founded:** 1904. **Geographic Preference:** Local.

36233 ▪ Greater Wasilla Chamber of Commerce (GWCC)
1155 E Depot Rd.
Wasilla, AK 99654
Ph: (907)376-1299
Co. E-mail: contact@wasillachamber.org
URL: http://wasillachamber.org
Contact: Kelsey McLeod, President
YouTube: www.youtube.com/channel/UCf5z56Aoc
ddlfKVoLywIqwQ
Description: Creates a positive economic and civic climate in the greater Wasilla area, thereby making possible for members and the community to grow and prosper. Provides education and information for members and the community. Facilitates group action on the part of the business community. **Founded:** 1978. **Geographic Preference:** Local.

36234 ▪ Haines Chamber of Commerce
219 Main St., Ste. 14
Haines, AK 99827
Ph: (907)766-2202
Co. E-mail: director.haineschamber@gmail.com
URL: http://www.haineschamber.org
Contact: Wendell Harren, President
Description: Promotes business and community development. Works to advance the interests of the area under the democratic system of free enterprise. Conducts activities beneficial to the community and its citizens. **Geographic Preference:** Local.

36235 ▪ Homer, Alaska Chamber of Commerce
201 Sterling Hwy.
Homer, AK 99603
Ph: (907)235-7740
Co. E-mail: membership@homeralaska.org
URL: http://www.homeralaska.org
Contact: Tom Soderholm, President
Facebook: www.facebook.com/VisitHomer
X (Twitter): x.com/visithomerak
Instagram: www.instagram.com/visithomer
YouTube: www.youtube.com/user/
HomerChamberVisito

Description: Promotes business and community development in Homer, AK. **Founded:** 1955. **Geographic Preference:** Local.

36236 ▪ Juneau Chamber of Commerce
9301 Glacier Hwy., Ste. 110
Juneau, AK 99801
Ph: (907)463-3488
Co. E-mail: info@juneauchamber.com
URL: http://juneauchamber.com
Contact: Craig E. Dahl, Executive Director
E-mail: cdahl@juneauchamber.com
Facebook: www.facebook.com/JuneauAK.Chamber
X (Twitter): x.com/Juneau_Chamber
Description: Promotes business and community development in the Juneau, AK area. **Geographic Preference:** Local.

36237 ▪ Kenai Chamber of Commerce
11471 Kenai Spur Hwy.
Kenai, AK 99611
Ph: (907)283-1991
Fax: (907)283-2230
URL: http://kenaichamber.org
Contact: Gregory D. Stein, President
Facebook: www.facebook.com/Kenaichamber
Description: Promotes business and community development in the Kenai, AK area. **Founded:** 1954. **Geographic Preference:** Local.

36238 ▪ Kodiak Chamber of Commerce (KCC)
100 E Marine Way, Ste. 300
Kodiak, AK 99615
Ph: (907)486-5557
Co. E-mail: chamber@kodiak.org
URL: http://www.kodiakchamber.org
Contact: Mary Beth Loewen, President
Facebook: www.facebook.com/Ko
diakChamberofCommerce
X (Twitter): x.com/kodiakchamber
Description: Promotes business and community development in the Kodiak, AK area. Co-sponsors Koniag's Kodiak Crab Festival and Comfish Alaska commercial fishing show. **Founded:** 1939. **Educational Activities:** ComFish Alaska (Annual). **Geographic Preference:** Local.

36239 ▪ Petersburg Chamber of Commerce
PO Box 649
Petersburg, AK 99833
Ph: (907)772-3646
Co. E-mail: pcoc@alaskan.com
URL: http://www.petersburg.org
Contact: David Kensinger, Vice President
Co-President
Description: Seeks to promote a strong and diversified economy. Serves the business community of Petersburg through leadership, service, marketing, and communications. **Geographic Preference:** Local.

36240 ▪ Prince of Wales Chamber of Commerce
PO Box 490
Klawock, AK 99925
Ph: (907)755-2626
Co. E-mail: info@princeofwalescoc.org
URL: http://princeofwalescoc.org
Contact: Abby Twyman, President
Facebook: www.facebook.com/
PrinceOfWalesChamberOfCommerce
Description: Promotes business and community development in Prince of Wales Island, AK. **Founded:** 1991. **Publications:** *Chamber POWer* (Monthly). **Educational Activities:** Monthly Board Meeting (Monthly). **Geographic Preference:** Local.

36241 ▪ Seldovia Chamber of Commerce
PO Box F
Seldovia, AK 99663
Ph: (907)234-7612
Co. E-mail: info@seldoviachamber.org
URL: http://www.youotterbehere.com
Contact: Crystal Collier, Board Member

Description: Promotes business and community development in Seldovia, AK. Conducts charitable activities. Sponsors festivals. Publications: none. **Awards:** Seldovia Chamber of Commerce Citizen of the Year Award (Annual). **Geographic Preference:** Local.

36242 ▪ Seward Area Chamber of Commerce
2001 Seward Hwy.
Seward, AK 99664
Ph: (907)224-8051
Co. E-mail: chamber@seward.com
URL: http://www.seward.com/chamber
Contact: Carole Tallman, President
Facebook: www.facebook.com/SewardChamber
Description: Promotes business and community development in the area. **Founded:** 1899. **Geographic Preference:** Local.

36243 ▪ Seward Chamber of Commerce
2001 Seward Hwy.
Seward, AK 99664
Ph: (907)224-8051
Fax: (907)224-5353
Co. E-mail: visitseward@seward.com
URL: http://www.seward.com
Contact: Carole Tallman, President
Facebook: www.facebook.com/VisitSeward
X (Twitter): x.com/SewardAK
Instagram: www.instagram.com/explore/locations/
234402488/seward-alaska
YouTube: www.youtube.com/channel/UCSI
2MKBQT7xG7_95gegmVUQ
Description: Promotes business and community development in the Seward, AK area. Sponsors festival and competitions. **Founded:** 1910. **Geographic Preference:** Local.

36244 ▪ Skagway Chamber of Commerce
701 State St.
Skagway, AK 99840
Ph: (907)983-1898
Fax: (907)983-2031
Co. E-mail: chamber@aptalaska.net
URL: http://skagwaychamber.org
Contact: Jackie Schaefer, President
E-mail: jjschaefer2009@gmail.com
Description: Strives to provide members with information of importance to business and residents of Skagway, AK. Represents members regarding city and state issues that affect Skagway. **Founded:** 1898. **Publications:** *Skagway Member Directory* (Annual). **Geographic Preference:** Local.

36245 ▪ *Skagway Member Directory*
701 State St.
Skagway, AK 99840
Ph: (907)983-1898
Fax: (907)983-2031
Co. E-mail: chamber@aptalaska.net
URL: http://skagwaychamber.org
Contact: Jackie Schaefer, President
E-mail: jjschaefer2009@gmail.com
URL(s): skagwaychamber.org/members-by-business
-type
Released: Annual **Description:** Covers comprehensive listing of area businesses. **Availability:** Online.

36246 ▪ Soldotna Chamber of Commerce (SCC)
44790 Sterling Hwy.
Soldotna, AK 99669
Ph: (907)262-9814
URL: http://visitsoldotna.com
Contact: Mike Frost, Treasurer Secretary
Description: Promotes business and community development in the Soldotna, AK area. Sponsors Soldotna Progress Days. **Founded:** 1959. **Publications:** *Soldotna Visitor Guide* (Annual); *Your Chamber Today*. **Awards:** Soldotna Chamber of Commerce/Vera Howarth Memorial Scholarship (Annual). **Geographic Preference:** Local.

36247 ▪ Talkeetna Chamber of Commerce
PO Box 334
Talkeetna, AK 99676
Co. E-mail: info@talkeetnachamber.org

URL: http://www.talkeetnachamber.org
Contact: Bill Rodwell, President
Facebook: www.facebook.com/TalkeetnaChamber
YouTube: www.youtube.com/user/TalkeetnaChamber
Description: Promotes business and community development in Talkeetna, AK area. **Founded:** 1975. **Awards:** Talkeetna Chamber of Commerce Post Secondary Education Scholarship (Annual). **Geographic Preference:** Local.

36248 ■ Tok Chamber of Commerce
PO Box 389
Tok, AK 99780
Ph: (907)883-5775
Co. E-mail: info@tokalaskainfo.com
URL: http://www.tokalaskainfo.com
Facebook: www.facebook.com/tok.chamber
Description: Promotes business and community development in Tok, AK area. **Geographic Preference:** Local.

36249 ■ Wrangell Chamber of Commerce (WCC)
107 Stikine Ave.
Wrangell, AK 99929
Contact: William Burr, President
Description: Aims to advance the business, professional, civic and cultural interests of the City of Wrangell. Encourages the growth of existing businesses. Supports activities beneficial to the community and its citizens. **Geographic Preference:** Local.

MINORITY BUSINESS ASSISTANCE PROGRAMS

36250 ■ Tanana Chiefs Conference (TCC)
122 1st Ave.
Fairbanks, AK 99701
Ph: (907)452-8251
Free: 800-478-6822
Co. E-mail: communications_dept@tananachiefs.org
URL: http://www.tananachiefs.org
Contact: Brian Ridley, Chairman
X (Twitter): x.com/americancancer
Instagram: www.instagram.com/americancancersociety
YouTube: www.youtube.com/user/TananaChiefs
Description: Provides a unified voice in advancing sovereign tribal governments through the promotion of physical and mental wellness, education, socioeconomic development, and culture of the Interior Alaska Native people. Covers an area of 235,000 square miles in interior Alaska. **Founded:** 1962.

36251 ■ YWCA Anchorage
3400 Spenard Rd., Ste. 200
Anchorage, AK 99503
Ph: (907)644-9600
Co. E-mail: ywcaoffice@ywcaak.org
URL: http://ywcaak.org
Contact: Ashley Johnson, Co-President

Facebook: www.facebook.com/YWCA.Alaska
X (Twitter): x.com/ywcaalaska
Instagram: www.instagram.com/ywcaak
YouTube: www.youtube.com/channel/UC08XcNQ1diqf47bk8fZ7T9g
Description: Provides business development services for women in Alaska who want to start or grow a business. **Geographic Preference:** Local.

INCUBATORS/RESEARCH AND TECHNOLOGY PARKS

36252 ■ Kenai Peninsula Economic Development District (KPEDD)
14896 Kenai Spur Hwy., Ste. 103-A
Kenai, AK 99611
Ph: (907)283-3335
URL: http://kpedd.org
Contact: Rusty Swan, President
Description: Assists with developing their business plans, preparing them for commercial loans, and providing access to capital and providing technical support.

EDUCATIONAL PROGRAMS

36253 ■ University of Alaska Anchorage - Matanuska-Susitna College
8295 E College Dr.
Palmer, AK 99645
Ph: (907)745-9774
Fax: (907)745-9711
Co. E-mail: uaa_mscinfo@alaska.edu
URL: http://matsu.alaska.edu
Contact: Dr. Talis J. Colberg, Director
E-mail: tjcolberg@alaska.edu
X (Twitter): x.com/MSCDragons
Instagram: www.instagram.com/matsu_college
YouTube: www.youtube.com/user/MatSuCollege
Description: Offers educational programs in in high-demand fields such as engineering, health, business and education, as well as in the liberal arts and sciences. **Founded:** 1958. **Awards:** Bill and Nell Biggs Scholarship (Annual); Pat and Cliff Rogers Nursing Scholarship; Dr. Orrin Rongstad Wildlife Scholarship (Annual).

CONSULTANTS

36254 ■ Alaska Business Development Center Inc. (ABDC)
840 K St., Ste. 202
Anchorage, AK 99501
Ph: (907)562-0335
Free: 800-478-3474
Fax: (907)562-6988
Co. E-mail: info@abdc.org
URL: http://www.abdc.org
Contact: Michelle Kern, President
YouTube: www.youtube.com/channel/UCF2SoogrnyYDKa64k9ORMEw

Description: Services: Consulting assistance to small businesses and commercial fishers. **Scope:** Services: Consulting assistance to small businesses and commercial fishers. **Founded:** 1978. **Training:** Volunteer Tax & Loan Program.

PUBLICATIONS

36255 ■ *Alaska Business Monthly*
501 W N Lights Blvd., Ste. 100
Anchorage, AK 99503
Ph: (907)276-4373
Fax: (907)279-2900
URL: http://www.akbizmag.com
Contact: Carter Damaska, Manager
E-mail: enews@akbizmag.com
URL(s): www.akbizmag.com
Facebook: www.facebook.com/AKBusinessMonth
Linkedin: www.linkedin.com/company/alaska-business-monthly
X (Twitter): x.com/akbusinessmonth
Instagram: www.instagram.com/akbizmag
YouTube: www.youtube.com/@alaskabusinessmagazine
Released: Monthly **Price:** $2.50, for per month online; $3.33, for per month online and print; $20.75, for per month total access. **Description:** Provides thorough and objective discussion and analysis of the issues and trends affecting Alaska's business sector; and by featuring stories on the individuals, organizations and companies that shape the Alaska economy. **Availability:** Print; Online.

36256 ■ *Alaska Business Monthly*
501 W N Lights Blvd., Ste. 100
Anchorage, AK 99503
Ph: (907)276-4373
Fax: (907)279-2900
URL: http://www.akbizmag.com
Contact: Carter Damaska, Manager
E-mail: enews@akbizmag.com
Facebook: www.facebook.com/AKBusinessMonth
Linkedin: www.linkedin.com/company/alaska-business-monthly
X (Twitter): x.com/akbusinessmonth
Instagram: www.instagram.com/akbizmag
YouTube: www.youtube.com/channel/UCiS1A4EdzzX2aA5nGi7Bwlw
Description: Publisher of business magazines. **Founded:** 1984. **Publications:** *Alaska Business Monthly* (Monthly).

VENTURE CAPITAL FIRM

36257 ■ Alaska Venture Partners, LLC
2964 Wentworth St.
Anchorage, AK 99508
Contact: John Wanamaker, Manager
Description: A venture capital firm specializing in early stage businesses, growth capital, management buyout, and mature and growing companies. The firm also provides incubation services and consulting services.

Arizona

ASSOCIATIONS AND OTHER ORGANIZATIONS

36258 ■ Arizona Business Alliance (ABA)
8821 N 7th St., No. 205
Phoenix, AZ 85014
Ph: (602)331-7249
Co. E-mail: office@azbizalliance.org
URL: http://arizonabusinessalliance.com
Facebook: www.facebook.com/ABABusinessAlliance
Description: Seeks to promote the businesses of Arizona by providing sales leads and networking opportunities. **Founded:** 1974.

36259 ■ Arizona Small Business Association (ASBA)
11811 N Tatum Blvd., Ste. P-195
Phoenix, AZ 85028
Ph: (602)306-4000
Co. E-mail: info@asba.com
URL: http://www.asba.com/default.aspx
Contact: Eric Knott, Chairman
Facebook: www.facebook.com/azsmallbiz
Linkedin: www.linkedin.com/company/asba
X (Twitter): x.com/asba
YouTube: www.youtube.com/channel/UCt16Hfq3il_SsrvhlnWmwTQ
Description: Focuses on four key fundamentals of business: effective small business education, dynamic professional connections, essential support resources, and public policy. **Founded:** 1972. **Publications:** The Business Edge (Bimonthly). **Educational Activities:** Celebration of Small Business. **Geographic Preference:** State.

36260 ■ Association of Fundraising Professionals Greater Arizona Chapter (AFP)
c/o Karolyn Kiburz
7375 E 6th Ave., Ste. 9
Scottsdale, AZ 85251
Ph: (480)947-3459
Fax: (480)990-1889
Co. E-mail: admin@afpaz.org
URL: http://community.afpglobal.org/afpazgreaterarizonachapter
Contact: Karolyn Kiburz, Administrator
Facebook: www.facebook.com/afpgreateraz
X (Twitter): x.com/afpgreateraz
Instagram: www.instagram.com/afpgreateraz
Description: Supports fundraising and nonprofit professionals in the Phoenix metro region. Seeks to advance philanthropy by fostering the development and growth of fundraising professionals and promoting ethical and effective fundraising standards. **Geographic Preference:** Local.

36261 ■ Association of Fundraising Professionals Southern Arizona
PO Box 41176
Tucson, AZ 85717
Ph: (520)748-2830
Co. E-mail: info@afpsoaz.org
URL: http://www.afpsoaz.org
Contact: Scott Matlick, President
E-mail: smatlick@rmhctucson.org
Facebook: www.facebook.com/AFPSOAZ
X (Twitter): x.com/afpsoaz
Description: Supports fundraising professionals in Tucson, Marana, Green Valley, and southern Arizona. **Founded:** 1960. **Geographic Preference:** Local.

36262 ■ Business Network International, Northern Arizona (BNI)
14301 N 87th St., Ste. 113
Scottsdale, AZ 85260
Ph: (602)788-1606
URL: http://bniarizona.com/find_a_chapter.php
Contact: Kelley Dominguez, Executive Director
Facebook: www.facebook.com/BNIArizona
X (Twitter): x.com/bniaz
Description: Provides both men and women a structured environment for the development and exchange of quality business referrals. Offers members the opportunity to share ideas and contacts. **Geographic Preference:** Local.

36263 ■ International Association of Women Phoenix Chapter
Phoenix, AZ
URL: http://www.iawomen.com/chapters/phoenix-chapter
Description: Serves as network of accomplished women united to achieve professional goals. Provides a forum for sharing ideas and experiences of professional women regarding career success. Promotes an active business and networking community from all industries. **Geographic Preference:** Local.

36264 ■ Minority and Small Business Alliance of Southern Arizona (MSBASA)
PO Box 22801
Tucson, AZ 85734
Co. E-mail: msbasarizona@gmail.com
URL: http://msbasa.org
Contact: Jo Anne Arvizu, Chairman
E-mail: jnarvizu@raytheon.com
Facebook: www.facebook.com/MSBAofAZ
X (Twitter): x.com/msbasa
YouTube: www.youtube.com/channel/UCIN2g4Y5t6zz0oujfvEsLkg/videos
Description: Provides educational programs, small business development opportunities, mentoring, and networking events to business owners in the Tucson area. **Founded:** 2009.

SMALL BUSINESS DEVELOPMENT CENTERS

36265 ■ Arizona Small Business Development Center
2411 W 14th St., Ste. 114
Tempe, AZ 85281
Ph: (480)731-8722
Fax: (480)731-8729
Co. E-mail: janice.washington@domail.maricopa.edu
URL: http://azsbdc.net
Contact: Janice Washington, Director
E-mail: janice.washington@domail.maricopa.edu
Facebook: www.facebook.com/arizonasbdc
Linkedin: www.linkedin.com/company/28130044
X (Twitter): x.com/AZSBDCNetwork
YouTube: www.youtube.com/channel/UCuGOIIBQasqR1l71DyxK_xA
Description: Provides small business owners and prospective owners with basic services: one-on-one confidential counseling help from an experienced small business practitioner in solving problems specific to the client's business, free of charge; practical, low-cost training offered; assistance in finding financing sources, specialized consulting and other services; access to reference materials, computers and software. **Geographic Preference:** State.

36266 ■ Arizona Western College Small Business Development Center (AZSBDC)
2411 W 14th St.
Tempe, AZ 85281
Ph: (480)731-8200
Co. E-mail: azsbdc@domail.maricopa.edu
URL: http://www.azsbdc.net/arizona-western-college
Facebook: www.facebook.com/arizonasbdc
X (Twitter): x.com/AZSBDC
Description: Represents and promotes the small business sector. Provides management assistance to current and prospective small business owners. Helps to improve management skills and expand the products and services of members. **Geographic Preference:** Local.

36267 ■ Central Arizona College Small Business Development Center (CAC)
8470 N Overfield Rd.
Coolidge, AZ 85128
Ph: (520)494-6450
Co. E-mail: sbdc@centralaz.edu
URL: http://centralaz.edu/small-business-development-center
Description: Represents and promotes the small business sector. Provides management assistance to current and prospective small business owners. Helps to improve management skills and expand the products and services of members. **Geographic Preference:** Local.

36268 ■ City of Phoenix
Phoenix City Hall 200 W Washington St.
Phoenix, AZ 85003
Ph: (602)262-6011
URL: http://www.phoenix.gov
Contact: Jeff Barton, Manager
E-mail: jeffrey.barton@phoenix.gov
Facebook: www.facebook.com/CityofPhoenixAZ
X (Twitter): x.com/cityofphoenixaz
Instagram: www.instagram.com/cityofphoenixaz
YouTube: www.youtube.com/user/cityofphoenixaz
Description: An entrepreneurial hub with the escalating growth of local incubators, accelerators, coworking and maker spaces. City of Phoenix leadership is

committed to startup success by supporting these organizations and pioneering innovative initiatives to foster economic growth and entrepreneurial development.

36269 ■ Coconino Community College Small Business Development Center
3000 N 4th St.
Flagstaff, AZ 86004
Ph: (928)526-7644
Co. E-mail: sbdc@coconino.edu
URL: http://www.coconino.edu/sbdc
Facebook: www.facebook.com/CoconinoSBDC
Linkedin: www.linkedin.com/company/coconino-sbdc
Instagram: www.instagram.com/coconino.sbdc
Description: Promotes the small business operations in Coconino County. **Geographic Preference:** Local.

36270 ■ Eastern Arizona College Small Business Development Center (EAC SBDC)
615 N Stadium Ave., No 113
Thatcher, AZ 85552
Ph: (928)428-8590
Fax: (928)428-2578
Co. E-mail: sbdc@eac.edu
URL: http://www.eac.edu/sbdc
Contact: Kevin Peck, Director
E-mail: kevin.peck@eac.edu
X (Twitter): twitter.com/eacsbdc
Description: Represents and promotes the small business sector. Provides management assistance to current and prospective small business owners. Helps to improve management skills and expand the products and services of members. **Geographic Preference:** Local.

36271 ■ LaunchPoint
245 W 2nd St.
Mesa, AZ 85201
URL: http://www.selectmesa.com/available-properties/launchpoint
Contact: Vincent Orleck, Project Manager
E-mail: vincent.orleck@mesaaz.gov
Description: A unique place for entrepreneurs and small companies that provides flexible space, business development assistance and networking and training opportunities in Mesa, Arizona.

36272 ■ Maricopa Community Colleges at Phoenix Small Business Development Center
108 N 40th St.
S Bldg.
Phoenix, AZ 85034
URL: http://www.maricopa.edu/business-workforce/small-business-development-center
Description: Represents and promotes the small business sector. Provides management assistance to current and prospective small business owners. Helps to improve management skills and expand the products and services of members. **Geographic Preference:** Local.

36273 ■ Mesa Minority/Micro Small Business Development Center (M3SBDC)
100 N 7th Ave., Ste. 400
Phoenix, AZ 85007
Ph: (602)845-1200
Fax: (602)845-1201
URL: http://www.azcommerce.com
Contact: Governor Doug Ducey, Chairman
Facebook: www.facebook.com/azcommerce
X (Twitter): x.com/azcommerce
YouTube: www.youtube.com/user/AZcommerce
Description: Provides management assistance to current and prospective small business owners in Mesa. **Geographic Preference:** Local.

36274 ■ Mohave Community College Small Business Development Center (MCC SBDC)
Home office: Mohave Community College
1971 Jagerson Ave., Bldg. 2000
Kingman, AZ 86409
URL: http://www.mohave.edu/about/sbdc
Contact: Stacy Klippenstein, President
Facebook: www.facebook.com/mohavecc
X (Twitter): x.com/mohavecc

YouTube: www.youtube.com/c/mohavecc
Description: Represents and promotes the small business sector. Provides management assistance to current and prospective small business owners. Helps to improve management skills and expand the products and services of members. **Geographic Preference:** Local.

36275 ■ Northland Pioneer College's Small Business Development Center (NPC:SBDC)
c/o Craig Boston
Director
NPC Show Low Campus, Goldwater Center, Rm. 1051001 W Deuce of Clubs
Show Low, AZ 85901
Ph: (928)532-6170
Co. E-mail: craig.boston@npc.edu
URL: http://www.npc.edu/sbdc
Contact: Craig Boston, Director
E-mail: craig.boston@npc.edu
Facebook: www.facebook.com/NPCSBDC
Description: Educational organization located in White Mountains of northeastern Arizona. **Geographic Preference:** Local.

36276 ■ Pima Community College Small Business Development Center
4905 E Broadway, Bldg. C, Rm. 117
Tucson, AZ 85709
Ph: (520)206-4580
Co. E-mail: soliver9@pima.edu
URL: http://www.pima.edu/business-industry/small-business.html
Description: Represents and promotes the small business sector. Provides management assistance to current and prospective small business owners. Helps to improve management skills and expand the products and services of members. **Geographic Preference:** Local.

SMALL BUSINESS ASSISTANCE PROGRAMS

36277 ■ Opportunity Through Entrepreneurship Foundation (OTEF)
14401 S 24th Way
Phoenix, AZ 85048
Ph: (602)456-9636
Co. E-mail: compliance@otef.org
URL: http://otef.org
Contact: Francine Hardaway, Executive Director
Description: Offers training and support to help at-risk youth and adults create and grow entrepreneurial ventures. **Founded:** 2005.

SCORE OFFICES

36278 ■ SCORE - ASU SkySong
1475 N Scottsdale Rd.
Scottsdale, AZ 85257
Ph: (480)884-1860
URL: http://greaterphoenix.score.org
Description: Provides expertise to help Phoenix area entrepreneurs prepare business plans, complete loan applications, protect their intellectual property, develop marketing strategies and gather valuable information about doing business.

36279 ■ SCORE - Carefree/Cave Creek Chamber
34250 N 60th St.
Scottsdale, AZ 85266
URL: http://greaterphoenix.score.org/mentors/bill-morgan
Contact: Bill Morgan, Contact
Description: Provides expertise to help Phoenix area entrepreneurs prepare business plans, complete loan applications, protect their intellectual property, develop marketing strategies and gather valuable information about doing business.

36280 ■ SCORE - Chandler Chamber of Commerce
4041 N Central Ave., No. 1000
Phoenix, AZ 85012

Ph: (480)963-4571
Co. E-mail: help@score.org
URL: http://greaterphoenix.score.org
Contact: Rod Houston, Contact
Facebook: www.facebook.com/SCOREGreaterPhoenix
X (Twitter): x.com/SCOREPhx
YouTube: www.youtube.com/c/ScorephoenixOrg
Pinterest: www.pinterest.com/phoenixscore
Description: Provides expertise to help Phoenix area entrepreneurs prepare business plans, complete loan applications, protect their intellectual property, develop marketing strategies and gather valuable information about doing business. Available at the Chandler Chamber of Commerce on the 1st and 3rd Friday of each month.

36281 ■ SCORE - Chandler Public Library
22 S Delaware St. Study Rm. 139
Chandler, AZ 85225
Co. E-mail: help@score.org
URL: http://www.score.org/greaterphoenix/about/our-locations
Description: Provides expertise to help Phoenix area entrepreneurs prepare business plans, complete loan applications, protect their intellectual property, develop marketing strategies and gather valuable information about doing business.

36282 ■ SCORE - Gilbert-EZ Spaces
1530 E William Field St., Ste. 201
Gilbert, AZ 85295
Ph: (480)207-1200
Co. E-mail: work@ezspaces.com
URL: http://greaterphoenix.score.org
Contact: John Mahon, Founder
E-mail: jmahon@ezspaces.com
URL(s): www.ezspaces.com
X (Twitter): x.com/ezspaces
Description: Provides expertise to help Phoenix area entrepreneurs prepare business plans, complete loan applications, protect their intellectual property, develop marketing strategies and gather valuable information about doing business.

36283 ■ SCORE - Goodyear Library
14455 W Ban Buren St., Ste. C101
Goodyear, AZ 85338
URL: http://www.score.org/greaterphoenix/about/our-locations
Description: Provides expertise to help Phoenix area entrepreneurs prepare business plans, complete loan applications, protect their intellectual property, develop marketing strategies and gather valuable information about doing business.

36284 ■ SCORE - Goodyear Valley Chamber of Commerce
289 N Litchfield Rd.
Goodyear, AZ 85338
Ph: (623)932-2260
Co. E-mail: info@southwestvalleychamber.org
URL: http://www.southwestvalleychamber.org/mentors.html
Contact: Jeffrey Campos, President
Description: Provides expertise to help Phoenix area entrepreneurs prepare business plans, complete loan applications, protect their intellectual property, develop marketing strategies and gather valuable information about doing business. Also eets at the Goodyear Library on the 2nd and 4th Saturdays of the month.

36285 ■ SCORE - Greater Phoenix
4041 N Central Ave., Ste. 1000
Phoenix, AZ 85012
Ph: (928)421-3778
Fax: (602)745-7210
Co. E-mail: help@score.org
URL: http://greaterphoenix.score.org
Linkedin: www.linkedin.com/company/greater-phoenix-score
X (Twitter): x.com/SCOREPhx
YouTube: www.youtube.com/c/ScorephoenixOrg
Pinterest: www.pinterest.com/phoenixscore

Description: Provides professional guidance and information to maximize the success of existing and emerging small businesses. Offers business counseling and workshops. **Geographic Preference:** Local.

36286 ■ SCORE - Greater Phoenix Better Business Bureau
4041 N Central Ave. 1000
Phoenix, AZ 85012
Ph: (928)421-3778
Fax: (602)745-7210
Co. E-mail: help@score.org
URL: http://greaterphoenix.score.org
Facebook: www.facebook.com/SCOREGreaterPhoenix
Linkedin: www.linkedin.com/company/greater-phoenix-score
X (Twitter): x.com/SCOREPhx
YouTube: www.youtube.com/c/ScorephoenixOrg
Pinterest: www.pinterest.com/phoenixscore

Description: Provides professional guidance and information to maximize the success of existing and emerging small businesses. Offers business counseling and workshops.

36287 ■ SCORE - Mesa Chamber of Commerce
165 N Centennial Way, Ste. 208
Mesa, AZ 85201
Ph: (602)745-7250
URL: http://greaterphoenix.score.org
Facebook: www.facebook.com/SCOREGreaterPhoenix
Linkedin: www.linkedin.com/company/greater-phoenix-score
X (Twitter): x.com/SCOREPhx
YouTube: www.youtube.com/c/ScorephoenixOrg
Pinterest: www.pinterest.com/phoenixscore

Description: Provides expertise to help Phoenix area entrepreneurs prepare business plans, complete loan applications, protect their intellectual property, develop marketing strategies and gather valuable information about doing business.

36288 ■ SCORE - North Phoenix Chamber of Commerce
16042 N 32nd St., Ste. D-10
Phoenix, AZ 85032
URL: http://greaterphoenix.score.org
Contact: Steve Sandler, Contact
E-mail: fmssteve@aol.com
Facebook: www.facebook.com/SCOREGreaterPhoenix
Linkedin: www.linkedin.com/company/greater-phoenix-score
X (Twitter): x.com/SCOREPhx
YouTube: www.youtube.com/c/ScorephoenixOrg
Pinterest: www.pinterest.com/phoenixscore

Description: Provides expertise to help Phoenix area entrepreneurs prepare business plans, complete loan applications, protect their intellectual property, develop marketing strategies and gather valuable information about doing business.

36289 ■ SCORE - Northern Arizona
1228 Willow Creek Rd., Ste.2
Prescott, AZ 86301
Ph: (928)778-7438
Co. E-mail: northernaz@scorevolunteer.org
URL: http://www.score.org/northernarizona
Facebook: www.facebook.com/SCORENorthernArizona
Linkedin: www.linkedin.com/company/northern-arizona-score
X (Twitter): x.com/SCOREArizona
Instagram: www.instagram.com/score_mentors

Description: Provides professional guidance and information to maximize the success of existing and emerging small businesses. Offers business counseling and workshops. **Founded:** 1964. **Geographic Preference:** Local.

36290 ■ SCORE - Oro Valley Library
1305 W Naranja Dr.
Oro Valley, AZ 85737

Description: Provides free professional guidance and information to maximize the success of existing and emerging small businesses in Tucson and the surrounding areas.

36291 ■ SCORE - Paradise Valley Community College (PVCC)
18401 N 32nd St.
Phoenix, AZ 85032
Ph: (602)787-7000
Co. E-mail: pvccinfo@paradisevalley.edu
URL: http://www.paradisevalley.edu/students/testing-services/course-placement-assessments
Contact: Paul A. Dale, President
X (Twitter): x.com/pvcc_official
YouTube: www.youtube.com/c/ParadiseValleyCommunityCollegePhoenixAz

Description: Provides expertise to help Phoenix area entrepreneurs prepare business plans, complete loan applications, protect their intellectual property, develop marketing strategies and gather valuable information about doing business. **Founded:** 1987.

36292 ■ SCORE - Phoenix Anthem Chamber of Commerce
3701 W Anthem Way
Phoenix, AZ 85086
Ph: (928)421-3778
URL: http://greaterphoenix.score.org/branch/north-phoenix-chamber-commerce
Facebook: www.facebook.com/SCOREGreaterPhoenix
Linkedin: www.linkedin.com/company/greater-phoenix-score
X (Twitter): x.com/SCOREPhx
YouTube: www.youtube.com/ScorephoenixOrg
Pinterest: www.pinterest.com/phoenixscore

Description: Provides professional guidance and information to maximize the success of existing and emerging small businesses. Offers business counseling and workshops.

36293 ■ SCORE - Phoenix Mesquite Public Library
4041 N Central Ave. No. 1000
Phoenix, AZ 85012
Ph: (928)421-3778
Co. E-mail: help@score.org
URL: http://greaterphoenix.score.org
Contact: Bill Morgan, Contact

Description: Provides expertise to help Phoenix area entrepreneurs prepare business plans, complete loan applications, protect their intellectual property, develop marketing strategies and gather valuable information about doing business.

36294 ■ SCORE - Pima County Library
101 N Stone Ave.
Tucson, AZ 85701
Ph: (520)594-5600
Fax: (520)594-5621
Co. E-mail: askalibrarian@pima.gov
URL: http://www.library.pima.gov
Contact: Amber Mathewson, Director
Facebook: www.facebook.com/pimacountylibrary
X (Twitter): x.com/pimalibrary
Instagram: www.instagram.com/pimacountylibrary
YouTube: www.youtube.com/user/pimacountylibrary

Description: Provides free professional guidance and information to maximize the success of existing and emerging small businesses in Tucson and the surrounding areas.

36295 ■ SCORE - Queen Creek Chamber of Commerce
22246 S Ellsworth Rd.
Queen Creek, AZ 85142
URL: http://greaterphoenix.score.org
Contact: Jim Warren, Contact
E-mail: jwwarren@cox.net
Facebook: www.facebook.com/SCOREGreaterPhoenix
Linkedin: www.linkedin.com/company/greater-phoenix-score
X (Twitter): x.com/SCOREPhx
YouTube: www.youtube.com/c/ScorephoenixOrg
Pinterest: www.pinterest.com/phoenixscore

Description: Provides expertise to help Phoenix area entrepreneurs prepare business plans, complete loan applications, protect their intellectual property, develop marketing strategies and gather valuable information about doing business.

36296 ■ SCORE - Scottsdale Chamber of Commerce
7501 E McCormick Pky., Ste. 202-N
Scottsdale, AZ 85258
Ph: (480)355-2700
Fax: (480)355-2710
Co. E-mail: info@scottsdalechamber.com
URL: http://greaterphoenix.score.org
Contact: Mark Stanton, President
URL(s): scottsdalechamber.com
Facebook: www.facebook.com/ScottsdaleChamber
X (Twitter): x.com/scottsdalechmbr
Instagram: www.instagram.com/scottsdalechamber

Description: Provides expertise to help Phoenix area entrepreneurs prepare business plans, complete loan applications, protect their intellectual property, develop marketing strategies and gather valuable information about doing business.

36297 ■ SCORE - Scottsdale Civic Center Library
4041 N Central Ave. No 1000
Phoenix, AZ 85012
Ph: (928)421-3778
Fax: (605)745-7210
Co. E-mail: help@score.org
URL: http://greaterphoenix.score.org
Contact: Jay Gladney, President
Linkedin: www.linkedin.com/company/greater-phoenix-score
X (Twitter): x.com/SCOREPhx
YouTube: www.youtube.com/c/ScorephoenixOrg
Pinterest: www.pinterest.com/phoenixscore

Description: Provides expertise to help Phoenix area entrepreneurs prepare business plans, complete loan applications, protect their intellectual property, develop marketing strategies and gather valuable information about doing business.

36298 ■ SCORE - Scottsdale Mustang Library
10101 N 90th St.
Scottsdale, AZ 85258
URL: http://www.score.org/greaterphoenix/about/our-locations

Description: Provides expertise to help Phoenix area entrepreneurs prepare business plans, complete loan applications, protect their intellectual property, develop marketing strategies and gather valuable information about doing business.

36299 ■ SCORE - Southern Arizona
Virtual
Tucson, AZ 85745
Ph: (520)302-5569
Co. E-mail: southernaz.score@gmail.com
URL: http://www.score.org/southernarizona
Contact: Armando Ojeda, Chairman
Facebook: www.facebook.com/SCOREsouthernarizona
Linkedin: www.linkedin.com/company/southern-arizona-score
Instagram: www.instagram.com/score_mentors

Description: Provides free professional guidance and information to maximize the success of existing and emerging small businesses in Tucson and the surrounding areas. **Founded:** 1964.

36300 ■ SCORE - Surprise AZ TechCelerator
12425 W Bell Rd. Building D
Surprise, AZ 85374
Ph: (602)745-7250
Co. E-mail: help@score.org
URL: http://greaterphoenix.score.org
URL(s): www.score.org/find-location

Description: Provides expertise to help Phoenix area entrepreneurs prepare business plans, complete loan applications, protect their intellectual property, develop marketing strategies and gather valuable information about doing business.

STATE LISTINGS   Arizona ■ 36315

36301 ■ SCORE - Tempe
Tempe, AZ 85281
Ph: (480)967-7891
Co. E-mail: help@score.org
URL: http://greaterphoenix.score.org
Description: Provides expertise to help Phoenix area entrepreneurs prepare business plans, complete loan applications, protect their intellectual property, develop marketing strategies and gather valuable information about doing business. Meets at the Tempe Public Library.

36302 ■ SCORE - Tempe Public Library
4041 N Central Ave. Ste. 1000
Phoenix, AZ 85012
Co. E-mail: help@score.org
URL: http://greaterphoenix.score.org/branch/tempe-public-library-wed-thurs-am-bric-room
Facebook: www.facebook.com/TempePublicLibrary
Instagram: www.instagram.com/tempepubliclibrary
Description: Provides expertise to help Phoenix area entrepreneurs prepare business plans, complete loan applications, protect their intellectual property, develop marketing strategies and gather valuable information about doing business.

36303 ■ Southern Arizona SCORE
5049 E Broadway Blvd., Ste. 314
Tucson, AZ 85711
Ph: (520)302-5569
Co. E-mail: southernaz@scorevolunteer.org
URL: http://www.score.org/southernarizona
Contact: Scott Harkins, Senior Vice President
Facebook: www.facebook.com/SCOREsouthernarizona
Linkedin: www.linkedin.com/company/southern-arizona-score
Founded: 1964.

BETTER BUSINESS BUREAUS

36304 ■ Better Business Bureau - Central, Northern and Western Arizona
4428 N 12th St.
Phoenix, AZ 85014-4585
Ph: (602)264-1721
Fax: (602)263-0997
Co. E-mail: info@arizonabbb.org
URL: http://www.bbb.org/us/nv/las-vegas/profile/college-and-university/university-of-phoenix-1086-55124
Contact: Paul Green, Director
Facebook: www.facebook.com/AZBBBNews
Description: Seeks to promote and foster the highest ethical relationship between businesses and the public through voluntary self-regulation, consumer and business education, and service excellence. Provides information to help consumers and businesses make informed purchasing decisions and avoid costly scams and frauds; settles consumer complaints through arbitration and other means. **Founded:** 1938. **Awards:** BBB of Central/Northern/Western Arizona Business Ethics Award (Annual). **Geographic Preference:** Local.

36305 ■ Better Business Bureau of Serving Southern Arizona (BBB)
120 N Stone Blvd., Ste. 200
Tucson, AZ 85701
Ph: (520)888-5353
Fax: (520)888-6262
Co. E-mail: info@tucson.bbb.org
URL: http://www.bbb.org/local-bbb/bbb-serving-southern-arizona
Contact: Pamela Crim, President
E-mail: pcrim@tucson.bbb.org
Facebook: www.facebook.com/soazbbb
Linkedin: www.linkedin.com/company/better-business-bureau-serving-southern-arizona
X (Twitter): x.com/tucsonbbb
Instagram: www.instagram.com/bbbsouthernarizona
YouTube: www.youtube.com/user/TucsonBBB
Description: Promote the highest ethical relationship between businesses and the public through voluntary self-regulation, consumer and business education, and service excellence. Provides information to help consumers and businesses make informed purchasing decisions and avoid costly scams and frauds; settles consumer complaints through arbitration and other means. **Founded:** 1952. **Geographic Preference:** Local.

CHAMBERS OF COMMERCE

36306 ■ Ahwatukee Foothills Chamber of Commerce (AFCC)
1345 E Chandler Blvd., Ste. 207
Phoenix, AZ 85048
Ph: (480)753-7676
Fax: (480)753-3898
Co. E-mail: info@ahwatukeechamber.com
URL: http://ahwatukeechamber.com
Contact: Andrew Hayes, Director
Facebook: www.facebook.com/AhwatukeeChamberofCommerce
X (Twitter): x.com/AhwatukeeCC
Description: Promotes business and community development in Ahwatukee Foothills, AZ. **Founded:** 1994. **Publications:** *The Forum*. **Geographic Preference:** Local.

36307 ■ Ajo District Chamber of Commerce
1 W Plz. St.
Ajo, AZ 85321
Ph: (520)387-7742
Fax: (520)387-3641
Co. E-mail: ajocofc@ajochamber.com
URL: http://www.ajochamber.com
Contact: Bo Johnson, Director
Description: Promotes business and community development in Ajo, AZ. Sponsors St. Patrick's Day celebration, Fourth of July festivities, and Octoberfest. **Geographic Preference:** Local.

36308 ■ Apache Junction Chamber of Commerce
567 W Apache Trl.
Apache Junction, AZ 85120
Ph: (480)982-3141
Co. E-mail: sales-marketing@ajchamber.com
URL: http://www.ajchamber.com
Contact: Mary Ann Przybylski, President
Facebook: www.facebook.com/AJChamber
X (Twitter): x.com/AJ_Chamber
Instagram: www.instagram.com/ajchamber
YouTube: www.youtube.com/channel/UChLCaB-VOC1WoXJIPbsUJIg
Description: Promotes business and community development in the Apache Junction, Gold Canyon and San Tan, AZ area. Sponsors Lost Dutchman Days festival. **Founded:** 1960. **Geographic Preference:** Local.

36309 ■ Arizona Chamber of Commerce and Industry
3200 N Central Ave., Ste. 1125
Phoenix, AZ 85012
Ph: (602)248-4430
Free: 866-275-5816
Fax: (602)391-2498
Co. E-mail: info@azchamber.com
URL: http://azchamber.com
Contact: Danny Seiden, President
Facebook: www.facebook.com/ArizonaChamber
X (Twitter): x.com/AZChamber
Description: Works to promote a business climate that enhances economic vitality and improves the quality of life for all Arizonans. **Founded:** 1974. **Publications:** *Accept Report* (Periodic); *Arizona Employment Law Handbook*; *VOX Negotium* (Periodic). **Geographic Preference:** State.

36310 ■ Arizona City Chamber of Commerce (AZC)
13640 S Sunland Gin Rd.
Arizona City, AZ 85123
Ph: (520)466-5141
Co. E-mail: azcitychamber@azci.net
URL: http://arizonacitychamberofcommerce.com
Contact: Linda Metz, President
Facebook: www.facebook.com/arizonacitychamber
Description: Promotes business and community development in the Arizona City, AZ area. **Founded:** 1959. **Geographic Preference:** Local.

36311 ■ Arizona Hispanic Chamber of Commerce (AZHCC)
1020 E Missouri Ave.
Phoenix, AZ 85014
Ph: (602)279-1800
Co. E-mail: info@azhcc.com
URL: http://www.azhcc.com
Contact: Monica Villalobos, President
Facebook: www.facebook.com/theAZHCC
Linkedin: www.linkedin.com/company/arizona-hispanic-chamber-of-commerce
X (Twitter): x.com/azhcc
Instagram: www.instagram.com/azhcc
YouTube: www.youtube.com/channel/UCEywoO1oBJWIMmp5VwvupDQ
Description: Promotes business and community development in the Hispanic community of Arizona. **Founded:** 1948. **Publications:** *Comercio*. **Geographic Preference:** State.

36312 ■ Asian Chamber of Commerce [Asian Chamber of Commerce Serving Arizona/Grand Canyon State]
1305 E Hatcher Rd.
Phoenix, AZ 85004
Ph: (602)529-8475
URL: http://azasianchamber.com
Contact: Anthony Bounxayavong Amphonephong, Chief Executive Officer
E-mail: anthony@azasianchamber.com
Facebook: www.facebook.com/AZAsianChamber
Linkedin: www.linkedin.com/company/az-asian-chamber-of-commerce
X (Twitter): x.com/AZAsianChamber
Instagram: www.instagram.com/azasianchamber
Description: Seeks to support, promote, and foster business, cultural, and educational relationships between chamber members and the general public. Provides consultancy and technical assistance to the members. **Founded:** 1993. **Publications:** *Asian SUNews* (Monthly). **Geographic Preference:** Local.

36313 ■ At-A-Glance
5800 W Glenn Dr., Ste. 275
Glendale, AZ 85301
Ph: (623)937-4754
Co. E-mail: info@glendaleazchamber.org
URL: http://www.glendaleazchamber.com
Contact: Robert Heidt, President
URL(s): www.glendaleazchamber.org/at-a-glance
Released: Biweekly **Description:** Contains members' issues, events, and other business news. **Availability:** PDF; Online.

36314 ■ Benson/San Pedro Valley Chamber of Commerce
168 E 4th St.
Benson, AZ 85602
Ph: (520)265-8031
Co. E-mail: info@bensonchamberaz.com
URL: http://www.bensonchamberaz.org
Contact: Lupe Diaz, Vice President
E-mail: lupe777diaz@gmail.com
Facebook: www.facebook.com/BensonChamberAZ
Description: Provide of business and community development in Benson, AZ. Conduct annual Butterflied Overland Stage Days. Sponsor local festivals. Convention/Meeting none. **Publications:** *Benson/San Pedro Valley Chamber of Commerce Newsletter* (Periodic). **Geographic Preference:** Local.

36315 ■ Black Chamber of Arizona (BCAZ)
2390 E Camelback Rd., Ste. 130
Phoenix, AZ 85016
Ph: (602)307-5200
URL: http://www.blackchamberaz.com
Contact: Robin S. Reed, President
X (Twitter): x.com/blackchamber_az
Description: Promotes economic development in the Greater Phoenix region. **Founded:** 1998. **Publications:** *Arizona Informant* (Weekly). **Awards:** GPBCC Small Business of the Year (Annual). **Geographic Preference:** Local.

Small Business Sourcebook • 42nd Edition   2411

36316 ■ Bouse Chamber of Commerce
44362 E Main St.
 Bouse, AZ 85325-0817
Ph: (928)851-2509
URL: http://bouseazchamber.com
Contact: Phil Sparks, President
Description: Strives to promote tourism in Bouse. Encourages senior citizen to retire to the community. **Founded:** 1981. **Geographic Preference:** Local.

36317 ■ Buckeye Valley Chamber of Commerce
508 E Monroe Ave.
 Buckeye, AZ 85326
Ph: (623)386-2727
Co. E-mail: info@buckeyevalleychamber.org
URL: http://www.buckeyevalleychamber.org
Contact: Deanna Kupcik, Officer
Facebook: www.facebook.com/buckeyechamber
X (Twitter): x.com/BuckeyeVChamber
Description: Strives to enhance community development in Buckeye, AZ. **Publications:** *Out in Front* (Monthly). **Geographic Preference:** Local.

36318 ■ Bullhead Area Chamber of Commerce
1251 Hwy. 95
 Bullhead City, AZ 86429
Ph: (928)754-4121
Co. E-mail: info@bullheadchamber.com
URL: http://bullheadareachamber.com
Contact: Bo Hellams, President
Facebook: www.facebook.com/bullheadchamber
X (Twitter): x.com/BullheadChamber
Description: Promotes business and community development in the Bullhead, AZ area. **Founded:** 1960. **Publications:** *Hot Prospects* (Annual); *Bullhead Area Chamber of Commerce--Membership Directory*; *The Business Frontline* (Monthly); *Bullhead City Profiles & Images* (Annual). **Geographic Preference:** Local.

36319 ■ *The Business Advocate*
1438 W Broadway Rd., Ste. 123
 Tempe, AZ 85283
Ph: (480)967-7891
Co. E-mail: info@tempechamber.org
URL: http://tempechamber.org
Contact: Anne Gill, President
E-mail: anne@tempechamber.org
URL(s): tempechamber.org/about-us
Released: Weekly (Tues.) **Availability:** Print; Online.

36320 ■ *Business Directory*
URL(s): www.dolanspringschamber.org/business-directory-1

36321 ■ *Business Directory*
165 N Centennial Way., Ste. 208
 Mesa, AZ 85201
Ph: (480)969-1307
Co. E-mail: info@mesachamber.org
URL: http://www.mesachamber.org
Contact: Sally Harrison, President
E-mail: sharrison@mesachamber.org
URL(s): business.mesachamber.org/list
Availability: Print; Online.

36322 ■ *Business Directory*
7120 Pav Way, Ste. 102
 Prescott Valley, AZ 86314
Ph: (928)772-8857
Fax: (928)772-4267
URL: http://www.pvchamber.org
Contact: Marnie Uhl, President
E-mail: marnie@pvchamber.org
URL(s): www.pvchamber.org/list
Availability: Online.

36323 ■ Chandler Chamber of Commerce
101 W Commonwealth Ave.
 Chandler, AZ 85225
Ph: (480)963-4571
Co. E-mail: info@chandlerchamber.com
URL: http://www.chandlerchamber.com
Contact: Terri Kimble, President
Facebook: www.facebook.com/ChandlerChamber
Linkedin: www.linkedin.com/company/chandler-chamber-of-commerce
X (Twitter): x.com/chandlerchamber
Instagram: www.instagram.com/chandlerchamber
YouTube: www.youtube.com/user/ChandlerChamber1
Description: Promotes business and community development in Chandler, AZ. **Founded:** 1912. **Publications:** *Business Connection* (Monthly). **Geographic Preference:** Local.

36324 ■ Chino Valley Area Chamber of Commerce (CVACC)
199 N Hwy. 89
 Chino Valley, AZ 86323
Ph: (928)636-2493
Co. E-mail: chamber@chinovalley.org
URL: http://www.chinovalley.org
Contact: Lorette Brashear, Director
Facebook: www.facebook.com/ChinoValleyChamber
Pinterest: www.pinterest.com/chinovalleyarea
Description: Promotes business growth in Chino. Serves members with professional development opportunities. Acts on public policy decisions for the benefit of the Chino business community. **Founded:** 1970. **Publications:** *The Chino Valley Connection* (Monthly). **Geographic Preference:** Local.

36325 ■ Chloride Chamber of Commerce (CCC)
PO Box 268
 Chloride, AZ 86431
Ph: (928)565-9777
Co. E-mail: chloridechamber@gmail.com
URL: http://www.visitchlorideaz.com
Contact: Angie Lee Nickoley, Director
Facebook: www.facebook.com/chloridearizonachamberofcommerce
Description: Promotes business and community development in Chloride, AZ. Sponsors community social and promotional events. **Geographic Preference:** Local.

36326 ■ Copper Basin Chamber of Commerce (CBCC)
355 Alden Rd.
 Kearny, AZ 85137
Ph: (520)363-7607
Co. E-mail: director@copperbasinaz.org
URL: http://copperbasinaz.org
Facebook: www.facebook.com/copperbasin.chamber
Instagram: www.instagram.com/copperbasinchamber
Description: Promotes business and community development in Hayden, Kearny, and Winkelman, AZ. Sponsors Pioneer Days and children's programs. Convention/Meeting: none. Publications: none. **Founded:** 1968. **Geographic Preference:** Local.

36327 ■ *Destination Flagstaff*
101 W Rte. 66
 Flagstaff, AZ 86001
Ph: (928)774-4505
Fax: (928)779-1209
Co. E-mail: info@flagstaffchamber.com
URL: http://www.flagstaffchamber.com
Contact: Julie Pastrick, President
E-mail: jpastrick@flagstaffchamber.com
URL(s): www.flagstaffchamber.com/membership-advantages
Released: Annual **Description:** Contains information on all things about Flagstaff – from business and education to arts and leisure. **Availability:** Print.

36328 ■ *Dolan Springs Information*
Released: Periodic **Availability:** Print.

36329 ■ Eloy Chamber of Commerce (ECC)
3725 N Camelot St.
 Eloy, AZ 85131
Ph: (520)466-3411
Co. E-mail: info@eloychamber.com
URL: http://eloychamber.com
Contact: Andrew Rodriguez, Executive Director
Description: Promotes business, tourism, and community development in the Eloy, AZ area. Provides referrals to members' businesses; conducts publicity campaigns for local tourist attractions. **Founded:** 1902. **Publications:** *Calendar of Events*; *The Chamber Voice* (Monthly); *Eloy Living Offers You* (Periodic). **Geographic Preference:** Local.

36330 ■ *Experience Sedona Guide*
45 Sunset Dr.
 Sedona, AZ 86336
Ph: (928)204-1123
Fax: (928)204-1064
Co. E-mail: info@sedonachamber.com
URL: http://sedonachamber.com
Contact: Michelle Conway, President
E-mail: mconway@sedonachamber.com
URL(s): sedonachamber.com/guide-books
Released: Annual **Description:** Offers all the information that needed to plan in Sedona itinerary - including accommodations, tours, activities, restaurant options and shopping excursions. **Availability:** Print; Online.

36331 ■ Flagstaff Chamber of Commerce
101 W Rte. 66
 Flagstaff, AZ 86001
Ph: (928)774-4505
Fax: (928)779-1209
Co. E-mail: info@flagstaffchamber.com
URL: http://www.flagstaffchamber.com
Contact: Julie Pastrick, President
E-mail: jpastrick@flagstaffchamber.com
Facebook: www.facebook.com/FlagstaffChamber
X (Twitter): x.com/flgchamber
Instagram: www.instagram.com/flagstaffchamber
Description: Promotes business and community development in Flagstaff, AZ. **Founded:** 1891. **Publications:** *Destination Flagstaff* (Annual); *Flagstaff Today* (Bimonthly). **Geographic Preference:** Local.

36332 ■ Fountain Hills Chamber of Commerce
16837 E Palisades Blvd.
 Fountain Hills, AZ 85268
Ph: (480)837-1654
URL: http://www.fountainhillschamber.com
Contact: Betsy LaVoie, President
E-mail: betsy@fountainhillschamber.com
Facebook: www.facebook.com/fountainhillschamber
X (Twitter): x.com/chamberfh
Instagram: www.instagram.com/fountainhillschamber
YouTube: www.youtube.com/user/fountainhillschamber
Description: Promotes business and community development in Fountain Hills, AZ. **Founded:** 1974. **Publications:** *News and Views* (Weekly). **Awards:** Fountain Hills Chamber of Commerce Business Person of the Year (Annual). **Geographic Preference:** Local.

36333 ■ Gilbert Chamber of Commerce (GCC)
119 N Gilbert Rd., Ste. 101
 Gilbert, AZ 85299-0527
Ph: (480)892-0056
Co. E-mail: info@gilbertchamber.com
URL: http://gilbertaz.com
Contact: Sarah Watts, President
E-mail: sarah@gilbertchamber.com
Facebook: www.facebook.com/GilbertChamber
Linkedin: www.linkedin.com/company/gilbert-chamber-of-commerce
X (Twitter): x.com/gilbertchamber
Instagram: www.instagram.com/gilbertchamber
YouTube: www.youtube.com/channel/UCo0KUGrzmE5l5yXcVYP4QRA
Description: Promotes business and community development in Gilbert, AZ. **Founded:** 1978. **Publications:** *Business Review* (Monthly); *Gilbert Chamber of Commerce Membership Directory* (Annual). **Geographic Preference:** Local.

36334 ■ Glendale Chamber of Commerce (GCC)
5800 W Glenn Dr., Ste. 275
 Glendale, AZ 85301
Ph: (623)937-4754
Co. E-mail: info@glendaleazchamber.org
URL: http://www.glendaleazchamber.com

STATE LISTINGS

Contact: Robert Heidt, President
Facebook: www.facebook.com/GlendaleAZchamber
Linkedin: www.linkedin.com/company/glendale-az-chamber-of-commerce
X (Twitter): x.com/glendalechamber
Instagram: www.instagram.com/glendaleazchamber
YouTube: www.youtube.com/channel/UCSIRyUMWYCt6QcDk93pNfQw
Description: Aims to foster tourism, as well as to protect and advance the commercial, industrial, cultural, educational, and civic interests of the City of Glendale. **Founded:** 1951. **Publications:** *At-A-Glance* (Biweekly). **Geographic Preference:** Local.

36335 ■ Globe-Miami Regional Chamber of Commerce
1360 N Broad St.
 Globe, AZ 85501
Ph: (928)425-4495
Co. E-mail: visitorinfo@globemiamichamber.com
URL: http://www.globemiamichamber.com
Contact: Christie Cothrun, President
Facebook: www.facebook.com/globemiamichamber
YouTube: www.youtube.com/channel/UCz5wf3AKVXfgIDMN8pNkE6Q
Description: Promotes tourism, community and economic development in Southern Gila County. **Founded:** 1992. **Geographic Preference:** Regional.

36336 ■ Graham County Chamber of Commerce
1051 W Thatcher Blvd.
 Safford, AZ 85546
Ph: (928)428-2511
Free: 888-837-1841
Co. E-mail: admin@grahamchamber.org
URL: http://grahamchamber.org
Contact: Vance Marcus Bryce, Chief Executive Officer
E-mail: vance@graham-chamber.com
Facebook: www.facebook.com/GrahamChamber
Description: Promotes business, industrial, agricultural, and community development in Graham County, Arizona. Seeks to increase public involvement in community improvement projects. **Founded:** 1881. **Publications:** *The Business Review* (Monthly). **Geographic Preference:** Local.

36337 ■ Grand Canyon Chamber of Commerce
PO Box 3007
 Grand Canyon, AZ 86023
Free: 844-638-2901
Fax: (928)638-4095
Co. E-mail: grandcanyonchamber@gmail.com
URL: http://grandcanyoncvb.org
Contact: Julie A. Aldaz, Contact
Facebook: www.facebook.com/grandcanyoncvb
Instagram: www.instagram.com/grandcanyoncvb
Description: Promotes business and community development in Grand Canyon, AZ. **Publications:** *Grand Canyon*. **Geographic Preference:** Local.

36338 ■ Greater Casa Grande Chamber of Commerce
575 N Marshall St.
 Casa Grande, AZ 85122
Ph: (520)836-2125
Free: 800-916-1515
Co. E-mail: info@casagrandechamber.org
URL: http://casagrandechamber.org
Contact: Renee Louzon-Benn, Executive Director
Linkedin: www.linkedin.com/company/greater-casa-grande-chamber-of-commerce
X (Twitter): x.com/cgazchamber
YouTube: www.youtube.com/user/ChamberWebsite
Description: Promotes business and community development in the Casa Grande, AZ area and tourism in Arizona and nationwide. **Founded:** 1925. **Publications:** *Community Book* (Annual); *The Voice of Business* (Monthly). **Geographic Preference:** State.

36339 ■ Greater Phoenix Chamber of Commerce
2575 E Camelback Rd., Ste. 410
 Phoenix, AZ 85016

Ph: (602)495-2195
Fax: (602)495-8913
Co. E-mail: info@phoenixchamber.com
URL: http://phoenixchamber.com
Contact: Todd Sanders, President
E-mail: tsanders@phoenixchamber.com
Facebook: www.facebook.com/phxchamber
Linkedin: www.linkedin.com/company/42478
X (Twitter): x.com/phxchamber
Instagram: www.instagram.com/phxchamber
YouTube: www.youtube.com/user/PhoenixChamber
Description: Supports the growth and development of business and the quality of life in the Phoenix, AZ area. Champions the voice of business in government, and keeps businesses informed, connected, and prosperous. **Founded:** 1888. **Publications:** *Greater Phoenix Chamber of Commerce Membership Directory & Business Services Guide*; *Arizona Industrial Directory* (Annual); *Business Services Guide* (Annual); *Greater Phoenix Ultimate Guide to Living Here* (Annual); *Greater Phoenix Chamber Membership List--Minority-Owned or Operated Businesses*; *Greater Phoenix Chamber Membership List--Women-Owned or Operated Businesses*; *Business Directory*; *Greater Phoenix Chamber Membership List--International Trade Businesses*; *Chamber Membership Directory/Consumer Guide*; *Arizona Software Industry Directory and Report*. **Educational Activities:** Greater Phoenix Chamber's Economic Outlook (Annual). **Geographic Preference:** Local.

36340 ■ *The Hassayampa Alert*
216 N Frontier St.
 Wickenburg, AZ 85390
Ph: (928)684-5479
Co. E-mail: info@wickenburgchamber.com
URL: http://www.wickenburgchamber.com
Contact: Kelly Blunt, President
E-mail: jbrooks@wickenburgchamber.com
URL(s): www.wickenburgchamber.com/newsletter
Released: Monthly **Availability:** PDF; Online.

36341 ■ Heber-Overgaard Chamber of Commerce
2774 Hwy. 260
 Overgaard, AZ 85933
Ph: (928)535-5777
Co. E-mail: coc@heberovergaard.org
URL: http://heberovergaard.org
Contact: Gary Martin, President
Facebook: www.facebook.com/heberovergaard.org
Linkedin: www.linkedin.com/in/heber-overgaard-chamber-of-commerce
Description: Promotes business and community development in Heber and Overgaard, AZ. **Publications:** *Splendor on the Rim*. **Geographic Preference:** Local.

36342 ■ Jerome Chamber of Commerce (JCC)
310 Hull Ave.
 Jerome, AZ 86331
Ph: (928)634-2900
Co. E-mail: info@jeromechamber.com
URL: http://jeromechamber.com
Contact: Kevin Savage, President
Facebook: www.facebook.com/jeromechamber
Description: Promotes business and community development in Jerome, AZ. Assists charitable programs and annual home tour. **Founded:** 1974. **Geographic Preference:** Local.

36343 ■ Kingman Area Chamber of Commerce
309 E Beale St.
 Kingman, AZ 86401
Ph: (928)753-6253
Co. E-mail: info@kingmanchamber.com
URL: http://kingmanchamber.com
Contact: Becky Fawson, Executive Director
E-mail: becky@kingmanchamber.com
Facebook: www.facebook.com/kingmanchamber
Pinterest: www.pinterest.com/KingmanChamber

Description: Promotes business and community development in the Kingman, AZ area. **Publications:** *Kingman Area Chamber Report* (Monthly). **Geographic Preference:** Local.

36344 ■ Lake Havasu Area Chamber of Commerce (LHACC)
314 London Bridge Rd.
 Lake Havasu City, AZ 86403
Ph: (928)855-4115
Co. E-mail: info@havasuchamber.com
URL: http://www.havasuchamber.com
Contact: Lisa Krueger, President
E-mail: lisak@havasuchamber.com
Facebook: www.facebook.com/havasuchamber
X (Twitter): x.com/HavasuChamber
Instagram: www.instagram.com/havasuchamber
YouTube: www.youtube.com/user/LakeHavasuChamber
Description: Promotes business and community development in west-central Arizona. Sponsors London Bridge Days. **Founded:** 1971. **Geographic Preference:** Local.

36345 ■ Marana Chamber of Commerce
13251 N Lon Adams Rd.
 Marana, AZ 85653
Ph: (520)682-4314
Co. E-mail: info@maranachamber.com
URL: http://www.maranachamber.com
Contact: Amanda Wiggins, President
E-mail: amandawiggins@maranachamber.com
Facebook: www.facebook.com/maranachamber
X (Twitter): x.com/maranachamber
Description: Promotes the community and the businesses in the community. Encourages the retention, expansion, and relocation of business locally. Provides value-added services to members by promoting business and providing assistance aimed at helping the community prosper. **Founded:** 1987. **Publications:** *Marana Chamber Newsletter*; *Marana Community Profile and Membership Directory* (Quarterly); *Marana Community Profile and Membership Directory* (Annual). **Educational Activities:** Marana Chamber of Commerce Luncheon. **Geographic Preference:** Local.

36346 ■ McMullen Valley Chamber of Commerce
66710 Hwy. 60
 Salome, AZ 85348-0700
Ph: (928)859-3846
Co. E-mail: mcmullencoc@gmail.com
URL: http://www.azoutback.net/Index.html
Contact: James Downing, President
Description: Promotes business and community development in Salome, Wenden, Harcuvar, Vicksburg and Brenda, AZ. **Founded:** 1989. **Geographic Preference:** Local.

36347 ■ Mesa Chamber of Commerce
165 N Centennial Way., Ste. 208
 Mesa, AZ 85201
Ph: (480)969-1307
Co. E-mail: info@mesachamber.org
URL: http://www.mesachamber.org
Contact: Sally Harrison, President
E-mail: sharrison@mesachamber.org
Facebook: www.facebook.com/MesaChamberofCommerce
Linkedin: www.linkedin.com/company/the-mesa-chamber-of-commerce
X (Twitter): x.com/mesachamber
Instagram: www.instagram.com/mesachamber
YouTube: www.youtube.com/channel/UCfr11hk-IgmT2D0k70dlbOw
Description: Promotes business, tourism, and community development in Mesa, AZ. Encourages civic involvement in tourism, community betterment, and winter visitor marketing. Conducts annual Business Showcase. **Publications:** *Business Directory*; *Inside Business* (Monthly). **Geographic Preference:** Local.

36348 ■ Nogales-Santa Cruz County Chamber of Commerce (NSCCC)
123 W Kino Pk. Pl.
 Nogales, AZ 85621

Ph: (520)287-3685
Co. E-mail: info@thenogaleschamber.org
URL: http://www.thenogaleschamber.org
Contact: Olivia Ainza-Kramer, President
Facebook: www.facebook.com/nogaleschamber
X (Twitter): x.com/NogalesChamber
Instagram: www.instagram.com/nogaleschamber
YouTube: www.youtube.com/channel/UCbXjweJwi-K
_AgPtAuK3qFg
Pinterest: www.pinterest.com/visitnogalesaz

Description: Promotes business and community development in Santa Cruz County, AZ. Sponsors festivals and parades; conducts competitions. Assists charitable efforts. **Founded:** 1914. **Publications:** *Discover* (Annual); *Santa Cruz County Visitors Guide* (Annual). **Educational Activities:** Business Expo (Annual). **Geographic Preference:** Local.

36349 ■ North Phoenix Chamber of Commerce (NPCC)
16042 N 32nd St., Ste. D-10
Phoenix, AZ 85032
Ph: (602)482-3344
Fax: (602)595-5651
Co. E-mail: info@northphoenixchamber.com
URL: http://www.northphoenixchamber.com
Contact: Tori Baker, Treasurer
Facebook: www.facebook.com/Nor
thPhoenixChamber
Linkedin: www.linkedin.com/company/north-phoenix
-chamber-of-commerce
X (Twitter): x.com/NorthPhxChamber
YouTube: www.youtube.com/user/NPhoenixChamber

Description: Strives to unite the people of commerce, industry, education, and of the professions to work together for the development of the greater North Phoenix area. **Founded:** 1963. **Geographic Preference:** Local.

36350 ■ Oatman-Gold Road Chamber of Commerce
PO Box 423
Oatman, AZ 86433
Ph: (928)234-0344
URL: http://www.oatmangoldroad.org
Contact: Leanne Toohey, Secretary

Description: Promotes business and community development in the Oatman, AZ area. Sponsors Gold Camp Days. Conducts International Burro Biscuit Throwing Contest. Offers "ghost town" atmosphere; wild burros petting areas and gunfights in the streets. **Geographic Preference:** Local.

36351 ■ *Out in Front*
508 E Monroe Ave.
Buckeye, AZ 85326
Ph: (623)386-2727
Co. E-mail: info@buckeyevalleychamber.org
URL: http://www.buckeyevalleychamber.org
Contact: Deanna Kupcik, Officer
URL(s): www.buckeyevalleychamber.org/membership
-benefits

Released: Monthly **Description:** Discusses business chapter news. **Availability:** Print.

36352 ■ Page-Lake Powell Chamber of Commerce (PLPCC) [The Chamber page lake powell]
48 S Lake Powell Blvd.
Page, AZ 86040
Ph: (928)645-2741
Co. E-mail: office@pagechamber.com
URL: http://pagelakepowellchamberofcommerce
.wpcomstaging.com
Contact: Judy Franz, Executive Director
E-mail: judy@pagechamber.com
Facebook: www.facebook.com/
ChamberPageLakePowell

Description: Promotes business and community development in the Page-Lake Powell area. Seeks to enhance the quality of life and promote relocation to the area. Sponsors area festivals. Operates a tourism information source and visitor guide. **Founded:** 1957. **Geographic Preference:** Local.

36353 ■ Parker Area Chamber of Commerce (PACC)
1217 S California Ave.
Parker, AZ 85344
Ph: (928)669-2174
Co. E-mail: info@parkeraz.org
URL: http://www.parkeraz.org
Contact: Kyleen Baldwin, Vice President, Finance
Facebook: www.facebook.com/ParkerAZChamber
Linkedin: www.linkedin.com/company/parker-area
-chamber-of-commerce/about
X (Twitter): x.com/azparker
YouTube: www.youtube.com/channel/
UCvPkSwGAVNtLoSJ5Kha0paQ

Description: Promotes business and community development in the Parker, AZ area. Encourages tourism; sponsors festivals. **Founded:** 1952. **Geographic Preference:** Local.

36354 ■ Peoria Chamber of Commerce (PCC)
24654 N Lake Pleasant Pky., No. 103-703
Peoria, AZ 85383
Ph: (623)979-3601
Co. E-mail: memberservices@peoriachamber.com
URL: http://www.peoriachamber.com
Contact: Rhonda Carlson, President
Facebook: www.facebook.com/peoriachamberaz
Linkedin: www.linkedin.com/company/peoria
-chamber-of-commerce-az
X (Twitter): x.com/peoriachamberaz
Instagram: www.instagram.com/peoriachamberaz

Description: Promotes business and community development in the Peoria, AZ area. **Founded:** 1919. **Geographic Preference:** Local.

36355 ■ Prescott Chamber of Commerce
117 W Goodwin St.
Prescott, AZ 86303
Ph: (928)445-2000
Free: 800-266-7534
Co. E-mail: chamber@prescott.org
URL: http://www.prescott.org
Contact: Sheri Heiney, President
E-mail: sheri@prescott.org
Facebook: www.facebook.com/PrescottChamber
Linkedin: www.linkedin.com/company/presco
tt-chamber-of-commerce
X (Twitter): x.com/prescottcofc
Instagram: www.instagram.com/prescottchamber
YouTube: www.youtube.com/channel/UCs-Av5cvrLYu
5mydJo2KPWQ
Pinterest: www.pinterest.com/prescottchamber

Description: Promotes business and community development in the Prescott, AZ area. Sponsors Bluegrass Festival and arts and crafts show. **Founded:** 1910. **Publications:** *Business Pages* (Monthly). **Geographic Preference:** Local.

36356 ■ Prescott Valley Chamber of Commerce
7120 Pav Way, Ste. 102
Prescott Valley, AZ 86314
Ph: (928)772-8857
Fax: (928)772-4267
URL: http://www.pvchamber.org
Contact: Marnie Uhl, President
E-mail: marnie@pvchamber.org
Facebook: www.facebook.com/presco
ttvalleychamber
Instagram: www.instagram.com/presco
ttvalleychamber
YouTube: www.youtube.com/channel/UC4Lfuf1L
dxyvqtlQbEDtGkQ

Description: Promotes business, industrial, and community development in North Central Arizona. Conducts monthly business mixer. **Founded:** 1978. **Publications:** *Member News Magazine* (Monthly); *Business Directory*. **Geographic Preference:** Local.

36357 ■ *Relocation Packet*
180 W 1st St., Ste. A
Yuma, AZ 85364
Ph: (928)782-2567
Free: 877-782-0438
Fax: (928)247-6509
Co. E-mail: info@yumachamber.org
URL: http://www.yumachamber.org
Contact: Kimberly Kahl, Executive Director
E-mail: kimberly@yumachamber.org
URL(s): www.yumachamber.org/relocation-informa
tion.html

Description: Includes chamber business directory, housing and apartment guide, and detailed map of Yuma. **Availability:** Print.

36358 ■ Rim Country Regional Chamber of Commerce
100 W Main St.
Payson, AZ 85541
Ph: (928)474-4515
Co. E-mail: info@rimcountrychamber.com
URL: http://www.rimcountrychamber.com
Contact: Tina McAllister Smith, President
E-mail: tinamcsmith72@gmail.com
Facebook: www.facebook.com/rimcountrychamber
X (Twitter): x.com/chamberrim
Instagram: www.instagram.com/rimcountrychamber

Description: Promotes business and community development in the Rim Country, AZ. Sponsors rodeo and parade, and June Festival. **Founded:** 1998. **Publications:** *Rim Country Regional Chamber of Commerce Newsletter* (Bimonthly); *Rim Country Chamber Visitors Guide* (Annual); *Spirit of Payson* (Periodic). **Educational Activities:** Strategic Retreat - Board of Directors (Annual). **Geographic Preference:** Local.

36359 ■ Scottsdale Area Chamber of Commerce
7501 E McCormick Pky., Ste. 202N
Scottsdale, AZ 85258
Ph: (480)355-2700
Co. E-mail: info@scottsdalechamber.com
URL: http://www.scottsdalechamber.com
Contact: Mark Stanton, President
E-mail: mstanton@scottsdalechamber.com
Facebook: www.facebook.com/ScottsdaleChamber
Linkedin: www.linkedin.com/company/scottsdale-area
-chamber-of-commerce
X (Twitter): x.com/scottsdalechmbr
Instagram: www.instagram.com/scottsdalechamber
YouTube: www.youtube.com/channel/UCT-WlmTl
15Q9mN4ZND3WKMg

Description: Seeks to build a vibrant and prosperous community through business leadership. **Founded:** 1947. **Publications:** *The Guide to Living in Scottsdale* (Monthly); *Scottsdale at Work*; *Start-Up Guide*. **Geographic Preference:** Local.

36360 ■ Sedona Chamber of Commerce
45 Sunset Dr.
Sedona, AZ 86336
Ph: (928)204-1123
Fax: (928)204-1064
Co. E-mail: info@sedonachamber.com
URL: http://sedonachamber.com
Contact: Michelle Conway, President
E-mail: mconway@sedonachamber.com
Facebook: www.facebook.com/Se
donaChamberofCommerce
Linkedin: www.linkedin.com/company/sedona
-chamber-of-commerce
X (Twitter): x.com/SedonaChamber
YouTube: www.youtube.com/channel/UCicClkX
_DeOA2-yE9gaxyBQ

Description: Promotes business and community development in Sedona, AZ and the Oak Creek Canyon area. **Founded:** 1950. **Publications:** *Experience Sedona Guide* (Annual). **Educational Activities:** Members Exhibition. **Geographic Preference:** Local.

36361 ■ Show Low Chamber of Commerce
81 E Deuce of Clubs
Show Low, AZ 85901
Ph: (928)537-2326
Co. E-mail: info@showlowchamber.com
URL: http://showlowchamber.com
Contact: Stefan Wehnau, President
X (Twitter): x.com/showlowchamber

Description: Promotes business and community development in Show Low, AZ. **Publications:** *Messenger*. **Geographic Preference:** Local.

STATE LISTINGS

Arizona ■ 36377

36362 ■ Sierra Vista Area Chamber of Commerce (SVAC)
21 E Wilcox Dr.
Sierra Vista, AZ 85635
Ph: (520)458-6940
Co. E-mail: media@svachamber.com
URL: http://www.svachamber.com
Contact: Melany Edwards-Barton, Chief Executive Officer
E-mail: ceo@svachamber.com
Facebook: www.facebook.com/SierraVistaChamber
Linkedin: www.linkedin.com/company/sierra-vista-area-chamber-of-commerce
X (Twitter): x.com/svachamber
Instagram: www.instagram.com/sierravistachamber
YouTube: www.youtube.com/channel/UCkilbmxBV8DvVfi8by9nqkA
Description: Promotes business and community development in the Sierra Vista, AZ area. **Founded:** 1959. **Publications:** *The Chamber Vista* (Monthly); *Sierra Vista Tourism* (Monthly). **Educational Activities:** Buffalo Soldier Days. **Geographic Preference:** Local.

36363 ■ Snowflake/Taylor Chamber of Commerce
113 N Main St., Ste. A
Snowflake, AZ 85937
Ph: (928)536-4331
Co. E-mail: admin@snowflaketaylorchamber.org
URL: http://snowflaketaylorchamber.org
Contact: Charles Carlson, III, President
Facebook: www.facebook.com/Snowflake-Taylor-Chamber-of-Commerce-482438121795674
Description: Promotes business, community development, and tourism in the Snowflake and Taylor, AZ area. Works to bring new industry and residents to area. **Publications:** *Chamber of Commerce Newsletter* (Monthly). **Geographic Preference:** Local.

36364 ■ Southwest Valley Chamber of Commerce
289 N Litchfield Rd.
Goodyear, AZ 85338
Ph: (623)932-2260
Co. E-mail: info@southwestvalleychamber.org
URL: http://www.southwestvalleychamber.org
Contact: Jeffrey Campos, President
E-mail: jeffrey@southwestvalleychamber.org
Facebook: www.facebook.com/SouthwestValleyCofC
X (Twitter): x.com/SWVChamber
Description: Promotes business and community development in the Southwest Valley areas of Avondale, Goodyear, Litchfield Park, and Tolleson, AZ. Sponsors festival. **Founded:** 1958. **Publications:** *Business Bylines* (Monthly). **Geographic Preference:** Local.

36365 ■ Springerville-Eagar Regional Chamber of Commerce
7 W Main St.
Springerville, AZ 85938
Ph: (928)333-2123
Co. E-mail: serccinfo@gmail.com
URL: http://springervilleeagarchamber.com
Facebook: www.facebook.com/springervilleeagarchamber
Description: Promotes business, tourism, and community development in the White Mountain, AZ area. Assists and cooperates with the Springerville and Eagar, AZ economic development commissions. Sponsors rodeos, parades, arts and crafts shows, and athletic tournaments. **Founded:** 1959. **Geographic Preference:** Local.

36366 ■ Superior Chamber of Commerce
165 Main St.
Superior, AZ 85173
Ph: (520)689-0200
URL: http://www.uschamber.com/co/chambers/arizona/superior
Contact: Carol Schumacher, Contact
URL(s): www.superiorarizonachamber.org
Facebook: www.facebook.com/iamsuperioraz
X (Twitter): x.com/iamsuperioraz
Instagram: www.instagram.com/superiorarizonachamber

Description: Promotes business and community development in Superior, AZ area. **Geographic Preference:** Local.

36367 ■ Swedish-American Chamber of Commerce Arizona (SACC AZ)
PO Box 5102
Scottsdale, AZ 85261-5102
Ph: (602)399-7300
Co. E-mail: contact@saccarizona.org
URL: http://www.saccarizona.org
Contact: Joacim Mattisson, President
Facebook: www.facebook.com/SACCArizona
Linkedin: www.linkedin.com/company/sacc-arizona
X (Twitter): x.com/sacc_az
Description: Promotes trade, commerce, and investments between Sweden and Arizona. **Founded:** 1996. **Geographic Preference:** State.

36368 ■ Tempe Chamber of Commerce
1438 W Broadway Rd., Ste. 123
Tempe, AZ 85283
Ph: (480)967-7891
Co. E-mail: info@tempechamber.org
URL: http://tempechamber.org
Contact: Anne Gill, President
E-mail: anne@tempechamber.org
Facebook: www.facebook.com/TempeCC
Linkedin: www.linkedin.com/company/tempe-chamber-of-commerce
X (Twitter): x.com/tempechamber
Instagram: www.instagram.com/tempechamber
YouTube: www.youtube.com/user/tempechamber
Description: Promotes business and community development in Tempe, AZ. **Founded:** 1908. **Publications:** *The Business Advocate* (Weekly (Tues.)); *Tempe Business Review* (Periodic). **Geographic Preference:** Local.

36369 ■ Tombstone Chamber of Commerce (TCC)
109 S 4th St.
Tombstone, AZ 85638
Ph: (520)457-9317
Co. E-mail: socialmedia@tombstonechamber.com
URL: http://www.tombstonechamber.com
Contact: Susan Wallace, President
Facebook: www.facebook.com/TombstoneChamberofCommerce
X (Twitter): x.com/TombstoneAZCofC
Instagram: www.instagram.com/tombstonechamberofcommerce
Description: Seeks to advance the general welfare and prosperity of the Tombstone area. **Founded:** 1809. **Geographic Preference:** Local.

36370 ■ Tubac Chamber of Commerce
1 Burruel St.
Tubac, AZ 85646
Ph: (520)398-2704
Co. E-mail: info@tubacaz.com
URL: http://www.tubacaz.com
Contact: Gale Thomssen, President
X (Twitter): x.com/TubacChamber
Description: Promotes business and community development in Tubac, AZ. **Founded:** 1691. **Geographic Preference:** Local.

36371 ■ Tucson Metro Chamber
212 E Broadway Blvd.
Tucson, AZ 85701
Ph: (520)792-1212
Co. E-mail: info@tucsonchamber.org
URL: http://tucsonchamber.org
Contact: Michael Guymon, President
E-mail: mguymon@tucsonchamber.org
Facebook: www.facebook.com/TheTucsonChamber
Linkedin: www.linkedin.com/company/tucson-metropolitan-chamber-of-commerce
X (Twitter): x.com/tucsonchamber
YouTube: www.youtube.com/user/TheTucsonChamber
Description: Promotes business and community development in the Tucson, AZ area. **Founded:** 1896. **Geographic Preference:** Local.

36372 ■ Visit Camp Verde Arizona
435 S Main St.
Camp Verde, AZ 86322
Ph: (928)554-0851
Co. E-mail: info@visitcampverde.com
URL: http://visitcampverde.com
Contact: Mary Kay, Director, Sales
Facebook: www.facebook.com/visitcampverde
Linkedin: www.linkedin.com/company/town-of-camp-verde
Description: Promotes business and community development in the Verde valley area of Arizona. **Geographic Preference:** Local.

36373 ■ Wickenburg Chamber of Commerce
216 N Frontier St.
Wickenburg, AZ 85390
Ph: (928)684-5479
Co. E-mail: info@wickenburgchamber.com
URL: http://www.wickenburgchamber.com
Contact: Kelly Blunt, President
E-mail: jbrooks@wickenburgchamber.com
Facebook: www.facebook.com/wickenburgchamber
X (Twitter): x.com/wickchamber
Instagram: www.instagram.com/visit_wickenburg
Description: Promotes business and community development in Wickenburg, AZ. **Founded:** 1863. **Publications:** *The Hassayampa Alert* (Monthly). **Educational Activities:** Fiesta Septiembre (Annual). **Geographic Preference:** Local.

36374 ■ Willcox Chamber of Commerce and Agriculture (WCCA)
101 S Railroad Ave.
Willcox, AZ 85643
Ph: (520)384-2272
Co. E-mail: info.willcoxchamber@gmail.com
URL: http://www.willcoxchamberofcommerce.com
Contact: Eddie Browning, President
E-mail: eddie.whitehat@gmail.com
Facebook: www.facebook.com/Willcoxchamber
Instagram: www.instagram.com/willcoxchamberofcommerce
Description: Promotes business, community, and agricultural development in Willcox, AZ and surrounding trade areas. **Founded:** 1915. **Publications:** *Business Directory* (Periodic). **Educational Activities:** Cowboy Hall of Fame (Annual). **Awards:** WCCA Citizen of the Year (Annual); Willcox Cowboy Hall of Fame Induction (Annual). **Geographic Preference:** Local.

36375 ■ Williams-Grand Canyon Chamber of Commerce (WGCCC)
200 W Railroad Ave.
Williams, AZ 86046
Ph: (928)635-4061
Co. E-mail: heather@frontburnermedia.com
URL: http://experiencewilliams.com
Description: Promotes business and community development in Williams and northern Arizona. Sponsors Rendezvous Days. **Founded:** 1974. **Publications:** *Business Directory* (Annual); *Chamber News.* **Geographic Preference:** Local.

36376 ■ Winslow Chamber of Commerce
523 W 2nd St.
Winslow, AZ 86047
Ph: (928)289-2434
Fax: (928)289-5660
Co. E-mail: winslowchamber@cableone.net
URL: http://winslowarizona.org
Contact: Bob Hall, Chief Executive Officer
Facebook: www.facebook.com/profile.php
Description: Promotes business and community development in Winslow, AZ. **Geographic Preference:** Local.

36377 ■ Yuma County Chamber of Commerce (YCCC)
180 W 1st St., Ste. A
Yuma, AZ 85364
Ph: (928)782-2567
Free: 877-782-0438
Fax: (928)247-6509
Co. E-mail: info@yumachamber.org
URL: http://www.yumachamber.org

36378 ■ Arizona

Contact: Kimberly Kahl, Executive Director
E-mail: kimberly@yumachamber.org
Facebook: www.facebook.com/YumaCoun tyChamberofCommerce
Linkedin: www.linkedin.com/company/yuma-county -chamber-of-commerce
X (Twitter): x.com/YumaChamber
Description: Works for the preservation of the free enterprise system in the Yuma, AZ area. **Founded:** 1905. **Publications:** *Relocation Packet*; *Vantage Point* (Monthly). **Educational Activities:** Good Morning YUMA (Monthly). **Geographic Preference:** Local.

MINORITY BUSINESS ASSISTANCE PROGRAMS

36378 ■ Arizona Minority Business Development Agency
1020 E Missouri Ave.
Phoenix, AZ 85014
Ph: (602)294-6087
URL: http://archive.mbda.gov/businesscenters/phoenix.html
Contact: Alika Kumar, Director
E-mail: alika@phoenixmbdacenter.com

36379 ■ Arizona Native American Business Development Center - National Center for American Indian Enterprise Development Center (NCAIED)
953 E Juanita Ave.
Mesa, AZ 85204
Ph: (602)325-8554
Co. E-mail: info@ncaied.org
URL: http://www.ncaied.org
Contact: Chris James, President
Facebook: www.facebook.com/NCAIED
Linkedin: www.linkedin.com/company/the-national -center-for-american-indian-enterprise-development
X (Twitter): x.com/ncaied
Instagram: www.instagram.com/ncaied
YouTube: www.youtube.com/channel/UC4ZAGk-GMn _1PFKwahezH6A
Founded: 1969.

36380 ■ Pacific Southwest Minority Supplier Development Council (PSWMSDC)
2030 W Baseline Rd., Ste. 182-547
Phoenix, AZ 85041
Ph: (602)495-9950
Co. E-mail: info@pswmsdc.org
URL: http://pswmsdc.org
Contact: Patricia Crenshaw, President
Facebook: www.facebook.com/PSWMSDC
Linkedin: www.linkedin.com/in/pswmsdc
X (Twitter): x.com/PSWMSDC
YouTube: www.youtube.com/channel/ UCW9jkO9YOHiXgsk87OwZDDA
Description: Provides a direct link between corporate America and minority-owned businesses. Increases procurement and business opportunities for minority businesses of all sizes. **Founded:** 1993. **Geographic Preference:** State.

FINANCING AND LOAN PROGRAMS

36381 ■ Arizona Tech Investors (ATI)
10645 N Tatum Blvd., Ste. 200-347
Phoenix, AZ 85028
URL: http://arizonatechinvestors.com
Contact: Bob DeLean, Chairman
Facebook: www.facebook.com/people/Arizona-Tech -Investors/100065547880803
Linkedin: www.linkedin.com/company/arizona techinvestors
Description: Funds high-growth see- and early-stage information technology and live science startups in the Southwest. **Founded:** 2007. **Industry Preferences:** SaaS; enterprise; ed tech; med tech; semiconductors; Internet of Things; medical devices and diagnostics; capital-efficient green tech.

36382 ■ Brookstone Venture Capital
7134 E Stetson Dr., Ste. B-400
Scottsdale, AZ 85251
Ph: (480)264-0238
Co. E-mail: info@canalpartners.com
URL: http://www.brookstoneventurecapital.com
Contact: Todd Belfer, Managing Partner
Description: Venture capital firm for B2B software and internet technologies companies. **Founded:** 2008. **Investment Policies:** Highly scalable revenue-generating companies with market-proven products and services, . **Industry Preferences:** Consumer services; human resources; financial services; health care technology; professional and business services; information technology.

36383 ■ Capital Insights L.L.C. (CI)
7328 E Deer Valley Rd., Ste. 105
Scottsdale, AZ 85255
Ph: (480)295-7100
Free: 866-635-5479
URL: http://cipinvest.com
Contact: Steven T. Nelson, Chief Executive Officer
E-mail: steve@cipinvest.com
Description: Firm provides financial and operational advisory services to companies in industries. **Preferred Investment Size:** $130,000 to $2,800,000. **Industry Preferences:** Communications and media, other products, semiconductors and other electronics, consumer related, industrial and energy.

36384 ■ Miller Capital Corp.
7025 N Scottsdale Rd., Ste. 235
Scottsdale, AZ 85253-3675
Ph: (602)225-0505
URL: http://www.themillergroup.net
Contact: Rudy R. Miller, President
Description: Provider of financial and strategic advisory services to both public and private middle-market companies. **Founded:** 1972. **Preferred Investment Size:** $1,000,000 to $5,000,000. **Industry Preferences:** Consumer related.

INCUBATORS/RESEARCH AND TECHNOLOGY PARKS

36385 ■ AZ TechCelerator
12425 W Bell Rd.
Surprise, AZ 85378
Ph: (623)222-8324
Co. E-mail: aztc@surpriseaz.gov
URL: http://www.aztechcelerator.com
Contact: Yuval Goren, President
Facebook: www.facebook.com/aztechcelerator
X (Twitter): x.com/AZTechCelerator
Instagram: www.instagram.com/aztechcelerator
Description: Provider of innovation, technology and entrepreneurship for business startups.

36386 ■ Center for Entrepreneurial Innovation (CEI)
275 N GateWay Dr.
Phoenix, AZ 85034
Ph: (602)286-8950
Co. E-mail: infocei@ceigateway.com
URL: http://www.ceigateway.com
Contact: Patti DuBois, Executive Director
E-mail: dubois@ceigateway.com
Facebook: www.facebook.com/ceigateway
X (Twitter): x.com/ceigateway
YouTube: www.youtube.com/channel/UCMw8u 3YVZg8QqOiYL4BIZCQ
Description: A business incubator that is dedicated to supporting technology-based businesses. Services include validation, product development, commercialization and growth. **Founded:** 2013.

36387 ■ CEO Focus
687 W Carob Pl.
Chandler, AZ 85248
Ph: (480)399-6013
Fax: (480)505-3581
URL: http://www.chandlerchamber.com

STATE LISTINGS

Description: A network of business improvement specialists who help business owners to quickly and systematically close the gap between their dreams and their realities. Also offers a business acceleration program to help build sustainable and profitable businesses.

36388 ■ Chandler Innovations
175 S Arizona Ave.
Chandler, AZ 85225
URL: http://www.chandleraz.gov
Description: A city-wide business incubation and entrepreneurial development program offering group coaching and one-on-one support to early stage founders, CEOs and entrepreneurs with tech-focused, scalable businesses. **Founded:** 2016.

36389 ■ City of Flagstaff Economic Development Department
c/o City of Flagstaff
211 W Aspen Ave.
Flagstaff, AZ 86001
Ph: (928)213-2906
Co. E-mail: econdevinfo@flagstaffaz.gov
URL: http://www.chooseflagstaff.com
Contact: David McIntire, Director
E-mail: dmcintire@flagstaffaz.gov
Description: Firm offers support services to entrepreneurs, startups and existing businesses to enhance the local economy and services include site selection, business retention and expansion, market analysis, business advocacy, incentives and grants and planning and design review.

36390 ■ City of Peoria Economic Development Services Department
9875 N 85th Ave.
Peoria, AZ 85345
Ph: (623)773-7735
URL: http://peoriaed.com
Contact: Amber Costa, Coordinator
E-mail: amber.costa@peoriaaz.gov
Description: Governs and supports businesses in the City of Peoria.

36391 ■ City of San Luis Economic Development Commission
1090 E Union St.
San Luis, AZ 85349
Ph: (928)341-8520
Free: 800-367-8939
URL: http://www.sanluisaz.gov/347/Economic -Development-Commission
Contact: Jenny Torres, Manager
E-mail: jtorres@sanluisaz.gov
Description: Promotes sustainable and economic growth and business start up services in the city of San Luis, AZ. Services include site location, zoning, business plans, business registration, and permits/ inspections.

36392 ■ DPR Construction
222 N 44th St.
Phoenix, AZ 85034
Ph: (602)808-0500
Co. E-mail: info@dpr.com
URL: http://www.dpr.com/#slide-0
Contact: Gretchen Kinsella, Leader
Facebook: www.facebook.com/DPRConstruction
Linkedin: www.linkedin.com/company/dpr-construc tion-inc
X (Twitter): x.com/DPRConstruction
Instagram: www.instagram.com/dprconstruction
YouTube: www.youtube.com/user/DPRConstruction
Description: A national technical builder specializing in highly complex and sustainable projects. Its core ideology is to build great things and operate with integrity, enjoyment, uniqueness and forward progression. **Founded:** 1994.

36393 ■ Eureka Loft
3839 N Drinkwater Blvd.
Scottsdale, AZ 85251
Ph: (480)312-7323
URL: http://ww.scottsdalelibrary.org/eurekaloft

Description: An innovative co-working space located in Scottsdale, Arizona, that supports a growing community of entrepreneurs and innovators with events and other amenities to help them on their paths to success.

36394 ■ Gangplank
22240 S Ellsworth Rd.
Queen Creek, AZ 85142
Co. E-mail: info@gangplankhq.com
URL: http://gangplankhq.com
Contact: Derek A. Neighbors, Manager
Facebook: www.facebook.com/GangplankQueenCreek
Instagram: www.instagram.com/gpqueencreek
Description: Firm provides marketing, financial management, and business planning services.

36395 ■ Hotwire Development L.L.C.
12304 E Poinsettia
Scottsdale, AZ 85259
Contact: Jeffrey S. Doss, Manager
Description: Works to ignite innovation by helping entrepreneurs realize their dreams. Partners with startup and early stage companies to decrease the cost and complexity of the product development process while increasing your product's (company's) likelihood of success.

36396 ■ James E. Rogers Community Law Group
1201 E Speedway
Tucson, AZ 85721
Ph: (520)621-1373
Co. E-mail: law-admissions@email.arizona.edu
URL: http://law.arizona.edu
Contact: Marc L. Miller, Dean
E-mail: marc.miller@law.arizona.edu
Description: Connects immigrants to a wide array of services and resources, both internally at the law school and the University, and externally through extensive partnerships with the nonprofit sector and private bar. **Founded:** 1915.

36397 ■ JumpStartbiz
15124 E Ridgeway Dr.
Fountain Hills, AZ 85268
Description: Business incubator/accelerator offering two structured programs that provide focus and accountability to the business owner.

36398 ■ Keap Inc.
1260 S Spectrum Blvd.
Chandler, AZ 85286
Ph: (480)499-6500
Free: 866-800-0004
Fax: (480)391-8177
Co. E-mail: sales@keap.com
URL: http://keap.com
Contact: Clate Mask, Chief Executive Officer
Facebook: www.facebook.com/Keap
Linkedin: www.linkedin.com/company/keap-growing
X (Twitter): x.com/keapgrowing
Instagram: www.instagram.com/keap
YouTube: www.youtube.com/user/infusionsoft
Pinterest: www.pinterest.com/keapgrowing
Description: Provides web-based application and portals for businesses selling online. **Founded:** 2001.

36399 ■ MAC 6 Leadership Academy
1430 W Broadway Rd.
Tempe, AZ 85282
URL: http://mac6.com/leadershipacademy
Description: Entrepreneurial investors who put monetary and intellectual capital in to growth stage businesses.

36400 ■ Moonshot
2225 N Gemini Dr.
Flagstaff, AZ 86001
Ph: (928)213-9234
Co. E-mail: info@moonshotaz.com
URL: http://www.moonshotaz.com
Contact: Scott Hathcock, President
Facebook: www.facebook.com/MoonshotAZ
Linkedin: www.linkedin.com/company/moonshotaz
X (Twitter): x.com/moonshotaz
Instagram: www.instagram.com/moonshotpioneers
Description: An incubator supporting the creation of science and technology-based businesses in Arizona. **Founded:** 2001.

36401 ■ San Luis Business Incubator (SLBI)
415 N Henry Chavez Ct.
San Luis, AZ 85349
Ph: (928)627-1627
Fax: (928)627-2166
URL: http://sanluisincubator.org
Contact: Jenny Torres, Manager
E-mail: jtorres@sanluisaz.gov
Description: Business incubator supporting the local economy. **Founded:** 1979.

36402 ■ Seed Spot
515 E Grant St.
Phoenix, AZ 85004
Ph: (602)456-9944
Co. E-mail: connect@seedspot.org
URL: http://seedspot.org
Contact: Brian Hill, Executive Director
Facebook: www.facebook.com/SEEDSPOT
Linkedin: www.linkedin.com/company/seedspot
X (Twitter): x.com/seedspot
Instagram: www.instagram.com/seedspot
Description: An incubator with a mission to educate, accelerate and invest in entrepreneurs who are creating solutions to social problems. Offers mentorship, an expansive network and creative space, as well as entrepreneurship curriculum.

36403 ■ Startup Tucson
PO Box 1214
Tucson, AZ 85702
Ph: (520)477-8278
Co. E-mail: info@startuptucson.com
URL: http://www.startuptucson.com
Contact: Fletcher McCusker, Chairman of the Board
Facebook: www.facebook.com/StartupTucson
X (Twitter): x.com/startuptucson
YouTube: www.youtube.com/channel/UCqD-jFzbCWda1slR6zRnJVw
Description: A community resource center offering a number of programs and events that support entrepreneurs.

36404 ■ Stealthmode Partners
2416 N Foote Dr.
Phoenix, AZ 85008
URL: http://www.stealthmodepartners.com
Contact: Francine Hardaway, Chief Executive Officer
E-mail: francine@stealthmode.com
Description: A network of people and companies working together behind the scenes to help its portfolio companies grow bigger, better, faster. **Founded:** 1999.

36405 ■ Swan/Starts
4640 E Skyline Dr.
Tucson, AZ 85718
Contact: Norman P. Soloway, Manager
Description: A business incubator that supports and invests in entrepreneurial companies seeking solutions to the world's grand challenges: clean energy & water, healthcare, safe & sustainable food production and education. **Founded:** 2014.

36406 ■ Tallwave LLC.
6720 N Scottsdale Rd.,Ste.140
Scottsdale, AZ 85253
Ph: (602)840-0400
Co. E-mail: info@tallwave.com
URL: http://tallwave.com
Contact: Jeff Pruitt, Chief Executive Officer
Facebook: www.facebook.com/Tallwave
Linkedin: www.linkedin.com/company/tallwave
X (Twitter): x.com/Tallwave
Instagram: www.instagram.com/tallwave
Description: Provides digital marketing and advertising agency services. **Founded:** 2010.

36407 ■ Tech Launch Arizona (TLA)
The Refinery at The Bridges, 1600 E Idea Ln., Ste. 110
Tucson, AZ 85713
Ph: (520)621-5000
Co. E-mail: info@tla.arizona.edu
URL: http://techlaunch.arizona.edu
Contact: Bruce Burgess, Director, Development
E-mail: bruceb@tla.arizona.edu
Facebook: www.facebook.com/UAZTechLaunch
Linkedin: www.linkedin.com/showcase/techlauncharizona-
X (Twitter): x.com/UAZTechLaunch
Description: An office of integrated teams creating an ecosystem of invention and commercialization. Creates social and economic impact through bringing the inventions of the UA from the lab to the world. It builds connections between the talents of our faculty and researchers and the experience of entrepreneurs and investors. It cultivates these conversations, fostering ideas that start in the lab, and grow them into new products and thriving businesses that benefit society. **Founded:** 2012.

36408 ■ Tech Parks Arizona
9070 S Rita Rd., Ste. 1750
Tucson, AZ 85747
Ph: (520)621-4088
Co. E-mail: info@uatechpark.org
URL: http://techparks.arizona.edu
Contact: Anita Bell, Director
E-mail: anitab@uaci.com
Facebook: www.facebook.com/UAZTechParks
X (Twitter): x.com/UAZTechParks
YouTube: www.youtube.com/channel/UChXj5OM0ETrYyzwyiMletqA
Description: Creates the place, environment and interactive ground that generates, attracts and retains technology companies and talent in alignment with the research, mission and goals of the University of Arizona.

36409 ■ TechBA Arizona
1626. Int. 205. Col. Del Valle, Delegación Benito Juárez
03100 Mexico City, México, Mexico
Ph: 52 555 200-0560
Co. E-mail: comunicacion@techba.org
URL: http://www.techba.org/indexE.php
Facebook: www.facebook.com/TechBACorporativo
Linkedin: www.linkedin.com/pub/techba-technology-business-accelerator/75/341/6b
X (Twitter): twitter.com/TechBA
YouTube: www.youtube.com/user/techbamexico
Description: A business accelerator program dedicated to helping Mexican technology companies expand to the United States in order to promote economic development and grow US-Mexico trade. **Founded:** 2005.

36410 ■ Territorial Normal School
1151 S Forest Ave.
Tempe, AZ 85281
Free: 855-278-5080
URL: http://economicdevelopment.asu.edu
Description: Connects with private industry, local governments, and community leaders to drive regional economic development that promotes human well-being.

36411 ■ Thunderbird Global Entrepreneurship Incubator
Thunderbird School of Global Management
1 Global Pl.
Glendale, AZ 85306
Ph: (602)978-7497
URL: http://www.thunderbird.edu
Contact: Charles Reeves, Executive Director
E-mail: charles.reeves.1@thunderbird.asu.edu
Description: A small business incubator offering entrepreneurs a unique environment to increase their chances for success, providing low-cast office space, professional and support services, and fostering entrepreneurial ideas from the early stages of company development until the graduation from the incubator.

36412 ■ University of Arizona Center for Innovation (AzCI)
9070 S Rita Rd., Ste. 1100
Tucson, AZ 85747

Ph: (520)382-3260
Co. E-mail: info@uacenterforinnovation.org
URL: http://www.uaci.com
Contact: Casey Carrillo, Executive Director
E-mail: ccarrillo@uaci.com
URL(s): techparks.arizona.edu/UACenterForInnovation
Facebook: www.facebook.com/UAZInnovation
Linkedin: www.linkedin.com/company/arizona-center-for-innovation
X (Twitter): x.com/UAZInnovation
Instagram: www.instagram.com/uazinnovation
YouTube: www.youtube.com/channel/UCfRIQHiX4jb74CJmo_ronUA
Description: A high-tech incubator promoting the development of high technology companies in Southern Arizona through a disciplined program of business development. **Founded:** 2003.

EDUCATIONAL PROGRAMS

36413 ■ Eastern Arizona College (EAC)
615 N Stadium Ave.
 Thatcher, AZ 85552
Ph: (928)428-8472
Free: 800-678-3808
URL: http://www.eac.edu
Contact: Todd Haynie, President
E-mail: todd.haynie@eac.edu
X (Twitter): x.com/eacmonsters
Instagram: www.instagram.com/eacadmissions
YouTube: www.youtube.com/user/EACAdmin
Description: Two-year college offering a small business management program. **Founded:** 1888. **Publications:** *The Gila Monster* (Monthly).

36414 ■ Rio Salado Community College (RSCC)
2323 W 14th St.
 Tempe, AZ 85281
Ph: (480)517-8000
Free: 800-729-1197
Co. E-mail: academic.advisement@riosalado.edu
URL: http://www.riosalado.edu
Contact: Kate Smith, President
Facebook: www.facebook.com/RioSaladoCollege
X (Twitter): x.com/riosaladoonline
Instagram: www.instagram.com/riosalado
YouTube: www.youtube.com/channel/UCrzVdHlicIw6BdV-IYvM-Ig
Description: Two-year college offering a program in small business management. **Founded:** 1978.

CONSULTANTS

36415 ■ Traklight
275 N Gateway Dr., Ste. 120
 Phoenix, AZ 85034
Ph: (360)230-8370
Free: 855-687-8785
Co. E-mail: info@traklight.com
URL: http://traklight.com
Contact: Mary Juetten, Chief Executive Officer
Facebook: www.facebook.com/traklight
X (Twitter): x.com/traklight
Description: Arizona-based software-as-a-service company that provides businesses a simple, automated, cost-effective way to minimize business risk and identify, manage, and protect valuable intangible assets including intellectual property. **Founded:** 2010.

PUBLISHERS

36416 ■ The GOALS Institute (TGI)
8390 E Via de Ventura F-110, Ste. 270
 Scottsdale, AZ 85258
Ph: (480)508-4460
Co. E-mail: info@goalsinstitute.com
URL: http://www.goalsinstitute.com
Contact: Peter J. Moriarty, Manager
Description: Services: Programs on teaching skills. Publisher: Books on soft skills. **Founded:** 1992.

36417 ■ Sohnen-Moe Associates, Inc. (SMA)
PO Box 86913
 Tucson, AZ 85754-6913
Ph: (520)743-3936
Fax: (520)743-3656
Co. E-mail: sma.info@sohnen-moe.com
URL: http://sohnen-moe.com
Contact: Cherie Sohnen-Moe, Chief Executive Officer
Facebook: www.facebook.com/SMA.biz
X (Twitter): x.com/SohnenMoe
Description: Publisher of materials for small business owners, especially healthcare practitioners. **Founded:** 1984.

36418 ■ Success Showcase Publishing
85 W Combs Rd., Ste. 101-343
 San Tan Valley, AZ 85140
URL: http://expertmarketpositioning.com
Description: Publisher of books on general business and marketing titles. **Founded:** 1996.

RESEARCH CENTERS

36419 ■ Arizona State University (ASU) - W. P. Carey School of Business - Center for Competitiveness and Prosperity Research
1151 S Forest Ave.
 Tempe, AZ 85281
URL: http://ccpr.wpcarey.asu.edu
Contact: L. William Seidman, Contact
Description: Publishes books on economics, real estate, consumer price index and demographics. Reports and documents in microform distributed by University Microfilms, Information Access Company and the Institute for Scientific Information. Printed publications available from the Center. Does not accept unsolicited manuscripts. **Founded:** 1986.

VENTURE CAPITAL FIRM

36420 ■ Alerion Capital Group
7702 E Doubletree Ranch Rd., Ste. 350
 Scottsdale, AZ 85258
Ph: (480)367-0900
URL: http://alerion.com
Contact: Jeff Unruh, Principal
Description: A private equity and management advisory firm investing in companies that will benefit most from their experience and knowledge. Centers around technology product and service providers.

36421 ■ Beechtree Capita,l LLC
34522 N Scottsdale Rd., Ste. 120-471
 Scottsdale, AZ 85266
Ph: (917)656-1066
URL: http://beechtreecapital.com
Contact: George M. Weiss, Chief Executive Officer
Description: Venture investment and management consulting firm for the advisory and investment activities of George M. Weiss, his family, and associated investors. Also operates out of New York and Dubai; primarily focused on emerging companies.

36422 ■ Biltmore Ventures
1825 W Knudsen, No. B-100
 Phoenix, AZ 85027
Ph: (480)510-5550
URL: http://www.biltmoreventures.com
Contact: Adam Bruss, Partner
Description: Venture capital firm for companies with an integral internet component. **Investment Policies:** Highly differentiated products and services with the ability to lead the market. **Industry Preferences:** Social networks and decentralized distribution.

36423 ■ Grayhawk Capital
4250 N Drinkwater Blvd., Ste. 300
 Scottsdale, AZ 85251
Ph: (602)956-8700
URL: http://www.grayhawk.vc
Contact: Brian N. Burns, Managing Partner
Description: Venture capital firm for early- and growth-stage companies primarily in the southwest. **Founded:** 1999. **Investment Policies:** Serial entrepreneurs; exceptional management teams; innovative and disruptive products; rapidly growing technology markets. **Industry Preferences:** Mobile; Cloud/Saas; enterprise software; security; business intelligence; finance; healthcare IT.

36424 ■ Pangaea Ventures Ltd.
5080 N 40th St., 105
 Phoenix, AZ 85018
URL: http://www.pangaeaventures.com
Contact: Tracy Hedberg, Director, Finance
Linkedin: www.linkedin.com/company/pangaea-ventures
X (Twitter): x.com/PangaeaVentures
Description: Venture capital firm for companies using advanced materials. Also has offices in Phoenix and Vancouver. **Founded:** 2000. **Industry Preferences:** Energy; electronics; sustainability; health.

Arkansas

SMALL BUSINESS DEVELOPMENT CENTERS

36425 ■ Arkansas Small Business and Technology Development Center - Lead Center (ASBTDC)
2801 S University Ave.
Little Rock, AR 72204
Ph: (501)916-3700
Free: 800-862-2040
Co. E-mail: leadcenter@asbtdc.org
URL: http://asbtdc.org/little-rock-lead-center
Contact: Laura Fine, Director
E-mail: lcfine@ualr.edu
Facebook: www.facebook.com/ASBTDC
X (Twitter): x.com/ASBTDC
Description: Provides management and technical assistance to small businesses in Arkansas. Provides individual consulting, research and training to small businesses. **Founded:** 1982. **Geographic Preference:** State.

36426 ■ Arkansas Small Business and Technology Development Center Monticello (ASBTDC)
140 University Pl.
Monticello, AR 71656
Ph: (870)460-1910
Co. E-mail: uam@asbtdc.org
URL: http://asbtdc.org/monticello
Contact: Aimee Weaver, Director
Facebook: www.facebook.com/uam.asbtdc
X (Twitter): x.com/ASBTDC_UAM
Description: Represents and promotes the small business sector. Provides management assistance to current and prospective small business owners. Helps to improve management skills and expand the products and services of members. **Founded:** 2002. **Geographic Preference:** Local.

36427 ■ Arkansas Small Business and Technology Development Center University of Arkansas, Fayetteville
240 N Block Ave., Ste. 100
Fayetteville, AR 72701
Ph: (479)575-5148
Co. E-mail: uaf@asbtdc.org
URL: http://asbtdc.org/fayetteville
Contact: Mary Beth Brooks, Director
E-mail: mebrooks@uark.edu
Facebook: www.facebook.com/UofAsbtdc
X (Twitter): x.com/ASBTDC_UArk
Description: Represents and promotes the small businesses in Fayetteville. **Geographic Preference:** Local.

36428 ■ Arkansas State University Small Business and Technology Development Center (ASU SBTDC)
319 University Loop W
Jonesboro, AR 72401
Ph: (870)972-3517
Fax: (870)972-3678
Co. E-mail: asusbtdc@astate.edu
URL: http://www.astate.edu/a/sbtdc
Contact: Laura Miller, Director
E-mail: lmiller@astate.edu
Facebook: www.facebook.com/ArkansasState
Linkedin: www.linkedin.com/company/arkansas-state-university-small-business-and-technology-development-center
X (Twitter): x.com/astate_sbtdc
Description: Represents and promotes the small business sector. Provides management assistance to current and prospective small business owners. Helps to improve management skills and expand the products and services of members. **Founded:** 1983. **Geographic Preference:** Local.

SCORE OFFICES

36429 ■ SCORE - Little Rock
2120 Riverfront Dr., Ste. 250
Little Rock, AR 72202
Ph: (501)324-7379
Co. E-mail: littlerockscore@sbcglobal.net
URL: http://www.score.org/littlerock
Facebook: www.facebook.com/SCORELittleRock
Linkedin: www.linkedin.com/in/score-of-little-rock-23aa3010a
Instagram: www.instagram.com/littlerockscore
Description: Provides professional guidance and information to maximize the success of existing and emerging small businesses. Offers business counseling and workshops. **Founded:** 1965. **Geographic Preference:** Local.

36430 ■ SCORE - Northwest Arkansas
1200 W Walnut St., Ste. 3411
Rogers, AR 72756
Free: 800-646-0450
Fax: (800)646-0450
Co. E-mail: help@score.org
URL: http://northwestarkansas.score.org
Contact: Bridget Weston, Chief Executive Officer
X (Twitter): x.com/SCORE_NWArkansa
Description: Provides professional guidance and information to maximize the success of existing and emerging small businesses. Offers business counseling and workshops. **Geographic Preference:** Local.

BETTER BUSINESS BUREAUS

36431 ■ Better Business Bureau of Arkansas
12521 Kanis Rd.
Little Rock, AR 72211
URL: http://www.bbb.org/local-bbb/bbb-serving-arkansas
Contact: Janet Robb, Contact
Description: Seeks to promote and foster the highest ethical relationship between businesses and the public through voluntary self-regulation, consumer and business education, and service excellence. Provides information to help consumers and businesses make informed purchasing decisions and avoid costly scams and frauds; settles consumer complaints through arbitration and other means. **Founded:** 1960. **Geographic Preference:** State.

CHAMBERS OF COMMERCE

36432 ■ Alma Chamber of Commerce (ACC)
PO Box 2607
Alma, AR 72921
URL: http://www.almachamber.com
URL(s): www.almanechamber.com
Description: Promotes business and community development in the Alma, KS area. **Founded:** 1984. **Geographic Preference:** Local.

36433 ■ Arkadelphia Area Chamber of Commerce
201 N 26th St.
Arkadelphia, AR 71923
Ph: (870)246-5542
Fax: (870)246-5543
Co. E-mail: info@arkadelphiaalliance.com
URL: http://www.arkadelphiaalliance.com/chamber-of-commerce/arkadelphia-area-chamber-of-commerce
Contact: J. L. Griffin, President
E-mail: griffin@arkadelphiaalliance.com
Description: Promotes business and community development in Arkadelphia, AR. **Geographic Preference:** Local.

36434 ■ Arkansas State Chamber of Commerce (ASCC)
1200 W Capitol Ave.
Little Rock, AR 72201-3008
Ph: (501)372-2222
URL: http://www.arkansasstatechamber.com
Contact: Randy Zook, President
E-mail: rzook@arkansasstatechamber.com
Facebook: www.facebook.com/ARStateChamber
X (Twitter): x.com/arstatechamber
YouTube: www.youtube.com/user/ArkansasStateChamber
Description: Promotes business and community development in Arkansas. **Founded:** 1928. **Geographic Preference:** State.

36435 ■ Bald Knob Area Chamber of Commerce
PO Box 338
Bald Knob, AR 72010-0338
Ph: (501)724-3140
URL: http://www.uschamber.com/co/chambers/arkansas/bald-knob
Description: Promotes business and community development in Bald Knob, AR. Sponsors annual Homefest. Publications: none. **Geographic Preference:** Local.

36436 ■ Batesville Area Chamber of Commerce (BACC)
409 Vine St.
Batesville, AR 72501
Ph: (870)793-2378

URL: http://chamber.batesvilleareaalliance.com
Contact: Crystal Johnson, Contact
E-mail: crystal.johnson@batesvilleareachamber.com
Facebook: www.facebook.com/BatesvilleChamber
X (Twitter): x.com/MyBatesville
Description: Promotes business and community development in Independence County, AR. **Founded:** 1919. **Publications:** *Batesville*; *City of Batesville/Independence County Maps*. **Educational Activities:** White River Water Carnival. **Geographic Preference:** Local.

36437 ■ Benton Area Chamber of Commerce
607 N Market St.
 Benton, AR 72015
Ph: (501)860-7002
Co. E-mail: reception@bentonchamber.com
URL: http://bentonchamber.com
Contact: Gary James, President
E-mail: gjames@bentonchamber.com
Facebook: www.facebook.com/BentonChamberOfCommerce
X (Twitter): x.com/BentonChamber
Instagram: www.instagram.com/bentonchamberofcommerce
Description: Provides business and community development in the Benton, AR area. **Geographic Preference:** Local.

36438 ■ Bentonville-Bella Vista Chamber of Commerce
702 SE 5th St., Ste. 40
 Bentonville, AR 72712
Ph: (479)273-2841
Co. E-mail: info@greaterbentonville.com
URL: http://greaterbentonville.com
Contact: Brandom Gengelbach, President
E-mail: bgengelbach@greaterbentonville.com
Facebook: www.facebook.com/greaterbentonville
Linkedin: www.linkedin.com/company/greaterbentonville
Instagram: www.instagram.com/greaterbentonville
YouTube: www.youtube.com/channel/UCSuoS8LKUNbrN16aMHm3WZg
Description: Promotes business and community development in Bentonville, AR area. **Founded:** 1926. **Publications:** *Bentonville/Bella Vista Chamber of Commerce--Business Directory*. **Geographic Preference:** Local.

36439 ■ Booneville Development Corporation - South Logan County Chamber of Commerce
210 E Main St.
 Booneville, AR 72927
Ph: (479)675-2666
URL: http://www.southlogan.com
Description: Promotes business and community development in Booneville, AR. **Founded:** 1828. **Geographic Preference:** Local.

36440 ■ Bradley County Chamber of Commerce
104 N Myrtle St.
 Warren, AR 71671
Ph: (870)226-5225
Co. E-mail: office@bradleychamber.com
URL: http://www.bradleychamber.com
Facebook: www.facebook.com/BradleyChamberofCommerce
X (Twitter): x.com/bradley_chamber
Description: Promotes business and community development in Bradley County, AR. **Founded:** 1924. **Geographic Preference:** Local.

36441 ■ Brinkley Chamber of Commerce
217 W Cypress St.
 Brinkley, AR 72021
Ph: (870)734-2262
Contact: Aaron Gifford, President
Facebook: www.facebook.com/BrinkleyChamberOfCommerce
Description: Promotes business and community development in Brinkley, AR. **Founded:** 2012. **Geographic Preference:** Local.

36442 ■ Bryant Chamber of Commerce (BCC)
109 Roya Ln.
 Bryant, AR 72022
Ph: (501)847-4702
Co. E-mail: info@bryantchamber.com
URL: http://www.bryantchamber.com
Contact: Jason Brown, Co-President Co-Chief Executive Officer
Facebook: www.facebook.com/BryantAreaChamberOfCommerce
X (Twitter): x.com/BryantChamber
Description: Promotes business and community development in Bryant, AR. **Founded:** 1974. **Geographic Preference:** Local.

36443 ■ Bull Shoals Lake White River Chamber of Commerce
612 Central Blvd.
 Bull Shoals, AR 72619
Ph: (870)445-4443
Co. E-mail: havefun@bullshoals.org
URL: http://www.bullshoals.org/contact-bull-shoals-chamber
Contact: Stacey Foster, Treasurer
Description: Promotes business and community development in Bull Shoals, AR. **Founded:** 1911. **Publications:** *Bull Shoals Lake - White River Visitor's Guide*. **Geographic Preference:** Local.

36444 ■ *Business News*
URL(s): www.bryant-ar.com/newsletter_5025_ct.aspx
Released: Periodic **Availability:** Print; Online.

36445 ■ Cabot Chamber of Commerce
110 S 1st St.
 Cabot, AR 72023
Ph: (501)843-2136
Fax: (501)843-1861
Co. E-mail: chamber@cabotcc.org
URL: http://www.cabotcc.org
Contact: Gina Jones, Co-President Co-Chief Executive Officer
E-mail: gina@cabotcc.org
Facebook: www.facebook.com/CabotChamberofCommerce
X (Twitter): x.com/cabotchamber
Instagram: www.instagram.com/cabotchamber
Description: Promotes business and community development in Cabot, AR. **Founded:** 1959. **Geographic Preference:** Local.

36446 ■ Clarksville-Johnson County Chamber of Commerce
101 N Johnson St.
 Clarksville, AR 72830-2949
Ph: (479)754-2340
URL: http://www.clarksvillejcochamber.com
Contact: Jessica Gunn, Executive Director
E-mail: jgunn@clarksvillejcochamber.com
Facebook: www.facebook.com/ClarksvilleChamber
X (Twitter): x.com/ClarksvilleAR
YouTube: www.youtube.com/channel/UCEFRaLGs9YXRtdmZM4ZEL0w
Description: Promotes business and community development in Clarksville and Johnson County, AR. **Founded:** 1921. **Publications:** *Johnson County Chamber Newsletter* (Weekly). **Geographic Preference:** Local.

36447 ■ Clinton Chamber of Commerce
290 Main St. Downtown Sq.
 Clinton, AR 72031
Ph: (501)745-6500
Co. E-mail: cltchamber@artelco.com
URL: http://exploreclintonar.com
Contact: Nancy Fowler, President
Facebook: www.facebook.com/clinton.chamber.9
Description: Promotes business and community development in Clinton, AR. **Founded:** 1936. **Geographic Preference:** Local.

36448 ■ Conway Area Chamber of Commerce (CACC)
900 Oak St.
 Conway, AR 72032
Ph: (501)327-7788
Co. E-mail: getsmart@conwayarkansas.org

URL: http://www.conwaychamber.org
Contact: Brad Lacy, President
Facebook: www.facebook.com/ConwayARChamber
Linkedin: www.linkedin.com/company/conway-area-chamber-of-commerce
X (Twitter): x.com/conway_chamber
YouTube: www.youtube.com/user/TheChamberLife
Description: Promotes business and community development in Conway, AR. **Founded:** 1890. **Publications:** *Directory of Manufacturing* (Annual). **Geographic Preference:** Local.

36449 ■ Corning Area Chamber of Commerce
1621 W Main St. US Hwy. 62
 Corning, AR 72422
Ph: (870)857-3874
Fax: (870)857-3874
Co. E-mail: corningar@gmail.com
URL: http://www.corningar.gov/chamber-of-commerce
Contact: Sherry Taylor, Secretary
Description: Promotes business and community development in the Corning, AR area. **Geographic Preference:** Local.

36450 ■ Cotter Gassville Chamber of Commerce
PO Box 489
 Cotter, AR 72626
Co. E-mail: info@centralwoodturners.org
URL: http://www.cotterarkansas.com
Facebook: www.facebook.com/cotter.chamber
Description: Works to the betterment of Cotter and its people. **Founded:** 1905. **Geographic Preference:** Local.

36451 ■ Cross County Chamber of Commerce and Economic Development Corp. (CCCEDC)
1790 Falls Blvd., Ste. 2
 Wynne, AR 72396
URL: http://www.crosscountychamber.org
Contact: Ashley Brumley, Director
E-mail: ashley@crosscountychamber.com
Description: Promotes business and community development in Wynne, AR. **Geographic Preference:** Local.

36452 ■ Crossett Area Chamber of Commerce (CACC)
101 W 1st Ave.
 Crossett, AR 71635
Ph: (870)364-6591
Fax: (870)364-7488
Co. E-mail: crossettchamber@windstream.net
URL: http://www.crossettchamber.org
Contact: Lindsey Mashburn Meeks, President
E-mail: lmeeks@murphysautobody.net
Facebook: www.facebook.com/crossettchamber
Description: Promotes business and community development in the Crossett, AR area. Sponsors annual Buddy Bass Tournament and Wiggins Cabin Festival. **Founded:** 1951. **Geographic Preference:** Local.

36453 ■ De Queen/Sevier County Chamber of Commerce
315 W Stillwell Ave.
 De Queen, AR 71832
Ph: (870)584-3225
Co. E-mail: dqchamber@gmail.com
URL: http://www.seviercountychamberofcommerce.org
Contact: Zahir Kamruddin, President
Description: Promotes business and community development in Sevier County, AR. **Geographic Preference:** Local.

36454 ■ Dermott Area Chamber of Commerce (DACC)
502 S Pecan
 Dermott, AR 71638
Ph: (870)538-5656
Fax: (870)538-5493
Co. E-mail: email@dermottchamber.com
URL: http://dermottchamber.com
Contact: Herb Green, Member

STATE LISTINGS																					Arkansas ■ 36470

Description: Promotes business and community development in Chicot County, AR. **Founded:** 1939. **Publications:** *McGohen Dermott Times News* (Monthly). **Educational Activities:** Dermott Crawfish Festival. **Geographic Preference:** Local.

36455 ■ Dierks Chamber of Commerce (DCC)
PO Box 292
  Dierks, AR 71833-0292
Ph: (870)286-3219
Fax: (870)286-2273
URL: http://www.chamber-commerce.net/dir/6236
Description: Promotes business and community development in Dierks, AR. **Geographic Preference:** Local.

36456 ■ Dover Area Chamber of Commerce (DACC)
9321 Market St.
  Dover, AR 72837
Ph: (479)331-3270
Co. E-mail: doverchambersecretary@gmail.com
Contact: Lisa Taylor, Director
Facebook: www.facebook.com/
  DoverAreaChamberofCommerce
Description: Promotes business and community development in the area. **Founded:** 1978. **Geographic Preference:** Local.

36457 ■ Dumas Chamber of Commerce
c/o Jann Farmer, Executive Director
  165 S Main
  Dumas, AR 71639
Ph: (870)382-5447
Co. E-mail: dumaschamber@dumasar.net
URL: http://www.dumasar.net
Contact: Jann Farmer, Executive Director
E-mail: mainstreetdumas@centurytel.net
Description: Promotes business industrial and community development in Southern Arkansas. Sponsors Dumas Ding Dong Days activities. **Founded:** 1870. **Geographic Preference:** Local.

36458 ■ El Dorado Chamber of Commerce (EDCC)
111 W Main St.
  El Dorado, AR 71730
Ph: (870)863-6113
Fax: (870)864-6758
Co. E-mail: chamber@goeldorado.com
URL: http://goeldorado.com/chamber
Contact: Bill Luther, President
E-mail: ceo@goeldorado.com
Facebook: www.facebook.com/ElDora
  doChamberofCommerce
Description: Promotes business and community development in El Dorado, AR. **Publications:** *The Chamber Newsletter* (Monthly). **Geographic Preference:** Local.

36459 ■ Fayetteville Chamber of Commerce (FCC)
21 W Mountain St., Ste. 300
  Fayetteville, AR 72701
Ph: (479)521-1710
Co. E-mail: chamber@fayettevillear.com
URL: http://www.fayettevillear.com
Contact: Steve Clark, President
E-mail: sclark@fayettevillear.com
Facebook: www.facebook.com/fayettevillechamber
X (Twitter): x.com/chamberfay
YouTube: www.youtube.com/channel/UCB9R_cpc9
  3NjHNl0ifGkzRw
Description: Promotes business and community development in Fayetteville, AR. **Founded:** 1889. **Geographic Preference:** Local.

36460 ■ Flippin Chamber of Commerce
PO Box 118
  Flippin, AR 72634
Ph: (870)405-4534
Co. E-mail: info@flippinchamber.org
URL: http://www.flippinchamber.org
Contact: Jennifer Cheek, Director

Description: Promotes business, community development, and tourism in Flippin and Marion counties, AR. Sponsors Ozark Mountain Air Festival. **Geographic Preference:** Local.

36461 ■ Fordyce Chamber of Commerce (FCC)
119 W 3rd St.
  Fordyce, AR 71742
Ph: (870)352-3520
Fax: (870)352-8090
Co. E-mail: fordyce@ipa.net
URL: http://www.chamber-commerce.net/dir/6647
Description: Aims to advance and promote the well-being of commerce, industry, agriculture, civic interests, and the citizenry of Fordyce and its trade territory. **Founded:** 1920. **Geographic Preference:** Local.

36462 ■ Forrest City Area Chamber of Commerce
203 N Izard St.
  Forrest City, AR 72335
Ph: (870)633-1651
Fax: (870)633-9500
Co. E-mail: info@forrestcitychamber.com
URL: http://www.forrestcitychamber.com
Facebook: www.facebook.com/ForrestCi
  tyAreaChamberOfCommerce
Description: Promotes business and community development in Forrest City, AR. Sponsors annual harvest festival, Christmas parade, and triathlon. Also conducts all industrial recruitment. **Publications:** *The Forum Express* (Monthly). **Geographic Preference:** Local.

36463 ■ Fort Smith Regional Chamber of Commerce
612 Garrison Ave.
  Fort Smith, AR 72901
Ph: (479)783-3111
Fax: (479)783-6110
Co. E-mail: info@fortsmithchamber.com
URL: http://www.fortsmithchamber.org
Contact: Tim Allen, President
E-mail: tallen@fortsmithchamber.com
Facebook: www.facebook.com/ftsmithchamber
X (Twitter): x.com/ftsmithchamber
Instagram: www.instagram.com/ftsmithchamber
YouTube: www.youtube.com/user/fortsmithchamber
Description: Promotes business and community development in Ft. Smith, AR. **Founded:** 1887. **Publications:** *Fort Smith Regional Community Guide*; *e-Catalyst!* (Monthly); *Forth Smith Regional Community Guide*; *Member Directory*. **Geographic Preference:** Local.

36464 ■ Grant County Chamber of Commerce (GCCC)
PO Box 907
  Sheridan, AR 72150
Ph: (870)942-3021
Co. E-mail: gccc@windstream.net
URL: http://www.grantcountychamber.com
X (Twitter): x.com/grantcochamber
Description: Promotes business and community development in Grant County, AR. **Founded:** 1900. **Geographic Preference:** Local.

36465 ■ Greater Blytheville Area Chamber of Commerce (BGCC)
300 W Walnut St.
  Blytheville, AR 72315
Ph: (870)762-2012
Co. E-mail: info@greaterblytheville.com
URL: http://mississippicountychamber.com
Contact: Sam Jackson, President
Facebook: www.facebook.com/misscochamber
X (Twitter): x.com/MissCoChamber
Instagram: www.instagram.com/misscountychamber
Description: Promotes business and community development in Blytheville, AR. Sponsors spring and fall festival. **Founded:** 1917. **Publications:** *E-Flash* (Monthly). **Geographic Preference:** Local.

36466 ■ Greater Eureka Springs Chamber of Commerce
PO Box 551
  Eureka Springs, AR 72632
Ph: (479)253-8737
Free: 800-638-7352
Co. E-mail: info@eurekaspringschamber.com
URL: http://www.eurekaspringschamber.com
Contact: Devin Henderson, Director, Operations
E-mail: devin@eurekaspringschamber.com
Facebook: www.facebook.com/
  EurekaSpringsChamber
X (Twitter): x.com/ESARChamber
Instagram: www.instagram.com/es_chamber
YouTube: www.youtube.com/channel/UC
  _JhOVzLnUrWIvqEB8EeMrQ
Pinterest: www.pinterest.com/EurekaSpringsAR
Description: Fosters personal, economic, and cultural growth of Eureka Springs community. **Geographic Preference:** Local.

36467 ■ Greater Hot Springs Chamber of Commerce (GHSCC)
659 Ouachita Ave.
  Hot Springs, AR 71901
Ph: (501)321-1700
Co. E-mail: info@growinghotsprings.com
URL: http://www.hotspringschamber.com
Contact: Gary Troutman, President
E-mail: gary.troutman@growinghotsprings.com
Facebook: www.facebook.com/HotSpringsChamber
X (Twitter): x.com/GHSChamber
Instagram: www.instagram.com/hs_chamber
Description: Promotes business, community development, and tourism in the Hot Springs, AR area. Sponsors Oktoberfest and Healthfest. **Founded:** 1897. **Publications:** *Greater Hot Springs Chamber of Commerce Newsletter* (Monthly). **Geographic Preference:** Local.

36468 ■ Greers Ferry Area Chamber of Commerce
8101 Edgemont Rd., Ste. 4
  Greers Ferry, AR 72067
Ph: (501)825-7188
Co. E-mail: info@greersferry.com
URL: http://www.greersferry.com
Facebook: www.facebook.com/gfchamber
Description: Promotes business and community development in Greers Ferry, AR. Sponsors events, including fishing tournaments, rodeos, Chamber Chili Challenge in November, Christmas Lighting Contest, and Christmas Tree Lighting. **Publications:** *The Heart of the Lake, Greers Ferry, Arkansas*. **Geographic Preference:** Local.

36469 ■ Harrison Chamber of Commerce (HCC)
303 N Main St., Ste. 301
  Harrison, AR 72601
Ph: (870)741-2659
Co. E-mail: cocinfo@harrison-chamber.com
URL: http://www.harrison-chamber.com
Contact: Wilson Marseilles, President
E-mail: wmarseilles@harrison-chamber.com
Facebook: www.facebook.com/HarrisonARChamber
X (Twitter): x.com/HarrisonCofC
Instagram: www.instagram.com/harrisonarchamber
Description: Promotes businesses in the area. **Founded:** 1958. **Publications:** *Membership Directory and Relocation Guide* (Annual). **Geographic Preference:** Local.

36470 ■ Heber Springs Area Chamber of Commerce
110 S 7th St.
  Heber Springs, AR 72543-2946
Ph: (501)362-2444
Co. E-mail: chamber@heber-springs.com
URL: http://www.heber-springs.com
Contact: Don Rodgers, President
Facebook: www.facebook.com/
  HeberSpringsChamber
X (Twitter): x.com/heberchamber
Instagram: www.instagram.com/heberchamber

36471 ■ Hope-Hempstead County Chamber of Commerce
101 W 2nd St.
Hope, AR 71801-4306
Ph: (870)777-3640
Co. E-mail: hopemelonfest@yahoo.com
URL: http://www.uschamber.com/co/chambers/arkansas/hope
Facebook: www.facebook.com/hopearkchamberofcommerce

Description: Promotes business and community development in Hempstead County, AR. Sponsors annual Hope Watermelon Festival in August. Holds seminars and periodic board meeting. **Publications:** *The Chamber* (Annual). **Educational Activities:** Hope Watermelon Festival (Annual). **Geographic Preference:** Local.

36472 ■ Horseshoe Bend Area Chamber of Commerce (HBACC)
707 Third St.
Horseshoe Bend, AR 72512
Ph: (870)670-5433
Co. E-mail: hsbchamberboard@gmail.com
URL: http://www.horseshoebend.org
Contact: Jeanette Hilliker, President
Facebook: www.facebook.com/hsbacc

Description: Promotes business and community development in the Horseshoe Bend, AR area. Sponsors annual Dogwood Days festival in April. **Founded:** 1969. **Geographic Preference:** Local.

36473 ■ Jonesboro Regional Chamber of Commerce
1709 E Nettleton Ave.
Jonesboro, AR 72403
Ph: (870)932-6691
Fax: (870)933-5758
URL: http://www.jonesborochamber.com
Contact: Mark Young, President
Facebook: www.facebook.com/JonesboroChamber
X (Twitter): x.com/jtownchamber
Instagram: www.instagram.com/jonesborochamber

Description: Promotes business and community development in the Craighead County, AR area. **Founded:** 1915. **Publications:** *Jonesboro Unlimited*. **Geographic Preference:** Local.

36474 ■ Lake Village Chamber of Commerce
111 Main St.
Lake Village, AR 71653
Ph: (870)265-5997
Co. E-mail: lvccdirector@sbcglobal.net
URL: http://lakevillagechamber.weebly.com
Contact: Joey Williamson, President
URL(s): www.lakevillagechamberofcommerce.org

Description: Promotes business and community development in Lake Village, AR. **Founded:** 1993. **Publications:** *News Exchange*. **Educational Activities:** General Membership. **Geographic Preference:** Local.

36475 ■ Lawrence County Chamber of Commerce (LCCC)
109 SW Front St.
Walnut Ridge, AR 72476
Ph: (870)886-3232
Fax: (870)886-1736
Co. E-mail: tourism@lawcochamber.org
URL: http://lawcochamber.org
Contact: Rachel King, Executive Director

Description: Promotes business and community development in the area. Sponsors events and festivals. **Publications:** *Let Us Point You in the Right Direction* (Annual). **Geographic Preference:** Local.

36476 ■ Little Rock Regional Chamber
One Chamber Plz.
Little Rock, AR 72201
Ph: (501)374-2001
Co. E-mail: chamber@littlerockchamber.com
URL: http://www.littlerockchamber.com
Contact: Jay Chesshir, President
Facebook: www.facebook.com/lrchamber
Linkedin: www.linkedin.com/company/littlerockregionalchamber
X (Twitter): x.com/lrchamber
Instagram: www.instagram.com/littlerockchamber
YouTube: www.youtube.com/littlerockchamber

Description: Promotes business and community development in the Little Rock, AR area. **Founded:** 1866. **Publications:** *Who's Who Membership Directory*; *Central Arkansas Manufacturing Directory*; *Greater Little Rock Guest Guide*; *Taking Care of Business*. **Educational Activities:** Columbus Day Chamber Ambassadors Golf Scramble (Annual). **Geographic Preference:** Local.

36477 ■ Magnolia-Columbia County Chamber of Commerce
211 W Main St.
Magnolia, AR 71753
Ph: (870)234-4352
Fax: (870)234-9291
Co. E-mail: ea@ccalliance.us
URL: http://www.magnoliachamber.com
Contact: Kimberly Jones, President
Facebook: www.facebook.com/magnoliacolumbiacountychamber

Description: Promotes economic and community development in Columbia County, AR. **Founded:** 1995. **Geographic Preference:** Local.

36478 ■ Marion Chamber of Commerce
13 Military Rd.
Marion, AR 72364
Ph: (870)739-6041
Co. E-mail: chamber@marionarkansas.org
URL: http://www.marionarchamber.org
Contact: Cheryl Starling, Administrator
Facebook: www.facebook.com/marionarchamber

Description: Promotes business and community development in Marion, AR. **Founded:** 1922. **Educational Activities:** Marion Chamber of Commerce Luncheon. **Geographic Preference:** Local.

36479 ■ Maumelle Area Chamber of Commerce (MACC)
115 Audubon Dr., No. 14
Maumelle, AR 72113
Ph: (501)851-9700
Fax: (501)851-6690
Co. E-mail: info@maumellechamber.com
URL: http://maumellechamber.com
Contact: Thomas Lipsmeyer, Co-President
Facebook: www.facebook.com/maumellechamber
X (Twitter): x.com/MaumelleChamber
Instagram: www.instagram.com/maumellechamber

Description: Seeks to promote high quality of business for members and community through leadership in economic and civic development. **Founded:** 1991. **Geographic Preference:** Local.

36480 ■ McGehee Chamber of Commerce
901 Holly St.
McGehee, AR 71654-2142
Ph: (870)222-4451
URL: http://www.themcgeheechamber.com
Contact: Pamela Blissitt, President

Description: Promotes business and community development in the McGehee, AR area. **Founded:** 1870. **Geographic Preference:** Local.

36481 ■ *Member Directory*
612 Garrison Ave.
Fort Smith, AR 72901
Ph: (479)783-3111
Fax: (479)783-6110
Co. E-mail: info@fortsmithchamber.org
URL: http://www.fortsmithchamber.org
Contact: Tim Allen, President
E-mail: tallen@fortsmithchamber.com
URL(s): public.fortsmithchamber.com/list
Availability: Online.

36482 ■ Monticello Drew County Chamber of Commerce
335 E Gaines St.
Monticello, AR 71655
Ph: (870)367-6741
URL: http://www.uschamber.com/co/chambers/arkansas/monticello

Description: Promotes business and community development in Drew County, AR. **Publications:** *Monticello Drew County Chamber of Commerce Newsletter* (Bimonthly). **Awards:** Drew County Industry of the Year (Annual); Drew County Man/Woman of the Year (Annual). **Geographic Preference:** Local.

36483 ■ Morrilton Area Chamber of Commerce (MACC)
115 E Broadway St.
Morrilton, AR 72110
Ph: (501)354-2393
Fax: (501)354-8642
Co. E-mail: chamber@morrilton.com
URL: http://www.morriltonarkansas.com
Contact: Stephanie Lipsmeyer, Director
E-mail: staphniel@morrilton.com

Description: Promotes business and community development in Morrilton, AR. Sponsors Great Arkansas Pig Out Festival. **Founded:** 1915. **Geographic Preference:** Local.

36484 ■ Mount Ida Area Chamber of Commerce
124 Hwy. 270 W
Mount Ida, AR 71957
Ph: (870)867-2723
Co. E-mail: director@mtidachamber.com
URL: http://www.mtidachamber.com
Contact: Pat Smith, Secretary
Facebook: www.facebook.com/MountIdaAreaChamberOfCommerce

Description: Promotes business and community development in Mt. Ida, AR area. Sponsors festival. **Founded:** 1960. **Publications:** *Mount Ida Area Visitor Guide*. **Geographic Preference:** Local.

36485 ■ *Mount Ida Area Visitor Guide*
124 Hwy. 270 W
Mount Ida, AR 71957
Ph: (870)867-2723
Co. E-mail: director@mtidachamber.com
URL: http://www.mtidachamber.com
Contact: Pat Smith, Secretary
URL(s): www.mtidachamber.com/relocation
Availability: Online.

36486 ■ Mountain Home Area Chamber of Commerce
1337 Hwy. 62 W
Mountain Home, AR 72653
Ph: (870)425-5111
Fax: (870)425-4446
Co. E-mail: info@enjoymountainhome.com
URL: http://enjoymountainhome.com
Contact: Dani Pugsley, President
E-mail: dani@enjoymountainhome.com
Facebook: www.facebook.com/EnjoyMountainHome
YouTube: www.youtube.com/channel/UCqqCKliA0MjrfQVMC4F-qdg

Description: Promotes business and community development in the Mountain Home area of Baxter and Marion counties, AR. **Founded:** 1888. **Publications:** *Spirit* (Monthly); *Three Rivers, Two Lakes... One Beautiful Life*. **Geographic Preference:** Local.

36487 ■ North Little Rock Chamber of Commerce (NLRCC)
100 Main St.
North Little Rock, AR 72114
Ph: (501)372-5959
Co. E-mail: nlrchamber@nlrchamber.org
URL: http://www.nlrchamber.org
Contact: Derrell Hartwick, President
E-mail: dhartwick@nlrchamber.org
Facebook: www.facebook.com/TheNLRChamber
X (Twitter): x.com/thenlrchamber
Instagram: www.instagram.com/thenlrchamber

STATE LISTINGS

Description: Promotes business and community development in North Little Rock, AR. Sponsors trade show. **Founded:** 1984. **Publications:** *Demographic Journal* (Periodic); *Maps* (Annual); *North Little Rock, Your Metropolitan Home: Industrial and Commercial Location Factors*. **Geographic Preference:** Local.

36488 ■ Osceola/South Mississippi County Chamber of Commerce
116 N Maple St.
Osceola, AR 72370
Ph: (870)563-2281
Fax: (870)563-5385
Co. E-mail: osceolachamber@sbcglobal.net
URL: http://www.osceolachamber.net
Contact: Ammi Tucker, Director
Facebook: www.facebook.com/OSMCChamber
X (Twitter): x.com/osmcchamber
Pinterest: www.pinterest.com/osmcchamber

Description: Promotes business and community development in southern Mississippi County, AR. **Founded:** 1947. **Publications:** *Leader Academy*. **Geographic Preference:** Local.

36489 ■ Paragould Regional Chamber of Commerce
300 W Ct. St.
Paragould, AR 72451-0124
Ph: (870)236-7684
Fax: (870)236-7142
URL: http://www.paragould.org
Contact: Allison Hestand, Chief Executive Officer
E-mail: ahestand@paragould.org
Facebook: www.facebook.com/pgouldchamber
X (Twitter): x.com/PgouldChamber
YouTube: www.youtube.com/channel/UC-T2Zw66u7DvbcOxD7DZbQw

Description: Promotes business and community development in the Paragould, AR area. **Founded:** 1915. **Geographic Preference:** Local.

36490 ■ Paris Area Chamber of Commerce (PACC)
301 W Walnut
Paris, AR 72855
Ph: (479)963-2244
Fax: (479)963-8321
Co. E-mail: pariscoc@gmail.com
URL: http://www.parisarkansas.com
Contact: Amber Mikles, Co-President
Facebook: www.facebook.com/ParisArkansasChamber
Instagram: www.instagram.com/parisarchamberofcommerce

Description: Promotes business and community development in northern Logan County, AR. Conducts Frontier Days Festivals and the Butterfly Festival. Participates in charitable programs. **Founded:** 1945. **Publications:** *Calendar of Events* (Monthly). **Geographic Preference:** Local.

36491 ■ Pine Bluff Regional Chamber of Commerce
510 Main St.
Pine Bluff, AR 71611
Ph: (870)535-0110
URL: http://jeffersoncountyalliance.com/chamber/about-chamber
Contact: John Lawson, Chairman of the Board
Facebook: www.facebook.com/pinebluffchamber

Description: Promotes business and community development in the Pine Bluff, AR area. **Founded:** 1911. **Publications:** *Investor's Report* (Monthly); *Who's Who in Pine Bluff Business* (Annual). **Geographic Preference:** Local.

36492 ■ Prairie Grove Chamber of Commerce
PO Box 23
Prairie Grove, AR 72753
Co. E-mail: pginfo@pgchamber.com
URL: http://www.pgchamber.com
Contact: Dale Reed, President

Description: Promotes business and community development in Prairie Grove, AR. **Geographic Preference:** Local.

36493 ■ Randolph County Chamber of Commerce
107 E Everett St.
Pocahontas, AR 72455
Ph: (870)892-3956
Co. E-mail: chamber@randolphchamber.com
URL: http://randolphchamber.com
Contact: Sydney Stevens, President
E-mail: sydney.wallace@hotmail.com
Facebook: www.facebook.com/randolphcountychamber
Linkedin: www.linkedin.com/in/randolph-county-chamber-of-commerce-b3a63137
X (Twitter): x.com/RandolphChamber
Instagram: www.instagram.com/randolphcountychamber

Description: Promotes business and community development in the Pocahontas, AR area. Conducts Agriculture Appreciation Day, Industry Appreciation Day, sports show, Christmas festival, and Veterans Day parade. **Founded:** 1856. **Publications:** *Randolph County Newsletter* (Weekly). **Geographic Preference:** Local.

36494 ■ Rector Chamber of Commerce
City Hall
409 S Stewart St.
Rector, AR 72461
Ph: (870)595-3035
URL: http://www.rectorarkansas.com/chamber-of-commerce.html

Description: Promotes business and community development in Rector, AR. **Founded:** 1887. **Geographic Preference:** Local.

36495 ■ Rogers-Lowell Area Chamber of Commerce (RLACC)
317 W Walnut St.
Rogers, AR 72756
Ph: (479)636-1240
Fax: (479)636-5485
Co. E-mail: memberservices@rogerslowell.com
URL: http://www.rogerslowell.com
Contact: Raymond Burns, President
Facebook: www.facebook.com/RLACC
Linkedin: www.linkedin.com/company/rogers-lowell-area-chamber-of-commerce
X (Twitter): x.com/RLACC
YouTube: www.youtube.com/channel/UCU-Z7BUOXVGvoSXdpiaHKLw

Description: Promotes business and community development in Rogers, AR. Sponsors Air Show. **Geographic Preference:** Local.

36496 ■ Russellville Chamber of Commerce
708 W Main St.
Russellville, AR 72801
Ph: (479)968-2530
Fax: (479)968-5894
Co. E-mail: chamber@russellvillechamber.com
URL: http://www.russellvillechamber.com
Contact: Paul Harvel, President
E-mail: pharvel@arkrivernow.com
Facebook: www.facebook.com/RsvlAreaChamber
X (Twitter): x.com/RsvlAreaChamber
Instagram: www.instagram.com/rsvlareachamber

Description: Promotes business and community development in Pope County, AR. Sponsors local festivals. **Founded:** 1920. **Publications:** *Business Connection* (Quarterly). **Educational Activities:** First Friday Luncheon (Monthly). **Awards:** Russellville Chamber of Commerce Citizen of the Year (Annual). **Geographic Preference:** Local.

36497 ■ Sherwood Chamber of Commerce (SCC)
7510 Hwy. 107
Sherwood, AR 72120
Ph: (501)835-7600
Co. E-mail: vvega@sherwoodchamber.net
URL: http://sherwoodchamber.net
Facebook: www.facebook.com/shwdchamber
Instagram: www.instagram.com/sherwoodchamberofficial

Description: Promotes business and community development in the area. **Publications:** *Sherwood Chamber of Commerce Business and Community Directory* (Annual); *Sherwood Chamber of Commerce Newsletter* (Bimonthly). **Geographic Preference:** Local.

36498 ■ Siloam Springs Chamber of Commerce (SSCC)
101 N Mt. Olive St.
Siloam Springs, AR 72761
Ph: (479)524-6466
Co. E-mail: info@siloamchamber.com
URL: http://siloamchamber.com
Contact: Arthur Hulbert, President
E-mail: arthur@siloamchamber.com
Facebook: www.facebook.com/siloamchamber
Instagram: www.instagram.com/siloamchamber
YouTube: www.youtube.com/channel/UCfnV_oh2iWcdu2A-l83GYjQ

Description: Promotes business and community development in Siloam Springs, AR. **Founded:** 1930. **Publications:** *News & Views* (Monthly). **Geographic Preference:** Local.

36499 ■ Spring River Area Chamber of Commerce (SRACC)
119 E Main St.
Highland, AR 72542
Ph: (870)856-3210
URL: http://www.sracc.org
Contact: Lauren Siebert, President
Facebook: www.facebook.com/springriverareachamberofcommerce

Description: Represents business interests of members in Northeastern Arkansas. Enhances members' success in business through programs, benefits and services, and other business related information. **Geographic Preference:** Local.

36500 ■ Springdale Chamber of Commerce (SCC)
202 W Emma Ave.
Springdale, AR 72764
Ph: (479)872-2222
Co. E-mail: info@chamber.springdale.com
URL: http://springdale.com
Contact: Bill Rogers, President
Facebook: www.facebook.com/SpringdaleCoC
Linkedin: www.linkedin.com/company/springdalecofc
X (Twitter): x.com/SpringdaleCofC
Instagram: www.instagram.com/springdalecofc

Description: Promotes business and community development in Springdale, AR. **Founded:** 1946. **Publications:** *Chamber Outlook* (Semimonthly). **Educational Activities:** Business After Hours (Monthly). **Geographic Preference:** Local.

36501 ■ Stuttgart Chamber of Commerce
507 S Main St.
Stuttgart, AR 72160
Ph: (870)673-1602
Co. E-mail: stuttgartchamber@centurylink.net
URL: http://www.stuttgartarkansas.org
Contact: Bethany Hildebrand, President
E-mail: bethany@stuttgartchamber.com
Facebook: www.facebook.com/stuttgartchamber
X (Twitter): x.com/Stuttgart_AR
Instagram: www.instagram.com/stuttgartchamber

Description: Promotes business and community development in Stuttgart, AR. **Founded:** 1940. **Publications:** *Chamber Talk*. **Geographic Preference:** Local.

36502 ■ Van Buren Area Chamber of Commerce
510 Main St.
Van Buren, AR 72956
Ph: (479)474-2761
Co. E-mail: info@vanburenchamber.org
URL: http://www.vanburenchamber.org
Contact: Julie Murray, President
Facebook: www.facebook.com/ChamberVanBuren
X (Twitter): x.com/ChamberVanBuren
Instagram: www.instagram.com/chambervanburen

Description: Promotes business and community development in the area. **Geographic Preference:** Local.

36503 ■ Van Buren Chamber of Commerce (VBCC)
510 Main St.
Van Buren, AR 72956
Ph: (479)474-2761
Co. E-mail: info@vanburenchamber.org
URL: http://www.vanburenchamber.org
Contact: Julie Murray, President
Facebook: www.facebook.com/ChamberVanBuren
X (Twitter): x.com/ChamberVanBuren
Instagram: www.instagram.com/chambervanburen
Description: Promotes business, tourism, and community development in Van Buren, AR. Sponsors community forums and social activities. Holds periodic board meeting. **Founded:** 1845. **Publications:** *Van Buren Today* (Monthly). **Geographic Preference:** Local.

36504 ■ White Hall Chamber of Commerce (WH)
102 Anderson Ave.
White Hall, AR 71602
Ph: (870)247-5502
Fax: (870)247-4870
Co. E-mail: whitehallchamber@gmail.com
URL: http://www.whitehallchamber.org
Contact: Kevin Bonnette, President
E-mail: kevin.bonnette.lp4s@statefarm.com
Facebook: www.facebook.com/WhiteHallChamber
Description: Promotes business and community development in White Hall, AR. **Founded:** 1964. **Geographic Preference:** Local.

36505 ■ Yellville Area Chamber of Commerce
414 W 3rd St.
Yellville, AR 72687
Ph: (870)449-4676
Co. E-mail: chamber@yellville.net
URL: http://www.yellvillechamber.org
Contact: Lyn Baker, President
Facebook: www.facebook.com/Yellville-Chamber-of-Commerce-1631754113504783
Description: Promotes business and community development in Yellville, AR. **Founded:** 1835. **Geographic Preference:** Local.

MINORITY BUSINESS ASSISTANCE PROGRAMS

36506 ■ Arkansas Economic Development Commission (AEDC)
1 Commerce Way, Ste. 601
Little Rock, AR 72202
Ph: (501)682-7306
Free: 800-275-2672
Co. E-mail: info@arkansasedc.com
URL: http://www.arkansasedc.com
Contact: Michael Preston, Executive Director
E-mail: mpreston@arkansasedc.com
Facebook: www.facebook.com/ArkansasEDC
Linkedin: www.linkedin.com/company/arkansasinc
X (Twitter): x.com/arkansasedc
YouTube: www.youtube.com/channel/UC8NHNFG0fF-AwE21YdkvVhw
Description: Firm provides marketing and consulting services. **Founded:** 1955. **Publications:** *Arkansas Agribusiness Directory* (Triennial).

FINANCING AND LOAN PROGRAMS

36507 ■ Arkansas Capital Corporation
200 River Market Ave., Ste. 400
Little Rock, AR 72201
Ph: (501)374-9247
Free: 800-216-7237
Co. E-mail: servicing@arcapital.com
URL: http://arcapital.com
Contact: Leslie Lane, President
Facebook: www.facebook.com/arcapitalcorp
Instagram: www.instagram.com/arcapitalcorp

Description: Involves in empowering entrepreneurs in Arkansas through partnerships with the lending community. **Founded:** 1957. **Preferred Investment Size:** $50,000 to $500,000. **Industry Preferences:** Communications and media, Internet specific, computer software and services, communications and computer hardware.

PROCUREMENT ASSISTANCE PROGRAMS

36508 ■ Arkansas APEX Accelerator (APAC)
University of Arkansas System Division of Agriculture
Cooperative Extension Service
2301 S University Ave.
Little Rock, AR 72204
Ph: (501)671-2390
Fax: (501)671-2394
Co. E-mail: apex@uada.edu
URL: http://www.uaex.uada.edu/business-communities/Arkansas-APEX-Accelerator/default.aspx
Contact: Melanie Berman, Program Director
Facebook: www.facebook.com/ArkansasAPEXAccelerator
Linkedin: www.linkedin.com/company/arapexaccelerator
Description: Provide training and resources that help Arkansas businesses generate revenues and thereby create or retain jobs for Arkansans through effective government contracting. **Founded:** 1993.

36509 ■ Arkansas APEX Accelerator (APAC)
University of Arkansas System Division of Agriculture
Cooperative Extension Service
2301 S University Ave.
Little Rock, AR 72204
Ph: (501)671-2390
Fax: (501)671-2394
Co. E-mail: apex@uada.edu
URL: http://www.uaex.edu/business-communities/arkansas-ptac/default.aspx
Contact: Melanie Berman, Program Director
E-mail: msberman@uada.edu
Facebook: www.facebook.com/ArkansasAPEXAccelerator
Linkedin: www.linkedin.com/company/arapexaccelerator
Description: Provide training and resources that help Arkansas businesses generate revenues and thereby create or retain jobs for Arkansans through effective government contracting. **Founded:** 1993.

36510 ■ Arkansas Procurement Technical Assistance Center - Satellite Office
Northwest Arkansas Community College
Bentonville, AR 72712
Ph: (501)650-6180
Fax: (501)671-2394
Co. E-mail: apac@uaex.edu
URL: http://www.uaex.edu/business-communities/arkansas-ptac/default.aspx
Description: Serves Arkansas businesses in all 75 counties at no charge from the main office in Malvern, supported by a fully staffed satellite office in Little Rock.

INCUBATORS/RESEARCH AND TECHNOLOGY PARKS

36511 ■ The ARK Challenge
1 E Center St., Ste. 270
Fayetteville, AR 72701
Ph: (479)200-3089
URL: http://arkchallenge.org
Contact: Jeannette Balleza Collins, Director
Facebook: www.facebook.com/arkchallenge
Linkedin: www.linkedin.com/company/the-ark-challenge
X (Twitter): twitter.com/arkchallenge
Instagram: www.instagram.com/arkchallenge
Description: A mentorship-driven accelerator program for technology startups.

36512 ■ BioVentures [UAMS BioVentures]
401 S Cedar St.
Little Rock, AR 72205
Ph: (501)686-6696
Co. E-mail: bioventures@uams.edu
URL: http://bioventures.tech
Contact: Kevin W. Sexton, President
Description: The Technology Licensing Office and the Life Science Business Incubator for the University of Arkansas for Medical Sciences (UAMS). **Founded:** 1879.

36513 ■ Catalyst Innovation Center
ABI, 504 University Loop E
State University, AR 72467
URL: http://catalystinnovation.org
Contact: Luna Acosta, Contact
E-mail: lacosta@astate.edu
Description: Offers creative, entrepreneurial space for research, learning, business and innovation. Offers dedicated space to house and incubate startup businesses including mentoring services, project support, and co-working space.

36514 ■ Delta Center for Economic Development (DCED)
319 University Loop 100 W
Jonesboro, AR 72401
Ph: (870)972-3000
Fax: (870)972-3806
Co. E-mail: dced@astate.edu
URL: http://www.astate.edu/deltaced
Description: Supports entrepreneurial and economic development in the area.

36515 ■ Delta Cuisine Commercial Kitchen and Business Incubator
2000 W Broadway ASU Mid-S
West Memphis, AR 72301
Ph: (870)733-6755
URL: http://deltacuisine.org
Description: A non-profit business incubator that focuses on assisting business launch in the food industry.

36516 ■ Economic Development Alliance of Jefferson County
510 Main St.
Pine Bluff, AR 71611
Ph: (870)535-0110
Co. E-mail: info@jeffersoncountyalliance.com
URL: http://jeffersoncountyalliance.com
Contact: Allison J. H. Thompson, President
E-mail: allison@jeffersoncountyalliance.com
Facebook: www.facebook.com/pinebluffchamber
Linkedin: www.linkedin.com/company/economic-development-alliance-jefferson-county-arkansas
X (Twitter): x.com/JeffersonCoAR
YouTube: www.youtube.com/channel/UC8xzskZLIOJIWfGFzfshW0g
Description: Firm is a non-profit company formed to unify community and economic development services. **Founded:** 1995.

36517 ■ University of Arkansas - GENESIS Technology Incubator
535 W Research Center Blvd.
Fayetteville, AR 72701
Ph: (479)575-6964
Fax: (479)575-5717
URL: http://artp.uark.edu/genesis-technology-incubator
Contact: David Snow, President
E-mail: desnow@uark.edu
Facebook: www.facebook.com/ARTechPark
Description: GENESIS provides office space and shared services to technology-based entrepreneurs, enhanced by the resources of the University of Arkansas. **Scope:** Support and nurture of small businesses involved in science and engineering. **Founded:** 1986. **Publications:** *GENESIS Quarterly Reports.* **Educational Activities:** GENESIS Technology Incubator Coffee Breaks, Covering topics relevant to technology and research firms.

PUBLICATIONS

36518 ■ *Arkansas Business*
114 Scott St.
 Little Rock, AR 72201
Ph: (501)372-1443
Free: 888-322-6397
URL: http://www.arkansasbusiness.com
Contact: Mitch Bettis, President
URL(s): www.arkansasbusiness.com
Facebook: www.facebook.com/ArkansasBusiness
X (Twitter): x.com/ArkBusiness
YouTube: www.youtube.com/user/ArkansasBusiness

Ed: Gwen Moritz. **Released:** Weekly **Description:** Business magazine on the Arkansas business community, covering people and recent news events statewide. **Availability:** Print; Online.

36519 ■ Arkansas Business Publishing Group
114 Scott St.
 Little Rock, AR 72201
Ph: (501)372-1443
Free: 888-322-6397
URL: http://www.arkansasbusiness.com
Contact: Mitch Bettis, President
Facebook: www.facebook.com/ArkansasBusiness
Linkedin: www.linkedin.com/company/arkansas
 -business-publishing-group
X (Twitter): x.com/ArkBusiness
YouTube: www.youtube.com/user/ArkansasBusiness

Description: Publisher of niche magazine and business journal. **Founded:** 1984. **Publications:** *Arkansas Bride* (Semiannual); *Greenhead* (Annual); *Arkansas Green Guide* (Annual); *Arkansas Next: A Guide to Life After High School* (Annual); *Little Rock Family* (Monthly); *Executive Golfer*; *Arkansas Business* (Weekly).

36520 ■ *Sherwood Chamber of Commerce Business and Community Directory*
7510 Hwy. 107
 Sherwood, AR 72120
Ph: (501)835-7600
Co. E-mail: vvega@sherwoodchamber.net
URL: http://sherwoodchamber.net
URL(s): business.sherwoodchamber.net/list

Released: Annual **Availability:** Print; Online.

RESEARCH CENTERS

36521 ■ University of Arkansas - Sam M. Walton College of Business - Center for Business and Economic Research (CBER)
CBER-WCOB-JBHT 404 1 University of Arkansas
 Fayetteville, AR 72701
Ph: (479)575-4151
Fax: (479)575-7687
Co. E-mail: cber@walton.uark.edu
URL: http://cber.uark.edu
Contact: Mervin Jebaraj, Director
E-mail: mjebara@uark.edu

Description: Integral unit of Sam M. Walton College of Business at University of Arkansas. Offers economic and demographic information about Arkansas. **Scope:** Business management, economics, and utilization of resources of the state, including studies on methods of increasing income of Arkansas citizens, more effective utilization of manpower and physical resources of the state, improved organization and management of business firms, wider markets for goods, and efficiency in government organization and operation. Collects economic data pertaining to the state. **Founded:** 1943. **Publications:** *Arkansas Business & Economic Review* (Quarterly); *CBER Bulletins*; *Project Reports*; *Series for Continuing Education in Business* (Occasionally).

EARLY STAGE FINANCING

36522 ■ Fund for Arksans Future II
201 E Broadway
 North Little Rock, AR 72114
URL: http://arkansasfund.com
Contact: Jeff Stinson, Executive Director

Description: Angel investment fund for early-stage companies in Arkansas. **Founded:** 2013.

VENTURE CAPITAL FIRM

36523 ■ Diamond State Ventures (DSV)
200 River Market Ave., Ste. 400
 Little Rock, AR 72201
Contact: Joe T. Hays, Contact
E-mail: jhays@dsvlp.com

Description: Offers debt and equity financing to lower middle-market companies in the United States. **Founded:** 1999.

California

START-UP INFORMATION

36524 ■ Tugboat Group
Description: Supports evergreen entrepreneurs with purpose-driven, scalable, profitable startups. **Founded:** 2006.

ASSOCIATIONS AND OTHER ORGANIZATIONS

36525 ■ Association of Fundraising Professionals California Valley Chapter (AFP-CV)
c/o Gary Pigg
2037 W Bullard Ave., PMB-323
Fresno, CA 93711
Ph: (559)898-2070
Fax: (888)491-7427
Co. E-mail: info@afpcaliforniavalley.org
URL: http://community.afpglobal.org/afpcavalleychapter/home
Contact: Gary Pigg, Treasurer
E-mail: garypigg@vbct.com
Facebook: www.facebook.com/AFPCAValley

Description: Fosters the development and growth of fundraising professionals. Promotes high ethical standards in the fundraising profession. Provides training opportunities for fundraising professionals. **Geographic Preference:** Local.

36526 ■ Association of Fundraising Professionals California, Yosemite Chapter
PO Box 1168
Modesto, CA 95353
Co. E-mail: afpyosemite@gmail.com
URL: http://community.afpnet.org/afpcayosemiteter/home
Contact: Arnold Chavez, President
Facebook: www.facebook.com/AFPYosemiteChapterModestoCA
X (Twitter): x.com/afpyosemite

Description: Fosters the development and growth of fundraising professionals. Promotes high ethical standards in the fundraising profession. Provides training opportunities for fundraising professionals. **Geographic Preference:** Local.

36527 ■ Association of Fundraising Professionals Greater Los Angeles Chapter (AFP-GLAC)
25943 Via Pera
Mission Viejo, CA 92691
Ph: (714)771-3685
Fax: (714)908-9777
Co. E-mail: office@afpglac.org
URL: http://community.afpglobal.org/afpcagreaterlosangeleschapter/home
Contact: Yvette Herrera, President
Facebook: www.facebook.com/afpglac
X (Twitter): x.com/afp_glac
Instagram: www.instagram.com/afpglac

Description: Supports professionals throughout the greater Los Angeles area who serve as development directors, fundraising consultants, grant writers, volunteer fundraisers, foundation executives, and other individuals dedicated to fundraising and philanthropy. **Geographic Preference:** Local.

36528 ■ Association of Fundraising Professionals Greater San Fernando Valley Chapter (AFPGSFV)
PO Box 7383
Northridge, CA 91327
Co. E-mail: info@afp-gsfv.org
URL: http://community.afpglobal.org/afpgsfv/home
Contact: Nancy Ackerman, President
X (Twitter): x.com/AFP_GSFV
Instagram: www.instagram.com/afp_gsfv

Description: Supports fundraising professionals from a wide range of nonprofit organizations and consulting firms throughout the Greater San Fernando Valley area, as well as Glendale, Pasadena, and Santa Clarita. **Founded:** 1992. **Geographic Preference:** Local.

36529 ■ Association of Fundraising Professionals Orange County Chapter (AFPOC)
PO Box 8133
Fountain Valley, CA 92728
Ph: (949)436-2939
Free: 800-666-3863
Co. E-mail: office@afpoc.org
URL: http://community.afpglobal.org/afpoc/home
Contact: Dominic Mumolo, President
Facebook: www.facebook.com/afpoc

Description: Supports fundraising professionals in Orange County, California. **Geographic Preference:** Local.

36530 ■ Association of Fundraising Professionals San Diego Chapter (AFPSD)
c/o Katie Gomez, Manager
PO Box 882088
San Diego, CA 92168-2088
Ph: (770)518-0776
Co. E-mail: katiegomez@afpsd.org
URL: http://community.afpglobal.org/afpcasandiegochapter/home
Contact: Katie Gomez, Manager
E-mail: katiegomez@afpsd.org
URL(s): afpglobal.org/chapters/afp-ca-san-diego-california-chapter
Facebook: www.facebook.com/AFPSD

Description: Seeks to advance philanthropy in San Diego and Imperial counties by empowering members, prospective members, and representatives of other organizations to practice effective and ethical fundraising. **Founded:** 1974. **Geographic Preference:** Local.

36531 ■ Association of Fundraising Professionals Santa Barbara/Ventura Counties Chapter
PO Box 1564
Santa Barbara, CA 93102
Co. E-mail: afpsbvreg@gmail.com
URL: http://community.afpnet.org/afpsbv/home
Contact: Gerry Pantoja, Co-President
E-mail: president@afpsbv.org
Facebook: www.facebook.com/afpsbv/photos/a.411630692196902/5917904621569454
X (Twitter): x.com/SbvAfp
YouTube: www.youtube.com/channel/UCBv3TBT5qBk2_qLpdTm2zSA/featured

Description: Fosters the development and growth of fundraising professionals. Promotes high ethical standards in the fundraising profession. Provides training opportunities for fundraising professionals. **Founded:** 1986. **Geographic Preference:** Local.

36532 ■ Association of Fundraising Professionals Silicon Valley Chapter
c/o Dawn Carroll, Administrator
PO Box 24938
San Jose, CA 95154
Ph: (408)744-0412
Fax: (408)228-8719
Co. E-mail: info@afpsv.org
URL: http://community.afpglobal.org/afpcasiliconvalleychapter/home
Contact: Matt Siegel, President
E-mail: president@afpsv.org
Facebook: www.facebook.com/AFPSV
X (Twitter): x.com/afpsvc

Description: Provides fundraising education, professional development opportunities, and peer-to-peer networking in the Bay Area. **Founded:** 1985. **Geographic Preference:** Local.

36533 ■ Bay Area Business Travel Association (BABTA)
San Francisco, CA
URL: http://babta.org
Contact: Carey Ann Pascoe, President
E-mail: president@babta.org
Facebook: www.facebook.com/pages/BABTA-Bay-Area-Business-Travel-Association/250003017431
Linkedin: www.linkedin.com/groups
X (Twitter): x.com/WeAreBABTA

Description: Represents travel managers and providers. Promotes the value of the travel manager in meeting corporate travel needs and financial goals. Cultivates a positive public image of the corporate travel industry. Protects the interests of members and their corporations in legislative and regulatory matters. Promotes safety, security, efficiency and quality travel. Provides a forum for the exchange of information and ideas among members. **Founded:** 1975. **Geographic Preference:** Local.

36534 ■ Business Development Association of Orange County (BDA/OC)
5198 Arlington Ave. no 81
Riverside, CA 92504
URL: http://bdaie.net/wp/links

Founded: 1984. **Geographic Preference:** Local.

STATE LISTINGS

36535 ■ Business Marketing Association Northern California Chapter
968 Inverness Way
Sunnyvale, CA 94087
Co. E-mail: info@norcalbusinessmarketing.org
URL: http://norcalbusinessmarketing.org
Contact: Tanya Salah, President
E-mail: roundtables@norcalbma.org
Facebook: www.facebook.com/norcalbma
X (Twitter): x.com/norcalbma
Instagram: www.instagram.com/norcalbma
Description: Promotes the development of business-to-business marketing and communications professionals through education, training and networking.
Founded: 1938. **Publications:** *COPY Magazine* (Monthly). **Geographic Preference:** Local.

36536 ■ Business Marketing Association Southern California Chapter (SoCal BMA)
PO Box 7372
Newport Beach, CA 92658-7372
Ph: (949)854-0449
Co. E-mail: info@socalbma.org
URL: http://www.socalbma.org
Facebook: www.facebook.com/SoCalBMA
Linkedin: www.linkedin.com/company/socalbma/about
X (Twitter): x.com/socalbma
Description: Promotes the development of business-to-business marketing and communications professionals through education, training and networking.
Founded: 1922. **Geographic Preference:** Local.

36537 ■ California Association of Business Brokers (CABB)
4747 N 1st St., Ste. 140
Fresno, CA 93726
Free: 866-972-2220
Fax: (559)227-1463
Co. E-mail: info@cabb.org
URL: http://www.cabb.org
Contact: Randy Katz, President
Facebook: www.facebook.com/CABB.org
Linkedin: www.linkedin.com/company/cabborg
X (Twitter): x.com/cabborg
Description: Represents professionals and firms in business brokerage, mergers and acquisitions. Provides business brokers education, conferences, professional designations, and networking opportunities in California. Works to become a leader in the exchange of business referrals, and to create professional relationships with successful business transaction advisors. **Founded:** 1986. **Geographic Preference:** State.

36538 ■ Environmental Entrepreneurs Southern California San Diego Chapter
San Diego, CA
URL: http://e2.org/chapters/san-diego
Contact: Carl Nettleton, Director
Description: Represents individual business leaders who advocate for good environmental policy while building economic prosperity. Provides information about pressing environmental issues to members. Tackles environmental issues through bipartisan efforts. **Founded:** 2010. **Geographic Preference:** Local.

36539 ■ The Indus Entrepreneurs South Coast (TIE)
5435 Oberlin Dr.
San Diego, CA 92121
Ph: (949)929-0916
Co. E-mail: executivedirector@southcoast.tie.org
URL: http://southcoast.tie.org
URL(s): hub.tie.org/c/tiesouthcoastold
Facebook: www.facebook.com/tiesouthcoast
X (Twitter): x.com/tiesouthcoast
Description: Seeks to enrich, foster, and facilitate entrepreneurship through mentoring, networking, and education. **Founded:** 2000. **Geographic Preference:** Local.

36540 ■ International Association of Business Communicators - San Francisco Bay Area (SF IABC)
330 N Wabash Ave., Ste. 2000
Chicago, IL 60611
Co. E-mail: communications@iabc.com
URL: http://sf.iabc.com
Contact: Kamna Narain, Co-President
Facebook: www.facebook.com/sfiabc
Linkedin: www.linkedin.com/company/sfiabc
Instagram: www.instagram.com/sfiabc
Description: Works with communicators and communications organizations to improve the effectiveness of organizational communication. Provides products, services, resources, activities, learning and networking opportunities, and other forms of professional and personal development. Conducts research in the field of communication. **Geographic Preference:** Local.

36541 ■ International Association of Women Bakersfield Chapter
Bakersfield, CA
URL: http://www.iawomen.com/chapters/bakersfield-chapter
Contact: Kelly Brown, President
E-mail: kelly@patbrownsystem.com
Description: Serves as network of accomplished women united to achieve professional goals. Provides a forum for sharing ideas and experiences of professional women regarding career success. Promotes an active business and networking community from all industries. **Geographic Preference:** Local.

36542 ■ International Association of Women Long Beach Chapter
Long Beach, CA
Co. E-mail: localchaptersoffice@iawomen.com
URL: http://community.iawomen.com/longbeach/home
Contact: Linda Kaplan, President
E-mail: designsbysilk1@sbcglobal.net
Facebook: www.facebook.com/IAWomenLongBeach
Description: Serves as network of accomplished women united to achieve professional goals. Provides a forum for sharing ideas and experiences of professional women regarding career success. Promotes an active business and networking community from all industries. **Geographic Preference:** Local.

36543 ■ International Association of Women Los Angeles Chapter
Los Angeles, CA
Free: 888-852-1600
Co. E-mail: losangeles@iawomen.com
URL: http://community.iawomen.com/losangeles/home
Contact: Corina Jimenez, President
E-mail: erica@mightysocialmedia.com
Facebook: www.facebook.com/IAWomenLosAngeles
Description: Serves as network of accomplished women united to achieve professional goals. Provides a forum for sharing ideas and experiences of professional women regarding career success. Promotes an active business and networking community from all industries. **Geographic Preference:** Local.

36544 ■ International Association of Women Oakland Chapter
Oakland, CA
Co. E-mail: oakland@iawomen.com
URL: http://community.iawomen.com/oakland/home
Description: Serves as network of accomplished women united to achieve professional goals. Provides a forum for sharing ideas and experiences of professional women regarding career success. Promotes an active business and networking community from all industries. **Geographic Preference:** Local.

36545 ■ International Association of Women Pasadena Chapter
Pasadena, CA
URL: http://community.iawomen.com/pasadena/home
Contact: Irma Vargas, President
E-mail: vrgsgrl@yahoo.com

Description: Serves as network of accomplished women united to achieve professional goals. Provides a forum for sharing ideas and experiences of professional women regarding career success. Promotes an active business and networking community from all industries. **Geographic Preference:** Local.

36546 ■ International Association of Women San Diego Chapter
San Diego, CA
Free: 888-852-1600
Co. E-mail: memberservices@iawomen.com
Facebook: www.facebook.com/IAWomenSanDiego
Description: Serves as network of accomplished women united to achieve professional goals. Provides a forum for sharing ideas and experiences of professional women regarding career success. Promotes an active business and networking community from all industries. **Geographic Preference:** Local.

36547 ■ International Association of Women San Fernando Valley Chapter
San Fernando, CA
URL: http://dev.iawomen.com/chapters
Description: Serves as a network for professional women seeking to promote their business, service, or product.

36548 ■ International Association of Women San Francisco Chapter
San Francisco, CA
URL: http://www.iawomen.com/chapters
URL(s): community.iawomen.com/home
Description: Serves as network of accomplished women united to achieve professional goals. Provides a forum for sharing ideas and experiences of professional women regarding career success. Promotes an active business and networking community from all industries. **Geographic Preference:** Local.

36549 ■ International Association of Women Santa Monica Chapter
Santa Monica, CA
URL: http://www.iawomen.com/chapters/santa-monica-chapter
Description: Serves as network of accomplished women united to achieve professional goals. Provides a forum for sharing ideas and experiences of professional women regarding career success. Promotes an active business and networking community from all industries. **Geographic Preference:** Local.

36550 ■ Los Angeles Venture Association (LAVA)
11301 Olympic Blvd., Ste. 376
Los Angeles, CA 90064
Co. E-mail: info@lava.org
URL: http://www.lava.org
Contact: Caroline Cherkassky, Chief Executive Officer
Linkedin: www.linkedin.com/company/los-angeles-venture-association
X (Twitter): x.com/LAVA310
Description: Promotes the development and financing of emerging growth and middle market companies. **Founded:** 1985.

36551 ■ Miami Valley Venture Association (MVVA)
202 Bicknell Ave.
Santa Monica, CA 90405
URL: http://mvva.org
Description: Serves entrepreneurs and investors by increasing the number of successfully funded businesses. Educates and improves the awareness of service providers in the area.

36552 ■ National Association of Women Business Owners Los Angeles (NAWBO-LA)
4500 Pk. Granada Ste. 202
Calabasas, CA 91302
URL: http://nawbola.org
Contact: Renee Young, President
Facebook: www.facebook.com/NAWBOLA
Linkedin: www.linkedin.com/company/nawbo-la
X (Twitter): x.com/nawbola

Description: Empowers women entrepreneurs into economic, social and political spheres of leadership by: strengthening the wealth creating capacity of members and promoting economic development within the entrepreneurial community creating innovative and effective changes in the business culture building strategic alliances, coalitions and affiliations transforming public policy and influencing opinion makers. **Founded:** 1979. **Awards:** NAWBO-LA Advocate of the Year Award (Annual); NAWBO-LA Hall of Fame (Annual); NAWBO-LA Rising Star of the Year (Annual); NAWBO-LA Trailblazer of the Year (Annual); Women Business Owner of the Year (Annual). **Geographic Preference:** Local.

36553 ■ National Association of Women Business Owners San Francisco Bay Area (NAWBO-SFBA)
237 Kearny St.
San Francisco, CA 94108
Co. E-mail: info@nawbo-sfba.org
URL: http://www.nawbo.org/san-francisco-bay-area
Contact: Nooshin Behroyan, President
Facebook: www.facebook.com/NAWBO.SanFranciscoBayArea
Linkedin: www.linkedin.com/company/nawbo-sfba
X (Twitter): x.com/nawbosfba
Description: Seeks to represent and support the interests of female business owners in San Francisco, Marin, Oakland/East Bay, and the Peninsula area of California. **Founded:** 1975. **Geographic Preference:** Local.

36554 ■ San Diego Business Travel Association (SDBTA)
PO Box 720596
San Diego, CA 92172
Co. E-mail: enquiries@gbta.org
URL: http://www.sdbta.org
Contact: Christine Ehly, President
E-mail: cehlygbta@gmail.com
X (Twitter): x.com/SDBTA
Description: Represents travel managers and providers. Promotes the value of the travel manager in meeting corporate travel needs and financial goals. Cultivates a positive public image of the corporate travel industry. Protects the interests of members and their corporations in legislative and regulatory matters. Promotes safety, security, efficiency and quality travel. Provides a forum for the exchange of information and ideas among members. **Geographic Preference:** Local.

36555 ■ Sand Hill Angels (SHA)
1060 La Avenida St.
Mountain View, CA 94043
Co. E-mail: info@sandhillangels.com
URL: http://www.sandhillangels.com
Facebook: www.facebook.com/sandhillangelsinc
Linkedin: www.linkedin.com/company/sand-hill-angels
X (Twitter): x.com/SandHillAngels
Description: Offer seed-stage investments for disruptive, scalable technologies typically in Northern California. **Founded:** 2000. **Preferred Investment Size:** $50,000 to $1,000,000. **Investment Policies:** Disruptive solutions to well-defined problems; developed products at the alpha/beta stage; large and growing markets; defensible technology; clear go-to-market plans; strong teams.

36556 ■ South of Market Community Action Network (SOMCAN)
1038 Mission st.
San Francisco, CA 94103
Ph: (415)255-7693
Fax: (415)552-5637
Co. E-mail: info@soman.org
URL: http://www.somcan.org
Contact: Angelica Cabande, Director
E-mail: acabande@somcan.org
Facebook: www.facebook.com/SOMCAN
Linkedin: www.linkedin.com/company/south-of-market-community-action-network--somcan-
Instagram: www.instagram.com/somcan.sf
YouTube: www.youtube.com/channel/UCHBw1K6ZdohUtQT6XLzww1A/featured
Description: Addresses gentrification issues within neighborhoods in San Francisco in order to give a voice to the resident base already established in those areas. **Founded:** 2000.

36557 ■ SYNERGY Business & Technology Center
1 N Calle Cesar Chavez, Ste. 102
Santa Barbara, CA 93103
Ph: (805)452-9542
Co. E-mail: info@synergybtc.com
URL: http://synergybtc.com
Contact: Michael Holliday, Director
Description: Offers a collaborative workplace environment for startups.

36558 ■ Tech Coast Angels (TCA)
5270 California Ave.
Irvine, CA 92617
URL: http://www.techcoastangels.com
Contact: Don Kasle, Treasurer
Facebook: www.facebook.com/techcoastangels
Linkedin: www.linkedin.com/company/techcoastangels
X (Twitter): x.com/techcoastangels
Description: Angel investor group for Southern California. **Founded:** 1997.

SMALL BUSINESS DEVELOPMENT CENTERS

36559 ■ Alameda County Small Business Development Center (ACSBDC)
25800 Carlos Bee Blvd., VBT 346
Hayward, CA 94542
Ph: (510)516-4118
Co. E-mail: info@acsbdc.org
URL: http://www.eastbaysbdc.org
Facebook: www.facebook.com/asksbdc
X (Twitter): x.com/AlamedaSBDC
Description: Represents and promotes the small business sector. Provides management assistance to current and prospective small business owners. Helps to improve management skills and expand the products and services of members. **Geographic Preference:** Local.

36560 ■ Alliance Small Business Development Center
IL
Free: 800-252-2923
URL: http://www.alliancesbdc.org
Description: Represents and promotes the small business sector. Provides management assistance to current and prospective small business owners. Helps to improve management skills and expand the products and services of members. **Geographic Preference:** Local.

36561 ■ Alpine County Small Business Development Center
56 S Lincoln St.
Stockton, CA 95203
Ph: (209)954-5089
Co. E-mail: aalopez@deltacollege.edu
Description: Represents and promotes the small business sector. Provides management assistance to current and prospective small business owners. Helps to improve management skills and expand the products and services of members. **Founded:** 1993. **Geographic Preference:** Local.

36562 ■ Amador County Small Business Development Center
5151 Pacific Ave.
Stockton, CA 95207
Ph: (209)954-5151
URL: http://www.deltacollege.edu/department/small-business-development-center
Contact: Nathan McBride, Director
E-mail: nmcbride@deltacollege.edu
Description: Represents and promotes the small business sector. Provides management assistance to current and prospective small business owners. Helps to improve management skills and expand the products and services of members. **Geographic Preference:** Local.

36563 ■ Butte College Small Business Development Center [Butte College SBDC]
2480 Notre Dame Blvd.
Chico, CA 95928
Ph: (530)895-9017
URL: http://www.buttecollegesbdc.com
Contact: Sophie Konuwa, Director
E-mail: konuwaso@butte.edu
Facebook: www.facebook.com/bcsbdc
Linkedin: www.linkedin.com/company/bcsbdc
X (Twitter): x.com/BCSBDC
Description: Represents and promotes the small business sector. Provides management assistance to current and prospective small business owners. Helps to improve management skills and expand the products and services of members. **Founded:** 1993. **Geographic Preference:** Local.

36564 ■ Calaveras County Small Business Development Center
c/o Steve Castellanos
8115 Hwy. 26
Valley Springs, CA 95252
URL: http://www.deltacollege.edu/about/district-map
Description: Provides management assistance to current and prospective small business owners in Calaveras County. **Geographic Preference:** Local.

36565 ■ California Fresno Small Business Development Center, Lead Office
390 W Fir Ave., Ste. 300
Clovis, CA 93611
Ph: (559)324-6403
URL: http://centralcasbdc.com/events/fresno-sba-government-contracting-workshop
Contact: Kurt Clark, Executive Director
E-mail: kclark5@ucmerced.edu
Description: Focuses on providing assistance to current and prospective small business owners in Fresno, California. **Geographic Preference:** Local.

36566 ■ California Los Angeles Region Small Business Development Center, Lead Office
c/o Long Beach Community College District, College Advancement and Economic Development
4900 E Conant St., Bldg. 2, Ste. 108
Long Beach, CA 90808
Ph: (562)938-5030
Free: 866-588-SBDC
URL: http://smallbizla.org/locations
Contact: Patrick Nye, Regional Director
Description: Provides business owners with assistance in business planning, management, marketing, sales, procurement, and strategic planning as well as access to financing. **Geographic Preference:** Local.

36567 ■ Capital Region SBDC
1792 Tribute Rd., Ste. 455
Sacramento, CA 95815
Ph: (916)655-2100
Co. E-mail: sbdc@metrochamber.org
URL: http://capitalregionvasbdc.com
Contact: SiewYee Lee, Director
Facebook: www.facebook.com/SacSBDC
Linkedin: www.linkedin.com/in/capital-region-sbdc-21a8a521
Description: Provides access to capital for small business owners and entrepreneurs. Business advisors provide guidance and consultation to improve businesses.

36568 ■ CDC Small Business Finance Corp. (CDCSBF)
2448 Historic Decatur Rd., No. 200
San Diego, CA 92106
Ph: (619)291-3594
Free: 800-611-5170
Co. E-mail: loaninfo@cdcloans.com
URL: http://cdcloans.com
Contact: Ellis Carr, President
Linkedin: www.linkedin.com/company/cdc-small-business-finance

STATE LISTINGS

X (Twitter): x.com/CDC_Loans
YouTube: www.youtube.com/user/
SmallBusinessFinance
Description: Offers a variety of low-interest financing loans that fit the needs of small businesses no matter where they are in the growth cycle. **Founded:** 1978.

36569 ■ **Central California Small Business Development Center Fresno**
390 W Fir Ave., Ste. 300
Clovis, CA 93611
Ph: (559)324-6403
Co. E-mail: vcsbdc@cloviscollege.edu
URL: http://valleycommunitysbdc.com
Contact: Rich Mostert, Director
E-mail: richard.mostert@cloviscollege.edu
Description: Represents and promotes the small business sector. Provides management assistance to current and prospective small business owners. Helps to improve management skills and expand the products and services of members. **Geographic Preference:** Local.

36570 ■ **Coachella Valley Small Business Development Center**
44-199 Monroe St., Ste. B.
Indio, CA 92201
Ph: (760)848-4096
URL: http://ociesmallbusiness.org/coachella-valley
Contact: Joaquin Tijerina, Director
Facebook: www.facebook.com/cvsbdc
X (Twitter): x.com/cvsbdc
Description: Represents and promotes the small business sector. Provides management assistance to current and prospective small business owners. Helps to improve management skills and expand the products and services of members. **Geographic Preference:** Local.

36571 ■ **College of the Canyons Small Business Development Center (COC SBDC)**
26455 Rockwell Canyon Rd.
Santa Clarita, CA 91355
Ph: (661)362-5900
Fax: (661)362-5596
URL: http://cocsbdc.org
Contact: Catherine Grooms, Director
Facebook: www.facebook.com/sbdcnola
X (Twitter): x.com/sbdcnola
Description: Provides management assistance to current and prospective small business owners in Canyons. **Geographic Preference:** Local.

36572 ■ **Contra Costa Small Business Development Center (CCSBDC)**
4071 Port Chicago Hwy.
Concord, CA 94520
Ph: (925)671-4570
Co. E-mail: admin@contracostasbdc.org
URL: http://www.eastbaysbdc.org/find-your-sbdc
Description: Represents and promotes the small business sector. Provides management assistance to current and prospective small business owners. Helps to improve management skills and expand the products and services of members. **Geographic Preference:** Local.

36573 ■ **El Camino College Small Business Development Center**
13430 Hawthorne Blvd.
Hawthorne, CA 90250-5806
Ph: (310)225-8277
Fax: (310)973-3132
URL: http://southbaysbdc.org
Contact: Starleen van Buren, Director
Description: Represents and promotes the small business sector. Provides management assistance to current and prospective small business owners. Helps to improve management skills and expand the products and services of members. **Geographic Preference:** Local.

36574 ■ **Imperial Valley Small Business Development Center at Imperial Valley College**
2799 S 4th St., El Centro
El Centro, CA 92243
Ph: (442)265-4951
Co. E-mail: imperial.valley@sdivsbdc.org
URL: http://sdivsbdc.org/imperial-valley-sbdc
Contact: Daniel Fitzgerald, Regional Director
Facebook: www.facebook.com/IVSBDC
X (Twitter): x.com/IVSBDC
Instagram: www.instagram.com/ivsbdc
Description: Represents and promotes the small business sector. Provides management assistance to current and prospective small business owners. Helps to improve management skills and expand the products and services of members. **Geographic Preference:** Local.

36575 ■ **Inland Empire North Small Business Development Center**
3780 Market St.
Riverside, CA 92501
Ph: (951)781-2345
URL: http://ociesmallbusiness.org/inland-empire
Contact: Paul Nolta, Director
E-mail: pnolta@iesmallbusiness.com
Description: Represents and promotes the small business sector. Provides management assistance to current and prospective small business owners. Helps to improve management skills and expand the products and services of members. **Geographic Preference:** Local.

36576 ■ **Inland Empire Small Business Development Center (IESBDC)**
603 N Euclid Ave.
Ontario, CA 91762
Ph: (909)983-5005
URL: http://entre.csusb.edu/content/sbdc-team
Contact: Paul Nolta, Program Director
E-mail: pnolta@iesmallbusiness.com
Founded: 1995. **Geographic Preference:** Local.

36577 ■ **Long Beach City College Small Business Development Center**
4900 E Conant St., Ste. 108
Long Beach, CA 90808
Ph: (562)938-5100
Fax: (562)938-5030
Co. E-mail: sbdcinfo@lbcc.edu
URL: http://longbeachsbdc.org
Contact: Brad Pollak, Director
Facebook: www.facebook.com/sbdclosangeles
X (Twitter): x.com/SBDCLosAngeles
Description: Represents and promotes the small business sector. Provides management assistance to current and prospective small business owners. Helps to improve management skills and expand the products and services of members. **Geographic Preference:** Local.

36578 ■ **Los Angeles Small Business Development Center Network (LA SBDC)**
4900 E Conant St., Bldg. 2, Ste. 108
Long Beach, CA 90808
Free: 866-588-7232
Fax: (562)938-5030
URL: http://smallbizla.org
Contact: Patrick Nye, Regional Director
Facebook: www.facebook.com/sbdclosangeles
Linkedin: www.linkedin.com/company/los-angeles-regional-sbdc-network
X (Twitter): x.com/SBDCLosAngeles
Description: Represents and promotes the small business sector. Provides management assistance to current and prospective small business owners. Helps to improve management skills and expand the products and services of members. **Geographic Preference:** Local.

36579 ■ **Mendocino Small Business Development Center**
345 N Franklin St.
Fort Bragg, CA 95437
Ph: (707)964-7571
URL: http://www.mendosbdc.org
Contact: Mary Anne Petrillo, Director
URL(s): www.westcenter.org/mendocino-sbdc
Description: Represents and promotes the small business sector. Provides management assistance to current and prospective small business owners. Helps to improve management skills and expand the products and services of members. **Geographic Preference:** Local.

36580 ■ **Napa-Sonoma SBDC**
Bldg. 3300
2277 Napa Vallejo Hwy.
Napa, CA 94558
Ph: (707)256-7250
Co. E-mail: sbdcclientservices@napavalley.edu
URL: http://napasonomasbdc.org
Contact: Cathy Balach, Advisor
Description: Represents and promotes the small business sector. Provides management assistance to current and prospective small business owners. Helps to improve management skills and expand the products and services of members. **Geographic Preference:** Local.

36581 ■ **North San Diego Small Business Development Center**
2075 Las Palmas Dr.
Carlsbad, CA 92011
URL: http://sdivsbdc.org/north-san-diego-sbdc
Contact: Amy Duncan, Director
Description: Represents and promotes the small business sector. Provides management assistance to current and prospective small business owners. Helps to improve management skills and expand the products and services of members. **Geographic Preference:** Local.

36582 ■ **Northcoast Small Business Development Center Del Norte**
Del Norte, CA
Ph: (707)464-2168
URL: http://www.northcoastsbdc.org/resource/starting-your-business
Contact: Leila Roberts, Director
E-mail: lroberts@northcoastsbdc.org
Description: Represents and promotes the small business sector. Provides management assistance to current and prospective small business owners. Helps to improve management skills and expand the products and services of members. **Geographic Preference:** Local.

36583 ■ **Northcoast Small Business Development Center Humboldt**
520 E St.
Eureka, CA 95501
Ph: (707)445-9720
URL: http://www.northcoastsbdc.org/team-members/leila-roberts
Contact: Leila Roberts, Director
Facebook: www.facebook.com/NorthCoastSBDC
Linkedin: www.linkedin.com/company/northcoastsbdc
X (Twitter): x.com/northcoastsbdc
Instagram: www.instagram.com/northcoastsbdc
Description: Represents and promotes the small business sector. Provides management assistance to current and prospective small business owners. Helps to improve management skills and expand the products and services of members. **Founded:** 1984. **Geographic Preference:** Local.

36584 ■ **Orange County Small Business Development Center (SBDC)**
1300 S Bristol St., 2nd Fl.
Santa Ana, CA 92704
Free: 800-616-7232
URL: http://ociesmallbusiness.org/orange-county/about-orange-county
Contact: Manal Richa, Director
Facebook: www.facebook.com/OCIESBDC
Linkedin: www.linkedin.com/company/orange-county-inland-empire-sbdc-network
X (Twitter): x.com/OCIESBDC
Instagram: www.instagram.com/ociesbdc
YouTube: www.youtube.com/channel/UC5d9GXJF0n5fNYvARD8fvfA
Description: Provides counseling and training to small business owners. **Founded:** 1991. **Geographic Preference:** Local.

36585 ■ California

STATE LISTINGS

36585 ■ Pacific Coast Regional Small Business Development Corp.
3255 Wilshire Blvd., Ste. 1501
  Los Angeles, CA 90010
Ph: (213)674-2696
Fax: (213)739-0639
URL: http://pcrsbdc.org
Contact: O. C. Issac, Senior Vice President Chief Credit Officer
Facebook: www.facebook.com/sbdclosangeles
Linkedin: www.linkedin.com/company/los-angeles-regional-sbdc-network
X (Twitter): x.com/SBDCLosAngeles
Description: Represents and promotes the small business sector. Provides management assistance to current and prospective small business owners. Helps to improve management skills and expand the products and services of members. **Geographic Preference:** Local.

36586 ■ San Francisco Small Business Development Center
1650 Mission St., Ste. 101
  San Francisco, CA 94103
Ph: (415)937-7232
URL: http://sfsbdc.org
Contact: Jossiel Cruseta, Director
Facebook: www.facebook.com/San-Francisco-SBDC-1386090498282523
X (Twitter): x.com/SanFranSBDC
Description: Represents and promotes the small business sector. Provides management assistance to current and prospective small business owners. Helps to improve management skills and expand the products and services of members. **Geographic Preference:** Local.

36587 ■ San Joaquin Delta College Small Business Development Center (SBDC)
6221 W Ln.
  Stockton, CA 95210
Ph: (209)868-1046
Co. E-mail: info@sanjoaquinsbdc.org
URL: http://www.sanjoaquinsbdc.org
Contact: Les Fong, Director
URL(s): www.deltacollege.edu/department/small-business-development-center
Facebook: www.facebook.com/SanJoaquinSBDC
Linkedin: www.linkedin.com/company/san-joaquin-sbdc
YouTube: www.youtube.com/channel/UCW__IqekWHrjn_2G2CK-TOA
Description: Represents and promotes the small business sector. Provides management assistance to current and prospective small business owners. Helps to improve management skills and expand the products and services of members. **Founded:** 1993. **Geographic Preference:** Local.

36588 ■ Santa Cruz Small Business Development Center
6500 Soquel Dr. No. 2100C
  Aptos, CA 95003
Ph: (831)479-6136
Co. E-mail: sbdc@cabrillo.edu
URL: http://www.santacruzsbdc.org
Contact: Brandon Napoli, Director, Finance Advisor
Linkedin: www.linkedin.com/company/santa-cruz-county-small-business-development-center
X (Twitter): x.com/CaliforniaSBDC
Instagram: www.instagram.com/sbdcsantacruzcounty
YouTube: www.youtube.com/channel/UC536BDZY4vdCLqwCczHOsfA
Description: Represents and promotes the small business sector. Provides management assistance to current and prospective small business owners. Helps to improve management skills and expand the products and services of members. **Founded:** 1985. **Geographic Preference:** Local.

36589 ■ Silicon Valley Center for Entrepreneurship (SVCE)
One Washington Sq.
  San Jose, CA 95192
Ph: (408)924-3593
URL: http://www.sjsu.edu/svce

Contact: Dr. Anuradha Basu, Director
E-mail: anu.basu@sjsu.edu
Description: Promotes effective entrepreneurship through knowledge creation and dissemination, collaborative partnerships, and outreach activities.

36590 ■ Silicon Valley Small Business Development Center at West Valley/Mission College (SBDC)
1887 Monterey Rd., 2nd Fl.
  San Jose, CA 95112
Ph: (408)385-9800
URL: http://www.svsbdc.org
Contact: Dennis King, Executive Director
Description: Represents and promotes the small business sector. Provides management assistance to current and prospective small business owners. Helps to improve management skills and expand the products and services of members. **Geographic Preference:** Local.

36591 ■ Small Business Development Center Greater Sacramento
One Capitol Mall, Ste. 700
  Sacramento, CA 95814
Ph: (916)319-4268
URL: http://www.sacramentovalleysbdc.org
Contact: SiewYee Lee, Director
Facebook: www.facebook.com/SacValleySBDC
Linkedin: www.linkedin.com/company/sacvalleysbdc
X (Twitter): x.com/SacValleySBDC
Instagram: www.instagram.com/sacvalleysbdc
Description: Represents and promotes the small business sector. Provides management assistance to current and prospective small business owners. Helps to improve management skills and expand the products and services of members. **Geographic Preference:** Local.

36592 ■ Small Business Development Center at Shasta College (SBDC)
1305 Sacramento St.
  Redding, CA 96001
Ph: (530)222-8323
URL: http://www.sbdcsc.org
Contact: Joe Rodola, Advisor
X (Twitter): x.com/sbdcshasta
YouTube: www.youtube.com/channel/UCYg7Bgifsbz76ptqLqKnO6w
Description: Represents and promotes the small business sector. Provides management assistance to current and prospective small business owners. Helps to improve management skills and expand the products and services of members. **Geographic Preference:** Local.

36593 ■ Small Business Development Centers of Northern California (SBDC)
1 Harpst St., House 71
  Arcata, CA 95521
URL: http://www.norcalsbdc.org
Contact: Kristin Johnson, Regional Director
E-mail: kristin.johnson@humboldt.edu
X (Twitter): x.com/californiasbdc
Description: Represents and promotes the small business sector. Provides management assistance to current and prospective small business owners. Helps to improve management skills and expand the products and services of members. **Geographic Preference:** Local.

36594 ■ Solano College Small Business Development Center
500 Chadbourne Rd.
  Fairfield, CA 94534
Ph: (707)646-1071
Co. E-mail: info@solanosbdc.org
URL: http://www.solanonapasbdc.org
Contact: Tim Murrill, Director
Facebook: www.facebook.com/solanonapasbdc
Instagram: www.instagram.com/solanonapasbdc
Description: Provides management assistance to current and prospective small business owners in Solano. **Geographic Preference:** Local.

36595 ■ TriTech Small Business Development Center
152 East 6th St.
  Corona, CA 92879
Ph: (951)571-6474
URL: http://www.rccd.edu/community/OED/Pages/TriTech-SBDC.aspx
Description: Represents and promotes the small business sector. Provides management assistance to current and prospective small business owners. Helps to improve management skills and expand the products and services of members. **Geographic Preference:** Local.

36596 ■ UC Merced Small Business Development Center Regional Network
655 W 18th St.
  Merced, CA 95340
Ph: (209)803-8076
Co. E-mail: ucmsbdc@ucmerced.edu
URL: http://centralcasbdc.com/contact/uc-merced-sbdc
Contact: Kurt Clark, Executive Director
E-mail: kclark5@ucmerced.edu
URL(s): ucmercedsbdc.com
Facebook: www.facebook.com/UCMercedSBDC
Linkedin: www.linkedin.com/company/ucmercedsbdc
X (Twitter): x.com/ucmercedsbdc
Instagram: www.instagram.com/ucmercedsbdc
Description: Represents and promotes the small business sector. Provides management assistance to current and prospective small business owners. Helps to improve management skills and expand the products and services of members. **Founded:** 2003. **Geographic Preference:** Local.

36597 ■ Woodland Small Business Development Center
300 1st St.
  Woodland, CA 95695
Ph: (530)661-5800
Fax: (530)661-5813
URL: http://cityofwoodland.org
Contact: Derrek Kaff, Chief of Police
Facebook: www.facebook.com/CityOfWoodland
X (Twitter): x.com/CityofWoodland
Description: Represents and promotes the small business sector. Provides management assistance to current and prospective small business owners. Helps to improve management skills and expand the products and services of members. **Geographic Preference:** Local.

36598 ■ Yuba Community College District Small Business Development Center
3301 E Onstott Rd.
  Yuba City, CA 95991
Co. E-mail: yccdchancellorsoffice@yccd.edu
URL: http://www.yccd.edu
Contact: Susan Alves, President
Description: Represents and promotes the small business sector. Provides management assistance to current and prospective small business owners. Helps to improve management skills and expand the products and services of members. **Geographic Preference:** Local.

SMALL BUSINESS ASSISTANCE PROGRAMS

36599 ■ American Small Business League (ASBL)
3910 Cypress Dr., Ste. B
  Petaluma, CA 94954
Ph: (707)789-9575
Fax: (707)789-9580
Co. E-mail: aprophet@asbl.com
URL: http://www.asbl.com
Contact: Lloyd Chapman, President
Description: Promotes and advocates policies that provide opportunity for small businesses. **Founded:** 2004. **Geographic Preference:** National.

36600 ■ Bankers Small Business Community Development Corp.
2448 Historic Decatur Rd., No. 200
San Diego, CA 92106
Ph: (619)291-3594
Free: 800-611-5170
Fax: (619)291-6954
URL: http://cdcloans.com
Contact: Ellis Carr, President
Linkedin: www.linkedin.com/company/cdc-small
-business-finance
Description: Offers small business loans. **Founded:** 1992.

36601 ■ California Department of General Services - Office of Small Business and Disabled Veteran Business Enterprise Services
707 3rd St.
West Sacramento, CA 95605
Ph: (916)375-4940
Co. E-mail: osdshelp@dgs.ca.gov
URL: http://www.dgs.ca.gov/PD/Services/Page-Content/Procurement-Division-Services-List-Folder/Certify-or-Re-apply-as-Small-Business-Disabled-Veteran-Business-Enterprise
Description: Assists small and disabled veteran businesses by participating in outreach events, providing resource guidance and supporting the businesses through advocacy. **Publications:** *California State Contracts Register* (Continuous).

36602 ■ California San Diego Small Business Development Center, Lead Office
Southwestern College
900 Otay Lakes Rd., Bldg. 660
Chula Vista, CA 91910
Ph: (619)482-6393
Co. E-mail: support@sandiegocitd.org
URL: http://www.sandiegocitd.org
Description: Helps small and medium-sized businesses with international trade. **Geographic Preference:** Local.

36603 ■ Governnor's of Business and Ecnomoic Development
1325 J St., Ste. 1800
Sacramento, CA 95818
Free: 877-345-4633
URL: http://www.business.ca.gov
Contact: Chris Dombrowski, Deputy Director
Facebook: www.facebook.com/CAGoBiz
Linkedin: www.linkedin.com/company/governor
X (Twitter): x.com/CAGoBiz
YouTube: www.youtube.com/channel/UCregW8KZRE4k1sXVZs2bPxw
Description: Offers small business assistance, permit assistance, regulatory guidance, trade development, expansion, and site selection services.

36604 ■ Renaissance Soma
275 5th St.
San Francisco, CA 94103
Ph: (415)541-8580
Co. E-mail: info@rencenter.org
URL: http://rencenter.org
Contact: Craig Jacoby, Chairman of the Board
Description: Helps entrepreneurs who traditionally lacked access to resources and information achieve financial self-sufficiency.

SCORE OFFICES

36605 ■ Central Valley SCORE
801 R St., Ste. 201
Fresno, CA 93721
Ph: (559)487-5791
Fax: (559)487-5636
Co. E-mail: info.0380@scorevolunteer.org
URL: http://centralvalley.score.org
Contact: Peter Fong, Director
Facebook: www.facebook.com/SCORECentralValley
Linkedin: www.linkedin.com/company/score-mentors
-central-valley
X (Twitter): x.com/SCORECentralVLY

YouTube: www.youtube.com/channel/UC9injk1ctFWtQpocxXPbC9A
Description: Unites active and retired business management professionals with men and women who are considering starting a small business, encountering problems with their business, or expanding their business.

36606 ■ Chico SCORE
1324 Mangrove Ave., Ste. 114
Chico, CA 95926
URL: http://greaterchicoarea.stage.score.org

36607 ■ Orange County SCORE
1415 S Main St.
Santa Ana, CA 92707
Ph: (714)550-7369
URL: http://www.score.org/orangecounty
Founded: 1964.

36608 ■ Santa Cruz County SCORE
826 Bay Ave. No. 543
Capitola, CA 95010
URL: http://www.score.org/centralcoast

36609 ■ SCORE - Alameda
College of Alameda-555 Ralph Appezzato pkwy.
Cougar Village Rm. 225
Alameda, CA 94501
Ph: (510)273-6611
URL: http://eastbay.score.org
Description: Provides professional guidance and information to maximize the success of existing and emerging small businesses. Offers business counseling and workshops.

36610 ■ SCORE - Alhambra
104 S 1st St.
Alhambra, CA 91801
Ph: (626)282-8481
URL: http://losangeles.score.org
Description: Provides professional guidance and information to maximize the success of existing and emerging small businesses. Offers business counseling and workshops.

36611 ■ SCORE - Atascadero
Atascadero Chamber of Commerce
6907 El Camino Real, Ste. A
Atascadero, CA 93422
Ph: (805)466-2044
Co. E-mail: info@atascaderochamber.org
URL: http://sanluisobispo.score.org/content/business
-resource-associations
Contact: Jacque Fields, Secretary
URL(s): www.atascaderochamber.org
X (Twitter): x.com/atownchamber
Instagram: www.instagram.com/atascadero_chamber
Description: Provides professional guidance and information to maximize the success of existing and emerging small businesses. Offers business counseling and workshops.

36612 ■ SCORE - Azusa
795 N Dalton
Azusa, CA 91702
Ph: (626)593-1120
Co. E-mail: score.chapter400@volunteer.org
URL: http://eastsangabrielvalley.score.org
Contact: Bridget Weston, Chief Executive Officer
Description: Provides professional guidance and information to maximize the success of existing and emerging small businesses. Offers business counseling and workshops.

36613 ■ SCORE - Banning
60 E Ramsey St.
Banning, CA 92220
Ph: (951)849-4695
Co. E-mail: help@score.org
URL: http://inlandempire.score.org
Description: Business counselors offering a full range of business counseling services as well as an array of in-person and online workshops covering a wide range of topics.

36614 ■ SCORE - Beaumont
726 Beaumont Ave.
Beaumont, CA 92223
Ph: (951)845-9541
URL: http://www.score.org/inlandempire/about
Description: Business counselors offering a full range of business counseling services as well as an array of in-person and online workshops covering a wide range of topics.

36615 ■ SCORE - Berkeley
Berkeley, CA
URL: http://eastbay.score.org/mentors/sandy-warren
Contact: Sandy Warren, Contact
Description: Provides professional guidance and information to maximize the success of existing and emerging small businesses. Offers business counseling and workshops.

36616 ■ SCORE - Calabasas
23564 Calabasas Rd., Ste. 101
Calabasas, CA 91302
Ph: (818)222-5680
Fax: (818)222-5690
Co. E-mail: info@calabasaschamber.com
URL: http://ventura.score.org
Contact: Bridget Weston, Chief Executive Officer
Description: Provides professional guidance and information to maximize the success of existing and emerging small businesses. Offers business counseling and workshops.

36617 ■ SCORE - Camarillo
638 Lindero canyon Rd. ste.,300
Oak Park, CA 91377
Ph: (805)204-6022
Co. E-mail: admin.0255@scorevolunteer.org
URL: http://www.ventura.score.org/resource/county
-offices-ventura-and-los-angeles-counties
Description: Provides professional guidance and information to maximize the success of existing and emerging small businesses. Offers business counseling and workshops.

36618 ■ SCORE - Campbell
Campbell, CA
Ph: (408)378-6252
URL: http://siliconvalley.score.org
Description: Provides professional guidance and information to maximize the success of existing and emerging small businesses. Offers business counseling and workshops.

36619 ■ SCORE - Canoga Park
7248 Owensmouth Ave.
Canoga Park, CA 91303
Ph: (818)884-4222
URL: http://losangeles.score.org
Description: Provides professional guidance and information to maximize the success of existing and emerging small businesses. Offers business counseling and workshops.

36620 ■ SCORE - Capital Corridor [SCORE - Sacramento]
6501 Sylvan Rd.
Citrus Heights, CA 95610
Free: 800-634-0245
Fax: (706)596-8331
Co. E-mail: sacinfo@scorevolunteer.org
URL: http://capitalcorridor.score.org
Facebook: www.facebook.com/SCORECapitalCorridor
Linkedin: www.linkedin.com/company/score-mentors
-capital-corridor
X (Twitter): x.com/SACSCORE
Description: Provides professional guidance and information to maximize the success of existing and emerging small businesses. Offers business counseling and workshops. **Founded:** 1978. **Geographic Preference:** Local.

36621 ■ SCORE - Castro Valley
Castro Valley, CA
URL: http://eastbay.score.org/branch/castro-valleye
den-area-chamber

Description: Provides professional guidance and information to maximize the success of existing and emerging small businesses. Offers business counseling and workshops.

36622 ■ SCORE - Central Coast [SCORE - Monterey Bay]
565 Hartnell St., Ste. 131
Monterey, CA 93942
Ph: (831)621-3735
Co. E-mail: central.coast@scorevolunteer.org
URL: http://centralcoast.score.org
Contact: Alexandra Navarro, Contact
Linkedin: www.linkedin.com/company/score-mentors-monterey-bay
Description: Provides professional guidance and information to maximize the success of existing and emerging small businesses. Offers business counseling and workshops. **Founded:** 1990. **Geographic Preference:** Local.

36623 ■ SCORE - Central Valley
801 R St., Ste. 201
Fresno, CA 93721
Ph: (559)487-5791
Fax: (559)487-5636
Co. E-mail: info.0380@scorevolunteer.org
URL: http://centralvalley.score.org
Contact: Peter W. Fong, Director
E-mail: peter.fong@scorevolunteer.org
Facebook: www.facebook.com/SCORECentralValley
Linkedin: www.linkedin.com/company/score-mentors-central-valley
X (Twitter): x.com/SCORECentralVLY
Description: Provides professional guidance and information to maximize the success of existing and emerging small businesses. Offers business counseling and workshops.

36624 ■ SCORE - Chamber of Commerce Ventura
1017 Thistlegate Rd.
Oak Park, CA 91377
Ph: (805)204-6022
Co. E-mail: info@scoreventura.org
URL: http://ventura.score.org
Contact: Bridget Weston, Chief Executive Officer
Facebook: www.facebook.com/SCOREVentura
Linkedin: www.linkedin.com/company/score-mentors-ventura-county
X (Twitter): x.com/VenturaSCORE
YouTube: www.youtube.com/user/VenturaSCORE
Description: Provides professional guidance and information to maximize the success of existing and emerging small businesses. Offers business counseling and workshops.

36625 ■ SCORE - Chino
Chaffey College-Info Tech Ctr.
13170 7th St.
Chino, CA 91710
Ph: (909)652-7649
URL: http://www.score.org/find-location
Description: Business counselors offering a full range of business counseling services as well as an array of in-person and online workshops covering a wide range of topics.

36626 ■ SCORE - Chino Hills
Chino Hills Community Ctr.
14250 Peyton Cr.
Chino Hills, CA 91709
URL: http://inlandempire.score.org/mentors/tom-roberts
Contact: Bob Henry, Contact
Description: Business counselors offering a full range of business counseling services as well as an array of in-person and online workshops covering a wide range of topics.

36627 ■ SCORE - Claremont
Claremont Chamber of Commerce
205 Yale Ave.
Claremont, CA 91711
URL: http://inlandempire.score.org/mentors/nitin-dvivedi
Contact: Nitin Dvivedi, Contact

Description: Provides professional guidance and information to maximize the success of existing and emerging small businesses. Offers business counseling and workshops.

36628 ■ SCORE - Coachella Valley
73-733 Fred Waring Dr.
Palm Desert, CA 92260
Ph: (760)773-6507
Co. E-mail: help@score.org
URL: http://www.score.org/coachellavalley
Facebook: www.facebook.com/coachellavalleyscore
Description: Provides professional guidance and information to maximize the success of existing and emerging small businesses. Offers business counseling and workshops.

36629 ■ SCORE - Concord
2280 Diamond Blvd., Ste. 200
Concord, CA 94520
Ph: (925)685-1181
URL: http://www.score.org/find-location
Description: Provides professional guidance and information to maximize the success of existing and emerging small businesses. Offers business counseling and workshops.

36630 ■ SCORE - Corona
Corona Chamber of Commerce
904 E 6th St.
Corona, CA 92879
Ph: (951)737-3350
Co. E-mail: help@score.org
URL: http://inlandempire.score.org
Description: Business counselors offering a full range of business counseling services as well as an array of in-person and online workshops covering a wide range of topics.

36631 ■ SCORE - Covina
2648 E Workman Ave., Ste. 267
West Covina, CA 91791
Ph: (951)652-4390
Co. E-mail: help@score.org
URL: http://eastsangabrielvalley.score.org
URL(s): www.score.org/find-location
Description: Provides professional guidance and information to maximize the success of existing and emerging small businesses. Offers business counseling and workshops.

36632 ■ SCORE - Culver City
6000 Sepulveda Blvd.
Culver City, CA 90230
Ph: (310)287-3850
URL: http://losangeles.score.org/score-los-angeles-locations
Description: Provides professional guidance and information to maximize the success of existing and emerging small businesses. Offers business counseling and workshops.

36633 ■ SCORE - Danville
Danville, CA
URL: http://eastbay.score.org
Description: Provides professional guidance and information to maximize the success of existing and emerging small businesses. Offers business counseling and workshops.

36634 ■ SCORE - Diamond Bar
Diamond Bar City Hall
21810 Copley Dr.
Diamond Bar, CA 91765
Co. E-mail: info@diamondbarca.gov
URL: http://inlandempire.score.org/esgv
URL(s): www.diamondbarca.gov/734/SCORE---Business-Resource
Description: Provides professional guidance and information to maximize the success of existing and emerging small businesses. Offers business counseling and workshops.

36635 ■ SCORE - Downey Chamber of Commerce
Downey Chamber of Commerce
11131 Brookshire Ave.
Downey, CA 90241

Ph: (562)923-2191
URL: http://www.downeychamber.org
Contact: Carmen Gonzalez, President
Facebook: www.facebook.com/downeychamber
X (Twitter): x.com/downeychamber
Instagram: www.instagram.com/downeychambercommerce
Description: Provides professional guidance and information to maximize the success of existing and emerging small businesses. Offers business counseling and workshops.

36636 ■ SCORE - Duarte
Duarte Chamber of Commerce
1735 Huntington Dr.
Duarte, CA 91009
Ph: (626)593-1120
URL: http://eastsangabrielvalley.score.org
Facebook: www.facebook.com/SCOREEastSanGabriel
X (Twitter): x.com/SCORESanGabriel
Description: Provides professional guidance and information to maximize the success of existing and emerging small businesses. Offers business counseling and workshops.

36637 ■ SCORE - Dublin
7080 Donlon Way
Dublin, CA 94568
Ph: (925)828-6200
URL: http://eastbay.score.org
Description: Provides professional guidance and information to maximize the success of existing and emerging small businesses. Offers business counseling and workshops.

36638 ■ SCORE - East Bay (EB Score)
College of Alameda, Cougar Village, Rm. 225
555 Ralph Appezzato Memorial Pkwy.
Alameda, CA 94501
Ph: (510)273-6611
Co. E-mail: info@eastbayscore.org
URL: http://eastbay.score.org
Facebook: www.facebook.com/ScoreEastBay
Linkedin: www.linkedin.com/company/score-east-bay
X (Twitter): x.com/ScoreEastBay
Description: Provides professional guidance and information to maximize the success of existing and emerging small businesses. Offers business counseling and workshops. **Founded:** 1964. **Geographic Preference:** Local.

36639 ■ SCORE - East San Gabriel Valley
3985 University Ave.
Riverside, CA 92501
Ph: (951)652-4390
Co. E-mail: help@score.org
URL: http://eastsangabrielvalley.score.org
Linkedin: www.linkedin.com/company/score-mentors-east-san-gabriel-valley
X (Twitter): x.com/SCORESanGabriel
Description: Provides professional guidance and information to maximize the success of existing and emerging small businesses. Offers business counseling and workshops.

36640 ■ SCORE - Eastvale
3985 University Ave.
Riverside, CA 92501
Ph: (951)652-4390
Co. E-mail: help@score.org
URL: http://inlandempire.score.org/branch/eastvale-city-hall
Facebook: www.facebook.com/SCOREInlandEmpire
Linkedin: www.linkedin.com/company/score-mentors-inland-empire
X (Twitter): x.com/SCOREInlandEmp
YouTube: www.youtube.com/user/SCOREIE
Description: Business counselors offering a full range of business counseling services as well as an array of in-person and online workshops covering a wide range of topics.

36641 ■ SCORE - Encino
4833 Balboa Ave.
Encino, CA 91316
Ph: (818)789-4711

STATE LISTINGS

URL: http://losangeles.score.org
Description: Provides professional guidance and information to maximize the success of existing and emerging small businesses. Offers business counseling and workshops.

36642 ■ SCORE - Fairfield, California
1111 Webster St.
Fairfield, CA 94533
Ph: (707)425-4625
URL: http://www.score.org/find-location
Description: Provides professional guidance and information to maximize the success of existing and emerging small businesses. Offers business counseling and workshops.

36643 ■ SCORE - Fontana
Fontana Chamber of Commerce
8491 Sierra Ave.
Fontana, CA 92335
Ph: (909)822-4433
URL: http://inlandempire.score.org/content/local-counseling-locations
Facebook: www.facebook.com/SCOREInlandEmpire
Linkedin: www.linkedin.com/company/score-mentors-inland-empire
X (Twitter): x.com/SCOREInlandEmp
YouTube: www.youtube.com/user/SCOREIE
Description: Business counselors offering a full range of business counseling services as well as an array of in-person and online workshops covering a wide range of topics.

36644 ■ SCORE - Foster City
100 Grand Ln., Ste. B
Foster City, CA 94404
Ph: (415)764-4964
URL: http://www.score.org/find-location?state=CA
Description: Provides professional guidance and information to maximize the success of existing and emerging small businesses. Offers business counseling and workshops.

36645 ■ SCORE - Fremont
39488 Stevenson Pl., Ste. 100
Fremont, CA 94539
URL: http://eastbay.score.org/branch/fremont-chamber-commerce
Description: Provides professional guidance and information to maximize the success of existing and emerging small businesses. Offers business counseling and workshops.

36646 ■ SCORE - Glendale
330 N Brand Blvd., Ste. 1200
Glendale, CA 91203
Ph: (818)552-3206
Fax: (818)547-1220
URL: http://losangeles.score.org/score-los-angeles-locations
Description: Provides professional guidance and information to maximize the success of existing and emerging small businesses. Offers business counseling and workshops. **Founded:** 1965. **Geographic Preference:** Local.

36647 ■ SCORE - Glendora
Glendora Chamber of Commerce
224 N Glendora Ave.
Glendora, CA 91741
Ph: (626)593-1120
URL: http://eastsangabrielvalley.score.org
Facebook: www.facebook.com/SCOREEastSanGabriel
X (Twitter): x.com/SCORESanGabriel
Description: Provides professional guidance and information to maximize the success of existing and emerging small businesses. Offers business counseling and workshops.

36648 ■ SCORE - Hemet
615 N San Jancinto St.
Hemet, CA 92543
Ph: (651)658-3211
Co. E-mail: help@score.org
URL: http://inlandempire.score.org/content/local-counseling-locations

Contact: Dennis Haffeman, Contact
Description: Business counselors offering a full range of business counseling services as well as an array of in-person and online workshops covering a wide range of topics.

36649 ■ SCORE - Hollywood
6255 Sunset Blvd., Ste. 150
Los Angeles, CA 90028
Ph: (323)469-8311
URL: http://losangeles.score.org/score-los-angeles-locations
Contact: Bridget Weston, Chief Executive Officer
Description: Provides professional guidance and information to maximize the success of existing and emerging small businesses. Offers business counseling and workshops.

36650 ■ SCORE - Inland Empire
3985 University Ave.
Riverside, CA 92501
Ph: (951)652-4390
Co. E-mail: help@score.org
URL: http://www.inlandempire.score.org
Contact: Jimmy Fraggos, Contact
Facebook: www.facebook.com/SCOREInlandEmpire
Linkedin: www.linkedin.com/company/score-mentors-inland-empire
X (Twitter): x.com/SCOREInlandEmp
YouTube: www.youtube.com/user/SCOREIE
Description: Provides professional guidance and information to maximize the success of existing and emerging small businesses. Offers business counseling and workshops. **Founded:** 1980. **Geographic Preference:** Local.

36651 ■ SCORE - Lafayette
Lafayette Chamber of Commerce
251 Lafayette Cir.
Lafayette, CA 94549
Ph: (925)284-7404
Co. E-mail: info@lafayettechamber.org
URL: http://lafayettechamber.org
Contact: John McCormick, President
Facebook: www.facebook.com/LafayetteChamber
Linkedin: www.linkedin.com/company/lafayette-chamber-of-commerce
X (Twitter): x.com/friendlychamber
YouTube: www.youtube.com/channel/UC23F-f9Kb2FuB3-ZtrG_u0A
Description: Provides professional guidance and information to maximize the success of existing and emerging small businesses. Offers business counseling and workshops. **Founded:** 1947.

36652 ■ SCORE - Lake Elsinore
3985 University Ave.
Riverside, CA 92501
Ph: (951)652-4390
URL: http://inlandempire.score.org
Contact: Robert Chabot, Contact
Linkedin: www.linkedin.com/company/score-mentors-inland-empire
X (Twitter): x.com/SCOREInlandEmp
YouTube: www.youtube.com/user/SCOREIE
Description: Business counselors offering a full range of business counseling services as well as an array of in-person and online workshops covering a wide range of topics.

36653 ■ SCORE - Livermore
2157 1st St.
Livermore, CA 94550
URL: http://eastbay.score.org/community-engagement
Description: Provides professional guidance and information to maximize the success of existing and emerging small businesses. Offers business counseling and workshops.

36654 ■ SCORE - Long Beach Chamber of Commerce
Long Beach, CA
Free: 800-634-0245
Co. E-mail: help@score.org
URL: http://www.score.org/longbeach
Contact: Tim Donahue, Contact

Facebook: www.facebook.com/SCORELongBeachCA
Linkedin: www.linkedin.com/company/score-long-beach-south-bay
Description: Provides professional guidance and information to maximize the success of existing and emerging small businesses. Offers business counseling and workshops. **Founded:** 1964.

36655 ■ SCORE - Long Beach Ironfire Coworking
2201 N Lakewood Blvd., No. 692
Long Beach, CA 90815
Ph: (562)528-6919
Co. E-mail: help@score.org
URL: http://longbeach.score.org
Contact: Bridget Weston, Chief Executive Officer
Facebook: www.facebook.com/SCORELongBeachCA
Linkedin: www.linkedin.com/company/score-long-beach-south-bay
Description: Provides professional guidance and information to maximize the success of existing and emerging small businesses. Offers business counseling and workshops.

36656 ■ SCORE - Long Beach Public Library - Michelle Obama Branch
5870 Atlantic Ave.
Long Beach, CA 90805
Ph: (562)528-6919
URL: http://longbeach.score.org
Description: Provides professional guidance and information to maximize the success of existing and emerging small businesses. Offers business counseling and workshops.

36657 ■ SCORE - Long Beach/South Bay
4811 Airport Plz. Dr.
Long Beach, CA 90815
Free: 800-634-0245
Co. E-mail: ch.admin0725@scorevolunteer.org
URL: http://www.score.org/longbeach
Contact: Jeff Salisbury, Contact
Facebook: www.facebook.com/SCORELongBeachCA
Linkedin: www.linkedin.com/company/score-long-beach-south-bay
Description: Provides professional guidance and information to maximize the success of existing and emerging small businesses. Offers business counseling and workshops. **Founded:** 1964.

36658 ■ SCORE - Los Altos
321 University Ave.
Los Altos, CA 94022
Ph: (408)453-6237
URL: http://siliconvalley.score.org/?_ga=2.7002290.1277302979.1626524310-1917805190.1626524308
Description: Provides professional guidance and information to maximize the success of existing and emerging small businesses. Offers business counseling and workshops.

36659 ■ SCORE - Los Angeles
6400 Playa Vista Dr.
Shadow Hills, CA 91040
Free: 800-634-0245
URL: http://www.score.org/losangeles
Contact: David A. Berkus, Contact
Linkedin: www.linkedin.com/company/score-greater-los-angeles
X (Twitter): x.com/scorelosangeles
Description: Provides professional guidance and information to maximize the success of existing and emerging small businesses. Offers business counseling and workshops. **Founded:** 1964.

36660 ■ SCORE - Los Angeles Public Library
312 N Spring St.
Los Angeles, CA 90012
Free: 800-634-0245
Co. E-mail: help@score.org
URL: http://losangeles.score.org
Facebook: www.facebook.com/SCORELosAngeles

Linkedin: www.linkedin.com/company/score-greater-los-angeles
X (Twitter): twitter.com/scorelosangeles
Description: Provides professional guidance and information to maximize the success of existing and emerging small businesses. Offers business counseling and workshops.

36661 ■ SCORE - Los Gatos
10 Station Way
Los Gatos, CA 95030
Ph: (408)453-6237
URL: http://siliconvalley.score.org
Description: Provides professional guidance and information to maximize the success of existing and emerging small businesses. Offers business counseling and workshops.

36662 ■ SCORE - Menlo Park
1100 Merrill St.
Menlo Park, CA 94025
Ph: (415)764-4964
URL: http://sanfrancisco.score.org
Description: Provides professional guidance and information to maximize the success of existing and emerging small businesses. Offers business counseling and workshops.

36663 ■ SCORE - Milpitas
828 N Hillview Dr.
Milpitas, CA 95035
Ph: (408)453-6237
URL: http://www.score.org/find-location
Description: Provides professional guidance and information to maximize the success of existing and emerging small businesses. Offers business counseling and workshops.

36664 ■ SCORE - Modesto-Merced
c/o C of C, 1114 J St.
Modesto, CA 95354
Free: 800-634-0245
Fax: (209)723-8189
Co. E-mail: help@score.org
URL: http://modestomerced.score.org
Contact: Bridget Weston, Chief Executive Officer
Description: Provides professional guidance and information to maximize the success of existing and emerging small businesses. Offers business counseling and workshops.

36665 ■ SCORE - Montebello
Montebelo Chamber of Commerce
109 N 19th St.
Montebello, CA 90640
Ph: (626)593-1120
URL: http://eastsangabrielvalley.score.org
Facebook: www.facebook.com/SCOREEastSanGabriel
X (Twitter): x.com/SCORESanGabriel
Description: Provides professional guidance and information to maximize the success of existing and emerging small businesses. Offers business counseling and workshops.

36666 ■ SCORE - Moreno Valley
12625 Frederick St., Ste. E-3
Moreno Valley, CA 92553
Ph: (951)697-4404
URL: http://inlandempire.score.org/content/local-counseling-locations
Contact: Diana Cescolini, Contact
Description: Business counselors offering a full range of business counseling services as well as an array of in-person and online workshops covering a wide range of topics.

36667 ■ SCORE - Morgan Hill
17485 Monterey Rd., Ste. 105
Morgan Hill, CA 95037
Co. E-mail: info@morganhill.org
URL: http://www.morganhill.org/score
Facebook: www.facebook.com/MorganHillChamber
Description: Provides professional guidance and information to maximize the success of existing and emerging small businesses. Offers business counseling and workshops.

36668 ■ SCORE - Mountain View
4701 Patrick Henry Dr. Mindrome Bldg 25
Santa Clara, CA 95054
URL: http://siliconvalley.score.org/free-business-management-consultants-small-business-owner
Description: Provides professional guidance and information to maximize the success of existing and emerging small businesses. Offers business counseling and workshops.

36669 ■ SCORE - Napa
PO Box 6083
Santa Rosa, CA 95406
URL: http://www.score.org/northcoast
Description: Provides professional guidance and information to maximize the success of existing and emerging small businesses. Offers business counseling and workshops.

36670 ■ SCORE - North Coast
PO Box 6083
Santa Rosa, CA 95406
Free: 800-634-0245
Co. E-mail: help@score.org
URL: http://www.score.org/northcoast
Contact: Bridget Weston, Chief Executive Officer
Facebook: www.facebook.com/SCORENorthCoast
Linkedin: www.linkedin.com/company/score-mentors-north-coast-score
Description: Provides professional guidance and information to maximize the success of existing and emerging small businesses. Offers business counseling and workshops. **Founded:** 1964. **Geographic Preference:** Local.

36671 ■ SCORE - Norwalk, California
Norwalk City Hall - Community Development Office
12700 Norwalk Blvd.
Norwalk, CA 90650
Ph: (626)593-1120
URL: http://eastsangabrielvalley.score.org
Facebook: www.facebook.com/SCOREEastSanGabriel
X (Twitter): x.com/SCORESanGabriel
Description: Provides professional guidance and information to maximize the success of existing and emerging small businesses. Offers business counseling and workshops.

36672 ■ SCORE - Oxnard
400 Esplanade Dr., Ste. 302
Oxnard, CA 93036
Ph: (805)204-6022
URL: http://ventura.score.org
Description: Provides professional guidance and information to maximize the success of existing and emerging small businesses. Offers business counseling and workshops.

36673 ■ SCORE - Palm Desert
73733 Fred Waring Dr.
Palm Desert, CA 92260
URL: http://www.score.org/coachellavalley
Contact: Juan Modesto, Officer
Description: Provides professional guidance and information to maximize the success of existing and emerging small businesses. Offers business counseling and workshops.

36674 ■ SCORE - Palms-Rancho Park Library
2920 Overland Ave.
Los Angeles, CA 90012
Ph: (310)840-2142
Free: 800-634-0245
Co. E-mail: office.0009@scorevolunteer.org
URL: http://losangeles.score.org/score-los-angeles-locations
URL(s): www.lapl.org/branches/palms
Instagram: www.instagram.com/palmsrancholapl
Description: Provides professional guidance and information to maximize the success of existing and emerging small businesses. Offers business counseling and workshops.

36675 ■ SCORE - Palo Alto
Palo Alto, CA

URL: http://siliconvalley.score.org/branch/palo-alto-chamber-commerce
Description: Provides professional guidance and information to maximize the success of existing and emerging small businesses. Offers business counseling and workshops.

36676 ■ SCORE - Pasadena
285 E Walnut St.
Pasadena, CA 91101
Ph: (626)744-4660
URL: http://losangeles.score.org
Description: Provides professional guidance and information to maximize the success of existing and emerging small businesses. Offers business counseling and workshops.

36677 ■ SCORE - Pico Rivera
Pico Rivera City Hall
6615 Passons Blvd.
Pico Rivera, CA 90660
Ph: (626)593-1120
URL: http://eastsangabrielvalley.score.org
Description: Provides professional guidance and information to maximize the success of existing and emerging small businesses. Offers business counseling and workshops.

36678 ■ SCORE - Playa Vista Branch, Los Angeles Public Library
6400 Playa Vista Dr.
Los Angeles, CA 90094
Ph: (310)437-6680
Fax: (310)437-6690
URL: http://www.score.org/losangeles
Contact: Henry Gambill, Senior Librarian
URL(s): www.lapl.org/branches/playa-vista
Description: Provides professional guidance and information to maximize the success of existing and emerging small businesses. Offers business counseling and workshops.

36679 ■ SCORE - Pleasanton
777 Peters Ave.
Pleasanton, CA 94566
URL: http://eastbay.score.org/branch/pleasanton-chamber-commerce
Description: Provides professional guidance and information to maximize the success of existing and emerging small businesses. Offers business counseling and workshops.

36680 ■ SCORE - Redwood City
1450 Veterans Blvd., Ste. 125
Redwood City, CA 94063
Ph: (415)764-4964
URL: http://sanfrancisco.score.org
Description: Provides professional guidance and information to maximize the success of existing and emerging small businesses. Offers business counseling and workshops.

36681 ■ SCORE - Richmond, California
3925 Macdonald Ave.
Richmond, CA 94805
Ph: (510)234-3512
URL: http://eastbay.score.org/find-location?state=CA
Description: Provides professional guidance and information to maximize the success of existing and emerging small businesses. Offers business counseling and workshops.

36682 ■ SCORE - San Diego
8825 Aero Dr., Ste. 101
San Diego, CA 92123
Ph: (858)283-1100
Co. E-mail: score0140@scorevolunteer.org
URL: http://sandiego.score.org
Facebook: www.facebook.com/SCORESanDiego
Linkedin: www.linkedin.com/company/score_2
X (Twitter): x.com/SanDiegoSCORE
Instagram: www.instagram.com/scoresandiego
YouTube: www.youtube.com/user/SanDiegoSCORE
Description: Provides professional guidance and information to maximize the success of existing and emerging small businesses. Offers business counseling and workshops. **Founded:** 1964.

STATE LISTINGS

36683 ■ SCORE - San Francisco
455 Market St., Ste. 600
San Francisco, CA 94105
Ph: (415)764-4964
Fax: (415)744-6750
Co. E-mail: sfscore@sfscore.org
URL: http://sanfrancisco.score.org
Contact: Pete Slosberg, Contact
Facebook: www.facebook.com/
SCORESanFranciscoCA
Linkedin: www.linkedin.com/company/score-mentors-san-francisco
X (Twitter): x.com/sfscore
Description: Provides professional guidance and information to maximize the success of existing and emerging small businesses. Offers business counseling and workshops. **Founded:** 1964. **Geographic Preference:** Local.

36684 ■ SCORE - San Jose
101 W Santa Clara St.
San Jose, CA 95113
Ph: (408)453-6237
URL: http://siliconvalley.score.org
Description: Provides professional guidance and information to maximize the success of existing and emerging small businesses. Offers business counseling and workshops.

36685 ■ SCORE - San Leandro
120 Estudillo Ave.
San Leandro, CA 94577
Ph: (510)317-1400
URL: http://eastbay.score.org
Description: Provides professional guidance and information to maximize the success of existing and emerging small businesses. Offers business counseling and workshops.

36686 ■ SCORE - San Luis Obispo
1228 Broad St.
San Luis Obispo, CA 93401
Ph: (805)547-0779
Co. E-mail: info@sloscore.org
URL: http://sanluisobispo.score.org
Contact: Horace Morana, Chairman
Facebook: www.facebook.com/
SCORESanLuisObispo
Linkedin: www.linkedin.com/company/score-mentors-san-luis-obispo
Description: Provides professional guidance and information to maximize the success of existing and emerging small businesses. Offers business counseling and workshops. **Founded:** 1964. **Educational Activities:** SCORE San Luis Obispo General assembly. **Geographic Preference:** Local.

36687 ■ SCORE - San Mateo
455 market St., Ste. 600
San Francisco, CA 94105
Ph: (415)764-4964
Fax: (415)744-6750
Co. E-mail: sfscore@sfscore.org
URL: http://sanfrancisco.score.org
Description: Provides professional guidance and information to maximize the success of existing and emerging small businesses. Offers business counseling and workshops.

36688 ■ SCORE - San Rafael
San Rafael, CA
URL: http://sanfrancisco.score.org
Contact: Art S. Leaffer, Contact
Description: Provides professional guidance and information to maximize the success of existing and emerging small businesses. Offers business counseling and workshops.

36689 ■ SCORE - Santa Ana
3631 S Harbor Blvd.
Santa Ana, CA 92704
Ph: (714)550-7369
URL: http://orangecounty.score.org/contact-orange-county-score
Description: Provides professional guidance and information to maximize the success of existing and emerging small businesses. Offers business counseling and workshops.

36690 ■ SCORE - Santa Barbara
PO Box 30602
Santa Barbara, CA 93101
Ph: (805)367-3292
Co. E-mail: info.sb@scorevolunteer.org
URL: http://www.score.org/santabarbara
Facebook: www.facebook.com/scoresantabarbara
Linkedin: www.linkedin.com/company/score-mentors-santa-barbara
Description: Provides professional guidance and information to maximize the success of existing and emerging small businesses. Offers business counseling and workshops. **Founded:** 1964. **Geographic Preference:** Local.

36691 ■ SCORE - Santa Clara
c/o San Jose Chamber of Commerce, PO Box 149
San Jose, CA 95103
Ph: (408)453-6237
URL: http://www.score.org/siliconvalley
Description: Provides professional guidance and information to maximize the success of existing and emerging small businesses. Offers business counseling and workshops.

36692 ■ SCORE - Santa Maria
1228 Broad St.
San Luis Obispo, CA 93401
Ph: (805)547-0779
Co. E-mail: info@sloscore.org
URL: http://sanluisobispo.score.org
Linkedin: www.linkedin.com/company/score-mentors-san-luis-obispo
X (Twitter): x.com/SCORESanLuisObi
Description: Provides professional guidance and information to maximize the success of existing and emerging small businesses. Offers business counseling and workshops.

36693 ■ SCORE - Santa Monica
1234 6th St.
Santa Monica, CA 90401
Ph: (310)393-9825
URL: http://losangeles.score.org/score-los-angeles-locations
Description: Provides professional guidance and information to maximize the success of existing and emerging small businesses. Offers business counseling and workshops.

36694 ■ SCORE - Santa Monica Public Library
601 Santa Monica Blvd.
Santa Monica, CA 90401
URL: http://losangeles.score.org/score-los-angeles-locations
Description: Provides professional guidance and information to maximize the success of existing and emerging small businesses. Offers business counseling and workshops.

36695 ■ SCORE - Saratoga
Saratoga, CA
URL: http://www.score.org/northeastny
Description: Provides professional guidance and information to maximize the success of existing and emerging small businesses. Offers business counseling and workshops.

36696 ■ SCORE - Silicon Valley - Business Library
c/o San Jose Chamber of Commerce, PO Box 149
San Jose, CA 95103
Ph: (408)453-6237
Co. E-mail: siliconvalley@scorevolunteer.org
URL: http://www.score.org/siliconvalley
Contact: Nader Radjy, Contact
Facebook: www.facebook.com/SCORESiliconValley
Linkedin: www.linkedin.com/company/silicon-valley-score
Description: Helps small business owners solve business challenges two ways: individual consulting sessions and educational programs. **Scope:** Small business. **Founded:** 1964. **Holdings:** Books and periodicals. **Geographic Preference:** Local.

36697 ■ SCORE - Simi Valley Chamber of Commerce
40 W Cochran St., Ste. 100
Simi Valley, CA 93065
Ph: (805)204-6022
Co. E-mail: info@simichamber.org
URL: http://www.simivalleychamber.org/business-resources.html
Contact: Kathi van Etten, President
Facebook: www.facebook.com/simi.chamber
Linkedin: www.linkedin.com/company/simi-valley-chamber-of-commerce/about
X (Twitter): x.com/home?lang=en
Instagram: www.instagram.com/simivalleychamber
YouTube: www.youtube.com/channel/UCEoTaotfTdXKKxG2xu1_H-w
Description: Provides professional guidance and information to maximize the success of existing and emerging small businesses. Offers business counseling and workshops.

36698 ■ SCORE - Simi Valley Public Library
2969 TaPO Canyon Rd.
Simi Valley, CA 93063
Ph: (805)526-1735
URL: http://ventura.score.org/resource/ventura-county-library-locations
Description: Provides professional guidance and information to maximize the success of existing and emerging small businesses. Offers business counseling and workshops.

36699 ■ SCORE - Sonora
197 Mono Way, Ste. B
Tuolumne County Chamber of Commerce
Sonora, CA 95370
Ph: (209)532-4316
Fax: (209)532-8068
Co. E-mail: tuolumnecountyscore@gmail.com
URL: http://tuolumnecounty.score.org
Contact: Bridget Weston, Chief Executive Officer
Facebook: www.facebook.com/
SCORETuolumneCounty
Description: Provides professional guidance and information to maximize the success of existing and emerging small businesses. Offers business counseling and workshops.

36700 ■ SCORE - Sunnyvale
CA
URL: http://www.score.org/siliconvalley/profile/ramesh-nair
Description: Provides professional guidance and information to maximize the success of existing and emerging small businesses. Offers business counseling and workshops.

36701 ■ SCORE - The Workplace Pacific Gateway
4811 Airport Plaza Dr., Ste. 200
Long Beach, CA 90815
URL: http://longbeach.score.org
Description: Provides professional guidance and information to maximize the success of existing and emerging small businesses. Offers business counseling and workshops.

36702 ■ SCORE - University of Southern California
3601 Trousdale Pky., Ste. 110
Los Angeles, CA 90089
Ph: (213)740-9104
URL: http://losangeles.score.org
Description: Provides professional guidance and information to maximize the success of existing and emerging small businesses. Offers business counseling and workshops.

36703 ■ SCORE - Vallejo
CA

URL: http://eastbay.score.org/branch/vallejo-chamber-commerce
Description: Provides professional guidance and information to maximize the success of existing and emerging small businesses. Offers business counseling and workshops.

36704 ■ SCORE - Ventura County
638 Lindero Canyon Rd., Ste. 300
Oak Park, CA 91377
Ph: (805)204-6022
Co. E-mail: admin.0255@scorevolunteer.org
URL: http://ventura.score.org
Facebook: www.facebook.com/SCOREVentura
Linkedin: www.linkedin.com/company/score-mentors-ventura-county
X (Twitter): x.com/VenturaSCORE
YouTube: www.youtube.com/user/VenturaSCORE
Description: Provides professional guidance and information to maximize the success of existing and emerging small businesses. Offers business counseling and workshops. **Founded:** 1971. **Geographic Preference:** Local.

36705 ■ SCORE - Walnut Creek
College of alameda-555 Ralpa Appezzata PKYW
Cougar Village Rm. 225
Alameda, CA 94501
Ph: (510)273-6611
URL: http://eastbay.score.org/branch/walnut-creek-chamber-commerce
Description: Provides professional guidance and information to maximize the success of existing and emerging small businesses. Offers business counseling and workshops.

36706 ■ SCORE - West Covina
West Covina City Hall
1444 W Garvey Ave.
West Covina, CA 91790
Ph: (626)593-1120
URL: http://www.westcovina.org/departments/community-development/community-and-economic-development/economic-development/score
Facebook: www.facebook.com/WestCovinaCity
Linkedin: www.linkedin.com/company/city-of-west-covina
X (Twitter): twitter.com/westcovinacity
Instagram: www.instagram.com/westcovinacity
Description: Provides professional guidance and information to maximize the success of existing and emerging small businesses. Offers business counseling and workshops. **Founded:** 1923.

36707 ■ SCORE - West Hollywood
8272 Santa Moncia Blvd.
West Hollywood, CA 90046
Ph: (323)650-2688
URL: http://losangeles.score.org
Description: Provides professional guidance and information to maximize the success of existing and emerging small businesses. Offers business counseling and workshops.

36708 ■ SCORE - Westlake Village
600 Hampshire Rd., Ste. 200
Westlake Village, CA 91361-2571
Ph: (805)370-0035
Fax: (805)370-1083
Co. E-mail: info@towlvchamber.org
URL: http://ventura.score.org/resource/local-chambers-commerce
Description: Provides professional guidance and information to maximize the success of existing and emerging small businesses. Offers business counseling and workshops.

36709 ■ SCORE - Whittier
Whittier Chamber of Commerce
8158 Painter Ave.
Whittier, CA 90602
Ph: (626)593-1120
URL: http://eastsangabrielvalley.score.org
Facebook: www.facebook.com/SCOREEastSanGabriel
X (Twitter): x.com/SCORESanGabriel

Description: Provides professional guidance and information to maximize the success of existing and emerging small businesses. Offers business counseling and workshops.

36710 ■ SCORE - Woodland Hills
6100 Topanga Canyon Blvd.
Woodland Hills, CA 91367
Ph: (818)347-4737
URL: http://losangeles.score.org
Contact: Bridget Weston, Chief Executive Officer
Facebook: www.facebook.com/SCORELosAngeles
Linkedin: www.linkedin.com/company/score-greater-los-angeles
X (Twitter): twitter.com/scorelosangeles
Description: Provides professional guidance and information to maximize the success of existing and emerging small businesses. Offers business counseling and workshops.

BETTER BUSINESS BUREAUS

36711 ■ Better Business Bureau of Central California
2600 W Shaw Ln.
Fresno, CA 93711-2767
Contact: Coleman Blair Looney, Contact
Description: Seeks to promote and foster ethical relationship between businesses and the public through voluntary self-regulation, consumer and business education, and service excellence. Provides information to help consumers and businesses make informed purchasing decisions and avoid costly scams and frauds; settles consumer complaints through arbitration and other means. **Founded:** 1950. **Geographic Preference:** Local.

36712 ■ Better Business Bureau of Los Angeles and Silicon Valley (BBBLASV)
835 Wilshire Blvd., No. 600
Los Angeles, CA 90017
Ph: (408)278-7400
Fax: (213)630-3410
Co. E-mail: info@lasvbbb.org
URL: http://www.bbb.org/local-bbb/bbb-of-los-angeles-and-silicon-valley
Facebook: www.facebook.com/BBBLASV
Linkedin: www.linkedin.com/showcase/los-angeles-silicon-valley-bbb
X (Twitter): x.com/BBBLASV
Instagram: www.instagram.com/bbblasv
YouTube: www.youtube.com/channel/UCIgQKPOMsWr9uwDgaC_s0gw
Description: Seeks to promote and foster the highest ethical relationship between businesses and the public through voluntary self-regulation, consumer and business education, and service excellence. Provides information to help consumers and businesses make informed purchasing decisions and avoid costly scams and frauds; settles consumer complaints through arbitration and other means. **Founded:** 1912. **Geographic Preference:** Local.

36713 ■ Better Business Bureau of Northeast California
10399 Old Placerville Rd.
Sacramento, CA 95827
Ph: (916)443-6843
Co. E-mail: info@necal.bbb.org
URL: http://www.bbb.org/local-bbb/bbb-of-northeast-california
Description: Seeks to promote and foster ethical relationship between businesses and the public through voluntary self-regulation, consumer and business education, and service excellence. Provides information to help consumers and businesses make informed purchasing decisions and avoid costly scams and frauds; settles consumer complaints through arbitration and other means. **Founded:** 1937. **Geographic Preference:** Local.

36714 ■ Better Business Bureau of San Mateo County
San Mateo, CA
URL: http://www.bbb.org/us/ca/san-mateo

Description: Seeks to promote and foster ethical relationship between businesses and the public through voluntary self-regulation, consumer and business education, and service excellence. Provides information to help consumers and businesses make informed purchasing decisions and avoid costly scams and frauds; settles consumer complaints through arbitration and other means. **Founded:** 1912. **Geographic Preference:** Regional; Local.

36715 ■ Better Business Bureau of Tri-Counties
211 E Victoria St., Ste. A
Santa Barbara, CA 93101
Ph: (805)963-8657
Co. E-mail: info@santabarbara.bbb.org
URL: http://www.bbb.org/local-bbb/bbb-of-the-tri-counties
Contact: Richard Copelan, Co-President Co-Chief Executive Officer
Facebook: www.facebook.com/bbbtricounties
Linkedin: www.linkedin.com/company/better-business-bureau-of-the-tri-counties
X (Twitter): x.com/bbbtricounties
Instagram: www.instagram.com/bbbtricounties
Description: Seeks to promote and foster ethical relationship between businesses and the public through voluntary self-regulation, consumer and business education, and service excellence. Provides information to help consumers and businesses make informed purchasing decisions and avoid costly scams and frauds; settles consumer complaints through arbitration and other means. **Founded:** 1945. **Geographic Preference:** Regional.

36716 ■ Business Consumer Alliance (BCA)
315 N La Cadena Dr.
Colton, CA 92324
Ph: (909)825-7280
Fax: (909)825-6246
Co. E-mail: info@checkbca.org
URL: http://www.checkbca.org
Contact: Kiry Peng, Chief Executive Officer
Facebook: www.facebook.com/businessconsumeralliance
Description: Promotes the ethical relationship between businesses and the public through voluntary self-regulation, consumer and business education, and service excellence. Provides information to help consumers and businesses make informed purchasing decisions and avoid costly scams and frauds; settles consumer complaints through arbitration and other means. **Founded:** 1928. **Geographic Preference:** North America.

36717 ■ *Consumer Guide*
URL(s): www.bbb.org/mbc/programs-services/consumer-guide
Released: Semiannual **Description:** Contains consumer information and membership directory. **Availability:** Print; Download; Online.

CHAMBERS OF COMMERCE

36718 ■ Acton-Agua Dulce Chamber of Commerce
PO Box 74
Acton, CA 93510
URL: http://www.actonaguadulceartscouncil.com/about.html
Contact: Paula Bradley, President
Description: Promotes Acton and its trade areas through educational, economic, legislative, civic, social and cultural programs and affairs. **Founded:** 1954. **Geographic Preference:** Local.

36719 ■ Alameda Chamber of Commerce - Library
2215-A S Shore Ctr.
Alameda, CA 94501
Ph: (510)522-0414
Co. E-mail: madlen@alamedachamber.com
URL: http://www.alamedachamber.com
Contact: Kelly E. Lux, Chairman
YouTube: www.youtube.com/channel/UCOj-SvHBTAfAY-_-WDsnSDQ

STATE LISTINGS

Description: Promotes business and community development in Alameda, CA. **Scope:** Craft. **Founded:** 1929. **Publications:** *Business Alameda Style* (Monthly). **Geographic Preference:** Local.

36720 ■ *Alert*
1215 K St., Ste. 1400
Sacramento, CA 95814
Ph: (916)444-6670
Free: 800-649-4921
Fax: (916)325-1272
Co. E-mail: techsupport@calchamber.com
URL: http://www.calchamber.com
Contact: Jennifer Barrera, President
URL(s): www.calchamber.com/free-newsletters
-signup?_gl=1*17qm8yg*_ga*MjA3NDQ1NjU3OC
4xNzE1NzY3NTg4*_ga_3K6SXWSVRP*MTcxNTc
2NzU4Ny4xLjEuMTcxNTc2NzY3OC4zNi4wLjA.
Released: Weekly; during legislative session. **Availability:** Print; PDF; Online.

36721 ■ Alhambra Chamber of Commerce
104 S 1st St.
Alhambra, CA 91801
Ph: (626)282-8481
Co. E-mail: ceo@alhambrachamber.org
URL: http://www.alhambrachamber.org
Contact: John Bwarie, Chief Executive Officer
E-mail: ceo@alhambrachamber.org
Facebook: www.facebook.com/
alhambrachamberofcommerce
X (Twitter): x.com/alhchamber
Instagram: www.instagram.com/alhambrachamber
Description: Works to encourage a strong local economy by promoting sound government and an informed membership and community. **Founded:** 1904. **Publications:** *Around Alhambra* (Monthly); *Alhambra Chamber of Commerce--Membership Directory* (Semiannual). **Educational Activities:** Business After Hours Mixers (Monthly). **Awards:** Alhambra Beautiful Award (Annual). **Geographic Preference:** Local.

36722 ■ Alpine Chamber of Commerce
1620 Alpine Blvd., Ste. 208
Alpine, CA 91901
Ph: (619)445-2722
Co. E-mail: info@alpinechamber.com
URL: http://www.alpinechamber.com
Contact: Chris Wiley, Chairman of the Board
Facebook: www.facebook.com/VisitAlpine
Linkedin: www.linkedin.com/company/alpinechamber
X (Twitter): x.com/alpinemtnchamb1
Instagram: www.instagram.com/visitalpine
Description: Works to advance the commercial, industrial, civic, agricultural, and general interest and prosperity of the community of Alpine and the East County region. **Founded:** 1961. **Geographic Preference:** Local.

36723 ■ Alpine County Chamber of Commerce (ACCC)
3 Webster St.
Markleeville, CA 96120
Ph: (530)694-2475
Co. E-mail: info@alpinecounty.com
URL: http://alpinecounty.com
Contact: Mark Schwartz, President
Facebook: www.facebook.com/VisitAlpineCounty
Instagram: www.instagram.com/alpinecoun
tychamber
YouTube: www.youtube.com/channel/UCVmF9DNj
tbgAqoWNi0qwVow
Description: Promotes business and community development in Alpine County, CA. Sponsors charitable events. **Founded:** 1928. **Geographic Preference:** Local.

36724 ■ Altadena Chamber of Commerce (ACC)
Altadena Community Ctr. Bldg.
730 E Altadena Dr.
Altadena, CA 91001
Ph: (626)794-3988
Co. E-mail: office@altadenachamber.org
URL: http://www.altadenachamber.org
Contact: Sandra Thomas, President

Facebook: www.facebook.com/AltadenaChamber
Description: Promotes commercial, industrial, civic, and general interests of the community of Altadena and its trade area. **Founded:** 1924. **Awards:** Altadena Chamber of Commerce Citizen of the Year (Annual). **Geographic Preference:** Local.

36725 ■ Alturas Chamber of Commerce
600 S Main St.
Alturas, CA 96101
Ph: (530)233-4434
Co. E-mail: alturaschamber@gmail.com
URL: http://alturaschamber.org
Facebook: www.facebook.com/profile.php
Description: Promotes business and community development in the Modoc County, CA area. **Founded:** 1992. **Geographic Preference:** Local.

36726 ■ Amador County Chamber of Commerce and Visitors Bureau
1 Prosperity Ct.
Sutter Creek, CA 95685
URL: http://amadorcountychamber.com
Description: Promotes business and community development in Amador County, CA. **Publications:** *Chamber News*. **Educational Activities:** Mixers. **Geographic Preference:** Local.

36727 ■ *Anaheim Business Advocate*
2099 S State College Blvd., Ste. 650
Anaheim, CA 92806
Ph: (714)758-0222
Fax: (714)758-0468
Co. E-mail: info@anaheimchamber.org
URL: http://www.anaheimchamber.org
Contact: Laura Cunningham, President
E-mail: laura@anaheimchamber.org
URL(s): www.anaheimchamber.org/newsletter
Released: Weekly **Availability:** Online.

36728 ■ Anaheim Chamber of Commerce
2099 S State College Blvd., Ste. 650
Anaheim, CA 92806
Ph: (714)758-0222
Fax: (714)758-0468
Co. E-mail: info@anaheimchamber.org
URL: http://www.anaheimchamber.org
Contact: Laura Cunningham, President
E-mail: laura@anaheimchamber.org
Facebook: www.facebook.com/AnaheimChamber
X (Twitter): x.com/AnaheimChamber
YouTube: www.youtube.com/user/AnaheimChamber
Description: Works to promote and support healthy diverse and broad-based economic growth in Anaheim. **Founded:** 1895. **Publications:** *Anaheim Business Advocate* (Weekly). **Geographic Preference:** Local.

36729 ■ Anderson Valley Chamber of Commerce
PO Box 275
Boonville, CA 95415
Ph: (707)895-2379
Co. E-mail: andersonvalleychamber@gmail.com
URL: http://www.andersonvalleychamber.com
Contact: Arline P. Bloom, Contact
Facebook: www.facebook.com/An
dersonValleyChamber
Description: Promotes business and community development in the Anderson Valley, CA. **Geographic Preference:** Local.

36730 ■ Angwin Community Council
PO Box 747
Angwin, CA 94508-0747
Ph: (707)965-1967
URL: http://www.uschamber.com/co/chambers/california/angwin
Description: Provides community service and representation to Angwin village and its citizen. **Geographic Preference:** Local.

36731 ■ Antioch Chamber of Commerce
101 H St., Unit. 4
Antioch, CA 94509
Ph: (925)757-1800
Fax: (925)757-5286

URL: http://antiochchamber.com
Contact: Daniel H. Sohn, Chief Executive Officer
Facebook: www.facebook.com/AntiochChamber
Description: Promotes business and community development in Antioch, CA. **Founded:** 1938. **Publications:** *The Voice of Business* (Monthly). **Geographic Preference:** Local.

36732 ■ Aptos Chamber of Commerce
7605-A Old Dominion Ct.
Aptos, CA 95003
Ph: (831)688-1467
Co. E-mail: info@aptoschamber.com
URL: http://aptoschamber.com
Contact: Karen Hibble, Contact
Facebook: www.facebook.com/Ap
tosChamberOfCommerce
Linkedin: www.linkedin.com/company/aptos-chamber
-of-commerce
X (Twitter): x.com/AptosChamber
Instagram: www.instagram.com/AptosChamber
Description: Promotes business and community development in Aptos, CA. **Publications:** *Business Bulletin*. **Geographic Preference:** Local.

36733 ■ *Arcadia California*
388 W Huntington Dr.
Arcadia, CA 91007
Ph: (626)447-2159
Co. E-mail: info@arcadiacachamber.org
URL: http://arcadiacachamber.org
Contact: Vicki Knight, President
URL(s): arcadiacachamber.org/about
Released: Biennial **Availability:** Print.

36734 ■ Arcadia Chamber of Commerce (ACC)
388 W Huntington Dr.
Arcadia, CA 91007
Ph: (626)447-2159
Co. E-mail: info@arcadiacachamber.org
URL: http://arcadiacachamber.org
Contact: Vicki Knight, President
Facebook: www.facebook.com/ArcadiaChamber
X (Twitter): x.com/ArcadiaChamber
Instagram: www.instagram.com/arcadiachamber
YouTube: www.youtube.com/user/TheArca
diaChamber
Description: Works to maintain a healthy business environment, contributes to the economic growth and to enhance the city's image. **Founded:** 1903. **Publications:** *Business Directory* (Biennial); *Arcadia California* (Biennial); *The Power of Connection* (Monthly). **Educational Activities:** Business Expo; Networking Breakfast (Monthly); Planning Conference (Annual). **Geographic Preference:** Local.

36735 ■ Arcata Chamber of Commerce (AACC)
1635 Heindon Rd.
Arcata, CA 95521
Ph: (707)822-3619
Co. E-mail: arcata@arcatachamber.com
URL: http://www.arcatachamber.com
Contact: Molly Steele, Executive Director
Facebook: www.facebook.com/arca
tachamberofcommerce
Instagram: www.instagram.com/arcatachamber
Description: Promotes business, tourism, and community development in Arcata, CA. Sponsors Fourth of July Jubilee. **Founded:** 1905. **Geographic Preference:** Local.

36736 ■ *Around Alhambra*
104 S 1st St.
Alhambra, CA 91801
Ph: (626)282-8481
Co. E-mail: ceo@alhambrachamber.org
URL: http://www.alhambrachamber.org
Contact: John Bwarie, Chief Executive Officer
E-mail: ceo@alhambrachamber.org
URL(s): www.alhambrachamber.org/Aroun
d-Alhambra
Released: Monthly **Description:** Features articles and events of the chamber and school district developments. **Availability:** Print; Online; Download; PDF.

36737 ■ Arvin Chamber of Commerce
PO Box 645
Arvin, CA 93203
Ph: (661)854-2265
Co. E-mail: arvinchamberofcommerce@yahoo.com
URL: http://www.arvinchamberofcommerce.com
Contact: Mark Marquez, President
Description: Promotes business and community development in Arvin, CA. **Geographic Preference:** Local.

36738 ■ Atascadero Chamber of Commerce
6907 El Camino Real, Ste. A
Atascadero, CA 93422
Ph: (805)466-2044
Co. E-mail: info@atascaderochamber.org
URL: http://www.atascaderochamber.org
Contact: Josh Cross, President
E-mail: josh@atascaderochamber.org
Facebook: www.facebook.com/atascaderochamberofcommerce
X (Twitter): x.com/atownchamber
Instagram: www.instagram.com/atascadero_chamber
Description: Promotes business and community development in Atascadero, CA. **Founded:** 1926. **Publications:** Business Reporter (11/year). **Geographic Preference:** Local.

36739 ■ Atwater Chamber of Commerce
1181 3rd St.
Atwater, CA 95301
Ph: (209)358-4251
Co. E-mail: info@atwaterchamberofcommerce.com
URL: http://www.atwaterchamberofcommerce.com
Contact: Don Borgwardt, President
E-mail: donb547@gmail.com
Description: Promotes business and community development in Atwater, CA. Sponsors fall festival. **Geographic Preference:** Local.

36740 ■ Auburn Chamber of Commerce (ACC)
1103 High, Ste. S 100
Auburn, CA 95603
Ph: (530)885-5616
Co. E-mail: info@auburnchamber.net
URL: http://www.auburnchamber.net
Contact: Gary Gilligan, President
Facebook: www.facebook.com/AuburnChamberofCommerce
X (Twitter): x.com/AuburnCAChamber
Instagram: www.instagram.com/auburnchamberofcommerce
Description: Promotes business, community, and economic development. **Founded:** 1906. **Publications:** Auburn Advantage (Quarterly). **Awards:** Auburn Chamber of Commerce Business of the Year (Annual). **Geographic Preference:** Local.

36741 ■ Azusa Chamber of Commerce
240 W Foothill Blvd.
Azusa, CA 91702
Ph: (626)334-1507
Fax: (626)334-5217
Co. E-mail: info@azusachamber.org
URL: http://www.azusachamber.org
Contact: Steven Castro, Chief Executive Officer
E-mail: steven@azusachamber.org
Facebook: www.facebook.com/AzusaChamberOfCommerce
Linkedin: www.linkedin.com/company/azusa-chamber-of-commerce
X (Twitter): x.com/AzusaChamber
Instagram: www.instagram.com/azusachamber
Description: Works to serve as a catalyst in transformation of business and economic climate, resulting in a healthier, more prosperous Azusa. **Publications:** Azusa Factbook (Periodic); The Azusan (Quarterly). **Geographic Preference:** Local.

36742 ■ Banning Chamber of Commerce
60 E Ramsey St.
Banning, CA 92220
Ph: (951)849-4695
Co. E-mail: info@thebanningchamber.com
URL: http://www.thebanningchamber.com
Facebook: www.facebook.com/banningchamberofcommerce
Instagram: www.instagram.com/banning_chamber1
Description: Advocates the commercial, industrial, civic and general interests of the City of Banning and the San Gorgonio Pass. **Founded:** 1928. **Publications:** Banning Mail Pouch (Monthly). **Geographic Preference:** Local.

36743 ■ Barstow Area Chamber of Commerce (BACC)
229 E Main St.
Barstow, CA 92311
Ph: (760)256-8617
Co. E-mail: bacc@barstowchamber.com
URL: http://barstowchamber.com
Contact: Eugene Butticci, Executive Director
E-mail: eugene.butticci@barstowchamber.com
X (Twitter): x.com/BarstowChamber
Description: Seeks to foster a better community by providing leadership which promotes economic success and enriches the quality of life. Sponsors leadership program, military mixer, community awards banquet, golf tournament, procurement seminar, and summer street festival. **Founded:** 1907. **Geographic Preference:** Local.

36744 ■ Bass Lake Chamber of Commerce
PO Box 126
Bass Lake, CA 93604
Ph: (559)642-3676
Co. E-mail: chamber@basslakechamber.com
URL: http://www.basslakechamber.com
Contact: Theresa Wilson, President
Facebook: www.facebook.com/basslakechamber
Description: Promotes business and community development in Bass Lake, CA. Sponsors local festival; holds competitions. Publications: none. **Founded:** 1976. **Geographic Preference:** Local.

36745 ■ Beaumont Chamber of Commerce
726 Beaumont Ave.
Beaumont, CA 92223
Ph: (951)845-9541
URL: http://www.beaumontcachamber.com
Contact: Sandy DeLeon, President
Facebook: www.facebook.com/BeaumontChamber
X (Twitter): x.com/BeaumontCA_CoC
Description: Works to help small business grow and succeed. Creates and maintains a climate for business growth and strong quality of life, serves as business advocate in city and provides credibility for business through association. **Founded:** 1954. **Geographic Preference:** Local.

36746 ■ Belmont Chamber of Commerce
1059A Alameda de las Pulgas
Belmont, CA 94002
Contact: Mary Morrissey Morrissey Parden, Contact
Description: Promotes business and community development in Belmont, CA. **Geographic Preference:** Local.

36747 ■ Benicia Chamber of Commerce and Visitors' Center [Benicia Chamber of Commerce]
601 1st St., Ste. 100
Benicia, CA 94510
Ph: (707)745-2120
Co. E-mail: info@beniciachamber.com
URL: http://www.beniciachamber.com
Contact: Carey Morgan, Chairman of the Board
Description: Promotes business and community development in Benicia, CA. **Founded:** 1847. **Geographic Preference:** Local.

36748 ■ Berkeley Chamber of Commerce
1834 University Ave.
Berkeley, CA 94703
Ph: (510)549-7000
Co. E-mail: info@berkeleychamber.com
URL: http://www.berkeleychamber.com
Contact: Fred Fassett, Chairman
Facebook: www.facebook.com/BerkeleyChamberofCommerce
Linkedin: www.linkedin.com/company/7064149
X (Twitter): x.com/berkeleycachamb
Instagram: www.instagram.com/berkeleychamber
Description: Works to represent Berkeley's business interests. Strives to join with the general community to promote understanding and act on issues of common concern. **Founded:** 1901. **Publications:** Berkeley Business Advocate (Bimonthly); BRJCC Directory (Annual). **Geographic Preference:** Local.

36749 ■ Bethel Island Chamber of Commerce
6163 Bethel Island Rd.
Bethel Island, CA 94511
Ph: (925)684-3220
Fax: (925)684-9025
Co. E-mail: bicc@bethelisland-chamber.com
URL: http://www.bethelisland-chamber.com
Contact: Andy Rowland, President
E-mail: andy.h.rowland@gmail.com
Description: Promotes business and community development in Bethel Island, CA. **Geographic Preference:** Local.

36750 ■ Beverly Hills Chamber of Commerce
9400 S Santa Monica Blvd., 2nd Fl.
Beverly Hills, CA 90210
Ph: (310)248-1000
Fax: (310)248-1020
Co. E-mail: info@beverlyhillschamber.com
URL: http://www.beverlyhillschamber.com
Contact: Farimah Fayyad, Chief Financial Officer
E-mail: fayyad@beverlyhillschamber.com
Facebook: www.facebook.com/BH.Chamber
Linkedin: www.linkedin.com/company/beverly-hills-chamber-of-commerce
X (Twitter): x.com/BH_Chamber
Instagram: www.instagram.com/bh_chamber
YouTube: www.youtube.com/channel/UCUjgC7AP6rYimmpikxH5-cw
Description: Promotes Beverly Hills businesses through marketing, advocacy, and education. **Founded:** 1923. **Geographic Preference:** Local.

36751 ■ Big Bear Chamber of Commerce
630 Bartlett Rd.
Big Bear Lake, CA 92315
Ph: (909)866-4607
Co. E-mail: contact@bigbearchamber.com
URL: http://www.bigbearchamber.com
Contact: Ellen Clarke, Executive Director
Facebook: www.facebook.com/bigbearchamberofcommerce
X (Twitter): x.com/BigBearChamber
Instagram: www.instagram.com/bblchamber
YouTube: www.youtube.com/user/bigbearchamber
Description: Promotes business and community development in the Big Bear Lake, CA area. **Founded:** 1947. **Publications:** Bear Valley Review (Periodic). **Geographic Preference:** Local.

36752 ■ Bishop Area Chamber of Commerce and Visitors Bureau
690 N Main St.
Bishop, CA 93514
Ph: (760)873-8405
Co. E-mail: info@bishopvisitor.com
URL: http://bishopvisitor.com
Facebook: www.facebook.com/visitBishop
X (Twitter): x.com/visitbishop
Instagram: www.instagram.com/visitbishop
YouTube: www.youtube.com/channel/UC9wcKJKf3OhFaVMb_LNJOWw
Pinterest: www.pinterest.com/visitbishop
Description: Promotes business, tourism, and community development in Bishop, CA. **Publications:** Bishop Chamber Bulletin (Quarterly). **Awards:** Bishop Chamber of Commerce Outstanding Citizen of the Year (Annual). **Geographic Preference:** Local.

36753 ■ Black Business Association (BBA)
PO Box 43159
Los Angeles, CA 90043
Ph: (323)291-9334
Fax: (323)291-7820
Co. E-mail: mail@bbala.org
URL: http://www.bbala.org
Contact: Sarah R. Harris, President
Facebook: www.facebook.com/BlackBusinessAssociation

STATE LISTINGS

California ■ 36773

Linkedin: www.linkedin.com/in/black-business
-association-3790a0b9
X (Twitter): x.com/BBANews
Instagram: www.instagram.com/
blackbusinessassociation
YouTube: www.youtube.com/user/
BlackBusinessAssoc
Description: Represents the interests of black-owned business entrepreneurs. **Founded:** 1970. **Geographic Preference:** Local.

36754 ■ Bonsall Chamber of Commerce
5256 S Mission Rd., Ste. 311
Bonsall, CA 92003
Ph: (760)630-1933
Co. E-mail: admin@bonsallchamber.org
URL: http://www.bonsallchamber.org
Contact: Marie Waldron, Contact
Facebook: www.facebook.com/
BonsallChamberofCommerce
Linkedin: www.linkedin.com/in/bonsall-chamber-of
-commerce-83053725
Description: Promotes business and community development in Bonsall, CA area. **Founded:** 1990. **Geographic Preference:** Local.

36755 ■ Boron Chamber of Commerce
26962 Twenty Mule Team Rd.
Boron, CA 93516-1560
Ph: (760)762-5810
URL: http://www.uschamber.com/co/chambers/california/boron
Description: Promotes business and community development in Boron, CA. **Founded:** 1953. **Geographic Preference:** Local.

36756 ■ Borrego Springs Chamber of Commerce
786 Palm Canyon Dr.
Borrego Springs, CA 92004-0420
Ph: (760)767-5555
Fax: (760)767-5976
Co. E-mail: info@borregospringschamber.com
URL: http://www.borregospringschamber.com
Contact: Clint Brandin, President
Facebook: www.facebook.com/BorregoSprings
Instagram: www.instagram.com/embraceborrego
YouTube: www.youtube.com/channel/UCBWixdvC
46vae6ZlOIOfXPQ/about
Description: Promotes business, tourism, and community development in Borrego Springs, CA. **Founded:** 1949. **Publications:** Chamber Views (Bimonthly). **Geographic Preference:** Local.

36757 ■ Brawley Chamber of Commerce
204 S Imperial Ave.
Brawley, CA 92227
Ph: (760)344-3160
URL: http://www.brawleychamber.com
Contact: Dr. Kathleen Lang, President
Facebook: www.facebook.com/BrawleyChamber
Description: Promotes business and community development in the Brawley, CA area. Sponsors Brawley Cattle Call Festival. **Founded:** 1904. **Publications:** Brawley Update (Monthly). **Geographic Preference:** Local.

36758 ■ Brea Chamber of Commerce (BCC)
1 Civic Center Cir., 2nd Fl.
Brea, CA 92821
Ph: (714)529-3660
Fax: (714)529-3657
Co. E-mail: answers@breachamber.com
URL: http://www.breachamber.com
Contact: Lacy Schoen, President
E-mail: lacy@breachamber.com
Facebook: www.facebook.com/breachamber
Linkedin: www.linkedin.com/company/breachamber
X (Twitter): x.com/breachamber
YouTube: www.youtube.com/channel/UC7KrpFiIR
-RsO_o_ApYb82w
Description: Promotes business and community development in Brea, CA. **Founded:** 1913. **Publications:** Business Directory. **Geographic Preference:** Local.

36759 ■ Brentwood Chamber of Commerce
35 Oak St.
Brentwood, CA 94513
Ph: (925)634-3344
Fax: (925)634-3759
Co. E-mail: info@brentwoodchamber.com
URL: http://www.brentwoodchamber.com
Contact: Tom Santamorena, Owner
Linkedin: www.linkedin.com/company/brentwood-ca
-chamber-of-commerce
X (Twitter): x.com/BrentwoodCoC
Instagram: www.instagram.com/brentwoodcoc
Description: Promotes business and community development in eastern Contra Costa County, CA. Conducts mixers, festivals, and parades; bestows Citizen of the Year Award. **Founded:** 1952. **Publications:** The Clarion (Monthly). **Geographic Preference:** Local.

36760 ■ Bridgeport Chamber of Commerce
PO Box 541
Bridgeport, CA 93517
Ph: (760)932-7500
URL: http://bridgeportcalifornia.com
Description: Promotes business and community development in Bridgeport, CA. **Geographic Preference:** Local.

36761 ■ Brisbane Chamber of Commerce
50 Pk. Pl., 2nd Fl.
Brisbane, CA 94005
Ph: (415)467-7283
Co. E-mail: madison@brisbanechamber.org
URL: http://brisbanechamber.org
Contact: Madison Davis, President
Description: Provides support and services to enhance business and residential community in Brisbane. **Founded:** 1944. **Publications:** The Luminary (Monthly). **Geographic Preference:** Local.

36762 ■ Buena Park Map
URL(s): www.wocrcoc.org
Released: every 18 months. **Availability:** Print.

36763 ■ Burbank Chamber of Commerce
200 W Magnolia Blvd.
Burbank, CA 91502
Ph: (818)846-3111
Co. E-mail: info@burbankchamber.org
URL: http://www.burbankchamber.org
Contact: Steve Mora, Officer
Facebook: www.facebook.com/BurbankChamber
X (Twitter): x.com/BurbankChamber
Description: Promotes business and community development in Burbank, CA. **Founded:** 1922. **Publications:** Burbank Business Journal (Monthly); Burbank Business Newsletter (Monthly). **Educational Activities:** Business Connection. **Geographic Preference:** Local.

36764 ■ Burlingame Business
417 California Dr.
Burlingame, CA 94010
Ph: (650)344-1735
Co. E-mail: info@burlingamechamber.org
URL: http://www.burlingamechamber.org
Contact: Tim Auran, Treasurer Secretary
URL(s): burlingamechamber.org/about-the-chamber/
newsletters
Released: Quarterly **Availability:** PDF; Online.

36765 ■ Burlingame Chamber of Commerce
417 California Dr.
Burlingame, CA 94010
Ph: (650)344-1735
Co. E-mail: info@burlingamechamber.org
URL: http://www.burlingamechamber.org
Contact: Tim Auran, Treasurer Secretary
Facebook: www.facebook.com/BurlingameChamber
X (Twitter): x.com/VisitBurlingame
Instagram: www.instagram.com/visitburlingame
Pinterest: www.pinterest.com/burlingame94010
Description: Promotes business and community development in Burlingame, CA. Sponsors community events. **Founded:** 1913. **Publications:** Burlingame Business (Quarterly); Welcome to Burlingame (Periodic). **Geographic Preference:** Local.

36766 ■ Burney Chamber of Commerce
36789 Main St.
Burney, CA 96013
Ph: (530)335-2111
Co. E-mail: burneycoc@gmail.com
URL: http://www.burneychamber.com
Contact: Jill Barnett, President
E-mail: sjillyb@frontiernet.net
Facebook: www.facebook.com/burney.chamber
Instagram: www.instagram.com/burneychamber
Description: Promotes business and community development in the Burney Basin, CA area. **Founded:** 1944. **Publications:** Intermountain Area Map. **Educational Activities:** Burney Basin Days (Annual). **Geographic Preference:** Local.

36767 ■ Business
1225 Pk. St.
Paso Robles, CA 93446
Ph: (805)238-0506
Fax: (805)238-0527
Co. E-mail: info@pasorobleschamber.com
URL: http://www.pasorobleschamber.com
Contact: Gina Fitzpatrick, President
E-mail: gina@pasorobleschamber.com
URL(s): www.pasorobleschamber.com/mission-vision
-core-values
Availability: Print.

36768 ■ Business
1321 Butte St., No. 100
Redding, CA 96001-1034
Ph: (530)225-4433
Co. E-mail: valerie@reddingchamber.com
URL: http://reddingchamber.com
Contact: Erin Hull, Vice President
URL(s): members.reddingchamber.com/list
Released: Annual **Description:** Contains list of member's businesses. **Availability:** Online.

36769 ■ The Business Connection
781 Los Osos Valley Rd.
Los Osos, CA 93402
Ph: (805)528-4884
Co. E-mail: info@lobpchamber.org
URL: http://lobpchamber.org
Contact: Tim Carstairs, President
URL(s): lobpchamber.org/newsletters
Released: Monthly **Availability:** Print; Online.

36770 ■ Business Directory
321 E La Habra Blvd.
La Habra, CA 90631
Ph: (562)697-1704
Co. E-mail: info@lahabrachamber.com
URL: http://www.lahabrachamber.com
Contact: Marie Laveaga, President
URL(s): business.lahabrachamber.com/list
Availability: Print.

36771 ■ Business Directory
388 W Huntington Dr.
Arcadia, CA 91007
Ph: (626)447-2159
Co. E-mail: info@arcadiacachamber.org
URL: http://arcadiacachamber.org
Contact: Vicki Knight, President
URL(s): web.arcadiacachamber.org/search?clear
templatecache=true
Released: Biennial **Availability:** Online.

36772 ■ Business Directory
180 E 4th St., Ste. 120
Chico, CA 95927
Ph: (530)891-5556
Co. E-mail: info@chicochamber.com
URL: http://www.chicochamber.com
Contact: Jeanette Joslyn, Bookkeeper Consultant
E-mail: jeanette@chicochamber.com
URL(s): web.chicochamber.com/directory/direc
toryemailform.aspx?listingid=6
Released: Annual **Availability:** Online.

36773 ■ Business Directory
2855 E Coast Hwy., Ste. 101
Corona del Mar, CA 92625
Ph: (949)673-4050

Fax: (949)673-3940
Co. E-mail: info@cdmchamber.com
URL: http://www.cdmchamber.com
Contact: Linda Leonhard, President
URL(s): www.cdmchamber.com/membership/marketing-opportunities
Availability: Print; Online.

36774 ■ *Business Directory*
2332 D St., Unit E
La Verne, CA 91750
Ph: (909)593-5265
Co. E-mail: lavernechamber@gmail.com
URL: http://www.lavernechamber.org
Contact: Leah Skinner, Executive Director
E-mail: leah@lavernechamber.org
URL(s): business.lavernechamber.org/list%20
Availability: Online.

36775 ■ *Business Directory*
15357 Paramount Blvd.
Paramount, CA 90723
Ph: (562)634-3980
Fax: (562)634-0891
Co. E-mail: inquire@paramountchamber.com
URL: http://www.paramountchamber.com
Contact: Alicia Valadez, President
URL(s): www.paramountchamber.com/business-directory
Description: Contains directory of Chamber members, important phone numbers, Chamber, City & School information and residential listing. **Availability:** Print.

36776 ■ *Business Directory*
44 N Mentor Ave.
Pasadena, CA 91106
Ph: (626)795-3355
Fax: (626)795-5603
Co. E-mail: info@pasadena-chamber.org
URL: http://www.pasadena-chamber.org
Contact: Paul Little, President
E-mail: paul@pasadena-chamber.org
URL(s): www.pasadena-chamber.org/directory
Availability: Online.

36777 ■ *Business Directory*
246 E Bonita Ave.
San Dimas, CA 91773
Ph: (909)592-3818
Fax: (909)592-8178
Co. E-mail: info@sandimaschamber.com
URL: http://www.sandimaschamber.com
Contact: Ben Lewis, General Manager
URL(s): chambermaster.sandimaschamber.org/list
Description: Contains information on the City, the Chamber, schools, shopping, parks, museums, and events as well as important contacts and phone numbers. **Availability:** Online.

36778 ■ *Business Directory*
817 Mission Ave.
San Rafael, CA 94901
Ph: (415)454-4163
Co. E-mail: frontdesk@srchamber.com
URL: http://srchamber.com
Contact: Joanne Webster, President
E-mail: jwebster@srchamber.com
URL(s): srchamber.com/list
Availability: Online.

36779 ■ *Business Directory*
PO Box 202
Venice, CA 90294
Ph: (310)822-5425
Co. E-mail: info@venicechamber.net
URL: http://venicechamber.net
Contact: George Francisco, President
URL(s): business.venicechamber.net/list
Availability: Online.

36780 ■ *Business Directory*
600 Hampshire Rd., Ste. 200
Westlake Village, CA 91361
Ph: (805)370-0035
Fax: (805)370-1083
Co. E-mail: chamber@conejochamber.org
URL: http://www.conejochamber.org
Contact: Danielle Borja, President
E-mail: dborja@conejochamber.org
URL(s): www.conejochamber.org/list
Availability: Print.

36781 ■ *Business Directory*
8158 Painter Ave.
Whittier, CA 90602
Ph: (562)698-9554
Fax: (562)693-2700
Co. E-mail: info@whittierchamber.com
URL: http://www.whittierchamber.com
Contact: Carol Crosby, President
URL(s): business.whittierchamber.com/list
Description: Lists important Whittier phone number, demographic and historical information, community service and a directory of all chamber members.
Availability: Print.

36782 ■ *Business Directory*
101 Golf Course Dr. C-7
Rohnert Park, CA 94928
Ph: (707)584-1415
Fax: (707)584-2945
Co. E-mail: info@rohnertparkchamber.org
URL: http://www.rohnertparkchamber.org
Contact: Lisa Orloff, Executive Director
E-mail: lisaorloff@rohnertparkchamber.org
URL(s): www.rohnertparkchamber.org/list
Description: Contains lists of members, businesses and information about city departments and services.
Availability: Print.

36783 ■ *Business Directory and Community Guide*
390 W 7th St.
San Pedro, CA 90731
Ph: (310)832-7272
Co. E-mail: info@sanpedrochamber.com
URL: http://www.sanpedrochamber.com
Contact: Elise Swanson, President
E-mail: eswanson@sanpedrochamber.com
URL(s): www.sanpedrochamber.com/member-benefits
Released: Annual **Availability:** Print; Online.

36784 ■ *Business Focus*
8158 Painter Ave.
Whittier, CA 90602
Ph: (562)698-9554
Fax: (562)693-2700
Co. E-mail: info@whittierchamber.com
URL: http://www.whittierchamber.com
Contact: Carol Crosby, President
URL(s): www.whittierchamber.com/business-focus
Released: Bimonthly **Description:** Features local news, chamber event, business tip, and community calendar. **Availability:** Print; PDF; Online.

36785 ■ *Business Insider*
13259 S St.
Cerritos, CA 90703
Ph: (562)467-0800
Fax: (562)467-0840
Co. E-mail: chamber@cerritos.org
URL: http://www.cerritos.org
Contact: May Peitzsch, President
E-mail: may@cerritos.org
URL(s): www.cerritos.org/insider-newsletter
Released: Monthly **Availability:** PDF; Online.

36786 ■ *Business Matters*
190 W Amado Rd.
Palm Springs, CA 92262
Ph: (760)325-1577
URL: http://pschamber.org
Contact: Brady Sandahl, President
E-mail: brady@bradysandahl.com
URL(s): pschamber.org/presidents-circle-sponsorship
Released: Weekly **Description:** Discusses chamber activities, partner member features, business articles, new products, promotions, location changes, and updates. **Availability:** Print.

36787 ■ *Business Resource Directory*
7 Main St.
San Andreas, CA 95249
Ph: (209)754-5400
Co. E-mail: chamber@calaveras.org
URL: http://calaveras.org
Contact: Sherri Reusche, President
URL(s): www.calaveras.org/resources
Availability: Print; Online.

36788 ■ *Business View*
224 N Glendora Ave.
Glendora, CA 91741-3336
Ph: (626)963-4128
Co. E-mail: info@glendora-chamber.org
URL: http://www.glendora-chamber.org
Contact: Joe Cina, President
URL(s): www.glendora-chamber.org/faq
Availability: Print; Online.

36789 ■ **Buttonwillow Chamber of Commerce**
104 W 2nd St.
Buttonwillow, CA 93206
Ph: (661)764-5406
Fax: (661)764-5406
URL: http://buttonwillowchamber.com/cms
Contact: Tori Ramay, President
Facebook: www.facebook.com/buttonwillowchamber
Description: Promotes business and community development in Buttonwillow, CA. Sponsors Cotton Harvest Festival, Country Christmas celebration, and Mayor's Race. **Geographic Preference:** Local.

36790 ■ *Byline*
10895 San Pablo Ave.
El Cerrito, CA 94530
Ph: (510)705-1202
Co. E-mail: info@elcerritochamber.org
URL: http://www.elcerritochamber.org
Contact: Jeffrey Wright, President
URL(s): www.elcerritochamber.org/byline
Ed: John C. Stashik. **Released:** Monthly **Price:** $60, for print 12 months. **Description:** Contains meeting notices and updates of chamber and community activities. **Availability:** Print; PDF; Online.

36791 ■ **Calabasas Chamber of Commerce**
23564 Calabasas Rd.
Calabasas, CA 91302
Ph: (818)222-5680
Co. E-mail: info@calabasaschamber.com
URL: http://www.calabasaschamber.com
Contact: Bridget Karl, President
X (Twitter): x.com/CalabChamber
Description: Promotes business and community development in Calabasas, CA. **Founded:** 1955. **Publications:** *Calabasas Newsletter* (Monthly). **Geographic Preference:** Local.

36792 ■ **Calaveras County Chamber of Commerce (CCCC)**
7 Main St.
San Andreas, CA 95249
Ph: (209)754-5400
Co. E-mail: chamber@calaveras.org
URL: http://calaveras.org
Contact: Sherri Reusche, President
Facebook: www.facebook.com/CalaverasChamber
Instagram: www.instagram.com/calaveraschamber
Description: Promotes business and community development in the Calaveras County, CA area. Sponsors community events and social activities. Maintains business resource center. **Founded:** 1948. **Publications:** *Business Resource Directory; Chamber Newsletter* (Weekly). **Educational Activities:** Mixer. **Geographic Preference:** Local.

36793 ■ **California Chamber of Commerce (CCC)**
1215 K St., Ste. 1400
Sacramento, CA 95814
Ph: (916)444-6670
Free: 800-649-4921
Fax: (916)325-1272
Co. E-mail: techsupport@calchamber.com
URL: http://www.calchamber.com
Contact: Jennifer Barrera, President

STATE LISTINGS

Facebook: www.facebook.com/CalChamber
Linkedin: www.linkedin.com/company/california-chamber-of-commerce
X (Twitter): x.com/calchamber
Description: Works to act as legislative advocate for all California business interests. Offers educational seminars. Issues publications. **Founded:** 1890. **Publications:** *Alert* (Weekly). **Geographic Preference:** State; Local.

36794 ■ California Israel Chamber of Commerce (CICC)
317 W Portal St.
San Francisco, CA 94127
Co. E-mail: info@ci-cc.org
URL: http://ci-cc.org
Contact: Sharon Vanek, Executive Director
Facebook: www.facebook.com/CICCtech
Linkedin: www.linkedin.com/company/the-california-israel-chamber-of-commerce-cicc-
X (Twitter): x.com/CICCtech
Description: Aims to strengthen business and trade relations between California and Israel. Serves as facilitator and active supporter for joint venture programs between the two communities. Conducts networking events, mentorship programs, investment forums, and educational seminars. **Founded:** 1997. **Geographic Preference:** State.

36795 ■ Calistoga Chamber of Commerce (CCC)
1133 Washington St.
Calistoga, CA 94515-1437
Ph: (707)942-6333
Fax: (707)942-9287
Co. E-mail: info@calistogachamber.com
URL: http://chamber.visitcalistoga.com
Contact: Bruce Kyse, Executive Director
Facebook: www.facebook.com/calistogachamber
Instagram: www.instagram.com/calistogachamber
Description: Seeks to promote business, tourism and community development in Calistoga, CA. Sponsors several entertainment shows and festivals. **Founded:** 1944. **Publications:** *Calistoga Visitors Guide*; *Guide to Calistoga* (Annual). **Geographic Preference:** Local.

36796 ■ Cambria Chamber of Commerce
767 Main St.
Cambria, CA 93428
Ph: (805)927-3624
Co. E-mail: info@cambriachamber.org
URL: http://cambriachamber.org
Contact: Mel McColloch, Chief Executive Officer
E-mail: mmccolloch@yahoo.com
Facebook: www.facebook.com/Cambria-Chamber-of-Commerce-113119142042857
Instagram: www.instagram.com/cambriachamber
Description: Promotes business and community development in Cambria, CA. **Geographic Preference:** Local.

36797 ■ Campbell Chamber of Commerce (CCC)
267 E Campbell Ave., Ste. C
Campbell, CA 95008
Ph: (408)378-6252
Fax: (408)378-0192
Co. E-mail: info@campbellchamber.net
URL: http://www.campbellchamber.com
Contact: Mike Lombardi, Treasurer
Linkedin: www.linkedin.com/company/campbell-chamber
YouTube: www.youtube.com/user/chambervideo1
Description: Promotes business and community development in Campbell, CA. Conducts business/education partnership programs. Sponsors festival. Informs Campbell business as to pending local, state, and federal legislation that will affect their business. **Founded:** 1958. **Publications:** *Campbell Connection* (Monthly). **Geographic Preference:** Local.

36798 ■ *Campbell Connection*
267 E Campbell Ave., Ste. C
Campbell, CA 95008
Ph: (408)378-6252
Fax: (408)378-0192

Co. E-mail: info@campbellchamber.net
URL: http://www.campbellchamber.com
Contact: Mike Lombardi, Treasurer
URL(s): www.campbellchamber.net/member-benefits
Released: Monthly **Description:** Contains current news and business activities of Campbell business and community. **Availability:** Print.

36799 ■ *Capitola*
716 Capitola Ave., Ste. G
Capitola, CA 95010
Ph: (831)475-6522
Fax: (831)475-6530
Co. E-mail: capcham@capitolachamber.com
URL: http://www.capitolachamber.com
Contact: Carrie Arnone, Chief Executive Officer
E-mail: carrie@capitolachamber.com
URL(s): www.capitolachamber.com/newsletter
Released: Monthly **Availability:** PDF; Online.

36800 ■ Capitola-Soquel Chamber of Commerce
716 Capitola Ave., Ste. G
Capitola, CA 95010
Ph: (831)475-6522
Fax: (831)475-6530
Co. E-mail: capcham@capitolachamber.com
URL: http://www.capitolachamber.com
Contact: Carrie Arnone, Chief Executive Officer
E-mail: carrie@capitolachamber.com
Description: Promotes Capitola business community. **Founded:** 1941. **Publications:** *Capitola* (Monthly). **Educational Activities:** Annual Capitola Begonia Festival (Annual). **Geographic Preference:** Local.

36801 ■ Cardiff-by-the-Sea Chamber of Commerce
122 Aberdeen Dr.
Cardiff, CA 92007
Ph: (760)436-0431
Fax: (760)733-0144
Co. E-mail: info@cardiffbythesea.org
URL: http://www.chamber-commerce.net/dir/5521/Cardiff-by-the-Sea-Chamber-of-Commerce-in-Cardiff-By-The-Sea
Description: Promotes business and community development within the city of Encinitas. **Geographic Preference:** Local.

36802 ■ *Carlsbad Business Journal*
5934 Priestly Dr.
Carlsbad, CA 92008
Ph: (760)931-8400
URL: http://carlsbad.org
Contact: Bret Schanzenbach, President
URL(s): carlsbad.org/blog/carlsbad-business-journal
Released: Monthly **Availability:** Print; PDF; Online.

36803 ■ Carlsbad Chamber of Commerce (CCC)
5934 Priestly Dr.
Carlsbad, CA 92008
Ph: (760)931-8400
URL: http://carlsbad.org
Contact: Bret Schanzenbach, President
Facebook: www.facebook.com/carlsbadchamber
Linkedin: www.linkedin.com/company/carlsbadchamber
X (Twitter): x.com/ChamberCarlsbad
Instagram: www.instagram.com/carlsbadchamber
YouTube: www.youtube.com/channel/UCqGgn4PS6OobsbOrEmZGa2Q
Description: Promotes business and community development in the Carlsbad, CA area. Sponsors Carlsbad Village Fair. **Founded:** 1923. **Publications:** *Carlsbad Chamber Members* (Annual); *Carlsbad Business Journal* (Monthly). **Awards:** Carlsbad Chamber of Commerce Outstanding Educational Program Award (Annual). **Geographic Preference:** Local.

36804 ■ Carmichael Chamber of Commerce (CCC)
6241 Fair Oaks Blvd., Ste. K
Carmichael, CA 95608
Ph: (916)481-1002

Co. E-mail: info@carmichaelchamber.com
URL: http://www.carmichaelchamber.com
Contact: Kelli Foley, President
E-mail: trilliumrealestateca@gmail.com
Description: Promotes business and community development in Carmichael, CA. Represents members' interests before state, local, and federal government agencies. Conducts public education campaigns. **Founded:** 1948. **Publications:** *Commentator* (Monthly). **Geographic Preference:** Local.

36805 ■ *Carpinteria Valley, Member Directory and Visitors Guide*
Released: Annual **Availability:** Print.

36806 ■ Carson Chamber of Commerce (CCC)
530 E Del Amo Blvd.
Carson, CA 90746
Ph: (310)217-4590
Fax: (310)217-4591
URL: http://www.carsonchamber.com
Contact: Barry Waite, President
E-mail: barrywaite@carsonchamber.com
Facebook: www.facebook.com/carsonchamberofcommerce
X (Twitter): x.com/CarsonChamber
Instagram: www.instagram.com/carsonchamber
YouTube: www.youtube.com/channel/UCPZOosiBxB75ARCKBg5EHkg
Description: Promotes business and community development in Carson, CA. **Founded:** 1962. **Geographic Preference:** Local.

36807 ■ Castro Valley/Eden Area Chamber of Commerce
4200 James Ave.
Castro Valley, CA 94546
Ph: (510)537-5300
Co. E-mail: info@castrovalleychamber.com
URL: http://www.edenareachamber.com
Contact: Julie Sumiki, President
Facebook: www.facebook.com/EdenAreaChamber
Linkedin: www.linkedin.com/company/cveachamber
X (Twitter): x.com/CVEACC
Pinterest: www.pinterest.com/edenareachamber
Description: Promotes business and community development in the eastern San Francisco Bay area of California. Conducts annual community festival and business exchange night. **Founded:** 1937. **Publications:** *Business Communique* (Monthly); *Community Guide* (Biennial). **Geographic Preference:** Local.

36808 ■ Catalina Island Chamber of Commerce & Visitors Bureau
No. 1 Green Pleasure Pier
Avalon, CA 90704
Ph: (310)510-1520
Co. E-mail: info@lovecatalina.com
URL: http://www.lovecatalina.com
Contact: Jim Luttjohann, Author
E-mail: jim@lovecatalina.com
Description: Promotes business, community development, and tourism on Santa Catalina Island, CA. **Publications:** *Visitor's Guide* (Annual). **Geographic Preference:** Local.

36809 ■ Cayucos Chamber of Commerce
PO Box 106
Cayucos, CA 93430
Ph: (805)995-1200
Co. E-mail: cayucoschamber@gmail.com
URL: http://www.cayucoschamber.com
Contact: Lori Stone, President
Facebook: www.facebook.com/cayucoschamberofcommerce
Instagram: www.instagram.com/cayucoschamber
Description: Promotes business and community development in Cayucos, CA. Sponsors semiannual antique sale, periodic flea market, and seafood festival. **Geographic Preference:** Local.

36810 ■ Central California Hispanic Chamber of Commerce (CCHCC)
1535 E Olive Ave., Ste. 102
Fresno, CA 93728

Ph: (559)549-4480
Co. E-mail: info@cchcc.biz
URL: http://cchcc.biz
Contact: Sonia Gardea-Arreguin, President
Facebook: www.facebook.com/cchccbiz
Linkedin: www.linkedin.com/in/central-california-hispanic-chamber-of-commerce-1717408b
X (Twitter): x.com/cchccbiz
Description: Seeks to promote, stimulate, and support Hispanic-owned businesses in the central California area by creating, maintaining, and improving a favorable business environment. **Founded:** 1983. **Geographic Preference:** Local.

36811 ■ Century City Chamber of Commerce
2029 Century Pk. E, Ste. 4392
 Los Angeles, CA 90067
Ph: (310)553-2222
Co. E-mail: contact@centurycitycc.com
URL: http://www.centurycitycc.com
Contact: Nancy Wood, President
Facebook: www.facebook.com/centurycitychamber
Linkedin: www.linkedin.com/companies/century-city-chamber-of-commerce
X (Twitter): x.com/centurycitycc
Instagram: www.instagram.com/centurycitycc
YouTube: www.youtube.com/user/CenturyCityChamber
Pinterest: www.pinterest.com/centurycitycc
Description: Promotes business and community development in Los Angeles, CA. **Founded:** 1969. **Geographic Preference:** Local.

36812 ■ Ceres Chamber of Commerce
2904 4th St.
 Ceres, CA 95307
Ph: (209)537-2601
Fax: (209)537-2699
Co. E-mail: info@cereschamber.com
URL: http://www.cereschamber.com
Contact: Herman Bhatti, President
Description: Encourages a strong local economy by maintaining and advancing business. Leadership provides an informed membership through the Chamber newsletter, the business directory, and business surveys. Serves as an active watchdog to review current legislation at the local, state and federal levels that impact the local business community. Promotes an advancement of business through information and recognition programs. **Publications:** *Ceres Directory and Fact Book* (Periodic); *Chamber Report* (Periodic). **Geographic Preference:** Local.

36813 ■ Cerritos Regional Chamber of Commerce
13259 S St.
 Cerritos, CA 90703
Ph: (562)467-0800
Fax: (562)467-0840
Co. E-mail: chamber@cerritos.org
URL: http://www.cerritos.org
Contact: May Peitzsch, President
E-mail: may@cerritos.org
Facebook: www.facebook.com/cerritosregionalchamberofcommerce
Linkedin: www.linkedin.com/company/cerritos-regional-chamber-of-commerce
X (Twitter): x.com/cerrregchamber
Description: Promotes business and community development in the Cerritos, CA area. Sponsors business expo. **Founded:** 1963. **Publications:** *Cerritos Regional Chamber of Commerce Business Directory*; *Business Insider* (Monthly). **Educational Activities:** Cerritos Chamber of Commerce Luncheon. **Geographic Preference:** Local.

36814 ■ *Cerritos Regional Chamber of Commerce Business Directory*
13259 S St.
 Cerritos, CA 90703
Ph: (562)467-0800
Fax: (562)467-0840
Co. E-mail: chamber@cerritos.org
URL: http://www.cerritos.org
Contact: May Peitzsch, President
E-mail: may@cerritos.org

URL(s): www.cerritos.org/business-directory
Released: Last Issue 2020. **Availability:** PDF.

36815 ■ Chamber of Commerce Mountain View
580 Castro St.
 Mountain View, CA 94041
Ph: (650)968-8378
Fax: (650)968-5668
Co. E-mail: info@chambermv.org
URL: http://chambermv.org
Contact: Bruce Humphrey, Director
Facebook: www.facebook.com/chambermv
Linkedin: www.linkedin.com/company/chamber-of-commerce-mountain-view
X (Twitter): x.com/chambermv
YouTube: www.youtube.com/user/WeLoveMountainView
Pinterest: www.pinterest.com/chambermv
Description: Promotes business and community development in Mountain View, CA. **Founded:** 1922. **Publications:** *Business News* (Monthly); *Chamber Annual Business and Community Directory* (Annual). **Geographic Preference:** Local.

36816 ■ *The Chamber Communicator*
3985 University Ave.
 Riverside, CA 92501
Ph: (951)683-7100
Fax: (951)683-2670
Co. E-mail: rchamber@riverside-chamber.com
URL: http://www.riverside-chamber.com
Contact: Cindy Roth, President
E-mail: croth@riverside-chamber.com
URL(s): www.riverside-chamber.com/faq.cfm
Released: Weekly **Description:** Contains updates on legislative action, meetings and events of the chamber. **Availability:** Online.

36817 ■ *Chamber Connection*
300 Pine St.
 Mount Shasta, CA 96067
Ph: (530)926-4865
Co. E-mail: info@mtshastachamber.com
URL: http://mtshastachamber.com
Contact: Thea Cowsky, President
URL(s): mtshastachamber.com/chamber/networking
Released: Quarterly; March, June, September and December. **Description:** Contains chamber news, business-related community issues, events calendar and schedule of business oriented meetings. **Availability:** Print.

36818 ■ *Chamber Membership Directory and Business Resource Guide*
350 S Bixel St.
 Los Angeles, CA 90017
Ph: (213)580-7500
Co. E-mail: info@lachamber.com
URL: http://www.lachamber.com
Contact: Maria S. Salinas, President
URL(s): lachamber.com/pages/membership
Released: Annual **Description:** Contains alphabetical listing of members and features a resource guide for business leaders throughout the Los Angeles area. **Availability:** Online.

36819 ■ *Chamber News*
901 National City Blvd.
 National City, CA 91950
Ph: (619)477-9339
Fax: (619)477-5018
Co. E-mail: thechamber@nationalcitychamber.org
URL: http://www.nationalcitychamber.org
Contact: Jacqueline L. Reynoso, President
E-mail: reynoso@nationalcitychamber.org
URL(s): www.nationalcitychamber.org/member/newmemberapp
Released: Quarterly **Description:** Contains information about chamber activities. **Availability:** Print.

36820 ■ *Chamber News*
197-B Mono Way
 Sonora, CA 95370
Ph: (209)532-4212
Co. E-mail: info@tcchamber.com
URL: http://tcchamber.com

Contact: Dave Souther, Co-President
URL(s): www.tcchamber.com/sponsorships
Released: Monthly **Availability:** Online.

36821 ■ *Chamber Newsletters*
1204 W Gardena Blvd., Ste. E
 Gardena, CA 90247
Ph: (310)532-9905
Co. E-mail: info@gardenachamber.org
URL: http://www.gardenachamber.org
Contact: Wanda Love, Executive Director
URL(s): www.gardenachamber.org/newsletters
Released: Monthly; latest issue April 20, 2011. **Description:** Contains Chamber activities, meetings and important events. **Availability:** Print; Online.

36822 ■ *Chamber Report*
100 Main St.
 Red Bluff, CA 96080
Ph: (530)527-6220
Fax: (530)527-2908
Co. E-mail: info@redbluffchamber.com
URL: http://redbluffchamber.com
Contact: Dave Gowan, Chief Executive Officer
E-mail: dave@redbluffchamber.com
Availability: PDF; Online.

36823 ■ Chatsworth Porter Ranch Chamber of Commerce (CPRCOC)
10038 Old Depot Plz. Rd.
 Chatsworth, CA 91311
Ph: (818)341-2428
Co. E-mail: info@chatsworthchamber.com
URL: http://www.chatsworthchamber.com
Contact: Nick Montano, President
Facebook: www.facebook.com/chatsworthchamber
X (Twitter): x.com/cprcoc
YouTube: www.youtube.com/channel/UCrdhcuYjwG0esb8ivhd23yA
Description: Promotes business and community development in Chatsworth, CA. **Founded:** 1914. **Geographic Preference:** Local.

36824 ■ Chico Chamber of Commerce
180 E 4th St., Ste. 120
 Chico, CA 95927
Ph: (530)891-5556
Co. E-mail: info@chicochamber.com
URL: http://www.chicochamber.com
Contact: Jeanette Joslyn, Bookkeeper Consultant
E-mail: jeanette@chicochamber.com
Facebook: www.facebook.com/ChicoChamberofCommerce
Linkedin: www.linkedin.com/company/chico-chamber-of-commerce
X (Twitter): x.com/ChicoChamber
Instagram: www.instagram.com/chicochamber
Description: Promotes business and community development in the Chico, CA area. Sponsors annual business-to-business and consumer trade shows, industrial barbecue, and promotes local economy and tourism. **Publications:** *Chico Business* (Monthly); *Business Directory* (Annual); *Chico Chamber of Commerce--Membership Directory*. **Geographic Preference:** Local.

36825 ■ Chino Valley Chamber of Commerce (CVCC)
13150 7th St.
 Chino, CA 91710
Ph: (909)627-6177
Co. E-mail: zwelborn@chinovalleychamber.com
URL: http://chinovalleychamber.com
Contact: Zeb Welborn, President
E-mail: zwelborn@chinovalleychamber.com
Facebook: www.facebook.com/ChinoValleyChamberOfCommerce
Linkedin: www.linkedin.com/company/chino-valley-chamber-of-commerce
X (Twitter): x.com/ChinoValleyCC
Instagram: www.instagram.com/chinovalleycc
YouTube: www.youtube.com/channel/UCKcxr-VvG_0QHutd39jF7bw
Description: Promotes business and community development in the Chino Valley, CA area. **Founded:** 1913. **Geographic Preference:** Local.

STATE LISTINGS

California ■ 36841

36826 ■ Chula Vista Chamber of Commerce
233 4th Ave.
  Chula Vista, CA 91910
Ph: (619)420-6603
Co. E-mail: info@chulavistachamber.org
URL: http://www.chulavistachamber.org
Contact: Susana Villegas, President
E-mail: lisa@chulavistachamber.org
Facebook: www.facebook.com/chamberchulavista
Linkedin: www.linkedin.com/company/chula-vista-chamber-of-commerce
X (Twitter): x.com/chambercv
Instagram: www.instagram.com/chamberchulavista
YouTube: www.youtube.com/channel/UCQexCt8NzB4nWO9yF45gMQw
Description: Seeks to enhance the partnership between business and professional people promoting free enterprise system. **Founded:** 1927. **Publications:** *News and Views* (Quarterly). **Geographic Preference:** Local.

36827 ■ Citrus Heights Chamber of Commerce
7625 Sunrise Blvd., Ste. 207
  Citrus Heights, CA 95610
Ph: (916)722-4545
Co. E-mail: chamber@chchamber.com
URL: http://www.chchamber.com
Contact: Ray Ward, President
Facebook: www.facebook.com/citrusheightschamber
Linkedin: www.linkedin.com/in/citrus-heights-chamber-of-commerce-50b51b9
YouTube: www.youtube.com/channel/UCpMDkT0gxDINgfo0fMSYm-g
Description: Promotes business and community development in Citrus Heights, CA. **Founded:** 1958. **Publications:** *Horizons* (Monthly). **Educational Activities:** Membership Luncheon (Monthly). **Geographic Preference:** Local.

36828 ■ *Clear Lake Chamber Newsletter*
3245 Bowers Ave.
  Clearlake, CA 95422
Ph: (707)994-3600
Fax: (707)994-3603
Co. E-mail: office@clearlakechamber.com
URL: http://www.clearlakearea.com
Contact: Joey Luiz, President
URL(s): www.clearlakearea.com/archive.asp
Released: Monthly **Description:** Includes calendar. **Availability:** Print; PDF; Online.

36829 ■ Cloverdale Chamber of Commerce
126 N Cloverdale Blvd.
  Cloverdale, CA 95425
Ph: (707)894-4470
Co. E-mail: info@cloverdalechamber.com
URL: http://cloverdalechamber.com
Contact: Erin Mewes, Director
Facebook: www.facebook.com/CloverdaleChamberofCommerce
Description: Promotes business and community development in Cloverdale, CA. **Founded:** 1926. **Publications:** *Business Update*. **Geographic Preference:** Local.

36830 ■ Clovis Chamber of Commerce
325 Pollasky Ave.
  Clovis, CA 93612
Ph: (559)299-7363
Fax: (559)299-2969
Co. E-mail: info@clovischamber.com
URL: http://www.clovischamber.com
Contact: Greg Newman, President
E-mail: greg@clovischamber.com
Facebook: www.facebook.com/ClovisChamber
Linkedin: www.linkedin.com/company/clovis-chamber-of-commerce
X (Twitter): x.com/ClovisChamber
Instagram: www.instagram.com/clovischamber
YouTube: www.youtube.com/channel/UCnaD1MoJ25-MtDeqscpYJPA
Pinterest: www.pinterest.com/clovischamber
Description: Strengthens the connections of homes, business, and community within Clovis area. **Founded:** 1912. **Publications:** *Clovis Directory and Visitor Guide* (Annual); *The Voice of Business* (Monthly). **Geographic Preference:** Local.

36831 ■ Colfax Chamber of Commerce
99 S Railroad St.
  Colfax, CA 95713
Ph: (530)346-8888
Co. E-mail: colfaxareachamber@gmail.com
URL: http://colfaxchamber.com
Contact: Tim Ryan, President
Facebook: www.facebook.com/Colfax-Area-Chamber-of-Commerce-362709669124
Instagram: www.instagram.com/colfaxareachamber
Description: Promotes business and community development in Colfax, CA. **Founded:** 1954. **Geographic Preference:** Local.

36832 ■ Colton Chamber of Commerce
655 N La Cadena Dr.
  Colton, CA 92324-2822
Ph: (909)825-2222
Fax: (909)824-1650
Co. E-mail: info@coltonchamber.org
URL: http://coltonchamber.org
Contact: Brian J. Chilstrom, Director
E-mail: brian.chilstrom@wcui.edu
Facebook: www.facebook.com/coltonchamberofcommerce
Description: Promotes business and community development in Colton, CA. **Founded:** 1887. **Geographic Preference:** Local.

36833 ■ Commerce Industrial Council Chamber of Commerce
6055 E Washington Blvd., No. 400
  Commerce, CA 90040
Ph: (323)728-7222
Co. E-mail: info@industrialcouncil.org
URL: http://www.industrialcouncil.org
Contact: Barbara Martine, Secretary
Facebook: www.facebook.com/CommerceIndustrialCouncil
X (Twitter): x.com/CIC_Chamber
Pinterest: www.pinterest.com/pin/363313894920282390
Description: Promotes commercial, industrial, education, and legislative actions that will benefit its members and all those concerned for the welfare of the community. **Founded:** 1959. **Geographic Preference:** Local.

36834 ■ *Community Guide*
1730 S Amphlett Blvd., Ste. 206
  San Mateo, CA 94402
Ph: (650)401-2440
Fax: (877)304-2441
Co. E-mail: info@sanmateochamber.org
URL: http://sanmateochamber.org
Contact: Cheryl Angeles, Chief Executive Officer
E-mail: cheryl@sanmateochamber.org
URL(s): sanmateochamber.org/2020-2021-business-directory-community-guide
Released: Annual **Availability:** Online.

36835 ■ *Community Guide and Membership Directory*
120 N E St.
  Madera, CA 93638
Ph: (559)673-3563
URL: http://maderachamber.com
Contact: Debi Bray, President
E-mail: dbray@maderachamber.com
URL(s): maderachamber.com/?page_id=844
Availability: Print; Online.

36836 ■ *Community and Visitor Guide*
44 N Mentor Ave.
  Pasadena, CA 91106
Ph: (626)795-3355
Fax: (626)795-5603
Co. E-mail: info@pasadena-chamber.org
URL: http://www.pasadena-chamber.org
Contact: Paul Little, President
E-mail: paul@pasadena-chamber.org
URL(s): www.pasadena-chamber.org/join/member-benefits
Description: Serves as a visitors' guide and is distributed to those interested in relocating, doing business or visiting Pasadena. **Availability:** Print; PDF.

36837 ■ Compton Chamber of Commerce
700 N Bulis Rd., Ste. 10A.
  Compton, CA 90221
Ph: (310)631-8611
Fax: (310)631-2066
Co. E-mail: cptchamber@aol.com
URL: http://www.comptonchamberofcommerce.org
Contact: Dr. Lestean M. Johnson, President
Facebook: www.facebook.com/compton.chamber
Linkedin: www.linkedin.com/company/compton-chamber-of-commerce
Description: Promotes business and community development in Compton, CA. Sponsors festival. **Publications:** none. **Founded:** 1888. **Geographic Preference:** Local.

36838 ■ Corning District Chamber of Commerce (CCC)
1110 Solano St.
  Corning, CA 96021
Ph: (530)824-5550
Co. E-mail: info@corningcachamber.org
URL: http://www.corningcachamber.org
Contact: Julie Kincheloe, President
URL(s): www.chamber-commerce.net/dir/6000/Corning-District-Chamber-of-Commerce-in-Corning
Facebook: www.facebook.com/corningcachamber
Description: Promotes business and community development in Corning, CA. **Founded:** 1921. **Publications:** *Chamber Reporter* (Monthly). **Geographic Preference:** Local.

36839 ■ Corona Chamber of Commerce
904 E 6th St.
  Corona, CA 92879
Ph: (951)737-3350
Co. E-mail: info@mychamber.org
URL: http://www.mychamber.org
Contact: Bobby Spiegel, Secretary
E-mail: bobby@mychamber.org
Facebook: www.facebook.com/CoronaChamber
Linkedin: www.linkedin.com/company/coronachamber
X (Twitter): x.com/Corona_Chamber
Instagram: www.instagram.com/coronachamber
YouTube: www.youtube.com/channel/UCER_HVYf_Q0jCpNS5hNUtIA
Description: Promotes business and community development in Corona, CA. Sponsors Street Faire. **Founded:** 1910. **Publications:** *Business Directory*; *Chamber News*. **Educational Activities:** Good Morning Corona (Annual); New Member Orientation (Monthly). **Geographic Preference:** Local.

36840 ■ Corona del Mar Chamber of Commerce (CDMCC)
2855 E Coast Hwy., Ste. 101
  Corona del Mar, CA 92625
Ph: (949)673-4050
Fax: (949)673-3940
Co. E-mail: info@cdmchamber.com
URL: http://www.cdmchamber.com
Contact: Linda Leonhard, President
Facebook: www.facebook.com/cdmchamber
X (Twitter): x.com/CdmChamber
Instagram: www.instagram.com/cdmchamber
Description: Promotes business and community development in Corona Del Mar, CA. **Founded:** 1957. **Publications:** *Business Directory*. **Geographic Preference:** Local.

36841 ■ Coronado Chamber of Commerce
1125 10th St.
  Coronado, CA 92118
Ph: (619)435-9260
Co. E-mail: info@coronadochamber.com
URL: http://coronadochamber.com
Contact: Rena Clancy, Executive Director
E-mail: rena@coronadochamber.com
Facebook: www.facebook.com/coronadochamber

Instagram: www.instagram.com/coronadochamber
Description: Promotes business and community development in Coronado, CA. Offers marketing consulting and relocation services. Conducts networking activities. Sponsors Christmas Open House. **Founded:** 1937. **Publications:** *Village Voice* (Monthly). **Geographic Preference:** Local.

36842 ■ **Corte Madera Chamber of Commerce**
129 Corte Madera Town Ctr.
 Corte Madera, CA 94925
Ph: (415)924-0441
Fax: (415)924-1839
Co. E-mail: chamber@cortemadera.org
URL: http://www.cortemadera.org
Contact: Stan Hoffman, President
E-mail: stan.hoffman@macerich.com
Description: Promotes business and community development in Corte Madera, CA area. **Geographic Preference:** Local.

36843 ■ **Costa Mesa Chamber of Commerce**
1870 Harbor Blvd. No. 105
 Costa Mesa, CA 92627
Ph: (714)885-9090
Fax: (714)885-9094
Co. E-mail: jharkness@costamesachamber.com
URL: http://www.costamesachamber.com
Contact: Jennifer Farrell, Attorney
E-mail: jfarrell@rutan.com
Linkedin: www.linkedin.com/company/costa-mesa-chamber-of-commerce
X (Twitter): x.com/CM_Chamber
Instagram: www.instagram.com/costamesa_commerce
YouTube: www.youtube.com/channel/UCJEq3_JEXt-p1AbDHxkOW5g
Description: Promotes business and community development in Costa Mesa, CA. **Publications:** *Business Outlook* (Periodic); *Daily Pilot*. **Geographic Preference:** Local.

36844 ■ **Cotati Chamber of Commerce**
216 E School St.
 Cotati, CA 94931
Ph: (707)795-5508
Co. E-mail: chamber@cotati.org
URL: http://cotati.org
Contact: Erin Armstrong, President
Facebook: www.facebook.com/cotati.ca.chamber
Description: Promotes business and community development in Cotati, CA. **Founded:** 1940. **Geographic Preference:** Local.

36845 ■ **Cottonwood Chamber of Commerce**
PO Box 584
 Cottonwood, CA 96022
Ph: (530)347-6800
Co. E-mail: info@cottonwoodchamberofcommerce.com
URL: http://www.cottonwoodchamberofcommerce.com
Contact: Amanda Dullen Fuller, President
Description: Promotes business and community development in Cottonwood, CA area. **Geographic Preference:** Local.

36846 ■ **Covina Chamber of Commerce**
1041 N Grand Ave., No. 351
 Covina, CA 91724
Ph: (626)967-4191
Co. E-mail: chamber@covina.org
URL: http://www.covina.org
Contact: Dawn Nelson, President
Facebook: www.facebook.com/CovinaChamberofCommerce
Linkedin: www.linkedin.com/company/covina-chamber-of-commerce
X (Twitter): x.com/covinachamber
Instagram: www.instagram.com/covinachamber
Description: Promotes business and community development in Covina, CA. **Founded:** 1900. **Publications:** *COVINA* (Monthly). **Awards:** Covina Chamber of Commerce Citizen of the Year (Annual). **Geographic Preference:** Local.

36847 ■ **Crescent City/Del Norte County Chamber of Commerce**
1001 Front St.
 Crescent City, CA 95531
Ph: (707)464-3174
URL: http://www.delnorte.org
Contact: Larry Timpe, President
Facebook: www.facebook.com/CCDNChamber
Description: Promotes business and community development in the Del Norte County, CA area. Sponsors festivals, Crab races, Fourth of July, Sea Cruise Car Show. **Founded:** 1857. **Geographic Preference:** Local.

36848 ■ **Crescenta Valley Chamber of Commerce (CVCC)**
3131 Foothill Blvd., Ste. D
 La Crescenta, CA 91214
Ph: (818)248-4957
Fax: (818)248-9625
Co. E-mail: info@crescentavalleychamber.org
URL: http://www.crescentavalleychamber.org
Contact: Michael Riley, President
E-mail: mriley@sprintmail.com
Facebook: www.facebook.com/cvchamber
X (Twitter): x.com/The_CV_Chamber
Description: Promotes business and community development in La Canada, La Crescenta, Montrose, and Sunland-Tujunga, CA. Sponsors Fourth of July Festival, Mayor's Prayer Breakfast, Tri-City Golf Tournament, 4 Cities Casino Night, annual Tea, Mary Pinola Smart-a-thon, and annual Family Festival of Fun. **Founded:** 1925. **Publications:** *Business and Community Services Directory*; *Foothill Business* (Monthly); *Business Directory CV Chamber*; *Crescenta Valley Chamber of Commerce Business Directory*. **Educational Activities:** Crescenta Valley Chamber of Commerce Banquet (Annual). **Awards:** Crescenta Valley Chamber of Commerce Business of the Year (Annual); Crescenta Valley Chamber of Commerce Man and Woman of the Year (Annual); Crescenta Valley Chamber of Commerce Volunteer of the Year (Annual). **Geographic Preference:** Local.

36849 ■ *Culver City Business Directory*
6000 Sepulveda Blvd., Ste. 1260
 Culver City, CA 90230
Ph: (310)287-3850
Co. E-mail: info@culvercitychamber.com
URL: http://www.culvercitychamber.com
Contact: Maria Jacobo, Chairman of the Board
URL(s): business.culvercitychamber.com/list
Released: Monthly **Availability:** Online.

36850 ■ **Culver City Chamber of Commerce**
6000 Sepulveda Blvd., Ste. 1260
 Culver City, CA 90230
Ph: (310)287-3850
Co. E-mail: info@culvercitychamber.com
URL: http://www.culvercitychamber.com
Contact: Maria Jacobo, Chairman of the Board
Facebook: www.facebook.com/culverchamber
Linkedin: www.linkedin.com/company/culver-city-chamber-of-commerce
X (Twitter): x.com/culverchamber
YouTube: www.youtube.com/channel/UCfH7AjL45Fl0hULse1mqqVA
Description: Promotes business and community development in Culver City, CA. **Founded:** 1921. **Publications:** *Culver City Business Directory* (Monthly). **Geographic Preference:** Local.

36851 ■ *Cupertino Business News*
20455 Silverado Ave.
 Cupertino, CA 95014
Ph: (408)252-7054
Co. E-mail: info@cupertino-chamber.org
URL: http://www.cupertino-chamber.org
Contact: Claudio Bono, President
URL(s): cupertino-chamber.org/newsletter
Released: Latest edition March 2023. **Availability:** Online.

36852 ■ **Cupertino Chamber of Commerce**
20455 Silverado Ave.
 Cupertino, CA 95014
Ph: (408)252-7054
Co. E-mail: info@cupertino-chamber.org
URL: http://www.cupertino-chamber.org
Contact: Claudio Bono, President
Facebook: www.facebook.com/CupChamber
X (Twitter): x.com/CupChamber
Instagram: www.instagram.com/cupchamber
YouTube: www.youtube.com/channel/UCVwbNbxFkmMIcXanwUZtVbg
Description: Promotes business and community development in Cupertino, CA. Collaborates with government, education, and private industry to assist and strengthen local businesses, to be an advocate for business, and affect the high quality of life for which Cupertino is known. Provides leadership and direction for community action. **Founded:** 1954. **Publications:** *Cupertino Business News*. **Awards:** Cupertino Chamber of Commerce Business of the Year (Annual); Cupertino Chamber of Commerce Citizen of the Year (Annual). **Geographic Preference:** Local.

36853 ■ **Cypress Chamber of Commerce**
9200 Valley View St., Business Bldg. 9, Rm. 101
 Cypress, CA 90630
Ph: (714)484-6015
Fax: (714)484-6016
Co. E-mail: execadmin@cypresschamber.org
URL: http://www.cypresschamber.org
Contact: Shelly Henderson, Chairman
Facebook: www.facebook.com/cypresschamber
X (Twitter): x.com/CypressChamber
Instagram: www.instagram.com/cypresschamber
YouTube: www.youtube.com/channel/UCqSg6EEiG8xR09X4bWYpA2w
Description: Promotes business and community development in Cypress, CA area. **Geographic Preference:** Local.

36854 ■ *Daily Pilot*
1870 Harbor Blvd. No. 105
 Costa Mesa, CA 92627
Ph: (714)885-9090
Fax: (714)885-9094
Co. E-mail: jharkness@costamesachamber.com
URL: http://www.costamesachamber.com
Contact: Jennifer Farrell, Attorney
E-mail: jfarrell@rutan.com
URL(s): www.latimes.com/socal/daily-pilot
Availability: Print.

36855 ■ **Daly City/Colma Chamber of Commerce**
362 Gellert Blvd.
 Daly City, CA 94015
Ph: (650)755-3900
Co. E-mail: staff@dccchamber.org
URL: http://dccchamber.org
Contact: Rebecca Husted, President
Facebook: www.facebook.com/DCCChamber
Linkedin: www.linkedin.com/in/dalycity-colmachamber
X (Twitter): x.com/dccchamber
Instagram: www.instagram.com/dalycitycolmachamber
YouTube: www.youtube.com/channel/UCl_-v4Likd4742AiQkq63Eg
Pinterest: www.pinterest.com/dccchamber
Description: Promotes business and community development in the Daly City/Colma, CA area. Sponsors annual festival and annual scholarship competition. **Founded:** 1953. **Geographic Preference:** Local.

36856 ■ **Dana Point Chamber of Commerce (DPCC)**
34183 Pacific Coast Hwy.
 Dana Point, CA 92629
Ph: (949)496-1555
Fax: (949)496-5321
URL: http://danapointchamber.com
Contact: Vickie McMurchie, President
Facebook: www.facebook.com/DanaPointChamberofCommerce
X (Twitter): x.com/danaptchamber
YouTube: www.youtube.com/user/DanaChamber
Pinterest: www.pinterest.com/danaptchamber

STATE LISTINGS

Description: Promotes business and community development in the Dana Point, CA area. **Publications:** *Dana Point Chamber of Commerce Business Directory.* **Geographic Preference:** Local.

36857 ■ Danville Area Chamber of Commerce
117-E Town and Country Dr.
Danville, CA 94526
Ph: (925)837-4400
Co. E-mail: ceo@danvilleareachamber.com
URL: http://www.danvilleareachamber.com
Contact: Glenn Bittner, Chairman
Facebook: www.facebook.com/DanvilleAreaChamber
Linkedin: www.linkedin.com/company/danville-area-chamber-of-commerce/about
X (Twitter): x.com/Danvilleareabiz
YouTube: www.youtube.com/channel/UCWkj tP9jyLhzoeEaHGWHMjw
Description: Promotes business and community development in the Danville, CA area. **Founded:** 1948. **Publications:** *Chamber Progress.* **Geographic Preference:** Local.

36858 ■ Davis Chamber of Commerce
604 3rd St.
Davis, CA 95616
Ph: (530)902-7699
Co. E-mail: communications@davischamber.com
URL: http://www.davischamber.com
Contact: Cory Koehler, Executive Director
E-mail: ckoehler@davischamber.com
Facebook: www.facebook.com/davischamber
X (Twitter): x.com/davischamber
Instagram: www.instagram.com/davischamber
YouTube: www.youtube.com/channel/UCAqiGaq2f 6kMm0snnon3N1Q
Description: Promotes business and community development in the Davis, CA area. Sponsors competitions and festivals. **Founded:** 1905. **Publications:** *Davis Chamber Viewpoint* (Quarterly). **Geographic Preference:** Local.

36859 ■ Delano Chamber of Commerce
931 High St.
Delano, CA 93215
Ph: (661)725-2518
Fax: (661)725-4743
Co. E-mail: info@delanochamberofcommerce.org
URL: http://delanochamberofcommerce.org
Contact: Victor Lopez, Chairman of the Board
Facebook: www.facebook.com/DelanoChamberofCommerce
YouTube: www.youtube.com/user/DelanoChamberofComme
Description: Promotes business and community development in Delano, CA. **Founded:** 1924. **Geographic Preference:** Local.

36860 ■ Desert Hot Springs Chamber of Commerce
12561 Palm Dr., Ste. C
Desert Hot Springs, CA 92240
Ph: (760)347-0676
URL: http://gcvcc.org/desert-hot-springs
Contact: David Conover, Chairman
Description: Promotes business and community development in Desert Hot Springs, CA. Operates visit information center. Sponsors monthly mixer. **Founded:** 2018. **Geographic Preference:** Local.

36861 ■ Dinuba Chamber of Commerce
210 N L St.
Dinuba, CA 93618
Ph: (559)591-2707
Co. E-mail: info@dinubachamber.com
URL: http://www.dinubachamber.com
Contact: Heathe Jones, President
E-mail: heathe@dinubachamber.com
Facebook: www.facebook.com/dinubachamber
Instagram: www.instagram.com/dinubachamber
Description: Promotes business and community development in Dinuba, CA. Conducts Raisin Day festival. **Geographic Preference:** Local.

36862 ■ Dixon District Chamber of Commerce
220 N Jefferson St.
Dixon, CA 95620
Ph: (707)678-2650
Co. E-mail: info@dixonchamber.org
URL: http://dixonchamber.org
Contact: Shauna Manina, President
Facebook: www.facebook.com/the dixonchamberofcommerce
Description: Promotes business and community development in the Dixon, CA area. **Founded:** 1909. **Awards:** Dixon District Chamber of Commerce Citizen of the Year (Annual). **Geographic Preference:** Local.

36863 ■ *Downey Business*
11131 Brookshire Ave.
Downey, CA 90241
Ph: (562)923-2191
Co. E-mail: info@downeychamber.com
URL: http://www.downeychamber.com
Contact: Sheila Tetangco-Bartolone, President
URL(s): www.downeychamber.org/Downey-Business-Newsletters.php
Released: 8/year **Description:** Features updates on chamber activities, future events and business community news. **Availability:** PDF.

36864 ■ Downey Chamber of Commerce (DCC)
11131 Brookshire Ave.
Downey, CA 90241
Ph: (562)923-2191
Co. E-mail: info@downeychamber.com
URL: http://www.downeychamber.com
Contact: Sheila Tetangco-Bartolone, President
Facebook: www.facebook.com/downeychamber
X (Twitter): x.com/downeychamber
Description: Promotes business and community development in Downey, CA. Seeks to advocate and support a healthy and profitable business environment which improves the quality of life in Downey. **Founded:** 1903. **Publications:** *Downey Business* (8/year); *Buyer's Guide and Chamber Directory* (Semiannual). **Geographic Preference:** Local.

36865 ■ *Duarte Business*
1735 Huntington Dr.
Duarte, CA 91010
Ph: (626)357-3333
Co. E-mail: info@duartechamber.com
URL: http://duartechamber.com
Contact: Adam Knight, President
URL(s): www.duartechamber.com/about
Released: Bimonthly **Availability:** Print.

36866 ■ Duarte Chamber of Commerce
1735 Huntington Dr.
Duarte, CA 91010
Ph: (626)357-3333
Co. E-mail: info@duartechamber.com
URL: http://duartechamber.com
Contact: Adam Knight, President
Facebook: www.facebook.com/DuarteChamber
Linkedin: www.linkedin.com/company/duarte-chamber-of-commerce
Instagram: www.instagram.com/duarte_chamber
Description: Promotes business and community development in Duarte, CA. **Publications:** *Duarte Business* (Bimonthly); *Duarte View* (Bimonthly); *Duarte Overview* (Annual). **Geographic Preference:** Local.

36867 ■ *Duarte View*
1735 Huntington Dr.
Duarte, CA 91010
Ph: (626)357-3333
Co. E-mail: info@duartechamber.com
URL: http://duartechamber.com
Contact: Adam Knight, President
URL(s): www.duartechamber.com/duarte-view
Ed: Jim Kirchner. **Released:** Bimonthly **Description:** Newspaper containing information about the general interests, columns and local business oriented news features of Duarte, CA. **Availability:** Print; Online; PDF.

36868 ■ Dublin Chamber of Commerce
6300 Village Pky., Ste. 100
Dublin, CA 94568
Ph: (925)828-6200
Co. E-mail: info@dublinchamberofcommerce.org
URL: http://www.dublinchamberofcommerce.org
Contact: Brent Herrera, Director
Facebook: www.facebook.com/DublinChamber
Instagram: www.instagram.com/dublinchamberca
YouTube: www.youtube.com/channel/UCcuyOiRhZryNq3oz5NC8t8w
Description: Promotes business and community development in Dublin, CA. **Founded:** 1968. **Geographic Preference:** Local.

36869 ■ Dunsmuir Chamber of Commerce
5915 Dunsmuir Ave.
Dunsmuir, CA 96025
Ph: (530)235-2177
URL: http://dunsmuir.com
Contact: Luann Wiegele, President
Facebook: www.facebook.com/dunsmuircoc
Description: Promotes business and community development in Dunsmuir, CA. **Founded:** 1949. **Geographic Preference:** Local.

36870 ■ Eagle Rock Chamber of Commerce
PO Box 41354
Eagle Rock, CA 90041
Ph: (323)257-2197
Co. E-mail: eaglerockchamberofcommerce@gmail.com
URL: http://www.eaglerockchamberofcommerce.com
Contact: Michael Nogueira, President
X (Twitter): x.com/ER_Chamber
Description: Promotes business and community development in Eagle Rock, CA area. **Geographic Preference:** Local.

36871 ■ East Los Angeles Chamber of Commerce
4716 E Cesar Chavez Ave.
Los Angeles, CA 90022
Ph: (323)263-2005
Co. E-mail: eastlachamber@icloud.com
URL: http://eastlachamber.com
Contact: Norma Aguirre, President
Facebook: www.facebook.com/eastlachamberofcommerce
X (Twitter): x.com/eastlacham
Description: Promotes business and community development in East Los Angeles, CA. **Founded:** 1988. **Geographic Preference:** Local.

36872 ■ *Eblast Newsletter*
40061 Hwy. 49, Ste. 102
Oakhurst, CA 93644
Ph: (559)683-7766
Co. E-mail: chamber@oakhurstchamber.com
URL: http://oakhurstchamber.com
Contact: Wade Wheeler, President
URL(s): www.oakhurstchamber.com/newsletter
Released: Weekly **Availability:** Online.

36873 ■ *Economic Report*
27758 Santa Margarita Pky., No. 378
Mission Viejo, CA 92691
Ph: (949)600-5470
Co. E-mail: info@economiccoalition.com
URL: http://www.economiccoalition.com
Contact: Mike Balsamo, Chairman
URL(s): www.economiccoalition.com/economic-report
Released: Annual **Availability:** Print; Download.

36874 ■ El Centro Chamber of Commerce and Visitors Bureau
1095 S 4th St.
El Centro, CA 92243
Ph: (760)352-3681
Fax: (760)352-3246
Co. E-mail: info@elcentrochamber.com
URL: http://www.elcentrochamber.org
Contact: Anne Irigoyen, President
Facebook: www.facebook.com/ElCentroChamber
X (Twitter): twitter.com/elcentrochamber
Instagram: www.instagram.com/elcentrochamber

36875 ■ California

Description: Promotes business and community development in El Centro, CA. **Awards:** El Centro Chamber of Commerce and Visitors Bureau Star Award (Monthly). **Geographic Preference:** Local.

36875 ■ The El Cerrito Chamber of Commerce (ECCC)
10895 San Pablo Ave.
El Cerrito, CA 94530
Ph: (510)705-1202
Co. E-mail: info@elcerritochamber.org
URL: http://www.elcerritochamber.org
Contact: Jeffrey Wright, President
Facebook: www.facebook.com/elcerritochamber
X (Twitter): x.com/cerritochamber

Description: Promotes business and community development in El Cerrito, CA. **Founded:** 1936. **Publications:** Byline (Monthly); California Chamber Advocate (Periodic); Membership and Business Directory (Periodic). **Geographic Preference:** Local.

36876 ■ El Dorado County Chamber of Commerce
542 Main St.
Placerville, CA 95667
Ph: (530)621-5885
Co. E-mail: chamber@eldoradocounty.org
URL: http://eldoradocounty.org
Contact: Leonard Grado, President
E-mail: lgrado@palosverdespropertiesinc.com
Facebook: www.facebook.com/ElDoradoCountyChamber

Description: Promotes business and community development in El Dorado County, CA. **Founded:** 1915. **Publications:** Business Directory; El Dorado Magazine; Ranch Marketing Guide. **Geographic Preference:** Local.

36877 ■ El Dorado Hills Chamber of Commerce
2085 Vine St., Ste. 105
El Dorado Hills, CA 95762
Ph: (916)933-1335
Fax: (916)933-5908
Co. E-mail: chamber@eldoradohillschamber.org
URL: http://www.eldoradohillschamber.com
Contact: Debbie Manning, President
E-mail: debbie@eldoradohillschamber.org
Facebook: www.facebook.com/pg/eldoradohillschamber
X (Twitter): x.com/EDHChamber
Instagram: www.instagram.com/edhchamber
YouTube: www.youtube.com/channel/UC11n_cSUGfNeBS-o2s8sq0Q
Pinterest: www.pinterest.com/edhchamber

Description: Aims to advance the interests of the business community in the City of El Dorado Hills, CA. **Geographic Preference:** Local.

36878 ■ El Segundo Chamber of Commerce
427 Main St.
El Segundo, CA 90245
Ph: (310)322-1220
Co. E-mail: info@elsegundochamber.org
URL: http://www.elsegundochamber.com
Contact: Marsha Hansen, Chief Executive Officer
Facebook: www.facebook.com/elsegundochamber

Description: Promotes business and community development in El Segundo, CA. Sponsors Main St. Run, Richmond St. Fair, and Christmas Parade. Conducts Business Outlook, business expo, seminars, and networking breakfasts. **Founded:** 1917. **Awards:** El Segundo Chamber of Commerce Business of the Year (Annual). **Geographic Preference:** Local.

36879 ■ El Sobrante Chamber of Commerce
3769 San Pablo Dam Rd.
El Sobrante, CA 94803
Ph: (510)223-0757
Co. E-mail: info@elsobrantechamber.com
URL: http://www.elsobrantecachamber.com
Contact: A. Scott Tuffnell, President
Facebook: www.facebook.com/elsobrantechamberofcommerce

Description: Promotes business and community development in the El Sobrante, CA area. **Geographic Preference:** Local.

36880 ■ Elk Grove Chamber of Commerce
8820 Elk Grove Blvd.
Elk Grove, CA 95624
Ph: (916)691-3760
Fax: (916)691-3810
Co. E-mail: chamber@elkgroveca.com
URL: http://www.elkgroveca.com
Contact: Angela Perry, President
E-mail: aperry@elkgroveca.com
Facebook: www.facebook.com/elkgrovechamber
Linkedin: www.linkedin.com/in/elk-grove-chamber-of-commerce-41930b39
X (Twitter): x.com/elkgrovechamber

Description: Promotes business and community development in Elk Grove, CA. **Founded:** 1952. **Publications:** Focus on Business (Quarterly). **Geographic Preference:** Local.

36881 ■ Encinitas Chamber of Commerce (ECC)
535 Encinitas Blvd., Ste. 116
Encinitas, CA 92024
Ph: (760)753-6041
Fax: (760)753-6270
Co. E-mail: support@encinitaschamber.com
URL: http://encinitaschamber.com
Contact: David DaCosta, Chairman
E-mail: david@dacostaproperties.com
Facebook: www.facebook.com/EncinitasChamberOfCommerce
Linkedin: www.linkedin.com/in/encinitas-chamber-of-commerce-63a55929
X (Twitter): x.com/encinitaschambe

Description: Promotes business and community development in Encinitas, CA. **Founded:** 1966. **Publications:** What to Know (Monthly). **Geographic Preference:** Local.

36882 ■ Encino Chamber of Commerce
4933 Balboa Blvd.
Encino, CA 91316
Ph: (818)789-4711
Fax: (818)789-2485
Co. E-mail: info@encinochamber.org
URL: http://www.encinochamber.org
Contact: Diana Donovan Duenas, Chief Executive Officer
E-mail: diana@encinochamber.org
Facebook: www.facebook.com/EncinoChamberofCommerce
X (Twitter): x.com/encinochamber
YouTube: www.youtube.com/encinochamber
Pinterest: www.pinterest.com/ceo0674

Description: Promotes business and community development in Encino, CA. **Founded:** 1936. **Publications:** Encino Chamber of Commerce Envoy (Monthly). **Geographic Preference:** Local.

36883 ■ Escalon Chamber of Commerce
PO Box 222
Escalon, CA 95320
Ph: (209)838-2793
Co. E-mail: escaloncofc@gmail.com
URL: http://www.escalonchamberofcommerce.org
Contact: Pat Brown, President

Description: Promotes business and community development in the Escalon, CA area. Conducts charitable activities; sponsors competitions and festivals. **Geographic Preference:** Local.

36884 ■ Escondido Chamber of Commerce
720 N Broadway
Escondido, CA 92025
Ph: (760)745-2125
Fax: (760)745-1183
Co. E-mail: info@escondidochamber.org
URL: http://escondidochamber.org
Contact: James Rowten, President
Facebook: www.facebook.com/Escochamber
Linkedin: www.linkedin.com/company/escondido-chamber-of-commerce
X (Twitter): x.com/escondidochambe
Instagram: www.instagram.com/escondidochamber

YouTube: www.youtube.com/user/EscondidoChamber

Description: Promotes business and community development in Escondido, CA. **Founded:** 1910. **Publications:** Business Resource Directory (Annual). **Awards:** Escondido Chamber of Commerce Business Leader of the Year (Annual). **Geographic Preference:** Local.

36885 ■ Esparto Regional Chamber of Commerce
16858 Yolo Ave.
Esparto, CA 95627
Ph: (530)787-3242
Co. E-mail: espartoregionalchamber@gmail.com
URL: http://www.espartoregionalchamber.com
Facebook: www.facebook.com/Espartoregionalchamber

Description: Promotes business and community development in Esparto District, CA. Sponsors Capay Valley Almond Festival. **Geographic Preference:** Local.

36886 ■ The Eureka Chamber Review
612 G St., Ste. 101
Eureka, CA 95501
Ph: (707)442-3738
URL: http://www.eurekachamber.com
Contact: Dane Valadao, Treasurer
URL(s): eurekachamber.com/eureka-chamber-newsletter

Released: Monthly **Description:** Features what is going on in the local business community. **Availability:** PDF; Online.

36887 ■ Events Calendar - Community
353 Camino El Estero
Monterey, CA 93940
Ph: (831)648-5350
Co. E-mail: info@montereychamber.com
URL: http://www.montereychamber.com
Contact: Monica Lal, President
E-mail: monica@montereychamber.com
URL(s): members.montereychamber.com/list

Released: Annual **Availability:** Online.

36888 ■ Exeter Chamber of Commerce
101 W Pine St.
Exeter, CA 93221
Ph: (559)592-2919
Fax: (559)592-3720
Co. E-mail: chamber@exeterchamber.com
URL: http://www.exeterchamber.com
Contact: John Guinn, Co-President
Facebook: www.facebook.com/exeterchamber
Instagram: www.instagram.com/exeterchamber

Description: Promotes and supports business and community development in Exeter, CA. **Founded:** 1909. **Publications:** Available Properties Listing Guide (Monthly); Chamber Report (3/year). **Educational Activities:** Annual Fall Festival (Annual). **Geographic Preference:** Local.

36889 ■ Fair Oaks Business Directory
PO Box 352
Fair Oaks, CA 95628
Ph: (916)967-2903
Co. E-mail: info@fairoakschamber.com
URL: http://www.fairoakschamber.com
Contact: Kimberley Pitillo, Executive Director
URL(s): www.fairoakschamber.com/business-directory

Availability: Online.

36890 ■ Fair Oaks Chamber of Commerce
PO Box 352
Fair Oaks, CA 95628
Ph: (916)967-2903
Co. E-mail: info@fairoakschamber.com
URL: http://www.fairoakschamber.com
Contact: Kimberley Pitillo, Executive Director
Facebook: www.facebook.com/TheFairOaksChamber
Instagram: www.instagram.com/myfairoaks

Description: Promotes business and community development in Fair Oaks, CA. Sponsors Fiesta, Business/Networking Fair, Octoberfest, Safe Hal-

STATE LISTINGS

California ■ 36904

loween, Business/Education Internships, Christmas in Village, and Summer Concerts In The Park. **Founded:** 1895. **Publications:** *Fair Oaks Business Directory; Burbank Business Newsletter* (Monthly). **Educational Activities:** Business Networking Mixers (Monthly). **Geographic Preference:** Local.

36891 ■ Fallbrook Chamber of Commerce
111 S Main Ave.
 Fallbrook, CA 92028
Ph: (760)728-5845
Fax: (760)728-4031
Co. E-mail: info@fallbrookchamberofcommerce.org
URL: http://fallbrookchamberofcommerce.org
Contact: Nicholas Beye, President
Facebook: www.facebook.com/FallbrookChamberofCommerce
Linkedin: www.linkedin.com/company/fallbrook-chamber-of-commerce
Instagram: www.instagram.com/fallbrookchamber
YouTube: www.youtube.com/channel/UCU8IPt73Iy4cydgb_gELv6A
Description: Promotes business and community development in Fallbrook, CA. Sponsors Avocado Harvest Festival and Avocado Open Golf Tournament. **Founded:** 1949. **Publications:** *Fallbrook's Chamber of Commerce Newsletter* (Weekly). **Educational Activities:** Sundowners (Monthly). **Geographic Preference:** Local.

36892 ■ *Fallbrook's Chamber of Commerce Newsletter*
111 S Main Ave.
 Fallbrook, CA 92028
Ph: (760)728-5845
Fax: (760)728-4031
Co. E-mail: info@fallbrookchamberofcommerce.org
URL: http://fallbrookchamberofcommerce.org
Contact: Nicholas Beye, President
URL(s): www.fallbrookchamberofcommerce.org/newsletters
Released: Weekly **Availability:** Online.

36893 ■ Folsom Chamber of Commerce
200 Wool St.
 Folsom, CA 95630
Ph: (916)985-2698
Co. E-mail: info@folsompartners.com
URL: http://www.folsomchamber.com
Contact: Nancy Christeson, Specialist
E-mail: nancyc@folsompartners.com
URL(s): www.choosefolsom.com
Facebook: www.facebook.com/FolsomChamberofCommerce
Instagram: www.instagram.com/folsomchamber
YouTube: www.youtube.com/user/folsomchamber
Description: Promotes business and community development in Folsom, CA. **Founded:** 1946. **Publications:** *Business Directory; All About Folsom Business* (Monthly); *Folsom Magazine* (Annual). **Geographic Preference:** Local.

36894 ■ Fontana Chamber of Commerce
8491 Sierra Ave.
 Fontana, CA 92335
Ph: (909)822-4433
Co. E-mail: info@fontanachamber.com
URL: http://www.fontanachamber.org
Contact: Phil Cothran, President
Facebook: www.facebook.com/fontanachamber
Linkedin: www.linkedin.com/company/fontana-chamber
X (Twitter): x.com/fontanachamber
Instagram: www.instagram.com/fontanachamber
Description: Promotes business and community development in the Fontana, CA area. **Founded:** 1914. **Geographic Preference:** Local.

36895 ■ Foresthill Divide Chamber of Commerce
24470 Main St., Ste. B
 Foresthill, CA 95631
Ph: (530)367-2474
Co. E-mail: foresthillchamber@sebastiancorp.net
URL: http://www.foresthillchamber.com
X (Twitter): x.com/foresthillcham1

Description: Promotes business and community development in Foresthill, CA. **Geographic Preference:** Local.

36896 ■ Fort Bragg - Mendocino Coast Chamber of Commerce
217 S Main St.
 Fort Bragg, CA 95437
Ph: (707)961-6300
Co. E-mail: chamber@mcn.org
URL: http://mendocinocoast.com
Contact: Curtis Bruchler, Chairman
Facebook: www.facebook.com/MendocinoCoastChamber
X (Twitter): x.com/Mendocinocoast
Instagram: www.instagram.com/mendocinocoast
YouTube: www.youtube.com/channel/UCMq7s1BsjPCmEANScFt5Tsg
Pinterest: www.pinterest.com/visitftbraggca
Description: Promotes business and community development in the Mendocino Coast area. Sponsors whale festivals every March. **Founded:** 1951. **Publications:** *The Current* (Monthly); *Medocino Coast Business Directory; Mendocino Map and Visitor Information Guide* (Annual). **Geographic Preference:** Local.

36897 ■ Fortuna Chamber of Commerce (FCC)
735 14th St.
 Fortuna, CA 95540
Ph: (707)725-3959
Free: 800-426-8166
Co. E-mail: ceo@fortunachamber.com
URL: http://fortunachamber.com/membership
Contact: Renee Lindsay, President
E-mail: ceo@fortunachamber.com
Facebook: www.facebook.com/fortunachamber
X (Twitter): x.com/fortunachamber
Instagram: www.instagram.com/fortunachamber
YouTube: www.youtube.com/channel/UCOkQeDMeUOdZX1TceqBfWzA
Description: Promotes business and community development in Fortuna, CA. Sponsors festival. **Founded:** 1920. **Geographic Preference:** Local.

36898 ■ Foster City Chamber of Commerce
100 Grand Ln., Ste. B
 Foster City, CA 94404
Ph: (650)573-7600
Co. E-mail: info@fostercitychamber.com
URL: http://business.fostercitychamber.com
Contact: Marah Curry, Director
E-mail: mcurry@fostercitychamber.com
Linkedin: www.linkedin.com/company/foster-city-chamber-of-commerce
X (Twitter): x.com/ThinkFosterCity
YouTube: www.youtube.com/channel/UCrEBQaICxYZkQVCZDo4ATCw
Description: Promotes business and community development in Foster City, CA. Sponsors annual Art and Wine Festival. **Founded:** 1972. **Geographic Preference:** Local.

36899 ■ Fountain Valley Chamber of Commerce
10055 Slater Ave., Ste. 250
 Fountain Valley, CA 92708
Ph: (714)962-3822
Co. E-mail: info@fvchamber.com
URL: http://www.fvchamber.com
Contact: Memory Bartlett, President
E-mail: ceo@fvchamber.com
Linkedin: www.linkedin.com/company/fountain-valley-chamber-of-commerce-ca
X (Twitter): x.com/FV_Chamber
Description: Promotes business and community development in Fountain Valley, CA. **Founded:** 1966. **Awards:** FV Chamber Ambassador of the Year (Annual). **Geographic Preference:** Local.

36900 ■ *Fremont Business Review*
39488 Stevenson Pl., Ste. 100
 Fremont, CA 94539
Ph: (510)795-2244
Fax: (510)795-2244
Co. E-mail: fmtcc@fremontbusiness.com

URL: http://www.fremontbusiness.com
Contact: Cindy Bonior, II, Chief Executive Officer
E-mail: cbonior@fremontbusiness.com
URL(s): www.fremontbusiness.com/advertising-opportunities1.html
Description: Includes promotional articles and meeting information. **Availability:** Print; Download; PDF; Online.

36901 ■ Fremont Chamber of Commerce (FCC)
39488 Stevenson Pl., Ste. 100
 Fremont, CA 94539
Ph: (510)795-2244
Fax: (510)795-2244
Co. E-mail: fmtcc@fremontbusiness.com
URL: http://www.fremontbusiness.com
Contact: Cindy Bonior, II, Chief Executive Officer
E-mail: cbonior@fremontbusiness.com
Facebook: www.facebook.com/FremontBusiness
X (Twitter): x.com/FremontBusiness
YouTube: www.youtube.com/user/FremontBusiness
Description: Promotes business and community development in Fremont, CA. Sponsors Festival of the Arts. Conducts business education and assistance programs. **Founded:** 1956. **Publications:** *Fremont Chamber of Commerce--Business Directory; Fremont Business Review; Fremont Chamber of Commerce Membership Directory and Guide.* **Geographic Preference:** Local.

36902 ■ *Fremont Chamber of Commerce Membership Directory and Guide*
39488 Stevenson Pl., Ste. 100
 Fremont, CA 94539
Ph: (510)795-2244
Fax: (510)795-2244
Co. E-mail: fmtcc@fremontbusiness.com
URL: http://www.fremontbusiness.com
Contact: Cindy Bonior, II, Chief Executive Officer
E-mail: cbonior@fremontbusiness.com
URL(s): www.fremontbusiness.com/marketing--advertising.html
Description: Contains membership listing and information about Fremont. **Availability:** Print; Online.

36903 ■ Galt District Chamber of Commerce (GCC)
604 N Lincoln Way
 Galt, CA 95632
Ph: (209)745-2529
Co. E-mail: galtchamber@gmail.com
URL: http://www.galtchamber.com
Contact: Kevin Borges, President
Facebook: www.facebook.com/GaltChamber
Instagram: www.instagram.com/galtchamber
YouTube: www.youtube.com/channel/UC-PL_RIYvnK4EPv_izywZjA
Description: Promotes business and community development in Galt, CA. Sponsors the Merchant's Fair and Galt Strawberry Festival. **Founded:** 1940. **Publications:** *Galt Today* (Bimonthly). **Geographic Preference:** Local.

36904 ■ Garden Grove Chamber of Commerce (GGCC)
12866 Main St.
 Garden Grove, CA 92840
Ph: (714)638-7950
Free: 800-959-5560
Co. E-mail: staff@gardengrovechamber.com
URL: http://gardengrovechamber.com
Contact: Cindy Spindle, Co-President Co-Chief Executive Officer
E-mail: ceo@gardengrovechamber.com
Facebook: www.facebook.com/gardengrovechamber
X (Twitter): x.com/GGChamber
YouTube: www.youtube.com/channel/UCIqUJW9q83Z_6orbo51tRQg
Description: Aims to serve the needs of the Garden Grove business community. Represents professionals from a wide variety of companies who are committed to promoting business in the community. **Founded:** 1907. **Geographic Preference:** Local.

36905 ■ Gardena Valley Chamber of Commerce (GVCC)
1204 W Gardena Blvd., Ste. E
Gardena, CA 90247
Ph: (310)532-9905
Co. E-mail: info@gardenachamber.org
URL: http://www.gardenachamber.org
Contact: Wanda Love, Executive Director
Facebook: www.facebook.com/GardenaValleyChamberofCommerce
X (Twitter): x.com/GardenaChamber
Instagram: www.instagram.com/gardenachamber
Description: Promotes business and community development in Gardena, CA. Conducts Business Expo and golf tournament. Sponsors fundraising activities. **Founded:** 1933. **Publications:** *Chamber Newsletters* (Monthly); *Gardena Valley Chamber of Commerce Membership directory*; *Gardena Valley Chamber of Commerce Directory*; *Gardena Valley Business Directory*. **Geographic Preference:** Local.

36906 ■ *Gardena Valley Chamber of Commerce Membership directory*
1204 W Gardena Blvd., Ste. E
Gardena, CA 90247
Ph: (310)532-9905
Co. E-mail: info@gardenachamber.org
URL: http://www.gardenachamber.org
Contact: Wanda Love, Executive Director
URL(s): www.gardenachamber.org/directory
Availability: Print.

36907 ■ Geyserville Chamber of Commerce (GCC)
PO Box 276
Geyserville, CA 95441
Ph: (707)276-6067
Co. E-mail: geyservillechamberofcommerce@gmail.com
URL: http://www.visitgeyserville.com
Contact: Bruce Lawton, President
Facebook: www.facebook.com/visitgeyserville
Instagram: www.instagram.com/visitgeyserville
Description: Promotes business and community development in Geyserville, CA. **Founded:** 1847. **Geographic Preference:** Local.

36908 ■ *Gilroy*
7471 Monterey St.
Gilroy, CA 95020
Ph: (408)842-6437
Co. E-mail: chamber@gilroy.org
URL: http://gilroy.org
Contact: Mark Turner, President
E-mail: mturner@gilroy.org
URL(s): cca.gilroy.org/businesssearch.aspx
Availability: Print.

36909 ■ Gilroy Chamber of Commerce (GCC)
7471 Monterey St.
Gilroy, CA 95020
Ph: (408)842-6437
Co. E-mail: chamber@gilroy.org
URL: http://gilroy.org
Contact: Mark Turner, President
E-mail: mturner@gilroy.org
Facebook: www.facebook.com/GilroyChamberofCommerce
Instagram: www.instagram.com/gilroychamber
Description: Seeks to promote economic vitality in the Gilroy community. Provides marketing opportunities for businesses for an increased network. Has partnerships with City of Gilroy, Gilroy Economic Development Corp., Gilroy Visitors Bureau, Leadership Gilroy, Gilroy Downtown Development Corp. and school district. **Founded:** 1952. **Publications:** *Gilroy*; *Gilroy Business Focus*. **Geographic Preference:** Local.

36910 ■ *Glendale Business*
701 N Brand Blvd., Ste. 120
Glendale, CA 91203
Ph: (818)240-7870
Fax: (818)240-2872
Co. E-mail: info@glendalechamber.com
URL: http://www.glendalechamber.com
Contact: Judee Kendall, President
E-mail: jkendall@glendalechamber.com
URL(s): www.glendalechamber.com/membership/marketing-opportunities
Availability: Online.

36911 ■ Glendale Chamber of Commerce (GCC)
701 N Brand Blvd., Ste. 120
Glendale, CA 91203
Ph: (818)240-7870
Fax: (818)240-2872
Co. E-mail: info@glendalechamber.com
URL: http://www.glendalechamber.com
Contact: Judee Kendall, President
E-mail: jkendall@glendalechamber.com
Facebook: www.facebook.com/GlendaleChamberCA
X (Twitter): x.com/GlendaleCAChmbr
Description: Promotes business and community development in Glendale, CA. **Founded:** 1910. **Publications:** *Glendale Business*. **Geographic Preference:** Local.

36912 ■ Glendora Chamber of Commerce
224 N Glendora Ave.
Glendora, CA 91741-3336
Ph: (626)963-4128
Co. E-mail: info@glendora-chamber.org
URL: http://www.glendora-chamber.org
Contact: Joe Cina, President
Facebook: www.facebook.com/GlendoraChamber
X (Twitter): x.com/glendorachamber
YouTube: www.youtube.com/user/glendorachamber
Description: Promotes business and community development in Glendora, CA. **Founded:** 1916. **Publications:** *Business View*. **Educational Activities:** Community Expo & Carrier Fair. **Geographic Preference:** Local.

36913 ■ Granada Hills Chamber of Commerce
17723 Chatsworth St.
Granada Hills, CA 91344
Ph: (818)368-3235
Fax: (818)366-7425
Co. E-mail: email@granadachamber.com
URL: http://www.granadachamber.com
Contact: Moe Biloo, President
Description: Promotes business and community development in Granada Hills, CA. **Founded:** 1927. **Geographic Preference:** Local.

36914 ■ Grand Terrace Area Chamber of Commerce
22400 Barton Rd., No. 21-306
Grand Terrace, CA 92313
Ph: (909)954-5003
Co. E-mail: info@gtchamber.org
URL: http://www.gtchamber.org
Contact: Claudia Cooley, President
URL(s): www.chamber-commerce.net/dir/6956
Description: Promotes business and community development in Grand Terrace, CA. Sponsors monthly luncheon, quarterly business mixers. **Founded:** 1963. **Geographic Preference:** Local.

36915 ■ Greater Bakersfield Chamber of Commerce
1725 Eye St.
Bakersfield, CA 93301
Ph: (661)327-4421
Co. E-mail: info@bakochamber.com
URL: http://www.bakersfieldchamber.org
Contact: Nick Ortiz, President
E-mail: nortiz@bakochamber.com
Facebook: www.facebook.com/bakochamber
Linkedin: www.linkedin.com/company/greater-bakersfield-chamber-of-commerce
Instagram: www.instagram.com/bakochamber
YouTube: www.youtube.com/user/BakersfieldChamber
Description: Bankers and beauticians, communications consultants and caterers. Provides leadership to promote a healthy environment for business through networking, advocacy, learning and community service. **Founded:** 1920. **Geographic Preference:** Local.

36916 ■ Greater Concord Chamber of Commerce
2280 Diamond Blvd., Ste. 200
Concord, CA 94520
Ph: (925)685-1181
Co. E-mail: info@concordchamber.com
URL: http://www.concordchamber.com
Contact: Marc Maier, Chairman
Facebook: www.facebook.com/concordchamberca
Linkedin: www.linkedin.com/company/greater-concord-chamber-of-commerce
X (Twitter): x.com/ConcordChamber1
YouTube: www.youtube.com/channel/UCF45RtmNEn2v0svmXbUWS8A
Description: Promotes business and community development in Concord, CA. **Founded:** 1937. **Geographic Preference:** Local.

36917 ■ Greater Conejo Valley Chamber of Commerce (GCVCC)
600 Hampshire Rd., Ste. 200
Westlake Village, CA 91361
Ph: (805)370-0035
Fax: (805)370-1083
Co. E-mail: chamber@conejochamber.org
URL: http://www.conejochamber.org
Contact: Danielle Borja, President
E-mail: dborja@conejochamber.org
Facebook: www.facebook.com/GreaterConejoValleyChamber
Linkedin: www.linkedin.com/company/greater-conejo-valley-chamber-of-commerce
X (Twitter): x.com/ConejoChamber1
Instagram: www.instagram.com/conejochamber
YouTube: www.youtube.com/channel/UCVRWIysoCw0HZ2NDHPSI6ag
Description: Business owners and individuals. Works together to advance the commercial, financial, industrial, and civic interests of the community. **Founded:** 1939. **Publications:** *Greater Conejo Valley Chamber of Commerce--Directory*; *Business Directory*; *Conejo Business Times* (Monthly). **Educational Activities:** Chamber After Five Mixer; Networking Breakfast of Champions. **Geographic Preference:** Local; Regional.

36918 ■ Greater Eureka Chamber of Commerce
612 G St., Ste. 101
Eureka, CA 95501
Ph: (707)442-3738
URL: http://www.eurekachamber.com
Contact: Dane Valadao, Treasurer
Facebook: www.facebook.com/eurekachamberofcommerce
X (Twitter): x.com/chambereureka
Description: Promotes business and community development in Eureka, CA. **Founded:** 1891. **Publications:** *The Eureka Chamber Review* (Monthly). **Geographic Preference:** Local.

36919 ■ Greater Fresno Area Chamber of Commerce [Fresno Chamber of Commerce]
2331 Fresno St.
Fresno, CA 93721
Ph: (559)495-4800
Fax: (559)495-4811
Co. E-mail: info@fresnochamber.com
URL: http://fresnochamber.com
Contact: Scott Miller, President
E-mail: smiller@fresnochamber.com
Facebook: www.facebook.com/FresnoChamberOfCommerce
X (Twitter): x.com/Fresno_Chamber
Instagram: www.instagram.com/fresno_chamber
Description: Promotes business and community development in the Fresno County, CA area. Serves as a voice of business on local and state level. **Founded:** 1885. **Publications:** *Fresno Business Newsletter* (Monthly); *Community Guide & Membership Directory*. **Educational Activities:** The Big Fresno Fair (Annual). **Geographic Preference:** Local.

STATE LISTINGS

36920 ■ Greater High Desert Chamber of Commerce (GHDCC)
15428 Civic Dr., Ste. 310
Victorville, CA 92392
Ph: (760)245-6506
URL: http://www.ghdcc.com
Contact: Mrk Creffield, President
E-mail: mark@ghdcc.com
Facebook: www.facebook.com/TheGHDCC
X (Twitter): x.com/GHDChamber
YouTube: www.youtube.com/channel/UCTApz_nyxUKo24k9K8_H7Lw
Description: Supports and sustains a thriving regional business community with a strong and unified voice that prospers through informed leaders and vital legislative support, and offers educational, high-level networking, and enhanced promotional opportunities. **Founded:** 2021. **Geographic Preference:** Local.

36921 ■ Greater Huntington Park Area Chamber of Commerce
6725 Seville Ave.
Huntington Park, CA 90255
Ph: (323)585-1155
Fax: (323)585-2176
Co. E-mail: info@hpchamber.org
URL: http://www.hpchamber.org
Contact: Andy Molina, President
Facebook: www.facebook.com/HPAreaChamber
Linkedin: www.linkedin.com/company/the-greater-huntington-park-area-chambr-of-commerce
X (Twitter): x.com/hpareaChamber
Instagram: www.instagram.com/hp_chamber_of_commerce
YouTube: www.youtube.com/channel/UCwX_FXc6PXysxZ1-mD2Cb6Q/featured
Description: Promotes business and community development in Huntington Park, CA. **Founded:** 1906. **Geographic Preference:** Local.

36922 ■ Greater Ontario Business Council (GOBC)
3200 Inland Empire Blvd., Ste. 130
Ontario, CA 91764
Ph: (909)984-2458
Co. E-mail: info@ontario.org
URL: http://www.ontario.org
Contact: Michael Gialluly, Treasurer
Facebook: www.facebook.com/greaterontariobusinesscouncil
X (Twitter): x.com/ontbuscouncil
Instagram: www.instagram.com/greaterontariobusinesscouncil
Description: Strives to help develop, enhance, and promote commerce in the city of Ontario and its trade area. Sponsors business golf tournament in April, police officers' recognition luncheon in May, Christmas on Euclid craft show, Police and Fire Safety Fair, health fair, chili cook, Christmas tree decorating contest for local schools and Nativity scene. **Founded:** 1910. **Publications:** *The Ontario Business Journal* (Monthly); *Who's Who in Chamber Membership* (Annual). **Educational Activities:** Ontario Chamber of Commerce Luncheon (Annual). **Geographic Preference:** Local.

36923 ■ Greater Redding Chamber of Commerce
1321 Butte St., No. 100
Redding, CA 96001-1034
Ph: (530)225-4433
Co. E-mail: valerie@reddingchamber.com
URL: http://reddingchamber.com
Contact: Erin Hull, Vice President
Facebook: www.facebook.com/ReddingChamberofCommerce
X (Twitter): x.com/redding_chamber
Instagram: www.instagram.com/reddingchamber
YouTube: www.youtube.com/channel/UC8Vzr4Sxc6a6Bmf3ZmBDG-g
Description: Promotes business and community development in the Greater Redding, CA area. **Founded:** 1910. **Publications:** *Business* (Annual); *Redding Directions* (Monthly). **Geographic Preference:** Local.

36924 ■ Greater Riverside Chambers of Commerce (GRCC)
3985 University Ave.
Riverside, CA 92501
Ph: (951)683-7100
Fax: (951)683-2670
Co. E-mail: rchamber@riverside-chamber.com
URL: http://www.riverside-chamber.com
Contact: Cindy Roth, President
E-mail: croth@riverside-chamber.com
Facebook: www.facebook.com/RiversideChamber
X (Twitter): x.com/RivChamber
YouTube: www.youtube.com/user/riversidechamber
Description: Promotes business and community development in the Riverside, CA area. **Founded:** 1962. **Publications:** *The Chamber Communicator* (Weekly). **Awards:** Raincross Trophy Dinner (Annual). **Geographic Preference:** Local.

36925 ■ Greater San Fernando Valley Chamber of Commerce
7120 Hayvenhurst Ave., Ste. 114
Van Nuys, CA 91406
Ph: (818)989-0300
Fax: (818)989-3836
URL: http://www.sanfernandovalleychamber.com
Contact: Mark L. Levinson, Attorney Chairman
X (Twitter): x.com/gsfvcc
Description: Promotes business and community development in the Van Nuys, CA area. **Founded:** 1911. **Publications:** *Chamber Today* (Monthly); *Speakers' Bureau Listing*. **Educational Activities:** Inaugural Ball (Annual). **Geographic Preference:** Local.

36926 ■ Greater Sherman Oaks Chamber of Commerce [Sherman Oaks Chamber of Commerce]
14827 Ventura Blvd., Ste. 207
Sherman Oaks, CA 91403
Ph: (818)906-1951
Fax: (818)206-0288
Co. E-mail: hello@shermanoakschamber.org
URL: http://www.shermanoakschamber.org
Contact: Tammy Scher, Chairperson
E-mail: tammy@shermanoakschamber.org
Facebook: www.facebook.com/ShermanOaksChamber
Linkedin: www.linkedin.com/in/shermanoakschamber
Instagram: www.instagram.com/shermanoakschamber
Description: Promotes business and community development in Sherman Oaks, CA. **Founded:** 1947. **Publications:** *Sherman Oaks Chamber NEWS*. **Geographic Preference:** Local.

36927 ■ Greater Stockton Chamber of Commerce (GSCC)
445 W Weber Ave., Ste. 220
Stockton, CA 95203
Ph: (209)547-2770
Fax: (209)466-5271
Co. E-mail: schamber@stocktonchamber.org
URL: http://stocktonchamber.org
Contact: Chris Kay, President
X (Twitter): x.com/StknChamber
YouTube: www.youtube.com/channel/UCVO2nGBrw7F_d-Jbw45Q2aQ
Description: Promotes business and community development in the Stockton, CA area. **Founded:** 1901. **Publications:** *Greater Stockton Chamber of Commerce--Membership Directory*; *Port O Call* (Monthly); *Industrial Directory, Stockton, San Joaquin County, California: Manufacturers, Wholesalers, Distributors* (Biennial). **Awards:** Greater Stockton Chamber of Commerce Agricultural Hall of Fame (Annual). **Geographic Preference:** Local.

36928 ■ Greater Tehachapi Chamber of Commerce (GTCC)
209 E Tehachapi Blvd.
Tehachapi, CA 93581
Ph: (661)822-4180
Fax: (661)822-9036
Co. E-mail: chamber@tehachapi.com
URL: http://www.tehachapi.com
Contact: Ida Perkins, President
E-mail: idaperkins@tehachapi.com
Description: Promotes business and community development in the greater Tehachapi, CA area. Sponsors rodeo and Mountain Festival. **Founded:** 1909. **Awards:** Greater Tehachapi Chamber of Commerce Business of the Year (Annual); Greater Tehachapi Chamber of Commerce Citizen of the Year (Annual). **Geographic Preference:** Local.

36929 ■ Greater Trinidad Chamber of Commerce
PO Box 356
Trinidad, CA 95570
Ph: (707)677-8645
Co. E-mail: greatertrinidadchamber@gmail.com
URL: http://www.exploretrinidadca.com
Contact: Brett Shuler, President
Facebook: www.facebook.com/TrinidadChamber
Description: Promotes business and community development in the greater Trinidad, CA area. **Founded:** 1950. **Geographic Preference:** Local.

36930 ■ Greater Ukiah Chamber of Commerce (GUCC)
200 S School St.
Ukiah, CA 95482
Ph: (707)462-4705
Fax: (707)462-5059
Co. E-mail: exploreukiah@gmail.com
URL: http://www.discoverukiah.com
Facebook: www.facebook.com/discoverukiah
Instagram: www.instagram.com/discoverukiah
Description: Promotes business and community development in the greater Ukiah, CA area. Conducts business networking and community promotional events. **Founded:** 1927. **Geographic Preference:** Local.

36931 ■ Gridley Area Chamber of Commerce
890 Hazel St.
Gridley, CA 95948
Ph: (530)846-3142
Co. E-mail: info@gridleyareachamber.org
URL: http://gridleyareachamber.org
Contact: Lynne Spencer, President
Facebook: www.facebook.com/GridleyAreaChamber
Description: Promotes business and community development in Gridley, CA. Sponsors Red Suspenders Day in May, the Pioneer Christmas Parade in December. **Founded:** 1946. **Publications:** *The Gridley Herald*; *Map of Gridley*; *Guide to Gridley* (Annual). **Geographic Preference:** Local.

36932 ■ Gustine Chamber of Commerce
375 5th St.
Gustine, CA 95322
Ph: (209)854-6975
Co. E-mail: gustinechamber@att.net
URL: http://www.gustinechamberofcommerce.com
Contact: Debbie Goularte, President
Facebook: www.facebook.com/gustinecofc
Instagram: www.instagram.com/gustinechamber
Description: Promotes business and community development in Gustine, CA. Sponsors Farmer's Market. **Founded:** 1913. **Publications:** *Business Directory*. **Geographic Preference:** Local.

36933 ■ Half Moon Bay Coastside Chamber of Commerce and Visitors Bureau
235 Main St.
Half Moon Bay, CA 94019
Ph: (650)726-8380
Co. E-mail: info@hmbchamber.com
URL: http://www.visithalfmoonbay.org/biz
Contact: Krystlyn Giedt, President
Facebook: www.facebook.com/VisitHalfMoonBay
X (Twitter): x.com/VisitHMB
Instagram: www.instagram.com/visithalfmoonbay
Pinterest: www.pinterest.com/visithmb
Description: Promotes business and community development in Half Moon Bay, CA. Sponsors community events. **Founded:** 1963. **Geographic Preference:** Local.

36934 ■ California | STATE LISTINGS

36934 ■ Healdsburg Chamber of Commerce and Visitors Bureau
217 Healdsburg Ave.
Healdsburg, CA 95448
Ph: (707)433-6935
Co. E-mail: info@healdsburg.com
URL: http://www.healdsburg.com
Contact: Tallia Hart, Chief Executive Officer
E-mail: tallia@healdsburg.com
Facebook: www.facebook.com/HealdsburgChamber
X (Twitter): x.com/healdsburg
Instagram: www.instagram.com/healdsburgchamber
YouTube: www.youtube.com/c/Healdsburg
Pinterest: www.pinterest.com/healdsburgcham
Description: Promotes business and community development in Healdsburg, CA. **Publications:** *Healdsburg Area Business* (Monthly). **Geographic Preference:** Local.

36935 ■ Hemet/San Jacinto Valley Chamber of Commerce
615 N San Jacinto St.
Hemet, CA 92543
Ph: (951)658-3211
URL: http://hemetsanjacintochamber.com
Contact: Cyndi Lemke, Director
Facebook: www.facebook.com/hsjvc
Linkedin: www.linkedin.com/company/hsjvc
X (Twitter): x.com/HSJV_C
Instagram: www.instagram.com/hemet_san_jacinto_chamber
Description: Promotes business and community development in Hemet, CA. **Founded:** 1920. **Publications:** *Chronicle*. **Geographic Preference:** Local.

36936 ■ Hercules Chamber of Commerce
500 Alfred Nobel Dr., Ste. 167
Hercules, CA 94547
Contact: Aida Torre, Contact
Description: Promotes business and community development in Hercules, CA area. **Geographic Preference:** Local.

36937 ■ Hermosa Beach Chamber of Commerce and Visitors Bureau
120 Pier Ave.
Hermosa Beach, CA 90254
Ph: (310)376-0951
Co. E-mail: info@hbchamber.net
URL: http://www.hbchamber.net
Contact: Andrea Jacobsson, Contact
X (Twitter): x.com/HermosaChamber
Instagram: www.instagram.com/hermosachamber
Description: Promotes business and community development in Hermosa Beach, CA. Sponsors arts and crafts show. **Founded:** 1906. **Geographic Preference:** Local.

36938 ■ High Desert Hispanic Chamber of Commerce (HDHCC)
12775 Fir St.
Oak Hills, CA 92344
Ph: (760)508-9120
URL: http://www.hdhcc.org
Facebook: www.facebook.com/profile.php
Linkedin: www.linkedin.com/in/hdhcc
X (Twitter): x.com/HDHCC
Description: Promotes the economic development of a culturally diverse business community through education, networking, and business community partnerships. **Geographic Preference:** Local.

36939 ■ Highland Area Chamber of Commerce (HCOC)
27255 Messina St.
Highland, CA 92346
Ph: (909)864-4073
Co. E-mail: hcoc@highlandchamber.org
URL: http://www.highlandchamber.org
Contact: Gail Shelton, President
Facebook: www.facebook.com/highlandareachamber
Description: Promotes business and community development in the Highland, CA area. Encourage residence through its maintenance, rehabilitation, development and occupation. **Founded:** 1906. **Geographic Preference:** Local.

36940 ■ Hispanic Chamber of Commerce of Sonoma County (HCCSC)
3033 Cleveland Ave., Ste. 306
Santa Rosa, CA 95403
Ph: (707)575-3648
Co. E-mail: hccadmin@hcc-sc.org
URL: http://sonomahispanicchamber.org/about
Contact: Alma Magallon, President
Facebook: www.facebook.com/hcocsc
Description: Focuses on building bridges by promoting and supporting Sonoma County businesses through education, civic, and economic engagement. **Founded:** 1987. **Geographic Preference:** Local.

36941 ■ *Historic Walking Tour*
584 Central Ave.
Pacific Grove, CA 93950
Ph: (831)373-3304
URL: http://www.pacificgrove.org
Contact: Moe Ammar, President
E-mail: moeammar@pacificgrove.org
URL(s): www.pacificgrove.org/discover-pacific-grove
Description: Provides information about 18 historic homes and buildings. **Availability:** Print.

36942 ■ Hollywood Chamber of Commerce
6255 Sunset Blvd., Ste. 150
Hollywood, CA 90028
Ph: (323)469-8311
Co. E-mail: info@hollywoodchamber.net
URL: http://hollywoodchamber.net
Contact: David Michael Jerome, President
Facebook: www.facebook.com/HollywoodChamberCA
Linkedin: www.linkedin.com/company/hollywood-chamber-of-commerce
X (Twitter): x.com/HollywoodArea
YouTube: www.youtube.com/user/TheHollywoodChamber
Description: Promotes business and community development in Hollywood, CA. **Founded:** 1921. **Publications:** *Hollywood Business Resource Book*; *Hollywood Business Weekly* (Weekly); *Hollywood Business* (Monthly). **Geographic Preference:** Local.

36943 ■ Holtville Chamber of Commerce
101 W 5th St.
Holtville, CA 92250
Ph: (760)356-2923
Fax: (760)356-2925
Co. E-mail: rosie@holtvillechamber.org
URL: http://www.holtvillechamber.org
Contact: Joseph Dhalliwal, President
Facebook: www.facebook.com/holtvillechamber
Instagram: www.instagram.com/holtvillechamber
Description: Promotes business and community development in Holtville, CA. **Geographic Preference:** Local.

36944 ■ Huntington Beach Chamber of Commerce
15744 Goldenwest St., Bldg. 22
Huntington Beach, CA 92647
Ph: (714)536-8888
Fax: (714)960-7654
Co. E-mail: hbchamber@hbcoc.com
URL: http://www.hbchamber.com
Contact: Barbara Mason, Secretary
Facebook: www.facebook.com/hbchamber
X (Twitter): x.com/hbcoc
Instagram: www.instagram.com/hbchamber
YouTube: www.youtube.com/user/thehbchamber
Description: Promotes business and supports the growth and development of the community in the Huntington Beach, CA area. **Founded:** 1904. **Publications:** *Chamber Business* (Monthly). **Educational Activities:** Economic Outlook Conference (Annual). **Awards:** Huntington Beach Chamber of Commerce Ambassador of the Year (Annual); Huntington Beach Chamber of Commerce Chairman's Member of the Year (Annual). **Geographic Preference:** Local.

36945 ■ Idyllwild Chamber of Commerce
54325 N Cir., Ste. 103
Idyllwild, CA 92549
Ph: (951)659-3259
Co. E-mail: info@idyllwildchamber.com
URL: http://www.idyllwildchamber.com
Contact: David Jerome, Contact
Facebook: www.facebook.com/pages/Idyllwild-Chamber-of-Commerce/107163772671868
Linkedin: www.linkedin.com/in/idyllwildchamber
X (Twitter): x.com/idyllwildcc
Description: Supports businesses by promoting Idyllwild and its surrounding areas as a visitor destination. Develops and participate in activities that benefit the community as a whole. Act as a communication network for businesses and citizens and to provide leadership in enhancing Idyllwild's quality of life. **Founded:** 1946. **Geographic Preference:** Local.

36946 ■ Imperial Beach Chamber of Commerce (IBCOC)
PO Box 506
Imperial Beach, CA 91933
Ph: (619)424-3151
Co. E-mail: info@ib-chamber.com
URL: http://www.ib-chamber.com
Contact: Olivia Pickering, President
X (Twitter): x.com/IBChamber
Description: Promotes business and community development in Imperial Beach, CA. **Founded:** 1951. **Publications:** *Biz Buzz* (Bimonthly). **Geographic Preference:** Local.

36947 ■ Imperial Chamber of Commerce
1095 S 4th St.
El Centro, CA 92243
Ph: (760)355-1244
URL: http://www.imperialchamber.org
Contact: Susan J. Paradis, Executive Director
E-mail: sparadis@imperialchamber.org
Description: Promotes business and community development in Imperial, CA. **Founded:** 1904. **Geographic Preference:** Local.

36948 ■ Indian Valley Chamber of Commerce (IVCC)
PO Box 516
Greenville, CA 95947
Ph: (530)285-0314
Co. E-mail: chamberofcommerceiv@gmail.com
URL: http://www.indianvalleychamber.com
Facebook: www.facebook.com/IVCoC
Description: Promotes business and community development in the area. Sponsors cultural programs and activities. **Publications:** *The Participant* (Bimonthly). **Geographic Preference:** Local; Regional.

36949 ■ Indio Chamber of Commerce
82-921 Indio Blvd.
Indio, CA 92201
Ph: (760)347-0676
Fax: (760)347-6069
Co. E-mail: info@indiochamber.org
URL: http://www.indiochamber.org
Contact: Joshua Bonner, President
E-mail: joshua@indiochamber.org
Facebook: www.facebook.com/indio.chamber.1
Description: Promotes business and community development in Indio, CA. Sponsors Southwest Arts Festival and International Tamale Festival. **Founded:** 1947. **Publications:** *Business Directory*; *East Valley Business* (Monthly); *Indio* (Annual). **Geographic Preference:** Local.

36950 ■ Industry Business Council (IMC)
15651 Mayor Dave Way.
City of Industry, CA 91744
Ph: (626)968-3737
Fax: (626)330-5060
Co. E-mail: info@industrybusinesscouncil.org
URL: http://www.industrybusinesscouncil.org
Contact: Dean Yamagata, Secretary Treasurer
E-mail: dyamagata@industrybusinesscouncil.org
Facebook: www.facebook.com/IndustryBC
X (Twitter): x.com/IndustryBC
Description: Works to serve the needs of its members and also provide services as a public relations agency for the City of Industry. **Founded:** 1962. **Publications:** *City of Industry News* (Monthly). **Geographic Preference:** Local.

STATE LISTINGS
California ■ 36966

36951 ■ Inglewood Airport Area Chamber of Commerce (IAACC)
330 E Queen St.
Inglewood, CA 90301
Ph: (310)677-1121
Fax: (310)677-1001
Co. E-mail: info@inglewoodchamber.org
URL: http://inglewoodchamber.org
Contact: Halimah Ginyard, President
Facebook: www.facebook.com/TheNewIAACC
X (Twitter): x.com/thenewiaacc
YouTube: www.youtube.com/channel/UCF8Lf6Bz66khqi0pCxotqYA
Description: Promotes business and community development in Inglewood, CA. **Founded:** 1922. **Publications:** Business Directory; Let's Talk Business (Monthly). **Geographic Preference:** Local.

36952 ■ Insights
16102 Arrow Hwy.
Irwindale, CA 91706
Ph: (626)960-6606
Co. E-mail: info@irwindalechamber.org
URL: http://www.irwindalechamber.org
Contact: Nicole Shahenian, President
E-mail: ceo@irwindalechamber.org
URL(s): www.irwindalechamber.org/newsletters
Released: Monthly **Availability:** PDF; Download; Online.

36953 ■ Irvine Chamber of Commerce (ICC)
36 Executive Pk., Ste. 100
Irvine, CA 92614
Ph: (949)660-9112
Fax: (949)660-0829
Co. E-mail: info@irvinechamber.com
URL: http://www.greaterirvinechamber.com
Contact: Bryan Starr, President
E-mail: bstarr@irvinechamber.com
Facebook: www.facebook.com/irvinechamber
Linkedin: www.linkedin.com/company/irvine-chamber-of-commerce
X (Twitter): x.com/irvinechamber
Instagram: www.instagram.com/irvinechamber
YouTube: www.youtube.com/user/TheIrvineChamber#p/a/u/1/nYWKaNxCKPs
Description: Promotes business and community development in Irvine, CA. **Founded:** 1979. **Publications:** Business Connection (Bimonthly). **Geographic Preference:** Local.

36954 ■ Irwindale Chamber of Commerce
16102 Arrow Hwy.
Irwindale, CA 91706
Ph: (626)960-6606
Co. E-mail: info@irwindalechamber.org
URL: http://www.irwindalechamber.org
Contact: Nicole Shahenian, President
E-mail: ceo@irwindalechamber.org
Facebook: www.facebook.com/Irwindalecoc
Linkedin: www.linkedin.com/company/irwindale-chamber-of-commerce
X (Twitter): x.com/IrwindaleCoC
Instagram: www.instagram.com/irwindalecc
YouTube: www.youtube.com/channel/UCrc3MEnlmXxszUvkQCovrGQ
Description: Promotes business and community development in Irwindale, CA. **Founded:** 1980. **Publications:** Insights (Monthly). **Awards:** Joe DiShanni Business of the Year Award (Annual); Irwindale Chamber of Commerce Citizen of the Year Award (Annual). **Geographic Preference:** Local.

36955 ■ Isleton Chamber of Commerce (ICC)
23 Main St.
Isleton, CA 95641
Ph: (916)777-4800
Co. E-mail: info@isletonchamber.com
URL: http://www.isletonchamber.com
Contact: Sue Tipp, President
Facebook: www.facebook.com/isletonchamber
Description: Promotes business and community development in Isleton, CA. **Founded:** 1970. **Geographic Preference:** Local.

36956 ■ Japanese Chamber of Commerce of Southern California (JCCSC)
244 S San Pedro St., Ste. 410
Los Angeles, CA 90012
Ph: (213)626-3067
Fax: (213)626-3070
Co. E-mail: office@jccsc.com
URL: http://www.jccsc.com
Contact: Jeff Yamazaki, President
Facebook: www.facebook.com/JapaneseChamberofCommerce
Description: Supports the business activities of Japanese and Japanese Americans in Southern California. Promotes mutual understanding and friendship between Japanese and Americans. Seeks to propagate the culture of Japan. **Geographic Preference:** Local.

36957 ■ Julian Chamber of Commerce
2129 Main St.
Julian, CA 92036
Ph: (760)765-1857
Co. E-mail: chamber@julianca.com
URL: http://visitjulian.com/chamber
Contact: Michael Raher, Vice President
E-mail: michael@journalpubs.com
Facebook: www.facebook.com/VisitJulian
X (Twitter): x.com/VisitJulianCA
Instagram: www.instagram.com/visitjulian
YouTube: www.youtube.com/channel/UCW_k4pFM5SJ4R6GBaNaYRyQ
Pinterest: www.pinterest.com/juliancalifornia
Description: Local businesses and individuals. Promotes tourism while maintaining the historic flavor of small town. **Publications:** Julian Guide (Semiannual); What to See and Do in Julian (Daily). **Geographic Preference:** Local.

36958 ■ Julian Guide
2129 Main St.
Julian, CA 92036
Ph: (760)765-1857
Co. E-mail: chamber@julianca.com
URL: http://visitjulian.com/chamber
Contact: Michael Raher, Vice President
E-mail: michael@journalpubs.com
URL(s): visitjulian.com/plan-your-trip/road-conditions-map
Released: Semiannual **Availability:** Print; PDF.

36959 ■ June Lake Loop Chamber of Commerce
PO Box 2
June Lake, CA 93529
Ph: (760)648-4651
Co. E-mail: danr@junelakeloop.org
URL: http://junelakeloop.org
Contact: Amanda Spencer, President
Facebook: www.facebook.com/junelakeloop
X (Twitter): x.com/junelakeloop
Instagram: www.instagram.com/junelakeloop
Description: Promotes business and community development in June Lake, California. **Geographic Preference:** Local.

36960 ■ Kerman Chamber of Commerce
783 S Madera Ave.
Kerman, CA 93630
Ph: (559)846-6343
Fax: (559)846-6344
Co. E-mail: info@kermanchamber.org
URL: http://www.kermanchamber.org
Contact: Kathy Scheidt, Treasurer
Facebook: www.facebook.com/KermanChamberOfCommerce
Description: Promotes business and community development in Kerman, CA. **Founded:** 1946. **Geographic Preference:** Local.

36961 ■ Kern River Valley Chamber of Commerce (KRVCC)
6416 Isabella Blvd., Ste. D
Lake Isabella, CA 93240
Ph: (760)379-5236
Co. E-mail: office@kernrivervalley.com
URL: http://www.kernrivervalley.com
Contact: Fred Clark, President
E-mail: fclark@farmersagent.com
Facebook: www.facebook.com/visitkernriver
Linkedin: www.linkedin.com/in/kern-river-valley-chamber-of-commerce-5b185254
X (Twitter): x.com/KRVCC
Description: Promotes business and community development and tourism in Lake Isabella and surrounding communities. **Publications:** Lake Lines (Monthly). **Awards:** KRVCC Man and Woman of the Year (Annual). **Geographic Preference:** Local.

36962 ■ Kernville Chamber of Commerce
11447 Kernville Rd.
Kernville, CA 93238
Ph: (760)376-2629
Co. E-mail: info@gotokernville.com
URL: http://www.gotokernville.com
Contact: Orion Sanders, President
Facebook: www.facebook.com/KernvilleChamber
X (Twitter): x.com/kernvillelife
YouTube: www.youtube.com/channel/UCnFWyv5t6x4nnMzqlaPOlfQ
Description: Promotes business, community development, and tourism in Kernville, CA. Works to attract visitors, new residents and jobs creating businesses in the area. Provides service and support to its members. **Founded:** 1957. **Publications:** Kernville Express (3/year). **Geographic Preference:** Local.

36963 ■ King City and Southern Monterey Chamber of Commerce and Agriculture
200 Broadway St., Ste. 40
King City, CA 93930
Ph: (831)385-3814
Fax: (831)386-9462
Co. E-mail: kcchambermanager@kingcitychamber.com
URL: http://kingcitychamber.com
Contact: Kathy Garcia, Director
Facebook: www.facebook.com/KingCityChamber
Instagram: www.instagram.com/kingcitychamber
Description: Promotes business and community development in King City, CA. **Founded:** 1911. **Publications:** Chamber Spotlight (Monthly). **Awards:** King City and Southern Monterey Chamber of Commerce and Agriculture Citizen of the Year Award (Annual). **Geographic Preference:** Local.

36964 ■ Kingsburg District Chamber of Commerce
1475 Draper St.
Kingsburg, CA 93631
Ph: (559)897-1111
Co. E-mail: info@kingsburgchamber.com
URL: http://www.kingsburgchamber.com
Contact: Reggie Gierke, President
Description: Promotes business and community development in Kingsburg, CA. Sponsors festival. Operates California Welcome Center. **Founded:** 1922. **Geographic Preference:** Local.

36965 ■ LA Area Chamber Voice
350 S Bixel St.
Los Angeles, CA 90017
Ph: (213)580-7500
Co. E-mail: info@lachamber.com
URL: http://www.lachamber.com
Contact: Maria S. Salinas, President
URL(s): lachamber.com/membership-benefits/get-involved
Released: Quarterly **Description:** Includes information about the chamber's activities. **Availability:** Print; Online.

36966 ■ La Canada Flintridge Chamber of Commerce and Community Association (LCF)
1 Civic Center Dr., Ste. A
La Canada Flintridge, CA 91011-3314
Ph: (818)790-4289
Fax: (818)790-8930
Co. E-mail: accounting@lacanadaflintridge.com
URL: http://www.lacanadaflintridge.com
Contact: Pat Anderson, President
E-mail: exec@lacanadaflintridge.com
Facebook: www.facebook.com/LCFChamber
X (Twitter): x.com/lcfchamber

Description: Promotes business and community development in La Canada Flintridge, CA. **Founded:** 1912. **Awards:** Miss La Canada Flintridge (Annual). **Geographic Preference:** Local.

36967 ■ La Habra Area Chamber of Commerce
321 E La Habra Blvd.
La Habra, CA 90631
Ph: (562)697-1704
Co. E-mail: info@lahabrachamber.com
URL: http://www.lahabrachamber.com
Contact: Marie Laveaga, President
Facebook: www.facebook.com/Lahabrachamber
X (Twitter): x.com/LaHabra_Chamber
Instagram: www.instagram.com/lahabrachamberofcommerce
Description: Works with businesses, retailers, and residents dedicated to commerce in its growing community. Serves as an advocate for its business membership as well as an essential link between business, government, and the community. **Founded:** 1914. **Publications:** Business Directory. **Geographic Preference:** Local.

36968 ■ La Mirada Chamber of Commerce
PO Box 1266
La Mirada, CA 90637-1266
Ph: (562)964-4142
Co. E-mail: info@lamiradachamber.com
URL: http://www.lamiradachamber.com
Contact: Richard Trujillo, President
Facebook: www.facebook.com/ChamberLaMirada
Linkedin: www.linkedin.com/company/lamiradachamber
YouTube: www.youtube.com/channel/UCkbOuNXmvV88xeQ8bsXwtVQ
Description: Promotes business and community development in La Mirada, CA. **Founded:** 1958. **Publications:** Business Directory; Your City Insider (Monthly). **Educational Activities:** La Mirada Morning View. **Geographic Preference:** Local.

36969 ■ La Quinta Chamber of Commerce (LQCC)
78015 Main St., Ste. 206
La Quinta, CA 92253
Ph: (760)347-0676
Co. E-mail: info@gcvcc.org
URL: http://gcvcc.org/la-quinta
Contact: Ray Dominguez, Chairman
Facebook: www.facebook.com/lqchambercommerce
Description: Promotes business and community development in La Quinta, CA. **Founded:** 1947. **Publications:** The Gem (Monthly). **Educational Activities:** Mayor's Luncheons (Bimonthly). **Geographic Preference:** Local.

36970 ■ La Verne Chamber of Commerce
2332 D St., Unit E
La Verne, CA 91750
Ph: (909)593-5265
Co. E-mail: lavernechamber@gmail.com
URL: http://www.lavernechamber.com
Contact: Leah Skinner, Executive Director
E-mail: leah@lavernechamber.org
Facebook: www.facebook.com/ChamberofCommerceLaVerne
X (Twitter): x.com/LaVerne_Chamber
Instagram: www.instagram.com/laverne_chamber
YouTube: www.youtube.com/channel/UCSxELU9VyP0oSj72RBNp2iA
Description: Promotes business and community development in La Verne, CA. Sponsors community marketplace and business showcase. **Founded:** 1909. **Publications:** Business Directory; The Exchange (Bimonthly). **Awards:** La Verne Chamber of Commerce Member of the Year (Annual). **Geographic Preference:** Local.

36971 ■ Lafayette Chamber of Commerce
251 Lafayette Cir., Ste. 150
Lafayette, CA 94549
Ph: (925)284-7404
Co. E-mail: info@lafayettechamber.org
URL: http://lafayettechamber.org
Contact: Brian Aiello, Director
Linkedin: www.linkedin.com/company/lafayette-chamber-of-commerce
X (Twitter): x.com/friendlychamber
YouTube: www.youtube.com/channel/UC23F-f9Kb2FuB3-ZtrG_u0A
Description: Promotes business and community development in Lafayette, CA. **Founded:** 1947. **Awards:** Lafayette Chamber Business Person of the Year (Annual). **Geographic Preference:** Local.

36972 ■ Laguna Beach Chamber of Commerce (LBCC)
357 Glenneyre
Laguna Beach, CA 92651
Ph: (949)494-1018
Co. E-mail: info@lagunabeachchamber.org
URL: http://www.lagunabeachchamber.org
Contact: Sandy Morales, President
E-mail: sandy@lagunabeachchamber.org
Facebook: www.facebook.com/LagunaBeachChamberofCommerce
X (Twitter): x.com/LagunaBeachCC
Instagram: www.instagram.com/chamberlb
YouTube: www.youtube.com/channel/UCWVhGe_KXYWBmvOY4DaAQpA
Description: Promotes business and community development in Laguna Beach, CA. **Founded:** 1917. **Publications:** Laguna Beach Business Directory & Relocation Guide (Annual); Laguna Beach Business News (Monthly); Laguna Beach Community Directory (Annual). **Educational Activities:** Mixers. **Geographic Preference:** Local.

36973 ■ Laguna Niguel Chamber of Commerce (LNCC)
30111 Crown Valley Pky., Ste. A
Laguna Niguel, CA 92677
Ph: (949)363-0136
Fax: (949)363-9026
Co. E-mail: lncc@lnchamber.com
URL: http://www.lnchamber.com
Contact: Scott Alevy, President
Facebook: www.facebook.com/lnchamber
Instagram: www.instagram.com/lagunaniguelchamber
Description: Promotes business and community development in Laguna Niguel, CA. **Founded:** 1982. **Publications:** Sea Country News (Monthly). **Geographic Preference:** Local.

36974 ■ Lake Almanor Area Chamber of Commerce
PO Box 1198
Chester, CA 96020
Ph: (530)258-2426
Co. E-mail: lakealmanorarea@gmail.com
URL: http://www.lakealmanorarea.com
Contact: Susan Bryner, Executive Director
E-mail: susan.bryner@gmail.com
Facebook: www.facebook.com/lakealmanorarea
Description: Promotes business and community development in the Chester and Lake Almanor, CA areas. **Founded:** 1939. **Geographic Preference:** Local.

36975 ■ Lake Arrowhead Communities Chamber of Commerce (LACCC)
28200 Hwy. 189, Ste. O-270
Lake Arrowhead, CA 92352-0219
Ph: (909)336-1547
Fax: (909)336-1548
Co. E-mail: askus@lakearrowheadchamber.com
URL: http://www.lakearrowheadchamber.com
Contact: Robin Bull, Executive Director
Facebook: www.facebook.com/LakeArrowheadCommunities
X (Twitter): x.com/lachamber
Instagram: www.instagram.com/ilovelakearrowhead
Description: Promotes business and community development in Lake Arrowhead, CA. Sponsors summer music festivals; supports charitable programs. **Founded:** 1950. **Geographic Preference:** Local.

36976 ■ Lake County Chamber of Commerce (LCCC)
875 Lakeport Blvd.
Lakeport, CA 95453
Ph: (707)263-5092
Fax: (707)263-5104
URL: http://www.lakecochamber.com
Contact: Helena Welsh, President
Facebook: www.facebook.com/lakecochamber
YouTube: www.youtube.com/channel/UChEYkK6mHtQqsMnVLxMivng
Description: Works to support and promote business and economic growth and encourage the improvement of tourism activities in Lakeport area, CA. **Geographic Preference:** Local.

36977 ■ Lake Elsinore Valley Chamber of Commerce
132 W Graham Ave.
Lake Elsinore, CA 92530
Ph: (951)245-8848
Co. E-mail: info@lakeelsinorechamber.com
URL: http://lakeelsinorechamber.com
Contact: Kim Joseph Cousins, President
E-mail: kim@lakeelsinorechamber.com
Facebook: www.facebook.com/LakeElsinoreChamber
Description: Promotes business and community development in the Lake Elsinore, CA area. Sponsors Frontier Days Rodeo, Play Days, and horse shows. **Founded:** 1949. **Publications:** Business Review (Monthly). **Awards:** Lake Elsinore Valley Chamber of Commerce Student of the Month (Annual). **Geographic Preference:** Local.

36978 ■ Lakeside Chamber of Commerce (LCC)
9924 Vine St.
Lakeside, CA 92040
Ph: (619)561-1031
Co. E-mail: info@lakesidechamber.org
URL: http://lakesidechamber.org
Contact: Kathy Kassel, President
Facebook: www.facebook.com/lakeside.chamber
X (Twitter): x.com/LakesideChamber
Instagram: www.instagram.com/lakesidechamber
Description: Promotes business and community development in Lakeside, CA. **Founded:** 1932. **Publications:** Lakeside Community and Business Directory; The Link (Monthly). **Educational Activities:** Lakeside Chamber of Commerce Board meeting; Chamber Networking Luncheon. **Geographic Preference:** Local.

36979 ■ Larkspur Chamber of Commerce
PO Box 819
Larkspur, CA 94977
Ph: (415)328-3401
Co. E-mail: info@larkspurchamber.org
URL: http://www.larkspurchamber.org
Contact: Sam Pahlavan, President
Facebook: www.facebook.com/LarkspurChamberCA
X (Twitter): twitter.com/LarkspurChamber
Instagram: www.instagram.com/larkspurchamber
YouTube: www.youtube.com/watch
Description: Promotes business and community development in Greenbrae, Kentfield, Larkspur, and Ross, CA. Sponsors local festivals. **Founded:** 1958. **Awards:** Larkspur Chamber of Commerce Business Citizen of the Year (Annual). **Geographic Preference:** Local.

36980 ■ Lassen County Chamber of Commerce (LCCC)
1516 Main, Ste.
Susanville, CA 96130
Ph: (530)257-4323
URL: http://www.lassencountychamber.org
Contact: Melanie Westbrook, Co-President
Facebook: www.facebook.com/Lassen-County-Chamber-of-Commerce-557136744437603
Description: Promotes business and community development in Susanville and Lassen County, CA. **Founded:** 1888. **Publications:** Chamber Chat (Monthly). **Geographic Preference:** Local.

36981 ■ Lee Vining Chamber of Commerce
PO Box 130
Lee Vining, CA 93541
Ph: (760)647-6629
Co. E-mail: info@monolake.org

STATE LISTINGS

URL: http://www.leevining.com
Description: Promotes business and community development in Lee Vining, CA. **Geographic Preference:** Local.

36982 ■ Lincoln Area Chamber of Commerce (LACC)
540 F St.
Lincoln, CA 95648
Ph: (916)645-2035
Fax: (916)645-9455
Co. E-mail: info@lincolnchamber.com
URL: http://www.lincolnchamber.com
Contact: Mark Luster, President
E-mail: mluster@spi-ind.com
Facebook: www.facebook.com/LincolnAreaChamberCA
X (Twitter): x.com/areaLincoln
Instagram: www.instagram.com/LincolnChamberca
Description: Promotes business and community development in Lincoln, CA. **Founded:** 1905. **Geographic Preference:** Local.

36983 ■ Linden-Peters Chamber of Commerce (LPCC)
PO Box 557
Linden, CA 95236
Ph: (209)547-3046
Co. E-mail: adondero@gmail.com
URL: http://lindenchamber.net
Contact: Vic Solari, President
Facebook: www.facebook.com/Linden-Peters-Chamber-of-Commerce-105026764414908
Description: Promotes business and community development in the Linden-Peters, CA area. **Geographic Preference:** Local.

36984 ■ Lindsay Chamber of Commerce
246 E Honolulu St.
Lindsay, CA 93247
Ph: (559)562-4929
Co. E-mail: info@thelindsaychamber.com
URL: http://thelindsaychamber.com
Contact: Henry Brower, President
Facebook: www.facebook.com/LindsayChamberofCommerce
Instagram: instagram.com/the_lindsay_chamber
Description: Promotes business and community development in Lindsay, OK. Sponsors golf tournament, kite festival, Christmas parade, fireworks display, Teacher Appreciation Day, and city-wide garage sale. **Founded:** 1920. **Publications:** *Chamber Communicant* (Monthly). **Geographic Preference:** Local.

36985 ■ Live Oak District Chamber of Commerce
PO Box 391
Live Oak, CA 95953-0391
Ph: (530)695-1519
URL: http://www.uschamber.com/co/chambers/california/live-oak
Description: Works to represent local business owners, organizations, churches, and individuals of Live Oak, California. **Founded:** 1946. **Geographic Preference:** Local.

36986 ■ *Livermore Chamber of Commerce Business Directory*
2157 1st St.
Livermore, CA 94550
Ph: (925)447-1606
Co. E-mail: lccinfo@livermorechamber.org
URL: http://www.livermorechamber.org
Contact: Dawn Argula, President
E-mail: dargula@livermorechamber.org
URL(s): business.livermorechamber.org/list
Availability: Print.

36987 ■ Livermore Valley Chamber of Commerce (LVCC)
2157 1st St.
Livermore, CA 94550
Ph: (925)447-1606
Co. E-mail: lccinfo@livermorechamber.org
URL: http://www.livermorechamber.org

Contact: Dawn Argula, President
E-mail: dargula@livermorechamber.org
Facebook: www.facebook.com/livermorevalleychamber
Linkedin: www.linkedin.com/company/livermore-valley-chamber-of-commerce
X (Twitter): x.com/livermorechambr
Instagram: www.instagram.com/livermorechamber
YouTube: www.youtube.com/channel/UCf0YzUWCO6WI_TNXF0bnrMg
Description: Promotes business and community development in Livermore, CA. **Founded:** 1937. **Publications:** *Chamber Business Journal* (Monthly); *Livermore Business Journal* (Monthly); *Livermore Chamber of Commerce Business Directory.* **Geographic Preference:** Local.

36988 ■ *Local Business Directory*
1401 Halyard Dr., Ste. 120
West Sacramento, CA 95691
Ph: (916)371-7042
Co. E-mail: info@westsacramentochamber.com
URL: http://www.westsacramentochamber.com
Contact: Andrea van Cleave, Director
E-mail: andrea@westsacramentochamber.com
URL(s): www.westsacramentochamber.com/members
Availability: Print.

36989 ■ Lodi Chamber of Commerce
35 S School St.
Lodi, CA 95240
Ph: (209)367-7840
Fax: (209)369-9344
Co. E-mail: frontdesk@lodichamber.com
URL: http://www.lodichamber.com
Contact: Pat Patrick, President
E-mail: ppatrick@lodichamber.com
Facebook: www.facebook.com/LodiChamber
X (Twitter): x.com/chamberlodi
Instagram: www.instagram.com/lodichamber
Description: Promotes business and community development in the area. Conducts community events. **Founded:** 1923. **Publications:** *Lodi Business* (Monthly). **Awards:** Lodi Area Chamber of Commerce Person of the Year (Annual). **Geographic Preference:** Local.

36990 ■ Loma Linda Chamber of Commerce (LLCC)
25541 Barton Rd., Ste. 4
Loma Linda, CA 92354
Ph: (909)799-2828
Fax: (909)799-2828
Co. E-mail: karen@lomalindachamber.org
URL: http://lomalindachamber.org
Contact: Victor J. Miller, President
Facebook: www.facebook.com/LomaLindaChamber
Description: Promotes business and community development in Loma Linda, CA. **Founded:** 1959. **Publications:** *Loma Linda Report* (Bimonthly). **Awards:** Loma Linda Chamber of Commerce Ambassador of the Year (Annual); Loma Linda Chamber of Commerce Business of the Year; Loma Linda Chamber of Commerce Citizen of the Year (Annual); Loma Linda City Employee of the Year (Annual); Loma Linda Chamber of Commerce Firefighter of the Year (Annual); Loma Linda Chamber of Commerce Board Member of the Year; Loma Linda Chamber of Commerce Police Officer of the Year (Annual). **Geographic Preference:** Local.

36991 ■ Lomita Chamber of Commerce
2315 Lomita Blvd., Ste. 410
Lomita, CA 90717
Ph: (424)378-7111
Fax: (424)263-5518
URL: http://www.lomitachamber.org
Contact: Heidi Butzine, President
E-mail: hi@lomitachamber.org
Facebook: www.facebook.com/LomitaAreaChamber
Linkedin: www.linkedin.com/company/lomita-chamber-of-commerce
X (Twitter): x.com/lomitachamber
Instagram: www.instagram.com/lomitachamber
YouTube: www.youtube.com/channel/UCn_PZi4CTQ_8KYxCQCzuokQ

Description: Promotes business and community development in Lomita, CA. Conducts charitable activities. Sponsors festival. **Founded:** 1907. **Geographic Preference:** Local.

36992 ■ Lompoc Valley Chamber of Commerce and Visitors' Bureau (LVCC&VB)
111 S I St.
Lompoc, CA 93436
Ph: (805)736-4567
Fax: (805)737-0453
Co. E-mail: chamber@lompoc.com
URL: http://www.lompoc.com
Contact: Amber Wilson, President
E-mail: amber@lompoc.com
Facebook: www.facebook.com/lompocvalleychamber
Pinterest: www.pinterest.com/lompocchamber
Description: Promotes business, community development, and tourism in the Lompoc, CA area. Operates committees responsible for business, tourism, governmental affairs, military aerospace affairs, and economic development. Maintains community resource center and tourist information center. Conducts downtown fair. **Founded:** 1903. **Publications:** *The Chamber* (Annual). **Geographic Preference:** Local.

36993 ■ Lone Pine Chamber of Commerce (LPCC)
120 S Main St.
Lone Pine, CA 93545
Ph: (760)876-4444
Fax: (760)876-9205
Co. E-mail: info@lonepinechamber.org
URL: http://lonepinechamber.org
Contact: Kathleen New, Executive Director
E-mail: director@lonepinechamber.org
Facebook: www.facebook.com/LonePineChamberofCommerce
Description: Promotes business, tourism, and economic development in southern Inyo County, CA. Sponsors bicycle road race. **Founded:** 1860. **Geographic Preference:** Local.

36994 ■ Long Beach Area Chamber of Commerce
1 World Trade Ctr., Ste. 1650
Long Beach, CA 90831
Ph: (562)436-1251
Fax: (562)436-7099
Co. E-mail: info@lbchamber.com
URL: http://www.lbchamber.com
Contact: Jeremy Harris, President
Facebook: www.facebook.com/lbchamber
X (Twitter): x.com/thelbchamber
YouTube: www.youtube.com/channel/UCxPmh7Wx8YBaHF6NdalzjzQ
Description: Promotes business and community development in the Long Beach, CA area. **Founded:** 1891. **Publications:** *Long Beach Business* (Monthly); *Member Referral Guide.* **Educational Activities:** Long Beach Young Professionals Networking Breakfast. **Geographic Preference:** Local.

36995 ■ *Long Beach Business*
1 World Trade Ctr., Ste. 1650
Long Beach, CA 90831
Ph: (562)436-1251
Fax: (562)436-7099
Co. E-mail: info@lbchamber.com
URL: http://www.lbchamber.com
Contact: Jeremy Harris, President
URL(s): www.lbchamber.com/business-councils
Released: Monthly **Availability:** Online.

36996 ■ Loomis Basin Chamber of Commerce
6090 Horseshoe Bar Rd.
Loomis, CA 95650
Ph: (916)652-7252
URL: http://www.loomischamber.com
Contact: Larry Thill, Executive Director
Facebook: www.facebook.com/LoomisChamber
Instagram: www.instagram.com/loomischamber
Description: Promotes business and community development in Loomis, CA. **Founded:** 1984. **Geographic Preference:** Local.

36997 ■ Los Alamitos Area Chamber of Commerce
3231 Katella Ave.
Los Alamitos, CA 90720
Ph: (562)598-6659
Fax: (562)598-7035
Co. E-mail: info@losalchamber.org
URL: http://losalchamber.org
Contact: Nesi Stewart, Chairman of the Board
E-mail: nesi@printmasterlosal.com
Facebook: www.facebook.com/LosAlamitosChamber
Description: Promotes business and community development in Los Alamitos, CA. **Publications:** *Los Alamitos Business* (Monthly). **Geographic Preference:** Local.

36998 ■ Los Altos Chamber of Commerce
321 University Ave.
Los Altos, CA 94022
Ph: (650)948-1455
Co. E-mail: info@losaltoschamber.org
URL: http://www.losaltoschamber.org
Contact: Tracie Murray, Chairman
Facebook: www.facebook.com/losaltoschamber
X (Twitter): x.com/losaltoschamber
Instagram: www.instagram.com/losaltoschamber
Description: Promotes business and community development in Los Altos, CA. Sponsors Los Altos Fall Festival. **Founded:** 1951. **Publications:** *The Chamber Advantage* (Monthly); *Los Altos Chamber of Commerce Business Directory*. **Educational Activities:** Los Altos Fall Festival (Annual). **Geographic Preference:** Local.

36999 ■ *Los Altos Chamber of Commerce Business Directory*
321 University Ave.
Los Altos, CA 94022
Ph: (650)948-1455
Co. E-mail: info@losaltoschamber.org
URL: http://www.losaltoschamber.org
Contact: Tracie Murray, Chairman
URL(s): business.losaltoschamber.org/list
Availability: Online.

37000 ■ Los Angeles Area Chamber of Commerce
350 S Bixel St.
Los Angeles, CA 90017
Ph: (213)580-7500
Co. E-mail: info@lachamber.com
URL: http://www.lachamber.com
Contact: Maria S. Salinas, President
Facebook: www.facebook.com/LAAreaChamber
Linkedin: www.linkedin.com/company/los-angeles-area-chamber-of-commerce
X (Twitter): x.com/LAAreaChamber
Instagram: www.instagram.com/laareachamber
YouTube: www.youtube.com/channel/UCV8TSNq28oZEQSPL_QWmQug
Pinterest: www.pinterest.com/laareachamber
Description: Promotes business and community development in the Los Angeles, CA area. **Founded:** 1888. **Publications:** *Southern California Business Trends* (Quarterly); *Chamber Membership Directory and Business Resource Guide* (Annual); *LA Area Chamber Voice* (Quarterly); *Southern California Business* (Monthly); *Chamber Membership Directory and Business Resource Guide* (Annual). **Educational Activities:** Referral Network (Monthly). **Geographic Preference:** Local.

37001 ■ *Los Angeles Business Journal*
11150 Santa Monica Blvd., Ste. 350
Los Angeles, CA 90025
Ph: (323)549-5225
Free: 855-293-9394
Fax: (323)549-5255
Co. E-mail: circulation1@labusinessjournal.com
URL: http://www.labusinessjournal.com
Contact: Josh Schimmels, Chief Executive Officer
E-mail: jschimmels@labusinessjournal.com
URL(s): labusinessjournal.com/about
Facebook: www.facebook.com/labusinessjournal
Linkedin: www.linkedin.com/company/los-angeles-business-journal
X (Twitter): x.com/LABJnews
Instagram: www.instagram.com/labusinessjournal
YouTube: www.youtube.com/channel/UCgxcHb58FSGcqNNJtHKhsGA
Released: Weekly **Price:** $149.95, for print and digital per year; $249.95, for 2 year print and online; $5, for back issue Jul. 8, 2024. **Description:** Newspaper (tabloid) covering local business news, business trends, executive profiles, and information for the Los Angeles area executive. **Availability:** Print; PDF; Online.

37002 ■ Los Angeles Gateway Chamber of Commerce
1517 Pacific Coast Hwy.
Harbor City, CA 90710
Ph: (310)430-8658
Co. E-mail: lagchamberwebinar@gmail.com
URL: http://www.lagateway.org
Contact: Emily Bastian, Contact
Instagram: www.instagram.com/lagchamber
Description: Promotes business and community development in Harbor City, CA. **Founded:** 1920. **Publications:** *Chamber Connection* (Monthly); *Chamber News* (Monthly). **Geographic Preference:** Local.

37003 ■ *Los Banos Chamber Directory*
932 6th St.
Los Banos, CA 93635
Ph: (209)826-2495
Fax: (209)826-9689
Co. E-mail: lbchamber@pacbell.net
URL: http://www.losbanos.com
Contact: Geneva Brett, President
URL(s): www.losbanos.com/members.html
Released: Periodic **Availability:** Print; Online.

37004 ■ Los Gatos Chamber of Commerce (TLGCC)
10 Station Way
Los Gatos, CA 95030
Ph: (408)354-9300
Fax: (408)399-1594
Co. E-mail: chamber@losgatoschamber.com
URL: http://www.losgatoschamber.com
Contact: Andrea Romano, President
Facebook: www.facebook.com/LosGatosChamberofCommerce
Linkedin: www.linkedin.com/company/los-gatos-chamber-of-commerce
Instagram: www.instagram.com/losgatoschamber
YouTube: www.youtube.com/channel/UCgKUpFfcM8mZJnz24USyObg
Description: Promotes business and community development in Los Gatos, CA. Offers programs, services and resources for business and community vitality. Operates the official Town of Los Gatos Information Office. **Founded:** 1999. **Publications:** *Art Guide - Cultural Arts in Los Gatos* (Periodic); *It's Our Business*. **Geographic Preference:** Local.

37005 ■ Los Osos/Baywood Park Chamber of Commerce
781 Los Osos Valley Rd.
Los Osos, CA 93402
Ph: (805)528-4884
Co. E-mail: info@lobpchamber.org
URL: http://lobpchamber.org
Contact: Tim Carstairs, President
Facebook: www.facebook.com/lobpchamber
Instagram: www.instagram.com/lobpchamber
Description: Promotes business and community development in the Los Osos-Baywood Park, CA area. **Founded:** 1955. **Publications:** *The Business Connection* (Monthly). **Educational Activities:** Chamber Board of Directors Meeting. **Awards:** LOBPCC Business of the Year; LOBPCC Citizen of the Year (Annual); LOBPCC Volunteer of the Year (Annual). **Geographic Preference:** Local.

37006 ■ Lost Sierra Chamber of Commerce
8989 Hwy. 89
Blairsden, CA 96103
Ph: (530)836-6811
Fax: (530)836-6809
Co. E-mail: epcc@psln.com
URL: http://www.lostsierrachamber.org
Contact: Kathi Burton, Treasurer
Facebook: www.facebook.com/LostSierraChamber
Instagram: www.instagram.com/lostsierrachamber
Description: Promotes business and community development in Eastern Plumas, CA. Sponsors local festivals; conducts competitions. **Geographic Preference:** Local.

37007 ■ Lucerne Valley Chamber of Commerce
32750 Old Woman Springs Rd.
Lucerne Valley, CA 92356
Ph: (760)248-7215
Fax: (760)248-2024
Co. E-mail: chamber@lucernevalley.net
URL: http://www.chamber-commerce.net/dir/8470
Description: Promotes business and community development in Lucerne Valley, CA. **Founded:** 1957. **Geographic Preference:** Local.

37008 ■ *The Luminary*
50 Pk. Pl., 2nd Fl.
Brisbane, CA 94005
Ph: (415)467-7283
Co. E-mail: madison@brisbanechamber.org
URL: http://brisbanechamber.org
Contact: Madison Davis, President
URL(s): www.brisbanechamber.org/the-luminary
Ed: Alison Wilson. **Released:** Monthly **Availability:** Print; Online; PDF.

37009 ■ Lynwood Chamber of Commerce
3651 E Imperial Hwy.
Lynwood, CA 90262
Ph: (310)537-6484
Fax: (310)537-8143
Co. E-mail: lynwoodchamber@aol.com
URL: http://www.chamber-commerce.net/dir/8490
Description: Promotes business and community development in Lynwood, CA. Conducts Career Day, Job Fair and scholarship competition. **Geographic Preference:** Local.

37010 ■ *Madera Business Beat*
120 N E St.
Madera, CA 93638
Ph: (559)673-3563
URL: http://maderachamber.com
Contact: Debi Bray, President
E-mail: dbray@maderachamber.com
URL(s): maderachamber.com/?page_id=677
Availability: Electronic publishing; Online.

37011 ■ Madera Chamber of Commerce
120 N E St.
Madera, CA 93638
Ph: (559)673-3563
URL: http://maderachamber.com
Contact: Debi Bray, President
E-mail: dbray@maderachamber.com
Facebook: www.facebook.com/MaderaChamber
Description: Promotes business and community development in Madera District, CA. **Founded:** 1911. **Publications:** *Community Guide and Membership Directory*; *Madera Business Beat*. **Educational Activities:** Business Extravaganza (Annual). **Geographic Preference:** Local.

37012 ■ Malibu Chamber of Commerce
PO Box 925
Malibu, CA 90265
Ph: (310)456-9025
Fax: (310)456-0195
Co. E-mail: ceo@malibu.org
URL: http://www.malibu.org
Contact: Barbara Bruderlin, Chief Executive Officer
E-mail: ceo@malibu.org
Linkedin: www.linkedin.com/company/malibuchamberofcommerce
X (Twitter): x.com/malibuchamber
Description: Promotes business and community development in Malibu, CA. **Founded:** 1948. **Publications:** *Malibu Business and Community Directory*. **Geographic Preference:** Local.

STATE LISTINGS

37013 ■ Manhattan Beach Chamber of Commerce (MBCC)
425 15th St.
Manhattan Beach, CA 90266
Ph: (310)545-5313
Co. E-mail: info@manhattanbeachchamber.com
URL: http://www.manhattanbeachchamber.com
Contact: David Archer, President
E-mail: david@manhattanbeachchamber.com
Facebook: www.facebook.com/ManhattanBeachChamberofCommerce
YouTube: www.youtube.com/channel/UCWdFfjxLaS4_qMVN5ZVLNag
Description: Promotes business and community development in Manhattan Beach, CA. Sponsors special events. **Founded:** 1941. **Publications:** *Sandollar* (Monthly). **Geographic Preference:** Local.

37014 ■ Manteca Chamber of Commerce
183 W N St., Ste. 6
Manteca, CA 95336
Ph: (209)823-6121
Fax: (209)239-6131
Co. E-mail: chamber@manteca.org
URL: http://manteca.org
Contact: Joann Beattie, Executive Director
Facebook: www.facebook.com/thingstodoinManteca
X (Twitter): x.com/mantecachamber
Description: Promotes business and community development in Manteca District, CA. **Founded:** 1923. **Publications:** *Manteca First* (Bimonthly). **Educational Activities:** Executive Board Meeting (Monthly). **Geographic Preference:** Local.

37015 ■ Marina Chamber of Commerce
PO Box 425
Marina, CA 93933
Co. E-mail: info@marinachamber.com
URL: http://www.marinachamber.com
Contact: Justin Sacoolas, Director
Description: Promotes business and community development in Marina, CA. **Geographic Preference:** Local.

37016 ■ Mariposa County Chamber of Commerce
5158 Hwy. 140
Mariposa, CA 95338
Ph: (209)966-2456
Co. E-mail: kyle@mariposachamber.org
URL: http://www.mariposachamber.org
Contact: Gabe Edwards, Chairman
Description: Promotes business and community development in Mariposa County, CA. Encourages travel and tourism. Sponsors monthly storytelling festival. **Publications:** *The Link* (Monthly). **Geographic Preference:** Local.

37017 ■ Mark West Area Chamber of Commerce
4787 Old Redwood Hwy., Ste. 101
Santa Rosa, CA 95403
Ph: (707)578-7975
Co. E-mail: office@markwest.org
URL: http://www.markwest.org
Contact: Alicia Mills, Secretary
E-mail: amills@mwusd.org
Facebook: www.facebook.com/MarkWestAreaChamber
YouTube: www.youtube.com/channel/UCNMXTHT0XaWzl4hy-2feJ4A
Description: Promotes business and community development in Mark West, CA area. **Founded:** 1980. **Geographic Preference:** Local.

37018 ■ Martinez Area Chamber of Commerce and Visitors and Information Center
603 Marina Vista
Martinez, CA 94553
Ph: (925)228-2345
Co. E-mail: info@martinezchamber.com
URL: http://martinezchamber.com
Contact: Julie Johnston, Co-President Co-Chief Executive Officer
Facebook: www.facebook.com/MartinezChamberVisitMartinez
Linkedin: www.linkedin.com/company/martinez-chamber-of-commerce
Description: Promotes business and community development in Martinez, CA. Conducts local 4th of July and Columbus Day festivities. **Founded:** 1936. **Publications:** *Networker* (Monthly). **Geographic Preference:** Local.

37019 ■ McCloud Chamber of Commerce (MCC)
303 Main St.
McCloud, CA 96057
Ph: (530)964-3113
Co. E-mail: info@mccloudchamber.com
URL: http://www.mccloudchamber.com
Contact: Airiel Scotti, Co-President
Facebook: www.facebook.com/McCloudChamber
X (Twitter): x.com/mccloudchamber
Pinterest: www.pinterest.com/mccloudchamber
Description: Strives to enhance and protect the natural and historic resources of McCloud to the benefit, enjoyment and pride of both local citizens and the tourists. Enhances existing businesses, encourages new opportunities and promotes tourism. **Geographic Preference:** Local.

37020 ■ McKinleyville Chamber of Commerce
1640 Central Ave.
McKinleyville, CA 95519
Ph: (707)839-2449
Co. E-mail: contact@mckinleyvillechamber.com
URL: http://mckinleyvillechamber.com
Contact: Jesse Miles, President
Description: Promotes business and community development in McKinleyville, CA. **Founded:** 1967. **Geographic Preference:** Local.

37021 ■ *Membership Directory*
1556 1st St., No. 104
Napa, CA 94559
Ph: (707)226-7455
URL: http://napachamber.com
Contact: Travis Stanley, President
E-mail: travis@napachamber.com
URL(s): napachamber.com/membership-overview
Availability: Online.

37022 ■ *Mendocino Map and Visitor Information Guide*
217 S Main St.
Fort Bragg, CA 95437
Ph: (707)961-6300
Co. E-mail: chamber@mcn.org
URL: http://mendocinocoast.com
Contact: Curtis Bruchler, Chairman
URL(s): mendocinocoast.com/visitor-guide
Released: Annual **Availability:** Download; PDF; Online.

37023 ■ Menifee Valley Chamber of Commerce
29737 New Hub Dr., Ste. 102
Menifee, CA 92586
Ph: (951)672-1991
Co. E-mail: info@menifeevalleychamber.com
URL: http://www.menifeevalleychamber.com
Contact: Maneesha Jones, President
Facebook: www.facebook.com/HollisterDowntownAssociation
Instagram: www.instagram.com/dwntwnhollister
YouTube: www.youtube.com/channel/UC1jtZZjGF_sT6xne6eLIkBQ
Description: Seeks to enhance the quality of individual living in Menifee Valley by promoting local business enterprise, strengthening the relationship of residents and businesses and establishing programs for development and economic growth. **Geographic Preference:** Local.

37024 ■ Menlo Park Chamber of Commerce (MPCC)
671 Oak Grove Ave., Ste. F
Menlo Park, CA 94025
Contact: Fran Dehn, Contact
Description: Promotes business and community development in Menlo Park, Portola Valley, and Atherton, CA. **Founded:** 1926. **Publications:** *The Acorn* (Monthly); *Community Directory* (Annual). **Educational Activities:** Women in Business Breakfast. **Geographic Preference:** Local.

37025 ■ *Mill Valley Business Directory*
85 Throckmorton Ave.
Mill Valley, CA 94941
Ph: (415)388-9700
Co. E-mail: info@millvalley.org
URL: http://www.millvalley.org
Contact: Paula Reynolds, Director, Operations
E-mail: preynolds88@gmail.com
URL(s): info.enjoymillvalley.com/directory
Released: Annual **Description:** Covers businesses, information centers, and conferences in Mill Valley, CA. **Availability:** Print; Online.

37026 ■ Mill Valley Chamber of Commerce (MVCC)
85 Throckmorton Ave.
Mill Valley, CA 94941
Ph: (415)388-9700
Co. E-mail: info@millvalley.org
URL: http://www.millvalley.org
Contact: Paula Reynolds, Director, Operations
E-mail: preynolds88@gmail.com
Facebook: www.facebook.com/MVChamber
X (Twitter): x.com/MVChamber
Description: Promotes business and community development in Mill Valley, CA. **Founded:** 1953. **Publications:** *Mill Valley Business* (Monthly); *Mill Valley Business Directory* (Annual). **Educational Activities:** Annual Mill Valley Wine, Beer and Gourmet Food Tasting (Annual). **Geographic Preference:** Local.

37027 ■ Millbrae Chamber of Commerce (MCC)
50 Victoria Ave., Ste. 103
Millbrae, CA 94030
Ph: (650)697-7324
Fax: (650)259-7918
Co. E-mail: millbraechamber@millbrae.com
URL: http://millbrae.com
Contact: Lorianne Richardson, President
E-mail: lorianne@millbrae.com
Facebook: www.facebook.com/MillbraeChamber
X (Twitter): x.com/MillbraeChamber
Description: Promotes business and community development in Millbrae, CA. Conducts forums and luncheons. Sponsors Art and Wine Festival, held on Labor Day weekend. **Founded:** 1949. **Publications:** *Business Directory* (Annual). **Awards:** Millbrae Chamber of Commerce Business of the Year (Annual); Millbrae Chamber of Commerce Chamber Excellence Award (Annual). **Geographic Preference:** Local.

37028 ■ Milpitas Chamber of Commerce
828 N Hillview Dr.
Milpitas, CA 95035
Ph: (408)262-2613
Co. E-mail: info@milpitaschamber.com
URL: http://www.milpitaschamber.com
Contact: Warren Wettenstein, President
E-mail: president@milpitaschamber.com
Facebook: www.facebook.com/milpitas.chamber
X (Twitter): x.com/MilpitasChamber
Description: Works to ensure a healthy economic environment for Milpitas area, CA. **Founded:** 1957. **Geographic Preference:** Local.

37029 ■ Modesto Chamber of Commerce
1114 J St.
Modesto, CA 95354
Ph: (209)577-5757
Co. E-mail: info@modchamber.org
URL: http://www.modchamber.org
Contact: Michael Gaffney, Board Member
Facebook: www.facebook.com/ModestoChamber
Linkedin: www.linkedin.com/company/modesto-chamber-of-commerce
X (Twitter): x.com/modchamber
YouTube: www.youtube.com/c/ModchamberOrg
Description: Promotes business and community development in Modesto, CA. **Publications:** *Progress* (Monthly); *United Way of Etowah County--*

Directory of Community Service Resources (Biennial); *Stanislaus County Industrial Directory*. **Educational Activities:** Oktoberfest (Annual). **Awards:** Modesto Chamber of Commerce Ambassador of the Year (Annual); Modesto Chamber of Commerce Distinguished Service Award (Annual); Chamber Member Of The Year Award; Modesto Chamber of Commerce Non-Profit Organization of the Year (Annual); Robert J. Cardoza Citizen of the Year Award; Modesto Chamber of Commerce Small Business of the Year (Annual); Modesto Chamber of CommerceW elcome Team Member of the Year (Annual). **Geographic Preference:** Local.

37030 ■ *Modesto Memo*
PO Box 76
Modesto, CA 95354
Ph: (209)450-3810
Co. E-mail: mickiemodestojc@yahoo.com
Contact: Vincent Sandoval, III, President
Released: Quarterly **Availability:** Print; PDF; Online.

37031 ■ **Monrovia Chamber of Commerce**
620 S Myrtle Ave.
Monrovia, CA 91016
Ph: (626)358-1159
Fax: (626)357-6036
Co. E-mail: chamber@monroviacc.com
URL: http://www.monroviacc.com
Contact: Kelly F. Ryan, President
Facebook: www.facebook.com/MonroviaChamber
X (Twitter): x.com/MonroviaChamber
Instagram: www.instagram.com/monroviachamber
Description: Promotes business and community development in the San Gabriel Valley, CA. Conducts workshops and expos. Holds community forum. **Founded:** 1897. **Publications:** *Monrovia Insider*; *Monrovia Chamber of Commerce--Membership Directory and Community Guide*. **Awards:** Iris Award (Annual); Monroe Award (Annual); Service to the Chamber Award (Annual). **Geographic Preference:** Local.

37032 ■ *Monrovia Insider*
620 S Myrtle Ave.
Monrovia, CA 91016
Ph: (626)358-1159
Fax: (626)357-6036
Co. E-mail: chamber@monroviacc.com
URL: http://www.monroviacc.com
Contact: Kelly F. Ryan, President
URL(s): www.monroviacc.com/pages/MembershipBenefits
Price: $36, By mail for annually. **Availability:** Online.

37033 ■ **Montclair Chamber of Commerce**
8880 Benson Ave., Ste. 110
Montclair, CA 91763
Ph: (909)985-5104
Co. E-mail: info@montclairchamber.com
URL: http://www.montclairchamber.com
Contact: Steve Hammitt, Chairman
Facebook: www.facebook.com/montclairchamber
Instagram: www.instagram.com/montclairchamber
Description: Promotes business and community development in Montclair, CA area. Supports local charities; conducts political and business networking forums. **Founded:** 1958. **Geographic Preference:** Local.

37034 ■ **Monte Rio Chamber of Commerce (MRCC)**
PO Box 220
Monte Rio, CA 95462
Ph: (707)865-6100
Co. E-mail: mrcc@sonic.net
URL: http://monterio.org
Contact: Marina Mctaggart, President
Description: Promotes business and community development in the Monte Rio and Russian River area of western Sonoma County, CA. **Geographic Preference:** Local.

37035 ■ **Montebello Chamber of Commerce**
109 N 19th St.
Montebello, CA 90640
Ph: (323)721-1153
Fax: (323)721-7946
Co. E-mail: info@montebellochamber.org
URL: http://www.montebellochamber.org
Contact: Greg Millsap, Chairman
X (Twitter): x.com/montebellocham
YouTube: www.youtube.com/user/montebellochamber
Description: Promotes business and community development in Montebello, CA. **Founded:** 1912. **Publications:** *SPOTLIGHT* (Bimonthly); *Annual Business Directory* (Annual). **Geographic Preference:** Local.

37036 ■ **Monterey Peninsula Chamber of Commerce (MPCC)**
353 Camino El Estero
Monterey, CA 93940
Ph: (831)648-5350
Co. E-mail: info@montereychamber.com
URL: http://www.montereychamber.com
Contact: Monica Lal, President
E-mail: monica@montereychamber.com
Facebook: www.facebook.com/MontereyPeninsulaChamber
X (Twitter): x.com/montereychamber
Instagram: www.instagram.com/montereychamber
YouTube: www.youtube.com/channel/UCKl5N6U98Pd551c7oQLkjhg
Description: Promotes business and community development in the Monterey Peninsula area of California. Meeting rooms and convention facilities available. **Founded:** 1908. **Publications:** *Action* (Monthly); *Monterey Peninsula Chamber of Commerce--Membership Directory & Business Referral Guide* (Continuous); *Business Resource Directory*; *Events Calendar - Community* (Annual). **Geographic Preference:** Local.

37037 ■ **Montrose-Verdugo City Chamber of Commerce (MVCC)**
3436 N Verdugo Rd., Ste. 100
Glendale, CA 91208
Ph: (818)249-7171
Fax: (818)249-8919
Co. E-mail: mvcc@montrosechamber.org
URL: http://www.montrosechamber.org
Contact: Adam Franko, President
Facebook: www.facebook.com/MontroseChamber
Description: Promotes business and community development in Montrose, Verdugo City, Glendale, and La Crescenta, CA. Sponsors charitable and service activities. Sponsors arts and crafts fairs, Memorial Day services, Oktoberfest, and Christmas Parade. **Founded:** 1923. **Publications:** *Business Connection* (Quarterly). **Educational Activities:** Mixers. **Awards:** Volunteer of the Year (Annual); MVCC Business Person of the Year (Annual). **Geographic Preference:** Local.

37038 ■ **Morgan Hill Chamber of Commerce (MHCC)**
17500 Depot St., Ste. 260
Morgan Hill, CA 95037
Ph: (408)779-9444
URL: http://www.morganhillchamber.org
Contact: Nick Gaich, President
Facebook: www.facebook.com/MorganHillChamber
Instagram: www.instagram.com/mhcoc
YouTube: www.youtube.com/channel/UCLGsLeX99iXvCglp6BiqIRg
Description: Promotes business and community development in Morgan Hill, CA. Sponsors business seminars. **Founded:** 1964. **Publications:** *Business Directory and Community Guide* (Annual); *Business Review* (Monthly). **Educational Activities:** Monthly Networking Mixers (Monthly); Wake Up Morgan Hill Networking Breakfast (Monthly). **Awards:** Morgan Hill Chamber of Commerce Volunteer of the Year (Annual); Morgan Hill Chamber of Commerce Educator of the Year (Annual); Morgan Hill Chamber of Commerce Man of the Year (Annual); Morgan Hill Chamber of Commerce Student of the Year (Annual); Morgan Hill Chamber of Commerce Woman of the Year (Annual). **Geographic Preference:** Local.

37039 ■ **Morro Bay Chamber of Commerce**
695 Harbor St.
Morro Bay, CA 93442
Ph: (805)772-4467
Co. E-mail: info@morrochamber.org
URL: http://www.morrochamber.org
Contact: Erica D. Crawford, President
Facebook: www.facebook.com/morro.chamber
Linkedin: www.linkedin.com/company/morro-bay-chamber-of-commerce
Instagram: www.instagram.com/morrobaychamber
Description: Promotes business and community development in Morro Bay, CA. **Founded:** 1923. **Publications:** *Business Referral Directory* (Semiannual); *Soundings*; *Business Referral Directory* (Annual). **Geographic Preference:** Local.

37040 ■ **Moss Landing Chamber of Commerce (MLCC)**
PO Box 41
Moss Landing, CA 95039
Ph: (831)633-4501
Co. E-mail: info@mosslandingchamber.com
URL: http://mosslandingchamber.com
Contact: Russ Jeffries, President
Facebook: www.facebook.com/mosslandingstreetfair
Description: Promotes business and community development in Moss Landing, CA. **Founded:** 1866. **Geographic Preference:** Local.

37041 ■ **Mount Shasta Chamber of Commerce**
300 Pine St.
Mount Shasta, CA 96067
Ph: (530)926-4865
Co. E-mail: info@mtshastachamber.com
URL: http://mtshastachamber.com
Contact: Thea Cowsky, President
Description: Promotes business and community development in Mt. Shasta, CA. **Founded:** 1939. **Publications:** *Chamber Connection* (Quarterly). **Awards:** Mount Shasta Chamber of Commerce Business of the Year (Annual); Mount Shasta Chamber of Commerce Citizen of the Year (Annual). **Geographic Preference:** Local.

37042 ■ **Napa Chamber of Commerce (NCC)**
1556 1st St., No. 104
Napa, CA 94559
Ph: (707)226-7455
URL: http://napachamber.com
Contact: Travis Stanley, President
E-mail: travis@napachamber.com
Facebook: www.facebook.com/NapaChamberOfCommerce
X (Twitter): x.com/NapaChamber
Instagram: www.instagram.com/napachamberofcommerce
YouTube: www.youtube.com/channel/UC847yKrDTWeu44eFsaJK3cA
Description: Promotes the Napa County, CA area's economic vitality and quality of life through leadership development, advocacy, facilitation, and education. **Founded:** 1900. **Publications:** *Commerce* (Monthly); *Community Economic Profile* (Annual); *Membership Directory*; *Visitor Booklet*. **Educational Activities:** Committee Meeting (Monthly). **Awards:** Napa Chamber of Commerce Business of the Year (Annual); Napa Chamber of Commerce Citizen of the Year (Annual); Napa Chamber of Commerce Healthcare Professional of the Year (Annual); Napa Chamber of Commerce Public Safety Officer of the Year (Annual); Napa Chamber of Commerce Teacher of the Year (Annual). **Geographic Preference:** Local.

37043 ■ **National City Chamber of Commerce (NCCC)**
901 National City Blvd.
National City, CA 91950
Ph: (619)477-9339
Fax: (619)477-5018
Co. E-mail: thechamber@nationalcitychamber.org
URL: http://www.nationalcitychamber.org
Contact: Jacqueline L. Reynoso, President
E-mail: reynoso@nationalcitychamber.org
Facebook: www.facebook.com/NationalCityChamber

STATE LISTINGS

Linkedin: www.linkedin.com/company/national-city-chamber-of-commerce
X (Twitter): x.com/ncccommerce
Instagram: www.instagram.com/nationalcitychamber
YouTube: www.youtube.com/channel/UCS5n3jqJ94J75Jzv5NzWpxQ

Description: Promotes business and community development in National City, CA. **Founded:** 1905. **Publications:** *Chamber News* (Quarterly); *Membership Directory and Business Referral Group*. **Geographic Preference:** Local.

37044 ■ Needles Chamber of Commerce
119 F St.
Needles, CA 92363
Ph: (760)326-2050
Co. E-mail: info@needleschamber.com
URL: http://www.needleschamber.com
Contact: George DeLeon, President
E-mail: george.deleon78@yahoo.com
Facebook: www.facebook.com/NeedlesChamberOfCommerce

Description: Promotes an active, healthy business environment throughout Needles so that its citizens and all of its business community shall prosper. **Geographic Preference:** Local.

37045 ■ Nevada City Chamber of Commerce (NCCC)
132 Main St.
Nevada City, CA 95959
Ph: (530)265-2692
Co. E-mail: info@nevadacitychamber.com
URL: http://www.nevadacitychamber.com
Contact: Gretchen Bond, President
Facebook: www.facebook.com/nevadacitychamber
X (Twitter): x.com/nevadacitychamb
Instagram: www.instagram.com/nevadacitychamber
YouTube: www.youtube.com/channel/UCrf9cJIySRyz_TwflGyh21A

Description: Promotes business and community development in Nevada City, CA. **Founded:** 1931. **Geographic Preference:** Local.

37046 ■ Newark Chamber of Commerce [North Silicon Valley Chamber of Commerce]
35501 Cedar Blvd.
Newark, CA 94560
Ph: (510)578-4500
Co. E-mail: info@newark-chamber.com
URL: http://www.newark-chamber.com
Contact: Debbie Montes, President
URL(s): www.ci.newark.ca.us/businesses/chamber-of-commerce
Facebook: www.facebook.com/NewarkChamberOfCommerce
X (Twitter): x.com/NewarkChamber

Description: Promotes business and community development in Newark, CA. Sponsors Winter Art and Wine Festival and Monarch Festival. **Founded:** 1906. **Publications:** *The Voice of Business* (Monthly). **Educational Activities:** Mixers (Monthly). **Geographic Preference:** Local.

37047 ■ Newport Beach Chamber of Commerce (NBCC)
4343 Von Karman Ave., Ste. 150-W
Newport Beach, CA 92660
Ph: (949)729-4400
Fax: (949)729-4417
URL: http://www.newportbeach.com
Contact: Steve Rosansky, President
E-mail: steve@newportbeach.com
Facebook: www.facebook.com/newportbeachchamber
Linkedin: www.linkedin.com/company/newport-beach-chamber-of-commerce
X (Twitter): x.com/newportchamber
Instagram: www.instagram.com/nbchamber
YouTube: www.youtube.com/channel/UCwH5q646uBFpzdaeuNA0GDA

Description: Promotes business and community development in the Newport Beach, CA area. **Founded:** 1907. **Publications:** *Lookout* (Monthly). **Educational Activities:** Newport Beach Fire and Lifeguard Appreciation (Annual). **Geographic Preference:** Local.

37048 ■ Norco Area Chamber of Commerce (NACC)
3954 Old Hamner Rd., Ste. B
Norco, CA 92860
Ph: (951)737-6222
Fax: (951)356-0555
Co. E-mail: info@norcoareachamber.org
URL: http://www.norcochamber.com
Contact: Jamie Ball, President
Facebook: www.facebook.com/norcoareachamber
Linkedin: www.linkedin.com/company/norco-area-chamber-of-commerce-and-visitors-center

Description: Promotes business and community development in Norco, CA. **Publications:** *Business News* (Monthly); *Business Roundup*. **Geographic Preference:** Local.

37049 ■ *North Monterey County Chamber*
10700 Merritt St.
Castroville, CA 95012
Ph: (831)633-2465
Co. E-mail: nmcchamber@gmail.com
URL: http://northmontereycountychamber.weebly.com
Contact: Sheila Rose, Co-President
URL(s): northmontereycountychamber.weebly.com/newsletter.html

Released: Monthly **Availability:** Online.

37050 ■ North Monterey County Chamber of Commerce
10700 Merritt St.
Castroville, CA 95012
Ph: (831)633-2465
Co. E-mail: nmcchamber@gmail.com
URL: http://northmontereycountychamber.weebly.com
Contact: Sheila Rose, Co-President

Description: Promotes business and community development in North Monterey County, CA. **Founded:** 1931. **Publications:** *North Monterey County Chamber* (Monthly). **Geographic Preference:** Local.

37051 ■ North Orange County Chamber of Commerce
100 W Valencia Mesa Dr., Ste. 207
Fullerton, CA 92835
Ph: (714)871-3100
Fax: (714)871-2871
Co. E-mail: nocc@nocchamber.com
URL: http://www.nocchamber.com
Contact: Andrew W. Gregson, President
Facebook: www.facebook.com/NOCChamberofCommerce
Linkedin: www.linkedin.com/company/fullerton-chamber-of-commerce
X (Twitter): x.com/NOCChamber
Instagram: www.instagram.com/nocchamber
YouTube: www.youtube.com/channel/UC5NVwvJBG5oLodufpepumZg

Description: Promotes business and community development in Fullerton, CA. **Founded:** 1893. **Publications:** *Fullerton Business Review* (Biweekly). **Geographic Preference:** Local.

37052 ■ North Sacramento Chamber of Commerce (NSCC)
PO Box 15468
Sacramento, CA 95851
Co. E-mail: connect@northsacramentochamber.org
URL: http://northsacramentochamber.org
Contact: Bob Poole, President
X (Twitter): x.com/N_SacChamber

Description: Promotes business and community development in Sacramento, CA area. **Founded:** 1923. **Geographic Preference:** Local.

37053 ■ North San Diego Business Chamber
10875 Rancho Bernardo Rd., Ste. 104
San Diego, CA 92127
Ph: (858)487-1767
Fax: (858)487-8051
Co. E-mail: admin@sdbusinesschamber.com
URL: http://www.sdbusinesschamber.com
Contact: Debra Rosen, President
E-mail: drosen@sdbusinesschamber.com

Description: Promotes business and community development in Rancho Penasquitos, Carmel Mountain Ranch, Sabre Springs, Mira Mesa/Miramar and Scripps Ranch, CA. Sponsors Miss Penasquitos Pageant, Carmel Mountain Ranch Fall Festival, Fiesta de Los Penasquitos Street Fair, education scholarships, and golf tournament. **Founded:** 1980. **Publications:** *Guide to the Area's Fifteen Shopping and Professional Centers* (Periodic); *Street and Area Map*. **Geographic Preference:** Local.

37054 ■ North Valley Regional Chamber of Commerce (NVRCC) [Northridge Chamber of Commerce]
9015 Wilbur Ave.
Northridge, CA 91324
Ph: (818)349-5676
Co. E-mail: info@nvrcc.org
URL: http://www.northridgechamber.org
Contact: Nancy Hofmeister, President
E-mail: nancy@nvrcc.org
Facebook: www.facebook.com/NorthridgeChamberofCommerce

Description: Promotes business and community development in North Valley area, CA. **Publications:** *Northridge and Chatsworth Business and Community News* (Monthly). **Geographic Preference:** Local.

37055 ■ Norwalk Chamber of Commerce
14783 Carmenita Rd.
Norwalk, CA 90650
Ph: (562)404-0909
Fax: (562)404-0911
Co. E-mail: info@norwalkchamber.com
URL: http://norwalkchamber.com
Contact: Rich LeGaspi, President
Facebook: www.facebook.com/Norwalk-Chamber-of-Commerce-278056065118
Linkedin: www.linkedin.com/organization-guest/company/norwalk-california-chamber-of-commerce
X (Twitter): x.com/norwalkchamber
Instagram: www.instagram.com/norwalkchamber

Description: Promotes business and community development in Norwalk, CA. **Founded:** 1923. **Publications:** *Norwalk Chamber News* (Monthly). **Geographic Preference:** Local.

37056 ■ Oakdale Chamber of Commerce
590 N Yosemite Ave.
Oakdale, CA 95361
Ph: (209)847-2244
Fax: (209)847-0826
Co. E-mail: membership@oakdalechamber.com
URL: http://www.oakdalechamber.com
Contact: Trisha K. Brown, Chief Executive Officer
Facebook: www.facebook.com/oakdalecachamber
Linkedin: www.linkedin.com/in/oakdale-chamber-227a23b3
X (Twitter): x.com/oakdalechamber
Instagram: www.instagram.com/oakdalechamber

Description: Promotes business and community development in Oakdale, CA. Sponsors annual Antique and Craft Show and Chocolate Festival. **Founded:** 1917. **Publications:** *Oakdale Business News* (Monthly). **Educational Activities:** Oakdale Chocolate Ball Chocolate Bliss (Annual). **Geographic Preference:** Local.

37057 ■ Oakhurst Area Chamber of Commerce (OACC)
40061 Hwy. 49, Ste. 102
Oakhurst, CA 93644
Ph: (559)683-7766
Co. E-mail: chamber@oakhurstchamber.com
URL: http://oakhurstchamber.com
Contact: Wade Wheeler, President
Facebook: www.facebook.com/OakhurstAreaChamber

37058 ■ California

X (Twitter): x.com/OakhurstChamber
Instagram: www.instagram.com/oakhurstchamber
Description: Works to advance the commercial, financial, industrial and civic interests of Oakhurst Area. **Founded:** 1959. **Publications:** *Eblast Newsletter* (Weekly). **Geographic Preference:** Local.

37058 ■ Oakland African-American Chamber of Commerce (OAACC)
Airport Plz. Bldg., Ste. 369
333 Hegenberger Rd.
Oakland, CA 94621
Ph: (510)268-1600
Co. E-mail: office@oaacc.org
URL: http://www.oaacc.org
Contact: Tammy Willis, Treasurer
Facebook: www.facebook.com/theoaacc
Instagram: www.instagram.com/theoaacc
Description: Promotes business and development for the African-American community in Oakland. **Founded:** 2003. **Geographic Preference:** Local.

37059 ■ Oakland Chinatown Chamber of Commerce (OCCC)
388 9th St., Ste. 290
Oakland, CA 94607
Ph: (510)893-8979
Fax: (510)893-8988
Co. E-mail: chinatownchamber@gmail.com
URL: http://www.oaklandchinatownchamber.org
Contact: Carl Chan, President
Facebook: www.facebook.com/chinatownchamber
X (Twitter): x.com/oaklandCTchambr
Instagram: www.instagram.com/oaklandchinatownchamber
Description: Promotes business and community development in Oakland, Chinatown area. **Founded:** 1985. **Geographic Preference:** Local.

37060 ■ Oakland Metropolitan Chamber of Commerce (OMCC)
1333 Broadway Plz. Level, Ste. 100
Oakland, CA 94612
Ph: (510)874-4800
URL: http://www.oaklandchamber.com
Contact: Barbara Leslie, President
E-mail: bleslie@oaklandchamber.com
Facebook: www.facebook.com/Oakbiz
X (Twitter): x.com/OaklandChamber
Instagram: www.instagram.com/oaklandchamber
YouTube: www.youtube.com/channel/UCeA0wlLSdBpI5spYOb0mFuw
Description: Promotes business and community development in Oakland, CA. **Founded:** 1905. **Publications:** *Focus on Business* (Monthly). **Educational Activities:** Oakland Metropolitan Chamber of Commerce Breakfast. **Awards:** Oakland on the Map Award (Annual). **Geographic Preference:** Local.

37061 ■ Oakley Chamber of Commerce
404 E Front St.
Oakley, CA 94561
URL: http://www.discoveroakley.com/144/Find
Description: Promotes business and community development in Oakley, CA area. **Founded:** 1985. **Geographic Preference:** Local.

37062 ■ Oceanside Chamber of Commerce (OCC)
928 N Coast Hwy.
Oceanside, CA 92054
Ph: (760)722-1534
Co. E-mail: info@oceansidechamber.com
URL: http://www.oceansidechamber.com
Contact: Tracy Millero-Chin, Chief Operating Officer
E-mail: tracy@oceansidechamber.com
Facebook: www.facebook.com/oceansidechamber
Linkedin: www.linkedin.com/company/oceanside-chamber-of-commerce
X (Twitter): x.com/osidecachamber
Instagram: www.instagram.com/oceansidechamber
YouTube: www.youtube.com/user/OceansideChamber
Pinterest: www.pinterest.com/osidecachamber

Description: Promotes business and community development in Oceanside, CA. **Founded:** 1896. **Publications:** *Oceanside Chronicle* (Monthly). **Geographic Preference:** Local.

37063 ■ Ojai Valley Chamber of Commerce (OVCofC)
206 N Signal St., Ste. P
Ojai, CA 93024
Ph: (805)646-8126
Co. E-mail: info@ojaichamber.org
URL: http://www.wheninojai.com/chamber
Contact: Barbara Haskins, President
Facebook: www.facebook.com/ojaichamber
Instagram: www.instagram.com/ojai_chamber
Description: Promotes business and community development in the Ojai, CA area. **Founded:** 1956. **Publications:** *Ojai Business Journal*. **Geographic Preference:** Local.

37064 ■ *Orange Business News*
34 Plz. Sqre
Orange, CA 92866
Ph: (714)538-3581
Co. E-mail: info@orangechamber.com
URL: http://www.orangechamber.com
Contact: Pat Buttress, Vice Chairman of the Board
URL(s): business.orangechamber.com/member/newmemberapp
Released: Weekly **Availability:** Print; Online.

37065 ■ Orange Chamber of Commerce
34 Plz. Sqre
Orange, CA 92866
Ph: (714)538-3581
Co. E-mail: info@orangechamber.com
URL: http://www.orangechamber.com
Contact: Pat Buttress, Vice Chairman of the Board
Facebook: www.facebook.com/orangechamber
Linkedin: www.linkedin.com/company/orange-chamber-of-commerce
X (Twitter): x.com/orangechamber
Instagram: www.instagram.com/orangechamber
YouTube: www.youtube.com/channel/UC3EobaQ29znHNE9fo8BVrfA
Description: Promotes business and community development in Orange, CA. **Founded:** 1921. **Publications:** *Orange Business News* (Weekly); *Orange Bytes* (Weekly). **Geographic Preference:** Local.

37066 ■ Orange County Business Council (OCBC)
2 Pk. Plz., Ste. 100
Irvine, CA 92614
Ph: (949)476-2242
Fax: (949)476-9240
URL: http://www.ocbc.org
Contact: Jeffrey Ball, President
E-mail: jball@ocbc.org
Facebook: www.facebook.com/BizCouncil
X (Twitter): x.com/OC_Biz_Council
Description: Promotes business and community development in Orange County, CA. **Founded:** 1888. **Publications:** *Orange County Business and Industrial Directory* (Annual); *The Indicator* (Biweekly); *Orange County Business and Industrial Directory*. **Educational Activities:** Economic Forecast Conference (Annual). **Geographic Preference:** Local.

37067 ■ Orange County Hispanic Chamber of Commerce (OCHCC)
5270 California Ave., Ste. 2. 286
Irvine, CA 92617
Ph: (714)953-4289
Fax: (714)953-0273
Co. E-mail: mail@ochcc.com
URL: http://www.ochcc.com
Contact: Reuben D. Franco, President
Facebook: www.facebook.com/theochcc
Linkedin: www.linkedin.com/in/ochcc
X (Twitter): x.com/OCHCC
Instagram: www.instagram.com/ochcc
YouTube: www.youtube.com/channel/UCJq59iWVAbR0pz4A4Y1K77g
Description: Promotes business and community development in Orange County, CA area. **Founded:** 1986. **Geographic Preference:** Local.

37068 ■ Orangevale Chamber of Commerce (OCC)
8897 Greenback Ln.
Orangevale, CA 95662
Ph: (916)988-0175
Co. E-mail: info@orangevalechamber.com
URL: http://www.orangevalechamber.com
Contact: Kim Bayne, Executive Director
X (Twitter): x.com/OVChamber
Description: Promotes business and community development in Sacramento County, CA. **Founded:** 1955. **Publications:** *Orangevale Chamber of Commerce Member Directory*; *Orangevale Juice* (Periodic). **Educational Activities:** Chamber Ambassador Meeting; Pow Wow Days (Annual). **Geographic Preference:** Local.

37069 ■ *Orangevale Chamber of Commerce Member Directory*
8897 Greenback Ln.
Orangevale, CA 95662
Ph: (916)988-0175
Co. E-mail: info@orangevalechamber.com
URL: http://www.orangevalechamber.com
Contact: Kim Bayne, Executive Director
URL(s): www.orangevalechamber.com/member-directory
Availability: Print.

37070 ■ Orinda Chamber of Commerce (OCC)
PO Box 2271
Orinda, CA 94563
Ph: (925)254-3909
Co. E-mail: info@orindachamber.org
URL: http://orindachamber.org
Contact: Kristen Southworth, Co-President
Facebook: www.facebook.com/OrindaChamberofCommerce
Instagram: www.instagram.com/orindachamberofcommerce
Description: Promotes business and community development in Contra Costa County, CA. **Founded:** 1985. **Publications:** *Orinda Chamber of Commerce Directory*. **Geographic Preference:** Local.

37071 ■ Oroville Area Chamber of Commerce (OACC)
1789 Montgomery St.
Oroville, CA 95965
Ph: (530)538-2542
Co. E-mail: info@orovillechamber.com
URL: http://www.orovillechamber.com
Contact: Eric Smith, President
Facebook: www.facebook.com/OrovilleChamberCa
Instagram: www.instagram.com/orovillechamberofcommerce
Description: Promotes business and community development in the Oroville, CA area. **Founded:** 1890. **Geographic Preference:** Local.

37072 ■ Oroville Chamber of Commerce
1789 Montgomery St.
Butte Valley, CA 95965
Ph: (530)538-2542
Co. E-mail: info@orovillechamber.com
URL: http://www.orovillechamber.com
Contact: Eric Smith, President
Facebook: www.facebook.com/OrovilleChamberCa
Instagram: www.instagram.com/orovillechamberofcommerce
Description: Promotes business and commerce in the area. **Founded:** 1977. **Publications:** *Oroville Chamber Update!* (Periodic). **Educational Activities:** Oroville Chamber of Commerce Meeting. **Geographic Preference:** Regional.

37073 ■ Otay Mesa Chamber of Commerce
8100 Gigantic St., Bldg. 4100
Office 4106
San Diego, CA 92154
Ph: (619)661-6111
Co. E-mail: otaymesachamberinfo@otaymesa.org
URL: http://www.otaymesa.org
Contact: Alejandra Mier Y. Teran, Executive Director
Facebook: www.facebook.com/Otay-Mesa-Chamber-of-Commerce-317420038339716

Linkedin: www.linkedin.com/in/otay-mesa-chamber-of-commerce-62505a160
YouTube: www.youtube.com/channel/UCS9hOIYX0Tsm7x1oAEjffRA
Description: Promotes business and community development in Otay Mesa, CA. Sponsors Trade Show. **Founded:** 1987. **Publications:** *Otay Action* (Bimonthly). **Geographic Preference:** Local.

37074 ■ Pacific Grove Chamber of Commerce (PGCC)
584 Central Ave.
Pacific Grove, CA 93950
Ph: (831)373-3304
URL: http://www.pacificgrove.org
Contact: Moe Ammar, President
E-mail: moeammar@pacificgrove.org
Facebook: www.facebook.com/PGChamber
X (Twitter): x.com/pgchamber
Instagram: www.instagram.com/pgchamber
YouTube: www.youtube.com/channel/UCtYthhV_ckfWaHtR4XGbdog/feed
Pinterest: www.pinterest.com/pgchamber
Description: Promotes business and community development and operates visitor information center in Pacific Grove, CA. **Founded:** 1915. **Publications:** *Historic Walking Tour*; *Wrap Up* (Quarterly). **Geographic Preference:** Local.

37075 ■ Pacific Palisades Chamber of Commerce
15330 Antioch St.
Pacific Palisades, CA 90272
Ph: (310)459-7963
Co. E-mail: ceo@mppcc.org
URL: http://www.palisadeschamber.com
Contact: Bob Benton, President
E-mail: ceo@mppcc.org
X (Twitter): x.com/palichamber
Instagram: www.instagram.com/palichamber
Description: Promotes business and community development in Pacific Palisades, CA. **Founded:** 1949. **Geographic Preference:** Local.

37076 ■ Pacifica Chamber of Commerce (PCC)
225 Rockaway Beach Ave., Ste. 1
Pacifica, CA 94044
Ph: (650)355-4122
Co. E-mail: info@pacificachamber.com
URL: http://www.pacificachamber.com
Contact: Lynn Gallo, President
Facebook: www.facebook.com/pacifica.chamber
X (Twitter): x.com/PacificaCoC
YouTube: www.youtube.com/user/PacificaChamber1
Pinterest: www.pinterest.com/PacificaChamber
Description: Promotes business and community development in Pacifica, CA. **Founded:** 1957. **Geographic Preference:** Local.

37077 ■ Pajaro Valley Chamber of Commerce
44 Brennan St.
Watsonville, CA 95077
Ph: (831)724-3900
URL: http://pajarovalleychamber.com
Contact: Shaz Roth, Chief Executive Officer
E-mail: shaz@pajarovalleychamber.com
Facebook: www.facebook.com/pajaro.chamber
Description: Promotes business and community development in the Watsonville and Pajaro Valley, CA area. **Publications:** *The Progress* (Quarterly). **Awards:** Pajaro Valley Chamber of Commerce Woman of the Year (Annual); Pajaro Valley Chamber of Commerce Business of the Year (Annual); Pajaro Valley Chamber of Commerce Man of the Year (Annual); Pajaro Valley Chamber of Commerce Organization of the Year (Annual). **Geographic Preference:** Local.

37078 ■ Palm Desert Area Chamber of Commerce
72-559 Hwy. 111
Palm Desert, CA 92260
Ph: (760)346-6111
Fax: (760)346-3263
Co. E-mail: ceo@pdacc.org
URL: http://www.pdacc.org
Contact: Randy Florence, President
Facebook: www.facebook.com/PalmDesertAreaChamber
Instagram: www.instagram.com/palmdesertareachamber
Description: Promotes business and community development in Palm Desert, CA. **Founded:** 1954. **Publications:** *Business to Business* (Monthly). **Awards:** Palm Desert Chamber of Commerce Business Person of the Year (Annual). **Geographic Preference:** Local.

37079 ■ Palm Springs Chamber of Commerce (PSCC)
190 W Amado Rd.
Palm Springs, CA 92262
Ph: (760)325-1577
URL: http://pschamber.org
Contact: Brady Sandahl, President
E-mail: brady@bradysandahl.com
Facebook: www.facebook.com/PalmSpringsChamber
Linkedin: www.linkedin.com/in/the-palm-springs-chamber-of-commerce-43063750
X (Twitter): x.com/pspringschamber
YouTube: www.youtube.com/user/PalmSpringsChamber
Description: Promotes business and community development in the Palm Springs, CA area. **Founded:** 1937. **Publications:** *Business Matters* (Weekly); *Business Referral* (Annual). **Educational Activities:** Board Retreat (Annual); Leadership Conference/Retreat. **Geographic Preference:** Local.

37080 ■ Palo Alto Chamber of Commerce
355 Alma St.
Palo Alto, CA 94301
Ph: (650)324-3121
Co. E-mail: info@paloaltochamber.com
URL: http://www.paloaltochamber.com
Contact: Charlie Weidanz, President
Facebook: www.facebook.com/paloaltochamberofcommerce
X (Twitter): x.com/PA_Chamber
YouTube: www.youtube.com/channel/UCdt-jdbDjSrKiUuJcHv_oJg
Description: Promotes business and community development in Palo Alto, CA. **Founded:** 1910. **Publications:** *Membership Directory & Community Guide* (Annual); *Business News Network* (Bimonthly). **Awards:** Palo Alto Chamber of Commerce Tall Tree Award (Annual). **Geographic Preference:** Local.

37081 ■ Palos Verdes Peninsula Chamber of Commerce
4040 Palos Verdes Dr. N, Ste. 205
Rolling Hills Estates, CA 90274
Ph: (310)377-8111
Co. E-mail: connect@palosverdeschamber.com
URL: http://www.palosverdeschamber.com
Contact: Eileen Hupp, President
E-mail: eileen@palosverdeschamber.com
Facebook: www.facebook.com/Palos-Verdes-Peninsula-Chamber-of-Commerce-618777738141796
X (Twitter): x.com/pvpchamber
Instagram: www.instagram.com/pvstreetfair
Pinterest: www.pinterest.com/pvpchamber
Description: Promotes business and community development in Palos Verdes Peninsula, California area. **Founded:** 1956. **Publications:** *Peninsula Business Journal* (Monthly). **Geographic Preference:** Regional.

37082 ■ Paradise Ridge Chamber of Commerce (PRCoC)
6161 Clark Rd., Ste. 1
Paradise, CA 95969
Ph: (530)877-9356
Co. E-mail: info@paradisechamber.com
URL: http://ww.paradisechamber.com
Contact: Kimball Shirey, President
Facebook: www.facebook.com/ParadiseRidgeChamberOfCommerce
Description: Promotes business and community development on the Paradise Ridge in Northern California. **Founded:** 1935. **Geographic Preference:** Local.

37083 ■ Paramount Chamber of Commerce (PCC)
15357 Paramount Blvd.
Paramount, CA 90723
Ph: (562)634-3980
Fax: (562)634-0891
Co. E-mail: inquire@paramountchamber.com
URL: http://www.paramountchamber.com
Contact: Alicia Valadez, President
Facebook: www.facebook.com/ParamountChamber
Instagram: www.instagram.com/paramountchamber
Description: Promotes business and community development in Paramount, CA. Maintains business resource center. **Founded:** 1924. **Publications:** *Pulse Beat* (Monthly); *Business Directory*; *City of Paramount Map*. **Educational Activities:** Paramount Fiesta. **Geographic Preference:** Local.

37084 ■ Pasadena Chamber of Commerce and Civic Association
44 N Mentor Ave.
Pasadena, CA 91106
Ph: (626)795-3355
Fax: (626)795-5603
Co. E-mail: info@pasadena-chamber.org
URL: http://www.pasadena-chamber.org
Contact: Paul Little, President
E-mail: paul@pasadena-chamber.org
Description: Promotes business and community development in Pasadena, CA. **Founded:** 1888. **Publications:** *Business Directory*; *Community and Visitor Guide*; *Pasadena Commerce* (Bimonthly). **Educational Activities:** Luncheon Alliance (Monthly). **Geographic Preference:** Local.

37085 ■ *Pasadena Commerce*
44 N Mentor Ave.
Pasadena, CA 91106
Ph: (626)795-3355
Fax: (626)795-5603
Co. E-mail: info@pasadena-chamber.org
URL: http://www.pasadena-chamber.org
Contact: Paul Little, President
E-mail: paul@pasadena-chamber.org
URL(s): www.pasadena-chamber.org/about/newsletter-archive
Released: Bimonthly **Availability:** Print; PDF.

37086 ■ Paso Robles Chamber of Commerce (PRCC)
1225 Pk. St.
Paso Robles, CA 93446
Ph: (805)238-0506
Fax: (805)238-0527
Co. E-mail: info@pasorobleschamber.com
URL: http://www.pasorobleschamber.com
Contact: Gina Fitzpatrick, President
E-mail: gina@pasorobleschamber.com
Facebook: www.facebook.com/PasoChamber
Linkedin: www.linkedin.com/company/paso-robles-chamber-of-commerce
X (Twitter): x.com/PasoChamber
Instagram: www.instagram.com/pasochamber
YouTube: www.youtube.com/channel/UCy4BOS8R1emmr3OjjcxXZBQ
Pinterest: www.pinterest.com/pasorobleschamber
Description: Promotes business and community development in northern San Luis Obispo County, CA. **Founded:** 1920. **Publications:** *Business*; *The Business News* (Monthly). **Educational Activities:** Business Expo. **Awards:** Roblan of the Year (Annual). **Geographic Preference:** Local.

37087 ■ Patterson-Westley Chamber of Commerce
PO Box 365
Patterson, CA 95363
Ph: (209)894-7900
URL: http://pattersonwestleychamber.org
Contact: Becky Campo, Co-President
Facebook: www.facebook.com/PattersonWestleyChamber
Instagram: www.instagram.com/Patterson_Westley_Chamber

Description: Promotes business and community development in the Patterson and Westley, CA area. Founded: 1923. Publications: *The Sentinel* (Quarterly). Geographic Preference: Local.

37088 ■ Perris Valley Chamber of Commerce
11 S D St.
Perris, CA 92570
Ph: (651)657-3555
Fax: (951)657-3085
Co. E-mail: pvcc@perrischamber.net
URL: http://www.perrischamber.net
Contact: Ignacio Valdivia, President
Facebook: www.facebook.com/perrischamber
Linkedin: www.linkedin.com/in/perrischamber
X (Twitter): x.com/Perrischamber
Instagram: www.instagram.com/perris.chamber
YouTube: www.youtube.com/channel/UCp4edxPtzEG6Xzdp0g_Bw1w
Description: Promotes business and community development in the Parris Valley, CA area. Founded: 1911. Geographic Preference: Local.

37089 ■ Petaluma Area Chamber of Commerce (PACC)
6 Petaluma Blvd. N, Ste. B-11
Petaluma, CA 94952
Ph: (707)762-2785
Co. E-mail: pacc@petalumachamber.com
URL: http://www.petalumachamber.com
Contact: Kevin Jones, President
E-mail: kevin.jones@fastsigns.com
Facebook: www.facebook.com/PetalumaAreaChamberOfCommerce
YouTube: www.youtube.com/user/PetalumaChamberVideo
Description: Promotes business and community development in the Petaluma Area, CA area. Founded: 1852. Publications: *Petaluma Business* (Monthly); *Petaluma Chamber Directory and Relocation Guide* (Annual); *Petaluma Street Map* (Annual). Awards: Petaluma Area Chamber of Commerce Citizen of the Year (Annual). Geographic Preference: Local.

37090 ■ *Petaluma Business*
6 Petaluma Blvd. N, Ste. B-11
Petaluma, CA 94952
Ph: (707)762-2785
Co. E-mail: pacc@petalumachamber.com
URL: http://www.petalumachamber.com
Contact: Kevin Jones, President
E-mail: kevin.jones@fastsigns.com
Ed: Marsha Trent. Released: Monthly Description: Newspaper containing information about business and community information within Petaluma Area, CA. Availability: Print.

37091 ■ Phelan Chamber of Commerce
PO Box 290010
Phelan, CA 92329-0010
Ph: (760)868-3291
Co. E-mail: phelanchamber@gmail.com
URL: http://www.phelanchamber.info
Contact: Rebecca Kujawa, President
E-mail: rebeccakujawa70@gmail.com
Description: Works to advance the general welfare and prosperity of the Phelan area. Founded: 1962. Geographic Preference: Local.

37092 ■ Pico Rivera Chamber of Commerce (PRCC)
c/o Julian Balderas Executive Director
5016 Passons Blvd.
Pico Rivera, CA 90660
Ph: (562)949-2477
Co. E-mail: julianbalderas@picoriverachamber.org
URL: http://www.picoriverachamber.org
Contact: Marco Zapien, President
E-mail: chefmz@zrgcorp.com
Facebook: www.facebook.com/picoriverachamber
X (Twitter): x.com/priverachambe
Instagram: www.instagram.com/picoriverachamber
Description: Promotes business and community development in Pico Rivera, CA. Conducts beautification and business of the year competitions. Sponsors business expo, golf tournaments, mixers, and other special events. Founded: 1958. Publications: *Business* (Monthly); *Business News* (Monthly). Geographic Preference: Local.

37093 ■ Pinon Hills Chamber of Commerce
10405 Moutain Rd.
Pinon Hills, CA 92372
Ph: (760)868-5801
Co. E-mail: info@pinonhillschamber.info
URL: http://pinonhillsthegateway.com
Contact: Lori Ann Weston, Contact
Facebook: www.facebook.com/PinonHillsChamber
Description: Promotes business and community development in Pinon Hills, CA area. Founded: 1934. Geographic Preference: Local.

37094 ■ *Pioneer*
246 E Bonita Ave.
San Dimas, CA 91773
Ph: (909)592-3818
Fax: (909)592-8178
Co. E-mail: info@sandimaschamber.com
URL: http://www.sandimaschamber.com
Contact: Ben Lewis, General Manager
URL(s): sandimaschamber.org/chamber-benefits
Released: Monthly Description: Features business articles, member profiles, and community events. Availability: Online.

37095 ■ Pismo Beach Chamber of Commerce
649 Dolliver St.
Pismo Beach, CA 93449
Ph: (805)773-4382
Fax: (805)773-6772
Co. E-mail: info@pismochamber.com
URL: http://www.pismochamber.com
Contact: Jeanette Vierra, President
Facebook: www.facebook.com/PismoBeachChamberofCommerce
X (Twitter): x.com/PismoChamber
YouTube: www.youtube.com/user/pismochamber
Description: Promotes business and community development in Pismo Beach, CA. Founded: 1947. Publications: *Business*. Geographic Preference: Local.

37096 ■ Pittsburg Chamber of Commerce
985 Railroad Ave.
Pittsburg, CA 94565
Ph: (925)432-7301
Co. E-mail: chamber@mypittsburgchamber.org
URL: http://www.mypittsburgchamber.org
Contact: Wolfgang Croskey, Chief Executive Officer
E-mail: wolfgang@mypittsburgchamber.org
Facebook: www.facebook.com/pittsburgc
Linkedin: www.linkedin.com/in/pittsburg-chamber-of-commerce-07347486
X (Twitter): x.com/chamber94565
Description: Promotes business and community development in Pittsburg, CA. Founded: 1910. Publications: *Business Today* (Monthly). Geographic Preference: Local.

37097 ■ Placentia Chamber of Commerce
117 N Main St.
Placentia, CA 92870
Ph: (714)528-1873
Co. E-mail: info@placentiachamber.com
URL: http://www.placentiachamber.com
Contact: Matthew Wolfe, President
Linkedin: www.linkedin.com/company/placentia-chamber-of-commerce
Instagram: www.instagram.com/placentiachamber
YouTube: www.youtube.com/channel/UCas3iO86ajh1kmJM2Or-f9g
Description: Promotes business and community development in northern Orange County, CA. Founded: 1924. Publications: *Placentia Chamber of Commerce Newsletter*. Geographic Preference: Local.

37098 ■ *Placentia Chamber of Commerce Newsletter*
117 N Main St.
Placentia, CA 92870
Ph: (714)528-1873
Co. E-mail: info@placentiachamber.com
URL: http://www.placentiachamber.com
Contact: Matthew Wolfe, President
URL(s): www.placentiachamber.com/privacy-policy
Availability: Print.

37099 ■ Pleasant Hill Chamber of Commerce (PHCC)
91 Gregory Ln., Ste. 11
Pleasant Hill, CA 94523
Ph: (925)687-0700
Fax: (925)676-7422
Co. E-mail: chamberinfo@pleasanthillchamber.com
URL: http://www.pleasanthillchamber.com
Contact: Margaret Manzo, President
Facebook: www.facebook.com/PleasantHillChamberofCommerce
Linkedin: www.linkedin.com/company-beta/1375381
X (Twitter): x.com/PHChamber_CA
Instagram: www.instagram.com/pleasanthillchamber
YouTube: www.youtube.com/channel/UCMW3tObpySYcYimtGs0N0yg
Description: Promotes business and community development in the central Contra Costa County, CA. Sponsors local festivals and charitable events. Conducts competitions. Founded: 1954. Publications: *Business News* (Monthly); *Pleasant Hill Chamber*. Educational Activities: Summer Bash; Art, Wine & Music Festival (Annual). Awards: Pleasant Hill Chamber of Commerce Citizen of the Year (Annual); Pleasant Hill Chamber of Commerce Teen of the Year (Annual). Geographic Preference: Local.

37100 ■ *Pomona Chamber Business Monthly*
101 W Mission Blvd., No. 218B
Pomona, CA 91766
Ph: (909)622-1256
Fax: (909)620-5986
Co. E-mail: info@pomonachamber.org
URL: http://pomonachamber.org
Contact: Monique Manzanares, President
E-mail: mmanzanares@pomonachamber.org
URL(s): pomonachamber.org/chamber-membership/join
Released: Monthly Description: Offers various articles and member advertising. Availability: Print.

37101 ■ Pomona Chamber of Commerce
101 W Mission Blvd., No. 218B
Pomona, CA 91766
Ph: (909)622-1256
Fax: (909)620-5986
Co. E-mail: info@pomonachamber.org
URL: http://pomonachamber.org
Contact: Monique Manzanares, President
E-mail: mmanzanares@pomonachamber.org
Facebook: www.facebook.com/pomonachamber
Linkedin: www.linkedin.com/in/pomona-chamber-of-commerce-ab55331a4
X (Twitter): x.com/PomonaChamberC
Instagram: www.instagram.com/pomonachamber
YouTube: www.youtube.com/channel
Description: Promotes business and community development in Pomona, CA. Founded: 1888. Publications: *Pomona Chamber Business Monthly* (Monthly); *Pomona Chamber of Commerce Membership Directory/Community Guide* (Annual). Geographic Preference: State.

37102 ■ Port Hueneme Chamber of Commerce (PHCC)
567 W Channel Islands Blvd., Ste., 583
Port Hueneme, CA 93041
Ph: (805)228-1366
Co. E-mail: chamberinfo@huenemechamber.com
URL: http://www.uschamber.com/co/chambers/california
Facebook: www.facebook.com/HuenemeChamber
Description: Promotes business and community development in Port Hueneme, Oxnard Harbor District, and surrounding areas. Founded: 1940. Geographic Preference: Local.

37103 ■ *Port O Call*
445 W Weber Ave., Ste. 220
Stockton, CA 95203
Ph: (209)547-2770
Fax: (209)466-5271

STATE LISTINGS

Co. E-mail: schamber@stocktonchamber.org
URL: http://stocktonchamber.org
Contact: Chris Kay, President
URL(s): stocktonchamber.org/port-o-call
Released: Monthly **Availability:** Print.

37104 ▪ Porterville Chamber of Commerce
93 N Main St.
Porterville, CA 93257
Ph: (559)784-7502
Co. E-mail: info@portervillechamber.org
URL: http://portervillechamber.org
Contact: Tony Benevento, President
Facebook: www.facebook.com/porterville.chamber
Description: Promotes business and community development in southeastern Tulare County, CA. Sponsors local festivals. **Founded:** 1907. **Publications:** *Business News* (Monthly); *Porterville Fact Book* (Biennial). **Educational Activities:** Spring Festival (Annual). **Geographic Preference:** Local.

37105 ▪ Poway Chamber of Commerce
14039 Midland Rd.
Poway, CA 92064
Ph: (858)748-0016
Fax: (858)748-1710
Co. E-mail: chamber@poway.com
URL: http://poway.com
Contact: Mike Leland, President
E-mail: mike@poway.com
Facebook: www.facebook.com/PowayChamber
Linkedin: www.linkedin.com/company/poway-chamber-of-commerce
X (Twitter): x.com/PowayChamber
Description: Promotes business and community development in Poway, CA. **Founded:** 1951. **Publications:** *Communique* (Monthly); *Poway Telephone Directory* (Annual). **Geographic Preference:** Local.

37106 ▪ *Progress*
1114 J St.
Modesto, CA 95354
Ph: (209)577-5757
Co. E-mail: info@modchamber.org
URL: http://www.modchamber.org
Contact: Michael Gaffney, Board Member
URL(s): www.modchamber.org/progress-magazine
Released: Monthly **Availability:** Print; PDF; Online.

37107 ▪ *The Progress*
44 Brennan St.
Watsonville, CA 95077
Ph: (831)724-3900
URL: http://pajarovalleychamber.com
Contact: Shaz Roth, Chief Executive Officer
E-mail: shaz@pajarovalleychamber.com
URL(s): pajarovalleychamber.com/membership
Released: Quarterly **Availability:** Print.

37108 ▪ *Pulse Beat*
15357 Paramount Blvd.
Paramount, CA 90723
Ph: (562)634-3980
Fax: (562)634-0891
Co. E-mail: inquire@paramountchamber.com
URL: http://www.paramountchamber.com
Contact: Alicia Valadez, President
URL(s): www.paramountchamber.com/publications
Ed: Peggy Lemons. **Released:** Monthly **Price:** $32, for month. **Availability:** PDF; Online.

37109 ▪ Quartz Hill Chamber of Commerce (QHCoC)
42043 50th St. W
Quartz Hill, CA 93536
Ph: (661)722-4811
Fax: (661)722-3235
Co. E-mail: contact@quartzhillchamber.com
URL: http://quartzhillchamber.com
Contact: Cheyenne Anderson-Hess, President
Facebook: www.facebook.com/QHCoC
Description: Promotes business and community development in Quartz Hill, CA. **Founded:** 1948. **Publications:** *Quartz Hill Breeze*. **Educational Activities:** Quartz Hill Chamber of Commerce Workshop. **Geographic Preference:** Local.

37110 ▪ Quincy Chamber of Commerce (QCC)
336 Main St.
Quincy, CA 95971
Ph: (530)394-0541
Co. E-mail: info@quincychamber.com
URL: http://www.quincychamber.com
Contact: Freddy Holman, President
Facebook: www.facebook.com/QuincyCAChamberofCommerce
X (Twitter): x.com/QuincyCofC
Instagram: www.instagram.com/quincycachamber
Description: Promotes business and community development in Quincy, CA. Sponsors community events. **Geographic Preference:** Local.

37111 ▪ *Ramona Business and Community News*
1306 Main St., Ste. 103
Ramona, CA 92065
Ph: (760)789-1311
Co. E-mail: rccstaff@ramonachamber.com
URL: http://www.ramonachamber.com
Contact: Joe Stupar, Executive Director
E-mail: joestupar@ramonachamber.com
URL(s): ramonachamber.com/newsletter
Released: Monthly **Availability:** PDF; Online.

37112 ▪ Ramona Chamber of Commerce (RCC)
1306 Main St., Ste. 103
Ramona, CA 92065
Ph: (760)789-1311
Co. E-mail: rccstaff@ramonachamber.com
URL: http://www.ramonachamber.com
Contact: Joe Stupar, Executive Director
E-mail: joestupar@ramonachamber.com
X (Twitter): x.com/RamonaChamber
Description: Promotes business and community development in Ramona, CA. Holds annual country fair, golf tournament, and rodeo. **Founded:** 1908. **Publications:** *Ramona Business and Community News* (Monthly). **Geographic Preference:** Local.

37113 ▪ Rancho Cordova Chamber of Commerce
2729 Prospect Pk. Dr., Ste. 117
Rancho Cordova, CA 95670
Ph: (916)273-5700
Fax: (916)384-2046
Co. E-mail: info@ranchocordova.org
URL: http://www.ranchocordova.org
Contact: Diann H. Rogers, President
E-mail: dhrogers@ranchocordova.org
Facebook: www.facebook.com/rancho.chamber
X (Twitter): x.com/RanchoChamber
Description: Promotes business and community development in the southeastern Sacramento, CA area. Conducts small business seminars and workshops; sponsors Talk to Expert series. Issues annual and monthly publications. **Founded:** 1963. **Publications:** *Chamber Report*. **Geographic Preference:** Local.

37114 ▪ Rancho Cucamonga Chamber of Commerce
10470 Foothill Blvd., Ste. 200
Rancho Cucamonga, CA 91730
Ph: (909)987-1012
Co. E-mail: info@ranchochamber.org
URL: http://ranchochamber.org
Contact: Robert Hufnagel, President
Facebook: www.facebook.com/RCChamberofCommerce
Linkedin: www.linkedin.com/company/rccoc
X (Twitter): x.com/rccoc
YouTube: www.youtube.com/channel/UCLkCTzR08SeM56Fy11hkslQ
Description: Promotes business and community development in Rancho Cucamonga, CA area. **Founded:** 1951. **Publications:** *Chamber Member Business and Resource Directory*; *The Shop Rancho Retail Guide and Service Directory* (Annual). **Educational Activities:** Business Connection Network. **Geographic Preference:** Local.

37115 ▪ Rancho Mirage Chamber of Commerce (RMCC)
71905 Hwy. 111, Ste. H
Rancho Mirage, CA 92270
Ph: (760)568-9351
Co. E-mail: info@ranchomirage.org
URL: http://ranchomiragechamber.org
Contact: Katie Stice, President
E-mail: katie.stice@ranchomirage.org
Facebook: www.facebook.com/ranchomiragechamber
X (Twitter): x.com/RMChamber_
Instagram: www.instagram.com/ranchomiragechamber
Description: Promotes business and community development in the Coachella Valley area of California. Sponsors Mayor's Breakfast. **Founded:** 1955. **Publications:** *The Business Advocate* (Monthly); *Rancho Mirage City Guide* (Annual); *Rancho Mirage Chamber of Commerce--Membership Directory & Buyers Guide* (Annual). **Geographic Preference:** Local.

37116 ▪ *Rancho Mirage City Guide*
71905 Hwy. 111, Ste. H
Rancho Mirage, CA 92270
Ph: (760)568-9351
Co. E-mail: info@ranchomirage.org
URL: http://ranchomiragechamber.org
Contact: Katie Stice, President
E-mail: katie.stice@ranchomirage.org
URL(s): ranchomiragechamber.org/city-guide-rancho-mirage
Released: Annual **Availability:** Online; PDF.

37117 ▪ Red Bluff-Tehama County Chamber of Commerce
100 Main St.
Red Bluff, CA 96080
Ph: (530)527-6220
Fax: (530)527-2908
Co. E-mail: info@redbluffchamber.com
URL: http://redbluffchamber.com
Contact: Dave Gowan, Chief Executive Officer
E-mail: dave@redbluffchamber.com
Facebook: www.facebook.com/redbluffchamber
X (Twitter): x.com/redbluffchamber
YouTube: www.youtube.com/channel/UCD8exKvswldY6fMgpyyhQfA
Description: Promotes business and community development in Red Bluff-Tehama County, CA. Sponsors Memorial Day Championship Drag Boat Races and art and crafts fair. **Publications:** *Chamber Report*. **Geographic Preference:** Local.

37118 ▪ Redlands Chamber of Commerce
47 N First St.
Redlands, CA 92373
Ph: (909)793-2546
Co. E-mail: info@redlandschamber.org
URL: http://redlandschamber.org
Contact: Ken Morse, President
Facebook: www.facebook.com/redlandschamber
Linkedin: www.linkedin.com/company/redlandschamber
X (Twitter): x.com/redlandschamber
Instagram: www.instagram.com/redlandschamber
Description: Promotes business and community development in Redlands, CA. Issues publications. **Founded:** 1893. **Publications:** *Chamber Membership Directory*; *Redlands Chamber Today* (Monthly). **Educational Activities:** Rise n Shine Redlands (Monthly). **Geographic Preference:** Local.

37119 ▪ Redondo Beach Chamber of Commerce and Visitors Bureau (RBCC)
1611 S Catalina Ave., Ste. 204
Redondo Beach, CA 90277
Ph: (310)376-6911
Co. E-mail: info@redondochamber.org
URL: http://www.redondochamber.org

Description: Promotes business and community development in Redondo Beach, CA. Sponsors festivals, competitions, and charitable events. **Founded:** 1907. **Publications:** *Beach Business* (Monthly); *Update* (Monthly). **Geographic Preference:** Local.

37120 ■ Rialto Chamber of Commerce
120 N Riverside Ave.
Rialto, CA 92376
Ph: (909)875-5364
Co. E-mail: lisa@rialtochamber.org
URL: http://www.rialtochamber.org
Facebook: www.facebook.com/rialto.chamber
Description: Promotes business and community development in Rialto, CA. Issues publications. **Founded:** 1907. **Geographic Preference:** Local.

37121 ■ Richmond Chamber of Commerce
3925 Macdonald Ave.
Richmond, CA 94805
Ph: (510)234-3512
Fax: (510)234-3540
Co. E-mail: staff@rcoc.com
URL: http://www.rcoc.com
Contact: James Lee, President
E-mail: james@rcoc.com
Facebook: www.facebook.com/richmon
 dchamberofcommerce
X (Twitter): x.com/RichmondCOC
Instagram: www.instagram.com/chamberrichmond
Description: Membership is made up of a dynamic range of businesses from sole-proprietors to major corporations. Provides a voice for each and encourages participation by all. Strives to provides services, resources, and advocacy to foster growth in the business community and benefit West Contra Costa County. Offers information about the city and its business opportunities, policies, and trends. **Founded:** 1924. **Publications:** *Richmond Chamber News* (Monthly); *Richmond Magazine*. **Educational Activities:** Chamber Breakfast for Business (Monthly). **Geographic Preference:** Local.

37122 ■ *Richmond Chamber News*
3925 Macdonald Ave.
Richmond, CA 94805
Ph: (510)234-3512
Fax: (510)234-3540
Co. E-mail: staff@rcoc.com
URL: http://www.rcoc.com
Contact: James Lee, President
E-mail: james@rcoc.com
URL(s): www.richmondchamber.ca/past-newsletters
Released: Monthly; Latest issue February 2023. **Availability:** Online.

37123 ■ *Richmond Magazine*
3925 Macdonald Ave.
Richmond, CA 94805
Ph: (510)234-3512
Fax: (510)234-3540
Co. E-mail: staff@rcoc.com
URL: http://www.rcoc.com
Contact: James Lee, President
E-mail: james@rcoc.com
URL(s): www.rcoc.com/about-the-chamber/our-mission-2
Description: Magazine containing a directory listing of all members alphabetically and by category, as well as articles about Richmond and display advertising. **Availability:** Print.

37124 ■ Ridgecrest Chamber of Commerce
128 E California Ave., Ste. B
Ridgecrest, CA 93555
Ph: (760)375-8331
Co. E-mail: chamber@ridgecrestchamber.com
URL: http://www.ridgecrestchamber.com
Contact: Tim Smith, Executive Director
Facebook: www.facebook.com/ridgecrestchamber1
YouTube: www.youtube.com/channel/UCm
 4xVl7glFiIv0J28euNH6A
Description: Promotes business and community development in eastern Kern County, CA. Sponsors Adopt-A-School program. Conducts Ridgecrest Follies, IWV Outlook Conference, Business Expo, Retail Promotion Seminars, and Military Shopping Tour. **Founded:** 1946. **Publications:** *Business Bylines* (Monthly). **Educational Activities:** Business After Hours (Monthly). **Geographic Preference:** Local.

37125 ■ Rio Linda/Elverta Chamber of Commerce
810 Oak Ln.
Rio Linda, CA 95673
Co. E-mail: info@riolindachamber.com
URL: http://www.riolindachamber.com
Contact: Wendy Stirnaman, President
E-mail: president@riolindachamber.com
Facebook: www.facebook.com/
 RLEChamberofCommerce
Description: Promotes business and community development in Rio Linda-Elverta, CA. **Founded:** 1983. **Publications:** *Welcome to Rio Linda-Elverta* (Monthly). **Geographic Preference:** Local.

37126 ■ Rio Vista Chamber of Commerce
33 N 2nd St.
Rio Vista, CA 94571
Ph: (707)374-2700
Co. E-mail: info@riovista.org
URL: http://www.riovista.org
Contact: Stacia Olson, President
E-mail: s.olson@californiadeltaliving.com
Facebook: www.facebook.com/riovis
 tachamberofcommerce
Instagram: www.instagram.com/riovis
 tachamberofcommerce
Description: Promotes business and community development in Rio Vista, CA. **Founded:** 1929. **Geographic Preference:** Local.

37127 ■ Ripon Chamber of Commerce - Friends of the Memorial Ripon Library
104 S Stockton Ave.
Ripon, CA 95366
Ph: (209)599-7519
Co. E-mail: info@riponchamber.org
URL: http://riponchamber.org
Contact: Kyle Wolterstorff, Chairman
E-mail: wolterstorff.kyle@principal.com
Facebook: www.facebook.com/
 RiponChamberofCommerce
X (Twitter): x.com/RiponChamber
Instagram: www.instagram.com/
 riponchamberofcommerce
Description: Promotes business and community development in Ripon, CA area. **Scope:** History. **Services:** Open to the public. **Holdings:** Books; audio books; CD's; DVD's. **Publications:** *The Communicator* (Quarterly). **Educational Activities:** Annual Almond Blossom Fashion Show (Annual). **Geographic Preference:** Local.

37128 ■ Rocklin Area Chamber of Commerce
3700 Rocklin Rd.
Rocklin, CA 95677
Ph: (916)624-2548
Co. E-mail: info@rocklinchamber.com
URL: http://www.rocklinchamber.com
Contact: Kent Ferrin, Chairman of the Board
Facebook: www.facebook.com/RocklinChamber
Linkedin: www.linkedin.com/company/rocklin-area
 -chamber-of-commerce
X (Twitter): x.com/rocklinchamber
Instagram: www.instagram.com/rocklinchamber
Description: Promotes business and community development in Rocklin, CA area. **Founded:** 1969. **Publications:** *Rocklin Chamber of Commerce City Guide and Membership Directory* (Annual); *Rocklin Chamber Membership Directory and Community Guide*. **Geographic Preference:** Local.

37129 ■ Rohnert Park Chamber of Commerce
101 Golf Course Dr. C-7
Rohnert Park, CA 94928
Ph: (707)584-1415
Fax: (707)584-2945
Co. E-mail: info@rohnertparkchamber.org
URL: http://www.rohnertparkchamber.org
Contact: Lisa Orloff, Executive Director
E-mail: lisaorloff@rohnertparkchamber.org
Facebook: www.facebook.com/RohnertParkChamber
Instagram: www.instagram.com/rpchamber
YouTube: www.youtube.com/channel/UCtqaxVZZqLq
 3DR357ulSJ8g
Description: Business people in the Rohnert Park, CA area committed to creating and maintaining an environment in which businesses can grow and prosper economically, socially, and culturally. Emphasis is placed on leadership, advocacy, building community, and partnerships. **Founded:** 1962. **Publications:** *Business Directory*; *Rohnert Park Chamber of Commerce Business News* (Bimonthly). **Educational Activities:** A. M. Rohnert Park. **Geographic Preference:** Local.

37130 ■ Rosamond Chamber of Commerce
2861 Diamond St.
Rosamond, CA 93560
Ph: (661)256-3248
URL: http://www.rosamondchamber.com
Contact: Gene Melchers, President
Facebook: www.facebook.com/Rosamon
 dChamberofCommerce
Description: Promotes business and community development in Rosamond, CA. **Educational Activities:** General Meeting (Monthly). **Geographic Preference:** Local.

37131 ■ Rosemead Chamber of Commerce (RCC)
3953 Muscatel Ave.
Rosemead, CA 91770
Ph: (626)288-0811
Co. E-mail: office@rosemeadchamber.org
URL: http://www.rosemeadchamber.org
Contact: Helen Romero Shaw, President
Facebook: www.facebook.com/rosemeadchamber
Instagram: www.instagram.com/rosemead_chamber
Description: Promotes business and community development in Rosemead, CA. Sponsors golf tournament and principal for a day program. **Founded:** 1927. **Publications:** *Rosemead Reports* (Irregular). **Geographic Preference:** Local.

37132 ■ *Rosemead Reports*
3953 Muscatel Ave.
Rosemead, CA 91770
Ph: (626)288-0811
Co. E-mail: office@rosemeadchamber.org
URL: http://www.rosemeadchamber.org
Contact: Helen Romero Shaw, President
URL(s): www.rosemeadchamber.org/rosemea
 d-reports-
Released: Irregular; last issue August 2022. **Description:** Newspaper containing news about Rosemead, CA; includes community news, business developments, membership updates and chamber activities. **Availability:** PDF.

37133 ■ Roseville Chamber of Commerce
650 Douglas Blvd.
Roseville, CA 95678
Ph: (916)783-8136
Co. E-mail: info@rosevillechamber.com
URL: http://rosevillechamber.com
Contact: Amy Triplett, Director
E-mail: amy@rosevilleareachamber.com
Facebook: www.facebook.com/RosevilleChamber
Linkedin: www.linkedin.com/in/
 rosevillechamberofcommerce
X (Twitter): x.com/RosevilleChambr
Instagram: www.instagram.com/rosevillechamber
Description: Promotes business and community development in Placer County, CA. **Founded:** 1947. **Publications:** *Roseville Insight* (Quarterly). **Geographic Preference:** Local.

37134 ■ *Roseville Insight*
650 Douglas Blvd.
Roseville, CA 95678
Ph: (916)783-8136
Co. E-mail: info@rosevillechamber.com
URL: http://rosevillechamber.com
Contact: Amy Triplett, Director
E-mail: amy@rosevilleareachamber.com
URL(s): www.rosevillechamber.com/advertising
 -opportunities

Released: Quarterly **Description:** Features chambers' activities, new members and articles on business matters. **Availability:** Print; Online.

37135 ■ Rough and Ready Chamber of Commerce
PO Box 801
Rough and Ready, CA 95975
Ph: (530)797-6729
Co. E-mail: info@roughandreadychamber.com
URL: http://www.roughandreadychamber.com
Contact: Sheridan Loungway, President
Description: Promotes business and community development in Rough and Ready, CA. **Founded:** 1849. **Awards:** Chili Cook-off (Annual). **Geographic Preference:** Local.

37136 ■ Running Springs Area Chamber of Commerce
2929 Running Springs School Rd.
Running Springs, CA 92382
Ph: (909)867-2411
Co. E-mail: info@runningspringschamber.com
URL: http://www.runningspringschamber.com
Contact: Kevin Somes, President
Facebook: www.facebook.com/
runningspringschamberofcommerce
Instagram: www.instagram.com/visitrunningsprings
Description: Promotes business and community development in Running Springs, CA. **Founded:** 1920. **Geographic Preference:** Local.

37137 ■ Russian River Chamber of Commerce
16209 1st St.
Guerneville, CA 95446
Ph: (707)869-9000
Free: 877-644-9001
Co. E-mail: news@russianriver.com
URL: http://russianriver.com/chamber-of-commerce
Contact: Bob Pullum, President
Instagram: www.instagram.com/russianriverchamber
YouTube: www.youtube.com/channel/UCeGxnnV
6jlJce8-Yj-fxFPA
Description: Promotes business and community development in Guerneville, CA. **Founded:** 1957. **Publications:** *Currents* (Monthly). **Geographic Preference:** Local.

37138 ■ Sacramento Black Chamber of Commerce (SBCC)
5960 S Land Pk., Dr.
Sacramento, CA 95822
Ph: (916)231-0416
Fax: (916)706-0477
Co. E-mail: info@sacblackchamber.org
URL: http://sacblackchamber.org
Contact: Azizza Davis Goines, President
Facebook: www.facebook.com/SacSBCC
Description: Local businesses within Greater Sacramento, CA region providing the latest information on local and national issues that may impact the community; brings local business owners together to create a solid economic structure within the Sacramento business community. **Founded:** 1984. **Publications:** *Capital Gains* (Quarterly). **Geographic Preference:** Local.

37139 ■ Sacramento Hispanic Chamber of Commerce (SHCC)
400 Capitol Mall, 9th Fl.
Sacramento, CA 95814
Ph: (916)486-7700
Co. E-mail: info@sachcc.org
URL: http://www.sachcc.org
Contact: Cathy Rodriguez Aguirre, President
E-mail: cathy@sachcc.org
Facebook: www.facebook.com/sachispanics
X (Twitter): x.com/SacHispanics
YouTube: www.youtube.com/channel/UCC5sLn1q
3-oba3PD_oSJgvQ
Description: Business owners, corporations, and individuals in Sacramento, CA. Creates and promotes a positive environment for Hispanic business. Coordinates efforts aimed at furthering economic and business development. Sponsors annual fundraisers and various festivals. **Founded:** 1972. **Publications:** *Sacramento Hispanic* (Monthly). **Awards:** SHCC Scholarships (Annual). **Geographic Preference:** Local.

37140 ■ Sacramento Metropolitan Chamber of Commerce
1017 L St., Ste. 557
Sacramento, CA 95814
Ph: (916)552-6800
Fax: (916)443-2672
Co. E-mail: communications@metrochamber.org
URL: http://metrochamber.org
Contact: Amanda Blackwood, President
Facebook: www.facebook.com/sacramentome
trochamber
Linkedin: www.linkedin.com/company/sacramento
-metro-chamber
X (Twitter): x.com/Metro_Chamber
Instagram: www.instagram.com/metro_chamber
YouTube: www.youtube.com/user/sacmetrochamber
Description: Promotes business and community development in the Sacramento, CA area. **Founded:** 1895. **Publications:** *Bizline*; *Metro Business* (Quarterly). **Awards:** Sacramento Metro Chamber of Commerce Business Hall of Fame (Annual); Sacramento Metro Chamber of Commerce Businessman and Businesswoman of the Year Awards (Annual). **Geographic Preference:** Local.

37141 ■ St. Helena Chamber of Commerce
1320 Main St. A
Saint Helena, CA 94574
Ph: (707)963-4456
Co. E-mail: admin@sthelena.com
URL: http://www.sthelenachamber.com
Contact: Amy Carabba, President
E-mail: amy@sthelena.com
Facebook: www.facebook.com/StHelenaCA
Linkedin: www.linkedin.com/company/st--helena
-chamber-of-commerce
X (Twitter): x.com/StHelenaCA
YouTube: www.youtube.com/user/sthelenachamber
Description: Promotes business and community development in St. Helena, CA. **Founded:** 1941. **Geographic Preference:** Local.

37142 ■ *Salinas Valley Chamber Business Journal*
119 E Alisal St.
Salinas, CA 93901
Ph: (831)751-7725
Co. E-mail: info@salinaschamber.com
URL: http://business.salinaschamber.com
Contact: Rodney Meeks, Chairman of the Board
URL(s): www.salinaschamber.com/business-journal
Availability: Print; PDF; Online.

37143 ■ Salinas Valley Chamber of Commerce
119 E Alisal St.
Salinas, CA 93901
Ph: (831)751-7725
Co. E-mail: info@salinaschamber.com
URL: http://business.salinaschamber.com
Contact: Rodney Meeks, Chairman of the Board
Facebook: www.facebook.com/
SalinasValleyChamberofCommerce
Linkedin: www.linkedin.com/company/
salinasvalleychamberofcommerce
X (Twitter): x.com/salinaschamber
Instagram: www.instagram.com/salinaschamber
Description: Promotes business and community development in the Salinas, CA area. **Publications:** *Chamber Membership Directory*; *Salinas Valley Chamber Business Journal*. **Awards:** Salinas Valley Chamber of Commerce Business Woman of the Year (Annual); Salinas Valley Chamber of Commerce Citizen of the Year (Annual). **Geographic Preference:** Local.

37144 ■ San Anselmo Chamber of Commerce (SACC)
PO BOX 2844
San Anselmo, CA 94979-2846
Ph: (415)233-7464
Co. E-mail: sananselmocc@gmail.com
URL: http://www.visitsananselmo.com/san-anselmo
-chamber-of-commerce
Contact: Benedetto Cico, President
Facebook: www.facebook.com/VisitSanAnselmo
X (Twitter): x.com/SanAnselmo12
Instagram: www.instagram.com/visitsananselmo
Description: Promotes business and community development in San Anselmo, CA area. **Geographic Preference:** Local.

37145 ■ San Benito County Chamber of Commerce
243 6th St., Ste. 100
Hollister, CA 95023-3988
Ph: (831)637-5315
Co. E-mail: ceo@sanbenitocountychamber.com
URL: http://www.sanbenitocountychamber.com
Contact: Michelle Leonard, President
E-mail: ceo@sanbenitocountychamber.com
Facebook: www.facebook.com/sanbenito.coun
tychamber
Description: Promotes business and community development in San Benito, CA. **Founded:** 1921. **Publications:** *Chamber e-News* (Monthly); *California.Calm, A Guide to San Benito County*. **Educational Activities:** Chamber Mixers (Monthly). **Geographic Preference:** Local.

37146 ■ San Bernardino Area Chamber of Commerce (SBACC)
546 W 6th St.
San Bernardino, CA 92410
Ph: (909)885-7515
Fax: (909)384-9979
Co. E-mail: sba.chamber@verizon.net
URL: http://www.sbachamber.org
Contact: Judi Penman, President
Facebook: www.facebook.com/sanbernardinocc
X (Twitter): x.com/SBAChamber
Instagram: www.instagram.com/sanbernardinocc
Description: Promotes business and community development in the San Bernardino, CA area. **Founded:** 1925. **Publications:** *San Bernardino Business* (Quarterly). **Geographic Preference:** Local.

37147 ■ San Clemente Chamber of Commerce (SCCC)
1231 Puerta Del Sol
San Clemente, CA 92673
Ph: (949)492-1131
Fax: (949)492-3764
Co. E-mail: info@scchamber.com
URL: http://www.scchamber.com
Contact: Ricky Rodriguez, Chairman of the Board
Facebook: www.facebook.com/SanClemen
teChamber
X (Twitter): x.com/SCChamber1
Instagram: www.instagram.com/sanclemen
techamber
YouTube: www.youtube.com/user/SanClemen
teChamber
Pinterest: www.pinterest.com/sanclementec
Description: Promotes business and community development in San Clemente, CA. **Founded:** 1925. **Publications:** *The San Clemente Current* (Monthly); *South Coast Area Directory* (Annual). **Educational Activities:** San Clemente Seafest (Annual). **Geographic Preference:** Local.

37148 ■ San Diego Coastal Chamber of Commerce (SDCC)
cø Nancy Wasko, President & CEO
11622 El Camino Real, Ste. 100.
San Diego, CA 92130
Ph: (858)755-4844
Fax: (858)408-3094
Co. E-mail: info@sandiegocoastalchamber.com
URL: http://www.delmarchamber.org
Contact: Nancy Wasko, President
E-mail: nancy@sandiegocoastalchamber.com
URL(s): www.sandiegocoastalchamber.com
Description: Promotes business and community development in the Del Mar, CA area. Conducts charitable activities. **Awards:** SDCCC Member of the Month (Monthly). **Geographic Preference:** Local.

37149 ■ San Diego County Hispanic Chamber of Commerce (SDCHCC)
Jacobs Ctr.
  404 Euclid Ave., No. 271 B
  San Diego, CA 92114
Ph: (858)268-0790
Co. E-mail: info@sdchcc.org
URL: http://www.sdchcc.org
Contact: Josie Clark, Co-President
Facebook: www.facebook.com/sdchcc
X (Twitter): x.com/sdchcc
Instagram: www.instagram.com/sdchcc
Description: Promotes business and community development in the Hispanic community of San Diego, CA. **Founded:** 1989. **Geographic Preference:** Local.

37150 ■ San Diego East County Chamber of Commerce (SDECCC)
201 S Magnolia Ave.
  El Cajon, CA 92020
Ph: (619)440-6161
Fax: (619)440-6164
Co. E-mail: events@eastcountychamber.org
URL: http://eastcountychamber.org
Contact: Rick Wilson, President
E-mail: rickw@eastcountychamber.org
Facebook: www.facebook.com/SanDiegoEastCountyChamber
X (Twitter): x.com/ecchamber
Instagram: www.instagram.com/sdeccc
YouTube: www.youtube.com/channel/UCawyOIglH-eb2G85BzNDsOQ
Description: Promotes business and community development in San Diego East County which includes El Cajon and La Mesa, CA. **Founded:** 1912. **Publications:** *East County Business News*. **Awards:** San Diego East County Chamber of Commerce Professional Services Industry Award (Annual). **Geographic Preference:** Local.

37151 ■ San Diego Regional Chamber of Commerce (SD)
402 W Broadway No.1000
  San Diego, CA 92101
Ph: (619)544-1300
URL: http://sdchamber.org
Contact: Jerry Sanders, President
Facebook: www.facebook.com/sdchamber
Linkedin: www.linkedin.com/company/san-diego-regional-chamber-of-commerce
X (Twitter): x.com/sdchamber
YouTube: www.youtube.com/user/2012SDChamber/feed
Description: Promotes business and community development in the Greater San Diego, CA area. **Scope:** Economics, including studies on demographics, housing, real estate, retail and wholesale, major industries, and population. **Founded:** 1870. **Publications:** *San Diego Metro Guide*; *Headquarters, San Diego County*; *Major Retail Centers, San Diego County*; *Real Estate Services, San Diego County* (Annual); *Directory & Referral Guide* (Annual); *Economic Bulletin* (Monthly); *San Diego World Trade Directory*; *Welcome* (Periodic); *California Bioscience Directory*; *Business Directory* (Annual); *Economic Profile* (Biennial); *San Diego Economic Bulletin* (Monthly); *World Trade Directory* (Periodic); *Chambers of Commerce* (Annual); *Small Business Assistance Directory*; *Executives Listing* (Annual); *Greater San Diego Chamber of Commerce Business Referral Directory* (Annual). **Educational Activities:** INSIGHTS; ERB San Diego Business; ERB San Diego's Economic Future. **Geographic Preference:** Local.

37152 ■ San Dimas Chamber of Commerce
246 E Bonita Ave.
  San Dimas, CA 91773
Ph: (909)592-3818
Fax: (909)592-8178
Co. E-mail: info@sandimaschamber.com
URL: http://www.sandimaschamber.com
Contact: Ben Lewis, General Manager
Facebook: www.facebook.com/sandimaschamber
Linkedin: www.linkedin.com/company/san-dimas-chamber-of-commerce/about
X (Twitter): x.com/sandimaschamber
Instagram: www.instagram.com/sandimaschamber
Description: Strives to foster and promote growth of business and professional community while enhancing the quality of life in San Dimas. **Founded:** 1914. **Publications:** *Pioneer* (Monthly); *Business Directory*; *The Business and Community Guide* (Biennial). **Geographic Preference:** Local.

37153 ■ San Francisco Chamber of Commerce (SFCC)
235 Montgomery St., Ste. 760
  San Francisco, CA 94104-2803
Ph: (415)392-4520
Fax: (415)392-0485
Co. E-mail: info@sfchamber.com
URL: http://sfchamber.com
Contact: Rodney Fong, President
Facebook: www.facebook.com/SFChamber
Linkedin: www.linkedin.com/company/san-francisco-chamber-of-commerce
X (Twitter): x.com/SF_Chamber
Instagram: www.instagram.com/sf_chamber
Description: Promotes business and community development in San Francisco, CA. Convention/Meeting: none. **Founded:** 1850. **Publications:** *San Francisco Chamber of Commerce Membership Directory*; *Northern California Business Directory*; *California Manufacturers Register: 2008 Edition* (Annual); *Directory of California Technology Companies*; *San Francisco Bay Area Silicon Valley International Business Directory*; *Business Meeting & More*; *Trade Association Directory--San Francisco Chamber of Commerce* (Annual); *World Trade Association International Business Directory* (Annual); *San Francisco Industry and Commerce Directory* (Annual); *San Francisco Business Resource Guide and International Business Directory* (Annual). **Geographic Preference:** Local.

37154 ■ San Gabriel Chamber of Commerce (SGCC)
620 W Santa Anita St.
  San Gabriel, CA 91776
Ph: (626)576-2525
Co. E-mail: rosco_sandy@yahoo.com
URL: http://sangabrielchamber.org
Contact: Sandy Rosco, Executive Director
E-mail: rosco_sandy@yahoo.com
Description: Promotes the interests of local businesses as well as its products and services. **Founded:** 1948. **Geographic Preference:** Local.

37155 ■ San Juan Capistrano Chamber of Commerce
31781 Camino Capistrano, Ste. 306
  San Juan Capistrano, CA 92693-1878
Ph: (949)493-4700
Co. E-mail: sales@sanjuancapistrano.net
URL: http://sanjuancapistrano.net
Contact: Abraham Lincoln, President
Facebook: www.facebook.com/sanjuanchamber
X (Twitter): x.com/sanjuanchamber
Description: Promotes business and community development in San Juan Capistrano, CA. **Founded:** 1956. **Geographic Preference:** Local.

37156 ■ San Leandro Chamber of Commerce (SLCC)
120 Estudillo Ave.
  San Leandro, CA 94577
Ph: (510)317-1400
Fax: (510)218-2644
Co. E-mail: info@sanleandrochamber.com
URL: http://www.sanleandrochamber.com
Contact: Emily Griego, President
E-mail: emilyg@sanleandrochamber.com
Facebook: www.facebook.com/SanLeandroChamberofCommerce
Linkedin: www.linkedin.com/company/san-leandro-chamber-of-commerce
Instagram: www.instagram.com/sanleandrochamber
Description: Promotes business and community development in San Leandro, CA. **Founded:** 1923. **Geographic Preference:** Local.

37157 ■ San Luis Obispo Chamber of Commerce
895 Monterey St.
  San Luis Obispo, CA 93401
Ph: (805)781-2670
Fax: (805)543-1255
Co. E-mail: slochamber@slochamber.org
URL: http://slochamber.org
Contact: Jim Dantona, President
E-mail: jim@slochamber.org
Facebook: www.facebook.com/slochamber
Linkedin: www.linkedin.com/company/san-luis-obispo-chamber-of-commerce
X (Twitter): x.com/slochamber
Instagram: www.instagram.com/slochamber
YouTube: www.youtube.com/user/SanLuisObispoChamber
Description: Promotes business and community development in San Luis Obispo, CA. Conducts lobbying activities. **Founded:** 1905. **Publications:** *San Luis Obispo Chamber of Commerce Visitors Guide*. **Educational Activities:** Chamber Mixer (Monthly). **Awards:** San Luis Obispo Citizen of the Year (Annual). **Geographic Preference:** Local.

37158 ■ *San Luis Obispo Chamber of Commerce Visitors Guide*
895 Monterey St.
  San Luis Obispo, CA 93401
Ph: (805)781-2670
Fax: (805)543-1255
Co. E-mail: slochamber@slochamber.org
URL: http://slochamber.org
Contact: Jim Dantona, President
E-mail: jim@slochamber.org
URL(s): slochamber.org/your-chamber/visitor-center
Availability: Print; Online.

37159 ■ San Marcos Chamber of Commerce (SMC)
251 N City Dr.
  San Marcos, CA 92078
Ph: (760)744-1270
Co. E-mail: info@sanmarcoschamber.com
URL: http://www.sanmarcoschamber.com
Contact: Rick Rungaitis, President
E-mail: rick@sanmarcoschamber.com
Facebook: www.facebook.com/SanMarcosChamber
Linkedin: www.linkedin.com/company/san-marcos-chamber-of-commerce
X (Twitter): x.com/SMChamberCA
Instagram: www.instagram.com/sanmarcoschamber
YouTube: www.youtube.com/c/Sanmarcoschamber
Pinterest: www.pinterest.com/SMChamberCA
Description: Promotes business and community development in San Marcos, CA. Offers networking service. Sponsors annual sanctioned Chili Cook-off. **Founded:** 1967. **Publications:** *San Marcos Business Update* (Monthly); *San Marcos Chamber of Commerce Business & Relocation Directory* (Annual). **Geographic Preference:** Local.

37160 ■ San Mateo Area Chamber of Commerce (SMCC)
1730 S Amphlett Blvd., Ste. 206
  San Mateo, CA 94402
Ph: (650)401-2440
Fax: (877)304-2441
Co. E-mail: info@sanmateochamber.org
URL: http://sanmateochamber.org
Contact: Cheryl Angeles, Chief Executive Officer
E-mail: cheryl@sanmateochamber.org
Facebook: www.facebook.com/sanmateochamber
Linkedin: www.linkedin.com/company/san-mateo-chamber-of-commerce/about
X (Twitter): x.com/sanmateochamber
YouTube: www.youtube.com/user/SanMateoChamber
Description: Promotes business and the public interest through representation, advocacy and sponsorship. Organizes and funds programs that support the economic, civic, cultural, and educational excellence of the San Mateo area. **Founded:** 1939. **Publications:** *Community Guide* (Annual). **Geographic Preference:** Local.

STATE LISTINGS

37161 ■ San Pablo Chamber of Commerce (SPCC)
1000 Gateway Ave.
San Pablo, CA 94806
Ph: (510)215-3000
URL: http://www.sanpabloca.gov
Contact: Matt Rodriguez, Manager
E-mail: mattr@sanpabloca.gov
Facebook: www.facebook.com/sanpabloca
X (Twitter): x.com/CityofSanPablo
Description: Promotes business and community development in San Pablo, CA. **Founded:** 1948. **Geographic Preference:** Local.

37162 ■ San Pedro Chamber of Commerce (SPCC)
390 W 7th St.
San Pedro, CA 90731
Ph: (310)832-7272
Co. E-mail: info@sanpedrochamber.com
URL: http://www.sanpedrochamber.com
Contact: Elise Swanson, President
E-mail: eswanson@sanpedrochamber.com
Facebook: www.facebook.com/SanPedroChamber
Instagram: www.instagram.com/sanpedrochamber
YouTube: www.youtube.com/channel/UCgoigvtVagMamMYgbm8s4Dg
Description: Promotes, supports and advocates the interests of the business community. **Founded:** 1906. **Publications:** *Business Beacon* (Monthly); *Business Directory and Community Guide* (Annual); *Visitors Guide* (Annual). **Educational Activities:** Taste in San Pedro (Annual); Taste in San Pedro (Annual). **Geographic Preference:** Local.

37163 ■ San Rafael Chamber of Commerce (SRCC)
817 Mission Ave.
San Rafael, CA 94901
Ph: (415)454-4163
Co. E-mail: frontdesk@srchamber.com
URL: http://srchamber.com
Contact: Joanne Webster, President
E-mail: jwebster@srchamber.com
Facebook: www.facebook.com/SanRafaelCoC
Linkedin: www.linkedin.com/company/san-rafael-chamber-of-commerce
X (Twitter): x.com/SanRafaelCoC
YouTube: www.youtube.com/user/SRChamberofCommerce
Description: Works to provide a strong voice in support of the economic vitality of the community. **Founded:** 1920. **Publications:** *Business Directory*. **Educational Activities:** Leadership Institute. **Geographic Preference:** Local.

37164 ■ San Ramon Chamber of Commerce (SRCC)
6101 Bollinger Canyon Rd., Ste. 355
San Ramon, CA 94583
Ph: (925)242-0600
Fax: (925)242-0603
Co. E-mail: info@sanramon.org
URL: http://sanramon.org
Contact: Kathy Fanning, President
E-mail: kathy.fanning@sanramon.org
Facebook: www.facebook.com/SanRamonChamber
Linkedin: www.linkedin.com/company/san-ramon-chamber-of-commerce
X (Twitter): x.com/SRChamber
Instagram: www.instagram.com/sanramonchamber
YouTube: www.youtube.com/user/sanramonchamber
Description: Works to enhance the quality of life and economic vitality of the San Ramon Valley by representing business and community interests. **Founded:** 1983. **Publications:** *B2B*. **Educational Activities:** East Bay Business Symposium. **Awards:** San Ramon Chamber of Commerce Citizen of the Year Award (Annual). **Geographic Preference:** Local.

37165 ■ San Simeon Chamber of Commerce
250 San Simeon Ave., Ste. 3A
San Simeon, CA 93452
Ph: (805)927-3500
URL: http://visitsansimeonca.com
Contact: Michael R. Hanchett, Contact
Facebook: www.facebook.com/VisitSanSimeonCA
X (Twitter): x.com/visit_sansimeon
Instagram: www.instagram.com/visitsansimeon
Description: Promotes business and community development in San Simeon, CA. **Founded:** 1836. **Geographic Preference:** Local.

37166 ■ San Ysidro Chamber of Commerce and Visitor Information Center
663 E San Ysidro Blvd.
San Ysidro, CA 92173
Ph: (619)428-5200
URL: http://www.sanysidrochamber.org
Description: Promotes business and commerce of the distinct community of San Ysidro through networking, communication of pertinent information, and sponsoring of community enhancing events, benefiting from its unique location along the international border. **Founded:** 1923. **Publications:** *San Ysidro in Motion* (Quarterly). **Educational Activities:** San Ysidro Chamber of Commerce and Visitor Information Center Board meeting (Monthly). **Geographic Preference:** Local.

37167 ■ Sanger District Chamber of Commerce
1789 Jensen Ave., Ste. B
Sanger, CA 93657
Ph: (559)875-4575
Fax: (559)875-0745
Co. E-mail: sangerchamber@gmail.com
URL: http://www.sanger.org
Contact: David Pearson, Secretary
E-mail: pd71dp@live.com
Facebook: www.facebook.com/sangerchamber
Instagram: www.instagram.com/sangerchamber
Description: Promotes business and community development in Sanger, CA. **Founded:** 1887. **Publications:** *Sanger District Chamber of Commerce--Business Directory* (Annual). **Geographic Preference:** Local.

37168 ■ Santa Ana Chamber (SAC)
1631 W Sunflower Ave., Ste. C-35
Santa Ana, CA 92704
Ph: (714)541-5353
Fax: (714)541-2238
Co. E-mail: info@santaanachamber.com
URL: http://santaanachamber.com
Contact: David Elliott, President
E-mail: delliott@santaanachamber.com
Facebook: www.facebook.com/SAChamberofCommerce
X (Twitter): x.com/santaanachamber
Instagram: www.instagram.com/santaanachamber
YouTube: www.youtube.com/channel/UCT2o0G60fEAYuNE2M26Vq0Q
Description: Promotes business and community development in the Santa Ana, CA area. **Founded:** 1889. **Publications:** *ChamberLine 2.0* (Biweekly); *CityLine* (Bimonthly); *Santa Ana Community Guide and Business Directory* (Annual). **Geographic Preference:** Local.

37169 ■ Santa Clarita Valley Chamber of Commerce (SCVCC)
28494 Westinghouse Pl., No. 114
Santa Clarita, CA 91355
Ph: (661)702-6977
Co. E-mail: hello@scvchamber.com
URL: http://www.scvchamber.com/cpages/home
Contact: Ivan Volschenk, President
Facebook: www.facebook.com/Santa-Clarita-Valley-Chamber-of-Commerce-364674386969338
Linkedin: www.linkedin.com/company/scvchamber
X (Twitter): x.com/SCVChamber
Description: Promotes business and community development in the Santa Clarita Valley, CA area. Sponsors business expo. **Founded:** 1923. **Publications:** *Business Focus* (Monthly); *Santa Clarita Valley Chamber of Commerce Business Directory*; *SCVCC E-News* (Weekly). **Educational Activities:** Business After Hours (Monthly); Business Expo (Annual). **Geographic Preference:** Local.

California ■ 37173

37170 ■ *Santa Clarita Valley Chamber of Commerce Business Directory*
28494 Westinghouse Pl., No. 114
Santa Clarita, CA 91355
Ph: (661)702-6977
Co. E-mail: hello@scvchamber.com
URL: http://www.scvchamber.com/cpages/home
Contact: Ivan Volschenk, President
URL(s): www.scvchamber.com/directory?current_page=1&sort_type=featured&search_for=company&asset_type=company_user&display_type=default
Availability: Online.

37171 ■ Santa Cruz County Chamber of Commerce [Santa Cruz Area Chamber of Commerce]
3121 Pk. Ave., Ste. C
Soquel, CA 95073
Ph: (831)457-3713
Co. E-mail: joinus@santacruzchamber.org
URL: http://www.santacruzchamber.org
Contact: Elana Solon, Director
Facebook: www.facebook.com/santacruzcountychamber
Linkedin: www.linkedin.com/company/santa-cruz-chamber-of-commerce
X (Twitter): x.com/santacruzbiz
Instagram: www.instagram.com/santacruzcountychamber
YouTube: www.youtube.com/user/sccoc1
Description: Promotes business and community development in the Santa Cruz, CA area. **Founded:** 1889. **Publications:** *Business Santa Cruz* (Monthly); *Santa Cruz Chamber of Commerce--Membership Directory*. **Educational Activities:** Women in Business EXTRAVAGANZA (Annual). **Awards:** Santa Cruz Chamber of Commerce Community Recognition Awards (Annual). **Geographic Preference:** Local.

37172 ■ Santa Fe Springs Chamber of Commerce
12016 E Telegraph Rd., Ste. 100
Santa Fe Springs, CA 90670
Ph: (562)944-1616
Co. E-mail: mail@sfschamber.com
URL: http://www.sfschamber.com
Contact: Kathie Fink, Chief Executive Officer
E-mail: kathie@sfschamber.com
Facebook: www.facebook.com/SFSChamber
X (Twitter): x.com/sfschamber
Instagram: www.instagram.com/sfschamber
YouTube: www.youtube.com/channel/UCG91Zu3rAizj2TAn91ocylA
Description: Promotes business and community development in Santa Fe Springs, CA. **Founded:** 1974. **Holdings:** Figures not available. **Awards:** SFS Destiny Fund Scholarship (Annual); The Don and Jackie Powell Grant (Annual). **Geographic Preference:** Local.

37173 ■ Santa Maria Valley Chamber of Commerce (SMVCC)
614 S Broadway
Santa Maria, CA 93454
Ph: (805)925-2403
Fax: (805)928-7559
Co. E-mail: info@santamaria.com
URL: http://santamaria.com
Contact: Glenn Morris, Co-President Co-Chief Executive Officer
E-mail: glenn@santamaria.com
Facebook: www.facebook.com/SMVCC
X (Twitter): x.com/SMVCC
Instagram: www.instagram.com/santamariachamberofcommerce
Description: Works to improve the economy and increase its tax base by attracting visitors to the Santa Maria Valley. **Founded:** 1902. **Publications:** *Chamber Challenge* (Monthly). **Educational Activities:** Santa Maria Valley Chamber of Commerce Christmas Luncheon. **Geographic Preference:** Local.

37174 ■ Santa Monica Chamber of Commerce (SMCC)
3019 Ocean Pk. Blvd., Ste. 332
Santa Monica, CA 90405
Ph: (310)393-9825
Fax: (310)394-1868
Co. E-mail: info@smchamber.com
URL: http://smchamber.com
Contact: Judy Kruger, Co-President Co-Chief Executive Officer
E-mail: judy.kruger@smchamber.com
X (Twitter): x.com/Santamonicabiz
YouTube: www.youtube.com/user/santamonicachamber
Description: Promotes business and community development in the Santa Monica, CA area. Provides information, research assistance, and business counseling. Offers business referrals and Certificates of Origin for members exporting goods overseas. Sponsors semiannual art festival. Holds annual community health fair. Offers business seminars. **Founded:** 1927. **Publications:** *Business Briefs* (Monthly); *Membership Directory and Buyers Guide* (Annual); *Mid-month Update* (Monthly); *Santa Monica Chamber of Commerce Business Profile and Membership Directory*. **Geographic Preference:** Local.

37175 ■ Santa Paula Chamber of Commerce
200 N 10th St.
Santa Paula, CA 93060
Ph: (805)525-5561
Co. E-mail: info@santapaulachamber.com
URL: http://www.santapaulachamber.com
Contact: John Marquez, Executive Director
Facebook: www.facebook.com/SantaPaulaChamber
Description: Promotes business and community development in Santa Paula, CA area. **Founded:** 1914. **Geographic Preference:** Local.

37176 ■ Santa Rosa Chamber of Commerce
50 Old Courthouse Sq., Ste. 110
Santa Rosa, CA 95404
Ph: (707)545-1414
Fax: (707)545-6914
URL: http://www.santarosametrochamber.com
Contact: Brad Calkins, Executive Director
Facebook: www.facebook.com/SantaRosaChamber
Linkedin: www.linkedin.com/company/santa-rosa-chamber-of-commerce
X (Twitter): x.com/SRMetroChamber
Description: Promotes business and community development in Santa Rosa, CA. **Founded:** 1906. **Publications:** *On Point* (Monthly); *On Point On Line* (Weekly). **Geographic Preference:** Local.

37177 ■ Santee Chamber of Commerce (SCC)
9625 Mission Gorge Rd., Ste. B2-315
Santee, CA 92071
Ph: (619)449-1515
Co. E-mail: info@santeechamber.com
URL: http://santeechamber.com
Contact: Melissa Dombo, Chairman
Facebook: www.facebook.com/santeechamber
X (Twitter): x.com/santeechamber
Instagram: www.instagram.com/santeechamber
Description: Seeks to encourage economic growth in a free enterprise environment and enhance the community's image through collaboration with various civic and governmental entities. **Founded:** 1955. **Publications:** *Echo* (Quarterly). **Educational Activities:** Business After Five Mixers. **Geographic Preference:** Local.

37178 ■ Saratoga Chamber of Commerce
14460 Big Basin Way
Saratoga, CA 95070
Ph: (408)867-0753
Co. E-mail: info@saratogachamber.org
URL: http://www.saratogachamber.org
Contact: Kelly Medrano, Manager, Operations
Facebook: www.facebook.com/SaratogaChamberCA
Linkedin: www.linkedin.com/company/saratoga-ca-chamber-of-commerce
Instagram: www.instagram.com/saratogachamberca
Description: Works to invigorate the business environment and enhance the quality of life in the community. **Founded:** 1956. **Publications:** *City Map* (Biennial); *Saratoga Business Focus* (Bimonthly); *Special Events Resource*. **Geographic Preference:** Local.

37179 ■ Sausalito Chamber of Commerce
22 El Portal
Sausalito, CA 94965
Ph: (415)331-7262
Co. E-mail: chamber@sausalito.org
URL: http://www.sausalito.org
Contact: Juli Vieira, Chief Executive Officer
Facebook: www.facebook.com/SausalitoChamberofCommerce
Instagram: www.instagram.com/sausalito_chamber
Description: Strives to promote the economic health and well-being of Sausalito, CA by providing leadership and representation for issues affecting the business community, the citizens and visitors. Seeks to promote business and community development in Sausalito. **Founded:** 1945. **Publications:** *Chamber Waves* (Monthly); *Sausalito Chamber of Commerce-- Membership Directory*. **Geographic Preference:** Local.

37180 ■ Scotts Valley Chamber of Commerce (SVCC)
King Village Shopping Ctr.
216-B Mt. Hermon Rd.
Scotts Valley, CA 95066
Ph: (831)438-1010
Fax: (831)438-6544
Co. E-mail: info@scottsvalleychamber.com
URL: http://scottsvalleychamber.com
Contact: Danny Reber, Executive Director
E-mail: dreber@scottsvalleychamber.com
Facebook: www.facebook.com/scottsvalleychamber
Linkedin: www.linkedin.com/in/scotts-valley-chamber-65781b120
X (Twitter): x.com/scottsvalley1
Instagram: www.instagram.com/scottsvalleychamber
Description: Promotes business and community development in Scotts Valley, CA. **Founded:** 1957. **Publications:** *Scotts Valley Business Today* (Monthly); *Scotts Valley Directory and Annual Review* (Annual). **Awards:** Scotts Valley Chamber of Commerce Beautification Project of the Year (Annual); Scotts Valley Chamber of Commerce Business of the Year (Annual); Alvin Scarborough Memorial Man of the Year (Annual); Scotts Valley Chamber of Commerce Organization of the Year (Annual); Scotts Valley Chamber of Commerce Annette Marcum Memorial (Annual). **Geographic Preference:** Local.

37181 ■ *SCVCC E-News*
28494 Westinghouse Pl., No. 114
Santa Clarita, CA 91355
Ph: (661)702-6977
Co. E-mail: hello@scvchamber.com
URL: http://www.scvchamber.com/cpages/home
Contact: Ivan Volschenk, President
URL(s): www.scvchamber.com/cpages/products-services
Released: Weekly **Availability:** Online.

37182 ■ Seal Beach Chamber of Commerce - California
201 8th St., Ste. 110
Seal Beach, CA 90740
Ph: (562)799-0179
Fax: (562)795-5637
Co. E-mail: info@sealbeachchamber.org
URL: http://sealbeachchamber.org
Contact: Rob Jahncke, President
Facebook: www.facebook.com/SealBeachChamber
Linkedin: www.linkedin.com/in/seal-beach-24997159
X (Twitter): x.com/sbchamber
Instagram: www.instagram.com/sealbeach_chamber
YouTube: www.youtube.com/channel/UCUjxu3nQ_0zt7uBh2_AwgQ
Description: Promotes business and community development in Seal Beach, CA. **Founded:** 1968. **Geographic Preference:** Local.

37183 ■ Sebastopol Area Chamber of Commerce and Visitors Center
265 S Main St.
Sebastopol, CA 95472
Ph: (707)823-3032
Co. E-mail: info@sebastopol.org
URL: http://www.sebastopol.org
Contact: Ambrosia Thomson, Co-President
Facebook: www.facebook.com/SebastopolChamber
X (Twitter): x.com/SebastopolChamb
Description: Promotes civic and commercial progress in the Sebastopol, CA area. **Founded:** 1921. **Publications:** *Chamber Action* (Weekly). **Educational Activities:** Business and Community Showcase. **Geographic Preference:** Local.

37184 ■ Selma District Chamber of Commerce (SDCC)
1821 Tucker St.
Selma, CA 93662
Ph: (559)891-2235
Fax: (559)896-7075
URL: http://www.selma-chamber.com
Contact: Char Tucker, President
YouTube: www.youtube.com/channel/UCpw6Z-C_pR7xn4labSMVEuw
Description: Large business/industry, small business, medical, professional, individual and retirees. Promotes business and community development in the Selma, CA area. Sponsors Annual Crab Feed & Auction, Raisin Festival, July 3rd Community Celebration, August Summer Concerts in the Park, Car Show Marching Band Festival & Field Competition and a Holiday Street Faire and Santa Arrival. Hosts fund raising event. **Founded:** 1890. **Publications:** *Selma Business* (Monthly). **Awards:** Selma District Chamber of Commerce Citizen of the Year (Annual). **Geographic Preference:** Local.

37185 ■ Shafter Chamber of Commerce (SCC)
336 Pacific Ave.
Shafter, CA 93263
Ph: (661)746-2600
Fax: (661)746-0607
Co. E-mail: shafterchamber@shafter.com
URL: http://www.shafter.com/30/Chamber-of-Commerce
Contact: Rachel Zermeno, Director
Facebook: www.facebook.com/CityOfShafter
Description: Promotes business and community development in Shafter, CA. Sponsors Street Faires, May Festival, Cinco de Mayo, and Business/Student Exchange Day. **Founded:** 1947. **Publications:** *Map/Directory* (Periodic). **Awards:** Shafter Chamber of Commerce Humanitarian (Annual); Shafter Chamber of Commerce Citizen of the Year (Annual). **Geographic Preference:** Local.

37186 ■ *Sherman Oaks Chamber NEWS*
14827 Ventura Blvd., Ste. 207
Sherman Oaks, CA 91403
Ph: (818)906-1951
Fax: (818)206-0288
Co. E-mail: hello@shermanoakschamber.org
URL: http://www.shermanoakschamber.org
Contact: Tammy Scher, Chairperson
E-mail: tammy@shermanoakschamber.org
URL(s): www.shermanoaksencinochamber.org/member-benefits.html
Description: Features member, new product, promotion and location changes. **Availability:** Print.

37187 ■ Shingle Springs/Cameron Park Chamber of Commerce
4095 Cameron Pk. Dr.
Shingle Springs, CA 95682
Ph: (530)677-8000
Co. E-mail: info@sscpchamber.org
URL: http://www.sscpchamber.org
Contact: Colette Thiel, President
E-mail: colette@thielhomes.com
Facebook: www.facebook.com/SSCPChamber
Description: "Connecting With the Community". Works to advocate, promote, and preserve the quality of life in the area by means of a strong, healthy,

STATE LISTINGS

and diverse business community. **Founded:** 1967. **Publications:** *Shingle Springs/Cameron Park Chamber of Commerce Member Directory*; *Shingle Springs/Cameron Park Chamber of Commerce Chamber News* (Monthly); *Shingle Springs/Cameron Park Chamber of Commerce Business Directory*; *Business Directory*. **Geographic Preference:** Local.

37188 ■ Shingle Springs/Cameron Park Chamber of Commerce Member Directory
4095 Cameron Pk. Dr.
Shingle Springs, CA 95682
Ph: (530)677-8000
Co. E-mail: info@sscpchamber.org
URL: http://www.sscpchamber.org
Contact: Colette Thiel, President
E-mail: colette@thielhomes.com
URL(s): www.sscpchamber.org/member-directory
Description: Contains history, shopping information and complete business listing. **Availability:** Online.

37189 ■ Sierra County Chamber of Commerce
PO Box 436
Sierra City, CA 96125
Free: 800-200-4949
Co. E-mail: info@sierracountychamber.com
URL: http://sierracountychamber.com
Contact: Mary Ervin, Contact
Facebook: www.facebook.com/sierracountychamberofcommercecalifornia
Description: Promotes business and community development in the area. Sponsors local events and festivals. **Founded:** 1950. **Publications:** *Chamber News*. **Geographic Preference:** Local.

37190 ■ Sierra Madre Chamber of Commerce
Adam's Pack Station, 80 W Sierra Madre Blvd., No. 340
Sierra Madre, CA 91024
Ph: (626)355-5111
Co. E-mail: smadrecc@gmail.com
URL: http://www.sierramadrechamber.com
Contact: Luther Tsinoglou, Contact
E-mail: luther@tsinoglou.com
Facebook: www.facebook.com/sierramadrechamber91024
Instagram: www.instagram.com/explore/locations/980994519/sierra-madre-chamber-of-commerce
Description: Promotes business and community development in Sierra Madre, CA. **Geographic Preference:** Local.

37191 ■ Signal Hill Chamber of Commerce (SHCC)
2201 E Willow St., Ste. D-138
Signal Hill, CA 90755
Free: 888-687-1718
Co. E-mail: president@signalhillchamber.org
URL: http://www.signalhillchamber.org
Contact: Adalita Silva, President
E-mail: asilva@comerica.com
Facebook: www.facebook.com/SignalHillChamber
Linkedin: www.linkedin.com/company/city-of-signal-hill-chamber-of-commerce
X (Twitter): x.com/SignalHillCOC
Description: Promotes business and community development in Signal Hill, CA. **Founded:** 1941. **Publications:** *Hill Street News* (Quarterly). **Geographic Preference:** Local.

37192 ■ The silicon valley organization (SVO)
101 W Santa Clara St.
San Jose, CA 95113
Ph: (408)291-5260
Co. E-mail: kathryns@thesvo.com
URL: http://www.sjchamber.com/blog-authors/the-silicon-valley-organization
Facebook: www.facebook.com/Thesiliconvalleyorganization
Linkedin: www.linkedin.com/company/the-silicon-valley-organization
Description: Promotes economic development and the improvement of quality of life in the Silicon Valley area of CA by being the leading voice for business through delivering innovative products and services, engaging in aggressive government advocacy, and producing premier networking opportunities. **Founded:** 1886. **Geographic Preference:** Local.

37193 ■ Silicon Valley Central Chamber of Commerce (SVCCC)
3350 Scott Blvd., Bldg. 54
Santa Clara, CA 95054
Ph: (408)244-8244
Co. E-mail: domarina.ebrahimi@svcentralchamber.com
URL: http://www.svcentralchamber.com
Contact: Christian D. Malesic, President
Facebook: www.facebook.com/SVCChamber
Linkedin: www.linkedin.com/company/svcchamber
X (Twitter): x.com/svcchamber
Instagram: www.instagram.com/svcchamber
YouTube: www.youtube.com/channel/UC7g6BZlnnHdiQ210PK8wOvA
Description: Promotes business, community development, tourism and the convention trade in Santa Clara, CA. **Founded:** 1960. **Geographic Preference:** Local.

37194 ■ Simi Valley Chamber of Commerce
40 W Cochran St., Ste. 100
Simi Valley, CA 93065
Ph: (805)526-3900
Co. E-mail: info@simichamber.org
URL: http://www.simivalleychamber.org
Contact: Kathi van Etten, President
E-mail: kathi@simichamber.org
Linkedin: www.linkedin.com/company/simi-valley-chamber-of-commerce
YouTube: www.youtube.com/channel/UCEoTaotfTdXKKxG2xu1_H-w
Description: Promotes business and community development in Simi Valley, CA. **Founded:** 1951. **Geographic Preference:** Local.

37195 ■ Solana Beach Chamber of Commerce
210 W Plz. St.
Solana Beach, CA 92075
Ph: (858)755-4775
Fax: (858)755-4889
Co. E-mail: info@solanabeachchamber.com
URL: http://solanabeachchamber.com
Contact: Greg Petre, President
Facebook: www.facebook.com/solanabeachchamber
Linkedin: www.linkedin.com/company/solanabeachchamber
X (Twitter): x.com/SolanaChamber
Instagram: www.instagram.com/solanabeachchamber
YouTube: www.youtube.com/channel/UCA9OlyzLDchquYln0CmKrqg
Pinterest: www.pinterest.com/sbcoc
Description: Works to promote and support local business by encouraging and facilitating tourism, business to business relationships, community involvement and communications with local county and regional governments. **Founded:** 1948. **Publications:** *Solana Business Sounds*. **Geographic Preference:** Local.

37196 ■ Solvang Chamber of Commerce (SCC)
485 Alisal Rd., Ste. 245
Solvang, CA 93463
Ph: (805)688-0701
Co. E-mail: solvangchamber@solvangcc.com
URL: http://www.solvangcc.com
Contact: Dan Cassara, President
E-mail: dan@ccwinery.com
Facebook: www.facebook.com/SolvangChamberOfCommerce
Linkedin: www.linkedin.com/company/solvang-chamber-of-commerce/about
Instagram: www.instagram.com/solvangchamber
Pinterest: www.pinterest.com/solvangchamber
Description: Promotes business and community development in Solvang, CA. **Founded:** 1921. **Geographic Preference:** Local.

37197 ■ Sonoma Valley Chamber of Commerce
651-A Broadway
Sonoma, CA 95476
Ph: (707)996-1033
Co. E-mail: info@sonomachamber.com
URL: http://www.sonomachamber.org
Contact: John Bast, Co-President
Facebook: www.facebook.com/sonomachamber
Linkedin: www.linkedin.com/company/sonomavalleychamber
X (Twitter): x.com/sonomachamber
Instagram: www.instagram.com/sonomachamber
Description: Promotes business and community development in the Sonoma Valley area of California. **Founded:** 1914. **Geographic Preference:** Local.

37198 ■ Sonora Chamber of Commerce (HSCC)
PO Box 3084
Sonora, CA 95370
Ph: (209)694-4008
Co. E-mail: info@sonorachamber.org
URL: http://www.sonorachamber.com
Contact: Katie Dunn, President
Facebook: www.facebook.com/sonorachamber
Description: Strives to develop an economically prosperous business district while maintaining the character and integrity of Historic Sonora, making it the "heartbeat" of the community. Promotes commerce, culture, trade, good fellowship, and cooperative relationships among individuals and businesses. **Founded:** 2000. **Geographic Preference:** Local.

37199 ■ South Orange County Economic Coalition (SOCEC)
27758 Santa Margarita Pky., No. 378
Mission Viejo, CA 92691
Ph: (949)600-5470
Co. E-mail: info@economiccoalition.com
URL: http://www.economiccoalition.com
Contact: Mike Balsamo, Chairman
Facebook: www.facebook.com/economiccoalition
Linkedin: www.linkedin.com/company/south-orange-county-economic-coalition
X (Twitter): x.com/socecoalition
Instagram: www.instagram.com/economiccoalition
Description: Promotes the social and economic development in South Orange County. **Founded:** 1967. **Publications:** *Economic Report* (Annual). **Educational Activities:** Legislative Action Committee (Monthly). **Geographic Preference:** Local.

37200 ■ South San Francisco Chamber of Commerce (SSF)
213 Linden Ave.
South San Francisco, CA 94080
Ph: (650)588-1911
Fax: (650)588-2534
Co. E-mail: info@ssfchamber.com
URL: http://www.ssfchamber.com
Contact: Paul Formosa, President
X (Twitter): x.com/SSFChamber94080
Description: Promotes business and community development in South San Francisco, CA. **Founded:** 1913. **Geographic Preference:** Local.

37201 ■ Southern Humboldt Chamber of Commerce (GRCC)
782 Redwood Dr.
Garberville, CA 95542
Ph: (707)923-2613
URL: http://garberville.org
Contact: Jenny Early, President
Facebook: www.facebook.com/SoHumChamber
Description: Promotes business, tourism, and community development in Southern Humboldt County, CA. Sponsors Shakespeare at Benbow Lake, Culpepper, and Merriweather circus. Operates visitor and business information center. **Founded:** 1941. **Geographic Preference:** Local.

37202 ■ SPOTLIGHT
109 N 19th St.
Montebello, CA 90640
Ph: (323)721-1153
Fax: (323)721-7946

Co. E-mail: info@montebellochamber.org
URL: http://www.montebellochamber.org
Contact: Greg Millsap, Chairman
URL(s): www.montebellochamber.org/spotlight-newspaper
Released: Bimonthly; February, April, June, august, October and December. **Description:** Contains industry-related topics, policy updates, industry news and updates on PTDA members. **Availability:** PDF.

37203 ■ Spring Valley Chamber of Commerce
3322 Sweetwater Springs Blvd., Ste. 202
Spring Valley, CA 91977
Ph: (619)670-9902
Fax: (619)670-9924
Co. E-mail: info@springvalleychamber.org
URL: http://www.springvalleychamber.org
Contact: Tina Carlson, President
Description: Promotes business and community development in Spring Valley, CA. Sponsors parade and business fair. **Founded:** 1935. **Publications:** *Chamber Communications* (Monthly). **Awards:** Spring Valley Chamber of Commerce Business of the Year (Annual); Spring Valley Chamber of Commerce Individual of the Year (Annual). **Geographic Preference:** Local.

37204 ■ Springville Chamber of Commerce
PO Box 104
Springville, CA 93265
Ph: (559)744-3810
Co. E-mail: chamber@springville.ca.us
URL: http://springville.ca.us
Contact: Regina Winton, President
Facebook: www.facebook.com/Springville-Chamber-of-Commerce-303370796367318
Description: Promotes business and communications among Springville citizens and its surroundings. **Founded:** 1952. **Geographic Preference:** Local.

37205 ■ *Stanton Chamber Directory*
Released: Annual **Availability:** Print.

37206 ■ Studio City Chamber of Commerce (SCCC)
4024 Radford Ave., Edit 2, Ste. F
Studio City, CA 91604
Ph: (818)655-5916
URL: http://www.studiocitychamber.com
Contact: Christine Alvarez, President
Facebook: www.facebook.com/studiocitychamberofcommerce
X (Twitter): x.com/SC_Chamber
Description: Promotes business and community development in Studio City, CA. Sponsors running and race walking competitions. **Founded:** 1920. **Publications:** *Studio City Business* (Monthly). **Geographic Preference:** Local.

37207 ■ Sunland Tujunga Chamber of Commerce
8250 Foothill Blvd.
Shadow Hills, CA 91040
Ph: (818)293-5388
Co. E-mail: stchamber91040@gmail.com
Facebook: www.facebook.com/SunlandTujungaChamber
Instagram: www.instagram.com/stchamber
Description: Promotes business and community development in the Sunland-Tujunga, CA area. **Geographic Preference:** Local.

37208 ■ Sunnyvale Chamber of Commerce
260 S Sunnyvale Ave., Ste. 7
Sunnyvale, CA 94086
Ph: (408)736-4971
Co. E-mail: info@svcoc.org
URL: http://www.svcoc.org
Contact: Dawn Maher, Chief Executive Officer
E-mail: dawn@svcoc.org
Facebook: www.facebook.com/SunnyvaleSVChamber
Linkedin: www.linkedin.com/company/sunnyvale-silicon-valley-chamber-of-commerce
X (Twitter): x.com/SVChamb
Instagram: www.instagram.com/sunnyvale_chamber

Description: Promotes policies designed to connect, educate, and energize the business community to achieve economic vitality. **Founded:** 1907. **Publications:** *Business Progress*. **Awards:** Murphy Awards (Annual). **Geographic Preference:** Local.

37209 ■ The Swedish-American Chamber of Commerce of Los Angeles (SACC-LA)
8549 Wilshire Blvd., Ste. 1087
Beverly Hills, CA 90211
Ph: (310)622-3616
Co. E-mail: info@sacc-la.org
URL: http://www.sacc-la.org
Contact: Gudrun Giddings, President
Facebook: www.facebook.com/sacc.gla
Linkedin: www.linkedin.com/company/the-swedish-american-chamber-of-commerce---los-angeles
X (Twitter): x.com/SACCLA
Instagram: www.instagram.com/sacc_la
YouTube: www.youtube.com/channel/UCNYGIePd0cjL1G-8b0s06Ug
Description: Seeks to create an effective network that enables and enhances the exchange of business opportunities between Swedish and American companies, particularly those in the Los Angeles area. **Founded:** 1988. **Geographic Preference:** Local.

37210 ■ Swedish-American Chamber of Commerce San Diego
4475 Mission Blvd., Ste. 217
San Diego, CA 92109
Ph: (760)500-9069
Co. E-mail: marketing@sacc-sandiego.org
URL: http://www.sacc-sandiego.org
Contact: Ted Stubner, President
E-mail: ted@thenorth-westpassage.com
Facebook: www.facebook.com/sacc.sandiego
Linkedin: www.linkedin.com/company/swedish-american-chamber-of-commerce---san-diego
X (Twitter): x.com/SACCsandiego
Instagram: www.instagram.com/saccsandiego
Description: Promotes, develops and increases the Swedish-American contacts and interactions in the San Diego area. Facilitates mutually beneficial relationships between Swedish and American companies. **Founded:** 1989. **Geographic Preference:** Local.

37211 ■ Taft District Chamber of Commerce [Taft Chamber of Commerce]
400 Kern St.
Taft, CA 93268
Ph: (661)765-2165
Fax: (661)765-6639
Co. E-mail: taftchamber@gmail.com
URL: http://www.taftchamber.com
Contact: Bart Hill, Treasurer
Facebook: www.facebook.com/taft.chamber
Description: Promotes business and community development in Taft, CA. Conducts annual fundraisers, Taft District Chamber of Commerce Gala and annual Taft District Chamber of Commerce Trout Derby. **Founded:** 1944. **Publications:** *Report to the Community* (Monthly). **Geographic Preference:** Local.

37212 ■ Temecula Valley Chamber of Commerce (TVCC)
26790 Ynez Ct., Ste. A
Temecula, CA 92591
Ph: (951)676-5090
Fax: (951)694-0201
URL: http://www.temecula.org
Contact: Brooke Nunn, President
E-mail: brooke@temecula.org
Facebook: www.facebook.com/temeculacc
Linkedin: www.linkedin.com/groups/3197530/profile
X (Twitter): x.com/TemValChamber
YouTube: www.youtube.com/user/temchamber
Description: Promotes business and community development in the Temecula Valley, CA area. **Founded:** 1966. **Publications:** *Chamber Directory* (Periodic); *E-Commerce Newsletter* (Monthly); *Temecula Today* (Bimonthly). **Geographic Preference:** Local.

37213 ■ Temple City Chamber of Commerce
5938 Kauffman Ave.
Temple City, CA 91780
Ph: (626)286-3101
Co. E-mail: info@templecitychamber.com
URL: http://www.templecitychamber.com
Contact: Peter Choi, President
E-mail: peter@templecitychamber.com
X (Twitter): x.com/TempleCityLife
Description: Promotes business and community development in Temple City, CA. **Founded:** 1924. **Publications:** *News and Views* (Monthly). **Geographic Preference:** Local.

37214 ■ Templeton Chamber of Commerce
321 Main St., Ste. C
Templeton, CA 93465
Ph: (805)434-1789
Co. E-mail: info@templetonchamber.com
URL: http://www.templetonchamber.com
Contact: Elizabeth Covert, Chairman of the Board
Facebook: www.facebook.com/TempletonChamberofCommerce
Description: Promotes business and community development in Templeton, CA. Sponsors local charities and festivals. **Founded:** 1913. **Geographic Preference:** Local.

37215 ■ Thousand Palms Chamber of Commerce
72-715 La Canada
Thousand Palms, CA 92276
Ph: (760)343-1988
Fax: (760)343-1988
Co. E-mail: info@thousandpalmschamber.com
URL: http://thousandpalmschamber.com/thousand_palms_chamber_of_commerce.htm
Facebook: www.facebook.com/thousandpalmschamber
Description: Promotes business and community development in Thousand Palms, CA. **Geographic Preference:** Local.

37216 ■ Three Rivers Chamber of Commerce
42268 Sierra Dr.
Three Rivers, CA 93271
Ph: (559)561-8101
Co. E-mail: threeriverschamber@gmail.com
URL: http://threeriverschamber.org
Contact: Mike Hand, President
Description: Promotes business and community development in the area. Sponsors events. **Geographic Preference:** Local.

37217 ■ Tiburon Peninsula Chamber of Commerce (TPCC)
46 B Main St.
Tiburon, CA 94920
Ph: (415)435-5633
Co. E-mail: deannbiss.tiburonchamber@gmail.com
URL: http://www.tiburonchamber.org
Contact: Natale Servino, President
Facebook: www.facebook.com/TiburonChamber
X (Twitter): x.com/TiburonChamber
Instagram: www.instagram.com/tiburonchamber
Description: Promotes business and community development in the Tiburon, CA area. Sponsors Chili Cook-off and Wine Festival. Conducts Fourth of July activities, picnic, and charitable activities. **Founded:** 1960. **Geographic Preference:** Local.

37218 ■ Torrance Area Chamber of Commerce (TACC)
3480 Torrance Blvd., Ste. 305
Torrance, CA 90503
Ph: (310)540-5858
URL: http://www.torrancechamber.com
Contact: Donna Duperron, President
E-mail: donna@torrancechamber.com
Facebook: www.facebook.com/torrancechamber
X (Twitter): x.com/torrancechamber
Instagram: www.instagram.com/torrancechamber
Description: Promotes business and community development in Torrance, CA area. **Publications:** *Torrance Area Chamber of Commerce--Membership Directory*. **Geographic Preference:** Local.

STATE LISTINGS California ■ 37234

37219 ■ Trinity County Chamber of Commerce (TCCC)
PO Box 517
 Weaverville, CA 96093
Co. E-mail: chamber@trinitycounty.com
URL: http://trinitycounty.com
Contact: Kelli Gant, President
Facebook: www.facebook.com/TrinityChamber
Description: Promotes business and community development in Trinity County, CA. **Founded:** 1966. **Geographic Preference:** Local.

37220 ■ Truckee Donner Chamber of Commerce
10065 Donner Pass Rd.
 Truckee, CA 96161
Ph: (530)587-8808
Fax: (530)587-2439
Co. E-mail: info@truckee.com
URL: http://truckee.com
Contact: Ruth Geresy, Manager, Operations
Facebook: www.facebook.com/truckeechamber
Description: Promotes and develops local business and tourism, while improving the community's quality of life. **Publications:** *Truckee Tracks* (Quarterly); *Truckee Chamber of Commerce--Business Directory*. **Geographic Preference:** Local.

37221 ■ Tuolumne County Chamber of Commerce
197-B Mono Way
 Sonora, CA 95370
Ph: (209)532-4212
Co. E-mail: info@tcchamber.com
URL: http://tcchamber.com
Contact: Dave Souther, Co-President
Linkedin: www.linkedin.com/tcchamber
X (Twitter): x.com/TuoCoChamber
Instagram: www.instagram.com/tuolumnecoun
 tychamber
Description: Works to provide leadership for a better business environment. Promotes the economic well-being of Tuolumne County, CA. **Founded:** 1908. **Publications:** *Chamber News* (Monthly). **Geographic Preference:** Local.

37222 ■ Turlock Chamber of Commerce
115 S Golden State Blvd.
 Turlock, CA 95380
Ph: (209)632-2221
Fax: (209)632-5289
Co. E-mail: info@turlockchamber.com
URL: http://www.turlockchamber.com
Contact: Gina Petros-Blom, Executive Officer
E-mail: ginab@turlockchamber.com
Description: Promotes business and community development in Turlock, CA. Conducts charitable activities. Sponsors Turlock Poultry and Dairy Festival. **Publications:** *TCC Business News* (Quarterly). **Geographic Preference:** Local.

37223 ■ Tustin Chamber of Commerce (TCC)
17390 17th St., Ste. C
 Tustin, CA 92780
Ph: (714)544-5341
Fax: (714)460-8191
URL: http://tustinchamber.org
Contact: Nathan Yeargin, Chairman
E-mail: drnathanyeargindc@gmail.com
Facebook: www.facebook.com/TustinChamber
Instagram: www.instagram.com/tustinchamber
YouTube: www.youtube.com/user/TheTustinChamber
Description: Promotes business and community development in Tustin, CA. **Founded:** 1957. **Publications:** *The Advocate* (Monthly); *Directory of Members & Buyers Guide*. **Geographic Preference:** Local.

37224 ■ Twain Harte Area Chamber of Commerce
23000 Meadow Dr., Ste. G
 Twain Harte, CA 95383
Ph: (209)586-4482
Co. E-mail: info@twainhartecc.com
URL: http://www.twainhartecc.com
Contact: Brian Todd, President
Facebook: www.facebook.com/TwainHarteChamber
Instagram: www.instagram.com/twainhartechamber

Description: Promotes business and community development in Twain Harte, CA area. **Founded:** 1955. **Geographic Preference:** Local.

37225 ■ Union City Chamber of Commerce
3939 Smith St.
 Union City, CA 94587
Ph: (510)952-9637
Co. E-mail: unioncitymi@gmail.com
URL: http://ucchamber.org
Facebook: www.facebook.com/UnionCi
 tyChamberOfCommerce
Description: Promotes business and community development in Union City, CA. **Founded:** 1912. **Geographic Preference:** Local.

37226 ■ Universal City North Hollywood Chamber of Commerce (UCNH)
6369 Bellingham Ave.
 North Hollywood, CA 91606-3202
Ph: (818)508-5155
Fax: (818)508-5156
Co. E-mail: info@noho.org
URL: http://www.noho.org
Contact: Brian Charles, President
Facebook: www.facebook.com/Universal-City-North
 -Hollywood-Chamber-of-Commerce-152882487402
Linkedin: www.linkedin.com/company/universal-city
 -north-hollywood-chamber-of-commerce
X (Twitter): x.com/ucnhchamber
Description: Promotes business and community development in the Universal City-North Hollywood, CA area. Conducts charitable activities. Sponsors festival. **Founded:** 1914. **Geographic Preference:** Local.

37227 ■ Upland Chamber of Commerce (UCC)
215 N 2nd Ave., Ste. D
 Upland, CA 91786
Ph: (909)204-4465
Fax: (909)204-4464
Co. E-mail: csanchez@uplandchamber.org
URL: http://www.uplandchamber.org
Contact: Kate Brown, Chairman
Facebook: www.facebook.com/Uplan
 dChamberOfCommerce
X (Twitter): x.com/UplandChamber
Instagram: www.instagram.com/uplandchamber
YouTube: www.youtube.com/channel/UC
 2jRyCMDpqhAJfl37YrCG7A
Description: Promotes business and community development in Upland, CA. **Founded:** 1963. **Publications:** *Business Directory and Community Guide*. **Educational Activities:** Ambassador Team Meeting (Irregular). **Geographic Preference:** Local.

37228 ■ Vacaville Chamber of Commerce (VCC)
411 Davis St., Ste. 101
 Vacaville, CA 95688
Ph: (707)448-6424
Co. E-mail: connect@vacavillechamber.com
URL: http://www.vacavillechamber.com
Contact: Debbie Egidio, Chief Executive Officer
E-mail: debbie@vacavillechamber.com
Facebook: www.facebook.com/vacavillechamber
Linkedin: www.linkedin.com/company/
 vacavillechamber
X (Twitter): x.com/vacachamber
Instagram: www.instagram.com/vacavillechamber
YouTube: www.youtube.com/channel/UCaGuTVn
 6oThsc6lX9XQCYMA
Description: Promotes business and community development in Vacaville, CA. Sponsors local charities and festivals. **Founded:** 1913. **Publications:** *Business Comments* (Bimonthly). **Awards:** Vacaville Chamber of Commerce Ambassador of the Year (Annual); Vacaville Chamber of Commerce Business of the Year (Annual). **Geographic Preference:** Local.

37229 ■ Vallejo Chamber of Commerce (VCC)
425 A Virginia St.
 Vallejo, CA 94590
Ph: (707)644-5551
Co. E-mail: info@vallejochamber.com
URL: http://www.vallejochamber.com

Contact: James Cooper, Co-Chief Executive Officer
 Co-President
E-mail: james@vallejochamber.com
Description: Promotes business and community development in Vallejo, CA. **Founded:** 1874. **Publications:** *Vallejo Chamber of Commerce--Business Directory and Visitors Guide* (Annual). **Geographic Preference:** Local.

37230 ■ Valley Center Chamber of Commerce (VCCC)
27350 Valley Ctr. Rd., Ste. E
 Valley Center, CA 92082
Ph: (760)749-8472
Co. E-mail: info@vcchamber.com
URL: http://www.vcchamber.com
Contact: Kim Cucinella, Co-President
Facebook: www.facebook.com/ValleyCenterChamber
Instagram: www.instagram.com/vc_chamber_of
 _commerce
Description: Promotes business and community development in Valley Center, CA. **Founded:** 1962. **Geographic Preference:** Local.

37231 ■ Venice Chamber of Commerce
PO Box 202
 Venice, CA 90294
Ph: (310)822-5425
Co. E-mail: info@venicechamber.net
URL: http://venicechamber.net
Contact: George Francisco, President
Description: Promotes business and community development in the Venice, CA area. **Founded:** 1922. **Publications:** *Business Directory*; *Venice Area Chamber of Commerce Newsletter*. **Educational Activities:** VAYP Annual Banquet (Annual); Venice Art Crawl Mixer at The Sidewalk Cafe (Annual). **Geographic Preference:** Local.

37232 ■ Ventura Chamber of Commerce
PO Box 24287
 Ventura, CA 93002
Ph: (805)643-7222
Fax: (805)653-8015
Co. E-mail: info@ventura-chamber.org
URL: http://venturachamber.org
Contact: Stephanie Caldwell, President
E-mail: stephanie@ventura-chamber.org
Facebook: www.facebook.com/venturachamber
Linkedin: www.linkedin.com/company/ventura
 -chamber-of-commerce
X (Twitter): x.com/venturachamber
YouTube: www.youtube.com/user/Ven
 turaChamberTV
Description: Promotes business and community development in the Ventura, CA area. **Founded:** 1899. **Publications:** *Ventura Business*; *Ventura Chamber Business Directory*; *Ventura County Industry Guide*. **Geographic Preference:** Local.

37233 ■ Vernon Chamber of Commerce
2724 Leonis Blvd.
 Vernon, CA 90058
Ph: (323)583-3313
Fax: (323)583-0704
Co. E-mail: info@vernonchamber.org
URL: http://www.vernonchamber.org/home
Contact: Marisa Olguin, President
Facebook: www.facebook.com/vernonchamberca
X (Twitter): x.com/vernonchamberca
Description: Seeks to enhance the economic and socio-economic health of Vernon community. **Founded:** 1951. **Geographic Preference:** Local.

37234 ■ Victorville Chamber of Commerce (VCC)
15428 Civic Dr., Ste. 310
 Victorville, CA 92392
Ph: (760)245-6506
Fax: (760)245-6505
URL: http://www.ghdcc.com
Contact: Mark Creffield, President
E-mail: mark@ghdcc.com
Description: Promotes business and community development in Victorville, CA. **Founded:** 1913. **Publications:** *Insight* (Quarterly); *Map*; *Victorville*

37235 ■ California　　　STATE LISTINGS

Chamber of Commerce Business Directory. **Educational Activities:** Mixers (Annual); High Desert Opportunity Business Conference. **Geographic Preference:** Local.

37235 ■ Vietnamese American Chamber of Commerce (VACOC)
Little Saigon, CA
Ph: (657)204-6987
Co. E-mail: contact@vacoc.com
URL: http://vacoc.org
Contact: Thanh Pham, President
Facebook: www.facebook.com/vachamberofcommerce
Description: Provides leadership for the community, promotes local resources, enhances local programs, and coordinates development efforts. **Founded:** 1985. **Geographic Preference:** Local.

37236 ■ Visalia Chamber of Commerce (VCC)
222 N Garden St., Ste. 300
Visalia, CA 93291
Ph: (559)734-5876
Co. E-mail: info@visaliachamber.org
URL: http://www.visaliachamber.org
Contact: Gail Zurek, President
X (Twitter): x.com/VisaliaBiz
Instagram: www.instagram.com/visaliachamber
Description: Promotes business and community development in Visalia, CA. Holds seminars. **Founded:** 1899. **Publications:** *Membership Directory and Community Guide to Visalia* (Annual); *Business Update* (Monthly). **Educational Activities:** Business Networking Breakfast; Christmas Tree Auction (Annual). **Awards:** Visalia Chamber of Commerce Large Business of the Year (Annual); Visalia Chamber of Commerce Man of the Year (Annual); Visalia Chamber of Commerce Small Business of the Year (Annual); Visalia Chamber of Commerce Woman of the Year (Annual). **Geographic Preference:** Local.

37237 ■ *Visitor's Guide*
No. 1 Green Pleasure Pier
Avalon, CA 90704
Ph: (310)510-1520
Co. E-mail: info@lovecatalina.com
URL: http://www.lovecatalina.com
Contact: Jim Luttjohann, Author
E-mail: jim@lovecatalina.com
URL(s): www.lovecatalina.com/island-info/visitors-guide/digital-visitors-guide
Released: Annual **Availability:** Print; Online.

37238 ■ *Visitors Guide*
390 W 7th St.
San Pedro, CA 90731
Ph: (310)832-7272
Co. E-mail: info@sanpedrochamber.com
URL: http://www.sanpedrochamber.com
Contact: Elise Swanson, President
E-mail: eswanson@sanpedrochamber.com
URL(s): www.sanpedrochamber.com/publications
Released: Annual **Availability:** Print.

37239 ■ Vista Chamber of Commerce
170 Eucalyptus Ave.
Vista, CA 92084
Ph: (760)726-1122
Fax: (760)726-8654
Co. E-mail: info@vistachamber.org
URL: http://vistachamber.org
Contact: Rachel Beld, President
Facebook: www.facebook.com/VistaChamber
Linkedin: www.linkedin.com/company/vista-chamber-of-commerce
X (Twitter): x.com/VistaChamber
YouTube: www.youtube.com/user/VistaChamberCommerce
Description: Promotes business and community development in Vista, CA. **Geographic Preference:** Local.

37240 ■ Walnut Creek Chamber of Commerce
1280 Civic Dr., No. 100
Walnut Creek, CA 94596
Ph: (925)934-2007
Fax: (925)934-2404
URL: http://www.walnut-creek.com
Contact: Bob Linscheid, Co-President Co-Chief Executive Officer
X (Twitter): x.com/WCChamberCA
YouTube: www.youtube.com/channel/UCViVUrS-0Ua2NmmDj-l0qTQ
Description: Promotes business and community development in Walnut Creek, CA. **Founded:** 1926. **Publications:** *Walnut Creek Business Focus* (Monthly); *Walnut Creek Chamber Membership Directory.* **Educational Activities:** Art and Wine (Annual); Ask the Experts. **Geographic Preference:** Local.

37241 ■ *Walnut Creek Chamber Membership Directory*
1280 Civic Dr., No. 100
Walnut Creek, CA 94596
Ph: (925)934-2007
Fax: (925)934-2404
URL: http://www.walnut-creek.com
Contact: Bob Linscheid, Co-President Co-Chief Executive Officer
URL(s): members.walnut-creek.com/list
Availability: Print.

37242 ■ Weed Chamber of Commerce (WCC)
34 Main St.
Weed, CA 96094
Ph: (530)938-4624
Free: 877-938-4624
Co. E-mail: weedchamber@ncen.org
URL: http://weedchamber.com
Contact: Garrett Greene, President
Facebook: www.facebook.com/weedchamberofcommerce
Description: Promotes business and community development in Weed, CA. **Founded:** 1953. **Publications:** *Weed Chamber News* (Quarterly). **Geographic Preference:** Local.

37243 ■ West Los Angeles Chamber of Commerce
907 Westwood Blvd., Ste. 222
Los Angeles, CA 90024
Co. E-mail: info@westlachamber.org
URL: http://www.westlachamber.org
Contact: Roozbeh Farahanipour, President
Facebook: www.facebook.com/wlacc
X (Twitter): x.com/westlachamber
Instagram: www.instagram.com/westlachamber
YouTube: www.youtube.com/channel/UC-k99AfvbQGJbrk_CfRKY9g
Description: Promotes business and community development in West Los Angeles, CA. **Founded:** 1945. **Publications:** *West Los Angeles Business Monthly* (Monthly). **Geographic Preference:** Local.

37244 ■ West Marin Chamber of Commerce
9920 Sir Francis Drake
Olema, CA 94950
Co. E-mail: info@pointreyes.org
URL: http://pointreyes.org
Contact: Frank Borodic, Contact
Description: Promotes business and community development in Point Reyes Station, CA. **Geographic Preference:** Local.

37245 ■ West Sacramento Chamber of Commerce
1401 Halyard Dr., Ste. 120
West Sacramento, CA 95691
Ph: (916)371-7042
Co. E-mail: info@westsacramentochamber.com
URL: http://www.westsacramentochamber.com
Contact: Andrea van Cleave, Director
E-mail: andrea@westsacramentochamber.com
Facebook: www.facebook.com/westsacchamber
X (Twitter): x.com/WestSacChamber
Instagram: www.instagram.com/westsacchamber
YouTube: www.youtube.com/user/WestSacChamber
Description: Promotes business and community development in the West Sacramento, CA area. Conducts toy drive and food drive. Sponsors golf tournament, port fest, annual barbecue, river front celebration, July 3 fireworks and community day parade. **Founded:** 1947. **Publications:** *Individual Map*; *The Insider*, *Local Business Directory.* **Educational Activities:** West Sacramento Business and Trade Fair. **Geographic Preference:** Local.

37246 ■ Western Association of Chamber Executives (WACE)
PO Box 1736
Sacramento, CA 95812
Ph: (916)442-2223
Co. E-mail: wace@calchamber.com
URL: http://www.waceonline.com
Contact: Dave Kilby, President
E-mail: dave.kilby@calchamber.com
Facebook: www.facebook.com/WACEPAGE
Description: Seeks to enhance and promote the professional growth and competence of Chamber of Commerce Executives. **Founded:** 1995. **Geographic Preference:** Local.

37247 ■ Westminster Chamber of Commerce
14491 Beach Blvd., Ste. B
Westminster, CA 92683
Ph: (714)898-9648
Fax: (714)898-9648
Co. E-mail: biz@westminsterchamber.org
URL: http://www.westminsterchamber.org
Contact: Sophak Ok, President
Facebook: www.facebook.com/WestminsterChamberOfCommerce
Linkedin: www.linkedin.com/company/westminster-chamber
X (Twitter): x.com/w_chamber
YouTube: www.youtube.com/channel/UCRH_--Z_jQQodYHR6dr1gvA
Description: Promotes business and community development in Westminster, CA. Sponsors Quarterly Breakfasts, Networking Luncheons & Mixers, Legislative Meetings & Mixer, Taste and Tour of Little Saigon, Business Expo, Bowling Tournament, Annual Business Awards Dinner and Business Forums. Conducts community activities including Salute to Seniors Luncheon and Public Service Awards luncheon. **Founded:** 1912. **Publications:** *DIRECTIONS* (Quarterly). **Awards:** Westminster Chamber of Commerce Citizen of the Year (Annual); Westminster Chamber of Commerce Organization of the Year (Annual); Westminster Chamber of Commerce Public Service Awards (Annual). **Geographic Preference:** Local.

37248 ■ Whittier Area Chamber of Commerce (WACC)
8158 Painter Ave.
Whittier, CA 90602
Ph: (562)698-9554
Fax: (562)693-2700
Co. E-mail: info@whittierchamber.com
URL: http://www.whittierchamber.com
Contact: Carol Crosby, President
Facebook: www.facebook.com/WhittierChamber
Linkedin: www.linkedin.com/company/whittier-area-chamber-of-commerce
Instagram: www.instagram.com/whittierchamber
YouTube: www.youtube.com/whittierchamber
Description: Promotes business and community development in the Whittier, CA area. **Founded:** 1914. **Publications:** *Whittier Area Chamber of Commerce--Membership Directory* (Semiannual); *Whittier Area Chamber of Commerce--Clubs and Organizations Directory* (Annual); *Clubs and Organizations Directory* (Annual); *Business Directory*, *Business Focus* (Bimonthly). **Educational Activities:** Hathaway Golf Classic (Annual); Wake Up Whittier. **Awards:** Whittier Area Chamber of Commerce Silver Shield Awards (Annual). **Geographic Preference:** Local.

37249 ■ Willits Chamber of Commerce (WCC)
299 E Commercial St.
Willits, CA 95490
Ph: (707)459-7910
Fax: (707)459-7914
Co. E-mail: info@willits.org
URL: http://www.willits.org
Contact: Lisa Kvasnicka, President
Facebook: www.facebook.com/willitschamber

STATE LISTINGS California ■ 37263

Description: Promotes business and community development in Willits, CA. Sponsors annual community festival. **Founded:** 1926. **Publications:** *Willits Chamber of Commerce--Membership Roster* (Periodic); *Chamber Updates* (Quarterly). **Educational Activities:** Willits Chamber of Commerce City Council Meeting (Semimonthly). **Geographic Preference:** Local.

37250 ■ Willow Creek Chamber of Commerce
PO Box 704
Willow Creek, CA 95573
Ph: (530)629-2693
Co. E-mail: info@willowcreekchamber.com
URL: http://www.willowcreekchamber.com
Contact: Katie Strause, Executive Director
Facebook: www.facebook.com/willowcreekchamber
Instagram: www.instagram.com/visitwillowcreek
Description: Promotes business and community development in Willow Creek, CA. **Geographic Preference:** Local.

37251 ■ Willows Chamber of Commerce
118 W Sycamore
Willows, CA 95988
Ph: (530)934-8150
Co. E-mail: thewillowschamber@gmail.com
URL: http://www.willowschamber.com
Contact: Jamie Millen, President
Facebook: www.facebook.com/willowschamber
Description: Promotes business and community development in the Willows, CA area. **Publications:** *Business Directory*; *Chamber Connection* (Monthly); *WACC Perspective* (Bimonthly). **Geographic Preference:** Local.

37252 ■ Wilmington Chamber of Commerce
Wilimington Municipal Bldg.
544 N Avalon Blvd., Ste. 104
Wilmington, CA 90744
Ph: (310)834-8586
Fax: (310)834-8887
Co. E-mail: info@wilmington-chamber.com
URL: http://www.wilmington-chamber.com
Contact: Sergio Carrillo, President
URL(s): www.wilmingtonchamber.org
Linkedin: www.linkedin.com/company/wilmington-ca-chamber-of-commerce
X (Twitter): x.com/wilmchamber
Description: Promotes business and community development in Wilmington, CA. **Geographic Preference:** Local.

37253 ■ Windsor Chamber of Commerce (WCC)
9001 Windsor Rd.
Windsor, CA 95492
Ph: (707)838-7285
Fax: (707)838-2778
Co. E-mail: info@windsorchamber.com
URL: http://www.windsorchamber.com
Contact: Shawn Nichols, Chairman
E-mail: shawn.nichols@fastsigns.com
Facebook: www.facebook.com/windsorchamber
X (Twitter): x.com/windsorchamber
Description: Promotes business and community development in Windsor, CA. Sponsors Windsor Day Festival and Windsor Business Expo. **Founded:** 1965. **Geographic Preference:** Local.

37254 ■ Winters Chamber of Commerce
201 First St.
Winters, CA 95694
Ph: (530)795-2329
Co. E-mail: director@winterschamber.com
URL: http://www.winterschamber.com
Contact: Chris Calvert, Chairman of the Board
Facebook: www.facebook.com/winterschamber
Instagram: www.instagram.com/WintersChamberCommerce
Description: Works to strengthen businesses and serve the community through involvement and volunteers. **Founded:** 1954. **Geographic Preference:** Local.

37255 ■ Woodland Area Chamber of Commerce (WCC)
400 Ct. St.
Woodland, CA 95695
Ph: (530)662-7327
Co. E-mail: hello@woodlandchamber.org
URL: http://woodlandchamber.org
Contact: Mark Ullrich, President
Facebook: www.facebook.com/WoodlandChamberOfCommerce
X (Twitter): x.com/woodlandchamber
Description: Promotes business and community development in the area. Sponsors festival. **Founded:** 1931. **Publications:** *Woodland Area Chamber of Commerce--Membership Directory*; *The Progress* (Monthly); *Membership Directory/Buyers Guide*. **Awards:** Woodland Chamber of Commerce Citizen of the Year (Annual). **Geographic Preference:** Local.

37256 ■ Wrightwood Chamber of Commerce
1350 Hwy. 2, Ste. E
Wrightwood, CA 92397
Ph: (760)249-4320
Co. E-mail: info@wrightwoodchamber.org
URL: http://www.wrightwoodchamber.org
Contact: Mal Youngblood, Contact
E-mail: maly@trinity.com
Facebook: www.facebook.com/wwchamberofcommerce
Instagram: www.instagram.com/wwchamberofcommerce
Description: Promotes business and community development in Wrightwood, CA. **Publications:** *Wellspring*. **Educational Activities:** Wrightwood Chamber of Commerce Board meeting. **Geographic Preference:** Local.

37257 ■ Yorba Linda Chamber of Commerce (YLCC)
17670 Yorba Linda Blvd.
Yorba Linda, CA 92886
Ph: (714)993-9537
Fax: (714)993-7764
Co. E-mail: info@yorbalindachamber.com
URL: http://www.yorbalindachamber.org
Contact: Susan Wan-Ross, Chief Executive Officer
E-mail: susan@yorbalindachamber.com
Facebook: www.facebook.com/YorbaLindaChamberofCommerce
Description: Promotes business and community development in Yorba Linda, CA. **Founded:** 1913. **Publications:** *Chamber Action* (Monthly). **Awards:** Yorba Linda Chamber of Commerce Senior High School Scholarships (Annual). **Geographic Preference:** Local.

37258 ■ Yountville Chamber of Commerce (YCC)
6484 Washington St., Ste. F
Yountville, CA 94599
Ph: (707)944-0904
Co. E-mail: info@yountville.com
URL: http://www.yountvillechamber.com
Contact: Whitney Diver McEvoy, President
E-mail: whitney@yountville.com
Facebook: www.facebook.com/YountvilleChamber
X (Twitter): x.com/yountvilleca
Instagram: www.instagram.com/yountvilleca
Pinterest: www.pinterest.com/yountvilleca
Description: Promotes business and community development in the Yountville, CA area. **Founded:** 1991. **Geographic Preference:** Local.

37259 ■ Yreka Chamber of Commerce (YCC)
1000 S Main St.
Yreka, CA 96097-3325
Ph: (530)842-1649
URL: http://business.mtshastachamber.com/list/member/yreka-chamber-of-commerce-yreka-277
Facebook: www.facebook.com/yrekachamber
Linkedin: www.linkedin.com/company/yreka-chamber-of-commerce
Instagram: www.instagram.com/yrekachamber
Description: Promotes business, tourism, and community development in Siskiyou County, CA. **Founded:** 1923. **Geographic Preference:** Local.

37260 ■ Yuba-Sutter Chamber of Commerce
1300 Franklin Rd.
Yuba City, CA 95993
Ph: (530)743-6501
Co. E-mail: info@yubasutterchamber.com
URL: http://www.yubasutterchamber.com
Contact: Maria Ball, Chairman
Facebook: www.facebook.com/YubaSutterChamber
Description: Promotes business and community development in Sutter and Yuba counties, CA. **Founded:** 1970. **Publications:** *Explore Yuba-Sutter* (Annual); *Business Today* (Weekly); *Chamber Notes* (Weekly); *Explore 99 Things* (Annual); *Innerview* (Monthly). **Educational Activities:** Business Connection Breakfasts (Monthly). **Awards:** Yuba-Sutter Chamber of Commerce Athena Award (Annual); Yuba-Sutter Chamber of Commerce Business of the Year (Annual); Yuba-Sutter Chamber of Commerce Civic Entrepreneur of the Year (Annual); Yuba-Sutter Chamber of Commerce Civic Organization of the Year (Annual); Yuba-Sutter Chamber of Commerce Non-Profit Business of the Year (Annual); Yuba-Sutter Chamber of Commerce Small Business of the Year (Annual). **Geographic Preference:** Local.

37261 ■ Yucaipa Valley Chamber of Commerce (YVCC)
35139 Yucaipa Blvd.
Yucaipa, CA 92399-4338
Ph: (909)790-1841
Co. E-mail: yucaipachamberofcommerce@gmail.com
URL: http://www.uschamber.com/co/chambers/california/yucaipa
Contact: Ellen Benefiel, Chief Executive Officer
E-mail: ellen@yucaipachamber.org
Facebook: www.facebook.com/YucaipaValleyChamberofCommerce
Description: Promotes a vibrant business environment by cooperative interaction between business, government and community. **Founded:** 1915. **Publications:** *The Chamber Times*; *Yucaipa Valley Chamber of Commerce Business Directory*. **Educational Activities:** Installation of Officers & Community Awards Banquet (Annual). **Awards:** YVCC Chamber Member of the Year (Annual); YVCC Citizen of the Year (Annual); YVCC Firefighter of the Year (Annual); YVCC Peace Officer of the Year (Annual). **Geographic Preference:** Local.

MINORITY BUSINESS ASSISTANCE PROGRAMS

37262 ■ ASIAN, Inc.
1167 Mission St., 4th Fl.
San Francisco, CA 94103
Ph: (415)928-5910
Fax: (415)921-0182
URL: http://www.asianinc.org
Contact: Lamar Heystek, President
Facebook: www.facebook.com/asianincsf
X (Twitter): x.com/ASIANInc
Instagram: www.instagram.com/asianincsf
YouTube: www.youtube.com/user/AsianincSF
Description: Assisting in the business development and growth of African Americans and other minorities in Northern California. **Founded:** 1971. **Geographic Preference:** National.

37263 ■ California Department of General Services - Office of Small Business and DVBE Services - Small & Minority Business
707 3rd St.
West Sacramento, CA 95605
URL: http://www.dgs.ca.gov
Description: Offers technical assistance to small and minority business and promotes their procurement of government contracts for purchases, construction, and services.

37264 ■ Los Angeles Minority Business Enterprise Center
1055 Wilshire Blvd., Ste. 900
Pasadena, CA 91107
URL: http://www.mbda.gov/business-center/los-angeles-mbda-business-center
Contact: Bo Sivanunsakul, Director
E-mail: bsivanunsakul@pacela.org
Description: Provider of access to educational and technical resources that foster business expansion and job creation throughout Los Angeles County. **Founded:** 2001.

37265 ■ Los Angeles Minority Business Opportunity Center
200 N Spring St., 13th Fl.
Los Angeles, CA 90012
Ph: (213)978-0671
Fax: (213)978-0780
Co. E-mail: losangelesmbdacenter@lacity.org
URL: http://mbcla.lacity.org
Contact: Sergio Gascon, Executive Director
E-mail: sgascon@mbdalosangeles.org
Description: LA MBOC's vision is to achieve entrepreneurial parity for local Minority Business Enterprises by actively promoting their ability to grow and compete in the global economy.

37266 ■ Northern California Minority Business Enterprise Center
3031 Tischway, Ste. 80
San Jose, CA 95128
Ph: (408)998-8058
URL: http://www.mbda.gov/business-center/san-jose-mbda-business-center
Contact: Tony Tang, Director
Description: Works to promote the growth and competitiveness of minority businesses in Northern California. Offers access to capital, contracting and technical assistance.

37267 ■ Southern California Minority Supplier Development Council (SCMSDC)
800 W 6th St., Ste. 850
Los Angeles, CA 90017
Ph: (213)689-6960
Co. E-mail: info@scmsdc.org
URL: http://www.scmsdc.org
Contact: Virginia Gomez, President
E-mail: vgomez@scmsdc.org
Facebook: www.facebook.com/SCMSDC
Linkedin: www.linkedin.com/company/southern-california-minority-supplier-development-council-scmsdc-
X (Twitter): x.com/scmsdc
Instagram: www.instagram.com/socalmsdc
YouTube: www.youtube.com/channel/UCRoerv0eAPmAHLro82C2eIg
Description: Provides a direct link between corporate America and minority-owned businesses. Increases procurement and business opportunities for minority businesses of all sizes. **Founded:** 1999. **Geographic Preference:** Local.

FINANCING AND LOAN PROGRAMS

37268 ■ 5AM Venture Management L.L.C.
501 Second St., Ste. 350
San Francisco, CA 94107
Ph: (415)993-8570
URL: http://5amventures.com
Contact: Lindsay Ziegler, Manager
Linkedin: www.linkedin.com/company/5amventures
X (Twitter): x.com/5amventures
Description: Venture capital firm. **Investment Policies:** Seed and early stage. **Industry Preferences:** Biotechnology.

37269 ■ 8VC
Pier 5, Ste. 101
San Francisco, CA 94111
URL: http://www.8vc.com
Contact: Bhaskar Ghosh, Chief Technology Officer
Facebook: www.facebook.com/eightVC
Linkedin: www.linkedin.com/company/8vc
Description: Partners with founders and entrepreneurs to build technology platforms and create long-term economic and societal value.

37270 ■ Aberdare Ventures
235 Montgomery St., Ste. 1230
San Francisco, CA 94104
Ph: (415)392-7442
Fax: (415)392-4264
URL: http://aberdare.com
Contact: Paul Klingenstein, Managing Partner
E-mail: pklingenstein@aberdare.com
Description: Equity firm provides seed, early and later-stage venture, private equity and grants investments for healthcare industry. **Founded:** 1999. **Preferred Investment Size:** $1,000,000 to $7,000,000. **Industry Preferences:** Healthcare technology, including biopharmaceutical products, medical devices, and related therapeutic technologies.

37271 ■ Accel
500 University Ave.
Palo Alto, CA 94301
Ph: (650)614-4800
URL: http://www.accel.com
Contact: Rich Wong, Partner
Linkedin: www.linkedin.com/company/accel-vc
X (Twitter): x.com/accel
Description: Venture capital firm. Funds startups in the seed, early, and growth stages. **Founded:** 1983.

37272 ■ Accel-KKR L.L.C.
Accel-KKR L.L.C.
2180 Sand Hill Rd., Ste. 300
Menlo Park, CA 94025
Ph: (650)289-2460
Fax: (650)289-2461
URL: http://www.accel-kkr.com
Contact: Steven Berman, Executive Director
X (Twitter): x.com/accelkkr
Description: Invests in software and IT enabled businesses. **Founded:** 2000. **Preferred Investment Size:** $10,000,000 to $50,000,000. **Industry Preferences:** Communications and media, Internet specific, computer related, and semiconductors and other electronics.

37273 ■ Accel Management Company Inc.
500 University Ave.
Palo Alto, CA 94301
Ph: (650)614-4800
URL: http://www.accel.com/india-home
Contact: Anne Rockhold, Chief Financial Officer
Description: Accel Partners is a venture capital investment firm that focuses its investments in the telecommunications, software, and life sciences industries. **Founded:** 1984. **Preferred Investment Size:** Venture capital firm. **Investment Policies:** Seed, start-up, and early stage. **Industry Preferences:** Internet specific, computer software and services, communications and media, semiconductors and other electronics, other products, medical and health, computer hardware, biotechnology, industrial and energy, and consumer related.

37274 ■ Accelerator Ventures (AV)
San Francisco, CA
URL: http://acceleratorventures.com
Contact: Alexander Lloyd, Founder Managing Partner Managing Director
Description: Early stage venture capital firm. . **Investment Policies:** Companies seeking first round of funding with capital efficiency, market disruption, and the ability to take advantage of technology. **Industry Preferences:** Technology.

37275 ■ Acorn Campus
3235 Kifer Rd., Ste. 150
Santa Clara, CA 95051
Ph: (408)598-4239
Co. E-mail: info@acorncampus.com
URL: http://www.acorncampus.com/default.html
Contact: Dr. Hsing Kung, Managing Partner Co-Founder
Description: Provider of venture capital and private equity investment services for communications, wireless, semiconductor, photonics, internet and life science field. **Preferred Investment Size:** $250,000 to $5,000,000. **Investment Policies:** Seed, start-up, and early stage. **Industry Preferences:** Communications, computer software, semiconductors and other electronics.

37276 ■ Advanced Technology Ventures (ATV)
2884 Sand Hill Rd., Ste. 121
Menlo Park, CA 94025
URL: http://www.atvcapital.com
Description: Firm provides venture capital investment services for information technology, healthcare, energy, software services and much more. **Preferred Investment Size:** $15,000,000 to $35,000,000. **Industry Preferences:** Internet specific, computer software and services, computer hardware, semiconductors and other electronics, communications and media, medical and health, biotechnology, industrial and energy, consumer related, and other products.

37277 ■ Agilent Technologies, Inc.
Agilent Technologies, Inc.
5301 Stevens Creek Blvd.
Santa Clara, CA 95051
Ph: (408)345-8886
Free: 877-424-4536
Fax: (408)345-8474
Co. E-mail: contact_us@agilent.com
URL: http://www.agilent.com
Contact: Mike McMullen, President
Facebook: www.facebook.com/Agilent.Tech
Linkedin: www.linkedin.com/company/agilent-technologies
X (Twitter): twitter.com/Agilent
YouTube: www.youtube.com/user/agilent
Description: Engaged in providing application-focused solutions including reagents, instruments, software, services, and consumables used in life sciences, diagnostics and applied chemical laboratory identification, interrogation, quantification and analysis applications. The company also conducts centralized order fulfillment and supply chain operations. **Founded:** 1999. **Publications:** "Using a design to test capability for LTE MIMO," Oct, 2009; "Test solutions soup up for 4G," Apr, 2009; "Why Use One Radio When Four Will Do," Oct, 2008; "3GPP LTE Introducing Single Carrier FDMA," Jan, 2008; "Examining the Design and Test Challenges of 3GPP LTE," Nov, 2007; "First Pass Accuracy with Momentum GX for WiMAX Design," Nov, 2007; "Addressing the new challenges of MIMO wireless LAN manufacturing test," Oct, 2006. **Educational Activities:** EMBL International PhD Symposium; American Chemical Society Southeastern Regional Meeting and Conference (SERMACS) (Annual). **Preferred Investment Size:** $500,000 to $10,000,000. **Industry Preferences:** Communications and media, semiconductors and other electronics, biotechnology, medical and health, and industrial and energy.

37278 ■ Allegis Capital L.L.C. / Media Technology Ventures
130 Lytton Ave., Ste. 210
Palo Alto, CA 94301
Ph: (650)687-0500
Fax: (650)687-0234
URL: http://www.mycapital.com/venture-capital-firms/allegis-capital.html
Contact: Robert R. Ackerman, Jr., Managing Director
Description: Provider of seed and early stage venture capital investments for technology entrepreneurs. **Founded:** 1996. **Preferred Investment Size:** $3,000,000 to $5,000,000. **Investment Policies:** Seed, start-up, early stage, and research and development. **Industry Preferences:** Internet specific, computer software and services, communications and media, semiconductors and other electronics, computer hardware, and other products.

37279 ■ Almaz Capital
3274 Alpine Rd.
Portola Valley, CA 94028
Ph: (650)644-4530

STATE LISTINGS

California ■ 37295

Co. E-mail: bayarea@almazcapital.com
URL: http://almazcapital.com
Contact: Tanya Dadasheva, Director
Facebook: www.facebook.com/AlmazCapital
YouTube: www.youtube.com/channel/UC3ozk-MHXtzmIQKWF46fNIQ

Description: Venture capital firm for tech companies serving global markets. Also operates out of Germany. **Founded:** 2008.

37280 ■ Alta Partners
23 Main St.
  Belvedere Tiburon, CA 94920
Ph: (415)362-4022
Co. E-mail: alta@altapartners.com
URL: http://www.altapartners.com
Contact: Dan Janney, Managing Director
E-mail: djanney@altapartners.com
Linkedin: www.linkedin.com/company/alta-partners

Description: Private equity and venture capital firm that provides investments to early stage and later stage companies. **Founded:** 1996. **Preferred Investment Size:** $2,000,000 to $15,000,000. **Industry Preferences:** Internet specific, computer software and services, industrial and energy, consumer related, communications and media, medical and health, computer hardware, biotechnology, semiconductors and other electronics, and other products.

37281 ■ Altos Ventures
2882 Sand Hill Rd., Ste. 100
  Menlo Park, CA 94025
URL: http://altos.vc

Description: Venture capital firm investing in software, mobile and internet companies. **Founded:** 1996. **Preferred Investment Size:** $1,000,000 to $3,000,000. **Industry Preferences:** Internet specific, computer software and services, other products, consumer related, communications and media.

37282 ■ American Infrastructure Funds LLC
950 Tower Ln., Ste. 800
  Foster City, CA 94404
Ph: (650)854-6000
Fax: (650)854-0853
Co. E-mail: lpinfo@aimlp.com
URL: http://www.aimlp.com

Description: Firm operating Investment services. **Founded:** 1984. **Preferred Investment Size:** $20,000,000 to $50,000,000. **Industry Preferences:** Consumer related, computer software and services, medical and health, Internet specific, communications and media, computer hardware, semiconductors and other electronics, industrial and energy, and other products.

37283 ■ Amgen Inc.
Amgen Inc.
  1 Amgen Center Dr.
  Thousand Oaks, CA 91320-1799
Ph: (805)447-1000
Free: 888-762-6436
Fax: (805)477-1010
Co. E-mail: medinfo@amgen.com
URL: http://amgen.com
Contact: Robert A. Bradway, Chief Executive Officer
Facebook: www.facebook.com/amgenbiotech
Linkedin: www.linkedin.com/company/amgen
X (Twitter): twitter.com/amgen
Instagram: www.instagram.com/amgenbiotech
YouTube: www.youtube.com/user/amgen

Description: Global independent biotechnology company focused on discovering, developing, manufacturing, and delivering innovative human therapeutics, using tools such as human genetics, pharmaceutical products include treatments for patients with rheumatoid arthritis, plaque psoriasis, active psoriatic arthritis, non-myeloid cancer, anemia caused by chronic kidney disease, and anemia due to chemotherapy. **Founded:** 1980. **Awards:** Amgen Award for Science Teaching Excellence Program (Annual). **Preferred Investment Size:** $1,000,000 to $3,000,000. **Investment Policies:** Early stage. **Industry Preferences:** Biotechnology.

37284 ■ Amgen Ventures
1 Amgen Center Dr.
  Thousand Oaks, CA 91320
URL: http://www.amgenbd.com
Contact: Samantha Palmer, Executive Director

Description: Corporate venture capital fund for emerging biotechnology companies. **Founded:** 2004. **Industry Preferences:** Human therapeutics.

37285 ■ Amidzad Partners Co.
370 Convention Way
  Redwood City, CA 94063
Ph: (650)216-2384
URL: http://www.amidzad.com
Contact: Rahim Amidi, Co-Founder Partner
E-mail: rahim@amidzad.com

Description: Venture capital firm provides investment services for seed and early-stage companies. **Investment Policies:** Seed and early stage. **Industry Preferences:** Technology and life sciences.

37286 ■ Analytics Ventures (AV)
6450 Lusk Blvd.
  San Diego, CA 92121
Co. E-mail: info@analyticsventures.com
URL: http://analyticsventures.com
Linkedin: www.linkedin.com/company/analytics-ventures

Description: Venture fund focused on artificial intelligence innovations; aims for a revenue-generating market launch within six months. **Founded:** 2016. **Industry Preferences:** Healthcare diagnostics and treatment; sustainable energy; distributed digital workload processing; advertising; stock trading.

37287 ■ Andreessen Horowitz (AH)
2865 Sand Hill Rd., Ste. 101
  Menlo Park, CA 94025
Co. E-mail: businessplans@a16z.com
URL: http://a16z.com
Contact: Ben Horowitz, Co-Founder Partner
Facebook: www.facebook.com/andreessenhorowitz
X (Twitter): twitter.com/a16z

Description: Venture capital firm investing in seed to late-stage technology companies. Seeks to connect investors, entrepreneurs, executives, engineers, academics, and industry experts in the technology ecosystem. **Founded:** 2009. **Industry Preferences:** Technology companies in the consumer, enterprise, bio/healthcare, crypto, and fintech services.

37288 ■ Anthem Venture Partners (AVP)
225 Arizona Ave., Ste. 200
  Santa Monica, CA 90401
Ph: (310)899-6225
Fax: (310)899-6234
URL: http://anthemvp.com
Contact: Bill Woodward, Partner

Description: Provider of venture capital, early-stage investment and operational guidance for technology companies. **Founded:** 2000. **Preferred Investment Size:** $500,000 to $400,000,000. **Investment Policies:** Early and later stage. **Industry Preferences:** Communications and media, Internet specific, computer hardware, consumer related, business services, computer software and services, semiconductors and other electronics, other products.

37289 ■ Applied Materials, Inc.
Applied Materials, Inc.
  3050 Bowers Ave.
  Santa Clara, CA 95054-3201
Ph: (408)727-5555
URL: http://www.appliedmaterials.com
Contact: Gary E. Dickerson, President
Facebook: www.facebook.com/AppliedMaterialsInc
Linkedin: www.linkedin.com/company/applied-materials
X (Twitter): twitter.com/Applied4Tech
Instagram: www.instagram.com/applied__materials/
YouTube: www.youtube.com/user/appliedschannel

Description: Firm provides manufacturing equipment, services and software to the global semiconductor, display, and related industries. **Founded:** 1967. **Educational Activities:** SEMICON China (Annual); Conference for Community Arts Education (Annual); SPIE Photomask Technology (Annual). **Investment Policies:** Seed and early stage. **Industry Preferences:** Communications.

37290 ■ Applied Ventures LLC (AV)
3050 Bowers Ave.
  Santa Clara, CA 95054-3299
URL: http://www.appliedmaterials.com/content/applied-materials/us/en/applied-ventures
Contact: Omkaram Nalamasu, President

Description: Stage-agnostic venture capital firm for technology and electronics businesses. Operates in India, China, Korea, Taiwan, and Japan. **Industry Preferences:** Advanced materials; energy conversion; data storage software and system.

37291 ■ Arcturus Capital
199 S Los Robles Ave., Ste. 535
  Pasadena, CA 91101
Ph: (626)578-5700
Fax: (626)578-5710
Co. E-mail: dana@hallcapitalmanagement.com
URL: http://arcturusvc.com
Contact: Donald Hall, Managing Director

Description: Venture capital firm for early-stage technology companies. **Industry Preferences:** Technology.

37292 ■ The Arcview Group
San Francisco, CA
Free: 855-892-1951
Co. E-mail: info@arcviewgroup.com
URL: http://www.arcviewgroup.com
Contact: Jeffrey Finkle, Chief Executive Officer
Facebook: www.facebook.com/ArcViewGroup
Linkedin: www.linkedin.com/company/arcviewgroup
X (Twitter): x.com/arcviewgroup
Instagram: www.instagram.com/arcviewgroup

Description: Private investment network and market research firm. Connects investors with opportunities in the cannabis sector.

37293 ■ Artiman Management LLC
1731 Embarcadero Rd., Ste. 212
  Palo Alto, CA 94303
Ph: (650)845-2020
Co. E-mail: info@artiman.com
URL: http://www.artiman.com
Contact: Yatin Mundkur, Partner

Description: Seeks entrepreneurs building white space communities. Sector agnostic. Specializes in incubation, seed, start-up, early stage, bridge, and growth capital investments. **Founded:** 2001.

37294 ■ Asset Management Company Venture Capital (AMV)
1300 El Camino Real, Ste. 100
  Menlo Park, CA 94025
Ph: (650)621-8808
Co. E-mail: plans@assetman.com
URL: http://assetman.com
Contact: Skip Fleshman, Partner
Linkedin: www.linkedin.com/company/asset-management-ventures
X (Twitter): x.com/AMV

Description: Firm provides private equity and venture capital services focused on digital health, technology and life sciences investments. **Founded:** 1962. **Preferred Investment Size:** $500,000 to $2,000,000. **Industry Preferences:** Computer software and services, medical and health, biotechnology, computer hardware, semiconductors and other electronics, Internet specific, communications and media, consumer related, industrial and energy, and other products.

37295 ■ Atel Capital Group
600 Montgomery St., 9th Fl.
  San Francisco, CA 94111
Ph: (415)989-8800
Co. E-mail: info@atel.com
URL: http://www.atel.com
Contact: Dean Cash, Chief Executive Officer
Linkedin: www.linkedin.com/company/atelcapitalgroup

Description: Financial services company. Offers equipment leasing, asset-based lending, venture leasing, lease administration, and asset management. **Founded:** 1977.

37296 ■ Atomic
One Letterman Dr.
San Francisco, CA 94129
Co. E-mail: info@atomic.vc
URL: http://atomic.vc
Contact: Justin Rubbo, Chief Financial Officer
Linkedin: www.linkedin.com/company/atomic-labs
X (Twitter): x.com/JoinAtomic
Instagram: www.instagram.com/atomic.vc
Description: Funds and creates promising companies; either from an idea within or from a co-founder. Ideates, researches, prototypes, validates, and funds. Also offers business support in accounting, design, engineering, finance, HR, IT, and recruiting. **Founded:** 2012.

37297 ■ August Capital
893A Folsom St.
San Francisco, CA 94107
URL: http://www.augustcap.com
Contact: Abby Hipps, General Counsel
Linkedin: www.linkedin.com/company/august-capital
X (Twitter): x.com/AugustCapital
Description: Investment firm provides of venture capital, growth capital and startup investments services. **Founded:** 1995. **Industry Preferences:** Internet specific, computer software, and services, communications and media, computer hardware, semiconductors and other electronics.

37298 ■ Avalon Ventures LLC
1134 Kline St.
La Jolla, CA 92037
Ph: (858)348-2180
Fax: (858)348-2183
Co. E-mail: info@avalon-ventures.com
URL: http://www.avalon-ventures.com
Contact: Kevin Kinsella, Founder
Description: Early-stage venture capital firm. **Industry Preferences:** Information technology and life sciences.

37299 ■ Azure Capital Partners
505 Sansome, Ste. 1575
San Francisco, CA 94111
Co. E-mail: info@azurecap.com
URL: http://www.azurecap.com
Contact: Andrea Drager, Partner
Linkedin: www.linkedin.com/company/azure-capital-partners
X (Twitter): x.com/azurecap
Description: Venture capital firm. Invests in post-sees and Series A technology businesses. **Founded:** 2000. **Industry Preferences:** Technology.

37300 ■ Bain Capital Ventures (BCV)
Bain Capital LP (BC)
301 Howard St., Ste. 2200
San Francisco, CA 94105
Ph: (617)516-2000
Fax: (617)516-2010
Co. E-mail: support@intralinks.com
URL: http://www.baincapital.com
Contact: Conrad White, Manager
X (Twitter): x.com/BainCapVC
Description: Invests in founders who transform major industries. Also operates out of New York and Boston. **Founded:** 1984. **Preferred Investment Size:** $1,000,000 in capital to $100,000 in growth equity. **Industry Preferences:** SaaS; infrastructure software; security; fintech; healthcare; consumer tech.

37301 ■ Band of Angels
750 Battery St., 7th Fl.
San Francisco, CA 94111
Ph: (650)695-0400
Co. E-mail: bandhq@bandangels.com
URL: http://www.bandangels.com
Contact: Sonja Markova, Executive Director
Linkedin: www.linkedin.com/company/band-of-angels

Description: Venture capital firm investing in seed technology and life sciences companies. **Founded:** 1994. **Preferred Investment Size:** $300,000 to $860,000. **Investment Policies:** Seed, early stage and balanced. **Industry Preferences:** Communications, computer software, semiconductors and other electronics, biotechnology, industrial and energy.

37302 ■ Baroda Ventures
9595 Wilshire Blvd., Ste. 310
Beverly Hills, CA 90212
URL: http://www.barodaventures.com
Contact: Paul Moore, Director
Description: Venture capital firm focused on the pre-seed and seed stages for companies primarily based in the Los Angeles area. **Founded:** 1998. **Industry Preferences:** Consumer internet; ecommerce; mobile; SaaS; blockchain; digtal media.

37303 ■ Battery Ventures L.P.
2882 Sand Hill Rd., Ste. 280
Menlo Park, CA 94025
Ph: (650)372-3939
URL: http://www.battery.com
Contact: Dharmesh Thakker, Partner
Linkedin: www.linkedin.com/company/battery-ventures
X (Twitter): x.com/batteryventures
YouTube: www.youtube.com/user/batteryventures
Description: Investment firm provides venture capital and private equity investment services for information technology sector. **Founded:** 1983. **Preferred Investment Size:** $300,000 to $50,000,000. **Industry Preferences:** Internet specific, computer software and services, communications and media, other products, semiconductors and other electronics, computer hardware, industrial and energy.

37304 ■ Bay City Capital LLC
1000 4th St., Ste. 500
San Rafael, CA 94901
Ph: (415)299-8196
URL: http://baycitycapital.com
Contact: David Beier, Managing Director
X (Twitter): x.com/baycitycapital
Description: Life sciences investment firm. **Founded:** 1997. **Industry Preferences:** Biopharmaceuticals; drug discovery and research tools; medical devices; diagnostics; healthcare IT; nutrition; agribusiness.

37305 ■ Bay Partners
2180 Sand Hill Rd., Ste. 345
Menlo Park, CA 94025
Ph: (650)854-1500
Fax: (650)854-1515
Co. E-mail: partners@baypartners.com
URL: http://www.baypartners.com
Contact: Stu Phillips, Partner
X (Twitter): x.com/baypartnersnews
Description: Firm provides venture capital and private equity investment services. **Founded:** 1976. **Preferred Investment Size:** $250,000. **Industry Preferences:** Communications and media, Internet specific, computer software and services, computer hardware, semiconductors and other electronics, consumer related, medical and health, and biotechnology.

37306 ■ Benchmark
140 New Montgomery St.
San Francisco, CA 94105
URL: http://benchmark.com
X (Twitter): x.com/benchmark
Description: Venture capital firm focused on early-stage investing. **Founded:** 1995. **Industry Preferences:** Enterprise software and services, communications, security, semiconductors, mobile computing, consumer/financial services.

37307 ■ Benchmark Capital
Academies Australasia Group Ltd.
2965 Woodside Rd.
Woodside, CA 94062
Ph: 61 2 9224-5500
Co. E-mail: info@academies.edu.au
URL: http://academies.edu.au

X (Twitter): x.com/benchmark
Description: Firm provides venture capital investment services. **Preferred Investment Size:** $100,000 to $15,000,000. **Industry Preferences:** Internet specific, communications and media, computer software and services, computer hardware, industrial and energy, semiconductors and other electronics, and consumer related.

37308 ■ Benhamou Global Ventures (BGV)
1600 El Camino Real, Ste. 280
Menlo Park, CA 94025
Ph: (650)324-3680
Co. E-mail: hello@bgv.com
URL: http://benhamouglobalventures.com
Contact: Amir Nayyerhabibi, Partner
Linkedin: www.linkedin.com/company/benhamou-global-ventures
X (Twitter): x.com/bgvcapital
Description: Venture capital firm for software startups. **Founded:** 2004. **Investment Policies:** Seeks disruptors with a thesis-driven approach. **Industry Preferences:** Digital transformation software.

37309 ■ Berkeley VC International LLC (BICC)
PO Box 591748
San Francisco, CA 94159-1748
Ph: (415)249-0450
Co. E-mail: info@berkeleyvc.com
URL: http://www.berkeleyvc.com
Contact: Arthur Trueger, Founder
Description: Finance: Venture capital firm. **Scope:** Firm provides financial advisory services. Assists companies seeking capital for new ventures. Active internationally. **Preferred Investment Size:** $1,000,000 to $50,000,000. **Industry Preferences:** Semiconductors and other electronics, communications and media, computer software and services, computer hardware, biotechnology, medical and health, other products, Internet specific, industrial and energy.

37310 ■ Bessemer Venture Partners (BVP)
889 Winslow St., Ste. 500
Redwood City, CA 94063
Ph: (650)853-7000
URL: http://www.bvp.com
Contact: Rob Arditi, Partner
YouTube: www.youtube.com/c/BessemerVenturePartners
Description: An investment firm that helps people from the seed stage to growth stage in creating companies. **Scope:** An investment firm that helps people from the seed stage to growth stage in creating companies. **Founded:** 1911. **Preferred Investment Size:** $1,000,000 to $10,000,000. **Industry Preferences:** Communications and media, Internet specific, computer software and services, semiconductors and other electronics, consumer related, medical and health, industrial and energy, and biotechnology, computer hardware, and other products.

37311 ■ Bison Capital Asset Management
233 Wilshire Blvd., Ste. 425
Santa Monica, CA 90401
URL: http://bisoncapital.com
Contact: Lou Caballero, Partner
E-mail: lcaballero@bisoncapital.com
Description: Middle-market capital investment firm. Also operates a New York office. **Founded:** 2001. **Investment Policies:** Established historically profitable businesses; proven management teams; $20-500 million in revenues; EBITDA of at least $5 million. **Industry Preferences:** Business and healthcare services; tech-enabled businesses; distribution/logistics.

37312 ■ Bloomberg Beta
140 New Montgomery St., 22nd Fl.
San Francisco, CA 94105
URL: http://github.com/Bloomberg-Beta/Manual
Contact: Roy Bahat, Contact

Description: Early stage venture capital firm funded solely by Bloomberg LP. **Founded:** 2013. **Investment Policies:** Looks for companies that make business work better. **Industry Preferences:** Machine intelligence.

37313 ■ Blumberg Capital Ventures
432 Bryant St.
San Francisco, CA 94107
Ph: (415)905-5000
Co. E-mail: info@blumbergcapital.com
URL: http://blumbergcapital.com
Contact: Gloria Hui, Director, Operations
Facebook: www.facebook.com/blumbergcapital
Linkedin: www.linkedin.com/company/blumberg-capital
X (Twitter): x.com/blumbergcapital

Description: Venture capital firm investing in seed and series A technology companies. **Founded:** 1991. **Preferred Investment Size:** $500,000 to $3,000,000. **Investment Policies:** Seed, early and first stage. **Industry Preferences:** Communications, computer software and internet specific.

37314 ■ Bonfire Ventures
725 Arizona Ave., Ste. 400
Santa Monica, CA 90401
URL: http://www.bonfirevc.com
Contact: Brett Queener, Partner Managing Director
E-mail: brett@bonfirevc.com
X (Twitter): x.com/bonfire_vc

Description: Venture capital firm. Invests in companies with software solutions redefining business. **Founded:** 2017.

37315 ■ BootstrapLabs
44 Tehama St.
San Francisco, CA 94105
Co. E-mail: info@bootstraplabs.com
URL: http://bootstraplabs.com
Contact: Nicolai Wadstrom, Chief Executive Officer
Facebook: www.facebook.com/bootstraplabs
Linkedin: www.linkedin.com/company/bootstraplabs
X (Twitter): x.com/bootstraplabs

Description: Venture capital firm focused on applied artificial intelligence. **Founded:** 2008. **Industry Preferences:** Transportation; logistics; energy; cybersecurity; IoT; health; fintech.

37316 ■ Boxador
714 Hampton Dr.
Venice, CA 90291
Ph: (310)910-9135
Co. E-mail: hello@boxador.com
URL: http://www.boxador.com
Contact: M. Bushnaq, Contact

Description: Builds companies around innovative, disruptive products. **Industry Preferences:** Enterprise software; SaaS; cloud; blockchain.

37317 ■ Brentwood Venture Capital
11150 Santa Monica Blvd., Ste. 1200
Los Angeles, CA 90025
Ph: (310)477-6611
Fax: (310)317-7200
Co. E-mail: info@brentwood.com
URL: http://www.brentwood.com
Contact: Crista Lewis, Director

Investment Policies: Seed, start-up, and second stage. **Industry Preferences:** Communications and media, computer software, Internet specific, biotechnology, and medical and health.

37318 ■ Breyer Capital
2180 Sand Hill Rd., Ste. 300
Menlo Park, CA 94025
Ph: (650)681-3069
Fax: (650)433-4243
Co. E-mail: info@breyercapital.com
URL: http://breyercapital.com
Contact: Jim Breyer, Chief Executive Officer
YouTube: www.youtube.com/channel/UCSq9shT1_u02vw9Rq7RrBdA

Description: Global venture capital and private equity investor focused on high-impact entrepreneurs in the United States and China. **Industry Preferences:** Media; social; data analytics; AI; financial technologies; digital health; security; blockchain.

37319 ■ Bullpen Capital
215 2nd St., Fl. 3
San Francisco, CA 94105
Ph: (415)525-3050
Co. E-mail: hello@bullpencap.com
URL: http://bullpencap.com
Contact: Eric Wiesen, Partner
Facebook: www.facebook.com/BullpenCapital
Linkedin: www.linkedin.com/company/bullpen-capital
X (Twitter): x.com/bullpencap

Description: Early-stage post-seed venture fund. Invests in tech companies funded by super-angels and institutional seed funds. **Founded:** 2010. **Industry Preferences:** Technology.

37320 ■ Caffeinated Capital
2969 Jackson St., Ste. 202
San Francisco, CA 94115
URL: http://caffeinatedcapital.com
Contact: Howie Liu, Chief Executive Officer
X (Twitter): x.com/caffeinatedcap
Founded: 2009.

37321 ■ California Business Bank (CBB)
3200 El Camino Real, Ste. 220
Irvine, CA 92602
Ph: (714)389-9964
Free: 866-495-4042
Co. E-mail: aalvarez@californiabusinessbank.com
URL: http://www.californiabusinessbank.com
Contact: Richard Tan, Chairman of the Board
Linkedin: www.linkedin.com/company/california-business-bank

Description: A state-chartered community oriented commercial bank that offers a wide range of business and loan products and services to individuals, professionals, and small to medium-sized businesses. **Founded:** 2005.

37322 ■ California Clean Energy Fund (CalCEF)
2150 Allston Way., Ste. 360
Berkeley, CA 94704
Contact: Daniel Ian Kennedy, Chief Executive Officer

Description: Supports entrepreneurs and investors specializing in clean energy transformation.

37323 ■ California Technology Ventures L.L.C. (CTV)
670 N Rosemead Blvd., Ste. 201
Pasadena, CA 91107
Ph: (626)351-3700
Co. E-mail: info@ctventures.com
URL: http://ctventures.com
Contact: William Hanna, Managing Director
E-mail: william@ctventures.com

Description: Firm specializing in investments in seed or start up companies. **Founded:** 1881. **Preferred Investment Size:** $250,000 to $2,000,000. **Investment Policies:** Early, first, second and later stage. **Industry Preferences:** Communications, computer software and hardware, Internet specific, semiconductors and other electronics, biotechnology, medical and health, and industrial and energy.

37324 ■ Canaan
2765 Sand Hill Rd.
Menlo Park, CA 94025
Ph: (650)854-8092
URL: http://www.canaan.com
Contact: Brent Ahrens, Partner
Linkedin: www.linkedin.com/company/canaan-partners
X (Twitter): x.com/canaanpartners

Description: Firm provides venture capital specializing in buyout investments. **Founded:** 1987. **Preferred Investment Size:** $3,000,000 to $25,000,000. **Industry Preferences:** Internet specific, computer software and services, computer hardware, medical and health, communications and media, biotechnology, semiconductors and other electronics, consumer related, and industrial and energy.

37325 ■ Canyon Creek Capital
1134 11th St.
Santa Monica, CA 90403
URL: http://canyoncreekcapital.com
Contact: Buck Jordan, Managing Partner
E-mail: buck.jordan@canyoncreekcapital.com

Description: Invests in disruptive startups at the "bridge to Series A" stage. **Investment Policies:** Prefers evidence of market adoption and/or traction before investing; strong CEOs.

37326 ■ Catamount Ventures
400 Pacific Ave., 3rd Fl.
San Francisco, CA 94133
URL: http://www.catamountventures.com
Contact: Mark Silverman, Managing Director
Linkedin: www.linkedin.com/company/catamount-ventures

Description: Venture capital firm. Invests in mission-driven companies that combine authentic brands with socially responsible products. **Founded:** 2000. **Investment Policies:** Looks for companies with significant market potential, sustainable competitive advantage, shared values, and sector leaders. **Industry Preferences:** Environment; core technology; consumer internet; educational services.

37327 ■ Catapult Capital LLC
665 3rd St., Ste. 150
San Francisco, CA 94107
URL: http://catapultcap.com
Contact: Jeff Bonforte, Managing Partner

Description: Private equity firm interested in funding relatively profitable enterprises that may not be growing. Specializes in business seeking revitalization. **Industry Preferences:** Internet, consumer, technology.

37328 ■ Cendana Capital
Two Embarcadero Ctr., 22nd Fl.
San Francisco, CA 94111
Co. E-mail: info@cendanacapital.com
Contact: Michael Kim, Contact
Facebook: www.facebook.com/CendanaCapital

Description: Invests in early-stage venture capital funds.

37329 ■ Cervin
705 Forest Ave.
Palo Alto, CA 94301
Co. E-mail: info@cervin.com
URL: http://www.cervin.com
Contact: Courtney McKee, Director, Finance
E-mail: courtney@cervin.com
Linkedin: www.linkedin.com/company/cervin-ventures
X (Twitter): x.com/cervinvc

Description: Venture capital firm. Offers either a traditional VC path or a capital-efficient path for high-growth companies. **Founded:** 2011.

37330 ■ Charles River Ventures (CRV)
300 Hamilton Ave., 3rd Fl.
Palo Alto, CA 94301
Ph: (650)687-5600
URL: http://www.crv.com
Contact: Sachin Sood, Chief Financial Officer
Facebook: www.facebook.com/CRVVC
Linkedin: www.linkedin.com/company/crvvc
X (Twitter): x.com/CRV
YouTube: www.youtube.com/channel/UCRibw5FGtD3nnklq787Znhw

Founded: 1970. **Preferred Investment Size:** $25,000 to $5,000,000. **Industry Preferences:** Internet specific, communications and media, computer software and services, computer hardware, other products, industrial and energy, semiconductors and other electronics, medical and health, consumer related, and biotechnology.

37331 ■ Charter Life Sciences (CLS)
325 E Middlefield Rd.
Mountain View, CA 94043
Ph: (650)318-5411

Fax: (650)318-3425
URL: http://www.clsvc.com
Contact: Andrew K. Klatt, Partner Chief Financial Officer
Description: Provider of venture capital and private equity investment services for life sciences companies, biotech and drug development companies, medical device companies and health care information technology companies. **Preferred Investment Size:** $1,000,000 to $5,000,000. **Investment Policies:** Early stage. **Industry Preferences:** Biotechnology, and medical and health.

37332 ■ Chemical Angel Network
42 Playa Cir.
 Aliso Viejo, CA 92656
URL: http://chemicalangels.com
Contact: Mark Vreeke, President
E-mail: mark.vreeke@chemicalangels.com
Linkedin: www.linkedin.com/company/chemical-angel-network
X (Twitter): x.com/ChemAngels
Description: Offers seed capital to chemistry-related startups. **Founded:** 2012.

37333 ■ Clearstone Venture Partners / Idealab! Capital Partners
725 Arizona Ave., Ste. 304
 Santa Monica, CA 90401
URL: http://www.clearstone.com
Contact: William Quigley, Managing Director
Linkedin: www.linkedin.com/company/clearstone-venture-partners
Description: Venture capital firm specializing in startups, early stage and mid venture companies. **Founded:** 1997. **Preferred Investment Size:** $2,000,000 to $10,000,000. **Industry Preferences:** Internet specific, computer software and services, computer hardware, communications and media, industrial and energy, semiconductors and other electronics and other products.

37334 ■ Clydesdale Ventures LLC
301 Mission st. No.36C
 San Francisco, CA 94105
Contact: Paul Klapper, Contact
Description: Venture capital firm at the seed and early stages. **Industry Preferences:** Health and wellness; natural products; healthy restaurant concepts.

37335 ■ Comcast Ventures
1 Kearny Bldg.
23 Geary St., 10th Fl.
 San Francisco, CA 94108
Ph: (415)926-5540
URL: http://comcastventures.com
Contact: Kyle Peters, Director, Finance
Facebook: www.facebook.com/ComcastVentures
Linkedin: www.linkedin.com/company/comcast-ventures
X (Twitter): x.com/comcastventures
Instagram: www.instagram.com/comcastventures
Founded: 1999.

37336 ■ Correlation Ventures (VC)
650 California St., 5th Fl.
 San Francisco, CA 94108
Ph: (415)890-5425
URL: http://correlationvc.com
Contact: Grace Chui-Miller, Chief Financial Officer
E-mail: gcm@correlationvc.com
Linkedin: www.linkedin.com/company/correlation-ventures
Description: Venture capital firm co-invests in U.S-based companies from seed to late stage. Uses predictive analytics to improve decision-making. Makes investment decisions within two weeks. Also operates out of San Diego and New York. **Founded:** 2006. **Preferred Investment Size:** $1,000,000 to $4,000,000.

37337 ■ Craft Ventures
590 Pacific
 Pleasant Hill, CA 94523
URL: http://www.craftventures.com
Contact: Mark Woolway, President
Linkedin: www.linkedin.com/company/craft-ventures
X (Twitter): twitter.com/craft_ventures
Description: Early-stage investment fund focused on the craft of building remarkable companies. The partners have all been founders or CEOs of their own successful companies and participated in other ventures as angel investors. **Founded:** 2017.

37338 ■ Credo Ventures
44 Tehama St.
 San Francisco, CA 94105
Ph: (650)722-2202
Co. E-mail: kiska@credoventures.com
URL: http://www.credoventures.com
Contact: Andrej Kiska, Partner
Facebook: www.facebook.com/CredoVentures
Linkedin: www.linkedin.com/company/credo-ventures
X (Twitter): twitter.com/credoventures
Description: Invests in early-stage entrepreneurs in Central Europe. Also operates out of Prague. **Founded:** 2009. **Industry Preferences:** IT; healthcare; internet.

37339 ■ CrossCoin Ventures, LLC
San Francisco, CA
URL: http://www.crosscoinventures.com
Contact: Gary Kremen, Contact
Description: Digital currency accelerator. Offers capital, mentoring, and networking.

37340 ■ Crosscut Ventures Management LLC
3110 Main St. PH
 Santa Monica, CA 90405
URL: http://crosscut.vc
Contact: Brett Brewer, Managing Director Co-Founder
Linkedin: www.linkedin.com/company/crosscut-ventures
X (Twitter): x.com/crosscutvc
Description: Partners with early-stage entrepreneurs to build high-growth tech companies from Seed to Series A. **Founded:** 2008.

37341 ■ Crosslink Capital (CC)
2180 Sand Hill Rd., Ste. 200
 Menlo Park, CA 94025
Ph: (415)617-1800
URL: http://www.crosslinkcapital.com
Contact: Anduena Zhubi, Director, Business Development
Description: Firm provides venture capital investment services. **Scope:** An independent venture capital and investment firm focused on strategic business and technology questions as well as to discuss tactical approaches to addressing these challenges. **Founded:** 1989. **Preferred Investment Size:** $8,000,000 to $20,000,000. **Industry Preferences:** Internet specific, computer software and services, semiconductors and other electronics, communications and media, biotechnology, computer hardware, other products, consumer related, medical and health, industrial and energy.

37342 ■ CRV
52 Zoe St.
 San Francisco, CA 94107
Ph: (415)960-3000
URL: http://www.crv.com
Contact: Sachin Sood, Chief Financial Officer
X (Twitter): x.com/CRV
YouTube: www.youtube.com/channel/UCRibw5FGtD3nnklq787Znhw
Description: Invests in high-growth technology companies. **Industry Preferences:** Enterprise; consumer; bioengineering.

37343 ■ DAG Ventures
251 Lytton Ave., Ste. 200
 Palo Alto, CA 94301
Ph: (650)543-8180
Fax: (650)328-2921
Co. E-mail: info@dagventures.com
URL: http://dagventures.com
Contact: Joe Zanone, Chief Financial Officer
Description: Venture capital firm at the mid-stage and growth financing rounds. **Founded:** 2004. **Industry Preferences:** Technology; energy; life science.

37344 ■ Data Elite
680 Mission St. Apt. 35B
 San Francisco, CA 94105
Contact: Stamatios Venios, Contact
Description: Venture lab and early-stage fund for big data startups and scientists. Offers workspace, support staff, and meaningful resources to transform founding teams into viable and impactful companies.

37345 ■ Defta Partners
111 Pine St., Ste. 1410
 San Francisco, CA 94111
Ph: (415)433-2262
Co. E-mail: information@deftapartners.com
URL: http://www.deftapartners.com
Contact: George Hara, Chief Executive Officer
Description: Provider of investment services for health care and IT services. **Founded:** 1984. **Preferred Investment Size:** $500,000 to $3,000,000. **Investment Policies:** Start-up, seed, and early stage. **Industry Preferences:** Computer software and services, semiconductors and other electronics, Internet specific, communications and media, medical and health, and computer hardware. **Geographic Preference:** National.

37346 ■ Delphi Ventures
204 E 2nd Ave., Ste. 406
 San Mateo, CA 94401
Ph: (650)854-9650
URL: http://www.delphiventures.com
Contact: Matthew Potter, Chief Financial Officer Partner
Description: Firm provides venture capital and private equity investment services. **Founded:** 1988. **Preferred Investment Size:** $500,000 to $12,000,000. **Industry Preferences:** Medical and health, and biotechnology.

37347 ■ Diamondhead Ventures L.P.
1350 Bayshore Hwy., Ste. 920
 Burlingame, CA 94010
Ph: (650)687-7550
URL: http://www.dhven.com
Contact: David Lane, Managing Director
Description: Provider of early stage venture capital investments for technology companies. **Founded:** 2000. **Preferred Investment Size:** $500,000 to $5,000,000. **Industry Preferences:** Communications and media, computer software, Internet specific, semiconductors and other electronics.

37348 ■ DN Capital
325 Sharon Pk., Dr.,752
 Menlo Park, CA 94025
Ph: (650)561-9300
URL: http://www.dncapital.com
Contact: Steve Schlenker, Co-Founder Managing Partner
Linkedin: www.linkedin.com/company/dn-capital
X (Twitter): x.com/dncapital
Description: Global early-stage venture firm for tech companies. Also operates out of London and Berlin. **Founded:** 2000. **Industry Preferences:** Fintech; proptech; travel; digital health; enterprise software; digital media.

37349 ■ Doll Capital Management (DCM)
2420 Sand Hill Rd., Ste. 200
 Menlo Park, CA 94025
Ph: (650)233-1400
Fax: (650)854-9159
Co. E-mail: businessplan@dcm.com
URL: http://www.dcm.com/en
Contact: Jason Krikorian, Partner
E-mail: jkrikorian@dcm.com
Facebook: www.facebook.com/dcmvc
X (Twitter): x.com/dcm_vc
Description: Firm focuses on start up companies in the business software, services, VC and empowering, consumer, digital media and components. **Founded:** 1996. **Preferred Investment Size:** $3,000,000 to $15,000,000. **Industry Preferences:** Internet specific, computer software and services, communications and media, semiconductors and other electronics, computer hardware, other products, and consumer related.

STATE LISTINGS

California ■ 37369

37350 ■ Dorset Capital L.L.C.
2930 Domingo Ave., No. 202
Berkeley, CA 94705-2443
Co. E-mail: mgmt@dorsetcapllc.com
URL: http://dorsetcapllc.com
Contact: James E. Burden, President

Description: Finance: Private equity investment company. **Founded:** 1999. **Preferred Investment Size:** $5,000,000 to $30,000,000. **Industry Preferences:** Consumer related, financial services, business service, and manufacturing.

37351 ■ Dot Edu Ventures
514 Bryant St., Ste. No.110
Palo Alto, CA 94301
Ph: (650)435-9042
Facebook: www.facebook.com/DotEduVentures

Description: Finance: Investments in technology businesses. **Founded:** 2000. **Industry Preferences:** Internet specific.

37352 ■ Draper Associates (DA)
55 E 3rd Ave.
San Mateo, CA 94401
Co. E-mail: plans@draper.vc
URL: http://www.draper.vc
Contact: Sarika Batra, Director
X (Twitter): x.com/DraperVC

Description: Seed-stage venture capital firm. **Founded:** 1985.

37353 ■ Draper International
1600 El Camino Real, Ste. 155
Menlo Park, CA 94025
Contact: William H. Draper, Manager

Description: Provider of investment management solutions. **Preferred Investment Size:** $250,000 to $1,000,000. **Industry Preferences:** Internet specific, computer hardware, computer software and services, consumer related, communications and media.

37354 ■ E! Entertainment Television L.L.C.
Comcast Corporation
5750 Wilshire Blvd.
Los Angeles, CA 90036
Ph: (215)286-1700
Co. E-mail: accessibility@comcast.com
URL: http://www.comcast.com

Description: Firm engages in the production and distribution of entertainment news and lifestyle-related programming. **Founded:** 1987. **Preferred Investment Size:** $2,000,000 to $10,000,000. **Industry Preferences:** Business and financial services, consumer products and services, and niche manufacturing.

37355 ■ EcoElectron Ventures
1106 Second St.
Encinitas, CA 92024
Ph: (760)635-1681
Fax: (760)635-1682
URL: http://ecoelectron.com
Contact: Josh Lampl, Investment Manager
E-mail: josh@ecoelectron.com

Description: Venture capital firm for entrepreneurs and technologists in the San Diego area. **Investment Policies:** Must see profit within thee years. Won't fund basic research and development. **Industry Preferences:** Renewable and clean energy; energy conservation; energy storage; power transmission innovations; energy control and communication software.

37356 ■ eCompanies L.L.C.
2120 Colorado Ave., 3rd Fl.
Santa Monica, CA 90404
URL: http://www.ecompanies.com

Description: Provider of incubation and seed capital services to companies. **Founded:** 1999. **Industry Preferences:** Internet specific, computer software and services, industrial and energy and other products.

37357 ■ El Dorado Ventures
355 Pacific Oaks Rd.
Goleta, CA 93117
Contact: Steven P. Kirkman, Chief Executive Officer

Preferred Investment Size: $250,000 to $1,000,000. **Industry Preferences:** Internet specific, computer software and services, computer hardware, communications and media, semiconductors and other electronics, medical and health, other products, consumer related, and biotechnology.

37358 ■ Electronics for Imaging, Inc. (EFI)
Electronics for Imaging, Inc. (EFI)
6453 Kaiser Dr.
Fremont, CA 94555
Ph: (650)357-3500
Fax: (650)357-3907
Co. E-mail: info@efi.com
URL: http://www.efi.com/en-gb
Contact: Jeff Jacobson, Chief Executive Officer
Facebook: www.facebook.com/EFIPrint
Linkedin: www.linkedin.com/company/efiprint
X (Twitter): twitter.com/EFIPrint
Instagram: www.instagram.com/efiprint
YouTube: www.youtube.com/user/EFIDigitalPrintTech

Description: Developer of pre-press management software. **Founded:** 1989.

37359 ■ Emergence Capital Partners (ECP)
Pier 5, Ste. 102
San Francisco, CA 94111
Ph: (650)573-3100
Co. E-mail: hello@emcap.com
URL: http://www.emcap.com
Contact: Julie Bell, Chief Operating Officer
E-mail: patti@emcap.com
Linkedin: www.linkedin.com/company/emergence
-capital-partners
X (Twitter): x.com/emergencecap

Founded: 2003. **Preferred Investment Size:** $1,000,000 to $10,000,000. **Investment Policies:** Start-up, seed, early stage, and expansion. **Industry Preferences:** Computer software, Internet specific, consumer related, financial services, and business service.

37360 ■ Felicis Ventures
2460 Sand Hill Rd., Ste. 100
Menlo Park, CA 94025
Ph: (650)800-7458
URL: http://www.felicis.com
Contact: Eric Wagner, Manager
Linkedin: www.linkedin.com/company/felicis-ventures
X (Twitter): x.com/felicis

Description: Boutique venture fund. **Founded:** 2006.

37361 ■ Finaventures
100 Jefferson Ave.
Redwood City, CA 94063
URL: http://finaventures.com
Contact: Rachid Sefrioui, Managing Director
Linkedin: www.linkedin.com/company/finaventures

Description: Provider of investment solutions in early and mid-stage companies. **Founded:** 1999. **Preferred Investment Size:** $500,000 to $3,000,000. **Investment Policies:** Early, first, and second stage, balanced, and expansion. **Industry Preferences:** Communications, computer software, and semiconductors and other electronics.

37362 ■ Floodgate
2462 Embarcadero Way
Palo Alto, CA 94301
URL: http://www.floodgate.com
Contact: Ann Miura-Ko, Partner
X (Twitter): twitter.com/floodgatefund

Description: Seed-stage venture capital firm. **Founded:** 2006.

37363 ■ Foothill Ventures
280 2nd St.
Los Altos, CA 94022
Co. E-mail: contact@foothill.ventures
URL: http://www.foothill.ventures
Contact: Dr. Xuhui Shao, Contact
Linkedin: www.linkedin.com/company/foothillventures
X (Twitter): x.com/FoothillVenture

Description: Technology-base venture fund invests in early-stage startups. **Industry Preferences:** AI; computer vision; cyber security; diagnostics; genetics; material science.

37364 ■ Forerunner Ventures
1161 Mission St., Ste.300
San Francisco, CA 94103
Contact: Kirsten Green, Manager

Description: Early stage venture capital firm for startups who can rewrite the rules of culture.

37365 ■ Foresight Capital
900 Larkspur Landing Cir., Ste. 150
Larkspur, CA 94939
Ph: (415)877-4887
URL: http://www.foresitecapital.com
Contact: Jim Tananbaum, Chief Executive Officer
Linkedin: www.linkedin.com/company/foresite-capital
-management
X (Twitter): x.com/foresitecapital

Description: Venture capital firm focused on the intersection of biology and big data in healthcare. Also operates out of New York. **Founded:** 2011. **Industry Preferences:** Therapeutics, devices, diagnostics, and services.

37366 ■ Forward Ventures
9255 Towne Centre Dr., Ste. 350
San Diego, CA 92121
Ph: (858)677-6077
Fax: (858)452-8799
Co. E-mail: info@forwardventures.com
URL: http://www.forwardventures.com
Contact: Caroline Barberio, Chief Financial Officer

Description: Invests in biomedical research and innovation community. **Founded:** 1990. **Preferred Investment Size:** $1,000,000 to $6,000,000. **Industry Preferences:** Biotechnology, medical and health, and Internet specific.

37367 ■ Foundation Capital
550 High St., 3rd Fl.
Palo Alto, CA 94301
Ph: (650)614-0500
URL: http://foundationcapital.com
Contact: Zach Noorani, Partner
Facebook: www.facebook.com/pg/foundationcap
Linkedin: www.linkedin.com/company/foundation
-capital
X (Twitter): twitter.com/foundationcap
Instagram: www.instagram.com/foundationcapital

Description: Venture capital firm offers networking, storage and telecommunications, mobile, cleantech, data communication, energy management, digital media, internet infrastructure and technologies, financial services, business-to-consumer e-commerce, internet media, and data networks. **Founded:** 1995. **Preferred Investment Size:** $1,000,000 to $10,000,000. **Industry Preferences:** Internet specific, communications and media, computer software and services, computer hardware, semiconductors and other electronics, industrial and energy, other products, industrial and energy, medical and health, and consumer related.

37368 ■ Founders Fund
1 Letterman Dr., Bldg. D 5th Fl.
San Francisco, CA 94129
Contact: Ken Howery, Manager

Description: Venture capital firm interested in science and technology companies solving difficult problems. Invests at all stages. **Founded:** 2005. **Industry Preferences:** Biotechnology, AI, aerospace, energy, and internet.

37369 ■ Founders Network
415 Jackson St.
Hayward, CA 94545
Ph: (415)489-0651
Co. E-mail: info@foundersnetwork.com
URL: http://foundersnetwork.com
Contact: Sonal Puri, Chief Executive Officer
Facebook: www.facebook.com/foundersnetwork
Linkedin: www.linkedin.com/company/founders-ne
twork
X (Twitter): x.com/foundersnetwork
Instagram: www.instagram.com/foundersnetwork
YouTube: www.youtube.com/user/foundersnetwork

Description: Community of tech start-up founders helping each other through peer mentoring. New members are nominated by current members. **Founded:** 2011.

37370 ■ Foundry
501 2nd St., Ste. 650
San Francisco, CA 94107
URL: http://foundryco.com
Contact: Mike Finnerty, President
Description: Venture capital firm provides investment services. **Founded:** 1964. **Preferred Investment Size:** 1,000,000 to $5,000,000. **Industry Preferences:** Internet specific, computer software and services, computer hardware, communications and media, medical and health, semiconductors and other electronics, biotechnology, consumer related, and other products.

37371 ■ Freestyle Capital
San Francisco, CA
Co. E-mail: info@freestyle.vc
URL: http://freestyle.vc
Contact: David Bill, Chief Technology Officer
Linkedin: www.linkedin.com/company/freestyle-capital
X (Twitter): x.com/freestylevc
Description: Venture capital firm for early-stage investments. Invests in 10-12 companies per year. **Founded:** 2009. **Preferred Investment Size:** $1,000,000. **Industry Preferences:** Technology; fintech; media; telecommunications; internet software; consumer and web-based technology companies.

37372 ■ FTV Management Company LP
601 California St., Fl. 19
San Francisco, CA 94108
Ph: (415)229-3000
Co. E-mail: info@ftvcapital.com
URL: http://ftvcapital.com
Contact: Arun Singh, Vice President
Linkedin: www.linkedin.com/company/ftv-capital
X (Twitter): x.com/ftvcapital
Description: Venture capital firm for companies in complex high-growth markets. **Founded:** 1998. **Investment Policies:** Looks for companies with at least $10 million annualized revenue; 20% historical and near-term revenue growth; blue chip customer relationships. **Industry Preferences:** Enterprise technology and services; financial services; payments and transaction processing.

37373 ■ FundersClub
2261 Market St., No 5081
San Francisco, CA 94114
Free: 888-405-9335
URL: http://fundersclub.com
Contact: Apoorva Mehta, Chief Executive Officer
Description: Uses software and community to source, vet, and fund startups. Invests at the Seed and Series A stages.

37374 ■ Gabriel Venture Partners
635 Mariners Island, Ste. 204
San Mateo, CA 94404
Ph: (650)551-5000
Fax: (650)551-5001
Co. E-mail: info@gabrielvp.com
URL: http://gabrielvp.com
Contact: Phil Samper, Co-Founder
Facebook: www.facebook.com/people/Gabriel-Venture-Partners/100065707890421
Linkedin: www.linkedin.com/company/elab-ventures
X (Twitter): x.com/GabrielVP
Description: Provider of venture capital investment services for communications, networking and information technology. **Founded:** 1999. **Preferred Investment Size:** $500,000 to $10,000,000. **Industry Preferences:** Internet specific, computer software and services, communications and media, computer hardware, semiconductors and other electronics, medical and health.

37375 ■ GGV Capital
3000 Sand Hill Rd., Bldg. 4, Ste. 230
Menlo Park, CA 94025
Contact: Hans Tung, Manager
Description: Venture capital firm focused on expansion-stage companies in the US and China. **Founded:** 2000.

37376 ■ Gideon Hixon Fund
23815 Stuart Ranch Rd., Ste. 302
Malibu, CA 90265
Ph: (805)963-2277
Fax: (805)565-0929
URL: http://www.gideonhixon.com
Contact: Dylan Hixon, Officer
Description: Provider of fund investments, direct investments and previous investments for entrepreneurs. **Founded:** 1990. **Preferred Investment Size:** $500,000 to $1,500,000. **Investment Policies:** Start-up, seed, first and second stage. **Industry Preferences:** Internet specific, medical and health, computer software and services, other products, and semiconductors and other electronics.

37377 ■ Glynn Capital Management (GCM)
3000 Sand Hill Rd., Bldg. 3, Ste. 230
Menlo Park, CA 94025
Ph: (650)854-2215
Co. E-mail: venture@glynncapital.com
URL: http://www.glynncapital.com
Contact: Amrita Tyagi, Manager
Description: Provider of technology investment, venture capital investment and public equity technology investment services for private and public technology growth companies. **Founded:** 1974. **Preferred Investment Size:** $300,000 to 500,000. **Industry Preferences:** Provider of technology investment, venture capital investment and public equity technology investment services for private and public technology growth companies.

37378 ■ GoAhead Ventures
535 Middlefield Rd., Ste. 280
Menlo Park, CA 94025
Co. E-mail: pitch@goaheadvc.com
URL: http://www.goaheadvc.com
Contact: Clancey Stahr, Contact
Description: Venture capital firm works with young entrepreneurs at the earliest stages. Works alongside the founders (often students or recent graduates) to delver tangible value.

37379 ■ Granite Ventures LLC (GV)
4120 Douglas Blvd., Ste. 306-327
Granite Bay, CA 95746
Ph: (916)351-5704
Co. E-mail: granitesuccess@gmail.com
URL: http://granitesuccess.com
Contact: Jeff Cooke, President
Description: Venture capital firm. **Founded:** 1992.

37380 ■ Granite Ventures LLC
300 Montgomery St., Ste. 638
San Francisco, CA 94104
Ph: (415)591-7700
Fax: (415)591-7720
URL: http://granitevc.com
Contact: Standish O'Grady, Managing Director
Facebook: www.facebook.com/Granite-Ventures-138307769528427
X (Twitter): x.com/granitev
Description: Invests in early-stage technology companies. **Founded:** 1992. **Preferred Investment Size:** $500,000-$4,000,000. **Investment Policies:** Proprietary technologies and sustainable competitive advantage.

37381 ■ GreatPoint Ventures (GPV)
744 Montgomery St., Ste. 500
San Francisco, CA 94111
Co. E-mail: info@gpv.com
URL: http://www.gpv.com
Contact: Ray Lane, Managing Partner
Linkedin: www.linkedin.com/company/greatpoint-ventures
X (Twitter): x.com/GreatPointVC
Description: Early-stage venture capital firm. Invests in revolutionary ideas that transform industries and benefit societies. **Founded:** 2015.

37382 ■ Greenhouse Capital Partners
1 Gate Six Rd., Ste. 203
Sausalito, CA 94965
Ph: (415)289-1141
Co. E-mail: info@greenhousecapital.net
URL: http://www.greenhousecap.com
Contact: Peter D. Henig, Managing Partner
E-mail: pete@greenhousecapital.net
Description: Growth capital for emerging businesses promoting health and sustainability. **Preferred Investment Size:** $500,000 to $5,000,000. **Investment Policies:** Revenue of $1,000,000 to $25,000,000; history of strong gross margins; positive (or nearly break-even) EBITDA; proven market fit; defensible market position in a growing industry. **Industry Preferences:** Environment and sustainability; food and agriculture.

37383 ■ Greylock Partners
2550 Sand Hill Rd., Ste. 200
Menlo Park, CA 94025
Ph: (650)493-5525
Fax: (650)493-5575
Co. E-mail: businessplans@greylock.com
URL: http://greylock.com
Contact: Allie Dalglish, Director
E-mail: allie@greylock.com
Facebook: www.facebook.com/Greylock
Linkedin: www.linkedin.com/company/greylock-partners
X (Twitter): x.com/GreylockVC
YouTube: www.youtube.com/user/greylockpartners
Description: Firm engages in venture investment related activities. **Founded:** 1965. **Preferred Investment Size:** $250,000 minimum. **Industry Preferences:** Diversified.

37384 ■ GSR Ventures
1300 El Camino Real, Ste. 100
Menlo Park, CA 94025
Ph: (650)331-7300
URL: http://gsrventuresglobal.com
Contact: Allen Zhu, Managing Director
E-mail: allen@gsrventures.com
Description: Venture capital firm for early-stage technology companies. Also operates out of Beijing and Shanghai. **Founded:** 2004.

37385 ■ Headline
101 Montgomery St., Ste. 200
San Francisco, CA 94129
Ph: (415)869-5200
URL: http://headline.com
Contact: Conrad Chu, Partner Chief Technology Officer
E-mail: conrad@headline.com
Linkedin: www.linkedin.com/company/headlinevc
X (Twitter): x.com/HeadlineVC
Description: Firm provides digital media, cloud services, software, networking equipment and services, internet infrastructure, internet community services, ecommerce, mobile, mobile applications, wireless telecommunication services and much more. **Founded:** 1998. **Preferred Investment Size:** $1,000,000 to $5,000,000. **Industry Preferences:** Communications and media, computer software and services, and Internet specific.

37386 ■ HighBar Partners
405 EL Camino Real, Ste. 361
Menlo Park, CA 94025
Ph: (650)900-4330
Co. E-mail: info@highbarpartners.com
URL: http://www.highbarpartners.com
Contact: John Kim, Co-Founder Managing Partner
Linkedin: www.linkedin.com/company/3109177
X (Twitter): x.com/HighBarPartners
Description: Provider of strategic growth capital to enterprise and infrastructure software companies. **Founded:** 1995. **Investment Policies:** Seed and early stage. **Industry Preferences:** Technology.

37387 ■ Hinge Capital, LLC
San Diego, CA
URL: http://www.hingecapital.com
Contact: Brandon Zeuner, Co-Founder Managing Director

X (Twitter): x.com/hingecapital

Description: Invests in entrepreneurs who use modern technology to solve difficult problems.

37388 ■ Horizon Ventures
232 Burke Rd.
 Los Altos, CA 94022
Contact: Jack Carsten, Contact

Description: Provider of venture capital investment to early and middle stage. **Founded:** 1999. **Preferred Investment Size:** $500,000 to $3,500,000. **Industry Preferences:** Internet specific, computer hardware, computer software and services, semiconductors and other electronics, medical and health, communications and media, and other products.

37389 ■ Icon Ventures
505 Hamilton Ave., Ste. 310
 Palo Alto, CA 94301
Co. E-mail: info@iconventures.com
URL: http://iconventures.com
Contact: Ted Kawahara, Director
Linkedin: www.linkedin.com/company/icon-ventures
X (Twitter): x.com/iconventures

Description: Provider of early venture and mid venture investment services for information technology sector. **Founded:** 2003. **Preferred Investment Size:** $4,000,000 to $8,000,000. **Industry Preferences:** Communications and media, computer software and services, and semiconductors and other electronics.

37390 ■ iD Ventures America, LLC
5201 Great America Pky., Ste. 355
 Santa Clara, CA 95054
Ph: (408)894-7900
Fax: (408)894-7939
URL: http://idsoftcapital.com
Contact: Dr. Ronald Chwang, President

Description: Provider of venture capital, bridge financing, growth capital investments and venture capital financing for energy technology, medical device, semiconductor and information technology sectors. **Founded:** 1998. **Preferred Investment Size:** $500,000 to $3,000,000. **Investment Policies:** Start-up, seed, first and second stage. **Industry Preferences:** Communications and media, computer software and hardware, Internet specific, semiconductors and other electronics, consumer related, and financial services.

37391 ■ Idealab
130 W Union St.
 Pasadena, CA 91103
Ph: (626)585-6900
Fax: (626)535-2701
Co. E-mail: contactus@idealab.com
URL: http://www.idealab.com
Contact: Marcia Goodstein, President
Facebook: www.facebook.com/idealab
Linkedin: www.linkedin.com/company/idealab
X (Twitter): x.com/idealab
YouTube: www.youtube.com/user/TheCoolNewStuff

Description: Provider of technology services including graphic design, marketing, financial advice, human resources, competitive research, legal, accounting and business development support and services. **Founded:** 1996. **Publications:** *The PointCast Network (PCN)*. **Investment Policies:** Innovation team supports start-ups. **Industry Preferences:** Innovation team supports start-ups.

37392 ■ Illumina Accelerator
200 Lincoln Centre Dr.
 Foster City, CA 94404
Ph: (650)376-9000
Co. E-mail: customercare@illumina.com
URL: http://sapac.illumina.com
Contact: Dr. Jacob Thaysen, Chief Executive Officer

Description: Business accelerator focused on establishing an innovative ecosystem for the genomics industry. Offers a six-month funding cyle with access to seed investment, sequencing systems and reagents, business guidance, and lab space. Also operates out of Cambridge, UK.

37393 ■ Illumina Ventures
200 Lincoln Centre Dr., Ste. 300-A
 Foster City, CA 94404
Co. E-mail: info@illuminaventures.com
URL: http://www.illuminaventures.com
Contact: Nick Naclerio, Founder Partner
X (Twitter): x.com/illuminaventure

Description: Invests in early-stage companies pioneering new applications of genomics and enabling precision medicine. **Industry Preferences:** Life science tools; clinical diagnostics; therapeutics; .

37394 ■ Illuminate Ventures
6114 La Salle Ave., Ste. 323
 Oakland, CA 94611
URL: http://illuminate.com
Contact: Cindy Padnos, Founder Managing Partner
Linkedin: www.linkedin.com/company/illuminate-ventures
X (Twitter): x.com/IlluminateVC
YouTube: www.youtube.com/user/IlluminateVC

Description: Venture capital firm specializing in funding B2B/enterprise cloud and mobile computing, particularly SaaS applications. **Founded:** 2010. **Investment Policies:** Innovative ideas let by talented teams; the intersection of creative destruction with new technologies to solve old problems in new ways.

37395 ■ Industry Ventures
522 Washington St.
 San Francisco, CA 94111
Ph: (415)273-4201
Fax: (415)483-7177
Co. E-mail: info@industryventures.com
URL: http://www.industryventures.com
Contact: Hans Swildens, Chief Executive Officer
E-mail: hans@industryventures.com
Facebook: www.facebook.com/Industryventures
Linkedin: www.linkedin.com/company/industry-ventures
X (Twitter): x.com/IndustryVC

Description: Provider of venture capital in secondary direct investments, limited partnership interests and much more. **Founded:** 2000. **Preferred Investment Size:** $250,000 to $250,000,000. **Industry Preferences:** Communications and media, computer software, Internet specific, consumer related, and business service.

37396 ■ Initialized Capital Management
464 Tehama St.
 San Francisco, CA 94103
Co. E-mail: contact@initialized.com
URL: http://initialized.com
Contact: Chi An, Controller
Facebook: www.facebook.com/InitializedCapital
Linkedin: www.linkedin.com/company/initialized-capital
X (Twitter): x.com/Initialized
Instagram: www.instagram.com/initialized
YouTube: www.youtube.com/channel/UC5fnPuszm7AarpX40Gjed8w

Description: Venture capital firm focused on software startups with promising engineers, designers, and product founders. Invests at the seed stage or earlier. **Founded:** 2016. **Industry Preferences:** Software.

37397 ■ Innovation Endeavors
1845 El Camino Real
 Palo Alto, CA 94306
Ph: (650)853-1236
Co. E-mail: info@innovationendeavors.com
URL: http://www.innovationendeavors.com
Contact: Eric Schmidt, Founder Partner
Facebook: www.facebook.com/Innovation.Endeavors
Linkedin: www.linkedin.com/company/innovation-endeavors
X (Twitter): x.com/iendeavors

Description: Invests in transformational technology, visionary founders, and emergent ecosystems. Also operates out of New York and Tel Aviv. **Founded:** 2010.

37398 ■ Inspiration Venture Partners LLC
330 Primrose Rd., Ste. 612.
 Burlingame, CA 94010
Co. E-mail: info@inspirationvc.com

URL: http://www.inspirationvc.com
Contact: Gady Nemirovsky, Partner
Linkedin: www.linkedin.com/company/inspiration-ventures
X (Twitter): x.com/insprVC

Description: Early stage venture capital firm for technological startups. Offers various assistance from concept creation to market validation and venture funding. **Industry Preferences:** Technology.

37399 ■ Institutional Venture Partners (IVP)
3000 Sand Hill Rd. Bldg. 2, Ste. 250
 Menlo Park, CA 94025
Ph: (650)854-0132
Free: 800-352-5267
URL: http://www.ivp.com
Contact: Kelly O'Kane, Senior Vice President, Investor Relations Senior Vice President, Business Development
Facebook: www.facebook.com/ivpvc
Linkedin: www.linkedin.com/company/ivpvc
X (Twitter): x.com/ivp

Description: Firm provides venture capital, later-stage venture capital, growth equity, investing in growth. **Founded:** 1980. **Preferred Investment Size:** $10,000,000 to $100,000,000. **Industry Preferences:** Internet specific, communications and media, computer hardware, computer software and services, semiconductors and other electronics, consumer related, and other products.

37400 ■ Intercept Ventures LLC
URL: http://www.interceptventures.com
Preferred Investment Size: $275,000 to $10,000,000. **Industry Preferences:** Internet specific, communications and media, computer hardware, medical and health, other products, computer software and services, semiconductors and other electronics.

37401 ■ Inventus Capital Partners (ICP)
400 S El Camino Real, Ste. 700
 San Mateo, CA 94402
URL: http://www.inventuscap.com
Contact: Kanwal Rekhi, Co-Founder Managing Director
Facebook: www.facebook.com/Inventusvc
X (Twitter): x.com/inventusvc

Description: Venture capital firm focused on consumer Internet and media, SaaS, mobile technology, and knowledge-based services to address end markets in India and across the world. **Founded:** 2005. **Industry Preferences:** Internet; mobile; cloud computing.

37402 ■ IVP
3000 Sand Hill Rd., Bldg. 2, Ste. 250
 Menlo Park, CA 94025
Ph: (650)854-0132
URL: http://ivp.com
Contact: Zack Willis, Vice President, Technology Development
X (Twitter): x.com/ivp

Description: Venture capital firm focused on later-stage companies. Specializes in venture growth, founder liquidity transactions, industry rollups, and public market investments. **Founded:** 1980. **Industry Preferences:** Technology and media.

37403 ■ Jane Capital Partners (JCP)
999 Green St. No. 2304
 San Francisco, CA 94133
URL: http://www.janecapital.com
Contact: Albert Nelson, Managing Director
E-mail: bnelson@janecapital.com

Description: Venture capital firm. Advised clients on mergers and acquisitions, strategic alliances, and financing. **Founded:** 2001. **Industry Preferences:** Energy; environment; information technology.

37404 ■ Javelin Venture Partners
221 Main St.
 San Francisco, CA 94105
Ph: (415)471-1300
Co. E-mail: info@javelinvp.com
URL: http://www.javelinvp.com
Contact: Alex Gurevich, Managing Director

Linkedin: www.linkedin.com/company/javelin-venture-partners
X (Twitter): x.com/javelinvp
Description: Early stage venture capital firm. Specialized in technology startups that leverage innovation to create world-changing companies. **Industry Preferences:** Digital social media; web services; ecommerce; mobile; cloud computing; enterprise health care; information technology.

37405 ■ K5 Ventures
Newport Beach, CA
URL: http://k5ventures.com
Contact: Amir Banifatemi, Managing Director
Description: Early-stage venture fund. Partners with and invests in tech-driven businesses in California and China. **Founded:** 2010.

37406 ■ K9 Ventures LLC
Palo Alto, CA
URL: http://www.k9ventures.com
Contact: Dr. Manu Kumar, Officer
Facebook: www.facebook.com/k9ventures
Linkedin: www.linkedin.com/company/k9-ventures
X (Twitter): x.com/k9ventures
Description: Technology-focused pre-seed venture capital firm. **Founded:** 2009. **Investment Policies:** Technology leaders; radically new markets or new core technologies; direct revenue (as opposed to companies built of media, commerce, or advertising); companies that make things. Won't invest in ecommerce.

37407 ■ Kaiser Permanente Ventures (KPV)
Kaiser Permanente Ventures (KPV)
One Kaiser Plz., 22nd Fl.
Oakland, CA 94612
URL: http://www.kpventures.com
Contact: Gina Crisosto, Consultant
Description: Provider of venture capital investments. **Founded:** 1997. **Preferred Investment Size:** $500,000 to $2,000,000. **Industry Preferences:** Biotechnology, and medical and health.

37408 ■ Kapor Capital (KC)
2148 Broadway
Oakland, CA 94612
Co. E-mail: info@kaporcapital.com
URL: http://www.kaporcapital.com
Contact: Tesheia van der Horst, Director
Facebook: www.facebook.com/KaporCapital
Linkedin: www.linkedin.com/company/kapor-capital
X (Twitter): x.com/KaporCapital
Description: Venture capital firm. Focuses on companies (at the pre-seed and see stages) who have a working version of their product/service with a small number of users. Believes startups can transform industries and address social needs. **Founded:** 2011. **Investment Policies:** Invests in companies with potential to realize significant financial returns and large-scale social impact, by expanding access to information/goods/services, economic opportunity in the marketplace or workplace, and increased efficient and competitive market-based solutions to social and economic problems.

37409 ■ Kearny Venture Partners (KVP)
Four Embarcadero Center, Ste. 2100
San Francisco, CA 94111
Ph: (415)875-7777
Co. E-mail: info@kearnyvp.com
URL: http://kearnyvp.com
Description: Healthcare investment firm. **Industry Preferences:** Emerging healthcare products.

37410 ■ Keiretsu Forum
44 Tehama St.
San Francisco, CA 94104
Co. E-mail: info@keiretsuforum.com
URL: http://www.keiretsuforum.com
Contact: Randy Williams, Chief Executive Officer
Description: Worldwide angel network of capital and resources with more than 50 chapters on three continents. **Founded:** 2000.

37411 ■ Kern Venture Group (KVG)
5001 California Ave., Ste. 214
Bakersfield, CA 93309
Ph: (661)343-1840
URL: http://www.kernventuregroup.com
Contact: Jacob Panero, Chief Executive Officer
Linkedin: www.linkedin.com/company/kern-venture-group
Description: Micro venture capital fund targets early-stage investments in disruptive technology. **Founded:** 2018.

37412 ■ Keybridge Venture Partners LLC
Los Altos, CA
URL: http://www.keybridgeventure.com
Contact: Grant Allen, Contact
Description: Angel investment firm. **Industry Preferences:** Robotics; applied AI; fintech; consumer services.

37413 ■ Khosla Ventures
2128 Sand Hill Rd.
Menlo Park, CA 94025
Ph: (650)376-8500
Fax: (650)926-9590
Co. E-mail: information@khoslaventures.com
URL: http://khoslaventures.com
Contact: Avisha Mehra, Director
E-mail: avisha@khoslaventures.com
URL(s): khoslaventuresacquisitionco.com
Linkedin: www.linkedin.com/company/khosla-ventures
X (Twitter): x.com/khoslaventures
YouTube: www.youtube.com/user/khoslaventures
Description: Venture capital firm interested in solving large problems with technology solutions. **Founded:** 2004. **Investment Policies:** Prefers technology or business innovation, the ability to disrupt large markets, short innovation cycles; favors technology risk over market risk. **Industry Preferences:** Consumer, enterprise, education, advertising, financial services, semiconductors, health, big data, agriculture, food, sustainable energy, and robotics.

37414 ■ Kleiner Perkins (KPCB)
2750 Sand Hill Rd.
Menlo Park, CA 94025
URL: http://www.kleinerperkins.com
Contact: Annie Case, Partner
X (Twitter): x.com/kleinerperkins
Description: Firm provides venture capital and private equity investment services. **Founded:** 1972. **Preferred Investment Size:** $500,000 minimum. **Industry Preferences:** Internet specific, computer software and services, computer hardware, communications and media, semiconductors and other electronics, medical and health, biotechnology, industrial and energy, consumer related, and other products.

37415 ■ KLM Capital Group
3080 Olcott St., Ste. 205C
Santa Clara, CA 95054
Ph: (408)970-8888
Fax: (408)378-5819
Co. E-mail: info@klmcapital.com
URL: http://www.klmtech.com
Contact: Mary Page, Chief Financial Officer
E-mail: mpage@klmcapital.com
Description: Provider of venture capital, seed, start up and early stage investments for communications, information technology and semiconductor industries. **Founded:** 1996. **Preferred Investment Size:** $500,000 to $5,000,000. **Industry Preferences:** Semiconductors and other electronics, Internet specific, computer software and services, communications and media, and consumer related.

37416 ■ KTB Ventures / KTB Venture Capital
310 De Guigne Dr.
Sunnyvale, CA 94085
URL: http://www.ktbvc.com
Description: Provider of private equity and venture capital investment services. **Founded:** 2000. **Preferred Investment Size:** $500,000 to $5,000,000. **Industry Preferences:** Internet specific, semiconductors and other electronics, communications and media, computer software and services, computer hardware, and consumer and business service.

37417 ■ Kyocera International Inc.
8611 Balboa Ave.
San Diego, CA 92123-1580
Ph: (858)576-2600
Free: 800-468-2957
Fax: (858)492-1456
Co. E-mail: salessupport@kyocera.de
URL: http://global.kyocera.com
Facebook: www.facebook.com/kyocera.global
Linkedin: www.linkedin.com/company/kyocera-global
YouTube: www.youtube.com/channel/UC0N82nDF_uBqzrnRHt8F8xA
Description: Manufacturer of ceramic semiconductor packages and laser printers, cameras and developer of prepackaged software. **Founded:** 1959. **Preferred Investment Size:** $300,000 to $500,000. **Industry Preferences:** Communications and media, computer related, semiconductors and other electronics, biotechnology, medical and health, consumer related, industrial and energy, business service, agriculture, forestry and fishing.

37418 ■ Labrador Ventures
535 Middlefield Ave., Ste. 190
Menlo Park, CA 94025
Ph: (650)366-6000
Co. E-mail: labrador@labrador.com
URL: http://www.labrador.com
Contact: Larry Kubal, Partner Founder
Description: Venture capital firm provides investment services. **Founded:** 1989. **Preferred Investment Size:** $1,000,000 to $6,000,000. **Investment Policies:** Start-up, seed, early and first stage. **Industry Preferences:** Communications, computer software, and semiconductors and other electronics.

37419 ■ Latterell Venture Partners (LVP)
2603 Camino Ramon, Ste. 2000
San Ramon, CA 94583
Ph: (925)242-2618
URL: http://www.lvpcapital.com
Contact: Ken Widder, Chief Executive Officer
E-mail: ken@lvpcapital.com
Description: Provider of startups and early stage investments for healthcare companies. **Founded:** 2001. **Preferred Investment Size:** $50,000 to $10,000,000. **Investment Policies:** Early stage and balanced. **Industry Preferences:** Biotechnology, and medical and health.

37420 ■ Levensohn Venture Partners (LVP)
999 Brannan St., Penthouse
San Francisco, CA 94103
Contact: Pascal Levensohn, Contact
Description: Venture capital firm. **Founded:** 1996.

37421 ■ LF USA Investment Inc.
4 Embarcadero Ctr., Ste. 1100
San Francisco, CA 94111
Ph: (415)315-7440
Co. E-mail: contact.usa@lf-investments.com
URL: http://www.lfvc.com
Contact: Michael Hsieh, Manager
Description: Provider of investment services to early and growth stage companies. **Founded:** 1992. **Preferred Investment Size:** $1,000,000 to $10,000,000. **Industry Preferences:** Consumer related, technology, software and services.

37422 ■ Life Science Angels, Inc.
1230 Bordeaux Dr.
Sunnyvale, CA 94089
Ph: (408)541-1152
Fax: (408)541-1418
URL: http://www.lifescienceangels.com
Contact: Allan May, Contact
Description: Angel investment group specializing in healthcare investing. **Founded:** 2005. **Industry Preferences:** Medical devices; diagnostics; pharmaceuticals; biotechnology; digital health.

STATE LISTINGS California ■ 37438

37423 ■ Lighthouse Capital Partners
336 Bon Air Ctr., Ste. 527
Greenbrae, CA 94904
Ph: (415)464-5900
Co. E-mail: info@lcpartners.com
URL: http://lcpartners.com
Description: Venture capital firm provides investment services to early-and growth-stage technology, life science and clean tech companies. **Preferred Investment Size:** $1,000,000 to $10,000,000. **Industry Preferences:** Internet specific, computer software and services, other products, semiconductors and other electronics, communications and media.

37424 ■ Lightspeed Venture Partners
Lightspeed Venture Partners
2200 Sand Hill Rd.
Menlo Park, CA 94025
Ph: (650)234-8300
Fax: (650)234-8333
Co. E-mail: info@lsvp.com
URL: http://lsvp.com
Contact: Nakul Mandan, Partner
E-mail: nakul@lsvp.com
Facebook: www.facebook.com/Lightspeed
Linkedin: www.linkedin.com/company/lightspeed-venture-partners
X (Twitter): x.com/lightspeedvp
Instagram: www.instagram.com/lightspeedventurepartners
Description: Lightspeed Venture Partners is a global venture capital firm managing more than $2 billion in capital. **Founded:** 1971. **Preferred Investment Size:** Engaged in venture capital management. **Industry Preferences:** Communications and media, Internet specific, computer software and services, computer hardware, semiconductors and other electronics, medical and health, industrial and energy, biotechnology, consumer related, and other products.

37425 ■ Lucas Venture Group (LVG)
545 Middlefield Rd., Ste. 220
Menlo Park, CA 94025
Co. E-mail: info@lucasvg.com
URL: http://www.lucasvg.com
Contact: Donald A. Lucas, Founder
Description: Venture capital firm. **Industry Preferences:** E-commerce; networking; software analytics; medical devices.

37426 ■ M13
1920 Olympic Blvd.
Santa Monica, CA 90404
URL: http://m13.co
Contact: Anna Barber, Partner
Linkedin: www.linkedin.com/company/m13-company
YouTube: www.youtube.com/channel/UCPChCbT252wiCvGxCdZ9thw
Description: Venture capital firm for scalable technology companies at every stage in lifecycle. Also operates out of New York. **Founded:** 2016.

37427 ■ Matrix Partners
535 Mission St., Ste. 2600
San Francisco, CA 94105
Ph: (650)798-1600
Co. E-mail: info@matrix.vc
URL: http://matrix.vc
Contact: Antonio Rodriguez, Contact
Description: Provider of business solutions for new and growing businesses. **Founded:** 1977. **Preferred Investment Size:** $2,000,000 to $10,000,000. **Industry Preferences:** Communications and media, Internet specific, computer software and services, computer hardware, semiconductors and other electronics.

37428 ■ Mayfield Fund, L.L.C. (MF)
2484 Sand Hill Rd.
Menlo Park, CA 94025
Ph: (650)854-5560
Co. E-mail: info@mayfield.com
URL: http://www.mayfield.com
Contact: Vikram Godse, Managing Partner
Facebook: www.facebook.com/MayfieldFund
Linkedin: www.linkedin.com/company/mayfield-fund
X (Twitter): x.com/MayfieldFund

Description: Investment company that invests in share capital of early stage companies and in turn earns income. **Founded:** 1969. **Preferred Investment Size:** $1,000,000 to $3,000,000. **Industry Preferences:** Computer software and services, computer hardware, Internet specific, communications and media, semiconductors and other electronics, consumer related, industrial and energy and other products.

37429 ■ Media Technology Ventures
200 Page Mill Rd., Ste. 100
Palo Alto, CA 94306
Ph: (650)687-0500
Co. E-mail: businessplans@allegiscyber.com
URL: http://allegiscyber.com
Contact: Tim Eades, Chief Executive Officer
Linkedin: www.linkedin.com/company/allegiscyber
X (Twitter): x.com/allegiscyber
Description: Firm provides investment services in technology, cyber-security, security companies, data analytics and virtualization. **Founded:** 1996. **Preferred Investment Size:** $3,000,000 to $5,000,000. **Industry Preferences:** Communications and media, Internet specific, and computer software and services, other products, computer hardware, semiconductors and other electronics.

37430 ■ Menlo Ventures
2884 Sand Hill Rd., Ste. 100
Menlo Park, CA 94025
Ph: (650)854-8540
Fax: (650)854-7059
Co. E-mail: contact@menlovc.com
URL: http://www.menlovc.com
Contact: Brent Fellows, Director
Linkedin: www.linkedin.com/company/menlo-ventures
X (Twitter): x.com/MenloVentures
Description: Venture capital firm provides investment for seed through growth technology companies. **Founded:** 1976. **Preferred Investment Size:** $5,000,000 to $20,000,000. **Industry Preferences:** Internet specific, communications and media, computer software and services, computer hardware, medical and health, semiconductors and other electronics, biotechnology, consumer related, industrial and energy, and other products.

37431 ■ Mesa Verde Venture Partners
4225 Executive Sq., Ste. 600
La Jolla, CA 92037
Co. E-mail: info@mesaverdevp.com
URL: http://www.mesaverdevp.com
Contact: Carey Ng, PhD, MBA, Managing Director
Description: Early-stage life science venture capital firm. Creates partnerships with entrepreneurs to build successful companies in the Southwest and other traditionally underrepresented areas.. **Founded:** 2006. **Preferred Investment Size:** $250,000 to $1,000,000. **Industry Preferences:** Therapeutics; medical devices; diagnostics; life science tools; healthcare wireless/IT.

37432 ■ MHS Capital
1301 Sansome St.
San Francisco, CA 94111
Co. E-mail: info@mhscapital.com
URL: http://www.mhscapital.com
Contact: Vijay Nagappan, Partner
Description: Early-stage investment firm backed by tech entrepreneurs. **Preferred Investment Size:** $500,000 to $1,000,000. **Investment Policies:** Solves interesting problem; strong product team; large market potential; disruptive advantage; capital efficiency. **Industry Preferences:** Internet; healthcare; education; mobile; ecommerce.

37433 ■ Michael S. Kenny & Company LLC
1710 S Amphlett Blvd., Ste. 302
San Mateo, CA 94402
Ph: (650)727-3985
Co. E-mail: info@michaelskenny.com
URL: http://michaelskenny.com
Contact: Michael S. Kenny, Managing Partner
Facebook: www.facebook.com/kennyandcompany
Linkedin: www.linkedin.com/company/kenny-&-company

X (Twitter): x.com/kennycompanyllc
Description: Management and business consulting firm. Offers strategy, operations, and technology consulting services. Also invests in select startups with high growth potential in disruptive technologies. **Preferred Investment Size:** $25,000 to $100,000.

37434 ■ Millennium Hanson
5855 Uplander Way, Ste. C
Los Angeles, CA 90230
Ph: (310)550-1995
Co. E-mail: corporateliaison@millenniumhanson.com
URL: http://millenniumhanson.com
Contact: Millennium Hanson, Manager
Description: Provider of venture capital for early stage investments. **Founded:** 1999. **Preferred Investment Size:** $1,000,000. **Investment Policies:** Early stage, expansion and acquisition. **Industry Preferences:** Internet specific.

37435 ■ Miramar Digital Ventures (MDV)
2101 E Coast Hwy., Ste. 300
Corona del Mar, CA 92625
Ph: (949)760-4450
Co. E-mail: info@miramarvp.com
URL: http://www.miramarvp.com
Contact: Bob Holmen, Officer
Description: Early-stage investment technology firm,. **Founded:** 2014. **Investment Policies:** Technology-driven companies with proprietary and defensible technology positions offering a competitive edge led by experienced management teams.

37436 ■ Mission Ventures
9255 Towne Centre Dr., Ste. 350
San Diego, CA 92121
Ph: (858)350-2100
URL: http://missionventures.com
Contact: Donna Pierzina, Controller
E-mail: donna@missionventures.com
Description: Company providing financing solutions to businesses. **Preferred Investment Size:** $2,000,000 to $10,000,000. **Industry Preferences:** Firm engaged in the investment for its investor include growth, emerging markets and providing significant assistance to those companies as they develop.

37437 ■ Montreux Growth Partners (MGP)
Four Embarcadero Ctr., Ste. 3720
San Francisco, CA 94111
Ph: (650)234-1200
Fax: (650)234-1250
Co. E-mail: info@mepvc.com
URL: http://www.mepvc.com
Contact: Daniel K. Turner, III, Contact
Description: Growth equity firm. **Founded:** 1993. **Preferred Investment Size:** $10,000,000-20,000,000. **Investment Policies:** Commercial stage companies with highly differentiated products, technologies, and services with $10-$100 million in revenue. **Industry Preferences:** Biopharmaceuticals; medical devices; healthcare.

37438 ■ New Enterprise Associates (NEA)
2855 Sand Hill Rd.
Menlo Park, CA 94025
Ph: (650)854-9499
Fax: (650)687-1854
Co. E-mail: lprelations@nea.com
URL: http://www.nea.com
Contact: Aaron Jacobson, Partner
Facebook: www.facebook.com/NEAvc
Linkedin: www.linkedin.com/company/new-enterprise-associates
Instagram: www.instagram.com/neavc
YouTube: www.youtube.com/user/NEAYVideos
Description: Provider of investments in venture growth equity at all stages. **Founded:** 1977. **Preferred Investment Size:** $200,000 to $20,000,000. **Industry Preferences:** Communications and media, Internet specific, medical and health, computer software and services, computer hardware, semiconductors and other electronics, biotechnology, consumer related, industrial and energy, and other products.

37439 ■ Nexit Ventures
470 Ramona St.
Palo Alto, CA 94301
Co. E-mail: info@nexitventures.com
URL: http://www.nexitventures.com
Contact: Risto Yli-Tainio, Chief Financial Officer Partner
E-mail: risto.yli-tainio@nexitventures.com
Description: Venture capital firm. Invests in disruptive and scalable Nordic companies. Based out of Silicon Valley and Finland. **Founded:** 1999.

37440 ■ Next47 Inc.
Siemens AG
537 Hamilton Ave., 2nd Fl.
Palo Alto, CA 94301
Ph: 49 89 3803 5491
Fax: 49 89 797 6664
Co. E-mail: contact@siemens.com
URL: http://www.siemens.com
Contact: Lak Ananth, Chief Executive Officer
Linkedin: www.linkedin.com/company/next47
X (Twitter): x.com/next47
Description: Global venture firm and accelerator backed by Siemens. **Founded:** 2016.

37441 ■ Nexus Venture Partners
3000 Sand Hill Rd.
Bldg. 1, Ste. 260
Menlo Park, CA 94025
Co. E-mail: plans@nexusvp.com
URL: http://nexusvp.com
Contact: Abhishek Sharma, Partner
E-mail: abhishek@nexusvp.com
Linkedin: www.linkedin.com/company/nexusvp
X (Twitter): x.com/nexusvp
Description: Venture capital firm based in Silicon Valley and India. **Founded:** 2006. **Investment Policies:** Capital-efficient business models; driven entrepreneurs; large market opportunities; innovation addressing a particular customer pain-point; clear differentiation.

37442 ■ Northern Light Venture Capital (NLVC)
2744 Sand Hill Rd., Ste. 100
Menlo Park, CA 94025
Ph: (650)585-5450
Fax: (650)585-5450
Co. E-mail: contact@nlvc.com
URL: http://nlvc.com
Linkedin: www.linkedin.com/company/northern-light-venture-capital
Description: Early-stage venture capital firm focused on China. **Founded:** 2005. **Industry Preferences:** Technology; media; telecommunication; clean technology; healthcare; consumer products.

37443 ■ Norwest Venture Partners XII, LP (NVP)
Wells Fargo & Company
525 University Ave., Ste. 800
Palo Alto, CA 94301
Ph: (415)396-7392
Free: 866-249-3302
Co. E-mail: corpcsf@wellsfargo.com
URL: http://www.wellsfargo.com
Contact: Brit Register Staveley, Director
X (Twitter): x.com/NorwestVP
Description: Investment firm provides venture capital and growth equity investment services for IT and health care sector. **Founded:** 1961. **Preferred Investment Size:** $1,000,000 to $30,000,000. **Industry Preferences:** Internet specific, computer software and services, communications and media, semiconductors and other electronics, consumer related, industrial and energy, medical and health, computer hardware, other products, and biotechnology.

37444 ■ Oak Investment Partners
3000 Sand Hill Rd., Ste. 3-245
Menlo Park, CA 94025
Ph: (650)614-3700
URL: http://www.oakvc.com
Contact: Ann Lamont, Managing Partner
Linkedin: www.linkedin.com/company/oak-investment-partners

Description: Investment firm provides venture capital investments, investment strategy, strategic assistance and management advisor services. **Founded:** 1978. **Preferred Investment Size:** $25,000,000 to $150,000,000. **Industry Preferences:** Communications and media, Internet specific, computer software and services, semiconductors and other electronics, computer hardware, consumer related, medical and health, biotechnology, industrial and energy, and other products.

37445 ■ Odyssey Venture Partners
2350 Mission College Blvd., Ste. 495
Santa Clara, CA 95054
Ph: (650)575-3236
URL: http://odysseyvp.com
Contact: Nikolas Pisanias, Partner
E-mail: npisanias@odysseyvp.com
Description: Funds and supports innovative Greek startups. Also operates out of Athens, Greece. **Industry Preferences:** Information and communication technology (ICT).

37446 ■ Okapi Venture Capital LLC
660 Newport Center Dr., Ste. 1600.
Newport Beach, CA 92660
URL: http://okapivc.com
Contact: Jeff Bocan, Managing Director
Description: Seed and early-stage venture capital fund focused on information technology and life science investments in southern California. **Founded:** 2005. **Investment Policies:** Capital-efficient startups with a sustainable competitive advantage focused growing markets based on early proofs of concept. **Industry Preferences:** Enterprise and consumer technology.

37447 ■ Omidyar Network (ON)
1991 Broadway, Ste. 200
Redwood City, CA 94063
Ph: (650)482-2500
Fax: (650)482-2525
Co. E-mail: info@omidyar.com
URL: http://omidyar.com
Contact: Mike Kubzansky, Chief Executive Officer
Facebook: www.facebook.com/OmidyarNetwork
Linkedin: www.linkedin.com/company/omidyar-network
X (Twitter): x.com/OmidyarNetwork
Description: Philanthropic investment firm committed to creating and fostering opportunity for people around the world. **Founded:** 2004.

37448 ■ Omninet Capital L.L.C.
9420 Wilshire Blvd., Ste. 400
Beverly Hills, CA 90212
Ph: (310)300-4100
Fax: (310)300-4101
Co. E-mail: info@omninet.com
URL: http://omninet.com
Contact: David Martin, Manager
Description: Engages in investing in real estate and venture capital. **Founded:** 1985. **Investment Policies:** Start-up and early stage. **Industry Preferences:** Communications, and Internet specific.

37449 ■ OneTraction
Stanford Research Pk.
3000 El Camino Real
Palo Alto, CA 94306
URL: http://www.onetraction.com
Facebook: www.facebook.com/onetraction
X (Twitter): x.com/OneTraction
Description: Offers on-demand innovation ventures and accelerator programs. **Founded:** 2014.

37450 ■ Onset Ventures
2400 Sand Hill Rd., Ste. 150
Menlo Park, CA 94025
URL: http://onset.com
Contact: Beatrice Pezino, Vice President, Finance
E-mail: finance@onset.com
Linkedin: www.linkedin.com/company/onset-ventures
Description: Venture capital firm specializing in early stage information technology. **Founded:** 1984. **Preferred Investment Size:** $8,000,000 to $12,000,000. **Industry Preferences:** Computer software and services, computer hardware, Internet specific, communications and media, semiconductors and other electronics, medical and health, other products, and biotechnology.

37451 ■ Opus Capital
CA
Ph: (650)543-2900
Co. E-mail: info@opuscapital.com
URL: http://www.opuscapitalventures.com
Contact: Evelyn Lassman, Controller
E-mail: evelyn@opuscapital.com
Description: Early-stage venture capital firm for technology startups. **Founded:** 2005. **Industry Preferences:** Enterprise application software and infrastructure; internet. semiconductors; wireless.

37452 ■ Oracle Venture Fund
500 Oracle Pky.
Redwood City, CA 94065
Ph: (737)867-1000
Free: 800-633-0738
URL: http://www.oracle.com
Facebook: www.facebook.com/Oracle
Linkedin: www.linkedin.com/company/oracle
X (Twitter): x.com/oracle
YouTube: www.youtube.com/oracle
Description: Provider of internet products and services including content management, storage electronic commerce, application services and much more. **Founded:** 1977. **Preferred Investment Size:** $2,000,000 to $5,000,000. **Industry Preferences:** Internet specific, computer software and services, medical and health, biotechnology, communications and media, computer hardware, and other products.

37453 ■ Pacific Ventures Group (PACV)
Los Angeles, CA 90015
Ph: (310)800-4556
Co. E-mail: info@pacvgroup.com
URL: http://pacvgroup.com
Contact: Shannon Masjedi, President
Description: Venture investment group focused on consumer productsI. **Industry Preferences:** Food; beverage; alcohol.

37454 ■ PacRim Venture Partners
535 Middlefield Rd., Ste. 280
Menlo Park, CA 94025
Ph: (650)330-0880
Fax: (650)330-0785
Co. E-mail: info@pacrimpartners.com
URL: http://www.pacrimpartners.com
Contact: Huoy-Ming Yeh, Director
E-mail: myeh@pacrimpartners.com
Description: Private venture capital fund with investors from the United States, Taiwan and Hong Kong. **Founded:** 1999. **Preferred Investment Size:** $100,000 to $2,000,000. **Industry Preferences:** Communications and media, computer hardware and software, Internet specific, semiconductors and other electronics.

37455 ■ Palo Alto Venture Partners
300 Hamilton Ave., 4th Fl.
Palo Alto, CA 94301
Ph: (650)462-1221
URL: http://www.pavp.com
Contact: Peter Ziebelman, Founder
E-mail: pziebelman@pavp.com
Description: Firm is engaged in seed, start up and early venture investments. **Founded:** 1996. **Preferred Investment Size:** $1,000,000 to $10,000,000. **Investment Policies:** Start-up, seed, early and first stage. **Industry Preferences:** Internet specific, computer software and services, communications and media, other products, and consumer related.

37456 ■ Palomar Ventures
18881 Von Karman Ave., Ste. 960
Irvine, CA 92612
Ph: (949)475-9455
Fax: (949)475-9456
Co. E-mail: sortiz@palomarventures.com
URL: http://www.palomarventures.com
Contact: Jim Gauer, Managing Director
E-mail: jgauer@palomarventures.com

Description: Firm providing investment in early stage information technology companies. **Founded:** 1999.

37457 ■ Partech Ventures
200 California St.
  San Francisco, CA 94111
Ph: (415)788-2929
URL: http://partechpartners.com
Contact: Jai Choi, Partner
Facebook: www.facebook.com/PartechPartners
Linkedin: www.linkedin.com/company/partech
X (Twitter): x.com/PartechPartners
Founded: 1982. **Preferred Investment Size:** $1,000,000 to $10,000,000. **Industry Preferences:** Internet specific, computer software, hardware and services, communications and media, semiconductors and other electronics, medical and health, consumer related, biotechnology, industrial and energy.

37458 ■ Pasadena Angels
Pasadena, CA
URL: http://www.pasadenaangels.com
Contact: Mike Krebs, Chairman of the Board
Facebook: www.facebook.com/people/Pasadena-Angels/100064862435521
Linkedin: www.linkedin.com/company/pasadena-angels
X (Twitter): x.com/pasadenaangels
Instagram: www.instagram.com/pasadenaangels
Description: Funds early-stage companies in Southern California. **Founded:** 2000.

37459 ■ Peninsula Ventures
Co. E-mail: info@peninsula.vc
URL: http://peninsula.vc
Description: Venture capital firm for early stage companies. **Investment Policies:** Capital efficiency or scale; disruptive or emerging markets; US-based companies. **Industry Preferences:** Software; infrastructure; core technology.

37460 ■ Persepolis Ventures
San Francisco, CA
Co. E-mail: inquires@persepolisventures.com
URL: http://www.persepolisventures.com
Contact: Ross Khosrovi, Founder Managing Partner
Description: Venture capital firm for seed stage healthcare companies. **Investment Policies:** Early proof of concept; optimal clinical and regulatory path to market; reach financial milestones in the first 12 to 18 months. **Industry Preferences:** Medical devices; digital health.

37461 ■ Phoenix Venture Partners (PVP)
1700 S El Camino Real, Ste. 355
  San Mateo, CA 94402
Ph: (650)349-3467
Fax: (650)349-3469
Co. E-mail: information@phoenix-vp.com
URL: http://phoenix-vp.com
Contact: Dr. Avinash Kant, Partner
Facebook: www.facebook.com/PhoenixVenturePartners
Description: Invests in innovative advanced materials/devices startups. Offers strategic and operational support.

37462 ■ Portfolia
San Mateo, CA 94402
Ph: (650)504-6841
Co. E-mail: info@portfolia.com
URL: http://www.portfolia.co
Contact: Trish Costello, Chief Executive Officer
Facebook: www.facebook.com/Portfolia1
Linkedin: www.linkedin.com/company/portfolia
X (Twitter): x.com/Portfolia1
Description: Seeks to create a best-in-class culture and community to empower women to invest in innovative companies with outsized potential for returns and imipact. Offers women the opportunity to learn about venture investing by watching pitch calls and doing diligence. Invests in emerging knowledge and solutions to improve longevity and vitality; also funds early-stage and growth companies in the US where people of color and LBGTQ investors see opportunities. **Founded:** 2013.

37463 ■ Prospect Venture Partners
525 University Ave., Ste. 1350
  Palo Alto, CA 94301
Ph: (650)327-8800
URL: http://www.prospectventures.com
Contact: Russell Hirsch, Managing Director
Linkedin: www.linkedin.com/company/prospect-venture-partners-lp
Description: Provider of venture capital investments for biopharmaceutical and medical device companies. **Founded:** 1997. **Preferred Investment Size:** $500,000 to $10,000,000. **Industry Preferences:** Biotechnology, medical and health, computer software and services, semiconductors and other electronics.

37464 ■ Quest Venture Partners (QVP)
540 Cowper St., Ste. 201
  Palo Alto, CA 94301
URL: http://www.questvp.com
Contact: Andrew Ogawa, Managing Partner
  Co-Founder
Description: Early stage venture capital firm. **Founded:** 2007.

37465 ■ Rally Ventures
702 Oak Grove Ave.
  Menlo Park, CA 94025
Ph: (650)854-1200
Co. E-mail: marketing@rallyventures.com
URL: http://www.rallyventures.com
Contact: Stephanie McCoy, Chief Financial Officer
Linkedin: www.linkedin.com/company/rallyventures
X (Twitter): x.com/rallyvc
Description: Invests in early-stage business technology companies. **Founded:** 2012. **Industry Preferences:** Big data; cloud technologies; infrastructure software; mobility; IoT; SaaS; security; storage.

37466 ■ Redleaf Venture Management
14395 Saratoga Ave., Ste. 130
  Saratoga, CA 95070
Contact: John D. Kohler, Contact
Preferred Investment Size: $1,000,000 to $20,000,000. **Industry Preferences:** Computer software and services, Internet specific, medical and health, communications and media, consumer related, and other products.

37467 ■ Rembrandt Venture Partners (RVP)
325 Sharon Pk. Dr., Ste. 325
  Menlo Park, CA 94025
Ph: (415)528-2900
Fax: (415)528-2901
Co. E-mail: inquiries@rembrandtvc.com
URL: http://rembrandtvc.com
Contact: Pauline Duffy, Chief Financial Officer
Description: Firm provides venture capital investment services. **Founded:** 2004. **Investment Policies:** Provider of capital management services. **Industry Preferences:** Communications, and Internet specific.

37468 ■ Ribbit Capital
364 University Ave.
  Palo Alto, CA 94301
URL: http://www.ribbitcap.com
Contact: Denise Gilbert, Contact
Description: Financial technology investment firm. Invests in disruptive financial services companies. **Founded:** 2012.

37469 ■ Richmond View Ventures (RVV)
901 Mission St.
  San Francisco, CA 94103
URL: http://rvv.tv
Contact: Julia Steigerwald, Founder
Description: Offers financing, business development, and strategic advice to B2B and B2C startups with high growth potential. Also operates out of Berlin. **Founded:** 2007. **Industry Preferences:** B2B and crowdsourcing; B2C, internet, mobile and media.

37470 ■ Riordan Lewis & Haden (RLH)
10900 Wilshire Blvd., Ste. 850
  Los Angeles, CA 90024
Ph: (310)405-7200
Fax: (310)405-7222
URL: http://www.rlhequity.com
Contact: Adam L. Frankinburger, Partner
E-mail: af@rlhequity.com
Description: Firm engages in private equity, building business, business IT consulting, business process outsourcing, information analytics. **Founded:** 1982. **Preferred Investment Size:** $10,000,000 to $50,000,000. **Industry Preferences:** Computer software, medical and health, consumer related, industrial and energy, transportation, business service, and manufacturing.

37471 ■ Rising Tide
101 Mission St., Ste. 380
  San Francisco, CA 94105
Ph: (650)486-2444
Co. E-mail: info@rtf.vc
URL: http://rtf.vc
Contact: Joseph Kell, Chief Financial Officer
Linkedin: www.linkedin.com/company/risingtidevc
X (Twitter): x.com/RisingTideVC
Description: Stage-agnostic venture capital firm focused on commitments, character, and results. **Founded:** 2007. **Industry Preferences:** Blockchain; healthcare; deep technology; artificial intelligence; .

37472 ■ Rocket Ventures
2200 Sand Hill Rd., Ste. 240
  Menlo Park, CA 94025
Ph: (650)561-9100
URL: http://www.rocketventures.com
Description: Firm provides venture capital and entrepreneurial resources. **Founded:** 2007. **Preferred Investment Size:** $1,000,000 to $8,000,000. **Industry Preferences:** Communications and media, computer software, and Internet specific.

37473 ■ Rubicon Venture Capital
CA
URL: http://www.rubicon.vc
Contact: Andrew Romans, Partner
Description: Venture capital firm backs software and internet technology companies in North America, the UK, and Northern Europe at the Late Seed, Series A, and Series B stages. Also operates out of New York. **Industry Preferences:** Artificial intelligence; machine learning; enterprise SaaS; big data; fintech; mobile; marketing tech; hospitality tech; B2B; B2C.

37474 ■ Runa Capital
459 Hamilton Ave., Office, Ste. 306
  Palo Alto, CA 94301
Ph: (650)644-1122
Linkedin: www.linkedin.com/company/runacapital
X (Twitter): x.com/runacapital
Description: Venture capital firm for tech companies. **Founded:** 2010. **Preferred Investment Size:** $1,000,000 to $10,000,000.

37475 ■ Sail Capital Partners
3161 Michelsen Dr., Ste. 750
  Irvine, CA 92612-4432
URL: http://www.sailcapital.com
Contact: Walter Schindler, Officer
Facebook: www.facebook.com/SAILCapital
Description: Venture capital firm for the cleantech sector. **Founded:** 2002. **Investment Policies:** Prefers customer-focused companies with realistic potential for positive cash flow. **Industry Preferences:** Energy; green innovation.

37476 ■ Saints Ventures
2020 Union St.
  San Francisco, CA 94123
Ph: (415)773-2080
URL: http://www.saintscapital.com
Contact: Allison Goldberg, Partner
X (Twitter): x.com/SaintsVentures
Description: Company offers liquidity solutions to investment companies. **Founded:** 2000. **Preferred Investment Size:** $5,000,000 to $100,000,000. **Investment Policies:** Special situation and acquisition. **Industry Preferences:** Consumer related, industrial, computer software, and Internet specific.

37477 ■ San Joaquin Angels (SJA)
c/o San Joaquin Partnership/Business Council In
2800 W March Ln., Ste. 470
Stockton, CA 95219
URL: http://sanjoaquinangels.weebly.com
Contact: Mark Plovnick, President
E-mail: mplovnick@pacific.edu
Description: Angel investment group investing in early-stage companies.

37478 ■ Sandalwood Ventures
100 Broadway St.
San Francisco, CA 94111
URL: http://www.sandalwoodventures.com
Linkedin: www.linkedin.com/company/sandalwood-ventures
Description: Boutique venture firm. **Founded:** 2017.

37479 ■ Sanderling Ventures
1300 S El Camino Real., Ste. 203
San Mateo, CA 94402
Ph: (650)401-2000
Fax: (650)375-7077
Co. E-mail: info@sanderling.com
URL: http://www.sanderling.com
Contact: Fred Middleton, Managing Director
Description: Firm provides investment services. **Founded:** 1979.

37480 ■ Sapphire Ventures (SV)
3408 Hillview Ave., Bldg. 5
Palo Alto, CA 94304
Ph: (650)382-1110
Co. E-mail: info@sapphireventures.com
URL: http://sapphireventures.com
Contact: Jai Das, President
YouTube: www.youtube.com/channel/UCU15ELvJ1AcdL-c_-n_JCjQ
Description: Venture capital firm investing in early- and expansion-stage technology companies in the US, Europe, and Israel. **Founded:** 1996.

37481 ■ Scale Capital
860 Via De La Paz E-1
Pacific Palisades, CA 90272
Co. E-mail: hello@scalecapital.com
URL: http://scalecapital.com
Contact: Kenneth Grunow, Partner
E-mail: kenneth@scalecapital.com
Description: Early-stage venture fund investing in Nordic scalable technology companies interested in entering the US market; focused on digitization, AI, and analytics. **Investment Policies:** Innovative technologies; scalable business models. **Industry Preferences:** Digitization; AI; analytics.

37482 ■ Scale Venture Partners
950 Tower Ln., Ste. 1150
Foster City, CA 94404
Ph: (650)378-6000
Fax: (650)378-6040
Co. E-mail: hello@scalevp.com
URL: http://www.scalevp.com
Contact: Alex Niehenke, Partner
E-mail: alex@scalevp.com
Facebook: www.facebook.com/scalevp
Linkedin: www.linkedin.com/company/scale-venture-partners
X (Twitter): x.com/scalevp
Description: Venture capital firm for companies building intelligent software. **Founded:** 2000. **Industry Preferences:** SaaS; cloud computing; mobile; internet.

37483 ■ SDL Ventures
4984 El Camino Real, Ste. 230
Los Altos, CA 94022
Ph: (650)559-9355
Fax: (650)559-9353
Co. E-mail: llewis@sdlventures.com
URL: http://www.sdlventures.com
Contact: Don Scifres, Managing Director
Description: Early-stage investment firm for technology and communications companies. **Preferred Investment Size:** $500,000 to $2,000,000. **Investment Policies:** Founders who are market insiders and offer significant sustainable technical advantage; meets unmet customer needs to ultimately address similar needs in the same (or adjacent) industry segments. **Industry Preferences:** Green technology; internet; medical and healthcare solutions; biotechnology.

37484 ■ Selby Venture Partners
PO Box Q
Menlo Park, CA 94026
Ph: (650)300-5882
URL: http://www.selbyventures.com
Contact: Doug Barry, Managing Director
E-mail: doug@selbyventures.com
Description: Firm provides investment services for developing software, information technology, communications and consumer sectors. **Founded:** 1998. **Preferred Investment Size:** $500,000 to $7,000,000. **Industry Preferences:** Internet specific, communications and media, consumer related, computer software, and services, computer hardware, semiconductors and other electronics.

37485 ■ Sequoia Capital
2800 Sand Hill Rd.
Menlo Park, CA 94025
Linkedin: www.linkedin.com/company/sequoia
Description: Venture capital firm provides investment services. **Founded:** 1972. **Preferred Investment Size:** $100,000 to $100,000,000. **Industry Preferences:** Internet specific, communications and media, computer software and services, computer hardware, other products, semiconductors and other electronics, medical and health, consumer related, biotechnology, industrial and energy.

37486 ■ Shepherd Ventures
5590 Meadows Del Mar
San Diego, CA 92130
Ph: (619)742-8228
Co. E-mail: info@shepherdventures.com
URL: http://shepherdventures.com
Contact: Tom Siegel, Managing Director
Description: Venture capital firm for technology and life sciences companies in Southern California and the Southwest. **Founded:** 2001. **Investment Policies:** Experienced management teams; compelling value propositions; extraordinary upside potential. **Industry Preferences:** Information technology; life sciences.

37487 ■ Sherpalo Ventures
2475 Hanover St., Ste. 100
Palo Alto, CA 94304
Co. E-mail: info@sherpalo.com
URL: http://www.sherpalo.com
Contact: Ram Shriram, Contact
Description: Mentor capital firm that supports the development and commercialization of early stage disruptive new technologies. **Founded:** 2000.

37488 ■ Shoreline Venture Management L.L.C.
3 Embarcadero Ctr, 26th Fl.
San Francisco, CA 94111
URL: http://shorelineventures.com
Contact: Bob Spears, Director
E-mail: rspears@shorelineventures.com
Description: Investment firm provides venture capital, partner funds, future funds and investment services for IT and health care sectors. **Founded:** 1998. **Investment Policies:** Seed and early stage. **Industry Preferences:** Consumer related, computer software and services, information technology, and medical and health.

37489 ■ Sierra Ventures
1400 Fashion Island Blvd., Ste. 1010
San Mateo, CA 94404
Ph: (650)854-1000
Co. E-mail: info@sierraventures.com
URL: http://www.sierraventures.com
Contact: Sarah Recinos, Office Manager
E-mail: sarah@sierraventures.com
Facebook: www.facebook.com/SierraVentures
Linkedin: www.linkedin.com/company/sierra-ventures
X (Twitter): x.com/Sierra_Ventures
Description: Firm provides investments in consumer and enterprise information technology. **Founded:** 1981. **Preferred Investment Size:** $2,000,000 to $25,000,000. **Industry Preferences:** Internet specific, computer software and services, computer hardware, communications and media, semiconductors and other electronics, industrial and energy, biotechnology, and consumer related.

37490 ■ Sigma Partners
2105 S Bascom Ave., Ste. 370.
Campbell, CA 95008
Ph: (650)853-1700
Fax: (650)853-1717
Co. E-mail: info@sigmapartners.com
URL: http://www.sigmapartners.com
Description: Venture capital firm specializing in startups, early stage and mid venture companies. **Founded:** 1984. **Preferred Investment Size:** $2,000,000 to $8,000,000. **Industry Preferences:** Internet specific, computer hardware, computer software and services, communications and media, semiconductors and other electronics, consumer related, and other products.

37491 ■ Skyline Ventures
525 University Ave., Ste. 1350
Palo Alto, CA 94301
Ph: (650)462-5800
Fax: (650)329-1090
URL: http://www.skylineventures.com
Contact: Eric M. Gordon, Co-Founder
Description: Firm provides investment services on healthcare companies such as molecule and protein therapeutics and medical devices. **Founded:** 1997. **Preferred Investment Size:** $15,000,000 to $25,000,000.

37492 ■ Sofinnova Ventures
3000 Sand Hill Rd., Bldg. 4, Ste. 250
Menlo Park, CA 94025
Ph: (650)681-8420
Fax: (650)322-2037
Co. E-mail: info@sofinnova.com
URL: http://www.sofinnova.com
Contact: Eric Delbridge, Manager
Linkedin: www.linkedin.com/company/sofinnova-partners
Description: Venture capital firm investing in internet, telecommunications and life-sciences seed stage and start-up companies. **Founded:** 1974. **Preferred Investment Size:** $100,000 to $30,000,000. **Industry Preferences:** Internet specific, computer software and services, computer hardware, communications and media, semiconductors and other electronics, and other products.

37493 ■ Storm Ventures
532 Emerson St.
Palo Alto, CA 94301
URL: http://www.stormventures.com
Contact: Arun Penmetsa, Partner
E-mail: arun@stormventures.com
Facebook: www.facebook.com/StormVentures
Linkedin: www.linkedin.com/company/storm-ventures
X (Twitter): x.com/stormventures
Description: Venture capital firm specializing in incubating and early-stage funding for information technology and networking companies. **Founded:** 2000. **Industry Preferences:** Mobile; SaaS; cloud computing.

37494 ■ Streamlined Ventures
University Ave.
Palo Alto, CA 94301
URL: http://www.streamlined.vc
Contact: Ullas Naik, Founder Partner
Linkedin: www.linkedin.com/company/streamlined-ventures
X (Twitter): x.com/streamlinedvc
Founded: 2013.

37495 ■ Strive Capital, Inc.
201 Spear St., Ste. 1100
San Francisco, CA 94105
Co. E-mail: report@strivecap.com
URL: http://www.strivecap.com

Contact: Nuno Gonçalves Pedro, Director
X (Twitter): x.com/strivecapital
Description: Early-stage venture capital firm investing exclusively in mobile companies. **Founded:** 2011. **Investment Policies:** Traction from end-users: reviews user adoption, retention, engagement, and sentiment. Also considers business models and operational models.

37496 ■ Summit Partners
200 Middlefield Rd., Ste. 200
 Menlo Park, CA 94025
Ph: (650)321-1166
Fax: (650)321-1188
URL: http://www.summitpartners.com
Contact: Peter Y. Chung, Chief Executive Officer
Linkedin: www.linkedin.com/company/summit-partners
X (Twitter): x.com/summitpartners
Description: Venture capital firm provides investment services. **Founded:** 1984. **Preferred Investment Size:** $5,000,000 to $500,000,000. **Industry Preferences:** Computer software and services, computer hardware, communications and media, Internet specific, semiconductors and other electronics, medical and health, business services, consumer related, biotechnology, industrial and energy, and other products.

37497 ■ Sutter Hill Ventures
755 Page Mill Rd., Ste. A- 200
 Palo Alto, CA 94304
Ph: (650)493-5600
Fax: (650)858-1854
Co. E-mail: shv@shv.com
URL: http://shv.com
Contact: James White, Manager
Description: Firm provides venture capital management services. **Founded:** 1962. **Preferred Investment Size:** $100,000 to $10,000,000. **Industry Preferences:** Private companies.

37498 ■ SV Angel (SVA)
950 mason St. Unit 1299
 San Francisco, CA 94108
URL: http://svangel.com
Contact: Topher Conway, Managing Partner
Linkedin: www.linkedin.com/company/sv-angel
X (Twitter): x.com/svangel
Description: Angel investment firm. Assists startups with financing, business development, and strategy. **Founded:** 2009.

37499 ■ SV Frontier
San Francisco, CA
Co. E-mail: info@svfrontier.com
URL: http://www.svfrontier.com
Contact: Yozo Suzuki, Founder
Facebook: www.facebook.com/svfrontier
Description: Venture capital fund for Japanese investors. Also offers consulting, business development, and employee training assistance. **Founded:** 2013.

37500 ■ Synopsys Inc.
Synopsys Inc.
 675 Almanor Ave.
 Sunnyvale, CA 94085
Ph: (650)584-5000
Free: 800-541-7737
Co. E-mail: contact@synopsys.com
URL: http://www.synopsys.com
Contact: Sassine Ghazi, President
Facebook: www.facebook.com/Synopsys
Linkedin: www.linkedin.com/company/synopsys
X (Twitter): twitter.com/synopsys
YouTube: www.youtube.com/user/synopsys
Description: Engaged in the provision of electronic design automation software, intellectual property products including pre-designed circuits, and technical support services and tools used by designers across the silicon-to-software spectrum, from engineers creating advanced semiconductors to software developers seeking to ensure the quality and security of their applications across a wide variety of industries including electronics, financial services, media, automotive, medicine, energy and industrials.

Founded: 1986. **Publications:** "Synopsys Insight "; "Design Ware Technical Bulletin"; "Verification Avenue Technical Bulletin"; "Synopsys Journal"; "Flexible Analysis is Key to Power Integrity," Oct, 2008; "Accelerate Rolls Power Plan," Oct, 2008; "Synopsys bets on mixed-signal implementation market," Sep, 2008; "Full frontal attack," Sep, 2008; "Synopsys revamps IC Complier with multi-threaded routing technology," May, 2008. **Training:** Verification Acceleration with CHIP it Automated Rapid Prototyping Series; Custom Design Solution Series; FPGA Implementation Series; Galaxy 2009Series; Introduction to 3GPP LTE Series; Manufacturing Asia Pacific Seminar Series; Reducing Costs and Improving Competitiveness for all your ASIC Projects; Reduce Semiconductor Technology Development Time and Cost; Hands-on Training for Synopsys Tools and Methodologies. **Educational Activities:** OSSC Annual Meeting (Annual). **Preferred Investment Size:** $500,000 to $5,000,000. **Industry Preferences:** Semiconductors and other electronics, computer software and services, manufacturing, and computer hardware. **Special Services:** Galaxy; Discovery; DesignWare IP.

37501 ■ TA Associates Management L.P.
64 Willow Pl., Ste. 100
 Menlo Park, CA 94025
Ph: (650)473-2200
URL: http://www.ta.com
Contact: Todd R. Crockett, Managing Director
E-mail: tcrockett@ta.com
Linkedin: www.linkedin.com/company/ta-associates
X (Twitter): x.com/taassociates
Description: Provider of investment and financial services. **Founded:** 1968. **Preferred Investment Size:** $60,000,000 to $500,000,000. **Industry Preferences:** Computer software and services, other products, communications and media, Internet specific, medical and health, semiconductors and other electronics, consumer related, computer hardware, financial and business services, medical and health.

37502 ■ Tallwood Venture Capital
325 Lytton Ave., Ste. 4A
 Palo Alto, CA 94301
Contact: Cheryl Kudelka, Chief Financial Officer
Description: Firm provides investments semiconductor related technologies products. **Investment Policies:** start-up, early stage, and balanced. **Industry Preferences:** Communications, and semiconductors and other electronics.

37503 ■ TAO Capital Partners
1 Letterman Dr., Ste. C4-420
 San Francisco, CA 94129
URL: http://www.taocap.com
Contact: Isaac E. Pritzker, Manager
Description: Invests in companies at various stages of their lifecycle. **Industry Preferences:** Technology; alternative energy and transportation; healthcare; education; sustainable food and agricultures; consumer; real estate.

37504 ■ Technology Partners
PO Box 1168
 Novato, CA 94948
Ph: (415)332-9999
URL: http://www.technologypartners.com
Contact: Jim Glasheen, Partner
E-mail: jim@technologypartners.com
Description: Involves in venture capital and investment. **Founded:** 1980. **Preferred Investment Size:** $1,000,000 to $15,000,000. **Industry Preferences:** Internet specific, medical and health, communications and media, computer software and services, consumer related, biotechnology, semiconductors and other electronics, computer hardware, industrial and energy, and other products.

37505 ■ TeleSoft Partners
601 California St., 19th Fl.
 San Francisco, CA 94111
Ph: (970)300-4700
Co. E-mail: contact@telesoftvc.com
URL: http://www.telesoftvc.com

Contact: Alan Howard, Chief Financial Officer
Description: Venture capital firm with partners in India, Europe, and Israel. **Founded:** 1996. **Industry Preferences:** Technology and energy.

37506 ■ Tenaya Capital
3280 Alpine Rd.
 Portola Valley, CA 94028
Description: Early-stage venture capital firm. Funds typically at the Series B and Series C stages. Also maintains an office in Wellesley, Mass. **Founded:** 1995. **Industry Preferences:** Software; consumer internet; information technology infrastructure; communication; electronics.

37507 ■ Threshold Ventures
2882 Sand Hill Rd., Ste. 150
 Menlo Park, CA 94025
Ph: (650)231-6900
Co. E-mail: info@threshold.vc
URL: http://threshold.vc
Contact: Emily Melton, Managing Partner
Linkedin: www.linkedin.com/company/thresholdvc
X (Twitter): x.com/thresholdvc
Description: An early-stage venture capital firm focusing on start-up companies involved in emerging markets offering fast growth. **Founded:** 2019.

37508 ■ TiE Silicon Valley (TiE SV)
480 S California Ave.Ste. 201
 Palo Alto, CA 94306
Ph: (408)484-6264
Co. E-mail: programs@tiesv.ai
URL: http://tiesv.ai
Contact: Anita Manwani, President
Facebook: www.facebook.com/TiESiliconValleyChapter
Linkedin: www.linkedin.com/company/tiesv
X (Twitter): x.com/tiesv
YouTube: www.youtube.com/user/tiesiliconvalley
Description: Angel investment group in Silicon Valley. Fosters entrepreneurship through funding, incubation, mentoring, networking, and education. **Founded:** 1992.

37509 ■ TransLink Capital
530 Lytton Ave., Ste. 300
 Palo Alto, CA 94301
Ph: (650)330-7353
Co. E-mail: info@translinkcapital.com
URL: http://translinkcapital.com
Contact: Brian Tomogane, Principal
E-mail: btomogane@translinkcapital.com
Description: Venture capital firm focused on technological companies in Japan, Korea, and Taiwan. Invests at the seed, early, and expansion stages. **Founded:** 2007. **Industry Preferences:** Mobile; cloud computing.

37510 ■ Triangle Peak Partners LP
505 Hamilton Ave., Ste. 300
 Palo Alto, CA 94301
Co. E-mail: info@trianglepeakpartners.com
URL: http://www.trianglepeakpartners.com
Contact: Michael C. Morgan, Chief Executive Officer
X (Twitter): x.com/TrianglePeak
Description: Multi-strategy asset management firm. Specializes in venture capital for technology and growth equity investments in energy. Also maintains offices in Carmel, CA, and Houston, TX.

37511 ■ Trinity Ventures
2480 Sand Hill Rd., Ste. 200
 Menlo Park, CA 94025
Ph: (650)854-9500
Co. E-mail: info@trinityventures.com
URL: http://www.trinityventures.com
Contact: Schwark Satyavolu, Partner
E-mail: schwark@trinityventures.com
Facebook: www.facebook.com/TrinityVentures
Linkedin: www.linkedin.com/company/trinity-ventures
X (Twitter): x.com/trinityventures
Description: Firm operating Investment services. **Founded:** 1986. **Preferred Investment Size:** $5,000,000 to $20,000,000. **Industry Preferences:** Internet specific, computer software and services, computer hardware, communications and media,

37512 ■ True Ventures
501 3rd St.
San Francisco, CA 94107
URL: http://trueventures.com
Contact: Dave Balter, Chief Executive Officer
Facebook: www.facebook.com/trueventures
X (Twitter): x.com/trueventures
Instagram: www.instagram.com/trueventures
Description: Venture capital firm investing in companies and the seed and Series A stages. **Founded:** 2006. **Industry Preferences:** Commerce; infrastructure services; media; mobile; software and services.

37513 ■ TSVC
153 2nd St., Ste. 108
Los Altos, CA 94022
URL: http://www.tsvcap.com
Contact: Chun Xia, Partner
E-mail: chun@tsvcap.com
Linkedin: www.linkedin.com/company/tsvcap
X (Twitter): x.com/TSVCap
Description: Early-stage venture capital firm for deep tech companies. **Founded:** 2010.

37514 ■ Ulu Ventures
115 Everett Ave.
Palo Alto, CA 94301
Co. E-mail: info@uluventures.com
URL: http://uluventures.com
Contact: Miriam Rivera, Chief Executive Officer
E-mail: miriam@uluventures.com
Linkedin: www.linkedin.com/company/ulu-ventures
X (Twitter): x.com/uluventures
Description: Seed stage venture fund for enterprise IT. **Founded:** 2008.

37515 ■ Uncork Capital
4 Palo Alto Sq., Fl. 2
Palo Alto, CA 94306
URL: http://uncorkcapital.com
Contact: Jeff Clavier, Founder Managing Partner
Facebook: www.facebook.com/uncorkcapital
X (Twitter): x.com/uncorkcap
Description: Seed-stage venture capital firm. **Founded:** 2004. **Industry Preferences:** SaaS; consumer and business marketplaces; hardware; VR; vehicle autonomy; blockchain; synthetic biology; bioinformatics.

37516 ■ U.S. Venture Partners (USVP)
1460 El Camino Real, Ste. 100
Menlo Park, CA 94025
Ph: (650)854-9080
Fax: (650)854-3018
Co. E-mail: contact@usvp.com
URL: http://www.usvp.com
Contact: Dale Holladay, Chief Financial Officer
E-mail: dale.h@usvp.com
Facebook: www.facebook.com/people/US-Venture-Partners-USVP/100032983676411
Linkedin: www.linkedin.com/company/u.s.-venture-partners
X (Twitter): x.com/USVP_
YouTube: www.youtube.com/channel/UChnA4oogiplHJWK1v9X78Lw
Description: Venture capital firm provides investment for startup, early-stage, late venture and growth capital. **Founded:** 1981. **Preferred Investment Size:** Venture capital firm. **Industry Preferences:** Internet specific, computer software and services, computer hardware, communications and media, semiconductors and other electronics, consumer related, medical and health, biotechnology, industrial and energy, and other products.

37517 ■ Upfront Ventures
1314 7th St., Ste. 600
Santa Monica, CA 90401
URL: http://upfront.com
Contact: Menyee Wu Zheng, Director
Facebook: www.facebook.com/UpfrontVC
Linkedin: www.linkedin.com/company/upfront-ventures

X (Twitter): x.com/upfrontvc
Instagram: www.instagram.com/upfrontvc
Description: Venture capital firm provides investment services. **Founded:** 1996. **Preferred Investment Size:** $3,000,000 to $25,000,000. **Industry Preferences:** Internet specific, consumer related, business and financial services, computer hardware, computer software and services, communications and media, and other products.

37518 ■ UpHonest Capital
950 Tower Ln., Ste. 2100
Foster City, CA 94404
Contact: Wei Guo, Contact
Description: Early stage venture capital firm. **Founded:** 2016. **Industry Preferences:** Technology, consumer, frontier, health, and enterprise.

37519 ■ Venrock
3340 Hillview Ave.
Palo Alto, CA 94304
Ph: (650)561-9580
Fax: (650)561-9180
URL: http://www.venrock.com
Contact: Bob Kocher, Partner
E-mail: bkocher@venrock.com
Facebook: www.facebook.com/venrock
Linkedin: www.linkedin.com/company/venrock
X (Twitter): x.com/Venrock
Description: Investment firm provides seed, early stage, late-stage, mezzanine, growth capital and first round investments for technology and healthcare sector. **Founded:** 1969. **Preferred Investment Size:** $5,000,000 to $15,000,000. **Industry Preferences:** Biotechnology, Internet specific, computer software and services, computer hardware, communications and media, medical and health, semiconductors and other electronics, industrial and energy, consumer related, and other products.

37520 ■ VentureTech Alliance LLC
2851 Junction Ave.
San Jose, CA 95134
URL: http://www.vtalliance.com
Contact: Becky Degeorge, Contact
Description: Venture investment management for early-stage semiconductor or emerging technology companies. **Founded:** 2001.

37521 ■ Versant Ventures
1 Sansome St., Ste. 3630
San Francisco, CA 94104
Ph: (415)801-8100
URL: http://versantventures.com
Contact: Alexander Mayweg, Managing Director
Linkedin: www.linkedin.com/company/versant-ventures
Founded: 1999. **Industry Preferences:** Healthcare.

37522 ■ Wavemaker Partners
1661 E Franklin Ave.
El Segundo, CA 90245
Co. E-mail: info@wavemaker.vc
URL: http://wavemaker.vc/us
Contact: Eric Manlunas, Founder Managing Partner
Linkedin: www.linkedin.com/company/wavemakerpartners
Description: Early stage venture capital firm. Dual-headquartered in California and Singapore. **Founded:** 2003. **Investment Policies:** Prefers scalable, sustainable, and capital-efficient companies who with thoughtful, mission-driven founders. **Industry Preferences:** Software; digital media.

37523 ■ Webb Investment Network (WIN)
16541 Cypress Way
Los Gatos, CA 95031
Contact: Maynard G. Webb, Chief Executive Officer
Description: Early-stage venture investor. **Founded:** 2010. **Preferred Investment Size:** $500,000 to $750,000 .

37524 ■ Wedbush Capital Partners
1000 Wilshire Blvd., Ste.830
Los Angeles, CA 90017
Ph: (213)688-8080
URL: http://www.wedbushcapital.com

Contact: Eric Wedbush, President
E-mail: eric.wedbush@wedbushcapital.com
Description: Firm provides banking and investment services. **Founded:** 1955. **Preferred Investment Size:** $500,000 minimum. **Industry Preferences:** Equity firm focus on recapitalizations, growth investments and management-led buyouts of lower middle-market companies.

37525 ■ Western States Investment Group (WSIG)
11585 Sorrento Valley Rd., Ste. 105
San Diego, CA 92121
Ph: (858)764-9954
Fax: (858)678-0900
Co. E-mail: info@wsig.com
URL: http://www.wsig.com
Contact: Terry Trzcinka, Liaison
Description: Firm provides investments services and also provides connections and strategic advice to small, emerging growth businesses. **Founded:** 1976. **Preferred Investment Size:** $1,000,000 minimum. **Industry Preferences:** Industrial and energy, medical and health, communications and media, semiconductors and other electronics, computer software and services, and biotechnology.

37526 ■ Western Technology Investment (WTI)
104 La Mesa Dr., Ste. 102
Portola Valley, CA 94028
Ph: (650)234-4300
Fax: (650)234-4343
Co. E-mail: info@westerntech.com
URL: http://www.westerntech.com
Contact: Maurice Werdegar, Chief Executive Officer
Description: Firm providing investment in technology and life sciences sectors. **Founded:** 1980. **Preferred Investment Size:** $250,000 to $30,000,000. **Industry Preferences:** Communications and media, semiconductors and other electronics, biotechnology, medical and health.

37527 ■ The Westly Group
2200 Sand Hill Rd., Ste. 250
Menlo Park, CA 94025
Ph: (650)275-7420
Co. E-mail: plans@westlygroup.com
URL: http://westlygroup.com
Contact: Dave Coglizer, Partner
Linkedin: www.linkedin.com/company/the-westly-group
X (Twitter): x.com/thewestlygroup
Description: Venture capital firm for early and mid-stage energy, utility, and sustainability-focused companies in North America. **Founded:** 2007.

37528 ■ WI Harper Group
50 California St., Ste. 2580
San Francisco, CA 94111
Ph: (415)397-6200
Fax: (415)397-6280
Co. E-mail: info@wiharper.com
URL: http://wiharper.com
Contact: Peter Liu, Chairman
Facebook: www.facebook.com/wiharpergroup
Linkedin: www.linkedin.com/company/wi-harper-group
X (Twitter): x.com/wiharpergroup
Description: Venture capital firm focused on early and expansion investments in China. Also maintains offices in Beijing and Taipei. **Founded:** 1993. **Industry Preferences:** Healthcare; biotech; artificial intelligence; robotics; fintech; insurtech; blockchain; sustainability; new media.

37529 ■ Wildcat Venture Partners (WVP)
2121 S El Camino Real, Ste. 200
San Mateo, CA 94403
Ph: (650)234-4840
Co. E-mail: ideas@wildcat.vc
URL: http://wildcat.vc
Contact: Elisa Jagerson, Managing Director
Linkedin: www.linkedin.com/company/wildcat-venture-partners
X (Twitter): x.com/WildcatVC

Description: Venture capital firms for B2B/B2B2C market disruptors and category leaders leveraging key technologies (machine learning/AI, IoT, and cloud/mobility. **Founded:** 2015. **Industry Preferences:** Digital health; EdTech; enterprise SaaS; FinTech.

37530 ■ Windward Ventures
3016 Tamburlaine Dr.
San Ramon, CA 94582
Contact: Chris Tom, Chief Executive Officer
Description: Firm provides investment management and investment advisory solutions. **Founded:** 1997.

37531 ■ Worldview Technology Partners Inc.
99 S Almaden Blvd., 6th Fl.
San Jose, CA 95113
Ph: (650)322-3800
Co. E-mail: wvfinance@worldview.com
URL: http://www.worldview.com
Description: Firm provides venture capital services focused on investing in technology companies. **Founded:** 1996. **Industry Preferences:** Communications and media, Internet specific, semiconductors and other electronics, computer software, and services, computer hardware, and other products.

37532 ■ Xfund (XF)
390 Lytton Ave.
Palo Alto, CA 94301
Ph: (650)204-1636
Co. E-mail: start@xfund.com
URL: http://www.xfund.com
Contact: Brandon Farwell, Partner
E-mail: brandon@xfund.com
Facebook: www.facebook.com/Xfund
Linkedin: www.linkedin.com/company/xfund
X (Twitter): x.com/xfund
Instagram: www.instagram.com/xfund
Description: Early-stage venture capital firm. Backs entrepreneurs who think laterally and experiment across disciplines. Partners with venture capital firms and research universities. **Founded:** 2014. **Industry Preferences:** Health; consumer; enterprise.

37533 ■ XG Ventures
713 Santa Cruz Ave., Ste. 10
Menlo Park, CA 94025
Co. E-mail: info@xg-ventures.com
URL: http://www.xg-ventures.com
Contact: Pietro Dova, Partner
Facebook: www.facebook.com/xgventures
X (Twitter): x.com/xgventures
Description: Invests in B2C and B2B seed-stage startups. **Founded:** 2008. **Investment Policies:** Innovative products and services. **Industry Preferences:** Mobile; ecommerce; enterprise; consumer; SaaS.

37534 ■ XSeed Capital
3130 Alpine Rd.
Portola Valley, CA 94028
Ph: (650)331-1230
Co. E-mail: info@xseedcap.com
URL: http://xseedcap.com
Contact: Alan Chiu, Partner
Facebook: www.facebook.com/xseedcapital
Linkedin: www.linkedin.com/company/xseed-capital
X (Twitter): x.com/xseedcapital
Description: Supports creative destruction by technological innovators. **Founded:** 2006. **Investment Policies:** Significant differentiation, innovation, and unique customer values. **Industry Preferences:** Software; computer science; IT.

PROCUREMENT ASSISTANCE PROGRAMS

37535 ■ California Procurement Technical Assistance Center - The Federal Technology Center (FTC)
4600 Roseville Rd., Ste. 100
North Highlands, CA 95660
Ph: (916)334-9388
Fax: (916)334-9078
URL: http://www.chchamber.com/list/member/federal-technology-center-the-north-highlands-209
Description: Promotes economic development by facilitating technology transfer between government and the private sector, and by helping small businesses successfully compete for government contracts.

37536 ■ California Procurement Technical Assistance Center - San Diego Contracting Opportunities Center (SDCOC)
880 National City Blvd.
National City, CA 91950
Ph: (619)216-6671
Co. E-mail: swcptac@swccd.edu
URL: http://socalptac.org
Contact: Brett Housholder, Officer
E-mail: bhousholder@swccd.edu
Facebook: www.facebook.com/socalPTAC
Linkedin: www.linkedin.com/company/socalptac
X (Twitter): x.com/socalptac
Instagram: www.instagram.com/socalptac
YouTube: www.youtube.com/channel/UCkDPPIrDFKgfZJpMRUwAB3g
Description: Assists small businesses with the information, resources, and technical assistance they need to effectively compete for and perform on federal, state, and local government contracts. **Founded:** 1994.

INCUBATORS/RESEARCH AND TECHNOLOGY PARKS

37537 ■ 500 Startups
814 Mission St., 6th Fl.
San Francisco, CA 94103
Co. E-mail: legal@500startups.com
URL: http://500.co
Contact: Christine Tsai, Chief Executive Officer
Linkedin: www.linkedin.com/company/500global
YouTube: www.youtube.com/user/500startups
Description: Business incubator providing networking, advice, curriculum, hands-on support and access to investors to startup companies. Also offers 4-month accelerator programs. **Founded:** 2010.

37538 ■ Access to Law Incubator (ALI)
225 Cedar St.
San Diego, CA 92101
URL: http://www.cwsl.edu/student-life/campus-resources/career-and-professional-development-office/students/services-for-students/available-programs
Contact: Matthew A. Lab, Director
E-mail: mlab@cwsl.edu
Description: A program created exclusively for graduates of California Western School of Law who intend to pursue solo practice. The mission is to provide tools and training to empower entrepreneurial and public service.

37539 ■ Access Plus Capital (APC)
1025 Fulton St., 2nd Fl.
Fresno, CA 93721
Ph: (559)263-1351
Fax: (559)263-1094
Co. E-mail: info@accesspluscapital.com
URL: http://www.accesspluscapital.com
Contact: Dorothy Thomas, President
Facebook: www.facebook.com/AccessPlusCapital
Linkedin: www.linkedin.com/company/accesspluscapital
X (Twitter): x.com/AccessPlusCap
YouTube: www.youtube.com/channel/UCxoopplnygScVCVHZt4gi4g
Description: Business incubator that helps startup companies to launch successfully. Offers loans, education, and training. **Founded:** 2008.

37540 ■ The Alchemist Accelerator (AA)
1355 Market St., Ste. 900
San Francisco, CA 94103
Ph: (415)527-0158
URL: http://www.alchemistaccelerator.com
Linkedin: www.linkedin.com/company/alchemistx
X (Twitter): x.com/alchemistacc
Instagram: www.instagram.com/alchemistxii
Description: An accelerator exclusively for startups whose revenue comes from enterprises, not consumers. The accelerator focuses on enterprise customer development, sales (direct and online), market validation, and a structured path to fundraising. **Founded:** 2012.

37541 ■ Ansir Cowork
7670 Opportunity Rd., Ste. 255
San Diego, CA 92111
Ph: (858)598-5025
Co. E-mail: info@ansirsd.com
URL: http://ansirsd.com
Contact: Ping Wang, Co-Founder
Facebook: www.facebook.com/Ansirsd
X (Twitter): x.com/AnsirSD
YouTube: www.youtube.com/channel/UCXC8dth_aV-xACIA4nJkqvg
Description: Startup hub dedicated to nurturing the startup ecosystem. Offers affordable co-working and private office space, meeting space, mentoring, and incubation for qualified companies. **Founded:** 2010.

37542 ■ APC Commercial Kitchen
2550 Monarch St.
Alameda, CA 94501
URL: http://apcollaborative.org/apc-commercial-kitchen
Contact: Suzanne Martin, Contact
E-mail: smartin@apcollaborative.org
Description: Culinary incubator offering commercial kitchen space to entrepreneurs.

37543 ■ Bay Area Kitchen Rental (BAKR)
49103 Milmont Dr.
Fremont, CA 94538
Ph: (510)329-0277
Co. E-mail: info@bayareakitchenrental.com
URL: http://www.bayareakitchenrental.com
Facebook: www.facebook.com/BayAreaKitchenRental
X (Twitter): x.com/bakr_talk
Instagram: www.instagram.com/bakrfremont
Description: Bay area culinary incubator. Offers food startups a hub to run their food business.

37544 ■ Bay Area Legal Incubator (BALI)
125 12th St., Ste. 100-BALI
Oakland, CA 94607
Ph: (510)473-5592
URL: http://www.bayarealegalincubator.org
Contact: Cynthia Chandler, Director
E-mail: cynthia@acbanet.org
Facebook: www.facebook.com/BayAreaLegalIncubator
Instagram: www.instagram.com/bayarealegalincubator
Description: A community of solo attorneys dedicated to providing affordable legal services and promoting social justice. Provides a two-year program to help attorneys accelerate the launch of solo practices serving low-and middle-income clients in a wide spectrum of practice areas.

37545 ■ Baylink LLC
2953 Bunker Hill Ln., Ste. 400
Santa Clara, CA 95054
Ph: (650)861-0299
Co. E-mail: info@baylink-llc.com
URL: http://www.baylink-llc.com
Contact: Dr. Harm TenHoff, Chief Executive Officer
Description: Medical device incubator and business accelerator for businesses in North America and Western Europe. Also operates out of the Netherlands. **Founded:** 2008.

37546 ■ Beckman Laser Institute Photonics Incubator
1002 Health Sciences Rd.
Irvine, CA 92697-1475
URL: http://www.bli.uci.edu/photonic-incubator
Contact: Dr. Arnold O. Beckman, Director

Description: Combines existing facilities, scientific and medical expertise, and extensive corporate contacts with newly constructed facilities to provide a unique, high impact resource for technology transfer in the area of medical photonics.

37547 ■ Berkeley Ventures
727 Allston Way
  Berkeley, CA 94710
Co. E-mail: info@berkeleyventures.com
URL: http://www.berkeleyventures.com
Contact: Barak Berkowitz, Chief Executive Officer
E-mail: chris@berkeleyventures.com

Description: An accelerator which helps serious entrepreneurs bring their innovations to the world. We are focused on helping startups in sectors including, but not limited to, internet, software, mobile, clean energy, and gaming. Offers access to mentors and advisors, introductions to investors, incubator space, connections to local talent/resources, and a year round program to help these companies grow.

37548 ■ blackbox
332 Cowper St.
  Palo Alto, CA 94301
Co. E-mail: info@blackbox.vc
URL: http://www.blackbox.org
Contact: Fadi Bishara, Contact
Facebook: www.facebook.com/blackbox.org
Linkedin: www.linkedin.com/company/blackboxdotorg
X (Twitter): x.com/blackboxvc

Description: An accelerator focused on helping purpose driven entrepreneurs and founders of born global startups learn, collaborate, and grow toward their full potential. **Founded:** 2011.

37549 ■ Blade Fire Labs
1013 Galleria Blvd., Ste. 215
  Roseville, CA 95678
URL: http://www.bladefirelabs.com

Description: Coworking space for startups and entrepreneurs.

37550 ■ Brand Knew (BK)
10351 Santa Monica Blvd., Ste. 200
  Los Angeles, CA 90025
Ph: (310)277-0918
Co. E-mail: info@brand-knew.com
URL: http://brand-knew.com
Contact: Zachary Suchin, Chief Executive Officer
Facebook: www.facebook.com/BrandKnewKnew
X (Twitter): x.com/BrandKnewKnew
Instagram: www.instagram.com/brandknewknew

Description: Accelerator program that provides qualified start-ups with affordable services and a productive, nurturing environment in which to navigate the often unpaved paths that lead nascent ventures on their trajectories towards success.

37551 ■ Business Technology Center of Los Angeles County (BTC)
Altadena, CA
URL: http://www.dogoodla.org/business-technology-center-la-co
Contact: Mark Lieberman, Administrator

Description: The BTC committed to developing high technology firms by providing financial, technical, and business management assistance. **Founded:** 1998.

37552 ■ Calbiotech
1935 Cordell Ct.
  El Cajon, CA 92020
Ph: (619)660-6162
URL: http://calbiotech.com
Contact: Noori Barka, President

Description: Manufacturer and developer of immunoassay products. **Founded:** 1998.

37553 ■ California Business Incubation Alliance (CBIA)
c/o California Technology Council
  5001 Great America Pky., Ste. 210
  Santa Clara, CA 95054
Co. E-mail: join@californiatechnology.org
URL: http://www.californiatechnology.org/cbia

Description: A best practices membership organization serving business incubators and business accelerators.

37554 ■ Capsity
3810 Broadway
  Sacramento, CA 95817
Ph: (916)619-0101
Co. E-mail: tours@capsity.com
URL: http://capsity.com
Contact: Dmitri Godamunne, Chief Executive Officer
Facebook: www.facebook.com/capsitycoworking
Linkedin: www.linkedin.com/company/capsity/about
Instagram: www.instagram.com/capsitycoworking

Description: Provides coworking, virtual, and private office spaces in Sacramento for entrepreneurs looking to develop their business.

37555 ■ Center for Cultural Innovation Arts Project Incubator (CCI)
244 S San Pedro St., Ste. 401
  Los Angeles, CA 90012
Co. E-mail: info@cciarts.org
URL: http://www.cciarts.org/incubator.htm
Contact: Angie Kim, President
E-mail: angie@cciarts.org

Description: Serves as both a "think tank" and research and development lab that works strategically with select teams of funders, artists, researchers, field practitioners and other innovation partners. **Founded:** 2007.

37556 ■ The Chamber Business Incubator
18300 Arosa Rd
  Tehachapi, CA 93561
Ph: (661)972-6346
URL: http://www.chamber101.com/2programs_committee/incubator/The%20Chamber.html

Description: Provides space, services, office equipment, group discounts and other services so that small businesses will be better equipped to succeed.

37557 ■ City of Coachella
53990 Enterprise Way
  Coachella, CA 92236
Ph: (760)398-3502
Fax: (760)888-1943
URL: http://www.coachella.org
Contact: Jason L. Rector, Founder
Facebook: www.facebook.com/yourcoachella
Linkedin: www.linkedin.com/company/city-of-coachella
X (Twitter): x.com/cityofcoachella
Instagram: www.instagram.com/officialcityofcoachella
YouTube: www.youtube.com/channel/UCNarFWjW6dMs57G2tDZ0PzA

Description: Business incubator aiding business startups and entrepreneurs. **Founded:** 1946.

37558 ■ CleanStart
801 K St., 28th Fl.
  Sacramento, CA 95814
Co. E-mail: info@cleanstart.org
URL: http://cleanstart.org
Contact: Thomas Hall, Executive Director
Facebook: www.facebook.com/CleanStartSacramento
Linkedin: www.linkedin.com/company/cleanstart-sacramento
X (Twitter): x.com/CleanTechSac
Instagram: www.instagram.com/cleanstart.inc

Description: Firm provides development of clean technology ventures. **Founded:** 2005.

37559 ■ The Cleantech Open
1000 N Alameda St., Ste. 240
  Los Angeles, CA 90012
Free: 888-989-6736
Co. E-mail: contact@cleantechopen.org
URL: http://www.cleantechopen.org/en
Contact: Rex Northen, Chief Executive Officer
Facebook: www.facebook.com/Cleantechopen
X (Twitter): x.com/cleantechopen

Description: Business accelerator that finds, funds and fosters entrepreneurs with big ideas that address today's most urgent energy, environmental and economic challenges. **Founded:** 2005.

37560 ■ Community Law Practice Incubator (CLPI)
301 Battery St., 3rd Fl.
  San Francisco, CA 94111
URL: http://www.americanbar.org/groups/delivery_legal_services/initiatives_awards/program_main/program_directory
Contact: Hamid Yazdan Panah, Coordinator
E-mail: hpanah@sfbar.org

Description: Legal incubator serving the professional needs of attorneys within their first three years of practice, and expand access to affordable legal services for low income persons.

37561 ■ Community Legal Aid SoCal (LEAP)
2101 N Tustin Ave.
  Santa Ana, CA 92705
Ph: (714)571-5200
URL: http://www.communitylegalsocal.org
Contact: Mei Tsang, President
Facebook: www.facebook.com/CommunityLegalAidSoCal
Linkedin: www.linkedin.com/company/communitylegalaidsocal
X (Twitter): x.com/LegalAidSoCal
Instagram: www.instagram.com/cla_socal
YouTube: www.youtube.com/user/LegalAidSocietyofOC

Description: Incubator that supplements the traditional law school curriculum by giving participants hands on, practical experience they need to successfully launch their own solo community. **Founded:** 1958.

37562 ■ Cowork Tahoe
3079 Harrison Ave., Ste. 12
  South Lake Tahoe, CA 96150
Ph: (530)600-3447
Co. E-mail: info@tahoemountainlab.com
URL: http://coworktahoe.com
Contact: David Orr, Co-Founder
Facebook: www.facebook.com/tahoemtnlab
X (Twitter): x.com/coworktahoe

Description: Firm provides co-working space for freelancers, entrepreneurs and remote workers. **Founded:** 2014.

37563 ■ Cuesta College - Business & Entrepreneurship Center (BEC)
26455 Rockwell Canyon Rd.
  Santa Clarita, CA 91355
URL: http://cocsbdc.org/partner/the-business-entrepreneurship-center-at-cuesta-college

Description: Works with public, private, and nonprofit resources to build strong and sustainable businesses. Offers assistance with marketing strategies and research, strategic planning, business plan creation, financial analysis, and business law.

37564 ■ Daly City Business Center
355 90 th St.
  Daly City, CA 94015
Ph: (650)991-8000
URL: http://www.dalycity.org
Facebook: www.facebook.com/dalycitygov
X (Twitter): x.com/dalycitygov
Instagram: www.instagram.com/dalycitygov
YouTube: www.youtube.com/user/DalyCityGov

Description: A small business incubator providing a proven growth environment for small businesses and entrepreneurs. **Founded:** 1995.

37565 ■ Digital Media Center (DMC)
2323 N Broadway
  Santa Ana, CA 92706-1640
URL: http://rsccd.edu/Departments/Educational-Services/Pages/Digital-Media-Center.aspx

Description: Provides business development education, leadership, and resources for creating innovative digital media businesses. **Founded:** 2006.

37566 ■ Downtown Works
550 W B St., 4th Fl.
  San Diego, CA 92101
Free: 888-535-9675
Co. E-mail: help@downtownworks.com
URL: http://www.downtownworks.com

Contact: Candace Vanderbilt, Manager
E-mail: candace@downtownworks.com
Facebook: www.facebook.com/downtownworks
Linkedin: www.linkedin.com/company/down
 townworks
X (Twitter): x.com/downtownworks
Instagram: www.instagram.com/downtownworks
Description: A coworking community for entrepreneurs, offering open desks, exclusive desks, private offices, virtual offices, flexible meeting rooms, podcast room, and video conferencing. **Founded:** 2016.

37567 ■ El Pajjaro Community Development Corp.
23 E Beach St., Ste. 209
 Watsonville, CA 95076
Ph: (831)722-1224
Fax: (831)722-3128
URL: http://www.elpajarocdc.org
Contact: Carmen Herrera-Mansir, Executive Director
Facebook: www.facebook.com/elpajarocdc
Instagram: www.instagram.com/elpajarocdc
Description: A small business incubator with more than twenty years of experience in the provider of bilingual/bicultural small business assistance and job creation for primarily minority and low-income entrepreneurs. **Founded:** 1979.

37568 ■ EvoNexus
5015 Shoreham Pl., Ste. 150
 San Diego, CA 92122
Co. E-mail: info@evonexus.org
URL: http://evonexus.org
Contact: Marco Thompson, President
Facebook: www.facebook.com/EvoNexus
Linkedin: www.linkedin.com/company/evonexus
X (Twitter): x.com/evonexus
Instagram: www.instagram.com/evonexus_incubator
Description: A startup technology incubator for Southern California's startup community helping entrepreneurs turn their ideas into formidable, commercially-viable companies. **Founded:** 2008.
Geographic Preference: Local.

37569 ■ Foodworks Culinary Center
736 F St.
 Arcata, CA 95521
Ph: (707)822-5951
Co. E-mail: citymgr@cityofarcata.org
URL: http://www.cityofarcata.org
Contact: David Loya, Director, Development
E-mail: dloya@cityofarcata.org
Facebook: www.facebook.com/cityofarcata
Instagram: www.instagram.com/cityofarcata
Description: Designed to facilitate small and start up food manufacturing businesses in support of Arcata's niche foods sector.

37570 ■ Foothill Entrepreneur Center (FEC)
12345 El Monte Rd.
 Los Altos Hills, CA 94022
Ph: (650)949-7325
URL: http://www.foothillentrepreneurs.com
Description: Firm educates students and community residents with business skills and leadership qualities needed to compete in the global market.

37571 ■ Founder Institute (FI)
265 Cambridge Ave., No. 60417
 Palo Alto, CA 94306
Co. E-mail: help@fi.co
URL: http://fi.co
Contact: Jonathan Greechan, Chief Executive Officer
Facebook: www.facebook.com/FounderInstitute
Linkedin: www.linkedin.com/school/the-founder-insti
 tute
X (Twitter): x.com/founding
Instagram: www.instagram.com/founding
YouTube: www.youtube.com/c/founderinstitute
Description: A pre-seed startup launch program for talented entrepreneurs with chapters in 65 countries. Provides a comprehensive step-by-step program that provides mentor support and other resources. **Founded:** 2009.

37572 ■ Founders Embassy (FE)
2398 Pacifiv Ave.
 San Francisco, CA 94115
Ph: (415)416-2750
Co. E-mail: founders@foundersembassy.com
URL: http://www.foundersembassy.com
Contact: Anastasia Crew, Co-Founder
Facebook: www.facebook.com/foundersembassy
X (Twitter): x.com/foundersembassy
Description: Equity-free accelerator designed for international and immigrant entrepreneurs. Offers access to Silicon Valley through bootcamp-style acceleration programs, events, and education. **Founded:** 2016.

37573 ■ Founders Space
450 Townsend St.
 San Francisco, CA 94107
Ph: (650)224-4344
URL: http://www.foundersspace.com
Contact: Steve Hoffman, Chief Executive Officer
Linkedin: www.linkedin.com/in/foundersspace
X (Twitter): x.com/foundersspace
Instagram: www.instagram.com/foundersspace
YouTube: www.youtube.com/c/FoundersSpace
Description: Small business accelerator & incubator for startups, helping talented entrepreneurs reach their full potential. Offers classes, workshops, mentoring sessions, and marketing plans.

37574 ■ Gateway
330 2nd St., 3rd Fl.
 Oakland, CA 94607
Co. E-mail: info@gtwy.co
URL: http://www.gtwy.co
Facebook: www.facebook.com/gatewayvc
Linkedin: www.linkedin.com/company/gateway
 -incubator
X (Twitter): twitter.com/gatewayvc
Instagram: www.instagram.com/gateway.vc
YouTube: www.youtube.com/channel/
 UCxOQs0sNrcH8_fxcaqB-eOA
Description: A business accelerator and seed investment program born out of Silicon Valley and located in the capital of cannabis advocacy and innovation. **Founded:** 2015.

37575 ■ Gateway Incubator, LLC
330 2nd St., 3rd Fl.
 Oakland, CA 94607
Contact: Carter Laren, Contact
Description: Business accelerator and seed investment program focused on cannabis advocacy and innovation.

37576 ■ Global Entrepreneurship Institute (GEI)
668 N Coast Hwy., Ste. 254
 Laguna Beach, CA 92651
URL: http://gcase.org
Contact: Robert W. Price, Executive Director
Linkedin: www.linkedin.com/company/gcaseorg
Description: Helps entrepreneurs launch new businesses, grow them across national borders, and create wealth for their shareholders. **Founded:** 1996.

37577 ■ Goleta Entrepreneurial Magnet (GEM)
130 Cremona Dr., Ste. B
 Goleta, CA 93117
Co. E-mail: info@goletaentrepreneurs.com
URL: http://goletaentrepreneurs.com
Contact: Jaime Valdez, Contact
Description: Provides critical support to new and growing science and technology entrepreneurs. **Founded:** 2012.

37578 ■ HanaHaus
456 University Ave.
 Palo Alto, CA 94301
Ph: (650)326-1263
Co. E-mail: info@hanahaus.com
URL: http://www.hanahaus.com
Contact: Dr. Hasso Plattner, Co-Founder
X (Twitter): x.com/hanahaus
YouTube: www.youtube.com/hanahaus
Description: Community workspace providing a culture of technology innovation, used by startups and entrepreneurs. **Founded:** 2015.

37579 ■ HAX Boost
479 Jessie St.
 San Francisco, CA 94103
URL: http://hax.co
Contact: Inder Sachdev, Director
Linkedin: www.linkedin.com/company/hax
X (Twitter): twitter.com/hax_co
Instagram: www.instagram.com/hax_co
Description: Hardware accelerator firm provides HAX covers invention, prototyping, sourcing, manufacturing, packaging, supply chain, strategy, marketing, distribution, fundraising, and financing. **Founded:** 2012.

37580 ■ Highway1
1040 Mariposa St.
 San Francisco, CA 94107
Co. E-mail: hello@highway1.io
URL: http://highway1.io
Description: A four-month tailored startup accelerator for design and development of your product and business, engineering for scale, and fundraising. Accepts up to 10 startups twice each year. **Founded:** 2013.

37581 ■ The Hood Kitchen Space
350 Clinton St., Ste. A
 Costa Mesa, CA 92626
Ph: (714)549-2430
URL: http://www.thehoodkitchen.com
Facebook: www.facebook.com/thehoodkitchenspace
Instagram: www.instagram.com/thehoodkitchen
Description: Culinary incubator with commercial kitchen space offered to entrepreneurs. **Founded:** 2012.

37582 ■ i3 Advanced Technology Incubator
26455 Rockwell Canyon Rd.
 Santa Clarita, CA 91355
Ph: (661)362-3241
Facebook: www.facebook.com/i3-Advanced-Technol
 ogy-Incubator-16820221614
Linkedin: www.linkedin.com/in/i3advancedincubator
Description: Business incubator providing support services to startups and entrepreneurs.

37583 ■ Imagine K12
335 Pioneer Way
 Mountain View, CA 94041
Co. E-mail: info@imaginek12.com
URL: http://www.imaginek12.com
Contact: Karen Lien, Director
Facebook: www.facebook.com/imaginek12
X (Twitter): x.com/imaginek12
Description: Accelerates education technology startups. **Founded:** 2011.

37584 ■ InCube Ventures, LLC
2051 Ringwood Ave.
 San Jose, CA 95131
Ph: (408)457-3700
Co. E-mail: contact@incubevc.com
URL: http://www.incubevc.com
Contact: Mir Imran, Founder
Description: Invests in promising, innovative life sciences companies. Venture arm of InCube Labs. **Founded:** 2008.

37585 ■ Indie Bio
479 Jessie St.
 San Francisco, CA 94103
URL: http://indiebio.co
Contact: Alex Kopelyan, Senior Director Partner
Facebook: www.facebook.com/indiebio
Linkedin: www.linkedin.com/company/indiebio
X (Twitter): x.com/indbio
YouTube: www.youtube.com/channel/UC0FFccwm
 1wbmYtKfX6HDncw
Description: Synthetic biology accelerator offers a new way for scientists, entrepreneurs, and tinkerers to shape their own destiny and make something that matters. **Founded:** 2015.

37586 ■ Ink People Center for the Arts
627 3rd St.
Eureka, CA 95501
Ph: (707)442-8413
Fax: (707)444-8722
Co. E-mail: inkers@inkpeople.org
URL: http://www.inkpeople.org
Contact: Leslie Castellano, Executive Director
Description: Connects the community to resources for cultural development. The DreamMaker Program supports over 70 self-directing projects created by people who want to make their community a better place through arts and culture.

37587 ■ InnoSpring
3401 EL Camino Real
Palo Alto, CA 94306
Contact: Wanfeng Liu, Chief Executive Officer
Description: Business accelerator and incubator that serves as an end-to-end launchpad for companies seeking US/China growth opportunities. **Founded:** 2012.

37588 ■ La Cocina
2948 Folsom St.
San Francisco, CA 94110
Ph: (415)824-2729
URL: http://lacocinasf.org
Contact: Caleb Zigas, Executive Director
E-mail: caleb@lacocinasf.org
X (Twitter): x.com/lacocinasf
Description: Cultivates low income food entrepreneurs as they formalize and grow their businesses. Provides affordable commercial kitchen space, technical assistance and access to market opportunities. **Founded:** 2005.

37589 ■ LabIX
120 8th St.
San Francisco, CA 94103
URL: http://flex.com/expertise/startups
Contact: François Barbier, President
Facebook: www.facebook.com/flexcorporate
Linkedin: www.linkedin.com/company/flexintl
X (Twitter): twitter.com/flexintl
Instagram: www.instagram.com/flexintl
YouTube: www.youtube.com/user/FlextronicsIntl
Description: A hardware venture eco-system/accelerator focused on technology platforms. Helps emerging technology startups, through investment and services, bring to market technologies that make tomorrow's disruptive products possible.

37590 ■ Launchpad LA (LPLA)
11870 Santa Monica Blvd., Ste. 106528
Los Angeles, CA 90025
Contact: Kyle Taylor, Contact
Description: Business accelerator providing startups with initial investments of $50,000 - $100,000 in exchange for 6 percent in the company. Provides office space and access to a network of mentors, advisors, and investors. **Founded:** 2009.

37591 ■ Lawyers for Family Justice
2151 Salvio St., Ste. 201
Concord, CA 94519
URL: http://www.cocofamilyjustice.org/services-before-import/safety/lawyers
Contact: Harry Gilbert, Contact
Description: Legal incubator program for new or transitioning attorneys starting their own solo, small firm, or nonprofit practice.

37592 ■ Lemnos Labs
2 Embarcadero Center 8Th Fl.
San Francisco, CA 94111
URL: http://www.lemnos.vc
Contact: Helen Zelman Boniske, Contact
Description: Incubator that supports early-stage hardware startups by providing access to capital and hands-on expertise. Invests in 8-12 startups per year. Incubation period is from 6-15 months. **Founded:** 2011.

37593 ■ LiteKey LLC
101 California St., Ste. 2710
San Francisco, CA 94111
Free: 866-862-1155
Fax: (866)214-0109
Co. E-mail: info@lite-key.com
URL: http://www.lite-key.com
X (Twitter): x.com/litekey
Description: Technology incubator. Offers help at the prototype, architect, construct, and evolve stages. Also operates out of Mexico. **Founded:** 2011.

37594 ■ Los Angeles Cleantech Incubator (LACI)
525 S Hewitt St.
Los Angeles, CA 90013
Ph: (213)358-6500
Co. E-mail: info@laincubator.org
URL: http://laincubator.org
Contact: Matt Petersen, President
Facebook: www.facebook.com/LACIncubator
Linkedin: www.linkedin.com/company/los-angeles-cleantech-incubator
X (Twitter): x.com/LACIncubator
Instagram: www.instagram.com/laincubator
Description: Business incubator that accelerates the development of cleantech startups by offering flexible office space, CEO coaching and mentoring, and access to a growing network of experts and capital. **Founded:** 2011.

37595 ■ Los Angeles Incubator Consortium (LAIC)
Los Angeles, CA
Ph: (323)741-2950
Co. E-mail: laincubatorconsortium@gmail.com
URL: http://www.laincubatorconsortium.com
Contact: Maria Hall, Director, Development
Facebook: www.facebook.com/LAIncubatorConsortium
X (Twitter): x.com/IncubatorLA
Description: A post-graduate incubator program to support and assist law school graduates in starting their own solo, small firm, or non-profit practices. Incubator participants receive the infrastructure and basic training needed to get their practices up and running, and serve the local community's legal needs at an affordable cost.

37596 ■ Matter
421 Bryant St.
San Francisco, CA 94107
Co. E-mail: info@matter.vc
URL: http://www.matter.vc
Facebook: www.facebook.com/mattervc
X (Twitter): twitter.com/mattervc
Description: Small business incubator accelerator supporting early stage media ventures.

37597 ■ MBC BioLabs
953 Indiana St.
San Francisco, CA 94107
Ph: (415)347-8287
URL: http://mbcbiolabs.com
Contact: Robert Blazej, Director
E-mail: rblazej@missionbiocapital.com
Facebook: www.facebook.com/mbcbiolabs
Linkedin: www.linkedin.com/company/mbc-biolabs
X (Twitter): x.com/MBiolabs
Instagram: www.instagram.com/mbcbiolabs
YouTube: www.youtube.com/channel/UCn-WzLxckk33iHf3FNT2iCw
Description: Dedicated to helping biotech startups get going quickly and inexpensively. Services include creative ways to get funding and equipment rental. **Founded:** 2013.

37598 ■ Mila Capital
9410 Owensmouth Ave.
Chatsworth, CA 91311
Co. E-mail: hello@mila.vc
URL: http://www.mila.vc
Contact: Carmen Palafox, Partner
Facebook: www.facebook.com/milacapitalvc
Linkedin: www.linkedin.com/company/milacapital
X (Twitter): x.com/milacapital
Description: Accelerator that empowers entrepreneurs and their business by making hardware not hard. Accepts seed stage companies, cultivates innovation, and grooms for execution. **Founded:** 2015.

37599 ■ Miller Center for Social Entrepreneurship
500 El Camino Real
Santa Clara, CA 95053
Ph: (408)551-6048
Co. E-mail: millercenter@scu.edu
URL: http://www.millersocent.org
Contact: Brigit Helms, Executive Director
Facebook: www.facebook.com/millersocent
X (Twitter): x.com/MillerSocent
Instagram: www.instagram.com/miller.socent
YouTube: www.youtube.com/user/SantaClaraCSTS
Description: Accelerates global, innovation-based entrepreneurship in service of humanity. Offers the Global Social Benefit Institute (GSBI) program. **Founded:** 1997.

37600 ■ Mr. C's Kitchen Rentals
CA
Ph: (805)461-3614
Co. E-mail: mrcscat@sbcglobal.net
URL: http://mrcscatering.com
Description: Culinary incubator with kitchen rental space for food entrepreneurs. **Founded:** 1977.

37601 ■ Mucker Capital (MC)
202 Bicknell Ave.
Santa Monica, CA 90405
URL: http://www.mucker.com
Contact: Erik Rannala, Co-Founder Partner
Facebook: www.facebook.com/MuckerCapital
Linkedin: www.linkedin.com/company/mucker
X (Twitter): x.com/mucker
YouTube: www.youtube.com/channel/UCKMs1hnGlrodkdr7tW50Sww
Description: Business incubator and accelerator supporting entrepreneurs in areas that are most critical to their success. Services include product development, customer development, business development, operational infrastructure, and recruiting. **Founded:** 2011.

37602 ■ MuckerLab
202 Bicknell Ave.
Santa Monica, CA 90405
URL: http://www.mucker.com
Description: A business accelerator that works with only ten companies a year. Supports startups in their earliest stages, provides mentors, and also helps raise venture capital.

37603 ■ New Economics For Women (NEW)
303 S Loma Dr.
Los Angeles, CA 90017
Ph: (213)483-2060
Fax: (213)483-7848
Co. E-mail: info@neworg.us
URL: http://neweconomicsforwomen.org
Contact: Beatríz Olvera Stotzer, President
Facebook: www.facebook.com/newecon4women
X (Twitter): x.com/newecon4women
Instagram: www.instagram.com/neweconomicsforwomen
Description: Virtual business incubator aiding women-owned business startups.

37604 ■ NexusLab
Ph: (818)744-3605
URL: http://nexuslab.com
Description: A U.S.-based company helping prospective entrepreneurs start and grow their businesses in the United States. Helps startups overcome challenges that are faced when launching an app.

37605 ■ Nordic Innovation House
470 Ramona St.
Palo Alto, CA 94301
Ph: (650)325-5500
Co. E-mail: post@nordicinnovationhouse.com
URL: http://www.nordicinnovationhouse.com/siliconvalley
Contact: Paula Salomaa, Director
E-mail: paula.salomaa@nordicinnovationhouse.com
Facebook: www.facebook.com/innovationhouse
Linkedin: www.linkedin.com/company/nordicinnovationhouse
X (Twitter): x.com/innorhouse

Instagram: www.instagram.com/nordicinnovationhousehk
Description: The U.S. headquarters for the Nordic Startup Community, allowing members to have a presence in Silicon Valley and New York, and providing a landing space and community of peers, partners, investors and service providers to entrepreneurs.

37606 ▪ One Million by One Million (1M/1M)
Co. E-mail: support@1mby1m.com
URL: http://1m1m.sramanamitra.com
Contact: Sramana Mitra, Founder Consultant
Facebook: www.facebook.com/1Mby1M
X (Twitter): x.com/1Mby1M
YouTube: www.youtube.com/user/1M1MRoundtables
Description: A global virtual incubator that aims to help one million entrepreneurs reach one million dollars in annual revenue. Offers education, video lectures, online strategy consulting, and introductions to customers, partners, and investors. **Founded:** 2010.

37607 ▪ One Valley (OV)
400 Concar Dr.
 San Mateo, CA 94402
Co. E-mail: marketing@theonevalley.com
URL: http://www.theonevalley.com
Contact: Nikhil Sinha, Chief Executive Officer
Facebook: www.facebook.com/theonevalley
Linkedin: www.linkedin.com/company/onevalley
X (Twitter): x.com/theonevalley
Instagram: www.instagram.com/_theonevalley
YouTube: www.youtube.com/channel/UCkZvIy0_eUyk1WIH0s7kcFQ
Description: Innovation platform. Accelerates start-ups and connects entrepreneurs to business models, technologies, and ideas. Also operates out of Boston. **Founded:** 2010.

37608 ▪ Orange Fab
Orange SA
c/o Orange Silicon Valley 60 Spear St.
 San Francisco, CA 94105
Ph: 33 1 44 44 22 22
Co. E-mail: csciw@orange.com
URL: http://www.orange.com
Facebook: www.facebook.com/orangefab
X (Twitter): twitter.com/OrangeFab
Description: Connects startups and corporations. Offers business development support and networking for high-potential entrepreneurs that could impact Orange's products and services.

37609 ▪ Outlet Coworking
2110 K St.
 Sacramento, CA 95816
Ph: (916)476-9606
URL: http://www.outletcoworking.com
Contact: Travis Reich, Manager
Facebook: www.facebook.com/outletcoworking
X (Twitter): x.com/outletcoworking
Instagram: www.instagram.com/outletcoworking
Description: Provides coworking space for independent workers and small business entrepreneurs. Features private offices, modern open space, conference rooms, and designer lounges. **Founded:** 2015.

37610 ▪ Parisoma
169 11th St.
 San Francisco, CA 94103
URL: http://www.fabernovel.com/contenu/openai-le-prototype-dun-capitalisme-de-concentration
Description: Supports entrepreneurs by offering co-working space, classes, events, mentoring, and partnerships. **Founded:** 2008.

37611 ▪ Plug and Play
440 N Wolfe Rd.
 Sunnyvale, CA 94085
Ph: (408)524-1400
Co. E-mail: info@pnptc.com
URL: http://www.plugandplaytechcenter.com
Contact: Neda Amidi, President
Facebook: www.facebook.com/plugandplaytechcenter
Linkedin: www.linkedin.com/company/plug-and-play-tech-center
X (Twitter): x.com/plugandplaytc
Description: Firm engages in investing in start-up companies.

37612 ▪ Plug and Play Tech Center
440 N Wolfe Rd.
 Sunnyvale, CA 94085
Ph: (408)524-1400
Co. E-mail: info@pnptc.com
URL: http://www.plugandplaytechcenter.com
Contact: Neda Amidi, President
Facebook: www.facebook.com/plugandplaytechcenter
Linkedin: www.linkedin.com/company/plug-and-play-tech-center
X (Twitter): x.com/plugandplaytc
Instagram: www.instagram.com/plugandplaytc
YouTube: www.youtube.com/plugandplaytc
Description: A global innovation platform connecting startups to corporations. Invests in over 100 companies each year.

37613 ▪ PortTech Los Angeles (LACI)
302 W 5th St., Ste. 201
 San Pedro, CA 90731
URL: http://www.porttechla.org
Linkedin: www.linkedin.com/company/porttech-los-angeles
Description: Brings together entrepreneurs, strategic partners, and investors to accelerate innovation, advance clean technologies and create economic opportunities.

37614 ▪ Prospect Silicon Valley [ProspectSV]
3031 Tisch Way, 110 Plz. W
 San Jose, CA 95128
Co. E-mail: hello@prospectsv.org
URL: http://www.prospectsv.org
Contact: Doug Davenport, Executive Director
Facebook: www.facebook.com/prospectsv
Linkedin: www.linkedin.com/company/prospect-silicon-valley
X (Twitter): x.com/ProspectSV
Instagram: www.instagram.com/prospectsiliconvalley
YouTube: www.youtube.com/channel/UCOkeP6A6ZLrZ1Kn9fYw5aVA
Description: Non-profit business incubator that supports emerging technology companies by providing access to facilities, platforms, partners, and market connections. **Founded:** 2013.

37615 ▪ QB3
2630 Bancroft Way
 Berkeley, CA 94720
URL: http://qb3.org
Contact: David Schaffer, Executive Director
Linkedin: www.linkedin.com/company/qb3
X (Twitter): x.com/qb3
YouTube: www.youtube.com/user/QB3TV
Description: Provides small spaces for biotech entrepreneurs to lay the foundations for their new startups. **Scope:** Understanding biological systems at all levels of complexity, from atoms and protein molecules to cells, tissue, organs and the entire organism, integrating the disciplines of mathematics, physics, chemistry, and engineering. **Founded:** 2000.

37616 ▪ ReadWrite Labs
100 Broadway
 San Francisco, CA 94111
URL: http://readwrite.com
Contact: Philippe Cases, Chief Executive Officer
Facebook: www.facebook.com/ReadWrite
X (Twitter): x.com/RWW
Instagram: www.instagram.com/readwritedotcom
YouTube: www.youtube.com/channel/UCIMPvTStrcn829w34OWNEPw
Description: Accelerates high-impact products to high-growth markets, serving the global IoT + wearables community. **Founded:** 2003.

37617 ▪ Renaissance Entrepreneur Center
275 Fifth St.
 San Francisco, CA 94103
Ph: (415)541-8580
Co. E-mail: info@rencenter.org
URL: http://rencenter.org
Contact: Bret Alexander Sweet, Director
E-mail: bsweet@rencenter.org
Facebook: www.facebook.com/RenaissanceEntrepreneurshipCenter
Linkedin: www.linkedin.com/company/renaissance-entrepreneurship-center
X (Twitter): x.com/RenCenter_
Instagram: www.instagram.com/rencenter
Description: Small business experts providing low-cost and free services to men and women with a business idea and a dream as well as those with many years working for him/her self who are ready to take their business to the next level. **Founded:** 1985.

37618 ▪ Renaissance Entrepreneurship Center
275 5th St.
 San Francisco, CA 94103
Ph: (415)541-8580
URL: http://rencenter.org
Contact: Craig Jacoby, Chairman of the Board
Facebook: www.facebook.com/RenaissanceEntrepreneurshipCenter
Linkedin: www.linkedin.com/company/renaissance-entrepreneurship-center
X (Twitter): x.com/RenCenter_
Instagram: www.instagram.com/rencenter
Description: Offers small business training, consulting, incubation, access to capital and networks, and emotional support. **Founded:** 1985.

37619 ▪ Rock Health
333 Bush St., 4th Fl.
 San Francisco, CA 94104
Ph: (415)869-8585
Co. E-mail: hello@rockhealth.com
URL: http://rockhealth.com
Contact: Megan Zweig, President
Linkedin: www.linkedin.com/company/rock-health
X (Twitter): x.com/rock_health
YouTube: www.youtube.com/user/RockHealth
Description: A venture fund dedicated to digital health, supporting companies that improve the quality, safety, and accessibility of our healthcare system. **Founded:** 2010.

37620 ▪ RocketSpace
535 Mission St. Flr. 14
 San Francisco, CA 94105
Contact: Duncan Logan, Chief Executive Officer
Description: A global network of technology campuses designed to help tech startups around the world. **Founded:** 2011.

37621 ▪ Runway Innovation Hub
160 Spear St., Ste. 1000
 San Francisco, CA 94105
Ph: (415)935-8122
URL: http://runway.is
Contact: Sandra Miller, Chief Executive Officer
Linkedin: www.linkedin.com/company/runwayinnovationhub
X (Twitter): twitter.com/RunwayInnovate
Instagram: www.instagram.com/runwayinnovationhub
YouTube: www.youtube.com/channel/UCHcmCHT4mMD0KBwzEJO3bmg
Description: Offers workspace, corporate innovation, and event services to fuel the growth of startups. **Founded:** 2013.

37622 ▪ The SABLE Accelerator
1494 Hamilton Way
 San Jose, CA 95125
Ph: (408)677-5333
URL: http://www.sablenetwork.com
Contact: Donovan Neale-May, Coordinator Managing Partner
E-mail: donovan@sablenetwork.com
Description: Furthers South Africa's economic interests through knowledge transfer and a network of expatriate South Africans contributing to their country of birth through mentoring, coaching, consulting, advising, teaching, funding, or donating.

37623 ■ Sae Kitchen
980 Los Vallecitos
San Marcos, CA 92069
Ph: (760)472-3711
Co. E-mail: support@saekitchen.com
URL: http://saekitchen.com
Contact: Lauren Perez, Owner
E-mail: lauren@saekitchen.com
Instagram: www.instagram.com/sae_kitchen
Description: Offers industrial equipment, production workspace, commissary storage, and industry support for culinary startups. Also maintains a Vista, California, location. **Founded:** 2009.

37624 ■ San Bernardino Employment & Training Agency
600 N Arrowhead Ave., Ste. 300
San Bernardino, CA 92401
Ph: (909)522-4656
Contact: Phillip Cothran, Chairman
Description: In addition to assisting job seekers and businesses with their employment needs, the agency provides business startup training and resources to entrepreneurs.

37625 ■ San Diego State University College of Business Administration - Lavin Entrepreneurship Center
William E Leonhard Entrepreneurship Ctr., Engineering & Interdisciplinary Sciences Complex, Ste 103
San Diego, CA 92182-1915
Ph: (619)594-2781
URL: http://lavincenter.sdsu.edu
Contact: Cathy Pucher, Executive Director
E-mail: cpucher@sdsu.edu
Facebook: www.facebook.com/sdsulavincenter
X (Twitter): twitter.com/SDSULavinCenter
Instagram: www.instagram.com/sdsulavincenter
YouTube: www.youtube.com/user/sdsuemc
Description: Provider of student entrepreneurs and local businesses the tools, resources and internships to achieve their goals. **Founded:** 1986.

37626 ■ San Diego Technology Incubator
1425 Russ Blvd., Ste. T-107
San Diego, CA 92101
URL: http://legacy.www.sbir.gov/node/353861
Contact: Michael Nicolaou, Investigator
E-mail: mnicolaou@yasoohealth.com
Description: Supports the economic development of the region by sheltering and supporting new technology ventures. Offers moderately priced office, lab and manufacturing facilities, and other support services to help early-stage and emerging companies with the edge they need to succeed during their incubation period of from one to three years.

37627 ■ San Joaquin Delta College - Northeastern California Small Business Development Center
110 N San Joaquin St., Ste. 402.
Stockton, CA 95202
Ph: (209)868-1046
URL: http://www.deltacollege.edu/department/small-business-development-center
Description: Virtual business incubator that provides services to help small businesses operate cost effectively.

37628 ■ San Jose BioCenter
5941 Optical Ct.
San Jose, CA 95138
Ph: (408)960-3807
Fax: (408)960-3822
Co. E-mail: info@sjbiocenter.com
URL: http://www.sjbiocenter.com
Contact: Melinda Richter, Executive Director
E-mail: melinda@sjbiocenter.com
Description: Life sciences incubator that provides wet labs, research equipment, and commercialization support to life sciences and other emerging technology companies. **Founded:** 2004.

37629 ■ San Jose BioCube
5941 Optical Ct.
San Jose, CA 95138
Ph: (408)960-3807
Co. E-mail: info@sjbiocube.com
URL: http://www.sanjosebiocube.com
Contact: Anthony Gonzalez, Chief Executive Officer
Description: Provides scalable office space, access to state-of-the-art lab facilities, and business support to promising life science, techno, and cleantech startup companies. **Founded:** 2004.

37630 ■ San Leandro Technology Center (SLTC)
Oakland, CA
URL: http://sl-tc.com
Description: Provides services to business startups.

37631 ■ Shared Kitchen Rentals
9932 Mesa Rim Rd., Ste. A
San Diego, CA 92121
Ph: (858)935-9924
URL: http://www.sharedkitchenrentals.com
Contact: R. Barry, Founder
Description: Shared commissary kitchen available to rent.

37632 ■ Sierra Commons (SC)
792 Searls Ave.
Nevada City, CA 95959
Ph: (530)265-8443
Co. E-mail: info@sierracommons.org
URL: http://www.sierracommons.org
Contact: Robert X. Trent, Executive Director
X (Twitter): x.com/Sierra_Commons
Description: Co-working and educational facility for Nevada County entrepreneurs. Offers meeting spaces, education, and mentoring. **Founded:** 2009.

37633 ■ Springboard
Springboard, Ste. 1100 22 Battery St.
San Francisco, CA 94111
Ph: (415)857-4459
Co. E-mail: contact@springboard.com
URL: http://www.springboard.com
Contact: Andrew Moers, President
Facebook: www.facebook.com/springboard
Linkedin: www.linkedin.com/school/springboard
X (Twitter): x.com/springboard
Instagram: www.instagram.com/springboard.hq
YouTube: www.youtube.com/springboard
Description: Offers a 13-week mentor-lead program at the Google campus in London and at ideaSpace at the University of Cambridge. Each year, Springboard invests in over 30 companies for between 3-6% common stock equity. **Founded:** 2013. **Educational Activities:** International Franchise Expo (IFE) (Annual).

37634 ■ Startup San Diego (SSD)
550 W B St., 4th Fl.
San Diego, CA 92101
Co. E-mail: info@startupsd.org
URL: http://startupsd.org
Contact: Lisa Barnhouse, Executive Director
Facebook: www.facebook.com/StartupSD
Linkedin: www.linkedin.com/company/startup-san-diego
X (Twitter): x.com/startupsandiego
Instagram: www.instagram.com/startupsandiego
Description: Offers events and programs to address development, funding, and leadership challenges that startups face. **Founded:** 2014.

37635 ■ StartX
2627 Hanover St.
Palo Alto, CA 94304
Co. E-mail: info@startx.stanford.edu
URL: http://startx.com
Contact: Joseph Huang, Chief Executive Officer
Facebook: www.facebook.com/StartX
X (Twitter): x.com/StartX
Description: An educational non-profit that accelerates the development of Stanford's top entrepreneurs through experiential education and collective intelligence. **Founded:** 2009.

37636 ■ The Story Lab
2700 Pennsylvania Ave., 2nd Fl.
Santa Monica, CA 90404
URL: http://www.storylab.com
Description: An incubator that is dedicated toward developing successful theatrical and digital content by amazing film, television, and virtual/360 content producers. **Founded:** 2012.

37637 ■ Tandem Capital
1450 Chapin Ave.
Burlingame, CA 94010
Ph: (650)342-1900
Co. E-mail: info@tandemcap.com
URL: http://tandemcap.com
Contact: David Wagonfeld, Partner
Facebook: www.facebook.com/TandemCap
X (Twitter): x.com/tandemcapital
Description: Seed fund backing startups and entrepreneurs as they build their brands.

37638 ■ Tech Liminal (TL)
344 Thomas L Berkley Way, (344 20th St)
Oakland, CA 94612
Co. E-mail: info@techliminal.com
URL: http://techliminal.com
Contact: Anca Mosoiu, Founder
Description: Supports business startups and entrepreneurs by providing accessible, technology-focused community space where diverse minds meet and learn to apply the right tools to solve the right problems. **Founded:** 2009.

37639 ■ Tech Startup School
Mountain View, CA
Co. E-mail: info@techstartupschool.com
URL: http://www.techstartupschool.com
Facebook: www.facebook.com/Tech.Startup.School
Linkedin: www.linkedin.com/company/tech-startup-school
X (Twitter): twitter.com/StartupSchl
Instagram: www.instagram.com/Tech.Startup.School
Description: Business accelerator. Offers training in innovation and entrepreneurship, expansion into new markets, mentoring, and an entrepreneurial ecosystem. Also runs programs in Turkey. **Founded:** 2015.

37640 ■ Temecula Valley Entrepreneur's Exchange (TVE2)
43200 Business Pk. Dr.
Temecula, CA 92590
Ph: (951)506-5180
Co. E-mail: info@tve2.org
URL: http://temeculaca.gov/912/TVE2-Temecula-Valley-Entrepreneurs-Excha
Description: A business incubator and regional resource center that fosters business growth and economic for startups and entrepreneurs. **Founded:** 2005.

37641 ■ TIPark Silicon Valley
1601 McCarthy Blvd.
Milpitas, CA 95035
Ph: (408)321-8218
Fax: (408)321-8206
Co. E-mail: contact@tiparksv.com
URL: http://www.tiparksv.com
Contact: Lucia Jiang, Contact
Facebook: www.facebook.com/TIParkSiliconValley
Linkedin: www.linkedin.com/company/tipark-silicon-valley
X (Twitter): x.com/TIParkSV
Description: Business incubator who encourages startups in the U.S. and China to expand overseas and to promote business communication and cooperation between Silicon Valley and China. Provides startups with low-cost office space. **Founded:** 2013.

37642 ■ The Trade Coffee & Coworking
2220 K St.
Sacramento, CA 95816
Ph: (916)538-6878
Co. E-mail: hello@thetradecollab.com
URL: http://www.thetradecollab.com
Contact: Amanda Kennedy, Owner
Facebook: www.facebook.com/TheTradeCollab
X (Twitter): x.com/thetradecollab

Description: A hybrid coffee and coworking business. Offers a variety of coworking memberships with office space for entrepreneurs and business startups. **Founded:** 2015.

37643 ■ Tumml
100 Broadway
   San Francisco, CA 94111
Contact: Julie Lein, Chief Executive Officer
Description: A startup hub for urban technology providing resources to early stage entrepreneurs tackling major urban challenges.

37644 ■ UpWest Labs
550 California Ave. No 1
   Palo Alto, CA 94306
Contact: Gil Ben-Artzy, Manager
Description: A seed stage fund investing in Israel's most promising entrepreneurs through a 4-month program. Provides seed funding, mentoring, and workspace. **Founded:** 2012.

37645 ■ US Market Access Center (USMAC)
101 Jefferson Dr.
   Menlo Park, CA 94025
Ph: (415)462-4633
Co. E-mail: info@usmarketaccess.com
URL: http://usmarketaccess.com
Contact: Paul Hynek, President
E-mail: paulhynek@gmail.com
Facebook: www.facebook.com/USMarketAccess
X (Twitter): x.com/usmarketaccess
Description: US Market Access Center is a non-profit business incubator sponsored by a collaboration of business, government, and academic organizations. The Center is a leading business gateway into the United States. Formerly International Business Incubator (IBI).

37646 ■ Valley Economic Development Centers (VEDC)
5121 Van Nuys Blvd., Ste. 200
   Sherman Oaks, CA 91403
Ph: (818)379-7000
Fax: (818)379-7077
Co. E-mail: info@economicalliance.org
URL: http://thevalley.net
Contact: Sonya Kay Blake, President
E-mail: sblake@economicalliance.org
Facebook: www.facebook.com/valleyeconomicalliance
X (Twitter): x.com/ValleyAlliance
Instagram: www.instagram.com/valleyeconomicalliance
YouTube: www.youtube.com/channel/UCS7Q4jvgqi1bnjkfo2FksqA
Description: Works to make small business dreams a reality by helping small businesses unable to qualify for traditional bank financing. Offers individualized service at a reasonable cost. **Founded:** 1995.

37647 ■ Ventura Ventures Technology Center (V2TC)
505 Poli St., 3rd Fl.
   Ventura, CA 93001
URL: http://ventura.chambermaster.com/list/member/ventura-ventures-technology-center-29303
Description: Provides business startup and acceleration help and offers flexible office space to early stage entrepreneurs as well as mentoring, access to funding sources, and entrepreneur-focus events and programs. **Founded:** 2009.

37648 ■ Vermont Slauson Economic Development Corporation (VSEDC)
1130 W Slauson Ave.
   Los Angeles, CA 90044
Ph: (323)753-2335
Fax: (323)753-6710
Co. E-mail: hq@vsedc.org
URL: http://vsedc.org
Contact: Joseph T. Rouzan, III, President
Facebook: www.facebook.com/VermontSlausonEconomicDevelopmentCorporation
X (Twitter): x.com/vsedc_
Instagram: www.instagram.com/vsedc

YouTube: www.youtube.com/channel/UCSLYP5EyeRcf3aYygOTQuhw
Description: VSEDC's Business Enterprise Center is a micro-business incubator offering affordable office space and support services to startup and established businesses. **Founded:** 1979. **Geographic Preference:** Local.

37649 ■ Vet-Tech
548 Market St., No. 59045
   San Francisco, CA 94104
Contact: Ryan Micheletti, Contact
Description: Startup accelerator for veterans.

37650 ■ WORK Petaluma
245 Kentucky St.
   Petaluma, CA 94952
Ph: (707)721-6540
Co. E-mail: info@workpetaluma.com
URL: http://workpetaluma.com
Contact: Matt Moller, Owner
E-mail: matt@workpetaluma.com
Facebook: www.facebook.com/WORKinPetaluma
X (Twitter): x.com/workpetaluma
Instagram: www.instagram.com/workpetaluma
Description: Provides coworking space and conference rooms for those in need of workspace, including startups and entrepreneurs. **Founded:** 2012.

37651 ■ Y Combinator Management, LLC
335 Pioneer Way
   Mountain View, CA 94041
Fax: (650)360-3189
Co. E-mail: yclegal@ycombinator.com
URL: http://www.ycombinator.com
Contact: Garry Tan, President
Facebook: www.facebook.com/YCombinator
Linkedin: www.linkedin.com/school/y-combinator
X (Twitter): x.com/ycombinator
YouTube: www.youtube.com/c/ycombinator
Description: Works with startups to help develop their ideas. Provides seed funding to help companies get through their first phase of business, to help them get to the point where they've built something impressive enough to raise money on a larger scale. **Founded:** 2005.

37652 ■ Zahn Innovation Platform Launchpad
5500 Campanile Dr.
   San Diego, CA 92182
Co. E-mail: ziplaunchpad@sdsu.edu
URL: http://ziplaunchpad.sdsu.edu
Contact: Cathy Pucher, Executive Director
E-mail: cpucher@sdsu.edu
Facebook: www.facebook.com/ZIPLaunchpad
X (Twitter): x.com/ziplaunchpad
Instagram: www.instagram.com/ziplaunchpad
Description: Commercial and social incubator that supports San Diego State University innovators and aspiring entrepreneurs as they transform their ideas into companies.

EDUCATIONAL PROGRAMS

37653 ■ American River College (ARC)
4700 College Oak Dr.
   Sacramento, CA 95841
Ph: (916)484-8011
Co. E-mail: info@arc.losrios.edu
URL: http://arc.losrios.edu
Contact: Lisa Cardoza, President
Facebook: www.facebook.com/americanrivercollege
Linkedin: www.linkedin.com/school/american-river-college
X (Twitter): x.com/ARCNewsToday
Instagram: www.instagram.com/arcnewstoday
YouTube: www.youtube.com/channel/UCbp0sT8Mm1GA__gpREFZXCQ
Description: Two-year college offering small business management classes. **Founded:** 1955. **Publications:** The Current.

37654 ■ Chabot College (CC) - Library
25555 Hesperian Blvd.
   Hayward, CA 94545

Ph: (510)723-6600
URL: http://www.chabotcollege.edu
Contact: Susan Sperling, President
Facebook: www.facebook.com/ChabotCollege
X (Twitter): x.com/chabot_college
Instagram: www.instagram.com/chabot_college
YouTube: www.youtube.com/user/chabotcollege
Description: Two-year college offering a program in entrepreneurship. **Scope:** Education materials. **Services:** Interlibrary loan. **Founded:** 1961. **Holdings:** E-books.

37655 ■ Cypress College (CC)
9200 Valley View St.
   Cypress, CA 90630
Ph: (714)484-7000
Co. E-mail: info@cypresscollege.edu
URL: http://www.cypresscollege.edu
Contact: Dr. JoAnna Schilling, President
Facebook: www.facebook.com/cypresscollege
Linkedin: www.linkedin.com/school/cypress-college
X (Twitter): x.com/CypressCollege
YouTube: www.youtube.com/user/CypressCC
Pinterest: www.pinterest.com/cypresscollege
Description: A two-year community college, offers certificates and associate degree programs. **Founded:** 1966.

37656 ■ De Anza College (DAC)
21250 Stevens Creek Blvd.
   Cupertino, CA 95014
Ph: (408)864-8817
Co. E-mail: dainternational@deanza.edu
URL: http://www.deanza.edu
Contact: Lloyd A. Holmes, President
E-mail: holmeslloyd@deanza.edu
Facebook: www.facebook.com/deanzacollege
X (Twitter): x.com/deanza_college
Instagram: www.instagram.com/deanzacollege
YouTube: www.youtube.com/user/DAWebTeam
Description: A two-year community college, offers certificates and associate degree programs. **Founded:** 1967. **Publications:** Red Wheelbarrow (Semiannual); La Voz: The Voice of De Anza (Weekly).

37657 ■ Empire College School of Business
3035 Cleveland Ave.
   Santa Rosa, CA 95403
Free: 877-395-8535
Co. E-mail: info@empcol.edu
URL: http://empcol.edu/school-of-business
Contact: Roy O. Hurd, President
Facebook: www.facebook.com/EmpireCollege.SchoolofLaw
Linkedin: www.linkedin.com/school/empire-college-school-of-law
X (Twitter): twitter.com/empcol
YouTube: www.youtube.com/user/empirecollege
Pinterest: www.pinterest.com/backup249225/empire-college
Description: An institute that offers career training programs in the field of Accounting, Business, Information Technology, Legal, Medical, Tourism and Hospitality, and GED Prep. **Founded:** 1961.

37658 ■ Lake Tahoe Community College (LTCC)
One College Dr.
   South Lake Tahoe, CA 96150
Ph: (530)541-4660
Fax: (530)541-7852
Co. E-mail: enrollmentservices@ltcc.edu
URL: http://ltcc.edu
Contact: Jeff DeFranco, President
Facebook: www.facebook.com/LakeTahoeCommunityCollege
X (Twitter): x.com/laketahoecc
Instagram: www.instagram.com/laketahoe_communitycollege
YouTube: www.youtube.com/user/LakeTahoeCommCollege
Description: Two-year college offering a small business management program. **Founded:** 1974. **Geographic Preference:** National.

37659 ■ Ohlone College
43600 Mission Blvd.
Fremont, CA 94539
Ph: (510)659-6000
Co. E-mail: admissions@ohlone.edu
URL: http://www.ohlone.edu
Contact: Dr. Eric Bishop, President
Facebook: www.facebook.com/ohlonecollege
X (Twitter): x.com/ohlonecollege
YouTube: www.youtube.com/ohlonecollege
Description: Two-year college offering a small business management program. **Founded:** 1967.

37660 ■ Saddleback College
28000 Marguerite Pky.
Mission Viejo, CA 92692
Ph: (949)582-4500
Co. E-mail: scadmissions@saddleback.edu
URL: http://www.saddleback.edu
Contact: Elizabeth Patricia Mccann, Chief Executive Officer
Facebook: www.facebook.com/SaddlebackCollege
X (Twitter): x.com/SaddlebackColl
Instagram: www.instagram.com/saddlebackcollege
Description: A two-year community college, offers certificates and associate degree programs. **Founded:** 1968.

37661 ■ Santa Ana College
1530 W 17th St.
Santa Ana, CA 92706-3398
Ph: (714)564-6000
Co. E-mail: studentoutreach@sac.edu
URL: http://www.sac.edu/Pages/default.aspx
Contact: Mario Robertson, Chairman
E-mail: robertson_mario@sac.edu
Facebook: www.facebook.com/SantaAnaCollege
Linkedin: www.linkedin.com/school/santa-ana-college
X (Twitter): x.com/SantaAnaCollege
Instagram: www.instagram.com/santaanacollege
Description: A two-year community college, offers certificates and associate degree programs. **Founded:** 1915.

37662 ■ Southwestern College (SWC)
900 Otay Lakes Rd.
Chula Vista, CA 91910-7297
Ph: (619)421-6700
Co. E-mail: admissions@swccd.edu
URL: http://www.swccd.edu
Contact: Mark Sanchez, President
E-mail: msanchez@swccd.edu
Description: A two-year community college, offers certificates and associate degree programs. **Founded:** 1961.

37663 ■ Stanford University - Center for Entrepreneurial Studies (CES)
Stanford Graduate School of Business
655 Knight Way
Stanford, CA 94305
URL: http://www.gsb.stanford.edu/experience/about/centers-institutes/ces
Contact: Stefanos Zenios, Director
Description: A dynamic global community of thought leaders supporting entrepreneurship through research, teaching, and student programs. **Founded:** 1996.

CONSULTANTS

37664 ■ Atlena
8383 Wilshire Blvd., Ste. 800
Beverly Hills, CA 90211
Ph: (323)456-8691
Co. E-mail: info@atlena.com
URL: http://www.atlena.com
Description: Research-centered consulting firm. Helps businesses at all stages fund and grow their operations and capture meaningful values.

37665 ■ California Coast Venture Forum (CCVF)
Stradling Yocca Carlson & Rauth 800 Anacapa St., Ste. A
Santa Barbara, CA 93101
Ph: (805)495-6962
Co. E-mail: forum@ccvf.org
URL: http://www.ccvf.org
Contact: Jerry Knotts, President
E-mail: jeknotts@ccvf.org
Description: Advises and promotes growing companies. Offers education, mentoring, referrals, and locating venture capital sources. **Founded:** 1996.

37666 ■ Capitol Services
3609 Bradshaw Rd., Ste. H 343
Sacramento, CA 95827
Free: 866-443-0657
Fax: (916)443-1908
Co. E-mail: info@cutredtape.com
URL: http://cutredtape.com
Contact: Shauna Krause, Consultant Principal
Description: Firm provides the registered agent, corporate and uniform commercial code services. **Scope:** Offers assistance to out-of-state businesses wishing to relocate or expand into California and to existing businesses within the State. Specific activities include helping construction trade firms secure a California contractors license, research and assistance in obtaining state and local government permits and licenses, assisting lawyers with public document search and retrieval and public policy analysis. Also helps with contractors licensing in California, Arizona and Nevada. **Founded:** 1978. **Publications:** "Handyman and CSLB Publications," Apr,2010; "Unlicensed Penalties, Suspensions and LLC's," Jan, 2010; "What every Contractor Should Know".

37667 ■ Cayenne Consulting (CC)
501 N El Camino Real, Ste. 200
San Clemente, CA 92672
URL: http://www.caycon.com
Contact: Akira Hirai, Chief Executive Officer
Facebook: www.facebook.com/cayenne.consulting
Linkedin: www.linkedin.com/company/cayenne-consulting
X (Twitter): x.com/CayenneBizPlan
YouTube: www.youtube.com/c/cayenneconsulting
Description: Business plan consultancy. Also offers market research and forecasting, exit planning, interim management, and financial projection services. **Founded:** 2001.

37668 ■ CFO Tools Inc.
San Francisco, CA
Ph: (408)320-7522
Co. E-mail: info@cfotools.net
URL: http://cfotools.net
Description: Offers financial consulting services to early stage technology companies in Silicon Valley. Specializes in implementing customized financial planning and reporting tools for clients. .

37669 ■ CFOs2Go
500 Ygnacio Valley Rd., Ste. 410
Walnut Creek, CA 94596
Ph: (925)299-4450
Fax: (925)935-1342
Co. E-mail: info@2goadvisorygroup.com
URL: http://www.2goadvisorygroup.com
Contact: Robert Weis, Chief Executive Officer
E-mail: rweis@cfos2go.com
Linkedin: www.linkedin.com/company/2go-advisory-group
X (Twitter): x.com/cfos2go
Description: Full service senior financial executive placement firm. Customizes staffing and consulting solutions to emerging and high growth companies. **Founded:** 1985.

37670 ■ Claggett Wolfe Associates (CWA)
3108 Sunshine Meadow Ln.
Auburn, CA 95602
Ph: (530)878-8016
Co. E-mail: info@claggettwolfe.com
URL: http://claggettwolfe.com
Contact: Charles Wolfe, Contact
Description: Firm provides management consulting and coaching to help individuals, organizations, and communities to be successful, productive, and effective, their social services consulting includes networks to lead planning, development, evaluation on anti-poverty, homelessness, vocational and mental health interventions especially with families, other services encompass collaborative grants and projects, planning and facilitation, community building, communication, executive and managerial coaching, project management, and team building. **Scope:** Firm provides management consulting and coaching to help individuals, organizations, and communities to be successful, productive, and effective, their social services consulting includes networks to lead planning, development, evaluation on anti-poverty, homelessness, vocational and mental health interventions especially with families, other services encompass collaborative grants and projects, planning and facilitation, community building, communication, executive and managerial coaching, project management, and team building.

37671 ■ Diverse Strategies (DSI)
300 Frank Ogawa Plz., Ste. 264
Oakland, CA 94612
Ph: (510)288-8390
Co. E-mail: info@diversestrategies.com
URL: http://diversestrategies.com
Contact: Nancy Lee, Executive Vice President Director, Finance
Facebook: www.facebook.com/diversestrat
X (Twitter): x.com/cliffordtong
Description: Venture consulting firm assists startups with the resources they need to launch, develop business strategies, and execute plans. **Founded:** 1990.

37672 ■ DragonVenture
2882 Sand Hill Rd., Ste. 150
Menlo Park, CA 94025
Ph: (650)233-9000
Fax: (650)234-8533
Co. E-mail: info@dragonventure.com
URL: http://www.dragonventure.com
Contact: Tony Luh, Co-Founder
Description: Early-stage investment and advisory services firm. Identifies and capitalizes on China-centric business and investment opportunities. Also maintains offices in Shanghai and Beijing. **Investment Policies:** Exceptional applications, management teams, and businesses based on defensible technologies and China-centric opportunities and clearly defined exit strategies.

37673 ■ Geneva Venture Partners
San Francisco, CA
Ph: (650)206-9449
URL: http://genevavp.com
Description: Early-stage venture-backed advisory services, particularly recruitment, for disruptive technology companies. **Founded:** 1983.

37674 ■ GeoVerde Corp.
28A Aladdin Ter.
San Francisco, CA 94133
Ph: (415)885-6813
Fax: (415)885-1205
Co. E-mail: jnikas@geoverde.com
URL: http://www.geoverde.com
Description: Consultant group. Assists small businesses navigate growth and turnaround. **Founded:** 1991.

37675 ■ Growthink (GT)
12130 Millennium Dr., Ste. 300
Los Angeles, CA 90094
Free: 800-506-5728
Co. E-mail: info@growthink.com
URL: http://www.growthink.com
Contact: Dave Lavinsky, President
Facebook: www.facebook.com/growthink
Linkedin: www.linkedin.com/company/growthink
X (Twitter): twitter.com/growthink
YouTube: www.youtube.com/user/growthink
Description: Offers professional advisory services. Provides business plan writing and consulting, corporate identity and branding, investment banking, strategy consulting, turnaround consulting, marketing strategy and consulting, private placement memorandum, and feasibility studies. Serves startups, small

STATE LISTINGS

and medium enterprises, middle market organizations, venture capital and private equity firms. **Founded:** 1999.

37676 ■ GrowthPoint Technology Partners
70 S Pk. St.
 San Francisco, CA 94107
Ph: (650)322-2500
Co. E-mail: info@gptpartners.com
URL: http://growthpoint.com
Contact: Alex Loukas, Director
E-mail: aloukas@gptpartners.com
Linkedin: www.linkedin.com/company/growthpoint-technology-partners
X (Twitter): x.com/GrowthPointTech

37677 ■ JCF Capital Markets, LLC
2173 Salk Ave., Ste. 250
 Carlsbad, CA 92008
Ph: (760)931-4761
Fax: (760)931-4850
Co. E-mail: info@jcfcapitalmarkets.com
URL: http://www.jcfcapitalmarkets.com
Contact: Justin C. Floyd, Managing Director
Facebook: www.facebook.com/people/JCF-Capital-Markets-LLC/100064032333614
Linkedin: www.linkedin.com/company/jcf-capital-advisors-llc
X (Twitter): x.com/jcfcapital
Description: Offers professional capital advisory, business consulting, and financial consulting services.

37678 ■ Lynch Financial Advisors, Inc. (LFA)
1700 Eureka Rd., Ste. 155
 Roseville, CA 95661
Ph: (916)772-3103
Fax: (916)772-3104
Co. E-mail: info@lynchfinancialadvisors.com
URL: http://lynchfinancialadvisors.com
Contact: Michael Lynch, Founder
Description: Financial and investment management. **Founded:** 2002.

37679 ■ Michael S. Kenny & Company LLC
1710 S Amphlett Blvd., Ste. 302
 San Mateo, CA 94402
Ph: (650)727-3985
Co. E-mail: info@michaelskenny.com
URL: http://michaelskenny.com
Contact: Michael S. Kenny, Managing Partner
Facebook: www.facebook.com/kennyandcompany
Linkedin: www.linkedin.com/company/kenny-&-company
X (Twitter): x.com/kennycompanyllc
Description: Management and business consulting firm. Offers strategy, operations, and technology consulting services. Also invests in select startups with high growth potential in disruptive technologies. **Preferred Investment Size:** $25,000 to $100,000.

37680 ■ PACE Finance Corporation (PFC)
1055 Wilshire Blvd., Ste. 900B
 Los Angeles, CA 90017
URL: http://pacelabdc.org/finance
Description: Offers no-cost advising services and low-cost educational programs for entrepreneurs. Offers one-on-sessions for marketing, management, sales, finance, and accounting.

37681 ■ Pro Business Plans
10880 Wilshire Blvd., Ste. 1101
 Los Angeles, CA 90024
Free: 800-409-4044
Fax: (800)409-4044
Co. E-mail: info@probusinessplans.com
URL: http://www.probusinessplans.com
Description: Business plan provider. Assists startups, early stage ventures, non-profits, and existing companies launch or expand their operations. **Founded:** 1999.

37682 ■ SEC Ventures
100 Pine St., Ste. 1250
 San Francisco, CA 94111
Ph: (415)462-5703
Co. E-mail: hello@secventures.com
URL: http://www.secventures.com
Contact: Steve Chen, Founder
Linkedin: www.linkedin.com/company/sec-ventures
Description: Offers investments, software solutions, and strategic advisory services to early-stage companies.

37683 ■ Small Business Advisory Group Inc.
1967 N Gateway Blvd., Ste. 103
 Fresno, CA 93727
Contact: Cindy Leddicotte, Chief Executive Officer
Description: Works with business owners who run companies that employ fewer than 500 employees and do not have the support of a professionally trained management team nor the staff of employees to take on peripheral projects. **Founded:** 2009.

37684 ■ Solid Vision Consulting (SVC)
111 N Market St., Ste. No 300
 San Jose, CA 95113
Ph: (408)625-1144
Fax: (408)625-1145
Co. E-mail: info@solidvisionconsulting.com
URL: http://www.solidvisionconsulting.com
Contact: Frank Kamal, Consultant
Linkedin: www.linkedin.com/company/solid-vision-consulting-llc
Description: Works with privately held small and mid-sized start-ups to run a stronger business. Also offers leadership coaching.

37685 ■ The Startup Garage (TSG)
211 4th st.
 Encinitas, CA 92024
Contact: Tyler Jensen, Contact
Description: Offers business consulting services; Provides market research, financial analysis, and start-up training programs. **Founded:** 2008.

37686 ■ STLGip [Soody Tronson Law Group]
2995 Woodside Rd., Ste. 400
 Woodside, CA 94062
Free: 866-325-7964
Fax: (866)325-7964
Co. E-mail: info@stlgip.com
URL: http://www.stlgip.com
Contact: Soody Tronson, Founder
Facebook: www.facebook.com/STLGip
Description: Full service boutique intellectual property firm. Counsels domestic and international entrepreneurs, investors, government agencies, institutions, and organizations, as well as early stage and larger more established companies.

37687 ■ Tennant Consulting (TC)
321 Frederick St.
 San Francisco, CA 94117
Ph: (925)788-1092
URL: http://tennantconsulting.com
Contact: Steve Tennant, Managing Director
Description: Management consulting firm for software and tech companies. Consults on marketing, sales, product development, revenue assessment, and fundraising. **Founded:** 2001.

37688 ■ TransAccel LLC
1159 Sonora Ct., Ste. 122
 Sunnyvale, CA 94086
Ph: (650)489-4151
Co. E-mail: info@transaccel.com
URL: http://www.transaccel.com
Contact: Wilson Chandra, Chief Executive Officer
Description: Fosters the growth of technology companies in the US and Asia. Also operates out of Asia and Australia. **Founded:** 2001.

37689 ■ VentureArchetypes (VA)
215 2nd St., at Howard,3rd. Fl.
 San Francisco, CA 94102
Free: 800-936-2594
URL: http://www.venturearchetypes.com
Contact: Nathan Beckord, Founder Consultant
E-mail: nathan@venturearchetypes.com
Facebook: www.facebook.com/VentureArchetypes
X (Twitter): x.com/startupventures
Description: Start-up consulting firm. Offers business development, strategy planning, and analysis services.

PUBLICATIONS

37690 ■ *Business Update*
222 N Garden St., Ste. 300
 Visalia, CA 93291
Ph: (559)734-5876
Co. E-mail: info@visaliachamber.org
URL: http://www.visaliachamber.org
Contact: Gail Zurek, President
URL(s): www.visaliachamber.org/business-update-newsletter
Released: Monthly **Availability:** Online.

37691 ■ *Business Update*
126 N Cloverdale Blvd.
 Cloverdale, CA 95425
Ph: (707)894-4470
Co. E-mail: info@cloverdalechamber.com
URL: http://cloverdalechamber.com
Contact: Erin Mewes, Director
Availability: Print.

37692 ■ *Comstock's: Business Insight for California's Capital Region*
2335 American River Dr., Ste. 410
 Sacramento, CA 95825-7088
Ph: (916)364-1000
Co. E-mail: ccpa@comstocksmag.com
URL: http://www.comstocksmag.com
Contact: Winnie Comstock-Carlson, President
E-mail: winnie@comstocksmag.com
URL(s): www.comstocksmag.com
Facebook: www.facebook.com/ComstocksMag
X (Twitter): x.com/comstocksmag
Instagram: www.instagram.com/comstocksmag
Released: Monthly **Price:** $25, for 1 year print; $40, for 2 yr. print; $50, for 3 years print; $4.95, for single copy. **Description:** Magazine highlighting business and industry trends, community issues, business leaders and their companies, and regional issues. **Availability:** Print; Online.

37693 ■ *Los Angeles Business Journal*
11150 Santa Monica Blvd., Ste. 350
 Los Angeles, CA 90025
Ph: (323)549-5225
Free: 855-293-9394
Fax: (323)549-5255
Co. E-mail: circulation1@labusinessjournal.com
URL: http://www.labusinessjournal.com
Contact: Josh Schimmels, Chief Executive Officer
E-mail: jschimmels@labusinessjournal.com
URL(s): labusinessjournal.com/about
Facebook: www.facebook.com/labusinessjournal
Linkedin: www.linkedin.com/company/los-angeles-business-journal
X (Twitter): x.com/LABJnews
Instagram: www.instagram.com/labusinessjournal
YouTube: www.youtube.com/channel/UCgxcHb58FSGcqNNJtHKhsGA
Released: Weekly **Price:** $149.95, for print and digital per year; $249.95, for 2 year print and online; $5, for back issue Jul. 8, 2024. **Description:** Newspaper (tabloid) covering local business news, business trends, executive profiles, and information for the Los Angeles area executive. **Availability:** Print; PDF; Online.

37694 ■ *Orange County Business Journal (OCBJ)*
18500 Von Karman Ave., Ste. 150
 Irvine, CA 92612
Ph: (949)833-8373
Co. E-mail: customerservice@ocbj.com
URL: http://www.ocbj.com
Contact: Richard Reisman, Chief Executive Officer
URL(s): www.ocbj.com/about
Facebook: www.facebook.com/OrangeCountyBusinessJournal
Linkedin: www.linkedin.com/company/ocbj/
X (Twitter): x.com/OCBizJournal
Instagram: www.instagram.com/ocbizjournal
YouTube: www.youtube.com/@orangecountybusinessjournal/featured

Ed: Pete Weitzner, Jerry Sullivan. **Released:** Weekly **Price:** $158, for 2 years 104 Issues; $99, for 1 year 52 Issues. **Description:** Delivers the complete package of news and information on Orange County's companies, industries and businesspeople. **Availability:** Print; Online.

37695 ■ Sacramento Business Journal
555 Capitol Mall, Ste. 200
Sacramento, CA 95814
Ph: (916)447-7661
Fax: (916)558-7898
Co. E-mail: sacramento@bizjournals.com
URL: http://www.bizjournals.com/sacramento
Contact: Stephanie Fretwell, Director
E-mail: sfretwell@bizjournals.com
Facebook: www.facebook.com/SacBiz
X (Twitter): x.com/Sacbiz
Instagram: www.instagram.com/sacbiz
Released: Weekly **Price:** $380, for nationwide access; $950, for nationwide + boI; $220, for print + online; $210, for online. **Description:** Local business newspaper. **Availability:** Print; Online; PDF. **Type:** Full-text.

37696 ■ San Diego Business Journal
4445 Eastgate Mall, Ste. 200
San Diego, CA 92121
Contact: Terri Cunningham, Contact
URL(s): www.sdbj.com
Facebook: www.facebook.com/people/San-Diego
 -Business-Journal/100067351284788
Linkedin: www.linkedin.com/company/san-diego
 -business-journal
X (Twitter): x.com/SDbusiness
YouTube: www.youtube.com/channel/UC7xBXg
 _LzaAkY1Ar8vy-Paw
Released: Weekly **Price:** $129, for 1 year print and online; $218, for 2 year print and online; $275, for 3 year print and online. **Description:** Metropolitan business newspaper specializing in investigative and enterprise reporting on San Diego County businesses and related issues. **Availability:** Print; PDF; Online.

37697 ■ Silicon Valley Business Journal
120 W Morehead St.
Charlotte, NC 28202
Co. E-mail: circhelp@bizjournals.com
URL: http://www.acbj.com
Contact: Mike Olivieri, Executive Vice President
URL(s): www.bizjournals.com/sanjose
Facebook: www.facebook.com/SVBizjournal
Linkedin: www.linkedin.com/company/san-jose-silicon
 -valley-business-journal
X (Twitter): x.com/svbizjournal
Instagram: www.instagram.com/
 siliconvalleybusinessjrnl
Ed: Cromwell Schubarth, Moryt Milo. **Released:** Weekly **Price:** $950, for premium unlimited 52 weeks; $350, for premium elite 52 weeks; $180, for digital only 52 weeks.; $190, for digital and print 52 weeks; $210, for digital only; $220, for digital + print; $380, for premium Nationwide Access; $220, for 1 year print; $4, for 4 weeks digital; $80, for 52 weeks digital access; $80, for 52 weeks digital & print. **Description:** Local business newspaper. **Availability:** Print; Online. **Type:** Full-text.

37698 ■ Uptown San Diego Examiner: Business News
3601 30th St.
San Diego, CA 92104
URL: http://uptownexaminer.com
URL(s): uptownexaminer.com
Released: Semiweekly (Wed. and Fri.) **Price:** $35, U.S. for annual subscription. **Description:** Newspaper of general circulation publishing all legal notices for both the City and County of San Diego. **Availability:** Print; Online.

PUBLISHERS

37699 ■ Bell Springs Publishing
PO Box 1240
Willits, CA 95490
Co. E-mail: publisher@bellsprings.com
URL: http://www.bellsprings.com
Description: Publishes small business and tax guidebooks also offers a pinball machine care and maintenance guidebook and its publications are available through online retailers and specialty shops. **Founded:** 1976. **Publications:** "Small Time Operator: How to Start Your Own Small Business, Keep Your Books, Pay Your Taxes & Stay Out of Trouble"; "422 Tax Deductions; Online Operator". **Training:** Small Business Workshops.

37700 ■ BizBest Media Corp.
860 Via de la Paz, Ste. E3-B
Pacific Palisades, CA 90272
Contact: Daniel Kehrer, Contact
Description: Publishes a small business resources directory. **Founded:** 1999.

37701 ■ California State University Press
2380 E Keats Ave., Mailstop MB99
Fresno, CA 93740-8024
Ph: (559)278-3056
Co. E-mail: benjaminkirk@mail.fresnostate.edu
URL: http://fresnostatecah.com/category/publishing/
 the-press-at-california-state-university-fresno
Description: Publishes books on art, drama, music, film, media, architecture, politics, business and autobiography. Reaches market through southern Illinois University Press. Does not accept unsolicited manuscripts. **Founded:** 1982.

37702 ■ Hunter Arts Publishing
PO Box 66578
Los Angeles, CA 90066
Ph: (310)842-8864
Fax: (310)842-8868
Co. E-mail: publisher@hunterarts.com
URL: http://www.headhuntersrevealed.com
Description: Publishes Headhunters Revealed! Career Secrets for Choosing and Using Professional Recruiters -an executive recruiter that exposes the mind and mechanics of the search industry to job-seeking professionals. Does not accept unsolicited manuscripts. **Founded:** 1999. **Publications:** *Headhunters Revealed: Career Secrets for Choosing and Using Professional Recruiters* (Quarterly).

37703 ■ Out of Your Mind..and Into the Marketplace
13381 White Sand Dr.
Tustin, CA 92780-4565
Ph: (714)544-0248
Fax: (714)730-1414
URL: http://www.business-plan.com
Contact: Linda Pinson, Contact
E-mail: lpinson@aol.com
Facebook: www.facebook.com/Out-of-Your-Mind-an
 d-Into-the-Marketplace-653552514664036
X (Twitter): x.com/omim2013
Description: Publishes on small and home-based business concerns, stressing step-by-step, hands-on approach to business start-up, record keeping, marketing and business plan preparation. Offers a business plan software program for windows. Reaches market through commission representatives, direct mail, trade sales and wholesalers. Does not accept unsolicited manuscripts. **Scope:** Business consulting firm that enables clients to create credible and defensible business plans that serve as guides throughout the lives of their business. Business plan software developer and consulting firm that specializes in step-by-step information for aspiring and current business owners. Provides information that is necessary to develop and/or expand marketable businesses. **Founded:** 1986. **Publications:** "Anatomy of a Business Plan"; "Steps to Small Business Start-up"; "The Hybrid Company"; "Keeping the Books"; "Starting your Home-Based Business"; "The Woman Entrepreneur"; "18 pasos para desarrollar tu negocio"; "Anatomia de un Plan del Negocio". **Training:** Be Your Own Boss: Steps to Small Business Start Up; Keeping Your Books: The Secret to Growth and Profit; Marketing: Developing and Implementing a Winning Marketing Strategy; Is Your Business Viable?: Pricing/Costing Your Product or Service; Propelling Your Company Into the Future: Write a Winning Business Plan; Business Planning Through the Use of Technology Using Automate Your Business Plan software in a computer laboratory. **Special Services:** Automate Your Business Plan.

37704 ■ Vince Emery Productions
PO Box 460279
San Francisco, CA 94146
Ph: (415)337-6000
Fax: (650)697-6048
Co. E-mail: returns@ipgbook.com
URL: http://www.emerybooks.com
Contact: Vince Emery, Contact
E-mail: vince@emery.com
Description: Publishes books on Internet businesses.

37705 ■ WBusiness Books
9682 Telstar Ave., Ste. 110
El Monte, CA 91731
Ph: (626)448-3448
Fax: (626)602-3817
Co. E-mail: info@academiclearningcompany.com
URL: http://www.newwinpublishing.com
Description: Publisher of business books, accepts unsolicited manuscripts and reaches the market through commission representatives. **Founded:** 2005.

37706 ■ Worthwhile Referral Sources (WRS)
13547 Ventura Blvd., No. 374
Sherman Oaks, CA 91423
Ph: (818)995-6646
Co. E-mail: info@wrswrs.com
URL: http://www.womensreferralservice.com
Contact: Nancy Sardella, President
URL(s): www.referral-guide.com
YouTube: www.youtube.com/user/WRSNetworking
Description: Publishes an annual directory of women-owned businesses, professional women, and their organizations and services. Reaches market through marketing representatives, direct mail, and telephone sales. Does not accept unsolicited manuscripts. **Founded:** 1977.

EARLY STAGE FINANCING

37707 ■ The Angels' Forum (TAF)
2665 Marine Way No. 1150
Mountain View, CA 94043
Contact: Carol M. Sands, Contact
Description: Early-stage investment group.

37708 ■ Arba Group
6300 Wilshire Blvd., Ste. 1800
Los Angeles, CA 90048
Contact: Ira Smedra, Chief Executive Officer
Description: Family-run investment group acting much like an angel investor to seed and fund companies in the Bay Area, Oregon, Seattle, and Chicago. **Industry Preferences:** Marketplace; fintech; SaaS; consumer/IOT; health and ed tech.

37709 ■ i/o ventures
San Francisco, CA
Co. E-mail: info@ventures.io
URL: http://ventures.io
Contact: Ashwin Navin, Partner
Description: An early-stage startup funding firm mentoring newly founded companies by providing seed funding, advice and connections. **Founded:** 2010.

37710 ■ Lombard Investments
950 John Daly Blvd., Ste. 260
Daly City, CA 94015
Ph: (415)397-5900
Fax: (415)397-5820
URL: http://lombardinvestments.com
Contact: Thomas Smith, Jr., Chief Executive Officer
Description: Private equity firm for companies in Southeast Asia. Also has offices in Thailand, Vietnam, and China. **Founded:** 1985. **Investment Policies:** Industry leaders with experienced and motivated management looking for equity in excess of $50 million. **Industry Preferences:** Food and beverages; retailing; financial services; media and entertainment; healthcare; education; energy.

STATE LISTINGS

37711 ■ North Bay Angels (NBA)
PO Box 1365
 Healdsburg, CA 95448
Ph: (707)431-4201
Co. E-mail: info@northbayangels.com
URL: http://www.northbayangels.com
Contact: Judy Puccioni, Executive Assistant
Description: Offers early-stage investment capital, advisory assistance, and mentoring to companies in the North Bay area. **Founded:** 1998. **Preferred Investment Size:** $250,000 to $1,000,000. **Investment Policies:** Unique market advantage addressing a critical need; functioning prototype of its product or business proposition; demonstrated market need for the product, service, or technology, . **Industry Preferences:** Healthcare; biotech; energy and cleantech; information technology; web-based businesses; communications technology; software.

37712 ■ Qualcomm Ventures
5775 Morehouse Dr.
 San Diego, CA 92121
URL: http://www.qualcommventures.com
Contact: Nan Zhou, Director
Linkedin: www.linkedin.com/company/qualcomm-ventures
X (Twitter): x.com/qualcommventure
Instagram: www.instagram.com/qcventures
YouTube: www.youtube.com/channel/UC4vkqVrgPzq_4YzyBf1E_ww
Description: Focused on innovation in the mobile ecosystem. Connects entrepreneurs to resources, relationships, and industry expertise. Also maintains offices in San Francisco, Israel, Europe, China, India, Korea, and Latin America. **Founded:** 2000. **Industry Preferences:** Mobile; artificial intelligence; automotive; digital health; internet.

EXPANSION AND GROWTH FINANCING

37713 ■ Costella Kirsch (CK)
3500 Alameda de las Pulgas, Ste. 150
 Menlo Park, CA 94025
Co. E-mail: info@costellakirsch.com
URL: http://www.costellakirsch.com
Contact: Beth Kelsey, Manager
E-mail: beth@costellakirsch.com
Description: Capital firm offering structured debt financing for emerging technology companies. . **Founded:** 1986.

VENTURE CAPITAL FIRM

37714 ■ Abingworth
3000 Sand Hill Rd., B1-145
 Menlo Park, CA 94025
Ph: (650)926-0600
Co. E-mail: info@abingworth.com
URL: http://www.abingworth.com
Contact: Kurt von Emster, Managing Partner
X (Twitter): x.com/Abingworthbio
Description: US arm of the transatlantic bioscience investment firm. Invests in drugs, devices, and diagnostics from seed-stage start-ups to publicly traded companies. **Founded:** 1973.

37715 ■ Accel
500 University Ave.
 Palo Alto, CA 94301
Ph: (650)614-4800
URL: http://www.accel.com
Contact: Rich Wong, Partner
Linkedin: www.linkedin.com/company/accel-vc
X (Twitter): x.com/accel
Description: Venture capital firm. Funds startups in the seed, early, and growth stages. **Founded:** 1983.

37716 ■ Alsop Louie Partners (ALP)
943 Howard St.
 San Francisco, CA 94103
Ph: (415)625-8752
URL: http://www.alsop-louie.com
Contact: Bill Crowell, Partner

Facebook: www.facebook.com/Alsop-Louie-Partners-100705716664097
X (Twitter): x.com/alsoplouie
Description: Early-stage risk-oriented technology venture capital firm. **Investment Policies:** Entrepreneurs with bold ideas and big dreams; new technologies and business models; companies that reshape the status quo.

37717 ■ AmBex Venture Partners LLC
1245 Oakmead Pky.
 Sunnyvale, CA 94085
Ph: (408)523-6000
Fax: (408)523-6060
Co. E-mail: info@ambex.com
URL: http://www.ambex.com
Contact: Chong-Moon Lee, Chief Executive Officer
Description: Venture capital firm for early- and growth-stage companies. **Founded:** 1996. **Investment Policies:** Information technology; pharmaceuticals; financial services; communication; Internet; bio science.

37718 ■ Amplify LA
1600 Main St.
 Venice, CA 90291
URL: http://amplify.la
Contact: Oded Noy, Managing Partner
Facebook: www.facebook.com/amplifyla
X (Twitter): x.com/amplifyla
Description: Amplifies startups by providing seed funding, access to additional capital, and an unmatched team of mentors and advisors who have a unique connection to media and entertainment. Every company accepted will receive up to $50K in seed funding and free workspace in our community entrepreneur facility in Venice.

37719 ■ Archer Venture Capital, LLC (AVC)
11390 W Olympic Blvd., Ste. 380
 Los Angeles, CA 90064
Co. E-mail: info@archervc.com
URL: http://www.archervc.com
Contact: George Bell, Senior Partner
Linkedin: www.linkedin.com/company/archervc
Description: Investment firm and start-up advisory platform for growth-stage technology companies. **Investment Policies:** Category-leading products in sizeable markets; passionate management teams; proven track record. **Industry Preferences:** Software; big data; digital media.

37720 ■ Asset Management Ventures (AMV)
1300 El Camino Real., Ste. 100
 Menlo Park, CA 94025
Ph: (650)621-8808
URL: http://assetman.com
Contact: Skip Fleshman, Partner
Linkedin: www.linkedin.com/company/asset-management-ventures
Description: Early-stage venture capital firm. **Founded:** 1965. **Investment Policies:** Integrity; transparency; deep technical and market knowledge. **Industry Preferences:** Digital health; technology; life science.

37721 ■ Backstage Capital
6121 Sunset Blvd.
 Los Angeles, CA 90028
URL: http://backstagecapital.com
Contact: Arlan Hamilton, Founder Managing Partner
X (Twitter): x.com/Backstage_Cap
Description: Invests in startups owned by people of color, women, and the LGBT community. **Founded:** 2015.

37722 ■ Base Ventures
Berkeley, CA
Co. E-mail: hello@base.ventures
URL: http://www.base.ventures
Contact: Erik Moore, Managing Director Co-Founder
Linkedin: www.linkedin.com/company/baseventures
X (Twitter): x.com/basevc
Description: Venture capital and private equity fund investing in technology companies. **Founded:** 2013.

California ■ 37728

37723 ■ Bessemer Venture Partners (BVP)
889 Winslow St., Ste. 500
 Redwood City, CA 94063
Ph: (650)853-7000
URL: http://www.bvp.com
Contact: Rob Arditi, Partner
YouTube: www.youtube.com/c/BessemerVenturePartners
Description: An investment firm that helps people from the seed stage to growth stage in creating companies. **Scope:** An investment firm that helps people from the seed stage to growth stage in creating companies. **Founded:** 1911. **Preferred Investment Size:** $1,000,000 to $10,000,000. **Industry Preferences:** Communications and media, Internet specific, computer software and services, semiconductors and other electronics, consumer related, medical and health, industrial and energy, and biotechnology, computer hardware, and other products.

37724 ■ Big Basin Capital
19925 Stevens Creek Blvd., Ste. 100
 Cupertino, CA 95014
Co. E-mail: ideas@bigbasincapital.com
URL: http://www.bigbasincapital.com
Contact: Taekkyung Lee, Partner
Linkedin: www.linkedin.com/company/big-basin-capital
Description: A venture capital firm based in Silicon Valley investing in early-stage startups in Korea and the United States. **Founded:** 2013.

37725 ■ Black Diamond Ventures
450 N Brand Blvd., Ste. 600
 Glendale, CA 91203
Ph: (818)245-6250
Co. E-mail: info@bdventures.com
URL: http://bdventures.com
Contact: Ana Quintana, Managing Partner
E-mail: ana@bdventures.com
Linkedin: www.linkedin.com/company/black-diamond-ventures
X (Twitter): x.com/bdventures1
Description: Venture capital firm focused on early- to mid-stage companies. **Founded:** 1998. **Preferred Investment Size:** $2,000,000 to $10,000,000. **Investment Policies:** Visionary entrepreneurs developing market-transforming technologies or products. **Industry Preferences:** Biotechnology; medical devices; semiconductor design; data analytics; mobile platforms.

37726 ■ Brainstorm Ventures
4 Embarcadero Ctr., Ste. 1400
 San Francisco, CA 94111
Co. E-mail: team@brainstorm.vc
URL: http://brainstorm.vc
Contact: Ariel Jaduszliwer, Managing Partner
Linkedin: www.linkedin.com/company/brainstormventures
X (Twitter): x.com/BrainstormVC
Description: Seed and early-stage venture capital firm. Also maintains an office in Mexico City. **Founded:** 1999. **Investment Policies:** Consumer or enterprise startups developing innovative technologies or applying existing technologies to new business models and markets.

37727 ■ ChinaVest
PO Box 470985
 San Francisco, CA 94147
Co. E-mail: info@chinavest.com.cn
URL: http://www.chinavest.com/index.aspx
Contact: Robert Theleen, Chief Executive Officer
Description: Private equity and venture capital arm of ChinaVest Merchant Bank. **Founded:** 1981.

37728 ■ Claremont Creek Ventures (CCV)
300 Frank H. Ogawa Plz., Ste. 350
 Oakland, CA 94612
Ph: (510)740-5001
URL: http://claremontcreek.com
Contact: Nat Goldhaber, Co-Founder Managing Director
Description: Seed and early-stage venture capital firm. Invests in digital solutions. **Founded:** 2005.

Small Business Sourcebook • 42nd Edition

37729 ■ The Column Group (TCG)
1 Letterman Dr. Bldg. D, Ste. DM-900
San Francisco, CA 94129
Ph: (415)865-2050
Fax: (415)255-2048
URL: http://www.thecolumngroup.com
Contact: Karina Tin, Manager
Linkedin: www.linkedin.com/company/the-column-group

Description: Science-driven venture capital firm for early-stage drug discovery companies.

37730 ■ Cycad Group
1270 Coast Village Cir., Ste. 100
Santa Barbara, CA 93108
Ph: (805)684-6515
URL: http://cycadvc.com
Contact: K. Leonard Judson, President

Description: Venture capital firm for early-stage technology-driven businesses. **Founded:** 2000. **Investment Policies:** Companies with disruptive technologies, innovative products, enabling solutions, and exceptional entrepreneurs. **Industry Preferences:** Life sciences (therapeutics, medical devices, diagnostics, analytical tools); energy technologies; advanced materials; chemical processes. .

37731 ■ DBL Partners
1 Montgomery St., Ste. 2375
San Francisco, CA 94104
Ph: (415)568-2901
Fax: (415)956-2561
URL: http://www.dbl.vc
Contact: Paula Uniacke, Director
E-mail: paula@dbl.vc

Description: Venture capital firm for innovation acceleration. Looks for social impact and financial success. Also has an office in Palo Alto. **Industry Preferences:** Cleantech; information technology; sustainable products and services; healthcare.

37732 ■ DragonVenture
2882 Sand Hill Rd., Ste. 150
Menlo Park, CA 94025
Ph: (650)233-9000
Fax: (650)234-8533
Co. E-mail: info@dragonventure.com
URL: http://www.dragonventure.com
Contact: Tony Luh, Co-Founder

Description: Early-stage investment and advisory services firm. Identifies and capitalizes on China-centric business and investment opportunities. Also maintains offices in Shanghai and Beijing. **Investment Policies:** Exceptional applications, management teams, and businesses based on defensible technologies and China-centric opportunities and clearly defined exit strategies.

37733 ■ Ecosystem Ventures
PO Box 3347
Saratoga, CA 95070
Ph: (408)426-8040
Co. E-mail: info@ecosystemventures.com
URL: http://ecosystemventures-ice.com
Contact: Alexander Fries, President
E-mail: fries@ecosystemventures.com

Description: Venture capital and strategic consulting firm for seed- and early-stage entrepreneurs dedicated to building sustainable companies around significant technologies. Also maintains an office Switzerland.

37734 ■ Emerging Technology Partners LLC (ETP)
425 Eccles Ave.
South San Francisco, CA 94080
Co. E-mail: info@etpvc.com
URL: http://etpvc.com
Contact: Dr. Wei-Wu He, Founder Partner

Description: Biomedical investment fund with a cross-border focus. Offers capital and assistance in building breakthrough diagnostic and therapeutic products in the United States and China. Facilitate strategic alliances, recruits management, and acquires new products and technologies. **Founded:** 2000. **Industry Preferences:** Life sciences.

37735 ■ Entertainment Media Ventures (EMV)
5225 Wilshire Blvd., Ste. 777
Los Angeles, CA 90036
Ph: (323)904-3777
Co. E-mail: info@emventures.com
URL: http://www.emventures.com
Contact: Sandford R. Climan, President

Description: Venture capital firm. Bridges the worlds of business, finance, and entertainment. Offers business acceleration services and global entertainment consulting. **Founded:** 1999.

37736 ■ Fenox Venture Capital
2680 N 1st St., Ste. 250
San Jose, CA 95134
Contact: M. D. Anis Uzzaman, Manager

Description: Venture capital firm for emerging technology companies. Specialized in assisting entrepreneurs with expansion in North America, Asia, and Europe. Operates out of 14 location in eight countries. **Industry Preferences:** IT; artificial intelligence; IoT; robotics; big data; virtual reality; augmented reality; finech; next generation technologies.

37737 ■ Finistere Ventures Inc. (FV)
17265 Amarillo Rd.
Ramona, CA 92065
Contact: Arama Kukutai, Manager

Description: Early-stage investment firm. **Founded:** 2006. **Industry Preferences:** Digital; life science; chemistry; agronomy.

37738 ■ Founders First Capital Partners (FFCP)
9920 Pacific Heights Blvd., Ste. 430
San Diego, CA 92121
Ph: (858)264-4102
Co. E-mail: info@f1stcp.com
URL: http://foundersfirstcapitalpartners.com
Contact: Kim T. Folsom, Chief Executive Officer
Facebook: www.facebook.com/f1stcp
Linkedin: www.linkedin.com/company/founders-first-capital-partners
X (Twitter): x.com/f1stcp
Instagram: www.instagram.com/f1stcp
YouTube: www.youtube.com/channel/UCadqC8UNVFH0c_6NBdkE-hA

Description: Venture capital firm providing support to startup companies owned by minorities, women, and military veterans. **Founded:** 2015.

37739 ■ GV Management Company, LLC
Alphabet Inc.
1600 Amphitheatre Pky.
Mountain View, CA 94043
Ph: (650)253-0000
URL: http://www.abc.xyz
Contact: David Krane, Chief Executive Officer

Description: Capital venture firm investing in the robotics, transportation, agriculture, and other various industries. **Founded:** 2009.

37740 ■ Hillcrest Venture Partners
950 N Isabel St.
Glendale, CA 91207
Ph: (818)492-9800
URL: http://www.hillcrestvp.com
Contact: Courtney Hall, Managing Director Co-Founder

Description: Venture capital firm for seed- to growth-stage technology companies. **Investment Policies:** Capital-efficient companies in California undergoing transformational change (hardware to software; services to SaaS; legacy products to new products; paid beta to commercial roll-out). **Industry Preferences:** Communications infrastructure; enterprise applications; financial technology; information technology infrastructure; life science research tools; wireless.

37741 ■ Impact Venture Capital
801 K St.
Sacramento, CA 95814
Ph: (650)837-3200
Co. E-mail: info@impactvc.com
URL: http://impactvc.com
Contact: Eric Ball, Partner
Facebook: www.facebook.com/impactVC
X (Twitter): x.com/VCimpact
YouTube: www.youtube.com/channel/UCXxumLFZkytZGG4INsbNOXg

Description: A business accelerator that works to identify, capitalize, and support the next generation of world-class IT startups. **Founded:** 2016.

37742 ■ Khosla Ventures
2128 Sand Hill Rd.
Menlo Park, CA 94025
Ph: (650)376-8500
Fax: (650)926-9590
Co. E-mail: information@khoslaventures.com
URL: http://khoslaventures.com
Contact: Avisha Mehra, Director
E-mail: avisha@khoslaventures.com
URL(s): khoslaventuresacquisitionco.com
Linkedin: www.linkedin.com/company/khosla-ventures
X (Twitter): x.com/khoslaventures
YouTube: www.youtube.com/user/khoslaventures

Description: Venture capital firm interested in solving large problems with technology solutions. **Founded:** 2004. **Investment Policies:** Prefers technology or business innovation, the ability to disrupt large markets, short innovation cycles; favors technology risk over market risk. **Industry Preferences:** Consumer, enterprise, education, advertising, financial services, semiconductors, health, big data, agriculture, food, sustainable energy, and robotics.

37743 ■ Kiva
986 Mission St., 4th Fl.
San Francisco, CA 94103
Ph: (828)479-5482
Co. E-mail: contactus@kiva.org
URL: http://www.kiva.org/borrow
Contact: Austin Choi, General Counsel
Facebook: www.facebook.com/kiva
Linkedin: www.linkedin.com/company/kiva-org
X (Twitter): x.com/Kiva
Instagram: www.instagram.com/kiva.org

Description: Helps small business owners in San Francisco get the financing they need to grow and create jobs. **Founded:** 2005.

37744 ■ Kleiner Perkins (KPCB)
2750 Sand Hill Rd.
Menlo Park, CA 94025
URL: http://www.kleinerperkins.com
Contact: Annie Case, Partner
X (Twitter): x.com/kleinerperkins

Description: Firm provides venture capital and private equity investment services. **Founded:** 1972. **Preferred Investment Size:** $500,000 minimum. **Industry Preferences:** Internet specific, computer software and services, computer hardware, communications and media, semiconductors and other electronics, medical and health, biotechnology, industrial and energy, consumer related, and other products.

37745 ■ Longitude Capital
2740 Sand Hill Rd., 2nd Fl.
Menlo Park, CA 94025
Ph: (650)854-5700
URL: http://www.longitudecapital.com
Contact: Brian Liu, Principal

Description: Venture growth firm specializing in biotechnology and medical technology companies that improve clinical outcomes, enhance quality of life, or reduce system costs. Also operates out of Greenwich, Connecticut. **Founded:** 2006.

37746 ■ Lucey Fund
Santa Monica, CA
URL: http://lucey.fund

Description: Venture capital firm that works to fund the development, design, branding, and marketing of their products. Guides startups through the development of their company and helps them choose the right direction.

37747 ■ MaC Venture Capital
6255 Sunset Blvd.
Los Angeles, CA 90028

URL: http://macventurecapital.com
Contact: Adrian Fenty, Managing Partner
Linkedin: www.linkedin.com/company/mac-venture-capital
X (Twitter): x.com/MaCVentureCap
Instagram: www.instagram.com/macventurecap
Description: Early stage venture capital firm investing in minority-owned tech companies. **Founded:** 2019.

37748 ■ Merus Capital
505 Hamilton Ave., Ste. 315
  Palo Alto, CA 94301
Contact: Becky DeGeorge, Contact
Description: Capital firm. Invests in real software solving real problems. **Founded:** 2008.

37749 ■ Mighty Capital
419 14th St.
  San Francisco, CA 94103
Linkedin: www.linkedin.com/company/mighty-capital
Description: Early-growth venture capital firm. **Founded:** 2017. **Investment Policies:** Strong leadership team; clear go-to-market strategy; proven product-market fit.

37750 ■ Mitsui Global Investment (MGI)
535 Middlefield Rd., Ste. 100
  Menlo Park, CA 94025
Ph: (650)234-5000
Fax: (650)323-1516
Co. E-mail: mgicontactsjfvz@mitsui.com
URL: http://mitsui-global.com
Contact: Kiyoshi Okubo, President
Description: Venture capital firm. Also maintains offices in Israel and Japan. **Industry Preferences:** IT and communication; healthcare; industrials.

37751 ■ MMC Technology Ventures (MMCT)
Marcus & Millichap, Inc.
777 S California Ave.
  Palo Alto, CA 94304
Ph: (818)212-2250
Fax: (818)212-2260
URL: http://www.marcusmillichap.com
Contact: Alex Yarmolinsky, Managing Partner
Description: Venture capital firm focused on early stage, post Series A investment. **Investment Policies:** Experienced management teams; ideas with traction. **Industry Preferences:** Real estate.

37752 ■ Moore Venture Partners (MVP)
San Diego, CA
Ph: (760)809-4791
URL: http://www.moorevp.com
Contact: Terry Moore, Managing Partner
E-mail: terry@moorevp.com
Linkedin: www.linkedin.com/company/moore-venture-partners
X (Twitter): x.com/thestorylab
Instagram: www.instagram.com/thestorylab
Description: Venture capital firm. Invests in early- and growth-stage opportunities from underserved markets in Southern California. **Founded:** 2011. **Industry Preferences:** Life science; technology.

37753 ■ NGP Capital (NGP)
418 Florence St.
  Palo Alto, CA 94301
Co. E-mail: finance@ngpcap.com
URL: http://www.ngpcap.com
Contact: Paul Asel, Partner
Linkedin: www.linkedin.com/company/ngpcapital
X (Twitter): x.com/NGPCapital
YouTube: www.youtube.com/channel/UCwqCHnifQ7HBF7Y3-d72qIQ
Description: Specializes in growth-stage investment-seeking entrepreneurs building intelligent devices and services connecting everybody and everything. **Founded:** 2005.

37754 ■ OMERS Ventures
537 Hamilton Ave.
  Palo Alto, CA 94301
Ph: (650)352-5868
Co. E-mail: info@omersventures.com
URL: http://www.omersventures.com

Contact: Michael Yang, Managing Partner
E-mail: myang@omersventures.com
Facebook: www.facebook.com/OMERSventures
X (Twitter): x.com/omersventures
Description: Multi-stage venture capital investor for scaling disruptive tech companies. Also has offices in Toronto and London.

37755 ■ O'Reilly Alpha Tech Ventures (OATV)
O'Reilly Media Inc.
1 Lombard St., Ste. 303
  San Francisco, CA 94111
Ph: (707)827-7000
Fax: (707)829-0104
Co. E-mail: orders@oreilly.com
URL: http://www.oreilly.com
Contact: Tim O'Reilly, Chief Executive Officer
Description: Early-stage investment firm for innovative technology companies. **Founded:** 2005.

37756 ■ Parakletos Ventures
175 Notech Pkwy., Ste. 200
  San Jose, CA 95134
Co. E-mail: info@parakletos.com
URL: http://www.parakletos.com
Contact: Dr. Paul H. J. Kim, Managing Partner
Description: Boutique venture capital firm for early-stage companies in Silicon Valley. **Industry Preferences:** Telecommunication infrastructure; semiconductor; wireless industries.

37757 ■ Precursor Ventures
580 Pacific Ave.
  San Francisco, CA 94133
Co. E-mail: hello@precursorvc.com
URL: http://precursorvc.com
Contact: Charles Hudson, Managing Partner
Facebook: www.facebook.com/precursorvc
X (Twitter): x.com/PrecursorVC
Description: Venture capital firm providing funding to technology startups. **Founded:** 2015.

37758 ■ Roda Group
2217 5th St.
  Berkeley, CA 94710-2216
Ph: (510)649-1900
Co. E-mail: info@rodagroup.com
URL: http://rodagroup.com
Contact: Mary Ahrens, Director, Finance
E-mail: mary@rodagroup.com
Description: Seed-stage venture capital firm focused on clean technology. **Founded:** 1997.

37759 ■ Samsung Ventures America (SVA)
2440 Sand Hill Rd., Ste. 303
  Menlo Park, CA 94025
URL: http://www.samsungventures.com
Contact: Liam Ahn, Contact
Description: Venture investment arm of Samsung Group for the discovery and development of small and medium-sized future-oriented businesses and technology, . **Industry Preferences:** Semiconductors; telecommunication; software; internet; bio engineering; medical.

37760 ■ SEC Ventures
100 Pine St., Ste. 1250
  San Francisco, CA 94111
Ph: (415)462-5703
Co. E-mail: hello@secventures.com
URL: http://www.secventures.com
Contact: Steve Chen, Founder
Linkedin: www.linkedin.com/company/sec-ventures
Description: Offers investments, software solutions, and strategic advisory services to early-stage companies.

37761 ■ Sequoia Capital
2800 Sand Hill Rd.
  Menlo Park, CA 94025
Linkedin: www.linkedin.com/company/sequoia
Description: Venture capital firm provides investment services. **Founded:** 1972. **Preferred Investment Size:** $100,000 to $100,000,000. **Industry Preferences:** Internet specific, communications and media, computer software and services, computer hardware, other products, semiconductors and other electronics, medical and health, consumer related, biotechnology, industrial and energy.

37762 ■ StartEngine (SE)
8300 McConnell Ave.
  Los Angeles, CA 90045
Co. E-mail: contact@startengine.com
URL: http://www.startengine.com
Contact: Howard Marks, Chief Executive Officer
Facebook: www.facebook.com/StartEngineLA
Linkedin: www.linkedin.com/company/startengined
X (Twitter): x.com/StartEngineLA
Instagram: www.instagram.com/startenginela
Description: Helps individuals invest in private companies on a public platform, thereby helping entrepreneurs achieve their dreams. **Founded:** 2011.

37763 ■ Startup Capital Ventures (SCV)
535 Middlefield Rd., Ste. 280
  Menlo Park, CA 94025
Ph: (650)461-8100
Co. E-mail: info@startupcv.com
URL: http://startupcv.com
Contact: Donavan Kealoha, Director
Description: Invests in early-stage capital-efficient B2B technology companies with proof of first revenue. Also maintains an office in Hawaii. **Founded:** 2005. **Preferred Investment Size:** $250,000 to $1,000,000. **Industry Preferences:** Fintech; Cloud/SaaS; security; healthcare IT; IoT.

37764 ■ Sunrise Ventures, LLC
6190 La Fremontia
  Rancho Santa Fe, CA 92067
Ph: (858)756-6820
Fax: (858)756-6838
Co. E-mail: sunrise@sunriseventures.com
URL: http://www.sunriseventures.com
Contact: Jason Karches, Partner
Description: Venture capital firm for early-stage private companies. . **Industry Preferences:** Internet/intranet infrastructure; enabling technology; ecommerce; enterprise application software; service and content sectors.

37765 ■ Thomvest Ventures (TV)
138 S Pk. St.
  San Francisco, CA 94107
Ph: (415)329-8400
Co. E-mail: info@thomvest.com
URL: http://thomvest.com
Contact: Eve Espinueva, Manager, Operations
Facebook: www.facebook.com/thomvest
X (Twitter): x.com/thomvest
YouTube: www.youtube.com/channel/UCJXoN2HLiQ_xzfYlkNAV97w
Description: Cross-stage venture capital fund for Peter Thomson, whose family owns the majority of Thomson Reuters. Works out of Silicon Valley and Toronto. **Founded:** 1996. **Industry Preferences:** Financial and real estate technology; cybersecurity and cloud infrastructure; sales and marketing technology.

37766 ■ TPG Growth II Management, LLC
TPG Inc.
345 California St., Ste. 3300
  San Francisco, CA 94104
Ph: (415)743-1500
Fax: (415)743-1501
URL: http://www.tpg.com
Contact: Arun Agarwal, Partner
Description: Specializes in growth equity and middle-market buyout opportunities across the U.S., Europe, Africa, and Asia. Draws on geographic-specific experience and global operational resources. **Founded:** 2007. **Industry Preferences:** Media; technology; industrials.

37767 ■ Transmedia Capital
717 Market St., Ste. 100
  San Francisco, CA 94103
Co. E-mail: info@transmediacapital.com
URL: http://transmediacapital.com
Contact: Chris Redlitz, Partner

Description: An early-stage technology venture fund providing deep domain expertise, operating experience, and advisory relationships.

37768 ■ Vertex Ventures
Vertex Venture Holdings Ltd.
345 California Ave.
Palo Alto, CA 94306
Ph: 65 6 828-8088
Fax: 65 6 828 8090
Co. E-mail: partnerships@vertexholdings.com
URL: http://www.vertexholdings.com
Contact: Raluca Mackey, Director
Facebook: www.facebook.com/vertexventuresofficial
Linkedin: www.linkedin.com/company/vertex-ventures
X (Twitter): x.com/VertexVentures

Description: Venture capital firm focused on transforming operations, technology and investments at foundational companies.

37769 ■ Vivo Capital (VC)
192 Lytton Ave.
Palo Alto, CA 94301
Ph: (650)688-0818
Co. E-mail: info@vivocapital.com
URL: http://vivocapital.com
Contact: Albert Chang, Executive Director

Description: Healthcare investment firm. Also maintains offices in Beijing, Shanghai, Taipei, and Hong Kong. **Founded:** 1996.

37770 ■ Walden Venture Capital (WVC)
2105 Woodside Rd.
Woodside, CA 94062
Ph: (415)391-7225
Co. E-mail: info@waldenvc.com
URL: http://www.waldenvc.com
Contact: Matt Miller, Managing Director

Description: Firm provides small business development, general management, marketing and financial management services through investment banking and venture capital. **Scope:** Firm provides small business development, general management, marketing and financial management services through investment banking and venture capital. **Founded:** 1970. **Special Services:** SaaS; Cloud.

37771 ■ Wasabi Ventures LLC (WVP)
San Mateo, CA
URL: http://www.wasabivp.com
Contact: Chris Yeh, Co-Founder Managing Partner

Description: Venture capital firm offering resources to emerging companies. Services include fundraising, business planning, product marketing, sales, technology, and development. Also maintains offices in New Hampshire, Maryland, and Ukraine. **Founded:** 2003.

Colorado

ASSOCIATIONS AND OTHER ORGANIZATIONS

37772 ■ Association of Fundraising Professionals Colorado Chapter
c/o DeAnn Acosta., Executive Director
PO Box 24745
Denver, CO 80224
Ph: (303)394-6388
Co. E-mail: info@afpcc.org
URL: http://community.afpglobal.org/afpcocolorado chapter/home
Contact: DeAnn Acosta, CFRE, Executive Director
E-mail: deann@afpcc.org
Facebook: www.facebook.com/afpcolo
X (Twitter): x.com/AFPColo
Description: Fosters the development and growth of fundraising professionals. Promotes high ethical standards in the fundraising profession. Provides training opportunities for fundraising professionals. **Geographic Preference:** State.

37773 ■ Business Network International Denver Metro
3430 Toringdon Way
Charlotte, NC 28277
Free: 855-264-2673
URL: http://bnicolorado.com
Contact: Jon Lyon, Managing Director
Description: Provides both men and women a structured environment for the development and exchange of quality business referrals. Offers members the opportunity to share ideas and contacts. **Geographic Preference:** Local.

37774 ■ Colorado Business Association (CBA)
1600 Broadway, Ste. 2500
Denver, CO 80202
Ph: (303)517-2568
Co. E-mail: info@coloradosbdc.org
URL: http://cbahq.com
Contact: Sharon King, Executive Director
E-mail: sharon.king@bouldersbdc.com
Facebook: www.facebook.com/coloradosbdc
X (Twitter): twitter.com/coloradosbdc
Instagram: www.instagram.com/coloradosbdc
YouTube: www.youtube.com/channel/UC3ofIWQN dHxmNFFHGsKZeKw/videos
Description: Seeks to promote the state of Colorado on a regional and national level with the goal of enabling economic and workforce growth within organizations.

37775 ■ International Association of Women South Denver Chapter
Denver, CO
URL: http://community.iawomen.com/denver/home
Contact: Katie Perry, Contact
Description: Serves as network of accomplished women united to achieve professional goals. Provides a forum for sharing ideas and experiences of professional women regarding career success. Promotes an active business and networking community from all industries. **Geographic Preference:** Local.

37776 ■ International Association of Women West Denver Chapter
Denver, CO
URL: http://community.iawomen.com/denver/home
Description: Serves as network of accomplished women united to achieve professional goals. Provides a forum for sharing ideas and experiences of professional women regarding career success. Promotes an active business and networking community from all industries. **Geographic Preference:** Local.

37777 ■ Pledge 1% Colorado (EFCO)
1123 Spruce St.
Boulder, CO 80302
URL: http://pledge1colorado.org
Contact: Matt Zwiebel, Sr., Executive Director
E-mail: matt@pledge1colorado.org
Facebook: www.facebook.com/Pledge1Colorado
Linkedin: www.linkedin.com/company/pledge 1colorado
X (Twitter): x.com/Pledge1CO
Description: Encourages philanthropic work within corporate communities. Provides volunteer day programs, training for nonprofit board service and seminars on corporate social responsibility and philanthropy to boost employee involvement. Offers resources, consulting services, and strategic and practical support to assist companies in establishing a culture of philanthropy and community participation. **Founded:** 2007. **Geographic Preference:** State.

37778 ■ Rocky Mountain Agribusiness Association (RMAA)
12110 N Pecos St., Ste. 220
Westminster, CO 80234
Ph: (303)280-5208
Co. E-mail: info@rmagbiz.org
URL: http://rmagbiz.org
Contact: Gary Leeper, Executive Director
E-mail: gary@imigroup.org
Facebook: www.facebook.com/RockyMoun tainAgribusinessAssociation
X (Twitter): x.com/RMAgBiz
Description: Serves as an advocate for agribusiness across the Rocky Mountain region. Provides information and programs to develop environmental concerns in the agribusiness industries in Colorado and adjoining states. **Geographic Preference:** Local.

37779 ■ Rocky Mountain Business Travel Association (RMBTA)
PO Box 890
Firestone, CO 80520
Co. E-mail: rmbtadenver@msn.com
URL: http://rockymountainbta.org
Contact: Laurie Etcheverry, President
E-mail: president@rockymountainbta.org
Facebook: www.facebook.com/GBTARockyMtn
X (Twitter): x.com/gbtarockymtn
Instagram: www.instagram.com/gbta_rm
Description: Represents travel managers and providers. Promotes the value of the travel manager in meeting corporate travel needs and financial goals. Cultivates a positive public image of the corporate travel industry. Protects the interests of members and their corporations in legislative and regulatory matters. Promotes safety, security, efficiency and quality travel. Provides a forum for the exchange of information and ideas among members. **Founded:** 1982. **Geographic Preference:** Regional.

37780 ■ Rocky Mountain Venture Capital Association (RMVCA)
798 Pope Dr.
Erie, CO 80516
Co. E-mail: support@rockymountainvca.com
URL: http://www.rockymountainvca.com
Contact: Nanette Schunk, Executive Director
E-mail: nanette@rockymountainvca.com
X (Twitter): x.com/RockyMtnVCA
Description: Represents entrepreneurs, venture capitals, and their service providers. **Industry Preferences:** Technology; cleantech; LOHAS; biotech; consumer products.

SMALL BUSINESS DEVELOPMENT CENTERS

37781 ■ Boulder Small Business Development Center (SBDC)
1001 Arapahoe Ave.
Boulder, CO 80302
Ph: (303)442-1475
Co. E-mail: admin@bouldersbdc.com
URL: http://www.bouldersbdc.com
Contact: Jamie Brandess, Director
E-mail: jamie.brandess@bouldersbdc.com
Facebook: www.facebook.com/bouldersbdc
Linkedin: www.linkedin.com/company/boulder-small -business-development-center
X (Twitter): x.com/bouldersbdc
YouTube: www.youtube.com/channel/UC3gFG 6RvKQYMIY2oMFp_wrA
Description: Represents and promotes the small business sector. Provides management assistance to current and prospective small business owners. Helps to improve management skills and expand the products and services of members. **Founded:** 1994. **Geographic Preference:** Local.

37782 ■ Colorado Small Business Development Center (CSBDC)
1600 Broadway, Ste. 2500
Denver, CO 80202
Ph: (303)892-3840
Co. E-mail: info@coloradosbdc.org
URL: http://www.coloradosbdc.org
Contact: Joey Jenkins, Director
E-mail: joey.jenkins@state.co.us
Facebook: www.facebook.com/coloradosbdc
X (Twitter): x.com/coloradosbdc
Instagram: www.instagram.com/coloradosbdc

YouTube: www.youtube.com/channel/UC3oflWQN
dHxmNFFHGsKZeKw

Description: Dedicated to helping existing and new businesses grow and prosper in Colorado by providing free and confidential consulting and no- or low-cost training programs. **Founded:** 1987. **Geographic Preference:** State.

37783 ■ Colorado Springs Small Business Development Center

559 E Pikes Peak Ave., Ste. 101
  Colorado Springs, CO 80903
Ph: (719)667-3803
Co. E-mail: sbdc@elpasoco.com
URL: http://www.pikespeaksbdc.org
Contact: Aikta Marcoulier, Executive Director
Facebook: www.facebook.com/pikespeaksbdc
Linkedin: www.linkedin.com/company/pikespeaksbdc
X (Twitter): x.com/pikespeakSBDC
Instagram: www.instagram.com/pikespeaksbdc
YouTube: www.youtube.com/channel/UChhNza8e
1qFj8HkyCxSAg7A

Description: Represents and promotes the small business sector. Provides management assistance to current and prospective small business owners. Helps to improve management skills and expand the products and services of members. **Geographic Preference:** Local.

37784 ■ Denver Metro Small Business Development Center

1445 Market St.
  Denver, CO 80202
Ph: (303)620-8076
Co. E-mail: info@denversbdc.org
URL: http://www.denversbdc.org
Contact: China Califf, Officer
Facebook: www.facebook.com/denversbdc
Linkedin: www.linkedin.com/company/denver-metro
  -sbdc
X (Twitter): x.com/denversbdc

Description: Represents and promotes the small business sector. Provides management assistance to current and prospective small business owners. Helps to improve management skills and expand the products and services of members. **Geographic Preference:** Local.

37785 ■ Grand Junction Small Business Development Center (SBDC)

2591 Legacy Way
  Grand Junction, CO 81503
Ph: (970)243-5242
Fax: (970)241-0771
Co. E-mail: frontdesk@gjincubator.org
URL: http://gjincubator.org/grand-junction-sbdc
Contact: Steve Ammentorp, President
Facebook: www.facebook.com/GJIncubator
Linkedin: www.linkedin.com/company/business
  -incubator-center
X (Twitter): x.com/Biz_Incubator
Instagram: www.instagram.com/gjincubator

Description: Represents and promotes the small business sector. Provides management assistance to current and prospective small business owners. Helps to improve management skills and expand the products and services of members. **Geographic Preference:** Local.

37786 ■ La Junta Small Business Development Center

1802 Colorado Ave.
  La Junta, CO 81050
Ph: (719)384-6800
Contact: Mickie Lewis, Executive Director
E-mail: mickie.lewis-gemici@ojc.edu

Description: Represents and promotes the small business sector. Provides management assistance to current and prospective small business owners. Helps to improve management skills and expand the products and services of members. **Geographic Preference:** Local.

37787 ■ Larimer County Small Business Development Center (SBDC)

320 E Vine Dr., Ste. 303
  Fort Collins, CO 80524
Ph: (970)498-9295
Co. E-mail: info@larimersbdc.org
URL: http://larimersbdc.org
Contact: Hope Hartman, Executive Director
Facebook: www.facebook.com/LarimerSBDC
Linkedin: www.linkedin.com/company/larimer-county
  -small-business-development-center-sbdc-
X (Twitter): x.com/LarimerSBDC
Instagram: www.instagram.com/larimer_sbdc

Description: Represents and promotes the small business sector. Provides management assistance to current and prospective small business owners. Helps to improve management skills and expand the products and services of members. **Founded:** 1987. **Geographic Preference:** Local.

37788 ■ Loveland Center for Business Development (LCBD)

5400 Stone Creek Cir., Ste. 200
  Loveland, CO 80538
Ph: (970)667-4106
Co. E-mail: info@lovelandbusiness.com
URL: http://www.lovelandbusiness.com
Contact: Mindy McCloughan, President
Linkedin: www.linkedin.com/company/loveland-busi-
  ness-development-center

Description: Provides management assistance to current and prospective small business owners in Loveland. **Founded:** 1990. **Geographic Preference:** Local.

37789 ■ Metro Small Business Development Center

1445 Market St.
  Denver, CO 80202
Ph: (303)620-8076
Co. E-mail: info@denversbdc.org
URL: http://www.denversbdc.org
Contact: China Califf, Executive Director
Facebook: www.facebook.com/denversbdc
Linkedin: www.linkedin.com/company/denver-metro
  -sbdc
X (Twitter): x.com/denversbdc

Description: Represents and promotes the small business sector. Provides management assistance to current and prospective small business owners. Helps to improve management skills and expand the products and services of members. **Geographic Preference:** Local.

37790 ■ North Metro Small Business Development Center

Front Range Community College
3645 W 112th Ave.
  Westminster, CO 80031
Ph: (303)460-1032
Co. E-mail: northmetro.sbdc@frontrange.edu
URL: http://northmetrosbdc.com
Contact: Angela Atkinson, Director
E-mail: angela.atkinson@frontrange.edu
Facebook: www.facebook.com/NorthMetroDenSBDC
Linkedin: www.linkedin.com/company/northme
  trosbdc
X (Twitter): x.com/NorthMetroSBDC
Instagram: www.instagram.com/northmetrosbdc
YouTube: www.youtube.com/channel/
  UCeQjUliPsBVq-aW6TAY_pNg
Pinterest: www.pinterest.com/northmetrodenversbdc

Description: Provides management assistance to current and prospective small business owners in North Metro. **Founded:** 1989. **Geographic Preference:** Local.

37791 ■ Northeast-East Central Colorado Small Business Development Center

800 17th St. Kepner Hall., Ste. 0025
  Greeley, CO 80639
Ph: (970)351-4274
Co. E-mail: info@eastcoloradosbdc.com
URL: http://eastcoloradosbdc.com
Contact: Lisa Hudson, Executive Director
E-mail: lisa@eastcoloradosbdc.com
Facebook: www.facebook.com/eastcosbdc
Linkedin: www.linkedin.com/company/east-colorado
  -sbdc
X (Twitter): x.com/eastcosbdc
Instagram: www.instagram.com/eastcosbdc

Description: Represents and promotes the small business sector. Provides management assistance to current and prospective small business owners. Helps to improve management skills and expand the products and services of members. **Founded:** 2009. **Geographic Preference:** Local.

37792 ■ Pueblo Small Business Development Center

121 W City Center Dr. No. 150
  Pueblo, CO 81003
URL: http://www.southerncoloradosbdc.org

Description: Provides management assistance to current and prospective small business owners in Pueblo. **Geographic Preference:** Local.

37793 ■ San Luis Valley Small Business Development Center

610 State Ave.
  Alamosa, CO 81101
Ph: (719)589-3682
URL: http://www.slv-sbdc.com
Contact: Jason C. Medina, Director
E-mail: jason@slv-sbdc.com
Facebook: www.facebook.com/slvsbdc

Description: Represents and promotes the small business sector. Provides management assistance to current and prospective small business owners. Helps to improve management skills and expand the products and services of members. **Geographic Preference:** Local.

37794 ■ South Metro Denver Small Business Development Center Aurora

15151 E Alameda Pky., Ste. 2300
  Aurora, CO 80012
Ph: (303)326-8686
Co. E-mail: info@aurora-southmetrosbdc.com
URL: http://www.aurora-southmetrosbdc.com
Contact: Marcia McGilley, Executive Director
E-mail: mmcgille@auroragov.org
Facebook: www.facebook.com/aurorasouthme
  trosbdc
Linkedin: www.linkedin.com/in/frankieanderson
X (Twitter): x.com/aurorasouthsbdc

Description: Represents and promotes the small business sector. Provides management assistance to current and prospective small business owners. Helps to improve management skills and expand the products and services of members. **Geographic Preference:** Local.

37795 ■ Southwest Colorado Small Business Development Center Durango

Education and Business Bldg., Rm. 140
1000 Rim Dr.
  Durango, CO 81301
Ph: (970)247-7009
URL: http://sbdcfortlewis.org
Contact: Mary Shepherd, Executive Director
E-mail: shepherd_m@fortlewis.edu
Facebook: www.facebook.com/southwestcolora
  dosbdc
Linkedin: www.linkedin.com/company/southwes
  t-colorado-sbdc
Instagram: www.instagram.com/southwestcolora
  dosbdc

Description: Represents and promotes the small business sector. Provides management assistance to current and prospective small business owners. Helps to improve management skills and expand the products and services of members. **Geographic Preference:** Local.

37796 ■ Southwest Colorado Small Business Development Center Pagosa

105 Hot Springs Blvd.
  Pagosa Springs, CO 81147
Ph: (970)264-2360
URL: http://sbdcfortlewis.org/who-we-are/locations
Contact: Mary Shepherd, Executive Director

Description: Represents and promotes the small business sector. Provides management assistance to current and prospective small business owners. Helps to improve management skills and expand the products and services of members. **Founded:** 1940. **Geographic Preference:** Local.

STATE LISTINGS   Colorado ■ 37812

37797 ■ Southwestern Colorado Small Business Development Center
835 Main Ave., Ste. 225
Durango, CO 81301
Ph: (970)903-5424
Co. E-mail: shepherd_m@fortlewis.edu
URL: http://www.coloradosbdc.org
Contact: Mary Shepherd, Executive Director
E-mail: shepherd_m@fortlewis.edu
URL(s): www.sbdcfortlewis.org
Facebook: www.facebook.com/southwestcoloradosbdc
Linkedin: www.linkedin.com/company/southwest-colorado-sbdc
Instagram: www.instagram.com/southwestcoloradosbdc
Description: Represents and promotes the small business sector. Provides management assistance to current and prospective small business owners. Helps to improve management skills and expand the products and services of members. **Geographic Preference:** Local.

37798 ■ West Central Small Business Development Center (SDBC)
145 S Cascade
Montrose, CO 81401
Ph: (970)765-3130
Co. E-mail: nancy@region10.net
URL: http://r10sbdc.org/who-we-are/contact-us
Contact: Nancy Murphy, Director
E-mail: nancy@region10.net
Description: Represents and promotes the small business sector. Provides management assistance to current and prospective small business owners. Helps to improve management skills and expand the products and services of members. **Geographic Preference:** Local.

37799 ■ West Central Small Business Development Center Chaffee and Lake County
145 S Cascade
Montrose, CO 81401
Ph: (970)765-3130
URL: http://r10sbdc.org
Contact: Nancy Murphy, Director
E-mail: nancy@region10.net
Description: Represents and promotes the small business sector. Provides management assistance to current and prospective small business owners. Helps to improve management skills and expand the products and services of members. **Geographic Preference:** Local.

SMALL BUSINESS ASSISTANCE PROGRAMS

37800 ■ Colorado Office of Economic Development and International Trade - Colorado International Trade Office
1600 Broadway, Ste. 2500
Denver, CO 80202
Ph: (303)892-3840
URL: http://choosecolorado.com
Contact: Eve Lieberman, Executive Director
Facebook: www.facebook.com/ColoradoEcoDevo
Linkedin: www.linkedin.com/company/colorado-office-of-economic-development-and-international-trade
YouTube: www.youtube.com/channel/UC_TXkdPgl4lh-FO6iNmt11w
Description: Promotes the export of Colorado's products and assists businesses in many aspects of exporting.

37801 ■ Colorado Office of Economic Development and International Trade (SBDC) - Small Business Development Center
1600 Broadway, Ste. 2500
Denver, CO 80202
Ph: (303)892-3840
Co. E-mail: info@coloradosbdc.org
URL: http://www.coloradosbdc.org
Contact: Sharon King, Executive Director
E-mail: sharon.king@bouldersbdc.com

Facebook: www.facebook.com/coloradosbdc
Linkedin: www.linkedin.com/company/coloradosmallbusinessdevelopmentcenternetwork
X (Twitter): x.com/coloradosbdc
Instagram: www.instagram.com/coloradosbdc
Description: Answers small business inquiries or refers them to an appropriate resource. Provides information on starting a business, marketing, financing, and other aspects of running a business. **Founded:** 1987.

37802 ■ Denver Metro Chamber of Commerce - Small Business Development Center (SBDC)
1445 Market St.
Denver, CO 80202
Ph: (303)620-8076
Co. E-mail: info@denversbdc.org
URL: http://www.denversbdc.org
Contact: China Califf, Executive Director
X (Twitter): x.com/denversbdc
Description: Assists companies with 100 or fewer employees. The Management Education Division provides management education and training; the Information/Networking Division sponsors meetings for small business chief executive officers for the exchange of information; and the Special Services Division is involved in such activities as legislative lobbying and sponsoring group health insurance programs for small businesses. **Founded:** 1990.

SCORE OFFICES

37803 ■ Grand Junction SCORE
2591 Legacy Way
Grand Junction, CO 81503
Ph: (970)243-5242
Co. E-mail: bob@ahinet.com

37804 ■ SCORE - Colorado Springs
13395 Voyager Pkwy Ste. 130
Colorado Springs, CO 80921
Ph: (719)377-3107
Co. E-mail: leaders@coloradospringsscore.org
URL: http://coloradosprings.score.org
Contact: Robyn Shaw, Treasurer
Facebook: www.facebook.com/SCOREColoradoSprings
Linkedin: www.linkedin.com/in/coloradospringsscore
X (Twitter): x.com/SCORECOSprings
Description: Provides professional guidance and information to maximize the success of existing and emerging small businesses. Offers business counseling and workshops. **Geographic Preference:** Local.

37805 ■ SCORE - Denver
721 19th St., Rm. 426
Denver, CO 80202
Ph: (303)927-3480
Co. E-mail: score62@scoredenver.org
URL: http://denver.score.org
Facebook: www.facebook.com/SCOREDenver
Linkedin: www.linkedin.com/company/score-denver
X (Twitter): x.com/SCOREDenver
Description: Provides professional guidance and information to maximize the success of existing and emerging small businesses. Offers business counseling and workshops. **Founded:** 1964. **Geographic Preference:** Local.

37806 ■ SCORE - Leadville
400 Harrison Ave., Ste. 100
Leadville, CO 80461
Ph: (719)293-2316
URL: http://coloradosprings.score.org
Description: Provides professional guidance and information to maximize the success of existing and emerging small businesses. Offers business counseling and workshops.

37807 ■ SCORE - Monument
166 Second St., Chamber of Commerce Bldg.
Monument, CO 80132
URL: http://coloradosprings.score.org/content/search-mentor?&local=1
Contact: Robert F. Mikulas, Contact

Description: Provides professional guidance and information to maximize the success of existing and emerging small businesses. Offers business counseling and workshops.

37808 ■ SCORE - Steamboat Springs
1131 Bob Adams Dr.
Steamboat Springs, CO 80487
Co. E-mail: help@score.org
URL: http://www.score.org/find-location
Description: Provides professional guidance and information to maximize the success of existing and emerging small businesses. Offers business counseling and workshops.

BETTER BUSINESS BUREAUS

37809 ■ Better Business Bureau of Denver/Boulder
3801 E Florida Ave., Ste. 350
Denver, CO 80210
Ph: (303)758-2100
URL: http://www.bbb.org/local-bbb/bbb-great-west-pacific
Description: Seeks to build and ensure a fair, honest, safe, marketplace in the Denver, CO area community by fostering ethical, fair, and honest relations between buyers and sellers. Promotes business self resolution in the traditional and electronic marketplace, while providing credibility and exceptional value for members. **Founded:** 1951. **Publications:** *Torch Report* (Bimonthly). **Geographic Preference:** Local.

37810 ■ Better Business Bureau Great West + Pacific [BBB Great West + Pacific]
PO Box 191279
Boise, ID 83719
Ph: (208)342-4649
URL: http://www.bbb.org/local-bbb/bbb-great-west-pacific
Linkedin: www.linkedin.com/company/bbbgwp
Instagram: www.instagram.com/bbbgwp
YouTube: www.youtube.com/bbbgwp
Description: Seeks to promote and foster the highest ethical relationship between businesses and the public through voluntary self-regulation, consumer and business education, and service excellence. Provides information to help consumers and businesses make informed purchasing decisions and avoid costly scams and frauds; settles consumer complaints through arbitration and other means. **Geographic Preference:** State.

37811 ■ Better Business Bureau of Northern Colorado and Wyoming
8020 S County Rd. 5, Ste. 100
Fort Collins, CO 80528
Ph: (970)484-1348
Fax: (970)221-1239
Co. E-mail: info@wynco.bbb.org
URL: http://www.bbb.org/local-bbb/bbb-serving-northern-colorado-and-wyoming
Contact: Shelley Polansky, President
E-mail: spolansky@wynco.bbb.org
Facebook: www.facebook.com/WyncoBBB
Linkedin: www.linkedin.com/company/better-business-bureau---northern-colorado-&-wyoming
X (Twitter): x.com/wyncobbb
Instagram: www.instagram.com/wyncobbb
YouTube: www.youtube.com/user/BBBWynco
Description: Seeks to promote and foster ethical relationship between businesses and the public through voluntary self-regulation, consumer and business education, and service excellence. Provides information to help consumers and businesses make informed purchasing decisions and avoid costly scams and frauds; settles consumer complaints through arbitration and other means. **Geographic Preference:** Local.

37812 ■ Better Business Bureau of Southern Colorado, Inc.
25 N Wahsatch Ave., Ste. 100
Colorado Springs, CO 80903
Ph: (719)636-1155

37813 ■ Colorado

Fax: (719)636-5078
Co. E-mail: info@bbbsc.org
URL: http://www.bbb.org/local-bbb/bbb-of-southern-colorado
Contact: Michelle Robinette, Chairman
Facebook: www.facebook.com/BBBSouthernColorado
Linkedin: www.linkedin.com/company/better-business-bureau-of-southern-colorado
Instagram: www.instagram.com/bbbsoutherncolorado
YouTube: www.youtube.com/user/BBBSouthernColorado
Description: Seeks to promote and foster the highest ethical relationship between businesses and the public through voluntary self-regulation, consumer and business education, and service excellence. Provides information to help consumers and businesses make informed purchasing decisions and avoid costly scams and frauds; settles consumer complaints through arbitration and other means. **Founded:** 1980. **Geographic Preference:** Local.

CHAMBERS OF COMMERCE

37813 ■ Alamosa County Chamber of Commerce (ACCC)
610 State Ave.
 Alamosa, CO 81101
Ph: (719)589-3681
Co. E-mail: alamosacountychamber@gmail.com
URL: http://www.alamosachamber.com
Contact: Kristy Esquibel, President
Facebook: www.facebook.com/alamosacountychamber
Instagram: www.instagram.com/alamosacountychamber
Description: Promotes business and community development in Alamosa County, CO. **Founded:** 1923. **Geographic Preference:** Local.

37814 ■ Arvada Chamber of Commerce (ACC)
7305 Grandview Ave.
 Arvada, CO 80002
Ph: (303)424-0313
URL: http://www.arvadachamber.org
Contact: Kami Welch, President
E-mail: kami@arvadachamber.org
Facebook: www.facebook.com/ArvadaChamberCommerce
X (Twitter): x.com/arvadachamber
YouTube: www.youtube.com/channel/UCRKbmd9FfmpDbyBlbNnRw3Q
Description: Promotes business and community development in the Arvada/Westminster area. Facilitates communication and cooperation among area businesspeople. **Founded:** 1925. **Publications:** *Insider* (Weekly); *Membership Directory/Community Resource Guide* (Annual); *Northwest Metro Business Network Book* (Annual). **Educational Activities:** Community Impact Breakfast; Arvada Chamber of Commerce Membership Luncheon. **Geographic Preference:** Local.

37815 ■ Aspen Chamber Resort Association (ACRA)
590 N Mill St.
 Aspen, CO 81611
Ph: (970)925-1940
Free: 877-702-7736
Fax: (970)920-1176
Co. E-mail: info@aspenchamber.org
URL: http://aspenchamber.org
Contact: Debbie Contini Braun, President
Facebook: www.facebook.com/AspenChamber
Linkedin: www.linkedin.com/company/aspen-chamber-resort-association
X (Twitter): x.com/aspenco
Instagram: www.instagram.com/aspenco
YouTube: www.youtube.com/user/AspenChamber
Pinterest: www.pinterest.com/Aspen_Co
Description: Serves the Aspen business and residential community by: attracting visitors to the resort, providing valuable services to member businesses, and facilitating community synergy among government and local civic organizations. **Founded:** 1960. **Geographic Preference:** Local.

37816 ■ Aurora Chamber of Commerce
14305 E Alameda Ave., Ste. 300
 Aurora, CO 80012
Ph: (303)344-1500
Fax: (303)344-1564
URL: http://www.aurorachamber.org
Contact: Kevin Hougen, President
E-mail: kevin.hougen@aurorachamber.org
Description: Strives to unite businesses and professionals to improve the business climate and to build a better community. **Founded:** 1901. **Publications:** *Impact* (Bimonthly). **Educational Activities:** Business for the Arts Committee. **Geographic Preference:** Local.

37817 ■ Basalt Chamber of Commerce
PO Box 500
 Basalt, CO 81621
Ph: (970)927-4031
Co. E-mail: info@basaltchamber.org
URL: http://www.basaltchamber.org
Contact: Kris Mattera, Executive Director
Facebook: www.facebook.com/BasaltChamberofCommerce
Linkedin: www.linkedin.com/company/basalt-co-chamber-of-commerce
X (Twitter): x.com/BasaltChamber
Description: Promotes business and community development in Basalt, Eljebel and old Snowmass, CO. **Founded:** 1983. **Geographic Preference:** Local.

37818 ■ Bent County Chamber of Commerce
702 Grove Ave.
 Las Animas, CO 81054
Ph: (719)456-0453
Co. E-mail: labcchamber@gmail.com
URL: http://labcchamber.com
Contact: Tiana Garcia, President
URL(s): bentcounty.org
Facebook: www.facebook.com/Las-AnimasBent-County-Chamber-of-Commerce-603518363088260
Description: Aims to promote trade, commerce, general prosperity, education, social and cultural interests, commercial uniformity, integrity and interdependence among businessmen; and to disseminate information relating to the commercial, financial, industrial and cultural interest of Las Animas and Bent County. **Geographic Preference:** Local.

37819 ■ Berthoud Area Chamber of Commerce
428 Mountain Ave.
 Berthoud, CO 80513
Ph: (970)532-4200
Co. E-mail: bcc@berthoudcolorado.com
URL: http://www.berthoudcolorado.com
Contact: Virginia Huppe, President
Description: Promotes business and community development in Berthoud, CO. **Publications:** *The Garden Spot of Colorado* (Monthly); *Berthoud Area Chamber of Commerce--Member Directory and Visitor Guide*. **Geographic Preference:** Local.

37820 ■ Boulder Chamber (BC)
2440 Pearl St.
 Boulder, CO 80302
Ph: (303)442-1044
Fax: (303)938-8837
Co. E-mail: info@boulderchamber.com
URL: http://boulderchamber.com
Contact: John Tayer, President
E-mail: john.tayer@boulderchamber.com
Facebook: www.facebook.com/boulderchamber
X (Twitter): x.com/BoulderChamber
Description: Promotes business and community development in Boulder, CO. **Founded:** 1905. **Publications:** *Chamber Today* (Monthly). **Geographic Preference:** Local.

37821 ■ Breckenridge Resort Chamber of Commerce (BRC)
111 Ski Hill Rd.
 Breckenridge, CO 80424
Ph: (970)453-2913
Co. E-mail: welcomecenter@gobreck.com
URL: http://www.gobreck.com
X (Twitter): x.com/GoBreck
Instagram: www.instagram.com/gobreck
Pinterest: www.pinterest.fr/GoBreck
Description: Promotes business, community development, and tourism in Breckenridge, CO. **Founded:** 1971. **Publications:** *Great Times*. **Geographic Preference:** Local.

37822 ■ Broomfield Chamber of Commerce [Chamber Serving the Broomfield Area]
105 Edgeview Dr., Ste. 410
 Broomfield, CO 80021
Ph: (303)466-1775
Fax: (303)466-4481
Co. E-mail: info@broomfieldchamber.com
URL: http://www.broomfieldchamber.com
Contact: Sam Taylor, President
E-mail: sam.taylor@broomfieldchamber.com
Linkedin: www.linkedin.com/company/broomfieldchamber
X (Twitter): x.com/BroomfieldCofC
Instagram: www.instagram.com/broomfieldchamber
YouTube: www.youtube.com/channel/UCXZ8uLyuGs0XlkuvX2Qitbg
Pinterest: www.pinterest.com/broomfieldcofc
Description: Promotes business and community development in the Broomfield, CO area. **Founded:** 1975. **Publications:** *The Broomfielder* (Monthly); *E-Updates* (Periodic). **Educational Activities:** Business After Hours (Irregular). **Geographic Preference:** Local.

37823 ■ *The Broomfielder*
105 Edgeview Dr., Ste. 410
 Broomfield, CO 80021
Ph: (303)466-1775
Fax: (303)466-4481
Co. E-mail: info@broomfieldchamber.com
URL: http://www.broomfieldchamber.com
Contact: Sam Taylor, President
E-mail: sam.taylor@broomfieldchamber.com
URL(s): www.broomfieldchamber.com/benefits
Released: Monthly **Description:** Contains information on the Broomfield, CO chamber events, activities and programs. **Availability:** Print.

37824 ■ Brush Area Chamber of Commerce
218 Clayton St.
 Brush, CO 80723
Ph: (970)842-2666
Co. E-mail: brushchamberexecdir@gmail.com
URL: http://www.brushchamberofcommerce.org
Contact: Carrie Ankrom, President
Facebook: www.facebook.com/BrushAreaChamber
Description: Promotes business and community development in the Brush, CO area. **Founded:** 1902. **Geographic Preference:** Local.

37825 ■ Buena Vista Chamber of Commerce
111 E Main St.
 Buena Vista, CO 81211
Ph: (719)395-6612
Co. E-mail: membership@buenavistacolorado.org
URL: http://www.buenavistacolorado.org
Facebook: www.facebook.com/bvchamber
X (Twitter): x.com/BuenaVistaCo
YouTube: www.youtube.com/channel/UCgf063a8COktB_ZcMq0ZJzg
Pinterest: www.pinterest.com/BuenaVistaCo
Description: Promotes business, community development, and tourism in Buena Vista, CO. Maintains visitor's bureau. Sponsors Fourth of July Celebration, Gold Rush Days, Christmas Opening, and trade show. **Founded:** 1976. **Publications:** *Buena Vista Chamber of Commerce Newsletter* (Weekly); *Business Directory*. **Educational Activities:** Business After Hours (Monthly). **Awards:** Buena Vista Area Chamber of Commerce Citizens of the Year (Annual). **Geographic Preference:** Local.

STATE LISTINGS

37826 ■ Carbondale Community Chamber of Commerce
520 S 3rd St., Ste. 3
Carbondale, CO 81623
Ph: (970)963-1890
Fax: (970)963-4719
Co. E-mail: tourism@carbondale.com
URL: http://www.carbondale.com
Contact: Andrea Stewart, Chief Executive Officer
E-mail: andrea@carbondale.com
Facebook: www.facebook.com/Carbondale
X (Twitter): x.com/carbondaleco
Instagram: www.instagram.com/carbondale

Description: Promotes business and community development in Carbondale, CO. **Founded:** 1947. **Publications:** *Membership Directory and Area Guide* (Annual). **Geographic Preference:** Local.

37827 ■ Castle Rock Chamber of Commerce (CRCC)
420 Jerry St.
Castle Rock, CO 80104
Ph: (303)688-4597
Co. E-mail: info@castlerock.org
URL: http://www.castlerock.org
Contact: Pam Ridler, Co-Chief Executive Officer Co-President
E-mail: pam@castlerock.org
Facebook: www.facebook.com/CastleRockChamber
Linkedin: www.linkedin.com/company/castle-rock-chamber-of-commerce
X (Twitter): x.com/CRChamber
Instagram: www.instagram.com/castlerockchamber
Pinterest: www.pinterest.com/pin/152559506103411749

Description: Promotes the economic well-being of Castle Rock, CO; provides a forum for members to promote their businesses; and serves as the voice of the Castle Rock business community. Sponsors art festival. **Founded:** 1955. **Geographic Preference:** Local.

37828 ■ Cedaredge Area Chamber of Commerce
245 W Main St.
Cedaredge, CO 81413

Description: Promotes business, community development, and tourism in Cedaredge, CO. Hosts Little Britches Rodeo; sponsors Apple Days Festival and other activities. **Founded:** 1976. **Geographic Preference:** Local.

37829 ■ *Chamber*
424 Main St.
Canon City, CO 81212
Ph: (719)275-2331
Free: 800-876-7922
Co. E-mail: membership @royalgorgechamberalliance.org
URL: http://www.canoncity.com
Contact: Cooper Trahern, President
URL(s): www.royalgorgechamberalliance.org/member-benefits

Released: Monthly **Description:** Contains information about the members and the activities of the association; published in the Canon City Daily Record. **Availability:** Print; PDF.

37830 ■ *The Chamber Connection*
2301 Main Ave.
Durango, CO 81302
Ph: (970)247-0312
Free: 888-414-0835
Fax: (970)385-7884
Co. E-mail: chamber@durangobusiness.org
URL: http://www.durangobusiness.org
Contact: Jack Llewellyn, Chief Executive Officer
E-mail: jack@durangobusiness.org
URL(s): www.durangobusiness.org/chamber-communications.html

Released: Monthly **Description:** Outlines events that are going on, updates the new membership, spotlights outstanding businesses and allows the board and executive director to reach to membership through articles. **Availability:** Print; PDF; Online.

37831 ■ Colorado River Valley Chamber (RACC)
100 E 11th St.
Rifle, CO 81650
Ph: (970)625-2085
Co. E-mail: info@coloradorivervalleychamber.com
URL: http://www.coloradorivervalleychamber.com
Contact: Larry Stewart, Chairman of the Board
E-mail: larrystewart@alpinebank.com
Facebook: www.facebook.com/coloradorivervalleychamber
X (Twitter): x.com/riflechamber
Instagram: www.instagram.com/westerngarcochamber

Description: Promotes business and community development in the Rifle, CO area. Sponsors County Fair Parade and other community events. **Publications:** *Rifle Chamber Scope* (Monthly). **Geographic Preference:** Local.

37832 ■ Conifer Chamber of Commerce
25997 Conifer Rd., Second Fl.
Conifer, CO 80433
Ph: (303)838-5711
Co. E-mail: director@goconifer.com
URL: http://www.goconifer.com
Contact: John Osborn, Co-President
Facebook: www.facebook.com/ConiferAreaChamberofCommerce
Linkedin: www.linkedin.com/company/conifer-chamber-of-commerce
X (Twitter): x.com/coniferchamber

Description: Provides leadership for the community, promotes local resources, enhances local programs, and coordinates development efforts. **Founded:** 1975. **Geographic Preference:** Local.

37833 ■ Cortez Area Chamber of Commerce (CACC)
20 W Main St.
Cortez, CO 81321
Ph: (970)565-3414
Co. E-mail: info@cortezchamber.com
URL: http://www.cortezchamber.com
Contact: Colton Black, Executive Director
Facebook: www.facebook.com/cortezchamber

Description: Promotes business and community development in the Cortez, CO area. Sponsors area festivals and charitable events. Conducts competitions. Convention/Meeting: none. **Founded:** 1926. **Publications:** *Chamber Commentaries* (Monthly). **Geographic Preference:** Local.

37834 ■ Craig Chamber of Commerce
775 Yampa Ave.
Craig, CO 81625
Ph: (970)824-5689
Co. E-mail: info@craigchamber.com
URL: http://www.craig-chamber.com
Contact: Randy Looper, President
Facebook: www.facebook.com/craigcochamber

Description: Promotes business, community development, and tourism in Moffat County, CO. **Founded:** 1947. **Geographic Preference:** Local.

37835 ■ Crawford Area Chamber of Commerce (CACC)
PO Box 22
Crawford, CO 81415
Co. E-mail: crawfordchamber@gmail.com
URL: http://www.crawfordcountry.org
Contact: Luke Finley, President

Description: Promotes cooperation among businesses, professionals and community citizens to improve the business environment of the Crawford area. **Geographic Preference:** Local.

37836 ■ Creede and Mineral County Chamber of Commerce
904 S Main St.
Creede, CO 81130
Ph: (719)658-2374
Fax: (719)658-2717
Co. E-mail: office@creede.com
URL: http://www.creede.com
Contact: Kathleen Murphy, Executive Director
Facebook: www.facebook.com/VisitCreede

Colorado ■ 37841

X (Twitter): x.com/visitcreede
Instagram: www.instagram.com/visitcreede
Pinterest: www.pinterest.com/visitcreede

Description: Seeks to encourage, foster, and protect the growth and integrity of the Mineral County, CO area through careful economic and community planning and promotion. **Geographic Preference:** Local.

37837 ■ Crested Butte/Mount Crested Butte Chamber of Commerce
601 Elk Ave.
Crested Butte, CO 81224
Ph: (970)349-6438
Free: 855-681-0941
URL: http://www.cbchamber.com
Contact: Joshua Futterman, President
Facebook: www.facebook.com/cbchamber
X (Twitter): x.com/chambercbmtcb
Instagram: www.instagram.com/cbchamber

Description: Promotes business and community development in Crested Butte, and Mt. Crested Butte, CO. **Geographic Preference:** Local.

37838 ■ Cripple Creek and Victor Chamber of Commerce
PO Box 650
Cripple Creek, CO 80813
Ph: (719)689-3461
URL: http://cripplecreekchamber.com

Description: Promotes business and community development in Cripple Creek, CO. **Founded:** 1984. **Geographic Preference:** Local.

37839 ■ Del Norte Chamber of Commerce (DNCC)
595 Grand Ave.
Del Norte, CO 81132
Ph: (719)657-9081
Co. E-mail: chamber@delnortechamber.org
URL: http://www.delnortechamber.org
Contact: Will Kreutzer, President
Facebook: www.facebook.com/DelNorteChamberofCommerce
Instagram: www.instagram.com/delnortechamberco

Description: Promotes business, community development, and tourism in Del Norte, CO. Sponsors Covered Wagon Days, Christmas Merchants' open house and logging events. **Founded:** 1872. **Geographic Preference:** Local.

37840 ■ Delta Area Chamber of Commerce, Inc.
301 Main St.
Delta, CO 81416
Ph: (970)874-8616
Fax: (970)874-8618
Co. E-mail: chamber@deltacolorado.org
URL: http://www.deltacolorado.org
Contact: Mariah Emond, President
Facebook: www.facebook.com/DeltaChamber
Linkedin: www.linkedin.com/company/delta-chamber-of-commerce
Instagram: www.instagram.com/deltaareachamber

Description: Promotes business and community development in the Delta, CO area. **Founded:** 1910. **Geographic Preference:** Local.

37841 ■ Denver Metro Chamber of Commerce (DMCC)
1445 Market St.
Denver, CO 80202
Ph: (303)534-8500
Fax: (303)534-3200
Co. E-mail: info@denverchamber.org
URL: http://denverchamber.org
Contact: Holli Riebel, Chief Operating Officer
Facebook: www.facebook.com/denvermetrochamber
Linkedin: www.linkedin.com/company/denver-metro-chamber-of-commerce
X (Twitter): x.com/DenChamber
Instagram: www.instagram.com/explore/locations/2931327/united-states/denver-colorado/denver-metro-chamber-of-commerce

Description: Promotes the development of civic leadership in the business community and fosters opportunities for increased cooperation among the private, public, and nonprofit sectors in Denver, CO

37842 ■ Colorado

area. **Founded:** 1876. **Publications:** *Denver Metro Chamber of Commerce--Membership Directory and Buyer's Guide*. **Geographic Preference:** Local.

37842 ■ Dolores Chamber of Commerce
201 Railroad Ave., 2nd St. Rail Rd.
Dolores, CO 81323
Ph: (970)882-4018
Co. E-mail: doloreschamber@gmail.com
URL: http://www.visitdolores.com
Contact: Susan Lisak, Executive Director
Facebook: www.facebook.com/DoloresChamber
Description: Promotes business and community development in Dolores, CO. **Founded:** 1900. **Geographic Preference:** Local.

37843 ■ Durango Chamber of Commerce
2301 Main Ave.
Durango, CO 81302
Ph: (970)247-0312
Free: 888-414-0835
Fax: (970)385-7884
Co. E-mail: chamber@durangobusiness.org
URL: http://www.durangobusiness.org
Contact: Jack Llewellyn, Chief Executive Officer
E-mail: jack@durangobusiness.org
Facebook: www.facebook.com/durangochamberofcommerce
Instagram: www.instagram.com/durangochamberofcommerce
YouTube: www.youtube.com/channel/UCa0wANorxyB9j3AoIKCszbw/featured
Description: Works to promote and support the local business community. Acts as a resource of information for its members, the community, and relocation inquirers. **Founded:** 1915. **Publications:** *The Chamber Connection* (Monthly). **Geographic Preference:** Local.

37844 ■ Eagle Chamber of Commerce
200 Broadway, Ste. 120
Eagle, CO 81631
Ph: (970)306-2262
Co. E-mail: info@eaglechamber.co
URL: http://www.eaglechamber.co
Contact: Dan Brown, President
Facebook: www.facebook.com/eaglechamberofcommerce
Description: Promotes business and community development in Eagle, CO. **Geographic Preference:** Local.

37845 ■ Elizabeth Area Chamber of Commerce (EACOC)
166 Main St., Ste. E
Elizabeth, CO 80107
Ph: (303)646-4287
Co. E-mail: director@elizabethchamber.org
URL: http://business.elizabethchamber.org
Contact: Nancy Shannon, President
Description: Promotes business and community development in Elizabeth, CO and the surrounding area in Elbert County. Sponsors ElizaBash, Harvest Festival, Olde Country Christmas and Art in the Pines. **Founded:** 1948. **Publications:** *EACOC Connection*. **Geographic Preference:** Local.

37846 ■ Erie Chamber of Commerce
235 Wells St.
Erie, CO 80516
Ph: (303)828-3440
Co. E-mail: erie@eriechamber.org
URL: http://eriechamber.org
Contact: Adam Ingersoll, Treasurer
Facebook: www.facebook.com/ErieChamber
X (Twitter): x.com/ErieChamber
Instagram: www.instagram.com/erie_chamber
Description: Works to advance the commercial, financial, industrial and civic interests of Erie, CO. **Geographic Preference:** Local.

37847 ■ Estes Park Resort
1700 Big Thompson Ave.
Estes Park, CO 80517
Ph: (970)577-6400
Free: 855-377-3778
Co. E-mail: info@theestesparkresort.com
URL: http://www.theestesparkresocom
Facebook: www.facebook.com/estesparkresort
Instagram: www.instagram.com/estesparkresort
Description: Promotes business and community development in the Estes Park, CO area. **Geographic Preference:** Local.

37848 ■ *Evergreen*
1524 Belford Ct.
Evergreen, CO 80439
Ph: (303)674-3412
Fax: (720)361-2994
Co. E-mail: admin@evergreenchamber.org
URL: http://www.evergreenchamber.org
Contact: Nancy Judge, President
E-mail: president@evergreenchamber.org
Description: Contains demographic information, frequently requested phone number, calendar of events, feature story and member listing. **Availability:** Download; Online.

37849 ■ Evergreen Area Chamber of Commerce (EACC)
1524 Belford Ct.
Evergreen, CO 80439
Ph: (303)674-3412
Fax: (720)361-2994
Co. E-mail: admin@evergreenchamber.org
URL: http://www.evergreenchamber.org
Contact: Nancy Judge, President
E-mail: president@evergreenchamber.org
Facebook: www.facebook.com/evergreenchamberofcommerceco
Linkedin: www.linkedin.com/company/evergreen-area-chamber-of-commerce
X (Twitter): x.com/EvergreenChmbr
Description: Promotes business and community development in Evergreen, CO. **Founded:** 1970. **Publications:** *Evergreen*. **Geographic Preference:** Local.

37850 ■ Florence Chamber of Commerce
116 N Pikes Peak Ave.
Florence, CO 81226
Ph: (719)784-3544
Co. E-mail: fcocofficemanager@gmail.com
URL: http://www.finditinflorence.com
Contact: Jenny Cristelli, President
Facebook: www.facebook.com/TheFlorenceChamberOfCommerce
Description: Promotes business and community development in eastern Fremont county, Florence, CO. Conducts Snowball Softball competition, annual Pioneer Day festival, and Hardscrabble 100 Mile Bicycle Race. Sponsors charitable Christmas activities. **Founded:** 1902. **Geographic Preference:** Local.

37851 ■ Fort Collins Area Chamber of Commerce
225 S Meldrum
Fort Collins, CO 80521
Ph: (970)482-3746
Co. E-mail: general@fcchamber.org
URL: http://www.fortcollinschamber.com
Contact: Ann Hutchison, II, President
Facebook: www.facebook.com/FortCollinsChamber
Linkedin: www.linkedin.com/company/fort-collins-area-chamber-of-commerce
X (Twitter): x.com/FCCOchamber
YouTube: www.youtube.com/user/FortCollinsChamber
Description: Promotes business and community development in the Ft. Collins, CO area. **Founded:** 1904. **Publications:** *The Chamber Compass*; *The Chamber Weekly* (Weekly (Tues.)). **Educational Activities:** Business Before Hours. **Geographic Preference:** Local.

37852 ■ Fort Morgan Area Chamber of Commerce (FMACC)
300 Main St.
Fort Morgan, CO 80701
Ph: (970)867-6702
Co. E-mail: info@fortmorganchamber.com
URL: http://www.fortmorganchamber.com
Contact: Jennifer Halligan, President
Facebook: www.facebook.com/fortmorganchamberofcommerce
Linkedin: www.linkedin.com/company/fmacc
Description: Promotes business and community development in the Ft. Morgan, CO area. **Founded:** 1919. **Publications:** *Advocate*. **Geographic Preference:** Local.

37853 ■ Fountain Valley Chamber of Commerce (FVCC)
10055 Slater Ave., Ste. 250
Fountain, CO 80817
Ph: (714)962-3822
Fax: (714)962-2045
Co. E-mail: info@fvchamber.com
URL: http://www.fvchamber.com
Contact: Brian Genovese, Chairman
Linkedin: www.linkedin.com/company/fountain-valley-chamber-of-commerce-ca
X (Twitter): x.com/FountainChamber
YouTube: www.youtube.com/watch
Description: Promotes business and community development in Fountain, CO. **Publications:** *Chamber Communique* (Monthly). **Geographic Preference:** Local.

37854 ■ Fruita Area Chamber of Commerce (FACC)
432 E Aspen Ave.
Fruita, CO 81521
Ph: (970)858-3894
Co. E-mail: info@fruitachamber.org
URL: http://fruitachamber.org
Contact: Kayla Brown, Executive Director
E-mail: kayla@fruitachamber.org
Facebook: www.facebook.com/fruitachamber.co
X (Twitter): x.com/WTFruitaChamber
Instagram: www.instagram.com/fruitachamber
Description: Promotes business and community development in Fruita, CO. **Geographic Preference:** Local.

37855 ■ Granby Chamber of Commerce (GCC)
516 E Agate Ave.
Granby, CO 80446
Ph: (970)887-2311
Co. E-mail: info@destinationgranby.com
URL: http://www.destinationgranby.com
Contact: Lauren Huber, Executive Director
E-mail: lauren@granbychamber.com
Facebook: www.facebook.com/VisitGranbyCO
Instagram: www.instagram.com/visitgranbyco
Description: Works to advance economic welfare and civic pride in the greater Granby area while preserving its unique cultural heritage and sense of community. **Founded:** 1947. **Publications:** *The Heart Beat* (Monthly). **Geographic Preference:** Local.

37856 ■ Grand Junction Area Chamber of Commerce
360 Grand Ave.
Grand Junction, CO 81501
Ph: (970)242-3214
Co. E-mail: info@gjchamber.org
URL: http://www.gjchamber.org
Contact: Candace Carnahan, Co-President Co-Chief Executive Officer
Facebook: www.facebook.com/grandjunctionchamber
Linkedin: www.linkedin.com/company/grand-junction-area-chamber-of-commerce
X (Twitter): x.com/GJChamber
Description: Promotes business and community development in the Grand Junction, CO area. **Publications:** *Grand Junction Area Chamber of Commerce--Business Directory*. **Geographic Preference:** Local.

37857 ■ Grand Lake Area Chamber of Commerce
14700 US Hwy. 34
Grand Lake, CO 80447
Ph: (970)627-3402
Free: 800-531-1019
Co. E-mail: glinfo@grandlakechamber.com

URL: http://gograndlake.com
Contact: Jim McComb, President
Facebook: www.facebook.com/gograndlake
X (Twitter): x.com/gograndlake
Instagram: www.instagram.com/gograndlake
YouTube: www.youtube.com/channel/UCpcBtsloO9owO8NWvqhn46A
Description: Promotes business and community development in the Grand Lake, CO area. **Founded:** 1946. **Publications:** *Investment Report* (Monthly). **Geographic Preference:** Local.

37858 ■ Greater Englewood Chamber of Commerce
3501 S Broadway, 2nd Fl.
Englewood, CO 80113
Ph: (303)789-4473
Co. E-mail: info@myenglewoodchamber.com
URL: http://myenglewoodchamber.com
Contact: Tracey Brummett, President
E-mail: tracey@onegoodturn.com
Facebook: www.facebook.com/myenglewoodchamber
Linkedin: www.linkedin.com/company/greater-englewood-chamber-of-commerce
Instagram: www.instagram.com/greaterenglewoodchamber
Description: Promotes business and community development in the Englewood, CO area. **Founded:** 1983. **Geographic Preference:** Local.

37859 ■ Greater Golden Chamber of Commerce
1010 Washington Ave.
Golden, CO 80401
Ph: (303)279-3113
Co. E-mail: info@goldenchamber.org
URL: http://goldenchamber.org
Contact: Dean Valdez, Chairman
Facebook: www.facebook.com/goldenchamber
Linkedin: www.linkedin.com/company/goldenchamberofcommerce
X (Twitter): x.com/GoldenChamber
Instagram: www.instagram.com/goldenchamberofcommerce
Description: Promotes business and community development in Golden, CO. **Founded:** 2002. **Publications:** *Greater Golden Chamber of Commerce Network* (Monthly). **Geographic Preference:** Local.

37860 ■ *Greater Golden Chamber of Commerce Network*
1010 Washington Ave.
Golden, CO 80401
Ph: (303)279-3113
Co. E-mail: info@goldenchamber.org
URL: http://goldenchamber.org
Contact: Dean Valdez, Chairman
URL(s): goldenchamber.org/newsletters/#
Released: Monthly **Availability:** PDF.

37861 ■ Greater Pueblo Chamber of Commerce (GPCC)
302 N Santa Fe Ave.
Pueblo, CO 81003-4102
Ph: (719)542-1704
Free: 800-233-3446
Co. E-mail: info@pueblochamber.net
URL: http://pueblochamber.org
Contact: Duane Nava, President
E-mail: duanen@pueblochamber.net
Facebook: www.facebook.com/greaterpueblochamber
Linkedin: www.linkedin.com/company/greater-pueblo-chamber-of-commerce
X (Twitter): x.com/pueblochamber
Instagram: www.instagram.com/visitpueblo
Pinterest: www.pinterest.com/pueblochamber
Description: Promotes business and community development in Pueblo County, CO. Acts as "the collective voice of 1,150 businesses and professionals working to improve and promote an atmosphere that not only enables the community to grow and prosper but be an outstanding place to visit, live and conduct business". **Founded:** 1910. **Publications:** *The Horizon*; *Passport to Pueblo*. **Geographic Preference:** Local.

37862 ■ Greater Woodland Park Chamber of Commerce
210 E Midland Ave.
Woodland Park, CO 80863
Ph: (719)687-9885
Fax: (719)687-8216
Co. E-mail: info@gwpcc.biz
URL: http://www.woodlandparkchamber.com
Contact: Debbie Miller, President
E-mail: debmiller@gwpcc.biz
X (Twitter): x.com/W_P_Chamber
Description: As the primary regional business advocate, the Greater Woodland Park Chamber of Commerce provides valuable member services, pro active leadership, economic opportunity and preservation of the free enterprise system. **Founded:** 1968. **Publications:** *Community and Economic Profile*. **Geographic Preference:** Local.

37863 ■ Greeley Chamber of Commerce
902 7th Ave.
Greeley, CO 80631
Ph: (970)352-3566
Co. E-mail: hello@greeleychamber.com
URL: http://www.greeleychamber.com
Contact: Jaime Henning, President
E-mail: jaime@greeleychamber.com
Facebook: www.facebook.com/GreeleyAreaChamberofCommerce
X (Twitter): x.com/chamberchatter
Instagram: www.instagram.com/greeleyareachamber
Pinterest: www.pinterest.com/greeleychamber
Description: Promotes business and community development in the Greeley and Weld County, CO area. Provides a small business development center. **Founded:** 1919. **Publications:** *Chamber Report* (3/year); *Greeleychamber.com*. **Educational Activities:** Business After Hours (Monthly); Business Before Hours (Monthly). **Geographic Preference:** Local.

37864 ■ *Greeleychamber.com*
902 7th Ave.
Greeley, CO 80631
Ph: (970)352-3566
Co. E-mail: hello@greeleychamber.com
URL: http://www.greeleychamber.com
Contact: Jaime Henning, President
E-mail: jaime@greeleychamber.com
URL(s): www.greeleychamber.com/chamber
Description: Contains information on legislative issues, chamber programs, new members, and other items of interest. **Availability:** Print.

37865 ■ Gunnison County Chamber of Commerce (GCCC)
500 E Tomichi Ave.
Gunnison, CO 81230
Ph: (970)641-1501
Co. E-mail: chamber@gunnison.com
URL: http://www.gunnisonchamber.com
Contact: Lacey Keane, Co-President
Facebook: www.facebook.com/GunnisonChamberofCommerce
YouTube: www.youtube.com/channel/UCifZHZUtUu9xKT3wdjZavuw
Description: Promotes business and community development in Gunnison County, CO. Sponsors local festivals. **Founded:** 1925. **Geographic Preference:** Local.

37866 ■ Haxtun Chamber of Commerce
145 S Colorado Ave.
Haxtun, CO 80731
Ph: (970)466-5540
Co. E-mail: director@welcometohaxtun.com
URL: http://welcometohaxtun.com
Contact: Jessica Allen Ayala, Executive Director
Description: Promotes business and community development in the Haxtun, CO area. **Founded:** 1909. **Geographic Preference:** Local.

37867 ■ Hispanic Chamber of Commerce of Metro Denver
444 Sherman St.
Denver, CO 80203
Ph: (303)534-7783
Fax: (303)595-8977
Co. E-mail: info@hispanicchamberdenver.org
URL: http://www.hispanicchamberdenver.com
Contact: Mike Ferrufino, President
E-mail: mferrufino@hispanicchamberdenver.org
X (Twitter): x.com/HispanicDenver
Description: Promotes business and community development in the Hispanic community Denver, CO. **Founded:** 1978. **Educational Activities:** Business After Hours. **Geographic Preference:** Local.

37868 ■ Holyoke Chamber of Commerce
118 N Interocean, Ste. A
Holyoke, CO 80734
Ph: (970)854-3517
Fax: (970)854-3517
Co. E-mail: director@holyokechamber.org
URL: http://www.holyokechamber.org
Contact: Casey Blake, President
Facebook: www.facebook.com/HolyokeChamberofCommerce
YouTube: www.youtube.com/channel/UCIqsPZzoFvihc4hkMMq8bYw
Description: Promotes business and community development in Holyoke, CO. **Geographic Preference:** Local.

37869 ■ *The Horizon*
302 N Santa Fe Ave.
Pueblo, CO 81003-4102
Ph: (719)542-1704
Free: 800-233-3446
Co. E-mail: info@pueblochamber.net
URL: http://pueblochamber.org
Contact: Duane Nava, President
E-mail: duanen@pueblochamber.net
URL(s): pueblochamber.org/member-benefits/advertising-sponsorship
Availability: Online.

37870 ■ Hotchkiss Community Chamber of Commerce (HCCC)
PO Box 158
Hotchkiss, CO 81419
Ph: (970)872-3226
Co. E-mail: chamberinfo@hotchkisschamber.com
URL: http://www.hotchkisschamber.com
Contact: Bill Long, Vice President
Facebook: www.facebook.com/hotchkisschamber
Description: Promotes business and community development in Hotchkiss area. Co-sponsors Hotchkiss Sheepcamp Stockdog trials and North Fork Valley Bluegrass Festival. **Founded:** 1950. **Geographic Preference:** Local.

37871 ■ Kremmling Area Chamber of Commerce and Visitor Center
203 Pk. Ave.
Kremmling, CO 80459
Ph: (970)724-3472
Fax: (970)724-0397
URL: http://www.kremmlingchamber.com
Facebook: www.facebook.com/kremmlingchambercommerce
X (Twitter): x.com/kremmlingco
Description: Provides leadership for the community, promotes local resources, enhances local programs, offers good places for relocation and coordinates development efforts. **Founded:** 1984. **Geographic Preference:** Local.

37872 ■ La Junta Chamber of Commerce (LJCC)
110 Santa Fe Ave.
La Junta, CO 81050
Ph: (719)384-7411
Co. E-mail: info@lajuntachamber.com
URL: http://www.lajuntachamber.com
Contact: Greg Kolomitz, President
Facebook: www.facebook.com/LaJuntaChamberofCommerce

Description: Promotes business and community development in La Junta, CO. Sponsors Early Settlers Day, community "Wake Up" breakfasts and other social and promotional events. **Founded:** 1930. **Awards:** La Junta Chamber of Commerce Community Service Award (Annual). **Geographic Preference:** Local.

37873 ■ La Veta/Cuchara Chamber of Commerce
305 S Main St.
 La Veta, CO 81055
Ph: (719)742-3676
URL: http://www.coloradodirectory.com/lave tacucharachamber

Description: Promotes business and community development in La Veta, CO. **Geographic Preference:** Local.

37874 ■ Lafayette Chamber of Commerce (LCC)
203 E Simpson St.
 Lafayette, CO 80026
Ph: (303)666-9555
Co. E-mail: info@lafayettecolorado.com
URL: http://www.lafayettecolorado.com
Contact: Vicki Trumbo, Executive Director
Facebook: www.facebook.com/LafayetteChamberCO
X (Twitter): x.com/LafayetteChmber

Description: Promotes business and community development in Lafayette, CO. **Founded:** 1954. **Publications:** *Business Directory*; *Lafayette Chamber Directory*. **Educational Activities:** Celebrate Lafayette. **Geographic Preference:** Local.

37875 ■ Lake City/Hinsdale County Chamber of Commerce (LCCCC)
800 Gunnison Ave.
 Lake City, CO 81235
Ph: (970)944-2527
Co. E-mail: chamber@lakecity.com
URL: http://www.lakecity.com
Contact: Cindy Young, Contact
Facebook: www.facebook.com/LakeCityCO
X (Twitter): x.com/LakeCityCO81235

Description: Promotes business, community development, and tourism in Hinsdale County, CO. **Founded:** 1953. **Geographic Preference:** Local.

37876 ■ Lamar Chamber of Commerce (LCC)
109A E Beech St.
 Lamar, CO 81052
Ph: (719)336-4379
Fax: (719)336-4370
Co. E-mail: lamarchamberofcommerce@gmail.com
URL: http://www.lamarchamber.org

Description: Promotes business and community development in Lamar, CO. **Founded:** 1897. **Geographic Preference:** Local.

37877 ■ Leadville/Lake County Chamber of Commerce
809 Harrison Ave.
 Leadville, CO 80461
Ph: (719)486-3900
Free: 888-LEA-DVILLE
Co. E-mail: leadville@leadvilleusa.com
URL: http://www.leadvilleusachamber.com
Contact: Tracy Purdy, President
Facebook: www.facebook.com/llcoc
X (Twitter): x.com/leadvillecoc

Description: Promotes business and community development in Lake County, CO. **Founded:** 1913. **Publications:** *Chamber E-News* (Monthly). **Geographic Preference:** Local.

37878 ■ Limon Chamber of Commerce
205 E Ave.
 Limon, CO 80828
Ph: (719)775-9418
Co. E-mail: limonchamberofcommerce@gmail.com
URL: http://www.limonchamber.us
Facebook: www.facebook.com/Limon.CO.CoC
X (Twitter): x.com/limonchamber

Description: Works to advance the commercial, financial, industrial and civic interests of Limon, CO. **Geographic Preference:** Local.

37879 ■ *Listing Business Directory*
125 Anglers Dr.
 Steamboat Springs, CO 80487
Ph: (970)879-0880
Fax: (970)285-3550
Co. E-mail: info@steamboatchamber.com
URL: http://www.steamboat-chamber.com
Contact: Kara Stoller, Co-Chief Executive Officer
E-mail: kara@steamboatchamber.com
URL(s): www.steamboatchamber.com/discover-s teamboat/business-directory

Availability: Print.

37880 ■ Logan County Chamber of Commerce
109 N Front St.
 Sterling, CO 80751
Ph: (970)522-5070
Free: 866-522-5070
Co. E-mail: info@logancountychamber.com
URL: http://www.logancountychamber.com
Contact: Brock Baseggio, Director
Facebook: www.facebook.com/logancoun tychamberofcommerce1
X (Twitter): x.com/LoganCommerce

Description: Promotes business and community development in Logan County, CO. **Founded:** 1937. **Publications:** *Chamber Highlights* (Periodic). **Awards:** Logan County Chamber Volunteer/Diplomat of the Year (Annual); Logan County Chamber of Commerce Small Business of the Year (Annual); Logan County Chamber of Commerce Business Person of the Year (Annual); Logan County Chamber of Commerce Citizen of the Year (Annual). **Geographic Preference:** Local.

37881 ■ Longmont Area Chamber of Commerce
528 Main St.
 Longmont, CO 80501
Ph: (303)776-5295
Co. E-mail: staff@longmontchamber.org
URL: http://www.longmontchamber.org
Contact: Scott Cook, Chief Executive Officer
E-mail: scook@longmontchamber.org
Facebook: www.facebook.com/longmontchamber
X (Twitter): x.com/longmontchamber
Instagram: www.instagram.com/longmontchamber
YouTube: www.youtube.com/user/LongmontChamber

Description: Promotes business and community development in the Longmont, CO area. **Publications:** *Longmont Area Best of Business Directory and Reference Guide* (Annual). **Geographic Preference:** Local.

37882 ■ Louisville Chamber of Commerce
901 Main St.
 Louisville, CO 80027
Ph: (303)666-5747
Fax: (303)666-4285
Co. E-mail: info@louisvillechamber.com
URL: http://www.louisvillechamber.com
Contact: Iona Kearney, President
E-mail: iona@speedysparklecarwash.com
Linkedin: www.linkedin.com/company/louisville -chamber-of-commerce

Description: Works to advance the commercial, financial, industrial and civic interests of Louisville, CO. **Geographic Preference:** Local.

37883 ■ Loveland Chamber of Commerce
5400 Stone Creek Cir.
 Loveland, CO 80538-6153
Ph: (970)744-4792
Fax: (970)667-5211
Co. E-mail: dixie@loveland.org
URL: http://www.loveland.org
Contact: Mindy McCloughan, President
E-mail: mmccloughan@loveland.org
Facebook: www.facebook.com/lovelandchamber
Linkedin: www.linkedin.com/groups/942547/profile
X (Twitter): x.com/LovelandChamber
YouTube: www.youtube.com/channel/ UC90eUSH7J0GHWIbJkc02f1A

Description: Promotes business and community development in the Loveland, CO area. Conducts Corn Roast Festival. **Founded:** 1902. **Publications:** *Aware* (Monthly); *Membership Directory/Relocation Guide* (Annual). **Geographic Preference:** Local.

37884 ■ Lyons Chamber of Commerce (LCC)
PO Box 426
 Lyons, CO 80540
Co. E-mail: admin@lyonschamber.org
URL: http://www.lyonschamber.org
Contact: Craig Ferguson, President
Facebook: www.facebook.com/LyonsColorado
X (Twitter): x.com/16lyonschamber

Description: Promotes business and community development in the area. **Founded:** 1970. **Publications:** *Lyons Directory* (Periodic). **Educational Activities:** Informational Safety Meeting. **Geographic Preference:** Local.

37885 ■ Manitou Springs Chamber of Commerce [Manitou Springs Chamber of Commerce and Visitors Bureau]
354 Manitou Ave.
 Manitou Springs, CO 80829
Ph: (719)685-5089
URL: http://manitousprings.org
Contact: Leslie E. Lewis, Contact
Facebook: www.facebook.com/visit.manitousprings
X (Twitter): x.com/Visit_Manitou
YouTube: www.youtube.com/channel/UCVWQml dKgNGcomyHQw_VsMg

Description: Promotes business, community development and tourism in Manitou Springs, CO. **Publications:** *News and Views* (Monthly). **Geographic Preference:** Local.

37886 ■ Meeker Chamber of Commerce
710 Market St.
 Meeker, CO 81641
Ph: (970)878-5510
URL: http://meekerchamber.com
Contact: Marie Hooks, President
Facebook: www.facebook.com/MeekerChamber

Description: Promotes business and community development in Meeker, CO. Sponsors yearly festival. **Founded:** 1885. **Geographic Preference:** Local.

37887 ■ *Membership Directory and Buyers' Guide*
Availability: Print.

37888 ■ Monte Vista Chamber of Commerce (MVCC)
947 1st Ave.
 Monte Vista, CO 81144
Ph: (719)852-2731
Co. E-mail: chamber@montevistachamber.org
URL: http://www.montevistachamber.org
Contact: Linda Burnett, President
E-mail: burnett.montevistachamber@gmail.com
Facebook: www.facebook.com/MonteVis taCOChamber

Description: Promotes business and community development in Monte Vista, CO. Gathers and disseminates business, industrial and general relocation information. Conducts business education programs. **Founded:** 1922. **Publications:** *Monte Vista F.Y.I.* (Monthly); *Mountain of Facts* (Annual). **Educational Activities:** Southern Rocky Mountain Agricultural Conference and Trade Fair (Annual); Potato-Grain Conference & Agricultural Exhibition. **Geographic Preference:** Local.

37889 ■ New Castle Chamber of Commerce
126 N 4th St.
 New Castle, CO 81647
Ph: (970)984-2897
Co. E-mail: newcastlecc@sopris.net
URL: http://www.newcastlechamber.org
Contact: Siobahn Milholm, President
Facebook: www.facebook.com/newcastleCOchamber

Description: Promotes new and existing businesses in the New Castle Area. Provides relocation and new resident packets to organizations and individuals. **Geographic Preference:** Local.

STATE LISTINGS   Colorado ■ 37906

37890 ■ Ouray Chamber Resort Association (OCRA)
1230 Main St.
Ouray, CO 81427
Ph: (970)325-3954
URL: http://www.visitouray.com
Description: Promotes business and community development in Ouray County, CO. Sponsors Octoberfest and New Year's Eve fireworks display. **Founded:** 1993. **Geographic Preference:** Local.

37891 ■ Pagosa Springs Area Chamber of Commerce (PSACC)
105 Hot Springs Blvd.
Pagosa Springs, CO 81147
Ph: (970)264-2360
Fax: (970)264-4625
Co. E-mail: info@pagosachamber.com
URL: http://pagosachamber.com
Contact: Meg Wempe, President
Facebook: www.facebook.com/PagosaSpringsChamber
X (Twitter): x.com/pagosasprings
Instagram: www.instagram.com/pagosaspringschamber
Description: Promotes business and community development in the Pagosa Springs, CO area. Sponsors Colorfest and Arts and Crafts Festival. Publications: none. **Founded:** 1976. **Geographic Preference:** Local.

37892 ■ Palisade Chamber of Commerce (PCC)
305 S Main St., Ste. 102
Palisade, CO 81526
Ph: (970)464-7458
Co. E-mail: info@palisadecoc.com
URL: http://palisadecoc.com
Contact: Jessica Burford, President
Description: Promotes agriculture, business and community development in the Palisade, CO area. Sponsors annual Palisade Peach Festival. **Founded:** 1982. **Publications:** *Fruit & Wine Directory* (Annual). **Educational Activities:** Awards Banquet. **Geographic Preference:** Local.

37893 ■ Parker Area Chamber of Commerce (PACC)
19751 E Main st., Ste. R16
Parker, CO 80138
Ph: (303)841-4268
Fax: (303)841-8061
Co. E-mail: info@parkerchamber.com
URL: http://www.parkerchamber.com
Contact: T. J. Sullivan, President
E-mail: tj@parkerchamber.com
Facebook: www.facebook.com/ParkerChamber
Instagram: www.instagram.com/parkercochamber
Description: Supports and promotes the success of the members through working, professional development, advocacy, leadership and community development. **Founded:** 1965. **Publications:** *Network*; *Parker Country Map* (Annual); *Parker Country Map* (Annual); *Parker Country Magazine* (Annual). **Educational Activities:** Parker Country Festival (Annual). **Geographic Preference:** Local.

37894 ■ Rangely Area Chamber of Commerce (RACC)
255 E Main St., Ste. A
Rangely, CO 81648
Ph: (970)675-5290
Co. E-mail: rangelychamber@gmail.com
URL: http://www.rangelychamber.com
Contact: Jodi Dillon, President
Facebook: www.facebook.com/rangelychamber
X (Twitter): x.com/rangelychamber
Instagram: www.instagram.com/rangelychamber
Description: Seeks to enhance the economic health and business climate of Rangely community. **Geographic Preference:** Local.

37895 ■ Royal Gorge Chamber Alliance (RGCA)
424 Main St.
Canon City, CO 81212
Ph: (719)275-2331
Free: 800-876-7922
Co. E-mail: membership@royalgorgechamberalliance.org
URL: http://www.canoncity.com
Contact: Cooper Trahern, President
Facebook: www.facebook.com/RoyalGorgeChamberAlliance
Description: Promotes business and community development in Canon City, CO. **Founded:** 1888. **Publications:** *Chamber* (Monthly). **Awards:** Canon City Chamber of Commerce Distinguished Citizen (Annual). **Geographic Preference:** Local.

37896 ■ Snowmass Tourism
130 Kearns Rd.
Snowmass Village, CO 81615
Ph: (970)922-2297
Co. E-mail: info@snowmasstoursim.com
URL: http://www.gosnowmass.com
Description: Promotes the social and economic development in Snowmass Village, CO. **Founded:** 1967. **Geographic Preference:** Local.

37897 ■ South Fork Visitors Center
28 Silverthread Ln.
South Fork, CO 81154
Ph: (719)873-5512
URL: http://www.southfork.org/south-fork/visitor-info
Description: Promotes business, tourism, and community development in South Fork, CO. **Founded:** 1992. **Geographic Preference:** Local.

37898 ■ South Metro Denver Chamber of Commerce
6972 s Vine St., Ste. 363
Centennial, CO 80122
Ph: (303)795-0142
Co. E-mail: info@bestchamber.com
URL: http://www.bestchamber.com
Contact: Jeff Keener, President
E-mail: jkeener@bestchamber.com
Facebook: www.facebook.com/bestchamber
Linkedin: www.linkedin.com/company/south-metro-denver-chamber-of-commerce
X (Twitter): x.com/BestChamber
YouTube: www.youtube.com/channel/UCh_q3SS5fFmEy2JJ6klxi_w
Description: Promotes business and community development in the southern metropolitan Denver, CO area. Conducts seminars. **Founded:** 1921. **Awards:** SMDC Small Business of the Year (Annual). **Geographic Preference:** Local.

37899 ■ Southern Colorado Women's Chamber of Commerce (SCWCC)
2424 Garden of the Gods Rd., Bldg. C, Ste. 250
Colorado Springs, CO 80949
Ph: (719)442-2007
Co. E-mail: info@scwcc.com
URL: http://www.scwcc.com
Contact: Lola Woloch, President
Facebook: www.facebook.com/scwcc
Linkedin: www.linkedin.com/company/scwcc
X (Twitter): x.com/SCWCC
Description: Promotes economic development among women-owned or operated businesses in Southern Colorado. **Founded:** 1993. **Publications:** *SCWCC Enews* (Monthly). **Geographic Preference:** Local.

37900 ■ Steamboat Springs Chamber Resort Association (SSCRA)
125 Anglers Dr.
Steamboat Springs, CO 80487
Ph: (970)879-0880
Fax: (970)285-3550
Co. E-mail: info@steamboatchamber.com
URL: http://www.steamboat-chamber.com
Contact: Kara Stoller, Co-Chief Executive Officer
E-mail: kara@steamboatchamber.com
Facebook: www.facebook.com/steamboatchamber
X (Twitter): x.com/SteamboatCO
YouTube: www.youtube.com/user/steamboatchamber
Pinterest: www.pinterest.com/Steamboat_CO
Description: Seeks to support, encourage and sustain a vibrant, healthy economy in Steamboat Springs, CO and the surrounding communities.

Publications: *Activity Guidelines*; *Dining Guide*; *Listing Business Directory*; *Visitors Guide* (Semiannual). **Geographic Preference:** Local.

37901 ■ *The Summit*
PO Box 5450
Frisco, CO 80443
Ph: (970)668-2051
Co. E-mail: info@summitchamber.org
URL: http://www.summitchamber.org
URL(s): summitchamber.org/member-benefits
Description: Contains information about the chamber and the community. **Availability:** Online.

37902 ■ Summit Chamber of Commerce
PO Box 5450
Frisco, CO 80443
Ph: (970)668-2051
Co. E-mail: info@summitchamber.org
URL: http://www.summitchamber.org
Facebook: www.facebook.com/SummitChamber
X (Twitter): x.com/summitchamber
Instagram: www.instagram.com/thesummitchamber
Description: Promotes business and community development in the area. **Founded:** 1971. **Publications:** *The Summit*; *Membership Directory and Buyers' Guide* (Annual). **Geographic Preference:** Local.

37903 ■ Swedish-American Chamber of Commerce Colorado (SACC-CO)
c/o Consulate of Sweden, 4100 E Mississippi Ave., Ste. 410
Denver, CO 80222
Ph: (720)515-9421
Co. E-mail: info@sacc-co.org
URL: http://sacc-co.org
Contact: Marie Forsgren-Mare, President
Facebook: www.facebook.com/SACCColorado
Linkedin: www.linkedin.com/company/sacc-colorado
X (Twitter): x.com/SACCColorado
Instagram: www.instagram.com/sacc_co
Description: Seeks to increase trade, commerce and investments between Sweden and Colorado. **Founded:** 1990. **Geographic Preference:** State.

37904 ■ Tri-Lakes Chamber of Commerce
166 2nd St.
Monument, CO 80132
Ph: (719)481-3282
Co. E-mail: julie@trilakeschamber.com
URL: http://www.trilakeschamber.com
Contact: Terri Hayes, President
E-mail: terri@trilakeschamber.com
Facebook: www.facebook.com/TriLakesChamberofCommerce
Linkedin: www.linkedin.com/company/tri-lakes-chamber-of-commerce-co
Instagram: www.instagram.com/trilakeschamber
YouTube: www.youtube.com/channel/UCL_Ju5t5bZVg0wmy-ljY4NA
Description: Promotes business and community development in Tri-Lakes, CO area. Conducts charitable activities. Sponsors area festivals. **Publications:** *Chamber Chat* (Weekly). **Geographic Preference:** Local.

37905 ■ Vallecito Lake Chamber of Commerce
18071 County Rd. 501
Bayfield, CO 81122
Ph: (970)247-1573
Co. E-mail: info@vallecitolakechamber.com
URL: http://vallecitolakechamber.com
Facebook: www.facebook.com/Vallecito-Lake-Chamber-of-Commerce-167016060018743
X (Twitter): x.com/vallecitolakecc
Description: Works to advance the commercial, financial, industrial and civic interests of the area. **Geographic Preference:** Local.

37906 ■ *Visitors Guide*
125 Anglers Dr.
Steamboat Springs, CO 80487
Ph: (970)879-0880
Fax: (970)285-3550
Co. E-mail: info@steamboatchamber.com
URL: http://www.steamboat-chamber.com

Contact: Kara Stoller, Co-Chief Executive Officer
E-mail: kara@steamboatchamber.com
URL(s): www.steamboatchamber.com/plan-your-trip/visitors-center/visitor-guide-request
Released: Semiannual **Description:** Feature maps of the Steamboat Springs area complete with a trail guide, a seasonal calendar of events, and a complete business directory. **Availability:** Print; Online.

37907 ■ West Metro Chamber Serving Jefferson County
1667 Cole Blvd., Bldg. 19, Ste. 400
Lakewood, CO 80401
URL: http://www.westmetrochamber.org
Contact: Jansen Tidmore, President
E-mail: jtidmore@jeffcoedc.org
Description: Seeks to support member businesses through business growth opportunities. **Founded:** 1947. **Geographic Preference:** Local.

37908 ■ West Yuma County Chamber of Commerce
14 W 2nd Ave.
Yuma, CO 80759
Ph: (970)848-2704
Co. E-mail: director@westyumachamber.com
URL: http://yumacochamber.com
Contact: Candy Gilliland, President
E-mail: c.gilliland@yumacolo.org
Description: Promotes business and community development in western Yuma County, CO. Holds Community Chest Drive and St. Patrick's Benefit Auction for local charity. Sponsors Yuma Fest, Old Threshers Day, and Business Expo. Conducts seminars and workshops. **Founded:** 1926. **Geographic Preference:** Local.

37909 ■ Westminster Chamber of Commerce
PO Box 1453
Westminster, CO 80036
Ph: (303)961-5975
Co. E-mail: info@westminsterchamber.biz
URL: http://www.westminsterchamber.biz
Facebook: www.facebook.com/WestminsterCC
Linkedin: www.linkedin.com/company/westminster-chamber-of-commerce
X (Twitter): x.com/westychamber
YouTube: www.youtube.com/channel/UCnXOusHDixyYRviqpn0EEsg
Description: Promotes business and community development in the area. **Founded:** 2013. **Geographic Preference:** Local.

37910 ■ Windsor Chamber of Commerce (WCC)
421 Main St.
Windsor, CO 80550-5129
Ph: (970)686-7189
Fax: (970)686-0352
Co. E-mail: information@windsorchamber.net
URL: http://windsorchamber.net
Contact: Michelle Vance, Executive Director
E-mail: michelle@windsorchamber.net
Facebook: www.facebook.com/windsorcochamber
Description: Promotes business and community development in Windsor, CO. Sponsors harvest and summer festival and pool day. Holds Business After Hours mixers. Conducts promotional campaigns. Presents Student of the Year award to high school students. Holds monthly board meeting. **Founded:** 1902. **Publications:** *Windsor Chamber of Commerce Newsletter* (Monthly). **Educational Activities:** Windsor Chamber of Commerce Dinner (Annual). **Geographic Preference:** Local.

37911 ■ Winter Park-Fraser Valley Chamber of Commerce
7881 US Hwy. 40
Winter Park, CO 80482
Ph: (970)726-4118
Free: 800-903-7275
Co. E-mail: visitorcenter@playwinterpark.com
URL: http://www.playwinterpark.com
Contact: Mindy O'Neil, President
E-mail: moneil@centennialbanking.com
Facebook: www.facebook.com/playwinterpark
X (Twitter): x.com/PlayWinterPark
Instagram: www.instagram.com/playwinterpark
YouTube: www.youtube.com/user/WinterParkChamber
Description: Promotes business, community development, and tourism in Winter Park and the Fraser River valley, CO. **Publications:** *Mountain Bike Trail Map* (Annual); *Valley View* (Monthly); *Visitors Guide*. **Geographic Preference:** Regional.

37912 ■ Wray Chamber of Commerce
110 E 3rd St.
Wray, CO 80758
Ph: (970)332-3484
URL: http://wraychamber.net
Contact: Brian Dean Clements, Contact
Facebook: www.facebook.com/wraychamber
X (Twitter): x.com/wraychamber
Instagram: www.instagram.com/wraychamber
Description: Promotes business and community development in Wray, CO. **Founded:** 1886. **Publications:** *Wray Chamber of Commerce News* (Monthly). **Geographic Preference:** Local.

MINORITY BUSINESS ASSISTANCE PROGRAMS

37913 ■ Colorado Office of Economic Development and International Trade - Minority Business Office
1600 Broadway, Ste. 2500
Denver, CO 80202
Co. E-mail: mbo@state.co.us
URL: http://oedit.colorado.gov/minority-business-office-of-colorado
Contact: Antonio Soto, Director
E-mail: antonio.soto@state.co.us
Facebook: www.facebook.com/mbocolorado
Linkedin: www.linkedin.com/company/minority-business-office
Instagram: www.instagram.com/mbocolorado
Description: Provides information and assistance to minority- and women-owned businesses in Colorado.

37914 ■ Mountain Plains Minority Supplier Development Council (MPMSDC)
6025 S Quebec St., Ste. 135
Centennial, CO 80111
Ph: (303)623-3037
Fax: (303)595-0027
URL: http://www.mpmsdc.org
Contact: Stan Sena, Chief Executive Officer
E-mail: stan@mpmsdc.org
Facebook: www.facebook.com/Mpmsdc
Linkedin: www.linkedin.com/company/mountain-plains-minority-supplier-development-council-mpmsdc-
X (Twitter): x.com/MPMSDC
Instagram: www.instagram.com/mpmsdc
Description: Provides a direct link between corporate America and minority-owned businesses. Increases procurement and business opportunities for minority businesses of all sizes. **Founded:** 1974. **Geographic Preference:** Regional.

FINANCING AND LOAN PROGRAMS

37915 ■ Access Venture Partners (AVP)
8787 Tpke., Dr., Ste. 260
Westminster, CO 80031
URL: http://accessvp.com
Contact: Tiffany Cholez, Chief Financial Officer
Linkedin: www.linkedin.com/company/access-venture-partners
X (Twitter): x.com/accessvp
Description: Firm provides venture capital in seed, early stage, early growth and expansion stage investments. **Founded:** 1999. **Preferred Investment Size:** $250,000 to $2,000,000. **Industry Preferences:** Internet specific, communications and media, biotechnology, computer software and services, semiconductors and other electronics, and industrial and energy.

37916 ■ Altira Group L.L.C.
205 Detroit St., Ste. 200
Denver, CO 80206
Ph: (303)592-5500
Fax: (303)592-5519
Co. E-mail: info@altiragroup.com
URL: http://www.altiragroup.com
Contact: Purcell Allen, Office Manager
Description: Provider of venture capital and private equity investments including early stage, mid stage, late stage, growth capital and follow-on investments for entrepreneurs and portfolio companies. **Founded:** 1996. **Preferred Investment Size:** $5,000,000 to $10,000,000. **Industry Preferences:** Industrial and energy, and environment.

37917 ■ Appian Ventures
4810 Prospect St.
Littleton, CO 80123
Ph: (303)830-2450
URL: http://www.appianvc.com
Description: Venture capital firm specializes in investments in software and technology companies. **Preferred Investment Size:** $1,000,000 to $2,000,000. **Investment Policies:** Seed, early and later stage. **Industry Preferences:** Communications, and computer software.

37918 ■ Aweida Venture Partners (AVP)
500 Discovery Pky., Ste. 300
Louisville, CO 80027
Contact: Kathy L. Mattison, Contact
Description: Provider of mezzanine, seed, early, mid and late venture capital investments for data storage, software and life sciences. **Founded:** 1988. **Preferred Investment Size:** $500,000 to $1,000,000. **Industry Preferences:** Computer software and hardware, Internet specific, biotechnology, and medical and health.

37919 ■ Centennial Ventures
8822 S Ridgeline Blvd., Ste. 250
Highlands Ranch, CO 80129
Contact: Tiffany Cholez, Contact
Description: Venture capital firm provides seed, early and later stage financing services. **Founded:** 1982. **Preferred Investment Size:** Venture capital firm. **Industry Preferences:** Communications and media, Internet specific, computer hardware, computer software and services, semiconductors and other electronics, medical and health, biotechnology, consumer related, other products, and industrial and energy.

37920 ■ FirstMile Ventures
630 Southpointe Ct., Ste. 200
Colorado Springs, CO 80906
Co. E-mail: info@firstmilevc.com
URL: http://www.firstmilevc.com
Contact: Bill Miller, Founder Managing Partner
Linkedin: www.linkedin.com/company/firstmile-ventures
X (Twitter): x.com/FirstMileVC
Description: Seed-stage, founder-driven venture capital firm. **Founded:** 2014. **Preferred Investment Size:** $50,000-$250,000. **Industry Preferences:** B2B software; infrastructure tech; distributed ledger.

37921 ■ Foundry Group
1050 Walnut St., Ste. 210
Boulder, CO 80302
Co. E-mail: foundrygroup@alterdomus.com
URL: http://foundry.vc
Contact: Seth Levine, Partner
E-mail: seth@foundry.vc
Linkedin: www.linkedin.com/company/foundry-vc
Description: Early-stage venture capital firm. Invests in technology companies throughout the US and Canada. **Founded:** 2007.

37922 ■ High County Venture, LLC (HCV)
831 Pearl St.
Boulder, CO 80302
Contact: Chris Marks, Contact
Description: Venture capital firm for innovative early-stage companies in Colorado. **Founded:** 2005. **Investment Policies:** Scalable, innovative technolo-

STATE LISTINGS

gies that address unmet needs or create efficiencies in the marketplace; markets with significant and rapid growth potential; visionary management.

37923 ■ Meritage Funds
501 S Cherry St., Ste. 550
Denver, CO 80246
Ph: (303)352-2040
Co. E-mail: info@meritage.vc
URL: http://www.meritage.vc
Contact: Jay Tankersley, Contact

Description: Private equity firm provides investment services. **Founded:** 1998. **Preferred Investment Size:** $5,000,000 to $15,000,000. **Industry Preferences:** Internet specific, communications and media, computer hardware, and computer software and services.

37924 ■ Next Wave Impact (NWI)
1031 33rd St.
Denver, CO 80205
Co. E-mail: info@nextwaveimpact.com
URL: http://nextwaveimpact.com
Contact: Dr. Alicia Robb, Chief Executive Officer
Facebook: www.facebook.com/nextwavenetwork
X (Twitter): x.com/nextwavenetwork

Description: Women-led firm drives impact, diversity, and inclusion in early-stage investing and the entrepreneurial ecosystem. **Preferred Investment Size:** $150,000-$200,000 in the first two years; $250,000-$500,000 in the third and fourth years. **Investment Policies:** Sustainable competitive advantage; well-balanced management team; market opportunity; balanced and diverse growth strategy; product/service differentiation; clear exit strategy; positive impact on people, communities, and the planet; shows traction in solving problems in health, education, food sustainability, clean energy, and the aging population.

37925 ■ Partisan Management Group
293 Pearl St.
Boulder, CO 80302
Contact: Karen J. Cassidy, Contact

Description: Venture capital firm for early-stage companies meeting unmet medical needs. . **Industry Preferences:** Medical devices; drug delivery.

37926 ■ Pennell Venture Partners II L.L.C.
PO Box 315
Boulder, CO 80306
Ph: (917)345-4134
Co. E-mail: info@pennell.com
URL: http://pennell.com
Contact: Thomas Pennell, Managing Partner

Description: Provider of venture capital investments including sourcing, closing and leading the post-closing integration services. **Preferred Investment Size:** $300,000 to $1,500,000. **Investment Policies:** Early stage. **Industry Preferences:** Computer software and business services.

37927 ■ Rockies Venture Club (RVC)
1415 Pk. Ave. W
Denver, CO 80205
Ph: (720)353-9350
URL: http://rockiesventureclub.wildapricot.org
Contact: Peter Adams, Executive Director
E-mail: peter@rockiesventureclub.org

Description: Angel investing club works to accelerate economic development. Offers events and education. **Founded:** 1985.

37928 ■ Roser Ventures LLC
1105 Spruce St.
Boulder, CO 80302
URL: http://roserventures.com
Contact: Al Valenti, Chief Financial Officer
E-mail: avalenti@roserventures.com

Founded: 1987. **Preferred Investment Size:** $100,000 to $3,000,000. **Industry Preferences:** Internet specific, communications and media, industrial and energy, semiconductors and other electronics, computer software and services, medical and health, computer hardware, other products, biotechnology, and consumer related.

37929 ■ Sequel Venture Partners
4430 Arapahoe Ave., Ste. 220
Boulder, CO 80303
Ph: (303)546-0400
Fax: (303)546-9728
URL: http://www.sequelvc.com
Contact: Tom Washing, Partner

Description: Provider of venture funding for early stage technology businesses. **Preferred Investment Size:** $2,000,000 to $12,000,000. **Industry Preferences:** Internet specific, computer software and services, medical and health, semiconductors and other electronics, biotechnology, communications and media, computer hardware, and other products.

PROCUREMENT ASSISTANCE PROGRAMS

37930 ■ Colorado Procurement Technical Assistance Center - Denver Small Business Development Procurement Center (SBDC)
1445 Market St.
Denver, CO 80202
Ph: (303)620-8076
Co. E-mail: info@denversbdc.org
URL: http://www.denversbdc.org
Contact: China Califf, Executive Director
Facebook: www.facebook.com/denversbdc
Linkedin: www.linkedin.com/company/denver-metro-sbdc
X (Twitter): x.com/denversbdc

Founded: 1990.

INCUBATORS/RESEARCH AND TECHNOLOGY PARKS

37931 ■ Boomtown Accelerator
2060 Broadway St., B-1
Boulder, CO 80302
Co. E-mail: hello@boomtownaccelerators.com
URL: http://boomtownaccelerators.com
Contact: Toby Krout, Chief Executive Officer
Facebook: www.facebook.com/BoomtownAccelerators
Linkedin: www.linkedin.com/company/boomtownaccelerators
X (Twitter): x.com/boomtown
Instagram: www.instagram.com/boomtownaccelerators
YouTube: www.youtube.com/channel/UCnawy9KXXNfd24QGWS4fVPQ

Description: Business accelerator specializing in tech and media companies. The 12-week program invests in people rather than ideas. **Founded:** 2013.

37932 ■ Business Incubator Center (BIC)
2591 Legacy Way
Grand Junction, CO 81503
Ph: (970)243-5242
Fax: (970)241-0771
Co. E-mail: frontdesk@gjincubator.org
URL: http://gjincubator.org
Contact: Jon Maraschin, Executive Director
E-mail: jmaraschin@gjincubator.org
Facebook: www.facebook.com/GJIncubator
X (Twitter): x.com/Biz_Incubator

Description: Assists entrepreneurs in the business start-up process and in managing new businesses. **Founded:** 1987. **Geographic Preference:** Local.

37933 ■ Business Incubator Center Kitchen (BIC)
2591 Legacy Way
Grand Junction, CO 81503
Ph: (970)243-5242
Fax: (970)241-0771
Co. E-mail: frontdesk@gjincubator.org
URL: http://gjincubator.org
Contact: Dalida Bollig, Chief Executive Officer
Facebook: www.facebook.com/GJIncubator
X (Twitter): x.com/Biz_Incubator
Instagram: www.instagram.com/gjbusincubator

Description: Supports the launch, growth, stabilization and long-term success of culinary business enterprises. **Founded:** 1987.

37934 ■ Canopy
1002 Walnut St., Ste. 300
Boulder, CO 80302
Ph: (303)586-4745
Co. E-mail: info@canopyboulder.com
URL: http://www.canopyboulder.com
Contact: Mark Nottoli, Co-Founder
Facebook: www.facebook.com/canopyboulder
Linkedin: www.linkedin.com/company/canopy-boulder
X (Twitter): twitter.com/CanopyBoulder
YouTube: www.youtube.com/channel/UCZ2CEKjstcxUwHsQeCgDeoA

Description: A seed-stage business accelerator and venture fund for the legal cannabis industry. Startups are awarded up to $80k in seed capital during the 16-week program, and connected with 100+ mentors, and the industry's largest investor network.

37935 ■ Denver Design Incubator (DDI)
2040 Clay St.
Denver, CO 80211
Ph: (720)213-6601
Co. E-mail: info@denverdesignincubator.com
URL: http://www.denverdesignincubator.com
Facebook: www.facebook.com/DenverDesignIncubator
Instagram: www.instagram.com/denverdesignincubator

Description: Offers resources, education, workspace, and professional development to the local community to support the sustainable and sewn products industry in Colorado. **Founded:** 2009.

37936 ■ DurangoSpace
101 W 11th St., Unit 108
Durango, CO 81301
Ph: (970)828-1340
URL: http://durangospace.com
Contact: Jasper Welch, Co-Founder
Facebook: www.facebook.com/people/DurangoSpace/100069207786244
X (Twitter): x.com/durangospace
YouTube: www.youtube.com/user/DurangoSpace

Description: Offers co-working shared space for startups and entrepreneurs in which ideas and resources can be shared and network opportunities exist. **Founded:** 1990.

37937 ■ Fitzsimons BioBusiness Incubator
12635 E Montview Blvd.
Aurora, CO 80045
Ph: (720)859-4100
Co. E-mail: info@fitzsimonsinnovation.com
URL: http://fitzsimonsinnovation.com
Contact: Dr. Afshin Safavi, President

Description: Business incubator that offers its clients business advisory services and programs in addition to facilities that include 20 pre-built labs and 21 executive office suites, shared scientific equipment and building wide services and amenities. **Founded:** 2000.

37938 ■ Fitzsimons Innovation Campus (FIC)
12635 E Montview Blvd.
Aurora, CO 80045
Ph: (720)859-4100
Co. E-mail: info@fitzsimonsinnovation.com
URL: http://fitzsimonsinnovation.com
Contact: Dr. Afshin Safavi, President
Facebook: www.facebook.com/FitzsimonsInnovationCommunity
Linkedin: www.linkedin.com/company/fitzsimons-innovation-community
X (Twitter): x.com/FIC_Colorado

Description: Offers an unrivaled range of opportunity to life sciences research and development companies of all sizes, from small start-ups to established industry leaders. Within the campus, more than six million square feet of corporate and bioresearch facility space are being developed for companies and firms focusing on the science and technology sectors.

37939 ■ Colorado   STATE LISTINGS

37939 ■ Fitzsimons Innovation Company (FIC)
12635 E Montview Blvd.
Aurora, CO 80045
Ph: (720)859-4100
Co. E-mail: info@fitzsimonsinnovation.com
URL: http://fitzsimonsinnovation.com
Contact: Dr. Afshin Safavi, President
Facebook: www.facebook.com/FitzsimonsInnovationCommunity
X (Twitter): x.com/FIC_Colorado
Description: An incubator dedicated to promoting the growth and success of bioscience businesses in Colorado, with a special emphasis on forming a bioscience cluster at Fitzsimons. Connects ideas, technology and people to deliver targeted assistance to start-up companies and entrepreneurs; unites industry experts, venture capitalists, private investors, and the researchers the move discoveries from the lab to the commercial marketplace.

37940 ■ Fitzsimons Life Science District
12635 E Montview Blvd.
Aurora, CO 80045
URL: http://fitzsimonsinnovation.com/collaborate/company-directory
Description: A development facility stimulating economic growth by creating a word-class scientific community at Fitzsimons which includes, but is not limited to, entrepreneurial life science organizations, related support services and high-quality amenities.

37941 ■ Fitzsimons Redevelopment Authority (FRA)
12635 E Montview Blvd.
Aurora, CO 80045
Ph: (720)859-4100
Co. E-mail: info@fitzsimonsinnovation.com
URL: http://fitzsimonsinnovation.com
Contact: Dr. Afshin Safavi, President
Facebook: www.facebook.com/FitzsimonsInnovationCommunity
X (Twitter): x.com/FIC_Colorado
Description: Firm provides bioscience incubator for early stage bioscience companies and offers plug and play offices and programming support to startups. **Founded:** 2000.

37942 ■ Fremont Economic Development Corp. (FEDC)
402 Valley Rd.
Canon City, CO 81212
Ph: (719)275-8601
Free: 855-942-4223
Co. E-mail: info@fedc.co
URL: http://www.fedc.co
Description: A small business incubator that assists entrepreneurs in the business start-up process and gives aid to new businesses to help ensure their survival. **Founded:** 1983.

37943 ■ Galvanize
1023 Walnut St.
Boulder, CO 80302
Ph: (303)749-0038
Co. E-mail: info@galvanize.com
URL: http://www.galvanize.com
Facebook: www.facebook.com/GalvanizeHQ
Linkedin: www.linkedin.com/company/galvanize-it
X (Twitter): x.com/galvanize
Instagram: www.instagram.com/GalvanizeHQ
Description: Business accelerator supporting entrepreneurs, engineers, mentors, and venture capitalists. Provides high speed internet, flexible workspace, conference rooms, and a variety of office amenities.

37944 ■ Global Accelerator Network (GAN)
1900 Grant St., Ste. 510
Denver, CO 80203
URL: http://morrow.co/accelerators
Contact: Patrick William Riley, Contact
Description: Helps startups acquire human and financial capital. **Founded:** 2010.

37945 ■ Innosphere
320 E Vine Dr., Ste. 101
Fort Collins, CO 80524
Ph: (970)221-1301
URL: http://innosphereventures.org
Contact: Aziza Syed, Director
Facebook: www.facebook.com/InnosphereVentures
Linkedin: www.linkedin.com/company/innosphereventures
X (Twitter): x.com/innosphere_v
Instagram: www.instagram.com/innosphere.ventures
YouTube: www.youtube.com/channel/UChpboJV07CgMx75tRmD1D2w
Description: A business incubator assisting startup companies and rapidly growing young firms. Formerly the Fort Collins Technology Incubator. **Founded:** 1999.

37946 ■ Innovation Pavilion
9200 E Mineral Ave.
Centennial, CO 80112
Contact: Waqar Ahmed, Contact
Facebook: www.facebook.com/InnovationPavilion
Description: Supports business startups by providing professional services from executive mentoring, legal and IT to marketing and education. **Founded:** 2011.

37947 ■ Kitchen CoOp (TKC)
8835 W 116th Cir., Ste. A
Broomfield, CO 80021
Free: 844-234-4235
Co. E-mail: info@the-kitchen-coop.com
URL: http://www.the-kitchen-coop.com
Contact: Jeff Greenberg, President
Facebook: www.facebook.com/TheKitchenCoop
Linkedin: www.linkedin.com/company/2527049
Description: Shared use kitchen for use by entrepreneurs, caterers, vendors, farmers market products, baking, confectioneries. **Founded:** 2007.

37948 ■ Kitchen Network
4986 Morrison Rd.
Denver, CO 80219
Ph: (303)922-0222
URL: http://www.kitchennetworkdenver.com
Description: Culinary incubator that helps emerging businesses grow. Provides pre-venture ideas to startups. **Founded:** 2004.

37949 ■ Pueblo Business and Technology Center
301 N Main St., Ste. 200
Pueblo, CO 81003
Ph: (719)544-2000
URL: http://www.pedco.org/btc
Contact: Crystal Lucero, Coordinator
E-mail: clucero@pedco.org
Description: A small business incubator that assists entrepreneurs in the business start-up process and gives aid to new businesses to help ensure their survival. **Founded:** 1920.

37950 ■ Pueblo Economic Development Corp. (PEDCO)
301 N Main St., Ste. 200
Pueblo, CO 81003
Ph: (719)544-2000
URL: http://www.pedco.org
Contact: Jeffery C. Shaw, President
E-mail: jshaw@pedco.org
Facebook: www.facebook.com/PuebloEconomicDevelopment
X (Twitter): x.com/puebloecondev
Description: A small business incubator offering startup help to entrepreneurs. **Founded:** 1981.

37951 ■ Rocky Mountain Center for Innovation and Technology
815 14th St. SW, Ste. C245
Loveland, CO 80537
Description: Provides a robust environment for innovative technology companies to incubate, grow and expand as cost effectively as possible.

37952 ■ Techstars
1050 Walnut St., Ste. 202
Boulder, CO 80302
Ph: (303)720-6559
Co. E-mail: info@techstars.com
URL: http://www.techstars.com
Contact: Maëlle Gavet, Chief Executive Officer
Facebook: www.facebook.com/techstars
Linkedin: www.linkedin.com/company/techstars
X (Twitter): x.com/techstars
Instagram: www.instagram.com/techstars
YouTube: www.youtube.com/user/techstarstv
Description: Partners with industry leaders to support innovative, high growth enterprise and industrial focused IoT startups. **Founded:** 2006.

37953 ■ Telluride Venture Network (TVA)
PO Box 4222
Telluride, CO 81435
URL: http://tellurideventurenetwork.com
Contact: Jesse Johnson, Founder
Description: Business accelerator for early stage entrepreneurs. Provides hands-on high-level mentoring, advice, practical business training, and access to capital. **Founded:** 2013.

37954 ■ Town of Parker, CO, Economic Development Department
20120 E Main St.
Parker, CO 80138
Ph: (303)841-0353
Co. E-mail: economicdevelopment@parkeronline.org
URL: http://www.p3parker.com/ped-parker-economic-development
Contact: Weldy Feazell, Director
Facebook: www.facebook.com/ParkerEDD
Linkedin: www.linkedin.com/company/parker-economic-development
Description: Firm provides economic and strategic management consulting services. **Founded:** 1864.

37955 ■ UNC BizHub Collaborative
Kepner Hall, No. 0025
800 17th St.
Greeley, CO 80639
Ph: (970)351-4274
Co. E-mail: info@eastcoloradosbdc.com
URL: http://eastcoloradosbdc.com
Contact: Lisa Hudson, Director
E-mail: lisa@eastcoloradosbdc.com
Description: Firm provides business management consulting services.

37956 ■ UpStart Inc.
428 Pratt St.
Longmont, CO 80501
Contact: Alex E. Sammoury, Contact
E-mail: alex@leninc.com
Description: Provides housing and laboratory space for young technology companies. A CTek venture center.

EDUCATIONAL PROGRAMS

37957 ■ Aims Community College
5401 W 20th St.
Greeley, CO 80634
Ph: (970)330-8008
Co. E-mail: communications@aims.edu
URL: http://www.aims.edu
Contact: Dr. Leah L. Bornstein, President
E-mail: leah.bornstein@aims.edu
Facebook: www.facebook.com/aimscc
Linkedin: www.linkedin.com/school/aims-community-college
X (Twitter): x.com/aimscc
Instagram: www.instagram.com/aims_cc
YouTube: www.youtube.com/user/AimsCeeCee
Description: Two-year college offering a small business management program. **Founded:** 1967.

37958 ■ Colorado Northwestern Community College (CNCC)
2801 W 9th St.
Craig, CO 81625
Free: 800-562-1105
Co. E-mail: infocentral@cncc.edu
URL: http://www.cncc.edu
Contact: Dr. Lisa Jones, President
Facebook: www.facebook.com/CNCC.SPARTANS

Linkedin: www.linkedin.com/edu/colorado-northwestern-community-college-32861
X (Twitter): x.com/cncc_spartans
Instagram: www.instagram.com/cncc.spartans
YouTube: www.youtube.com/user/ColoradoNorthwestern
Description: Two-year college offering a small business management program. **Founded:** 1962.

37959 ■ Emily Griffith Technical College (EGTC)
1860 Lincoln St., 4th fl.
Denver, CO 80203
Ph: (720)423-4700
Co. E-mail: learnenglish@emilygriffith.edu
URL: http://www.emilygriffith.edu
Contact: Jeff A. Barratt, Executive Director
Facebook: www.facebook.com/EmilyGriffithTech
Linkedin: www.linkedin.com/school/emily-griffith-technical-college
X (Twitter): x.com/EGtechcollege
Instagram: www.instagram.com/emilygriffithtechcollege
YouTube: www.youtube.com/user/EGTechnicalCollege
Description: A public technical college that offers technical courses. **Founded:** 1915.

37960 ■ Lamar Community College (LCC)
2401 S Main St.
Lamar, CO 81052
Ph: (719)336-2248
Co. E-mail: admissions@lamarcc.edu
URL: http://cccs.edu/college/lamar-community-college
Description: A two-year community college, offers certificates and associate degree programs. **Founded:** 1937.

CONSULTANTS

37961 ■ Four Corners Management Systems (FCMS)
2004 Glenisle Ave.
Durango, CO 81301
Ph: (970)259-1000
URL: http://jasperwelch.org
Contact: Jasper Welch, Officer
Description: Offers management consultation to small businesses to help facilitate organizational and team development. **Founded:** 1991.

PUBLICATIONS

37962 ■ *The Business Times*
609 N Ave., Ste. 5
Grand Junction, CO 81501
Ph: (970)424-5133
Co. E-mail: publisher@thebusinesstimes.com
URL: http://www.thebusinesstimes.com
Contact: Craig Hall, Publisher
URL(s): thebusinesstimes.com
Facebook: www.facebook.com/GrandValleyBusinessTimes
Ed: Phil Castle. **Released:** Biweekly **Price:** $30, Individuals for one year. **Description:** Newspaper covering local business. **Availability:** Print; PDF; Online.

37963 ■ Colorado Springs Business Journal (CSBJ)
235 S Nevada Ave.
Colorado Springs, CO 80903
Ph: (719)634-5905
Fax: (719)577-4545
Co. E-mail: digital@csbj.com
URL: http://www.csbj.com
Contact: John Weiss, Chairman of the Board
Facebook: www.facebook.com/csbusinessjournal
Linkedin: www.linkedin.com/company/113432
X (Twitter): x.com/CSBIZJournal
Instagram: www.instagram.com/cosbusinessjournal
YouTube: www.youtube.com/user/csbjwebadmin
Description: Publishes a business journal serving the Colorado Springs area.

37964 ■ Denver Business Journal (DBJ)
1660 Lincoln St., Ste. 1700
Denver, CO 80264
Ph: (303)803-9200
Fax: (303)803-9203
Co. E-mail: denver@bizjournals.com
URL: http://www.bizjournals.com/denver
Contact: Kevin Pitts, Publisher President, Marketing
E-mail: kpitts@bizjournals.com
Facebook: www.facebook.com/denverbusiness
Linkedin: www.linkedin.com/company/denver-business-journal
X (Twitter): x.com/denbizjournal
Instagram: www.instagram.com/denbizjournal
Description: Publisher of business newspaper. **Founded:** 1985. **Publications:** *Denver Business Journal--Top Twenty-Five Book of Lists Issue* (Annual); *Denver Business Journal-Technology Directory of Colorado* (Annual).

EARLY STAGE FINANCING

37965 ■ Greater Colorado Venture Fund (GCVF)
69 1/2 Main St.
College Heights Durango, CO 81301
URL: http://www.greatercolorado.vc
Contact: Jamie Finney, Partner
Description: Venture capital fund for early stage companies in rural Colorado outside of the Front Range. Works to inspire innovation in places often overlooked by venture funds. **Founded:** 2008.

VENTURE CAPITAL FIRM

37966 ■ Crawley Ventures
600 S Cherry St., Ste. 1125
Denver, CO 80246
Ph: (303)592-1135
URL: http://www.crawleyventures.com
Contact: Brian Zimbelman, Principal
Description: Venture capital firm specializing in high-growth opportunities. **Founded:** 1995. **Preferred Investment Size:** $250,000 to $1,500,000. **Investment Policies:** Prefers strong leadership teams, differentiated products or services, an understanding of customers, and early revenue.

37967 ■ Greenmont Capital Partners
1634 Walnut St., Ste. 301
Boulder, CO 80302
Ph: (303)444-0599
Co. E-mail: contact@greenmontcapital.com
URL: http://www.greenmontcapital.com
Contact: Todd Woloson, Managing Director
Description: Early stage venture capital firm. **Founded:** 2004. **Preferred Investment Size:** $1,000,000 to $5,000,000. **Investment Policies:** Privately held growth-stage companies in the United States. **Industry Preferences:** Consumer products; LOHAS (Lifestyles of Health and Sustainability).

37968 ■ Harbinger Ventures
PO Box 21465
Boulder, CO 80308
URL: http://harbingerventures.com
Contact: Megan Bent, Founder Managing Partner
Description: Early-stage growth-equity firm. Identifies and scales high-growth companies in the consumer sector.

37969 ■ Iron Gate Capital
842 W S Boulder Rd., Ste. 200
Louisville, CO 80027
Ph: (303)395-1335
Co. E-mail: info@irongatecapital.com
URL: http://irongatecapital.com
Contact: Ryan Pollock, Managing Partner
Description: Venture capital firm for early-stage companies. Seeks to generate 3-5X ROI in five years. **Preferred Investment Size:** $3,000,000 to $5,000,000. **Investment Policies:** Revenues from $2,000,000 to $15,000,000; well considered market and product strategies; sustainable competitive advantage; meaningful base of customers. **Industry Preferences:** B2B technology.

Connecticut

ASSOCIATIONS AND OTHER ORGANIZATIONS

37970 ■ Angel Investor Forum (AIF)
50 Skating Pond Rd.
Trumbull, CT 06611-1487
URL: http://www.angelinvestorforum.com
Contact: Marty Isaac, President

Description: Invests in early stage companies in the Northeastern US, particularly Connecticut. **Founded:** 2004. **Investment Policies:** Scalable activities; substantial business models and growth potential; clear path to exit in three to five year. **Industry Preferences:** Biotechnology; business products; clean technology; computers and peripherals; education; electronics/instrumentation; financial services; healthcare services; energy; internet/web services; IT services; marketing; media and entertainment; medical devices; mobile; nanotechnology; networking; semiconductors; software. telecommunications.

37971 ■ Ashford Business Association (ABA)
PO Box 342
Ashford, CT 06278
URL: http://service.ct.gov/business/s/
onlinebusinesssearch?businessNameEn=yaJ
3dxjAAK0nSW7z6C9
3upTxNwzvhAmsKgrGRRvMPF%2FqHYzhjJ8rJO
1QE7HiqGm8
Contact: Natale Caminiti, Treasurer

Description: Represents small business owners. Promotes the interests of small businesses. Provides government relations services, educational information and member benefit programs. **Geographic Preference:** Local.

37972 ■ Association of Fundraising Professionals Fairfield County Connecticut Chapter (FCC)
c/o Kathy Hoile, Administrator
PO Box 83
Fairfield, CT 06825
Ph: (203)644-7609
Co. E-mail: kathy@afpfairfield.org
URL: http://www.afpfairfield.org
Contact: Kathy Hoile, Administrator
E-mail: kathy@afpfairfield.org
Facebook: www.facebook.com/AFPFairfieldCoun
tyChapter

Founded: 1993. **Geographic Preference:** Local.

37973 ■ Business Network International Connecticut
88 Day Hill Rd.
Windsor, CT 06095
Ph: (203)605-3301
URL: http://bniwne.com/ct-northern-connecticut-val-ley-bni/en-US/index
Contact: Matthew Busey, President
Facebook: www.facebook.com/BNIConnecticut

Description: Provides both men and women a structured environment for the development and exchange of quality business referrals. Offers members the opportunity to share ideas and contacts. **Geographic Preference:** State.

37974 ■ Connecticut Pharmacists Association (CPA) - Academy of Medical Marijuana Dispensaries
35 Cold Spring Rd., Ste. 121
Rocky Hill, CT 06067
URL: http://ctpharmacists.org/academy-of-medical
-marijuana-dispensaries
Contact: Marissa Salvo, President

Description: Offers communication, expertise, information, experiences, and suggestions to advance medical marijuana dispensaries in Connecticut. **Founded:** 2014.

37975 ■ Entrepreneurs' Organization - Connecticut Chapter (EO)
409 Canal St.
Milldale, CT 06467
Co. E-mail: eoconnecticut@outlook.com
URL: http://www.eoct.org
Contact: Ernie Lawas, Chairman
URL(s): www.eonetwork.org/connecticut/about-our
-chapter
Facebook: www.facebook.com/eoconnecticut
Linkedin: www.linkedin.com/company/eo-connecticut
Instagram: www.instagram.com/eoconnecticut

Description: Supports entrepreneurs and business owners in Connecticut. Members must be founders, owners, or controlling shareholders of a company grossing more than $1 million annually. **Founded:** 1998.

37976 ■ International Association of Business Communicators Connecticut (CT-IABC)
CT
URL: http://iabcheritage.com/about

Description: Represents the interests of communication managers, public relations directors, writers, editors and audiovisual specialists. Encourages establishment of college-level programs in organizational communication. Conducts surveys on employee communication effectiveness and media trends. Conducts research in the field of communication. **Geographic Preference:** State.

37977 ■ International Association of Women Fairfield County Chapter
CT
URL: http://www.iawomen.com/chapters

Description: Serves as network of accomplished women united to achieve professional goals. Provides a forum for sharing ideas and experiences of professional women regarding career success. Promotes an active business and networking community from all industries. **Geographic Preference:** Local.

37978 ■ International Association of Women Hartford County Chapter
Hartford, CT

URL: http://www.iawomen.com/chapters/hartfor
d-county-chapter
Contact: Jessica Riley, Vice President

Description: Serves as network of accomplished women united to achieve professional goals. Provides a forum for sharing ideas and experiences of professional women regarding career success. Promotes an active business and networking community from all industries. **Geographic Preference:** Local.

37979 ■ National Federation of Independent Business Connecticut
Hartford, CT
Ph: (860)248-6342
Co. E-mail: andrew.markowski@nfib.org
URL: http://www.nfib.com/connecticut
Contact: Andrew Markowski, Director
E-mail: andrew.markowski@nfib.org
X (Twitter): x.com/nfib_ct

Description: Represents small and independent businesses. Aims to promote and protect the rights of members to own, operate and grow their businesses. **Geographic Preference:** State.

SMALL BUSINESS DEVELOPMENT CENTERS

37980 ■ Connecticut Small Business Development Center (CTSBDC)
222 Pitkin St.
East Hartford, CT 06108
Ph: (860)942-2186
Co. E-mail: ctsbdc@uconn.edu
URL: http://ctsbdc.uconn.edu
Contact: Joe Ercolano, Director
E-mail: joseph.ercolano@uconn.edu
Facebook: www.facebook.com/ctsbdc
Linkedin: www.linkedin.com/company/ctsbdc
X (Twitter): x.com/ctsbdc
Instagram: www.instagram.com/ctsbdc
YouTube: www.youtube.com/channel/
UCMonjNggFamnG1AfBKn1wLg

Description: Provides no-cost, confidential advising services to both prospective and existing entrepreneurs to help them start or grow their business. **Founded:** 2013. **Geographic Preference:** State.

SMALL BUSINESS ASSISTANCE PROGRAMS

37981 ■ AdvanceCT (CERC)
470 James St., Ste. 09
New Haven, CT 06513
Ph: (860)571-7136
Co. E-mail: admin@advancect.org
URL: http://www.advancect.org
Contact: John Bourdeaux, Chief Executive Officer
E-mail: jbourdeaux@advancect.org
Facebook: www.facebook.com/AdvanceConnecticut
Linkedin: www.linkedin.com/company/advancect
X (Twitter): x.com/advance_ct

YouTube: www.youtube.com/channel/UCM
4mnl0vkcgbdjs_8vYNApg
Description: Provides managerial assistance and assists in preparing applications for financing.
Founded: 2020.

37982 ■ Department of Economic & Community Development - Office of Business and Economic Development
450 Columbus Blvd., Ste. 5
Hartford, CT 06103
URL: http://portal.ct.gov/DECD/Services/Business
-Development
Contact: Patricia Paesani, Contact
E-mail: patricia.paesani@ct.gov
Description: Promotes trade; publishes a brochure on licensing and joint ventures; and administers the Exporters Revolving Loan Fund for small and medium-sized businesses.

SCORE OFFICES

37983 ■ Northwest Connecticut SCORE
59 Field St.
Torrington, CT 06790
Ph: (860)482-6586
Co. E-mail: contactus@score.org
URL: http://www.score.org/northwestconnecticut
Facebook: www.facebook.com/scorenwconnecticut
Linkedin: www.linkedin.com/company/score-mentors
-northwest-connecticut
X (Twitter): x.com/SCORE_NWCT
Founded: 1964.

37984 ■ SCORE - Branford
Branford, CT
URL: http://newhaven.score.org
Description: Provides professional guidance and information to maximize the success of existing and emerging small businesses. Offers business counseling and workshops.

37985 ■ SCORE - Bridgeport
900 Lafayette Blvd., Ste. 337
Bridgeport, CT 06604
Ph: (203)831-0065
URL: http://fairfieldcounty.score.org
Description: Provides professional guidance and information to maximize the success of existing and emerging small businesses. Offers business counseling and workshops.

37986 ■ SCORE - Bristol
440 N Main St.
Bristol, CT 06010
Ph: (860)584-4718
URL: http://www.score.org/find-location
Description: Provides professional guidance and information to maximize the success of existing and emerging small businesses. Offers business counseling and workshops. **Geographic Preference:** Local.

37987 ■ SCORE - Cheshire
195 S Main St.
Cheshire, CT 06410
URL: http://newhaven.score.org
Description: Provides professional guidance and information to maximize the success of existing and emerging small businesses. Offers business counseling and workshops.

37988 ■ SCORE - Connecticut
100 Riverview Ctr., Ste. 230
Middletown, CT 06457
URL: http://www.score.org/easternct
Description: Provides professional guidance and information to maximize the success of existing and emerging small businesses. Offers business counseling and workshops.

37989 ■ SCORE - Danbury
155 Deer Hill Ave. c/o Danbury City Hall
Danbury, CT 06810
Ph: (203)794-1404
Co. E-mail: westernconnecticutscore@scorevolun
teer.org
URL: http://westernconnecticut.score.org

Contact: Bridget Weston, Chief Executive Officer
Description: Provides professional guidance and information to maximize the success of existing and emerging small businesses. Offers business counseling and workshops.

37990 ■ SCORE - East Hartford
840 Main St.
East Hartford, CT 06108
Ph: (860)290-4331
URL: http://greaterhartford.score.org
Contact: Scott Harkins, Chairman of the Board
Description: Provides professional guidance and information to maximize the success of existing and emerging small businesses. Offers business counseling and workshops.

37991 ■ SCORE - Fairfield County
111 E Ave., Ste. 317
Norwalk, CT 06851
Ph: (203)831-0065
Co. E-mail: score.fairfieldcounty@gmail.com
URL: http://www.score.org/fairfieldcounty
Contact: Roy Anderson, Chairman
E-mail: royandersonsr@yahoo.com
Facebook: www.facebook.com/ScoreFairfieldCounty
Linkedin: www.linkedin.com/company/scorefairfiel
dcounty
Instagram: www.instagram.com/scorefairfieldcounty
YouTube: www.youtube.com/channel/
UCcslYPTzkAZZSVtogJGD1Eg
Description: Provides professional guidance and information to maximize the success of existing and emerging small businesses. Offers business counseling and workshops. **Founded:** 1964. **Geographic Preference:** Local.

37992 ■ SCORE - Farmington
6 Montieth Dr.
Farmington, CT 06032
Ph: (860)673-6791
Co. E-mail: help@score.org
URL: http://greaterhartford.score.org
URL(s): www.score.org/find-location
YouTube: www.youtube.com/channel/
UCAcXTbJc9QBixeOuMdGR9fw
Description: Provides professional guidance and information to maximize the success of existing and emerging small businesses. Offers business counseling and workshops.

37993 ■ SCORE - Glastonbury
280 Trumbull St.
Hartford, CT 06103
Ph: (860)519-5851
Co. E-mail: help@score.org
URL: http://greaterhartford.score.org
Contact: Bridget Weston, Chief Executive Officer
Description: Provides professional guidance and information to maximize the success of existing and emerging small businesses. Offers business counseling and workshops.

37994 ■ SCORE - Greater Hartford
280 Trumbull St.
Hartford, CT 06103
Ph: (860)519-5851
Co. E-mail: help@score.org
URL: http://greaterhartford.score.org
Contact: Scott Harkins, Chairman of the Board
Facebook: www.facebook.com/SCOREGreaterHar
tford
Linkedin: www.linkedin.com/company/score---greater
-hartford
X (Twitter): x.com/HartfordSCORE
YouTube: www.youtube.com/channel/
UCAcXTbJc9QBixeOuMdGR9fw
Description: Provides professional guidance and information to maximize the success of existing and emerging small businesses. Promotes entrepreneur education in Greater Hartford area, Connecticut. **Founded:** 1964. **Geographic Preference:** Local.

37995 ■ SCORE - Greenwich
101 W Putnam Ave.
Greenwich, CT 06830
Ph: (203)831-0065

Co. E-mail: score.fairfieldcounty@gmail.com
URL: http://fairfieldcounty.score.org/mentors/jeff-ford
Contact: Jeff Ford, Contact
Description: Provides professional guidance and information to maximize the success of existing and emerging small businesses. Offers business counseling and workshops.

37996 ■ SCORE - Guilford
400 Church St.
Guilford, CT 06437
Ph: (860)388-9508
Fax: (860)388-9508
Co. E-mail: scorechapter@gmail.com
URL: http://sect.score.org/content/about-us-198
Linkedin: www.linkedin.com/company/score-mentors
-southeastern-connecticut
X (Twitter): twitter.com/SCORESECT
Description: Provides professional guidance and information to maximize the success of existing and emerging small businesses. Offers business counseling and workshops.

37997 ■ SCORE - Hamden
2901 Dixwell Ave.
Hamden, CT 06518
URL: http://newhaven.score.org
Description: Provides professional guidance and information to maximize the success of existing and emerging small businesses. Offers business counseling and workshops.

37998 ■ SCORE - Madison, Connecticut
859 Boston Post Rd.
Madison, CT 06443
URL: http://www.score.org/easternct/content/contac
t-eastern-ct-score
Description: Provides professional guidance and information to maximize the success of existing and emerging small businesses. Offers business counseling and workshops.

37999 ■ SCORE - Manchester, Connecticut
20 Hartford Rd.
Manchester, CT 06040
Ph: (860)519-5851
URL: http://greaterhartford.score.org
Description: Provides professional guidance and information to maximize the success of existing and emerging small businesses. Offers business counseling and workshops.

38000 ■ SCORE - Meriden
Meriden, CT
URL: http://www.score.org/newhaven
Description: Provides professional guidance and information to maximize the success of existing and emerging small businesses. Offers business counseling and workshops.

38001 ■ SCORE - Milford, Connecticut
5 Broad St.
Milford, CT 06460
URL: http://newhaven.score.org
Description: Provides professional guidance and information to maximize the success of existing and emerging small businesses. Offers business counseling and workshops.

38002 ■ SCORE - Mystic
62 Greenmanville Ave.
Mystic, CT 06355
Ph: (860)388-9508
Fax: (860)388-9508
Co. E-mail: scorechapter@gmail.com
URL: http://sect.score.org/contact-southeastern-c
t-score
Contact: Bill Pryor, Contact
Description: Provides professional guidance and information to maximize the success of existing and emerging small businesses. Offers business counseling and workshops.

38003 ■ SCORE - New Britain
Hartford, CT
URL: http://www.score.org/greaterhartford
Contact: Stephen Mahoney, Contact

38004 ■ Connecticut

Facebook: www.facebook.com/SCOREMentors
Linkedin: www.linkedin.com/company/score---greater-hartford
X (Twitter): x.com/HartfordSCORE
Description: Provides professional guidance and information to maximize the success of existing and emerging small businesses. Offers business counseling and workshops.

38004 ■ SCORE - New Haven
110 Washington Ave., 3rd fl.
North Haven, CT 06473
Ph: (203)234-6305
Co. E-mail: help@score.org
URL: http://www.score.org/newhaven
Contact: Jordan Arovas, Contact
Facebook: www.facebook.com/SCORENewHaven
Linkedin: www.linkedin.com/company/score-mentors-new-haven
Description: Provides professional guidance and information to maximize the success of existing and emerging small businesses. Offers business counseling and workshops. **Founded:** 1964.

38005 ■ SCORE - New London
63 Huntington St.
New London, CT 06320
Ph: (860)388-9508
URL: http://www.score.org/find-location?state=CT
Description: Provides professional guidance and information to maximize the success of existing and emerging small businesses. Offers business counseling and workshops.

38006 ■ SCORE - New Milford
c/o Danbury City Hall
155 Deer Hill Ave.
Danbury, CT 06810
Ph: (203)794-1404
Co. E-mail: westernconnecticutscore@scorevolunteer.org
URL: http://westernconnecticut.score.org
Contact: Bridget Weston, Chief Executive Officer
Facebook: www.facebook.com/SCOREWConnecticut
Linkedin: www.linkedin.com/company/score-mentors-western-connecticut
Description: Provides professional guidance and information to maximize the success of existing and emerging small businesses. Offers business counseling and workshops.

38007 ■ SCORE - Newtown
3 Primrose St.
Newtown, CT 06470
Ph: (203)794-1404
URL: http://westernconnecticut.score.org
Description: Provides professional guidance and information to maximize the success of existing and emerging small businesses. Offers business counseling and workshops.

38008 ■ SCORE - North Haven
110 Washington Ave., 3rd Fl.
North Haven, CT 06473
Ph: (203)865-7645
URL: http://www.score.org/newhaven
Facebook: www.facebook.com/SCORENewHaven
Linkedin: www.linkedin.com/company/score-mentors-new-haven
Description: Offers free workshops and seminars on all aspects of business. Volunteers with a wide range of expertise, provides free confidential business counseling, guidance and information to maximize the success of existing and emerging small businesses. Promotes entrepreneur education in New Haven County area, Connecticut. **Founded:** 1964. **Geographic Preference:** Local.

38009 ■ SCORE - Northwest Connecticut (SCORE-NWCT)
59 Field St.
Torrington, CT 06790
Ph: (860)482-6586
URL: http://www.score.org/northwestconnecticut
Facebook: www.facebook.com/scorenwconnecticut
Linkedin: www.linkedin.com/company/score-mentors-northwest-connecticut

X (Twitter): x.com/SCORE_NWCT
Description: Provides professional guidance and information to maximize the success of existing and emerging small businesses. Offers business counseling and workshops. **Founded:** 1964. **Geographic Preference:** Local.

38010 ■ SCORE - Norwich
290 Salem Tpke.
Norwich, CT 06360
Ph: (860)388-9508
URL: http://www.score.org/find-location
Description: Provides professional guidance and information to maximize the success of existing and emerging small businesses. Offers business counseling and workshops.

38011 ■ SCORE - Ridgefield
472 Main St.
Ridgefield, CT 06877
Ph: (203)794-1404
URL: http://westernconnecticut.score.org/about-us-38
URL(s): pittsburgh.score.org/find-location
Description: Provides professional guidance and information to maximize the success of existing and emerging small businesses. Offers business counseling and workshops.

38012 ■ SCORE - Rocky Hill
33 Church St.
Rocky Hill, CT 06067
Ph: (860)519-5851
URL: http://greaterhartford.score.org/find-location?state=CT
Description: Provides professional guidance and information to maximize the success of existing and emerging small businesses. Offers business counseling and workshops.

38013 ■ SCORE - Shelton
111 E Ave., Ste. 317
Norwalk, CT 06851
Ph: (203)831-0065
Co. E-mail: score.fairfieldcounty@gmail.com
URL: http://fairfieldcounty.score.org
Facebook: www.facebook.com/SCOREFairfieldCounty
Linkedin: www.linkedin.com/company/scorefairfieldcounty
Instagram: www.instagram.com/scorefairfieldcounty
YouTube: www.youtube.com/channel/UCcslYPTzkAZZSVtogJGD1Eg
Description: Provides professional guidance and information to maximize the success of existing and emerging small businesses. Offers business counseling and workshops.

38014 ■ SCORE - Simsbury
280 Trumbull St.
Hartford, CT 06103
Ph: (860)519-5851
URL: http://greaterhartford.score.org
Description: Provides professional guidance and information to maximize the success of existing and emerging small businesses. Offers business counseling and workshops.

38015 ■ SCORE - Simsbury Library
725 Hopmeadow St.
Simsbury, CT 06070
Ph: (860)658-7663
URL: http://greaterhartford.score.org/find-location?state=CT
Description: Provides professional guidance and information to maximize the success of existing and emerging small businesses. Offers business counseling and workshops.

38016 ■ SCORE - South Windsor
22 Morgan Farms Dr.
South Windsor, CT 06074
Ph: (860)519-5851
Co. E-mail: help@score.org
URL: http://www.score.org/find-location

STATE LISTINGS

Description: Provides professional guidance and information to maximize the success of existing and emerging small businesses. Offers business counseling and workshops.

38017 ■ SCORE - Southeastern Connecticut (SECT)
PO Box 283
Old Saybrook, CT 06475
Ph: (860)388-9508
Fax: (860)388-9508
URL: http://www.score.org/easternct/sponsors-and-partners
Contact: Margo Weitekamp, Contact
Facebook: www.facebook.com/SCORESEConnecticut
X (Twitter): x.com/SCORESECT
Description: Provides professional guidance and information to maximize the success of existing and emerging small businesses. Offers business counseling and workshops. **Geographic Preference:** Local.

38018 ■ SCORE - Torrington
333 Kennedy Dr., Ste. 101
Torrington, CT 06790
Ph: (860)482-6586
Co. E-mail: help@score.org
URL: http://northwestconnecticut.score.org
Contact: Bridget Weston, Chief Executive Officer
Facebook: www.facebook.com/scorenwconnecticut
Linkedin: www.linkedin.com/company/score-mentors-northwest-connecticut
X (Twitter): twitter.com/SCORE_NWCT
Description: Provides professional guidance and information to maximize the success of existing and emerging small businesses. Offers business counseling and workshops.

38019 ■ SCORE - Vernon
30 Lafayette Sq.
Vernon Rockville, CT 06066
Ph: (860)872-0587
URL: http://greaterhartford.score.org
Contact: Bridget Weston, Contact
Description: Provides professional guidance and information to maximize the success of existing and emerging small businesses. Offers business counseling and workshops.

38020 ■ SCORE - Wallingford
50 N Main St.
Wallingford, CT 06492
URL: http://newhaven.score.org
Contact: James A. G. Krupp, Contact
Description: Provides professional guidance and information to maximize the success of existing and emerging small businesses. Offers business counseling and workshops.

38021 ■ SCORE - Waterbury
Silas Bronson Library
267 Grand St.
Waterbury, CT 06702
Ph: (203)574-8225
Co. E-mail: westernconnecticutscore@scorevolunteer.org
URL: http://westernconnecticut.score.org/about-us-38
Description: Provides professional guidance and information to maximize the success of existing and emerging small businesses. Offers business counseling and workshops.

38022 ■ SCORE - Waterford
914 Hartford Tpk.
Waterford, CT 06385
URL: http://www.score.org/easternct/content/contact-eastern-ct-score
Description: Provides professional guidance and information to maximize the success of existing and emerging small businesses. Offers business counseling and workshops.

38023 ■ SCORE - West Hartford
948 Farmington Ave.
West Hartford, CT 06107
Ph: (860)521-2300

STATE LISTINGS

URL: http://greaterhartford.score.org/find-location?state=CT
Description: Provides professional guidance and information to maximize the success of existing and emerging small businesses. Offers business counseling and workshops.

38024 ■ SCORE - Western Connecticut
155 Deer Hill Ave.
Danbury, CT 06810
Ph: (203)794-1404
Co. E-mail: westernconnecticutscore@scorevolunteer.org
URL: http://westernconnecticut.score.org
Contact: Will Meikle, Chairman
Facebook: www.facebook.com/SCOREWConnecticut
Linkedin: www.linkedin.com/company/score-mentors-western-connecticut
Description: Provides professional guidance and information to maximize the success of existing and emerging small businesses. Offers business counseling and workshops.

38025 ■ Southeastern Connecticut SCORE (SECT)
PO Box 283
Old Saybrook, CT 06475
Ph: (860)388-9508
Co. E-mail: scorechapter@gmail.com
URL: http://www.score.org/easternct
Facebook: www.facebook.com/SCOREEasternCT
Linkedin: www.linkedin.com/company/score-mentors-eastern-ct
X (Twitter): x.com/SCORESECT
Founded: 1964.

BETTER BUSINESS BUREAUS

38026 ■ Better Business Bureau of Connecticut
29 Berlin Rd.
Cromwell, CT 06416
Ph: (860)740-4500
Fax: (860)740-4515
Co. E-mail: info@ct.bbb.org
URL: http://www.bbb.org/local-bbb/bbb-serving-connecticut
Contact: Paulette Scarpetti, President
E-mail: pscarpetti@ct.bbb.org
Facebook: www.facebook.com/bbbservingct
Linkedin: www.linkedin.com/company/bbbservingct
X (Twitter): x.com/bbbservingct
Instagram: www.instagram.com/bbbservingct
YouTube: www.youtube.com/user/bbbservingct
Description: Promotes the highest ethical relationship between businesses and the public. Provides arbitration, mediation, conciliation services, and educational marketplace information. **Founded:** 1928. **Publications:** *BBB Consumer Guide* (Annual); *Marketplace Report* (Periodic); *What Is a Better Business Bureau*. **Awards:** Connecticut BBB Torch Award for Marketplace Ethics (Annual). **Geographic Preference:** State.

CHAMBERS OF COMMERCE

38027 ■ Avon Chamber of Commerce (ACOC)
412 W Avon Rd.
Avon, CT 06001
Ph: (860)675-4832
Co. E-mail: avonchamber@sbcglobal.net
URL: http://www.avonchamber.com
Contact: Bryan Keilty, President
Facebook: www.facebook.com/avon.ofcommerce
Description: Works to advance the economic and civic development of the community. **Founded:** 1965. **Geographic Preference:** Local.

38028 ■ Bethel Chamber of Commerce
184 Greenwood Ave.
Bethel, CT 06801-2530
Ph: (203)743-6500
Co. E-mail: bethelchamberct@gmail.com
URL: http://www.bethelmaine.com
Contact: Kristen Keil, Chairman
Description: Promotes business and community development in Bethel, CT area. **Founded:** 1953. **Geographic Preference:** Local.

38029 ■ *BizLink*
10 Progress Dr., 2nd Fl.
Shelton, CT 06484
Ph: (203)925-4981
Fax: (203)925-4984
Co. E-mail: info@greatervalleychamber.com
URL: http://www.greatervalleychamber.com
Contact: Bill Purcell, President
URL(s): greatervalleychamber.com/inform-educate
Released: Weekly **Description:** Weekly e-news publication for the Chamber. Includes event information and business news and tips. **Availability:** Online.

38030 ■ Bloomfield Chamber of Commerce (BCC)
717 Bloomfield Ave.
Bloomfield, CT 06002
Ph: (860)242-3710
Co. E-mail: info@bloomfieldchamber.org
URL: http://bloomfieldchamber.org
Contact: Brian Cuddeback, President
Facebook: www.facebook.com/BloomfieldCtChamber
Description: Strives to be the principal advocate, networking organization, and service and resource provider for local businesses. Supports business and community efforts so that Bloomfield continues to be an economically attractive place to live and do business. **Founded:** 1965. **Publications:** *The Forum* (Bimonthly). **Geographic Preference:** Local.

38031 ■ Bradley Regional Chamber of Commerce
PO Box 1335
East Granby, CT 06026
Ph: (860)653-3833
URL: http://bradleyregionalchamber.org
Contact: Dave Renouf, Treasurer
Facebook: www.facebook.com/BradleyRegionalChamberofCommerce
Description: Promotes business and community development in Windsor Locks and East Granby Area, CT. **Founded:** 2013. **Publications:** *News and Views* (Weekly). **Geographic Preference:** Local.

38032 ■ Bridgeport Regional Business Council (BRBC)
10 Middle St., 14th Fl.
Bridgeport, CT 06604
Ph: (203)335-3800
Fax: (203)366-0105
Co. E-mail: onofrio@brbc.org
URL: http://www.brbc.org
Contact: Dan Onofrio, President
Facebook: www.facebook.com/BptRegionalBusinessCouncil
Linkedin: www.linkedin.com/company/bridgeport-regional-business-council
X (Twitter): x.com/brbc
Description: Promotes business and community development in Bridgeport region. **Founded:** 1986. **Publications:** *enews* (Monthly); *IMPACT* (Quarterly). **Geographic Preference:** Local.

38033 ■ Chamber of Commerce of Eastern Connecticut
914 Hartford Tpke., Ste. 206
Waterford, CT 06385
Ph: (860)701-9113
Free: 866-274-5587
Fax: (860)701-9902
Co. E-mail: info@chamberect.com
URL: http://www.chamberect.com
Contact: Courtney Assad, Director
Facebook: www.facebook.com/chamberect
X (Twitter): x.com/chamberect
Instagram: www.instagram.com/chamberect
Description: Promotes business and community development in New London County, CT. **Publications:** *Chamber Update*. **Awards:** Chamber of Commerce of Eastern Connecticut Citizen of the Year Award (Annual). **Geographic Preference:** Regional.

38034 ■ Chamber of Commerce of Newtown (CCN)
45 Main St.
Newtown, CT 06470
Ph: (203)426-2695
Co. E-mail: chamber@newtown-ct.com
URL: http://www.newtown-ct.com
Contact: Judith Miller, President
E-mail: judithmiller@newtown-ct.com
Facebook: www.facebook.com/NewtownChamber
Description: Promotes business and community development in Newtown, CT. Sponsors Christmas Tree Poster contest, Christmas Tree Lighting, and Pizza and Politics Forum for local candidates. **Founded:** 1996. **Geographic Preference:** Local.

38035 ■ Chamber of Commerce of Northwest Connecticut
333 Kennedy Dr., Ste. R101
Torrington, CT 06790
Ph: (860)482-6586
Fax: (860)489-8851
Co. E-mail: info@nwctchamberofcommerce.org
URL: http://nwctchamberofcommerce.org
Contact: JoAnn M. Ryan, President
E-mail: joann@nwctchamberofcommerce.org
Facebook: www.facebook.com/NWCTChamber
Linkedin: www.linkedin.com/company/chamber-of-commerce-of-northwest-connecticut-inc
X (Twitter): x.com/nwctchamber
Description: Promotes business and community development in Northwestern Connecticut. **Founded:** 1901. **Publications:** *Personal Services Booklet*. **Geographic Preference:** Local.

38036 ■ Chamber of Commerce - Windham Region
1320 Main St.
Willimantic, CT 06226
Ph: (860)423-6389
Co. E-mail: info@windhamchamber.com
URL: http://windhamchamber.com
Contact: Pam Atwood, Chairman of the Board
E-mail: pam@atwooddementiagroup.com
Description: Works in building a vibrant, growing regional community that supports a 21st century lifestyle. **Founded:** 2008. **Geographic Preference:** Local.

38037 ■ *Chamber Directory*
320 Boston Post Rd., Ste. 180-169
Darien, CT 06820
Ph: (203)655-3600
URL: http://www.darienctchamber.com
Contact: Kesti Aysseh, Executive Director
URL(s): www.darienctchamber.com/business-directory
Availability: Online.

38038 ■ Cheshire Chamber of Commerce (CCC)
195 S Main St., Ste. 2
Cheshire, CT 06410
Ph: (203)272-2345
Fax: (203)271-3044
Co. E-mail: jean@cheshirechamber.org
URL: http://cheshirechamber.org
Contact: Yetta Augur, President
E-mail: yetta@cheshirechamber.org
Description: Promotes business and community development in Cheshire, CT. **Publications:** *Business Review* (Quarterly). **Geographic Preference:** Local.

38039 ■ Clinton Chamber of Commerce
50 E Main St.
Clinton, CT 06413
Ph: (860)669-3889
Co. E-mail: chamber@clintonctchamber.com
URL: http://www.clintonct.com
Contact: Paul Orsini, Executive Director
Facebook: www.facebook.com/ClintonCTChamber
Description: Promotes business and community development in Clinton, CT. Sponsors business expo, summer concert series. **Founded:** 1983. **Publications:** *Chamber News*. **Geographic Preference:** Local.

38040 ■ Connecticut Business and Industry Association (CBIA)
350 Church St.
Hartford, CT 06103
Ph: (860)244-1900
URL: http://www.cbia.com
Contact: Chris DiPentima, President
Facebook: www.facebook.com/CBIAfb
Instagram: www.instagram.com/cbia_
YouTube: www.youtube.com/user/CBIAvideos
Description: Promotes a regulatory system that responds to businesses' needs. **Founded:** 1815. **Publications:** *George D. Hall's Directory of Connecticut Manufacturers*. **Geographic Preference:** State.

38041 ■ Connecticut River Valley Chamber of Commerce (CRVCC)
2400 Main St., Ste. 2
Glastonbury, CT 06033
Ph: (860)659-3587
Fax: (860)659-0102
URL: http://www.crvchamber.org
Contact: Paul Haas, Contact
Facebook: www.facebook.com/CTRiverValleyChamber
Linkedin: www.linkedin.com/company/ct-river-valley-chamber-of-commerce
X (Twitter): x.com/CRVChamber
Instagram: www.instagram.com/crvchamber
YouTube: www.youtube.com/channel/UCOIgujLC7q7tg0ahFFxUSLw
Description: Promotes business and community development in Glastonbury, CT. Sponsors Apple Harvest Festival and the summer music series. **Founded:** 1902. **Publications:** *Connecticut River Valley Chamber of Commerce Business Directory*; *Chamber Pulse* (Monthly); *Glastonbury Connecticut Fact Book and Information Guide* (Continuous). **Geographic Preference:** Local.

38042 ■ Darien Chamber of Commerce (DCC)
320 Boston Post Rd., Ste. 180-169
Darien, CT 06820
Ph: (203)655-3600
URL: http://www.darienctchamber.com
Contact: Kesti Aysseh, Executive Director
Facebook: www.facebook.com/DarienCTChamber
Linkedin: www.linkedin.com/company/darien-chamber-of-commerce
X (Twitter): x.com/DarienChamber
Instagram: www.instagram.com/darienctchamber
Pinterest: www.pinterest.com/darienchamberct
Description: Promotes business and community development in Darien, IL. Sponsors Easter Gala, tree lighting ceremony, and annual festival. **Founded:** 1984. **Publications:** *Chamber Directory*; *The Guide* (Annual). **Geographic Preference:** Local.

38043 ■ East Haven Chamber of Commerce (EHCC)
PO Box 120055
East Haven, CT 06512
Ph: (203)467-4305
Co. E-mail: easthavenchamber01@gmail.com
URL: http://easthavenchamber.com
Contact: Jennifer Higham, President
Facebook: www.facebook.com/EastHavenChamber
X (Twitter): x.com/EHCC01
Instagram: www.instagram.com/easthavenchamber
Description: Promotes business and community development in East Haven, CT area. **Geographic Preference:** Local.

38044 ■ Fairfield Chamber of Commerce
1597 Post Rd.
Fairfield, CT 06824
Ph: (203)255-1011
Fax: (203)256-9990
Co. E-mail: info@fairfieldct.chamber.com
URL: http://www.fairfieldctchamber.com
Contact: Beverly A. Balaz, President
E-mail: beverly@fairfieldctchamber.com
Facebook: www.facebook.com/fairfieldchamber
X (Twitter): x.com/fairfieldchambr
Instagram: www.instagram.com/fairfieldctchamber
Description: Promotes business and community development in Fairfield, CT. Sponsors holiday events and revitalization efforts. Encourages cultural involvement. **Founded:** 1946. **Publications:** *Resource Guide* (Annual); *Fairfield Town Map* (Annual). **Geographic Preference:** Local.

38045 ■ Granby Chamber of Commerce (GCC)
2 Pk., Pl. Business Ctr.
Granby, CT 06035
Description: Promotes business and community development in Granby, CT area. **Founded:** 1965. **Geographic Preference:** Local.

38046 ■ Greater Danbury Chamber of Commerce (GDCC)
1 Ives St., Ste. 301
Danbury, CT 06810
Ph: (203)743-5565
Co. E-mail: info@danburychamber.com
URL: http://www.danburychamber.com
Contact: Cynthia C. Merkle, President
YouTube: www.youtube.com/channel/UCgxbyghO4CDmiVn4qh--WVQ
Description: Represents the ten town Connecticut business community of Bethel, Bridgewater, Brookfield, Danbury, New Fairfield, New Milford, Newtown, Redding, Ridgefield, Sherman and the surrounding area. Promotes business and community development. **Founded:** 1684. **Publications:** *Danbury Difference* (Bimonthly); *Greater Danbury Business Directory and Buyers Guide*; *Inside Business* (Quarterly). **Geographic Preference:** Local.

38047 ■ Greater Manchester Chamber of Commerce (GMCC)
20 Hartford Rd.
Manchester, CT 06040
Ph: (860)646-2223
Fax: (860)646-5871
Co. E-mail: staffgmcc@manchesterchamber.com
URL: http://www.manchesterchamber.com
Contact: April DiFalco, President
E-mail: april@manchesterchamber.com
Facebook: www.facebook.com/ctmancheterchamber
Instagram: www.instagram.com/ctmancheterchamber
YouTube: www.youtube.com/channel/UCGdGEi1kU6BInUAU2zXRHFA
Description: Promotes business and community development in the Manchester, CT area. **Founded:** 1901. **Publications:** *News and Views* (Bimonthly). **Geographic Preference:** Local.

38048 ■ Greater New Britain Chamber of Commerce (GNBCC)
One Liberty Sq.
New Britain, CT 06050-1118
Ph: (860)229-1665
URL: http://greaternewbritainchamber.com
Contact: Frank D. Marrocco, Treasurer
E-mail: frankfdmcpa@gmail.com
Facebook: www.facebook.com/GNBCOC
X (Twitter): x.com/newbritainchamb
Description: Promotes business and community development in New Britain, CT area. **Publications:** *Positively New Britain* (Monthly). **Geographic Preference:** Local.

38049 ■ Greater New Haven Chamber of Commerce (GNHCC)
900 Chapel St., 10th Fl.
New Haven, CT 06510
Ph: (203)787-6735
Fax: (203)782-4629
URL: http://www.gnhcc.com
Contact: Garrett Sheehan, President
Facebook: www.facebook.com/gnhcc
X (Twitter): x.com/GNHCC
YouTube: www.youtube.com/channel/UCYDOMaQAo9iIXRn4uJu7qZA
Description: Provides leadership in marshalling the physical, economic, and human resources of the South Central Connecticut region. **Founded:** 1794. **Geographic Preference:** Local.

38050 ■ Greater New Milford Chamber of Commerce (GNMCC)
11 Railroad St.
New Milford, CT 06776
Ph: (860)354-6080
Fax: (860)354-8526
Co. E-mail: nmcc@newmilford-chamber.com
URL: http://newmilford-chamber.com
Contact: Jennifer Birdseye, President
E-mail: jbirdseye@websterbank.com
Facebook: www.facebook.com/greaternewmilfordchamber
Description: Promotes business and community development in New Milford, CT. Sponsors Village Fair and Business Expo. **Founded:** 1931. **Publications:** *New Milford Living Magazine* (Monthly); *New Milford Visitor's Guide* (Periodic). **Geographic Preference:** Local.

38051 ■ Greater Norwalk Chamber of Commerce
101 E Ave.
Norwalk, CT 06851
Ph: (203)866-2521
Co. E-mail: info@greaternorwalkchamber.com
URL: http://www.greaternorwalkchamber.com
Contact: Brian Griffin, President
E-mail: bgriffin@norwalkchamberofcommerce.com
Facebook: www.facebook.com/GreaterNorwalk
Linkedin: www.linkedin.com/company/greaternorwalk
X (Twitter): x.com/GreaterNorwalk
Instagram: www.instagram.com/greaternorwalk
Description: Promotes business and community development in the Norwalk, CT area. **Founded:** 1889. **Publications:** *Cutting Edge* (Bimonthly); *Who's Who Greater Norwalk Business Directory*. **Geographic Preference:** Local.

38052 ■ Greater Southington Chamber of Commerce
31 Liberty St.
Southington, CT 06489
Ph: (860)628-8036
Co. E-mail: info@southingtonchamber.com
URL: http://www.southingtonchamber.com
Contact: Barbara Coleman-Hekeler, President
Facebook: www.facebook.com/southingtonchamber1
Description: Promotes business and community development in the Southington, CT area. **Founded:** 1938. **Publications:** *Southington at a Glance* (Annual); *Southington CC Express* (Weekly). **Awards:** Southington Chamber of Commerce Beautification Award (Annual); Business Person of the Year, Riccio Brothers Award (Biennial); Southington Chamber of Commerce Community Spirit Award (Annual); Greater Southington Chamber of Commerce Employee of the Year (Annual). **Geographic Preference:** Local.

38053 ■ *Greater Valley Business and Resource Guide*
10 Progress Dr., 2nd Fl.
Shelton, CT 06484
Ph: (203)925-4981
Fax: (203)925-4984
Co. E-mail: info@greatervalleychamber.com
URL: http://www.greatervalleychamber.com
Contact: Bill Purcell, President
URL(s): greatervalleychamber.com/business-directory
Description: Features demographic and relocation information. **Availability:** Online.

38054 ■ Greater Valley Chamber of Commerce (GVCC)
10 Progress Dr., 2nd Fl.
Shelton, CT 06484
Ph: (203)925-4981
Fax: (203)925-4984
Co. E-mail: info@greatervalleychamber.com
URL: http://www.greatervalleychamber.com
Contact: Bill Purcell, President
Facebook: www.facebook.com/thegreatervalleychamber
X (Twitter): x.com/Valley_Chamber
Instagram: www.instagram.com/greatervalleychamber

STATE LISTINGS

Connecticut ■ 38068

YouTube: www.youtube.com/user/Grea
terValleyChamber
Description: Represents the business community of Ansonia, Beacon Falls, Derby, Oxford, Seymour, Shelton and the surrounding area. **Founded:** 1964. **Publications:** *BizLink* (Weekly); *Business Matters* (Bimonthly); *Greater Valley Business and Resource Guide.* **Awards:** Greater Valley Chamber of Commerce Platinum Award (Annual); Greater Valley Chamber of Commerce Silver Medal Award (Annual); Greater Valley Gold Seal Award (Annual). **Geographic Preference:** Local.

38055 ■ Greenwich Chamber of Commerce (GCC)
45 E Putnam Ave., Ste. 121
Greenwich, CT 06830
Ph: (203)869-3500
Fax: (203)869-3502
Co. E-mail: greenwichchamber@greenwichchamber.com
URL: http://www.greenwichchamber.com
Contact: Marcia O'Kane, President
Facebook: www.facebook.com/
GreenwichCTChamber
Linkedin: www.linkedin.com/company/greenwich
-chamber-of-commerce-ct
X (Twitter): x.com/GreenwichCC
Instagram: www.instagram.com/greenwichchamber
YouTube: www.youtube.com/channel/UCZJ0
3BqeBhwnsUcD9ysrYIw
Description: Promotes business and community development in Greenwich, CT. **Founded:** 1917. **Publications:** *Company List.* **Geographic Preference:** Local.

38056 ■ Hamden Regional Chamber of Commerce
3074 Whitney Ave.
Hamden, CT 06518
Ph: (203)288-6431
Co. E-mail: hcc@hamdenchamber.com
URL: http://hamdenregionalchamber.com
Contact: Nancy Dudchik, President
X (Twitter): x.com/HamdenChamber1
Description: Promotes business and community development in Hamden, CT. **Founded:** 1925. **Publications:** *In Hamden* (Monthly). **Geographic Preference:** Local.

38057 ■ Kent Chamber of Commerce
PO Box 124
Kent, CT 06757
Ph: (860)592-0061
Co. E-mail: info@kentct.com
URL: http://kentct.com
Contact: David Schreiber, President
Facebook: www.facebook.com/kentc
tchamberofcommerce
Instagram: www.instagram.com/kentctchamber
Description: Promotes business and community development in Kent, CT area. **Founded:** 1739. **Geographic Preference:** Local.

38058 ■ Madison Chamber of Commerce (MCC)
12 School St.
Madison, CT 06443
Ph: (203)245-7394
Co. E-mail: chamber@madisonct.com
URL: http://www.madisonct.com
Contact: Paul Harris, President
E-mail: paul.harris@nmvfc.org
Facebook: www.facebook.com/ma
disonchamberofcommerce
Description: Promotes business and community development in the area. **Founded:** 1948. **Publications:** *Chamber Waves* (Semimonthly). **Educational Activities:** Madison Expo. **Geographic Preference:** Local.

38059 ■ Middlesex County Chamber of Commerce
393 Main St.
Middletown, CT 06457
Ph: (860)347-6924
Co. E-mail: info@middlesexchamber.com

URL: http://www.middlesexchamber.com
Contact: Larry McHugh, President
E-mail: larry@middlesexchamber.com
Facebook: www.facebook.com/mdsxchamber
Linkedin: www.linkedin.com/company/middlesex
-county-chamber-of-commerce
X (Twitter): x.com/MdsxChamber
Instagram: www.instagram.com/mdsxchamber
YouTube: www.youtube.com/channel/UCu4S5VNV
tz7iZl5OGn2WyZw
Pinterest: www.pinterest.com/mdsxchamber
Description: Promotes business and community development in Middlesex County, CT. Sponsors Business After Hours program. **Founded:** 1983. **Publications:** *Middlesex Magazine and Business Review* (Monthly); *We're on the Move.* **Educational Activities:** Central Business Bureau Meeting (Monthly). **Awards:** Middlesex Chamber Distinguished Citizen Award (Annual); Judge Raymond E. Baldwin Scholarship (Annual). **Geographic Preference:** Local.

38060 ■ Midstate Chamber of Commerce (MCC)
546 S Broad St., Ste. 2C
Meriden, CT 06450
Ph: (203)235-7901
Co. E-mail: info@midstatechamber.com
URL: http://www.midstatechamber.com
Contact: Rosanne P. Ford, President
Facebook: www.facebook.com/MidstateCoC
Linkedin: www.linkedin.com/company/midstate
-chamber-of-commerce
X (Twitter): x.com/midstatecoc
Instagram: www.instagram.com/midsta
techamberofcommerce
YouTube: www.youtube.com/channel/UC
tqXPEzHPL8ZnWkYf60-y5g
Description: Encourages and promotes commerce, industry, and community. **Founded:** 1896. **Publications:** *Chamber News*; *Community Profile and Membership Directory.* **Educational Activities:** Business Expo (Annual); Business After Hours (Bimonthly). **Geographic Preference:** Local.

38061 ■ Milford Regional Chamber of Commerce
1201 Boston Post Rd., Unit 1100
Milford, CT 06460
Ph: (203)878-0681
Fax: (203)876-8517
Co. E-mail: chamber@milfordct.com
URL: http://www.milfordct.com
Contact: Michael Moses, President
E-mail: mmoses@milfordct.com
Facebook: www.facebook.com/milfordctchamber
Linkedin: www.linkedin.com/company/milford-regional
-chamber-of-commerce
X (Twitter): x.com/MilfordChamber
YouTube: www.youtube.com/channel/
UCjwuoxqFWhALKlyhUfHVCkA
Description: Promotes business and community development in Milford, CT. **Founded:** 1954. **Geographic Preference:** Local.

38062 ■ Monroe Chamber of Commerce (MCC)
411 Monroe Tpke.
Monroe, CT 06468-2201
Ph: (203)268-6518
Co. E-mail: info@monroectchamber.com
URL: http://www.monroectchamber.com
Contact: Ray Giovanni, President
E-mail: rgiovanni@unionsavings.com
Facebook: www.facebook.com/MonroeCOC
Description: Promotes business and community development in the Monroe, CT area. Sponsors Monroe Spirit Week festival. **Founded:** 1966. **Publications:** *Business*; *Monroe Business Bulletin* (Monthly). **Geographic Preference:** Local.

38063 ■ New Canaan Chamber of Commerce (NCCC)
91 Elm St.
New Canaan, CT 06840
Ph: (203)966-2004
Co. E-mail: info@newcanaanchamber.com

URL: http://newcanaanchamber.com
Contact: Meredith Bach, President
E-mail: mbach@randinsurance.com
Facebook: www.facebook.com/NewCanaanChamber
Linkedin: www.linkedin.com/company/new-canaan
-chamber-of-commerce
Description: Promotes business and community development in New Canaan, CT. Bestows Citizen's Award. Sponsors village fair. **Founded:** 1956. **Geographic Preference:** Local.

38064 ■ *New Milford Living Magazine*
11 Railroad St.
New Milford, CT 06776
Ph: (860)354-6080
Fax: (860)354-8526
Co. E-mail: nmcc@newmilford-chamber.com
URL: http://newmilford-chamber.com
Contact: Jennifer Birdseye, President
E-mail: jbirdseye@websterbank.com
URL(s): newmilford-chamber.com/member-directory
-listings/new-milford-living-magazine
Released: Monthly **Availability:** Print.

38065 ■ Newington Chamber of Commerce (NCC)
171 Market Sq., Ste. 101
Newington, CT 06111
Ph: (860)666-2089
Co. E-mail: office@newingtonchamber.com
URL: http://www.newingtonchamber.com
Contact: Katie Kiss, President
Facebook: www.facebook.com/newingtonchamber
Linkedin: www.linkedin.com/company/newing
tonchamber
Instagram: www.instagram.com/newingtonchamber
YouTube: www.youtube.com/channel/
UCQPFyimouhD95qjpP25oGCw
Description: Promotes business and community development in Newington, CT. **Founded:** 1945. **Geographic Preference:** Local.

38066 ■ North Central Connecticut Chamber of Commerce (NCCCC)
PO Box 123
Enfield, CT 06083
Ph: (860)741-3838
Co. E-mail: info@ncccc.org
URL: http://www.ncccc.org
Contact: Peter DiMaria, President
Facebook: www.facebook.com/northcentralctcham
ber
Description: Promotes business and community development in North Central, CT area. **Founded:** 1894. **Geographic Preference:** Regional.

38067 ■ Northeastern Connecticut Chamber of Commerce (NCCC)
210 Westcott Rd.
Danielson, CT 06239
Ph: (860)774-8001
Co. E-mail: info@nectchamber.com
URL: http://www.nectchamber.com
Contact: Betti Kuszaj, Executive Director
Facebook: www.facebook.com/Northeastern-Connec
ticut-Chamber-of-Commerce-266217953714
X (Twitter): x.com/nectchamber
Instagram: www.instagram.com/ne_ct_chamber
Description: Promotes business and community development in Danielson, CT area. **Geographic Preference:** Local.

38068 ■ Old Saybrook Chamber of Commerce
1 Main St.
Old Saybrook, CT 06475
Ph: (860)388-3266
Fax: (860)388-9433
Co. E-mail: info@oldsaybrookchamber.com
URL: http://www.oldsaybrookchamber.com
Contact: Bob Bradley, President
E-mail: robert.bradley@rate.com
X (Twitter): x.com/OSchamber
Instagram: www.instagram.com/oschamber
Pinterest: www.pinterest.com/oschamber

Description: Provides leadership, support, and networking within the business community of Old Saybrook. **Founded:** 1939. **Publications:** *Chamberlights* (Monthly). **Geographic Preference:** Local.

38069 ■ Orange Chamber of Commerce
605A Orange Center Rd.
Orange, CT 06477-2913
Ph: (203)795-3328
Co. E-mail: director@orangectchamber.com
URL: http://www.orangectchamber.com
Contact: Theodore Novicki, President
E-mail: ted.novicki@uinet.com
Facebook: www.facebook.com/OrangeCTChamberofCommerce
X (Twitter): x.com/orangedirector
Description: Promotes business and community development in Orange, CT. **Founded:** 1962. **Geographic Preference:** Local.

38070 ■ Quinnipiac Chamber of Commerce
50 N Main St., 2nd Fl.
Wallingford, CT 06492
Ph: (203)269-9891
Fax: (203)269-1358
Co. E-mail: gary@quinncham.com
URL: http://www.quinncham.com
Contact: Garrett Sheehan, President
E-mail: gsheehan@gnhcc.com
Facebook: www.facebook.com/quinncham
X (Twitter): x.com/QuinnChamNews
Instagram: www.instagram.com/quinncham
YouTube: www.youtube.com/channel/UCgLhiuaaH_RFEQTj29u3QMw
Description: Promotes business and community development in Wallingford and North Haven, CT. Active lobbying and activities in educational arena. Sponsors seminars; conducts Business After Hours mixers. Maintains Women's Council, Industrial Council, Mayor's Advisory Council, and Legislative Committee, Real Estate Advisory Committee, and Small Business Council. **Founded:** 1978. **Publications:** *Chamber Connections* (Monthly). **Educational Activities:** Business After Hours (Monthly). **Geographic Preference:** Local.

38071 ■ Ridgefield Chamber of Commerce
383 Main St., 2B
Ridgefield, CT 06877
Ph: (203)438-5992
Co. E-mail: info@ridgefieldchamber.org
URL: http://chamber.inridgefield.com
Contact: Diana Spence, Executive Director
Facebook: www.facebook.com/ridgefieldchamber
Linkedin: www.linkedin.com/company/ridgefield-chamber-of-commerce
Instagram: www.instagram.com/destinationridgefieldct
YouTube: www.youtube.com/channel/UCtx_10szs5pvkcvoe-VfB1A
Description: Promotes business and community development in Ridgefield, CT. Sponsors Halloween Walk, Holiday Tree Lighting, Gift certificate program, Sale-a-brations, and home based entrepreneur workshop. **Founded:** 1966. **Publications:** *Getting To Know Ridgefield* (Annual). **Geographic Preference:** Local.

38072 ■ Rocky Hill Chamber of Commerce
2264 Silas Deane Hwy.
Rocky Hill, CT 06067
URL: http://www.rhchamber.org
Description: Promotes business and community development in Rocky Hill, CT. Maintains governmental affairs, economic development, civic affairs, education, public relations, membership, retention, meetings, and budget committees. **Founded:** 1989. **Geographic Preference:** Local.

38073 ■ Shoreline Chamber of Commerce
2614 Boston Post Rd., Guilford
Guilford, CT 06437
Ph: (203)488-5500
Fax: (203)405-8189
Co. E-mail: info@shorelinechamberct.com
URL: http://www.shorelinechamberct.com
Contact: Dee Jacob, President
Facebook: www.facebook.com/shorelinechamberct
Linkedin: www.linkedin.com/company/shoreline-ct-chamber-of-commerce
X (Twitter): x.com/CTShoreline
Instagram: www.instagram.com/shorelinechamberct
Pinterest: www.pinterest.com/chamberct
Description: Works to enhance business opportunity for the economic success of Branford, CT. **Publications:** *Moving Forward* (Quarterly). **Geographic Preference:** Local.

38074 ■ Simsbury Chamber of Commerce (SCOC)
720 Hopmeadow St.
Simsbury, CT 06070
Ph: (860)651-7307
Fax: (860)651-1933
Co. E-mail: info@simsburycoc.org
URL: http://www.simsburycoc.org
Contact: Joseph Beale, President
E-mail: jbeale@liberty-bank.com
Facebook: www.facebook.com/simsburycoc
X (Twitter): x.com/SimsburyCOC
Description: Promotes business and community development in Simsbury, CT. **Founded:** 1961. **Geographic Preference:** Local.

38075 ■ Stamford Chamber of Commerce
970 Summer St.
Stamford, CT 06905
Ph: (203)359-4761
Fax: (203)614-9979
Co. E-mail: stamfordchamber@stamfordchamber.com
URL: http://www.stamfordchamber.com
Contact: Heather Cavanagh, President
E-mail: hcavanagh@stamfordchamber.com
Facebook: www.facebook.com/stamfordchamberofcommerce
Linkedin: www.linkedin.com/company/stamford-chamber-of-commerce
X (Twitter): x.com/stamfordchamber
Instagram: www.instagram.com/stamfordchamber
Description: Aims to advance the civic and economic vitality of Stamford, Connecticut. **Geographic Preference:** Local.

38076 ■ Suffield Chamber of Commerce (SCC)
PO Box 741
Suffield, CT 06078
URL: http://www.suffieldchamber.com
Description: Works to promote economic and community development within the region by offering networking opportunities, educational seminars and special programs to its members. **Founded:** 1994. **Geographic Preference:** Regional.

38077 ■ Tolland County Chamber of Commerce (TCCC)
30 Lafayette Sq.
Vernon, CT 06066
Ph: (860)872-0587
Co. E-mail: tccc@tollandcountychamber.org
URL: http://tollandcountychamber.org
Contact: Angie Chirico, President
Facebook: www.facebook.com/tollandcountychamber
Linkedin: www.linkedin.com/in/candice-corcione-09446614
X (Twitter): x.com/TollandChamber
Instagram: www.instagram.com/tollandcountychamber
YouTube: www.youtube.com/channel/UC7OSbIRSiqeQ2P0Op6k55aQ
Description: Promotes business and community development in Tolland County. **Founded:** 1955. **Publications:** *Bare Bones* (Quarterly). **Educational Activities:** Consumer Showcase. **Geographic Preference:** Local.

38078 ■ Tri-State Chamber of Commerce (TSC) [Salisbury Chamber of Commerce]
386 Main St.
Lakeville, CT 06039
Ph: (860)393-9171
Co. E-mail: info@tristatechamber.com
URL: http://tristatechamber.com
Facebook: www.facebook.com/TriStateChamberOfCommerce
Description: Promotes business and community development in Lakeville, CT. **Founded:** 2006. **Publications:** *Tri-State Chamber of Commerce-- Printed Directory* (Annual). **Geographic Preference:** Regional.

38079 ■ West Hartford Chamber of Commerce (WHCC)
948 Farmington Ave.
West Hartford, CT 06107
Ph: (860)521-2300
Fax: (860)521-1996
Co. E-mail: info@whchamber.com
URL: http://www.whchamber.com
Contact: Christopher Conway, President
E-mail: cconway@whchamber.com
Facebook: www.facebook.com/westhartford.chamber
Linkedin: www.linkedin.com/company/west-hartford-chamber-of-commerce
X (Twitter): x.com/wh_chamber
Description: Promotes business and community development in West Hartford, CT. **Founded:** 1908. **Educational Activities:** Evening Networking Function. **Awards:** Noah Webster Awards (Annual). **Geographic Preference:** Local.

38080 ■ West Haven Chamber of Commerce (WHCC)
355 Main St.
West Haven, CT 06516
Ph: (203)933-1500
URL: http://www.uschamber.com/co/chambers/connecticut/west-haven
Facebook: www.facebook.com/westhavenchamber
X (Twitter): x.com/wsthavenchamber
Description: Promotes business and community development in West Haven, CT. **Founded:** 1919. **Awards:** West Haven Scholarship Award (Annual). **Geographic Preference:** Local.

38081 ■ Westport-Weston Chamber of Commerce (WWCC)
41 Riverside Ave.
Westport, CT 06880
Ph: (203)227-9234
Fax: (203)454-4019
Co. E-mail: info@westportwestonchamber.com
URL: http://www.westportchamber.com
Contact: Matthew Mandell, Director
E-mail: matthew@westportwestonchamber.com
Facebook: www.facebook.com/WestportWeston
Linkedin: www.linkedin.com/company/westport-weston-chamber-of-commerce
Instagram: www.instagram.com/westportwestonchamber
Description: Promotes business and community development in Westport and Weston, CT. Sponsors Golf and Tennis Classic, Business Expo, and Business After Hours Lead-Generators. **Founded:** 1931. **Publications:** *Chamber of Commerce Newsletter* (Monthly); *Member and Business Directory* (Annual). **Educational Activities:** Business After Hours; Westport/Weston Chamber of Commerce Workshop. **Geographic Preference:** Local.

38082 ■ Wethersfield Chamber of Commerce
200 Main St.
Wethersfield, CT 06109
Ph: (860)721-6200
Co. E-mail: wethersfield@sbcglobal.net
URL: http://www.wethersfieldchamber.com
Contact: Pat DePerry, President
E-mail: patdeperry@bhhsne.com
Facebook: www.facebook.com/WethChamber
Description: Promotes business and community development in Wethersfield, CT. Convention/Meeting: none. **Founded:** 1986. **Geographic Preference:** Local.

38083 ■ Wilton Chamber of Commerce
86 Old Ridgefield Rd.
Wilton, CT 06897
Ph: (203)762-0567
Co. E-mail: info@wiltonchamber.com
URL: http://wiltonchamber.com

STATE LISTINGS

Contact: Susan Goldman, President
Description: Aims to advance the commercial and civic interests of the town of Wilton. **Founded:** 1989. **Publications:** *Chamber News* (Monthly). **Geographic Preference:** Local.

38084 ■ Windsor Chamber of Commerce (WCC)
261 Broad St.
 Windsor, CT 06095
Ph: (860)688-5165
Fax: (860)688-0809
Co. E-mail: info@windsorcc.org
URL: http://www.windsorcc.org
Contact: Mary-Lynn Kinney, Treasurer
Description: Seeks to provide a voice for the business community on issues of public policy. Strives to help businesses work together for their mutual benefit. Advocates initiatives that enhance the region's economic vitality and quality of life. Sponsors annual auction, Nightmare on Broad Street at Halloween, golf tournament, school-to-career, Winter Magic, Businesses Fueling Minds and new teacher reception. **Founded:** 1949. **Publications:** *Business United* (Bimonthly). **Awards:** Frank Parker Beautification Award (Annual); The Jerry Hallas Memorial Award (Annual). **Geographic Preference:** Local.

MINORITY BUSINESS ASSISTANCE PROGRAMS

38085 ■ University of Hartford Entrepreneurial Center - Women's Business Center (EC)
222 Pitkin St.
 East Hartford, CT 06108
URL: http://www.hartford.edu/barney/about/centers-and-institutes/entrepreneurial-center-splash.aspx
Description: Provides business counseling, business workshops and resources, and referrals to SBA programs for start-up and established businesses. Serves both men and women, but emphasis is on women-owned enterprises. **Founded:** 1985.

FINANCING AND LOAN PROGRAMS

38086 ■ Ash Creek Capital Advisors LLC
131 Doubling Rd.
 Greenwich, CT 06830-4040
URL: http://ashcreekadvisors.com
Contact: Steven Landis, Managing Director
Description: Offers capital funding and advisory services. **Investment Policies:** Proven business model; revenues in excess of $5 million; niche/expanding markets; sustainable competitive advantage; short-term opportunity or problem; .

38087 ■ Canaan Partners
285 Riverside Ave., Ste. 250
 Westport, CT 06880
Ph: (203)855-0400
Co. E-mail: hello@canaan.com
URL: http://www.canaan.com
Contact: Sarah Johnson, Manager
X (Twitter): x.com/canaanpartners
Description: Venture capital firm specializing in seed, early-stage technology and healthcare startups. **Founded:** 1987. **Preferred Investment Size:** $3,000,000 to $25,000,000. **Industry Preferences:** Internet specific, computer software and services, medical and health, communications and media, biotechnology, other products, computer hardware, semiconductors and other electronics, consumer related, industrial and energy.

38088 ■ Catterton Partners
599 W Putnam Ave.
 Greenwich, CT 06830
Ph: (203)629-4901
Fax: (203)629-4903
Co. E-mail: info@lcatterton.com
URL: http://www.lcatterton.com
Contact: Chinta Bhagat, Managing Partner
Linkedin: www.linkedin.com/company/l-catterton

X (Twitter): x.com/L_Catterton
Description: Investment firm provides of venture capital and private equity investment services for consumer industry. **Founded:** 1989. **Preferred Investment Size:** $5,000,000 minimum. **Industry Preferences:** Consumer related, communications and media, other products.

38089 ■ Cava Capital
679 Post Rd.
 Darien, CT 06820
Ph: (203)210-7477
Co. E-mail: info@cavacapital.com
URL: http://cavacapital.com
Contact: Bob Geiman, Managing Partner
 Co-Founder
Facebook: www.facebook.com/CavaCapital
X (Twitter): x.com/CavaCapital
Description: Venture capital firm. Invests from seed to Series B stages. **Founded:** 2007. **Investment Policies:** Companies with some market validation and scalable, highly efficient business models; entrepreneurs with domain expertise. **Industry Preferences:** Technology (mobile, commerce, SaaS, marketplaces, and on-demand economy); consumer products and services (wellness and active lifestyle).

38090 ■ Centricap
65 High Ridge Rd., Ste. 439
 Stamford, CT 06905
Ph: (203)326-7600
URL: http://www.centricap.com
Contact: Steven Chrust, Senior Partner Managing Director
E-mail: schrust@centricap.com
X (Twitter): x.com/CentripetalVC
Description: Early stage and growth equity venture capital firm. **Investment Policies:** Companies where the MVP (minimal viable product) is complete and market tested; have generated first revenues, proven their basic business model, or have proven traction. **Industry Preferences:** Health and wellness; impact; market reimagination.

38091 ■ CHL Medical Partners
113 Post Rd., E
 Westport, CT 06880
Ph: (203)324-7700
Fax: (203)724-1999
Co. E-mail: info@chlmedical.com
URL: http://www.chlmedical.com
Contact: David Steffy, Partner
Description: Firm provides investment for healthcare businesses. **Founded:** 2001. **Preferred Investment Size:** $250,000 to $6,000,000. **Industry Preferences:** Medical and health, biotechnology, and Internet specific.

38092 ■ Connecticut Innovations Inc. (CI)
470 James St., Ste. 8
 New Haven, CT 06513
Ph: (860)563-5851
Co. E-mail: info@ctinnovations.com
URL: http://ctinnovations.com
Contact: Matthew McCooe, Chief Executive Officer
Facebook: www.facebook.com/ctinnovations
Linkedin: www.linkedin.com/company/67435
X (Twitter): x.com/CT_Innovate
Instagram: www.instagram.com/ct_innovations
Description: Venture capital and investment firm. **Founded:** 1989. **Preferred Investment Size:** $100,000 to $2,000,000. **Industry Preferences:** Internet specific, computer software and services, semiconductors and other electronics, biotechnology, medical and health, industrial and energy, communications and media, other products, computer hardware, and consumer related.

38093 ■ Elm Street Ventures (ESV)
33 Whitney Ave.
 New Haven, CT 06510
Ph: (203)401-4201
Co. E-mail: venture@elmvc.com
URL: http://www.elmvc.com
Contact: Rob Bettigole, Founder Managing Partner

Connecticut ■ 38099

Description: Venture capital firm and the seed and early stages for the life sciences. Yale University it its largest investor. **Industry Preferences:** Life sciences (therapeutics, laboratory tools, diagnostics, medical devices); software; materials; sustainable technology.

38094 ■ Galen Partners (GP)
680 Washington Blvd., 10th Fl.
 Stamford, CT 06901
Ph: (203)653-6400
URL: http://www.galen.com
Contact: David Jahns, Managing Director
E-mail: djahns@galen.com
Description: Early stage venture capital firm that invests in firms already generating revenue. Focuses on health care technology enabled services, medical devices, and specialty pharmaceutical companies. **Founded:** 1990. **Industry Preferences:** Information technology services; medical technology; specialty pharmaceuticals.

38095 ■ Generation Partners
Two Lafayette Ct.
 Greenwich, CT 06830
Ph: (203)422-8212
URL: http://www.generation.com
Contact: Andrew Hertzmark, Managing Partner
E-mail: hertzmark@generation.com
Linkedin: www.linkedin.com/company/generation-partners
Description: Finance: Venture capital and buyout firm. **Founded:** 1995. **Preferred Investment Size:** $10,000,000 to $40,000,000. **Industry Preferences:** Computer software and services, Internet specific, business services, communications and media, consumer related, healthcare services and technology.

38096 ■ Great Point Partners, LLC (GPP)
165 Mason St., 3rd Fl.
 Greenwich, CT 06830
Ph: (203)971-3300
Co. E-mail: info@gppfunds.com
URL: http://gppfunds.com
Contact: Christopher Baviello, Assistant Vice President, Finance
E-mail: cbaviello@gppfunds.com
Description: Offers growth equity for healthcare companies. **Founded:** 2003.

38097 ■ Landmark Angels
2 Greenwich Office Pk., Ste. 300
 Greenwich, CT 06831
Ph: (203)552-1445
Co. E-mail: admin@landmarkangels.com
URL: http://www.landmarkangels.com
Contact: William S. Podd, Executive Director
Description: Angel investor group. **Founded:** 2008. **Industry Preferences:** Life science; healthcare services; medical devices; digital health; energy; ed tech; fin tech; ag tech; consumer products.

38098 ■ Landmark Partners Inc.
Ares Management Corporation
 10 Mill Pond Ln.
 Simsbury, CT 06070
Ph: (310)201-4100
Co. E-mail: investorrelations@aresmgmt.com
URL: http://www.aresmgmt.com
Contact: Timothy L. Haviland, President
E-mail: timothy.haviland@landmarkpartners.com
Description: Provides secondary investing across alternative asset classes. **Founded:** 1989. **Preferred Investment Size:** $500,000 minimum. **Industry Preferences:** Other products, computer software and services, computer hardware, semiconductors and other electronics, Internet specific, biotechnology, medical and health, consumer related, industrial and energy.

38099 ■ LaunchCapital
195 Church St., Ste. 1700
 New Haven, CT 06510
URL: http://www.launchcapital.com
Contact: Alice Smith, Director, Finance Director, Administration
E-mail: alice@launchcapital.com

Description: Seed-stage venture capital firm. Backed by the Pritzker Vlock Family Office (PVFO). **Founded:** 2008. **Investment Policies:** Capital-efficient companies; innovative thinkers; creative solutions.

38100 ■ NTC Group Inc.
104 Field Point Rd.
Greenwich, CT 06830
Ph: (203)862-2800
URL: http://ntcgroup.com
Contact: Anthony Adler, Director
E-mail: aadler@ntcgroup.com
Description: Provides investment and management services. **Founded:** 1985.

38101 ■ RFE Investment Partners
36 Grove St., 2nd Fl.
New Canaan, CT 06840
Ph: (203)966-2800
Co. E-mail: info@rfeip.com
URL: http://www.rfeip.com
Contact: Michael Rubel, Managing Director
E-mail: mrubel@rfeip.com
Description: Firm is engaged in business and strategy management such as healthcare, technology, media, and much more services. **Scope:** Firm is engaged in business and strategy management such as healthcare, technology, media, and much more services. **Founded:** 1979. **Preferred Investment Size:** $10,000,000 to $25,000,000. **Industry Preferences:** Other products, business services, medical and health, industrial and energy, consumer related, computer software and services, computer hardware, semiconductors and other electronics, and biotechnology.

38102 ■ Saugatuck Capital Company L.P.
4 Armstrong Rd., Ste. 230
Shelton, CT 06484
Ph: (203)348-6669
Fax: (203)324-6995
Co. E-mail: saugatuck@saugatuckcapital.com
URL: http://www.saugatuckcapital.com
Contact: Gary L. Goldberg, Managing Director
E-mail: ggoldberg@saugatuckcapital.com
Description: Private investment firm. **Founded:** 1982. **Preferred Investment Size:** $4,000,000 to $7,000,000. **Industry Preferences:** Other products, medical and health, consumer related, communications and media, industrial and energy, computer hardware, semiconductors and other electronics, computer software and services, and Internet specific.

38103 ■ Turnstone Capital
PO Box 253
Rowayton, CT 06853
Co. E-mail: info@turnstonecapital.com
URL: http://www.turnstonecapital.com
Contact: Marc J. La Magna, Managing Partner
Description: Funds and develops disruptive technology ventures.

PROCUREMENT ASSISTANCE PROGRAMS

38104 ■ Connecticut Procurement Technical Assistance Center (CT PTAC)
19-B Thames St.
Groton, CT 06340
Ph: (860)437-4659
Fax: (860)437-4662
Co. E-mail: ptac@ctptac.org
URL: http://ctptac.org
Contact: Yu-Han Yang, Database Manager
Facebook: www.facebook.com/CTPTAC
Linkedin: www.linkedin.com/company/ctptac
Description: Provides marketing and procurement assistance to Connecticut businesses interested in selling their goods or services to federal, state, or local governments.

38105 ■ Connecticut Procurement Technical Assistance Center (CTSBDC) - Small Business Development Procurement Center
19 Thames St.
Groton, CT 06340
Ph: (860)437-4659
Fax: (860)437-4662
Co. E-mail: ptac@ctptac.org
URL: http://ctptac.org/resources/informational
Description: Covers activities for the VA Medical Center (West Haven, CT), Naval Submarine base (Groton, CT), and the U.S. Coast Guard Academy (New London, CT).

INCUBATORS/RESEARCH AND TECHNOLOGY PARKS

38106 ■ Bridgeport Innovation Center (BIC)
Time Equities Inc. (TEI)
955 Connecticut Ave., Ste. 5103
Bridgeport, CT 06607
Ph: (212)206-6000
Co. E-mail: receptionist@timeequities.com
URL: http://timeequities.com
Description: Bridgeport Innovation Center provides an entrepreneurial environment for small to mid-sized growth businesses. As a Bridgeport business your company may qualify for the city's liberal tax incentives and/or for Connecticut State tax abatements, personnel job training, and/or financial assistance programs.

38107 ■ Central Connecticut State University - Institute of Technology and Business Development (ITBD)
185 Main St., Ste. 218
New Britain, CT 06051
URL: http://www.ccsu.edu/trio/enroll-your-student
Contact: Lisette Velasquez, Contact
E-mail: lisette.velasquez@ccsu.edu
Description: A small business incubator that assists entrepreneurs in the business start-up process and gives aid to new businesses to help ensure their survival. **Scope:** Manufacturing and engineering, human resources, and management. **Founded:** 1986.
Publications: *ITBD Quarterly newsletter* (Quarterly).

38108 ■ Connecticut Center for Advanced Technology, Inc. (CCAT)
222 Pitkin St., Ste. 101
East Hartford, CT 06108
Ph: (860)291-8832
Fax: (860)291-8874
Co. E-mail: info@ccat.us
URL: http://www.ccat.us
Contact: Ron Angelo, President
E-mail: rangelo@ccat.us
Facebook: www.facebook.com/CTCenterforAdvancedTech
Linkedin: www.linkedin.com/company/ccat
X (Twitter): x.com/CCATInc
Description: A non-profit corporation funded under federal and state sponsored grants to develop a national center that addresses military and civilian industrial manufacturing needs; promotes energy planning and policy initiatives; stimulates innovation; and enhances workforce development issues concerning technology competitiveness. **Founded:** 2004.

38109 ■ Hamden Business Incubator
3074 Whitney Ave., Bldg. 1
Hamden, CT 06518
URL: http://www.hamdeneconomicdevelopment.org
Contact: Steven R. Rolnick, President
Description: Firm engages in business consulting services.

38110 ■ Institute for Technology & Business Development (ITBD)
1615 Stanley St.
New Britain, CT 06050
Ph: (860)832-2277
Co. E-mail: coned@ccsu.edu
URL: http://ce.ccsu.edu
Description: Business incubator aiding the growth of existing businesses as well as startups, turning ideas into ventures.

38111 ■ Stamford Innovation Center (SIC)
175 Atlantic St.
Stamford, CT 06901
Ph: (203)226-8701
Co. E-mail: team@stamfordcenter.com
URL: http://stamfordcenter.com
Contact: Barry Schwimmer, Manager
Facebook: www.facebook.com/stamfordicenter
Linkedin: www.linkedin.com/company/stamford-innovation-center
X (Twitter): x.com/StamfordiCenter
Instagram: www.instagram.com/stamfordicenter
YouTube: www.youtube.com/user/StamfordiCenter
Description: A hub for innovation and entrepreneurship that supports a diverse community of small business owners, freelancers, innovators, and entrepreneurs by providing resources such as classes, events, and workspace.

38112 ■ University of Connecticut Technology Incubation Program (UCONN TIP)
438 Whitney Rd. Ext., Unit 1006
Storrs, CT 06269-1006
Co. E-mail: tip@uconn.edu
URL: http://innovation.uconn.edu/technology-incubation-program
Contact: Mostafa Analoui, Executive Director
E-mail: mostafa.analoui@uconn.edu
Description: A program that aims to accelerate the successful establishment and development of entrepreneurial companies by providing laboratory/office space and an array of support resources and services which are available through the various departments and functions at the University.

38113 ■ Univiersity of Connecticut (CCEI) - Connecticut Center for Entrepreneurship and Innovation
100 Constitution Plz., 3rd Fl.
Hartford, CT 06103
Ph: (860)728-2101
Co. E-mail: ccei@uconn.edu
URL: http://ccei.uconn.edu
Contact: Jennifer Mathieu, Executive Director
Facebook: www.facebook.com/UConnCCEI
Linkedin: www.linkedin.com/company/connecticutcenterforentrepreneurshipandinnovation
X (Twitter): x.com/uconnccei
Instagram: www.instagram.com/uconnccei
Description: Promotes entrepreneurship and innovation. Supports new venture development through funding and programs, engages students in innovation through courses and research, and connects the University with the entrepreneurial ecosystem in the state. **Founded:** 2007.

CONSULTANTS

38114 ■ Brand New Matter (BNM)
23 Old Kings Hwy. S
Darien, CT 06820
Co. E-mail: info@brandnewmatter.com
URL: http://brandnewmatter.com
Contact: Krish Jagirdar, Partner
Linkedin: www.linkedin.com/company/bnmcapital
X (Twitter): x.com/brandnewmatter
Description: Strategic advisory and venture capital firm. **Founded:** 2013.

38115 ■ Start U Up
20 Hollow Tree Ridge Rd.
Darien, CT 06820
URL: http://www.startuup.net
Contact: Jeffrey M. Glick, President
E-mail: jmg@startuup.net
Description: Offers professional executive management services on an outsourced basis. Specializes in management support for financial services entrepreneurs.

PUBLISHERS

38116 ■ Alliance of Area Business Publishers (AABP)
287 Richards Ave.
Norwalk, CT 06850
Ph: (203)515-9294
Co. E-mail: sandersonmgt@gmail.com

URL: http://www.bizpubs.org
Contact: Cate Sanderson, Executive Director
E-mail: cate@sandersonmgt.com

Description: Local area business publications. Encourages high journalistic standards among area business publications. Acts as a forum for the exchange of ideas and information, especially on common issues such as editorial excellence, postal regulations, government regulations, and advertising. Compiles statistics of business patterns in markets of members and engages in cooperative member market research. **Founded:** 1979. **Publications:** *Association of Area Business Publications--Directory* (Annual); *Alliance of Area Business Publications--Membership Directory*. **Awards:** AABP Editorial Excellence Awards (Annual). **Geographic Preference:** National.

38117 ■ Business Books International
194 Putnam Rd.
 New Canaan, CT 06840
Ph: (203)219-2321
URL: http://businessbooksusa.com

Description: Publishes reference books for business and library use on regions of the world, does not accept unsolicited manuscripts and reaches the market through advertising, direct mail, trade sales, and wholesalers. **Founded:** 1982.

38118 ■ Hannacroix Creek Books Inc.
1127 High Ridge Rd., PMB No. 110
 Stamford, CT 06905
Contact: Jan Yager, Director

Description: Publisher of books and audio cassettes in the areas of deafness, friendship, business, time management and relationships. **Founded:** 1996.

38119 ■ Hunt-Scanlon Corporation
20 Signal Rd.
 Stamford, CT 06902
URL: http://huntscanlon.com
Contact: Christopher Hunt, President

Description: Publishes business directories for business-to-business applications. It also publishes CD-ROMs and software, as well as a newsletter. Reaches the market through direct mail. **Founded:** 1988. **Publications:** *The Job Seekers Guide to Executive Recruiters*; *Job Seekers Guide to Personnel Managers*; *RecruiterLink* (Annual); *Personnel Locator*; *Hunt-Scanlon's Select Guide to Human Resource Executives* (Annual); *Hunt-Scanlon's Select Guide to Finance Executives* (Annual); *Hunt-Scanlon's Select Guide to Sales & Marketing Executives* (Annual); *Hunt-Scanlon's Select Guide to Information Technology Executives*; *Hunt-Scanlon's Executive Recruiters of North America* (Annual); *Hunt-Scanlon's Executive Recruiters of North America - Contingency Firms* (Annual); *4 Data Base* (Annual); *ExecutiveSelect - Human Resource Executives Edition* (Annual); *ExecutiveSelect - Finance Executives Edition* (Annual); *ExecutiveSelect - Sales & Marketing Executives Edition*; *ExecutiveSelect - Information Technology Executives Edition* (Annual); *Diversity in Corporate America* (Biennial).

EARLY STAGE FINANCING

38120 ■ Palm Ventures LLC
Greenwich, CT
Ph: (203)302-7000
Co. E-mail: info@palmventures.com
URL: http://palmventures.com
Contact: James Walker, III, Chief Executive Officer
Founded: 1992.

EXPANSION AND GROWTH FINANCING

38121 ■ Palm Ventures LLC
Greenwich, CT
Ph: (203)302-7000
Co. E-mail: info@palmventures.com
URL: http://palmventures.com
Contact: James Walker, III, Chief Executive Officer
Founded: 1992.

Delaware

ASSOCIATIONS AND OTHER ORGANIZATIONS

38122 ▪ First State Innovation (FSI)
1 Richter Pkwy., Ste. 150
Wilmington, DE 19803
Ph: (302)690-1260
Co. E-mail: info@firststateinnovation.org
URL: http://www.firststateinnovation.org
Contact: Ernest J. Dianastasis, Chairman of the Board
Description: Helps early-stage technology-base businesses find seed capital, alternative funding, human capital, intellectual capital, commercialization assistance, and other resources. Works to accelerate Delaware's entrepreneurial economy. **Founded:** 2006.

38123 ▪ National Federation of Independent Business Delaware (NFIB)
Annapolis, MD
Ph: (301)335-1063
URL: http://www.nfib.com/delaware
Contact: Julianna Rauf, Manager
E-mail: julianna.rauf@nfib.org
X (Twitter): x.com/nfib_de
Description: Represents small and independent businesses. Aims to promote and protect the rights of members to own, operate and grow their businesses. **Founded:** 1943. **Geographic Preference:** State.

SMALL BUSINESS DEVELOPMENT CENTERS

38124 ▪ Delaware Small Business Development Center (DSBDC) [Newark SBDC]
1 Innovation Way, Ste. 301
Newark, DE 19711
Ph: (302)831-4283
Fax: (302)831-1423
Co. E-mail: delaware-sbdc@udel.edu
URL: http://delawaresbdc.org
Contact: J. Michael Bowman, Director
E-mail: jmbowman@udel.edu
Facebook: www.facebook.com/delawareSBDC
Linkedin: www.linkedin.com/company/delaware-sbdc
X (Twitter): x.com/dsbdc
Instagram: www.instagram.com/de_sbdc
YouTube: www.youtube.com/user/DSBTDC
Founded: 1984. **Geographic Preference:** State.

38125 ▪ Delaware Small Business Development Center (DSBDC) [Georgetown SBDC]
103 W Pine St.
Georgetown, DE 19947
Ph: (302)856-1555
Co. E-mail: delaware-sbdc@udel.edu
URL: http://delawaresbdc.org
Contact: David Root, Director
Instagram: www.instagram.com/de_sbdc
YouTube: www.youtube.com/user/DSBTDC

Description: Represents and promotes the small business sector. Provides management assistance to current and prospective small business owners. Helps to improve management skills and expand the products and services of members. **Founded:** 1984.

38126 ▪ Dover Small Business Development Center
Bank of America Bldg., Rm. 108
1200 N DuPont Hwy.
Dover, DE 19901
Ph: (302)831-1555
URL: http://delawaresbdc.org/contact
Description: Provides management assistance to current and prospective small business owners in Dover. **Geographic Preference:** Local.

SCORE OFFICES

38127 ▪ SCORE - Delaware
1105 Market St., Lobby Level, Ste. 02
Wilmington, DE 19801
Ph: (302)661-2366
Co. E-mail: contact.0042@scorevolunteer.org
URL: http://delaware.score.org
Contact: Bridget Weston, Chief Executive Officer
Linkedin: www.linkedin.com/company/score-delaware
X (Twitter): x.com/scoredelaware
YouTube: www.youtube.com/channel/UCvUiZZ7ZRL-iL0DBRFGdUSQ
Description: Provides professional guidance and information to maximize the success of existing and emerging small businesses. Offers business counseling and workshops. **Geographic Preference:** Local.

38128 ▪ SCORE - Georgetown
PO Box 0000 (Len Kidwell)
Georgetown, DE 19947
URL: http://delaware.score.org
Linkedin: www.linkedin.com/company/score-delaware
X (Twitter): x.com/scoredelaware
YouTube: www.youtube.com/channel/UCvUiZZ7ZRL-iL0DBRFGdUSQ
Description: Provides professional guidance and information to maximize the success of existing and emerging small businesses. Offers business counseling and workshops.

38129 ▪ SCORE - Kent
PO Box 0000 (Herb Konowitz)
Dover, DE 19901
URL: http://delaware.score.org
Contact: Bridget Weston, Chief Executive Officer
Description: Provides professional guidance and information to maximize the success of existing and emerging small businesses. Offers business counseling and workshops.

BETTER BUSINESS BUREAUS

38130 ▪ Better Business Bureau of Delaware
60 Reads Way
New Castle, DE 19720

Ph: (302)221-5255
Fax: (302)221-5265
Co. E-mail: info@delaware.bbb.org
URL: http://ww.bbb.org/local-bbb/bbb-serving-delaware
Contact: Christine Sauers, President
Facebook: www.facebook.com/bbbdelaware
X (Twitter): x.com/bbbdelaware
YouTube: www.youtube.com/channel/UCFMvpf1XMK5h_ls2NH2eaKQ
Description: Seeks to promote and foster ethical relationship between businesses and the public through voluntary self-regulation, consumer and business education, and service excellence. Provides information to help consumers and businesses make informed purchasing decisions and avoid costly scams and frauds; settles consumer complaints through arbitration and other means. **Founded:** 1965. **Publications:** BBB Consumer Resource Guide and Membership Directory. **Awards:** Edward M. Rush, Sr. Memorial Award (Annual); Better Business Bureau of Delaware Torch Awards for Marketplace Ethics (Annual). **Geographic Preference:** State.

CHAMBERS OF COMMERCE

38131 ▪ Bethany-Fenwick Area Chamber of Commerce
36913 Coastal Hwy.
Fenwick Island, DE 19944
Ph: (302)539-2100
Co. E-mail: info@bethany-fenwick.org
URL: http://thequietresorts.com
Contact: Jamie Hayman, President
Facebook: www.facebook.com/BethanyFenwickAreaChamberOfCommerce
Linkedin: www.linkedin.com/company/bethany-fenwick-area-chamber-of-commerce
X (Twitter): x.com/TheQuietResorts
Instagram: www.instagram.com/thequietresorts
Description: Promotes business and community development in Bethany Beach, Fenwick Island and surrounding areas in Delaware. Holds semiannual surf fishing tournament, annual golf tournament and ocean-to-bay bike tour. **Founded:** 1976. **Publications:** Map and Business Guide; Map and Visitors Guide (Annual). **Geographic Preference:** Local.

38132 ▪ Central Delaware Chamber of Commerce (CDCC)
435 N DuPont Hwy.
Dover, DE 19901
Ph: (302)734-7513
Fax: (302)678-0189
Co. E-mail: info@cdcc.net
URL: http://www.cdcc.net
Contact: Dina C. Vendetti, President
Facebook: www.facebook.com/CentralDelawareChamber
Description: Promotes business and community development in central Delaware. **Founded:** 1919. **Publications:** Central Delaware Info Book (Annual); Chamber News. **Geographic Preference:** Local.

STATE LISTINGS

38133 ■ Chamber of Commerce for Greater Milford (CCGM)
24 NW Front St., Ste. 101
 Milford, DE 19963
Ph: (302)422-3344
Fax: (302)422-7503
Co. E-mail: milford@milfordchamber.com
URL: http://www.milfordchamber.com
Contact: Angel Hodges, President
Facebook: www.facebook.com/CCGMofMilford
Description: Seeks to advance Greater Milford economy through promotion of civic, industrial, commercial, educational, agricultural, and social interests of communities within the area. **Founded:** 1989. **Geographic Preference:** Local.

38134 ■ Delaware State Chamber of Commerce (DSCC)
1201 N Orange St.
 Wilmington, DE 19899
Ph: (302)655-7221
Co. E-mail: info@dscc.com
URL: http://www.dscc.com
Contact: Michael Quaranta, President
E-mail: mquaranta@dscc.com
Facebook: www.facebook.com/DelawareStateChamber
Linkedin: www.linkedin.com/company/delaware-state-chamber-of-commerce
X (Twitter): x.com/destatechamber
YouTube: www.youtube.com/user/DEStateChamber
Description: Promotes business and community development in Delaware. **Founded:** 1837. **Publications:** *Delaware Legislative Roster* (Annual); *Delaware Directory of Commerce and Industry* (Annual); *Delaware State Chamber Business Journal* (Biweekly); *Legislative Roster* (Annual). **Awards:** Marvin S. Gilman Superstars in Business Awards (Annual); Josiah Marvel Cup Award (Annual); DSCC Superstars in Education (Annual). **Geographic Preference:** Local.

38135 ■ *Legislative Roster*
1201 N Orange St.
 Wilmington, DE 19899
Ph: (302)655-7221
Co. E-mail: info@dscc.com
URL: http://www.dscc.com
Contact: Michael Quaranta, President
E-mail: mquaranta@dscc.com
URL(s): www.dscc.com/roster.html
Released: Annual **Price:** $35, for 26 copies and up; $45, for 1-10 copies; $40, for 11-25 copies. **Description:** Provides the names and addresses of members of the Delaware General Assembly, the Congressional delegation and state and local government leaders. **Availability:** Print; Download; PDF.

38136 ■ Lewes Chamber of Commerce and Visitors Bureau, Inc.
120 Kings Hwy.
 Lewes, DE 19958
Ph: (302)645-8073
Free: 877-465-3937
Fax: (302)645-8412
Co. E-mail: inquiry@leweschamber.com
URL: http://www.leweschamber.com
Description: Promotes business and community development in Lewes, DE. Sponsors kite festival, garden tour, and Christmas parade. **Founded:** 1935. **Publications:** *Visitors Guide* (Annual). **Geographic Preference:** Local.

38137 ■ New Castle County Chamber of Commerce (NCCCC)
920 Justison St.
 Wilmington, DE 19801
Ph: (302)737-4343
Fax: (302)322-3593
Co. E-mail: info@ncccc.com
URL: http://www.ncccc.com
Contact: Bob Chadwick, President

E-mail: chadwickb@ncccc.com
X (Twitter): x.com/NCC_Chamber
YouTube: www.youtube.com/channel/UCdp0xR1DtjxJ3T4NgAUHDrg
Description: Creates a prosperous economic environment in New Castle County, DE. Strives to be the premier resource for business growth by providing programs and services that contribute to the success of the community. Offers value-added benefits, connection to business opportunities, local representation on major issues of public policy, and timely communication so that members can be proactive in growing their businesses. **Founded:** 1922. **Publications:** *Business Matters* (Monthly). **Awards:** David J. Freschman Entrepreneur of the Year Award (Annual). **Geographic Preference:** Local.

38138 ■ Rehoboth Beach-Dewey Beach Chamber of Commerce (RBDBCC)
501 Rehoboth Ave.
 Rehoboth Beach, DE 19971-0216
Ph: (302)227-2233
Free: 800-441-1329
Fax: (302)227-8351
Co. E-mail: rehoboth@beach-fun.com
URL: http://www.beach-fun.com
Contact: Carrie Lingo, Chairman
Description: Promotes business and community development in the Rehoboth Beach-Dewey Beach area. Sponsors Sea Witch Weekend Festival. **Founded:** 1940. **Publications:** *Delaware Coast Vacationland* (Annual); *FocusOn* (Irregular); *Map and Visitors Guide* (Annual). **Educational Activities:** Sand Castle Contest (Annual). **Geographic Preference:** Local.

38139 ■ *Visitors Guide*
120 Kings Hwy.
 Lewes, DE 19958
Ph: (302)645-8073
Free: 877-465-3937
Fax: (302)645-8412
Co. E-mail: inquiry@leweschamber.com
URL: http://www.leweschamber.com
URL(s): www.leweschamber.com/membership/invitation-join
Released: Annual **Availability:** Print.

MINORITY BUSINESS ASSISTANCE PROGRAMS

38140 ■ Wilmington Minority Business Enterprise Office (SMBEO)
800 N French St., 3rd Fl.
 Wilmington, DE 19801
Fax: (302)571-4326
URL: http://www.wilmingtonde.gov/business/minority-business-development-program
Contact: James C. Williams, Manager
E-mail: jcwilliams@wilmingtonde.gov
Description: Allows the solicitation and assistance to disadvantage businesses to participate in the procurement process and performance of City contracts.

FINANCING AND LOAN PROGRAMS

38141 ■ Blue Rock Capital
3524 Silverside Rd., Ste. 35B
 Wilmington, DE 19810
Preferred Investment Size: $250,000 to $2,000,000. **Industry Preferences:** Internet specific, semiconductors and other electronics, communications and media, consumer related, computer software and services, and computer hardware.

INCUBATORS/RESEARCH AND TECHNOLOGY PARKS

38142 ■ Delaware Kitchen Share
10 E Ave.
 New Castle, DE 19720
Free: 866-294-2046
Co. E-mail: info@dekitchenshare.com
URL: http://www.dekitchenshare.com
Contact: Antoinette Stanley, Founder
Facebook: www.facebook.com/DelawareKitchenShare
Description: Culinary incubator supporting startup food businesses. **Founded:** 2010.

38143 ■ Delaware Technology Park Inc. (DTP)
1 Innovation Way
 Newark, DE 19711
Ph: (302)452-1100
URL: http://deltechpark.org
Contact: J. Michael Bowman, President
Facebook: www.facebook.com/delawaretechpark
X (Twitter): x.com/deltechpark
Description: Provides development-stage life science, information technology, advanced materials and renewable energy companies with access to resources needed to accelerate their success. **Founded:** 1992.

38144 ■ Emerging Enterprise Center (EEC)
920 Justison St.
 Wilmington, DE 19801
Ph: (302)737-4343
Co. E-mail: info@eecincubator.com
URL: http://eecincubator.com
Facebook: www.facebook.com/emergingenterprisecenter
Linkedin: www.linkedin.com/company/emerging-enterprise-center
X (Twitter): x.com/EECincubator
Instagram: www.instagram.com/eecincubator
YouTube: www.youtube.com/channel/UCe4GjKBVHJ1HwZpCJBuF5mQ
Description: Provides affordable office space and support services to startup companies, connecting businesses with a comprehensive network of partners, mentors, bankers, attorneys and accountants so that early stage businesses can focus on growth and development. **Founded:** 2008.

38145 ■ The Menagerie LLC
PO Box 802
 Greenwood, DE 19950
Ph: (302)265-8845
Co. E-mail: tmllc@icloud.com
URL: http://www.the-menagerie-llc.com
Facebook: www.facebook.com/TheMenagerieLLC
Description: Culinary incubator offering kitchen space for food entrepreneurs wanting to expand their brand.

LEGISLATIVE ASSISTANCE

38146 ■ State of Delaware Senate Small Business Committee
Legislative Hall
 411 Legislative Ave.
 Dover, DE 19901
Ph: (302)744-4298
Co. E-mail: lc_reception@delaware.gov
URL: http://legis.delaware.gov/LIS/LIS147.NSF/*/3E6C4C7B89FBBBAC85257811006D9509/?opendocument&nav=Senate
Contact: Harris B. McDowell, Chairman

District of Columbia

FEDERAL GOVERNMENT FINANCING PROGRAM

38147 ■ U.S. International Development Finance Corporation (DFC)
1100 New York Ave. NW
  Washington, DC 20527
Ph: (202)336-8400
Co. E-mail: info@dfc.gov
URL: http://www.dfc.gov
Contact: Scott A. Nathan, Chief Executive Officer
Facebook: www.facebook.com/DFCgov
Linkedin: www.linkedin.com/company/dfcgov
X (Twitter): x.com/DFCgov
Instagram: www.instagram.com/dfcgov
YouTube: www.youtube.com/channel/UCX6mvT0jM3R-1iuliisYXNg
Founded: 2019. **Industry Preferences:** Healthcare; technology; critical infrastructure; energy.

MINORITY BUSINESS DEVELOPMENT AGENCY

38148 ■ MBDA Business Centers
1401 Constitution Ave. NW
  Washington, DC 20230
URL: http://www.mbda.gov/business-resources/business-centers
Description: Provides assistance to small and minority businesses in New Mexico.

ASSOCIATIONS AND OTHER ORGANIZATIONS

38149 ■ Association of Fundraising Professionals Washington DC Metro Area Chapter
1717 K St., Ste. 900
  Washington, DC 20006
Ph: (202)845-7450
Co. E-mail: info@afpdc.org
URL: http://community.afpglobal.org/afpdc/home
Contact: Lori Woehrle, President
Facebook: www.facebook.com/AFPWashingtonDC
Linkedin: www.linkedin.com/company/afp-dc
X (Twitter): x.com/afpdc
Description: Supports fundraising professionals in the Washington DC area. **Founded:** 1965.

38150 ■ District of Columbia Small Business Development Center (DCSBDC)
2600 6th St. NW Rm. 128
  Washington, DC 20059
Ph: (202)806-1551
Fax: (202)806-1777
Co. E-mail: dcsbdc@aedc.net
URL: http://dcsbdc.org
Contact: Carl E. Brown, Jr., Director
E-mail: carl.brown@howard.edu
Facebook: www.facebook.com/DCSBDC
Linkedin: www.linkedin.com/company/dc-small-business-development-center-network
X (Twitter): x.com/DCSBDC
Description: Provides free management and technical assistance and affordable training in all phases of business development to District of Columbia based small businesses. **Geographic Preference:** State.

38151 ■ Entrepreneurs' Organization - Washington, DC Chapter (EO DC)
Washington, DC
Co. E-mail: jkopp@eodcnetwork.org
URL: http://www.eonetwork.org/dc
Facebook: www.facebook.com/EODCchapter
Description: Provides local resources to members which includes networking events, mentorship, live forums, and leadership development. **Founded:** 1991.

38152 ■ Mid-Atlantic Venture Association (MAVA)
1400 K St. NW, No. 1100
  Washington, DC 20005
Co. E-mail: mava@mava.org
URL: http://www.mava.org
Linkedin: www.linkedin.com/company/morethanventure
Description: Creates a forum for business interaction between investors, service providers, and entrepreneurs in the Mid-Atlantic region. Offers programs, information, and forums designed to stimulate revenue and company growth, facilitate deal flow, and foster relationships among entrepreneurs, investors, strategic partners, and customers. **Founded:** 1987.

38153 ■ Monte Jade Science and Technology Association of Greater Washington
1015 15th St. NW, Ste. 1050
  Washington, DC 20005
Co. E-mail: mjdc168@gmail.com
URL: http://www.montejadedc.org
Contact: Terry Hsiao, Contact
E-mail: terry.hsiao@hookmobile.com
Facebook: www.facebook.com/MonteJadeDC
X (Twitter): x.com/montejadedc
Description: Members include executives, managers, and directors leading, operating, and developing science and technology firms in the Greater Washington area. Seeks to provide the Asian community in Washington DC with resources for starting, funding, and growing high technology business.

38154 ■ National Advisory Council, Small Business Administration (NAC)
Small Business Administration
  409 3rd St. SW
  Washington, DC 20416
Free: 800-827-5722
URL: http://www.sba.gov/about-sba/organization
Founded: 1953.

SMALL BUSINESS DEVELOPMENT CENTERS

38155 ■ Aspen Network for Developing Entrepreneurs (ANDE)
2300 N St. NW, Ste. 700
  Washington, DC 20037-1122
Ph: (202)736-2298
Co. E-mail: ande.info@aspeninst.org
URL: http://www.andeglobal.org
Contact: Richenda van Leeuwen, Executive Director
Facebook: www.facebook.com/AspenANDE
Linkedin: www.linkedin.com/company/aspenande
X (Twitter): x.com/aspenande
YouTube: www.youtube.com/channel/UCJIK4o_8QIaK3P5B9JuvlUA
Description: A global membership network of organizations that advance entrepreneurship in emerging markets. Provides financial, educational, and business support services to small and growing businesses. **Founded:** 2009.

38156 ■ District of Columbia Small Business Development Center at University of District of Columbia (DC SBDC)
2600 6th St. NW, Rm. 128
  Washington, DC 20059
Ph: (202)806-1550
Co. E-mail: info@dcsbdc.org
URL: http://dcsbdc.org
Contact: Carl E. Brown, Jr., Executive Director
Facebook: www.facebook.com/DCSBDC
Linkedin: www.linkedin.com/company/dc-small-business-development-center-network
X (Twitter): x.com/DCSBDC
Description: Represents and promotes the small business sector. Provides management assistance to current and prospective small business owners. Helps to improve management skills and expand the products and services of members. **Geographic Preference:** Local.

38157 ■ National Small Business Development Center Advisory Board
409 3rd St., SW
  Washington, DC 20416
URL: http://www.sba.gov/document/support-sbdc-advisory-board-member-profiles
Description: Provides assistance to small businesses and aspiring entrepreneurs throughout the United States and its territories.

38158 ■ Small Business Administration District Advisory Councils
US Small Business Administation
  409 3rd St. SW
  Washington, DC 20416
URL: http://www.sba.gov/about-sba/organization
Description: Provides information on advisory committees, rules around the advisory committee establishment, committee membership and operations.

STATE LISTINGS   District of Columbia ■ 38170

38159 ■ Washington, D.C. Small Business Development Center at Howard University (DC SBDC)
Rm 128, 2600 6th St. NW
Washington, DC 20059
Ph: (202)806-1550
Co. E-mail: info@dcsbdc.org
URL: http://dcsbdc.org
Contact: Carl E. E. Brown, Jr., Executive Director
E-mail: carl.brown@howard.edu
Facebook: www.facebook.com/DCSBDC
Linkedin: www.linkedin.com/company/dc-small-business-development-center-network
X (Twitter): x.com/DCSBDC
Description: Represents and promotes the small business sector. Provides management assistance to current and prospective small business owners. Helps to improve management skills and expand the products and services of members. **Founded:** 1979. **Geographic Preference:** Local.

SMALL BUSINESS ASSISTANCE PROGRAMS

38160 ■ District of Columbia Office of the Deputy Mayor Planning and Economic Development (DMPED)
John A. Wilson Bldg.
1350 Pennsylvania Ave. NW, Ste. 317
Washington, DC 20004
Ph: (202)727-6365
Fax: (202)727-6703
Co. E-mail: dmped.eom@dc.gov
URL: http://dmped.dc.gov
Contact: Sharon Carney, Chief of Staff
E-mail: sharon.carney@dc.gov
Facebook: www.facebook.com/DCDMPED
Linkedin: www.linkedin.com/company-beta/22338462
X (Twitter): x.com/dmpeddc
Instagram: www.instagram.com/dmped
Description: Works to attract new businesses and retain existing ones. The Financial Services Division offers SBA 503/504 loans and other loan programs. The Small Business Incubator Facility Program provides affordable facilities and management assistance to new and small businesses. The Neighborhood Commercial Services Division provides loans and technical assistance to encourage the revitalization of neighborhood commercial districts.

38161 ■ Government of the District of Columbia (DSLBD) - Department of Small and Local Business Development
441 4th St. NW, Ste. 850 N
Washington, DC 20001
Ph: (202)727-3900
Fax: (202)654-6032
Co. E-mail: dslbd@dc.gov
URL: http://dslbd.dc.gov
Contact: Kristi C. Whitfield, Director
Facebook: www.facebook.com/smallbizdc
Linkedin: www.linkedin.com/company/dc-department-of-small-local-business-development-dslbd
X (Twitter): x.com/SmallBizDC
Instagram: www.instagram.com/smallbizdc
YouTube: www.youtube.com/channel/UCEMuNh_ZSIKG9ADq2Iz-kCA/featured
Description: The mission of the Department of Small and Local Business Development is to foster economic growth and the development of local, small, and disadvantaged business enterprises through supportive legislation, business development programs, and agency and public/private contract compliance.

SCORE OFFICES

38162 ■ SCORE - Washington, DC
409 3rd St., SW Ste. 100A
Washington, DC 20002
Ph: (202)619-1000
URL: http://www.score.org/washingtondc
Facebook: www.facebook.com/SCOREWashingtonDC
Linkedin: www.linkedin.com/company/score-mentors-washington-dc
X (Twitter): x.com/DCSCORE
Description: Provides professional guidance and information to maximize the success of existing and emerging small businesses. Offers business counseling and workshops. **Founded:** 1964. **Publications:** *SCORE Today.* **Awards:** SCORE Washington DC Client of the Year (Annual). **Geographic Preference:** Regional.

BETTER BUSINESS BUREAUS

38163 ■ Better Business Bureau Serving Metro Washington DC and Eastern Pennsylvania
1411 K St. NW, 10th Fl.
Washington, DC 20005
Ph: (202)393-8000
Fax: (202)393-1198
URL: http://www.bbb.org/local-bbb/bbb-serving-metro-washington-dc-metro-philadelphia-and-eastern-pennsylvania
Facebook: www.facebook.com/BBBservingMetroDCandEasternPA
Linkedin: www.linkedin.com/company/bbbdcpa
X (Twitter): x.com/BBB_DCPA
YouTube: www.youtube.com/channel/UCHzIvqkQ_po71d4uUWLkp0A
Description: Business and professional. Helps the local community to make a better place to live. Promotes integrity and business ethics through self-regulation in the marketplace. **Founded:** 1920. **Publications:** *BBB Rules of Arbitration*; *BBB Rules of Mediation*; *Memberline* (Periodic). **Geographic Preference:** Regional.

CHAMBERS OF COMMERCE

38164 ■ *Alliance Newsletter*
1518 K St. NW 2nd Fl.
Washington, DC 20005
Ph: (202)638-1526
Fax: (202)638-4664
Co. E-mail: info@naeh.org
URL: http://endhomelessness.org
Contact: Shalom Mulkey, President
URL(s): endhomelessness.org/help-end-homelessness/follow-the-alliance
Description: Contains latest news and information on Watertown Belmont Chamber of Commerce. **Availability:** Print.

38165 ■ Capitol Hill Association of Merchants and Professionals (CHAMPS)
PO Box 15486
Washington, DC 20003
Ph: (202)547-7788
Co. E-mail: champs@capitolhill.org
URL: http://capitolhill.org
Contact: Brad Johnson, President
Facebook: www.facebook.com/CHAMPS.dc
X (Twitter): x.com/champsdc
Instagram: www.instagram.com/champs.dc
Description: Advocates for businesses and the community's economic development in Washington, D.C. Provides an online directory, events calendar, newsletters, blog, and networking opportunities.

38166 ■ DC Chamber of Commerce (DCCC)
1133 21st St. NW, Ste. M200
Washington, DC 20036
Ph: (202)347-7201
Co. E-mail: contact@dcchamber.org
URL: http://dcchamber.org
Contact: Angela Franco, President
E-mail: afranco@dcchamber.org
Facebook: www.facebook.com/DCCofCommerce
Linkedin: www.linkedin.com/company/dc-chamber-of-commerce
X (Twitter): x.com/dcchamber
Instagram: www.instagram.com/dcchamber
Description: Promotes business and community development in Washington, DC. **Founded:** 1956. **Publications:** *DC Chamber of Commerce-- Membership Directory*. **Geographic Preference:** Local.

38167 ■ National Association of Small Business Contractors (NASBC)
700 12th St. NW, Ste. 700
Washington, DC 20005
Free: 888-861-9290
Co. E-mail: notify@americansbcc.org
URL: http://www.nasbc.org
Contact: Cris Young, President
Description: Serves and advances the interests of small business contractors. Seeks to establish opportunities for small business owners to meet with state and federal agencies, prime contractors, potential teaming partners and procurement experts. Strives to create a strong and respected voice for advocacy in support of small business' interests. **Geographic Preference:** National.

38168 ■ National Black Chamber of Commerce (NBCC)
601 Pennsylvania Ave. NW, Ste. 900, S Bldg.
Washington, DC 20004
Ph: (202)220-3060
Co. E-mail: info@nationalbcc.org
URL: http://www.nationalbcc.org
Contact: Charles H. DeBow, III, President
Facebook: www.facebook.com/NationalBCC
X (Twitter): x.com/NationalBCC
YouTube: www.youtube.com/user/Nationalbcc
Description: Represents Black owned businesses. Seeks to empower and sustain African American communities through entrepreneurship and capitalistic activity. Provides advocacy, training and education to Black communities. **Founded:** 1993. **Publications:** *The Small Business Resource Guide*. **Geographic Preference:** Multinational; Local.

MINORITY BUSINESS ASSISTANCE PROGRAMS

38169 ■ Government of the District of Columbia (DSLBD) - Department of Small and Local Business Development
441 4th St. NW, Ste. 850 N
Washington, DC 20001
Ph: (202)727-3900
Fax: (202)654-6032
Co. E-mail: dslbd@dc.gov
URL: http://dslbd.dc.gov
Contact: Kristi C. Whitfield, Director
Facebook: www.facebook.com/smallbizdc
Linkedin: www.linkedin.com/company/dc-department-of-small-local-business-development-dslbd
X (Twitter): x.com/SmallBizDC
Instagram: www.instagram.com/smallbizdc
YouTube: www.youtube.com/channel/UCEMuNh_ZSIKG9ADq2Iz-kCA/featured
Description: The mission of the Department of Small and Local Business Development is to foster economic growth and the development of local, small, and disadvantaged business enterprises through supportive legislation, business development programs, and agency and public/private contract compliance.

38170 ■ Washington DC Women's Business Center (DCWBC)
740 15th St. NW, 4th Fl.
Washington, DC 20005
Ph: (202)393-8307
Co. E-mail: info@dcwbc.org
URL: http://www.dcwbc.org
Contact: LaToria Brent, Specialist
Facebook: www.facebook.com/TheDCWBC
X (Twitter): x.com/thedcwbc
Instagram: www.instagram.com/thedcwbc
Pinterest: www.pinterest.com/dcwbc
Description: Provides business development and support for women-owned businesses in the field of federal procurements. **Founded:** 2010.

FINANCING AND LOAN PROGRAMS

38171 ▪ Core Capital Partners
1233 20th St. NW, Ste. 460
Washington, DC 20036
Ph: (202)589-0090
Fax: (202)589-0091
Co. E-mail: nalmasi@core-capital.com
URL: http://www.core-capital.com
Contact: Randy Klueger, Chief Financial Officer
E-mail: rklueger@core-capital.com
Description: Firm provides early stage ventures focusing on seed or series A rounds, small to mid sized, emerging growth companies. **Founded:** 1999. **Industry Preferences:** Firm provides early stage ventures focusing on seed or series A rounds, small to mid sized, emerging growth companies.

38172 ▪ MIT Alumni Angels of Washington DC (MITAADC)
Washington, DC
Co. E-mail: mitalumniangelsdc@gmail.com
URL: http://www.mitalumniangelsdc.com
Contact: Terry Hsiao, Director
Description: Connects MIT alumni investors with entrepreneurs in the Washington DC area. **Founded:** 2018.

38173 ▪ Oxantium Ventures
2600 Virgina Ave. NW, Ste. 512
Washington, DC 20037
Co. E-mail: info@oxantium.com
URL: http://oxantium.com
Contact: Dr. Richard Wirt, Contact
Description: Invests in a diversified range of companies at the seed, early, and growth stages. **Preferred Investment Size:** $2-6 million.

PROCUREMENT ASSISTANCE PROGRAMS

38174 ▪ Procurement Center Representative (PCR)
409 3rd St. SW, 2nd Fl.
Washington, DC 20416
URL: http://www.sba.gov/federal-contracting/counseling-help/procurement-center-representative-directory
Contact: Michael Baltzgar, Contact
E-mail: michael.baltzgar@sba.gov
Description: Covers activities for Department of Health and Human Services (Washington, DC), Army Corps of Engineers (Baltimore, MD), Social Security Administration (Baltimore, MD).

38175 ▪ U.S. Small Business Administration - Office of Government Contracting & Business Development
409 Third St. SW, Ste. 8000
Washington, DC 20416
Ph: (202)205-6459
URL: http://www.sba.gov/about-sba/sba-locations/headquarters-offices/office-government-contracting-business-development
Contact: Larry Stubblefield, Officer
Description: Covers activities for NASA, Goddard Space Flight Center (Greenbelt, MD), NASA Headquarters (Washington, DC), LABCOM Adelphi Lab Center (Adelphi, MD), and Navy Surface Warfare Center (Indian Head, MD).

INCUBATORS/RESEARCH AND TECHNOLOGY PARKS

38176 ▪ AGORA Partnerships
1314 Massachusetts Ave. SE
Washington, DC 20003
Ph: (505)227-0270
Co. E-mail: info@agora2030.org
URL: http://agora2030.org
Facebook: www.facebook.com/AgoraPartnerships
Linkedin: www.linkedin.com/company/agora-partnerships
X (Twitter): x.com/Agora2030
Instagram: www.instagram.com/agora_2030
YouTube: www.youtube.com/user/agorapartnerships
Description: Business accelerator providing high-potential, early- and growth-stage companies solving social and environmental challenges with in-depth consulting support and access to mentors, investors, and a community of peers. **Founded:** 2005.

38177 ▪ EatsPlace
3607 Georgia Ave. NW
Washington, DC 20010
Ph: (202)656-3287
Co. E-mail: info@eatsplace.com
URL: http://eatsplace.com
Contact: Katy Chang, Founder
Facebook: www.facebook.com/EatsPlace
X (Twitter): x.com/eatsplace
Instagram: www.instagram.com/eatsplace
Pinterest: www.pinterest.com/eatsplace
Description: A food incubator and accelerator supporting food startups. **Founded:** 2012.

38178 ▪ Forum Ventures
Washington, DC
URL: http://www.forumvc.com
Contact: Mike Cardamon, Chief Executive Officer
Description: Works closely with early stage enterprise SaaS companies to help them scale. We are passionate about building a strong community around entrepreneurship and disruptive technology that changes the way we work across every industry.

38179 ▪ Halcyon
3400 Prospect St. NW
Washington, DC 20007
Ph: (202)796-4240
Co. E-mail: inquiry@halcyonhouse.org
URL: http://www.halcyonhouse.org
Contact: Kate Goodall, Chief Executive Officer
Facebook: www.facebook.com/pg/halcyoninspires
X (Twitter): x.com/HalcyonInspires
Instagram: www.instagram.com/halcyoninspires
YouTube: www.youtube.com/halcyoninspires
Description: Supports innovators and creators who seek to make the world a better place. Offers an incubator and arts lab.

38180 ▪ Mess Hall
703 Edgewood St. NE
Washington, DC 20017
Ph: (202)248-0230
URL: http://messhalldc.com
Facebook: www.facebook.com/MessHallDC
X (Twitter): x.com/MessHallDC
Instagram: www.instagram.com/messhalldc
Description: A culinary incubator supporting up-and-coming food entrepreneurs by providing commercial kitchens, combined with institutional knowledge and extraordinary opportunities. **Founded:** 2014.

38181 ▪ Potential Energy DC (PEDC)
Washington, DC
URL: http://www.potentialenergydc.org
Contact: Dave McCarthy, Executive Director
E-mail: dave@potentialenergydc.org
Linkedin: www.linkedin.com/company/potential-energy-dc
Description: Incubator for clean energy startups.

38182 ▪ Union Kitchen
1369 New York Ave. NE
Washington, DC 20002
Ph: (202)792-7850
Co. E-mail: info@unionkitchendc.com
URL: http://www.unionkitchen.com
Contact: Carson Garfield, Member
Facebook: www.facebook.com/UnionKitchenDC
Linkedin: www.linkedin.com/company/union-kitchen-dc
Instagram: www.instagram.com/unionkitchendc
Description: A business incubator for small food businesses, launching small businesses to success by saving time, augmenting sales, reducing costs, and helping entrepreneurs gain the edge, savvy, and market share to grow. **Founded:** 2012.

LEGISLATIVE ASSISTANCE

38183 ▪ Council of the District of Columbia (CDC)
1350 Pennsylvania Ave. NW
Washington, DC 20004
Ph: (202)724-8000
URL: http://dccouncil.gov
Contact: Phil Mendelson, Chairman
E-mail: pmendelson@dccouncil.gov
Facebook: www.facebook.com/councilofdc
X (Twitter): x.com/councilofdc
YouTube: www.youtube.com/channel/UCXTTGvPOwbn3QSov4FaQU-w

PUBLICATIONS

38184 ▪ *Washington Business Journal*
120 W Morehead St.
Charlotte, NC 28202
Co. E-mail: circhelp@bizjournals.com
URL: http://www.acbj.com
Contact: Mike Olivieri, Executive Vice President
URL(s): www.bizjournals.com/washington
Linkedin: www.linkedin.com/company/washington-business-journal
X (Twitter): x.com/WBJonline
Instagram: www.instagram.com/wbjnewsroom
Released: Weekly **Price:** $70, for Digital Access or Digital & Print; $245, for Nationwide Access; $180, for next year; $4, for digital. **Description:** Metropolitan business newspaper (tabloid). **Availability:** Print; PDF; Download; Online.

PUBLISHERS

38185 ▪ Friends of the Earth (FOE)
1101 15th St. NW 11th Fl.
Washington, DC 20005
Ph: (202)783-7400
Fax: (202)783-0444
URL: http://foe.org
Contact: Erich Pica, President
E-mail: epica@foe.org
Facebook: www.facebook.com/foe.us
X (Twitter): x.com/foe_us
Instagram: www.instagram.com/foe_us
YouTube: www.youtube.com/user/FriendsoftheEarthUS
Description: Dedicated to protecting the planet from environmental disaster; preserving biological and ethnic diversity; empowers citizens to have an effective voice in environmental decision; promotes use of tax dollars to protect the environment; other interests include groundwater and ozone protection, toxic waste cleanup, and reforming the World Bank and sustainable development which addressed the need to reduce over-consumption in the U.S. **Scope:** Energy conservation, water, coal, oil, gas, nuclear energy, synthetic fuels, oceans and coasts, and agricultural resources, including studies on surface mining, biotechnology, rural land, groundwater protection, water conservation, protection of natural resources internationally, nuclear waste storage, and nuclear weapons testing and production. Serves as a national information center on federal and international appropriations and tax incentives for conservation. **Publications:** *Friends of the Earth Newsmagazine* (Quarterly). **Geographic Preference:** Local; National.

38186 ▪ Gallaudet University Press
800 Florida Ave. NE
Washington, DC 20002-3695
Ph: (202)651-5488
Fax: (202)651-5489
Co. E-mail: gupress@gallaudet.edu
URL: http://gupress.gallaudet.edu
Facebook: www.facebook.com/GallaudetUniversityPress
X (Twitter): x.com/gallaudetpress
Instagram: www.instagram.com/gallaudetpress
YouTube: www.youtube.com/channel/UCirJP-oRh4ftYT1RH2sRwlQ

Description: Publishes reference books, biographies for and about deaf and hard of hearing people, deaf culture and deaf studies. Accepts unsolicited manuscripts. Reaches market through direct mail, reviews, listings, wholesalers and distributors. **Publications:** *Sign Language Studies (SLS)* (Quarterly).

38187 ■ International Council for Small Business (ICSB)
2201 G St. NW Funger Hall, Ste. 315
Washington, DC 20052
Ph: (202)994-0704
Fax: (202)994-4930
Co. E-mail: info@icsb.org
URL: http://icsb.org
Contact: Dr. Ayman El Tarabishy, President
E-mail: ayman@gwu.edu
Facebook: www.facebook.com/icsb.org
Linkedin: www.linkedin.com/company/international-council-for-small-business-icsb-
X (Twitter): x.com/icsb
Instagram: www.instagram.com/icsbglobal
YouTube: www.youtube.com/channel/UCvWy8wfz5nMk9a6yr5ZS0hQ

Description: Promotes and supports the interests and advancement of small businesses globally. **Founded:** 1955. **Publications:** *Journal of Small Business Management (JSBM)* (6/year). **Geographic Preference:** Multinational.

38188 ■ International Franchise Association (IFA) - Library
1900 K St., NW, Ste. 700
Washington, DC 20006
Ph: (202)628-8000
Co. E-mail: info@franchise.org
URL: http://www.franchise.org
Contact: Matthew Haller, President
E-mail: mhaller@franchise.org
Facebook: www.facebook.com/IFA.DC
Linkedin: www.linkedin.com/company/international-franchise-association
X (Twitter): x.com/franchising411
Instagram: www.instagram.com/franchising411
YouTube: www.youtube.com/user/ifadc

Description: Firms in 100 countries utilizing the franchise method of distribution for goods and services in all industries. **Scope:** Franchise. **Founded:** 1960. **Holdings:** Figures not available. **Publications:** *Franchises Directory; Franchising World* (6/year; Annual); *International Franchise Association--Franchise Opportunities Guide* (Semiannual). **Educational Activities:** International Franchise Expo (IFE) (Annual); IFA Legal Symposium (Annual); IFA Annual Convention (Annual). **Awards:** Don Debolt Franchising Scholarship Program (Annual); Franchise Law Diversity Scholarship Awards (Annual); IFA Entrepreneur of the Year (Annual); Bonny LeVine Award (Annual); IFA Hall of Fame Award (Annual). **Geographic Preference:** Multinational.

38189 ■ Kiplinger Washington Editors Inc.
1100 13th St. NW, Ste. 1000
Washington, DC 20005
Ph: (202)887-6400
Free: 800-544-0155
Co. E-mail: sub.services@kiplinger.com
URL: http://www.kiplinger.com
Contact: W. M. Kiplinger, Founder
Facebook: www.facebook.com/KiplingerPersonalFinance
Linkedin: www.linkedin.com/company/kiplinger-washington-editors
X (Twitter): x.com/kiplinger
Instagram: www.instagram.com/kiplingerfinance
YouTube: www.youtube.com/user/kiplinger

Description: Publisher of personal finance and business forecasting books for both professionals and the public. **Founded:** 1920. **Publications:** *The Agriculture Letter* (Bimonthly); *The Kiplinger Tax Letter* (Biweekly); *The Kiplinger Letter* (Weekly); *Kiplinger's Retirement Report* (Monthly); *Kiplinger Finance & Forecasts (KFF)* (Monthly); *Kiplinger's Personal Finance* (Monthly); *Changing Times Financial Services Directory*.

38190 ■ National Association for Business Economics (NABE)
1020 19th St. NW Ste. 550
Washington, DC 20036
Ph: (202)463-6223
Fax: (202)463-6239
Co. E-mail: nabe@nabe.com
URL: http://www.nabe.com
Contact: Paul Volcker, President
Facebook: www.facebook.com/national-association-for-business-economics-48820424893
Linkedin: www.linkedin.com/company/national-association-for-business-economics
X (Twitter): twitter.com/business_econ

Description: Maintains placement service for members; conducts several seminars per year. Maintains speakers' bureau. **Founded:** 1959. **Publications:** *Business Economics: Designed to Serve the Needs of People Who Use Economics in Their Work* (Quarterly); *Nabe Outlook* (Quarterly); *Careers in Business Economics*; *Salary Survey* (Biennial); *National Association for Business Economics--Membership Directory*; *NABE News* (Quarterly); *NABE Policy Survey* (Semiannual); *Business Economics--Membership Directory Issue*; *Business Economics* (Quarterly). **Educational Activities:** National Association Business Economics Annual Meeting (Annual). **Awards:** Adolph G. Abramson Award (Annual). **Geographic Preference:** National.

38191 ■ National Small Business Association (NSBA)
1156 15th St. NW, Ste. 502
Washington, DC 20005
Free: 800-345-6728
Co. E-mail: info@nsba.biz
URL: http://www.nsba.biz
Contact: Todd McCracken, President
Facebook: www.facebook.com/NSBAAdvocate
Linkedin: www.linkedin.com/company/2061777
X (Twitter): x.com/NSBAAdvocate

Description: Small businesses including manufacturing, wholesale, retail, service, and other firms. Works to advocate at the federal level on behalf of smaller businesses. **Founded:** 1937. **Educational Activities:** Small Business Meetup Day. **Awards:** Lewis A. Shattuck Small Business Advocate of the Year Award (Annual). **Geographic Preference:** National.

38192 ■ U.S. Small Business Administration (SBA)
409 3rd St. SW
Washington, DC 20416
Ph: (202)205-6766
Free: 800-827-5722
Fax: (202)205-7064
Co. E-mail: answerdesk@sba.gov
URL: http://www.sba.gov
Facebook: www.facebook.com/SBAgov
Linkedin: www.linkedin.com/company/us-small-business-administration
X (Twitter): x.com/sbagov
Instagram: www.instagram.com/sbagov
YouTube: www.youtube.com/user/sba

Description: Continues to help small business owners and entrepreneurs pursue the american dream. **Founded:** 1953. **Publications:** *Directory of Operating Small Business Investment Companies* (Semiannual); *www.BusinessLaw.gov*; *SBA Online*; *U.S. Business Advisor*. **Awards:** U.S. SBA Entrepreneurial Success Award (Annual); U.S. SBA Small Business Advocates of the Year (Annual); U.S. SBA Small Business Exporter of the Year (Annual); U.S. SBA National Small Business Person of the Year (Annual); Phoenix Award for Small Business Disaster Recovery (Annual); Phoenix Award for Outstanding Contributions to Disaster Recovery (Annual).

VENTURE CAPITAL FIRM

38193 ■ Humble Ventures
Washington, DC
URL: http://humble.vc
Contact: Ajit Verghese, Co-Founder
X (Twitter): x.com/humbleventures

Description: Venture capital firm focusing on startup businesses owned by women and minority groups.

38194 ■ Potomac Equity Partners
5111 Yuma Pl. NW, Ste. 200
Washington, DC 20016
Ph: (202)827-6050
Co. E-mail: general@potomacequitypartners.com
URL: http://www.potomacequitypartners.com
Contact: Chris Blythe, Partner
Linkedin: www.linkedin.com/company/potomac-equity-partners

Description: Private equity investment firm specializing in government-regulated sectors in North America. **Founded:** 2012. **Investment Policies:** Small to mid-market; enterpise values from $10,000,000 to $150,000,000. **Industry Preferences:** Business services; education and training; healthcare; information services; software and technology.

38195 ■ Revolution
1717 Rhode Island Ave. NW, Ste. 1000
Washington, DC 20036
Ph: (202)776-1400
URL: http://revolution.com
Contact: John Sabin, Chief Financial Officer
X (Twitter): x.com/revolution
Instagram: www.instagram.com/revolutionllc

Description: Builds disruptive, innovative companies that offer choice, convenience, and control for consumers and businesses. . **Founded:** 1985. **Investment Policies:** Companies attacking conventional industries with innovative products and services; entrepreneurs who want to change the world. .

38196 ■ Village Capital
1101 K St. NW, Ste. 920
Washington, DC 20005
Co. E-mail: info@vilcap.com
URL: http://vilcap.com
Contact: Allie Burns, Chief Executive Officer
X (Twitter): x.com/villagecapital
Instagram: www.instagram.com/villagecapital

Description: Finds, trains, and invests in entrepreneurs solving real-world problems. **Founded:** 2009.

Florida

ASSOCIATIONS AND OTHER ORGANIZATIONS

38197 ■ Association of Fundraising Professionals Miami Chapter
3090 Alton Rd.
Miami Beach, FL 33140
Co. E-mail: info@afpmiami.org
URL: http://community.afpglobal.org/miami/home
Contact: Jaime Bayo, President
E-mail: jaime@acespace.org
Facebook: www.facebook.com/AFPMiami
X (Twitter): x.com/AFPMiami

Description: Fosters the development and growth of fundraising professionals. Promotes high ethical standards in the fundraising profession. Provides training opportunities for fundraising professionals. **Founded:** 1975. **Geographic Preference:** Local.

38198 ■ Association of Fundraising Professionals Treasure Coast Chapter
PO Box 543
Palm City, FL 34991
Co. E-mail: info@afptreasurecoast.org
URL: http://www.afptreasurecoast.org
Contact: Elisabeth Glynn, Director
E-mail: eglynn@unitedwaymartin.org
X (Twitter): x.com/AFP_TC

Description: Fosters the development and growth of fundraising professionals. Promotes high ethical standards in the fundraising profession. Provides training opportunities for fundraising professionals. **Founded:** 1994. **Geographic Preference:** Local.

38199 ■ BNI Southwest Florida
c/o Terri West
7282 55th Ave. E, Ste. 141
Bradenton, FL 34203
Ph: (941)545-3102
Free: 855-264-2673
URL: http://bniswfl.com/en-US/index
Contact: Terri West, Contact
Facebook: www.facebook.com/BNIswfl

Description: Provides both men and women a structured environment for the development and exchange of quality business referrals. Offers members the opportunity to share ideas and contacts. **Geographic Preference:** Local.

38200 ■ Business Brokers of Florida (BBF)
6122 US Hwy. 98
Sebring, FL 33876
Ph: (863)655-3085
Fax: (863)655-2670
Co. E-mail: support@bbms.biz
URL: http://www.bbfmls.com
Contact: Joe Shemansky, President

Description: Represents professionals and firms in business brokerage, mergers and acquisitions. Provides business brokers education, conferences, professional designations, and networking opportunities in Florida. Works to become a leader in the exchange of business referrals, and to create professional relationships with successful business transaction advisors. **Founded:** 1985. **Geographic Preference:** State.

38201 ■ Business Development Board of Martin County (BDBMC)
1002 SE Monterey Commons Blvd., Ste. 207
Stuart, FL 34996
Ph: (772)221-1380
Co. E-mail: info@bdbmc.org
URL: http://bdbmc.org
Contact: Jeff Leslie, President
Facebook: www.facebook.com/BDBMC
Linkedin: www.linkedin.com/company/bdbmc
YouTube: www.youtube.com/user/BDBMartinCounty

Description: Promotes balanced and orderly economic growth in Martin County by retaining and assisting existing businesses and attracting desirable new businesses while preserving quality of life, and expanding educational and employment opportunities. **Founded:** 1991. **Geographic Preference:** Local.

38202 ■ Business Law Section of the Florida Bar
651 E Jefferson St.
Tallahassee, FL 32399
Ph: (850)561-5630
Fax: (850)561-5825
Co. E-mail: flabizlaw@gmail.com
URL: http://flabizlaw.org
Contact: Kacy Donlon, Chairman
E-mail: kdonlon@jclaw.com
Facebook: www.facebook.com/flabizlaw/wall
X (Twitter): x.com/FlaBizLaw

Description: Furthers the development of business law, educating section members in business law and related professional responsibilities. Improves the practice of both in-house and outside business counsel through seminars, legislation, and committee activity in a wide variety of areas, such as high technology, small business, bankruptcy, banking, and commercial law. **Geographic Preference:** State.

38203 ■ Business Network International, Central West Florida (BNI WCF)
3430 Torigdon Way
Charlotte, NC 28277
Free: 855-264-2673
URL: http://bniwcf.com/en-US/index
Contact: Nola Moon, Managing Director
E-mail: nolamoon@bni.com

Description: Provides both men and women a structured environment for the development and exchange of quality business referrals. Offers members the opportunity to share ideas and contacts. **Geographic Preference:** Local.

38204 ■ Business Network International Miami Dade
3430 Torigdon Way
Charlotte, NC 28277
Free: 855-264-2673
URL: http://bnimiami.com/en-US/findachapter
Contact: Ron Leonard, Managing Director
E-mail: ronleonard@bni.com
X (Twitter): x.com/BNIMiamiDade
Instagram: www.instagram.com/bnimiamidade
YouTube: www.youtube.com/channel/UCOBk-CsMiKdMBQ9j3EUnJ-A

Description: Provides both men and women a structured environment for the development and exchange of quality business referrals. Offers members the opportunity to share ideas and contacts. **Geographic Preference:** Local.

38205 ■ Central & North Florida Business Travel Association (CNFBTA)
9150 International Dr.
Orlando, FL 32803-5127
Co. E-mail: membership@cnfbta.org
URL: http://cnfbta.org
Contact: Darren LAppanna, Co-President

Description: Represents travel managers and providers. Promotes the value of the travel manager in meeting corporate travel needs and financial goals. Cultivates a positive public image of the corporate travel industry. Protects the interests of members and their corporations in legislative and regulatory matters. Promotes safety, security, efficiency and quality travel. Provides a forum for the exchange of information and ideas among members. **Founded:** 1989. **Geographic Preference:** Local.

38206 ■ Entrepreneurs' Organization - South Florida Chapter (EO)
7580 NW 5th St., Unit 16987
Plantation, FL 33318
Ph: (954)274-2729
Co. E-mail: admin@eosofla.org
URL: http://www.eosoflo.com
URL(s): www.eonetwork.org/southflorida
Linkedin: www.linkedin.com/in/eosouthflorida
X (Twitter): x.com/eosofla

Description: Seeks to help entrepreneurs achieve their full potential in their business and personal lives through networking, shared experiences, and collaborative learning.

38207 ■ Entrepreneurs' Organization - Tampa Bay Chapter (EO)
Tampa, FL
URL: http://www.eonetwork.org/tampabay
Contact: Rhonda Robinson, Manager
E-mail: rhonda@eotampabay.com
X (Twitter): x.com/EntrepreneurOrg
Instagram: www.instagram.com/entrepreneursorg

Description: Provides local resources to members which includes networking events, mentorship, live forums, and leadership development. **Founded:** 1987.

38208 ■ Florida Chapter of the Data Management Association - Library
1433 Swan Ct.
Poinciana, FL 34759-5107
Co. E-mail: cfemperor@hotmail.com

URL: http://dama.org/content/dama-florida-south
Description: Represents leaders in the field of information management. Promote the understanding, development and practice of managing information and data as a key enterprise asset. **Scope:** Data management. **Holdings:** Figures not available. **Geographic Preference:** State.

38209 ■ International Association of Women Coral Gables Chapter
Coral Gables, FL
Ph: (305)310-0616
URL: http://www.iawomen.com/chapters/coral-gables-chapter
Contact: Teresa Safie, Contact
Description: Serves as network of accomplished women united to achieve professional goals. Provides a forum for sharing ideas and experiences of professional women regarding career success. Promotes an active business and networking community from all industries. **Geographic Preference:** Local.

38210 ■ International Association of Women Miami Chapter
Miami, FL
Co. E-mail: iaweasternrm@iawomen.com
URL: http://www.iawomen.com/chapters
Description: Serves as a network for women who want to promote their business, product, or service.

38211 ■ International Association of Women Ocala Chapter
Ocala, FL
URL: http://dev.iawomen.com/chapters
Description: Serves as network of accomplished women united to achieve professional goals. Provides a forum for sharing ideas and experiences of professional women regarding career success. Promotes an active business and networking community from all industries. **Geographic Preference:** Local.

38212 ■ International Association of Women Orlando Chapter
Orlando, FL
URL: http://www.iawomen.com/chapters
Description: Serves as network of accomplished women united to achieve professional goals. Provides a forum for sharing ideas and experiences of professional women regarding career success. Promotes an active business and networking community from all industries. **Geographic Preference:** Local.

38213 ■ International Association of Women Pembroke Pines Chapter
Pembroke Pines, FL
URL: http://www.iawomen.com/chapters/pembroke-pines-chapter
Contact: Sylvia Doane-Ward, President
E-mail: sgdward@gmail.com
Description: Serves as network of accomplished women united to achieve professional goals. Provides a forum for sharing ideas and experiences of professional women regarding career success. Promotes an active business and networking community from all industries. **Geographic Preference:** Local.

38214 ■ National Association of Women Business Owners Lakeland Metro
122 E Main St., Ste. 237
Lakeland, FL 33801
Ph: (863)606-8631
Co. E-mail: info@nawbolakeland.com
URL: http://nawbolakeland.com
Contact: Liz Dederer, President
Description: Represents female entrepreneurs across all industries in the Lakeland area of Florida. **Geographic Preference:** Local.

38215 ■ National Association of Women Business Owners South Florida
Miami, FL 33166
Co. E-mail: info@nawbosouthflorida.com
URL: http://nawbosouthflorida.com
Contact: Carol Wechsler, Contact
Facebook: www.facebook.com/NAWBOSouthFlorida
Linkedin: www.linkedin.com/company/nawbo-south-fl
Instagram: www.instagram.com/nawbosouthflorida
Description: Promotes and supports women-owned businesses. **Geographic Preference:** Local.

SMALL BUSINESS DEVELOPMENT CENTERS

38216 ■ Florida A&M University - Small Business Development Center (SBDC)
625 E Tennessee St. Ste. 200
Tallahassee, FL 32308
Ph: (850)599-3407
Fax: (850)561-2049
Co. E-mail: sbdcfamu@gmail.com
URL: http://sbdcfamu.org
Contact: Barbara Boles, Secretary
Facebook: www.facebook.com/fsbdcatfamu
X (Twitter): x.com/SBDCrattlers
YouTube: www.youtube.com/channel/UCDNbLcGg2vU80p9FqcTEMJw
Description: Works with existing and startup small businesses to help them grow and compete in today's global economy. **Scope:** Management fundamentals to assist small business owners and potential owners in making sound decisions for the successful operations of their businesses. **Founded:** 1983.

38217 ■ Florida SBDC at Indian River State College, Fort Pierce
3209 Virginia Ave., Bldg. Y-303
Fort Pierce, FL 34981-5541
URL: http://floridasbdc.org/success-stories/story/ishkabibbles-with-florida-sbdc-at-irsc
Contact: Tom Kindred, Regional Director
Description: Provides management assistance to current and prospective small business owners in Fort Pierce. **Geographic Preference:** Local.

38218 ■ Florida SBDC at USF: Counties of Sarasota and Manatee
222 10th St., W
Bradenton, FL 34205
Ph: (813)396-2721
URL: http://sbdctampabay.com/sarasota
Contact: Brad Mix, Consultant
Description: Represents and promotes the small business sector. Provides management assistance to current and prospective small business owners. Helps to improve management skills and expand the products and services of members. **Geographic Preference:** Local.

38219 ■ Florida Small Business Development Center at Daytona State College (FSBDC)
1200 W International Speedway Blvd.
Bldg., 140, Ste. 203
Daytona Beach, FL 32114
Ph: (386)506-4723
Co. E-mail: sbdc@daytonastate.edu
URL: http://www.daytonastate.edu/in-the-community/small-business-development-center/index.html
Contact: Trecia Marchand, Director
E-mail: trecia.marchand@daytonastate.edu
Facebook: www.facebook.com/SBDCDaytonaBch
X (Twitter): x.com/SBDCDaytonaBch
Instagram: www.instagram.com/sbdcdaytonabch
Description: Provides management assistance to current and prospective small business owners in Florida. **Founded:** 1973. **Geographic Preference:** Local.

38220 ■ Florida Small Business Development Center at Eastern Florida State College Melbourne (FSBDC)
c/o Robin Braswell, Director
1519 Clearlake Rd., Bldg. 3, Rm. 114
Cocoa, FL 32922
Ph: (321)433-5573
Fax: (321)433-5708
Co. E-mail: braswellr@easternflorida.edu
URL: http://www.easternflorida.edu/sbdc/index.php
Contact: Robin Braswell, Director
E-mail: braswellr@easternflorida.edu
Description: Represents and promotes the small business sector. Provides management, accounting, finance, marketing, operations, new venture planning, and technical assistance to prospective entrepreneurs and existing small business owners. **Founded:** 1990. **Geographic Preference:** Local.

38221 ■ Florida Small Business Development Center Network (FSBDCN)
11000 University Pky., Bld. 38
Pensacola, FL 32514
Ph: (850)685-9801
Co. E-mail: info@floridasbdc.org
URL: http://floridasbdc.org
Contact: Greg Britton, Director
E-mail: gbritton@uwf.edu
Facebook: www.facebook.com/floridasbdcn
Linkedin: www.linkedin.com/company/florida-small-business-development-center-network
X (Twitter): x.com/FloridaSBDCN
Instagram: www.instagram.com/floridasbdcn
YouTube: www.youtube.com/user/Floridasbdcn
Description: Represents and promotes the small business sector. Provides management, accounting, finance, marketing, operations, new venture planning, and technical assistance to prospective entrepreneurs and existing small business owners. **Founded:** 1976. **Geographic Preference:** State.

38222 ■ Florida Small Business Development Center at Seminole Community College (FSBDC)
1445 Dolgner Pl.
Sanford, FL 32771
Ph: (407)321-3495
Fax: (407)321-4184
Co. E-mail: slodyskob@seminolestate.edu
URL: http://sbdc.seminolestate.edu
Contact: Hunt Dawkins, Consultant
Description: Represents and promotes the small business sector. Provides management, accounting, finance, marketing, operations, new venture planning, and technical assistance to prospective entrepreneurs and existing small business owners. **Founded:** 1993. **Geographic Preference:** Local.

38223 ■ Florida Small Business Development Center at South Florida State College
600 W College Dr.
Bldg. H
Avon Park, FL 33825
Ph: (863)784-7378
URL: http://sbdctampabay.com/highlands
Contact: Greg Manning, Consultant
Description: Represents and promotes the small business sector. Provides management assistance to current and prospective small business owners. Helps to improve management skills and expand the products and services of members. **Geographic Preference:** Local.

38224 ■ Florida Small Business Development Center at the University of Central Florida (FSBDC)
3201 E Colonial Dr., Ste. A-20
Orlando, FL 32803
Ph: (407)420-4850
Fax: (407)420-4862
Co. E-mail: sbdc@ucf.edu
URL: http://sbdcorlando.com
Contact: Eunice Choi, Regional Director
E-mail: eunice.choi@ucf.edu
Facebook: www.facebook.com/SBDCOrlando
Linkedin: www.linkedin.com/company/florida-sbdc-at-the-university-of-central-florida
X (Twitter): x.com/sbdcorlando
YouTube: www.youtube.com/c/Sbdcorlando
Description: Represents and promotes the small business sector. Provides management, accounting, finance, marketing, operations, new venture planning, and technical assistance to prospective entrepreneurs and existing small business owners. **Founded:** 1980.

38225 ■ Florida Small Business Development Center at the University of West Florida (FSBDC)
11000 University Pky., Bldg. 76, Ste. 109
Pensacola, FL 32514
Ph: (850)474-2528

URL: http://sbdc.uwf.edu
Contact: Jamie Hardy, Office Manager
Linkedin: www.linkedin.com/company/floridasbdca
   tuwf
X (Twitter): x.com/FloridaSBDC_UWF
YouTube: www.youtube.com/channel/UCAWRfsha
   1qjiG_Mk8ieY2Mg
Description: Represents and promotes the small business sector. Provides management, accounting, finance, marketing, operations, new venture planning, and technical assistance to prospective entrepreneurs and existing small business owners. **Founded:** 1976.

38226 ■ Small Business Development Center at Florida A&M University Perry
428 N Jefferson St.
   Perry, FL 32347
Ph: (850)584-5366
Co. E-mail: sbdcfamu@gmail.com
URL: http://sbdcfamu.org
Facebook: www.facebook.com/fsbdcatfamu
Description: Provides management assistance to current and prospective small business owners in Perry. **Geographic Preference:** Local.

38227 ■ Small Business Development Center at Florida A&M University Tallahassee
625 E Tennessee St., Ste. 200
   Tallahassee, FL 32308
Ph: (850)599-3407
Fax: (850)561-2049
Co. E-mail: sbdcfamu@gmail.com
URL: http://sbdcfamu.org
Contact: Barbara Boles, Secretary
Facebook: www.facebook.com/fsbdcatfamu
X (Twitter): x.com/SBDCrattlers
YouTube: www.youtube.com/channel/UCDNbLcGg
   2vU80p9FqcTEMJw
Description: Represents and promotes the small business sector. Provides management assistance to current and prospective small business owners. Helps to improve management skills and expand the products and services of members. **Founded:** 1976. **Geographic Preference:** Local.

38228 ■ Small Business Development Center at Florida Atlantic University - Boca Raton
777 Glades Rd.
   Boca Raton, FL 33431
URL: http://www.fau.edu/sbdc
Contact: Dr. Sandra D. Marin Ruiz, Regional Director
E-mail: smarinruiz@fau.edu
Description: Represents and promotes the small business sector. Provides management assistance to current and prospective small business owners. Helps to improve management skills and expand the products and services of members. **Geographic Preference:** Local.

38229 ■ Small Business Development Center at Florida Atlantic University Downtown Campus
111 E Las Olas Blvd.
   Fort Lauderdale, FL 33301
Ph: (954)236-1000
URL: http://www.fau.edu/about/locations
Description: Represents and promotes the small business sector. Provides management assistance to current and prospective small business owners. Helps to improve management skills and expand the products and services of members. **Geographic Preference:** Local.

38230 ■ Small Business Development Center at Florida Atlantic University - Florida Keys Community College (FAU)
1101 Brickell Ave., S Tower Penthouse, 11th Fl.
   Miami
   Key West, FL 33040
URL: http://www.fau.edu/academic/freshman/fice/#FL
Description: Represents and promotes the small business sector. Provides management assistance to current and prospective small business owners. Helps to improve management skills and expand the products and services of members. **Geographic Preference:** Local.

38231 ■ Small Business Development Center at Florida Atlantic University - Treasure Coast
500 NW California Blvd.
   Port Saint Lucie, FL 34986
Ph: (772)873-3700
Fax: (772)873-3369
URL: http://www.fau.edu/education/centersandprograms/card/cardsites
Description: Represents and promotes the small business sector. Provides management assistance to current and prospective small business owners. Helps to improve management skills and expand the products and services of members. **Geographic Preference:** Local.

38232 ■ Small Business Development Center at Florida Gulf Coast University Cape Coral
1231 Lafayette St.
   Cape Coral, FL 33904
Ph: (239)745-3700
Co. E-mail: sbdc@fgcu.edu
URL: http://fsbdcswfl.org/contact/#locationscape
   -coral-office
Description: Provides management assistance to current and prospective small business owners in Cape Coral. **Geographic Preference:** Local.

38233 ■ Small Business Development Center at Florida Gulf Coast University Clewiston (SBDCFGCU) [SBDC at FGCU - Clewiston]
Lucas Hall, 3rd Fl., 10501 FGCU Blvd. S
   Fort Myers, FL 33965
Ph: (239)745-3700
Co. E-mail: sbdc@fgcu.edu
URL: http://fsbdcswfl.org
Facebook: www.facebook.com/FGCUSBDC
YouTube: www.youtube.com/channel/UC_TstNR
   2lFPjXSIw8KtedRg
Description: Represents and promotes the small business sector. Provides management assistance to current and prospective small business owners. Helps to improve management skills and expand the products and services of members. **Geographic Preference:** Local.

38234 ■ Small Business Development Center at Florida Gulf Coast University Fort Myers
Florida Gulf Coast University
   10501 FGCU Blvd. S
   Fort Myers, FL 33965
Ph: (239)745-3700
URL: http://fsbdcswfl.org
Description: Represents and promotes the small business sector. Provides management assistance to current and prospective small business owners. Helps to improve management skills and expand the products and services of members. **Geographic Preference:** Local.

38235 ■ Small Business Development Center at Florida Gulf Coast University Immokalee
10501 FGCU Blvd., S
   Fort Myers, FL 33965
Ph: (239)745-3700
Co. E-mail: sbdc@fgcu.edu
URL: http://fsbdcswfl.org/contact-us-locations/
   immokalee-office
Facebook: www.facebook.com/FGCUSBDC
X (Twitter): x.com/fgcusbdc
YouTube: www.youtube.com/c/FloridaSBDCa
   tFGCUFortMyers
Description: Represents and promotes the small business sector. Provides management assistance to current and prospective small business owners. Helps to improve management skills and expand the products and services of members. **Geographic Preference:** Local.

38236 ■ Small Business Development Center at Florida Gulf Coast University Port Charlotte
2702 Tamiami Trl.
   Port Charlotte, FL 33952-5129
Ph: (941)627-2222
URL: http://floridasbdc.org/locations
Description: Represents and promotes the small business sector. Provides management assistance to current and prospective small business owners. Helps to improve management skills and expand the products and services of members. **Geographic Preference:** Local.

38237 ■ Small Business Development Center Fort Lauderdale
111 E Las Olas Blvd.
   Fort Lauderdale, FL 33301
Ph: (954)236-1000
URL: http://www.fau.edu/broward/about/fort-lauder
   dale
Description: Represents and promotes the small business sector. Provides management assistance to current and prospective small business owners. Helps to improve management skills and expand the products and services of members. **Founded:** 1978. **Geographic Preference:** Local.

38238 ■ Small Business Development Center at Gulf Coast State College
5230 W US Hwy 98
   Panama City, FL 32401
Ph: (850)474-2528
URL: http://clients.floridasbdc.org/center.aspx?center
   =41010&subloc=45
Description: Provides management assistance to current and prospective small business owners in Gulf Coast. **Geographic Preference:** Local.

38239 ■ Small Business Development Center at Indian River State College Stuart
2400 SE Salerno Rd.
   Stuart, FL 34997
Ph: (772)336-6285
Co. E-mail: fsbdc@irsc.edu
URL: http://floridasbdc.org
Description: Represents and promotes the small business sector. Provides management assistance to current and prospective small business owners. Helps to improve management skills and expand the products and services of members. **Geographic Preference:** Local.

38240 ■ Small Business Development Center Miami-Dade Hialeah Gardens
The Church in the Gardens
   13090 NW 107th Ave.
   Hialeah Gardens, FL 33018
Ph: (305)515-8609
URL: http://clients.floridasbdc.org/DocumentMaster
   .aspx?doc=2691
Description: Represents and promotes the small business sector. Provides management assistance to current and prospective small business owners. Helps to improve management skills and expand the products and services of members. **Geographic Preference:** Local.

38241 ■ Small Business Development Center at Palm Beach Community College Boca Raton
777 Glades Rd.
   Boca Raton, FL 33431
URL: http://www.fau.edu/jupiter/about/history
Facebook: www.facebook.com/PalmBeachSta
   teCollege
X (Twitter): x.com/pbstatecollege
Description: Represents and promotes the small business sector. Provides management assistance to current and prospective small business owners. Helps to improve management skills and expand the products and services of members. **Geographic Preference:** Local.

38242 ■ Small Business Development Center at State College of Florida Manatee Sarasota
220 W Garden St., Ste. 301
   Pensacola, FL 32502
URL: http://floridasbdc.org
Contact: Sandra Saft, President
Description: Represents and promotes the small business sector. Provides management assistance to current and prospective small business owners.

STATE LISTINGS

Helps to improve management skills and expand the products and services of members. **Geographic Preference:** Local.

38243 ■ **Small Business Development Center at University of Central Florida Kissimmee**
1425 E Vine St.
Kissimmee, FL 34744
URL: http://sbdcorlando.com/satellite-service-centers
Description: Represents and promotes the small business sector. Provides management assistance to current and prospective small business owners. Helps to improve management skills and expand the products and services of members. **Geographic Preference:** Local.

38244 ■ **Small Business Development Center at University of Central Florida Orlando**
3201 E Colonial Dr., Ste. A-20
Orlando, FL 32803
Ph: (407)420-4850
Fax: (407)420-4862
URL: http://sbdcorlando.com
Contact: Eunice Choi, Regional Director
E-mail: eunice.choi@ucf.edu
Facebook: www.facebook.com/sbdcorlando
X (Twitter): x.com/sbdcorlando
Instagram: www.instagram.com/sbdcorlando
YouTube: www.youtube.com/channel/UCGDAG2PnnrVT-alP0fOL4xg
Description: Represents and promotes the small business sector. Provides management assistance to current and prospective small business owners. Helps to improve management skills and expand the products and services of members. **Geographic Preference:** Local.

38245 ■ **Small Business Development Center at University of North Florida Gainesville**
c/o Gainesville Technology Enterprise Ctr
2153 SE Hawthorne Rd.
Gainesville, FL 32641
URL: http://www.unf.edu/sbdc/locations.html
Description: Provides management assistance to current and prospective small business owners in Gainesville. **Geographic Preference:** Local.

38246 ■ **Small Business Development Center at University of North Florida Jacksonville**
c/o Adam W Herbert
12000 Alumni Dr.
Jacksonville, FL 32224
Ph: (904)620-2476
Free: 800-450-4624
Co. E-mail: smallbiz@unf.edu
URL: http://www.unf.edu/sbdc
Contact: Heather Mudd, President
Facebook: www.facebook.com/UNFSBDC
Linkedin: www.linkedin.com/company/the-small-business-development-center-at-unf
X (Twitter): x.com/SBDCatUNF
Instagram: www.instagram.com/fsbdc_unf
YouTube: www.youtube.com/user/SBDCatUNF
Description: Represents and promotes the small business sector. Provides management assistance to current and prospective small business owners. Helps to improve management skills and expand the products and services of members. **Founded:** 1976. **Geographic Preference:** Local.

38247 ■ **Small Business Development Center at University of North Florida Ocala/Marion County**
3003 SW College Rd.,Bldg. 42, Ste. 107F
Ocala, FL 34474
Free: 866-998-8332
URL: http://www.unf.edu/sbdc/locations.html
Contact: Dr. Phil Geist, Consultant
Description: Represents and promotes the small business sector. Provides management assistance to current and prospective small business owners. Helps to improve management skills and expand the products and services of members. **Geographic Preference:** Local.

38248 ■ **Small Business Development Center at University of South Florida: Hillsborough County**
2101 E Palm Ave.
Tampa, FL 33605
Ph: (813)204-9267
Fax: (813)277-1387
URL: http://sbdctampabay.com/hillsborough
Contact: Carol Minor, Consultant
Description: Represents and promotes the small business sector. Provides management assistance to current and prospective small business owners. Helps to improve management skills and expand the products and services of members. **Geographic Preference:** Local.

38249 ■ **Small Business Development Center at University of South Florida St. Petersburg (SBDC)**
140 7th Ave., S, LPH 122D
Saint Petersburg, FL 33701
Ph: (727)453-7200
URL: http://sbdctampabay.com/pinellas
Contact: Kris Manning, Business Manager
Description: Represents and promotes the small business sector. Provides management assistance to current and prospective small business owners. Helps to improve management skills and expand the products and services of members. **Geographic Preference:** Local.

38250 ■ **Small Business Development Center at University of South Florida: Tampa**
Tampa Port Authority Bldg., Ste. 210
1101 Channelside Dr.
Tampa, FL 33602
Ph: (813)905-5800
URL: http://sbdctampabay.com/tampa
Contact: Carl Hadden, Regional Director
Description: Represents and promotes the small business sector. Provides management assistance to current and prospective small business owners. Helps to improve management skills and expand the products and services of members. **Geographic Preference:** Local.

38251 ■ **Small Business Development Center at University of West Florida Fort Walton Beach**
1170 Martin Luther King Jr Blvd., Bldg. 2
Fort Walton Beach, FL 32547
Ph: (850)474-2528
Co. E-mail: sbdc@uwf.edu
URL: http://sbdc.uwf.edu/location/fort-walton-beach
Description: Represents and promotes the small business sector. Provides management assistance to current and prospective small business owners. Helps to improve management skills and expand the products and services of members. **Geographic Preference:** Local.

38252 ■ **University of West Florida - Small Business Development Center (SBDC)**
11000 University Pky., Bldg., 76, Ste. 109
Pensacola, FL 32514
Ph: (850)474-2528
Co. E-mail: sbdc@uwf.edu
URL: http://sbdc.uwf.edu
Contact: Kelly Massey, Regional Director
Facebook: www.facebook.com/SBDCatUWF
X (Twitter): x.com/FloridaSBDC_UWF
Instagram: www.instagram.com/fsbdc_uwf
YouTube: www.youtube.com/channel/UCAWRfsha1qjiG_Mk8ieY2Mg
Description: Delivers, through certified professionals, consulting, training and information to help businesses succeed and create a positive impact for the Florida economy. **Scope:** Support for small businesses in four Florida counties: Escambia, Santa Rosa, Okaloosa, and Walton. Offers consulting services. **Founded:** 1976. **Publications:** *Highlights Newsletter* (Quarterly).

SMALL BUSINESS ASSISTANCE PROGRAMS

38253 ■ **Barry University The Entrepreneurial Institute**
11300 NE 2nd Ave.
Miami Shores, FL 33161-6695
URL: http://my.barry.edu/biced/entrepreneurial-institute
Description: Developed as an educational training and economic development technical assistance program. The institute focuses on the economic disparity that exists in many Miami-Dade communities and provides on-site assistance as well as services on campus by appointment. **Founded:** 1940.

38254 ■ **Broward County Office of Economic and Small Business Development (OESBD)**
115 S Andrews Ave., Rm. 114
Fort Lauderdale, FL 33301
Ph: (954)357-7270
URL: http://www.broward.org/EconDev/Pages/BusinessAssistance.aspx
Description: Offers services and technical assistance, including financing opportunities.

38255 ■ **Enterprise Florida Inc.-Marketing And Development Div. (EFI)**
800 N Magnolia Ave., Ste. 1100
Orlando, FL 32803
Ph: (407)956-5600
Fax: (407)956-5599
URL: http://www.enterpriseflorida.com
Contact: Angela Adams Suggs, Chief Executive Officer
Facebook: www.facebook.com/EnterpriseFlorida
Linkedin: www.linkedin.com/company/enterprise-florida
X (Twitter): x.com/enterprisefl
Instagram: www.instagram.com/enterpriseflorida
YouTube: www.youtube.com/c/EnterpriseFlorida
Description: Provider of economic development services for aviation, aerospace, life sciences, information technology, defense and homeland security sectors. **Founded:** 1996.

38256 ■ **Florida Business Development Corporation (FBDC)**
1715 N Westshore Blvd., Ste. 780
Tampa, FL 33607
Ph: (561)433-0233
Co. E-mail: info@fbdc.net
URL: http://www.fbdc.net
Contact: Bill Habermeyer, President
Facebook: www.facebook.com/Florida-Business-Development-Corporation-251541018194749
Linkedin: www.linkedin.com/company/florida-business-development-corporation
X (Twitter): x.com/FBDC504
Description: Seeks to promote business through economic and community development. Assists businesses in their expansion and financing needs. Enhances the quality of life and fosters the growth of good jobs within the community. **Founded:** 1989. **Geographic Preference:** State.

38257 ■ **Veterans Business Outreach Center (VBOC)**
Gulf Coast State College
Student Union W, Rooms 326-3305230 W Hwy. 98
Panama City, FL 32401
Free: 800-542-7232
URL: http://vboc.org
Contact: Brenton Peacock, Director
E-mail: bpeacock@gulfcoast.edu
Facebook: www.facebook.com/VBOCFlorida
Linkedin: www.linkedin.com/company/vbocfl
X (Twitter): x.com/VBOC_FLORIDA
YouTube: www.youtube.com/channel/UCvB9RNUaHwwffiKe1Tb-_eA
Description: Serves active duty personnel, veterans, and military spouses who want to start a small business in Florida. Offers business counseling and assistance with business plans, locating funding, understanding taxes, developing marketing, and considering government contracting. **Founded:** 1998.

38258 ■ Florida

SCORE OFFICES

38258 ■ Mid-Florida SCORE
11962 County Rd. 101, Ste. 302-259
 The Villages, FL 32162
Ph: (352)399-0050
Co. E-mail: midflorida@scorevolunteer.org
URL: http://midflorida.score.org
Contact: Byron Zuidema, Chairman of the Board
E-mail: byron.zuidema@scorevolunteer.org
Facebook: www.facebook.com/SCOREMidFlorida
Linkedin: www.linkedin.com/company/score-mentors
 -mid-florida

Description: Unites active and retired business management professionals with men and women who are considering starting a small business, encountering problems with their business, or expanding their business. Serves the Florida counties of Sumter, Marion, and Lake. **Founded:** 1964.

38259 ■ SCORE - Amelia Island
961687 Gateway Blvd., Ste. 101G
 Saint Augustine, FL 32086
URL: http://jacksonville.score.org

Description: Provides professional guidance and information to maximize the success of existing and emerging small businesses. Offers business counseling and workshops.

38260 ■ SCORE - Boynton Beach
500 S Australian Ave., Ste. 115
 West Palm Beach, FL 33401
URL: http://palmbeachcounty.score.org/mentors/jerry
 -siegel
Contact: Jerry Siegel, President

Description: Provides professional guidance and information to maximize the success of existing and emerging small businesses. Offers business counseling and workshops.

38261 ■ SCORE - Brooksville
15588 Aviation Loop Dr.
 Spring Hill, FL 34604
Ph: (727)842-4638
URL: http://pascohernando.score.org

Description: Provides professional guidance and information to maximize the success of existing and emerging small businesses. Offers business counseling and workshops.

38262 ■ SCORE - Broward
299 E Broward Blvd., Ste. 123
 Fort Lauderdale, FL 33301
Ph: (954)356-7263
Fax: (954)356-7145
Co. E-mail: mail@browardscore.org
URL: http://broward.score.org
Contact: George Gremse, President
Linkedin: www.linkedin.com/company/broward-score
X (Twitter): x.com/BrowardSCORE

Description: Provides professional guidance and information to maximize the success of existing and emerging small businesses. Offers business counseling and workshops. **Founded:** 1964. **Geographic Preference:** Local.

38263 ■ SCORE - Broward County Main Library
100 S Andrews Ave.
 Fort Lauderdale, FL 33301
URL: http://broward.score.org

Description: Provides professional guidance and information to maximize the success of existing and emerging small businesses. Offers business counseling and workshops.

38264 ■ SCORE - Callahan
542196 U. S. Hwy. 1
 Callahan, FL 32011
URL: http://jacksonville.score.org/contact-jacksonville
 -score

Description: Provides professional guidance and information to maximize the success of existing and emerging small businesses. Offers business counseling and workshops.

38265 ■ SCORE - Central Florida
100 S Kentucky Ave., Ste. 230
 Lakeland, FL 33801
Ph: (863)284-5607
Fax: (863)680-4070
Co. E-mail: info@centralflscore.org
URL: http://centralflorida.score.org
Contact: Bridget Weston, Chief Executive Officer
Linkedin: www.linkedin.com/company/central-florida
 -score

Description: Provides resources and expertise to maximize the success of existing and emerging small businesses. Offers business counseling and workshops. **Geographic Preference:** Local.

38266 ■ SCORE - Clay County [SCORE - Orange Park]
1726 Kingsley Ave., Ste. 2B
 Orange Park, FL 32073
URL: http://www.score.org/jacksonville/content/con
 tact-jacksonville-score

Description: Provides professional guidance and information to maximize the success of existing and emerging small businesses. Offers business counseling and workshops.

38267 ■ SCORE - Clermont
c/o S Lake Chamber of Commerce
 620 W Montrose St.
 Clermont, FL 34711
URL: http://midflorida.score.org/branch/clermon
 t-branch

Description: Provides professional guidance and information to maximize the success of existing and emerging small businesses. Offers business counseling and workshops.

38268 ■ SCORE - DeLand
336 N Woodland Blvd.
 Deland, FL 32720
Ph: (386)255-6889
Fax: (386)255-0229
Co. E-mail: info@score87.org
URL: http://volusiaflagler.score.org/deland-office
Contact: Stephen Barnett, Contact

Description: Provides professional guidance and information to maximize the success of existing and emerging small businesses. Offers business counseling and workshops.

38269 ■ SCORE - Fleming Island
1845 Town Center Blvd., Bldg. 400, Ste. 410
 Fleming Island, FL 32003
Ph: (904)264-2651
URL: http://jacksonville.score.org/contact-jacksonville
 -score

Description: Provides professional guidance and information to maximize the success of existing and emerging small businesses. Offers business counseling and workshops.

38270 ■ SCORE - Fort Pierce
3220 S Us Hwy. 1, Ste. No. 2
 Fort Pierce, FL 34982
Ph: (772)489-0548
Fax: (772)489-9548
Co. E-mail: ch.admin0308@scorevolunteer.org
URL: http://treasurecoast.score.org

Description: Provides professional guidance and information to maximize the success of existing and emerging small businesses. Offers business counseling and workshops.

38271 ■ SCORE - Hobe Sound
8958 SE Bridge Rd.
 Hobe Sound, FL 33455
Ph: (772)546-4724
URL: http://www.score.org/find-location

Description: Provides professional guidance and information to maximize the success of existing and emerging small businesses. Offers business counseling and workshops.

38272 ■ SCORE - Hollywood/Pembroke Pines
6565 Taft St., Ste. 403
 Hollywood, FL 33024
Ph: (954)356-7263

Co. E-mail: help@score.org
URL: http://broward.score.org/broward-mentoring
 -locations
URL(s): www.score.org/find-location?page=1

Description: Provides professional guidance and information to maximize the success of existing and emerging small businesses. Offers business counseling and workshops.

38273 ■ SCORE - Jacksonville
7825 Baymeadows Way, Ste. 100B
 Jacksonville, FL 32256
Ph: (904)443-1911
Fax: (904)443-1980
Co. E-mail: help@score.org
URL: http://jacksonville.score.org
Facebook: www.facebook.com/SCOREJacksonville
Linkedin: www.linkedin.com/company/score
 -jacksonville
X (Twitter): x.com/SCOREJacksonvil
YouTube: www.youtube.com/channel/
 UCSwryxRxeqsDkvgMse6lOAQ

Description: Provides professional guidance and information to maximize the success of existing and emerging small businesses. Offers business counseling and workshops. **Founded:** 1965. **Geographic Preference:** Local.

38274 ■ SCORE - JAX Chamber Office
3 Independent Dr.
 Jacksonville, FL 32202
Ph: (904)366-6618
URL: http://jacksonville.score.org

Description: Provides professional guidance and information to maximize the success of existing and emerging small businesses. Offers business counseling and workshops.

38275 ■ SCORE - Jensen Beach
1960 NE Jensen Beach Blvd.
 Jensen Beach, FL 34957
Ph: (772)489-0548
URL: http://treasurecoast.score.org

Description: Provides professional guidance and information to maximize the success of existing and emerging small businesses. Offers business counseling and workshops.

38276 ■ SCORE - Jupiter
705 Military Tr.
 Jupiter, FL 33458
URL: http://palmbeachcounty.score.org/mentors/
 richard-f-calcote
Contact: Richard F. Calcote, Contact

Description: Provides professional guidance and information to maximize the success of existing and emerging small businesses. Offers business counseling and workshops.

38277 ■ SCORE - Manasota
2801 Fruitville Rd., Ste. 280
 Sarasota, FL 34237
Ph: (941)955-1029
Co. E-mail: susan.jojo@scorevolunteer.org
URL: http://manasota.score.org
Contact: Dennis Zink, Contact
Facebook: www.facebook.com/SCOREManasota
Linkedin: www.linkedin.com/company/manasota
 -score
X (Twitter): x.com/SCOREManasota

Description: Provides professional guidance and information to maximize the success of existing and emerging small businesses. Offers business counseling and workshops. **Founded:** 1964. **Awards:** SCORE - Manasota Small Business of the Year (Annual). **Geographic Preference:** Local.

38278 ■ SCORE - Melbourne
1600 Sarno Rd., Ste. 205
 Melbourne, FL 32935
Ph: (321)254-2288
Co. E-mail: score.chapter400@volunteer.org
URL: http://spacecoast.score.org

Description: Provides professional guidance and information to maximize the success of existing and emerging small businesses. Offers business counseling and workshops.

38279 ■ SCORE - Merritt Island
400 Fortenberry Rd.
Merritt Island, FL 32952
Ph: (321)459-2200
URL: http://spacecoast.score.org/content/counseling-schedule-1
Description: Provides professional guidance and information to maximize the success of existing and emerging small businesses. Offers business counseling and workshops.

38280 ■ SCORE - Miami-Dade
2000 Ponce de Leon Blvd., Ste. 600
Miami, FL 33134
Ph: (786)425-9119
Co. E-mail: admin0029@scorevolunteer.org
URL: http://miamidade.score.org
Description: Provides professional guidance and information to maximize the success of existing and emerging small businesses. Offers business counseling and workshops. **Geographic Preference:** Local.

38281 ■ SCORE - Mid Florida
11962 Co Rd. 101, No. 302-259
The Villages, FL 32162
Ph: (352)399-0050
URL: http://midflorida.score.org
Description: Provides professional guidance and information to maximize the success of existing and emerging small businesses. Offers business counseling and workshops.

38282 ■ SCORE - Miramar
299 E Broward Blvd., No. 123
Fort Lauderdale, FL 33301
Ph: (954)356-7263
Fax: (954)356-7145
Co. E-mail: mail@browardscore.org
URL: http://broward.score.org
Facebook: www.facebook.com/SCOREBroward
X (Twitter): x.com/BrowardSCORE
Description: Provides professional guidance and information to maximize the success of existing and emerging small businesses. Offers business counseling and workshops.

38283 ■ SCORE - Naples
900 Goodlette Rd. N
Naples, FL 34102
Ph: (239)430-0081
Co. E-mail: info@scorenaples.org
URL: http://naples.score.org
Contact: Cheryl McDonnell, Chairman
E-mail: cheryl.mcdonnell@scorevolunteer.org
Linkedin: www.linkedin.com/company/score-of-naples
X (Twitter): x.com/naplesscore
Instagram: www.instagram.com/naplesscore
YouTube: www.youtube.com/channel/UCVIN5cDwFz-QHRZ59dv3PIQ
Description: Creates opportunities for small business owners and potential small business owners to achieve success. Provides entrepreneur education in Naples area, in Florida. Offers individual counseling, workshops, seminars and literature. **Founded:** 1988. **Geographic Preference:** Local.

38284 ■ SCORE - New Smyrna Beach
115 Canal St.
New Smyrna Beach, FL 32168
Ph: (386)255-6889
Fax: (386)255-0229
Co. E-mail: info@score87.org
URL: http://volusiaflagler.score.org/new-smyrna-office
Facebook: www.facebook.com/SCOREVolusiaFlagler
Linkedin: www.linkedin.com/company/score87
X (Twitter): twitter.com/SCOREChapter87
YouTube: www.youtube.com/channel/UC3QZ8qlRC7HremwEj_PYJ_Q
Description: Provides professional guidance and information to maximize the success of existing and emerging small businesses. Offers business counseling and workshops.

38285 ■ SCORE - North Central Florida
101 SE 2nd Pl., Ste. 104
Gainesville, FL 32601
Ph: (352)251-3622
Co. E-mail: help@score.org
URL: http://northcentralflorida.score.org
Facebook: www.facebook.com/SCORENorthCentralFlorida
Linkedin: www.linkedin.com/company/score-mentors-north-central-florida
X (Twitter): x.com/SCOREGainesvill
Description: Provides professional guidance and information to maximize the success of existing and emerging small businesses. Offers business counseling and workshops. **Founded:** 1964.

38286 ■ SCORE - Northeast Fort Lauderdale
2400 E Commercial Blvd., Ste. 1100
Fort Lauderdale, FL 33308
Ph: (954)356-7263
URL: http://broward.score.org/broward-mentoring-locations
Contact: Richard Kirshen, Contact
Description: Provides professional guidance and information to maximize the success of existing and emerging small businesses. Offers business counseling and workshops.

38287 ■ SCORE - Orlando
3201 E Colonial Dr., Ste. A-20
Orlando, FL 32803
Ph: (407)420-4844
Fax: (407)420-4849
Co. E-mail: score@nationalec.org
URL: http://orlando.score.org
Contact: Bo Harvey, Contact
Facebook: www.facebook.com/SCOREorlando
Linkedin: www.linkedin.com/company/score-orlando
YouTube: www.youtube.com/user/SCOREOrlando
Description: Provides professional guidance and information to maximize the success of existing and emerging small businesses. Offers business counseling and workshops. **Founded:** 1966. **Geographic Preference:** Local.

38288 ■ SCORE - Ormond Beach
165 W Granada Blvd.
Ormond Beach, FL 32174
URL: http://www.score.org/volusiaflagler/content/locations
Description: Provides professional guidance and information to maximize the success of existing and emerging small businesses. Offers business counseling and workshops.

38289 ■ SCORE - Palm Bay
4100 Dixie Hwy. NE
Palm Bay, FL 32905
Ph: (321)951-9998
URL: http://spacecoast.score.org/content/counseling-schedule-1
Contact: Jim Youngquist, Chairman
E-mail: jim.youngquist@scorevolunteer.org
Description: Provides professional guidance and information to maximize the success of existing and emerging small businesses. Offers business counseling and workshops.

38290 ■ SCORE - Palm Beach
500 S Australian Ave., Ste. 115
West Palm Beach, FL 33401
Ph: (561)981-5180
Fax: (561)833-1470
Co. E-mail: wpbadmin@scorevolunteer.org
URL: http://palmbeachcounty.score.org
Facebook: www.facebook.com/SCOREPalmBeachCounty
Linkedin: www.linkedin.com/company/score-palm-beach-county
Description: Provides professional guidance and information to maximize the success of existing and emerging small businesses. Offers business counseling and workshops. **Founded:** 1976. **Geographic Preference:** Local.

38291 ■ SCORE - Palm City
2601 SW High Meadow Ave.
Palm City, FL 34990
Ph: (772)489-0548
URL: http://www.score.org/treasurecoast/about/score-treasure-coast-mentoring-locations
Description: Provides professional guidance and information to maximize the success of existing and emerging small businesses. Offers business counseling and workshops.

38292 ■ SCORE - Palm Coast
160 Lake Ave.
Palm Coast, FL 32164
URL: http://www.score.org/volusiaflagler/content/locations
Description: Provides professional guidance and information to maximize the success of existing and emerging small businesses. Offers business counseling and workshops.

38293 ■ SCORE - Parkland
FL
URL: http://broward.score.org
Description: Provides professional guidance and information to maximize the success of existing and emerging small businesses. Offers business counseling and workshops.

38294 ■ SCORE - Pasco-Hernando [Pasco-Hernando County SCORE - Chapter 439]
4532 US Hwy. 19, Ste. 6
New Port Richey, FL 34652
Ph: (727)842-4638
Co. E-mail: info@score439.org
URL: http://pascohernando.score.org
Facebook: www.facebook.com/SCOREPascoHernando
Linkedin: www.linkedin.com/company/pasco-hernando-score-chapter-439
X (Twitter): x.com/score439
Description: Provides professional guidance and information to maximize the success of existing and emerging small businesses. Offers business counseling and workshops. **Founded:** 1964. **Geographic Preference:** Local.

38295 ■ SCORE - Pensacola
15500 Perdido Key Dr.
Pensacola, FL 32507
Ph: (850)492-4660
Co. E-mail: panamacity@scorevolunteer.org
URL: http://floridapanhandle.score.org
Contact: Bridget Weston, Chief Executive Officer
Description: Provides professional guidance and information to maximize the success of existing and emerging small businesses. Offers business counseling and workshops.

38296 ■ SCORE - Pinellas County
4707 140th Ave. N, Ste. 311
Clearwater, FL 33762
Ph: (727)437-0990
Co. E-mail: pinellas.county@scorevolunteer.org
URL: http://www.pinellascounty.score.org
Facebook: www.facebook.com/scorepinellas
Linkedin: www.linkedin.com/company/score-pinellas-county
X (Twitter): x.com/SCOREMentors
Description: Provides professional guidance and information to maximize the success of existing and emerging small businesses. Offers business counseling and workshops. **Geographic Preference:** Local.

38297 ■ SCORE - Pompano Beach
Pompano Beach, FL
URL: http://broward.score.org/mentors/dale-m-long
Contact: Dale M. Long, Contact
Description: Provides professional guidance and information to maximize the success of existing and emerging small businesses. Offers business counseling and workshops.

38298 ■ SCORE - Port Charlotte
1777 Tamiami Trl., Ste. 411
Port Charlotte, FL 33948
Ph: (941)743-6179
Co. E-mail: port.charlotte@scorevolunteer.org
URL: http://www.score.org/portcharlotte
X (Twitter): x.com/Charlottecscore

Description: Provides professional guidance and information to maximize the success of existing and emerging small businesses. Offers business counseling and workshops. **Founded:** 1964.

38299 ■ SCORE - Port Saint Lucie
500 California Blvd.
 IRSC Pruitt Campus, Bldg. F, 1st Fl.
 Port Saint Lucie, FL 34986
Ph: (772)879-4199
Co. E-mail: help@score.org
URL: http://treasurecoast.score.org
URL(s): www.score.org/find-location
Description: Provides professional guidance and information to maximize the success of existing and emerging small businesses. Offers business counseling and workshops.

38300 ■ SCORE - St. Augustine
100 Southpark Blvd., Ste. 405
 Saint Augustine, FL 32086
Ph: (904)829-5681
URL: http://jacksonville.score.org/contact-jacksonville-score
Description: Provides professional guidance and information to maximize the success of existing and emerging small businesses. Offers business counseling and workshops.

38301 ■ SCORE - Sebastian
700 Main St.
 Sebastian, FL 32958
Ph: (772)589-5969
Co. E-mail: help@score.org
URL: http://treasurecoast.score.org/treasure-coast-mentoring-locations
Description: Provides professional guidance and information to maximize the success of existing and emerging small businesses. Offers business counseling and workshops.

38302 ■ SCORE - South Palm Beach
7999 N Federal Hwy., Ste. 201
 Boca Raton, FL 33487
Ph: (561)981-5180
Co. E-mail: ch.admin0224@scorevolunteer.org
URL: http://palmbeachcounty.score.org
Contact: Hal Finkelstein, Chairman
Linkedin: www.linkedin.com/company/score-palm-beach-county
Description: Provides professional guidance and information to maximize the success of existing and emerging small businesses. Offers business counseling and workshops. **Founded:** 1964. **Geographic Preference:** Local.

38303 ■ SCORE - Southwest Florida
2201 2 nd St., Ste. 500
 Fort Myers, FL 33966
Ph: (239)533-3102
Co. E-mail: swflscore@gmail.com
URL: http://southwestflorida.score.org
Facebook: www.facebook.com/SCORESouthwestFlorida
Linkedin: www.linkedin.com/company/score-mentors-southwest-florida%C2%A0
X (Twitter): x.com/SCORESWFlorida
Description: Provides professional guidance and information to maximize the success of existing and emerging small businesses. Offers business counseling and workshops. **Geographic Preference:** Local.

38304 ■ SCORE - Space Coast
Melbourne Professional Complex
 1600 Sarno Rd., Ste. 205
 Melbourne, FL 32935
Ph: (321)254-2288
Fax: (321)254-1346
Co. E-mail: scorechapter400@bellsouth.net
URL: http://spacecoast.score.org
Contact: Karla Micka, Vice Chairman of the Board
E-mail: karla.micka@scorevolunteer.org
Description: Provides professional guidance and information to maximize the success of existing and emerging small businesses. Offers business counseling and workshops. **Geographic Preference:** Local.

38305 ■ SCORE - Stuart
2400 SE Salerno Rd.
 Stuart, FL 34997
Ph: (772)489-0548
Co. E-mail: help@score.org
URL: http://treasurecoast.score.org
Description: Provides professional guidance and information to maximize the success of existing and emerging small businesses. Offers business counseling and workshops.

38306 ■ SCORE - Sunrise
10001 W Oakland Pk. Blvd., Ste. 302
 Sunrise, FL 33351
Co. E-mail: mail@browardscore.org
URL: http://broward.score.org/broward-mentoring-locations
Description: Provides professional guidance and information to maximize the success of existing and emerging small businesses. Offers business counseling and workshops.

38307 ■ SCORE - Tampa
2101 E Palm Ave., Ste. A
 Tampa, FL 33605
Ph: (813)448-2311
Co. E-mail: ed.datz@scorevolunteer.org
URL: http://tampa.score.org
Description: Provides professional guidance and information to maximize the success of existing and emerging small businesses. Offers business counseling and workshops.

38308 ■ SCORE - Titusville
2000 S Washington Ave.
 Titusville, FL 32780
Ph: (321)267-3036
URL: http://spacecoast.score.org/content/counseling-schedule-1
Description: Provides professional guidance and information to maximize the success of existing and emerging small businesses. Offers business counseling and workshops.

38309 ■ SCORE - Treasure Coast
3220 S US Hwy. 1., Ste. 2
 Fort Pierce, FL 34982
Ph: (772)489-0548
Co. E-mail: ch.admin0308@scorevolunteer.org
URL: http://www.score.org/treasurecoast
Contact: Roger Lebida, Contact
Facebook: www.facebook.com/SCORETreasureCoast
Linkedin: www.linkedin.com/company/treasure-coast-score
X (Twitter): x.com/SCORETrCoast
Description: Provides resources and expertise to maximize the success of existing and emerging small businesses. Offers business counseling and workshops. **Founded:** 1964. **Geographic Preference:** Local.

38310 ■ SCORE - Venice
597 S Tamiami Tr.
 Venice, FL 34285
Ph: (941)488-2236
URL: http://greaterhartford.score.org/find-location?state=FL
Description: Provides professional guidance and information to maximize the success of existing and emerging small businesses. Offers business counseling and workshops.

38311 ■ SCORE - Vero Beach Chamber of Commerce
1957 14th Ave.
 Vero Beach, FL 32960
Ph: (772)226-5459
URL: http://treasurecoast.score.org
Description: Provides professional guidance and information to maximize the success of existing and emerging small businesses. Offers business counseling and workshops.

38312 ■ SCORE - Volusia/Flagler
601 Innovation Way, Ste., 134
 Daytona Beach, FL 32114
Ph: (386)255-6889
Co. E-mail: volusia-flagler@scorevolunteer.org
URL: http://www.score.org/volusiaflagler
Facebook: www.facebook.com/SCOREVolusiaFlagler
Linkedin: www.linkedin.com/company/score-mentors-volusia-flagler-county
X (Twitter): x.com/SCOREChapter87
YouTube: www.youtube.com/channel/UC3QZ8qIRC7HremwEj_PYJ_Q
Description: Provides professional guidance and information to maximize the success of existing and emerging small businesses. Offers business counseling and workshops. **Founded:** 1964. **Geographic Preference:** Local.

38313 ■ SCORE - Wellington
7999 N Federal Hwy., Ste. 201
 Boca Raton, FL 33487
Ph: (561)981-5180
Co. E-mail: ch.admin0224@scorevolunteer.org
URL: http://palmbeach.score.org
Contact: Ron Klein, President
Description: Provides professional guidance and information to maximize the success of existing and emerging small businesses. Offers business counseling and workshops.

38314 ■ Tallahassee SCORE
300 E Pk. Ave.
 Tallahassee, FL 32301
Ph: (615)504-7458
URL: http://columbusga.score.org/locations-13
Description: Unites active and retired business management professionals with men and women who are considering starting a small business, encountering problems with their business, or expanding their business. Serves the Big Bend and Capitol region of Florida. **Founded:** 1964.

38315 ■ Tampa SCORE
2101 E Palm Ave., Ste. A
 Tampa, FL 33605
Ph: (813)448-2311
URL: http://tampa.score.org
Contact: George R. Boraiko, President
Description: Unites active and retired business management professionals with men and women who are considering starting a small business, encountering problems with their business, or expanding their business.

BETTER BUSINESS BUREAUS

38316 ■ Better Business Bureau of Central Florida
1600 S Grant St.
 Longwood, FL 32750
Ph: (407)621-3300
Free: 800-275-6614
Fax: (407)786-2625
Co. E-mail: info@findbbb.org
URL: http://www.bbb.org/local-bbb/bbb-serving-central-florida
Contact: Salmons Holly, President
Linkedin: www.linkedin.com/company/better-business-bureau---central-florida
X (Twitter): x.com/BBBCFL
Description: Seeks to promote and foster ethical relationship between businesses and the public through voluntary self-regulation, consumer and business education, and service excellence. Provides information to help consumers and businesses make informed purchasing decisions and avoid costly scams and frauds; settles consumer complaints through arbitration and other means. **Founded:** 1983. **Publications:** *BBB Central Florida Times* (Quarterly). **Educational Activities:** Golf Outing (Annual). **Geographic Preference:** Local.

38317 ■ Better Business Bureau of Northeast Florida and the Southeast Atlantic
4417 Beach Blvd., Ste. 202
 Jacksonville, FL 32207
Ph: (904)721-2288
Fax: (904)721-7373
Co. E-mail: info@bbbnefla.org

STATE LISTINGS   Florida ■ 38332

URL: http://www.bbb.org/local-bbb/bbb-of-northeast-florida-and-the-southeast-atlantic
Contact: Tom Stephens, Chief Executive Officer
Linkedin: www.linkedin.com/company/bbb-serving-northeast-florida-&-the-southeast-atlantic
X (Twitter): x.com/BBBJacksonville
Description: Seeks to promote and foster ethical relationship between businesses and the public through voluntary self-regulation, consumer and business education, and service excellence. Provides information to help consumers and businesses make informed purchasing decisions and avoid costly scams and frauds; settles consumer complaints through arbitration and other means. **Founded:** 1987. **Geographic Preference:** Local; Regional.

38318 ■ Better Business Bureau of Northwest Florida
912 E Gadsden St.
  Pensacola, FL 32501
Ph: (850)429-0002
Fax: (850)429-0006
Co. E-mail: info@nwfl.bbb.org
URL: http://www.bbb.org/local-bbb/bbb-of-northwest-florida
Facebook: www.facebook.com/nwfl.bbb
X (Twitter): x.com/nwflbbb
Description: Seeks to promote and foster ethical relationship between businesses and the public through voluntary self-regulation, consumer and business education, and service excellence. Provides information to help consumers and businesses make informed purchasing decisions and avoid costly scams and frauds; settles consumer complaints through arbitration and other means. **Founded:** 1985. **Awards:** BBB of Northwest Florida Customer Service Excellence Award (Annual); BBB of Northwest Florida Student Ethics Scholarship (Annual); BBB of Northwest Florida Torch Award for Marketplace Ethics (Annual). **Geographic Preference:** Local.

38319 ■ Better Business Bureau of West Florida
2655 McCormick Dr.
  Clearwater, FL 33759
Ph: (727)535-5522
Fax: (727)539-6301
Co. E-mail: info@bbbwestflorida.org
URL: http://www.bbb.org/local-bbb/bbb-of-west-florida
Contact: Karen Nalven, President
E-mail: knalven@bbbwestflorida.org
Facebook: www.facebook.com/BBBWestFlorida
Linkedin: www.linkedin.com/company/better-business-bureau-serving-west-florida
X (Twitter): x.com/BBBWestFlorida
YouTube: www.youtube.com/user/BBBWestFL
Description: Seeks to promote and foster ethical relationship between businesses and the public through voluntary self-regulation, consumer and business education, and service excellence. Provides information to help consumers and businesses make informed purchasing decisions and avoid costly scams and frauds; settles consumer complaints through arbitration and other means. **Founded:** 1984. **Publications:** *Better Business Bureau of West Florida Year in Review* (Annual). **Geographic Preference:** Local.

CHAMBERS OF COMMERCE

38320 ■ Alachua Chamber of Commerce
14801 Main St.
  Alachua, FL 32615
Ph: (386)462-3333
Co. E-mail: communications@alachuachamber.com
URL: http://www.alachua.com
Contact: Mitch Glaeser, President
Description: Promotes business growth and community development in Alachua, FL. **Geographic Preference:** Local.

38321 ■ Anna Maria Island Chamber of Commerce
5313 Gulf Dr.
  Holmes Beach, FL 34217
Ph: (941)778-1541

Co. E-mail: info@annamariaislandchamber.org
URL: http://annamariaislandchamber.org
Contact: Wayne Gunter, Treasurer
Facebook: www.facebook.com/amichamber
Linkedin: www.linkedin.com/company/anna-maria-island-chamber-of-commerce
X (Twitter): x.com/amichamber
Instagram: www.instagram.com/amichamber
Pinterest: www.pinterest.com/amicoc2013
Description: Promotes business and community development in Anna Maria Island area of FL. Promotes tourism. Conducts workshops, seminars, trade shows, and festivals. **Founded:** 1949. **Publications:** *Anna Maria Island Vacation Guide* (Annual). **Geographic Preference:** Local.

38322 ■ Apalachicola Bay Chamber of Commerce (ABCC)
17 Ave., E
  Apalachicola, FL 32320
Ph: (850)653-9419
Co. E-mail: info@apalachicolabay.org
URL: http://www.apalachicolabay.org
Contact: John C. Solomon, Executive Director
E-mail: execdirector@apalachicolabay.org
Facebook: www.facebook.com/ApalachicolaBayChamber
X (Twitter): x.com/ApalachicolaFL
Description: Promotes business, tourism, and community development in Franklin County, FL. **Publications:** *Apalachicola Bay Area of Franklin County*; *Chuck Spicer's Coastline*. **Geographic Preference:** Local.

38323 ■ Apopka Area Chamber of Commerce
180 E Main St.
  Apopka, FL 32703
Ph: (407)886-1441
URL: http://www.apopkachamber.org
Contact: Cate Manley, President
E-mail: cate@apopkachamber.org
Facebook: www.facebook.com/ApopkaChamber
Linkedin: www.linkedin.com/company/apopka-area-chamber-commerce
X (Twitter): x.com/ApopkaAreaCC
Instagram: www.instagram.com/apopka_chamber
YouTube: www.youtube.com/channel/UCTYiKW408 6IE5OH9MQGOIfQ
Description: Promotes business and community development in the Apopka, FL area. Monitors issues concerning business community. Sponsors student government day. **Founded:** 1913. **Publications:** *Foliage Locator*; *Membership Books* (Annual). **Geographic Preference:** Local.

38324 ■ Auburndale Chamber of Commerce
2701 Lake Myrtle Pk. Rd.
  Auburndale, FL 33823
Ph: (863)967-3400
Fax: (863)967-0880
Co. E-mail: auburndalechamber@live.com
URL: http://www.myauburndalechamber.com
Contact: Sandra Hall, Executive Director
Description: Promotes business and community development in the Auburndale, FL area. Holds monthly board meeting, luncheons, seminars, socials, and town meetings. **Founded:** 1997. **Geographic Preference:** Local.

38325 ■ Avon Park Chamber of Commerce (APCC)
28 E Main St.
  Avon Park, FL 33825
Ph: (863)453-3350
Co. E-mail: members@theapcc.net
URL: http://www.theapcc.net
Contact: Tina Thompson, President
Facebook: www.facebook.com/TheAPCC1904
X (Twitter): x.com/APChamberFL
Description: Promotes business and community development in Avon Park, FL. Sponsors annual Arts and Crafts Show and Jararanda Festival for fine arts. **Founded:** 1904. **Publications:** *Downtown Merchant Directory*. **Geographic Preference:** Local.

38326 ■ Baker County Chamber of Commerce
20 E Macclenny Ave.
  Macclenny, FL 32063
Ph: (904)259-6433
URL: http://www.bakerchamberfl.com
Contact: Darryl Register, Executive Director
E-mail: dregister@bakerchamberfl.com
Facebook: www.facebook.com/Baker-County-Florida-Chamber-of-Commerce-148574765198343
X (Twitter): x.com/bakercounty_coc
Description: Promotes business and community development in Baker County, FL. **Publications:** *Baker Bulletin* (Monthly). **Geographic Preference:** Local.

38327 ■ *Bay Biz*
235 W 5th St.
  Panama City, FL 32401
Ph: (850)785-5206
Co. E-mail: information@baychamberfl.com
URL: http://www.panamacity.org
Contact: Carol Roberts, President
E-mail: carol@baychamberfl.com
URL(s): panamacity.org/about/publications
Released: Weekly; Biweekly **Availability:** Online.

38328 ■ *Bay Biz Magazine*
235 W 5th St.
  Panama City, FL 32401
Ph: (850)785-5206
Co. E-mail: information@baychamberfl.com
URL: http://www.panamacity.org
Contact: Carol Roberts, President
E-mail: carol@baychamberfl.com
URL(s): panamacity.org/about/publications
Released: Quarterly; winter, spring, summer, fall. **Price:** $5, Single issue. **Availability:** Print; Online.

38329 ■ Bay County Chamber of Commerce (BCCC)
235 W 5th St.
  Panama City, FL 32401
Ph: (850)785-5206
Co. E-mail: information@baychamberfl.com
URL: http://www.panamacity.org
Contact: Carol Roberts, President
E-mail: carol@baychamberfl.com
Facebook: www.facebook.com/baychamberfl
X (Twitter): x.com/baychamberfl
YouTube: www.youtube.com/channel/UC2ayf2P_E 14yvcGa0Vq1Asw
Description: Strives to develop, enhance, and maintain a viable business climate and to provide leadership in the development of economic growth and quality of life. **Founded:** 1913. **Publications:** *Bay Biz* (Weekly; Biweekly); *Bay Biz Magazine* (Quarterly). **Geographic Preference:** Local.

38330 ■ Belle Glade Chamber of Commerce
540 S Main St.
  Belle Glade, FL 33430
Ph: (561)996-2745
Fax: (561)996-2743
Co. E-mail: info@belleglade chamber.com
URL: http://www.belleglade chamber.com
Contact: Kathy Rhodes, Co-President
Facebook: www.facebook.com/belleglade chamber
Description: Promotes business and community development in Belle Glade, FL. **Founded:** 1938. **Geographic Preference:** Local.

38331 ■ *The Biz Insider*
URL(s): hollywoodchamber.org/publications
Released: Biweekly **Price:** Free for members. **Description:** Contains news and area events about the chamber and its members. **Availability:** Print; Online.

38332 ■ Boca Grande Area Chamber of Commerce
471 Pk. Ave., Ste. 3
  Boca Grande, FL 33921
Ph: (941)964-0568
Fax: (941)964-0620
Co. E-mail: info@bocagrandechamber.com
URL: http://bocagrandechamber.com

Small Business Sourcebook • 42nd Edition   2537

38333 ■ Florida   STATE LISTINGS

Contact: Gary Cross, Executive Director
Facebook: www.facebook.com/bgacc
Pinterest: www.pinterest.com/bocagrandecoc
Description: Seeks to enhance members' business and economic growth of Boca Grande area. **Geographic Preference:** Local.

38333 ■ Boynton Beach Business Monthly
Released: Monthly **Availability:** Print.

38334 ■ *The Bridge*
1945 Fruitville Rd.
Sarasota, FL 34236
Ph: (941)955-8187
Co. E-mail: communications@sarasotachamber.com
URL: http://www.sarasotachamber.com
Contact: Heather Kasten, President
E-mail: hkasten@sarasotachamber.com
URL(s): www.sarasotachamber.com/the-bridge-magazine.html
Released: Quarterly **Availability:** Print; Online.

38335 ■ British American Chamber of Commerce of Central Florida
10 N Pk. Ave., Ste. 1B
Apopka, FL 32703
URL: http://www.baccorlando.com/corporate-sponsors
Contact: Nick Grounds, Director
E-mail: nickgrounds1@gmail.com
Description: Promotes trade and investment. Facilitates social and commercial interaction among members. Provides a forum in which members can exchange information and ideas. **Geographic Preference:** Local.

38336 ■ *Business Directory*
1100 Reid St.
Palatka, FL 32177
Ph: (386)328-1503
Fax: (386)328-7076
Co. E-mail: chamber@chamberpc.com
URL: http://www.putnamcountychamber.com
Contact: Dana Jones, President
E-mail: danajones@chamberpc.com
URL(s): members.putnamcountychamber.com/list
Availability: Print.

38337 ■ *Business Directory*
100 E Call St.
Starke, FL 32091
Ph: (904)964-5278
Fax: (904)964-2863
URL: http://northfloridachamber.com
Contact: Pam Whittle, President
E-mail: pam@northfloridachamber.com
URL(s): www.northfloridachamber.com/membership-application.php
Availability: Online.

38338 ■ *Business Online*
2702 Tamiami Trl.
Port Charlotte, FL 33952
Ph: (941)627-2222
Fax: (941)627-9730
Co. E-mail: askus@charlottecountychamber.org
URL: http://www.charlottecountychamber.org
Contact: Stephen Lineberry, President
E-mail: president@charlottecountychamber.org
URL(s): www.charlottecountychamber.org/business-online-2
Released: Weekly **Availability:** PDF; Online.

38339 ■ *Business Watch*
401 N Flagler Dr.
West Palm Beach, FL 33401
Ph: (561)833-3711
Fax: (561)833-5582
Co. E-mail: chamber@palmbeaches.org
URL: http://www.palmbeaches.org
Contact: Richard Reikenis, President
URL(s): www.palmbeaches.org/business-watch
Released: Monthly **Availability:** PDF; Online.

38340 ■ Cape Coral Chamber of Commerce
2051 Cape Coral Pky. E
Cape Coral, FL 33904
Ph: (239)549-6900
Fax: (239)549-9609
Co. E-mail: info@capecoralchamber.com
URL: http://capecoralchamber.com
Contact: Donna Germain, President
E-mail: donna@capecoralchamber.com
Facebook: www.facebook.com/ChamberofCommerceofCapeCoral
Linkedin: www.linkedin.com/company/capecoralchamber
X (Twitter): x.com/capechamber
Instagram: www.instagram.com/chamberofcapecoral
Description: Advocates business interest, tourism, and community development in Cape Coral, FL. **Founded:** 1989. **Publications:** *Chamber Trends* (Quarterly). **Geographic Preference:** Local.

38341 ■ Cedar Key Chamber of Commerce (CKACOC)
450 2nd St.
Cedar Key, FL 32625
Ph: (352)543-5600
Co. E-mail: info@cedarkey.org
URL: http://cedarkey.org
Contact: Ben Iversen, Vice President Co-President
Facebook: www.facebook.com/CedarKeyWelcomeCenter
Description: Promotes business and community development in the Cedar Key, FL area. Promotes commercial aquaculture, fishing, and tourism. Conducts annual fine arts fair and annual seafood festival. **Founded:** 1983. **Publications:** *Business Directory.* **Geographic Preference:** Local.

38342 ■ Central Palm Beach County Chamber of Commerce
12794 W Forest Hill Blvd., Ste. 19
Wellington, FL 33414
Ph: (561)790-6200
Co. E-mail: info@cpbchamber.com
URL: http://www.cpbchamber.com
Contact: Mary Lou Bedford, Chief Executive Officer
E-mail: marylou@cpbchamber.com
Facebook: www.facebook.com/cpbchamber
X (Twitter): x.com/cpbchamber
Description: Promotes business and community development in the Acreage, Loxahatchee, Royal Palm Beach, Greenacres and Wellington areas. **Founded:** 1983. **Awards:** Central Palm Beach County Small Business of the Year (Annual). **Geographic Preference:** Local.

38343 ■ Chamber of Commerce of Okeechobee County
55 S Parrott Ave.
Okeechobee, FL 34972
Ph: (863)467-6246
Co. E-mail: info@okeechobeebusiness.com
URL: http://www.okeechobeebusiness.com
Contact: Tabitha Trent, President
Facebook: www.facebook.com/OkeeChamber
X (Twitter): x.com/Okee_Chamber
YouTube: www.youtube.com/channel/UCE0z110a5qi_NeyuelRVuGQ
Description: Promotes business and community development in Okeechobee County, FL. **Founded:** 2011. **Geographic Preference:** Local.

38344 ■ Chamber of Commerce of the Palm Beaches
401 N Flagler Dr.
West Palm Beach, FL 33401
Ph: (561)833-3711
Fax: (561)833-5582
Co. E-mail: chamber@palmbeaches.org
URL: http://www.palmbeaches.org
Contact: Richard Reikenis, President
X (Twitter): x.com/chamberupdate
Instagram: www.instagram.com/chamberupdate
YouTube: www.youtube.com/user/chamberupdate
Description: Advances the economic, industrial and civic interests of the Palm Beaches. Strives to support projects that lead to a stronger economy and an improved quality of life. **Founded:** 1913. **Publications:** *Education Guide to the Palm Beaches* (Irregular); *Entrepreneur Guide to the Palm Beaches*; *Guide to the Palm Beaches*; *Business Watch* (Monthly). **Awards:** Chamber of Commerce of the Palm Beaches ATHENA Awards (Annual); Chamber of Commerce of the Palm Beaches Small Business Person of the Year (Annual). **Geographic Preference:** Local.

38345 ■ *Chamber Connection*
12222 Overseas Hwy.
Marathon, FL 33050
Ph: (305)743-5417
Free: 800-262-7284
Co. E-mail: info@floridakeysmarathon.com
URL: http://floridakeysmarathon.com
Contact: Daniel Samess, Chief Executive Officer
E-mail: ceo@floridakeysmarathon.com
URL(s): floridakeysmarathon.com/about/newsletters
Released: Monthly **Description:** Contains information on the current events of the organization. **Availability:** Download; PDF; Online.

38346 ■ *Chamber Insider*
136 S Bronough St.
Tallahassee, FL 32301
Ph: (850)521-1200
Co. E-mail: info@flchamber.com
URL: http://www.flchamber.com
Contact: Mark Wilson, President
E-mail: mwilson@flchamber.com
URL(s): www.flchamber.com/chamber-insider-spotlight-world-kinect
Availability: Print; Online.

38347 ■ *Chamber Review*
URL(s): centralpascochamber.com/?page=Newsletter
Released: Monthly **Price:** Included in membership. **Description:** Features latest news and events in the chamber of commerce. **Availability:** Print; PDF; Online.

38348 ■ Chamber South (CS)
6410 SW 80th St.
South Miami, FL 33143
Ph: (305)661-1621
Fax: (305)666-0508
Co. E-mail: info@chambersouth.com
URL: http://www.chambersouth.com
Contact: Brittnie Bassant, President
E-mail: bbassant@chambersouth.com
Facebook: www.facebook.com/ChamberSouth
X (Twitter): x.com/chambersouth
YouTube: www.youtube.com/user/chambersouth1
Description: Promotes business and community development in South Dade/Kendall and Miami, FL. Sponsors South Miami Art Festival and other special events. Conducts local festivals. **Founded:** 1931. **Publications:** *Compass Points* (Monthly); *Southword* (Monthly). **Geographic Preference:** Local.

38349 ■ *Chamber Trends*
2051 Cape Coral Pky. E
Cape Coral, FL 33904
Ph: (239)549-6900
Fax: (239)549-9609
Co. E-mail: info@capecoralchamber.com
URL: http://capecoralchamber.com
Contact: Donna Germain, President
E-mail: donna@capecoralchamber.com
URL(s): capecoralchamber.com/chamber-trends
Ed: Stephanie Roberson. **Released:** Quarterly **Availability:** PDF; Online.

38350 ■ Charlotte County Chamber of Commerce
2702 Tamiami Trl.
Port Charlotte, FL 33952
Ph: (941)627-2222
Fax: (941)627-9730
Co. E-mail: askus@charlottecountychamber.org
URL: http://www.charlottecountychamber.org
Contact: Stephen Lineberry, President
E-mail: president@charlottecountychamber.org
Facebook: www.facebook.com/charlottecountychamber
Linkedin: www.linkedin.com/company/charlotte-county-chamber-of-commerce

STATE LISTINGS

Description: Promotes business and community development in Charlotte County, FL. **Founded:** 1925. **Publications:** *Business Online* (Weekly); *Perspective* (Quarterly). **Geographic Preference:** Local.

38351 ■ Citrus County Chamber of Commerce - Crystal River
915 n Suncoast Blvd.
Crystal River, FL 34429
Ph: (352)795-3149
Fax: (352)795-1921
URL: http://www.citruscountychamber.com
Contact: Josh Wooten, President
E-mail: josh@citruscountychamber.com
Facebook: www.facebook.com/CitrusChamber
X (Twitter): x.com/citruschamber
Description: Promotes business and community development in Crystal River, FL area. **Founded:** 1974. **Publications:** *The Wisecracker*. **Geographic Preference:** Local.

38352 ■ Clay County Chamber of Commerce
1845 Town Center Blvd., Ste. 410
Fleming Island, FL 32003
Ph: (904)264-2651
Co. E-mail: claychamber@claychamber.com
URL: http://www.claychamber.com
Contact: Randy Bowman, Chairman
Facebook: www.facebook.com/ClayCountyChamber
Linkedin: www.linkedin.com/company/clay-chamber-of-commerce
X (Twitter): x.com/claychamber
Instagram: www.instagram.com/claychamberfl
Description: Promotes business and community development in Clay County, FL. Sponsors annual Health Screening, Business and Health Expo, Military Appreciation, Industry Appreciation, Golf Tournament. In addition, promote economic, tourism and film development for the county. **Founded:** 1962. **Publications:** *Links* (Monthly); *Membership and Marketplace Guide* (Semiannual). **Geographic Preference:** Local.

38353 ■ Clewiston Chamber of Commerce
109 Central Ave.
Clewiston, FL 33440
Ph: (863)983-7979
Co. E-mail: clewistonchamber@embarqmail.com
URL: http://clewiston-fl.gov
Contact: Hillary Hyslope, Executive Director
Facebook: www.facebook.com/clewistonchamber
Description: Promotes business and community development in Clewiston, FL. **Founded:** 1946. **Publications:** *Clewiston Chamber of Commerce Newsletter*. **Educational Activities:** Clewiston Sugar Festival (Annual). **Geographic Preference:** Local.

38354 ■ *Coastlines*
34 Miracle Strip Pky. SE
Fort Walton Beach, FL 32548
Ph: (850)244-8191
Fax: (850)244-1935
Co. E-mail: info@fwbchamber.org
URL: http://www.fwbchamber.org
Contact: Ted Corcoran, President
E-mail: ted@fwbchamber.org
URL(s): www.fwbchamber.org/coastlines
Released: Weekly **Description:** Contains information about Chamber members and about upcoming community events. **Availability:** Print; Online.

38355 ■ Cocoa Beach Regional Chamber of Commerce (CBRCC)
400 Fortenberry Rd.
Merritt Island, FL 32952
Ph: (321)459-2200
Fax: (321)459-2232
Co. E-mail: cclark@cocoabeachchamber.com
URL: http://cocoabeachchamber.com
Contact: Jimmy Lane, President
Facebook: www.facebook.com/CocoaBeachRegionalChamberofCommerce
X (Twitter): x.com/_CBRCC
YouTube: www.youtube.com/user/CocoaBeachChamber
Description: Promotes business and community development in central Brevard County, FL. **Founded:** 1925. **Publications:** *Discover Our Spirit* (Monthly); *Economic Development Council Newsletter* (Monthly); *Tourism and Convention Council Newsletter* (Periodic). **Awards:** Cocoa Beach Area Chamber of Commerce Business of the Year (Annual). **Geographic Preference:** Local.

38356 ■ Coconut Grove Chamber of Commerce (CGCC)
3015 Grand Ave.
Coconut Grove, FL 33133
Ph: (305)444-7270
Fax: (305)444-2498
Co. E-mail: info@coconutgrovechamber.com
URL: http://coconutgrove.com/business/coconut-grove-chamber-of-commerce
Facebook: www.facebook.com/CoconutGroveChamber
X (Twitter): x.com/cgrovechamber
Description: Works to advance the commercial, financial, industrial and civic interests of Coconut Grove, FL. **Founded:** 1946. **Awards:** Coconut Grove Chambe - Golden Coconut Award (Annual). **Geographic Preference:** Local.

38357 ■ *The Communicator*
24214 Sorrento Ave.
Sorrento, FL 32776
Ph: (352)383-8801
Co. E-mail: chamber@elcchamber.com
URL: http://www.elcchamber.com
Contact: Pam Jennelle, President
URL(s): www.elcchamber.com/newsletter
Released: Monthly **Description:** Twelve pages, local info. **Availability:** PDF.

38358 ■ *Connection*
1800 N Dixie Hwy.
Boca Raton, FL 33432
Ph: (561)395-4433
Fax: (561)392-3780
Co. E-mail: info@bocachamber.com
URL: http://www.bocaratonchamber.com
Contact: Troy M. McLellan, Co-Chief Executive Officer Co-President
E-mail: tmclellan@bocachamber.com
URL(s): www.bocaratonchamber.com/boca-chamber-quarterly-connection-newsletter.html
Released: Quarterly **Description:** Includes helpful business information, networking tips, recent and upcoming events, recognition of members and a planning calendar. **Availability:** Print; Download; Online.

38359 ■ *ConTACt*
2000 S Washington Ave.
Titusville, FL 32780-4747
Ph: (321)267-3036
Fax: (321)264-0127
Co. E-mail: info@titusville.org
URL: http://titusville.org
Contact: Erin Akins VanDyke, Co-President
URL(s): titusville.org/contact-us
Released: Weekly (Thurs.) **Availability:** Online.

38360 ■ Coral Gables Chamber of Commerce (CGCC)
224 Catalonia Ave.
Coral Gables, FL 33134
Ph: (305)446-1657
Fax: (305)446-9900
Co. E-mail: info@coralgableschamber.org
URL: http://coralgableschamber.org
Contact: Mark A. Trowbridge, President
E-mail: mtrowbridge@coralgableschamber.org
X (Twitter): x.com/gableschamber
Instagram: www.instagram.com/gableschamber
YouTube: www.youtube.com/user/GablesCommunications
Description: Strives to foster and enhance the economic interests and quality of life in the Coral Gables community. **Founded:** 1925. **Geographic Preference:** Local.

38361 ■ Coral Springs Chamber of Commerce
9500 W Sample Rd.
Coral Springs, FL 33065
Ph: (954)752-4242
Co. E-mail: info@csccrchamber.com
URL: http://www.csccrchamber.com
Contact: Cindy Brief, President
Facebook: www.facebook.com/CSCCRChamberofCommerce
Linkedin: www.linkedin.com/company/coral-springs-chamber-of-commerce
X (Twitter): x.com/CSCCRChamber
Instagram: www.instagram.com/csccrchamber
YouTube: www.youtube.com/channel/UCGIZ4aj5qOTaA8UFDxXIBQg
Description: Promotes business and community development in Coral Gables, FL. Sponsors the town festival. **Founded:** 1997. **Publications:** *The Chamber Focus* (Monthly). **Awards:** Coral Springs Chamber of Commerce Small Business Leader of the Year (Annual); Coral Springs Chamber of Commerce Veteran Small Business Leader of the Year (Annual). **Geographic Preference:** Local.

38362 ■ Crestview Area Chamber of Commerce (CACC)
1447 Commerce Dr.
Crestview, FL 32539
Ph: (850)682-3212
Fax: (850)682-7413
Co. E-mail: info@crestviewchamber.com
URL: http://www.crestviewchamber.com
Contact: Sandra Wilson, Executive Director
Facebook: www.facebook.com/CrestviewAreaChamber
X (Twitter): x.com/crestviewchamb1
Description: Promotes business and community development in the Crestview, FL area. **Founded:** 1956. **Educational Activities:** Crestview Kiwanis and Rotary Meeting. **Geographic Preference:** Local.

38363 ■ Davie-Cooper City Chamber of Commerce (DCCC)
6191 Orange Dr., Ste. 6177
Davie, FL 33314
Ph: (954)581-0790
Co. E-mail: info@davie-coopercity.org
URL: http://www.davie-coopercity.org
Contact: Dr. Aimee Sanchez-Zadak, President
Facebook: www.facebook.com/DavieCooperCityChamber
X (Twitter): x.com/DavieCCChamber
Description: Promotes business and community development in the Davie/Cooper City, FL area. Seeks to protect the public against fraud and unethical practices; earn and maintain the public's confidence in the free enterprise system; and promote tourism. Sponsors Orange Blossom festival, and the Pro-Rodeo in November. **Founded:** 1935. **Publications:** *Chamber Chronicle* (Monthly); *Membership Directory and Buyer's Guide* (Annual). **Educational Activities:** Business After Hours/Business Mixers (Monthly). **Geographic Preference:** Local.

38364 ■ Daytona Regional Chamber of Commerce [Chamber, Daytona Beach and Halifax Area]
126 E Orange Ave.
Daytona Beach, FL 32114
Ph: (386)255-0981
Fax: (386)258-5104
Co. E-mail: info@daytonachamber.com
URL: http://www.daytonachamber.com
Contact: Nancy Keefer, President
E-mail: nancy@daytonachamber.com
Facebook: www.facebook.com/daytona.chamber
Linkedin: www.linkedin.com/company/daytona-regional-chamber-of-commerce
X (Twitter): x.com/DaytonaChamber
YouTube: www.youtube.com/channel/UCPL8Qh8lyzXPQ5JXDD4q3Eg
Description: Promotes business and community development in the Daytona Beach, FL area. **Founded:** 1920. **Publications:** *Official Guide* (Annual). **Geographic Preference:** Local.

38365 ■ DeLand Area Chamber of Commerce (DACC)
City Hall Complex, 2nd Fl.
120 S Florida Ave.
Deland, FL 32720
Ph: (386)734-4331
Fax: (386)734-4333
Co. E-mail: connect@delandchamber.org
URL: http://www.delandchamber.org
Contact: Elizabeth Godwin, President
Facebook: www.facebook.com/DeLandAreaChamberofCommerce
X (Twitter): x.com/delandchamber
Instagram: www.instagram.com/delandchamber
YouTube: www.youtube.com/channel/UC7KpY-HF7gIgIDyMXJCgW-Q

Description: Promotes business and community development in western Volusia County, FL. Seeks improved public education and transportation. Sponsors Restaurant Show and Home Show. Sponsors Leadership De Land. Administers Industrial and Tourism Development programs. **Founded:** 1890. **Publications:** *The Business Exchange* (Monthly); *Buyer's Guide* (Annual); *DeLand Data* (Bimonthly). **Geographic Preference:** Local.

38366 ■ DeSoto County Chamber of Commerce
222 E Oak St.
Arcadia, FL 34266
Ph: (863)494-4033
Co. E-mail: chamber@desotochamberfl.com
URL: http://desotochamberfl.com
Contact: Debbie Wertz, Executive Director

Description: Promotes business and community development in DeSoto County, FL. Provides staffed Welcome Center for local information. Sponsors All-Florida Championship Rodeo, Christmas card lane and Harvest Festival. **Founded:** 1926. **Publications:** *Chamber News* (Monthly). **Educational Activities:** Harvest Festival. **Geographic Preference:** Local.

38367 ■ Destin Area Chamber of Commerce
4484 Legendary Dr., Ste. A
Destin, FL 32541
Ph: (850)837-6241
Co. E-mail: mail@destinchamber.com
URL: http://www.destinchamber.com
Contact: Shane A. Moody, President
E-mail: ceo@destinchamber.com
Facebook: www.facebook.com/destinchamber
Linkedin: www.linkedin.com/company/destin-area-chamber-of-commerce
X (Twitter): x.com/destinchamber
Instagram: www.instagram.com/destinchamber
YouTube: www.youtube.com/destinchamber
Pinterest: www.pinterest.com/destinchamber

Description: Promotes business and community development in the Destin, FL area. **Founded:** 1966. **Publications:** *Chamber Progress* (Bimonthly); *Mini-Guide Brochure*. **Educational Activities:** Destin Area Chamber of Commerce Breakfast. **Geographic Preference:** Local.

38368 ■ Dixie County Chamber of Commerce
PO Box 547
Cross City, FL 32628
Ph: (352)498-5572
Co. E-mail: info@dixiechamber.org
URL: http://www.dixiechamber.org
Contact: Carol M. West, President

Description: Promotes business and community development in Dixie County, FL. **Geographic Preference:** Local.

38369 ■ Dunedin Chamber of Commerce
301 Main St.
Dunedin, FL 34698
Ph: (727)733-3197
Co. E-mail: chamber@dunedinfl.com
URL: http://dunedinfl.com
Contact: Pam Pravetz, President
Facebook: www.facebook.com/DunedinChamber
Instagram: www.instagram.com/dunedinchamber

Description: Promotes business and community development in the Dunedin, FL area. **Founded:** 1926. **Publications:** *Business Times* (Monthly). **Geographic Preference:** Local.

38370 ■ Dunnellon Chamber & Business Association (DCBA)
20500 E Pennsylvania Ave.
Dunnellon, FL 34432
Ph: (352)489-2320
Co. E-mail: dunnellonchambercommerce@gmail.com
URL: http://www.dunnellonchamber.com
Contact: Joanne Black, President
Facebook: www.facebook.com/dunnellonchambercommerce

Description: Promotes business and community development in the Dunnellon, FL area. Sponsors Boomtown Days festival, 4th of July Festival. **Founded:** 1887. **Publications:** *Boomtown Gazette* (Annual). **Geographic Preference:** Local.

38371 ■ East Lake County Chamber of Commerce
24214 Sorrento Ave.
Sorrento, FL 32776
Ph: (352)383-8801
Co. E-mail: chamber@elcchamber.com
URL: http://www.elcchamber.com
Contact: Pam Jennelle, President
Facebook: www.facebook.com/elcchamber
X (Twitter): x.com/EastLakeChamber
Instagram: www.instagram.com/elcchamber
Pinterest: www.pinterest.com/eastlakecountyc

Description: Promotes business and community development in East Lake County. **Founded:** 1985. **Publications:** *The Communicator* (Monthly). **Geographic Preference:** Local.

38372 ■ East Lee County Chamber of Commerce
25 Homestead Rd. N, No. 41
Lehigh Acres, FL 33936
Ph: (239)369-3322
Co. E-mail: info@elccoc.org
URL: http://elccoc.org
Contact: Michael J. Welch, Officer
Facebook: www.facebook.com/EastLeeChamber
X (Twitter): x.com/EastLeeChamber
Instagram: www.instagram.com/eastleechamberofcommerce

Description: Promotes business and community development in Lehigh Acres, FL. **Publications:** *Biennial Guide* (Biennial); *Business Beat* (Monthly). **Educational Activities:** Membership Meeting. **Geographic Preference:** Local.

38373 ■ *East Oranger*
12301 Lake Underhill Rd., Ste. 245
Orlando, FL 32828
Ph: (407)277-5951
Co. E-mail: eocc@eocc.org
URL: http://www.eocc.org
Contact: Andrew Cole, President
URL(s): www.eocc.org/about-us
Released: Weekly **Availability:** Online.

38374 ■ East Orlando Chamber of Commerce (EOCC)
12301 Lake Underhill Rd., Ste. 245
Orlando, FL 32828
Ph: (407)277-5951
Co. E-mail: eocc@eocc.org
URL: http://www.eocc.org
Contact: Andrew Cole, President
Linkedin: www.linkedin.com/company/east-orlando-chamber-of-commerce
X (Twitter): x.com/EastOrlandoCC
Instagram: www.instagram.com/eastorlandocc
YouTube: www.youtube.com/user/eastorlandocc

Description: Promotes business and community development in East Orange County, FL. Maintains visitor's center; provides business and personal relocation assistance. **Publications:** *East Oranger* (Weekly); *Relo Directory* (Annual). **Geographic Preference:** Local.

38375 ■ Englewood Florida Chamber of Commerce
601 S Indiana Ave.
Englewood, FL 34223
Ph: (941)474-5511
Co. E-mail: business@englewoodchamber.com
URL: http://www.englewoodchamber.com
Contact: Kathleen Callahan, President
Facebook: www.facebook.com/englewoodchamber

Description: Advocates responsible business and economic growth in Englewood community. **Geographic Preference:** Local.

38376 ■ *Estero*
9210 Estero Pk., Commons Blvd., Ste. 9
Estero, FL 33928
Ph: (239)390-1137
Co. E-mail: info@esterochamber.org
URL: http://esterochamber.org
Contact: Pamela Mueller, President
URL(s): esterochamber.org/our-magazine
Released: Annual **Availability:** Print; Online.

38377 ■ Estero Chamber of Commerce
9210 Estero Pk., Commons Blvd., Ste. 9
Estero, FL 33928
Ph: (239)390-1137
Co. E-mail: info@esterochamber.org
URL: http://esterochamber.org
Contact: Pamela Mueller, President
Facebook: www.facebook.com/EsteroChamberOfCommerce
Linkedin: www.linkedin.com/company/esterochamber
X (Twitter): x.com/esteroflchamber
Instagram: www.instagram.com/esterochamber

Description: Seeks to foster and achieve a business and economic climate for all the citizens of the Estero area. **Publications:** *Estero* (Annual). **Geographic Preference:** Local.

38378 ■ *Every Monday*
75 S Ivanhoe Blvd.
Orlando, FL 32804
Ph: (407)425-1234
Fax: (407)839-5020
Co. E-mail: info@orlando.org
URL: http://www.orlando.org
Contact: Jacob V. Stuart, President
E-mail: jacob.stuart@orlando.org
URL(s): www.orlando.org
Released: Weekly **Price:** Free. **Availability:** Print; Online.

38379 ■ *Fantastic Flagler Visitor, Newcomer & Resident Guide*
20 Airport Rd., Ste. C
Palm Coast, FL 32164
Ph: (386)437-0106
Co. E-mail: info@flaglerchamber.org
URL: http://www.flaglerchamber.org
URL(s): www.flaglerchamber.org/relocation-guide
Released: Annual **Description:** Magazine containing general information about the community, business information, and a visitor's guide to Flagler County, Florida. **Availability:** Print; Online.

38380 ■ *First Monday*
75 S Ivanhoe Blvd.
Orlando, FL 32804
Ph: (407)425-1234
Fax: (407)839-5020
Co. E-mail: info@orlando.org
URL: http://www.orlando.org
Contact: Jacob V. Stuart, President
E-mail: jacob.stuart@orlando.org
URL(s): www.orlando.org/index.php?src=gendocs&ref=FirstMonday%20Archives&category=About%20the%20chamber
Released: Monthly **Availability:** Print; PDF; Online.

38381 ■ Flagler County Chamber of Commerce
20 Airport Rd., Ste. C
Palm Coast, FL 32164
Ph: (386)437-0106
Co. E-mail: info@flaglerchamber.org
URL: http://www.flaglerchamber.org

X (Twitter): x.com/aarpky
Description: Promotes business and community development in Flagler Beach, FL. **Founded:** 1962. **Publications:** *Fantastic Flagler Visitor, Newcomer & Resident Guide* (Annual). **Geographic Preference:** Local.

38382 ■ Florida Chamber of Commerce (FCC)
136 S Bronough St.
Tallahassee, FL 32301
Ph: (850)521-1200
Co. E-mail: info@flchamber.com
URL: http://www.flchamber.com
Contact: Mark Wilson, President
E-mail: mwilson@flchamber.com
Facebook: www.facebook.com/flchamber
Linkedin: www.linkedin.com/company/florida-chamber-of-commerce
X (Twitter): x.com/FlChamber
Description: Promotes business and community development in the state of Florida. **Founded:** 1916. **Publications:** *Chamber Insider*; *People under the Sun*; *Directory of Chambers of Commerce in Florida*; *Virginia Industrial Directory* (Annual); *Guide to Florida High-Tech Industries*; *Directory of Florida Industries* (Annual). **Geographic Preference:** Local.

38383 ■ Frostproof Chamber of Commerce
17 E Wall St.
Frostproof, FL 33843
Ph: (863)635-9112
Co. E-mail: info@frostproofchamberofcommerce.com
URL: http://www.frostproofchamberofcommerce.com
Facebook: www.facebook.com/FrostproofChamber
Description: Promotes business and community development in Frostproof, FL. **Geographic Preference:** Local.

38384 ■ Gadsden County Chamber of Commerce
304 W King St.
Quincy, FL 32351
Ph: (850)627-9231
Co. E-mail: gadsdencc@tds.net
URL: http://www.gadsdencc.com
Contact: Bradford May, Chairman of the Board
Description: Promotes business and economic development in Gadsden County, Fl. **Geographic Preference:** Local.

38385 ■ Gainesville Area Chamber of Commerce
300 E University Ave., Ste. 100
Gainesville, FL 32601
Ph: (352)334-7100
Fax: (352)334-7141
URL: http://gainesvillechamber.com
Contact: Eric Godet, Sr., President
E-mail: egodet@gainesvillechamber.com
Facebook: www.facebook.com/GNVChamber
X (Twitter): x.com/gnvchamber
Instagram: www.instagram.com/gainesvillechamber
YouTube: www.youtube.com/user/GainesvilleChamber
Description: Promotes business and community development in the Gainesville, FL area. **Founded:** 1924. **Publications:** *Business Journal Newsletter* (Weekly); *Community and Buyer's Guide* (Annual). **Educational Activities:** Business Showcase; Chamber After Hours. **Geographic Preference:** Local.

38386 ■ Gilchrist County Chamber of Commerce
112 S Main St.
Trenton, FL 32693
Ph: (352)463-3467
Co. E-mail: chamber@gilchristcounty.com
URL: http://gilchristcounty.com
Contact: Leah Myrick, President
Facebook: www.facebook.com/GilchristCountyChamber
Description: Promotes business and community development in Gilchrist County, FL. **Publications:** *The Chamber Monthly Review* (Monthly). **Geographic Preference:** Local.

38387 ■ Greater Bartow Chamber of Commerce (GBCC)
510 N Broadway Ave.
Bartow, FL 33830
Ph: (863)533-7125
Fax: (863)533-3793
Co. E-mail: virginia@bartowchamber.com
URL: http://www.bartowchamber.com
Contact: Shannon Medley, President
Facebook: www.facebook.com/BartowChamberofCommerce
Description: Works to recruit new businesses and industries to Bartow, FL and promotes cultural life. **Founded:** 1887. **Publications:** *Bartow Chamber News* (Monthly). **Geographic Preference:** Local.

38388 ■ Greater Boca Raton Chamber of Commerce (GBRCC)
1800 N Dixie Hwy.
Boca Raton, FL 33432
Ph: (561)395-4433
Fax: (561)392-3780
Co. E-mail: info@bocachamber.com
URL: http://www.bocaratonchamber.com
Contact: Troy M. McLellan, Co-Chief Executive Officer Co-President
E-mail: tmclellan@bocachamber.com
Facebook: www.facebook.com/bocachamber
Linkedin: www.linkedin.com/in/bocachamber
X (Twitter): x.com/bocachamber
YouTube: www.youtube.com/channel/UCuvy_dSIQCkOG8kckyk5aQw
Description: Promotes business and community development in the Boca Raton, FL area. Provides member services such as discount health insurance, networking, business development workshops, etc. **Founded:** 1952. **Publications:** *Boca Raton Annual* (Annual); *Connection* (Quarterly). **Awards:** Greater Boca Raton Chamber of Commerce Business Leader of the Year (Annual); Greater Boca Raton Chamber of Commerce Small Business Leader of the Year (Annual). **Geographic Preference:** Local.

38389 ■ Greater Brandon Chamber of Commerce (GBCC)
1463 Oakfield Dr., Ste. 134
Brandon, FL 33511
Ph: (813)689-1221
Co. E-mail: info@brandonchamber.com
URL: http://www.brandonchamber.com
Contact: Matt Lettelleir, President
E-mail: president@brandonchamber.com
Facebook: www.facebook.com/thebrandonchamber
Linkedin: www.linkedin.com/company/brandonchamber
Instagram: www.instagram.com/thebrandonchamber
Description: Promotes business and community development in the Brandon, FL area. Operates visitors' bureau. Holds seminars and networking opportunities. **Founded:** 1959. **Publications:** *Brandon Business* (Monthly). **Educational Activities:** Coffee Club; Business After Hours (Monthly). **Awards:** Greater Brandon Community Leadership Award (Annual). **Geographic Preference:** Local.

38390 ■ Greater Chiefland Area Chamber of Commerce
PO Box 1397
Chiefland, FL 32644
Ph: (352)493-1849
URL: http://chieflandchamber.com
Contact: Melanie Hutchison, President
Description: Fosters population, commerce and finance advancement, civic and social improvement, and other sphere of interests within greater Chiefland area. **Awards:** Greater Chiefland Area Citizen of the Year. **Geographic Preference:** Local.

38391 ■ Greater Dade City Chamber of Commerce
14112 8th St.
Dade City, FL 33525
Ph: (352)567-3769
Co. E-mail: jmoors@dadecitychamber.org
URL: http://www.dadecitychamber.org
Contact: John Moors, President

E-mail: jmoors@dadecitychamber.org
Facebook: www.facebook.com/DadeCityChamber
Linkedin: www.linkedin.com/in/gdcchamber
X (Twitter): x.com/GDCChamber
Pinterest: www.pinterest.com/dadecitychamber
Description: Promotes business and community development in the Dade City, FL area. **Publications:** *Greater Dade City Chamber of Commerce--Annual Membership Directory* (Annual); *Annual Membership Directory* (Annual). **Geographic Preference:** Local.

38392 ■ Greater Dania Beach Chamber of Commerce
102 W Dania Beach Blvd.
Dania Beach, FL 33004
Ph: (954)926-2323
Fax: (954)926-2384
Co. E-mail: rshane@daniabeachchamber.org
URL: http://www.daniabeachchamber.org
Contact: Pat Chukerman, President
Description: Promotes business and community development in Dania, FL. **Awards:** Greater Dania Beach Chamber of Commerce Small Business Person of the Year (Annual). **Geographic Preference:** Local.

38393 ■ Greater Delray Beach Chamber of Commerce
140 NE 1st St.
Delray Beach, FL 33444
Ph: (561)278-0424
Co. E-mail: info@vupmedia.com
URL: http://www.delraybeach.com
Contact: David Schmidt, Chairman of the Board
Facebook: www.facebook.com/delraybeach
Linkedin: www.linkedin.com/in/delray-chamber-bb010550/%20
X (Twitter): x.com/delraychamber
Instagram: www.instagram.com/delraychamber
YouTube: www.youtube.com/channel/UC_OHOUmQ3EkmuOKMvbZNLGg
Description: Seeks to promote and perpetuate business growth, economic development, civic interest, general welfare and prosperity of the Greater Delray Beach area. Aims to stimulate public interest to these ends. **Founded:** 1912. **Publications:** *TradeWinds* (Bimonthly). **Awards:** Greater Delray Beach Chamber of Commerce Business of the Year (Annual); Greater Delray Beach Chamber of Commerce Business Recognition Awards (Annual); Ken Ellingsworth Community Service Awards (Annual); Greater Delray Beach Chamber of Commerce Small Business Person of the Year (Annual). **Geographic Preference:** Local.

38394 ■ Greater Fort Lauderdale Chamber of Commerce (GFLCC)
512 NE 3rd Ave.
Fort Lauderdale, FL 33301
Ph: (954)462-6000
Fax: (954)527-9430
Co. E-mail: info@ftlchamber.com
URL: http://www.ftlchamber.com
Contact: Dan Lindblade, President
E-mail: dan@ftlchamber.com
Facebook: www.facebook.com/ftlchamber
X (Twitter): x.com/ftlchamber
Instagram: www.instagram.com/ftlchamber
YouTube: www.youtube.com/channel/UC6poMQbbx9lT8ltWGIRU2eA
Description: Promotes business, tourism, and community development in the Greater Ft. Lauderdale, FL area. **Founded:** 1910. **Publications:** *The Challenge* (Monthly); *Guide to Greater Fort Lauderdale* (Annual); *Chamber Link* (Monthly); *The Guide* (Biennial). **Geographic Preference:** Local.

38395 ■ Greater Fort Myers Chamber of Commerce (GFMCC)
2310 Edwards Dr.
Fort Myers, FL 33901
Ph: (239)332-2930
Co. E-mail: info@fortmyers.org
URL: http://fortmyers.org
Contact: Brian Hamman, President
Facebook: www.facebook.com/gfmcc
X (Twitter): x.com/FtMyersChamber

Instagram: www.instagram.com/greaterfor
tmyerschamber
Description: Promotes civic and commercial progress of Greater Fort Myers' community. **Founded:** 1989. **Publications:** *Greater Network E-News* (Bi-monthly). **Geographic Preference:** Local.

38396 ■ Greater Fort Walton Beach Chamber of Commerce (FWB)
34 Miracle Strip Pky. SE
Fort Walton Beach, FL 32548
Ph: (850)244-8191
Fax: (850)244-1935
Co. E-mail: info@fwbchamber.org
URL: http://www.fwbchamber.org
Contact: Ted Corcoran, President
E-mail: ted@fwbchamber.org
Facebook: www.facebook.com/FWBChamber
X (Twitter): x.com/fwbchamber
Instagram: www.instagram.com/greaterfwbchamber
YouTube: www.youtube.com/user/fwbchamber
Description: Promotes business and community development in the Ft. Walton Beach, FL area. **Founded:** 1946. **Publications:** *Lifestyles* (Annual); *Coastlines* (Weekly); *Lifestyles*. **Educational Activities:** Billy Bowlegs Pirate Festival; First Friday Coffees (Monthly). **Geographic Preference:** Local.

38397 ■ Greater Hernando County Chamber of Commerce (GHCCC)
15588 Aviation Loop Dr.
Brooksville, FL 34604
Ph: (352)796-0697
Co. E-mail: info@hernandochamber.com
URL: http://www.hernandochamber.com
Contact: Morris Porton, President
E-mail: president@hernandochamber.com
Facebook: www.facebook.com/hernandocoun
tychamber
X (Twitter): x.com/HernandoChamber
Description: Business and professional men and women who promote civic, commercial, and industrial progress. **Publications:** *The Business Edge* (Monthly). **Educational Activities:** Leadership Hernando. **Geographic Preference:** Local.

38398 ■ Greater Hollywood Chamber of Commerce (GHCC)
330 N Federal Hwy.
Hollywood, FL 33020
Ph: (954)923-4000
Free: 800-231-5562
Fax: (954)923-8737
Co. E-mail: information@hollywoodchamber.org
URL: http://www.hollywoodchamber.org
Contact: Dr. Natacha Yacinthe, President
Facebook: www.facebook.com/HollywoodChamber
Instagram: www.instagram.com/hollywoodchamber
Description: Promotes business and community development in the Hollywood, FL area. **Founded:** 1922. **Publications:** *Visitor Guide* (Annual). **Geographic Preference:** Local.

38399 ■ Greater Lake Placid Chamber of Commerce
18 N Oak Ave.
Lake Placid, FL 33852
Ph: (863)465-4331
Co. E-mail: chamberexecutive@lpfla.com
URL: http://www.lpfla.com
Contact: Donald Clarke, President
E-mail: donald@clarkepestcontrol.com
Facebook: www.facebook.com/VisitLakePlacid
Instagram: www.instagram.com/lpchamber
Description: Promotes business and community development in the Lake Placid, FL area. **Publications:** *Chamber News* (Monthly); *Lake Placid Map*. **Educational Activities:** Lake Placid Chamber of Commerce Luncheon (Monthly). **Geographic Preference:** Local.

38400 ■ Greater Marathon Chamber of Commerce (GMCC)
12222 Overseas Hwy.
Marathon, FL 33050
Ph: (305)743-5417
Free: 800-262-7284

Co. E-mail: info@floridakeysmarathon.com
URL: http://floridakeysmarathon.com
Contact: Daniel Samess, Chief Executive Officer
E-mail: ceo@floridakeysmarathon.com
Facebook: www.facebook.com/pages/Greater-Mara
thon-Chamber-of-Commerce/131017336915343
Description: Promotes business and community development in the Marathon, FL area. **Founded:** 1939. **Publications:** *Chamber Connection* (Monthly). **Geographic Preference:** Local.

38401 ■ Greater Miami Chamber of Commerce (GMCC)
1601 Biscayne Blvd., Ballroom Level
Miami, FL 33132
Ph: (305)350-7700
Co. E-mail: president@miamichamber.com
URL: http://www.miamichamber.com
Contact: Alfred Sanchez, President
Facebook: www.facebook.com/miamichamber
Linkedin: www.linkedin.com/company/miamichamber
X (Twitter): x.com/MiamiChamber
Instagram: www.instagram.com/miami_chamber
YouTube: www.youtube.com/user/Grea
terMiamiChamber/videos
Description: Promotes business and community development in the Miami, FL area. **Founded:** 1907. **Publications:** *CEO Report* (Quarterly); *CEO Report Update* (Monthly); *Greater Miami Chamber Membership Directory* (Annual); *New Member Profile* (Semiannual); *NewsBreak* (Weekly). **Awards:** Greater Miami Chamber of Commerce Health Care Heroes (Annual). **Geographic Preference:** Local.

38402 ■ *Greater Miami Chamber Membership Directory*
1601 Biscayne Blvd., Ballroom Level
Miami, FL 33132
Ph: (305)350-7700
Co. E-mail: president@miamichamber.com
URL: http://www.miamichamber.com
Contact: Alfred Sanchez, President
URL(s): www.miamichamber.com/member-directory
Released: Annual **Availability:** Print.

38403 ■ Greater Miami Shores Chamber of Commerce
9620 NE 2nd Ave., Ste. 201
Miami Shores, FL 33138
Ph: (305)754-5466
Co. E-mail: chamberinfo@miamishores.com
URL: http://www.miamishores.com
Contact: Catherine McLaney, President
Linkedin: www.linkedin.com/company/greater-miami
-shores-chamber-of-commerce
X (Twitter): x.com/ShoresChamber
Description: Strives to provide leadership for the advancement of the economic vitality, civic affairs and quality of life of the total community in Miami shores, FL. **Founded:** 1949. **Geographic Preference:** Local.

38404 ■ Greater Mulberry Chamber of Commerce (GMCC)
705 N Church Ave.
Mulberry, FL 33860
Ph: (863)425-4414
Fax: (863)425-3837
Co. E-mail: chamber@mulberrychamber.org
URL: http://www.mulberrychamber.org
Contact: Cindy Bryson, Secretary
Description: Promotes business and community development in Mulberry, FL. Helps to bring educational information to the local businesses and helps to promote the sports and tourism in the Central Florida Area. **Publications:** *Mulberry Magic* (Monthly). **Geographic Preference:** Local.

38405 ■ The Greater Naples Chamber of Commerce (GNCC)
2390 Tamiami Trl. N, Ste. 210
Naples, FL 34103
Ph: (239)262-6376
Co. E-mail: info@napleschamber.org
URL: http://www.napleschamber.org
Contact: Michael Dalby, President
E-mail: michael@napleschamber.org

Facebook: www.facebook.com/NaplesChamber
X (Twitter): x.com/NaplesChamber
Description: Promotes business and community development in the Naples, FL area. **Founded:** 1947. **Publications:** *Currents* (Monthly); *Naples on the Gulf* (Annual). **Geographic Preference:** Local.

38406 ■ Greater Nassau County Chamber of Commerce
961687 Gateway Blvd., Ste. 101-G
Fernandina Beach, FL 32034
Ph: (904)261-3248
Co. E-mail: info@nassaucountyflchamber.com
URL: http://www.islandchamber.com
Contact: Regina Duncan, President
Facebook: www.facebook.com/NassauCoun
tyFLChamberofCommerce
Linkedin: www.linkedin.com/company/nassau-county
-fl-chamber-of-commerce
X (Twitter): x.com/AmeliaIsland
Instagram: www.instagram.com/nassau_county
_chamber
YouTube: www.youtube.com/channel/UCzwl
dcujnaaurGBDZO5ha2A
Description: Promotes business and community development in Nassau County, FL. **Founded:** 1956. **Publications:** *Greater Nassau Chamber News*. **Geographic Preference:** Local.

38407 ■ Greater North Miami Beach Chamber of Commerce
16901 NE 19th Ave., Ste. A
North Miami Beach, FL 33162
Ph: (305)944-8500
Co. E-mail: chamber@nmbchamber.com
URL: http://www.nmbchamber.com
Contact: Evan Piper, President
Facebook: www.facebook.com/thegrea
ternmbchamber
X (Twitter): x.com/NMBCoC
Description: Promotes business and community development in North Miami, FL. Sponsors annual Career Shadowing Day. **Founded:** 1947. **Publications:** *The Pink Sheet* (Monthly). **Educational Activities:** Business After Hours Expo (Monthly). **Geographic Preference:** Local.

38408 ■ Greater Palm Harbor Area Chamber of Commerce (GPHACC)
1151 Nebraska Ave.
Palm Harbor, FL 34683
Ph: (727)784-4287
Co. E-mail: phcc@palmharborchamber.com
URL: http://palmharborchamber.com
Contact: Margie Swope, Treasurer
Facebook: www.facebook.com/Grea
terPalmHarborAreaChamberofCommerce
Description: Promotes business and community development in the Palm Harbor, FL area. **Founded:** 1997. **Publications:** *Communicator* (Bimonthly). **Geographic Preference:** Local.

38409 ■ Greater Pensacola Chamber
418 W Garden St.
Pensacola, FL 32502
Ph: (850)475-4999
Co. E-mail: support@pensacolachamber.com
URL: http://www.pensacolachamber.com
Contact: Todd Thomson, President
E-mail: cingram@pensacolachamber.com
Facebook: www.facebook.com/PensacolaChamber
Linkedin: www.linkedin.com/company/greater
-pensacola-chamber
X (Twitter): x.com/pcolachamber
Instagram: www.instagram.com/pensacolachamber
YouTube: www.youtube.com/channel/UCyTBl5k7Z
-1ZQiYhl7rYPTw
Description: Promotes business and community development in the Pensacola, FL area. **Founded:** 1889. **Geographic Preference:** Local.

38410 ■ Greater Pine Island Chamber of Commerce (GPICC)
PO Box 325
Matlacha, FL 33993
Ph: (239)283-0888
Co. E-mail: info@pineislandchamber.com

URL: http://pineislandchamber.org
Contact: Larry Solinger, President
Facebook: www.facebook.com/Greater-Pine-Island-Chamber-of-Commerce-181770921876671
Description: Promotes business, community development, and tourism in Pine Island, FL. Sponsors fundraising activities. **Founded:** 1961. **Publications:** *Chamber Connection* (Monthly). **Educational Activities:** Business Card Exchange (Monthly). **Geographic Preference:** Local.

38411 ■ Greater Plant City Chamber of Commerce
106 N Evers St.
Plant City, FL 33563
Ph: (813)754-3707
Co. E-mail: info@plantcity.org
URL: http://www.plantcity.org
Contact: Christine Miller, President
E-mail: christine@plantcity.org
Description: Promotes business and community development in the Plant City, FL area. **Founded:** 1975. **Publications:** *Greater Plant City Chamber of Commerce--Membership Directory*. **Geographic Preference:** Local.

38412 ■ Greater Plantation Chamber of Commerce (GPCC)
7401 NW 4th St.
Plantation, FL 33317
Ph: (954)587-1410
Co. E-mail: info@plantationchamber.org
URL: http://plantationchamber.org
Contact: Siobhan Edwards, President
Facebook: www.facebook.com/plantationchamber
Description: Promotes business and community development in the Plantation, FL area. Encourages orderly development and growth. **Founded:** 1961. **Publications:** *Plantation Annual* (Annual). **Geographic Preference:** Local.

38413 ■ Greater Pompano Beach Chamber of Commerce
2200 E Atlantic Blvd.
Pompano Beach, FL 33062
Ph: (954)941-2940
Free: 888-939-5711
Fax: (954)785-8358
Co. E-mail: info@pompanobeachchamber.com
URL: http://www.pompanobeachchamber.com
Contact: Jeff Wolfe, Director
Facebook: www.facebook.com/pompanobeachchamber
Description: Promotes business and community development in Pompano Beach, FL. **Awards:** Greater Pompano Beach Chamber of Commerce Small Business Person of the Year (Annual). **Geographic Preference:** Local.

38414 ■ Greater Riverview Chamber of Commerce (GRCC)
6152 Delancey Station St., Ste. 205
Riverview, FL 33578
Ph: (813)234-5944
Co. E-mail: info@riverviewchamber.com
URL: http://www.riverviewchamber.com
Contact: Michelle Mosher, President
Facebook: www.facebook.com/theriverviewchamber
Linkedin: www.linkedin.com/company/riverviewchamber
Description: Promotes business and community development in Riverview, FL. Sponsors run. **Founded:** 1966. **Geographic Preference:** Local.

38415 ■ The Greater Sanford Regional Chamber of Commerce
230 E First St.
Sanford, FL 32771
Ph: (407)322-2212
Co. E-mail: kim@sanfordchamber.com
URL: http://www.sanfordchamber.com
Contact: Nicolet Severe, President
Facebook: www.facebook.com/SanfordChamberofCommerce
X (Twitter): x.com/OfSanford
Instagram: www.instagram.com/sanfordchamber
YouTube: www.youtube.com/channel/UCAdoidhCo5oqr6UiT4yuwTg
Description: Promotes business and community development in Sanford and Seminole County. **Founded:** 1920. **Publications:** *The Channel* (Bimonthly). **Educational Activities:** Bikefest. **Geographic Preference:** Local.

38416 ■ Greater Sarasota Chamber of Commerce (GSCC)
1945 Fruitville Rd.
Sarasota, FL 34236
Ph: (941)955-8187
Co. E-mail: communications@sarasotachamber.com
URL: http://www.sarasotachamber.com
Contact: Heather Kasten, President
E-mail: hkasten@sarasotachamber.com
Facebook: www.facebook.com/greatersarasotachamber
Linkedin: www.linkedin.com/company/greater-sarasota-chamber-of-commerce
X (Twitter): x.com/GSCC
Instagram: www.instagram.com/greatersarasotachamber
YouTube: www.youtube.com/channel/UCEI8ECbIC9yhDNrLWdejvew
Description: Promotes business and community development in Sarasota County, FL. **Founded:** 1921. **Publications:** *The Bridge* (Quarterly); *Catalyst* (Monthly); *ePoint!* (Bimonthly); *Guide to Greater Sarasota*; *The Point* (Quarterly). **Awards:** Greater Sarasota Chamber of Commerce Small Business of the Year Award (Annual). **Geographic Preference:** Local.

38417 ■ Greater Sebring Chamber of Commerce (GSCC)
227 US 27 N
Sebring, FL 33870
Ph: (863)385-8448
Fax: (863)385-8810
Co. E-mail: admin@sebring.org
URL: http://www.sebring.org
Contact: Tenille Drury-Smith, President
E-mail: ceo@sebring.org
Facebook: www.facebook.com/greatersebringchamber
X (Twitter): x.com/SebringChamber
Description: Promotes business and community development in the Sebring, FL area. **Founded:** 1925. **Publications:** *Communicator* (Bimonthly); *Lifestyle Sebring* (Annual). **Geographic Preference:** Local.

38418 ■ Greater Seffner Area Chamber of Commerce
1209 Kingsway Rd.
Brandon, FL 33510
Ph: (813)627-8686
Co. E-mail: info@seffnerchamber.com
URL: http://seffnerchamber.com
Contact: Rachel Roetter, Director
Description: Promotes business and community development in the Seffner, Mango, Dover, and Valrico FL area. **Founded:** 1986. **Geographic Preference:** Local.

38419 ■ Greater Seminole Area Chamber of Commerce
9200 113th St.
Seminole, FL 33772
Ph: (727)392-3245
Fax: (727)397-7753
Co. E-mail: admin@myseminolechamber.com
URL: http://myseminolechamber.com
Contact: Allison Bean, Chairperson
Facebook: www.facebook.com/greaterseminolechamberofcommerce/www.facebook.com/greaterseminolechamberofcommerce/www.facebook.com/greaterseminolechamberofcommerce
Linkedin: www.linkedin.com/company/seminolechamberofcommercefl
X (Twitter): x.com/seminolechambr
Description: Seeks to advance Seminole's economy and quality of life. **Founded:** 1963. **Geographic Preference:** Local.

38420 ■ Greater Sunrise Chamber of Commerce
6800 Sunset Strip
Sunrise, FL 33313
Ph: (954)835-2428
Fax: (954)561-9685
Co. E-mail: sunrisechamber@sunrisechamber.org
URL: http://sunrisechamber.org
Contact: Brian Feuer, Executive Director
E-mail: executivedirector@sunrisechamber.org
Description: Promotes business and community development in Sunrise, FL. **Founded:** 1975. **Publications:** *Sunlines* (Monthly). **Geographic Preference:** Local.

38421 ■ Greater Tallahassee Chamber of Commerce
300 E Pk. Ave.
Tallahassee, FL 32301
Ph: (850)224-8116
Fax: (850)561-3860
Co. E-mail: info@talchamber.com
URL: http://talchamber.com
Contact: Sue Dick, President
E-mail: sdick@talchamber.com
Facebook: www.facebook.com/talchamber
Linkedin: www.linkedin.com/company/greater-tallahassee-chamber-of-commerce
X (Twitter): x.com/talchamber
Instagram: www.instagram.com/talchamber
YouTube: www.youtube.com/user/talchamber
Description: Promotes business and community development in Tallahassee, FL. **Founded:** 1923. **Publications:** *Business Views*; *Market Directory* (Annual). **Awards:** Greater Tallahassee Chamber of Commerce Small Business Excellence Awards (Annual). **Geographic Preference:** Local.

38422 ■ Greater Winter Haven Chamber of Commerce
401 Ave. B NW
Winter Haven, FL 33881
Ph: (863)293-2138
Co. E-mail: info@winterhavenchamber.com
URL: http://www.winterhavenchamber.com
Contact: Sara Beth Wyatt, President
E-mail: sarabeth@winterhavenchamber.com
Facebook: www.facebook.com/WinterHavenChamber
Linkedin: www.linkedin.com/company/greater-winter-haven-chamber-of-commerce
X (Twitter): x.com/whchamber
Instagram: www.instagram.com/winterhavenchamber
YouTube: www.youtube.com/channel/UCOl-ATPZ0MZ1NCcf0xvLdGw
Description: Promotes business and community development in Winter Haven, FL. **Founded:** 1910. **Publications:** *Winter Haven* (Annual). **Geographic Preference:** Local.

38423 ■ *The Guide*
512 NE 3rd Ave.
Fort Lauderdale, FL 33301
Ph: (954)462-6000
Fax: (954)527-9430
Co. E-mail: info@ftlchamber.com
URL: http://www.ftlchamber.com
Contact: Dan Lindblade, President
E-mail: dan@ftlchamber.com
URL(s): www.ftlchamber.com/the-chamber/guide-archives
Released: Biennial **Description:** Includes information about the General Fort Lauderdale area, the Chamber, business and industry, media, facts and figures, and transportation. **Availability:** Online.

38424 ■ *Guide to the Palm Beaches*
401 N Flagler Dr.
West Palm Beach, FL 33401
Ph: (561)833-3711
Fax: (561)833-5582
Co. E-mail: chamber@palmbeaches.org
URL: http://www.palmbeaches.org

Contact: Richard Reikenis, President
URL(s): www.palmbeaches.org/publications
Released: Latest edition 2024. **Description:** Covers businesses in the Palm Beaches. **Availability:** Online.

38425 ■ Gulf Breeze Area Chamber of Commerce
3044 Gulf Breeze Pky.
Gulf Breeze, FL 32563
Ph: (850)932-7888
Co. E-mail: reception@gulfbreezechamber.com
URL: http://www.gulfbreezechamber.com
Contact: Grace Arneault, Co-Chief Executive Officer Co-President
Facebook: www.facebook.com/GulfBreezeChamber
Linkedin: www.linkedin.com/company/gulf-breeze-area-chamber
X (Twitter): x.com/gbreezechamber
YouTube: www.youtube.com/user/GBChamberLive
Description: Develops an attractive business environment that provides opportunity for economic growth while improving the quality of life and enhancing the standard of living for the entire Gulf Breeze area. **Founded:** 1988. **Publications:** *Gulf Breeze Magazine* (Quarterly); *Gulf Breeze Area Chamber of Commerce--Membership Directory and Relocation Guide* (Annual). **Geographic Preference:** Local.

38426 ■ Gulf County Chamber of Commerce
321 B Reid Ave.
Port Saint Joe, FL 32456
Ph: (850)227-1223
Co. E-mail: info@gulfchamber.org
URL: http://www.gulfchamber.org
Contact: Aaron Little, Chairman of the Board
Facebook: www.facebook.com/GulfCoChamberofCommerce
X (Twitter): x.com/gulf_chamber
Pinterest: www.pinterest.com/gulfcountychamb
Description: Promotes the growth of local businesses by keeping members informed of news that may affect their businesses; by discovering and communicating members' interests on questions affecting the welfare of cities, county, state and the country at large; by linking the people of the entire communities together in a common enterprise; and by making possible great public and business-forward movements. **Founded:** 1938. **Geographic Preference:** Local.

38427 ■ Hardee County Chamber of Commerce (HCCC)
135 E Main St.
Wauchula, FL 33873
Ph: (863)773-6967
Free: 866-866-5545
Co. E-mail: director@hardeecc.com
URL: http://www.hardeecc.com
Contact: Heather Nedley, Executive Chairman of the Board
Facebook: www.facebook.com/hardeecc
YouTube: www.youtube.com/channel/UC40Eu8s2a9A7dp1rcQYXyxw
Description: Promotes business and community development in Hardee County, FL. **Publications:** *Chamber Bulletin* (Monthly); *The Voice of Business* (Monthly). **Geographic Preference:** Local.

38428 ■ Hawthorne Area Chamber of Commerce
6800 SE US Hwy. 301
Hawthorne, FL 32640
Ph: (352)363-5125
Co. E-mail: hawthornechamber@hotmail.com
URL: http://www.hawthorneareachamber.org/index.php
Contact: Donna Boles, President
Facebook: www.facebook.com/Hawthorne-Area-Chamber-of-Commerce-146320612073599
Description: Promotes business and community development in Hawthorne, FL area. **Founded:** 1840. **Geographic Preference:** Local.

38429 ■ Hialeah Chamber of Commerce and Industries (HCC&I)
240 E 1st Ave., Ste. 217
Hialeah, FL 33010
Ph: (305)888-7780
Co. E-mail: info@hialeahchamber.org
URL: http://hialeahchamber.org
Contact: Daniel Hernandez, President
YouTube: www.youtube.com/channel/UCDRuxSsjTsCd6NcEkGq6EHA
Description: Provides information to small, medium, and large sized businesses in the community. Develops business opportunities throughout the community through the use of trade missions to Latin America, the Caribbean, and Europe. **Founded:** 1979. **Geographic Preference:** Local.

38430 ■ High Springs Chamber of Commerce (HSCC)
23517 NW 185th Rd.
High Springs, FL 32643
Ph: (386)454-3120
Co. E-mail: chamber@highsprings.com
URL: http://highsprings.com
Contact: Sharon Decker, President
Facebook: www.facebook.com/HSChamberOfCommerce
Description: Promotes business and community development in High Springs, FL. Sponsors annual Pioneer Days festival. **Geographic Preference:** Local.

38431 ■ Hobe Sound Chamber of Commerce
8958 SE Bridge Rd., 2nd Fl., Hobe Sound Centre Bldg.
Hobe Sound, FL 33455
Ph: (772)546-4724
Fax: (772)546-9969
Co. E-mail: info@hobesound.org
URL: http://www.hobesound.org
Contact: Dorothy J. Flemming, President
Facebook: www.facebook.com/hobesoundchamber
Instagram: www.instagram.com/hobesoundchamber
Description: Promotes business and community development in Hobe Sound, FL. **Geographic Preference:** Local.

38432 ■ Immokalee Chamber of Commerce
Immokalee, FL 34142
Ph: (239)657-3237
Co. E-mail: immokaleechamber@comcast.net
URL: http://www.immokaleechamber.com
Contact: Danny Gonzalez, President
Description: Promotes business and community development in Immokalee, FL. **Founded:** 1873. **Geographic Preference:** Local.

38433 ■ Indian River County Chamber of Commerce
1216 21st St.
Vero Beach, FL 32960
Ph: (772)567-3491
Co. E-mail: info@indianriverchamber.com
URL: http://www.indianriverchamber.com
Contact: Dori Stone, President
E-mail: doris@indianriverchamber.com
Facebook: www.facebook.com/IndianRiverChamber
X (Twitter): x.com/IRCChamber
Instagram: www.instagram.com/ircchamber
Description: Business and professional membership. Promotion, expansion and retention of business. Provides leadership for growth and change. Promotes tourism. **Founded:** 1923. **Publications:** *ChamberLink* (Monthly). **Geographic Preference:** Local.

38434 ■ Indiantown Western Martin County Chamber of Commerce
16656 SW Warfield Blvd.
Indiantown, FL 34956
Ph: (772)597-2184
Co. E-mail: info@indiantownchamber.com
URL: http://www.indiantownchamber.com
Contact: Joe Catrambone, Executive Director
E-mail: jcat@stuartmartinchamber.org
Facebook: www.facebook.com/itownchamber
Description: Promotes business growth and community development in Indiantown, FL. **Geographic Preference:** Local.

38435 ■ Islamorada Chamber of Commerce
87100 Overseas Hwy., Mile Marker 87 Bayside
Islamorada, FL 33036
Ph: (305)664-4503
Free: 800-FAB-KEYS
Co. E-mail: info@islamoradachamber.com
URL: http://islamoradachamber.com
Contact: Christina Steele, President
Description: Promotes business and community development in Islamorada, FL. **Founded:** 1962. **Geographic Preference:** Local.

38436 ■ Jackson County Chamber of Commerce
4318 Lafayette St.
Marianna, FL 32447
Ph: (850)482-8060
Co. E-mail: info@jacksoncounty.com
URL: http://www.jacksoncounty.com
Contact: Tiffany Wilson Garling, President
Description: Promotes economic and community development in Jackson County, FL. Provides public relations services. **Founded:** 1822. **Geographic Preference:** Local.

38437 ■ JAX Chamber [Jacksonville Regional Chamber of Commerce]
3 Independent Dr.
Jacksonville, FL 32202
Ph: (904)366-6600
Co. E-mail: info@myjaxchamber.com
URL: http://www.myjaxchamber.com
Contact: Daniel Davis, President
E-mail: daniel.davis@myjaxchamber.com
Facebook: www.facebook.com/JaxChamber
Linkedin: www.linkedin.com/company/jacksonville-regional-chamber-of-commerce
X (Twitter): x.com/JAXChamber
Instagram: www.instagram.com/jaxchamber
Description: Promotes business and community development in Jacksonville, FL. Conducts seminars and other programs. **Founded:** 1884. **Geographic Preference:** Local.

38438 ■ Jensen Beach Chamber of Commerce
1912 NE Jensen Beach Blvd.
Jensen Beach, FL 34957
Ph: (772)334-3444
Co. E-mail: info@jensenbeach.biz
URL: http://jensenbeachflorida.info
Contact: Ronald Rose, Chief Executive Officer
Facebook: www.facebook.com/jbchamber
X (Twitter): x.com/JensenBeachBuzz
YouTube: www.youtube.com/user/JensenBeachFlorida
Description: Seeks to promote business and community development in Jensen Beach, FL. **Founded:** 1950. **Publications:** *The BeachBiz* (Irregular). **Geographic Preference:** Local.

38439 ■ Key Largo Chamber of Commerce [Key Largo Chamber of Commerce and Florida Keys Visitor Center]
106000 Overseas Hwy.
Key Largo, FL 33037
Ph: (305)451-1414
Free: 800-822-1088
Co. E-mail: info@keylargochamber.org
URL: http://www.keylargochamber.org
Contact: Eileen Eadie, Vice President Co-President
E-mail: vicepresident@keylargochamber.org
Facebook: www.facebook.com/KeyLargoChamber
Description: Promotes business and community development in Key Largo, Plantation Key, and the Everglades area of Florida. Operates welcome center. Provides information to visitors and businesses and individuals considering moving to the area. **Founded:** 1970. **Publications:** *The Legend* (Monthly); *Legendary Key Largo: A Guide to Island Living* (Monthly). **Geographic Preference:** State.

38440 ■ *Key Newsletter*
5114 Ocean Blvd.
Siesta Key, FL 34242
Ph: (941)349-3800
URL: http://www.siestakeychamber.com

Contact: Ann Frescura, Executive Director
E-mail: ann@siestakeychamber.com
URL(s): www.siestakeychamber.com/siesta-key-chamber/benefits/member-event-policy
Released: Monthly **Availability:** Online.

38441 ■ Key West Chamber of Commerce (KWCC)
510 Greene St., 1st Fl.
Key West, FL 33040
Ph: (305)294-2587
Co. E-mail: info@keywestchamber.org
URL: http://www.keywestchamber.org
Contact: Scott Atwell, Chief Executive Officer
Facebook: www.facebook.com/KeyWestChamber
X (Twitter): x.com/keywestchamber
Instagram: www.instagram.com/keywestchamber
YouTube: www.youtube.com/keywestchamber
Pinterest: www.pinterest.com/keywestchamber
Description: Promotes business and community development in the Key West, FL area. Issues tourist information. **Founded:** 1822. **Publications:** *Chamber Chowder* (Monthly). **Educational Activities:** Fantasy Fest (Annual). **Geographic Preference:** Local.

38442 ■ Kissimmee - Osceola County Chamber of Commerce
1425 E Vine St.
Kissimmee, FL 34744
Ph: (407)847-3174
Fax: (407)870-8607
Co. E-mail: info@kissimmeechamber.com
URL: http://kissimmeechamber.com
Contact: John Newstreet, President
E-mail: jnewstreet@kissimmeechamber.com
X (Twitter): x.com/kisschamber
Description: Provides valuable member benefits, expands economic base, supports quality education, promotes tourism, and encourages good government. **Publications:** *The Chamber Roadmap* (Monthly); *The Journal of Osceola County Business* (Bimonthly). **Educational Activities:** Back to School, Back to Business Expo; Business After Hours (Monthly). **Geographic Preference:** Local.

38443 ■ Lady Lake Area Chamber of Commerce
106 US Hwy. 441
Lady Lake, FL 32159
Ph: (352)753-6029
Co. E-mail: leslie@ladylakechamber.com
URL: http://www.ladylakechamber.com
Contact: Vicki Kerley, President
Facebook: www.facebook.com/Lady-Lake-Area-Chamber-of-Commerce-164853090252729
Description: Promotes business and community development in Lady Lake, FL. **Publications:** *The Heritage Express*. **Geographic Preference:** Local.

38444 ■ Lake Alfred Chamber of Commerce (LACC)
115 E Pomelo St.
Lake Alfred, FL 33850
Ph: (863)875-7800
Co. E-mail: lachamber1@gmail.com
URL: http://www.lakealfredchamber.com
Contact: Kristina Henderson, President
Facebook: www.facebook.com/lakealfredchamberofcommerce
Description: Promotes business and community development in Lake Alfred, FL. **Geographic Preference:** Local.

38445 ■ Lake City Chamber of Commerce
162 S Marion Ave.
Lake City, FL 32025
Ph: (386)752-3690
Co. E-mail: info@lakecitychamber.com
URL: http://www.lakecitychamber.com
Contact: Steve Smith, President
Facebook: www.facebook.com/lakecitycolumbiacountychamber
Linkedin: www.linkedin.com/company/lake-city-columbia-county-chamber-of-commerce
X (Twitter): x.com/FloridasGateway
Instagram: www.instagram.com/iamlakecity

Description: Promotes business and community development in Lake City, WA. Sponsors festival and awards scholarships. **Founded:** 1958. **Publications:** *Chamber Chat* (Monthly). **Geographic Preference:** Local.

38446 ■ Lake Eustis Area Chamber of Commerce [Eustis Area Chamber of Commerce (ECC)]
1 W Orange Ave.
Eustis, FL 32726
Ph: (352)357-3434
Fax: (352)357-1392
Co. E-mail: info@eustischamber.com
URL: http://eustischamber.com
Contact: Tami Roundtree, President
Facebook: www.facebook.com/lakeeustisareachamberofcommerce
Description: Promotes business and community development in the Eustis, FL area. Sponsors Washington Birthday Festival. **Publications:** *The Chamber Connection* (Biweekly); *Eustis Book* (Annual); *Eustis Brochure and Membership Directory*. **Educational Activities:** Eustis Area Chamber of Commerce Breakfast (Monthly). **Geographic Preference:** Local.

38447 ■ *Lake Placid Map*
18 N Oak Ave.
Lake Placid, FL 33852
Ph: (863)465-4331
Co. E-mail: chamberexecutive@lpfla.com
URL: http://www.lpfla.com
Contact: Donald Clarke, President
E-mail: donald@clarkepestcontrol.com
URL(s): www.lpfla.com/membership/promotional-opportunities
Availability: Print.

38448 ■ Lake Wales Area Chamber of Commerce and EDC (LWACC)
340 W Central Ave.
Lake Wales, FL 33853
Ph: (863)676-3445
Fax: (863)676-3446
Co. E-mail: lori@lakewaleschamber.com
URL: http://www.lakewaleschamber.com
Contact: Derrick Epley, Chairman
Facebook: www.facebook.com/lakewaleschamber
Description: Promotes business and community development in Lake Wales, FL. **Publications:** *Lake Wales Area Chamber of Commerce--Membership Directory/Buyers Guide* (Annual); *Membership Directory/Buyers Guide* (Annual); *Progressions* (Monthly); *Membership Directory/Buyers Guide* (Annual); *Membership Directory/Buyers Guide* (Annual). **Geographic Preference:** Local.

38449 ■ Lakeland Area Chamber of Commerce
35 Lake Morton Dr.
Lakeland, FL 33801
Ph: (863)688-8551
Fax: (863)683-7454
Co. E-mail: info@lakelandchamber.com
URL: http://www.lakelandchamber.com
Contact: Amy Wiggins, President
E-mail: president@lakelandchamber.com
Facebook: www.facebook.com/LakelandChamber
Linkedin: www.linkedin.com/company/lakeland-area-chamber-of-commerce
X (Twitter): x.com/LakelandChamber
YouTube: www.youtube.com/user/lakelandchamber
Description: Promotes business and community development in the Lakeland, FL area. **Founded:** 1921. **Publications:** *Forum 2.0* (Weekly). **Awards:** Scott Linder Small Business of the Year Award (Annual). **Geographic Preference:** Local.

38450 ■ Lauderdale-By-The-Sea Chamber of Commerce (LSCC)
4201 N Ocean Dr.
Fort Lauderdale, FL 33308
Ph: (954)776-1000
Co. E-mail: info@lbts.com
URL: http://www.lbts.com
Contact: Howard Goldberg, Chairman

E-mail: howard@goldbergsells.com
Facebook: www.facebook.com/Lauderdale-By-The-Sea-Florida-82502273669
Description: Promotes business and community development in Lauderdale-by-the-Sea, FL. **Founded:** 1955. **Geographic Preference:** Local.

38451 ■ Leesburg Area Chamber of Commerce
600 Market St.
Leesburg, FL 34748
Ph: (352)787-2131
Co. E-mail: info@leesburgchamber.com
URL: http://www.leesburgchamber.com
Contact: Sandi Moore, President
Facebook: www.facebook.com/LeesburgChamber
Linkedin: www.linkedin.com/company/leesburg-area-chamber-of-commerce
X (Twitter): x.com/LeesburgChamber
Instagram: www.instagram.com/leesburgchamber
YouTube: www.youtube.com/channel/UCcrFYOfM6lynrLTO27ZxTZQ
Description: Promotes business and community development in the Leesburg, FL area. Maintains committees; sponsors parades; conducts fishing tournaments. **Founded:** 1924. **Publications:** *Community and Commerce* (Monthly). **Geographic Preference:** Local.

38452 ■ *The Legend*
106000 Overseas Hwy.
Key Largo, FL 33037
Ph: (305)451-1414
Free: 800-822-1088
Co. E-mail: info@keylargochamber.org
URL: http://www.keylargochamber.org
Contact: Eileen Eadie, Vice President Co-President
E-mail: vicepresident@keylargochamber.org
URL(s): www.keylargochamber.org/member-center
Released: Monthly **Description:** Contains community news and events concerning the chamber and its members. **Availability:** Print.

38453 ■ Longboat Key Chamber of Commerce (LKCC)
5390 Gulf of Mexico Dr., Ste. 102
Longboat Key, FL 34228
Ph: (941)383-2466
Fax: (941)383-8217
Co. E-mail: info@lbkchamber.com
URL: http://www.longboatkeychamber.com
Contact: Gail Loefgren, President
Facebook: www.facebook.com/lbkchamber
X (Twitter): x.com/lbkchamber
Instagram: www.instagram.com/lbkchamber
Description: Promotes business and community development in Longboat Key, FL. Provides business resource information and convention/meeting planning, relocation, and tourist assistance. Holds seminars. Sponsors fishing and golfing tournaments and annual one-day Islandfest and Business Expo. **Founded:** 1958. **Publications:** *Map of Longboat Key, Florida*; *Restaurant and Accommodations Directory* (Periodic); *Vacation Guide* (Periodic). **Geographic Preference:** Local.

38454 ■ Lower Keys Chamber of Commerce (LKCC)
31020 Overseas Hwy.
Big Pine Key, FL 33043
Ph: (305)872-2411
Free: 800-872-3722
Co. E-mail: info@lowerkeyschamber.com
URL: http://www.lowerkeyschamber.com
Contact: Leslie Valant, President
E-mail: leslie@leewardwealth.com
Facebook: www.facebook.com/LKCofC
Instagram: www.instagram.com/lowerkeyschamberofcommerce
Description: Promotes business and community development in the lower Florida keys. Holds monthly business social and three fundraising events per year. Conducts annual Jazz Festival, Dolphin Fishing

38455 ■ Florida
STATE LISTINGS

Tournament and Underwater Music Festival. **Founded:** 1963. **Publications:** *Chamber Channel* (Monthly); *Visitors Guide.* **Geographic Preference:** Local.

38455 ■ Madison County Chamber of Commerce
182 NW College Lp.
 Madison, FL 32341
Ph: (850)973-2788
Co. E-mail: chamber@madisonfl.org
URL: http://madisonfl.org
Facebook: www.facebook.com/madisoncoun
 tyflchamber

Description: Promotes business and community development in Madison County, FL. Conducts local charitable projects; sponsors annual Down Home Days festival. **Founded:** 1962. **Publications:** *Madison Magazine* (Periodic); *C/N Chamber News* (Monthly); *Reflections of Madison County* (Annual). **Geographic Preference:** Local.

38456 ■ Maitland Area Chamber of Commerce
500 N Maitland Ave., Ste. 100
 Maitland, FL 32751
Ph: (407)644-0741
Co. E-mail: info@maitlandchamber.com
URL: http://www.maitlandchamber.com
Contact: Dawn Aiello, President
Facebook: www.facebook.com/Maitlan
 dAreaChamber
Instagram: www.instagram.com/maitlandchamber

Description: Promotes business and community development in southern Seminole County, FL. Sponsors Annual Spring Festival during the third weekend in April, the Live and Silent Auction the third Friday in August, and Business Expo and non-profit showcase in October. **Founded:** 1958. **Geographic Preference:** Local.

38457 ■ Manatee Chamber of Commerce
222 10th St. W
 Bradenton, FL 34205
Ph: (941)748-3411
Fax: (941)745-1877
Co. E-mail: info@manateechamber.com
URL: http://www.manateechamber.com
Contact: Jacki Dezelski, President
E-mail: jackid@manateechamber.com
Facebook: www.facebook.com/ManateeChamber
Linkedin: www.linkedin.com/company/manatee
 -chamber-of-commerce
X (Twitter): x.com/ManateeChamber
Instagram: www.instagram.com/ManateeChamber

Description: Promotes business and community development in the Manatee County, FL area. **Founded:** 1962. **Geographic Preference:** Local.

38458 ■ *Marco Island*
1102 N Collier Blvd.
 Marco Island, FL 34145
Ph: (239)394-7549
Fax: (239)394-3061
Co. E-mail: info@marcoislandchamber.org
URL: http://marcoislandchamber.org
Contact: Tiffany Homuth, President
URL(s): marcoislandchamber.org/request-a-copy

Ed: Donna Niemczyk, Katherine O'Hara. **Released:** Annual **Description:** Contains photographic and editorial coverage of the Marco Island area. **Availability:** Print; PDF; Online.

38459 ■ Marco Island Area Chamber of Commerce
1102 N Collier Blvd.
 Marco Island, FL 34145
Ph: (239)394-7549
Fax: (239)394-3061
Co. E-mail: info@marcoislandchamber.org
URL: http://marcoislandchamber.org
Contact: Tiffany Homuth, President
Facebook: www.facebook.com/MarcoChamber

Description: Promotes business and community development in the Marco, FL area. **Founded:** 1977. **Publications:** *Marco Island Chamber of Commerce Newsletter* (Monthly); *Marco Island* (Annual). **Geographic Preference:** Local.

38460 ■ Melbourne Regional Chamber of the East Central Florida [Melbourne-Palm Bay Area Chamber of Commerce (M-PBACC)]
1005 E Strawbridge Ave.
 Melbourne, FL 32901-4782
Ph: (321)724-5400
URL: http://www.melbourneregionalchamber.com
Contact: Michael Ayers, President
E-mail: michael@melbourneregionalchamber.com
YouTube: www.youtube.com/user/
 MelbourneChamberFLA/videos

Description: Promotes business and economic development in South Brevard County, FL. **Founded:** 1960. **Publications:** *The Chamber Weekly Connection!* (Weekly); *Drug Resource Guide* (Annual); *Relocation Guide*; *Visitor Guide* (Annual). **Educational Activities:** Corporate Health Challenge. **Geographic Preference:** Local.

38461 ■ *Miami Beach Chamber Business Directory*
1920 Meridian Ave., 3rd fl.
 Miami Beach, FL 33139
Ph: (305)674-1300
Co. E-mail: info@miamibeachchamber.com
URL: http://www.miamibeachchamber.com
Contact: Jerry Libbin, President
E-mail: jerry@miamibeachchamber.com
URL(s): business.miamibeachchamber.com/list

Availability: Print.

38462 ■ Miami Beach Chamber of Commerce
1920 Meridian Ave., 3rd fl.
 Miami Beach, FL 33139
Ph: (305)674-1300
Co. E-mail: info@miamibeachchamber.com
URL: http://www.miamibeachchamber.com
Contact: Jerry Libbin, President
E-mail: jerry@miamibeachchamber.com
Facebook: www.facebook.com/MiamiBeachChamber
Linkedin: www.linkedin.com/company/miami-beach
 -chamber-of-commerce
X (Twitter): x.com/MiamiBeachBiz
YouTube: www.youtube.com/user/
 miamibeachchamber

Description: Promotes business and community development in Miami Beach, FL. **Founded:** 1921. **Publications:** *E-Currents* (Weekly); *Miami Beach Chamber Business Directory*. **Educational Activities:** Miami Beach Chamber of Commerce Luncheon. **Awards:** Miami Beach Chamber of Commerce Citizen of the Year (Annual); Jan Pfeiffer Distinguished Service Award (Annual); Leonard A. 'Doc' Baker Lifetime Achievement Award (Annual). **Geographic Preference:** Local.

38463 ■ Miami-Dade County Chamber of Commerce (MDCC)
100 S Biscayne Blvd., Ste. 300
 Miami, FL 33131
Ph: (305)751-8648
Co. E-mail: mdcc@m-dcc.org
URL: http://www.m-dcc.org
Contact: Gordon Eric Knowles, President
E-mail: eknowles@m-dcc.org
Facebook: www.facebook.com/MiaDadeChamber
X (Twitter): x.com/Mia_DadeChamber
Instagram: www.instagram,com/mia_dadechamber

Description: Promotes business and economic interest of the black community throughout Dade County. **Founded:** 1974. **Geographic Preference:** Local.

38464 ■ Miramar Pembroke Pines Regional Chamber of Commerce
15800 Pines Blvd., Ste. 323
 Pembroke Pines, FL 33027
Ph: (954)432-9808
Co. E-mail: info@miramarpembrokepines.org
URL: http://www.miramarpembrokepines.org
Contact: Patty Archer, President

Facebook: www.facebook.com/
 miramarpembrokepineschamber
Linkedin: www.linkedin.com/company/
 miramarpembrokepineschamber
X (Twitter): x.com/MPPRChamber
YouTube: www.youtube.com/channel/UCnjKt8ZVNE
 _pkaWvnweC_LA
Pinterest: www.pinterest.com/mpprcc

Description: Works to provide a variety of venues to assist the business owners of the region to become better businesses by becoming better business leaders. **Founded:** 1969. **Publications:** *Insight for Business.* **Geographic Preference:** Local.

38465 ■ Monticello-Jefferson County Chamber of Commerce - Library
420 Washington St.
 Monticello, FL 32344
Ph: (850)997-5552
Co. E-mail: info@monticellojeffersonfl.com
URL: http://www.monticellojeffersonfl.com
Contact: Tami Lester, President
Facebook: www.facebook.com/mon
 ticellohamberofcommerce

Description: Promotes business and community development in Jefferson County, FL. **Scope:** Classics; politics; mystery. **Services:** Interlibrary loan; copying. **Founded:** 1957. **Holdings:** Books; Critically acclaimed DVDs; Audiobooks; Ebooks. **Geographic Preference:** Local.

38466 ■ Mount Dora Area Chamber of Commerce (MDACC)
341 Alexander St.
 Mount Dora, FL 32757
Ph: (352)383-2165
Co. E-mail: admin@mountdora.com
URL: http://www.mountdora.com
Contact: Rachel O'Ryan, President
Facebook: www.facebook.com/MountDoraChamber
Instagram: www.instagram.com/mountdorachamber
YouTube: www.youtube.com/channel/UCbWc
 13TaNOMFMKvXPWv4K-A

Description: Promotes business and community development in the Mount Dora, FL area. Sponsors community activities. **Founded:** 1923. **Publications:** *Community Guide and Directory* (Annual). **Geographic Preference:** Local.

38467 ■ *Naples on the Gulf*
2390 Tamiami Trl. N, Ste. 210
 Naples, FL 34103
Ph: (239)262-6376
Co. E-mail: info@napleschamber.org
URL: http://www.napleschamber.org
Contact: Michael Dalby, President
E-mail: michael@napleschamber.org
URL(s): www.napleschamber.org/member-benefits/
 marketing-opportunities

Released: Annual **Availability:** Print; Online.

38468 ■ Navarre Beach Area Chamber of Commerce
1804 Prado St.
 Navarre, FL 32566
Ph: (850)939-3267
Co. E-mail: exec@navarrechamber.com
URL: http://www.navarrechamber.com
Contact: Chanda Ryan, President
E-mail: chanda.ryan@navarrechamber.com
Facebook: www.facebook.com/NavarreChamber
Linkedin: www.linkedin.com/company/navarre-beach
 -area-chamber-of-commerce
Instagram: www.instagram.com/navarrechamber
YouTube: www.youtube.com/user/navarrechamber

Description: Promotes business and community development in the Navarre, FL area. Encourages industrial development and tourism. Sponsors local festival. **Founded:** 1975. **Geographic Preference:** Local.

38469 ■ *NewsBreak*
1601 Biscayne Blvd., Ballroom Level
 Miami, FL 33132
Ph: (305)350-7700
Co. E-mail: president@miamichamber.com
URL: http://www.miamichamber.com

Contact: Alfred Sanchez, President
URL(s): www.miamichamber.com/committees/marketing-membership/customer-care
Released: Weekly **Description:** Contains information on current events, opportunities and special offers for members. **Availability:** Print.

38470 ■ Niceville Valparaiso Chamber of Commerce [Niceville Valparaiso Bay Area Chamber of Commerce]
1055 E John Sims Pky.
 Niceville, FL 32578
Ph: (850)678-2323
Fax: (850)678-2602
Co. E-mail: info@nicevillechamber.com
URL: http://www.nicevillechamber.com
Contact: Tricia Brunson, President
E-mail: triciabrunson@nicevillechamber.com
Facebook: www.facebook.com/Nicevillechamber
YouTube: www.youtube.com/user/
 NicevilleValpChamber
Description: Promotes business and community development in Niceville and Valparaiso, FL area. Sponsors business seminars and leadership school. **Founded:** 1956. **Geographic Preference:** Local.

38471 ■ North Dade Regional Chamber of Commerce
2761 N 29th Ave.
 Hollywood, FL 33020
Ph: (305)690-9123
Fax: (954)272-7100
Co. E-mail: joelr@thechamber.cc
URL: http://www.thechamber.cc
Description: Promotes business and community development in North Dade area. **Founded:** 1974. **Geographic Preference:** Local.

38472 ■ North Florida Regional Chamber of Commerce
100 E Call St.
 Starke, FL 32091
Ph: (904)964-5278
Fax: (904)964-2863
URL: http://northfloridachamber.com
Contact: Pam Whittle, President
E-mail: pam@northfloridachamber.com
Description: Promotes business and community development in Bradford County, FL. Sponsors Arts Festival, Christmas Parade, and a Fourth of July celebration. Operates small business resource library. **Founded:** 1945. **Publications:** *Business Directory*; *Tri County Connection* (Quarterly). **Geographic Preference:** Local.

38473 ■ North Fort Myers Chamber of Commerce
2787 N Tamiami Trl., Unit 10
 North Fort Myers, FL 33903
Ph: (239)997-9111
Co. E-mail: info@nfmchamber.org
URL: http://www.nfmchamber.org
Contact: Carolyn Graves, Director
Description: Promotes business and community development in North Ft. Myers, FL. Sponsors Cracker Festival. **Founded:** 1958. **Publications:** *Focus* (Weekly); *Bulletin* (Periodic). **Geographic Preference:** Local.

38474 ■ North Port Area Chamber of Commerce (NPACC)
1337 N Sumter Blvd.
 North Port, FL 34286
Ph: (941)564-3040
Co. E-mail: info@northportareachamber.com
URL: http://www.northportareachamber.com
Contact: Kelly Louke, President
E-mail: klouke@csbtfl.com
Facebook: www.facebook.com/NPACC
Description: Promotes business and community development in North Port, FL. **Geographic Preference:** Local.

38475 ■ Northeast Polk Chamber of Commerce
35610 Hwy. 27
 Haines City, FL 33845
Ph: (863)422-3751
Fax: (863)422-4704
Co. E-mail: info@hainescitychamber.com
URL: http://www.northeastpolkchamber.com
Contact: Lana Stripling, Executive Director
Facebook: www.facebook.com/northeas
 tpolkchamber
X (Twitter): x.com/NEPChamber
Instagram: www.instagram.com/northeas
 tpolkchamber
Description: Promotes business and community development in Haines City, FL. **Founded:** 1960. **Publications:** *Heart-Beat* (Monthly). **Geographic Preference:** Local.

38476 ■ Northern Palm Beach County Chamber of Commerce
5520 PGA Blvd., Ste. 200
 Palm Beach Gardens, FL 33418
Ph: (561)746-7111
Co. E-mail: info@pbnchamber.com
URL: http://www.pbnchamber.com
Contact: Noel Martinez, President
E-mail: noel@pbnchamber.com
Facebook: www.facebook.com/pbnchamber
Linkedin: www.linkedin.com/company/the-northern
 -palm-beach-county-chamber-of-commerce
X (Twitter): x.com/pbnchamber
Instagram: www.instagram.com/pbnchamber
Description: Promotes business and community development in northern Palm Beach County. **Founded:** 2007. **Publications:** *E-Communicator* (Monthly). **Geographic Preference:** Local.

38477 ■ Ocala/Marion County Chamber & Economic Partnership
310 SE 3rd St.
 Ocala, FL 34471
Ph: (352)629-8051
Fax: (352)629-7651
Co. E-mail: info@ocalacep.com
URL: http://ocalacep.com
Contact: Kevin Sheilley, President
Facebook: www.facebook.com/OcalaCEP
X (Twitter): x.com/OcalaCEP
Description: Works with business agencies, business people and local economic developers and educators in pursuing economic growth and expansion. Provides support and resources for business development needs and programs. Assists in the retention and expansion of existing firms and the attraction of new businesses. **Scope:** Works with public to promote Marion County for industrial and business development. **Founded:** 1954. **Publications:** *Sunlines* (Monthly); *Who's Who in Business* (Annual). **Training:** Involves in choosing career options; Resume development; Networking for jobs; Self marketing strategies; Negotiating the job offer. **Geographic Preference:** Local.

38478 ■ *Official Guide to Wellington*
12161 Ken Adams Way, Ste. 183
 Wellington, FL 33414
Ph: (561)792-6525
Fax: (561)792-6200
Co. E-mail: info@wellingtonchamber.com
URL: http://www.wellingtonchamber.com
Contact: Michela Green, Executive Director
URL(s): www.wellingtonchamber.com/about-us/abou
 t-the-chamber
Released: Annual **Availability:** Print; Online.

38479 ■ Ormond Beach Chamber of Commerce
165 W Granada Blvd.
 Ormond Beach, FL 32174
Ph: (386)677-3454
Fax: (386)677-4363
Co. E-mail: info@ormondchamber.com
URL: http://www.ormondchamber.com
Contact: Debbie Cotton, President
E-mail: dcotton@ormondchamber.com
Facebook: www.facebook.com/ormondchamber
Linkedin: www.linkedin.com/company/ormond-beach
 -chamber-of-commerce
YouTube: www.youtube.com/channel/UCgWH
 dFDL8QvEAyCSvXnj6NA
Description: Promotes business and community development in Ormond Beach, FL. Sponsors art show and jazz festival. **Awards:** Ormond Beach Chamber of Commerce Beautification Awards (Quarterly). **Geographic Preference:** Local.

38480 ■ Oviedo-Winter Springs Regional Chamber of Commerce (OWSRCC)
376 N Central Ave.
 Oviedo, FL 32765
Ph: (407)365-6500
Co. E-mail: info@owsrcc.org
URL: http://www.owsrcc.org
Contact: Dan Lacich, Chairman
Facebook: www.facebook.com/OWSRCC
X (Twitter): x.com/owschamber
YouTube: www.youtube.com/channel/UC00eV49-M
 -cqHFt7qcTS5Dg
Pinterest: www.pinterest.com/OWSChamber
Description: Promotes business and community development in the Oviedo, FL area. **Founded:** 1982. **Geographic Preference:** Local.

38481 ■ Pahokee Chamber of Commerce
115 E Main St.
 Pahokee, FL 33476
Ph: (561)924-5579
URL: http://www.uschamber.com/co/chambers/flori
 da/pahokee
Description: Promotes business and community development in Pahokee, FL. **Geographic Preference:** Local.

38482 ■ Palm Beach Chamber of Commerce (PBCC)
400 Royal Palm Way, Ste. 106
 Palm Beach, FL 33480
Ph: (561)655-3282
Co. E-mail: mo@palmbeachchamber.com
URL: http://www.palmbeachchamber.com
Contact: Laurel Baker, Chief Executive Officer
Facebook: www.facebook.com/
 PalmBeachChamberofCommerce
X (Twitter): x.com/PB_Chamber
Instagram: www.instagram.com/palmbeachchamber
Description: Provides leadership, education, and advocacy for the Town of Palm Beach to continue to thrive. **Founded:** 1929. **Publications:** *Palm Beach Guide*. **Educational Activities:** Palm Beach Chamber of Commerce Breakfast. **Geographic Preference:** Local.

38483 ■ *Palm Beach Guide*
400 Royal Palm Way, Ste. 106
 Palm Beach, FL 33480
Ph: (561)655-3282
Co. E-mail: mo@palmbeachchamber.com
URL: http://www.palmbeachchamber.com
Contact: Laurel Baker, Chief Executive Officer
URL(s): www.palmbeachchamber.com/about
Description: Contains all information needed in order to have a fabulous time wining, dining, shopping, and learning about Palm Beach. **Availability:** Print.

38484 ■ Palm City Chamber of Commerce (PCCC)
3168 SW Martin Downs Blvd.
 Palm City, FL 34990
Ph: (772)286-8121
Co. E-mail: info@palmcitychamber.com
URL: http://www.palmcitychamber.com
Contact: Christina Franco, President
Description: Promotes business and community development in Palm City, FL. Participates in community and environmental projects. Holds monthly social networking meeting. **Founded:** 1927. **Publications:** *The Bridge*; *Business* (Monthly). **Educational Activities:** Palm City Chamber of Commerce Breakfast (Monthly). **Geographic Preference:** Local.

38485 ■ Panama City Beach Chamber of Commerce
309 Richard Jackson Blvd., Ste. 101
 Panama City Beach, FL 32407
Ph: (850)235-1159
Fax: (850)235-2301
Co. E-mail: chamber@pcbeach.org

URL: http://www.pcbeach.org
Contact: Kristopher McLane, President
Facebook: www.facebook.com/PCBeachChamber
X (Twitter): x.com/PCBChamber
Instagram: www.instagram.com/mypcbchamber
Description: Promotes business and community development in Panama City Beach, FL. **Founded:** 1987. **Geographic Preference:** Local.

38486 ■ Pinellas Park/Gateway Chamber of Commerce
5851 Pk. Blvd.
 Pinellas Park, FL 33781
Ph: (727)544-4777
Fax: (727)209-0837
Co. E-mail: office@pinellasparkchamber.com
URL: http://www.pinellasparkchamber.com
Contact: Dr. Daniel Strauss, President
Facebook: www.facebook.com/PPGCofC
X (Twitter): x.com/PPKChamber
Description: Promotes business and economic development in the Pinellas Park, FL area. Conducts annual Legislative Day and Country in the Park. Maintains high-tech work center. **Founded:** 1915. **Publications:** *News and Views* (Monthly). **Educational Activities:** Corporate Golf Tournament. **Geographic Preference:** Local.

38487 ■ Port Orange/South Daytona Chamber of Commerce
3431 Ridgewood Ave.
 Port Orange, FL 32129
Ph: (386)761-1601
Fax: (386)788-9165
Co. E-mail: info@pschamber.com
URL: http://www.pschamber.com
Contact: Patty Tropea, Office Manager
Facebook: www.facebook.com/PortOrangeSouthDaytonaChamber
X (Twitter): x.com/POSDChamber
Instagram: www.instagram.com/po_sdchamber
Description: Promotes business and community development in the Port Orange, FL area. **Founded:** 1974. **Publications:** *Community Directory and Buyers' Guide* (Annual); *TradeWinds*. **Geographic Preference:** Local.

38488 ■ Putnam County Chamber of Commerce
1100 Reid St.
 Palatka, FL 32177
Ph: (386)328-1503
Fax: (386)328-7076
Co. E-mail: chamber@chamberpc.com
URL: http://www.putnamcountychamber.com
Contact: Dana Jones, President
E-mail: danajones@chamberpc.com
Facebook: www.facebook.com/PutnamCountyFL
X (Twitter): x.com/putnamcochamber
YouTube: www.youtube.com/channel/UCC8WNAOFAT0Dk0uN-SnZGhQ
Description: Promotes business and community development in Putnam County, FL. **Founded:** 1926. **Publications:** *Business Directory*; *Return on Investment* (Monthly). **Geographic Preference:** Local.

38489 ■ *Relax*
20 Airport Rd., Ste. C
 Palm Coast, FL 32164
Ph: (386)437-0106
Fax: (386)437-5700
Co. E-mail: info@flaglerchamber.org
URL: http://www.flaglerchamber.org
Contact: Rebecca DeLorenzo, President
Description: Features information on hotels and visitors. **Availability:** Print.

38490 ■ *Relocation Guide and Membership Directory*
201 N Franklin St., Ste. 201
 Tampa, FL 33602
Ph: (813)228-7777
Co. E-mail: info@tampabaychamber.com
URL: http://www.tampabaychamber.com/pages/about
Contact: Dr. Bob Rohrlack, Secretary
URL(s): www.tampabaychamber.com/pages/membership
Availability: Print; Online.

38491 ■ Safety Harbor Chamber of Commerce (SHCC)
200 Main St.
 Safety Harbor, FL 34695
Ph: (727)726-2890
Fax: (727)726-2733
Co. E-mail: info@safetyharborchamber.com
URL: http://www.safetyharborchamber.com
Contact: James Poulter, Director
Facebook: www.facebook.com/safetyharborchamberofcommerce
X (Twitter): x.com/VisitSafetyHarb
Instagram: www.instagram.com/safetyharborfl
Description: Promotes business and community development in Safety Harbor, FL. Sponsors Safety Harbor Sprints, Arbor Day Volleyball Tournament, and Safety Harbor Fall Street Festival. Donates to local and national charities. **Founded:** 1930. **Publications:** *Harbor News* (Monthly). **Geographic Preference:** Local.

38492 ■ St. Cloud Greater Osceola Chamber of Commerce
1200 New York Ave.
 Saint Cloud, FL 34769
Ph: (407)892-3671
Fax: (407)892-5289
Co. E-mail: accounting@stcloudflchamber.com
URL: http://www.stcloudflchamber.com
Contact: Dirk Webb, President
Facebook: www.facebook.com/StCloudChamber
Linkedin: www.linkedin.com/company/st.-cloud-chamber-of-commerce
X (Twitter): x.com/stcloudchamber
Instagram: www.instagram.com/st.cloudchamber
YouTube: www.youtube.com/channel/UCsNeG7dZ8bJReVrGvVvKhaQ
Description: Promotes business and community development in St. Cloud, FL. Economic development, tourism, governmental affairs and education in Osceola County. **Founded:** 1927. **Publications:** *Osceola Business Journal* (Monthly); *St. Cloud Visitors Guide and Area Map*. **Geographic Preference:** Local.

38493 ■ St. Lucie County Chamber of Commerce
2937 W Midway Rd.
 Fort Pierce, FL 34981
Ph: (772)595-9999
Fax: (772)595-9990
Co. E-mail: info@stluciechamber.org
URL: http://stluciechamber.org
Contact: Terissa Aronson, President
E-mail: president@stluciechamber.org
Facebook: www.facebook.com/SLCChamber
X (Twitter): x.com/stluciechamber
Instagram: www.instagram.com/stluciechamber
YouTube: www.youtube.com/user/CityPortStLucie
Description: Promotes business and community development in Ft. Pierce and St. Lucie County, FL. **Founded:** 1906. **Publications:** *Business & Community Guide*. **Geographic Preference:** Local.

38494 ■ St. Petersburg Area Chamber of Commerce
100 2nd Ave. N, Ste. 150
 Saint Petersburg, FL 33701-3351
Ph: (727)388-0685
Co. E-mail: lcissna@stpete.com
URL: http://www.stpete.com
Contact: Chris Steinocher, President
Facebook: www.facebook.com/StPeteChamber
Linkedin: www.linkedin.com/company/stpetechamber
X (Twitter): x.com/StPeteChamber
Instagram: www.instagram.com/stpetechamber
YouTube: www.youtube.com/user/StPetersburgChamber
Description: Promotes business and community development in the St. Petersburg, FL area. **Geographic Preference:** Local.

38495 ■ Sanibel-Captiva Islands Chamber of Commerce
1159 Cswy., Rd.
 Sanibel, FL 33957
Ph: (239)472-1080
Fax: (239)472-1070
Co. E-mail: office@sanibel-captiva.org
URL: http://sanibel-captiva.org/sanibel-captiva-island-chamber-of-commerce
Contact: John Lai, President
E-mail: john@sanibel-captiva.org
Facebook: www.facebook.com/SanibelCaptivaChamber
Linkedin: www.linkedin.com/company/sanibel-captiva-chamber-of-commerce
X (Twitter): x.com/sancapchamber
Description: Promotes business and community development in Sanibel, FL and the Captiva Islands. **Founded:** 1954. **Publications:** *Island Guide*. **Geographic Preference:** Local.

38496 ■ Santa Rosa County Chamber of Commerce
4315 Avalon Blvd.
 Milton, FL 32583
Ph: (850)623-2339
Co. E-mail: info@srcchamber.com
URL: http://www.srcchamber.com
Contact: Donna Tucker, President
E-mail: ceo@srcchamber.com
Description: Promotes business and community development in Santa Rosa County, FL. Provides advice to prospective business owners. **Publications:** *Santa Rosan* (Monthly). **Awards:** Santa Rosa County Chamber of Commerce Business of the Year (Annual); Santa Rosa County Chamber of Commerce Community Achievement Award; Santa Rosa County Chamber of Commerce Community Leader of the Year (Annual); Santa Rosa County Chamber of Commerce Emerging Leader of the Year (Annual); Santa Rosa County Chamber of Commerce Hall of Fame Award (Annual); Santa Rosa County Chamber of Commerce Industry of the Year; Santa Rosa County Chamber of Commerce Man of the Year (Annual); Santa Rosa County Chamber of Commerce Woman of the Year (Annual). **Geographic Preference:** Local.

38497 ■ *Santa Rosan*
4315 Avalon Blvd.
 Milton, FL 32583
Ph: (850)623-2339
Co. E-mail: info@srcchamber.com
URL: http://www.srcchamber.com
Contact: Donna Tucker, President
E-mail: ceo@srcchamber.com
URL(s): srcchamber.com/category/the-santa-rosan
Released: Monthly **Availability:** Online.

38498 ■ Sebastian River Area Chamber of Commerce
700 Main St.
 Sebastian, FL 32958
Ph: (772)589-5969
Fax: (772)589-5993
Co. E-mail: info@sebastianchamber.com
URL: http://business.sebastianchamber.com
Contact: Cheryl Thibault, President
Facebook: www.facebook.com/SebastianChamber
X (Twitter): x.com/sebastianfl
Instagram: www.instagram.com/visitsebastianriverareafl
YouTube: www.youtube.com/user/sebastianriverarea
Pinterest: www.pinterest.com/visitsebastian
Description: Promotes business and community development in the Sebastian, FL area. **Founded:** 1958. **Publications:** *Lodging, Dining and Things To Do* (Annual). **Educational Activities:** Tourism Committee Meeting (Quarterly). **Geographic Preference:** Local.

38499 ■ Seminole County Regional Chamber of Commerce
1055 AAA Dr., Ste. 153
 Heathrow, FL 32746
Ph: (407)708-4600
Fax: (407)708-4615
Co. E-mail: info@seminolebusiness.org

URL: http://www.seminolebusiness.org
Contact: Jason Brodeur, Co-President Co-Chief Executive Officer
E-mail: jbrodeur@seminolebusiness.org
Facebook: www.facebook.com/SeminoleCountyChamber
X (Twitter): x.com/SeminoleChamber
Instagram: www.instagram.com/seminolechamber
YouTube: www.youtube.com/channel/UCCKkLOi838h05V3LEllo5lw
Description: Promotes business and economic growth in the Seminole County, FL area. **Founded:** 1921. **Geographic Preference:** Local.

38500 ■ Siesta Key Chamber of Commerce (SKCC)
5114 Ocean Blvd.
Siesta Key, FL 34242
Ph: (941)349-3800
URL: http://www.siestakeychamber.com
Contact: Ann Frescura, Executive Director
E-mail: ann@siestakeychamber.com
Facebook: www.facebook.com/SiestaKeyChamber
Linkedin: www.linkedin.com/company/siestakeychamber
X (Twitter): x.com/SKChamber
Instagram: www.instagram.com/siestakeychamber
Description: Promotes business and community development in, and provides visitor information in Siesta Key, FL. Conducts Christmas parade, Sand Fest, July 4th Fireworks. **Founded:** 1959. **Publications:** *Accommodations Guide to Siesta Key* (Annual); *Beach Business* (Monthly); *Key Newsletter* (Monthly); *Visitor's Guide* (Annual). **Educational Activities:** Siesta Key Chamber 4th of July Fireworks (Annual). **Geographic Preference:** Local.

38501 ■ South Dade Chamber of Commerce
47 N Krome Ave.
Homestead, FL 33030
Ph: (305)247-2332
Co. E-mail: sdccinfo@southdadechamber.org
URL: http://southdadechamber.org
Contact: Lucia Soria, Chairman of the Board
Description: Promotes business and economic development in South Miami-Dade County Florida. **Founded:** 1915. **Publications:** *Chamber Times* (Monthly); *Festival and Events Guide*; *Business Directory* (Annual). **Geographic Preference:** Local.

38502 ■ South Lake Chamber of Commerce (SLCC)
620 W Montrose St.
Clermont, FL 34711
Ph: (352)394-4191
Fax: (352)394-5799
Co. E-mail: office@southlakechamber-fl.com
URL: http://www.southlakechamber-fl.com
Contact: Aimee Stanley, Owner
Facebook: www.facebook.com/SouthLakeChamberFL
X (Twitter): x.com/SLChamberFL
Description: Promotes business and community development in Clermont, FL. Sponsors Labor Day Festival, Light Up Clermont Christmas Festival, and Business Expo. **Founded:** 1947. **Publications:** *Business Beat* (Monthly). **Awards:** South Lake Chamber of Commerce Citizen of the Year (Annual). **Geographic Preference:** Local.

38503 ■ South Tampa Chamber of Commerce (STCOC)
3415 W Bay to Bay Blvd.
Tampa, FL 33629
Ph: (813)637-0156
Co. E-mail: ceo@southtampachamber.org
URL: http://www.southtampachamber.org
Contact: Kelly Flannery, Co-President Co-Chief Executive Officer
Facebook: www.facebook.com/SouthTampaChamber 1926
Linkedin: www.linkedin.com/company/south-tampa-chamber-of-commerce
X (Twitter): x.com/s_tampachamber
Instagram: www.instagram.com/southtampachamber
YouTube: www.youtube.com/channel/UCX1oBqSdrAWKzMWhHx0c1uA
Description: Promotes business and community development in the southern section of Tampa, FL. Supports local charities; conducts political and business networking forums. **Founded:** 1926. **Awards:** South Tampa Chamber of Commerce Small Business of the Year (Annual); South Tampa Chamber of Commerce Citizen of the Year (Annual). **Geographic Preference:** Local.

38504 ■ Southeast Volusia Chamber of Commerce
115 Canal St.
New Smyrna Beach, FL 32168
Ph: (386)428-2449
Co. E-mail: sevinfo@sevchamber.com
URL: http://www.sevchamber.com
Contact: Scott Steger, President
Facebook: www.facebook.com/SoutheastVolusiaChamberOfCommerce
Instagram: www.instagram.com/SEVolusiaCoC
YouTube: www.youtube.com/channel/UCMNMViK0qO8RzVubv8lbXCQ
Description: Promotes business and community development in southeastern Volusia County, FL. **Founded:** 1932. **Publications:** *Business/Investors Directory and Visitor's Guide* (Annual); *Official SE Volusia County Map* (Annual); *Southeast Volusia focus* (Monthly). **Educational Activities:** East Coast Cruiser Night; Membership Meeting. **Geographic Preference:** Local.

38505 ■ Suwannee County Chamber of Commerce
212 N Ohio Ave.
Live Oak, FL 32064
Ph: (386)362-3071
Fax: (386)362-4758
Co. E-mail: staff@suwanneechamber.com
URL: http://www.suwanneechamber.com
Contact: Hillary Cannon, Executive Director
Facebook: www.facebook.com/SuwanneeChamber
Description: Promotes business and community development in Suwannee County, FL. Sponsors Christmas on the Square Festival and Suwanee Bicycle Festival. **Founded:** 1946. **Publications:** *Membership Directory and Buyers Guide* (Periodic); *Suwanee Notes* (Periodic). **Geographic Preference:** Local.

38506 ■ SWFL Inc.
25071 Chamber of Commerce Dr.
Bonita Springs, FL 34135
Ph: (239)992-2943
Co. E-mail: communications@swflinc.com
URL: http://swflinc.com
Contact: Tiffany Esposito, President
E-mail: tiffany@swflinc.com
Facebook: www.facebook.com/SWFLinc
Linkedin: www.linkedin.com/company/swfl-inc
X (Twitter): x.com/SWFLinc
Instagram: www.instagram.com/swfl_inc
YouTube: www.youtube.com/user/BonitaChamber
Description: Business and community leaders promoting business and community development in Bonita Springs, FL. **Founded:** 1967. **Publications:** *Chamber Focus* (Monthly). **Geographic Preference:** Local.

38507 ■ Tampa Bay Beaches Chamber of Commerce
6990 Gulf Blvd.
Saint Pete Beach, FL 33706-2030
Ph: (727)360-6957
Fax: (727)360-2233
Co. E-mail: info@tampabaybeaches.com
URL: http://www.tampabaybeaches.com
Contact: Robin Miller, President
Facebook: www.facebook.com/TampaBayBeachesChamber
Instagram: www.instagram.com/buybeachesfirst
YouTube: www.youtube.com/user/BeachesChamber
Description: Promotes business and community development in the Pinellas County beaches area of Florida. Sponsors a triathlon, and the Taste of the Beaches festival. **Founded:** 1997. **Publications:** *Beach Waves* (Monthly); *Guidebook* (Annual). **Geographic Preference:** Local.

38508 ■ Tampa Bay Chamber of Commerce (GTCC)
201 N Franklin St., Ste. 201
Tampa, FL 33602
Ph: (813)228-7777
Co. E-mail: info@tampabaychamber.com
URL: http://www.tampabaychamber.com/pages/about
Contact: Dr. Bob Rohrlack, Secretary
Facebook: www.facebook.com/tampabaychamber
Linkedin: www.linkedin.com/company/tampabaychamber
X (Twitter): x.com/TB_Chamber
YouTube: www.youtube.com/user/TampaChamber
Description: Promotes business growth and community development in Greater Tampa area. **Founded:** 1885. **Publications:** *Directory of Industries--Tampa and Greater Tampa Metropolitan Area*; *Inside View* (Quarterly); *Relocation Guide and Membership Directory*. **Awards:** Greater Tampa Chamber of Commerce Small Business of the Year (Annual). **Geographic Preference:** Local.

38509 ■ Tarpon Springs Chamber of Commerce (TSCC)
1 N Pinellas Ave.
Tarpon Springs, FL 34689
Ph: (727)937-6109
URL: http://www.tarponspringschamber.org
Contact: Jean Hungiville, President
E-mail: president@tarponspringschamber.org
Description: Promotes business and community development in the Tarpon Springs, FL area. **Founded:** 1921. **Publications:** *Guide Book* (Annual). **Geographic Preference:** Local.

38510 ■ Titusville Area Chamber of Commerce
2000 S Washington Ave.
Titusville, FL 32780-4747
Ph: (321)267-3036
Fax: (321)264-0127
Co. E-mail: info@titusville.org
URL: http://titusville.org
Contact: Erin Akins VanDyke, Co-President
Facebook: www.facebook.com/titusvillechamber
Linkedin: www.linkedin.com/company/titusvillechamber
YouTube: www.youtube.com/channel/UCIM2W-xS9wQRxrBu3lSzUHw
Description: Promotes business and community development in the Titusville, FL area. **Founded:** 1924. **Publications:** *ConTACt* (Weekly (Thurs.)). **Geographic Preference:** Local.

38511 ■ Umatilla Chamber of Commerce
PO Box 300
Umatilla, FL 32784
Ph: (352)669-3511
Co. E-mail: umatilla@umatillachamber.org
URL: http://www.umatillachamber.org
Contact: Ray Powers, President
Facebook: www.facebook.com/umatillaflchamber
Description: Promotes business and community development in Umatilla, FL. Sponsors festival. **Founded:** 1904. **Geographic Preference:** Local.

38512 ■ Upper Tampa Bay Regional Chamber of Commerce
101 State St. W
Oldsmar, FL 34677
Ph: (813)855-4233
Fax: (813)854-1237
Co. E-mail: mhowe@utbchamber.com
URL: http://www.utbchamber.com
Contact: Mark Howe, President
E-mail: mhowe@utbchamber.com
Facebook: www.facebook.com/UpperTampaBayChamberofCommerce
X (Twitter): x.com/OldsmarNews
Instagram: www.instagram.com/utbchamber
Description: Promotes business and community development in Upper Tampa Bay Region. **Founded:** 1960. **Publications:** *Horizon Lines* (Monthly); *Visitors Guide* (Annual). **Educational Activities:** Oldsmar Days and Nights (Annual). **Geographic Preference:** Local.

38513 ■ **Uptown Chamber of Commerce**
9385 N 56th St. Ste. 101
Temple Terrace, FL 33617
Ph: (813)989-7004
Co. E-mail: info@uptownchamber.org
URL: http://www.uptownchamber.org
Contact: Kenneth Lawson, President
Facebook: www.facebook.com/UTChamber
Linkedin: www.linkedin.com/company/utchamber
X (Twitter): x.com/utchamber
Instagram: www.instagram.com/UTChamber
Description: Promotes business and community development in Temple Terrace, FL. Holds art festival, Fourth of July parade and celebration, and business expo. **Founded:** 1963. **Publications:** *News and Views* (Monthly). **Awards:** Greater Temple Terrace Chamber of Commerce Citizen of the Year (Annual); Ed Hanna Business of the Year (Annual); Greater Temple Terrace Chamber of Commerce Small Business of the Year (Annual); Greater Temple Terrace Chamber of Commerce Students of the Year Award (Annual). **Geographic Preference:** Local.

38514 ■ **Venice Area Chamber of Commerce (VACC)**
597 Tamiami Trl. S
Venice, FL 34285
Ph: (941)488-2236
Fax: (941)484-5903
Co. E-mail: vchamber@venicechamber.com
URL: http://www.venicechamber.com
Contact: Kathy Lehner, President
E-mail: klehner@venicechamber.com
Facebook: www.facebook.com/VeniceAreaChamberofCommerce
Linkedin: www.linkedin.com/company/venice-area-chamber-of-commerce
X (Twitter): x.com/veniceareacc
Instagram: www.instagram.com/venicefloridachamber
Description: Promotes business and community development in the Venice, FL area. **Founded:** 1925. **Publications:** *Members in Action*. **Geographic Preference:** Local.

38515 ■ *Visitors Guide*
URL(s): lbts-chamber.opt2webinc.com/guide
Description: Provides a wealth of information about the area for visitors and newcomers. **Availability:** Print; Online.

38516 ■ *Visitor's Guide*
5114 Ocean Blvd.
Siesta Key, FL 34242
Ph: (941)349-3800
URL: http://www.siestakeychamber.com
Contact: Ann Frescura, Executive Director
E-mail: ann@siestakeychamber.com
URL(s): www.siestakeychamber.com/plan-your-trip/visitors-guide
Released: Annual **Availability:** Print; Online.

38517 ■ **Wakulla County Chamber of Commerce (WCCC)**
23 High Dr.
Crawfordville, FL 32326
Ph: (850)926-1848
Co. E-mail: info@wakullacountychamber.com
URL: http://wakullacountychamber.com
Contact: Amy Geiger, President
Facebook: www.facebook.com/wakullacountychamber
X (Twitter): x.com/wakullachamber
Instagram: www.instagram.com/wakullachamber
Description: Promotes business and community development in Wakulla County, FL. **Founded:** 1843. **Geographic Preference:** Local.

38518 ■ **Walton Area Chamber of Commerce**
63 S Centre Trl.
Santa Rosa Beach, FL 32459
Ph: (850)267-0683
Fax: (850)267-0603
Co. E-mail: hannah@waltonareachamber.com
URL: http://www.waltonareachamber.com
Contact: Megan Harrison, President
E-mail: ceo@waltonareachamber.com
Facebook: www.facebook.com/WaltonAreaChamberOfCommerce
Linkedin: www.linkedin.com/company/waltonareachamber
X (Twitter): x.com/ChamberOfWalton
Instagram: www.instagram.com/ChamberofWalton
Description: Works to help members improve and enhance their business. Provides vision leadership within Walton County. **Founded:** 1925. **Publications:** *Chamber Connection* (Monthly); *Official Buyer's Guide* (Annual); *Chamber Connection* (Monthly). **Educational Activities:** Walton County Chamber of Commerce Breakfast (Annual). **Geographic Preference:** Local.

38519 ■ **Washington County Chamber of Commerce (WCCC)**
672 5th St.
Chipley, FL 32428
Ph: (850)638-4157
Co. E-mail: info@washcomall.com
URL: http://www.washcomall.com
Contact: Tracy Andrews, President
Facebook: www.facebook.com/WashingtonCountyChamberofCommerce
X (Twitter): x.com/WcChamberFl
YouTube: www.youtube.com/channel/UCE-cpiBq4tDrDX5aBC_FHIA
Description: Promotes business and community development in Washington County, FL. **Publications:** *The Believer* (Monthly). **Geographic Preference:** Local.

38520 ■ **Wellington Chamber of Commerce**
12161 Ken Adams Way, Ste. 183
Wellington, FL 33414
Ph: (561)792-6525
Fax: (561)792-6200
Co. E-mail: info@wellingtonchamber.com
URL: http://www.wellingtonchamber.com
Contact: Michela Green, Executive Director
Facebook: www.facebook.com/WellingtonChamber
X (Twitter): x.com/WellyChamber
Pinterest: www.pinterest.com/wellchamber
Description: Promotes the general welfare and prosperity of the village of Wellington as well as its economic, civic, cultural, industrial, security and educational interests. **Founded:** 1996. **Publications:** *Official Guide to Wellington* (Annual). **Geographic Preference:** Local.

38521 ■ **West Orange Chamber of Commerce (WOCC)**
12184 W Colonial Dr.
Winter Garden, FL 34787
Ph: (407)656-1304
URL: http://wochamber.com
Contact: Stina D'Uva, President
E-mail: sduva@wochamber.com
Facebook: www.facebook.com/westorangechamber
Linkedin: www.linkedin.com/company/westorangechamber
X (Twitter): x.com/WOChamber
Instagram: www.instagram.com/westorangechamber
YouTube: www.youtube.com/user/wochamber
Description: Promotes business and community development in western Orange County, FL. Conducts charitable activities. Sponsors educational programs. **Founded:** 1972. **Publications:** *Chamber Matters* (Monthly); *Newsline* (Monthly). **Geographic Preference:** Local.

38522 ■ **West Pasco Chamber of Commerce (WPCC)**
5443 Main St.
New Port Richey, FL 34652
Ph: (727)842-7651
Co. E-mail: chamber@greaterpasco.com
URL: http://greaterpasco.com
Contact: Tim McClain, President
E-mail: tim@greaterpasco.com
Description: Promotes business and community development in New Port Richey, FL. **Publications:** *Chamber News*; *West Pasco Chamber of Commerce--Member Directory*. **Geographic Preference:** Local.

38523 ■ **West Volusia Regional Chamber of Commerce**
184 Treemonte Dr.
Orange City, FL 32763
Ph: (386)218-0540
Co. E-mail: ask@westvolusiaregionalchamber.org
URL: http://www.westvolusiaregionalchamber.org
Contact: Patricia Parte, Chairman
Facebook: www.facebook.com/westvolusiaregionalchamber.org
X (Twitter): x.com/WestVolRChamber
Instagram: www.instagram.com/wvolusiaregchamber
Description: Promotes business and community development in the Orange City, FL area. Encourages public service. Sponsors community social and promotional activities. Maintains tourism center. **Publications:** *City Directory* (Biennial); *Dateline* (Monthly). **Educational Activities:** Breakfast Connection. **Geographic Preference:** Local.

38524 ■ **Williston Area Chamber of Commerce**
50 NW Main St.
Williston, FL 32696
Ph: (352)528-5552
URL: http://www.willistonflchamber.com
Contact: Kurt Richardson, President
Facebook: www.facebook.com/Williston-FL-Area-Chamber-of-Commerce-1817918615139308
Description: Promotes business and community development in the Williston, FL area. **Founded:** 1985. **Publications:** *Chamber Music* (Monthly). **Educational Activities:** Levelup - The Chamber Business Conference. **Geographic Preference:** Local.

38525 ■ *Winter Haven*
401 Ave. B NW
Winter Haven, FL 33881
Ph: (863)293-2138
Co. E-mail: info@winterhavenchamber.com
URL: http://www.winterhavenchamber.com
Contact: Sara Beth Wyatt, President
E-mail: sarabeth@winterhavenchamber.com
URL(s): www.winterhavenchamber.com/market-your-business.html
Released: Annual **Description:** Includes tourism and travel information. **Availability:** Online.

38526 ■ **Winter Park Chamber of Commerce (WPCC)**
151 W Lyman Ave.
Winter Park, FL 32789
Ph: (407)644-8281
Co. E-mail: wpcc@winterpark.org
URL: http://winterpark.org
Contact: Betsy Gardner Eckbert, President
E-mail: bgardnereckbert@winterpark.org
Facebook: www.facebook.com/WinterParkChamber
Linkedin: www.linkedin.com/company/winter-park-chamber-of-commerce
X (Twitter): x.com/WPChamberFL
Instagram: www.instagram.com/winterparkchamber
YouTube: www.youtube.com/c/WinterParkChamberofCommerce
Description: Strives to develop, promote, and sustain a vital, thriving business climate throughout the community. Seeks to support and enhance the civic, educational, economical well-being of the Winter Park, FL area. **Founded:** 1923. **Publications:** *Winter Park Outlook* (Annual). **Geographic Preference:** Local.

38527 ■ **Ybor City Chamber of Commerce**
1800 E 9th Ave.
Tampa, FL 33605
Ph: (813)248-3712
Co. E-mail: membership@ybor.org
URL: http://www.ybor.org
Contact: Lee Bell, President
E-mail: lee.bell@ybor.org
Facebook: www.facebook.com/YborCityChamber
Description: Represents and assists local businesses. **Founded:** 1886. **Publications:** *La Setima* (Monthly). **Geographic Preference:** Local.

38528 ■ Zephyrhills Chamber of Commerce
38550 5th Ave.
Zephyrhills, FL 33542
Ph: (813)782-1913
Co. E-mail: admin@zephyrhillschamber.org
URL: http://www.zephyrhillschamber.org
Contact: Melonie Monson, President
E-mail: director@zephyrhillschamber.org
Facebook: www.facebook.com/zephyrhillschamber
Linkedin: www.linkedin.com/company/zephyrhillschamber
X (Twitter): x.com/ZHillsCOC
Instagram: www.instagram.com/zephyrhillschamber
YouTube: www.youtube.com/channel/UCU6XQeDHI7nT-oxHqTCnU0A
Description: Promotes business and community development in Zephyrhills, FL. **Publications:** Business. **Geographic Preference:** Local.

MINORITY BUSINESS ASSISTANCE PROGRAMS

38529 ■ Florida Black Business Investment Board (BBIF)
301 E Pine St., Ste. 175
Orlando, FL 32801
Ph: (407)649-4780
Co. E-mail: info@bbif.com
URL: http://bbif.com
Contact: Inez Long, President
Facebook: www.facebook.com/bbifflorida
Linkedin: www.linkedin.com/company/bbifflorida
X (Twitter): x.com/bbifflorida
Description: Obtains and provides loans for Black-owned and -operated businesses. **Founded:** 1987.

38530 ■ Florida State Minority Supplier Development Council (FSMSDC)
9499 NE 2nd Ave., Ste. 201
Miami, FL 33138
Ph: (305)762-6151
Fax: (305)762-6158
Co. E-mail: fsmsdc@fsmsdc.org
URL: http://fsmsdc.org
Contact: Beatrice Louissaint, President
E-mail: beatrice@fsmsdc.org
Facebook: www.facebook.com/FSMSDC
Linkedin: www.linkedin.com/company/floridastatemsdc
X (Twitter): x.com/fsmsdc
Instagram: www.instagram.com/fsmsdc
YouTube: www.youtube.com/user/TheSFMSDC
Description: Private-sector corporation that promotes the procurement of goods and services from minority businesses. Provides technical assistance and referral services to minority businesses. **Founded:** 1975.

38531 ■ Palm Beach County Resource Center Inc. (PBCRC)
2001 Broadway, Ste. 250
Riviera Beach, FL 33404
Ph: (561)863-0895
Fax: (561)863-0897
URL: http://www.pbcrc.org
Description: Strives to promote small businesses in Palm Beach county.

38532 ■ U.S. Department of Commerce - Minority Business Development Agency Business Center
c/o Marie Gill, Project Director
970 SW 1St. St., Ste. 406
Miami, FL 33130
Ph: (786)515-0670
Co. E-mail: marie@mgillonline.com
URL: http://www.mbda.gov/mbda-programs/business-centers
Contact: Marie Gill, Director
E-mail: marie@mgillonline.com
Description: Providing general and specific business assistance, counseling and training to help establish, maintain and grow eligible minority business enterprises.

FINANCING AND LOAN PROGRAMS

38533 ■ Cannabis Business Solutions, Inc. (CBS)
GL Brands, Inc.
2202 N Westshore Blvd., Ste. 200
Tampa, FL 33607
Ph: (720)717-3646
Free: 888-811-4367
Co. E-mail: info@glbrands.com
URL: http://glbrands.com
Contact: Catherine M. Zito, Chief Executive Officer
Facebook: www.facebook.com/pages/category/Medical-Cannabis-Dispensary/Cannabis-Business-Solutions-Inc-102222854455470
X (Twitter): x.com/CatherineMZito
Description: Provides various services for the cannabis industry, including investment opportunities for cannabis businesses, special events and webinars, in addition to banking and payment solutions.

38534 ■ CEO Advisors
848 Brickell Ave., Ste. 603
Miami, FL 33131
Ph: (305)371-8560
URL: http://www.ceoadvisors.us
Contact: Roberto Arguello, Jr., President
Facebook: www.facebook.com/CEOAdvisors9
Linkedin: www.linkedin.com/company/wix-com
Description: Provider of clients services in strategy, mergers and acquisitions, corporate finance and advisory, supply chain management, government relations and public affairs. **Scope:** Provider of clients services in strategy, mergers and acquisitions, corporate finance and advisory, supply chain management, government relations and public affairs. **Founded:** 1989. **Preferred Investment Size:** $300,000 to $500,000. **Industry Preferences:** Communications and media, computer hardware and software, semiconductors and other electronics, biotechnology, medical and health, consumer related.

38535 ■ GoBeyond Investing
3756 Mahogany Bend Dr.
Naples, FL 34114
Co. E-mail: info@gobeyondinvesting.com
URL: http://gobeyondinvesting.com
Description: Early-stage investing firm with locations in Florida, Zurich, Luxembourg, Malta, and Dubai. **Founded:** 2008. **Industry Preferences:** Technology; industrial; consumer; internet; mobile; impact.

38536 ■ Goldcoast Angel Investors
801 Bricknell Ave., Ste. 900
Miami, FL 33131
Ph: (305)423-1529
URL: http://goldcoastangels.vc
Contact: Bo Megginson, Managing Partner
Description: Early-stage investment group.

38537 ■ Ignition Point Capital Group
411 N New River Dr. E, Ste. 605
Fort Lauderdale, FL 33301
Ph: (954)372-7820
URL: http://ignitionpnt.com
Description: Member-managed private equity group invests in early-stage growth companies in South Florida. **Founded:** 2012. **Investment Policies:** High growth; sustainable competitive advantage; strong market position.

38538 ■ Lovett Miller & Co., Inc.
3304 Jean Cir.
Tampa, FL 33629
Ph: (813)222-1477
Fax: (813)222-1478
Co. E-mail: info@lovettmiller.com
URL: http://www.lovettmiller.com
Contact: Rad Lovett, Co-Founder
E-mail: rad@lovettmiller.com
Description: Operates a private equity investment firm. **Founded:** 1997. **Preferred Investment Size:** $3,000,000 to $10,000,000. **Industry Preferences:** Computer software and services, Internet specific, communications and media, consumer related, business services, financial services, medical and health, and other products.

38539 ■ Orchid Black
1601 3rd St. S, Ste. F
Saint Petersburg, FL 33701
Ph: (727)900-5389
URL: http://www.orchid.black
Linkedin: www.linkedin.com/company/orchidblack
Description: Venture capital, private equity, and consulting firm founded on the idea that industry knowledge, pragmatic engineering expertise, and a repeatable playbook produce results. Helps build and scale technology businesses. Also operates out of New York.

38540 ■ Tamiami Angel Funds
3003 Tamiami Trl. N, Ste. 410
Naples, FL 34103
Ph: (239)262-6300
Fax: (239)262-2212
URL: http://www.tamiamiangels.com
Contact: Timothy J. Cartwright, Chairman Managing Director
Facebook: www.facebook.com/tamiamiangels
Linkedin: www.linkedin.com/company/tamiamiangelfunds
X (Twitter): x.com/TamiamiAngels
Description: Invests in early-stage accelerated growth companies. **Founded:** 2008.

PROCUREMENT ASSISTANCE PROGRAMS

38541 ■ Florida APEX Accelerator (PTAC)
University of West Florida
9999 University Pky.
Pensacola, FL 32514-5732
Ph: (850)898-3485
Co. E-mail: info@floridaptac.org
URL: http://fptac.org
Facebook: www.facebook.com/flapexaccelerator
Linkedin: www.linkedin.com/company/flapexaccelerator
Description: Helps Florida businesses interested in obtaining contracts with the Department of Defense, other federal agencies, and state/local government agencies and participating prime contractors covering the Pensacola area. **Founded:** 1985.

38542 ■ Florida Department of Management Services - Agency Purchasing
4050 Esplanade Way, Ste. 260
Tallahassee, FL 32399
Co. E-mail: dms.purchasing@dms.fl.gov
URL: http://www.dms.myflorida.com/agency_administration/agency_purchasing
Description: Publishes Doing Business with the State of Florida. Potential vendors should contact each state agency's purchasing office, since the Department of General Services does not make purchases for all agencies.

38543 ■ Florida Gulf Coast University-Florida Procurement Technical Assistance Center (PTAC)
10501 FGCU Blvd South - CLI, Lutgert COB Unit 2320
Fort Myers, FL 33965-6502
Ph: (239)745-3708
Co. E-mail: info@floridaptac.org
URL: http://fptac.org/location/fort-myers
Contact: Mark Odell, Specialist
E-mail: modell@fgcu.edu
Description: Helps Florida businesses interested in obtaining contracts with the Department of Defense, other federal agencies, and state/local government agencies and participating prime contractors covering Lee, Collier, Charlotte, Glades, and Hendry counties.

38544 ■ Florida Procurement Center Representatives (Fl PCR)
c/o Scott Nirk
Office of Government Contracting, Area III South Florida District Office 51 SW 1ST Ave. Ste. 201
Miami, FL 33131
Ph: (305)536-5769
Fax: (202)741-6625
Co. E-mail: scott.nirk@sba.gov
URL: http://www.sba.gov/federal-contracting/counseling-help/procurement-center-representative-directory#id-area---al-fl-ga-ky-ms-nc-sc-tn
Contact: Scott Nirk, Contact
E-mail: scott.nirk@sba.gov
Description: Covers activities for Naval Training Systems Center (Orlando, FL). McDill Air Force Base (Tampa, FL), Patrick Air Force Base (Cocoa Beach, FL), and NASA, Kennedy Space Flight Center (Cape Canaveral, FL).

38545 ■ The Florida Procurement Technical Assistance Center (PTAC)
3201 E Colonial Dr., Ste. A-20
Orlando, FL 32803-5140
Ph: (407)420-4850
Co. E-mail: info@floridaptac.org
URL: http://fptac.org
Contact: Steve South, Specialist
E-mail: steve.south@ucf.edu
Description: Helps Florida businesses interested in obtaining contracts with the Department of Defense, other federal agencies, and state/local government agencies and participating prime contractors covering the Orlando area.

38546 ■ Florida Procurement Technical Assistance Center-University of South Florida-Pinellas Park
13805 58th St., N
Clearwater, FL 33760
Ph: (727)453-7200
URL: http://fptac.org/location/clearwater
Contact: Yolanda Cowart, Specialist
E-mail: ygoodloe@co.pinellas.fl.us
Description: Helps Florida businesses interested in obtaining contracts with the Department of Defense, other federal agencies, and state/local government agencies and participating prime contractors covering St. Petersburg, Sarasota, and Pasco Counties.

38547 ■ JAX Chamber Small Business Center
3 Independent Dr.
Jacksonville, FL 32202
Ph: (904)366-6618
URL: http://jaxchamber.com/localcontacts
Description: Engages in mentoring, education, consulting and networking opportunities for small business entrepreneurs through meetings, workshops, development programs and seminars. The organization also provides a resource library with telecommunication equipment and reference materials. **Founded:** 1884. **Publications:** Jacksonville Magazine--International Business Guide.

38548 ■ University of South Florida-Florida Procurement Technical Assistance Center-Tampa Office
4202 E Fowler Ave.
Tampa, FL 33620
URL: http://www.usf.edu/locations/tampa-campus.aspx
Description: Helps Florida businesses interested in obtaining contracts with the Department of Defense, other federal agencies, and state/local government agencies and participating prime contractors covering Tampa, Bartow, Ocala, and Melbourne areas.

38549 ■ University of West Florida - Fort Walton Beach Office Procurement Technical Assistance Center
Coastal Bank & Trust Bldg., Ste. A
815 Beal Pkwy. NW
Fort Walton Beach, FL 32547
Ph: (815)229-7500
URL: http://fptac.org/location/fort-walton-beach
Contact: John DiGiacomo, Specialist
E-mail: jdigiacomo@uwf.edu
Description: Helps Florida businesses interested in obtaining contracts with the Department of Defense, other federal agencies, and state/local government agencies and participating prime contractors covering Ft. Walton Beach and Crestview areas.

INCUBATORS/RESEARCH AND TECHNOLOGY PARKS

38550 ■ Apex Brasil
Miami Center Bldg. 201 S Biscayne Blvd., Ste. 1200
Miami, FL 33131
Ph: (305)704-3500
Fax: (305)704-3505
Co. E-mail: escritorio.usa@apexbrasil.com.br
URL: http://apexbrasil.com.br
Facebook: www.facebook.com/apexbrasil
Linkedin: www.linkedin.com/company/apex-brasil
Instagram: www.instagram.com/apexbrasil
YouTube: www.youtube.com/user/ApexBrasil
Description: Firm provides trade and investment promotion agency services. **Founded:** 1997.

38551 ■ ARCEO Executive Office Program
3606 Enterprise Ave., Ste. 200
Naples, FL 34104
Ph: (239)260-4332
Fax: (239)529-1085
URL: http://londonexecutivesuites.com
Description: Firm provides start-ups with infrastructure, staff and technology support services.

38552 ■ Beaver Street Enterprise Center (BSEC)
1225 W Beaver St.
Jacksonville, FL 32204
Ph: (904)265-4700
Co. E-mail: info@bsecenter.net
URL: http://bsecenter.net
Contact: Theresa Johnson, Managing Director
E-mail: theresa.johnson@bsecenter.net
Facebook: www.facebook.com/BeaverStreetEnterpriseCenter
X (Twitter): x.com/bsecenter
Description: A small business incubator established to launch new businesses, to assist existing business through growing pains, to create jobs and enhance economic development in Jacksonville. **Founded:** 2001.

38553 ■ BUILDING.CO
120 SW 8th St.
Miami, FL 33130
Ph: (305)702-0403
URL: http://building.co
Contact: Jose Rasco, Co-Founder
Facebook: www.facebook.com/BUILDINGMiami
X (Twitter): x.com/buildingco
Instagram: www.instagram.com/buildingco
Description: Provides shared workspace for growing tech companies and individuals serving the tech ecosystem.

38554 ■ The Center for Technology, Enterprise & Development Business Incubator
401 W Atlantic Ave., Ste. 09
Delray Beach, FL 33444
Ph: (561)265-3790
Free: 866-353-3790
Fax: (561)265-0806
URL: http://www.tedcenter.org
Contact: Tony Newbold, President
Description: Agency that transforms communities through collaborative partnerships and educational programs.

38555 ■ CityDesk
350 S Miami Ave., Ste. A
Miami, FL 33130
Ph: (305)680-6030
Co. E-mail: info@citydeskmiami.com
URL: http://citydeskmiami.com
Facebook: www.facebook.com/citydeskmiami
X (Twitter): x.com/citydeskmiami
Instagram: www.instagram.com/citydeskmiami
Description: A modern workspace community for startups and entrepreneurs. Provides private offices, coworking desks, meeting rooms, and virtual offices.

38556 ■ Commercial Kitchen Fort Myers (CKFM)
11770-A Metro Pky.
Fort Myers, FL 33966
Ph: (239)462-3589
Co. E-mail: ckfm@comcast.net
URL: http://www.commercialkitchenfortmyers.com
Description: Operator of fully equipped commercial kitchen and kitchen incubator for rent that supports caterers, personal chefs, bakers, street vendors, cake decorators and producers of specialty food items such as condiments and candies.

38557 ■ Cowork Tampa
3104 N Armenia Ave., Ste. 2
Tampa, FL 33607
Free: 800-531-2986
Co. E-mail: vip@coworktampa.com
URL: http://coworktampa.com
Contact: Chris Arnoldi, Founder
X (Twitter): x.com/CoWorkTampa
Instagram: www.instagram.com/coworktampa
Description: Provides coworking space to tech startups and entrepreneurs. **Founded:** 2011.

38558 ■ Enterprise Development Corporation of South Florida
313 Datura St., Ste. 200
Boca Raton, FL 33487
Ph: (561)425-8918
URL: http://techhubsouthflorida.org
Contact: Louis Balbirer, Chairman of the Board
Facebook: www.facebook.com/SouthFloridaTechHub
Linkedin: www.linkedin.com/company/techhubsouthflorida
X (Twitter): x.com/techhubfl
Description: A non profit organization that assists emerging science and technology companies.

38559 ■ Entrepreneurship Development Institute (EDI)
3209 Virginia Ave.
Fort Pierce, FL 34981
Ph: (772)462-7630
Free: 888-283-1177
URL: http://www.irscbiz.com
Contact: Joe Gorham, Coordinator
E-mail: jgorham@irsc.edu
Description: Provides management and employee development programs.

38560 ■ FAU Tech Runway
901 NW 35th St.
Boca Raton, FL 33431
Ph: (561)297-8000
Co. E-mail: techrunway@fau.edu
URL: http://www.fau.edu/techrunway
Contact: Connor Lynch, Chief Executive Officer
Facebook: www.facebook.com/fautechrunway
Linkedin: www.linkedin.com/company/fautechrunway
X (Twitter): x.com/fautechrunway
Instagram: www.instagram.com/fau_techrunway
YouTube: www.youtube.com/channel/UCo6_BhpJNtc1xriY66B_ybg
Description: Fosters technology startups. Offers a collaborative workspace for entrepreneurs to house, educate, mentor, and fund their companies from inception through venture funding. **Founded:** 2014.

38561 ■ FIT Business Innovation Center
1050 W Nasa Blvd.
Melbourne, FL 32901
URL: http://wjconstruction.com/our-projects/fit-business-innovation-center
Description: Supports business startups and entrepreneurs by providing office space, coaching, and training to help clients achieve success.

38562 ■ Florida Atlantic Research and Development Authority (FARDA)
3651 FAU Blvd., Ste. 400
Boca Raton, FL 33431

Ph: (561)416-6092
Co. E-mail: info@research-park.org
URL: http://www.research-park.org
Facebook: www.facebook.com/ResearchParkFAU
Linkedin: www.linkedin.com/company/researchparkfau
Instagram: www.instagram.com/researchparkfau
YouTube: www.youtube.com/channel/UCHRak85-Bbp29nztDAR9mVA

Description: Research and development facility offering applied research directed at the industry partners' specific needs. **Founded:** 1985.

38563 ■ Florida Atlantic University - Technology Business Incubator
777 Glades Rd.
Boca Raton, FL 33431
Co. E-mail: llsboca@fau.edu
URL: http://www.fau.edu

Description: Assists companies in the early stages of development.

38564 ■ Florida State University College of Business - Jim Moran Institute for Global Entrepreneurship
111 S Monroe St.
Tallahassee, FL 32301-1536
Ph: (850)644-3372
Fax: (850)644-5950
Co. E-mail: jimmoraninstitute@fsu.edu
URL: http://jimmoraninstitute.fsu.edu
Contact: Randy Blass, Executive Director
E-mail: rblass@jimmoraninstitute.fsu.edu
Facebook: www.facebook.com/JimMoranInstitute
Linkedin: www.linkedin.com/company/jim-moran-institute-for-global-entrepreneurship
X (Twitter): x.com/jimmoraninst
Instagram: www.instagram.com/jimmoraninstitute

Description: Provide students, faculty, entrepreneurs and business owners with the tools and expertise necessary to develop strategies that establish and sustain the startup of new business ventures. **Founded:** 1995.

38565 ■ FloridaWest
3 W Garden St., Ste. 618
Pensacola, FL 32502
Ph: (850)898-2201
Fax: (850)898-2201
Co. E-mail: inquiries@floridawesteda.com
URL: http://www.floridawesteda.com
Contact: Rick Byars, President
Facebook: www.facebook.com/floridawesteda
X (Twitter): x.com/FloridaWestEDA
Instagram: www.instagram.com/floridawesteda

Description: Works to connect the assets, resources and skilled workforce of the Greater Pensacola region with business and industry to build a thriving industrial and professional community for the ongoing economic growth and prosperity of the region.

38566 ■ Gainesville Technology Enterprise Center (GTEC)
2153 SE Hawthorne Rd., Ste. 101
Gainesville, FL 32641
Ph: (352)395-5053
Fax: (352)395-5086
URL: http://www.sfcollege.edu/incubators
Contact: Bill Dorman, Director
E-mail: bill.dorman@sfcollege.edu

Description: A community organization providing early stage technology startup companies with the tools, training and infrastructure to become self-sufficient, financially-viable technology enterprises. **Founded:** 2014.

38567 ■ Gainesville Technology Entrepreneurship Center (GTEC)
2153 SE Hawthorne Rd., Ste. 101
Gainesville, FL 32641
Ph: (352)395-5053
Fax: (352)395-5086
URL: http://www.sfcollege.edu/incubators
Contact: Bill Dorman, Director
E-mail: bill.dorman@sfcollege.edu

Description: A community program providing early stage startup companies with tools, training and infrastructure to help them get started, grow and develop into financially viable enterprises. **Founded:** 1965.

38568 ■ Gazelle Lab
Tampa, FL
URL: http://gazellelab.com

Description: A Tampa Bay based seed stage investment fund. A three-month, seed stage investment program offering $6,000 per founder to companies that make its list for up to 3 founders. In return, Gazelle Lab takes 6% equity in the company in common/founders stock. **Founded:** 2011.

38569 ■ Greenwood Consulting Group (GCGI)
1150 Junonia St.
Sanibel, FL 33957
Ph: (239)395-9446
Co. E-mail: gail@g-jgreenwood.com
URL: http://www.g-jgreenwood.com
Contact: Jim Greenwood, Contact
E-mail: gail-jim@g-jgreenwood.com
Facebook: www.facebook.com/2008/fbml

Description: Provides a host of services to small businesses including incubation as well as an innovation research program.

38570 ■ Healthy Food Factory
Boca Raton, FL
Ph: (561)394-7466
URL: http://www.healthyfoodfactory.com
Contact: Brigitte Lang, Founder
E-mail: brlang@aol.com
URL(s): www.healthyfoodfactory.eu
Facebook: www.facebook.com/HealthyFoodFactory

Description: Culinary incubator offering shared kitchen space for food startups. **Founded:** 2013.

38571 ■ Hour Cucina L.L.C.
411 S Federal Hwy.
Boynton Beach, FL 33435
Ph: (561)739-3789
Co. E-mail: info@hourcucina.com
URL: http://www.hourcucina.com
Contact: Lester S. Albert, Member
Facebook: www.facebook.com/HourCucina
X (Twitter): x.com/hourcucina
Instagram: www.instagram.com/hourcucina

Description: Culinary incubator offering kitchen space for food startups.

38572 ■ Innovation Hub at Broward College
111 E Las Olas Blvd.
Fort Lauderdale, FL 33301
Ph: (954)201-7350
Co. E-mail: bcrecruiting@broward.edu
URL: http://www.broward.edu
Contact: Gregory Adam, President
Facebook: www.facebook.com/BrowardCollege
Linkedin: www.linkedin.com/company/broward-college
X (Twitter): x.com/BrowardCollege
Instagram: www.instagram.com/browardcollege
YouTube: www.youtube.com/user/browardEdu
Pinterest: www.pinterest.com/browardcollege

Description: A mixed-use business incubator, focusing on housing a dynamic community of entrepreneurs, start-ups, mentors, advisors and investors and serving as a one-stop resource for business owners, innovators and committed individuals pursuing their entrepreneurial ambitions.

38573 ■ Innovation Hub at the University of Florida (UF Innovate)
747 SW 2nd Ave.
Gainesville, FL 32601
Ph: (352)294-0885
URL: http://innovate.research.ufl.edu
Contact: Jim O'Connell, Vice President
E-mail: jimoconnell@ufl.edu
Facebook: www.facebook.com/UFInnovate
X (Twitter): x.com/UFInnovate

Description: An elite entrepreneurial program available to selected applicants. Programs available in three tracks, Resident Startups, Hatchery Members and Affiliate Members. **Founded:** 2011.

38574 ■ Let's Eat Fresh Commissary Kitchen & Catering
809 N Magnolia Ave.
Ocala, FL 34475
Ph: (352)299-5233
Co. E-mail: letseatfresh@yahoo.com
URL: http://www.letseatfresh.net
Contact: Rosaria Delprete, Owner
Facebook: www.facebook.com/LEF.CommissaryKitchen
Instagram: www.instagram.com/letseatfreshkitchen

Description: Firm offers kitchen for caterers, food trucks, and independent cooks.

38575 ■ National Entrepreneur Center (NEC)
3201 E Colonial Dr., Ste. A-20
Orlando, FL 32803
Ph: (407)420-4848
Co. E-mail: info@nationalec.org
URL: http://nationalec.org
Contact: Jerry Ross, President
Facebook: www.facebook.com/NationalEC
X (Twitter): x.com/nationalec
YouTube: www.youtube.com/nationalec

Description: Firm provides start-ups and entrepreneurs by providing one-on-one business coaching, low-cost business seminars, networking events, access to business resources, advisory board programs and connections to procurement assistance. **Founded:** 2003.

38576 ■ Ooo La La!
2413 SE Dixie Hwy.
Stuart, FL 34996
Ph: (772)233-0456
URL: http://ooolalalife.com
Contact: Lorna Day, Owner
E-mail: lorna@ooolalalife.com
Facebook: www.facebook.com/ooolalacaters

Description: Producer of food products.

38577 ■ Pathlight Kitchens
3200 W Colonial Dr.
Orlando, FL 32808
Ph: (407)480-1657
Co. E-mail: info@pathlighthome.org
Facebook: www.facebook.com/PathlightKitchen

Description: Helps culinarians and small business achieve professional goals at a low cost. Offers fully equipped commercial culinary kitchens and bake shop.

38578 ■ Power Plant Business Incubator
405 SE Osceola Ave.
Ocala, FL 34471
Ph: (352)629-8051
URL: http://ocalacep.com/growing-jobs/create-your-business
Contact: Jessica McCallum, Director, Operations
E-mail: jessica@ocalacep.com
Facebook: www.facebook.com/powerplantincubator
Instagram: www.instagram.com/powerplantbusinessincubator

Description: Firm provides a nurturing climate and sustainable system services.

38579 ■ Proton Enterprises (PE)
1150 Central Ave.
Naples, FL 34102
Co. E-mail: hello@protonenterprises.com
URL: http://www.protonenterprises.com
Linkedin: www.linkedin.com/company/proton-enterprises

Description: A business incubator whose goal is to accelerate the growth and success of companies through an array of business support services and resources.

38580 ■ Seminole Technology Business Incubation Center (STBIC)
1445 Dolgner Pl.
Sanford, FL 32771

Ph: (407)321-3495
Fax: (407)321-4184
Co. E-mail: templer@seminolestate.edu
URL: http://www.seminoleinc.com
Contact: Kyle Kilger, Contact
Description: Firm provides nurturing environment for technology based companies in the early stages of development.

38581 ■ SMARTstart Pasco Business Incubator
15029 14th St.
Dade City, FL 33525
URL: http://smartstartpasco.com
Contact: Daniel Mitchell, Program Director
E-mail: dmitchell@pascoedc.com
Description: Business incubator who helps entrepreneurs and business startups and services include consulting and mentoring, resource networks, financing, business plan assistance, marketing and product commercialization.

38582 ■ Southwest Florida Enterprise Center
3903 Dr. Martin Luther King, Jr. Blvd., Ste. 5
Fort Myers, FL 33916
Ph: (239)321-7085
URL: http://cityftmyers.com
Contact: Phyllis R. Calloway, Director
Description: Firm provides accounting assistance, business planning, legal assistance and procurement services. **Founded:** 2009.

38583 ■ Spark Growth (SG)
912 7th Ave. E
Bradenton, FL 34202
Ph: (941)877-1599
Co. E-mail: info@sparkgrowth.net
URL: http://sparkgrowth.net
Contact: Sara Hand, Chief Executive Officer
E-mail: sara@sparkgrowth.net
Facebook: www.facebook.com/SparkGrowth
Linkedin: www.linkedin.com/company/spark-growth-us
X (Twitter): x.com/Spark_Growth
Description: Firm provides entrepreneurial ecosystem development services. **Founded:** 2013.

38584 ■ Tampa Bay Innovation Center (TBIC)
501 1st Ave. N, Ste. 901
Saint Petersburg, FL 33701
Ph: (727)547-7340
Fax: (727)547-7350
Co. E-mail: info@tbinnovates.com
URL: http://tbinnovates.com
Contact: Tonya Elmore, President
E-mail: elmoret@tbinnovates.com
Facebook: www.facebook.com/tbinnovationcenter
Linkedin: www.linkedin.com/company/tampa-bay-innovation-center/about
X (Twitter): x.com/tbinnovates
Instagram: www.instagram.com/tbinnovates
Description: Provider of business incubation program provides clients with access to networks, experts, international markets, industry peers, market research, service providers, university support systems, and funding. **Founded:** 2003.

38585 ■ Tampa Bay Kitchen
25778 US Hwy., 19 N
Clearwater, FL 33763
Ph: (727)432-2317
Co. E-mail: info@tampabaykitchen.com
URL: http://www.tampabaykitchen.com
Facebook: www.facebook.com/TampaBayKitchen
Description: Culinary incubator with a commercial kitchen for rent to food startups.

38586 ■ Tampa Bay Technology Incubator (TBTI)
3702 Spectrum Blvd., Ste. 165
Tampa, FL 33612
URL: http://www.usf.edu/research-innovation/rf/usf-connect/tbti
Description: Helps to grow successful companies. Supports technology research as a catalyst for economic development.

38587 ■ Tampa Bay WaVE Inc.
500 E Kennedy Blvd., Ste. 300
Tampa, FL 33602
Free: 866-928-3066
Co. E-mail: hello@tampabaywave.org
URL: http://www.tampabaywave.org
Contact: Linda Olson, President
Facebook: www.facebook.com/TampaBayWaVE
Linkedin: www.linkedin.com/company/tampa-bay-wave
X (Twitter): x.com/tampabayWaVE
Instagram: www.instagram.com/tampabaywave
YouTube: www.youtube.com/user/tampabaywave/videos
Pinterest: www.pinterest.com/tampabaywave
Description: Firm that helps entrepreneurs turn ideas into growing tech businesses. **Founded:** 2008.

38588 ■ Technology Business Incubator (TBI)
3651 FAU Blvd., Ste. 400
Boca Raton, FL 33431
Ph: (561)416-6092
URL: http://www.research-park.org/technology-business-incubator
Contact: Bob Swindell, Chairman
Description: Designed to assist companies in the early stages of development and to the greatest extent possible, lighten the burdens of running a business for the entrepreneur, thereby letting him/her focus on developing the technology and finding new customers. **Founded:** 2010.

38589 ■ The TED Center
401 W Atlantic Ave., Ste. O9
Delray Beach, FL 33444
Ph: (561)265-3790
Fax: (561)265-0806
URL: http://tedcenter.org
Contact: Tony Newbold, President
Facebook: www.facebook.com/TheTEDcenter
Description: Business incubator committed to helping individuals realize their dreams and aspirations to successfully enter the world of entrepreneurship and business.

38590 ■ Travel Startups Incubator (TSI)
7901 4th St. N, Ste. 300
Saint Petersburg, FL 33702
Ph: (207)460-0740
Co. E-mail: matt@travelstartups.co
URL: http://www.travelstartupsincubator.com
Contact: Matt Zito, Managing Partner
Description: Team of veteran travel entrepreneurs, startup advisors, and mentors dedicated to investing in talented travel entrepreneurs and early seed-stage travel technology ideas.

38591 ■ Treasure Coast Research Park [St. Lucie County]
2300 Virginia Ave.
Fort Pierce, FL 34982
Ph: (772)462-1100
Fax: (772)462-1153
Co. E-mail: utilities_customer_service@stlucieco.org
URL: http://www.stlucieco.gov
Contact: Peter J. Tesch, President
E-mail: ptesch@youredc.com
Facebook: www.facebook.com/StLucieGOV
X (Twitter): x.com/stluciegov
Instagram: www.instagram.com/stluciegov
YouTube: www.youtube.com/stluciegov
Description: Operator of research, education and development park for food and agricultural sciences research. **Founded:** 1905.

38592 ■ UF Innovate
747 SW 2nd Ave.
Gainesville, FL 32601
Ph: (352)294-0885
URL: http://innovate.research.ufl.edu
Contact: Dr. Jackson Streeter, Director
E-mail: jstreeter@ufl.edu
Facebook: www.facebook.com/UFInnovate
Linkedin: www.linkedin.com/school/uf-innovate/mycompany
X (Twitter): x.com/UFInnovate
Description: Umbrella organization for the innovation ecosystem an University of Florida. Includes Tech Licensing, Ventures, and two business incubators (The Hub and Sid Martin Biotech). Helps transition research from the laboratory to the market; connects innovators with entrepreneurs; fosters the economy in order to make the world a better place.

38593 ■ University of Central Florida Business Incubation Program (UCFBIP)
3259 Progress Dr.
Orlando, FL 32826
Ph: (407)635-9880
URL: http://incubator.ucf.edu
Contact: Julie Driskel, Office Manager
E-mail: julie.driskel@ucf.edu
X (Twitter): x.com/ucfbip
Description: Helps early-stage business develop into financially stable companies by providing tools, training and infrastructure. **Founded:** 1999.

38594 ■ University of Florida - Sid Martin Biotechnology Incubator
University of Florida
Gainesville, FL 32611
URL: http://www.ufl.edu
Contact: Merrie Shaw, Director
URL(s): innovate.research.ufl.edu/sid-martin-biotech
Description: Business incubator supporting biotechnology startups and entrepreneurs. **Scope:** Biotechnology development. **Founded:** 1987.

38595 ■ University of Florida - Sid Martin Biotechnology Institute
12085 Research Dr.
Alachua, FL 32615
Ph: (386)462-0880
URL: http://www.innovate.research.ufl.edu/accelerate-2/#sid-martin-biotech
Description: Biotechnology business incubator with laboratories and specialized equipment, mentors, advisors, and collaborators.

38596 ■ Venture Hive
1010 NE 2nd Ave.
Miami, FL 33132
Ph: (305)735-1274
Co. E-mail: info@venturehive.com
URL: http://www.venturehive.com
Contact: Susan Amat, Chief Executive Officer
Facebook: www.facebook.com/VentureHive
Linkedin: www.linkedin.com/company/venturehive
X (Twitter): x.com/venturehive
Description: Accelerator/incubator offering a 12-week program and on-going residency and support to entrepreneurs. **Founded:** 2013.

38597 ■ weVENTURE
2202 S Babcock St., 1st Fl.
Melbourne, FL 32901
Ph: (321)674-7007
Co. E-mail: weventure@fit.edu
URL: http://weventure.fit.edu
Contact: Kathryn Rudloff, Executive Director
E-mail: krudloff@fit.edu
Facebook: www.facebook.com/weVENTURE
Description: Provider of innovative mentoring programs and award-winning training curriculum that builds local businesses.

EDUCATIONAL PROGRAMS

38598 ■ Florida Keys Community College
5901 College Rd.
Key West, FL 33040
Ph: (305)296-9081
Co. E-mail: recruiter@fkcc.edu
URL: http://www.cfk.edu
Contact: Dr. Jonathan Gueverra, President
Facebook: www.facebook.com/TheCollegeoftheFloridaKeys
Linkedin: www.linkedin.com/company/the-college-of-the-florida-keys
Instagram: www.instagram.com/collegeflkeys
YouTube: www.youtube.com/user/myfkcc

Description: A two-year community college, offers certificates and associate degree programs. **Founded:** 1965.

38599 ■ The Idea Center (IC)
315 NE 2nd Ave., Bldg. 8, 5th Fl.
 Miami, FL 33132
Ph: (305)237-7809
Co. E-mail: ideacenter@mdc.edu
URL: http://theideacenter.co
Contact: Alejandro D. Gonzalez, Executive Director
Facebook: www.facebook.com/ideacenterMDC
Linkedin: www.linkedin.com/company/ideacentermdc
X (Twitter): x.com/ideacentermdc
Instagram: www.instagram.com/ideacentermdc
YouTube: www.youtube.com/channel/UCGhl_jK3gl6jTPWEMYV2_oQ
Description: Offers a support network for Miami Dade College students and community members to make creative, innovative, and entrepreneurial ideas come to fruition. **Founded:** 2014.

38600 ■ St. John's River State College (SJRSC)
5001 St. John's Ave.
 Palatka, FL 32177
Ph: (386)312-4050
Fax: (386)312-4048
Co. E-mail: helpdesk@vikings.sjrstate.edu
URL: http://www.sjrstate.edu
Contact: Joe H. Pickens, JD, President
Facebook: www.facebook.com/SJRstate
Instagram: www.instagram.com/sjrstate
YouTube: www.youtube.com/user/SJRstate
Description: Two-year college offering a small business management program. **Founded:** 1958.

38601 ■ Santa Fe College (SF)
3000 NW 83rd St.
 Gainesville, FL 32606
Ph: (352)395-5000
Co. E-mail: information@sfcollege.edu
URL: http://www.sfcollege.edu
Contact: Paul Broadie, II, President
Facebook: www.facebook.com/santafecollege
Linkedin: www.linkedin.com/school/santa-fe-college
X (Twitter): x.com/santafecollege
Instagram: www.instagram.com/santafecollege
YouTube: www.youtube.com/user/SantaFeCollege
Pinterest: www.pinterest.com/santafecollege352
Description: Two-year college offering a program in small business management. **Founded:** 1966.

38602 ■ Seminole State College of Florida (SSC)
100 Weldon Blvd.
 Sanford, FL 32773
Ph: (407)708-4722
Co. E-mail: helpdesk@seminolestate.edu
URL: http://www.seminolestate.edu
Contact: Dr. Georgia Lorenz, President
Facebook: www.facebook.com/seminolestate
Linkedin: www.linkedin.com/school/seminole-state-college-of-florida
X (Twitter): x.com/SeminoleState
Instagram: www.instagram.com/seminolestate
YouTube: www.youtube.com/user/SeminoleStateCollege
Description: Two-year college offering a small business administration program. **Founded:** 1965.

TRADE SHOWS AND CONVENTIONS

38603 ■ Florida Bar Convention
URL(s): www.floridabar.org
Frequency: Annual. **Description:** Networking conference for lawyers in Florida. **Principal Exhibits:** Networking conference for lawyers in Florida.

CONSULTANTS

38604 ■ Business Confidant
3231 Huntington Place Dr.
 Sarasota, FL 34231
Ph: (415)282-1044
Fax: (650)754-1496
Co. E-mail: info@businessconfidant.net
URL: http://www.businessconfidant.net
Contact: Rick Shepherd, Owner Consultant
Description: Specialized in creating business plans. **Founded:** 2000.

38605 ■ Orchid Black
1601 3rd St. S, Ste. F
 Saint Petersburg, FL 33701
Ph: (727)900-5389
URL: http://www.orchid.black
Linkedin: www.linkedin.com/company/orchidblack
Description: Venture capital, private equity, and consulting firm founded on the idea that industry knowledge, pragmatic engineering expertise, and a repeatable playbook produce results. Helps build and scale technology businesses. Also operates out of New York.

PUBLICATIONS

38606 ■ *Jacksonville Business Journal*
120 W Morehead St.
 Charlotte, NC 28202
Co. E-mail: circhelp@bizjournals.com
URL: http://www.acbj.com
Contact: Mike Olivieri, Executive Vice President
URL(s): www.bizjournals.com/jacksonville
Facebook: www.facebook.com/JBJNews
Linkedin: www.linkedin.com/company/jacksonville-business-journal
X (Twitter): x.com/JaxBizJournal
Instagram: www.instagram.com/jaxbizjournal
Price: $70, for online only; $70, for 1 year online and online; $245, for nationwide access; $180, for online only; $190, for print and online; $350, for nationwide access; $950, for nationwide + bol. **Description:** Local business news coverage. **Availability:** Print; Online. **Type:** Full-text.

38607 ■ *Orlando Business Journal* (OBJ)
255 S Orange Ave., Ste. 650
 Orlando, FL 32801
Ph: (407)649-8470
Fax: (407)420-1625
Co. E-mail: orlando@bizjournals.com
URL: http://www.bizjournals.com/orlando
Contact: Julie Swyers, Director
E-mail: jswyers@bizjournals.com
Facebook: www.facebook.com/objupdate
Linkedin: www.linkedin.com/company/orlando-business-journal
X (Twitter): x.com/OBJUpdate
Instagram: www.instagram.com/orlandobizjrnl
Description: Publisher of newspaper covering general business news, major events. **Founded:** 1984. **Publications:** *Book of Lists* (Annual); *Health Care Directory* (Annual).

38608 ■ *South Florida Business Journal*
120 W Morehead St.
 Charlotte, NC 28202
Co. E-mail: circhelp@bizjournals.com
URL: http://www.acbj.com
Contact: Mike Olivieri, Executive Vice President
URL(s): www.bizjournals.com/southflorida
Linkedin: www.linkedin.com/company/south-florida-business-journal
X (Twitter): x.com/SFBJNews
Instagram: www.instagram.com/sfbjnews
Released: Weekly **Price:** $180, for per year digital; $70, for digital access or Digital & Print; $245, for Nationwide Access; $4, for digital. **Description:** Newspaper covering business in Miami, Fort Lauderdale, and West Palm Beach. **Availability:** Print; PDF; Download; Online.

38609 ■ *Tampa Bay Business Journal* (TBBJ)
4890 W Kennedy Blvd., Ste. 850
 Tampa, FL 33609
Ph: (813)873-8225
Fax: (813)876-1827
Co. E-mail: tampabay@bizjournals.com
URL: http://www.bizjournals.com/tampabay
Contact: Ian Anderson, President
E-mail: ianderson@bizjournals.com
Facebook: www.facebook.com/TampaBusinessJournal
X (Twitter): x.com/tbbjnewsroom
Description: Publisher of journal covering flash news, daily local business news, events. **Founded:** 2012.

38610 ■ *Vero Beach Christian Business Association--Directory*
1275 US Hwy. 1, Ste. 2
 Vero Beach, FL 32960
Co. E-mail: info@vbcba.org
URL: http://www.vbcba.org
Contact: Maureen Nicolace, President
URL(s): members.vbcba.org
Released: Annual **Description:** Covers christian business leaders in Vero Beach, Florida. **Availability:** Print.

PUBLISHERS

38611 ■ Famaco Publishers L.L.C.
6001-21 Argyle Forest Blvd. 323
 Jacksonville, FL 32244-6127
Ph: (904)434-5901
Co. E-mail: sales@famacopublishers.com
URL: http://famacopublishers.com
Contact: M. A. Muhammad, Manager
Facebook: www.facebook.com/famacopublishers
X (Twitter): x.com/famacopublisher
Description: Publishes scholarly nonfiction works on religion, politics and social commentary. Does not accept unsolicited manuscripts. Reaches market through commission representatives, direct mail, telephone sales, wholesalers and distributors and broadcast Internet. **Founded:** 1996.

EARLY STAGE FINANCING

38612 ■ Bling Capital
135 Palm Ave.
 Miami Beach, FL 33139
URL: http://www.blingcap.com
Contact: Ankur Pansari, Principal
Description: Venture capital firm offering funding to seed stage startups. **Industry Preferences:** Consumer tech, internet, mobile, marketplace, data, fintech, SaaS, and automation.

38613 ■ New World Angels
1900 Glades Rd., Ste. 500-07
 Boca Raton, FL 33431
Ph: (561)372-6309
Co. E-mail: info@newworldangels.com
URL: http://www.newworldangels.com
Contact: Ron Tarro, President
Facebook: www.facebook.com/newworldangels
Linkedin: www.linkedin.com/company/new-world-angels
Description: Consists of accredited private investors, operators, and entrepreneurs providing equity capital to early-stage companies in Florida. **Founded:** 2014.

EXPANSION AND GROWTH FINANCING

38614 ■ Arsenal Growth
750 S Orlando Ave., Ste. 200
 Winter Park, FL 32789
Ph: (407)838-1400
Co. E-mail: deal@arsenalgrowth.com
URL: http://arsenalgrowth.com
Contact: Amy Brooks, Director, Finance
Linkedin: www.linkedin.com/company/arsenal-growth
X (Twitter): x.com/ArsenalGrowth
Description: Growth equity firm specializing in the intersection of government, large corporations, and emerging technology companies. **Investment Poli-**

cies: Tech-enabled businesses with recurring revenues targeting large markets. **Industry Preferences:** Commerce/logistics; enterprise; healthcare IT.

VENTURE CAPITAL FIRM

38615 ■ Ballast Point Ventures (BPV)
401 E Jackson St., Ste. 2300
Tampa, FL 33602
Ph: (813)906-8500
Fax: (813)906-8514
Co. E-mail: info@ballastpointventures.com
URL: http://ballastpointventures.com
Contact: Drew Graham, Managing Partner

Description: Offers financing, operational advice, and strategic consulting to entrepreneurs in Florida, the Southeast, and Texas. Prefers being the lead investor. **Founded:** 2001. **Investment Policies:** Large and growing market; exceptional management team; revenue generating; .

38616 ■ CapStone Holdings, Inc.
2655 N Airport Rd., No. 60439
Fort Myers, FL 33907-1430
Contact: Keith Stone, President

Description: Provides funding and an incubator environment from which promising fintech startups can find the resources and tools needed to grow their business. **Founded:** 2019.

38617 ■ H.I.G. Biohealth Partners
1450 Brickell Ave., 31st Fl.
Miami, FL 33131
Ph: (305)379-2322
Fax: (305)379-2013
Co. E-mail: info@higbio.com
URL: http://higbio.com
Contact: Brian Schwartz, Co-President

Description: Offers capital to small and medium-sized companies with growth potential. Maintains offices in Miami, New York, Chicago, Boston, Dallas, Los Angeles, San Francisco, Atlanta, Hamburg, London. Luxembourg, Madrid, Milan, Paris, Bogotá, Rio de Janeiro, and São Paulo. **Founded:** 1993. **Investment Policies:** Companies developing novel products for unmet medical needs. **Industry Preferences:** Therapeutics (small molecules, protein therapeutics, antibodies); medical devices; diagnostics.

38618 ■ NewGate Capital
2250 Lee Rd., Ste. 100
Winter Park, FL 32789
Ph: (407)647-8752
Co. E-mail: info@newgategroup.net
URL: http://newgatecapitalpartners.com
Contact: Chris Shenefelt, Partner
Facebook: www.facebook.com/newgatecapital
Linkedin: www.linkedin.com/company/new-gate-capital-partners
X (Twitter): x.com/NewGateCapital

Description: A group of accredited investors offering funding for early-stage entrepreneurs. **Founded:** 2000. **Preferred Investment Size:** $25,000 to $250,000 for individual transaction; up to $2,000,000 for a syndicated group.

Georgia

ASSOCIATIONS AND OTHER ORGANIZATIONS

38619 ■ Association of Fundraising Professionals Greater Atlanta Chapter
c/o Jenna Brown Executive Director
PO Box 868
Lagrange, GA 30241
Free: 877-845-0704
Co. E-mail: jbrown@asginfo.net
URL: http://community.afpnet.org/afpgaatlantachapter/home
Contact: Jenna Brown, Executive Director
E-mail: jbrown@asginfo.net
Facebook: www.facebook.com/afpgreateratl
Linkedin: www.linkedin.com/company/afpgreateratl
X (Twitter): x.com/afpgreateratl
Description: Fosters the development and growth of fundraising professionals. Promotes high ethical standards in the fundraising profession. Provides training opportunities for fundraising professionals. **Geographic Preference:** Local.

38620 ■ Entrepreneurs' Organization - Atlanta Chapter (EO)
Atlanta, GA
URL: http://www.eonetwork.org/atlanta
Description: Provides local resources to members which includes networking events, mentorship, live forums, and leadership development. **Founded:** 1994.

38621 ■ Georgia Agribusiness Council (GAC)
1655 S Elm St.
Commerce, GA 30529
Ph: (706)336-6830
Fax: (706)336-6898
URL: http://www.ga-agribusiness.org
Contact: Will Bentley, President
E-mail: wbentley@ga-agribusiness.org
Facebook: www.facebook.com/GAagribusiness
X (Twitter): x.com/GAagribusiness
YouTube: www.youtube.com/user/GAagribusiness
Description: Advances the business of agriculture through economic development, environmental stewardship and education to improve the quality of life. **Founded:** 1966. **Publications:** *AgOutlook* (Monthly). **Geographic Preference:** State.

38622 ■ Georgia Association of Business Brokers (GABB)
4780 Ashford Dunwoody Rd., Ste. A-241.
Atlanta, GA 30338-5564
Ph: (770)744-3639
Co. E-mail: georgiabusinessbrokers@gmail.com
URL: http://www.gabb.org
Contact: Judy J. Mims, President
E-mail: judy@childcare.properties
Facebook: www.facebook.com/GeorgiaAssociationBusinessBrokersGABB
Linkedin: www.linkedin.com/company/georgia-association-of-business-brokers
X (Twitter): x.com/GABB_Brokers

Description: Represents professionals and firms in business brokerage, mergers and acquisitions. Provides business brokers education, conferences, professional designations, and networking opportunities in Georgia. Works to become a leader in the exchange of business referrals, and to create professional relationships with successful business transaction advisors. **Founded:** 1986. **Geographic Preference:** State.

38623 ■ International Association of Business Communicators Atlanta [IABC Atlanta]
Atlanta, GA 30355
Co. E-mail: admin@iabcatl.com
URL: http://atlanta.iabc.com
Contact: Eric Berrios, Vice President
E-mail: eberrios@realmco.com
Facebook: www.facebook.com/IABCAtlanta
Linkedin: www.linkedin.com/company/744806/admin
X (Twitter): x.com/IABCAtlanta
Description: Represents the interests of communication managers, public relations directors, writers, editors and audiovisual specialists. Encourages establishment of college-level programs in organizational communication. Conducts surveys on employee communication effectiveness and media trends. Conducts research in the field of communication. **Founded:** 1970. **Awards:** IABC/Atlanta Catalyst Award (Annual); IABC/Atlanta Golden Flame Award (Annual). **Geographic Preference:** Local.

38624 ■ International Association of Women Atlanta Chapter
Atlanta, GA
Co. E-mail: atlanta@iawomen.com
URL: http://community.iawomen.com/atlanta/home
Contact: Susan Simmons-Stevenson, President
Description: Serves as network of accomplished women united to achieve professional goals. Provides a forum for sharing ideas and experiences of professional women regarding career success. Promotes an active business and networking community from all industries. **Geographic Preference:** Local.

38625 ■ International Association of Women DeKalb-Gwinnett Chapter
Duluth, GA
URL: http://www.iawomen.com/chapters/dekalb-gwinnett-chapter
Description: Serves as network of accomplished women united to achieve professional goals. Provides a forum for sharing ideas and experiences of professional women regarding career success. Promotes an active business and networking community from all industries. **Geographic Preference:** Local.

38626 ■ Kirkwood Business Owners' Association (KBOA)
Atlanta, GA 30317
Co. E-mail: kirkwoodbiz@gmail.com
URL: http://www.kirkwoodbiz.com
Contact: Sam Mugavero, President

Description: Represents small business owners. Promotes the interests of small businesses. Provides government relations services, educational information and member benefit programs. **Founded:** 2007. **Geographic Preference:** Local.

38627 ■ National Federation of Independent Business Georgia
2020 Howell Mill Rd. NW, Ste. D-589
Atlanta, GA 30318-1732
Ph: (404)522-1290
URL: http://www.nfib.com/georgia
Contact: Nathan Humphrey, Director
X (Twitter): x.com/nfib_ga
Description: Represents small and independent businesses. Aims to promote and protect the rights of members to own, operate and grow their businesses. **Geographic Preference:** State.

SMALL BUSINESS DEVELOPMENT CENTER LEAD OFFICE

38628 ■ University of Georgia - Small Business Development Center - State Office
382 E Broad St.
Athens, GA 30602-5412
Ph: (706)542-2762
Fax: (706)542-7935
URL: http://www.georgiasbdc.org
Contact: Allan Adams, Director
E-mail: aadams@georgiasbdc.org
URL(s): www.georgiasbdc.org/state-office; www.georgiasbdc.org/espanol
Founded: 1977. **Geographic Preference:** State.

SMALL BUSINESS DEVELOPMENT CENTERS

38629 ■ Georgia Southern University - College of Business Administration - Small Business Development Center [University of Georgia Small Business Development Center at Georgia Southern University; University of Georgia - Small Business Development Center - Southern Coastal Office]
1332 S Dr.
Statesboro, GA 30458
Ph: (912)478-4636
URL: http://www.georgiasouthern.edu
Contact: Kyle Marrero, President
URL(s): www.georgiasbdc.org/southern-coastal
Facebook: www.facebook.com/GeorgiaSouthern
Linkedin: www.linkedin.com/school/georgia-southern-university
X (Twitter): x.com/georgiasouthern
Instagram: www.instagram.com/georgiasouthernuniversity
YouTube: www.youtube.com/user/GeorgiaSouthernUniv

38630 ■ Georgia

38630 ■ Georgia Southern University Small Business Development Center (UGA SBDC)
382 E Broad St.
Athens, GA 30602-5412
Ph: (706)542-2762
Fax: (706)542-7935
URL: http://www.georgiasbdc.org
Contact: Allan Adams, Director
E-mail: aadams@georgiasbdc.org
Facebook: www.facebook.com/ugasbdc
X (Twitter): x.com/ugasbdc
Instagram: www.instagram.com/uga_sbdc
YouTube: www.youtube.com/channel/UCCKVo-4TZ9z2cClt0xOwZxw

Description: Represents and promotes the small business sector. Provides management assistance to current and prospective small business owners. Helps to improve management skills and expand the products and services of members. **Founded:** 1977.
Geographic Preference: Local.

38631 ■ Georgia State University - J. Mack Robinson College of Business - Small Business Development Center (SBDC) - Reference Collection [University of Georgia Small Business Development Center at Georgia State University; University of Georgia - Small Business Development Center - Atlanta Office]
75 Piedmont Ave., Ste. 700
Atlanta, GA 30303
Ph: (404)413-7830
Fax: (404)413-7832
Co. E-mail: atlanta@georgiasbdc.org
URL: http://sbdc.robinson.gsu.edu
Contact: Alicia Johnson, Coordinator
E-mail: ajohnson@georgiasbdc.org
URL(s): www.georgiasbdc.org/atlanta-office
Facebook: www.facebook.com/ugasbdcgsu
Linkedin: www.linkedin.com/company/ugasbdcgsu
X (Twitter): x.com/ugasbdcgsu
Instagram: www.instagram.com/ugasbdcgsu

Description: Integral unit of Georgia State University. **Scope:** Small business, marketing, finance, international business, and government procurement. **Services:** Counseling; Center open to the public for reference use only. **Founded:** 1977. **Holdings:** Business directories; government publications and journals, periodicals, training manuals and videotapes. **Subscriptions:** 11 journals and other serials.
Geographic Preference: Local.

38632 ■ Small Business Development Center University of West Georgia (UGA SBDC)
105 Aycock Dr., Ste. 124E-I
Carrollton, GA 30118
Ph: (678)839-5082
Fax: (678)839-5083
URL: http://www.westga.edu/sbdc
Contact: Todd Anduze, Director
E-mail: tanduze@westga.edu
X (Twitter): x.com/UnivWestGa
YouTube: www.youtube.com/user/uwgucm

Description: Represents and promotes the small business sector. Provides management assistance to current and prospective small business owners. Helps to improve management skills and expand the products and services of members. **Founded:** 1906.
Geographic Preference: Local.

38633 ■ University of Georgia - Small Business Development Center - Albany Office
414 N Westover Blvd., Ste. F
Albany, GA 31707
Ph: (229)420-1144
Fax: (229)430-3933
URL: http://georgiasbdc.org/albany-office
Contact: Nema Etheridge, Director
E-mail: netheridge@georgiasbdc.org

Description: Represents and promotes the small business sector. Provides management assistance to current and prospective small business owners. Helps to improve management skills and expand the products and services of members. **Geographic Preference:** Local.

38634 ■ University of Georgia - Small Business Development Center - Augusta Office
2907 Professional Pkwy., Ste. B
Augusta, GA 30907
Ph: (706)650-5655
Co. E-mail: augusta@georgiasbdc.org
URL: http://georgiasbdc.org/augusta-office
Contact: Rick McMurtrey, Director
E-mail: rmcmurtrey@georgiasbdc.org
Geographic Preference: Local.

38635 ■ University of Georgia - Small Business Development Center - Brunswick Office (UGA SBDC)
501 Gloucester St., Ste. 200
Brunswick, GA 31520
Ph: (912)264-7343
Co. E-mail: brunswick@georgiasbdc.org
URL: http://georgiasbdc.org/brunswick-office
Contact: David Lewis, Director
URL(s): georgiasbdc.org/locations
Facebook: www.facebook.com/ugasbdc.bwick
X (Twitter): x.com/ugasbdc
Instagram: www.instagram.com/uga_sbdc
Geographic Preference: Local.

38636 ■ University of Georgia Small Business Development Center at Clayton State University (SBDC) [Clayton State University - College of Business - Small Business Development Center; University of Georgia - Small Business Development Center - Morrow Office]
2000 Clayton State Blvd.
Morrow, GA 30260
Ph: (678)466-5100
URL: http://www.clayton.edu/business/centers-and-initiatives/small-business-development-center
Contact: Kimberly Knight, Director
E-mail: kimberlyknight@clayton.edu
URL(s): www.georgiasbdc.org/morrow-office

Description: Provides economic development assistance for small businesses with no-cost consulting services and low cost educational programs. **Founded:** 1969. **Geographic Preference:** Local.

38637 ■ University of Georgia - Small Business Development Center - Columbus Office (SBDC)
3100 Gentian Blvd., Ste. 119
Columbus, GA 31907
Ph: (706)569-2651
Co. E-mail: columbus@georgiasbdc.org
URL: http://georgiasbdc.org/columbus-office
Contact: Todd Carlisle, Director
E-mail: tcarlisle@georgiasbdc.org
Facebook: www.facebook.com/ugasbdccolumbus
Geographic Preference: Local.

38638 ■ University of Georgia - Small Business Development Center - DeKalb Office
1990 Lakeside Pkwy., Ste. 250
Tucker, GA 30084
Ph: (770)414-3110
Co. E-mail: dekalb@georgiasbdc.org
URL: http://www.georgiasbdc.org/dekalb-office
Contact: Mark Collier, Director
E-mail: mcollier@georgiasbdc.org
Facebook: www.facebook.com/ugasbdc.dekalb

Description: Represents and promotes the small business sector. Provides management assistance to current and prospective small business owners. Helps to improve management skills and expand the products and services of members. **Geographic Preference:** Local.

38639 ■ University of Georgia - Small Business Development Center - Gainesville Office
303 Jesse Jewell Pkwy. SE, Ste. 400
Gainesville, GA 30501
Ph: (770)531-5681
Co. E-mail: gainesville@georgiasbdc.org
URL: http://georgiasbdc.org/gainesville-office
Contact: Dr. W. Patrick Fulbright, Director
E-mail: pfulbright@georgiasbdc.org
Facebook: www.facebook.com/SBDCGainesvilleGA
Geographic Preference: Local.

38640 ■ University of Georgia - Small Business Development Center - Gwinnett Office
2530 Sever Rd., Ste. 202
Lawrenceville, GA 30043
Ph: (678)985-6820
Co. E-mail: gwinnett@georgiasbdc.org
URL: http://georgiasbdc.org/gwinnett-office
Contact: Todd Anduze, Director
E-mail: tanduze@georgiasbdc.org
Geographic Preference: Local.

38641 ■ University of Georgia Small Business Development Center at Kennesaw State University (UGA SBDC) [Kennesaw State University - Michael J. Coles College of Business - Small Business Development Center; University of Georgia - Small Business Development Center - Kennesaw Office]
3333 Busbee Dr., Ste. 500
Kennesaw, GA 30144
Ph: (470)578-6450
Co. E-mail: kennesaw@georgiasbdc.org
URL: http://www.kennesaw.edu/coles/centers/small-business-development-center
Contact: Drew Tonsmeire, Director
E-mail: dtonsmeire@georgiasbdc.org
Facebook: www.facebook.com/kennesawsbdc

Description: Represents and promotes the small business sector. Provides management assistance to current and prospective small business owners. Helps to improve management skills and expand the products and services of members. **Geographic Preference:** Local.

38642 ■ University of Georgia - Small Business Development Center - Macon Office
4875 Riverside Dr., Ste. 202
Macon, GA 31210
Ph: (478)757-3609
Co. E-mail: macon@georgiasbdc.org
URL: http://georgiasbdc.org/macon-office
Contact: Josh Walton, Director
E-mail: jwalton@georgiasbdc.org
Facebook: www.facebook.com/ugasbdcmacon
Geographic Preference: Local.

38643 ■ University of Georgia - Small Business Development Center - Rome Office (UGA SBDC)
901 N Broad St., Ste. 320
Rome, GA 30161
Ph: (706)622-2006
Co. E-mail: rome@georgiasbdc.org
URL: http://georgiasbdc.org/rome-office
Contact: Patricia Devlin, Consultant
E-mail: pdevlin@georgiasbdc.org
Geographic Preference: Local.

38644 ■ University of Georgia - Small Business Development Center - Savannah Office (UGA SBDC) [University of Georgia - Small Business Development Center - Southern Coastal; University of Georgia Small Business Development Center at Georgia Southern University]
316 E Bay St.
Savannah, GA 31401
Ph: (912)651-3200
Fax: (912)651-3209
Co. E-mail: southerncoastal@georgiasbdc.org
URL: http://georgiasbdc.org/southern-coastal
Contact: Becky Brownlee, Director
E-mail: rbrownlee@georgiasbdc.org
Geographic Preference: Local.

38645 ■ University of Georgia Small Business Development Center at Valdosta State University [Valdosta State University - Harley Langdale, Jr. College of Business Administration - Small Business Development Center; University of Georgia - Small Business Development Center - Valdosta Office]
100 Thaxton Hall.
 Valdosta, GA 31698
Ph: (229)245-3738
Fax: (229)245-3741
URL: http://www.valdosta.edu/colleges/business/
 small-business-development-center
Contact: Walt Moore, Consultant
E-mail: wkmoore@valdosta.edu
URL(s): valdostastate.info/colleges/business/small
 -business-development-center; www.georgiasbdc
 .org/valdosta-office
Facebook: www.facebook.com/ugasbdc.valdosta
Geographic Preference: Local.

38646 ■ University of West Georgia - Richards College of Business - Small Business Development Center (UWG SBDC) [University of Georgia Small Business Development Center at University of West Georgia; University of West Georgia - Small Business Development Center - Carrollton Office]
105 Aycock Dr., Ste. 124
 Carrollton, GA 30118
Ph: (678)839-5082
Co. E-mail: carrollton@georgiasbdc.org
URL: http://www.westga.edu/academics/business/
 sbdc
Contact: Todd Anduze, Director
E-mail: tanduze@georgiasbdc.org
URL(s): www.georgiasbdc.org/carrollton-office
Facebook: www.facebook.com/ugasbdc
X (Twitter): x.com/ugasbdc
Instagram: www.instagram.com/uga_sbdc
YouTube: www.youtube.com/c/georgiasbdcorg1
Founded: 1977.

SMALL BUSINESS ASSISTANCE PROGRAMS

38647 ■ Georgia Department of Community Affairs - Business and Financial Assistance Div.
60 Executive Pk. S NE
 Atlanta, GA 30329-2231
Ph: (404)679-4940
Free: 800-781-8346
URL: http://www.dca.ga.gov
Contact: Audrey King, Chairman
Facebook: www.facebook.com/GeorgiaDCA
Linkedin: www.linkedin.com/company/georgia-depar
 tment-of-community-affairs
X (Twitter): x.com/GA_DCA
Instagram: www.instagram.com/ga_dca
YouTube: www.youtube.com/channel/UCQn
 _zKD8Fo0SvAsL6Oxqa6Q
Description: Coordinates technical and financial assistance programs for rural development.

38648 ■ Georgia Department of Economic Development - Entrepreneur and Small Business Office
Technology Sq., 75 5th St. NW, Ste. 1200
 Atlanta, GA 30308
URL: http://www.georgia.org/small-business
Facebook: www.facebook.com/georgiaesb
X (Twitter): x.com/GeorgiaESB
Description: Promotes the interests of small businesses at trade fairs and through a network of resources.

SCORE OFFICES

38649 ■ Northeast Georgia SCORE
1000 Dawsonville Hwy.
 Gainesville, GA 30504
Ph: (470)465-0717
Co. E-mail: help@score.org
URL: http://negeorgia.score.org
Facebook: www.facebook.com/SCORENEGeorgia
Description: Unites active and retired business management professionals with men and women who are considering starting a small business, encountering problems with their business, or expanding their business. Serves the Georgia area of Athens, Dahlonega, and Gainesville as well as surrounding counties. **Founded:** 2016. **Geographic Preference:** Local.

38650 ■ SCORE - Alpharetta
5960 N Point Pky.
 Alpharetta, GA 30022
URL: http://northmetroatlanta.score.org
Facebook: www.facebook.com/SCORENorthMe
 troATL
X (Twitter): x.com/SCORENorthMetro
Description: Provides professional guidance and information to maximize the success of existing and emerging small businesses. Offers business counseling and workshops.

38651 ■ SCORE - Atlanta
233 Peachtree St., NE Ste. 300
 Atlanta, GA 30303
Ph: (404)331-0121
Co. E-mail: admin.0048@scorevolunteer.org
URL: http://atlanta.score.org
Linkedin: www.linkedin.com/company/score-mentors
 -atlanta
X (Twitter): x.com/SCORE_Atlanta
Description: Provides professional guidance and information to maximize the success of existing and emerging small businesses. Offers business counseling and workshops. **Founded:** 1964. **Awards:** SCORE - Atlanta PRNews Platinum Award (Annual). **Geographic Preference:** Local.

38652 ■ SCORE - Blue Ridge
Fanin Chamber of Commerce
 152 Orvin Lance Dr.
 Blue Ridge, GA 30513
Ph: (540)283-7064
URL: http://www.score.org/blueridge
Description: Provides professional guidance and information to maximize the success of existing and emerging small businesses. Offers business counseling and workshops.

38653 ■ SCORE - Brunswick
111 E Liberty St., Ste. 103
 Savannah, GA 31401
Ph: (912)652-4335
Co. E-mail: scoresav70@gmail.com
URL: http://www.score.org/savannah
Description: Provides professional guidance and information to maximize the success of existing and emerging small businesses. Offers business counseling and workshops.

38654 ■ SCORE - Cobb Chamber of Commerce
240 Interstate N Pky.
 Atlanta, GA 30339
Ph: (770)859-2321
URL: http://northmetroatlanta.score.org
Facebook: www.facebook.com/SCOREAtlantaGA
Linkedin: www.linkedin.com/company/score-mentors
 -atlanta
X (Twitter): x.com/SCORE_Atlanta
Description: Provides professional guidance and information to maximize the success of existing and emerging small businesses. Offers business counseling and workshops.

38655 ■ SCORE - Cobb Sewell Mill Library
2051 Lower Roswell Rd.
 Marietta, GA 30068
URL: http://www.score.org/northmetroatlanta/about/
 score-north-metro-atlanta-mentoring-locations
Description: Provides professional guidance and information to maximize the success of existing and emerging small businesses. Offers business counseling and workshops.

38656 ■ SCORE - College Park
College Park, GA
URL: http://atlanta.score.org
Description: Provides professional guidance and information to maximize the success of existing and emerging small businesses. Offers business counseling and workshops.

38657 ■ SCORE - Columbus, Georgia
1127 Broadway Ste. B
 Columbus, GA 31901
Ph: (706)596-8331
Co. E-mail: score671@bellsouth.net
URL: http://columbusga.score.org
Contact: Scott Harkins, Chairman of the Board
Facebook: www.facebook.com/ColumbusGASCORE
X (Twitter): x.com/ColumbusGAscore
Instagram: www.instagram.com/scorecolumbusga
Pinterest: www.pinterest.com/ColumbusGaSCORE
Description: Provides professional guidance and information to maximize the success of existing and emerging small businesses. Offers business counseling and workshops. **Founded:** 2002. **Geographic Preference:** Local.

38658 ■ SCORE - Cumming
505 Peachtree Pky.
 Cumming, GA 30041
URL: http://northmetroatlanta.score.org
Description: Provides professional guidance and information to maximize the success of existing and emerging small businesses. Offers business counseling and workshops.

38659 ■ SCORE - Duluth City Hall
3167 Main St.
 Duluth, GA 30096
URL: http://northmetroatlanta.score.org/score-north
 -metro-atlanta-mentoring-locations
Description: Provides professional guidance and information to maximize the success of existing and emerging small businesses. Offers business counseling and workshops.

38660 ■ SCORE - Dunwoody
1200 Ashwood Pky., Ste. 155
 Dunwoody, GA 30338
URL: http://northmetroatlanta.score.org/score-north
 -metro-atlanta-mentoring-locations
Description: Provides professional guidance and information to maximize the success of existing and emerging small businesses. Offers business counseling and workshops.

38661 ■ SCORE - Evans
1000 Business Blvd.
 Evans, GA 30809
Ph: (706)651-0018
URL: http://greateraiken.score.org/about-aiken-score
Contact: Cynthia McKinley, Contact
URL(s): www.score.org/find-location
Description: Provides professional guidance and information to maximize the success of existing and emerging small businesses. Offers business counseling and workshops.

38662 ■ SCORE - Hinesville
425 W Oglethorpe Hwy.
 Hinesville, GA 31313
Ph: (912)652-4335
URL: http://savannah.score.org
Description: Provides professional guidance and information to maximize the success of existing and emerging small businesses. Offers business counseling and workshops.

38663 ■ SCORE - Marietta
55 Atlanta St. SE
 Marietta, GA 30060
URL: http://northmetroatlanta.score.org/mentors/
 frank-perkowski
Contact: Frank Perkowski, Contact

Description: Provides professional guidance and information to maximize the success of existing and emerging small businesses. Offers business counseling and workshops.

38664 ■ Georgia   STATE LISTINGS

38664 ■ SCORE - Middle Georgia
Greater Macon Chamber of Commerce
305 Coliseum Dr.
Macon, GA 31217
Ph: (478)207-6829
Co. E-mail: middlegeorgia@scorevolunteer.org
URL: http://middlegeorgia.score.org
Contact: Bridget Weston, Chief Executive Officer
Facebook: www.facebook.com/SCOREmiddlegeorgia
Linkedin: www.linkedin.com/company/score-mentors-middle-georgia
X (Twitter): x.com/SCOREMiddleGA
YouTube: www.youtube.com/user/SCORESmallBusiness
Pinterest: www.pinterest.com/scorementors
Description: Provides professional guidance and information to maximize the success of existing and emerging small businesses. Offers business counseling and workshops. **Founded:** 1964.

38665 ■ SCORE - Moultrie
116 First Ave. SE
Moultrie, GA 31768-0487
URL: http://columbusga.score.org
Contact: Greg Icard, Contact
E-mail: gicard@selectmoultrie.com
Description: Provides professional guidance and information to maximize the success of existing and emerging small businesses. Offers business counseling and workshops.

38666 ■ SCORE - Norcross
10 College St.
Norcross, GA 30071
URL: http://northmetroatlanta.score.org/score-north-metro-atlanta-mentoring-locations
Description: Provides professional guidance and information to maximize the success of existing and emerging small businesses. Offers business counseling and workshops.

38667 ■ SCORE - North Metro Atlanta
1425 Market Blvd., Ste., 530
Roswell, GA 30076
Ph: (678)506-0718
Co. E-mail: ch.admin0718@scorevolunteer.org
URL: http://www.score.org/northmetroatlanta
Contact: Sanjay Gadre, Contact
Facebook: www.facebook.com/SCORENorthMetroATL
Description: Provides professional guidance and information to maximize the success of existing and emerging small businesses. Offers business counseling and workshops.

38668 ■ SCORE - Northeast Georgia
1000 Dawsonville Hwy.
Gainesville, GA 30504
Ph: (470)465-0717
Co. E-mail: help@score.org
URL: http://negeorgia.score.org
Facebook: www.facebook.com/SCORENEGeorgia
Linkedin: www.linkedin.com/company/score-mentors-ne-georgia
Description: Provides professional guidance and information to maximize the success of existing and emerging small businesses. Offers business counseling and workshops.

38669 ■ SCORE - Peachtree City
225 Willow Bend Rd.
Peachtree City, GA 30269
URL: http://atlanta.score.org/about-score-atlanta
Description: Provides professional guidance and information to maximize the success of existing and emerging small businesses. Offers business counseling and workshops.

38670 ■ SCORE - Peachtree Corners
107 Technology Pky.
Peachtree Corners, GA 30092
Co. E-mail: northmetroatl@scorevolunteer.org
URL: http://northmetroatlanta.score.org/score-north-metro-atlanta-mentoring-locations
Description: Provides professional guidance and information to maximize the success of existing and emerging small businesses. Offers business counseling and workshops.

38671 ■ SCORE - Sandy Springs
1 Galambos Way
Sandy Springs, GA 30328
URL: http://northmetroatlanta.score.org/branch/sandy-springs-virtual
Description: Provides professional guidance and information to maximize the success of existing and emerging small businesses. Offers business counseling and workshops.

38672 ■ SCORE - Savannah
111 E Liberty St., Ste. 103
Savannah, GA 31401
Ph: (912)652-4335
Fax: (912)652-4184
Co. E-mail: help@score.org
URL: http://savannah.score.org
Contact: Michael Siegel, Contact
Facebook: www.facebook.com/SCORESavannah
Linkedin: www.linkedin.com/company/savannah-score
YouTube: www.youtube.com/channel/UCqi9rf2iQDPtWXfB_4NC7YA
Description: Provides professional guidance and information to maximize the success of existing and emerging small businesses. Develops business plans and evaluates financial projections. Identifies problems and potential solutions. **Founded:** 1964. **Geographic Preference:** Local.

38673 ■ SCORE - Smyrna
100 Village Green Cir.
Smyrna, GA 30080
Ph: (678)506-0718
URL: http://www.score.org/find-location
Description: Provides professional guidance and information to maximize the success of existing and emerging small businesses. Offers business counseling and workshops.

38674 ■ SCORE - Snellville
2342 Oak Rd.
Snellville, GA 30078
URL: http://northmetroatlanta.score.org/score-north-metro-atlanta-mentoring-locations
Description: Provides professional guidance and information to maximize the success of existing and emerging small businesses. Offers business counseling and workshops.

38675 ■ SCORE - Statesboro
58 E Main St.
Statesboro, GA 30460
Ph: (912)478-0872
URL: http://savannah.score.org
Description: Provides professional guidance and information to maximize the success of existing and emerging small businesses. Offers business counseling and workshops.

38676 ■ SCORE - Sugar Hill
4988 W Broad St.
Sugar Hill, GA 30518
Ph: (678)506-0718
URL: http://northmetroatlanta.score.org
URL(s): pittsburgh.score.org/find-location
Description: Provides professional guidance and information to maximize the success of existing and emerging small businesses. Offers business counseling and workshops.

38677 ■ SCORE - Warner Robins
1228 Watson Blvd.
Warner Robins, GA 31093
Co. E-mail: middlegeorgia@scorevolunteer.org
URL: http://middlegeorgia.score.org/content/take-workshop-300
Contact: Bridget Weston, Contact
Facebook: www.facebook.com/SCOREmiddlegeorgia
Linkedin: www.linkedin.com/company/score-mentors-middle-georgia
X (Twitter): x.com/SCOREMiddleGA
YouTube: www.youtube.com/user/SCORESmallBusiness
Pinterest: www.pinterest.com/scorementors
Description: Provides professional guidance and information to maximize the success of existing and emerging small businesses. Offers business counseling and workshops.

BETTER BUSINESS BUREAUS

38678 ■ Better Business Bureau of Metro Atlanta, Athens and Northeast Georgia
235 Peachtree St. N Twr., Ste. 900
Atlanta, GA 30303
Ph: (404)766-0875
Free: 877-651-4222
Co. E-mail: info@atlanta.bbb.org
URL: http://www.bbb.org/local-bbb/bbb-of-metro-atlanta-athens-and-ne-georgia
Contact: Lisa Blakley, Officer
Facebook: www.facebook.com/BBBAtlanta
Linkedin: www.linkedin.com/company/bbbatlanta
X (Twitter): x.com/BBBAtlanta
Instagram: www.instagram.com/bbbatlanta
YouTube: www.youtube.com/channel/UCQRqj_yy8DP6rRMVpvLUijA
Description: Seeks to promote and foster the highest ethical relationship between businesses and the public through voluntary self-regulation, consumer and business education, and service excellence. Provides information to help consumers and businesses make informed purchasing decisions and avoid costly scams and frauds; settles consumer complaints through arbitration and other means. **Geographic Preference:** Local.

38679 ■ Better Business Bureau Serving the Fall Line Corridor, Inc.
277 Martin Luther King Jr., Blvd., Ste. 201
Macon, GA 31201-3495
Ph: (478)742-7999
Fax: (478)742-8191
URL: http://www.bbb.org/local-bbb/better-business-bureau-serving-the-fall-line-corridor-inc
Contact: Kelvin Collins, Chief Executive Officer
E-mail: blair@ccie.bbb.org
Description: Seeks to promote and foster ethical relationship between businesses and the public through voluntary self-regulation, consumer and business education, and service excellence. Provides information to help consumers and businesses make informed purchasing decisions and avoid costly scams and frauds; settles consumer complaints through arbitration and other means. **Geographic Preference:** Local.

38680 ■ Better Business Bureau of West Georgia - East Alabama
233 12th St., Ste. 911 B
Columbus, GA 31901
Ph: (706)324-0712
Fax: (706)324-2181
URL: http://www.bbb.org/local-bbb/better-business-bureau-serving-the-fall-line-corridor-inc
Description: Seeks to promote and foster the highest ethical relationship between businesses and the public through voluntary self-regulation, consumer and business education, and service excellence. Provides information to help consumers and businesses make informed purchasing decisions and avoid costly scams and frauds; settles consumer complaints through arbitration and other means. **Awards:** BBB Torch Awards (Annual); Students of Integrity Scholarship Award (Biennial). **Geographic Preference:** Regional.

CHAMBERS OF COMMERCE

38681 ■ Adel-Cook County Chamber of Commerce
100 S Hutchinson Ave.
Adel, GA 31620
Ph: (229)896-2281
Fax: (229)896-8201
Co. E-mail: cookcochamber@windstream.net

URL: http://www.adelcookchamber.org
Contact: Heather Green, President
E-mail: heather.green@adelcookchamber.org
Facebook: www.facebook.com/adelcookchamber
Instagram: www.instagram.com/adelcookchamber
Description: Promotes business and community development in Cook County, GA. Sponsors local festival. **Founded:** 1958. **Publications:** *The Informer* (Quarterly). **Geographic Preference:** Local.

38682 ■ Albany Area Chamber of Commerce - Georgia
225 W Broad Ave.
Albany, GA 31701
Ph: (229)434-8700
Fax: (229)434-8716
URL: http://albanyga.com
Contact: Don Gray, Chairman
E-mail: dgray@albanyga.com
Description: Promotes business and community development in the Albany-Daugherty County, GA area. **Founded:** 1909. **Publications:** *Business Magazine* (Bimonthly); *Business* (Bimonthly); *Business in Brief* (Bimonthly); *Manufacturing Directory*. **Geographic Preference:** Local.

38683 ■ Alma/Bacon County Chamber of Commerce
504 N Pierce St., Ste. 102, 230 Ga Hwy. 64
Alma, GA 31510
URL: http://almagachamber.org
Contact: Reece Turner, President
Description: Promotes business and community development in Bacon County, GA. **Founded:** 1912. **Geographic Preference:** Local.

38684 ■ Americus-Sumter County Chamber of Commerce
Rees Pk. Economic Development Ctr., 409 Elm Ave.
Americus, GA 31709
Ph: (229)924-2646
Fax: (229)924-8784
Co. E-mail: info@sumtercountychamber.com
URL: http://www.sumtercountychamber.com
Contact: Amber Batchelor, President
E-mail: chamber@sumtercountychamber.com
Description: Promotes business and community development in Sumter County, GA. **Founded:** 1920. **Publications:** *What's News* (Quarterly). **Geographic Preference:** Local.

38685 ■ Ashburn Turner County Chamber of Commerce
238 E College Ave.
Ashburn, GA 31714
Ph: (229)567-9696
Co. E-mail: turnercountychamber@gmail.com
URL: http://www.turnerchamber.com
Contact: Ashley Miller, Executive Director
Facebook: www.facebook.com/ashburn turnerchamber
Instagram: www.instagram.com/atcchamber
Description: Promotes business and community development in Turner County, GA. **Geographic Preference:** Local.

38686 ■ Athens Area Chamber of Commerce (AACC)
246 W Hancock Ave.
Athens, GA 30601
Ph: (706)549-6800
Fax: (706)549-5636
Co. E-mail: info@athensga.com
URL: http://www.athenschamber.net
Contact: Doc Eldridge, President
E-mail: doc@athensga.com
Facebook: www.facebook.com/AthensChamber
X (Twitter): x.com/AthensGAChamber
Description: Promotes business and community development in the Athens, GA area. **Founded:** 1982. **Publications:** *It's Your Business* (Semimonthly); *Athens Area Chamber of Commerce Basic Package*; *Athens Area Chamber of Commerce Deluxe Package*; *Athens Area Chamber of Commerce Largest Employers*; *Athens Area Chamber of Commerce Manufacturer's Guide*; *Athens Area Chamber of Commerce Membership Directory*. **Awards:** Spirit of Athens Award (Annual). **Geographic Preference:** Local.

38687 ■ ATL Airport Chamber, Inc.
600 S Central Ave., Ste. 100
Atlanta, GA 30354
Ph: (404)209-0910
Fax: (404)389-0271
Co. E-mail: info@airportchamber.com
URL: http://airportchamber.com
Contact: Carmenlita Scott, President
Facebook: www.facebook.com/ATLAirportChamber
Description: Promotes business and community development in Airport area, GA. **Founded:** 1945. **Geographic Preference:** Regional.

38688 ■ *The Augusta Chronicle*
One 10th St., Ste. 120
Augusta, GA 30901
Ph: (706)821-1300
Fax: (706)821-1300
URL: http://www.augustametrochamber.com
Contact: Sue Parr, President
URL(s): profile.augustachronicle.com/newsletters/manage
Released: Monthly **Description:** Contains information about the chamber and the community. **Availability:** Print.

38689 ■ Augusta Metro Chamber of Commerce (AMCC)
One 10th St., Ste. 120
Augusta, GA 30901
Ph: (706)821-1300
Fax: (706)821-1300
URL: http://www.augustametrochamber.com
Contact: Sue Parr, President
Facebook: www.facebook.com/AugustaMetroChamber
Linkedin: www.linkedin.com/company/augusta-metro-chamber-of-commerce
X (Twitter): x.com/Augusta_Chamber
Instagram: www.instagram.com/augusta_chamber
YouTube: www.youtube.com/user/AugustaChamber
Description: Promotes business and community development in the Augusta, GA area. **Founded:** 1908. **Publications:** *The Augusta Chronicle* (Monthly); *Capitol Updates* (Semimonthly). **Geographic Preference:** Local.

38690 ■ Bainbridge-Decatur County Chamber of Commerce
100 Boat Basin Cir.
Bainbridge, GA 39817
Ph: (229)246-4774
Co. E-mail: info@bainbridgegachamber.com
URL: http://www.bainbridgegachamber.com
Contact: Lauren Minor, President
E-mail: lauren@bainbridgegachamber.com
Description: Promotes business and community development in Decatur County, GA. **Founded:** 1924. **Geographic Preference:** Local.

38691 ■ Banks County Chamber of Commerce (BCCC)
PO Box 57
Homer, GA 30547
Ph: (706)335-4866
Co. E-mail: alicia@bankscountyga.info
URL: http://www.bankscountyga.biz
Description: Promotes business and community development in Banks County, GA. Banks County Holiday Festival for arts and crafts. **Founded:** 1972. **Publications:** *The Chamber Connection* (Biweekly). **Geographic Preference:** Local.

38692 ■ Barnesville-Lamar County Chamber of Commerce
100 Commerce Pl.
Barnesville, GA 30204
Ph: (404)733-7034
Co. E-mail: president@barnesville.org
URL: http://barnesville.org
Contact: Bianca Romero, President
Facebook: www.facebook.com/BarnesvilleChamber
Instagram: www.instagram.com/barnesville_lamar_cc
Description: Promotes business and community development in Lamar County, GA. Sponsors Health Fair and Buggy Days festival. **Founded:** 1959. **Publications:** *Business Builder* (Monthly). **Geographic Preference:** Local.

38693 ■ Barrow County Chamber of Commerce (BCCC)
6 Porter St.
Winder, GA 30680
Ph: (770)867-9444
Co. E-mail: vkeibler@barrowchamber.com
URL: http://www.barrowchamber.com/home
Contact: Tommy Jennings, President
E-mail: trjennings@barrowchamber.com
Facebook: www.facebook.com/BarrowCountyChamber
Instagram: www.instagram.com/barrowcountychamber
Description: Promotes business and community development in Barrow County, GA. Sponsors annual Summer's End Festival. **Founded:** 1948. **Publications:** *Barrowvision Newsletter* (Monthly); *Chamber Chat* (Monthly). **Educational Activities:** Barrow County Chamber of Commerce Meeting (Monthly). **Awards:** Barrow County Chamber of Commerce Citizen of the Year (Annual); Barrow County Chamber of Commerce Star Student of the Year (Annual). **Geographic Preference:** Local.

38694 ■ Baxley-Appling County Chamber of Commerce
305 W Parker St.
Baxley, GA 31513
Ph: (912)367-7731
Fax: (912)367-2073
Co. E-mail: chamber@baxley.org
URL: http://www.baxley.org/chamber-of-commerce
Contact: Keri Crosby, Executive Director
Facebook: www.facebook.com/BaxleyApplingCounty-Chamber-of-Commerce-386966021447535
X (Twitter): x.com/BaxleyChamber
Description: Promotes business and community development in Appling County, GA. **Founded:** 1972. **Publications:** *Partners in Progress* (Weekly); *South Georgia Business* (Monthly). **Geographic Preference:** Local.

38695 ■ Berrien County Chamber of Commerce
Berrien County Administration Bldg.
201 N Davis St., Rm. 133
Nashville, GA 31639
Ph: (229)686-5123
Fax: (229)686-1905
Co. E-mail: berrienchamber@windstream.net
URL: http://www.berrienchamber.com
Contact: Lisa Smart, Executive Director
E-mail: berrienchamber.lisa@windstream.net
Facebook: www.facebook.com/berrienchamber1
Instagram: www.instagram.com/berrienchamber
Description: Promotes business and community development in Berrien County, GA. **Founded:** 1856. **Geographic Preference:** Local.

38696 ■ Blairsville - Union County Chamber of Commerce (BUCCC)
129 Union County Recreation Rd.
Blairsville, GA 30514
Free: 877-745-5789
Co. E-mail: info@blairsvillechamber.com
URL: http://www.visitblairsvillega.com
Contact: Steve Rowe, President
E-mail: president@blairsvillechamber.com
YouTube: www.youtube.com/channel/UCqwx9Ka_V9iPSy4l1Lb8luw
Description: Seeks to develop leadership qualities in individuals that have the potential to affect great, positive change in Union County through their particular economic, civic, and social responsibilities and interactions with current and future contributing members of the community. **Founded:** 1835. **Publications:** *BUCCC Monthly News* (Weekly). **Geographic Preference:** Regional.

38697 ■ Blakely-Early County Chamber of Commerce
214 Ct., Sq.
Blakely, GA 39823
Ph: (229)723-3741
Co. E-mail: info@blakelyearlycountychamber.org
URL: http://www.blakelyearlycountychamber.org/home
Contact: Celia Bostwick, President
Facebook: www.facebook.com/BlakelyEarlyCountyChamberofCommerce
X (Twitter): x.com/EarlyChamber
Description: Promotes business and community development in Early County, GA. **Geographic Preference:** Local.

38698 ■ Brunswick-Golden Isles Chamber of Commerce (BGICC)
1505 Richmond St., 2nd Fl.
Brunswick, GA 31520
Ph: (912)265-0620
Co. E-mail: info@bgicoc.com
URL: http://www.brunswickgoldenisleschamber.com
Contact: Ralph Staffins, III, President
E-mail: rstaffins@bgicoc.com
Facebook: www.facebook.com/bgicoc
Linkedin: www.linkedin.com/company/brunswick-golden-isles-chamber-of-commerce-inc
X (Twitter): x.com/bgicoc
Instagram: www.instagram.com/bgichamber
Description: Promotes business and community development in Glynn County, GA. **Founded:** 1954. **Publications:** *Brunswick-Golden Isles Today* (Annual); *Chamber Clipper*. **Geographic Preference:** Local.

38699 ■ *Business*
200 Northside Dr.
Carrollton, GA 30117
Ph: (770)832-2446
Co. E-mail: carrollchamber@carroll-ga.org
URL: http://carroll-ga.org
Contact: Dr. Karen Handel, Chief Executive Officer
E-mail: karen@carroll-ga.org
URL(s): carroll-ga.chambermaster.com/list
Availability: Print; Online.

38700 ■ *Business*
225 W Broad Ave.
Albany, GA 31701
Ph: (229)434-8700
Fax: (229)434-8716
URL: http://albanyga.com
Contact: Don Gray, Chairman
E-mail: dgray@albanyga.com
URL(s): albanyga.com/benefits
Released: Bimonthly **Description:** Contains chamber activities and items of interest to businesses. **Availability:** Print; Online.

38701 ■ *Business Directory*
300 S Wall St.
Calhoun, GA 30701
Ph: (706)625-3200
Co. E-mail: communications@gordoncountychamber.com
URL: http://www.gordoncountychamber.com
Contact: Kathy Johnson, President
E-mail: kjohnson@gordoncountychamber.com
URL(s): www.gordoncountychamber.com/list
Availability: Online.

38702 ■ Camden County Chamber of Commerce
531 N Lee St.
Kingsland, GA 31548
Ph: (912)729-5840
Co. E-mail: membership@camdenchamber.com
URL: http://www.camdenchamber.com
Contact: Alison Shores, President
E-mail: president@camdenchamber.com
Facebook: www.facebook.com/CamdenCountyChamber
X (Twitter): x.com/CamdenChamber
Instagram: www.instagram.com/camden_chamberofcommerce

Description: Promotes business and community development in Camden-Kings Bay area of Georgia. **Publications:** *Teamwork, Leadership, Commitment*. **Geographic Preference:** Local.

38703 ■ Camilla Chamber of Commerce
212 E Broad St.
Camilla, GA 31730
Ph: (229)336-5255
Co. E-mail: camillachamber@gmail.com
URL: http://www.camillageorgia.com
Contact: Jennifer Burnum, Executive Director
E-mail: jennifer@camillageorgia.com
Facebook: www.facebook.com/camilla.chamber
Description: Promotes business and community development in Camilla, GA. Sponsors Gnat Days Summer Celebration. **Founded:** 1858. **Geographic Preference:** Local.

38704 ■ Carroll County Chamber of Commerce
200 Northside Dr.
Carrollton, GA 30117
Ph: (770)832-2446
Co. E-mail: carrollchamber@carroll-ga.org
URL: http://carroll-ga.org
Contact: Dr. Karen Handel, Chief Executive Officer
E-mail: karen@carroll-ga.org
Facebook: www.facebook.com/carrollchambergeorgia
Linkedin: www.linkedin.com/company/carroll-county-chamber
X (Twitter): x.com/Carroll_Chamber
Instagram: www.instagram.com/carrollcountychamber
YouTube: www.youtube.com/channel/UCIXNIGBxuZaixIDhhhJ_8-Q
Description: Promotes business and community development in Carroll County, GA. **Founded:** 1955. **Publications:** *Business*; *Chamber News* (Monthly); *Existing Industry Resource*. **Geographic Preference:** Local.

38705 ■ Cartersville-Bartow County Chamber of Commerce (CBC)
122 W Main St.
Cartersville, GA 30120
Ph: (770)382-1466
Fax: (770)382-2704
Co. E-mail: reception@cartersvillechamber.com
URL: http://www.cartersvillechamber.com
Contact: Cindy Williams, Chief Executive Officer
E-mail: cindy@cartersvillechamber.com
Facebook: www.facebook.com/CartersvilleBartowChamber
Linkedin: www.linkedin.com/company/cartersville-bartow-county-chamber-of-commerce
X (Twitter): x.com/ChamberResource
Instagram: www.instagram.com/cartersvilletowchamber
YouTube: www.youtube.com/user/CartersvilleBartow
Description: Promotes business and community development in Bartow County, GA. **Founded:** 1889. **Geographic Preference:** Local.

38706 ■ Catoosa County Chamber of Commerce
264 Catoosa Cir.
Ringgold, GA 30736
Ph: (706)965-5201
Fax: (706)965-8224
Co. E-mail: info@catoosachamberofcommerce.com
URL: http://www.catoosachamberofcommerce.com/home.php
Contact: Amy L. Jackson, President
E-mail: ajackson@catoosachamberofcommerce.com
Facebook: www.facebook.com/catoosacochamber
Linkedin: www.linkedin.com/company/catoosa-county-chamber-of-commerce
X (Twitter): x.com/catoosachamber
Instagram: www.instagram.com/catoosachamber
Description: Promotes business and community development in the Catoosa County, GA area. **Founded:** 1929. **Publications:** *Chamber Network* (Bimonthly); *Common Cents* (Biweekly). **Geographic Preference:** Local.

38707 ■ *Chamber In Motion*
416 N Ashley St.
Valdosta, GA 31601
Ph: (229)247-8100
Co. E-mail: kbrockington@valdostachamber.com
URL: http://www.valdostachamber.com
Contact: Christie Moore, President
E-mail: cmoore@valdostachamber.com
URL(s): www.valdostachamber.com/south-georgia-military-affairs-council
Availability: Online.

38708 ■ *Chamber News*
200 Northside Dr.
Carrollton, GA 30117
Ph: (770)832-2446
Co. E-mail: carrollchamber@carroll-ga.org
URL: http://carroll-ga.org
Contact: Dr. Karen Handel, Chief Executive Officer
E-mail: karen@carroll-ga.org
URL(s): www.carrollcountychamber.org/join-the-chamber
Released: Monthly **Availability:** Print; Online.

38709 ■ *ChamberLink*
11605 Haynes Bridge Rd., Ste. 100
Alpharetta, GA 30009
Ph: (770)993-8806
Free: 866-840-5770
Co. E-mail: info@gnfcc.com
URL: http://www.gnfcc.com
Contact: Kali Boatright, President
E-mail: kboatright@gnfcc.com
URL(s): www.gnfcc.com/membership/marketing-opportunities
Released: Weekly **Availability:** Online.

38710 ■ Chatsworth-Murray County Chamber of Commerce
126 N 3rd Ave.
Chatsworth, GA 30705
Ph: (706)695-6060
URL: http://www.murraycountychamber.org
Facebook: www.facebook.com/MurrayCountyChamberofCommerce
Instagram: www.instagram.com/murrayco_chamber
Description: Promotes business and community development in Murray County, GA. Sponsors North Georgia Mountain Christmas Parade. **Founded:** 1977. **Publications:** *Chamber Report* (3/year); *Quality of Life*; *Quality of Life*. **Awards:** Chatsworth-Murray County Chamber of Commerce Business of the Year (Annual); Chatsworth-Murray County Chamber of Commerce Business Man of the Year (Annual); Chatsworth-Murray County Chamber of Commerce Business Woman of the Year (Annual). **Geographic Preference:** Local.

38711 ■ Chattooga County Chamber of Commerce
44 GA-Highway 48
Summerville, GA 30747
Ph: (706)857-4033
Co. E-mail: info@chattoogachamber.com
URL: http://www.chattoogachamber.org
Contact: Bryan Edge, Officer
Description: Promotes tourism, business and community development in Chattooga County, GA. Conducts educational and leadership development programs. **Founded:** 1986. **Publications:** *Essentials* (Monthly). **Geographic Preference:** Local.

38712 ■ Cherokee County Chamber of Commerce
3605 Marietta Hwy.
Canton, GA 30114
Ph: (770)345-0400
Fax: (770)345-0030
Co. E-mail: info@cherokeechamber.org
URL: http://cherokeechamber.com
Contact: Pamela W. Carnes, President
E-mail: pam@cherokeechamber.com
Facebook: www.facebook.com/CherokeeCountyChamber
YouTube: www.youtube.com/user/CherokeeChamber

Description: Promotes business and community development in Cherokee County. **Founded:** 1970. **Publications:** *Visions* (Bimonthly). **Geographic Preference:** Local.

38713 ■ Claxton-Evans County Chamber of Commerce
302 W Railroad St.
Claxton, GA 30417
Ph: (912)739-1391
Fax: (912)739-3827
Co. E-mail: info@claxtonevanschamber.com
URL: http://www.claxtonevanschamber.com
Contact: Paul Coley, President
Facebook: www.facebook.com/claxtonevanschamber
YouTube: www.youtube.com/channel/UCiyTlrrvRCK0gMiRMqJoqVg
Pinterest: www.pinterest.com/0dxqc10arsv1atu
Description: Promotes business and community development in Evans County, GA. **Founded:** 1953. **Publications:** *It's Good for Business*; *Membership Notes* (Monthly); *The Only Thing Missing*. **Geographic Preference:** Local.

38714 ■ Clayton County Chamber of Commerce
2270 Mt. Zion Rd.
Jonesboro, GA 30236
Ph: (678)610-4021
Fax: (678)610-4025
Co. E-mail: info@claytonchamber.org
URL: http://www.claytonchamber.org
Contact: Valencia Williamson, President
E-mail: vwilliamson@claytonchamber.org
Facebook: www.facebook.com/ClaytonCountyChamberofCommerce
X (Twitter): x.com/Clayton_Chamber
Description: Promotes business growth and enhances the overall business climate for a prosperous Clayton County. **Founded:** 1953. **Publications:** *FOCUS* (Monthly); *Economic Focus* (Quarterly). **Geographic Preference:** Local.

38715 ■ Cobb Chamber of Commerce
1100 Cir. 75 Pkyw., Ste. 1000
Atlanta, GA 30339
Ph: (770)980-2000
Co. E-mail: info@cobbchamber.org
URL: http://www.cobbchamber.org
Contact: Sharon Mason, President
E-mail: smason@cobbchamber.org
Facebook: www.facebook.com/cobbchamber
YouTube: www.youtube.com/c/CobbChamberofCommerceAtlanta
Description: Promotes business and community development in the Marietta, GA area. **Founded:** 1942. **Publications:** *Cobb Chamber of Commerce--Business Directory* (Annual); *Direct* (Monthly). **Geographic Preference:** Local.

38716 ■ Colquitt - Miller County Chamber of Commerce (CMCCOC)
302 E College St.
Colquitt, GA 39837
Ph: (229)758-2400
Fax: (229)758-8140
Co. E-mail: colquittmillercoc@gmail.com
URL: http://www.colquitt-georgia.com
Contact: Ashley Middleton, Secretary
Facebook: www.facebook.com/Colquitt-Miller-County-Chamber-of-Commerce-133615416694300
X (Twitter): x.com/ColquittGA_Cham
Description: Works to improve the economic and cultural vitality of the community. **Founded:** 1856. **Geographic Preference:** Local.

38717 ■ Conyers-Rockdale Chamber of Commerce
936 Green St., SW
Conyers, GA 30012
Ph: (770)483-7049
Fax: (770)922-8415
URL: http://conyers-rockdale.com
Contact: Fred J. Boscarino, President
E-mail: fred@conyers-rockdale.com
Facebook: www.facebook.com/ConyersRockdaleChamberOfCommerce
X (Twitter): x.com/conyersrockdale
Description: Promotes business and community development in the Conyers/Rockdale area. **Founded:** 1954. **Geographic Preference:** Local.

38718 ■ Cordele-Crisp Chamber of Commerce
502 S 2nd St.
Cordele, GA 31010
Ph: (229)273-1668
Fax: (229)273-5132
Co. E-mail: info@cordele-crisp-chamber.com
URL: http://visitcordele.com
Contact: Monica Simmons, President
E-mail: monica@visitcordele.com
X (Twitter): x.com/CordeleChamber
Description: Works to advance the economic, industrial, professional, cultural, and civic welfare of Crisp County, GA. Sponsors annual Watermelon Festival. **Founded:** 1888. **Publications:** *Cordele-Crisp Chamber of Commerce--Business Directory*. **Geographic Preference:** Local.

38719 ■ Cumming-Forsyth County Chamber of Commerce
212 Webb St.
Cumming, GA 30040
Ph: (770)887-6461
Fax: (770)781-8800
Co. E-mail: fccoc@focochamber.org
URL: http://www.focochamber.org
Contact: James McCoy, President
Facebook: www.facebook.com/ForsythCountyChamber
X (Twitter): x.com/forsythchamber
Instagram: www.instagram.com/forsythchamber
Description: Promotes business and community development in Forsyth County, GA. **Founded:** 1954. **Publications:** *Minds for Business* (Monthly). **Geographic Preference:** Local.

38720 ■ Dahlonega Lumpkin County Chamber of Commerce & Visitors Bureau
342 Courthouse Hill, Ste. E
Dahlonega, GA 30533
Ph: (706)867-3762
Co. E-mail: info@dlcchamber.org
URL: http://www.dlcchamber.org
Contact: Robb Nichols, Executive Director
E-mail: robb@dahlonega.org
Facebook: www.facebook.com/DahlonegaLumpkinChamber
Linkedin: www.linkedin.com/company/dahlonega-lumpkin-county-chamber-of-commerce
Instagram: www.instagram.com/dahlonegalumpkinchamber
YouTube: www.youtube.com/channel/UC4_J-2bwaHcmOe8Cn6X1YOw
Description: Promotes business and community development in Lumpkin County, GA. **Geographic Preference:** Local.

38721 ■ Darien-McIntosh Chamber of Commerce
111 Magnolia Bluff Way No. 410
Darien, GA 31305
Ph: (912)437-4837
Co. E-mail: info@discoverdarien.com
URL: http://discoverdarien.com
Instagram: www.instagram.com/discoverdarien
Description: Promotes economic growth, represents the business community and enhances the quality of life while protecting cultural and natural resources. **Founded:** 1736. **Publications:** *The Bagpiper*. **Geographic Preference:** Local.

38722 ■ Dawson County Chamber of Commerce
44 Commerce Dr.
Dawsonville, GA 30534
Ph: (706)265-6278
Free: 877-302-9271
Co. E-mail: info@dawson.org
URL: http://www.dawsonchamber.org
Contact: Mandy Power, President
Facebook: www.facebook.com/dawsoncountychamber
X (Twitter): x.com/dawsonchamber
YouTube: www.youtube.com/channel/UC1gl_gnt-OFtABrJZVIyDJw
Description: Businesses, professionals, retirees and concerned individuals representing the best interest of Dawson County. Promotes, assists, and encourages the development of Dawson County's economic, educational, social, and natural resources in a manner consistent with preserving the county's uniquely desirable quality of life. **Geographic Preference:** Local.

38723 ■ Donalsonville/Seminole County Chamber of Commerce
122 E 2nd St.
Donalsonville, GA 39845
Ph: (229)524-2588
Co. E-mail: shavery.seminolega@outlook.com
URL: http://www.donalsonville-seminole.org
Contact: Sarah Avery, President
E-mail: shavery.seminolega@outlook.com
Facebook: www.facebook.com/donalsonvillechamberofcommerce
Description: Promotes business and community development in Seminole County, GA. Contributes weekly newspaper column and radio report. Sponsors Harvest Festival. **Founded:** 1920. **Geographic Preference:** Local.

38724 ■ Dooly County Chamber of Commerce
110 E Union St.
Vienna, GA 31092
Ph: (229)268-8275
Fax: (229)268-8200
Co. E-mail: rhonda@bigpigjig.com
URL: http://www.doolychamber.com
Contact: Jimmy Carter, President
Facebook: www.facebook.com/Georgia.DoolyCountyChamber
Description: Promotes business and community development in Dooly County, GA. **Founded:** 1821. **Geographic Preference:** Local.

38725 ■ Douglas - Coffee County Chamber of Commerce
144 N Peterson Ave., Ste. 205
Douglas, GA 31533
Ph: (912)384-1873
Co. E-mail: chamber@douglasga.org
URL: http://douglasga.org
Contact: Emily Courson, Executive Director
E-mail: ecourson@douglasga.org
Facebook: www.facebook.com/coffeegachamber
X (Twitter): x.com/coffeegachamber
YouTube: www.youtube.com/channel/UC1TsjtXdRyN1nmvMowXH92g
Description: Entrepreneurs, small business partners, and industries. Enhances the quality of life in Douglas-Coffee County, Georgia. **Founded:** 2012. **Geographic Preference:** Local.

38726 ■ Douglas County Chamber of Commerce
6658 Church St.
Douglasville, GA 30134
Ph: (770)942-5022
Fax: (770)942-5022
Co. E-mail: info@douglascountygeorgia.com
URL: http://douglascountygeorgia.com
Contact: Sara Ray, President
Facebook: www.facebook.com/douglascountychamber
Linkedin: www.linkedin.com/company/douglascountychamber
X (Twitter): x.com/DC_Chamber
Instagram: www.instagram.com/douglascountychamber
YouTube: www.youtube.com/user/DCChamber
Description: Promotes business and community development in Douglas County, GA. Sponsors local festivals; conducts promotional activities. **Founded:** 1941. **Publications:** *New Horizons* (Monthly). **Awards:** Douglas County Chamber of Commerce

Citizen of the Year (Annual); Douglas County Chamber of Commerce Small Business of the Year (Annual). **Geographic Preference:** Local.

38727 ■ **Dublin - Laurens County Chamber of Commerce**
1200 Bellevue Ave.
Dublin, GA 31021
Ph: (478)272-5546
Co. E-mail: chamber@dublin-georgia.com
URL: http://www.dublin-georgia.com
Contact: Heath Taylor, President
Facebook: www.facebook.com/Dlchamber
Description: Promotes business and community development in Dublin, Georgia. **Founded:** 1911. **Publications:** *The Chamber Clarion* (Quarterly). **Geographic Preference:** Local.

38728 ■ **Eastman - Dodge County Chamber of Commerce**
1646 College St.
Eastman, GA 31023
Ph: (478)374-4723
URL: http://eastman-georgia.com
Contact: Paula McCain, President
Description: Works for the advancement of the economic, commercial, industrial, professional, educational, cultural and civic welfare of the Dodge County area. Encourages the growth of existing industries and businesses while giving all proper assistance to any new firms or individuals seeking to locate to the area. **Geographic Preference:** Local.

38729 ■ **Eatonton-Putnam County Chamber of Commerce**
305 N Madison Ave.
Eatonton, GA 31024
Ph: (706)485-7701
Co. E-mail: info@eatonton.com
URL: http://eatonton.com
Contact: Maggie Milner, President
E-mail: president@eatonton.com
Facebook: www.facebook.com/epchamber
X (Twitter): x.com/eatontonchamber
Description: Promotes business and community development in Putnam County, GA. **Founded:** 1979. **Publications:** *Chamber Corner* (Monthly); *Community Magazine* (Biennial); *Eatonton and Putnam County* (Annual). **Geographic Preference:** Local.

38730 ■ **Effingham County Chamber of Commerce**
520 W 3rd St.
Springfield, GA 31329
Ph: (912)754-3301
Co. E-mail: info@effinghamcountychamber.org
URL: http://www.effinghamcounty.com
Contact: Brandt Herndon, Contact
Facebook: www.facebook.com/EffinghamChamber
Linkedin: www.linkedin.com/company/effingham-county-chamber-of-commerce
X (Twitter): x.com/EffinghamOf
Instagram: www.instagram.com/effinghamchamber
YouTube: www.youtube.com/channel/UC554BcS3lPl0YjtDfsUCdJw
Description: Promotes economic development in Effingham County. Helps existing businesses become more competitive. Encourages new businesses to locate in the county. Facilitates cooperation among governmental leaders in addressing growth management issues. **Founded:** 1986. **Geographic Preference:** Local.

38731 ■ **Fannin County Chamber of Commerce**
152 Orvin Lance Dr.
Blue Ridge, GA 30513
Ph: (706)632-5680
Free: 800-899-6867
Fax: (706)632-2241
Co. E-mail: info@blueridgemountains.com
URL: http://www.blueridgemountains.com/chamber
Contact: Jan Hackett, Officer
E-mail: janhackett@blueridgemountains.com
Facebook: www.facebook.com/visitblueridge
X (Twitter): x.com/BlueRidgeGA
Instagram: www.instagram.com/visitblueridgega
YouTube: www.youtube.com/user/blueridgega
Pinterest: www.pinterest.com/VisitBlueRidgeGa
Description: Promotes business and community development in northwestern Georgia and Polk County, TN. Encourages tourism in the area. Convention/Meeting: none. **Founded:** 1983. **Publications:** *Mountain Update* (Quarterly). **Geographic Preference:** Local.

38732 ■ **Forsyth-Monroe County Chamber of Commerce**
PO Box 5795
Forsyth, GA 31029
Ph: (478)994-9239
Free: 888-642-4628
Co. E-mail: admin@forsyth-monroechamber.com
URL: http://www.forsyth-monroechamber.com
Contact: Simonia Blassingame, Contact
E-mail: sblassingame@forsyth-monroechamber.com
X (Twitter): x.com/FMCCOC1
Description: Promotes business and community development in Monroe County, GA. Provides funding for the Monroe County Historical Society. **Founded:** 1950. **Publications:** *Keynotes* (Monthly). **Geographic Preference:** Local.

38733 ■ **Georgia Chamber of Commerce (GCC)**
270 Peachtree St. NW, Ste. 2200
Atlanta, GA 30303
Ph: (404)223-2264
Co. E-mail: communications@gachamber.com
URL: http://www.gachamber.com
Contact: Chris Clark, President
E-mail: cclark@gachamber.com
Facebook: www.facebook.com/georgiachamber
Linkedin: www.linkedin.com/company/georgia-chamber-of-commerce
X (Twitter): x.com/GAChamber
Instagram: www.instagram.com/gachamber1915
YouTube: www.youtube.com/channel/UCaPfeLsXF2Dc5vN2kro5AOg
Description: Serves as the voice of business community. Advocates the business viewpoint in the shaping of public policy, encouraging ethical business practices and ensuring the state's future as economically prosperous, educationally competitive, and environmentally responsible. **Founded:** 1915. **Publications:** *Profile* (Monthly); *Georgia Manufacturing Directory* (Annual). **Geographic Preference:** State.

38734 ■ **Georgia Hispanic Chamber of Commerce (GHCC)**
270 Peachtree St. NW, Ste. 2200
Atlanta, GA 30303
Ph: (404)929-9998
Co. E-mail: info@ghcc.org
URL: http://ghcc.org/en
Contact: Veronica Maldonado-Torres, President
E-mail: veronica@ghcc.org
Facebook: www.facebook.com/ghcc1
X (Twitter): x.com/GHCC_news
Instagram: www.instagram.com/ghcc_news
YouTube: www.youtube.com/channel/UCKaLAjSM2DiCJg1eJHoCk7A
Description: Promotes business and community development in the Hispanic community of the State of Georgia. **Founded:** 1984. **Publications:** *Comercio* (Quarterly). **Awards:** GHCC Legislative Award (Annual). **Geographic Preference:** Local.

38735 ■ **Gilmer County Chamber of Commerce**
696 1st Ave.
East Ellijay, GA 30540
Ph: (706)635-7400
Fax: (706)635-7410
Co. E-mail: info@gilmerchamber.com
URL: http://www.gilmerchamber.com
Contact: Jennifer Grimmer, President
E-mail: president@gilmerchamber.com
Facebook: www.facebook.com/gilmerchamber
Description: Promotes business and community development in Ellijay and East Ellijay, GA. Sponsors Georgia Apple Festival. Convention/Meeting: none. Publications: none. **Founded:** 1978. **Geographic Preference:** Local.

38736 ■ **Gordon County Chamber of Commerce**
300 S Wall St.
Calhoun, GA 30701
Ph: (706)625-3200
Co. E-mail: communications@gordoncountychamber.com
URL: http://www.gordoncountychamber.com
Contact: Kathy Johnson, President
E-mail: kjohnson@gordoncountychamber.com
Facebook: www.facebook.com/people/Gordon-County-Chamber-of-Commerce/100064471010307
Description: Promotes business and community development in Gordon County, GA. Convention/Meeting: none. **Founded:** 1953. **Publications:** *Business Directory*; *Foresight* (Monthly). **Geographic Preference:** Local.

38737 ■ **Greater Columbus Georgia Chamber of Commerce**
1200 6th Ave.
Columbus, GA 31902
Ph: (706)327-1566
Free: 800-360-8552
Fax: (706)327-7512
Co. E-mail: info@columbusgachamber.com
URL: http://columbusgachamber.com
Contact: Jerald Mitchell, President
E-mail: jmitchell@columbusgachamber.com
Facebook: www.facebook.com/GreaterColumbusGeorgiaChamberofCommerce
X (Twitter): x.com/colsgachamber
Instagram: www.instagram.com/columbusga_chamber
YouTube: www.youtube.com/channel/UCueniMw81Uxi2elBmr_uxIw
Description: Promotes business and community development in Columbus, GA. Sponsors Columbus Day celebration. Conducts 10K Run and Criterium. **Founded:** 1827. **Publications:** *Business Progress*; *The Chamber Express* (Semimonthly). **Geographic Preference:** Local.

38738 ■ **Greater Dalton Chamber of Commerce (GDCC)**
100 S Hamilton St.
Dalton, GA 30720
Ph: (706)278-7373
Co. E-mail: info@daltonchamber.org
URL: http://daltonchamber.org
Contact: Rob Bradham, President
E-mail: bradham@daltonchamber.org
Facebook: www.facebook.com/greaterdaltonchamberofcommerce
Linkedin: www.linkedin.com/company/greater-dalton-chamber-of-commerce
X (Twitter): x.com/daltonchamber
Instagram: www.instagram.com/greaterdaltonchambe
YouTube: www.youtube.com/channel/UCjWoNktbnqjxnThnoyaGK_w
Pinterest: www.pinterest.com/greaterdaltonch
Description: Promotes business and community development in Dalton and Whitfield County, GA. **Founded:** 1940. **Publications:** *The Chamber Link* (Irregular); *Manufacturer's Directory*. **Geographic Preference:** Local.

38739 ■ **Greater Hall Chamber of Commerce (GHCC)**
230 E E Butler Pky.
Gainesville, GA 30501
Ph: (770)532-6206
Fax: (770)535-8419
Co. E-mail: info@ghcc.com
URL: http://www.ghcc.com
Contact: Kit Dunlap, President
E-mail: kit@ghcc.com
Linkedin: www.linkedin.com/company/greater-hall-chamber-of-commerce/about
YouTube: www.youtube.com/channel/UC-GxIUU42IeYIYw5Dl46gjw

Description: Promotes business and community development in Hall County, GA. **Founded:** 1908. **Publications:** *BusinessLink* (Monthly). **Geographic Preference:** Local.

38740 ■ Greater Haralson County Chamber of Commerce
70 Murphy Campus Blvd.
Waco, GA 30182
Ph: (770)537-5594
URL: http://haralson.org
Contact: Eric McDonald, President
Facebook: www.facebook.com/grea
terharalsonchamber
Linkedin: www.linkedin.com/company/greater
-haralson-chamber-of-commerce
Instagram: www.instagram.com/grea
terharalsonchamber
Description: Promotes the civic, educational civic and industrial progress of the community. **Publications:** *Chamber News*. **Geographic Preference:** Local.

38741 ■ The Greater Helen Area Chamber of Commerce, Inc.
1074 Edelweiss Strasse
Helen, GA 30545
Ph: (706)878-1908
Co. E-mail: helenchamber@helenchamber.com
URL: http://www.helenchamber.com
Facebook: www.facebook.com/Helen-Chamber-of
-Commerce-978295758904870
Description: Local merchants. Sponsors 7 major events during the year to bring tourists to the area. **Founded:** 1968. **Geographic Preference:** Local.

38742 ■ Greater Macon Chamber of Commerce (GMCC)
305 Coliseum Dr.
Macon, GA 31217
Ph: (478)621-2000
Fax: (478)621-2021
Co. E-mail: info@maconchamber.com
URL: http://www.maconchamber.com
Contact: Cristen Carter, Treasurer
Facebook: www.facebook.com/maconchamber
X (Twitter): x.com/macon_chamber
Instagram: www.instagram.com/macon_chamber
Description: Promotes business and community development in Macon, GA. **Founded:** 1861. **Publications:** *Business Macon* (Monthly). **Geographic Preference:** Local.

38743 ■ Greater North Fulton Chamber of Commerce (GNFCC)
11605 Haynes Bridge Rd., Ste. 100
Alpharetta, GA 30009
Ph: (770)993-8806
Free: 866-840-5770
Co. E-mail: info@gnfcc.com
URL: http://www.gnfcc.com
Contact: Kali Boatright, President
E-mail: kboatright@gnfcc.com
Facebook: www.facebook.com/GNFCC
Linkedin: www.linkedin.com/company/greater-north
-fulton-chamber-of-commerce
X (Twitter): x.com/gnfcc
Description: Promotes business and community development in northern Fulton County, GA. **Founded:** 1972. **Publications:** *ChamberLink* (Weekly); *Your Business Connection* (Monthly). **Educational Activities:** Business After Hours (Monthly). **Geographic Preference:** Local.

38744 ■ Greater Tattnall Chamber of Commerce
108 W Brazell St.
Reidsville, GA 30453
Ph: (912)557-4335
URL: http://www.tattnallcountyga.com/greater-tattnall
-chamber.cfm
Description: Promotes business and community development in Tattnall County, GA. **Founded:** 1801. **Geographic Preference:** Local.

38745 ■ Greater Vidalia Chamber
2805 E 1st St.
Vidalia, GA 30474
URL: http://www.greatervidaliachamber.com
Contact: Michele Johnson, President
E-mail: michelej@greatervidaliachamber.com
Facebook: www.facebook.com/greatervi
daliachamber
Description: Promotes business and community development in Toombs County, GA. **Publications:** *Chamber News*. **Geographic Preference:** Local.

38746 ■ Greene County Chamber of Commerce
102 N E St.
Greensboro, GA 30642
Ph: (706)453-7592
Co. E-mail: hello@greeneccoc.org
URL: http://www.greeneccoc.org
Contact: Mika Mills, President
Facebook: www.facebook.com/greeneccoc
Linkedin: www.linkedin.com/company/greene-county
-chamber-of-commerce-greensboro-ga
X (Twitter): x.com/GreeneGaCCOC
Pinterest: www.pinterest.com/gccoc
Description: Promotes business and community development in Greene County, GA. Sponsors Lake Ocunee/Downtown Festival. **Founded:** 1967. **Publications:** *Chamber Focus* (Monthly); *The Greene Pages* (Annual). **Geographic Preference:** Local.

38747 ■ Griffin-Spalding Chamber of Commerce
143 N Hill St.
Griffin, GA 30223-3340
Ph: (770)228-8200
Co. E-mail: griffinchamber@cityofgriffin.com
URL: http://www.griffinchamber.com
Contact: Chuck Copeland, President
Facebook: www.facebook.com/griffinschamber
Instagram: www.instagram.com/griffinschamber
YouTube: www.youtube.com/channel/UCoQsxpeoxM
1kxlr7dN1CpSA
Description: Promotes business and community development in Spalding County, GA. Sponsors Mayfling festival and Business After Hours. Holds annual retreat and board meeting. **Publications:** *Action* (Monthly). **Educational Activities:** Business After Hours (Annual). **Awards:** General Griffin Nomination (Annual); Lon Touchstone Small Business of the Year Award (Annual); Griffin-Spalding Chamber of Commerce Outstanding Citizen Award (Annual); Griffin-Spalding Chamber of Commerce Outstanding Organization Award (Annual). **Geographic Preference:** Local.

38748 ■ Gwinnett Chamber of Commerce
6500 Sugarloaf Pky.
Duluth, GA 30097
Ph: (770)232-3000
Co. E-mail: info@gwinnettchamber.org
URL: http://www.gwinnettchamber.org
Contact: Nick Masino, President
E-mail: nick@gwinnettchamber.org
Facebook: www.facebook.com/gwinnettchamber
Linkedin: www.linkedin.com/company/gwinne
tt-chamber-of-commerce
X (Twitter): x.com/gwinnettchamber
YouTube: www.youtube.com/user/GwinnettChamber
Description: Works to promote and sustain a responsible pro-business environment in Gwinnett County. **Founded:** 1947. **Publications:** *Inside Gwinnett* (11/year); *Inside Gwinnett* (Quarterly). **Geographic Preference:** Local.

38749 ■ Habersham County Chamber of Commerce
668 U. S. 441 Business
Cornelia, GA 30531
Ph: (706)778-4654
Co. E-mail: habchamber@windstream.net
URL: http://www.habershamchamber.com
Contact: Ellie van Doornum, Co-President
Facebook: www.facebook.com/habershamcoun
tychamber
Description: Promotes business and community development in Habersham, Hall, Rabun, Stephens, and White counties, GA. **Founded:** 1818. **Publications:** *Apple Blossom* (Monthly). **Geographic Preference:** Local.

38750 ■ Harris County Chamber of Commerce
159 S College St.
Hamilton, GA 31811
Ph: (706)628-0010
Co. E-mail: info@harriscountychamber.org
URL: http://www.harriscountychamber.org
Contact: Gloria Boyer, Co-President Co-Chief Executive Officer
Facebook: www.facebook.com/harriscountychamber
X (Twitter): x.com/hcgachamber
YouTube: www.youtube.com/user/HarrisCoun
tyChamber1
Description: Provides leadership aimed at promoting controlled growth, economic development and, in general, to enhance and preserve the quality of life experienced by all citizens of Harris County, Georgia. **Founded:** 1991. **Geographic Preference:** Local.

38751 ■ Hart County Chamber of Commerce
10 S Carolina St.
Hartwell, GA 30643
Ph: (706)376-8590
Co. E-mail: hartchamber@hartcom.net
URL: http://www.hart-chamber.org
Contact: Nikki Peters, Co-Chairman of the Board
Facebook: www.facebook.com/hartgachamber
X (Twitter): x.com/VisitHartwellGA
Pinterest: www.pinterest.com/hartgachamber
Description: Promotes business and community development in Hart County, GA. Sponsors Antique Boat Festival and Lake Hartwell Dam Run. **Founded:** 1949. **Geographic Preference:** Local.

38752 ■ Hawkinsville-Pulaski County Chamber of Commerce
42 S Lumpkin St.
Hawkinsville, GA 31036
Ph: (478)783-1717
Co. E-mail: info@hawkinsvillechamber.org
URL: http://hawkinsvillechamber.org
Contact: John Jones, Chairman
Facebook: www.facebook.com/chamberhawkinsville
Instagram: www.instagram.com/chamberhawkinsville
Description: Promotes business and community development in Pulaski County, GA. **Geographic Preference:** Local.

38753 ■ Henry Area Chamber of Commerce
1709 Hwy. 20 W
McDonough, GA 30253
Ph: (770)957-5786
URL: http://www.henrycounty.com
Contact: Joseph B. Henning, President
E-mail: jhenning@henrycounty.com
Facebook: www.facebook.com/HenryCoun
tyChamberofCommerce
X (Twitter): x.com/Henry_Chamber
Instagram: www.instagram.com/henrychamber
YouTube: www.youtube.com/user/HenryChamber
Description: Promotes business and community development in Henry area. **Founded:** 1967. **Geographic Preference:** Local.

38754 ■ Homerville - Clinch County Chamber of Commerce
101 S College St.
Homerville, GA 31634-3401
Ph: (912)487-2360
URL: http://www.uschamber.com/co/chambers/geor
gia/homerville
Description: Promotes business and community development in Clinch County, GA area. **Geographic Preference:** Local.

38755 ■ Jackson County Area Chamber of Commerce
270 Athens St.
Jefferson, GA 30549
Ph: (706)387-0300
Co. E-mail: info@jacksoncountyga.com

38756 ■ Georgia

URL: http://www.jacksoncountyga.com
Contact: Jim Shaw, President
E-mail: jshaw@jacksoncountyga.com
Facebook: www.facebook.com/jacksoncoun tychamberga
X (Twitter): x.com/JacksonCoGA
YouTube: www.youtube.com/channel/UCo9N _pbOEsQf3bH0vtplntA
Description: Works to encourage the growth of existing industries and businesses while giving all proper assistance to any new firms or individuals seeking to locate in the Jackson County area. **Publications:** *The Chamber Connection* (Quarterly). **Geographic Preference:** Local.

38756 ■ LaGrange - Troup County Chamber of Commerce
111 Bull St.
Lagrange, GA 30240
Ph: (706)884-8671
Co. E-mail: info@lagrangechamber.com
URL: http://www.lagrangechamber.com
Contact: Jamey Jackson, Chairman of the Board
Facebook: www.facebook.com/LaGrangeTroupCOC
X (Twitter): x.com/troupcoc
Pinterest: www.pinterest.com/visitlagrange
Description: Promotes international understanding through cultural exchange. **Founded:** 1911. **Publications:** *Burbank Business Newsletter* (Monthly). **Geographic Preference:** Local.

38757 ■ Lee County Chamber of Commerce
106 Walnut Ave., N
Leesburg, GA 31763
Ph: (229)759-2422
Fax: (229)759-9224
Co. E-mail: ldavis@lee.ga.us
URL: http://www.leechamber.net
Contact: Lisa Davis, President
E-mail: ldavis@lee.ga.us
Facebook: www.facebook.com/lee.chamber
Description: Aims to advance the economic, civic, and cultural growth in the community, to enhance the quality of life, and to work continuously to improve the area as a desirable place to live and conduct business. **Founded:** 1826. **Geographic Preference:** Local.

38758 ■ Liberty County Chamber of Commerce
208 E Ct. St.
Hinesville, GA 31313
Ph: (912)368-4445
Co. E-mail: info@libertycounty.org
URL: http://libertycounty.org/chamber-of-commerce
Contact: Jimmy Shanken, Executive
Facebook: www.facebook.com/libertycountychamber
YouTube: www.youtube.com/user/libertycoun tychamber
Description: Businesses, professionals, and individuals interested in promoting a healthy business climate and supporting economic development and improved quality of life in Liberty County, GA. Sponsors festival. **Founded:** 1976. **Publications:** *The Chamber Chat* (Monthly). **Geographic Preference:** Local.

38759 ■ Lincolnton - Lincoln County Chamber of Commerce
112 Washington St.
Lincolnton, GA 30817
Ph: (706)359-6512
Co. E-mail: info@lincolngachamber.org
URL: http://www.lincolngachamber.org
Contact: Wendi Qualls, Chairman
URL(s): www.lincolncountyga.org
Facebook: www.facebook.com/LincolnCoun tyGAChamber
YouTube: www.youtube.com/channel/ UCpONcNTxTpnkMwUwVw9bjXg
Description: Promotes business and community development in Lincolnton, GA area. **Geographic Preference:** Local.

38760 ■ Madison County Chamber of Commerce (MCCC)
800 Madison St.
Danielsville, GA 30633

Ph: (706)795-2191
Co. E-mail: astrickland@madisoncountyga.org
URL: http://www.madisoncountyga.org
Contact: Kim Shupe, Chairman
YouTube: www.youtube.com/channel/UCswA 3FPFbwiXZcirgJihuTw
Description: Promotes business and community development in Madison County, Georgia. **Founded:** 1811. **Geographic Preference:** Local.

38761 ■ Madison-Morgan County Chamber of Commerce
118 N Main St.
Madison, GA 30650
Ph: (706)438-3120
Co. E-mail: info@madisonga.org
URL: http://madisonga.org
Contact: Bob Hughes, President
E-mail: bhughes@madisonga.org
Facebook: www.facebook.com/ma disonmorganchamber
X (Twitter): x.com/MMCCOC
Description: Promotes business and community development in Madison, GA. **Founded:** 1984. **Publications:** *Community Image* (Biennial). **Geographic Preference:** Local.

38762 ■ Meriwether County Chamber of Commerce (MCCC)
1 Broad St.
Warm Springs, GA 31830
Ph: (706)655-2558
Fax: (706)655-2812
URL: http://www.meriwethercoun tychamberofcommerce.com
Contact: Carolyn McKinley, President
Facebook: www.facebook.com/MeriwetherCoun tyChamber
Description: Promotes business and community development in Meriwether County, GA. **Publications:** *MCCC Newsletter* (Monthly). **Geographic Preference:** Local.

38763 ■ Metro Atlanta Chamber of Commerce (MAC)
191 Peachtree St. NE, Ste. 3400
Atlanta, GA 30303
Ph: (404)880-9000
URL: http://www.metroatlantachamber.com
Contact: Dan Corso, President
Facebook: www.facebook.com/metroatlantachamber
Linkedin: www.linkedin.com/company/metro-atlanta -chamber
X (Twitter): x.com/atlchamber
Description: Aims to improve the quality of life and promote economic growth in Atlanta. **Founded:** 1859. **Publications:** *Metro Atlanta Area Health Care Facilities Directory* (Biennial); *Atlanta Chamber of Commerce--Transportation* (Biennial); *Metro Atlanta Top Employers*; *Arts and Business Council*; *Atlanta Area Hospitals*; *Education*; *New Business Quarterly* (Quarterly); *Sports and Recreation*; *Atlanta Consular Corps*; *Atlanta Consulates, Trade and Tourism Offices and Foreign-American Chambers of Commerce* (Annual); *International Atlanta* (Annual); *Atlanta Business Chronicle's Book of Lists*; *Metro Atlanta Chamber of Commerce--Who's Who in Metro Atlanta Business: Membership Directory* (Annual); *Atlanta Employment Services* (Annual); *Atlanta Chamber of Commerce--Education Directory* (Biennial); *Metro Atlanta Chamber of Commerce--Who's Who in Metro Atlanta Business*; *Metropolitan Atlanta Manufacturing Directory* (Biennial); *Bioscience Directory*; *Fortune 1000 Companies in Metro Atlanta*; *Media Guide for Metro Atlanta*; *Executive Recruiting Agencies*; *Atlanta Larger Employers* (Biennial); *Who's Who in Metro Atlanta Business: Membership Directory & Buyers Guide* (Annual). **Geographic Preference:** Local.

38764 ■ Metter-Candler Chamber of Commerce
1210 S Lewis St.
Metter, GA 30439
Ph: (912)685-2159
Co. E-mail: metterchamber@gmail.com
URL: http://everythingsbetterinmetter.com/better -opportunity-about.php

Contact: Victoria Gaitten, Executive Director
E-mail: metterchamber@gmail.com
Facebook: www.facebook.com/mettercan dlerchamber
X (Twitter): x.com/betterinmetter
YouTube: www.youtube.com/channel/UCBz tZbQDnTMIPxZmvCARK-A
Pinterest: www.pinterest.com/betterinmetter/every thing-better-in-metter-metter-ga
Description: Promotes business and community development in Metter and Candler County, GA. **Founded:** 1956. **Geographic Preference:** Local.

38765 ■ Milledgeville-Baldwin County Chamber of Commerce
130 S Jefferson St.
Milledgeville, GA 31061
Ph: (478)453-9311
URL: http://milledgevillega.com
Contact: Kara Lassiter, President
E-mail: klassiter@milledgevillega.com
Facebook: www.facebook.com/milledgevillechamber
Linkedin: www.linkedin.com/company/milledgeville -baldwin-county-chamber-ga
X (Twitter): x.com/mbcchamberga
YouTube: www.youtube.com/user/Mille dgevilleChamber
Description: Promotes business and community development in Baldwin County. **Founded:** 1947. **Geographic Preference:** Local.

38766 ■ Monticello-Jasper County Chamber of Commerce
119 W Washington St.
Monticello, GA 31064
Ph: (706)468-8994
Co. E-mail: jasperchamber@bellsouth.net
URL: http://jaspercountycoc.com
Contact: Mandi Tanner, Executive Director
Facebook: www.facebook.com/mon ticellojasperchamberofcommerce
Description: Promotes business and community development in Monticello, GA. Sponsors Jasper Jubilee festival and Fourth of July celebration. **Founded:** 1959. **Geographic Preference:** Local.

38767 ■ Moultrie-Colquitt County Chamber of Commerce
116 1st Ave., SE
Moultrie, GA 31776
Ph: (229)985-2131
Free: 888-408-4748
Fax: (229)890-2638
Co. E-mail: contact@moultriechamber.com
URL: http://business.moultriechamber.com
Contact: Tommie Beth Willis, President
E-mail: tbwillis@moultriechamber.com
Facebook: www.facebook.com/moultriechamber1
X (Twitter): x.com/moultriechamber
Instagram: www.instagram.com/moultriechamber
Description: Promotes business and community development in Moultrie, GA. **Founded:** 1910. **Geographic Preference:** Local.

38768 ■ Ocilla - Irwin Chamber of Commerce
620 S Irwin Ave.
Ocilla, GA 31774
Ph: (229)468-9114
URL: http://www.ocillachamber.net
Contact: Tammy Vickers, Executive Secretary
Description: Promotes business and community development in Ocilla - Irwin, GA area. **Geographic Preference:** Local.

38769 ■ Oconee County Chamber of Commerce
55 Nancy Dr.
Watkinsville, GA 30677
Ph: (706)769-7947
Fax: (706)769-7948
Co. E-mail: areese@oconeechamber.org
URL: http://www.oconeechamber.org
Contact: Courtney Bernardi, President
E-mail: cbernardi@oconeechamber.org
Facebook: www.facebook.com/oconeechamber
Linkedin: www.linkedin.com/company/oconee-county -chamber-of-commerce

STATE LISTINGS

X (Twitter): x.com/oconeechamber
Instagram: www.instagram.com/oconeechamber
Description: Promotes business and community development in Oconee County, GA. Sponsors Fall Craft Festival. **Founded:** 1975. **Awards:** Larry Risse Agribusiness Person of the Year (Annual); Sharon Johnson Volunteer of the Year (Annual); Oconee County Chamber of Commerce Student/Teacher Award Recognition (STAR) (Annual); Oconee County Chamber of Commerce Teacher of the Year (Annual). **Geographic Preference:** Local.

38770 ■ Okefenokee Chamber and Development Authority
3795 Main St.
Folkston, GA 31537
Ph: (912)496-2536
Fax: (912)496-4601
Co. E-mail: info@folkston.com
URL: http://okefenokeechamber.com
Contact: Dana O'Quinn, Executive Director
E-mail: dana@folkston.com
Facebook: www.facebook.com/visitfolkston
Linkedin: www.linkedin.com/company/okefenokee-chamber-of-commerce
Instagram: www.instagram.com/okefenokee.chamber
Description: Promotes business and community development in Charlton County, GA. Encourages tourism. Sponsors annual Okefenokee Festival. **Founded:** 1965. **Geographic Preference:** Local.

38771 ■ *Paulding Chamber Business Directory*
455 Jimmy Campbell Pky.
Dallas, GA 30132
Ph: (770)445-6016
URL: http://www.pauldingchamber.org
Contact: Stacy Hamby, President
E-mail: shamby@pauldingchamber.org
URL(s): members.pauldingchamber.org/list
Availability: Print.

38772 ■ Paulding Chamber of Commerce
455 Jimmy Campbell Pky.
Dallas, GA 30132
Ph: (770)445-6016
URL: http://www.pauldingchamber.org
Contact: Stacy Hamby, President
E-mail: shamby@pauldingchamber.org
Facebook: www.facebook.com/PauldingChamberofCommerce
Description: Promotes community and economic development in Paulding County, GA. Assists existing business and industry with planned expansions and/or local relocations. Sponsors fundraisers and events for investors. **Publications:** *The Outlook* (Monthly); *Paulding Chamber Business Directory*; *Paulding Chamber Quality of Life* (Biennial). **Educational Activities:** Paulding Chamber of Commerce Banquet (Annual); First Thursday Forum. **Geographic Preference:** Local.

38773 ■ *Progress*
URL(s): www.oeh.ac.at/mediadaten
Released: Semiannual **Price:** Free to members.
Availability: Print; Online.

38774 ■ Quitman-Brooks County Chamber of Commerce
220 E Screven St.
Quitman, GA 31643
Ph: (229)263-2085
Co. E-mail: qbccdirector@gmail.com
URL: http://www.uschamber.com/co/chambers/georgia/quitman
Contact: Katheryn Patrick, Chief Executive Officer
Facebook: www.facebook.com/QBCChamber
Description: Promotes economic development in Quitman, GA and Brooks County. **Publications:** *Quitman-Brooks County Chamber of Commerce Newsletter*. **Geographic Preference:** Local.

38775 ■ Rabun County Chamber of Commerce
10 Seed Tick Rd. Hwy. 441
Clayton, GA 30525
Ph: (706)782-4812

URL: http://rabunchamber.com
Contact: Rick Story, President
X (Twitter): x.com/RabunOf
YouTube: www.youtube.com/channel/UCg8UXpmjhqZNL0iNfE9QkUw
Description: Promotes business and community development in Rabun County, GA. **Founded:** 1976. **Publications:** *Special Events* (Periodic). **Geographic Preference:** Local.

38776 ■ Roberta - Crawford County Chamber of Commerce
39 Wright Ave.
Roberta, GA 31078
Ph: (478)836-3825
Co. E-mail: robertacrawfordcoc@gmail.com
URL: http://robertacrawfordchamber.org
Contact: Patti Temple, Executive Director
Facebook: www.facebook.com/RobertaCrawfordCountyChamberOfCommerce
Description: Advances the commercial, financial, industrial, educational, and civic interests of the county. **Founded:** 1910. **Geographic Preference:** Local.

38777 ■ Robins Regional Chamber [Robins Regional Chamber of Commerce]
1228 Watson Blvd.
Warner Robins, GA 31093
Ph: (478)922-8585
Co. E-mail: info@robinsregion.com
URL: http://www.warner-robins.com
Contact: April Bragg, President
E-mail: abragg@robinsregion.com
Facebook: www.facebook.com/Robinsregion
Linkedin: www.linkedin.com/company/robins-regional-chamber-of-commerce
X (Twitter): x.com/robinsregional
YouTube: www.youtube.com/user/RobinsRegion
Description: Promotes business and community development in the Warner Robins, GA area. **Founded:** 1949. **Publications:** *Business Bulletin* (Quarterly). **Awards:** Robins Regional Chamber of Commerce Small Business of the Year (Annual). **Geographic Preference:** Local.

38778 ■ Savannah Area Chamber of Commerce (SACC)
101 E Bay St.
Savannah, GA 31401
Ph: (912)644-6400
Co. E-mail: info@savannahchamber.com
URL: http://www.savannahchamber.com
Contact: William W. Hubbard, President
E-mail: bhubbard@savannahchamber.com
X (Twitter): x.com/savchamber
Instagram: www.instagram.com/savchamber
YouTube: www.youtube.com/channel/UCKjjujmVotFwZkwchpweJ4w
Description: Promotes business and community development in the Savannah, GA area. **Founded:** 1806. **Publications:** *Outlook* (Monthly); *Sharing Savannah* (Weekly); *Small Street* (Quarterly). **Geographic Preference:** Local.

38779 ■ Screven County Chamber of Commerce (SCCC)
101 S Main St.
Sylvania, GA 30467
Ph: (912)564-7878
Co. E-mail: screvencountychamber@gmail.com
URL: http://screvencountychamber.com/index.html
Contact: Brett Warren, Chief Executive Officer
Facebook: www.facebook.com/screvencountychamber
Instagram: www.instagram.com/screvencochamber
Description: Works to build a shared vision for the future, promote lifelong learning, provide community leadership, achieve economic growth, and improve the quality of life and represent the interests of members. **Publications:** *Community Connection* (Biweekly). **Geographic Preference:** Local.

38780 ■ Soperton - Treutlen Chamber of Commerce
488 2nd St. S
Soperton, GA 30457

URL: http://treutlenchamber.com
Description: Promotes business and community development in Treutlen County, GA. **Geographic Preference:** Local.

38781 ■ South Fulton Chamber of Commerce (SFCC)
4405 Mall Blvd., Ste. 120
Union City, GA 30291
Ph: (770)964-1984
Co. E-mail: info@southfultonchamber.com
URL: http://www.southfultonchamber.com
Contact: Walter W. Vinson, Chairman
Facebook: www.facebook.com/SouthFultonChamber
X (Twitter): x.com/sfultonchamber
YouTube: www.youtube.com/channel/UCedPmDbc61tTJ6EuVLEsVCA
Description: Promotes business and community development in southern Fulton County, GA. Supports local vocational center. Sponsors golf tournament. **Founded:** 1962. **Geographic Preference:** Local.

38782 ■ Statesboro-Bulloch Chamber of Commerce
841 Buckhead Dr., Ste. 3
Statesboro, GA 30458
Ph: (912)764-6111
URL: http://statesboro-chamber.org
Contact: Jennifer Davis, President
E-mail: jennifer@statesborochamber.com
Facebook: www.facebook.com/statesborochamber
Instagram: www.instagram.com/statesborochamber
Description: Promotes business and economic development in Bulloch County, GA. **Founded:** 1925. **Publications:** *Chamber Connection* (Monthly). **Geographic Preference:** Local.

38783 ■ Swainsboro/Emanuel County Chamber of Commerce
102 S Main St.
Swainsboro, GA 30401
Ph: (478)237-6426
Fax: (478)237-7460
Co. E-mail: info@goemanuel.org
URL: http://www.emanuelchamber.org/home
Contact: Ken Warnock, Chief Executive Officer
E-mail: kjcw@goemanuel.org
Facebook: www.facebook.com/swainsboroemanuelcountychamber
Linkedin: www.linkedin.com/company/swainsboro-emanuel-county-chamber-of-commerce
X (Twitter): x.com/SECCHAMBER
Instagram: www.instagram.com/emanuelchamber
Description: Promotes business and community development in Emanuel County, GA. **Founded:** 1954. **Educational Activities:** Wash Pot Festival. **Geographic Preference:** Local.

38784 ■ Telfair County Chamber of Commerce (TCCC)
9 E Oak St.
McRae Helena, GA 31055
Ph: (229)868-6365
Fax: (888)575-2477
URL: http://www.telfairco.org/home.html
Contact: Laura Smith, Secretary
Description: Promotes commercial and industrial development, as well as community development throughout Telfair County, GA. **Founded:** 1940. **Geographic Preference:** Local.

38785 ■ Terrell County Chamber of Commerce
211 W Lee St.
Dawson, GA 39842
Ph: (229)995-2011
Co. E-mail: tcchamberdirector@gmail.com
URL: http://www.terrellga.com
Contact: Daniel Beaver, Chairman
Facebook: www.facebook.com/terrellcountychamber
Description: Promotes business and community development in Terrell County, GA. **Founded:** 1947. **Geographic Preference:** Local.

38786 ■ **Thomaston - Upson Chamber of Commerce**
110 W Main St.
Thomaston, GA 30286
Ph: (706)647-9686
URL: http://www.thomastongachamber.com
Contact: Lori Showalter Smith, Co-President
Facebook: www.facebook.com/ThomastonUpsonChamber
Instagram: www.instagram.com/tuchamber
YouTube: www.youtube.com/channel/UCDZHzdcuJgQxeRoJhDkDxtQ
Description: Promotes business and community development in Upson County, GA. **Founded:** 1947. **Publications:** *Chamber Comment* (Monthly). **Geographic Preference:** Local.

38787 ■ **Thomasville-Thomas County Chamber of Commerce**
401 S Broad St.
Thomasville, GA 31799
Ph: (229)226-9600
Fax: (229)226-9603
Co. E-mail: chamber@thomasvillechamber.com
URL: http://www.thomasvillechamber.com
Contact: Andrea Collins, Director
E-mail: andrea@thomasvillechamber.com
X (Twitter): x.com/TvilleGAChamber
YouTube: www.youtube.com/channel/UCMqiVy00UY08bunWTF-TiMg
Description: Promotes business and community development in Thomas County, GA. Sponsors festival and competitions; conducts charitable activities. **Founded:** 1921. **Geographic Preference:** Local.

38788 ■ **Towns County Chamber of Commerce**
1411 Jack Dayton Cir.
Young Harris, GA 30582
Ph: (706)896-4966
Free: 800-984-1543
Co. E-mail: candacelee@brmemc.net
URL: http://www.golakechatuge.com
Facebook: www.facebook.com/TownsCountyChamber
Linkedin: www.linkedin.com/company/towns-county
X (Twitter): x.com/golakechatuge
Instagram: www.instagram.com/townscountychamber
Description: Provides support, leadership, and education through planned development, marketing, and communications to enhance the quality of life while maintaining the heritage of Towns County. **Founded:** 1998. **Geographic Preference:** Local.

38789 ■ **Valdosta-Lowndes County Chamber of Commerce (VLCCC)**
416 N Ashley St.
Valdosta, GA 31601
Ph: (229)247-8100
Co. E-mail: kbrockington@valdostachamber.com
URL: http://www.valdostachamber.com
Contact: Christie Moore, President
E-mail: cmoore@valdostachamber.com
Facebook: www.facebook.com/vlcchamber
Linkedin: www.linkedin.com/company/valdosta-lowndes-county-chamber-of-commerce
X (Twitter): x.com/ValdostaChamber
Instagram: www.instagram.com/valdostachamber
YouTube: www.youtube.com/user/vlcchamber1
Description: Promotes business and community development in Lowndes County, GA. **Founded:** 1912. **Publications:** *Chamber Focus* (Weekly); *Chamber In Motion*. **Geographic Preference:** Local.

38790 ■ **Walker County Chamber of Commerce**
10052 N Hwy. 27
Rock Spring, GA 30739
Ph: (706)375-7702
Co. E-mail: info@walkerchochamber.com
URL: http://www.walkerrocks.com
Contact: Cindy Scoggins, Chairman
Facebook: www.facebook.com/walkercountychamber
Instagram: www.instagram.com/visitwalkercountyga
YouTube: www.youtube.com/channel/UCZz7x46b3p_CWAtajH5YDdQ
Description: Promotes business and community development in the Walker County, GA area. **Founded:** 1991. **Publications:** *The Chamber ADVANTAGE* (Monthly); *Future Focus* (Monthly); *News Blast* (Weekly (Mon.)); *Quality of Life*. **Geographic Preference:** Local.

38791 ■ **Walton County Chamber of Commerce (WCCC)**
207 N Wayne St.
Monroe, GA 30655
Ph: (770)267-6594
Fax: (770)267-0961
Co. E-mail: staff@waltonchamber.org
URL: http://www.waltonchamber.org
Contact: Teri Smiley, President
E-mail: teri@waltonchamber.org
Facebook: www.facebook.com/WaltonCountyChamber
X (Twitter): x.com/WaltonChamber
Instagram: www.instagram.com/waltonchamber
Description: Promotes business and community development in Walton County, GA. **Founded:** 1819. **Publications:** *Official Buyer's Guide* (Annual). **Geographic Preference:** Local.

38792 ■ **Warren County Chamber of Commerce**
46 S Norwood St.
Warrenton, GA 30828
Ph: (706)465-9604
Co. E-mail: chamber@warrencountyga.com
URL: http://warrencountyga.com
Contact: Jeffrey D. Fowler, President
E-mail: jeffrey@warrencountyga.gov
Facebook: www.facebook.com/WarrenCountyChamberGA
Linkedin: www.linkedin.com/company/warren-county-chamber-of-commerce
X (Twitter): x.com/chamber_warren
Instagram: www.instagram.com/warrencountychamber
YouTube: www.youtube.com/channel/UCtX_R-r3j6eGzlTw081IE6g
Description: Promotes business and community development in Warren County, GA. **Founded:** 1990. **Geographic Preference:** Local.

38793 ■ **Washington County Chamber of Commerce**
603 S Harris St.
Sandersville, GA 31082
Ph: (478)552-3288
Fax: (478)552-1449
Co. E-mail: chamber@washingtoncountyga.com
URL: http://www.washingtoncountyga.com
Contact: Katie Moncus, President
E-mail: kmoncus@washingtoncountyga.com
Facebook: www.facebook.com/pg/washingtoncountygachamber
X (Twitter): x.com/WashCoChamberPA
Description: Promotes business and community development in Washington County, GA. **Founded:** 1911. **Geographic Preference:** Local.

38794 ■ **Washington-Wilkes Chamber of Commerce**
26 W Sq.
Washington, GA 30673
Ph: (706)678-2013
Co. E-mail: wwchamberofcommerce@gmail.com
URL: http://www.washingtonwilkes.org
Contact: Ruthie Clements, President
Facebook: www.facebook.com/HistoricWashingtonWilkes
Description: Businesses, organizations, and individuals concerned with the socioeconomic climate of Washington-Wilkes. Promotes business and community development in the Washington, GA area. **Founded:** 1780. **Holdings:** Figures not available. **Geographic Preference:** Local.

38795 ■ **Wayne County Chamber of Commerce**
261 W Plum St.
Jesup, GA 31545
Ph: (912)427-2028
Co. E-mail: chamberoffice@waynechamberga.com
URL: http://www.waynechamberga.com
Contact: Deena Bennett, Executive Director
E-mail: dbennett@waynechamberga.com
Facebook: www.facebook.com/WayneCountyChamber
Description: Promotes business and community development in Wayne County, GA. **Founded:** 1891. **Geographic Preference:** Local.

38796 ■ **Wheeler County Chamber of Commerce**
6 W Railroad Ave.
Alamo, GA 30411
Ph: (912)568-7808
Co. E-mail: chamber@wheelercounty.org
URL: http://www.wheelercounty.org
Contact: Janice Mock, President
Description: Promotes business and community development in Wheeler County, Georgia. **Geographic Preference:** Local.

38797 ■ **White County Chamber of Commerce**
122 N Main St.
Cleveland, GA 30528
Ph: (706)865-5356
Co. E-mail: info@whitecountychamber.org
URL: http://www.whitecountychamber.org
Contact: Beth Truelove, President
E-mail: cindy@whitecountychamber.org
Facebook: www.facebook.com/whitecountychamberofcommerce
Linkedin: www.linkedin.com/in/whitecountychamberofcommerce
X (Twitter): x.com/WhiteCoChamber
YouTube: www.youtube.com/channel/UC2H4l71syqJSWQPSbXsV13Q
Pinterest: www.pinterest.com/whitecounty
Description: Promotes business and community development in White County, GA. Sponsors Easter Eggstravaganza Festival. **Founded:** 1983. **Publications:** *The Chamber Advocate* (Monthly); *Industrial Development Brochure* (Semiannual); *Tourism Brochure* (Annual); *Tourism Brochure* (Annual). **Educational Activities:** Business After Hours (Monthly). **Geographic Preference:** Local.

38798 ■ **Wrightsville - Johnson County Chamber of Commerce**
8679 N Marcus St.
Wrightsville, GA 31096
Ph: (478)864-7200
Co. E-mail: wrightsville.johnsonctychamber@gmail.com
URL: http://wrightsville-johnsonctychamber.com/chamber
Facebook: www.facebook.com/WJCCoC
Instagram: www.instagram.com/wrightsvillejohnsonctychamber
YouTube: www.youtube.com/channel/UCr9m6QJqykGYjp4HL1i8RFg
Description: Works to advance the commercial, agricultural, industrial, civic, and general interests of the City of Wrightsville, Johnson County, Georgia and its trade area. **Geographic Preference:** Local.

MINORITY BUSINESS ASSISTANCE PROGRAMS

38799 ■ **Georgia Minority Supplier Development Council (GMSDC)**
759 W Peachtree St. NE, Ste. 107
Atlanta, GA 30308
Ph: (404)589-4929
Co. E-mail: info@gmsdc.org
URL: http://www.gmsdc.org
Contact: Stacey J. Key, President
E-mail: stacey@gmsdc.org
Facebook: www.facebook.com/GMSDC.org

STATE LISTINGS
Georgia ■ 38815

Linkedin: www.linkedin.com/company/georgia-minori
ty-supplier-development-council-gmsdc-
X (Twitter): x.com/gmsdc
YouTube: www.youtube.com/user/
GMSDCTVChannel

Description: Provides a direct link between corporate America and minority-owned businesses. Increases procurement and business opportunities for minority businesses of all sizes. **Founded:** 1975. **Geographic Preference:** State.

38800 ■ Georgia Tech Minority Business Development Agency Business Center (MBDA)
75 5th St. NW, Ste. 3000
Atlanta, GA 30308
Ph: (404)894-2096
URL: http://georgiambdabusinesscenter.org
Contact: Donna Ennis, Operator Representative
E-mail: donna.ennis@innovate.gatech.edu

Description: Provides emerging and existing minority businesses with business development and technical assistance.

38801 ■ Urban League of Greater Atlanta (ULGATL)
230 Peachtree St. NE, Ste. 2600
Atlanta, GA 30303-1600
Ph: (404)659-1150
Co. E-mail: info@ulgatl.org
URL: http://ulgatl.org
Contact: Randy Koporc, Chief Executive Officer
Facebook: www.facebook.com/ULGATL
Linkedin: www.linkedin.com/company/urban-league
-of-greater-atl
X (Twitter): x.com/ulgatl
Instagram: www.instagram.com/ulgatl

Description: Provides business mentoring and networking services to minority business owners in Atlanta. **Founded:** 1920. **Geographic Preference:** Local.

FINANCING AND LOAN PROGRAMS

38802 ■ Accuitive Medical Ventures L.L.C./ AMV Partners
2905 Premiere Pky., Ste. 150
Duluth, GA 30097
Ph: (678)812-1101

Description: Provider of venture capital, venture financing and management for healthcare industry. **Investment Policies:** Early stage and expansion. **Industry Preferences:** Medical and health.

38803 ■ Ariel Southeast Angel Partners (ASAP)
11258 Ford Ave., Ste. 2
Richmond Hill, GA 31324
Ph: (912)656-5603
Co. E-mail: hello@asap-invests.com
URL: http://asap-invests.com
Contact: Carl D. Francis, Chairman of the Board
Facebook: www.facebook.com/ArielSAVPartners
Linkedin: www.linkedin.com/company/ariel-savannah
-angel-partners

Description: Angel investor group supporting start-up and early-stage high-growth businesses in the Southeast. **Investment Policies:** Potential to exit within 3-5 years.

38804 ■ Atlanta Technology Angels (ATA)
3423 Piedmont Rd., NE
Atlanta, GA 30307
Co. E-mail: info@angelatlanta.com
URL: http://angelatlanta.com
Contact: Steven Lustig, Chief Executive Officer
Facebook: www.facebook.com/Atlan
taTechnologyAngels
Linkedin: www.linkedin.com/company/atlanta
-technology-angels
X (Twitter): x.com/Angel_Atlanta
YouTube: www.youtube.com/channel/UC
_vxDnSkRDw7hyPMp8d108A

Description: Angel investors offering seed- and early-stage capital to high-growth technology companies. **Founded:** 1998. **Preferred Investment Size:** $200,000 to $2,000,000. **Industry Preferences:** Hardware; software; digital media; consumer products and services; financial services; life science; healthcare; CleanTech; industrial technologies.

38805 ■ Cedar Ventures LLC
2870 Peachtree Rd., No. 450
Atlanta, GA 30305
Ph: (404)239-8416
Fax: (404)239-8417
URL: http://cedarventures.com
Contact: David Gaither, Consultant
E-mail: principal@cedarventures.com
Linkedin: www.linkedin.com/company/cedar-ventures
-llc

Description: Financial advisory and investment banking firm. Raises debt and equity capital. Offers associates in the Middle East and China. **Founded:** 2000. **Industry Preferences:** Real estate, manufacturing, alternative energy, port facilities, and infrastructure projects.

38806 ■ Croft & Bender LP (C&B)
4401 Northside Pky., Ste. 395
Atlanta, GA 30327
Ph: (404)841-3131
Fax: (404)841-3135
Co. E-mail: info@croft-bender.com
URL: http://www.croft-bender.com
Contact: Lee Anderson, Chief Financial Officer
Linkedin: www.linkedin.com/company/croft-&-bender

Description: Firm that provides private equity investment services. **Founded:** 1996. **Industry Preferences:** Internet specific, computer software and services, medical and health, industrial, communications and media.

38807 ■ EGL Ventures
Eleven Piedmont Ctr.
3495 Piedmont Rd., Ste. 412
Atlanta, GA 30305
Ph: (404)949-8300
Fax: (404)949-8311
Co. E-mail: info@eglventures.com
URL: http://www.eglventures.com
Contact: Dr. David Ellis, Partner

Description: Provider of private equity and venture capital investment services for seed, startup, early, mid and late stage equity investments. **Founded:** 1988. **Preferred Investment Size:** $500,000 to $6,000,000. **Industry Preferences:** Provider of private equity and venture capital investment services for seed, startup, early, mid and late stage equity investments.

38808 ■ Equity-South Advisors L.L.C.
2855 Marconi Dr., Ste. 370
Alpharetta, GA 30005
Ph: (678)612-9876
URL: http://www.equity-south.com
Contact: Douglas Diamond, Partner
E-mail: dld@equity-south.com

Description: Firm provides investment consulting advice services. **Founded:** 1995. **Preferred Investment Size:** $1,000,000 to $6,000,000. **Industry Preferences:** Communications, computer software, semiconductors and other electronics, medical and health, consumer related, industrial and energy, business service, and manufacturing.

38809 ■ Invest Georgia (IG)
1388 Cornell Rd. NE
Atlanta, GA 30306
URL: http://investgeorgia.net
Contact: John F. Carter, Chief Executive Officer
X (Twitter): x.com/InvestGeorgia

Description: Long-term investment program backed by the State of Georgia. Helps grow and mentor current, new, and future Georgia venture capital and private equity investment funds to create new companies and jobs. . **Founded:** 2014.

38810 ■ Noro-Moseley Partners (NMP)
3284 Northside Pky. NW, Ste. 525
Atlanta, GA 30327-2337
Ph: (404)233-1966
URL: http://noromoseley.com
Contact: Beth Warchol, Vice President Controller
X (Twitter): x.com/norovc

Description: Investment firm provides venture capital and private equity investment services for information technology and healthcare markets. **Founded:** 1983. **Preferred Investment Size:** $3,000,000 to $10,000,000. **Industry Preferences:** Internet specific, computer software and services, medical and health, consumer related, other products, communications and media, computer hardware, semiconductors and other electronics, industrial and energy, and biotechnology.

38811 ■ River Capital Inc.
4200 Northside Pky. N, Bldg. 14, Ste. 250
Atlanta, GA 30327
Ph: (404)873-2166
Co. E-mail: info@river-capital.bwpsites.com
URL: http://river-capital.com
Contact: Jerry D. Wethington, President

Description: Investment Firm provides capital and recapitalization services. **Founded:** 1983.

38812 ■ Seraph Group
W Peachtree St. NW
Atlanta, GA 30309
Linkedin: www.linkedin.com/company/seraph-group

Description: Invests in venture-scalable technology companies at the seed and early stages. **Founded:** 2004.

38813 ■ Small Business Assistance Corporation (SBAC)
111 E Liberty St., Ste. 100
Savannah, GA 31401
Ph: (912)232-4700
Co. E-mail: sbac@sbacsav.com
URL: http://sbacsav.com
Contact: Tony O'Reilly, President
Facebook: www.facebook.com/SBACSAV
Linkedin: www.linkedin.com/company/small-business
-assistance-corporation
Instagram: www.instagram.com/sbacsav
YouTube: www.youtube.com/channel/UC
t4dubxjbnQFc76_d3edNiw

Description: Offers loans and technical assistance for businesses in Southeast Georgia and the Low Country of South Carolina. **Founded:** 1989.

38814 ■ UPS Strategic Enterprise Fund
755 Battery Ave. SE
Atlanta, GA 30339
Free: 800-PIC-KUPS
URL: http://www.ups.com/us/en/Home.page

Description: Firm providing partnerships and investments services. **Preferred Investment Size:** $250,000 to $1,500,000. **Industry Preferences:** Internet specific, computer software and services, other products, computer hardware, communications and media, semiconductors and other electronics.

38815 ■ Vocap Partners (VP)
75 5th St. NW, Ste. 3210
Atlanta, GA 30308
URL: http://vocappartners.com
Contact: Wendy Coya, Chief Financial Officer
Partner
Facebook: www.facebook.com/VocapInvestmentPar
tners
Linkedin: www.linkedin.com/company/vocap-inves
tment-partners
X (Twitter): x.com/vocappartners

Description: Invests in disruptive Series A technology companies. Also operates out of Vero Beach, Florida. **Founded:** 2011. **Investment Policies:** $1,000,000 to $10,000,000 in revenue; large market potential; clear change drivers; software/tech-enabled solution; recurring revenue business model. **Industry Preferences:** Enterprise software; healthcare IT; fintech; marketing technology; data and analytics; media and ecommerce.

PROCUREMENT ASSISTANCE PROGRAMS

38816 ■ Georgia Tech Procurement Assistance Center Albany Office (GTPAC)
230 S Jackson St., Ste. 218
  Albany, GA 31701
Ph: (229)573-7035
URL: http://gtpac.org/directions/albany
Contact: Bridget Bennett, Counselor

Description: Provides marketing and procurement technical assistance to Georgia businesses, large and small, operating in the government procurement markets at the federal, state, and local levels as a prime contractor or subcontractor.

38817 ■ Georgia Tech Procurement Assistance Center Augusta Office (GTPAC)
2907 Professional Pky., Ste. B
  Augusta, GA 30907
URL: http://gtpac.org/directions/augusta

Description: Provides marketing and procurement technical assistance to Georgia businesses, large and small, operating in the government procurement markets at the federal, state, and local levels as a prime contractor or subcontractor.

38818 ■ Georgia Tech Procurement Assistance Center Carrollton Office (GTPAC)
500 Old Bremen Rd.
  Carrollton, GA 30117
URL: http://gtpac.org/directions/carrollton

Description: Provides marketing and procurement technical assistance to Georgia businesses, large and small, operating in the government procurement markets at the federal, state, and local levels as a prime contractor or subcontractor.

38819 ■ Georgia Tech Procurement Assistance Center Columbus Office (GTPAC)
3100 Gentian Blvd., Ste. 115
  Columbus, GA 31907
Ph: (229)430-4189
URL: http://members.napex.us/members/?id=75097764
Contact: Bridget L. Bennett, Contact
E-mail: bridget.bennett@innovate.gatech.edu

Description: Provides marketing and procurement technical assistance to Georgia businesses, large and small, operating in the government procurement markets at the federal, state, and local levels as a prime contractor or subcontractor.

38820 ■ Georgia Tech Procurement Assistance Center (EII) - Enterprise Innovation Institute
151 Osigian Blvd., Ste. 157
  Warner Robins, GA 31088
Ph: (478)953-1460
URL: http://gtpac.org
Contact: Aileen Zoellner, Counselor
E-mail: aileen.zoellner@innovate.gatech.edu

Description: Provides marketing and procurement technical assistance to Georgia businesses, large and small, operating in the government procurement markets at the federal, state, and local levels as a prime contractor or subcontractor. Founded: 1948.

38821 ■ Georgia Tech Procurement Assistance Center Gainesville Office (GTPAC)
3041 Landrum Education Dr. Rm 133
  Gainesville, GA 30504
URL: http://gtpac.org/directions/gainesville

Description: Provides marketing and procurement technical assistance to Georgia businesses, large and small, operating in the government procurement markets at the federal, state, and local levels as a prime contractor or subcontractor.

38822 ■ Georgia Tech Procurement Assistance Center Savannah Office (GTPAC)
210 Technology Cir., Rm. 230
  Savannah, GA 31407-3038
URL: http://pe.gatech.edu/savannah

Description: Provides marketing and procurement technical assistance to Georgia businesses, large and small, operating in the government procurement markets at the federal, state, and local levels as a prime contractor or subcontractor.

INCUBATORS/RESEARCH AND TECHNOLOGY PARKS

38823 ■ 24/7 Shared Kitchen
245 Scenic Hwy.
  Lawrenceville, GA 30046
Ph: (404)484-4588
URL: http://247sharedkitchen.com
Contact: Cornelia Florea, Contact
E-mail: corneliaflorea@yahoo.com

Description: Offers a fully equipped rental kitchen to new entrepreneurs.

38824 ■ Arthur K. Williams Microbusiness Enterprise Center
230 S Jackson St.
  Albany, GA 31701
Ph: (229)483-7650
Co. E-mail: albanymbec@gmail.com
URL: http://asalh.org/venue/arthur-k-williams-micro-business-enterprise-center
Facebook: www.facebook.com/albanymbec
X (Twitter): x.com/albanymbec1
Instagram: www.instagram.com/albanymbec

Description: Provider of resources and facility to stimulate small business formation, growth, and survival.

38825 ■ Augusta University Life Sciences Business Development Center (LSBDC)
1120 15th St.
  Augusta, GA 30912
URL: http://www.augusta.edu/research/oic/biobusiness-incubator.php

Description: A facility that is dedicated to incubating great ideas through innovative startup companies. A bio business incubator designed with a full spectrum of amenities that faculty, staff and student researchers require to commercialize technologies that can change lives.

38826 ■ The Burson Center
500 Old Bremen Rd.
  Carrollton, GA 30117
Ph: (678)890-2333
Co. E-mail: burson@carroll-ga.org
URL: http://bursoncenter.com
Facebook: www.facebook.com/bursoncenter

Description: Research center focuses on the development of information technology and healthcare.

38827 ■ Business Incubator at Breanu University (BIBU)
Featherstone Ctr. 999 Chestnut St.
  Gainesville, GA 30501
Ph: (770)535-9220
Co. E-mail: bibu@brenau.edu
URL: http://www.brenau.edu/incubator
Contact: Matt Thomas, Vice President
E-mail: mthomas@brenau.edu

Description: Works with startups, inventors, and entrepreneurs to develop standalone businesses in Northeast Georgia, Gainesville, and Hall County.

38828 ■ Business Innovation Group (BIG)
Georgia Southern University
  58 E Main St., Ste. D
  Statesboro, GA 30458
Ph: (912)478-0872
Co. E-mail: big@georgiasouthern.edu
URL: http://www.georgiasouthern.edu/research/big/2016/04/01/business-innovation-group-now-accepting-innovation-incubator-applications-for-summer-2016
Contact: Dominique Halaby, Contact
E-mail: dhalaby@georgiasouthern.edu
Facebook: www.facebook.com/GeorgiaSouthernBIG
X (Twitter): x.com/GaSouthernBIG
Instagram: www.instagram.com/gasouthernbig

Description: Provides students and community members with the skills and training needed to successfully launch a new business enterprise.

38829 ■ CollabTech Incubator
c/o Collab Tech Manager
  58 Edgewood Ave. NE, Rm. 113
  Atlanta, GA 30303
Ph: (404)413-3556
URL: http://research.gsu.edu/georgia-state-technology-transfer/collabtech-incubator

Description: A downtown Atlanta business incubator offering collaboration with world-class researchers in a modern and unique working environment. Founded: 2015.

38830 ■ CoreCard Corporation
CoreCard Corporation
  1 Meca Way
  Norcross, GA 30093
Ph: (770)381-2900
Fax: (770)381-2808
Co. E-mail: comments@intelsys.com
URL: http://www.intelsys.com
Contact: J. Leland Strange, President
Linkedin: www.linkedin.com/company/intelligent-systems-corporation

Description: Invests in and provides management resources and investment advice for early stage companies in the financial technology and software industry. Founded: 1973.

38831 ■ Cunningham Enterprise Center at Columbus State University
3100 Gentian Blvd.
  Columbus, GA 31907
Ph: (706)568-5101
Fax: (706)569-2693
URL: http://www.columbusstate.edu/conference-center
Contact: Tammy Whorton, Executive Director
E-mail: whorton_tammy@columbusstate.edu
Facebook: www.facebook.com/CunninghamCenter
X (Twitter): x.com/CunninghamCentr

Description: A non-profit organization dedicated to housing and nurturing new companies by providing the space and the support needed to grow technology-related jobs in the Chattahoochee Valley area.

38832 ■ Georgia BioBusiness Center (GBBC)
220 Riverbend Rd.
  Athens, GA 30602-7411
Ph: (706)542-1214
Fax: (706)542-0995
URL: http://www.uga.edu/a-z/location/gbbc-address.html
Contact: Jere W. Morehead, President
E-mail: president@uga.edu

Description: A small business incubator affiliated with several established and startup bioscience companies with research and technology ties to UGA. The program enables bioscience startup companies to accelerate their early growth through access to management expertise and state-of-the-art instrumentation.

38833 ■ Georgia Hispanic Chamber of Commerce Business Development Center
270 Peachtree St. NW, Ste. 2200
  Atlanta, GA 30303
Ph: (404)929-9998
Co. E-mail: marketing@ghcc.org
URL: http://ghcc.org/en
Contact: Verónica Maldonado-Torres, President
E-mail: veronica@ghcc.org
Facebook: www.facebook.com/ghcc1
Linkedin: www.linkedin.com/company/georgia-hispanic-chamber-of-commerce
X (Twitter): twitter.com/GHCC_news
YouTube: www.youtube.com/channel/UCKaLAjSM2DiCJg1eJHoCk7A

Description: Provider of in-house programming and consultations through the business development center. Founded: 1984.

38834 ■ Georgia Institute of Technology - Advanced Technology Development Center (ATDC)
Tech Sq.
75 5th St. NW Ste. 2000
Atlanta, GA 30308
Ph: (404)894-3575
Fax: (404)894-4545
Co. E-mail: ivy@atdc.org
URL: http://atdc.org
Contact: John Avery, Director
E-mail: john.avery@atdc.org
URL(s): catalog.gatech.edu/academics/research
 -support-facilities/advanced-technology
 -development-center
Facebook: www.facebook.com/atdcgt
Linkedin: www.linkedin.com/company/atdc
X (Twitter): x.com/atdc
Instagram: www.instagram.com/theatdc
YouTube: www.youtube.com/channel/UCX6GcHHK
 2E0_XlcSwkfOdrw
Description: A start-up accelerator helping technology entrepreneurs in Georgia. **Scope:** Promotes the development of advanced technology-based companies throughout Georgia. including firms involved in advanced structural materials, electronic equipment, biotechnology, health and medical products, artificial intelligence, environmental sciences, telecommunications, aerospace systems, instrumentation and test equipment, robotics, and related technologies. **Founded:** 1980. **Publications:** *Technology Partners* (Quarterly).

38835 ■ The Innovation Factory (TIF)
2905 Premier Pky., Ste. 150
Duluth, GA 30097
Free: 888-935-4411
Co. E-mail: info@tif.net
URL: http://www.tif.net
Contact: Anthony V. Lando, Chief Operating Officer
E-mail: alando@tif.net
Description: Acquires novel medical technology ideas from individual inventors, corporations and universities, and develops ideas comprehensively from proof of concept to FDA approval into marketable products, and then launches businesses around those products.

38836 ■ Lawyers for Equal Justice (L4EJ)
2960 Pharr Ct. S Unit N4
Atlanta, GA 30305
Contact: Hulett Askew, Chief Executive Officer
Description: Legal incubator providing the support and training needed to start a successful solo or small firm practice.

38837 ■ MicroBusiness Enterprise Center
230 S Jackson St.
Albany, GA 31701
Ph: (229)483-7650
Fax: (229)430-2737
URL: http://www.albanymbec.biz
Contact: Barbara Francis, Contact
E-mail: bfrancis@albanyga.gov
Facebook: www.facebook.com/albanymbec
X (Twitter): x.com/albanymbec1
Instagram: www.instagram.com/albanymbec
Description: A community resource providing assistance and facilities to create an environment that will stimulate small business formation, growth and survival. **Founded:** 1990.

38838 ■ Prep
3300 Marjan Dr.
Atlanta, GA 30340
Ph: (404)920-4150
Co. E-mail: info@prepatl.com
URL: http://www.prepkitchens.com
Contact: Mitch Jaffe, Chief Executive Officer
E-mail: mitchj@prepatl.com
Facebook: www.facebook.com/PREPKITCHENS
X (Twitter): x.com/PREPKITCHENS
Instagram: www.instagram.com/prepkitchens
YouTube: www.youtube.com/channel/
 UCFrNzgQxkiXNkCjwik50_XQ

Description: Firm provides shared kitchen, dedicated kitchen facility, food trucks and studio kitchen and other related services. **Founded:** 2013.

38839 ■ Southwest Georgia Business Development Center
110 E Union St.
Vienna, GA 31092
URL: http://www.doolychamber.com/member-list
Description: A small business incubator established to create an environment for the development, growth, and success of emerging service and light manufacturing businesses in the southwest region of Georgia.

38840 ■ TechSquare Labs
850 W Peachtree St. NW Unit C-1
Atlanta, GA 30308
Ph: (404)385-7275
Co. E-mail: hello@techsquare.co
URL: http://techsquare.co
Contact: Janet Mulroy, Chief Financial Officer
Description: A coworking space, venture fund, and community supporting tech startups and entrepreneurs.

38841 ■ University of Georgia - Innovation Gateway
110 Terrell Hall
 210 S Jackson St.
Athens, GA 30602
Ph: (706)542-1404
Co. E-mail: gateway@uga.edu
URL: http://research.uga.edu/gateway
Contact: Derek Eberhart, Executive Director
E-mail: dereke@uga.edu
Linkedin: www.linkedin.com/showcase/innovationa
 tuga
X (Twitter): x.com/uga_innovation
Description: Business incubator for startups or early-stage companies that are involved in the research and development of new products and services. **Founded:** 1999.

EDUCATIONAL PROGRAMS

38842 ■ Berry College Entrepreneurial Program
2277 Martha Berry Hwy. NW, Green 420
 Mount Berry, GA 30149
Ph: (706)378-2854
Co. E-mail: cseed@berry.edu
URL: http://www.berry.edu/c-seed/entrepreneurship
Description: Supports current and former students to contribute in meaningful ways in their communities. Offers entrepreneurship classes to facilitate knowledge as students begin their business startups.

38843 ■ East Georgia State College (EGSC)
131 College Cir.
Swainsboro, GA 30401
Ph: (478)289-2000
Co. E-mail: ask_egsc@ega.edu
URL: http://www.ega.edu
Contact: Dr. David Schecter, President
Facebook: www.facebook.com/EastGeorgiaSta
 teCollege
X (Twitter): x.com/EastGaCollege
YouTube: www.youtube.com/user/EastGaCollege
Description: Offers several associate's degree and targeted bachelor's degree courses. **Founded:** 1971.

38844 ■ Georgia Highlands College - Floyd Campus (GHC)
3175 Cedartown Hwy.
 Rome, GA 30161
Ph: (706)802-5000
Fax: (706)295-6341
URL: http://www.highlands.edu/campus-locations/floy
 d-campus
Contact: Brad Gilmore, Manager
E-mail: bgilmore@highlands.edu
Description: College in Georgia that serves the northwestern parts of the state. **Founded:** 1970.

38845 ■ University of West Georgia (UWG) - Richards College of Business
1601 Maple St.
 Carrollton, GA 30118
Ph: (678)839-6467
Co. E-mail: business@westga.edu
URL: http://www.westga.edu/business
Facebook: www.facebook.com/RichardsCollege
Linkedin: www.linkedin.com/company/richards
 -college-of-business
Description: Presents business-related courses, seminars, and workshops to persons interested in professional and staff development. Also provides counseling, databases, and case studies to those interested in starting or building a small business. **Founded:** 1967.

LEGISLATIVE ASSISTANCE

38846 ■ Georgia House of Representatives
c/o David Ralston, Speaker of the House,332 State
 Capitol
Atlanta, GA 30334
Ph: (404)656-5020
Fax: (404)656-5644
Co. E-mail: david.ralston@house.ga.gov
URL: http://www.legis.ga.gov/house
Contact: Spiro Amburn, Chief of Staff
E-mail: spiro.amburn@house.ga.gov
Description: Provides information on Georgia's elected house members, pending legislation, and historical information.

CONSULTANTS

38847 ■ Flashpoint (FP)
828 W Peachtree St., NW
Atlanta, GA 30308
Co. E-mail: info@flashpointgt.com
URL: http://flashpoint.co
Contact: Dr. Merrick Furst, Director
Facebook: www.facebook.com/FlashpointGT
X (Twitter): x.com/FlashpointGT
Description: Unique program helps founders manage and accelerate their startups.

38848 ■ JDC Consultancy
6175 Hickory Flat Hwy., Ste. 110-264
 Canton, GA 30115
Ph: (678)367-3794
Co. E-mail: email@jdcconsultancy.com
URL: http://jdcconsultancy.com
Contact: Jason Coles, President
Facebook: www.facebook.com/jdcconsultancy
Description: Assists with immigration business plans for entrepreneurs interested in a business visa to live and work in the United States.

PUBLICATIONS

38849 ■ Atlanta Business Chronicle (ABC)
3384 Peachtree Rd. ste. 900
Atlanta, GA 30326
URL: http://www.bizjournals.com/atlanta
Contact: David Rubinger, President
E-mail: drubinger@bizjournals.com
Facebook: www.facebook.com/atlbizchron
Linkedin: www.linkedin.com/company/atlanta
 -business-chronicle
X (Twitter): x.com/AtlBizChron
Instagram: www.instagram.com/atlbizchron
Description: Publisher of newspapers covering news, business, sports. **Founded:** 1978. **Publications:** *Atlanta Business Chronicle* (Weekly).

38850 ■ The Atlanta Small Business Monthly

38851 ■ Savannah Business Journal
2 E Bryan St., Ste., 400
Savannah, GA 31401
URL: http://coastalempirenews.com
Contact: Louise D. Phelps, Owner Publisher
URL(s): www.savannahbusinessjournal.com/site/con
 tact.html
X (Twitter): x.com/SavBusiness

Ed: Donald R. Blum. **Released:** 9/year **Price:** $25, for 1 year; $3, for 1 month; $1, for 1 day. **Description:** Business journal with a focus on Savannah, Georgia. **Availability:** Print; Online.

PUBLISHERS

38852 ■ Franklin-Sarrett Publishers L.L.C. (FSP)
3761 Vineyard Trace, NE
 Marietta, GA 30062-5227
Ph: (770)578-9410
Co. E-mail: info@franklin-sarrett.com
URL: http://www.franklin-sarrett.com
Contact: Kay Borden, Contact
Description: Publisher of Newspapers and magazines. **Founded:** 1992.

RESEARCH CENTERS

38853 ■ Georgia Southwestern State University School of Business Administration - Center for Business and Economic Development (CBED)
800 GSW State University Dr.
 Americus, GA 31709
URL: http://www.gsw.edu/foundation/giving-opportunities/fund-summary
Contact: Dr. Gaynor Cheokas, Dean Professor
E-mail: gaynor.cheokas@gsw.edu

Description: Integral unit of School of Business Administration, Georgia Southwestern State University. **Scope:** Business and economics. **Publications:** *Journal of Applied Financial Research*.

38854 ■ Valdosta State University College of Business Administration - Center for Business and Economic Research (CBER)
1500 N Patterson St.
 Valdosta, GA 31698
Ph: (229)333-7878
Fax: (229)259-5504
URL: http://www.valdosta.edu/colleges/business/business-and-economic-research
Contact: Mike Beverly, Director
E-mail: hmbeverly@valdosta.edu
Description: Integral unit of College of Business Administration, Valdosta State University. **Scope:** Business and economic research, focusing on regional economic and business development issues. **Publications:** *Cost of Living Index Reports* (Quarterly); *South Georgia Business Outlook* (Quarterly).

VENTURE CAPITAL FIRM

38855 ■ Kugarand Capital Holdings
108 Brookwood Path, Ste. 200
 Peachtree City, GA 30269
Contact: Karen Rands, Contact
Description: Venture capital firm. **Industry Preferences:** High tech; biomed/science; B2C; B2B.

38856 ■ TechOperators LLC
1 Buckhead Plz.
 3060 Peachtree Rd. NW, Ste. 720
 Atlanta, GA 30305
Ph: (404)537-2525
Co. E-mail: info@techoperators.com
URL: http://www.techoperators.com
Contact: Bill Jones, Vice President
E-mail: bill.jones@techoperators.com
Linkedin: www.linkedin.com/company/techoperators-llc
X (Twitter): x.com/techoperators
Description: Venture capital firm for emerging software companies. **Founded:** 2008. **Preferred Investment Size:** $2,000,000 to $4,000,0000. **Investment Policies:** Emerging growth-stage companies with high growth potential and defensible positions in large and growing markets.

38857 ■ TTV Capital
1230 Peachtree St. NE, Ste. 1150
 Atlanta, GA 30309
Ph: (404)347-8400
Co. E-mail: info@ttvcapital.com
URL: http://ttvcapital.com
Contact: Krista Gammon, Director
Linkedin: www.linkedin.com/company/ttv-capital
Description: Venture capital firm focused on fintech companies. **Founded:** 2000. **Industry Preferences:** Banking; data analytics; security.

Hawaii

ASSOCIATIONS AND OTHER ORGANIZATIONS

38858 ■ Association of Fundraising Professionals Aloha Chapter
PO Box 11899
Honolulu, HI 96828-0899
Ph: (808)527-2426
Co. E-mail: office@afphawaii.org
URL: http://community.afpglobal.org/afphialohachapter
Contact: Angela Britten, Treasurer
E-mail: nominations@afphawaii.org
Facebook: www.facebook.com/afphawaii
Linkedin: www.linkedin.com/company/afphawaii
X (Twitter): x.com/afphawaii
Description: Professional association for individuals on Oahu, Maui, Kauai, and the Big Island who are involved in non-profit development, non-profit management, and fundraising consulting. **Founded:** 1983. **Geographic Preference:** State.

38859 ■ Business Network International Hawaii
3430 Toringdon Way
Charlotte, NC 28277
Free: 855-264-2673
URL: http://www.bnihawaii.com
Contact: Benjamin Tabios, Managing Director
E-mail: benjamintabios@bni.com
Facebook: www.facebook.com/BNIHawaii
Description: Provides both men and women a structured environment for the development and exchange of quality business referrals. Offers members the opportunity to share ideas and contacts. **Geographic Preference:** State.

38860 ■ Entrepreneurs Foundation of Hawaii (EFH)
2800 Woodlawn Dr., Ste. 265
Honolulu, HI 96822
URL: http://www.efhawaii.org
Contact: John Dean, Sr., Chairman of the Board
X (Twitter): x.com/EFHawaii
Description: Encourages philanthropic work within corporate communities. Provides volunteer day programs, training for nonprofit board service, and seminars on corporate social responsibility and philanthropy to boost employee involvement. Offers resources, consulting services, and strategic and practical support to assist companies in establishing a culture of philanthropy and community participation. **Founded:** 2005. **Geographic Preference:** State.

38861 ■ International Association of Women Honolulu Chapter
PO Box 2295
Honolulu, HI 96804-2295
Co. E-mail: ewihonoluluchapter@gmail.com
URL: http://www.ewihonolulu.org
Contact: Jenni Liu, President
Facebook: www.facebook.com/ewihonolulu
X (Twitter): x.com/EWIHonolulu
Description: Serves as a network for businesswomen to promote their service or product.

SMALL BUSINESS DEVELOPMENT CENTERS

38862 ■ Hawaii SBDc - O'ahu
677 Ala Moana Blvd., Ste. 612
Honolulu, HI 96813
Ph: (808)945-1430
Fax: (808)945-1432
URL: http://www.hisbdc.org/locations/oahu
Contact: Joseph Burns, Associate Director
E-mail: joseph.burns@hisbdc.org
X (Twitter): x.com/HawaiiSBDC
Description: Represents and promotes the small business sector. Provides management assistance to current and prospective small business owners. Helps to improve management skills and expand the products and services of members. **Founded:** 1990. **Geographic Preference:** Local.

38863 ■ Hawaii Small Business Development Center Lead Office
677 Ala Moana Blvd., Ste. 612
Honolulu, HI 96813
Ph: (808)974-1430
URL: http://www.hisbdc.org
Contact: Joseph Burns, Director
Description: Represents and promotes the small business sector. Provides management assistance to current and prospective small business owners. Helps to improve management skills and expand the products and services of members. **Founded:** 1990. **Geographic Preference:** State.

38864 ■ Kaua'i Small Business Development Center
2970 Kele St., Ste. 101
Lihue, HI 96766
Ph: (808)241-3148
Fax: (808)241-3229
URL: http://hisbdc.org/locations/kauai
Contact: Robbie Melton, Director
E-mail: robbie.melton@hisbdc.org
Description: Represents and promotes the small business sector. Provides management assistance to current and prospective small business owners. Helps to improve management skills and expand the products and services of members. **Founded:** 1990. **Geographic Preference:** Local.

38865 ■ Maui Small Business Development Center
590 Lipoa Pky., Ste. 264
Kihei, HI 96753
Ph: (808)875-5990
Fax: (808)875-5989
URL: http://hisbdc.org/Locations/Maui.aspx
Contact: Wayne Wong, Director
E-mail: wayne.wong@hisbdc.org
Facebook: www.facebook.com/SBDC.Maui.HBRL
Description: Represents and promotes the small business sector. Provides management assistance to current and prospective small business owners. Helps to improve management skills and expand the products and services of members. **Founded:** 1990. **Geographic Preference:** Local.

SMALL BUSINESS ASSISTANCE PROGRAMS

38866 ■ Chamber of Commerce Hawaii (COCHi)
733 Bishop St., Makai Twr. Ste., 1200
Honolulu, HI 96813
Ph: (808)545-4300
Fax: (808)545-4369
Co. E-mail: info@cochawaii.org
URL: http://www.cochawaii.org
Contact: Sherry Menor-McNamara, President
E-mail: sherrymenor-mcnamara@cochawaii.org
Facebook: www.facebook.com/ChamberOfCommerceHawaii
Linkedin: www.linkedin.com/company/the-chamber-of-commerce-of-hawaii
X (Twitter): x.com/cochawaii
Instagram: www.instagram.com/cochawaii
YouTube: www.youtube.com/channel/UCLrevhdWIwMYUY8ijEsJZkQ
Description: Offers business referrals, financial planning, loan packaging, and business, marketing, and entrepreneurship counseling. **Founded:** 1850. **Publications:** *Chamber of Commerce of Hawaii--Business Networking Member Directory* (Annual); *Who's Who in Government in Hawaii* (Biennial); *Business Networking Directory*. **Geographic Preference:** State.

38867 ■ Hawaii Department of Business, Economic Development and Tourism - Strategic Marketing & Support
No. 1 Capitol District Bldg.
250 S Hotel St.
Honolulu, HI 96813
Ph: (808)586-2355
Co. E-mail: dbedt.director@hawaii.gov
URL: http://dbedt.hawaii.gov
Contact: Luis P. Salaveria, Director
Facebook: www.facebook.com/DBEDT.HIgov
Instagram: www.instagram.com/dbedthigov
YouTube: www.youtube.com/channel/UC0Hoj9WILVmKobM6FG5Uz3g/videos
Description: Promotes new enterprise development in Hawaii from the U.S. mainland and international business centers.

SCORE OFFICES

38868 ■ SCORE - Hawaii
500 Ala Moana Blvd., Ste. 1-306A
Honolulu, HI 96813
Ph: (808)547-2700
Fax: (808)547-2728
Co. E-mail: scorehawaii@scorevolunteer.org

URL: http://hawaii.score.org
Contact: Kunio Hasebe, Director
Facebook: www.facebook.com/scorehawaiimentors
Instagram: www.instagram.com/scorehawaii
Description: Creates opportunities for small business owners and potential business owners to achieve success. Provides business assistance to develop business plans, stimulate business growth and identify problems and potential solutions. Promotes entrepreneur education in Hawaii. **Geographic Preference:** State.

38869 ■ SCORE - Maui County
110 'ala'ihi St., Ste. 209
Kahului, HI 96732
Ph: (808)879-5389
Fax: (808)875-4616
Co. E-mail: help@score.org
URL: http://maui.score.org
Contact: Bridget Weston, Chief Executive Officer
Description: Provides professional guidance and information to maximize the success of existing and emerging small businesses. Offers business counseling and workshops.

BETTER BUSINESS BUREAUS

38870 ■ Better Business Bureau Great West + Pacific [BBB Great West + Pacific]
PO Box 191279
Boise, ID 83719
Ph: (208)342-4649
URL: http://www.bbb.org/local-bbb/bbb-great-west-pacific
Linkedin: www.linkedin.com/company/bbbgwp
Instagram: www.instagram.com/bbbgwp
YouTube: www.youtube.com/bbbgwp
Description: Seeks to promote and foster the highest ethical relationship between businesses and the public through voluntary self-regulation, consumer and business education, and service excellence. Provides information to help consumers and businesses make informed purchasing decisions and avoid costly scams and frauds; settles consumer complaints through arbitration and other means. **Geographic Preference:** State.

CHAMBERS OF COMMERCE

38871 ■ Chamber of Commerce Hawaii (COCHi)
733 Bishop St., Makai Twr. Ste., 1200
Honolulu, HI 96813
Ph: (808)545-4300
Fax: (808)545-4369
Co. E-mail: info@cochawaii.org
URL: http://www.cochawaii.org
Contact: Sherry Menor-McNamara, President
E-mail: sherrymenor-mcnamara@cochawaii.org
Facebook: www.facebook.com/ChamberOfCommerceHawaii
Linkedin: www.linkedin.com/company/the-chamber-of-commerce-of-hawaii
X (Twitter): x.com/cochawaii
Instagram: www.instagram.com/cochawaii
YouTube: www.youtube.com/channel/UCLrevhdWlwMYUY8ijEsJZkQ
Description: Offers business referrals, financial planning, loan packaging, and business, marketing, and entrepreneurship counseling. **Founded:** 1850. **Publications:** Chamber of Commerce of Hawaii--Business Networking Member Directory (Annual); Who's Who in Government in Hawaii (Biennial); Business Networking Directory. **Geographic Preference:** State.

38872 ■ Hawaii Island Chamber of Commerce (HICC)
1321 Kinoole St.
Hilo, HI 96720
Ph: (808)935-7178
Co. E-mail: admin@hicc.biz
URL: http://www.hicc.biz
Contact: Miles Yoshioka, Executive Officer
E-mail: miles.yoshioka@hicc.biz

Facebook: www.facebook.com/HawaiiIslandChamberofCommerce
Linkedin: www.linkedin.com/company/hawaii-island-chamber-of-commerce
YouTube: www.youtube.com/channel/UCl958kA2mtl4GK1cdr0fAbA
Description: Business and professional people in the community who work together to make Hawaii Island a better place to live and do business. Provides leadership via services and advocacy for the business community and to promote the economic well-being of the community as a whole. **Founded:** 1898. **Publications:** The Chamber Connection; The Hawaii Island Chamber of Commerce Directory & Guide (Annual). **Awards:** Hawaii Island Chamber of Commerce ATHENA Award (Annual). **Geographic Preference:** Local.

38873 ■ Hawaii Island Portuguese Chamber of Commerce (HIPCC)
PO Box 1839
Hilo, HI 96720
Co. E-mail: hawaiiportuguesechamber@gmail.com
URL: http://hipcc.org
Contact: Marlene Hapai, President
Facebook: www.facebook.com/HIPCC
Instagram: www.instagram.com/hiportuguesechamber
Description: Promotes commerce, industry, and agriculture throughout the County and State of Hawaii. **Founded:** 1982. **Awards:** HIPCC Scholarships (Annual). **Geographic Preference:** State.

38874 ■ Hawaii Korean Chamber of Commerce (HKCC)
PO Box 2296
Honolulu, HI 96804
Ph: (808)544-3581
URL: http://www.hawaiikoreanchamber.org
Contact: Gina Kim Nakamura, Vice President
E-mail: gina.nakamura@centralpacificbank.com
Description: Strives to fulfill the goals and purposes of supporting the Korean people and its business community. **Founded:** 1940. **Awards:** HKCC Scholarship Award (Annual). **Geographic Preference:** Local.

38875 ■ Honolulu Japanese Chamber of Commerce (HJCC)
2454 S Beretania St., Ste. 201
Honolulu, HI 96826
Ph: (808)949-5531
Fax: (808)949-3020
URL: http://www.hjcc.org
Contact: Steve Teruya, President
Facebook: www.facebook.com/HonoluluJapaneseChamber
Instagram: www.instagram.com/hjcc808
Description: Represents business owners in Hawaii. Promotes trade between the U.S. and Japan. **Founded:** 1900. **Publications:** Shoko Newsletter (Monthly); Honolulu Japanese Chamber of Commerce--Membership Directory. **Awards:** HJCC Charitable Corporation Scholarship Fund (Annual). **Geographic Preference:** National; Local.

38876 ■ Honolulu Japanese Junior Chamber of Commerce (HJJCC)
PO Box 1105
Aiea, HI 96701
Co. E-mail: info@hjjcc.com
URL: http://www.hjjcc.com
Contact: Kari Kiyota, President
Facebook: www.facebook.com/hjjcc
X (Twitter): x.com/HonJapaneseJC
Description: Aims to provide young people of Honolulu a medium for leadership training and civic improvement. **Founded:** 1949. **Publications:** SHOKO. **Geographic Preference:** Local.

38877 ■ Kailua Chamber of Commerce (KCOC)
PO Box 1496
Kailua, HI 96734
Ph: (808)261-2727
Co. E-mail: info@kailuachamber.com
URL: http://www.kailuachamber.com

Contact: Michael Fry, President
Facebook: www.facebook.com/kailuachamberofcommerce
Instagram: www.instagram.com/kailua_chamber
Description: Promotes Kailua as a community, and supports members and businesses individually and collectively. **Founded:** 1957. **Geographic Preference:** Local.

38878 ■ Kauai Chamber of Commerce (KCC)
4268 Rice St.
Lihue, HI 96766
Ph: (808)245-7363
Co. E-mail: info@kauaichamber.org
URL: http://www.kauaichamber.org
Contact: Mark Perriello, President
E-mail: mark@kauaichamber.org
Facebook: www.facebook.com/KauaiChamber
X (Twitter): x.com/kauaichamber
Instagram: www.instagram.com/kauaichamber
Description: Businesses and professional men and women. Represents all elements of Kauai's business and industry. Works to advance the commercial, financial, industrial, civic and social well-being of the county of Kaua'i and the state of Hawaii. **Founded:** 1913. **Publications:** Update (Monthly); Kauai Chamber of Commerce--Community Guide & Business Directory. **Geographic Preference:** Local.

38879 ■ Kona Kohala Chamber of Commerce (KKCC)
75-5737 Kaukini Hwy., Ste. 208
Kailua Kona, HI 96740
Ph: (808)329-1758
Co. E-mail: info@kona-kohala.com
URL: http://www.kona-kohala.com
Contact: Wendy J. Laros, President
X (Twitter): x.com/KKCCChat
Description: Promotes business and community development in West Hawaii. **Founded:** 1968. **Educational Activities:** Membership Meeting (Annual). **Geographic Preference:** Local.

38880 ■ Maui Chamber of Commerce
62 N Market St., Ste. 302
Wailuku, HI 96793
Ph: (808)224-0081
Fax: (808)244-0083
Co. E-mail: office@mauichamber.com
URL: http://www.mauichamber.com
Contact: Pamela Tumpap, President
Facebook: www.facebook.com/maui.chamber
X (Twitter): x.com/MauiChamber
Instagram: www.instagram.com/mauichamber
Description: Promotes a healthy economic environment for business. Advocates responsive government and quality education, while preserving the unique community characteristics of Maui. Supports civic, social, and cultural programs designed to increase the functional and aesthetic values of the community. **Founded:** 1910. **Publications:** Reasons to Believe (Bimonthly). **Geographic Preference:** Local.

38881 ■ Moloka'i Chamber of Commerce
PO Box 515
Kaunakakai, HI 96748
Ph: (808)658-0608
Co. E-mail: info@molokaichamber.org
URL: http://molokaichamber.org
Contact: Robert Stephenson, President
Facebook: www.facebook.com/molokaichamber
X (Twitter): x.com/molokaichamber
Description: Promotes business and community development in the Moloka'i area. **Geographic Preference:** Local.

38882 ■ Native Hawaiian Chamber of Commerce (NHCC)
PO Box 597
Honolulu, HI 96809
Ph: (808)369-1470
Co. E-mail: nhccoahu@gmail.com
URL: http://www.nativehawaiianchamberofcommerce.org
Contact: Timmy Wailehua, President

Facebook: www.facebook.com/Na
 tiveHawaiianChamberOfCommerce
Linkedin: www.linkedin.com/company/native
 -hawaiian-chamber-of-commerce
Description: Participates in economic, social, and public affairs in Hawaiian community. **Founded:** 1974. **Publications:** *The Voice of Hawaiian Business* (Monthly). **Geographic Preference:** State.

MINORITY BUSINESS ASSISTANCE PROGRAMS

38883 ▪ Honolulu Minority Business Enterprise Center
University of Hawaii, Shidler College of Business
 2404 Maile Way A414b
 Honolulu, HI 96822
Ph: (808)956-0850
Fax: (808)956-0851
Co. E-mail: info@honolulumbdacenter.com
URL: http://hawaiimbda.com
Contact: Chris Rachal, Program Director
E-mail: crachal@honolulumbdacenter.com
URL(s): www.mbda.gov/business-center/hawaii-mb
 da-business-center
Facebook: www.facebook.com/HawaiiMBDA
Description: Established to increase the number of minority-owned businesses and strengthen existing ones.

FINANCING AND LOAN PROGRAMS

38884 ▪ XLR8HI
900 Fort St. Mall
 Honolulu, HI 96813
Co. E-mail: aloha@xlr8hi.com
URL: http://xlr8hi.com
Contact: Tarik Sultan, Member
Facebook: www.facebook.com/Xlr8hi
Linkedin: www.linkedin.com/company/xlr8hi
X (Twitter): x.com/xlr8hi
Instagram: www.instagram.com/xlr8_hi
Description: Promotes a culture of innovation and inclusion in Hawaii's startup community. Offers workspace, workshops, and speakers series. **Founded:** 2012.

INCUBATORS/RESEARCH AND TECHNOLOGY PARKS

38885 ▪ Blue Startups
55 Merchant St., Ste. 1700
 Honolulu, HI 96813
Ph: (808)954-6180
Co. E-mail: info@bluestartups.com
URL: http://www.bluestartups.com
Contact: Chenoa Farnsworth, Managing Partner
 Co-Founder
Facebook: www.facebook.com/BlueStartups
X (Twitter): x.com/BlueStartups
YouTube: www.youtube.com/channel/UC35BGT
 tXaHjk82nY5ZnXUAQ
Description: Focused on helping technology companies compete on a global scale. **Founded:** 2012.

38886 ▪ GoFarm Hawaii
3050 Maile Way, Gilmore 115
 Honolulu, HI 96828-0270
Free: 800-956-3530
Co. E-mail: info@gofarmhawaii.org
URL: http://gofarmhawaii.org
Contact: Janel Yamamoto, Program Director
Facebook: www.facebook.com/gofarm.hawaii
X (Twitter): x.com/gofarmhawaii
Instagram: www.instagram.com/gofarmhawaii
YouTube: www.youtube.com/gofarmhawaii

Description: A small business incubator providing business consulting services to agriculture-related businesses throughout the State of Hawaii, maximizing their chance of business viability and success, in order to grow the State's diversified agriculture industry.

38887 ▪ Hana Kitchens (HK)
55 Merchant St., Ste. 20
 Honolulu, HI 96813
Ph: (808)888-8886
Co. E-mail: info@hanakitchens.com
URL: http://www.hanakitchens.com
Facebook: www.facebook.com/HanaKitchensHawaii
X (Twitter): x.com/hanakitchens
Instagram: www.instagram.com/hanakitchens_hawaii
Description: Offers commercial kitchen space for rent to entrepreneurs in the food industry both start up and established businesses.

38888 ▪ Hawaii Technology Development Corporation (HDTC)
521 Ala Moana Blvd., Ste. 255
 Honolulu, HI 96813
Ph: (808)539-3806
Fax: (808)539-3795
Co. E-mail: info@htdc.org
URL: http://www.htdc.org
Contact: Sandra Fujiyama, Executive Director
Facebook: www.facebook.com/htdcorg
X (Twitter): x.com/HTDCorg
Instagram: www.instagram.com/htdcorg
Description: Facilitates the development and growth of Hawaii's commercial high technology industry. HTDC has multiple incubation centers throughout the islands, where companies have access to advanced connectivity, state-of-the-art facilities, and shared support services. **Founded:** 1983. **Publications:** *Hawaii High Technology Business Directory*.

38889 ▪ Manoa Innovation Center (MIC)
2800 Woodlawn Dr.
 Honolulu, HI 96822
URL: http://research.hawaii.edu/manoa-innovation
 -center
Contact: Paul Yee, Contact
E-mail: pyee@chaneybrooks.com
Description: The MIC is a high technology small business incubator that forges ties between entrepreneurs and university-oriented research and development.

38890 ▪ Maui Research and Technology Center (MRTC)
590 Lipoa Pky.
 Kihei, HI 96753
Ph: (808)875-5978
Co. E-mail: mrtc@htdc.org
Facebook: www.facebook.com/
 MauiResearchTechCenter
Description: State agency. Accelerates Hawaii's technology industry by offering capital, building infrastructure, and developing talent to foster innovation. Affiliated with the Department of Business, Economic Development and Tourism (DBEDT). **Founded:** 1983.

38891 ▪ Nalukai Foundation
67-1185 Mamalahoa Hwy., Ste. D-104, PMB: 165
 Kamuela, HI 96743
Ph: (808)657-4309
Co. E-mail: aloha@nalukai.org
URL: http://nalukai.org
Contact: David Clarke, Executive Director
E-mail: david@nalukai.org
Facebook: www.facebook.com/nalukaifoundation
Description: Offers a startup camp that brings together a group of Hawaii's most ambitious and inquisitive students to give them tools and skills to be successful entrepreneurs.

LEGISLATIVE ASSISTANCE

38892 ▪ Hawaii State Legislature - House Committee on Labor & Public Employment
415 S Beretania St.
 Honolulu, HI 96813
URL: http://www.capitol.hawaii.gov/committeepage
 .aspx?comm=LAB&year=2018
Contact: Aaron Ling Johanson, Chairman
E-mail: repjohanson@capitol.hawaii.gov
Description: Works on programs relating to employment, government operations and efficiency, employee pay and benefits, employee recruitment, classification and training, career development, employee performance, and employment conditions.

38893 ▪ Hawaii State Legislature - Senate Committee on Commerce, Consumer Protection, and Health
c/o Rosalyn H. Baker, Chairman
 Vice Chairman
 Senate District 6
 Hawaii State Capitol, Rm. 230
 Honolulu, HI 96813
Ph: (808)586-6070
Fax: (808)586-6071
Co. E-mail: senbaker@capitol.hawaii.gov
URL: http://www.capitol.hawaii.gov/committeepage
 .aspx?comm=CPH&year=2016
Contact: Rosalyn H. Baker, Chairman Vice Chairman of the Board
E-mail: senbaker@capitol.hawaii.gov
Description: Focuses on programs relating to business regulation, professional and vocational licensing, consumer protection, financial institutions, insurance regulation, public utility regulation, and telecommunications regulation.

38894 ▪ Hawaii State Legislature - Senate Committee on Water, Land, and Agriculture
c/o Mike Gabbard, Chairperson
 Senate District 20
 Hawaii State Capitol, Rm. 201
 Honolulu, HI 96813
Ph: (808)586-6830
Fax: (808)586-6679
Co. E-mail: sengabbard@capitol.hawaii.gov
URL: http://www.capitol.hawaii.gov/legislature/commi
 tteepage.aspx?comm=WLA&year=2016
Contact: Mike Gabbard, Chairman of the Board
E-mail: sengabbard@capitol.hawaii.gov
URL(s): www.capitol.hawaii.gov/memberpage.aspx
 ?member=gabbard; www.capitol.hawaii.gov/legisla
 ture/legislators.aspx
Description: Promotes programs relating to state planning, sustainability, land and water management, forest management and reserve, coastal zone management, land reclamation, naturally occurring fisheries, and ocean resource.

TRADE SHOWS AND CONVENTIONS

38895 ▪ Hawaii Buildings, Facilities, and Property Management Expo
Frequency: Annual. **Description:** Tradeshow featuring products and services geared towards the operation, renovation, maintenance, and sustainability needs of buildings on the islands of Hawaii. Seminars are also presented. **Principal Exhibits:** Tradeshow featuring products and services geared towards the operation, renovation, maintenance, and sustainability needs of buildings on the islands of Hawaii. Seminars are also presented.

PUBLICATIONS

38896 ▪ *Hawaii Business*
1000 Bishop St., Ste. 202
 Honolulu, HI 96813

Ph: (808)534-7555
Co. E-mail: info@aiohawaii.com
URL: http://www.aiohawaii.com
Contact: Duane Kurisu, Founder Chairman
URL(s): www.hawaiibusiness.com
Facebook: www.facebook.com/hawaiibusiness
Linkedin: www.linkedin.com/company/hawaii
 -business-magazine
X (Twitter): x.com/hawaiibusiness
Instagram: www.instagram.com/
 hawaiibusinessmagazine

Released: Monthly **Price:** $24.99, Individuals for 1 year. **Description:** Covers the major issues affecting the state's businesses, and provides useful information to owners and managers. **Availability:** Print; Online.

EARLY STAGE FINANCING

38897 ■ Hawaii Angels
335 Merchant St., No. 516
 Honolulu, HI 96813
Co. E-mail: info@hawaiiangels.org
URL: http://www.hawaiiangels.org
Contact: Robert J. Robinson, Founder

Description: Investment network for seed-level private equity investors. **Founded:** 2002. **Investment Policies:** Strong teams, proprietary technology, and large potential markets.

Idaho

SMALL BUSINESS DEVELOPMENT CENTERS

38898 ■ College of Southern Idaho Small Business Development Center
315 Falls Ave.
Twin Falls, ID 83303-1238
Ph: (208)732-6450
Co. E-mail: isbdc@csi.edu
URL: http://www.csi.edu/isbdc
Contact: Dean Fisher, President
URL(s): idahosbdc.org
Facebook: www.facebook.com/idahosbdc
Linkedin: www.linkedin.com/company/idaho-sbdc
X (Twitter): x.com/IdahoSBDC
YouTube: www.youtube.com/channel/UCo87FNsl0 3UxUigC0Lhlznw
Description: Represents and promotes the small business sector. Provides management assistance to current and prospective small business owners. Helps to improve management skills and expand the products and services of members. **Founded:** 1986. **Geographic Preference:** Local.

38899 ■ Idaho Small Business Development Center State Office (SBDC)
2360 W University Dr., Ste. 2132
Boise, ID 83725
Ph: (208)426-2034
Fax: (208)426-3877
Co. E-mail: dougcovey@boisestate.edu
URL: http://idahosbdc.org
Contact: Doug Covey, Director
E-mail: dougcovey@boisestate.edu
Facebook: www.facebook.com/Idaho.SBDC.State
Linkedin: www.linkedin.com/company/idaho-sbdc
X (Twitter): x.com/IdahoSBDC
Instagram: www.instagram.com/idaho_sbdc
YouTube: www.youtube.com/channel/UCo87FNsl0 3UxUigC0Lhlznw
Founded: 1986. **Publications:** *Your Idaho Business Plan*. **Geographic Preference:** State.

SMALL BUSINESS ASSISTANCE PROGRAMS

38900 ■ University of Idaho Office of Economic Development (ORED)
875 Perimeter Dr.
Moscow, ID 83844-3003
Ph: (208)885-6689
URL: http://www.uidaho.edu/research/business/economic-development
Contact: Jeremy Tamsen, Contact
E-mail: tamsen@uidaho.edu
Description: Connects businesses, industries, non-profits and communities to support the expansion of local businesses.

SCORE OFFICES

38901 ■ SCORE - Boise Public Library
380 E Parkcenter Blvd., Ste. 330
Boise, ID 83706
URL: http://www.score.org/treasurevalley/content/resource-partners-treasure-valley-score
URL(s): www.boisepubliclibrary.org
Description: Provides professional guidance and information to maximize the success of existing and emerging small businesses. Offers business counseling and workshops.

38902 ■ SCORE - Eastern Idaho
2300 N Yellowstone Hwy., Ste. 100
Idaho Falls, ID 83401
Ph: (208)360-2094
Fax: (208)528-7127
Co. E-mail: help@score.org
URL: http://easternidaho.score.org
Contact: Bridget Weston, Chief Executive Officer
Description: Provides professional guidance and information to maximize the success of existing and emerging small businesses. Offers business counseling and workshops. **Founded:** 1985. **Geographic Preference:** Local.

38903 ■ SCORE - Treasure Valley
380 E Parkcenter Blvd., No. 330
Boise, ID 83706
Ph: (208)509-5301
URL: http://www.score.org/treasurevalley
Contact: Tom N. French, Contact
Linkedin: www.linkedin.com/company/score-mentors-treasure-valley
X (Twitter): x.com/SCOREMentors
YouTube: www.youtube.com/channel/UCJFjfyCS-ncNa3pXgnrjEpw
Description: Provides professional guidance and information to maximize the success of existing and emerging small businesses. Offers business counseling and workshops. **Founded:** 1964. **Geographic Preference:** Local.

BETTER BUSINESS BUREAUS

38904 ■ Better Business Bureau Great West + Pacific [BBB Great West + Pacific]
PO Box 191279
Boise, ID 83719
Ph: (208)342-4649
URL: http://www.bbb.org/local-bbb/bbb-great-west-pacific
Linkedin: www.linkedin.com/company/bbbgwp
Instagram: www.instagram.com/bbbgwp
YouTube: www.youtube.com/bbbgwp
Description: Seeks to promote and foster the highest ethical relationship between businesses and the public through voluntary self-regulation, consumer and business education, and service excellence. Provides information to help consumers and businesses make informed purchasing decisions and avoid costly scams and frauds; settles consumer complaints through arbitration and other means. **Geographic Preference:** State.

CHAMBERS OF COMMERCE

38905 ■ Bayview Chamber of Commerce
PO Box 121
Bayview, ID 83803
Ph: (208)683-8040
URL: http://bayviewidaho.org
Contact: Marsha Ritzheimer, President
E-mail: peteritz@frontier.com
Description: Promotes business, community development, and tourism in Bayview, ID. Sponsors Bayview Days and July 4th Festival. **Founded:** 1958. **Geographic Preference:** Local.

38906 ■ Boise Metro Chamber of Commerce (BMCC)
1101 W Front St., Ste. 100
Boise, ID 83702
Ph: (208)472-5205
Co. E-mail: info@boisechamber.org
URL: http://www.boisechamber.org
Contact: Bill Connors, President
E-mail: bconnors@boisechamber.org
Facebook: www.facebook.com/boisemetrochamber
Instagram: www.instagram.com/boisechamber
Description: Promotes business and community development in the Boise, ID area. **Founded:** 1900. **Publications:** *Boise Metro Business Today* (Monthly). **Geographic Preference:** Local.

38907 ■ Buhl Chamber of Commerce
716 Hwy. 30 E
Buhl, ID 83316
Ph: (208)543-6682
Co. E-mail: admin@buhlchamber.org
URL: http://www.buhlchamber.org
Contact: Michelle Olsen, Contact
E-mail: michelleo@buhlchamber.org
Description: Promotes business and community development in Buhl, ID. **Founded:** 1920. **Geographic Preference:** State.

38908 ■ *Business Guide and Business Relocation*
160 Sun Valley Rd. W
Ketchum, ID 83340
Ph: (208)726-3423
Free: 800-634-3347
Fax: (208)726-4533
Co. E-mail: info@visitsunvalley.com
URL: http://www.visitsunvalley.com
Contact: Scott Fortner, Executive Director
E-mail: scott@visitsunvalley.com
URL(s): visitsunvalley.com/about-sun-valley/community-resources
Availability: Print.

38909 ■ Caldwell Chamber of Commerce
1001 Blaine st.
Caldwell, ID 83605

Small Business Sourcebook • 42nd Edition

38910 ■ Idaho

Ph: (208)459-7493
Co. E-mail: info@caldwellchamber.org
URL: http://www.caldwellchamber.org
Contact: Jerry Summers, Executive Director
E-mail: jsummers@caldwellchamber.org
Facebook: www.facebook.com/CaldwellChamber
X (Twitter): x.com/caldwellchamber
Instagram: www.instagram.com/caldwellchamberofcommerce
YouTube: www.youtube.com/channel/UCq503YrESgPcWiRwAmWtARw
Description: Promotes business and community development in Caldwell, ID. **Founded:** 1887. **Publications:** *Business News* (Monthly). **Geographic Preference:** Local.

38910 ■ Cascade Chamber of Commerce (CCC)
101 S Main St.
Cascade, ID 83611
Ph: (208)382-3833
Co. E-mail: info@cascadechamber.com
URL: http://www.cascadechamber.com
Contact: Tom Reinhardt, President
Facebook: www.facebook.com/cascadeidaho
Instagram: www.instagram.com/cascade_idaho_chamber
YouTube: www.youtube.com/channel/UCylyO0Skcm2IZ3Phme2pUUw
Description: Promotes business and community development in Cascade, ID. Sponsors Thunder Mountain Days, Winter Jamboree, and Annual Christmas Lighting Contest. **Publications:** *Business Directory*. **Geographic Preference:** Local.

38911 ■ Coeur d'Alene Chamber of Commerce [Coeur d'Alene Area Chamber of Commerce (CDACC)]
105 N 1st St.
Coeur d Alene, ID 83814
Co. E-mail: info@cdachamber.com
URL: http://cdachamber.com
Contact: Linda Coppess, Member
Facebook: www.facebook.com/cdachamber
X (Twitter): x.com/cdachamber
Instagram: www.instagram.com/cdachamberofcommerce
YouTube: www.youtube.com/channel/UCWWVLPy0H-K8YKK1Td0ErSg
Description: Promotes business and community development in Kootenai County, ID. **Publications:** *A Report to Membership* (Monthly); *Visitor Guide*. **Educational Activities:** Upbeat Breakfast (Monthly; Annual). **Geographic Preference:** Local.

38912 ■ Council Chamber of Commerce (CCC)
201 N Dartmouth St.
Council, ID 83612
Co. E-mail: info@councilchamberofcommerce.com
URL: http://www.councilchamberofcommerce.com
Contact: Lyle L. Sall, Contact
Facebook: www.facebook.com/councilidahochamberofcommerce
Description: Strives to promote and perpetuate the business, commercial, manufacturing, agriculture, and civic interests of the City of Council and its nearby territory. **Geographic Preference:** Local.

38913 ■ Donnelly Area Chamber of Commerce
169 Halferty St.
Donnelly, ID 83615
URL: http://donnellychamber.com
Contact: Belinda Provancher, President
Facebook: www.facebook.com/donnellyidaho
Description: Promotes business and community development in the Donnelly, ID area. Sponsors festivals and hall of fame; presents business and service awards. Operates county welcome center and tourism development. **Founded:** 1886. **Geographic Preference:** Local.

38914 ■ Gem County Chamber of Commerce (GCCC)
1022 S Washington Ave.
Emmett, ID 83617
Ph: (208)365-3485
Fax: (208)365-3220
Co. E-mail: chamber@emmettidaho.com
URL: http://emmettidaho.com
Contact: Teena Turner, President
E-mail: teena@evansrealtyllc.com
Facebook: www.facebook.com/gemchamber
Linkedin: www.linkedin.com/profile/view
X (Twitter): x.com/GemChamber
Instagram: www.instagram.com/gemcountychamberofcommerce
YouTube: www.youtube.com/user/GemChamber
Description: Promotes business and community development in Gem County, ID. **Publications:** *Chamber Reminder* (Weekly). **Geographic Preference:** Local.

38915 ■ Glenns Ferry Chamber of Commerce (GFCC)
7 E 1st Ave.
Glenns Ferry, ID 83623
Co. E-mail: gfchamber@centurylink.net
URL: http://glennsferrychamber.org/home
Contact: Mickie Zuiderveld, President
E-mail: mz.gfchamber@gmail.com
Facebook: www.facebook.com/GlennsFerryChamberOfCommerce
Description: Promotes business and community development in Glenns Ferry, ID. Sponsors annual Oregon Trail historical re-enactment. Conducts charitable activities. **Publications:** *Glenns Ferry Directory*. **Geographic Preference:** Local.

38916 ■ Grangeville Chamber of Commerce
Hwy. 95 Pine St.
Grangeville, ID 83530
Ph: (208)983-0460
Fax: (208)983-1429
URL: http://grangevilleidaho.com/chamber-of-commerce
Contact: Dina Cervantes, Executive Director
Description: Promotes business and community development in Grangeville, ID. **Geographic Preference:** Local.

38917 ■ Greater Blackfoot Area Chamber of Commerce
70 W Judicial St.
Blackfoot, ID 83221
Ph: (208)785-0510
Co. E-mail: chamber@blackfootchamber.org
URL: http://blackfootchamber.org
Contact: Cindy Reese, Co-President
Facebook: www.facebook.com/BlackfootChamber
X (Twitter): x.com/BlackfootChambe
Instagram: www.instagram.com/blackfootchamber
Description: Promotes business and community development in the Blackfoot, ID area. **Founded:** 1952. **Geographic Preference:** Local.

38918 ■ Greater Bonners Ferry Chamber of Commerce (GBFCC)
PO Box X
Bonners Ferry, ID 83805-1288
Ph: (208)267-5922
URL: http://www.uschamber.com/co/chambers/idaho/bonners-ferry
Description: Promotes business, community development, and tourism in Boundary County, ID. **Founded:** 1908. **Geographic Preference:** Local.

38919 ■ Greater Preston Idaho Business Association
70 W Oneida
Preston, ID 83263
Ph: (208)852-1817
Fax: (208)852-1820
Co. E-mail: julies@prestonid.us
URL: http://prestonidaho.org
Contact: Linda Acock, Officer
E-mail: lindaa@prestonid.us
Description: Promotes business and community development in the Preston, ID area. **Founded:** 1900. **Geographic Preference:** Local.

STATE LISTINGS

38920 ■ Greater Sandpoint Chamber of Commerce (GSCC)
1202 5th Ave.
Sandpoint, ID 83864
Ph: (208)263-2161
Fax: (208)265-5289
Co. E-mail: info@sandpointchamber.com
URL: http://sandpointchamber.org
Contact: Sean Mirus, Chairman
E-mail: smirus@schweitzer.com
Facebook: www.facebook.com/Chamber7B
Linkedin: www.linkedin.com/company/greater-sandpoint-chamber-of-commerce/about
X (Twitter): x.com/chamber7b
YouTube: www.youtube.com/chamber7b
Description: Promotes business and community development in the Sandpoint, ID area. **Founded:** 1978. **Publications:** *Business Lines* (Monthly). **Awards:** Greater Sandpoint Chamber of Commerce Business of the Month (Monthly). **Geographic Preference:** Local.

38921 ■ Hagerman Valley Chamber of Commerce (HVCC)
380 State St.
Hagerman, ID 83332
Ph: (208)837-9131
Free: 800-255-8946
Co. E-mail: hagermanchamber@gmail.com
URL: http://hagermanvalleychamber.com
Contact: Judy Osborne, Contact
Facebook: www.facebook.com/hagermanchamber
X (Twitter): x.com/hagermanchamber
Instagram: www.instagram.com/explore/locations/113995888630625/hagerman-valley-chamber-of-commerce
Description: Promotes business and community development in the Hagerman, ID area. **Geographic Preference:** Local.

38922 ■ Hailey Chamber of Commerce
781 S Main St.
Hailey, ID 83333
Ph: (208)788-3484
Co. E-mail: info@valleychamber.org
URL: http://haileyidaho.com
Contact: Mike McKenna, Executive Director
E-mail: mike@valleychamber.org
Description: Promotes business and community development in Hailey, ID. **Publications:** *Hailey Chamber News* (Weekly). **Geographic Preference:** Local.

38923 ■ Historic Silver Valley Chamber of Commerce
10 E Station Ave.
Kellogg, ID 83837
Ph: (208)784-0821
Co. E-mail: director@silvervalleychamber.com
URL: http://www.silvervalleychamber.com
Contact: Diannah Fields-Brown, President
E-mail: diannah.fields.brown@gmail.com
Facebook: www.facebook.com/silvervalleychamber
Linkedin: www.linkedin.com/company/historic-silver-valley-chamber-of-commerce
X (Twitter): x.com/SilverValley_ID
Instagram: www.instagram.com/silvervalleychamber
YouTube: www.youtube.com/channel/UCIBlzWZQe742xOnUnYoHqpA
Pinterest: www.pinterest.com/silvervalleyid
Description: Promotes business and community development in Kellogg and the Silver Valley, ID area. **Founded:** 1930. **Geographic Preference:** Local.

38924 ■ Historic Wallace Chamber of Commerce
10 River St.
Wallace, ID 83873
Ph: (208)753-7151
URL: http://www.wallaceid.fun
Description: Promotes business and community development in Wallace, ID and surrounding Silver Valley area. Sponsors Huckleberry/Heritage Festival, 5K Fun Run, Yuletide Lighting Celebration, and Joint Chamber Auction. **Founded:** 1964. **Geographic Preference:** Local.

38925 ■ Jerome Chamber of Commerce
104 W Main St., Ste. 106
Jerome, ID 83338
Ph: (208)324-2711
Co. E-mail: director@visitjeromeidaho.com
URL: http://visitjeromeidaho.com
Contact: Jason L. Peterson, Contact
X (Twitter): x.com/visitjerome
Description: Promotes business and community development in Jerome, ID. **Founded:** 1920. **Publications:** *News and Views* (Quarterly). **Educational Activities:** General Membership. **Geographic Preference:** Local.

38926 ■ Kamiah Chamber of Commerce
518 Main St.
Kamiah, ID 83536
Ph: (208)935-2290
URL: http://www.kamiahchamber.com
Contact: Dallon Wheeler, Co-President
Description: Promotes business and community development in Kamiah, ID. **Geographic Preference:** Local.

38927 ■ Kuna Chamber of Commerce
333 N Ave. C, Ste. 1A
Kuna, ID 83634
Ph: (208)922-9254
Co. E-mail: info@kunachamber.com
URL: http://www.kunachamber.org/#
Contact: Bobby Rossadillo, Co-President
Facebook: www.facebook.com/KunaChamber
Linkedin: www.linkedin.com/in/kuna-information-3ab34a133
X (Twitter): x.com/KunaChamber
Description: Promotes business and community development in Kuna, ID. **Publications:** *Kuna Directory* (Periodic); *Business Connection* (Quarterly). **Geographic Preference:** Local.

38928 ■ Lava Hot Springs Chamber of Commerce (LHSCC)
PO Box 238
Lava Hot Springs, ID 83246
Ph: (208)776-5500
Co. E-mail: findout@lavahotsprings.org
URL: http://lavahotsprings.org
Contact: Collin Petrun, President
Facebook: www.facebook.com/LavaHotSpringsChamber
X (Twitter): x.com/LavaChamber
YouTube: www.youtube.com/user/lavahotspringscoc
Description: Promotes business and community development in the Lava Hot Springs, ID area. **Geographic Preference:** Local.

38929 ■ Meridian Chamber of Commerce
215 E Franklin Rd.
Meridian, ID 83642
Ph: (208)888-2817
Fax: (208)888-2682
Co. E-mail: info@meridianchamber.org
URL: http://meridianchamber.org
Contact: Sean Evans, Chief Executive Officer
E-mail: michelle.leverett@meridianchamber.org
Facebook: www.facebook.com/MeridianChamber
Linkedin: www.linkedin.com/company/meridian-chamber-of-commerce
X (Twitter): x.com/meridianchamber
YouTube: www.youtube.com/channel/UCvRI_Ehz6HEK4TguxLL2UCQ
Description: Provides ways to become involved in the community through leadership opportunities, business advocacy, networking, and promotion of individual businesses in Meridian, ID. **Founded:** 1958. **Publications:** *Member Spotlight* (Monthly); *Meridian Buyer's Guide* (Annual). **Educational Activities:** Business After Hours (Monthly). **Awards:** Meridian Small Business Person of the Year (Annual); Meridian Small Business of the Year (Annual). **Geographic Preference:** Local.

38930 ■ Mini-Cassia Chamber of Commerce
1177 7th St.
Heyburn, ID 83336
Ph: (208)679-4793
Fax: (208)679-4794
Co. E-mail: info@minicassiachamber.com
URL: http://www.minicassiachamber.com
Contact: Melissa Aston, Chairman
Facebook: www.facebook.com/MiniCassiaChamber
Linkedin: www.linkedin.com/company/mini-cassia-chamber-of-commerce
X (Twitter): x.com/mcchamber
Description: Promotes business and community development and tourism in the Minidoka/Cassia County, IL area. Sponsors festivals. **Founded:** 1993. **Geographic Preference:** Local.

38931 ■ Moscow Chamber of Commerce (MCC)
411 S Main St.
Moscow, ID 83843
Ph: (208)882-1800
Co. E-mail: info@moscowchamber.com
URL: http://www.moscowchamber.com
Contact: Traci Hacker, President
Facebook: www.facebook.com/moscow.chamber
X (Twitter): x.com/ChamberMoscow
Instagram: www.instagram.com/moscowchamber
YouTube: www.youtube.com/user/TheMoscowChamber
Description: Promotes business, community development, and tourism in the Moscow, Idaho area. **Founded:** 1949. **Publications:** *Business Journal* (Quarterly). **Educational Activities:** The Business Forum. **Geographic Preference:** Local.

38932 ■ Mountain Home Chamber of Commerce
205 N 3rd E
Mountain Home, ID 83647
Ph: (208)587-4334
Fax: (208)587-0042
Co. E-mail: chamber@mountainhomechamber.com
URL: http://www.mountainhomechamber.com
Contact: Josh Dison, President
E-mail: jtdison22@aol.com
YouTube: www.youtube.com/channel/UCKmJpav4eykl28Nhfwh3mdQ
Description: Provides a format in which members can share and grow in ideas, leadership, community commitment and economic vitality. Promotes business and community development. Sponsors Air Force Appreciation Day. **Geographic Preference:** Local.

38933 ■ Nampa Chamber of Commerce
101 11th Ave. S, Ste. 105
Nampa, ID 83651
Ph: (208)466-4641
Co. E-mail: nampachamberofcommerce@nampa.com
URL: http://www.nampa.com
Contact: Mitch Minnette, President
E-mail: mitch@nampa.com
Facebook: www.facebook.com/NampaChamber
X (Twitter): x.com/nampachamber
Instagram: www.instagram.com/nampachamber
Description: Promotes business and community development in Nampa, ID. **Founded:** 1892. **Publications:** *Nampa Chamber* (Monthly). **Geographic Preference:** Local.

38934 ■ Pocatello-Chubbuck Chamber of Commerce
324 S Main St.
Pocatello, ID 83204
Ph: (208)233-1525
URL: http://www.pocatelloidaho.com
Contact: Matt Hunter, President
E-mail: matthew@pocatelloidaho.com
Facebook: www.facebook.com/PocatelloChubbuckChamber
X (Twitter): x.com/PocatelloChmber
Description: Promotes business and community development in the Pocatello, ID area. Sponsors leadership program. **Founded:** 1901. **Publications:** *Chamber Notes* (Monthly); *Chamber Today* (Monthly); *Welcome to Pocatello* (Semiannual). **Geographic Preference:** Local.

38935 ■ Post Falls Chamber of Commerce (PFCC)
201 E 4th Ave.
Post Falls, ID 83854
Ph: (208)773-5016
Free: 800-292-2553
Co. E-mail: info@postfallschamber.com
URL: http://www.postfallschamber.com
Contact: Christina Petit, President
Facebook: www.facebook.com/pages/PFchamber-Commerce/227583730606504
X (Twitter): x.com/PFChamber
Description: Promotes business and community development in Post Falls, ID. Sponsors Old-Time Fiddler's Contest, Post Falls Pioneer Festival, Christmas tree lighting ceremony, and Summer Community Picnic. **Founded:** 1964. **Geographic Preference:** Local.

38936 ■ Priest Lake Chamber of Commerce (PLCC)
PO Box 174
Coolin, ID 83821
Ph: (208)443-3191
Co. E-mail: info@priestlake.org
URL: http://priestlake.org
Contact: Sandra Vandeventer, Contact
Facebook: www.facebook.com/priestlakechamber
Instagram: www.instagram.com/priestlakechamber
Description: Promotes business and community development in the Coolin, ID area. **Geographic Preference:** Local.

38937 ■ Priest River Chamber of Commerce
50 Main St., Ste. 102
Priest River, ID 83856
Ph: (208)448-2721
Co. E-mail: priestrivercoc@gmail.com
URL: http://www.visitpriestriver.com
Contact: Ashley Scribner, President
Description: Unites local businesses and citizens towards the common goal of prosperity for the community. **Founded:** 1890. **Geographic Preference:** Local.

38938 ■ Rexburg Chamber of Commerce
167 W Main St., Ste. 2
Rexburg, ID 83440
Ph: (208)356-5700
Fax: (208)356-5799
Co. E-mail: info@rexburgchamber.com
URL: http://rexburgchamber.org
Contact: Chris Mann, Chief Executive Officer
E-mail: chris@rexburgchamber.com
Facebook: www.facebook.com/rexburgchamberofcommerce
X (Twitter): x.com/rexcc
Instagram: www.instagram.com/rexchamber
Pinterest: www.pinterest.com/rexcc
Description: Enhances the vitality and economic health of Rexburg and Madison County. Sponsors many activities throughout the year to bring thousands of people to Rexburg like Sunbird Program, Idaho International Dance and Music Festival, and July 4th Whoopee Days Celebrations. **Publications:** *Membership Directory and Buyers' Guide* (Annual); *Rexburg Chamber of Commerce--Membership Directory and Buyers Guide* (Annual). **Educational Activities:** Folk Dance. **Geographic Preference:** Local.

38939 ■ St. Maries Chamber of Commerce
538 Main Ave.
Saint Maries, ID 83861
Ph: (208)245-3563
URL: http://stmarieschamber.org
Contact: Shirley Ackerman, Director
Description: Promotes business and community development in St. Maries, ID and the surrounding area. **Publications:** *Chamber of Commerce Newsletter* (Monthly). **Geographic Preference:** Local.

38940 ■ Salmon River Chamber of Commerce
PO Box 289
Riggins, ID 83549
Ph: (208)628-2783
Co. E-mail: salmonriverchamber@gmail.com

URL: http://rigginsidaho.com
Contact: Cody D. Killmar, Contact
Facebook: www.facebook.com/
 SalmonRiverChamberOfCommerce
Instagram: www.instagram.com/visitrigginsidaho
Description: Promotes business and community development in Salmon River, ID area. **Geographic Preference:** Local.

38941 ■ Salmon Valley Chamber of Commerce
Co. E-mail: info@salmonchamber.com
URL: http://www.salmonchamber.com
Contact: George Miley, President
Description: Works to generate support for and promote the well-being of the businesses in the greater Salmon Valley. **Founded:** 1977. **Geographic Preference:** Local.

38942 ■ Soda Springs Chamber of Commerce
9 W 2nd S
 Soda Springs, ID 83276
Ph: (208)547-2600
Co. E-mail: sodacoc@sodachamber.com
URL: http://www.sodachamber.com
Contact: Alan Skinner, Treasurer Secretary
Facebook: www.facebook.com/Soda-Springs-Idaho
 -Chamber-of-Commerce-203355813022437
Pinterest: www.pinterest.com/pin/3880836928617
 17458
Description: Promotes business and community development in Soda Springs, ID. **Geographic Preference:** Local.

38943 ■ Stanley-Sawtooth Chamber of Commerce
PO Box 8
 Stanley, ID 83278
Ph: (208)774-3411
Co. E-mail: information@stanleycc.org
URL: http://stanleycc.org
Contact: Jason Bosley, Director
Facebook: www.facebook.com/StanleyIdaho
X (Twitter): twitter.com/Stanley_Idaho
Description: Helps to promote the Stanley area. **Geographic Preference:** Local.

38944 ■ Sun Valley-Ketchum Chamber and Visitors Bureau
160 Sun Valley Rd. W
 Ketchum, ID 83340
Ph: (208)726-3423
Free: 800-634-3347
Fax: (208)726-4533
Co. E-mail: info@visitsunvalley.com
URL: http://www.visitsunvalley.com
Contact: Scott Fortner, Executive Director
E-mail: scott@visitsunvalley.com
Facebook: www.facebook.com/visitsunvalley
X (Twitter): x.com/visitsunvalley
Instagram: www.instagram.com/visitsunvalley
YouTube: www.youtube.com/user/SunValleyIdaho/fea
 tured
Pinterest: www.pinterest.com/visitsunvalley
Description: Promotes business development and tourism in the Sun Valley-Ketchum, ID area. **Publications:** *Business Guide and Business Relocation*; *Vacation Planner* (Annual). **Geographic Preference:** Local.

38945 ■ Teton Valley Chamber of Commerce
60 S Main St.
 Driggs, ID 83422
Co. E-mail: info@trec-biz.org
URL: http://discovertetonvalley.com
Contact: Brian McDermott, Executive Director
E-mail: brianm@trec-biz.org
Description: Promotes business and community development in Driggs, ID. **Publications:** *Come Out and Play*. **Geographic Preference:** Local.

38946 ■ Twin Falls Area Chamber of Commerce
2015 Neilsen Point Pl., Ste. 100
 Twin Falls, ID 83301
Ph: (208)733-3974
Free: 866-894-6325
Fax: (208)733-9216
Co. E-mail: info@twinfallschamber.com
URL: http://twinfallschamber.com
Contact: Shawn Barigar, President
E-mail: shawn@twinfallschamber.com
Facebook: www.facebook.com/pages/Twin-Falls
 -Area-Chamber-of-Commerce/345601455005
Linkedin: www.linkedin.com/company/twin-falls-area
 -chamber-of-commerce
Instagram: www.instagram.com/tfchamber
Description: Promotes business and community development in the Twin Falls, ID area. **Founded:** 1920. **Geographic Preference:** Local.

38947 ■ Weiser Chamber of Commerce
309 State St.
 Weiser, ID 83672
Ph: (208)414-0452
Co. E-mail: info@weiserchamber.com
URL: http://weiserchamber.info
Contact: Sally Frye, President
Facebook: www.facebook.com/
 ShopingLocalinWeiser
Instagram: www.instagram.com/weiser_chamber
Description: Promotes business and community development in Weiser, ID. Sponsors National Old-time Fiddlers' Contest, Christmas Parade, Spring Crab Feed and Auction, and Fall Chili Cook-Off and Mud Bog. Operates Vendome Event Center. **Founded:** 1948. **Publications:** *Chamber News*. **Geographic Preference:** Local.

FINANCING AND LOAN PROGRAMS

38948 ■ Boise Angel Alliance (BAA)
7154 W State St., No 252
 Boise, ID 83714
Ph: (208)629-7290
Co. E-mail: info@boiseangels.org
URL: http://www.boiseangels.org
Contact: Amy Curry, President
E-mail: amy@boiseangels.org
Facebook: www.facebook.com/BoiseAngelAlliance
Instagram: www.instagram.com/BoiseAngels
Description: Identifies and invests in early-stage disruptive companies solving real problems in the Treasure Valley. **Founded:** 2004. **Investment Policies:** Generates revenue (or is nearly there); business models based on a sustainable or unique product, service, or technology; sizable market opportunity; well-defined exit strategy.

INCUBATORS/RESEARCH AND TECHNOLOGY PARKS

38949 ■ Bonner Business Center (BBC)
804 Airport Way
 Sandpoint, ID 83864
URL: http://bonnerbusinesscenter.com
Description: A small business incubator assisting the development of new firms in Northern Idaho. Also equipped with a fully licensed shared-use food production facility.

38950 ■ Butte Business Center
159 N Idaho St.
 Arco, ID 83213-0641
Ph: (208)527-3060
URL: http://arcobuttebusinesscenter.blogspot.com
Description: Business incubator helping to provide opportunities for new entrepreneurs to get their business off the ground.

38951 ■ CSI Business Incubator
College of Southern Idaho 315 Falls Ave., Evergreen Bldg. C77
 Twin Falls, ID 83301-1238
Ph: (208)733-9554
Free: 800-680-0274
Co. E-mail: info@csi.edu
URL: http://www.csi.edu
Contact: Julie J. D. Golder, Vice President
E-mail: jgolder@acct.org
Facebook: www.facebook.com/CollegeofSouthernI
 daho
Linkedin: www.linkedin.com/edu/school
X (Twitter): x.com/csieagles
Instagram: www.instagram.com/collegeofsourtherni
 daho
YouTube: www.youtube.com/user/CSIEagles
Description: A small business incubator providing entrepreneurs with adequate facilities and resources needed to develop new businesses; expanding the economic base of South-Central Idaho by assisting value-added, non-competing new businesses; creating jobs in the Magic Valley area; and improving new businesses' chances for success.

38952 ■ Idaho Innovation Center Inc. (IIC)
2300 N Yellowstone
 Idaho Falls, ID 83401
Ph: (208)523-1026
Fax: (208)528-7127
URL: http://innovateidaho.org
Contact: Bryan Magleby, Executive Director
E-mail: bryan@iictr.com
Facebook: www.facebook.com/innovateidaho
Description: A small business incubator providing large business resources to small, fledgling companies so that entrepreneurs can confidently and aggressively start and grow their small businesses.

38953 ■ Salmon Valley Business and Innovation Center (SVBIC)
803 Monroe
 Salmon, ID 83467
URL: http://lceda.net/svbic
Contact: Tammy Stringham, Executive Director
Description: A project developed to encourage new business growth in the community while creating greater employment opportunities for residents of the Salmon Valley.

EDUCATIONAL PROGRAMS

38954 ■ BYU Idaho
210 W 4th S
 Rexburg, ID 83460
Ph: (208)496-1411
Co. E-mail: ask@byui.edu
URL: http://www.byui.edu
Contact: Henry J. Eyring, President
X (Twitter): x.com/byuidaho
Description: General studies associates degrees.

38955 ■ College of Eastern Idaho (CEI)
1600 S 25th E
 Idaho Falls, ID 83404
Ph: (208)524-3000
Free: 800-662-0261
Co. E-mail: info@cei.edu
URL: http://cei.edu
Contact: Dr. Rick Aman, President
E-mail: rick.aman@cei.edu
Facebook: www.facebook.com/CEI.Falcons
Linkedin: www.linkedin.com/company/college-of-eas
 tern-idaho
Instagram: www.instagram.com/collegeofeasterni
 daho
YouTube: www.youtube.com/user/EITC1969
Description: Vocation-technical school offering customized training; industry-specific upgrade training; independent business and agribusiness management training; entry/re-entry training; and retraining for displaced workers. **Founded:** 1969.

38956 ■ College of Southern Idaho School of Vo-Tech Education
315 Falls Ave.
 Twin Falls, ID 83303
Ph: (208)733-9554
Free: 800-680-0274
Fax: (208)736-4705
Co. E-mail: info@csi.edu
URL: http://www.csi.edu
Contact: Dr. Dean Fisher, President
Facebook: www.facebook.com/CollegeofSouthernI
 daho
Linkedin: www.linkedin.com/edu/school

STATE LISTINGS

X (Twitter): x.com/csieagles
Instagram: www.instagram.com/collegeofsoutherni daho
YouTube: www.youtube.com/user/CSIEagles
Description: Vocation-technical school offering customized training; industry-specific upgrade training; independent business and agribusiness management training; entry/re-entry training; and retraining for displaced workers. **Founded:** 1965.

38957 ■ Idaho State University College of Technology (ISU)
1999 Alvin Ricken Dve.
  Pocatello, ID 83209
Ph: (208)282-2622
Fax: (208)282-5195
Co. E-mail: ctech@isu.edu
URL: http://www.isu.edu/tech
Contact: Tom Putnam, Executive Director
E-mail: thomasputnam@isu.edu
X (Twitter): x.com/idahostateu
Description: Vocation-technical school offering customized training; industry-specific upgrade training; independent business and agribusiness management training; entry/re-entry training; and retraining for displaced workers. **Founded:** 1901.

38958 ■ Lewis-Clark State College School of Technology (LCSC)
500 8th Ave.
  Lewiston, ID 83501
Ph: (208)792-2220
Fax: (208)792-2816
Co. E-mail: admissions@lcsc.edu
URL: http://www.lcsc.edu/ti
Contact: Dr. Cynthia L. Pemberton, President
E-mail: president@lcsc.edu
Description: Vocation-technical school offering customized training; industry-specific upgrade training; independent business and agribusiness management training; entry/re-entry training; and retraining for displaced workers. **Founded:** 1893.

38959 ■ North Idaho College Professional-Technical Education
1000 W Garden Ave.
  Coeur d Alene, ID 83814
URL: http://www.nic.edu/cte
Description: Vocation-technical school offering customized training; industry-specific upgrade training; independent business and agribusiness management training; entry/re-entry training; and retraining for displaced workers. **Founded:** 1933.

LEGISLATIVE ASSISTANCE

38960 ■ Idaho Department of Commerce (IDC)
700 W State St. fl.
  Boise, ID 83720
Ph: (208)334-2470
Free: 800-842-5858
Co. E-mail: info@commerce.idaho.gov
URL: http://commerce.idaho.gov
Contact: Tom Kealey, Director
E-mail: tom.kealey@commerce.idaho.gov
Facebook: www.facebook.com/IdahoCommerce
X (Twitter): x.com/IdahoCommerce
Instagram: www.instagram.com/visitidaho
Founded: 1958.

PUBLICATIONS

38961 ■ Idaho Business Review (IBR)
4696 W Overland Rd., Ste. 180
  Boise, ID 83705
Ph: (208)336-3768
Free: 877-615-9536
Fax: (208)336-5534
URL: http://idahobusinessreview.com
Contact: Autumn Kersey, Sales Executive
E-mail: akersey@idahobusinessreview.com
Facebook: www.facebook.com/IdahoBusinessReview
Linkedin: www.linkedin.com/company/idaho-business-review
X (Twitter): x.com/IBRnews
Instagram: www.instagram.com/ibrnews
YouTube: www.youtube.com/channel/UC59PCuG4AfDCN_TkgX26x2A
Description: Publisher of newspaper covering commercial real estate, construction, financial sector and business development news and much more. **Founded:** 1984.

38962 ■ North Idaho Business Journal
PO Box 6200
  Coeur d Alene, ID 83816
URL(s): businessjournalnorthidaho.com
Facebook: www.facebook.com/NIBusinessJournal
Availability: Print.

RESEARCH CENTERS

38963 ■ University of Idaho - Center for Business Development and Entrepreneurship (CBDE)
875 Perimeter Dr. 264
  Moscow, ID 83844-4264
URL: http://www.webpages.uidaho.edu/catalog/2010/research.htm
Description: Integral unit of College of Business and Economics at University of Idaho. **Scope:** Business and economics, including studies on market and labor force, regional economics. **Founded:** 1974.

Illinois

ASSOCIATIONS AND OTHER ORGANIZATIONS

38964 ▪ Association of Fundraising Professionals Chicago Chapter (AFP Chicago)
400 E Randolph St., Ste. 2305
Chicago, IL 60601
Ph: (312)500-1410
Co. E-mail: info@afpchicago.org
URL: http://www.afpchicago.org
Contact: Nathan Armstrong, President
Facebook: www.facebook.com/afpchicago
X (Twitter): x.com/AFPCHICAGO
Instagram: www.instagram.com/afpchicago
YouTube: www.youtube.com/channel/UC2QKAmH
t6gWckxk_-IHEJxA
Description: Supports fundraising professionals in the Chicago area. **Geographic Preference:** Regional.

38965 ▪ Association of Fundraising Professionals East Central Illinois Chapter (AFPECI)
PO Box 6252
Champaign, IL 61826-6252
Co. E-mail: afpeci@gmail.com
URL: http://afpeci.org
Contact: Angela Hatfield Marker, Co-President
Facebook: www.facebook.com/afpeci
X (Twitter): x.com/afpeci
Description: Provides education, training, mentoring, research, credentialing, and advocacy to fundraising professionals in the Champaign-Urbana, Danville, Mattoon, Charleston, Effingham, and Decatur communities of east-central Illinois. Hosts monthly educational networking events on a variety of topics related to fundraising and advancement. **Founded:** 1989. **Geographic Preference:** Local.

38966 ▪ Business Marketing Association Chicago Chapter
Chicago, IL
Co. E-mail: info@chicagobusinessmarketing.net
URL: http://chicagobusinessmarketing.net
Contact: Bill Furlong, Chief Executive Officer
Facebook: www.facebook.com/ANAB2BCHI
Linkedin: www.linkedin.com/company/business
-marketing-association-chicago-bma-
X (Twitter): x.com/ANAB2B
Description: Promotes the development of business-to-business marketing and communications professionals through education, training and networking. **Founded:** 1922. **Geographic Preference:** Local.

38967 ▪ Business Network International, Central and Southern Illinois
3430 Toringdon Way
Charlotte, NC 28277
Free: 855-264-2673
Co. E-mail: michaelpenny@bni.com
URL: http://bni-il.com
Contact: Mike Penny, Managing Director
Description: Provides both men and women a structured environment for the development and exchange of quality business referrals. Offers members the opportunity to share ideas and contacts. **Geographic Preference:** Local.

38968 ▪ Business Network International Mid America
2082 Quarry Rd.
O'Fallon, IL 62269
Ph: (314)822-1030
URL: http://bnimidamerica.com/en-US/findachapter
Contact: Victor Muzquiz, Executive Director
Description: Provides both men and women a structured environment for the development and exchange of quality business referrals. Offers members the opportunity to share ideas and contacts. **Founded:** 1994. **Geographic Preference:** Regional.

38969 ▪ Chicago Business Travel Association (CBTA) [Global Business Travel Association - Chicago Chapter]
PO Box 877
Chicago, IL 60690
Co. E-mail: info@chicagobta.org
URL: http://chicagobta.org
Contact: Wayne Urbanek, Chairperson
Facebook: www.facebook.com/ChicagoBTA
X (Twitter): x.com/chicagobta
Instagram: www.instagram.com/chicagobusiness
travel
Description: Promotes the value of business travel management by representing corporate travel managers and travel service providers. Monitors developments in the business travel field and provides current, critical industry information.

38970 ▪ Entrepreneurs' Organization - Chicago Chapter (EO)
318 W Adams, Ste. 1600
Chicago, IL 60616
Ph: (847)702-4700
Co. E-mail: marketing@eochicago.org
URL: http://eochicago.org
Contact: Bobby Achettu, President
URL(s): www.eonetwork.org/chicago
Facebook: www.facebook.com/EOChicago
Linkedin: www.linkedin.com/company/eo-chicago
-chapter
X (Twitter): x.com/eochicago10
Instagram: www.instagram.com/eochicago
Description: Provides local resources to members which includes networking events, mentorship, live forums, and leadership development. **Founded:** 1994.

38971 ▪ Family Firm Institute - Midwest Study Group (FFI-MWC)
711 Atlantic Ave. 6th Fl.
Boston, MA 02111
URL: http://www.ffi.org/about/study-groups/midwes
t-chapter
Contact: Shannon Zur, Chairman
E-mail: shannonz@vogelcg.com
Description: Professional membership association for individuals and organizations working the in family enterprise field. **Geographic Preference:** Local.

38972 ▪ Illinois Venture Capital Association (IVCA)
27 N Wacker Dr., No. 405
Chicago, IL 60606
URL: http://illinoisvc.org
Contact: Jim TenBroek, Chairman of the Board
Linkedin: www.linkedin.com/company/ivca
X (Twitter): x.com/ivcaillinois
Description: Works with entrepreneurial organizations in the Midwest to encourage innovation and business creation. Promotes institutional investment in local private equity firms. **Founded:** 2000.

38973 ▪ The Indus Entrepreneurs Midwest
Chicago, IL
URL: http://www.hub.tie.org/c/TiEMidwest
Description: Advocates for the advancement of entrepreneurship and exchange of ideas. Works in fostering entrepreneurship and nurturing entrepreneurs, providing a networking platform for members and helping members integrate with the mainstream community. **Founded:** 1998. **Geographic Preference:** Regional.

38974 ▪ International Association of Women Chicago Chapter (IAW)
Chicago, IL
URL: http://www.iawomen.com/chapters/chicago
-chapter
Contact: Vicki Sowa, President
E-mail: mscrystalspaeth@gmail.com
Description: Serves as network of accomplished women united to achieve professional goals. Provides a forum for sharing ideas and experiences of professional women regarding career success. Promotes an active business and networking community from all industries. **Geographic Preference:** Local.

38975 ▪ International Association of Women Schaumburg Chapter
Schaumburg, IL
URL: http://community.iawomen.com/schaumburg/
home
Contact: Dr. Denise Styer, President
Description: Serves as network of accomplished women united to achieve professional goals. Provides a forum for sharing ideas and experiences of professional women regarding career success. Promotes an active business and networking community from all industries. **Geographic Preference:** Local.

38976 ▪ Midwest Business Brokers and Intermediaries (MBBI)
1018 W Madison Ave., Ste. 9
Chicago, IL 60607
Ph: (847)847-7703
URL: http://www.mbbi.org
Contact: Raymond Horn, III, Contact
E-mail: rhorn@mpslaw.com
Facebook: www.facebook.com/MBBIAssociation
Linkedin: www.linkedin.com/company/mbbi

X (Twitter): x.com/MBBIAssociation
YouTube: www.youtube.com/channel/UCzO7uJf15eX5difyTCyguKg
Description: Represents industry leaders involved in the buying, funding, and selling of small businesses. **Geographic Preference:** Regional.

38977 ■ River North Business Association (RNBA)
620 N Lasalle St., Ste. 320
Chicago, IL 60654
Ph: (312)645-1047
Fax: (312)645-1151
Co. E-mail: info@greaterrnba.com
URL: http://greaterrnba.com
Contact: Marty Padilla, President
E-mail: president@greaterrnba.com
Facebook: www.facebook.com/Greaterrnba
X (Twitter): x.com/rivernorthchi
Instagram: www.instagram.com/greaterrnba
YouTube: www.youtube.com/user/rnbachicago
Description: Represents businesses and provides member services to help them succeed. **Publications:** *River North Directory* (Annual); *River North News* (Quarterly). **Educational Activities:** Business Exchange and Exposition (Annual); Fraud: Preparing for Holiday Business. **Geographic Preference:** Local.

38978 ■ Society of Financial Service Professionals Quad City Chapter - VTC Library
1701 1st Ave.
Rock Island, IL 61201
Ph: (309)786-6481
Co. E-mail: connie.teshak@modern-woodmen.org
URL: http://societyoffsp.org/quadcity
Contact: Mike Hetrick, Sr., President
Description: Represents the interests of financial advisers. Fosters the development of professional responsibility. Helps clients achieve their personal and business-related financial goals. **Scope:** Finance. **Founded:** 1928. **Holdings:** Videos. **Geographic Preference:** Regional.

SMALL BUSINESS DEVELOPMENT CENTERS

38979 ■ Illinois SBDC at Harper College
1200 W Algonquin Rd.
Palatine, IL 60067
Ph: (847)925-6000
URL: http://www.harpercollege.edu/business/sbdc/index.php
Contact: Tom Cassell, Director
Description: Represents and promotes the small business sector. Provides management assistance to current and prospective small business owners. Helps to improve management skills and expand the products and services of members. **Geographic Preference:** Local.

38980 ■ Illinois Small Business Development Center at Chicago State University (SBDC)
9501 S King Dr.
Chicago, IL 60653
Ph: (773)995-2000
Facebook: www.facebook.com/chicagostateuniversity
X (Twitter): x.com/ChicagoState
Description: Represents and promotes the small business sector. Provides management assistance to current and prospective small business owners. Helps to improve management skills and expand the products and services of members. **Geographic Preference:** Local.

38981 ■ Illinois Small Business Development Center at College of DuPage (SBDC)
535 Duane St., Office 233
Glen Ellyn, IL 60137
Ph: (630)942-2600
Co. E-mail: bdc@cod.edu
URL: http://www.cod.edu/business-development-center/sbdc/index.aspx
Contact: Ute Westphal, Program Manager
E-mail: westphalu@cod.edu

Description: Represents and promotes the small business sector. Provides management assistance to current and prospective small business owners. Helps to improve management skills and expand the products and services of members. **Geographic Preference:** Local.

38982 ■ Illinois Small Business Development Center at College of Lake County
Rm. E186, 19351 W Washington St.
Grayslake, IL 60030-1198
Ph: (847)543-2033
Co. E-mail: illinoissbdc@clcillinois.edu
URL: http://www.clcillinois.edu/businesses/illinois-small-business-development-center
Description: Represents and promotes the small business sector. Provides management assistance to current and prospective small business owners. Helps to improve management skills and expand the products and services of members. **Founded:** 1969. **Geographic Preference:** Local.

38983 ■ Illinois Small Business Development Center at Danville Area Community College (ILSBDC-DACC)
c/o Earle Steiner, Director, 2000 E Main St., Bremer Conference Ctr.
Danville, IL 61832
Ph: (217)554-1669
Co. E-mail: ilsbdc@dacc.edu
URL: http://www.dacc.edu/catalog-2021-2022/small-business-development-center
Contact: Earle Steiner, Director
E-mail: esteiner@dacc.edu
Description: Represents and promotes the small business sector. Provides management assistance to current and prospective small business owners. Helps to improve management skills and expand the products and services of members. **Geographic Preference:** Local.

38984 ■ Illinois Small Business Development Center at Elgin Community College (ECC)
1700 Spartan Dr., Bldg. E, Rm. E105
Elgin, IL 60123-7193
Ph: (847)214-7488
Fax: (847)931-3911
Co. E-mail: sbdc@elgin.edu
URL: http://elgin.edu/business
Contact: John Duffy, Secretary
Description: Provides management assistance to current and prospective small business owners in Elgin. **Geographic Preference:** Local.

38985 ■ Illinois Small Business Development Center at Highland Community College
c/o Highland Campus
2998 W Pearl City Rd.
Freeport, IL 61032
Ph: (815)599-3481
Co. E-mail: businessinstitute@highland.edu
URL: http://highland.edu/businessinstitute/small-business-development
Description: Represents and promotes the small business sector. Provides management assistance to current and prospective small business owners. Helps to improve management skills and expand the products and services of members. **Geographic Preference:** Local.

38986 ■ Illinois Small Business Development Center at Illinois Eastern Community College
218 E Main St.
Olney, IL 62450
Ph: (618)395-3011
Co. E-mail: brumfielb@iecc.edu
URL: http://resources.istcoalition.org/illinois-eastern-community-college-small-business-development-center
Contact: Barney Brumfiel, Contact
E-mail: brumfielb@iecc.edu
Description: Represents and promotes the small business sector. Provides management assistance to current and prospective small business owners. Helps to improve management skills and expand the products and services of members. **Geographic Preference:** Local.

38987 ■ Illinois Small Business Development Center at Illinois Valley Community College
815 N Orlando Smith Ave.
Oglesby, IL 61348
URL: http://www.ivcc.edu/continuingandprofessionaleducation/smallbusinessdevelopment.php
Description: Represents and promotes the small business sector. Provides management assistance to current and prospective small business owners. Helps to improve management skills and expand the products and services of members. **Geographic Preference:** Local.

38988 ■ Illinois Small Business Development Center at Industrial Council of Nearwest Chicago
320 N Damen Ave., Ste. 100
Chicago, IL 60612
Ph: (312)433-7656
URL: http://americassbdc.org/find-your-sbdc
Description: Represents and promotes the small business sector. Provides management assistance to current and prospective small business owners. Helps to improve management skills and expand the products and services of members. **Geographic Preference:** Local.

38989 ■ Illinois Small Business Development Center Joliet Junior College (ISBDCJJC)
1215 Houbolt Rd.
Joliet, IL 60431
URL: http://www.jjc.edu/small-business-development-center
Contact: Ellen Scalpelli, Secretary
E-mail: escalpel@jjc.edu
URL(s): resources.istcoalition.org/joliet-junior-college-small-business-development-center
Description: Represents and promotes the small business sector. Provides management assistance to current and prospective small business owners. Helps to improve management skills and expand the products and services of members. **Geographic Preference:** Local.

38990 ■ Illinois Small Business Development Center at the Joseph Center
7600 W Roosevelt Rd.
Forest Park, IL 60130
Ph: (708)697-6200
Fax: (708)697-6222
Co. E-mail: sbdc@josephcenter.com
URL: http://josephcenter.com
Contact: Andy Pham, Director
URL(s): josephcenter.homestead.com
Facebook: www.facebook.com/people/Illinois-SBDC-ITC-PTAC-at-The-Joseph-Center/100068080554602
Linkedin: www.linkedin.com/in/illinois-sbdc-ptac-itc-at-the-joseph-center
Instagram: www.instagram.com/jc_sbdc_itc_ptac
Description: Represents and promotes the small business sector. Provides management assistance to current and prospective small business owners. Helps to improve management skills and expand the products and services of members. **Founded:** 2005. **Geographic Preference:** Local.

38991 ■ Illinois Small Business Development Center at Kankakee Community College
100 College Dr.
Kankakee, IL 60901-6505
Ph: (815)802-8222
URL: http://www.dhs.state.il.us/page.aspx?item=73553
Description: Represents and promotes the small business sector. Provides management assistance to current and prospective small business owners. Helps to improve management skills and expand the products and services of members. **Geographic Preference:** Local.

38992 ■ Illinois Small Business Development Center at Kaskaskia College
International Trade Ctr.
325 S Poplar St.
Centralia, IL 62801

URL: http://www.kaskaskia.edu/media/web-assets/
documents/institutional-assessment/03-25-2020
-UPDATED-MFIP-Static-Document-Board-Approve
d.pdf
Description: Represents and promotes the small business sector. Provides management assistance to current and prospective small business owners. Helps to improve management skills and expand the products and services of members. **Geographic Preference:** Local.

38993 ■ Illinois Small Business Development Center at Lincoln Land Community College (ISBDC LLCC)
5250 Shepherd Rd.
 Springfield, IL 62794-9256
Ph: (217)786-2200
Free: 800-727-4161
Co. E-mail: info@llcc.edu
URL: http://www.llcc.edu
Contact: Ken Elmore, Chairman
Description: Provides management assistance to current and prospective small business owners in Springfield. **Geographic Preference:** Local.

38994 ■ Illinois Small Business Development Center at McHenry County College (ISBDC)
4100 W Shamrock Ln.
 McHenry, IL 60050
Ph: (815)455-6098
Co. E-mail: sbdc@mchenry.edu
URL: http://www.mchenry.edu/isbdc/index.html
Description: Represents and promotes the small business sector. Provides management assistance to current and prospective small business owners. Helps to improve management skills and expand the products and services of members. **Geographic Preference:** Local.

38995 ■ Illinois Small Business Development Center at Rend Lake College
468 N Ken Gray Pky.
 Ina, IL 62846
Ph: (618)437-5321
Free: 800-369-5321
Fax: (618)437-5677
URL: http://www.rlc.edu/index.php
Contact: Cathy DeJarnette, Director
E-mail: dejarnettec@rlc.edu
Facebook: www.facebook.com/rendlakecollege
X (Twitter): x.com/rendlakecollege
Instagram: www.instagram.com/rendlakecollege
YouTube: www.youtube.com/user/RendLakeCollege
Description: Represents and promotes the small business sector. Provides management assistance to current and prospective small business owners. Helps to improve management skills and expand the products and services of members. **Geographic Preference:** Local.

38996 ■ Illinois Small Business Development Center at Rock Valley College
605 Fulton Ave.
 Rockford, IL 61103
Ph: (815)921-2081
URL: http://www.rockvalleycollege.edu/Community/
 SBDC
Description: Represents and promotes the small business sector. Provides management assistance to current and prospective small business owners. Helps to improve management skills and expand the products and services of members. **Geographic Preference:** Local.

38997 ■ Illinois Small Business Development Center at Shawnee Community College (SBDC)
8364 Shawnee College Rd.
 Ullin, IL 62992
URL: http://shawneecc.edu/community-services/cce
 d/illinois-small-business-development-center
Description: Represents and promotes the small business sector. Provides management assistance to current and prospective small business owners. Helps to improve management skills and expand the products and services of members. **Geographic Preference:** Local.

38998 ■ Illinois Small Business Development Center at SIU-E/East St. Louis
601 James R. Thompson Dr., Rm. 2009
 East Saint Louis, IL 62201-1200
Ph: (618)482-6913
Co. E-mail: sbdcedw@gmail.com
URL: http://www.siue.edu/eslc
Contact: Dr. Timothy Staples, Executive Director
E-mail: tstaple@siue.edu
Description: Represents and promotes the small business sector. Provides management assistance to current and prospective small business owners. Helps to improve management skills and expand the products and services of members. **Founded:** 1941. **Geographic Preference:** Local.

38999 ■ Illinois Small Business Development Center at Southeastern Illinois College
3575 College Rd.
 Harrisburg, IL 62946
Ph: (618)252-5400
Free: 866-338-2742
URL: http://www.sic.edu/audience/business-industry/
 small-business-development-center
Contact: Lori Cox, Director
E-mail: lori.cox@sic.edu
Description: Provides management assistance to current and prospective small business owners in Southeastern Illinois. **Geographic Preference:** Local.

39000 ■ Illinois Small Business Development Center at Southern Illinois University
6 Hairpin Dr.
 Edwardsville, IL 62026-1107
Ph: (618)650-2929
Fax: (618)650-2647
Co. E-mail: sbdcedw@gmail.com
URL: http://www.siue.edu/business/sbdc
Contact: Jo Ann May, Director
E-mail: gdimagg@siue.edu
Description: Provides management assistance to current and prospective small business owners in Southern Illinois. **Geographic Preference:** Local.

39001 ■ Illinois Small Business Development Center at Waubonsee Community College
18 S River St.
 Aurora, IL 60506-4134
Ph: (630)801-7900
Co. E-mail: sbdc@waubonsee.edu
URL: http://www.waubonsee.edu/community
 -offerings/illinois-small-business-development-cen
 ter-waubonsee
Facebook: www.facebook.com/waubonsee.sbdc
Description: Provides management assistance to current and prospective small business owners in Waubonsee. **Geographic Preference:** Local.

39002 ■ Illinois Small Business Development Center at Western Illinois University
304 Sea Hall
 Western Illinois University
 Macomb, IL 61455
Ph: (309)298-3040
Fax: (309)298-3041
Co. E-mail: sb-center@wiu.edu
URL: http://wiusbdc.org
Facebook: www.facebook.com/
 IllinoisSmallBusinessDevelopmentCenter
Description: Provides management assistance to current and prospective small business owners in Western Illinois. **Founded:** 1989. **Geographic Preference:** Local.

39003 ■ Pike County Economic Development Center
1301 E Washington
 Pittsfield, IL 62363
Ph: (217)440-5101
URL: http://www.pikeedc.org
Contact: Patrick Conley, Chairman of the Board
Facebook: www.facebook.com/PCEDC
X (Twitter): x.com/PikeCoWorks
Description: A small business incubator that serves entrepreneurs and startups. Services include affordable lease rates, low startup costs, small business counseling, business seminars, business plan assistance, and financial planning and assistance. **Founded:** 1999.

SMALL BUSINESS ASSISTANCE PROGRAMS

39004 ■ Illinois Department of Commerce and Economic Opportunity - Energy and Recycling
500 E Monroe
 Springfield, IL 62701-1643
Ph: (217)785-3416
Free: 800-785-6055
URL: http://www.illinoisenergy.org
Description: Intervenes in the utility rate-setting process and in disputes between small businesses and utility companies. Assists in financing energy conservation measures.

SCORE OFFICES

39005 ■ Chicago SCORES
600 W Cermak Rd.
 Chicago, IL 60616
Ph: (312)666-0496
Co. E-mail: info@chicagoscores.org
URL: http://www.chicagoscores.org
Contact: Jessica Mater, Executive Director (Acting)
Facebook: www.facebook.com/
 AmericaSCORESChicago
Linkedin: www.linkedin.com/company/america-scores
 -chicago
Instagram: www.instagram.com/
 americascoreschicago
Description: Aims to empower students in urban communities with the use of soccer, writing with creative expression and service-learning. **Founded:** 2000. **Geographic Preference:** Local.

39006 ■ Decatur SCORE
1430 W William St.
 Decatur, IL 62522
Ph: (217)381-5143
URL: http://decatur.score.org
Contact: John C. Bury, Contact
Facebook: www.facebook.com/SCOREDecaturIL
Linkedin: www.linkedin.com/company/score-mentors
 -decatur
Description: Works to strengthen the formation, growth and success of small businesses nationwide. **Founded:** 1964. **Geographic Preference:** Local.

39007 ■ E. Central Illinois (ECI) SCORE
403 N E Jefferson St.
 Peoria, IL 61603
URL: http://www.score.org/peoria/content

39008 ■ Peoria SCORE
403 NE Jefferson St.
 Peoria, IL 61603
Ph: (309)676-0755
Co. E-mail: score.peoria@scorevolunteer.org
URL: http://www.score.org/peoria
Contact: Andrew Fograscher, President
Facebook: www.facebook.com/SCOREPeoria
Linkedin: www.linkedin.com/company/peoria-score
 .org
X (Twitter): x.com/scorepeoria
YouTube: www.youtube.com/user/
 SCORESmallBusiness
Pinterest: www.pinterest.com/scorementors
Founded: 1965.

39009 ■ Quad Cities SCORE
331 W 3rd St.
 Davenport, IA 52801
Ph: (309)797-0082
Co. E-mail: help@score.org
URL: http://quadcities.score.org
Contact: Rieva Lesonsky, Contact
Facebook: www.facebook.com/SCOREQuadCities
Description: Provides professional guidance and information to maximize the success of existing and emerging small businesses. Develops business plans

STATE LISTINGS

and evaluate financial projections. Promotes entrepreneur education in the western Illinois/eastern Iowa Quad Cities area including Moline and Rock Island IL and Davenport and Bettendorf, IA. **Founded:** 1978. **Publications:** *Quad Cities SCORE Newsletter* (Bimonthly). **Geographic Preference:** Local.

39010 ■ SCORE - Antioch
440 Lake Str.
Antioch, IL 60002
URL: http://northchicago.score.org
Description: Provides professional guidance and information to maximize the success of existing and emerging small businesses. Offers business counseling and workshops.

39011 ■ SCORE - Arlington Heights Chamber of Commerce (AHCC)
3400 W Stonegate Blvd.
Arlington Heights, IL 60005
Ph: (847)253-1703
Fax: (847)253-9133
Co. E-mail: info@arlingtonhcc.com
URL: http://arlingtonhcc.com
Contact: Marc Poulos, Chairman of the Board
Facebook: www.facebook.com/arlingtonheightschamber
Linkedin: www.linkedin.com/company/arlington-heights-chamber-of-commerce
X (Twitter): x.com/ArlHtsChamber
YouTube: www.youtube.com/ArlingtonHtsChamber
Description: Provides professional guidance and information to maximize the success of existing and emerging small businesses. Offers business counseling and workshops.

39012 ■ SCORE - Arlington Heights Library
500 N Dunton Ave.
Arlington Heights, IL 60004
Co. E-mail: scorensclc@gmail.com
URL: http://www.northchicago.score.org/arlington-heights-library
Description: Provides professional guidance and information to maximize the success of existing and emerging small businesses. Offers business counseling and workshops.

39013 ■ SCORE - Aurora Santori Library
Aurora, IL
URL: http://foxvalley.score.org/branch/aurora-santori-library
Description: Provides professional guidance and information to maximize the success of existing and emerging small businesses. Offers business counseling and workshops.

39014 ■ SCORE - Barrington Bank and Trust
201 S Hough St.
Barrington, IL 60010
URL: http://northchicago.score.org/barrington-bank
Description: Provides professional guidance and information to maximize the success of existing and emerging small businesses. Offers business counseling and workshops.

39015 ■ SCORE - Barrington Library
505 N NW Hwy.
Barrington, IL 60010
URL: http://northchicago.score.org/barrington-library
Description: Provides professional guidance and information to maximize the success of existing and emerging small businesses. Offers business counseling and workshops.

39016 ■ SCORE - Bloomingdale
104 S Bloomingdale Rd.
Bloomingdale, IL 60108
Ph: (630)980-9082
Co. E-mail: info@bloomingdalechamber.com
URL: http://www.bloomingdalechamber.com/score
Contact: Chris Karountzos, Chairman of the Board
Description: Provides professional guidance and information to maximize the success of existing and emerging small businesses. Offers business counseling and workshops. **Founded:** 1982.

39017 ■ SCORE - Bolingbrook
198 S Bolingbrook Dr.
Bolingbrook, IL 60440
Ph: (630)633-5930
URL: http://greaterhartford.score.org/find-location?state=IL
Description: Provides professional guidance and information to maximize the success of existing and emerging small businesses. Offers business counseling and workshops.

39018 ■ SCORE - Buffalo Grove
1954 First Ave., Ste. 193
Highland Park, IL 60035
Ph: (224)372-3432
URL: http://greaterhartford.score.org/find-location?state=IL
Description: Provides professional guidance and information to maximize the success of existing and emerging small businesses. Offers business counseling and workshops.

39019 ■ SCORE - Chicago
500 W Madison St., Ste. 1150
Chicago, IL 60661
Ph: (312)725-0123
Fax: (312)886-4879
Co. E-mail: info@scorechicago.org
URL: http://chicago.score.org
Facebook: www.facebook.com/scorechicago
Linkedin: www.linkedin.com/company/score-chicago
X (Twitter): x.com/SCOREChicago
Instagram: www.instagram.com/scorechicago
YouTube: www.youtube.com/user/ScoreChicagoVideo
Pinterest: www.pinterest.com/SCOREChicago
Description: Provides professional guidance and information to maximize the success of existing and emerging small businesses. Offers business counseling and workshops. **Geographic Preference:** Local.

39020 ■ SCORE - Chicago Beverly Area Planning Association
500 W Madison St., Ste. 1150
Chicago, IL 60661
Ph: (312)353-7724
Fax: (312)886-4879
Co. E-mail: toma.talpa@scorevolunteer.org
URL: http://chicago.score.org
Linkedin: www.linkedin.com/company/score-chicago
X (Twitter): x.com/scorechicago
Instagram: www.instagram.com/scorechicago
YouTube: www.youtube.com/user/ScoreChicagoVideo
Pinterest: www.pinterest.com/SCOREChicago
Description: Provides professional guidance and information to maximize the success of existing and emerging small businesses. Offers business counseling and workshops.

39021 ■ SCORE - Chicago City Hall
c/o BACP City Hall, Rm. 800
121 N LaSalle St.
Chicago, IL 60602
Ph: (312)744-2086
Co. E-mail: toma.talpa@scorevolunteer.org
URL: http://chicago.score.org
Contact: Robert L. Nevin, President
Description: Provides professional guidance and information to maximize the success of existing and emerging small businesses. Offers business counseling and workshops.

39022 ■ SCORE - Chicago Harold Washington Library Center
500 W Madison St., Ste., 1150
Chicago, IL 60661
Ph: (312)353-7724
Fax: (312)886-4879
Co. E-mail: toma.talpa@scorevolunteer.org
URL: http://chicago.score.org
Contact: Hannah Fernandez, Chairman
URL(s): pittsburgh.score.org/find-location
Linkedin: www.linkedin.com/company/score-chicago
X (Twitter): x.com/scorechicago
YouTube: www.youtube.com/user/ScoreChicagoVideo
Pinterest: www.pinterest.com/SCOREChicago
Description: Provides professional guidance and information to maximize the success of existing and emerging small businesses. Offers business counseling and workshops. **Founded:** 1974.

39023 ■ SCORE - Chicago Lakeview
3179 N Clark St., 2nd Floor of 5th 3rd Bank Bldg.
Chicago, IL 60657
Ph: (773)303-0167
Co. E-mail: scorechicago@scorevolunteer.org
URL: http://www.score.org/chicago/about/our-locations
Description: Provides professional guidance and information to maximize the success of existing and emerging small businesses. Offers business counseling and workshops.

39024 ■ SCORE - Chicago Logan Square
500 W Madison St. Ste. 1150
Chicago, IL 60661
Co. E-mail: toma.talpa@scorevolunteer.org
URL: http://chicago.score.org
Linkedin: www.linkedin.com/company/score-chicago
X (Twitter): x.com/scorechicago
YouTube: www.youtube.com/user/ScoreChicagoVideo
Pinterest: www.pinterest.com/SCOREChicago
Description: Provides professional guidance and information to maximize the success of existing and emerging small businesses. Offers business counseling and workshops.

39025 ■ SCORE - Chicago Ravenswood
500 W Madison St. Ste. 1150
Chicago, IL 60661
Ph: (312)353-7724
Fax: (312)886-4879
Co. E-mail: info@scorechicago.org
URL: http://chicago.score.org
Contact: Hannah Fernandez, Chairman
Linkedin: www.linkedin.com/company/score-chicago
X (Twitter): x.com/scorechicago
Instagram: www.instagram.com/scorechicago
YouTube: www.youtube.com/user/ScoreChicagoVideo
Description: Provides professional guidance and information to maximize the success of existing and emerging small businesses. Offers business counseling and workshops.

39026 ■ SCORE - Countryside
6734 Joliet Rd.
Countryside, IL 60525
Ph: (630)908-0088
Co. E-mail: toma.talpa@scorevolunteer.org
URL: http://chicago.score.org/score-chicago-branch-locations
Description: Provides professional guidance and information to maximize the success of existing and emerging small businesses. Offers business counseling and workshops.

39027 ■ SCORE - Darien
401 Plainfield Rd.
Darien, IL 60561
Ph: (630)692-1162
Co. E-mail: help@score.org
URL: http://foxvalley.score.org
Description: Provides professional guidance and information to maximize the success of existing and emerging small businesses. Offers business counseling and workshops.

39028 ■ SCORE - Decatur
907 W Marketview Dr., Ste. 10
Champaign, IL 61822
Ph: (217)381-5143
URL: http://decatur.score.org
Facebook: www.facebook.com/SCOREDecaturIL
Linkedin: www.linkedin.com/company/score-mentors-decatur
Description: Provides professional guidance and information to maximize the success of existing and emerging small businesses. Offers business counseling and workshops.

39029 ■ SCORE - Deerfield
405 Lake Cook Rd., Ste. 200
Deerfield, IL 60015
URL: http://www.score.org/northchicago/content/about/north-chicago-branches
Description: Provides professional guidance and information to maximize the success of existing and emerging small businesses. Offers business counseling and workshops.

39030 ■ SCORE - DeKalb
775 S Annie Glidden Rd.
DeKalb, IL 60115
URL: http://foxvalley.score.org
Description: Provides professional guidance and information to maximize the success of existing and emerging small businesses. Offers business counseling and workshops.

39031 ■ SCORE - Des Plaines
1400 E Touhy, Ste. 145
Des Plaines, IL 60018
Ph: (847)824-4200
Co. E-mail: scorensclc@gmail.com
URL: http://northchicago.score.org/desplaines-chamber
Description: Provides professional guidance and information to maximize the success of existing and emerging small businesses. Offers business counseling and workshops.

39032 ■ SCORE - Elgin Gail Borden Library
Elgin, IL
Co. E-mail: help@score.org
URL: http://foxvalley.score.org/content/about-us-62
Description: Provides professional guidance and information to maximize the success of existing and emerging small businesses. Offers business counseling and workshops.

39033 ■ SCORE - Elgin State Bank
1001 S Randall Rd.
Elgin, IL 60123
Ph: (630)692-1162
URL: http://foxvalley.score.org
Description: Provides professional guidance and information to maximize the success of existing and emerging small businesses. Offers business counseling and workshops.

39034 ■ SCORE - Elk Grove Village
1001 Wellington Ave.
Elk Grove Village, IL 60007
URL: http://northchicago.score.org/find-location
Description: Provides professional guidance and information to maximize the success of existing and emerging small businesses. Offers business counseling and workshops.

39035 ■ SCORE - Elmhurst
125 S Prospect Ave.
Elmhurst, IL 60126
Ph: (630)279-8696
URL: http://foxvalley.score.org
Description: Provides professional guidance and information to maximize the success of existing and emerging small businesses. Offers business counseling and workshops.

39036 ■ SCORE - Evanston
1703 Orrington Ave.
Evanston, IL 60201
URL: http://northchicago.score.org
Contact: Randall Smith, President
Description: Provides professional guidance and information to maximize the success of existing and emerging small businesses. Offers business counseling and workshops.

39037 ■ SCORE - Fox Valley
902 S Randall Rd., Ste. C 314
Saint Charles, IL 60174
Ph: (630)692-1162
Co. E-mail: help@score.org
URL: http://foxvalley.score.org
Contact: Louis J. Dries, Contact
Facebook: www.facebook.com/SCOREFoxValley
Linkedin: www.linkedin.com/company/score-fox-valley-chapter-289
Description: Strives for the formation, growth and success of small businesses. Provides professional guidance and information to maximize the success of existing and emerging small businesses. Promotes entrepreneur education in Fox Valley area, Illinois.
Founded: 1964. **Geographic Preference:** Local.

39038 ■ SCORE - Frankfort
Frankfort, IL
Co. E-mail: toma.talpa@scorevolunteer.org
URL: http://chicago.score.org/mentors/john-schneider
Description: Provides professional guidance and information to maximize the success of existing and emerging small businesses. Offers business counseling and workshops.

39039 ■ SCORE - Glen Ellyn
357 Roosevelt Rd.
Glen Ellyn, IL 60137
URL: http://foxvalley.score.org
Contact: Tom Drouin, Contact
Description: Provides professional guidance and information to maximize the success of existing and emerging small businesses. Offers business counseling and workshops.

39040 ■ SCORE - Glenview Park Center
2400 Chestnut
Glenview, IL 60025
URL: http://northchicago.score.org/glenview-park-cender
Description: Provides professional guidance and information to maximize the success of existing and emerging small businesses. Offers business counseling and workshops.

39041 ■ SCORE - Glenview Public Library
1930 Glenview Rd.
Glenview, IL 60025
Ph: (847)729-7500
URL: http://northchicago.score.org/glenview-public-library
URL(s): pittsburgh.score.org/find-location
Description: Provides professional guidance and information to maximize the success of existing and emerging small businesses. Offers business counseling and workshops.

39042 ■ SCORE - Glenview State Bank
2222 Chestnut Ave.
Glenview, IL 60026
URL: http://northchicago.score.org/glenview-state-bank
Contact: Emil Winograd, Contact
Description: Provides professional guidance and information to maximize the success of existing and emerging small businesses. Offers business counseling and workshops.

39043 ■ SCORE - Gurnee
Warren Newport Library
224 N O'Plaine Rd.
Gurnee, IL 60031
URL: http://northchicago.score.org/gurnee-warren-newport-library
Contact: Richard McFarlane, Contact
Description: Provides professional guidance and information to maximize the success of existing and emerging small businesses. Offers business counseling and workshops.

39044 ■ SCORE - Highland Park
1954 First Ave., Ste. 193
Highland Park, IL 60035
Ph: (224)372-3432
URL: http://northchicago.score.org
Contact: John Fisher, President
Description: Provides professional guidance and information to maximize the success of existing and emerging small businesses. Offers business counseling and workshops.

39045 ■ SCORE - Hoffman Estates
2200 W Higgins Rd.
Hoffman Estates, IL 60169
URL: http://www.score.org/northchicago/content/about/north-chicago-branches
Description: Provides professional guidance and information to maximize the success of existing and emerging small businesses. Offers business counseling and workshops.

39046 ■ SCORE - Lake Bluff
4 E Scranton Ave.
Lake Bluff, IL 60044
URL: http://northchicago.score.org/lake-bluff-lake-forest-bank-and-trust
Description: Provides professional guidance and information to maximize the success of existing and emerging small businesses. Offers business counseling and workshops.

39047 ■ SCORE - Lake Forest
717 Forest Ave., 2nd Fl.
Lake Forest, IL 60045
URL: http://www.score.org/northchicago/content/about/north-chicago-branches
Description: Provides professional guidance and information to maximize the success of existing and emerging small businesses. Offers business counseling and workshops.

39048 ■ SCORE - Lake Zurich
444 S Rand Rd.
Lake Zurich, IL 60047
URL: http://northchicago.score.org/lake-zurich-chamber
Description: Provides professional guidance and information to maximize the success of existing and emerging small businesses. Offers business counseling and workshops.

39049 ■ SCORE - Libertyville
507 N Milwaukee Ave.
Libertyville, IL 60048
Co. E-mail: scorensclc@gmail.com
URL: http://northchicago.score.org/libertyville-bank-and-trust
Description: Provides professional guidance and information to maximize the success of existing and emerging small businesses. Offers business counseling and workshops.

39050 ■ SCORE - Lincolnshire
300 Olde Half Day Rd.
Lincolnshire, IL 60069
Co. E-mail: scorensclc@gmail.com
URL: http://northchicago.score.org
Contact: Arnold Goldberg, Contact
Description: Provides professional guidance and information to maximize the success of existing and emerging small businesses. Offers business counseling and workshops.

39051 ■ SCORE - Matteson
4821 Southwick Dr.
Matteson, IL 60443
Co. E-mail: toma.talpa@scorevolunteer.org
URL: http://chicago.score.org
Description: Provides professional guidance and information to maximize the success of existing and emerging small businesses. Offers business counseling and workshops.

39052 ■ SCORE - McHenry
4100 W Shamrock Ln.
McHenry, IL 60050
URL: http://foxvalley.score.org
Description: Provides professional guidance and information to maximize the success of existing and emerging small businesses. Offers business counseling and workshops.

39053 ■ SCORE - Mount Prospect
10 S Emerson St.
Mount Prospect, IL 60056
URL: http://www.score.org/northchicago/content/about/north-chicago-branches
Description: Provides professional guidance and information to maximize the success of existing and emerging small businesses. Offers business counseling and workshops.

STATE LISTINGS

39054 ■ SCORE - Mundelein
Wintrust Community Bank
1110 W Maple Ave.
Mundelein, IL 60060
URL: http://www.score.org/northchicago/content/abou t/north-chicago-branches
Description: Provides professional guidance and information to maximize the success of existing and emerging small businesses. Offers business counseling and workshops.

39055 ■ SCORE - Naperville
Naperville, IL
URL: http://foxvalley.score.org/success-story/ riverwalk-adult-day-services-score-fox-valley-success-story
Description: Provides professional guidance and information to maximize the success of existing and emerging small businesses. Offers business counseling and workshops.

39056 ■ SCORE - Naperville Public Library Nichols Library
200 W Jefferson
Naperville, IL 60540
URL: http://foxvalley.score.org/branch/naperville -public-library-nichols-library
Description: Provides professional guidance and information to maximize the success of existing and emerging small businesses. Offers business counseling and workshops.

39057 ■ SCORE - Niles
6960 W Oakton St.
Niles, IL 60714
URL: http://northchicago.score.org/niles-maine-distric t-library
Contact: Mark Lieberman, Contact
Description: Provides professional guidance and information to maximize the success of existing and emerging small businesses. Offers business counseling and workshops.

39058 ■ SCORE - North Chicago
1954 First Ave. Ste. 193
Highland Park, IL 60035
Ph: (224)372-3432
Co. E-mail: scorensclc@gmail.com
URL: http://northchicago.score.org
Contact: John Fisher, President
Description: Provides professional guidance and information to maximize the success of existing and emerging small businesses. Offers business counseling and workshops.

39059 ■ SCORE - North Cook and Lake Counties
1954 First Ave., Ste. 193
Highland Park, IL 60035
Ph: (224)372-3432
Co. E-mail: scorensclc@gmail.com
URL: http://northchicago.score.org
Contact: Bridget Weston, Chief Executive Officer
Facebook: www.facebook.com/SCORENorthCookan dLakeCounties
Linkedin: www.linkedin.com/company/score-mentors -north-cook-and-lake-counties
X (Twitter): x.com/ScoreCook
YouTube: www.youtube.com/channel/UC2hkHcemM 2BXtoW3rLPtPWg
Description: Provides professional guidance and information to maximize the success of existing and emerging small businesses. Offers business counseling and workshops.

39060 ■ SCORE - Northbrook
1201 Cedar Ln.
Northbrook, IL 60062
URL: http://www.score.org/northchicago/content/abou t/north-chicago-branches
Description: Provides professional guidance and information to maximize the success of existing and emerging small businesses. Offers business counseling and workshops.

39061 ■ SCORE - Northbrook Bank and Trust
1100 Waukegan Rd.
Northbrook, IL 60062
Co. E-mail: scorensclc@gmail.com
URL: http://northchicago.score.org/northbrook-bank -and-trust
Description: Provides professional guidance and information to maximize the success of existing and emerging small businesses. Offers business counseling and workshops.

39062 ■ SCORE - Northbrook Chamber of Commerce
1954 1st Ave.
Highland Park, IL 60035
Ph: (224)372-3432
Co. E-mail: scorensclc@gmail.com
URL: http://northchicago.score.org
Facebook: www.facebook.com/SCORENorthCookan dLakeCounties
Linkedin: www.linkedin.com/company/score-mentors -north-cook-and-lake-counties
X (Twitter): x.com/ScoreCook
Description: Provides professional guidance and information to maximize the success of existing and emerging small businesses. Offers business counseling and workshops.

39063 ■ SCORE - Northfield
245 Waukegan Rd.
Northfield, IL 60093
Co. E-mail: scorensclc@gmail.com
URL: http://northchicago.score.org
Facebook: www.facebook.com/SCORENorthCookan dLakeCounties
X (Twitter): twitter.com/ScoreCook
Description: Provides professional guidance and information to maximize the success of existing and emerging small businesses. Offers business counseling and workshops.

39064 ■ SCORE - Oak Forest
16333 S Kilbourn Ave. - BCI, Ste. 5350
Oak Forest, IL 60452
Ph: (708)596-2000
URL: http://chicago.score.org/branch/oak-forest
Description: Provides professional guidance and information to maximize the success of existing and emerging small businesses. Offers business counseling and workshops.

39065 ■ SCORE - Oak Park
Oak Park, IL
URL: http://chicago.score.org
Contact: Jonathan M. Berman, Contact
Description: Provides professional guidance and information to maximize the success of existing and emerging small businesses. Offers business counseling and workshops.

39066 ■ SCORE - Oak Park Public Library (OPPL)
834 Lake St.
Oak Park, IL 60301
Ph: (708)383-8200
Fax: (708)697-6917
URL: http://www.oppl.org/research-learn
Contact: David J. Seleb, President
E-mail: davids@oppl.org
X (Twitter): x.com/oakparklibrary
YouTube: www.youtube.com/user/ OakParkPublicLibrary
Description: Provides professional guidance and information to maximize the success of existing and emerging small businesses. Offers business counseling and workshops. **Founded:** 1948.

39067 ■ SCORE - Palatine Bank & Trust
110 W Palatine Rd.
Palatine, IL 60067
URL: http://northchicago.score.org/palatine-bank-an d-trust
Description: Provides professional guidance and information to maximize the success of existing and emerging small businesses. Offers business counseling and workshops.

39068 ■ SCORE - Palatine Public Library
700 N Ct.
Palatine, IL 60067
Ph: (224)372-3432
URL: http://www.score.org/northchicago/content/abou t/north-chicago-branches
Contact: David Kirshner, Contact
Description: Provides professional guidance and information to maximize the success of existing and emerging small businesses. Offers business counseling and workshops.

39069 ■ SCORE - Palos Hills
9000 W Collegea Pky.
Workforce Development & Community Service, Bldg. M, Rm. 150
Palos Hills, IL 60465
Ph: (708)974-5468
Co. E-mail: toma.talpa@scorevolunteer.org
URL: http://chicago.score.org/score-chicago-branch -locations
Description: Provides professional guidance and information to maximize the success of existing and emerging small businesses. Offers business counseling and workshops.

39070 ■ SCORE - Park Ridge
20 S Prospect Ave.
Park Ridge, IL 60068
URL: http://northchicago.score.org/park-ridge-public -library
Description: Provides professional guidance and information to maximize the success of existing and emerging small businesses. Offers business counseling and workshops.

39071 ■ SCORE - Peoria
403 NE Jefferson St.
Peoria, IL 61603
Ph: (309)676-0755
Fax: (309)676-7534
Co. E-mail: score.peoria@scorevolunteer.org
URL: http://peoria.score.org
Linkedin: www.linkedin.com/company/peoria-score .org
X (Twitter): x.com/scorepeoria
Description: Provides professional guidance and information to maximize the success of existing and emerging small businesses. Offers business counseling and workshops. **Founded:** 1965. **Geographic Preference:** Local.

39072 ■ SCORE - Plainfield
Plainfield, IL
Co. E-mail: help@score.org
URL: http://foxvalley.score.org
Description: Provides professional guidance and information to maximize the success of existing and emerging small businesses. Offers business counseling and workshops.

39073 ■ SCORE - Rockford
Rockford Public Library
6685 E State St.
Rockford, IL 61108
URL: http://foxvalley.score.org/mentors/jaron-hite
Contact: Jaron Hite, Contact
Description: Counsels small businesses on start-up, writing a business plan, addressing problems with cash flow, inventory control, and other business-related issues. **Publications:** *Scoreboard* (Monthly). **Educational Activities:** Starting a Small Business/ Writing a Business Plan. **Geographic Preference:** Regional.

39074 ■ SCORE - Rosemont
9700 W Higgins Rd.
Rosemont, IL 60018
URL: http://northchicago.score.org
Facebook: www.facebook.com/SCORENorthCookan dLakeCounties
Linkedin: www.linkedin.com/company/score-mentors -north-cook-and-lake-counties
X (Twitter): x.com/ScoreCook

Description: Provides professional guidance and information to maximize the success of existing and emerging small businesses. Offers business counseling and workshops.

39075 ■ SCORE - Schaumburg Bank & Trust
1180 E Higgins Rd.
Schaumburg, IL 60173
URL: http://northchicago.score.org/schaumburg-bank-and-trust
Description: Provides professional guidance and information to maximize the success of existing and emerging small businesses. Offers business counseling and workshops.

39076 ■ SCORE - Schaumburg Public Library
130 S Roselle Rd.
Schaumburg, IL 60193
URL: http://northchicago.score.org/schaumburg-public-library
Description: Provides professional guidance and information to maximize the success of existing and emerging small businesses. Offers business counseling and workshops.

39077 ■ SCORE - Skokie
5215 Oakton St.
Skokie, IL 60077
URL: http://northchicago.score.org
Description: Provides professional guidance and information to maximize the success of existing and emerging small businesses. Offers business counseling and workshops.

39078 ■ SCORE - Springfield, Illinois
3330 Ginger Creek Dr.
Springfield, IL 62711
Ph: (217)381-5143
Co. E-mail: help@score.org
URL: http://decatur.score.org/springfieldbranch
Description: Provides professional guidance and information to maximize the success of existing and emerging small businesses. Offers business counseling and workshops. **Founded:** 1964. **Geographic Preference:** Local.

39079 ■ SCORE - Streamwood
1405 S Pk. Ave.
Streamwood, IL 60107
URL: http://northchicago.score.org
Description: Provides professional guidance and information to maximize the success of existing and emerging small businesses. Offers business counseling and workshops.

39080 ■ SCORE - Wheaton
225 N Cross St.
Wheaton, IL 60187
Ph: (630)668-1374
Co. E-mail: help@score.org
URL: http://www.score.org/find-location?state=IL
Contact: Chris Wilson, Contact
Description: Provides professional guidance and information to maximize the success of existing and emerging small businesses. Offers business counseling and workshops.

39081 ■ SCORE - Wheeling
355 Schoenbeck Rd.
Wheeling, IL 60090
URL: http://northchicago.score.org
Description: Provides professional guidance and information to maximize the success of existing and emerging small businesses. Offers business counseling and workshops.

39082 ■ SCORE - Wilmette
1242 Wilmette Ave.
Wilmette, IL 60091
URL: http://northchicago.score.org/wilmette-public-library
Description: Provides professional guidance and information to maximize the success of existing and emerging small businesses. Offers business counseling and workshops.

BETTER BUSINESS BUREAUS

39083 ■ Better Business Bureau of Central Illinois
8100 N University St.
Peoria, IL 61615
Ph: (309)688-5124
Co. E-mail: info@mybbb.org
URL: http://www.bbb.org/local-bbb/bbb-of-central-illinois
Contact: Jessica Tharp, President
Facebook: www.facebook.com/HOIBBB
X (Twitter): x.com/BBBHOI
Instagram: www.instagram.com/bbbcentralil
YouTube: www.youtube.com/channel/UCSeeeeCLntPyY_oDs3soGnA
Description: Seeks to promote and foster the highest ethical relationship between businesses and the public through voluntary self-regulation, consumer and business education, and service excellence. Provides information to help consumers and businesses make informed purchasing decisions and avoid costly scams and frauds; settles consumer complaints through arbitration and other means. **Geographic Preference:** Local.

39084 ■ Better Business Bureau of Chicago and Northern Illinois
121 W Wacker Dr., Ste. 2000
Chicago, IL 60601
Ph: (312)832-0500
Free: 888-982-0210
Fax: (312)595-9760
Co. E-mail: bbbinfo@chicago.bbb.org
URL: http://www.bbb.org/local-bbb/bbb-of-chicago-and-northern-illinois
Contact: Steve J. Bernas, President
Facebook: www.facebook.com/ChicagoBBB
Linkedin: www.linkedin.com/company/chicagobbb
X (Twitter): x.com/ChicagoBBB
Instagram: www.instagram.com/chicagobbb
YouTube: www.youtube.com/bbbchicago
Description: Seeks to promote and foster the highest ethical relationship between businesses and the public through voluntary self-regulation, consumer and business education, and service excellence. Provides information to help consumers and businesses make informed purchasing decisions and avoid costly scams and frauds; settles consumer complaints through arbitration and other means. **Founded:** 1926. **Publications:** *BBB Alert* (Bimonthly); *The Consumer Resource Guide* (Quarterly). **Geographic Preference:** Local.

CHAMBERS OF COMMERCE

39085 ■ Addison Chamber of Commerce and Industry (ACCI)
1 Friendship Plz.
Addison, IL 60101
Ph: (630)543-4300
URL: http://www.addisonadvantage.org/business/chamber_of_commerce
Contact: Dee LaRocca, Executive Director
Description: Promotes the retention and further development of business in Addison, IL, and the representation of businesses to local and national county, state, and national governmental agencies. **Founded:** 1991. **Publications:** *Accent on Members* (Biennial); *Addison Community Directory*; *Shoptalk*. **Educational Activities:** Five Star Business EXPO. **Geographic Preference:** Local.

39086 ■ Albany Park Chamber of Commerce
3403 W Lawrence Ave., Ste. 201
Chicago, IL 60625
Ph: (773)478-0202
Co. E-mail: info@northrivercommission.org
URL: http://northrivercommission.org/chamber-of-commerce
Facebook: www.facebook.com/albanyparkchamber
X (Twitter): x.com/albanypkchamber
Description: Promotes business and community development in the Albany Park area of Chicago, IL. **Founded:** 1927. **Geographic Preference:** Local.

39087 ■ Algonquin - Lake in the Hills Chamber of Commerce
2200 Harnish Dr.
Algonquin, IL 60102
Ph: (847)658-5300
Co. E-mail: info@alchamber.com
URL: http://www.alchamber.com
Contact: Denny White, Chairman
Facebook: www.facebook.com/ALChamber
Linkedin: www.linkedin.com/company/algonquin-lake-in-the-hills-chamber-of-commerce
X (Twitter): x.com/alcoc
Description: Aims to bring area businesses and individuals together to improve the business climate and quality of life for all citizens. **Publications:** *Chamber Connections* (Monthly). **Geographic Preference:** Local.

39088 ■ Alsip Chamber of Commerce
12159 S Pulaski Rd.
Alsip, IL 60803
Ph: (708)597-2668
Fax: (708)597-5962
Co. E-mail: info@alsipchamber.org
URL: http://alsipchamber.org
Contact: Marigrace Sinnott-Snooks, Executive Director
Description: Promotes businesses in Alsip. **Founded:** 1961. **Geographic Preference:** Local.

39089 ■ Antioch Chamber of Commerce and Industry (ACCI)
882 Main St.
Antioch, IL 60002
Ph: (847)395-2233
Co. E-mail: office@antiochchamber.org
URL: http://www.antiochchamber.org
Contact: Marty Geweke, President
Facebook: www.facebook.com/AntiochChamberofCommerce
Description: Promotes business and community development in Antioch, IL. Sponsors art and craft fair, Christmas program, Easter Program, and Taste of Antioch. **Geographic Preference:** Local.

39090 ■ Arcola Chamber of Commerce
135 N Oak St.
Arcola, IL 61910
Ph: (217)268-4530
Co. E-mail: staff@arcolachamber.com
URL: http://www.arcolachamber.com
Facebook: www.facebook.com/amazingarcola
Description: Promotes business and community development in Arcola, IL area. **Geographic Preference:** Local.

39091 ■ Arlington Heights Chamber of Commerce (AHCC)
3400 W Stonegate Blvd.
Arlington Heights, IL 60005
Ph: (847)253-1703
Fax: (847)253-9133
Co. E-mail: info@arlingtonhcc.com
URL: http://www.arlingtonhcc.com
Contact: Jon Ridler, Executive Director
Facebook: www.facebook.com/arlingtonheightschamber
Linkedin: www.linkedin.com/company/arlington-heights-chamber-of-commerce
X (Twitter): x.com/ArlHtsChamber
YouTube: www.youtube.com/user/ArlingtonHtsChamber
Description: Promotes business and community development in Arlington Heights, IL. **Geographic Preference:** Local.

39092 ■ Barrington Area Chamber of Commerce (BACC)
190 E James St.
Barrington, IL 60010
Ph: (847)381-2525
Co. E-mail: email@barringtonchamber.com
URL: http://barringtonchamber.com
Contact: Suzanne Corr, President
E-mail: suzanne@barringtonchamber.com
Facebook: www.facebook.com/Barrington-Area-Chamber-of-Commerce-BACC-369925886352262

Linkedin: www.linkedin.com/company/barrington-area
-chamber-of-commerce
X (Twitter): x.com/bacc_tweet
YouTube: www.youtube.com/channel/UCjfQ1LjqIVbk
2iC4RjXAQ6g
Description: Aims to promote a dynamic business environment for the community. **Founded:** 1969. **Geographic Preference:** Local.

39093 ■ Bartlett Chamber of Commerce
335 S Main St.
Bartlett, IL 60103
Ph: (630)830-0324
Co. E-mail: nan@bartlettareachamber.com
URL: http://www.bartlettareachamber.com
Contact: Nanette Gudenkauf, President
Facebook: www.facebook.com/Bartle
ttAreaChamberIL
X (Twitter): x.com/ChamberBartlett
YouTube: www.youtube.com/channel/UC7wiilv3Z
_WgwkkUgCDa5dA
Description: Promotes business and community development in Bartlett, IL. **Founded:** 1977. **Publications:** *Bartletter Business and Chamber of Commerce Directory* (Annual); *Business Beat* (Monthly). **Geographic Preference:** Local.

39094 ■ Batavia Chamber of Commerce (BCC)
106 W Wilson St.
Batavia, IL 60510
Ph: (630)879-7134
Fax: (478)242-6237
Co. E-mail: info@bataviachamber.org
URL: http://www.bataviachamber.org
Contact: Margaret Perreault, President
Facebook: www.facebook.com/BataviaChamber
Linkedin: www.linkedin.com/company/batavia
-chamber-of-commerce
X (Twitter): x.com/bataviachamber
Description: Businesses, organizations, and individuals interested in business and community development in Batavia, IL. Supports community improvement projects. **Founded:** 1953. **Publications:** *Batavia Business* (Monthly). **Geographic Preference:** Local.

39095 ■ Beardstown Chamber of Commerce (BCC)
101 W 3rd St.
Beardstown, IL 62618
Ph: (217)323-3271
Co. E-mail: info@beardstownil.org
URL: http://www.beardstownil.org
Contact: Jack Bell, Contact
Facebook: www.facebook.com/chamber.commerce.5
Description: Promotes business and community development in Beardstown, IL. **Geographic Preference:** Local.

39096 ■ Beecher Chamber of Commerce
PO Box 292
Beecher, IL 60401-0292
Ph: (708)946-6803
Co. E-mail: info@beecherchamber.org
URL: http://beecherchamber.org
Contact: Larry Sanders, Jr., President
Facebook: www.facebook.com/
BeecherChamberOfCommerce
Description: Promotes business and community development in the Beecher, IL area. **Founded:** 1970. **Geographic Preference:** Local.

39097 ■ Belmont-Central Chamber of Commerce (BCCC)
5534 W Belmont Ave.
Chicago, IL 60641
Ph: (773)647-1644
Co. E-mail: belmontcentralcc@sbcglobal.net
URL: http://belmontcentral.org
Facebook: www.facebook.com/belmontcen
tralchamber
Description: Maintains a strong and viable commercial district at Belmont-Central. **Founded:** 1930. **Geographic Preference:** Local.

39098 ■ Belvidere Area Chamber of Commerce (BACC)
404 S State St.
Belvidere, IL 61008
Ph: (815)544-4357
Co. E-mail: info@belviderechamber.com
URL: http://www.belviderechamber.com
Contact: Amy Ohlsen, President
Facebook: www.facebook.com/BelvidereChamber
X (Twitter): x.com/BelvChamber
Instagram: www.instagram.com/belviderechamber
Description: Promotes business and community development in the Boone County, IL area. **Founded:** 1915. **Publications:** *Chamber HELP* (Annual); *Chamber News*. **Geographic Preference:** Local.

39099 ■ Benton-West City Area Chamber of Commerce
211 N Main St.
Benton, IL 62812
Ph: (618)438-2121
Co. E-mail: info@bentonwestcitychamber.com
URL: http://www.bentonwestcitychamber.com
Contact: Heston Mays, President
Facebook: www.facebook.com/BentonWestCi
tyAreaChamberOfCommerce
X (Twitter): x.com/benwCchamber
Description: Promotes business and community development in the Benton, IL area. Holds area festival. **Founded:** 1951. **Geographic Preference:** Local.

39100 ■ Berwyn Development Corp. (BCD)
3322 S Oak Pk. Ave., 2nd Fl.
Berwyn, IL 60402
Ph: (708)788-8100
Fax: (708)788-0966
Co. E-mail: info@berwyn.net
URL: http://www.berwyn.net
Contact: Diane Salemi, President
E-mail: dsalemi@republicebank.com
Facebook: www.facebook.com/WhyBerwyn
Linkedin: www.linkedin.com/company/berwyn
-development-corporation
X (Twitter): x.com/WhyBerwyn
Instagram: www.instagram.com/whyberwyn
YouTube: www.youtube.com/user/BerwynBDC
Description: Promotes business and community development in Berwyn, IL. Conducts charitable activities. **Founded:** 1983. **Publications:** *BDC Annual Report* (Annual); *Berwyn Business Briefs* (Quarterly); *Berwyn Community Business Directory* (Annual). **Awards:** Charles E. Piper Award (Annual). **Geographic Preference:** Local.

39101 ■ Black Chamber of Commerce of Lake County (BCCCL)
668 Lenox Ave.
Waukegan, IL 60085-6402
Ph: (847)596-2910
Fax: (847)596-2912
Co. E-mail: info@bcclcinc.org
URL: http://www.bcclcinc.org
Contact: Dan Davis, Treasurer Vice President
E-mail: dan.davis@bccoflakecounty.com
URL(s): bcclc.org
Facebook: www.facebook.com/bccoflakecounty
Description: Represents Black owned businesses. Seeks to empower and sustain African American communities through entrepreneurship and capitalistic activity. Provides advocacy, training and education to Black communities. **Founded:** 2006. **Geographic Preference:** Local.

39102 ■ Bloomingdale Chamber of Commerce (BCC)
104 S Bloomingdale Rd.
Bloomingdale, IL 60108
Ph: (630)980-9082
Co. E-mail: info@bloomingdalechamber.com
URL: http://www.bloomingdalechamber.com
Contact: Cindy Allston, President
Facebook: www.facebook.com/Blooming
daleChamber#!/pages/Bloomingdale-Chamber-of
-Commerce/256616857345
X (Twitter): x.com/Chamber60108
Description: Strives to promote the growth of local business for the benefit of Bloomingdale Chamber of Commerce and the community. **Founded:** 1982. **Publications:** *Chamber Outlook* (Monthly). **Awards:** Bloomingdale Chamber of Commerce Large Business of the Year (Annual); Bloomingdale Chamber of Commerce Ambassador of the Year (Annual). **Geographic Preference:** Local.

39103 ■ Blue Island Area Chamber of Commerce and Industry
2434 Vermont St.
Blue Island, IL 60406
Ph: (708)388-1000
Co. E-mail: sara@blueislandchamber.org
URL: http://www.blueislandchamber.org
Facebook: www.facebook.com/BlueIslandChamber
Description: Coordinates marketing and networking efforts, as well as acting as a liaison with various municipal bodies. **Founded:** 1952. **Geographic Preference:** Local.

39104 ■ Bolingbrook Area Chamber of Commerce (BACC)
201-B Canterbury Ln.
Bolingbrook, IL 60440
Ph: (630)226-8420
Fax: (630)226-8426
Co. E-mail: info@bolingbrookchamber.org
URL: http://bolingbrook.org
Contact: Kevin O'Keeffe, Executive Director
Facebook: www.facebook.com/bbchamber60440
Linkedin: www.linkedin.com/company/bolingbrook
-area-chamber-of-commerce
X (Twitter): x.com/bbchamber60440
Instagram: www.instagram.com/bolingbrook_chamber
YouTube: www.youtube.com/user/BolingbrookChamber
Description: Fosters a competitive enterprise system of business and promotes the growth and development of businesses in the community. **Founded:** 1978. **Educational Activities:** Business to Business Showcase (Periodic). **Geographic Preference:** Local.

39105 ■ Breese Chamber of Commerce
PO Box 132
Breese, IL 62230
URL: http://breesechamber.com
Contact: Nick Lampen, President
Description: Works hand-in-hand with the city of Breese to promote business and residential growth and encourage tourism and shopping. Aims to improve the existing facilities and the historical aspects of the city. **Geographic Preference:** Local.

39106 ■ Bridgeview Chamber of Commerce & Industry
7940 S Harlem Ave.
Bridgeview, IL 60455
Ph: (708)594-2525
Fax: (708)598-1709
Co. E-mail: info@bridgeviewchamber.net
URL: http://www.bridgeview-il.gov/chamber
Contact: Lara Al-Ali, President
Facebook: www.facebook.com/bri
dgeviewchamberofcommerceindustry
Description: Provides information from local, state and federal sources on a variety of issues that may affect the business community. Sponsors community programs such as the Toys for Needy Children Drive at Christmas, scholarships to deserving students, Fire Prevention Poster Contest, and Christmas Tree Lighting Ceremony. **Geographic Preference:** Local.

39107 ■ Brookfield Chamber of Commerce (BCC)
PO Box 38
Brookfield, IL 60513
Ph: (708)268-8080
Co. E-mail: info@brookfieldchamber.net
URL: http://www.brookfieldchamber.net
Facebook: www.facebook.com/BfieldChamber
Description: Promotes business and community development in Brookfield, IL area. **Founded:** 1953. **Geographic Preference:** Local.

39108 ■ Buffalo Grove Lincolnshire Chamber of Commerce (BGLCC)
50 1/2 Raupp Blvd.
Buffalo Grove, IL 60089
Ph: (847)541-7799
Fax: (847)541-7819
Co. E-mail: info@bglcc.org
URL: http://www.bglcc.org
Contact: Brad Schencker, President
Description: Promotes business and community development in Buffalo Grove, IL and surrounding communities. **Founded:** 1972. **Publications:** *Around Town* (Monthly). **Geographic Preference:** Local.

39109 ■ Bushnell Chamber of Commerce
PO Box 111
Bushnell, IL 61422
Co. E-mail: info@bushnellchamber.org
URL: http://www.bushnellchamber.org
Contact: Don Swartzbaugh, President
E-mail: dswartzbaugh@bushnellbank.com
Facebook: www.facebook.com/bushnellchamber
Instagram: www.instagram.com/bushnellchamber
Description: Works to build a strong economic base through the promotion of local businesses and activities. **Geographic Preference:** Local.

39110 ■ *Business*
200 E Railroad St.
Monticello, IL 61856
Ph: (217)762-7921
Co. E-mail: info@monticellochamber.org
URL: http://www.monticellochamber.org
Contact: Sarah Ross, Vice President
E-mail: sross@kirbyhealth.org
URL(s): monticellochamber.org/directory
Availability: Online.

39111 ■ *Business Directory*
1 N Research Dr.
Edwardsville, IL 62025
Ph: (618)656-7600
Fax: (618)656-7611
Co. E-mail: office@edglenchamber.com
URL: http://www.edglenchamber.com
Contact: Desiree Bennyhoff, President
URL(s): www.edglenchamber.com/business-directory.html
Availability: Print.

39112 ■ *Business Directory*
5002 Oakton St.
Skokie, IL 60077
Ph: (847)673-0240
Fax: (847)673-0249
Co. E-mail: info@skokiechamber.org
URL: http://skokiechamber.org
Contact: Scott F. Schoeller, President
URL(s): members.skokiechamber.org/list
Availability: Online.

39113 ■ Byron Area Chamber of Commerce
232 W 2nd St.
Byron, IL 61010
Ph: (815)234-5500
Co. E-mail: office@byronchamber.com
URL: http://www.byronchamber.com
Contact: Shawn McCammond, President
Facebook: www.facebook.com/byronchamber
Description: Promotes business and community development in Byron, IL. **Founded:** 1958. **Publications:** *Byron Chamber News* (Monthly). **Geographic Preference:** Local.

39114 ■ Cahokia Area Chamber of Commerce (CCC)
509 Camp Jackson Rd.
Cahokia, IL 62206
Ph: (618)623-5109
Co. E-mail: events@cahokiaheightschamber.org
URL: http://cahokiaheightschamber.org
Contact: Darwyn Buchanan, President
Facebook: www.facebook.com/cahokiaheightschamber
Description: Promotes business in the Cahokia, IL area. **Geographic Preference:** Local.

39115 ■ Canton Area Chamber of Commerce (CACC)
2 N Main St.
Canton, IL 61520
Ph: (309)647-2677
URL: http://www.cantonillinois.org/chamber
Contact: Jana Emmons, President
Facebook: www.facebook.com/CACC61520
Linkedin: www.linkedin.com/company/canton-illinois-chamber-of-commerce
Description: Businesses, organizations, and individuals promoting economic and community development in the Canton, IL area. **Founded:** 1925. **Publications:** *Chamber Courier* (Monthly). **Awards:** Canton Area Chamber of Commerce Citizen of the Year (Annual); Canton Area Chamber of Commerce Educator of the Year (Annual). **Geographic Preference:** Local.

39116 ■ Carbondale Chamber of Commerce (CCC)
131 S Illinios Ave.
Carbondale, IL 62901
Ph: (618)549-2146
Fax: (618)529-5063
Co. E-mail: info@carbondalechamber.com
URL: http://www.carbondalechamber.com
Contact: Steve Quinn, President
Linkedin: www.linkedin.com/company/carbondale-chamber-of-commerce
X (Twitter): x.com/cdalechamber
YouTube: www.youtube.com/channel/UCx2Ii0HJko6xZ3e2XFwNNM
Description: Promotes business and community development in the Carbondale, IL area. **Founded:** 1916. **Publications:** *The Communicator* (Bimonthly); *Membership Directory and Buyer's Guide* (Annual). **Awards:** Carbondale Chamber of Commerce Business Leader of the Year (Annual); Carbondale Chamber of Commerce Business of the Year (Annual); Carbondale Chamber of Commerce Citizen of the Year (Annual). **Geographic Preference:** Local.

39117 ■ Carlinville Community Chamber of Commerce
112 N Side Sq.
Carlinville, IL 62626
Ph: (217)854-2141
Co. E-mail: info@carlinville.com
URL: http://www.carlinville.com
Contact: Tim Rhodus, President
Facebook: www.facebook.com/carlinvillechamberofcommerce
Description: Promotes business and community development in Carlinville, IL. **Founded:** 1976. **Publications:** *Chamber Insider*. **Educational Activities:** Christmas Market (Annual). **Geographic Preference:** Local.

39118 ■ Carmi Chamber of Commerce (CCC)
108 N Main Cross
Carmi, IL 62821
Ph: (618)382-7606
Co. E-mail: chamber@cityofcarmi.com
URL: http://www.cityofcarmi.org/the-chamber
Contact: Kelly Northcott, Executive Director
Description: Aims to sustain and further develop a thriving economy in the area and enhance the community's quality of life. Sponsors several activities including community food basket drives at Thanksgiving. **Founded:** 1944. **Geographic Preference:** Local.

39119 ■ Carol Stream Chamber of Commerce
150 S Gary Ave.
Carol Stream, IL 60188
Ph: (630)665-3325
Co. E-mail: info@carolstreamchamber.com
URL: http://carolstreamchamber.com
Contact: Tracy Conn, President
Facebook: www.facebook.com/carolstreamchamber
Linkedin: www.linkedin.com/company/carolstreamchamber
X (Twitter): x.com/cs_chamber
Description: Represents businesses and professional people. Works to advance the economic well-being of the greater Carol Stream area and its nearby vicinity. Offers a variety of programs to keep the members at their competitive best. **Founded:** 1992. **Publications:** *Chamber Connection* (Monthly). **Geographic Preference:** Local.

39120 ■ Carterville Chamber of Commerce
120 N Greenbriar
Carterville, IL 62918
Ph: (618)985-6942
Fax: (618)985-6942
URL: http://www.cartervillechamber.com
Contact: Winter Campanella, President
Facebook: www.facebook.com/cartervillechambe
Linkedin: www.linkedin.com/company/carterville-chamber-of-commerce
X (Twitter): x.com/3cchamber
Description: Enhances the business and social climate of the Carterville area which helps individual businesses prosper. **Founded:** 1984. **Geographic Preference:** Local.

39121 ■ Carthage Area Chamber of Commerce (CACC)
PO Box 247
Carthage, IL 62321
Ph: (217)357-3024
Co. E-mail: chamber@carthage-il.com
URL: http://www.carthage-il.com
Contact: Cynthia Stewart, President
Description: Promotes business and community development in Hancock County, IL. **Geographic Preference:** Local.

39122 ■ Cary Grove Area Chamber of Commerce
445 Pk. Ave.
Cary, IL 60013
Ph: (847)639-2800
Co. E-mail: info@carygrovechamber.com
URL: http://www.carygrovechamber.com
Contact: Lynn Caccavallo, President
E-mail: lynn@carygrovechamber.com
Facebook: www.facebook.com/carygrovechamber
X (Twitter): x.com/carygrove
Description: Promotes business and community development in the Cary, IL area. Holds bimonthly board meeting. Sponsors Home and Business Expo. **Founded:** 1964. **Publications:** *Insights*; *Minutes of Board Meeting*. **Geographic Preference:** Local.

39123 ■ Chamber 630
2001 Butterfield Rd., Ste. 105
Downers Grove, IL 60515
Ph: (630)968-4050
Co. E-mail: info@chamber630.com
URL: http://www.chamber630.com
Contact: Laura Crawford, President
E-mail: laura@chamber630.com
Facebook: www.facebook.com/Chamber630
Linkedin: www.linkedin.com/company/chamber630
X (Twitter): x.com/Chamber630
Instagram: www.instagram.com/chamber630
Description: Promotes business and community development in the Woodridge, IL area. **Founded:** 1951. **Publications:** *Chamber Connections* (Monthly); *Connecticut River Valley Chamber of Commerce Business Directory*; *ChamberLine* (Monthly); *Village and Business* (Annual). **Geographic Preference:** Local.

39124 ■ *Chamber Chat*
3 S Pk. Ave.
Herrin, IL 62948
Ph: (618)942-5163
Co. E-mail: director@herrinchamber.com
URL: http://www.herrinchamber.com
Contact: Quinn Laird, President
URL(s): www.herrinchamber.com/join-us-today
Released: Monthly **Availability:** Online.

39125 ■ Chamber of Commerce of Southwestern Madison County (SWMC)
3600 Nameoki Rd., Ste. 101
Granite City, IL 62040
Ph: (618)876-6400
Fax: (618)876-6448
Co. E-mail: chamber@chamberswmc.org

URL: http://www.chamberswmc.org
Contact: David Stoecklin, Officer
Facebook: www.facebook.com/Chamber-of-Commerce-Southwestern-Madison-County-106917149432337
X (Twitter): x.com/ChamberSWMC
Description: Promotes business in Southwestern Madison County. **Founded:** 1896. **Geographic Preference:** Local.

39126 ■ *Chamber Courier*
2 N Main St.
Canton, IL 61520
Ph: (309)647-2677
URL: http://www.cantonillinois.org/chamber
Contact: Jana Emmons, President
URL(s): www.cantonillinois.org/chamber/chamber-courier
Released: Monthly **Description:** Contains information on chamber events and member activities. **Availability:** Download; PDF; Online.

39127 ■ *Chamber Review*
155 W Morton Ave.
Jacksonville, IL 62650
Ph: (217)245-2174
Fax: (217)245-0661
Co. E-mail: chamber2@jacksonvilleareachamber.org
URL: http://www.jacksonvilleareachamber.org
Contact: Adam Withee, Treasurer
URL(s): www.jacksonvilleareachamber.org/membership-benefits
Released: Monthly **Description:** Contains information on current chamber issues and activities. **Availability:** Print.

39128 ■ *Chambergram*
8799 W 151st St.
Orland Park, IL 60462
Ph: (708)349-2972
Fax: (708)349-7454
Co. E-mail: info@orlandparkchamber.org
URL: http://orlandparkchamber.org
Contact: Ramzi Hassan, President
URL(s): orlandparkchamber.org/chambergram-magazines
Ed: Bonnie Hollaway. **Released:** Monthly **Availability:** PDF; Online.

39129 ■ Champaign County Black Chamber of Commerce (CCBCC)
408 Taylor Thomas Ln.
Champaign, IL 61820
Co. E-mail: wkyles@ilbcc.org
URL: http://www.theccbcc.org
Contact: William Kyles, President
E-mail: wkyles@ilbcc.org
Facebook: www.facebook.com/theccbcc
Description: Represents Black owned businesses. Seeks to empower and sustain African American communities through entrepreneurship and capitalistic activity. Provides advocacy, training and education to Black communities. **Founded:** 2002. **Geographic Preference:** Local.

39130 ■ Champaign County Chamber of Commerce
303 W Kirby Ave.
Champaign, IL 61820
Ph: (217)359-1791
Co. E-mail: info@champaigncounty.org
URL: http://www.champaigncounty.org
Contact: Laura E. Weis, President
E-mail: lauraw@champaigncounty.org
Facebook: www.facebook.com/ccountychamber
X (Twitter): x.com/ccountychamber
YouTube: www.youtube.com/user/cctychamber
Description: Works to ensure a healthy economic and socio-economic base to benefit the community. **Publications:** *Commerce Connection* (Bimonthly); *Images of Champaign County* (Annual); *Champaign County Chamber of Commerce--Membership Directory* (Annual). **Educational Activities:** Business After Hours. **Awards:** Champaign County ATHENA Award (Annual); Champaign County Most Valuable Citizen (Annual); Champaign County Small Business of the Year (Annual); Champaign County Chamber Top Investors (Annual). **Geographic Preference:** Local.

39131 ■ Charleston Area Chamber of Commerce (CACC)
501 Jackson Ave.
Charleston, IL 61920
Ph: (217)345-7041
Co. E-mail: cacc@charlestonchamber.com
URL: http://www.charlestonchamber.com
Contact: Doug Abolt, President
Facebook: www.facebook.com/CharlestonAreaChamber
Linkedin: www.linkedin.com/in/charleston-illinois-chamber-of-commerce-b7511a31
Description: Promotes the economic climate in the greater Charleston, Illinois area. Acts as the marketing/promoting agent for the Charleston area in collaboration with other community organizations. **Founded:** 1919. **Publications:** *Chamber Focus* (Monthly); *Membership Directory & Buyers' Guide* (Annual); *Charleston Area Chamber of Commerce--Membership Directory & Buyer's Guide* (Annual). **Geographic Preference:** Local.

39132 ■ Chatham Area Chamber of Commerce (CACC)
106 E Mulberry St.
Chatham, IL 62629
Ph: (217)483-6450
Co. E-mail: coordinator@chatham-il-chamber.com
URL: http://www.chatham-il-chamber.com
Contact: Tracy Formea, President
Facebook: www.facebook.com/chathamilchamber
Description: Promotes business and community development in Chatham, NJ. **Geographic Preference:** Local.

39133 ■ Chicago Chinatown Chamber of Commerce
2169B S China Pl.
Chicago, IL 60616
Ph: (312)326-5320
Co. E-mail: info@chicagochinatown.org
URL: http://www.chicagochinatown.org
Contact: Patrick McShane, President
Facebook: www.facebook.com/ChicagoChinatownChamberofCommerce
X (Twitter): x.com/Chinatown312
Instagram: www.instagram.com/chinatownchamber
Description: Strives to improve and expand business opportunities and to educate others on the history, culture, and customs of the Chinese American community. **Founded:** 1983. **Publications:** *The Chamber News* (Monthly). **Geographic Preference:** State.

39134 ■ Chicagoland Chamber of Commerce (CCOC)
The Wrigley Bldg.
410 N Michigan Ave., Ste. 900
Chicago, IL 60611
Ph: (312)494-6700
Co. E-mail: info@chicagolandchamber.org
URL: http://www.chicagolandchamber.org
Contact: Jack Lavin, President
Facebook: www.facebook.com/ChicagolandChamber
X (Twitter): x.com/chicagolandcmbr
YouTube: www.youtube.com/channel/UCdBFeZNrlmqnKxAlaEksleg
Description: Promotes business and community development in Chicago, IL. Conducts drug-free workplace program. **Founded:** 1904. **Publications:** *Business Resource Guide and Membership Directory*; *Commerce--International Banking Issue* (Monthly); *Directory of Foreign Consulates and Other International Representation* (Semiannual). **Geographic Preference:** Local.

39135 ■ Chillicothe Chamber of Commerce
1028 N Second St.
Chillicothe, IL 61523
Ph: (309)274-4556
Fax: (309)274-3603
Co. E-mail: office@chillicothechamber.com
URL: http://www.chillicothechamber.com
Contact: Sarah Sights, President
Facebook: www.facebook.com/chillicothechamber
Description: Promotes business and community development in Chillicothe, IL. **Geographic Preference:** Local.

39136 ■ Clinton Area Chamber of Commerce and Tourism Bureau [Clinton Area Chamber of Commerce (CACC)]
100 S Ctr. St., Ste. 101
Clinton, IL 61727
Ph: (217)935-3364
Co. E-mail: chamber@clintonilchamber.com
URL: http://www.clintonilchamber.com
Contact: Josh Shofner, President
Description: Promotes business and community development in Clinton, IL. Sponsors Clinton May Days Festival and Community Expo. **Founded:** 1953. **Publications:** *Chamber Scoop* (Monthly). **Geographic Preference:** Local.

39137 ■ Collinsville Chamber of Commerce
221 W Main St.
Collinsville, IL 62234
Ph: (618)344-2884
Co. E-mail: info@discovercollinsville.com
URL: http://www.discovercollinsville.com
Contact: Jason Rehg, Advisor
Facebook: www.facebook.com/CollinsvilleChamber
Description: Promotes business and community development in Collinsville, IL. **Founded:** 1928. **Geographic Preference:** Local.

39138 ■ *Commerce Connection*
303 W Kirby Ave.
Champaign, IL 61820
Ph: (217)359-1791
Co. E-mail: info@champaigncounty.org
URL: http://www.champaigncounty.org
Contact: Laura E. Weis, President
E-mail: lauraw@champaigncounty.org
URL(s): www.champaigncounty.org/publications
Released: Bimonthly **Description:** Contains information on Chamber activities, issues of concern to members, committee reports, special events, and new member updates. **Availability:** PDF; Online.

39139 ■ *Common Ground*
1 N Research Dr.
Edwardsville, IL 62025
Ph: (618)656-7600
Fax: (618)656-7611
Co. E-mail: office@edglenchamber.com
URL: http://www.edglenchamber.com
Contact: Desiree Bennyhoff, President
URL(s): www.edglenchamber.com/common-ground.html
Released: Monthly **Description:** Includes news about chamber events. **Availability:** Online; PDF.

39140 ■ *Communicator*
URL(s): www.freeportilchamber.com/pages/Newsletter
Released: Monthly **Availability:** Print; PDF; Online.

39141 ■ *Community Guide*
1257 N Green St.
McHenry, IL 60050
Ph: (815)385-4300
Fax: (815)385-9142
Co. E-mail: info@mchenrychamber.com
URL: http://mchenrychamber.com
Contact: Molly Ostap, President
E-mail: molly@mchenrychamber.com
URL(s): mchenrychamber.com/membership-levels-and-benefits
Description: Includes organization lists, calendar of events, and editorials. **Availability:** Online.

39142 ■ *Community Guide*
2200 W Higgins Rd., Ste. 201
Hoffman Estates, IL 60169
Ph: (847)781-9100
Fax: (847)781-9172
Co. E-mail: info@hechamber.com
URL: http://www.hechamber.com
Contact: Tricia O'Brien, President

URL(s): www.hechamber.com/prospective-members
Released: Annual **Description:** Features lists of businesses and highlights of the Hoffman Estates community. **Availability:** Online.

39143 ■ *Community Guide (Crystal Lake)*
427 W Virginia St.
Crystal Lake, IL 60014
Ph: (815)459-1300
Co. E-mail: info@clchamber.com
URL: http://www.clchamber.com
Contact: Randy Smith, Chairman of the Board
URL(s): www.clchamber.com/site-map
Description: Covers business, professionals, and community organizations in Crystal Lake. **Availability:** PDF; Download; Online.

39144 ■ *Community Guide and Business Directory*
662 E NW Hwy.
Mount Prospect, IL 60056
Ph: (847)392-1200
Co. E-mail: info@mountprospectchamber.org
URL: http://www.mountprospectchamber.org
Contact: Trisha Chokshi, Chairman
URL(s): www.mountprospectchamber.org/list
Availability: Online.

39145 ■ *Community Guide and Shopping, Dining, Lodging Guide, and a Street Map*
655 Deerfield Rd., Ste. 100-310
Deerfield, IL 60015
Ph: (847)945-4660
Fax: (847)715-9129
Co. E-mail: info@dbrchamber.com
URL: http://www.dbrchamber.com
Contact: Victoria Street, Executive Director
E-mail: victoriastreet@dbrchamber.com
URL(s): www.dbrchamber.com/faq
Released: Annual **Availability:** Print.

39146 ■ Crete Area Chamber of Commerce
PO Box 263
Crete, IL 60417-0263
Ph: (708)672-9216
Co. E-mail: cretechamber.info@gmail.com
URL: http://www.cretechamber.com
Contact: Judy Petrungaro, President
Facebook: www.facebook.com/CreteChamber
Description: Promotes business and community development in Crete, IL area. Sponsors 2-antique show, Wine Tasting, ribbon cutting, and grants scholarship. **Founded:** 1984. **Publications:** *Crete Record* (Weekly). **Geographic Preference:** Local.

39147 ■ Crystal Lake Chamber of Commerce
427 W Virginia St.
Crystal Lake, IL 60014
Ph: (815)459-1300
Co. E-mail: info@clchamber.com
URL: http://www.clchamber.com
Contact: Randy Smith, Chairman of the Board
Facebook: www.facebook.com/clchamberc
Linkedin: www.linkedin.com/company/crystallakechamber
X (Twitter): x.com/clchamber
Instagram: www.instagram.com/crystallakechamber
YouTube: www.youtube.com/channel/UCpc0rhHt1YyIFJ-BzWSJBHA
Description: Provides businesses, professionals, and community organizations in the area with opportunities to meet, share interests, and develop business relationships. **Founded:** 1940. **Publications:** *Community Guide*; *News & Views* (Monthly); *Shopping and Dining Guide*. **Awards:** Carl E. Wehde Award (Annual); Robert O. Covey Business of the Year Award (Annual). **Geographic Preference:** Local.

39148 ■ Deerfield, Bannockburn, Riverwoods Chamber of Commerce (DBR)
655 Deerfield Rd., Ste. 100-310
Deerfield, IL 60015
Ph: (847)945-4660
Fax: (847)715-9129
Co. E-mail: info@dbrchamber.com
URL: http://www.dbrchamber.com
Contact: Victoria Street, Executive Director
E-mail: victoriastreet@dbrchamber.com
Facebook: www.facebook.com/dbrchamberofcommerce
Pinterest: www.pinterest.com/DBRChamber
Description: Strives to enhance the local business climate and to promote business and community development in the Deerfield, Bannockburn, and Riverwoods, IL areas. **Founded:** 1925. **Publications:** *Community Guide and Shopping, Dining, Lodging Guide, and a Street Map* (Annual). **Awards:** Deerfield, Bannockburn, Riverwoods Chamber of Commerce College Scholarship (Annual). **Geographic Preference:** Local.

39149 ■ DeKalb Chamber of Commerce
130 W Lincoln Hwy., Ste. 200
DeKalb, IL 60115
Ph: (815)756-6306
Co. E-mail: chamber@dekalb.org
URL: http://dekalb.org
Contact: Matt Duffy, Executive Director
Facebook: www.facebook.com/dekalbilchamber
Linkedin: www.linkedin.com/company/dekalb-chamber-of-commerce
X (Twitter): x.com/dekalbilchamber
Instagram: www.instagram.com/dekalbilchamber
Description: Promotes business and community development in DeKalb County, GA. **Founded:** 1923. **Publications:** *Access DeKalb*; *DeKalb Chamber Membership Guide* (Annual); *DeKalb County Map* (Semiannual). **Educational Activities:** DeKalb Chamber of Commerce Meeting (Semimonthly). **Geographic Preference:** Local.

39150 ■ Des Plaines Chamber of Commerce and Industry
1400 E Touhy Ave., Ste. 145
Des Plaines, IL 60018
Ph: (847)824-4200
Fax: (847)824-7932
Co. E-mail: abiwer@dpchamber.com
URL: http://www.dpchamber.com
Contact: Andrea Biwer, Executive Director
E-mail: abiwer@dpchamber.com
X (Twitter): x.com/dpchamberil
YouTube: www.youtube.com/channel/UCPXI6wjQRd5bUB909nJsQvg
Description: Promotes, supports, and assists the Des Plaines business community through effective communication and quality service. Improves the quality of life for all citizens of the area. **Publications:** *The Business Advocate* (Monthly); *Directory and Community Guide* (Annual). **Geographic Preference:** Local.

39151 ■ *Directory and Community Guide*
1400 E Touhy Ave., Ste. 145
Des Plaines, IL 60018
Ph: (847)824-4200
Fax: (847)824-7932
Co. E-mail: abiwer@dpchamber.com
URL: http://www.dpchamber.com
Contact: Andrea Biwer, Executive Director
E-mail: abiwer@dpchamber.com
URL(s): www.dpchamber.com/members-benefits/marketing
Released: Annual **Availability:** Print.

39152 ■ Dixon Chamber of Commerce & Main Street [Dixon Chamber of Commerce]
87 S Hennepin Ave.
Dixon, IL 61021
Ph: (815)284-3361
Co. E-mail: info@dixonnow.com
URL: http://www.discoverdixon.com
Contact: Jeremy Englund, Agent
Description: Businesspersons, manufacturers, professionals, and non-profit organizations interested in promoting business and community development in the Dixon, IL area. **Publications:** *Dixon Area Business News* (Monthly); *Membership and Business Services Directory* (Annual). **Geographic Preference:** Local.

39153 ■ Du Quoin Chamber of Commerce
PO Box 57
Du Quoin, IL 62832
Ph: (618)542-9570
Co. E-mail: dqchamber@nwcable.net
URL: http://duquoin.org/chamber-of-commerce
Contact: Tim Leake, President
Description: Promotes the common interests and community welfare of the residents in Du Quoin, IL. Seeks to enhance the city's image and develop and encourage the various commercial, industrial, professional, financial, and civic interests of the city. **Geographic Preference:** Local.

39154 ■ *E-Newsletter*
1313 Delany Rd., 2
Gurnee, IL 60031
Ph: (847)249-3800
Co. E-mail: info@lakecountychamber.com
URL: http://www.lakecountychamber.com
Contact: Shaunese L. Teamer, Executive Director
URL(s): www.lakecountychamber.com/faqs
Released: Weekly **Price:** $100, for other. **Availability:** Online.

39155 ■ *East Peoria Business Directory*
201 Clock Tower Dr.
East Peoria, IL 61611
Ph: (309)699-6212
Fax: (309)699-6220
Co. E-mail: epcc@epcc.org
URL: http://www.epcc.org
Contact: Mike Unes, President
URL(s): business.epcc.org/list
Availability: Online.

39156 ■ East Peoria Chamber of Commerce
201 Clock Tower Dr.
East Peoria, IL 61611
Ph: (309)699-6212
Fax: (309)699-6220
Co. E-mail: epcc@epcc.org
URL: http://www.epcc.org
Contact: Mike Unes, President
Facebook: www.facebook.com/EastPeoriaCC
Linkedin: www.linkedin.com/company/east-peoria-chamber-of-commerce/about
X (Twitter): x.com/EastPeoriaCC
Instagram: www.instagram.com/eastpeoriacc
Description: Represents businesses interested in promoting East Peoria, IL. **Founded:** 1948. **Publications:** *East Peoria Business Directory*; *EP Update* (Monthly); *The FOLEPI Guide*. **Educational Activities:** Business After Hours (Monthly). **Geographic Preference:** Local.

39157 ■ Edwardsville/Glen Carbon Chamber of Commerce
1 N Research Dr.
Edwardsville, IL 62025
Ph: (618)656-7600
Fax: (618)656-7611
Co. E-mail: office@edglenchamber.com
URL: http://www.edglenchamber.com
Contact: Desiree Bennyhoff, President
Linkedin: www.linkedin.com/company/edwardsville-glen-carbon-chamber-of-commerce
X (Twitter): x.com/EdGlenChamber
Description: Promotes business and community development in Madison County, IL. Holds monthly Business After Hours party; sponsors annual Halloween Parade, Harvest Hometest and Annual Golf Scramble. Organizes ribbon cutting events for new local businesses. **Founded:** 1924. **Publications:** *Business Directory*; *Common Ground* (Monthly). **Awards:** Albert Cassens Award for Outstanding Community Achievement (Annual); Tallerico Leadership Award (Annual). **Geographic Preference:** Local.

39158 ■ Effingham Chamber of Commerce and Industry
903 N Keller Dr.
Effingham, IL 62401
Ph: (217)342-4147
Fax: (217)342-4228
Co. E-mail: chamber@effinghamcountychamber.com
URL: http://effinghamccoc.chambermaster.com

STATE LISTINGS

Contact: Lucinda Hart, President
E-mail: lhart@effinghamcountychamber.com
Description: Promotes business and community development in the Effingham, IL area. Sponsors rodeo. **Founded:** 1917. **Publications:** *Effingham Business* (Quarterly); *Take Five* (Monthly). **Awards:** Chamber Community Scholarship (Annual). **Geographic Preference:** Local.

39159 ■ Elgin Area Chamber of Commerce (EACC)
31 S Grove Ave.
   Elgin, IL 60120
Ph: (847)741-5660
Fax: (847)741-5677
Co. E-mail: info@elginchamber.com
URL: http://www.elginchamber.com
Contact: Carol Gieske, President
Facebook: www.facebook.com/elginareachamber
Linkedin: www.linkedin.com/company/elgin-area-chamber
X (Twitter): x.com/ElginAreaChambe
Instagram: www.instagram.com/elginareachamber
YouTube: www.youtube.com/channel/UCLHxxO4WqqmyZ4omZn5oKdw
Description: Promotes economic and community development in northern Kane County, IL. **Founded:** 1908. **Publications:** *Elgin Area Chamber Business Review* (Monthly). **Geographic Preference:** Local.

39160 ■ Elizabeth Chamber of Commerce
PO Box 371
   Elizabeth, IL 61028
Ph: (815)990-8618
Co. E-mail: elizabeth.area.chamber@gmail.com
URL: http://www.elizabeth-il.org
Contact: Cheryl Rife, President
E-mail: thethreeelizabeths@gmail.com
Facebook: www.facebook.com/EnergizeElizabethShopLocal
Instagram: www.instagram.com/village_of_elizabethillinois
Description: Promotes business and community development in Elizabeth, IL area. **Founded:** 1986. **Geographic Preference:** Local.

39161 ■ Elmhurst Chamber of Commerce and Industry
300A W Lake St., Ste. 201
   Elmhurst, IL 60126-3301
Ph: (630)834-6060
Co. E-mail: info@elmhurstchamber.org
URL: http://www.elmhurstchamber.org
Contact: John R. Quigley, President
Facebook: www.facebook.com/elmhurstchamber
Linkedin: www.linkedin.com/company/elmhurst-chamber-of-commerce-&-industry
X (Twitter): x.com/elmhurstchamber
Description: Business and professional men and women. Sponsors annual Elmfest. Offers services, programs and events that provide opportunities for networking and referral, business education, development and promotion, governmental representation and community involvement. **Founded:** 1918. **Publications:** *Focus* (Weekly); *Elmhurst Community* (Annual). **Geographic Preference:** Local.

39162 ■ *Elmhurst Community*
300A W Lake St., Ste. 201
   Elmhurst, IL 60126-3301
Ph: (630)834-6060
Co. E-mail: info@elmhurstchamber.org
URL: http://www.elmhurstchamber.org
Contact: John R. Quigley, President
URL(s): www.elmhurstchamber.org/2024-elmhurst-community-directory
Released: Annual **Availability:** Online.

39163 ■ Evanston Chamber of Commerce (ECC)
1007 Church St., Ste. 106
   Evanston, IL 60201
Ph: (847)328-1500
Fax: (847)328-1510
Co. E-mail: info@evchamber.com
URL: http://www.evchamber.com
Contact: Nasutsa Mabwa, President

Facebook: www.facebook.com/evanstonchamber
Linkedin: www.linkedin.com/company/evanston-chamber-of-commerce
X (Twitter): x.com/EvanstonChamber
Instagram: www.instagram.com/evanstonchamber
YouTube: www.youtube.com/channel/UCyuazYeCpivxbxFD0jmVXqg
Description: Promotes business and community development in Evanston, WY. **Founded:** 1921. **Publications:** *Destination Evanston* (Annual); *Evanston Community Guide* (Annual); *Evanston Marketplace* (Bimonthly). **Awards:** Evanston Chamber of Commerce Community Leadership Award (Annual). **Geographic Preference:** Local.

39164 ■ *Evanston Community Guide*
1007 Church St., Ste. 106
   Evanston, IL 60201
Ph: (847)328-1500
Fax: (847)328-1510
Co. E-mail: info@evchamber.com
URL: http://www.evchamber.com
Contact: Nasutsa Mabwa, President
URL(s): www.evchamber.com/the-evanston-community/evanston-community-guide
Released: Annual **Availability:** Online.

39165 ■ Evergreen Park Chamber of Commerce (EPCC)
9449 S Kedzie Ave., Ste. 196
   Evergreen Park, IL 60805
Ph: (708)423-1118
Co. E-mail: info@evergreenparkchamber.org
URL: http://www.evergreenparkchamber.org
Contact: Frank Murray, Co-President
Facebook: www.facebook.com/EPChamberofCommerce
Description: Serves the business community by creating a positive business environment. Promotes commerce by developing and providing information and advocacy in a responsive and ethical manner. **Founded:** 1947. **Geographic Preference:** Local.

39166 ■ Fairbury Chamber of Commerce
101 E Locust St.
   Fairbury, IL 61739
Ph: (815)692-3899
Co. E-mail: fairburychamber@maxwire.net
URL: http://fairburychamber.com
Contact: Rebekah Fehr, Executive Director
Description: Advances the commercial, industrial, civic and professional interest of the City of Fairbury by supporting the growth of existing industries and assisting those firms or individuals seeking to locate in the area. **Founded:** 1857. **Publications:** *Member Directory & Community Guide*. **Geographic Preference:** Local.

39167 ■ Forest Park Chamber of Commerce and Development (FPC)
PO Box 617
   Forest Park, IL 60130
Ph: (708)366-2543
Co. E-mail: info@exploreforestpark.com
URL: http://exploreforestpark.com
Contact: Neil Rembos, Co-President
Facebook: www.facebook.com/forestparkchamber
X (Twitter): x.com/ForestPkChamber
Description: Local businesses, organizations and community-minded individuals working together to promote business and a sense of community. Provides a climate where business can grow by strengthening, supporting, and promoting the economic viability, social needs and community cohesion of the Village of Forest Park. **Founded:** 1912. **Publications:** *Forest Park Community Guide* (Annual). **Geographic Preference:** Local.

39168 ■ Fox Lake/Richmond/Spring Grove Area Chamber of Commerce (FLRSGAC)
10910 B N Main St.
   Richmond, IL 60071
Ph: (815)403-5155
Co. E-mail: info@flrsgac.com
URL: http://business.chainolakeschamber.com/list/member/chain-o-lakes-area-chamber-of-commerce-richmond-619

Illinois ■ 39172

Contact: Hailey Tuohy, Executive Director
Linkedin: www.linkedin.com/company/fox-lake-richmond-spring-grove-chamber-of-commerce
Description: Provides favorable business climate by acting as a vehicle to promote the area's economic progress. **Founded:** 2019. **Geographic Preference:** Local.

39169 ■ Frankfort Chamber of Commerce
123 Kansas St.
   Frankfort, IL 60423
Ph: (815)469-3356
Co. E-mail: office@frankfortchamber.com
URL: http://www.frankfortchamber.com
Contact: Tom van Dellen, President
Facebook: www.facebook.com/frankfort.chamberofcommerce
Linkedin: www.linkedin.com/company/frankfort-chamber-of-commerce
YouTube: www.youtube.com/channel/UC2Er75HtON7k_k52Vb9detA
Description: Promotes the commercial, industrial, and civic welfare of the Frankfort area. Provides many civic and business development programs. Sponsors fund-raising events like Labor Day Weekend Festival and Frankfort Fall Festival. **Founded:** 1967. **Publications:** *Frankfort Business* (Weekly). **Geographic Preference:** Local.

39170 ■ French American Chamber of Commerce Chicago (FACC-Chicago) [FACC Chicago Chapter]
35 E Wacker Dr., Ste. 650
   Chicago, IL 60601
Ph: (312)578-0444
Co. E-mail: information@facc-chicago.com
URL: http://www.facc-chicago.com
Contact: Alexandra Gantier-Hochart, Executive Director
E-mail: agantierh@facc-chicago.com
Facebook: www.facebook.com/faccchicago
Linkedin: www.linkedin.com/company/french-american-chamber-of-commerce-chicago-chapter
X (Twitter): x.com/faccchicago
Instagram: www.instagram.com/faccofchicago
Description: Promotes and develops commercial and financial relations between France and the United States in Chicago land. Offers commercial services and organizes professional events to bring members together in the spirit of establishing contacts and expanding the economic relationship between both countries. **Founded:** 1978. **Geographic Preference:** Local.

39171 ■ Fulton Chamber of Commerce
415 11th Ave.
   Fulton, IL 61252
Ph: (815)589-2616
Co. E-mail: info@cityoffulton.us
URL: http://www.cityoffulton.us/city/city-information.html
Contact: Karrie Kenney, Contact
E-mail: karrie.kenney@central-bank.com
Description: Represents small business owners, individuals, and large corporations. Enhances the economic climate and promotes the business community for the benefit of the greater Fulton area. **Founded:** 1835. **Geographic Preference:** Local.

39172 ■ Galena Area Chamber of Commerce (GACC)
PO Box 204
   Galena, IL 61036
URL: http://galenachamber.com
Contact: Cindy Foley, President
Facebook: www.facebook.com/galenaareachamber
Description: Organized on behalf of its members to promote the economic welfare of the business community and contribute to the quality of life in the Galena area. Events sponsored include a business and trade showcase, 2 golf outings, Festival of Quilts, Ladies Getaway, Business After Hours, Business A.M., Halloween Parade, Night of the Luminaria, and various community education meetings. **Founded:**

Small Business Sourcebook • 42nd Edition

1838. **Publications:** *Community Development Guide and Membership Directory* (Annual); *Galenian* (Semiannual); *Nexus* (Monthly). **Geographic Preference:** Local.

39173 ■ Galesburg Area Chamber of Commerce
200 E Main St., Ste. 200
Galesburg, IL 61401
Ph: (309)343-1194
Co. E-mail: chamber@galesburg.org
URL: http://www.galesburg.org
Contact: Pam Gaither, Executive Director
E-mail: pgaither@galesburg.org
Facebook: www.facebook.com/GalesburgAreaChamber
Linkedin: www.linkedin.com/in/GalesburgAreaChamber
Description: Promotes business and community development in Galesburg, IL area. **Geographic Preference:** Local.

39174 ■ Geneva Chamber of Commerce (GCC)
8 S 3rd St.
Geneva, IL 60134-0481
Ph: (630)232-6060
Fax: (630)232-6083
Co. E-mail: chamberinfo@genevachamber.com
URL: http://www.genevachamber.com
Contact: Paula Schmidt, President
E-mail: pschmidt@genevachamber.com
Facebook: www.facebook.com/GenevaILChamber
X (Twitter): x.com/GenevaILChamber
Instagram: www.instagram.com/genevailchamber
YouTube: www.youtube.com/user/genevachamber
Description: Promotes business and community development in Geneva, IL. Sponsors local festivals. **Publications:** *Soundings* (Monthly). **Geographic Preference:** Local.

39175 ■ Gibson Area Chamber of Commerce
PO Box 294
Gibson City, IL 60936
Co. E-mail: info@gibsonareachamber.org
URL: http://gibsoncityillinois.com/business/chamber-of-commerce
Contact: Bill Kirby, President
Description: Promotes business and community development in the Gibson, IL area. **Geographic Preference:** Local.

39176 ■ Glen Ellyn Chamber of Commerce (GECOC)
810 N Main St.
Glen Ellyn, IL 60137
Ph: (630)469-0907
Fax: (630)469-0426
Co. E-mail: admin@glenellynchamber.com
URL: http://www.glenellynchamber.com
Contact: J. P. Lacour, President
Facebook: www.facebook.com/GlenEllynChamberofCommerce
Linkedin: www.linkedin.com/company/glenellynchamberofcommerce
X (Twitter): x.com/gechamber
YouTube: www.youtube.com/channel/UCrNXKNwR996OoNhm1WG7dtw
Description: Promotes business and community development in the Glen Ellyn, IL area. **Founded:** 1949. **Publications:** *Chamber Goods and Services Guide* (Annual); *Navigator* (Monthly). **Geographic Preference:** Local.

39177 ■ Glenview Chamber of Commerce
2222 Chestnut
Glenview, IL 60026
Ph: (847)724-0900
Co. E-mail: info@glenviewchamber.com
URL: http://www.glenviewchamber.com
Contact: Michael Moylan, President
Facebook: www.facebook.com/GlenviewChamberofCommerce
Linkedin: www.linkedin.com/in/glenviewchamber
X (Twitter): x.com/GlenviewChamber
Instagram: www.instagram.com/glenview_chamber_of_commerce

Description: Works for the advancement of commercial, industrial, professional and civic interests of Glenview. Provides programs that increase visibility, customers and education. **Founded:** 1923. **Publications:** *Community Resource Directory* (Biennial); *Community Resource Directory* (Biennial). **Educational Activities:** Business After Hours (Monthly). **Geographic Preference:** Local.

39178 ■ GLMV Chamber of Commerce
1123 S Milwaukee Ave.
Libertyville, IL 60048
Ph: (847)680-0750
Co. E-mail: info@glmvchamber.org
URL: http://www.glmvchamber.org
Contact: Steven Kopala, Chairman
Facebook: www.facebook.com/glmvchamberofcommerce
X (Twitter): x.com/glmvchamber
YouTube: www.youtube.com/user/glmvchambercommerce
Description: Promotes business and community development in Green Oaks, Libertyville, Mundelein, and Vernon Hills, Illinois area. **Founded:** 1946. **Publications:** *Images*; *GLMV Chamber of Commerce--Membership Directory*. **Geographic Preference:** Local.

39179 ■ Grand Corridor Chamber of Commerce (GCCC)
11 Conti Pky.
Elmwood Park, IL 60707
Ph: (708)456-8000
Fax: (708)456-8680
Co. E-mail: info@grandchamber.org
URL: http://grandchamber.org
Contact: Katie Muellner, President
Facebook: www.facebook.com/MCEPChamberOfCommerce
Description: Works on bridging the gap between the business community, political community, community organizations, and the area residents. **Geographic Preference:** Local.

39180 ■ Grayslake Area Chamber of Commerce
10 S Seymour Ave.
Grayslake, IL 60030
Ph: (847)223-6888
Co. E-mail: thegreatergrayslakechamber@gmail.com
URL: http://www.grayslakechamber.com
Contact: Steve Lawrence, President
Facebook: www.facebook.com/GrayslakeAreaChamber
Linkedin: www.linkedin.com/company/grayslake-chamber-of-commerce
Description: Represents commercial, industrial, professional service and retail businesses. Acts as a liaison between the Village of Grayslake, the Township, Lake County, the State and local citizens on matters concerning the well-being of the Grayslake business community. Plans, organizes and funds community events that are designed to promote the Village and the businesses in it. **Founded:** 1950. **Publications:** *Community Resource Guide*. **Educational Activities:** Arts Festival & Wine Tasting (Annual). **Awards:** Joanne W. Lawrence Scholarship (Annual). **Geographic Preference:** Local.

39181 ■ Grayville Chamber of Commerce (GCC)
109 N Ct., St.
Grayville, IL 62844
Ph: (317)658-4055
Co. E-mail: grayvillecofc109@gmail.com
URL: http://grayvillechamber.com
Facebook: www.facebook.com/GrayvilleChamber
Description: Promotes business and community development in Grayville, IL. Sponsors annual Grayville Days. **Geographic Preference:** Local.

39182 ■ Greater Aurora Chamber of Commerce (GACC)
43 W Galena Blvd.
Aurora, IL 60506
Ph: (630)256-3180
URL: http://www.aurorachamber.com

Contact: Jessica Linder Gallo, President
E-mail: jlindergallo@aurora-chamber.com
Linkedin: www.linkedin.com/company/aurora-regional-chamber
X (Twitter): x.com/aurorailchamber
YouTube: www.youtube.com/channel/UCvz4nGG_kT-m6_aEf1wQu0g
Description: Promotes business and community development in the Aurora, IL area. **Founded:** 1920. **Publications:** *The Spencer Chamber Monthly* (Monthly). **Geographic Preference:** Local.

39183 ■ Greater Belleville Chamber of Commerce
216 E A St.
Belleville, IL 62220
Ph: (618)233-2015
Fax: (618)233-2077
Co. E-mail: info@bellevillechamber.org
URL: http://www.bellevillechamber.org
Contact: Wendy J. Pfeil, President
E-mail: wpfeil@bellevillechamber.org
Facebook: www.facebook.com/GreaterBellevilleChamber
YouTube: www.youtube.com/channel/UCk2peMYbSpywies_ymADaSQ
Description: Works to support and advance business and community interests, as well as the quality of life. **Geographic Preference:** Local.

39184 ■ Greater Centralia Chamber of Commerce
210 E Broadway
Centralia, IL 62801
Ph: (618)532-6789
Co. E-mail: office@centraliachamber.com
URL: http://centraliachamber.com
Contact: Marcus Holland, Executive Director
E-mail: marcus@centraliachamber.com
Facebook: www.facebook.com/CentraliaChamber
X (Twitter): x.com/CentraliaFest
Instagram: www.instagram.com/centraliachamber
Description: Improves the Centralia Area Business Climate by working diligently for positive community planning and change. **Founded:** 1924. **Publications:** *CHAMBER DATELINE* (Monthly). **Geographic Preference:** Local.

39185 ■ Greater Decatur Chamber of Commerce
101 S Main St., Ste. 102
Decatur, IL 62523
Ph: (217)422-2200
Co. E-mail: communication@decaturchamber.com
URL: http://www.decaturchamber.com
Contact: Mirinda Rothrock, President
Facebook: www.facebook.com/DecaturRegionalChamberOfCommerce
Linkedin: www.linkedin.com/company/greater-decatur-chamber-of-commerce/about
X (Twitter): x.com/DecRegChamber
Instagram: www.instagram.com/decaturregionalchamber
YouTube: www.youtube.com/channel/UCJXioarQaHThJH8WGtMF9MQ
Description: Promotes business and community development in Greater Decatur, IL area. **Founded:** 1903. **Publications:** *Chamber of Commerce Business Directory* (Annual); *Membership Directory* (Annual); *Decatur Chamber of Commerce Business Directory*; *Friday Facts* (Weekly). **Geographic Preference:** Local.

39186 ■ Greater Fairfield Area Chamber of Commerce
121 E Main
Fairfield, IL 62837
Ph: (618)842-6116
Co. E-mail: chamber@fairfieldilcitygov.us
URL: http://cityoffairfieldillinois.com/chamber-of-commerce
Description: Represents businesses, professionals, and interested others. Promotes agricultural, business, community, and industrial development in the

Fairfield, IL area. **Publications:** *Greater Fairfield Area Chamber of Commerce News* (Quarterly). **Geographic Preference:** Local.

39187 ■ Greater Fayette County Chamber of Commerce
210 S 5th St., 2nd Fl.
Vandalia, IL 62471
Ph: (618)431-2281
Co. E-mail: greaterfaycochamber@gmail.com
URL: http://www.gfcchamber.org
Contact: Dr. Jennifer Garrison, President
E-mail: jgarrison@vandals203.org
Facebook: www.facebook.com/greaterfayettecoun tychamberofcommerce

Description: Aims to advance the interest of business, professional, and service organizations in the Vandalia area through acting as their voice in governmental and social affairs, communicating their needs and enhancing the quality of life. **Founded:** 1914. **Geographic Preference:** Local.

39188 ■ Greater Shelbyville Chamber of Commerce
143 E Main St.
Shelbyville, IL 62565-1653
Contact: Regina Agney, Contact

Description: Promotes business and community development in Shelbyville, IL. **Founded:** 1930. **Publications:** *Chamber of Commerce.* **Geographic Preference:** Local.

39189 ■ Greater Springfield Chamber of Commerce (GSCC)
501 E Capitol Ave., Ste. A
Springfield, IL 62701
Ph: (937)325-7621
Free: 800-803-1553
Fax: (937)521-1941
Co. E-mail: receptiondesk@gscc.org
URL: http://www.gscc.org
Contact: Mike Murphy, President
E-mail: mmurphy@gscc.org
URL(s): www.greaterspringfield.com
Facebook: www.facebook.com/TheSpringfieldChamber
X (Twitter): x.com/growsangamon

Description: Promotes the businesses of the greater Springfield region of Ohio. **Founded:** 2010. **Publications:** *ManuFacts: Sangamon County Directory of Manufacturers* (Annual); *miniUPDATE e-mail newsletter* (Semimonthly); *eUpdate* (Weekly). **Awards:** Greater Springfield Small Business Person of the Year Awards (Annual). **Geographic Preference:** Local.

39190 ■ Greenville Chamber of Commerce
102 N Second
Greenville, IL 62246
Ph: (618)664-9272
Free: 844-404-9272
Co. E-mail: greenvileilchamber@gmail.com
URL: http://www.greenvilleilchamber.org
Contact: Elaine McNamara, Executive Director
E-mail: elaine@greenvillesmart.com
Facebook: www.facebook.com/GreenvilleILChamber
Instagram: www.instagram.com/greenvilleilchamber

Description: Promotes business and community development in Greenville, IL area. **Founded:** 2011. **Geographic Preference:** Local.

39191 ■ Hamilton County Chamber of Commerce
PO Box 456
McLeansboro, IL 62859
Ph: (618)643-9394
Co. E-mail: info@hamcochamber.org
URL: http://www.hamcochamber.org
Contact: Jamie Green, President
Facebook: www.facebook.com/hamcochamber

Description: Promotes business and community development in Hamilton County, FL. **Founded:** 1958. **Geographic Preference:** Local.

39192 ■ Hampshire Area Chamber of Commerce
113 W Oak Knoll Dr.
Hampshire, IL 60140
Ph: (847)683-1122
Co. E-mail: hampshirechamber@gmail.com
URL: http://www.hampshirechamber.org
Contact: Robbi Burklow, President
E-mail: robenette.burklow@gmail.com
Facebook: www.facebook.com/hampshireareachamber
X (Twitter): x.com/hampchamber1
YouTube: www.youtube.com/channel/UCu5LWQfZ08 4gg3OvTcixBSA

Description: Promotes business and community development in Hampshire, IL. Organizes annual Coon Creek Day. **Geographic Preference:** Local.

39193 ■ Harvard Area Chamber of Commerce
36 N Ayer St.
Harvard, IL 60033
Ph: (815)943-4404
Co. E-mail: info@harvcc.net
URL: http://harvardchamber.com
Contact: Susan Dale, President

Description: Promotes business and community development in the Harvard, IL area. **Founded:** 1930. **Publications:** *Chamber News* (Bimonthly). **Geographic Preference:** Local.

39194 ■ Harvey Area Chamber of Commerce (HACC)
174 E 154th St.
Harvey, IL 60426
Ph: (708)581-6422
Co. E-mail: haccbiz@harveyareachamberil.com
URL: http://harveyareachamberil.com/contact
Contact: Andrea A. Paxton, Contact
Facebook: www.facebook.com/harveyarea.chamber

Description: Promotes business and community development in the Harvey, ND area. **Founded:** 2004. **Publications:** *At Work* (Monthly). **Geographic Preference:** Local.

39195 ■ Havana Area Chamber of Commerce
PO Box 116
Havana, IL 62644
Ph: (309)543-6580
Fax: (309)543-6633
Co. E-mail: havanachamber@gmail.com
URL: http://www.havanail.gov/chamber-of-commerce
Contact: April Burgett, President
Facebook: www.facebook.com/havanachamber

Description: Works with other community resources to promote local tourism, create jobs, and recruit new businesses in Havana, IL. Sponsors community events. **Geographic Preference:** Local.

39196 ■ Heritage Corridor Business Alliance (HCBAQ)
418 Main St.
Lemont, IL 60439
Ph: (630)257-5997
Co. E-mail: info@myhcba.com
URL: http://www.myhcba.com
Contact: Jeff Hawthorne, President
E-mail: jhawtho@citgo.com
Facebook: www.facebook.com/HeritageCorri dorAlliance
X (Twitter): x.com/HCBA416

Description: Aims to promote the community and make it a better place to live, work, and conduct business. **Founded:** 1948. **Publications:** *Chamber Chords* (Monthly). **Geographic Preference:** Local.

39197 ■ Herrin Chamber of Commerce
3 S Pk. Ave.
Herrin, IL 62948
Ph: (618)942-5163
Co. E-mail: director@herrinchamber.com
URL: http://www.herrinchamber.com
Contact: Quinn Laird, President
Linkedin: www.linkedin.com/company/herrin-chamber -of-commerce
X (Twitter): x.com/herrinchamber

Description: Serves and supports the economic good of the greater Herrin area with priority given to economic development and the assistance necessary to acquire and retain business and industry in Herrin and the surrounding region. **Founded:** 1943. **Publications:** *Chamber Chat* (Monthly). **Geographic Preference:** Local.

39198 ■ Herscher Chamber of Commerce
272 E 2nd St.
Herscher, IL 60941
Ph: (815)426-2131
URL: http://herscher.net/herscher-chamber-of -commerce
Contact: Dan Martin, President

Description: Provides park improvements and various community projects to the village of Herscher. **Founded:** 1916. **Geographic Preference:** Local.

39199 ■ Highland Chamber of Commerce
1216 Main St.
Highland, IL 62249
Ph: (618)654-3721
Co. E-mail: info@highlandillinois.com
URL: http://www.highlandillinois.com
Contact: Hillarie Holzinger, Executive Director
E-mail: hillarie@highlandillinois.com
Facebook: www.facebook.com/Highlan dChamberOfCommerce

Description: Promotes business, tourism, and community development in Highland, IL. **Founded:** 1924. **Holdings:** Figures not available. **Publications:** *Available Site Location Guide* (Annual); *Chamber News.* **Geographic Preference:** Local.

39200 ■ Highland Park Chamber of Commerce (HPCC)
508 Central Ave., Ste. 202
Highland Park, IL 60035
Ph: (847)432-0284
Co. E-mail: info@chamberhp.com
URL: http://www.chamberhp.com
Contact: Ginny Anzelmo Glasner, President
Facebook: www.facebook.com/Highlan dParkChamberofCommerce
Linkedin: www.linkedin.com/company/highland-park -illinois-chamber-of-commerce
X (Twitter): x.com/hpilcc
YouTube: www.youtube.com/channel/UCa1_DR 2fFhG3IJHSNFVv26w

Description: Promotes business and community development in Highland Park, IL. Conducts charitable activities. Sponsors festival. **Founded:** 1911. **Geographic Preference:** Local.

39201 ■ Hills Chamber of Commerce
8632 W 103rd St., Ste. A
Palos Hills, IL 60465
Ph: (708)233-6860
Fax: (708)233-6852
Co. E-mail: info@thehillschamber.org
URL: http://www.thehillschamber.org
Contact: Phyllis Majka, President
E-mail: phyllis@mica-associates.com
Facebook: www.facebook.com/ thehillschamberofcommerce

Description: Promotes business and community development in Palos Hills, IL. **Geographic Preference:** Local.

39202 ■ Hinsdale Chamber of Commerce
22 E 1st St.
Hinsdale, IL 60521
Ph: (630)323-3952
Fax: (630)323-3953
Co. E-mail: staff@hinsdalechamber.com
URL: http://www.hinsdalechamber.com
Contact: Eva Field, President
Facebook: www.facebook.com/hins dalechamberofcommerce
Instagram: www.instagram.com/hinsdalechamber

Description: Promotes business and community development in Hinsdale, IL. Holds annual Fine Arts Fair, Farmers' Market, and other social events. Sponsors Christmas walk, annual garage, Halloween

Parade, sidewalk sales. Operates welcome service. **Publications:** *Hinsdale Community Directory* (Annual). **Geographic Preference:** Local.

39203 ■ *Hinsdale Community Directory (Illinois)*
22 E 1st St.
Hinsdale, IL 60521
Ph: (630)323-3952
Fax: (630)323-3953
Co. E-mail: staff@hinsdalechamber.com
URL: http://www.hinsdalechamber.com
Contact: Eva Field, President
URL(s): www.hinsdalechamber.com/about-us
Released: Annual **Description:** Covers member businesses, clubs and organizations, public and private schools, public officials and community services in Hinsdale, Illinois. Includes maps. **Entries include:** Company name, address, phone, name and title of contact. **Arrangement:** Alphabetical. **Availability:** PDF.

39204 ■ **Hoffman Estates Chamber of Commerce (HECC)**
2200 W Higgins Rd., Ste. 201
Hoffman Estates, IL 60169
Ph: (847)781-9100
Fax: (847)781-9172
Co. E-mail: info@hechamber.com
URL: http://www.hechamber.com
Contact: Tricia O'Brien, President
Facebook: www.facebook.com/hechamber
X (Twitter): x.com/hechamber
YouTube: www.youtube.com/user/HoffmanEstatesIL
Description: Promotes business and community development in Hoffman Estates, IL area. **Founded:** 1990. **Publications:** *Community Guide* (Annual). **Geographic Preference:** Local.

39205 ■ **Huntley Area Chamber of Commerce**
11704 Coral St.
Huntley, IL 60142
Ph: (847)669-0166
Fax: (847)669-0170
Co. E-mail: info@huntleychamber.org
URL: http://huntleychamber.org
Contact: Ben Beallis, Secretary
Facebook: www.facebook.com/HuntleyAreaChamberofCommerce
X (Twitter): x.com/HuntleyChamber
Description: Promotes business and community development in Huntley, IL area. **Founded:** 1987. **Publications:** *The Chamber Review* (Monthly); *Community Guide* (Annual). **Geographic Preference:** Local.

39206 ■ **Illinois Association of Chamber of Commerce Executives (IACCE)**
PO Box 9436
Springfield, IL 62791-9436
Ph: (217)585-2995
URL: http://www.iacce.org
Contact: Todd Maisch, Chief Executive Officer
Facebook: www.facebook.com/IACCE4me
Linkedin: www.linkedin.com/company/iacce
X (Twitter): x.com/iacce
Description: Serves as an access and valued resource for the professional development of Chamber of Commerce executives and staff in Illinois. **Founded:** 1915. **Publications:** *IACCE News* (Monthly); *Resource Guide* (Annual); *Directory of Chambers of Commerce in Illinois*. **Awards:** Illinois Association of Chamber of Commerce Executives Scholarships (Annual); Distinguished Illinois Chamber of Commerce Executive Award (Irregular). **Geographic Preference:** State.

39207 ■ **Illinois Black Chamber of Commerce (ILBCC)**
411 Hamilton Blvd., Ste. 1404
Peoria, IL 61602
Ph: (309)740-4430
Fax: (309)672-1379
Co. E-mail: icontact@ilbcc.org
URL: http://www.ilbcc.org
Contact: Larry D. Ivory, President
Facebook: www.facebook.com/IllinoisBlackChamber
Linkedin: www.linkedin.com/company/illinoisblackchamber
X (Twitter): x.com/IllinoisBCC
YouTube: www.youtube.com/channel/UCeWuc0vIfYCHHEms4jhR9kw
Description: Represents Black owned businesses. Seeks to empower and sustain African American communities through entrepreneurship and capitalistic activity. Provides advocacy, training and education to Black communities. **Founded:** 1997. **Geographic Preference:** State.

39208 ■ **Illinois Chamber of Commerce - Library**
70 W Madison, Ste. 200
Chicago, IL 60602
Ph: (312)983-7100
URL: http://ilchamber.org
Contact: Jim Bajt, Director
X (Twitter): x.com/ILChamber
Instagram: www.instagram.com/illinoischamber
YouTube: www.youtube.com/user/TheIllinoisChamber
Description: Chamber of commerce engaged in educating and persuading policy makers business. **Founded:** 1917. **Holdings:** Webinars and seminars; publication and posters; business and hr webinar series.

39209 ■ **Illinois Valley Area Chamber of Commerce and Economic Development (IVACED)**
1320 Peoria St.
Peru, IL 61354
Ph: (815)223-0227
Fax: (815)223-4827
Co. E-mail: ivaced@ivaced.org
URL: http://www.ivaced.org
Contact: Jeff Borelli, President
Facebook: www.facebook.com/iamivac
X (Twitter): x.com/i_am_ivac
Instagram: www.instagram.com/i_am_ivac
Description: Promotes business and community development in portions of Bureau, La Salle, Marshall, and Putnam counties, IL. **Founded:** 1911. **Publications:** *Agri-Business Brochure*; *Airport Brochure*; *Major Annual Events*; *Membership Memo* (Monthly); *Transportation Brochure*. **Educational Activities:** IVAC Business Breakfast Seminar (Annual). **Geographic Preference:** Local.

39210 ■ *International Marketplace Newsletter*
6445 N W, Ste. 304
Chicago, IL 60645
Ph: (773)743-6022
Co. E-mail: info@westridgechamber.org
URL: http://www.westridgechamber.org
Contact: Irv Loundy, President
E-mail: iloundy@devonbank.com
Availability: Print.

39211 ■ **Jacksonville Area Chamber of Commerce**
155 W Morton Ave.
Jacksonville, IL 62650
Ph: (217)245-2174
Fax: (217)245-0661
Co. E-mail: chamber2@jacksonvilleareachamber.org
URL: http://www.jacksonvilleareachamber.org
Contact: Adam Withee, Treasurer
Facebook: www.facebook.com/jacksonvilleareachamber
Description: Promotes business and community development in the Jacksonville, IL area. **Founded:** 1889. **Publications:** *Chamber Review* (Monthly). **Awards:** Jacksonville Area Business of the Year - 25 or More Employees (Annual); Jacksonville Area Business of the Year - Fewer than 25 Employees (Annual); Jacksonville Area Not-For-Profit Business of the Year (Annual). **Geographic Preference:** Local.

39212 ■ **Jefferson County Chamber of Commerce (JCCC)**
200 Potomac Blvd., Ste. 4
Mount Vernon, IL 62864
Ph: (618)242-5725
Fax: (618)242-5130
Co. E-mail: chamberinfo@southernillinois.com
URL: http://www.southernillinois.com
Contact: Jamie Storey, Executive Director
E-mail: chamberexec@southernillinois.com
Description: Promotes business and community development in Jefferson County, IL. Holds Business After Hours parties and board meetings. **Founded:** 1921. **Publications:** *Business News* (Monthly). **Geographic Preference:** Local.

39213 ■ **Jefferson Park Chamber of Commerce**
5214 W Lawrence Ave., Ste. 5
Chicago, IL 60630
Ph: (773)736-6697
Fax: (773)736-5008
Co. E-mail: info@jeffersonparkchamber.com
URL: http://www.jeffersonparkchamber.com
Contact: Brian Nadig, President
Facebook: www.facebook.com/jeffparkchamber
Description: Helps maintain the viability of the community through promotion and development of business in Jefferson Park. **Founded:** 1934. **Geographic Preference:** Local.

39214 ■ **Jersey County Business Association (JCBA)**
c/o Becky Wayne, Director
209 N State St.
Jerseyville, IL 62052
Ph: (618)639-5222
Co. E-mail: beth@jcba-il.us
URL: http://www.jcba-il.us
Contact: Becky Wayne, Director
Description: Promotes business and community development in Jersey County, IL. Sponsors golf day, car show, and craft shows. **Founded:** 1955. **Publications:** *The Business News* (Monthly). **Geographic Preference:** Local.

39215 ■ **Joliet Region Chamber of Commerce & Industry**
116 N Chicago St., Ste. 110
Joliet, IL 60432
Ph: (815)727-5371
Fax: (815)727-5374
Co. E-mail: info@jolietchamber.com
URL: http://www.jolietchamber.com
Contact: Jen Howard, President
E-mail: jhoward@jolietchamber.com
X (Twitter): x.com/jolietchamber
Instagram: www.instagram.com/joliet.chamber
YouTube: www.youtube.com/user/JolietChamber
Description: Promotes business environment to enhance the quality of life in Joliet Region, IL. Serves as the voice in governmental and social affairs in the community. **Founded:** 1914. **Publications:** *Vision* (Monthly); *Joliet Region Chamber of Commerce and Industry--Membership Directory*. **Geographic Preference:** Local.

39216 ■ **Kankakee County Chamber of Commerce**
200 E Ct., St., Ste. 502
Kankakee, IL 60901
Ph: (815)351-9068
Co. E-mail: info@kankakeecountychamber.com
URL: http://www.kankakeecountychamber.com
Contact: Ashley Villarreal, President
E-mail: ashley@kankakeecountychamber.com
Facebook: www.facebook.com/kankakeechamber
Linkedin: www.linkedin.com/company/kankakeecountychamber
Instagram: www.instagram.com/kankakeecountychamber
YouTube: www.youtube.com/channel/UCwIS3atQSK8CBLlj1FGIRYQ
Description: Promotes business and community development in the Kankakee County, IL area. **Founded:** 2010. **Publications:** *News and Views* (Monthly). **Geographic Preference:** Local.

39217 ■ **Kewanee Chamber of Commerce**
113 E 2nd St.
Kewanee, IL 61443
Ph: (309)852-2175
Co. E-mail: chamber@kewanee-il.com
URL: http://www.kewanee-il.com

Contact: Mark Mikenas, Executive Vice President
Facebook: www.facebook.com/people/Kewanee
-Chamber-of-Commerce/100060329371193
Description: Promotes business and community development in Kewanee, IL. **Founded:** 1888. **Geographic Preference:** Local.

39218 ■ Lake County Chamber of Commerce (LCCC)
1313 Delany Rd., 2
Gurnee, IL 60031
Ph: (847)249-3800
Co. E-mail: info@lakecountychamber.com
URL: http://www.lakecountychamber.com
Contact: Shaunese L. Teamer, Executive Director
Description: Businesses and individuals in Lake County, IL. Promotes: tourism; trade between local and foreign businesses; community and county development; friendly relations between local industry and business leaders. **Founded:** 1915. **Publications:** E-Newsletter (Weekly). **Geographic Preference:** Local.

39219 ■ Lake Forest - Lake Bluff Chamber of Commerce
207 E Westminster, Lower Level
Lake Forest, IL 60045
Ph: (847)234-4282
Fax: (847)234-4297
Co. E-mail: info@lflbchamber.com
URL: http://www.lflbchamber.com
Contact: Joanna Rolek, Executive Director
Facebook: www.facebook.com/LakeFores
tLakeBluffChamberofCommerce
Linkedin: www.linkedin.com/in/lflbchamber
X (Twitter): x.com/lflbchamber
Instagram: www.instagram.com/lakefores
tlakebluffchamber
YouTube: www.youtube.com/user/LFLBChamber
Description: Promotes the economic and civic interest of the community. **Founded:** 1953. **Publications:** Community Guide (Annual); Shopping and Dining Guide. **Geographic Preference:** Local.

39220 ■ Lake Zurich Area Chamber of Commerce (LZACC) [LZ Area Chamber of Commerce]
33 E Main St.
Lake Zurich, IL 60047
Ph: (847)438-5572
Fax: (847)438-5574
Co. E-mail: info@lzacc.com
URL: http://lzacc.com
Contact: Claire Slattery, Executive Director
E-mail: cslattery@lzacc.com
Facebook: www.facebook.com/LZACC
Linkedin: www.linkedin.com/in/lz-area-chamber-of
-commerce-0565b913b
X (Twitter): x.com/lzareacc
Description: Retailers, industrial concerns, professionals, and service organizations that promote business and industry in the Lake Zurich Area (including Deer Park, Hawthorn Woods, Kildeer, Long Grove, and North Barrington), IL. Sponsors Business After Hours seminars, retail promotions, and community recognition and beautification programs. Conducts social activities, sponsors scholarships. Sponsors Community Recognition Program and a Community and Business EXPO. **Founded:** 1915. **Publications:** Chatter (Monthly); Guide to Lake Zurich (Annual). **Educational Activities:** Lake Zurich Area Chamber of Commerce Seminar. **Geographic Preference:** Local.

39221 ■ Lakeshore Chamber of Commerce (LCC)
7120 Indianapolis Blvd.
Hammond, IN 46324-2221
Ph: (219)931-1000
Fax: (219)937-8778
Co. E-mail: info@lakeshorechamber.com
URL: http://www.lakeshorechamber.com
Contact: Dave Ryan, Executive Director
E-mail: dryan@lakeshorechamber.com
Description: Enhances the economic environment of its local business community. **Founded:** 1912. **Publications:** News and Views (Quarterly); Community Directory and Buyers Guide (Biennial); Greater Hammond Community Map; Greater Hammond Transit Map; Summer Events Tabloid (Annual). **Geographic Preference:** Local.

39222 ■ Lakeview East Chamber of Commerce (LVECC)
3138 N Broadway
Chicago, IL 60657
Ph: (773)348-8608
Co. E-mail: info@lakevieweast.com
URL: http://lakevieweast.com
Contact: Marc Engel, President
Facebook: www.facebook.com/LakeViewEast
Linkedin: www.linkedin.com/company/lakeview-eas
t-chamber-of-commerce
X (Twitter): x.com/lakevieweast
Instagram: www.instagram.com/lakevieweast
YouTube: www.youtube.com/channel/UCY7mT
-ZeHYvY8sEMwIVC48Q
Pinterest: www.pinterest.com/lakevieweastcoc
Description: Promotes business and community development in the Lakeview area of Chicago. **Publications:** Chamber Report (3/year); Lakeview Directory & Neighborhood Guide (Annual); Official Guide to Lakeview East (Annual). **Geographic Preference:** Local.

39223 ■ Lebanon Chamber of Commerce
221 W Saint Louis St.
Lebanon, IL 62254
Ph: (618)537-8420
Fax: (312)292-9348
Co. E-mail: chamber@lebanonil.us
URL: http://lebanonil.us
Description: Aims to promote business and resident growth, encourage tourism and shopping, and improve the existing facilities and historical aspects of the city of Lebanon. **Geographic Preference:** Local.

39224 ■ Legislative Guide to Elected & Appointed Officials
3400 W Stonegate Blvd.
Arlington Heights, IL 60005
Ph: (847)398-3730
Fax: (847)398-3745
Co. E-mail: office@rmchamber.org
URL: http://rmchamber.org
Contact: Michael Hutchins, President
E-mail: michael.hutchins@ngc.com
URL(s): rmchamber.org/member-services/economic
-development
Availability: Print; PDF.

39225 ■ LGBT Chamber of Commerce of Illinois
661 W Lake St.
Chicago, IL 60661
Ph: (773)303-0167
Co. E-mail: chamber@lgbtcc.com
URL: http://lgbtcc.com
Linkedin: www.linkedin.com/company/lgbt-chamber
-of-commerce-of-illinois
X (Twitter): x.com/lgbtccillinois
YouTube: www.youtube.com/channel/UCdyVklfg6r
5x8h3s2wq838Q
Description: Seeks to help gay, lesbian, bisexual and transgender business community through networking, promotions, marketing and attracting tourism. **Founded:** 1996. **Geographic Preference:** Local.

39226 ■ Lincoln Park Chamber of Commerce (LPCC)
2468 N Lincoln
Chicago, IL 60614
Ph: (773)880-5200
Co. E-mail: info@lincolnparkchamber.com
URL: http://www.lincolnparkchamber.com
Contact: Kim Schilf, President
E-mail: kim@lincolnparkchamber.com
Facebook: www.facebook.com/ChamberLincolnPark
X (Twitter): x.com/lpcc09
Instagram: www.instagram.com/lincolnparkchamber
Description: Works to develop membership services. Advocates for the protection and advancement of economic and business development. Promotes the Lincoln Park area and its businesses. Encourages relationships and communication between and among the community and its governmental bodies. **Founded:** 1947. **Publications:** Resident's Guide to Lincoln Park; The Source (Monthly). **Geographic Preference:** Local.

39227 ■ Lincolnwood Chamber of Commerce & Industry (LCCI)
4433 W Touhy Ave.
Lincolnwood, IL 60712
Ph: (847)752-4111
Co. E-mail: info@lincolnwoodchamber.com
URL: http://www.lincolnwoodchamber.com
Contact: Kari Fleck Gutstein, President
Facebook: www.facebook.com/lincolnwoo
dILchamber
Linkedin: www.linkedin.com/company/lincolnwoo
d-chamber-of-commerce-and-industry
Instagram: www.instagram.com/lincolnwoo
dchamberofcommerce
Description: Promotes business and community development in Lincolnwood, IL. **Founded:** 1978. **Awards:** Lincolnwood Chamber of Commerce and Industry Corporate Citizens of the Year (Annual); Madeleine Grant Memorial College Scholarship (Annual). **Geographic Preference:** Local.

39228 ■ Lindenhurst - Lake Villa Chamber of Commerce
500 E Grand
Lake Villa, IL 60046
Ph: (847)306-6713
Co. E-mail: director@llrchamber.com
URL: http://llrchamber.com
Contact: Katie Burau, President
E-mail: kburau@firstambank.com
Instagram: www.instagram.com/llrchamber
YouTube: www.youtube.com/channel/UCx8CGeWO
6TQmMAMvjP8CsNA
Description: Helps to promote a sound economic climate in Northeastern Illinois. Helps the members enhance business activity through education, networking opportunities, and cost saving benefits. **Publications:** On the Move (Quarterly). **Geographic Preference:** Local.

39229 ■ Lisle Area Chamber of Commerce (LCC)
925 Burlington Ave.
Lisle, IL 60532
Ph: (331)801-0098
Co. E-mail: info@lislechamber.com
URL: http://lislechamber.com
Contact: Jill Eidukas, Executive Director
Facebook: www.facebook.com/LisleChamber
Linkedin: www.linkedin.com/in/lisle-area-chamber-67
451960
X (Twitter): x.com/lislechamber1
Instagram: www.instagram.com/lislechamber
Description: Promotes business and community development in the Lisle, IL area. **Founded:** 1983. **Publications:** Community Profile on Village of Lisle (Biennial); Membership Directory and Product/Services Guide (Annual). **Geographic Preference:** Local.

39230 ■ Litchfield Chamber of Commerce
400 N State St.
Litchfield, IL 62056
Ph: (217)324-2533
Co. E-mail: info@litchfieldchamber.com
URL: http://www.litchfieldchamber.com
Contact: Kassidy Paine, Co-President
E-mail: kassidyp@gmail.com
Facebook: www.facebook.com/litchfieldilchamber
Linkedin: www.linkedin.com/company/litchfield-il
-chamber-of-commerce

Description: Aims to promote and stimulate the economic growth within the greater Litchfield area by mobilizing the talents and energies of the chamber's members. **Founded:** 1898. **Publications:** *Chamber World* (Monthly). **Geographic Preference:** Local.

39231 ■ *Lockport*
222 E 9th St., 3rd Fl.
Lockport, IL 60441
Ph: (815)838-3357
Fax: (815)838-2653
Co. E-mail: office@lockportchamber.com
URL: http://lockportchamber.com
Contact: Tim Gaba, President
URL(s): www.lockportchamber.com/member-benefits
Description: Contains listing of member businesses as well as local information; distributed to new residents and businesses. **Availability:** Print; Online.

39232 ■ Lockport Chamber of Commerce (LCC)
222 E 9th St., 3rd Fl.
Lockport, IL 60441
Ph: (815)838-3357
Fax: (815)838-2653
Co. E-mail: office@lockportchamber.com
URL: http://lockportchamber.com
Contact: Tim Gaba, President
Facebook: www.facebook.com/lockportchamber
Description: Promotes business and community development in Lockport, IL. Sponsors parades as well as a variety of social and promotional activities. **Founded:** 1974. **Publications:** *Lockport*; *Lockport Connections* (Monthly); *Lockport Map*. **Educational Activities:** Business Expo (Annual); Holiday Business After Hours (Annual); Lockport Chamber of Commerce Board Meeting (Monthly). **Awards:** Lockport Chamber of Commerce Dollars for Scholars (Annual). **Geographic Preference:** Local.

39233 ■ Lombard Area Chamber of Commerce and Industry
10 Lilac Ln.
Lombard, IL 60148
Ph: (630)627-5040
Co. E-mail: info@lombardchamber.com
URL: http://www.lombardchamber.com
Contact: Melissa Boltz, President
E-mail: melissa@lombardchamber.com
Facebook: www.facebook.com/LombardChamber
Description: Promotes business and community development in the Lombard, IL area. Sponsors Lilac Festival and Lilac Ball. Sponsors golf outing. **Founded:** 1953. **Publications:** *Lombard Business Directory*; *The Sourcebook: Directory of Goods and Services*; *Village*. **Geographic Preference:** Local.

39234 ■ Loves Park - Machesney Park Chamber of Commerce
100 Heart Blvd.
Loves Park, IL 61111
Ph: (815)633-3999
Co. E-mail: info@parkschamber.com
URL: http://www.parkschamber.com
Contact: Josh Aurand, Treasurer
Facebook: www.facebook.com/parkschamber
Linkedin: www.linkedin.com/company/the-parks-chamber
YouTube: www.youtube.com/channel/UCqIBvQkTMsENSaWT-4JqS4w
Description: Works to build a healthy economy and improve the quality of life in the community. **Publications:** *Chamber Chatter* (Monthly). **Geographic Preference:** Local.

39235 ■ Mahomet Area Chamber of Commerce (MACC)
401 Oak St.
Mahomet, IL 61853
Ph: (217)586-3165
Co. E-mail: office@mahometchamberofcommerce.com
URL: http://mahometchamberofcommerce.com
Contact: Alan Singleton, Director
Facebook: www.facebook.com/pages/Mahomet-Area-Chamber-of-Commerce
X (Twitter): x.com/mahometchamber

Description: Works to advance the general welfare and prosperity of the Mahomet area. **Founded:** 1985. **Publications:** *Mahomet Connection* (Monthly). **Awards:** Mahomet Area Chamber of Commerce Scholarship (Annual). **Geographic Preference:** Local.

39236 ■ Manhattan Chamber of Commerce (MCC)
PO Box 357
Manhattan, IL 60442
Ph: (815)478-3811
Co. E-mail: chamber@manhattan-il.com
URL: http://www.manhattan-il.com
Contact: Kevin Molloy, President
Facebook: www.facebook.com/ManhattanChamber
Description: Promotes business and community development in Manhattan, IL. **Founded:** 1886. **Geographic Preference:** Local.

39237 ■ Marengo Union Chamber of Commerce
116 S State St.
Marengo, IL 60152
Ph: (815)568-6680
Co. E-mail: chamber@marengo-union.com
URL: http://www.marengo-union.com
Contact: Colleen Helfers, Executive Director
Description: Promotes business and community development in McHenry County, IL. Sponsors annual Settlers Day. **Founded:** 1970. **Publications:** *Chamber Talk*. **Geographic Preference:** Local.

39238 ■ Marion Chamber of Commerce
2305 W Main St.
Marion, IL 62959
Ph: (618)997-6311
Fax: (618)997-4665
Co. E-mail: info@marionillinois.com
URL: http://www.marionillinois.com
Contact: Karen Mullins, Executive Director
Facebook: www.facebook.com/marionilchamber
Linkedin: www.linkedin.com/company/marion-chamber-of-commerce
X (Twitter): x.com/marion_chamber
Instagram: www.instagram.com/marionilchamber
YouTube: www.youtube.com/channel/UCiDaBavvX57ORrkrCZXFwbg
Description: Promotes business and community development in the Marion, IL area. **Founded:** 1923. **Geographic Preference:** Local.

39239 ■ Marshall Area Chamber of Commerce
708 Archer Ave.
Marshall, IL 62441
Ph: (217)826-2034
Co. E-mail: marshallilchamber@gmail.com
URL: http://www.marshallilchamber.com
Contact: Anne Sheehy, President
Facebook: www.facebook.com/marshallilchamber
Pinterest: www.pinterest.com/marshallilchamber
Description: Represents industries and businesses organized to promote agricultural, business, community, and tourism development in the Marshall, IL area. **Founded:** 1982. **Geographic Preference:** Local.

39240 ■ Mattoon Chamber of Commerce
1518 Broadway Ave.
Mattoon, IL 61938
Ph: (217)235-5661
Fax: (217)235-5786
Co. E-mail: matchamber@consolidated.net
URL: http://www.mattoonchamber.com
Contact: Ed Dowd, Executive Director
E-mail: director@mattoonchamber.com
Facebook: www.facebook.com/MattoonChamberofCommerce
Description: Business and professional firms. Seeks to support community and economic development in Coles County, IL. Sponsors Bagelfest. **Founded:** 1905. **Publications:** *Business Directory and Buyer's Guide* (Annual). **Awards:** Mattoon Chamber of Commerce Citizen of the Year (Annual). **Geographic Preference:** Local.

39241 ■ Maywood Chamber of Commerce (MCC)
PO Box 172
Maywood, IL 60153
Ph: (708)345-7077
Co. E-mail: info@maywoodchamber.com
URL: http://www.maywood-il.org
Contact: Edwin H. Walker, IV, President
Description: Businesses, churches, organizations, government agencies, and individuals interested in promoting business and community development in Maywood, IL. Conducts charitable activities. **Founded:** 1935. **Publications:** *Community Guide* (Annual); *Maywood Chamber of Commerce--Community Guide: Maywood Community Guide* (Annual); *Business Guide*. **Geographic Preference:** Local.

39242 ■ McHenry Area Chamber of Commerce (MACC)
1257 N Green St.
McHenry, IL 60050
Ph: (815)385-4300
Fax: (815)385-9142
Co. E-mail: info@mchenrychamber.com
URL: http://mchenrychamber.com
Contact: Molly Ostap, President
E-mail: molly@mchenrychamber.com
Facebook: www.facebook.com/mchenryareachamber
Linkedin: www.linkedin.com/company/mchenry-area-chamber-of-commerce
YouTube: www.youtube.com/channel/UCwNLqVRSSMf7cDZA-HHutxw
Description: Represents businesses and professional men and women working together to provide support to the growth and development of the business community and continually improve the quality of life for those who work and live in McHenry. **Founded:** 1952. **Publications:** *Community Guide*; *Up Front* (Monthly). **Educational Activities:** Business Council; Country Meadows Craft Show. **Geographic Preference:** Local.

39243 ■ McLean County Chamber of Commerce (MCC)
2203 E Empire St., Ste. B
Bloomington, IL 61702-1586
Ph: (309)829-6344
Fax: (309)827-3940
Co. E-mail: chamber@mcleancochamber.org
URL: http://www.mcleancochamber.org
Contact: Charlie Moore, President
E-mail: charlie@mcleancochamber.org
Facebook: www.facebook.com/mcleancochamber
X (Twitter): x.com/mcleancochamber
Instagram: www.instagram.com/mcleancochamber
YouTube: www.youtube.com/channel/UCZWFy5PP5JZb8wEjVv7GnxA
Description: Represents businesses and individuals investing time and money in a continual community development program. Improves the economic, civic and cultural well-being of McLean County. **Founded:** 1900. **Publications:** *McLean County News* (Weekly); *News, Views & Issues* (Monthly); *Business Directory*. **Educational Activities:** Business After Hours (Monthly). **Geographic Preference:** Local.

39244 ■ Melrose Park Chamber of Commerce and Community Development (MPCCCD)
900 N 25th Ave.
Melrose Park, IL 60160
Ph: (708)731-3715
Co. E-mail: info@mpcccd.org
URL: http://mpcccd.org
Contact: Isaac Bazbaz, Executive Director
E-mail: ibazbaz@mpcccd.org
X (Twitter): x.com/mpcccd
YouTube: www.youtube.com/channel/UC69cWAwKTYs9m-AnNMkHF0g
Description: Helps different companies to recognize their business. **Founded:** 2018. **Publications:** *Chamber Business and Community Guide* (Annual); *Chamber Chit-Chat* (Quarterly). **Geographic Preference:** Local.

STATE LISTINGS

39245 ▪ *Membership Directory & Buyers' Guide*
501 Jackson Ave.
Charleston, IL 61920
Ph: (217)345-7041
Co. E-mail: cacc@charlestonchamber.com
URL: http://www.charlestonchamber.com
Contact: Doug Abolt, President
URL(s): charlestonchamber.com/membership-benefits
Released: Annual; January. **Description:** Serves as an excellent resource for business leads and contacts and a great sales tool. **Availability:** Print; Online.

39246 ▪ *Membership List*
211 Locust St.
Sterling, IL 61081
Ph: (815)625-2400
Fax: (815)625-9361
Co. E-mail: knoble@saukvalleyareachamber.com
URL: http://www.saukvalleyareachamber.com
Contact: Lance Buser, President
URL(s): www.saukvalleyareachamber.com/membership-benefits
Availability: Print.

39247 ▪ **Mendota Area Chamber of Commerce**
800 Washington St.
Mendota, IL 61342
Ph: (815)539-6507
Fax: (815)539-6025
Co. E-mail: sweide@mendotachamber.com
URL: http://www.mendotachamber.com
Contact: Sam Setchell, Co-President Co-Chief Executive Officer
Facebook: www.facebook.com/mendotachamber
Description: Promotes business and community development in Mendota, IL. **Founded:** 1945. **Geographic Preference:** Local.

39248 ▪ **Metro-East Regional Chamber of Commerce**
4387 N Illinois St., Ste. 200
Swansea, IL 62226
Ph: (618)233-3938
Co. E-mail: chamber@metroeastchamber.org
URL: http://metroeastchamber.org
Contact: Amy Kempfer, President
Facebook: www.facebook.com/MetroEastChamber
Description: Aims to bring businesses together for the purpose of developing and promoting balanced economic growth and business opportunities that in harmony with the objectives of the entire community. Welcomes all businesses, organizations, and individuals regardless of race, religion, color, or national origin who demonstrate an interest in maintaining and promoting a healthy economic climate in the Village of Swansea, Illinois. **Founded:** 1969. **Publications:** *Chamber Communicator* (Monthly); *E-Chamber Update* (Weekly). **Geographic Preference:** Local.

39249 ▪ **Metropolis Chamber of Commerce**
516 Market St.
Metropolis, IL 62960
Ph: (618)524-2714
Co. E-mail: office@metropolischamber.com
URL: http://www.metropolischamber.com
Contact: Kelly Lunsford, President
Facebook: www.facebook.com/metrochamber
Instagram: www.instagram.com/metrochamber
Description: Promotes business and community development in Metropolis, IL area. **Publications:** *Chamberlink* (Monthly). **Geographic Preference:** Local.

39250 ▪ *MGCCI It's Your Business*
6101 Capulina Ave.
Morton Grove, IL 60053-2902
Ph: (847)965-0330
Fax: (847)965-0349
URL: http://mgcci.org
Contact: Jim Broderick, President
URL(s): mgcci.org/member-benefits
Availability: Print; Online.

39251 ▪ **Mokena Chamber of Commerce**
11104 Front St., Ste. 1B
Mokena, IL 60448
Ph: (708)479-2468
Fax: (708)479-7144
Co. E-mail: chamber@mokena.com
URL: http://www.mokena.com
Contact: Melissa M. Fedora, Executive Director
Facebook: www.facebook.com/MokenaCC
X (Twitter): x.com/mokenachamber
Instagram: www.instagram.com/mokenachamber
YouTube: www.youtube.com/user/mokenachamber
Description: Promotes business and community development in the Mokena, IL area. **Publications:** *Chambergram* (Quarterly). **Geographic Preference:** Local.

39252 ▪ **Momence Chamber of Commerce**
PO Box 34
Momence, IL 60954
Ph: (815)472-4620
URL: http://www.momence.org
Contact: Veronica Smith, President
Description: Provides it's members with the opportunity to network and make business contacts. **Founded:** 1938. **Geographic Preference:** Local.

39253 ▪ **Monmouth Area Chamber of Commerce**
89 Public Sq.
Monmouth, IL 61462
Ph: (309)734-3181
Co. E-mail: info@monmouthilchamber.com
URL: http://monmouthilchamber.com
Contact: Jenna Clayton, President
Facebook: www.facebook.com/MonmouthChamberEvents
Description: Represents businesses and professional persons interested in promoting business and community development in the Monmouth, IL area. Sponsors prime beef festival. **Founded:** 1912. **Publications:** *Chamber Communicator* (Monthly). **Educational Activities:** Good Morning Monmouth. **Geographic Preference:** Local.

39254 ▪ **Monticello Chamber of Commerce**
200 E Railroad St.
Monticello, IL 61856
Ph: (217)762-7921
Co. E-mail: info@monticellochamber.org
URL: http://www.monticellochamber.org
Contact: Sarah Ross, Vice President
E-mail: sross@kirbyhealth.org
Facebook: www.facebook.com/MonticelloChamber
X (Twitter): x.com/monticellochamb
Instagram: www.instagram.com/makeitmonticello
Pinterest: www.pinterest.com/makeitmonticello
Description: Works to create an environment where businesses can succeed. **Founded:** 1999. **Publications:** *Business*. **Educational Activities:** Lunch with Santa on the Train (Annual). **Geographic Preference:** Local.

39255 ▪ **Morrison Chamber of Commerce**
221 W Main St.
Morrison, IL 61270
Ph: (815)772-3757
Fax: (815)772-3757
Co. E-mail: morrisonchamber@morrisonil.org
URL: http://morrisonchamber.com
Contact: Kevin Schisler, President
Facebook: www.facebook.com/morrisonchamberofcommerce
Description: Aims to promote Morrison and support its members through structure and events that unite the community. **Founded:** 1927. **Geographic Preference:** Local.

39256 ▪ **Morton Chamber of Commerce**
415 W Jefferson St.
Morton, IL 61550
Ph: (309)263-2491
Fax: (309)263-2401
Co. E-mail: info@mortonillinois.org
URL: http://www.mortonchamber.org
Contact: Jeff Schieferle Uhlenbrock, President
Facebook: www.facebook.com/mortonchamber
Linkedin: www.linkedin.com/company/mortonchamber
X (Twitter): x.com/mortonchamber
Instagram: www.instagram.com/mortonchamberofcommerce
YouTube: www.youtube.com/user/MortonChamberofComm
Description: Businesses. Promotes business and community development in the area. Sponsors retail promotions and annual festivals and events. **Founded:** 1955. **Publications:** *Morton Matters* (Monthly). **Geographic Preference:** Local.

39257 ▪ **Morton Grove Chamber of Commerce and Industry (MGCCI)**
6101 Capulina Ave.
Morton Grove, IL 60053-2902
Ph: (847)965-0330
Fax: (847)965-0349
URL: http://mgcci.org
Contact: Jim Broderick, President
Facebook: www.facebook.com/mgcci.org
Linkedin: www.linkedin.com/company/morton-grove-chamber-of-commerce
Description: Promotes business and community development in Morton Grove, IL. **Founded:** 1920. **Publications:** *Morton Grove Community Guide* (Biennial; Semiannual); *MGCCI It's Your Business*. **Educational Activities:** Business After Hours (6/year); Golf Outing (Annual). **Geographic Preference:** Local.

39258 ▪ *Morton Matters*
415 W Jefferson St.
Morton, IL 61550
Ph: (309)263-2491
Fax: (309)263-2401
Co. E-mail: info@mortonillinois.org
URL: http://www.mortonchamber.org
Contact: Jeff Schieferle Uhlenbrock, President
URL(s): www.mortonchamber.org/member-services
Released: Monthly **Availability:** Electronic publishing; Online.

39259 ▪ **Mount Carroll Chamber of Commerce**
320 N Main St., Ste. 101
Mount Carroll, IL 61053
Ph: (815)244-4424
Co. E-mail: info@mtcarrollil.org
URL: http://mtcarrollil.org
Contact: Pam Sorg, President
Facebook: www.facebook.com/mountcarrollchamber
Description: Promotes business and community development in Mt. Carroll, IL. **Geographic Preference:** Local.

39260 ▪ **Mount Greenwood Chamber of Commerce**
3052 W 111th St.
Chicago, IL 60655
Ph: (773)238-6103
Co. E-mail: info@mtgcc.org
Facebook: www.facebook.com/people/Mount-Greenwood-Chamber-of-Commerce/100064374742116
Description: Promotes business and community development in the Mt. Greenwood area of Chicago, IL. **Geographic Preference:** Local.

39261 ▪ **Mount Prospect Chamber of Commerce**
662 E NW Hwy.
Mount Prospect, IL 60056
Ph: (847)392-1200
Co. E-mail: info@mountprospectchamber.org
URL: http://www.mountprospectchamber.org
Contact: Trisha Chokshi, Chairman
Facebook: www.facebook.com/mountprospectchamber
Linkedin: www.linkedin.com/in/the-mount-prospect-chamber-of-commerce-a6b49514
X (Twitter): x.com/MP_Chamber
YouTube: www.youtube.com/user/mountprospectchamber

39262 ■ Mount Zion Chamber of Commerce (ZCC)
1400 Mt. Zion Pky.
Mount Zion, IL 62549
Ph: (217)864-2526
Co. E-mail: mtzionilchamber@gmail.com
URL: http://www.mtzionchamber.org
Contact: Jay Woodrum, President
X (Twitter): x.com/mt_zionChamber
Description: Promotes business and community development in the Mt. Zion, IL area. Participates in Pony Express Days; sponsors Small Business Expo. **Founded:** 1987. **Geographic Preference:** Local.

Description: Promotes business and community development in Mt. Prospect, IL. **Founded:** 1926. **Publications:** *Chamber Matters* (Bimonthly); *Community Guide and Business Directory*. **Geographic Preference:** Local.

39263 ■ Murphysboro Chamber of Commerce
1709 Walnut St., Ste. A
Murphysboro, IL 62966
Ph: (618)684-6421
Fax: (618)684-2010
URL: http://murphysborochamber.com
Contact: Gene Basden, President
Description: Promotes business and community development in Murphysboro, IL. **Founded:** 1923. **Publications:** *Chamber Directory* (Periodic); *City Directory* (Periodic). **Geographic Preference:** Local.

39264 ■ Naperville Area Chamber of Commerce (NACC)
55 S Main St., No. 351
Naperville, IL 60540
Ph: (630)355-4141
Co. E-mail: chamber@naperville.net
URL: http://www.naperville.net
Contact: Raymond E. Krouse, Jr., Partner
E-mail: ray.krouse@sikich.com
Facebook: www.facebook.com/NapervilleChamber
Linkedin: www.linkedin.com/company/naperville-area-chamber-of-commerce
X (Twitter): x.com/NaperChamber
Instagram: www.instagram.com/naperchamber
YouTube: www.youtube.com/user/NapervilleChamber
Description: Promotes business and community development in Naperville, IL area. **Founded:** 1913. **Publications:** *Commerce* (Monthly); *Community Resource Guide and Relocation Handbook*; *Directory of Members & Buyers Guide*. **Awards:** Naperville Area Small Business of the Year Awards (Annual). **Geographic Preference:** Local.

39265 ■ Nauvoo Chamber of Commerce
Tourism Office
1295 Mulholland St.
Nauvoo, IL 62354
Ph: (217)453-6648
URL: http://www.beautifulnauvoo.com/nauvoo-chamber-of-commerce.html
Contact: Thomas E. Grant, Jr., Contact
Description: Works to advance the general welfare and prosperity of Nauvoo. Promotes the economic, civic, commercial, cultural, industrial, and education interest of the area. **Founded:** 1839. **Geographic Preference:** Local.

39266 ■ *The Networker*
5120 Museum Dr.
Oak Lawn, IL 60453
Ph: (708)424-8300
Fax: (708)229-2236
Co. E-mail: office@oaklawnchamber.com
URL: http://www.oaklawnchamber.com
Contact: Jim Makina, President
URL(s): www.oaklawnchamber.com/bi-monthly-newsletter
Released: 6/year **Availability:** Print; PDF.

39267 ■ New Lenox Chamber of Commerce (NLCC)
1 Veterans Pky.
New Lenox, IL 60451
Ph: (815)485-4241
URL: http://www.newlenoxchamber.com
Contact: Emily Johnson, Chief Executive Officer
E-mail: emily@newlenoxchamber.com
Facebook: www.facebook.com/newlenoxchamber
X (Twitter): x.com/NewLenoxChamber
YouTube: www.youtube.com/channel/UCYXJtZNnhYwLCa8m1QZQX5w
Description: Promotes business and community development in New Lenox Township, IL. Sponsors area festival; conducts community awards, scholarships and partnership with schools. **Founded:** 1960. **Publications:** *Business Bulletin*; *New Lenox, IL: The Community With the Ability to Grow*; *Welcome to New Lenox*. **Awards:** New Lenox Chamber of Commerce Business of the Year (Annual). **Geographic Preference:** Local.

39268 ■ Niles Chamber of Commerce and Industry
8060 Oakton St.
Niles, IL 60714
Ph: (847)268-8180
Fax: (847)268-8186
Co. E-mail: office@nileschamber.com
URL: http://www.nileschamber.com
Contact: Suzanne Wulf, First Vice President
X (Twitter): x.com/Niles_Chamber
Description: Promotes business and community development in Niles, IL. **Founded:** 1971. **Publications:** *Chamber Scene*; *NCCI Community Guide* (Annual). **Awards:** Niles Citizen of the Year Award (Annual); Ken Scheel Chamber Member of the Year Award (Annual). **Geographic Preference:** Local.

39269 ■ Northbrook Chamber of Commerce and Industry (NCCI)
2002 Walters Ave.
Northbrook, IL 60062
Ph: (847)498-5555
Co. E-mail: info@northbrookchamber.org
URL: http://www.northbrookchamber.org
Contact: Tensley Garris, Executive Director
E-mail: tensley@northbrookchamber.org
Facebook: www.facebook.com/NorthbrookChamber
Description: Promotes business and economic development in Northbrook, IL. **Founded:** 1901. **Publications:** *Membership Directory and Buyer's Guide*; *Northbrook Chamber of Commerce and Industry--Membership Directory and Buyer's Guide*. **Geographic Preference:** Local.

39270 ■ Norwood Park Chamber of Commerce and Industry
6088 N NW Hwy.
Chicago, IL 60631-2502
Ph: (773)763-3606
Fax: (773)763-3620
Co. E-mail: info@norwoodpark.org
URL: http://www.norwoodpark.org
Contact: Kim Bronder, President
Facebook: www.facebook.com/Norwood.Park.Chamber
Linkedin: www.linkedin.com/company/norwood-park-chamber-of-commerce
X (Twitter): x.com/norwoodparkcoc
Instagram: www.instagram.com/norwoodparkcoc
Description: Works to provide leadership, visions and strategy to the business community. **Geographic Preference:** Local.

39271 ■ Oak Forest - Crestwood Area Chamber of Commerce
15440 S Central
Oak Forest, IL 60452
Ph: (708)687-4600
Co. E-mail: info@oc-chamber.org
URL: http://oc-chamber.org
Contact: Kim Malecky-Iles, Director
Facebook: www.facebook.com/occhamber
Description: Aims to protect and enhance the investments of the Oak Forest businesses. **Founded:** 1975. **Publications:** *FYI*; *Oak Leaf* (Monthly). **Geographic Preference:** Local.

39272 ■ Oak Lawn Chamber of Commerce
5120 Museum Dr.
Oak Lawn, IL 60453
Ph: (708)424-8300
Fax: (708)229-2236
Co. E-mail: office@oaklawnchamber.com
URL: http://www.oaklawnchamber.com
Contact: Jim Makina, President
Facebook: www.facebook.com/Oak-Lawn-Chamber-of-Commerce-184315644995163
Description: Works to represent and advance the Oak Lawn business community; strives with constant integrity, fairness and cooperation to promote and to improve the economic atmosphere, business climate and image of Oak Lawn. **Founded:** 1947. **Publications:** *The Networker* (6/year). **Geographic Preference:** Local.

39273 ■ Oak Park-River Forest Chamber of Commerce (OPRF)
143 S Oak Pk. Ave.
Oak Park, IL 60302
Ph: (708)613-0550
Co. E-mail: info@oprfchamber.org
URL: http://www.oprfchamber.org
Contact: Darien Marion Burton, President
E-mail: darien@dmburton.co
Facebook: www.facebook.com/OPRFChamber
Linkedin: www.linkedin.com/company/oak-park---river-forest-chamber-of-commerce
X (Twitter): x.com/oprfchamber
YouTube: www.youtube.com/channel/UCtoPfkdIOtF50CB4tJO4XFA
Description: Promotes economic and community development in Oak Park and River Forest, IL. **Founded:** 1905. **Publications:** *Business Connection* (Bimonthly); *Community Guide* (Annual); *Portrait*. **Educational Activities:** Consumer Expo. **Geographic Preference:** Local.

39274 ■ *Official Guide to Lakeview East*
3138 N Broadway
Chicago, IL 60657
Ph: (773)348-8608
Co. E-mail: info@lakevieweast.com
URL: http://lakevieweast.com
Contact: Marc Engel, President
URL(s): lakevieweast.com/advertising
Released: Annual **Description:** Includes membership directory. **Availability:** Print.

39275 ■ Okawville Chamber of Commerce
PO Box 506
Okawville, IL 62271
Ph: (618)243-5694
Co. E-mail: tourokawville@606front.net
URL: http://okawvillecc.com
Description: Promotes business and community development in Okawville. **Founded:** 1838. **Geographic Preference:** Local.

39276 ■ Oregon Chamber of Commerce
122 N 4th St.
Oregon, IL 61061
Ph: (815)732-2100
Co. E-mail: chamber.director@oregonil.com
URL: http://oregonil.com
Contact: Donna Marie Mann, President
Facebook: www.facebook.com/OregonILAreaChamber
Description: Promotes business and community development in Oregon, IL. Sponsors Autumn on Parade Festival. **Geographic Preference:** Local.

39277 ■ Orland Park Area Chamber of Commerce (OPACC)
8799 W 151st St.
Orland Park, IL 60462
Ph: (708)349-2972
Fax: (708)349-7454
Co. E-mail: info@orlandparkchamber.org
URL: http://orlandparkchamber.org
Contact: Ramzi Hassan, President
Facebook: www.facebook.com/OrlandParkChamber
Linkedin: www.linkedin.com/company/orland-park-area-chamber-of-commerce
X (Twitter): x.com/orlandchamber1
Instagram: www.instagram.com/orlandparkareachamber

39278 ■ Oswego Chamber of Commerce
73 W Van Buren St.
Oswego, IL 60543
Ph: (630)554-3505
Fax: (630)554-0050
Co. E-mail: info@oswegochamber.org
URL: http://www.oswegochamber.org
Contact: Angie Hibben, President
E-mail: angie@oswegochamber.org
X (Twitter): x.com/oswegochamber

Description: Aims to make business in Oswego grow and succeed. **Founded:** 1984. **Publications:** *Chamber News*. **Geographic Preference:** Local.

39279 ■ Ottawa Area Chamber of Commerce and Industry
633 La Salle St., Ste. 401
Ottawa, IL 61350
Ph: (815)433-0084
Fax: (815)433-2405
Co. E-mail: info@ottawachamberillinois.com
URL: http://www.ottawachamberillinois.com
Contact: Jeff Hettrick, Executive Director
E-mail: j.hettrick@ottawachamberillinois.com
Facebook: www.facebook.com/OttawaChamberIllinois
Linkedin: www.linkedin.com/company/ottawa-area-chamber-of-commerce
X (Twitter): x.com/ottawachamberil
Instagram: www.instagram.com/ottawachamberillinois
YouTube: www.youtube.com/channel/UCBV9LAkv2itejOL7ONyMvAg

Description: Retailers, professionals, corporations, and individuals united to promote tourism, generate new business, aid downtown merchants, and improve the quality of life in the Ottawa, IL area. Sponsors Welcomburger festival, Farmers Market, Legislative and State of the City Luncheons, Small Business Seminars and IVLead Leadership Series. **Founded:** 1916. **Publications:** *ED Update* (Monthly); *Manufacturer's Guide* (Periodic). **Geographic Preference:** Local.

39280 ■ Palatine Area Chamber of Commerce (PACC)
3400 W Stonegate Blvd.
Arlington Heights, IL 60005
Ph: (847)359-7200
Fax: (847)359-7246
Co. E-mail: info@palatinechamber.com
URL: http://www.palatinechamber.com
Contact: Steven Gaus, Director
E-mail: sgaus@palatinechamber.com
Facebook: www.facebook.com/PalatineChamber
X (Twitter): x.com/PalatineChamber
YouTube: www.youtube.com/channel/UCFAgqmcOadi2bhGiouU8kSg

Description: Promotes business and community development in Palatine, IL. **Founded:** 1950. **Publications:** *The Chamber Guide* (Annual); *Community Guide* (Monthly); *The Key* (Monthly); *The Chamber Guide* (Annual). **Geographic Preference:** Local.

39281 ■ Pana Chamber of Commerce
120 E 3rd St.
Pana, IL 62557
Ph: (217)562-4240
Co. E-mail: panachamber@consolidated.net
URL: http://www.panachamber.net
Contact: Al Stupek, Director
E-mail: al@yourtccu.net
Facebook: www.facebook.com/people/Pana-Chamber/100010010831405

Description: Promotes business and community development in Pana, IL. Sponsors annual Pana Heritage Days, Chamber Week, Downtown Block Party, Car Show, Illinois State Championship Antique Bicycle Show, Blacksmith Hammer in & Antique Tractor Show and Christmas Week. **Founded:** 1930. **Publications:** *Business and Professional Memo* (Quarterly). **Geographic Preference:** Local.

39282 ■ Paris Area Chamber of Commerce & Tourism (PACCT)
105 N Central St.
Paris, IL 61944
Ph: (217)465-4179
Co. E-mail: info@parisilchamber.com
URL: http://www.parisilchamber.com
Contact: Paige Moreschi, President

Description: Promotes business and community development in Paris, IL. Sponsors Honey Bee Festival. **Founded:** 1903. **Awards:** Paris Area Chamber of Commerce and Tourism Parisian of the Year (Annual). **Geographic Preference:** Local.

39283 ■ Pekin Area Chamber of Commerce (PACC)
402 Ct., St.
Pekin, IL 61554
Ph: (309)346-2106
Co. E-mail: info@pekinchamber.com
URL: http://pekinchamber.com
Contact: Chris Deverman, President
Facebook: www.facebook.com/PekinChamber
X (Twitter): x.com/PekinChamber
Instagram: www.instagram.com/pekinchamber

Description: Promotes the growth of the Pekin area through collective efforts. **Founded:** 1911. **Publications:** *Focus* (Weekly). **Educational Activities:** Business After Hours (Irregular). **Geographic Preference:** Local.

39284 ■ Peoria Area Chamber of Commerce (PACC)
403 NE Jefferson Ave.
Peoria, IL 61603
Ph: (309)495-5900
Co. E-mail: editor@peoriachamber.org
URL: http://www.peoriachamber.org
Contact: Joshua Gunn, President
E-mail: jgunn@peoriachamber.org
Facebook: www.facebook.com/PeoriaChamber
Linkedin: www.linkedin.com/company/peoriaareachamber
X (Twitter): x.com/Peoriachamber
Instagram: www.instagram.com/peoriaareachamber

Description: Promotes business and community development in the Peoria, IL area. **Founded:** 1910. **Publications:** *Chamber Communicator* (Weekly). **Educational Activities:** Business After Hours (Monthly). **Geographic Preference:** Local.

39285 ■ Petersburg Chamber of Commerce (PCC)
PO Box 452
Petersburg, IL 62675
Ph: (217)691-0004
Co. E-mail: petersburgilchamber@gmail.com
URL: http://www.petersburgilchamber.com
Contact: Kelly Spivey, President
Facebook: www.facebook.com/PetersburgILChamberofCommerce

Description: Promotes business and community development in Menard County, IL. Sponsors Petersburg Harvest Fest and Christmas in Petersburg. **Geographic Preference:** Local.

39286 ■ Pike County Chamber of Commerce
224 W Washington St.
Pittsfield, IL 62363
Ph: (217)285-2971
Co. E-mail: pikechamber@casscomm.com
URL: http://www.pikeil.org
Contact: Coy Bainter, President
Facebook: www.facebook.com/PikeCountyIllinoisChamber
Linkedin: www.linkedin.com/company/pike-county-il-chamber-of-commerce/about
X (Twitter): x.com/PikeCoChamber
YouTube: www.youtube.com/channel/UCMHOzhXXMXZi2fiyJKEW6eA

Description: Promotes business and community development in Pike County, IL. **Founded:** 1987. **Geographic Preference:** Local.

39287 ■ Pinckneyville Chamber of Commerce
4 S Walnut St.
Pinckneyville, IL 62274
Ph: (618)357-3243
Co. E-mail: chamber.pville@gmail.com
URL: http://pinckneyville.com
Contact: Ashley Bathon, Chairman
Facebook: www.facebook.com/pinckneyville.chamber

Description: Provides a venue in which people can take effective action for the progress of the community. Organizes convention, sales meetings and other gatherings. **Geographic Preference:** Local.

39288 ■ Plainfield Area Chamber of Commerce (PACC)
24109 W Lockport St.
Plainfield, IL 60544
Ph: (815)436-4431
Co. E-mail: pacc@plainfieldchamber.org
URL: http://www.plainfieldchamber.com
Contact: Brian Minnis, Member
Facebook: www.facebook.com/plainfieldchamber
Linkedin: www.linkedin.com/company/plainfield-area-chamber-of-commerce
X (Twitter): x.com/plainfieldacc
Instagram: www.instagram.com/explore/locations/367222166761/plainfield-area-chamber-of-commerce
YouTube: www.youtube.com/channel/UCu0Gc1eWDBq7yUvJqqU8-Sw

Description: Promotes business and community growth and development. Strives to make the Plainfield area a better place to live, work, worship, learn, and conduct business. **Founded:** 1972. **Geographic Preference:** Local.

39289 ■ Polo Chamber of Commerce
115 N Franklin Ave.
Polo, IL 61064
Ph: (815)946-3131
Co. E-mail: polochamber@gmail.com
URL: http://www.poloil.org/ChamberCommerce.html
Contact: Tammy Merdian, President
Facebook: www.facebook.com/poloilchamber

Description: Promotes business and community development in Polo, IL. Sponsors festivals. **Geographic Preference:** Local.

39290 ■ Pontiac Area Chamber of Commerce (PACC)
210 N Plum St.
Pontiac, IL 61764
Ph: (815)844-5131
Co. E-mail: info@pontiacchamber.org
URL: http://pontiacchamber.org/web
Contact: Debi Ores, Treasurer

Description: Promotes business and community development in the Pontiac, IL area. Jointly sponsors annual Bluegrass Festival. **Founded:** 1917. **Publications:** *Chamber Plus* (Quarterly). **Geographic Preference:** Local.

39291 ■ Portage Park Chamber of Commerce (PPCC)
PO Box 346163
Chicago, IL 60634-6091
Ph: (773)777-2020
Co. E-mail: info@portageparkchamber.org
URL: http://www.portageparkchamber.org
Contact: Lawrence Pahlke, President
Facebook: www.facebook.com/PortageParkChamber
X (Twitter): x.com/gsborovik
Instagram: www.instagram.com/portageparkchamber

Description: Promotes business and community development in the Portage Park area of Chicago, IL. Markets the six corners business district. Sponsors community events and promotional activities. **Founded:** 1937. **Geographic Preference:** Local.

39292 ■ Princeton Area Chamber of Commerce
435 S Main St.
Princeton, IL 61356
Ph: (815)875-2616
Co. E-mail: jcole@princeton-il.com
URL: http://princetonchamber-il.com
Contact: Dave Shouse, President
Facebook: www.facebook.com/PrincetonILChamber

Description: Serves as a clearinghouse of business and community information, to legislative issues and reliable business referrals. **Founded:** 1870. **Geographic Preference:** Local.

39293 ■ Quincy Area Chamber of Commerce (QACC)
300 Civic Center Plz., Ste. 245
Quincy, IL 62301
Ph: (217)222-7980
URL: http://www.quincychamber.org
Contact: Bruce Guthrie, Co-President Co-Chief Executive Officer
Facebook: www.facebook.com/quincychamber
X (Twitter): x.com/quincychamber
Description: Promotes activities for members who enhance the economic well being and quality of life in the Quincy area. **Founded:** 1887. **Publications:** *Mini Update* (Weekly). **Geographic Preference:** Local.

39294 ■ Rantoul Area Chamber of Commerce (RACC)
120 E Sangamon Ave.
Rantoul, IL 61866
Ph: (217)714-7316
URL: http://www.rantoulchamber.com
Contact: George Papametro, President
Facebook: www.facebook.com/rantoulareachamber
Instagram: www.instagram.com/rantoulareachamber
Description: Promotes business and community development in Rantoul, IL. Sponsors Fourth of July celebration. **Founded:** 1989. **Geographic Preference:** Local.

39295 ■ Riverside Chamber of Commerce
PO Box 7
Riverside, IL 60546
URL: http://riversidechamber.us
Contact: Greg Gorski, President
Facebook: www.facebook.com/RiversideChamber
YouTube: www.youtube.com/user/riversidechamber
Description: Promotes business and community development in Riverside, IL area. **Founded:** 1993. **Geographic Preference:** Local.

39296 ■ Rochelle Chamber of Commerce
501 W 6th Ave.
Rochelle, IL 61068
Ph: (815)562-4189
Co. E-mail: rochellechamber@gmail.com
Facebook: www.facebook.com/RochelleAreaChamber
Description: Represents, educates and supports member businesses, promoting economic vitality and enhancing the quality of life. **Founded:** 1939. **Publications:** *Community Guide* (Annual). **Geographic Preference:** Local.

39297 ■ Rock Falls Chamber of Commerce (RFCC)
601 W 10th St.
Rock Falls, IL 61071
Ph: (815)625-4500
URL: http://www.rockfallschamber.com
Contact: Bethany Bland, Co-Chief Executive Officer Co-President
E-mail: bland@rockfallschamber.com
Facebook: www.facebook.com/rockfallschamber
Instagram: www.instagram.com/rockfallschamber
Description: Promotes business and community development in Whiteside County, IL. **Founded:** 1956. **Publications:** *Chamber News Highlights* (Monthly). **Awards:** Rock Falls Chamber of Commerce Shoulder to the Wheel Award (Annual). **Geographic Preference:** Local.

39298 ■ Rockford Chamber of Commerce
308 W State St., Ste. 190
Rockford, IL 61101
Ph: (815)987-8100
Co. E-mail: info@rockfordchamber.com
URL: http://www.rockfordchamber.com
Contact: Lynette Jacques, Vice President
E-mail: ljacques@rockfordchamber.com
Facebook: www.facebook.com/RockfordChamberOfCommerce
Linkedin: www.linkedin.com/company/rockford-chamber-of-commerce
X (Twitter): x.com/rockfordchamber
Description: Members help other members increase sales, control costs, network effectively, advocate improvements in the business climate. **Founded:** 1910. **Publications:** *The Voice* (Monthly); *Manufacturers Directory* (Annual); *Membership and Business Directory* (Annual); *Rockford Area Map*. **Geographic Preference:** Local.

39299 ■ Rockford Regional Chamber of Commerce Business Women's Council
308 W State St., Ste. 190.
Rockford, IL 61101
URL: http://www.rockfordchamber.com/councils--committees.html
Contact: Caitlin Pusateri, President
Description: Aims to enhance the economic vitality of its members. **Publications:** *The Voice* (Monthly). **Educational Activities:** Rockford Regional Chamber of Commerce Business Women's Council Luncheon. **Geographic Preference:** Regional.

39300 ■ Rolling Meadows Chamber of Commerce (RMCC)
3400 W Stonegate Blvd.
Arlington Heights, IL 60005
Ph: (847)398-3730
Fax: (847)398-3745
Co. E-mail: office@rmchamber.org
URL: http://rmchamber.org
Contact: Michael Hutchins, President
E-mail: michael.hutchins@ngc.com
YouTube: www.youtube.com/channel/UCyi7PD_C7itfBtRjwk98-rQ
Description: Promotes business, industrial, professional, cultural, and civic development in the Rolling Meadows, IL area. Monitors legislation; partners with city to oversee economic development. **Founded:** 1961. **Publications:** *The Connector* (Monthly); *Dining Guide* (Semiannual); *Legislative Guide to Elected & Appointed Officials*. **Educational Activities:** Golf Outing (Annual); Networking/Social Function. **Geographic Preference:** Local.

39301 ■ Romeoville Area Chamber of Commerce
North Campus Bldg., 101 Airport Rd.
Romeoville, IL 60446
Ph: (815)886-2076
Co. E-mail: info@romeovillechamber.org
URL: http://www.romeovillechamber.org
Contact: Joel Sanabria, Chief Executive Officer
E-mail: director@romeovillechamber.org
Facebook: www.facebook.com/RomeovilleAreaChamber
Linkedin: www.linkedin.com/company/romeoville-area-chamber-of-commerce
Description: Serves as communication vehicle of business, professional and service organization in governmental and social affairs in Romeoville. **Founded:** 1978. **Geographic Preference:** Local.

39302 ■ *Roselle Chamber Business News*
c/o Gail Croson, Executive Director
1350 W Lake St., Ste. A
Roselle, IL 60172
Ph: (630)894-3010
Fax: (630)894-3042
Co. E-mail: executivedirector@rosellechamber.com
URL: http://www.rosellechamber.com
Contact: Gail Croson, Executive Director
E-mail: executivedirector@rosellechamber.com
URL(s): www.rosellechamber.com/news_forms
Released: Monthly **Availability:** PDF.

39303 ■ Roselle Chamber of Commerce and Industry
c/o Gail Croson, Executive Director
1350 W Lake St., Ste. A
Roselle, IL 60172
Ph: (630)894-3010
Fax: (630)894-3042
Co. E-mail: executivedirector@rosellechamber.com
URL: http://www.rosellechamber.com
Contact: Gail Croson, Executive Director
E-mail: executivedirector@rosellechamber.com
Description: Promotes business and community development in Roselle, IL. Conducts networking, social activities and business seminars; sponsors community parade, entertainment tents at annual festival and business expo; participates in or contributes to other business and community projects and events. **Founded:** 1949. **Publications:** *Roselle Chamber Business News* (Monthly). **Awards:** Brian K. Healy Service Award (Annual); Roselle Chamber of Commerce and Industry Business Person of the Year Award (Annual). **Geographic Preference:** Local.

39304 ■ Round Lake Area Chamber of Commerce and Industry
2007 N Civil Center Way.
Round Lake Beach, IL 60073
Ph: (847)546-2002
Co. E-mail: info@rlchamber.org
URL: http://www.rlchamber.org
Contact: Marci DiProva, President
Description: Promotes business and community development in the Round Lake, IL area. Conducts annual Home and Trade Fair. **Publications:** *Chamber News*. **Geographic Preference:** Local.

39305 ■ St. Charles Chamber of Commerce
1601 E Main St. St. D
Saint Charles, IL 60174
Ph: (630)584-8384
Co. E-mail: info@stcharleschamber.com
URL: http://www.stcharleschamber.com
Contact: Jim di Ciaula, President
Facebook: www.facebook.com/StCharlesCoC
Linkedin: www.linkedin.com/company/st.-charles-chamber-of-commerce
X (Twitter): x.com/StCharlesCoC
Description: Promotes business and community development in St. Charles, IL area. **Founded:** 1922. **Publications:** *Chamber Communique* (Monthly). **Awards:** The Charlemagne Award (Annual). **Geographic Preference:** Local.

39306 ■ Sandwich Area Chamber of Commerce
128 E Railroad St.
Sandwich, IL 60548
Ph: (815)786-9075
Co. E-mail: infor@sandwich-il.org
URL: http://www.sandwichilchamber.org
Contact: Bill Novicki, President
Facebook: www.facebook.com/sandwichchamber
Linkedin: www.linkedin.com/company/sandwich-chamber-of-commerce
Instagram: www.instagram.com/sandwichareachamber
Description: Works to provide a favorable business climate by acting as a vehicle to help promote the area's economic progress. Supports the development of the business community and to improve the quality of life for those that live and work in the area. Sponsors community events. **Founded:** 1979. **Publications:** *Business Connection* (Monthly). **Geographic Preference:** Local.

39307 ■ Sauk Valley Area Chamber of Commerce (SVACC)
211 Locust St.
Sterling, IL 61081
Ph: (815)625-2400
Fax: (815)625-9361
Co. E-mail: knoble@saukvalleyareachamber.com
URL: http://www.saukvalleyareachamber.com
Contact: Lance Buser, President
Facebook: www.facebook.com/SaukValleyChamber
Linkedin: www.linkedin.com/company/sauk-valley-area-chamber-of-commerce
X (Twitter): x.com/sva_cc
Instagram: www.instagram.com/sva_cc
Description: Promotes business and community development in the Sauk Valley Area. Conducts Business Expo, Seasonal Sights and Sounds, and Community Carnival. **Founded:** 1912. **Publications:** *Ac-*

tion Report (Monthly); Membership List; Sterling/Rock Falls Restaurant and Lodging Guide (Periodic). **Geographic Preference:** Local.

39308 ■ Savanna Chamber of Commerce (SCC)
313 Main St.
 Savanna, IL 61074
Ph: (815)273-2722
Co. E-mail: chamber@savannail.com
URL: http://www.savanna-il.com
Contact: Amy Johnston, President
Description: Promotes business and community development in Savanna, IL. Sponsors annual trade shows and seminars, annual Car Cruise and Beach Party, annual Gingerbread Christmas and Cookie Walk, and other social and promotional activities. **Founded:** 1949. **Publications:** Outlook (Monthly). **Geographic Preference:** Local.

39309 ■ Skokie Chamber of Commerce (SCC)
5002 Oakton St.
 Skokie, IL 60077
Ph: (847)673-0240
Fax: (847)673-0249
Co. E-mail: info@skokiechamber.org
URL: http://skokiechamber.org
Contact: Scott F. Schoeller, President
Instagram: www.instagram.com/skokiechamberofcommerce
Description: Promotes business and community development in the Skokie, IL area. **Founded:** 1925. **Publications:** Business Directory; Chamber Connection (Monthly); Industrial Directory. **Geographic Preference:** Local.

39310 ■ *Soundings*
8 S 3rd St.
 Geneva, IL 60134-0481
Ph: (630)232-6060
Fax: (630)232-6083
Co. E-mail: chamberinfo@genevachamber.com
URL: http://www.genevachamber.com
Contact: Paula Schmidt, President
E-mail: pschmidt@genevachamber.com
URL(s): genevachamber.com/geneva-chamber-soundings
Released: Monthly **Availability:** Print.

39311 ■ Stateline Chamber
5386 Williams Dr.
 Roscoe, IL 61073
Ph: (815)623-9065
Co. E-mail: info@statelinechamber.com
URL: http://statelinechamber.com
Contact: John Broda, President
Facebook: www.facebook.com/statelinechamber
Linkedin: www.linkedin.com/company/10661291
X (Twitter): x.com/statelinecc
Instagram: www.instagram.com/statelinechamber
Description: Promotes business and community development in the Rockton, IL area. **Founded:** 1951. **Geographic Preference:** Regional.

39312 ■ Staunton Chamber of Commerce (SCC)
229 W Main
 Staunton, IL 62088
Ph: (618)635-8356
Co. E-mail: info@stauntonchamber.com
URL: http://www.stauntonchamber.com
Contact: Carrie Borgini, President
E-mail: mayfield@madisontelco.com
Facebook: www.facebook.com/stauntonilchamber
Description: Promotes business and community development in Staunton, IL area. **Founded:** 1859. **Geographic Preference:** Local.

39313 ■ Streator Area Chamber of Commerce and Industry (SACCI)
320 E Main St.
 Streator, IL 61364
Ph: (815)672-2921
Co. E-mail: sacci@mchsi.com
URL: http://www.streatorchamber.com
Contact: Jennifer Bunker Skerston, President
Facebook: www.facebook.com/StreatorChamber
Description: Businesses organized to promote economic and community development in Streator, IL. **Founded:** 1915. **Geographic Preference:** Local.

39314 ■ Sullivan Chamber and Economic Development (SCED)
101 E Jefferson St.
 Sullivan, IL 61951
Ph: (217)728-4223
Co. E-mail: info@sullivanchamber.com
URL: http://www.sullivan-chamber.com
Contact: Linda Huber, President
Facebook: www.facebook.com/SullyChamber
X (Twitter): x.com/Sullychamber
Description: Promotes business and community development in Moultrie County, IL. Promotes tourism. Sponsors annual Christmas parade, Christmas lighting contest, Safe Trick or Treat, and Festival of Stars in May. **Founded:** 2016. **Publications:** Sullivan Spark. **Geographic Preference:** Local.

39315 ■ *Sullivan Spark*
101 E Jefferson St.
 Sullivan, IL 61951
Ph: (217)728-4223
Co. E-mail: info@sullivanchamber.com
URL: http://www.sullivan-chamber.com
Contact: Linda Huber, President
URL(s): www.sullivanchamber.com/sullivan-spark
Facebook: www.facebook.com/sullivanilspark
Availability: Print.

39316 ■ Swedish-American Chamber of Commerce Chicago
121 W Wacker Dr., Ste. 618
 Chicago, IL 60601
Ph: (312)257-3002
Co. E-mail: sacc@sacc-chicago.org
URL: http://sacc-chicago.org
Contact: Carl Källén, President
Facebook: www.facebook.com/SACC.Chicago
Linkedin: www.linkedin.com/company/3028439
X (Twitter): x.com/SACCChicago
Instagram: www.instagram.com/sacc_chicago
Description: Business organization that promotes trade, commerce, and investment between Sweden and Chicago as well as the states of Illinois, Indiana, Iowa, Missouri, and Wisconsin. **Geographic Preference:** Local.

39317 ■ Sycamore Chamber of Commerce
519 W State St.
 Sycamore, IL 60178
Ph: (815)895-3456
Co. E-mail: office@sycamorechamber.com
URL: http://sycamorechamber.com
Contact: Robert Heck, President
Facebook: www.facebook.com/SycamoreChamber
X (Twitter): x.com/sycamorechamber
Instagram: www.instagram.com/sycamorechamber
Description: Promotes economic and social development in Sycamore, IL. **Founded:** 1915. **Publications:** Chamber Focus. **Geographic Preference:** Local.

39318 ■ Tinley Park Chamber of Commerce (TPCC)
17316 S Oak Pk. Ave.
 Tinley Park, IL 60477
Ph: (708)532-5700
Fax: (708)532-1475
Co. E-mail: info@tinleychamber.org
URL: http://tinleychamber.org
Contact: Brandy Cafarelli, President
Facebook: www.facebook.com/tinleyparkchamber
Linkedin: www.linkedin.com/in/tinley-park-chamber-of-commerce-90314332
X (Twitter): x.com/TinleyPkChamber
YouTube: www.youtube.com/channel/UCvkajB6dzuXL-g8K7uGjLGg
Description: Promotes business and community development in Tinley Park, IL. **Founded:** 1955. **Publications:** Chamber News and Views (Weekly (Tues.)). **Geographic Preference:** Local.

39319 ■ Troy/Maryville/St. Jacob/Marine Area Chamber of Commerce
647 E US Hwy. 40
 Troy, IL 62294
Ph: (618)667-8769
Co. E-mail: info@troymaryvillecoc.com
URL: http://www.troycoc.com
Contact: Ryan Sautman, President
Facebook: www.facebook.com/tmscoc
Linkedin: www.linkedin.com/company/troy-maryville-st-jacob-marine-chamber-of-commerce
X (Twitter): x.com/tmscoc
Instagram: www.instagram.com/tmsmcoc
Description: Promotes business development and networking in order to enhance the growth and self sufficiency within the community and surrounding areas. **Founded:** 1984. **Geographic Preference:** Local.

39320 ■ Tuscola Chamber of Commerce (TCC)
PO Box 454
 Tuscola, IL 61953
Ph: (217)253-5678
URL: http://dawnheacock.wixsite.com/tuscolacoc
Contact: Jerry Hall, President
Description: Promotes business and community development in Tuscola, IL area. **Geographic Preference:** Local.

39321 ■ Uptown Chamber of Commerce
4619 N Broadway
 Chicago, IL 60640
Ph: (773)878-1064
URL: http://exploreuptown.org/about-us/uptown-chamber-of-commerce
Facebook: www.facebook.com/UptownUnited
X (Twitter): x.com/uptownunited
Instagram: www.instagram.com/exploreuptownchi
Description: Promotes business and community development in the uptown area of Chicago, IL. **Founded:** 1923. **Publications:** Chambergram (Monthly). **Geographic Preference:** Local.

39322 ■ Vermilion Advantage (VA)
15 N Walnut St.
 Danville, IL 61832
Ph: (217)442-6201
Co. E-mail: contact@vermilionadvantage.com
URL: http://www.vermilionadvantage.com
Contact: Timothy Dudley, President
E-mail: ceo@vermilionadvantage.com
Facebook: www.facebook.com/VermilionAdvantage
YouTube: www.youtube.com/channel/UCxFfa_Dy5m_7LWaEkh8127Q
Description: Promotes business and community development in the Vermilion County, IL area. **Founded:** 1899. **Publications:** The Commerce Communicator (Monthly). **Geographic Preference:** Local.

39323 ■ Villa Park Chamber of Commerce
10 W Pk. Blvd.
 Villa Park, IL 60181
Ph: (630)941-9133
Co. E-mail: vpchamber@sbcglobal.net
URL: http://www.villaparkchamber.org
Contact: Laura Schnettler, Author
Facebook: www.facebook.com/VillaParkChamberofCommerce
X (Twitter): x.com/VPChamber
Description: Promotes business and community development in Villa Park, IL area. **Founded:** 1948. **Publications:** Chamber Connections (Irregular). **Geographic Preference:** Local.

39324 ■ *The Voice*
308 W State St., Ste. 190.
 Rockford, IL 61101
URL: http://www.rockfordchamber.com/councils--committees.html
Contact: Caitlin Pusateri, President
URL(s): www.rockfordchamber.com/the-voice
Released: Monthly **Availability:** Print; Online.

39325 ■ Walnut Chamber of Commerce (WCC)
PO Box 56
Walnut, IL 61376
Ph: (815)866-9352
Co. E-mail: director@walnutillinois.com
URL: http://www.walnutillinois.com
Contact: Brent William Jamison, Contact
Facebook: www.facebook.com/WalnutIllinoisChamberofCommerce
Description: Promotes business and community development in the Walnut, IL area. **Founded:** 1972. **Geographic Preference:** Local.

39326 ■ Washington Chamber of Commerce (WCC)
105 S Spruce St.
Washington, IL 61571
Ph: (309)444-9921
Co. E-mail: info@washingtoncoc.com
URL: http://washingtonilcoc.com
Contact: Tina Glidewell, President
Facebook: www.facebook.com/WashingtonChamberofCommerce
X (Twitter): x.com/WashingtonILCOC
Instagram: www.instagram.com/washington_coc
Description: Promotes business and community development in the area. **Founded:** 1935. **Geographic Preference:** Local.

39327 ■ Waterloo Chamber of Commerce
118 E 3rd St.
Waterloo, IL 62298
Ph: (618)939-5300
Fax: (618)939-1805
Co. E-mail: chamber@htc.net
URL: http://www.enjoywaterloo.com
Contact: Bethany Prange Booher, President
Facebook: www.facebook.com/waterloochamberofcommerce
Description: Helps promote a prosperous business climate and quality of life for the businesses and people of Waterloo. **Geographic Preference:** Local.

39328 ■ Watseka Area Chamber of Commerce (WACC)
110 S 3rd St.
Watseka, IL 60970
Ph: (815)432-2416
Co. E-mail: watsekaareachamber@gmail.com
URL: http://www.watsekachamber.org
Contact: Bob Burd, Contact
E-mail: bob.burd@countryfinancial.com
Facebook: www.facebook.com/WatsekaAreaChamber
X (Twitter): x.com/WatsekaChamber
Description: Promotes business and community development in the Watseka, IL area. **Founded:** 1945. **Publications:** WACC Report (Monthly). **Educational Activities:** Business Showcase. **Geographic Preference:** Local.

39329 ■ Wauconda Area Chamber of Commerce (WCC)
100 N Main St.
Wauconda, IL 60084
Ph: (847)526-5580
Co. E-mail: info@waucondachamber.org
URL: http://www.waucondachamber.org
Contact: Tracy Lehmann, President
Facebook: www.facebook.com/waucondachamber
X (Twitter): x.com/waucondachamofc
Description: Businesses and industries united to promote and foster the commercial, industrial, professional, civic, and general interests of Wauconda Township, IL. Provides information to the public and business community about the area. Sponsors Miss Wauconda Pageant and the Wauconda Rodeo; holds dinner meetings; conducts Thanksgiving and Christmas community activities. Awards scholarships to local students. **Founded:** 1948. **Publications:** Wauconda Community Guide (Annual); Wauconda Wave (Bimonthly). **Geographic Preference:** Local.

39330 ■ WCC Community Guide
351 Linden Ave.
Wilmette, IL 60091
Ph: (847)251-3800
Co. E-mail: info@wilmettekenilworth.com
URL: http://www.wilmettekenilworth.com
Contact: Charles E. Hutchinson, President
E-mail: charles@charleshutchinsonlaw.com
URL(s): www.wilmettekenilworth.com/2024/04/10/wilmette-kenilworth-community-guide
Released: Annual **Availability:** Online.

39331 ■ West Suburban Chamber of Commerce and Industry (WSCCI) - McCook Public Library
PO Box 187
La Grange, IL 60525
Ph: (708)387-7550
Fax: (708)387-7556
Co. E-mail: info@wscci.org
URL: http://www.wscci.org
Contact: Scott Stephens, President
Facebook: www.facebook.com/wscci
Linkedin: www.linkedin.com/company/west-suburban-chamber-of-commerce-and-industry
X (Twitter): x.com/WSCCI_IL
YouTube: www.youtube.com/channel/UCdhnjj7rlFgt5P07JFMdUXA
Description: Advocates for business by striving to enhance and promote the stability and well-being of the community. Sponsors job fair, golf outing, awards gala, and New Teachers' Welcome Breakfast. **Scope:** Local history; boundaries of the village. **Founded:** 1902. **Holdings:** Books; DVDs; CDs; ebooks; magazine; newspaper; audiobooks. **Publications:** Outlook. **Geographic Preference:** Local.

39332 ■ Westchester Chamber of Commerce
PO Box 7309
Westchester, IL 60154
Ph: (708)240-8400
Co. E-mail: info@westchesterchamber.org
URL: http://www.westchesterchamber.org
Contact: Maria Vasos, Officer
Facebook: www.facebook.com/westchesterchamber
X (Twitter): x.com/westchamber2013
YouTube: www.youtube.com/user/westchesterchamber1
Description: Promotes growth and health of businesses in the community of Westchester. **Founded:** 1954. **Geographic Preference:** Local.

39333 ■ Western DuPage Chamber of Commerce (WDCC)
306 Main St.
West Chicago, IL 60185
Ph: (630)231-3003
Fax: (630)231-3009
Co. E-mail: team@westerndupagechamber.com
URL: http://www.westerndupagechamber.com
Contact: David J. Sabathne, President
Facebook: www.facebook.com/WesternDuPageChamber
YouTube: www.youtube.com/user/westerndupagechamber
Description: Retail businesses, banks, professional service organizations, and individuals. Promotes business and community development in the Winfield, IL area. Sponsors festival. **Founded:** 1975. **Publications:** Winfield STUFF! (Monthly). **Geographic Preference:** Local.

39334 ■ Westmont Chamber of Commerce and Tourism Bureau (WCCTB)
1 S Cass Ave., Ste. 101
Westmont, IL 60559
Ph: (630)960-5553
Fax: (630)960-5554
Co. E-mail: wcctb@westmontchamber.com
URL: http://www.westmontchamber.com
Contact: Becky Rheintgen, President
X (Twitter): x.com/WestmontChamber
Instagram: www.instagram.com/westmontchamber
Description: Works to improve the economic environment of Westmont by fostering the development of business growth and prosperity of the entire community. **Geographic Preference:** Local.

39335 ■ Westridge Chamber of Commerce (WRCC)
6445 N W, Ste. 304
Chicago, IL 60645
Ph: (773)743-6022
Co. E-mail: info@westridgechamber.org
URL: http://www.westridgechamber.org
Contact: Irv Loundy, President
E-mail: iloundy@devonbank.com
Facebook: www.facebook.com/OnDevonFestival
X (Twitter): x.com/WestRidgecofc
Instagram: www.instagram.com/ondevonfestival
Description: Local chamber of commerce. Represents members' interests; holds seminars, workshops, and other promotional activities. **Founded:** 1992. **Publications:** International Marketplace Newsletter. **Geographic Preference:** Local.

39336 ■ Wheaton Chamber of Commerce
108 E Wesley St.
Wheaton, IL 60187
Ph: (630)668-6464
URL: http://www.wheatonchamber.com
Contact: Vickie Austin, President
E-mail: president@wheatonchamber.com
Facebook: www.facebook.com/Wheatonchamber
Linkedin: www.linkedin.com/company/wheaton-chamber-of-commerce
X (Twitter): x.com/WheatonChamber
Instagram: www.instagram.com/wheatonchamber
YouTube: www.youtube.com/user/WheatonCoC
Pinterest: www.pinterest.com/wheatonchamber
Description: Fosters meaningful business relationships, advocates on issues impacting the local economy, and develops business education and marketing opportunities. **Founded:** 1916. **Publications:** Wheaton Chamber of Commerce Membership Directory (Annual); Business and Community Directory; Wheaton Map. **Geographic Preference:** Local.

39337 ■ Wheeling-Prospect Heights Area Chamber of Commerce and Industry (WPHACCI)
2 Community Blvd.
Wheeling, IL 60090
Ph: (847)892-7900
Co. E-mail: info@wheelingareachamber.com
URL: http://www.wheelingareachamber.com
Contact: Matt Eggemeyer, President
Facebook: www.facebook.com/GreaterWheelingAreaChamber
Linkedin: www.linkedin.com/company/wheelingareachamber
Description: Promotes business and community development in the Wheeling and Prospect Heights, IL area. **Founded:** 1929. **Publications:** Wheeling Area Chamber of Commerce and Industry--Community Guide (Biennial); Buying Guide (Annual); Chamber Connections (Monthly). **Educational Activities:** Business EXPO (Semiannual). **Geographic Preference:** Local.

39338 ■ Will County Center for Economic Development (CED)
203 N Ottawa St., Ste. 100
Joliet, IL 60432
Ph: (815)723-1800
Fax: (815)723-6972
URL: http://willcountyced.com
Contact: John E. Greuling, President
Facebook: www.facebook.com/WillCountyCED
Linkedin: www.linkedin.com/company/will-county-center-for-economic-development
X (Twitter): x.com/willcountyced
Instagram: www.instagram.com/WillCountyCED
YouTube: www.youtube.com/channel/UCRRIHgTjSPYiNvQoFEeJeOg
Description: Provides information and assistance in locating or expanding a business in Will County. Offers services such as county development data, business incentive programs and government relations. **Founded:** 1981. **Geographic Preference:** State.

STATE LISTINGS

Illinois ■ 39353

39339 ■ Willowbrook/Burr Ridge Chamber of Commerce and Industry
7850 S Quincy St.
Willowbrook, IL 60527
Ph: (630)654-0909
Co. E-mail: info@wbbrchamber.org
URL: http://www.wbbrchamber.org
Contact: Kyle Wetzel, President
E-mail: kwetzel@farmersagent.com
Facebook: www.facebook.com/pg/officialWBBRChamber/posts
Linkedin: www.linkedin.com/in/willowbrook-burr-ridge-chamber-09971336
X (Twitter): x.com/wbbrchamber
Instagram: www.instagram.com/wbbrchamber
Description: Provides community leadership, facilitates communication, promotes education, supports local causes and represents the interest and advancement of its members. **Founded:** 1985. **Geographic Preference:** Local.

39340 ■ Wilmette/Kenilworth Chamber of Commerce
351 Linden Ave.
Wilmette, IL 60091
Ph: (847)251-3800
Co. E-mail: info@wilmettekenilworth.com
URL: http://www.wilmettekenilworth.com
Contact: Charles E. Hutchinson, President
E-mail: charles@charleshutchinsonlaw.com
Facebook: www.facebook.com/wilmettekenilworthchamber
X (Twitter): x.com/WilmetteChamber
Instagram: www.instagram.com/wkchamber
YouTube: www.youtube.com/user/TheWilmetteChamber
Description: Promotes business and community development in the Wilmette, IL area. Sponsors sidewalk sale. **Publications:** *WCC Community Guide* (Annual); *Wilmette Chamber Headline News*. **Geographic Preference:** Local.

39341 ■ Wilmington Chamber of Commerce
PO Box 724
Wilmington, IL 60481
Ph: (815)476-5991
Co. E-mail: info@wilmingtonilchamber.org
URL: http://wilmingtonilchamber.org
Contact: Steve Evans, President
E-mail: steve@wilmingtonilchamber.org
Linkedin: www.linkedin.com/company/wilmington-il-chamber-of-commerce
YouTube: www.youtube.com/channel/UCgH6GT0ezXHF-sNogErfnSw
Description: Promotes business and community development in Wilmington, IL area. **Publications:** *Newsbriefs* (Monthly). **Educational Activities:** Chamber Christmas Party. **Geographic Preference:** Local.

39342 ■ Wood Dale Chamber of Commerce
PO Box 353
Wood Dale, IL 60191-0353
Ph: (630)595-0505
Co. E-mail: info@wooddalechamber.com
URL: http://www.thegoa.com/wood-dale-chamber.html
Contact: Mike Melone, Treasurer
Facebook: www.facebook.com/wooddalechamber
Description: Works for the advancement of the economic, industrial, professional, cultural and civic welfare of businesses while giving all proper assistance to any new firms or individuals seeking to locate in Wood Dale. Supports beneficial activity for the community. **Publications:** *Chamber Update*. **Geographic Preference:** Local.

39343 ■ Woodstock Chamber of Commerce and Industry (WCCI)
127 E Calhoun St.
Woodstock, IL 60098
Ph: (815)338-2436
Co. E-mail: chamber@woodstockilchamber.com
URL: http://www.woodstockilchamber.com
Contact: Brad Ball, President
Linkedin: www.linkedin.com/company/woodstock-chamber-of-commerce-&-industry

X (Twitter): x.com/wdstkchamber
Description: Promotes business and community development in Woodstock, IL. Sponsors festivals; hosts art fairs, craft fairs, and business exposition. Conducts charitable activities. **Founded:** 1945. **Publications:** *Connection* (Monthly). **Geographic Preference:** Local.

39344 ■ Yorkville Area Chamber of Commerce (YACC)
26 W Countryside Pky.
Yorkville, IL 60560
Ph: (630)553-6853
Fax: (630)553-0702
Co. E-mail: support@yorkvillechamber.org
URL: http://www.yorkvillechamber.org
Contact: Sarah Allen, Treasurer
Facebook: www.facebook.com/yorkvillechamber
Description: Promotes the business and community development in Yorkville, IL. **Founded:** 1971. **Geographic Preference:** Local.

MINORITY BUSINESS ASSISTANCE PROGRAMS

39345 ■ Chicago Minority Business Opportunity Center
216 W Jackson Blvd., Ste. 600
Chicago, IL 60606
Ph: (312)755-8880
Co. E-mail: info@chicagombdacenter.com
URL: http://www.chicagomsdc.org
Contact: J. Vincent Williams, President
Linkedin: www.linkedin.com/in/chicagomsdc
X (Twitter): x.com/ChicagoMSDC
YouTube: www.youtube.com/user/ChicagoMSDC
Description: Works to foster and promote the growth of minority-owned businesses in the Chicago area. **Founded:** 1968.

39346 ■ Chicago Minority Supplier Development Council (MSDC)
216 W Jackson Blvd., Ste. 600
Chicago, IL 60606
Ph: (312)755-8880
Co. E-mail: info@chicagomsdc.org
URL: http://www.chicagomsdc.org
Contact: Debra Jenings Johnson, President
Facebook: www.facebook.com/chicagomsdc
Linkedin: www.linkedin.com/in/chicagomsdc
X (Twitter): x.com/ChicagoMSDC
YouTube: www.youtube.com/user/ChicagoMSDC
Founded: 1968.

FINANCING AND LOAN PROGRAMS

39347 ■ Adams Street Partners LLC (ASP)
1 N Wacker Dr., Ste. 2700
Chicago, IL 60606-2823
Ph: (312)553-7890
Fax: (313)553-7891
URL: http://www.adamsstreetpartners.com
Contact: Quintin Kevin, Partner Chief Financial Officer
Linkedin: www.linkedin.com/company/adams-street-partners
Description: Employee-owned investment firm. Manages private equity for companies seeking first round of capital. Deals with primary, secondary, and direct investments. **Founded:** 1972. **Industry Preferences:** Technology; life science,.

39348 ■ Allstate Private Equity
3075 Sanders Rd., Ste. G5
Northbrook, IL 60062
URL: http://www.allstateinvestments.com
Contact: Michael Barzyk, Managing Director
Description: Provider of insurance for private equity fund, sponsors and investors. **Preferred Investment Size:** $15,000,000-$20,000,000. **Industry Preferences:** Communications and media, computer hardware and software, semiconductors and other electronics, biotechnology, medical and health, consumer related, industrial and energy, financial services, and manufacturing.

39349 ■ Alpha Capital Partners Ltd.
122 S Michigan Ave., Ste. 1700
Chicago, IL 60603
Ph: (312)322-9800
Co. E-mail: info@alphacapital.com
URL: http://www.alphacapital.com
Contact: Andrew H. Kalnow, Chief Executive Officer
Description: Private equity investment firm which provides equity financing for promising growth businesses. **Scope:** A venture capital management organization that provides equity financing for promising growth businesses and buyouts or recapitalization of established companies. **Founded:** 1984. **Preferred Investment Size:** $500,000 to $5,000,000. **Industry Preferences:** Computer software and services, consumer related, other products, communications and media, medical and health, biotechnology, semiconductors and other electronics, Internet specific, industrial and energy, and computer hardware.

39350 ■ Arch Venture Partners L.P.
8775 W Higgins Rd., Ste. 1025
Chicago, IL 60631
Ph: (773)380-6600
Fax: (773)380-6606
Co. E-mail: emailinquiries@archventure.com
URL: http://www.archventure.com
Contact: Keith Crandell, Co-Founder Managing Director
Linkedin: www.linkedin.com/company/avpvc
Description: Provider of early-stage venture capital investment services. **Founded:** 1986.

39351 ■ Beecken Petty O'Keefe & Co. (BPOC)
131 S Dearborn St., Ste. 2800
Chicago, IL 60603
Ph: (312)435-0300
Fax: (312)435-0371
Co. E-mail: partners@bpoc.com
URL: http://www.bpoc.com
Contact: Adam Hentze, Principal
E-mail: ahentze@bpoc.com
Description: Firm provides financial services and private equity management services for healthcare sector. **Founded:** 1996. **Preferred Investment Size:** $5,000,000 to $500,000,000. **Industry Preferences:** Medical and health, computer software and services, Internet specific, other products, communications and media.

39352 ■ Cornerstone Angels
2100 Sanders Rd., Ste. 170
Northbrook, IL 60062
Ph: (847)739-0100
URL: http://www.cornerstoneangels.com
Contact: Michael Gruber, Founder
Facebook: www.facebook.com/CornerstoneAngels
Linkedin: www.linkedin.com/company/cornerstone-angels
YouTube: www.youtube.com/user/CornerstoneAngels
Description: Offers financial capital, mentoring, and advisory support to high-growth organizations primarily in the Midwest. **Founded:** 2006.

39353 ■ DN Partners L.L.C.
180 N LaSalle, Ste. 3001
Chicago, IL 60601
URL: http://www.dnpartners.net
Contact: Janet Powaga, Director, Research Vice President
Description: Firm providing investment in middle-market companies. **Founded:** 1995. **Industry Preferences:** Communications, computer hardware, Internet specific, semiconductors and other electronics, medical and health, consumer related, industrial and energy, transportation, financial services, business service, manufacturing, agriculture, forestry and fishing.

39354 ■ Dresner Capital Resources Inc. [Dresner Partners]
10 S LaSalle St., Ste. 2170
  Chicago, IL 60603
Ph: (312)726-3600
Fax: (312)726-7448
URL: http://www.dresnerpartners.com
Contact: Steven M. Dresner, President
E-mail: sdresner@dresnerco.com
X (Twitter): x.com/dresnerpartners

Description: Provider of investment banking solutions in middle-market companies. **Founded:** 1991.

39355 ■ First Analysis Securities Corp. (FASC)
1 S Wacker Dr., Ste. 3900
  Chicago, IL 60606
Ph: (312)258-1400
Free: 800-866-3272
URL: http://www.firstanalysis.com
Contact: James MacDonald, Managing Director

Description: Analyzes stocks of environmental firms for institutional investors. Industries served include United States investors, corporations, and institutions. **Scope:** Analyzes stocks of environmental firms for institutional investors. Industries served include United States investors, corporations, and institutions. **Founded:** 1981.

39356 ■ Frontenac Co.
Frontenac Co.
  One S Wacker, Ste. 2980
  Chicago, IL 60606
Ph: (312)368-0044
Fax: (312)368-9520
Co. E-mail: reception@frontenac.com
URL: http://www.frontenac.com
Contact: Elizabeth C. Williamson, Managing Director
E-mail: ewilliamson@frontenac.com
Linkedin: www.linkedin.com/company/frontenac

Description: Provider of buyouts, recapitalization, growth capital, PIPES transactions, and lower middle market investments. **Founded:** 1971. **Preferred Investment Size:** $10,000,000 to $50,000,000. **Industry Preferences:** Consumer related, other products, Internet specific, computer software and services, medical and health, communications and media, industrial and energy, computer hardware, semiconductors and other electronics, and biotechnology.

39357 ■ Golub Capital
150 S Wacker Dr., 5th Fl.
  Chicago, IL 60606
Ph: (312)205-5050
Fax: (312)201-9167
URL: http://golubcapital.com
Contact: David B. Golub, President

Description: Provider of financial services. **Founded:** 1994. **Preferred Investment Size:** $4,000,000 to $25,000,000. **Industry Preferences:** Medical and health, consumer related, industrial and energy, transportation, business service, and manufacturing.

39358 ■ GTCR L.L.C.
GTCR L.L.C.
  300 N LaSalle St., Ste. 5600
  Chicago, IL 60654
Ph: (312)382-2200
Co. E-mail: info@gtcr.com
URL: http://www.gtcr.com
Contact: Cameron Rouzer, Director

Description: Firm provides private equity investors in healthcare. **Scope:** A private equity investment firm and long-term strategic partner for management teams. Currently manages more than 2 billion dollar in equity capital invested in a wide range of companies and industries. Primary industry focus includes marketing services, distribution, healthcare services, information technology services, outsourced business services and transaction processing. **Founded:** 1980. **Preferred Investment Size:** $10,000,000 to $300,000,000. **Industry Preferences:** Communications, other products, computer software and services, consumer related, semiconductors and other electronics, medical and health, Internet specific, computer hardware.

39359 ■ High Street Capital (HSC)
150 N Wacker Dr., Ste. 2420
  Chicago, IL 60606
Ph: (312)423-2650
Fax: (312)267-2861
Co. E-mail: info@highstreetcapital.com
URL: http://www.highstreetcapital.com
Contact: Christopher E. Brewster, Chief Financial Officer
E-mail: chris@highstreetcapital.com

Description: Provider of private equity, growth equity investments for control and non-control, outsourced business services, value-added distribution and logistics, niche manufacturing. **Founded:** 1997. **Preferred Investment Size:** $2,000,000 to $8,000,000. **Industry Preferences:** Communications, computer software, semiconductors and other electronics, medical and health, industrial and energy, business service, and manufacturing.

39360 ■ Illinois Ventures
200 S, Wacker Fl., 20, Ste. 2000
  Chicago, IL 60606
Ph: (312)996-9853
URL: http://www.illinoisventures.com
Contact: Nancy Sullivan, Chief Executive Officer
Linkedin: www.linkedin.com/company/illinoisventures
X (Twitter): x.com/IllinoisVC

Founded: 2000. **Industry Preferences:** Healthcare; technology.

39361 ■ IrishAngels Inc.
Vitalize Venture Group
  415 N LaSalle Dr.
  Chicago, IL 60654
URL: http://www.vitalize.vc
Contact: Caroline Gash, Contact

Description: Invests in seed-stage startups with growth potential in the United States. **Founded:** 2012. **Investment Policies:** Prefers startups looking to raise $1,000,000-$3,000,000; term sheet issued from a lead investor; pre-money valuation less than $10,000,000; potential 10x CoC ROI; early revenues indicating product-market fit; entrepreneurial experience; . **Industry Preferences:** B2B SaaS; consumer tech or products; medical device or diagnostics.

39362 ■ JKandB Capital
Two Prudential Plaza
  180 N Stetson Ave., Ste. 4300
  Chicago, IL 60601
Ph: (312)946-1200
URL: http://www.jkbcapital.com
Contact: David Kronfeld, Chairman Founder

Description: Firm provides investment services in communications, information technology, and health care markets. **Preferred Investment Size:** $5,000,000 to $30,000,000. **Industry Preferences:** Internet specific, communications and media, computer software and services, semiconductors and other electronics, industrial and energy, and consumer related.

39363 ■ KB Partners
600 Central Ave., Ste. 325
  Highland Park, IL 60035
Ph: (847)681-1270
Co. E-mail: info@kbpartners.com
URL: http://kbpartners.com
Contact: John Garabedian, Partner
E-mail: john@kbpartners.com
Linkedin: www.linkedin.com/company/kb-partners
X (Twitter): x.com/KBPartnersVC

Description: Investment firm provides angel funded and venture capital investment services. **Founded:** 1996. **Preferred Investment Size:** $1,000,000 to $5,000,000. **Industry Preferences:** Internet specific, computer software and services, industrial and energy, communications and media, semiconductors and other electronics, medical and health, and other products.

39364 ■ Lake Capital Partners Inc.
980 N Michigan Ave., Ste. 1300
  Chicago, IL 60611
Ph: (312)640-7050
Fax: (312)640-7051
Co. E-mail: info@lakecapital.com
URL: http://www.lakecapital.com
Contact: Christopher Scales, Vice President

Description: Provider of investments for middle market services companies. **Founded:** 1998. **Preferred Investment Size:** $50,000,000 to $100,000,000. **Industry Preferences:** Technology, financial services, healthcare and business services.

39365 ■ LaSalle Capital
LaSalle Capital
  145 S Wells St., Ste. 1800
  Chicago, IL 60606
Ph: (312)236-7041
Co. E-mail: contact@lasallecapital.com
URL: http://www.lasallecapitalgroup.com
Contact: David R. Murav, Partner
E-mail: dmurav@lasallecapital.com
X (Twitter): x.com/LaSalle_Capital

Founded: 2004. **Preferred Investment Size:** $5,000,000 to $15,000,000. **Industry Preferences:** Communications, consumer related, semiconductors and other electronics, medical and health, industrial and energy, business service, manufacturing, and agriculture, forestry and fishing.

39366 ■ Madison Dearborn Partners L.L.C. (MDP)
Madison Dearborn Partners L.L.C. (MDP)
  70 W Madison St., Ste. 4600
  Chicago, IL 60602
Ph: (312)895-1000
Fax: (312)895-1001
Co. E-mail: info@mdcp.com
URL: http://www.mdcp.com
Contact: Drew Macha, Director

Description: Finance: Venture capital firm. **Founded:** 1992. **Preferred Investment Size:** $100,000,000 to $600,000,000. **Industry Preferences:** Communications and media, Internet specific, consumer related, semiconductors and other electronics, medical and health, industrial and energy, computer software and services, computer hardware, and other products.

39367 ■ Mesirow Financial Private Equity
Mesirow Financial Holdings Inc.
  353 N Clark St.
  Chicago, IL 60654
Ph: (312)595-6000
Free: 800-453-0600
URL: http://www.mesirow.com
Contact: Ben Blakney, Co-President
Facebook: www.facebook.com/mesirowfinancial
Linkedin: www.linkedin.com/company/mesirow-financial
X (Twitter): x.com/MesirowFin
YouTube: www.youtube.com/user/MesirowFinancial

Description: Private equity firm provides investment services. **Founded:** 1937. **Preferred Investment Size:** $2,000,000 to $10,000,000. **Industry Preferences:** Computer software and services, other products, computer hardware, consumer related, Internet specific, communications and media, industrial and energy, semiconductors and other electronics, medical and health.

39368 ■ Mosaix Ventures
1822 N Mohawk St.
  Chicago, IL 60614
Ph: (312)274-0988
Co. E-mail: rlal@mosaixventures.com
URL: http://www.mosaixventures.com
Contact: Ranjan Lal, Partner
E-mail: rlal@mosaixventures.com

Description: Provider of private equity and venture capital investments for medical devices, technology-enabled services and purpose-built applications targeting niche markets. **Founded:** 2000. **Preferred Investment Size:** $1,000,000 to $4,000,000. **Industry Preferences:** Medical and health, and biotechnology.

39369 ■ North American Funds L.L.C.
1244 N Stone St., Apt. 9
Chicago, IL 60610-5201
Contact: R. David Bergonia, Manager
Description: Provider of investment and business development assistance to smaller and lower middle market companies. **Preferred Investment Size:** $500,000 minimum. **Industry Preferences:** Manufacturing and service.

39370 ■ OCA Ventures
351 W Hubbard St., Ste. 600
Chicago, IL 60654
URL: http://www.ocaventures.com
Contact: David Zyer, Partner
Linkedin: www.linkedin.com/company/oca-ventures
X (Twitter): x.com/ocaventures
Description: Venture capital firm focused on seed, Series A, and Series B companies. Invests highly scalable service and technology companies with dramatic growth potential. **Founded:** 1999. **Industry Preferences:** Technology; financial services; education; healthcare technology.

39371 ■ Open Prairie Ventures
400 E Jefferson
Effingham, IL 62401
Ph: (217)347-1000
URL: http://www.openprairie.com
Contact: Patrick Morand, President
Description: Investment firm provides of fund deployment, advisory and strategic planning services. **Founded:** 1997. **Preferred Investment Size:** $250,000 to $2,500,000. **Industry Preferences:** Communications and media, computer hardware and software, Internet specific, computer related, semiconductors and other electronics, biotechnology, medical and health, industrial and energy.

39372 ■ Polestar Venture Capital
180 N Michigan Ave., Ste. 1905
Chicago, IL 60601
Ph: (312)984-9090
Fax: (312)984-9877
Co. E-mail: info@polestarvc.com
URL: http://www.polestarvc.com
Contact: Derrick K. Collins, Partner
E-mail: dkcollins@polestarvc.com
Description: Investment firm provides financing, mezzanine capital, private equity and venture capital, capital advisory and investment services. **Industry Preferences:** Communications and media, computer software, computer related, and manufacturing.

39373 ■ Prism Capital
2700 Patriot Blvd., Ste. 250
Glenview, IL 60026
Ph: (312)464-7900
Co. E-mail: robert@prismfund.com
URL: http://www.prismfund.com
Contact: Robert Finkel, Managing Partner
E-mail: robert@prismfund.com
Description: Investment firm provides private equity and venture capital investment services for smaller businesses. **Founded:** 1999. **Preferred Investment Size:** $2,000,000 to $15,000,000. **Industry Preferences:** Computer software and services, Internet specific, and consumer related, medical and health, semiconductors and other electronics, computer hardware, and other products.

39374 ■ Pritzker Group Venture Capital (PGVC)
110 N Wacker Dr., Ste. 4350
Chicago, IL 60606
Ph: (312)447-6001
URL: http://www.pritzkergroup.com/venture-capital
Contact: Chris Girgenti, Managing Partner
X (Twitter): x.com/PritzkerVC
Description: Provider of venture capital investments. **Founded:** 1996. **Preferred Investment Size:** $5,000,000 to $12,000,000. **Industry Preferences:** Internet specific, communications and media, medical and health, and computer software and services.

39375 ■ Serra Ventures
520 N Neil, Ste. 510
Champaign, IL 61820
Ph: (217)819-5200
Co. E-mail: info@serraventures.com
URL: http://www.serraventures.com
Contact: Tim Hoerr, Chief Executive Officer
Facebook: www.facebook.com/SerraVentures
Linkedin: www.linkedin.com/company/serra-ventures
X (Twitter): x.com/SerraVentures
Description: Early-stage venture capital firm for technology companies in emerging Midwest technology centers and underserved West Coast markets. **Investment Policies:** Capital-efficient business model; teams with strong industry and/or technical experience; demonstrated product-market fit; established customer base; strong patent or technology advantage. **Industry Preferences:** Information technology; devices/instrumentation; agricultural technologies.

39376 ■ Sterling Partners (SP)
167 N Green St. 4th Fl.
Chicago, IL 60607
Ph: (312)465-7000
Fax: (312)465-7001
URL: http://sterlingpartners.com
Contact: Michelle Shuster, Director
Linkedin: www.linkedin.com/company/sterling-partners
Description: Firm is engaged in business and healthcare services. **Founded:** 1983. **Preferred Investment Size:** Up to $200,000,000. **Industry Preferences:** Communications and media, computer software, medical and health, consumer related, business service, and manufacturing.

39377 ■ Thinker Ventures
317 W Jefferson St.
Rockford, IL 61101
Ph: (815)516-0500
Co. E-mail: info@thinkerventures.com
URL: http://thinkerventures.com
Facebook: www.facebook.com/thinkerventures
YouTube: www.youtube.com/channel/UCNV5PW06AUlu8LrHOCLx7Kw
Description: Offers business development and funding for small and medium-sized companies. **Founded:** 2002.

39378 ■ Third Coast Capital Advisors L.L.C.
131 S Dearborn St., Ste. 2170
Chicago, IL 60603
Ph: (312)332-6484
URL: http://www.thirdcoastca.com
Contact: Jeff Olsick, Director
E-mail: jolsick@thirdcoastca.com
Linkedin: www.linkedin.com/company/third-coast-capital-advisors-llc
Description: Provider of financial advisory solutions. **Founded:** 2008.

39379 ■ Thoma Cressey Bravo, Inc. (TCB)
110 N Wacker Dr., 32nd Fl.
Chicago, IL 60606
Ph: (312)254-3300
Fax: (312)254-3301
URL: http://www.tcb.com
Contact: Thoma Cressey Bravo, Manager
Description: Firm offers capital investment. **Founded:** 1998. **Preferred Investment Size:** $10,000,000 to $100,000,000. **Industry Preferences:** Other products, medical and health, computer software and services, Internet specific, consumer related, computer hardware, and biotechnology.

39380 ■ Urbana-Champaign Angel Network (UCAN)
1817 S Neil St., Ste. 100
Champaign, IL 61820
Ph: (217)539-6261
Co. E-mail: edc@champaigncountyedc.com
URL: http://www.champaigncountyedc.org
Contact: Robert Flider, Member
Description: Matches startups with capital provider. Offers a forum for accredited investors to review selected opportunities. Furthers economic development in Champaign county.

39381 ■ VCapital Management
901 W Jackson Blvd., Ste. 503
Chicago, IL 60607
Ph: (312)690-4171
URL: http://vcapital.com
Contact: Peter Banas, Vice President Chief Financial Officer
Linkedin: www.linkedin.com/company/vcapital
Description: Venture capital firm provides investment services. **Founded:** 2015. **Preferred Investment Size:** $500,000 to $3,000,000. **Industry Preferences:** Computer software and services, medical and health, Internet specific, communications and media, biotechnology, industrial and energy, computer hardware, other products, semiconductors and other electronics, and consumer related.

39382 ■ Vitalize Venture Group
Vitalize Venture Group
415 N LaSalle Dr.
Chicago, IL 60654
URL: http://www.vitalize.vc
Contact: Gale Wilkinson, Founder Managing Partner
Linkedin: www.linkedin.com/company/vitalizevc
X (Twitter): twitter.com/VitalizeVC
Description: Investment platform for early-stage companies via IrishAngels and VitalizeVC. **Founded:** 2017.

39383 ■ VitalizeVC
Vitalize Venture Group
415 N La Salle Dr.
Chicago, IL 60654
URL: http://www.vitalize.vc
Contact: Gale Wilkinson, Founder Managing Partner
Linkedin: www.linkedin.com/company/vitalizevc
X (Twitter): x.com/VitalizeVC
Description: Invests in early-stage B2B startups with growth potential in the United States. **Founded:** 2018. **Investment Policies:** Prefers startups looking to raise $1,000,000-$3,000,000; term sheet issued from a lead investor; pre-money valuation less than $20,000,000; potential 30x CoC ROI; early revenues indicating product-market fit; entrepreneurial experience; . **Industry Preferences:** B2B SaaS .

39384 ■ West Suburban Angels (WSA)
1750 W Ogden Ave., Unit 4051
Naperville, IL 60567-1254
Co. E-mail: westsuburbanangels@gmail.com
URL: http://www.westsuburbanangels.com
Contact: Kenn Miller, Director
Facebook: www.facebook.com/people/West-Suburban-Angels/100067583014610
Linkedin: www.linkedin.com/company/west-suburban-angels
X (Twitter): x.com/wsangels
Description: Connects high-growth early-stage startups looking for capital and mentorship with investors interested in financial return and community impact. **Founded:** 2014. **Industry Preferences:** Innovative information technology; business services; industrial technology; financial services; consumer/industrial products; healthcare services/technology.

39385 ■ William Blair Capital Partners
The William Blair Bldg., 150 N Riverside Plz.
Chicago, IL 60606
Ph: (312)236-1600
Free: 800-621-0687
Co. E-mail: info@williamblair.com
URL: http://www.williamblair.com
Contact: Christoph B. Fuchs, Manager
E-mail: cfuchs@williamblair.com
Facebook: www.facebook.com/WilliamBlairCo
X (Twitter): x.com/WilliamBlair
Instagram: www.instagram.com/williamblaircompany
Description: Firm provides investment banking and wealth management services. **Founded:** 1935. **Preferred Investment Size:** $7,000,000 to $35,000,000. **Industry Preferences:** Consumer related, medical and health, computer software,

hardware and services, biotechnology, industrial and energy, communications and media, semiconductors and other electronics.

39386 ■ Wind Point Partners
676 N Michigan Ave., Ste. 3700
Chicago, IL 60611
Ph: (312)255-4800
Fax: (312)255-4820
Co. E-mail: exec@wppartners.com
URL: http://www.wppartners.com
Contact: Alex Washington, Managing Director
Description: Provider of an investment management firm. **Founded:** 1984. **Preferred Investment Size:** $30,000,000 to $150,000,000. **Industry Preferences:** Industrial and energy, consumer related, other products, communications and media, medical and health, Internet specific, biotechnology, computer software and services, computer hardware, semiconductors and other electronics.

PROCUREMENT ASSISTANCE PROGRAMS

39387 ■ College of DuPage Center for Entrepreneurship - Illinois Procurement Technical Assistance Center (PTAC)
535 Duane St., Office 233
Glen Ellyn, IL 60137
URL: http://www.cod.edu/business-development-center/apex/index.html
Contact: Ileen Kelly, Contact
E-mail: kellyi421@cod.edu
Description: Provides one-on-one counseling, technical information, marketing assistance and training to existing businesses that are interested in selling their products and/or services to local, state, or federal government agencies.

39388 ■ Defense Information Systems Agency, Continental United States (DISA CONUS)
IL
Free: 844-347-2457
Co. E-mail: disa.mpeo@mail.mil
URL: http://www.disa.mil
Contact: Christopher S. Argo, Chief of Staff
Facebook: www.facebook.com/USdisa
Linkedin: www.linkedin.com/company/defenseinformationsystemsagency
X (Twitter): twitter.com/usdisa
YouTube: www.youtube.com/usdisa
Description: Covers activities for Defense Information & Technological Contracting (Scott Air Force Base, IL), 375th Airlift Wing (Scott Air Force Base, IL), and USAF AMC Contracting Flight (Scott Air Force Base, IL).

39389 ■ Illinois Procurement Technical Assistance Center - College of DuPage
535 Duane St., Office 233
Glen Ellyn, IL 60137
Ph: (630)942-2600
URL: http://www.cod.edu/business-development-center/apex/index.html
Contact: Ileen Kelly, Director, Business Development Program Manager
E-mail: kellyi421@cod.edu
Description: Assists with doing business with the government, or to improve your current level of government contracting.

39390 ■ Illinois Procurement Technical Assistance Center-Illinois Hispanic Chamber of Commerce (IHCC)
222 W Merchandise Mart Plz.
Ste. 1212 c/o 1871
Chicago, IL 60654
Ph: (312)425-9500
Co. E-mail: info@ihccbusiness.net
URL: http://ihccbusiness.net/ihcc-procurement-technical-assistance
Contact: Jaime di Paulo, President
E-mail: jaime@ihccbusiness.net
Facebook: www.facebook.com/ihccbusiness
X (Twitter): x.com/ihccbusiness
Instagram: www.instagram.com/ihccbusiness
YouTube: www.youtube.com/channel/UCl3R5Qx9EFAWn_Yemv0EOFQ
Description: Promotes the growth and success of Hispanic firms and serves as a strong advocate for business issues.

39391 ■ Illinois Procurement Technical Assistance Center - North Business & Industrial Council (PTAC)
8420 W Bryn Mawr Ave., 1020
Chicago, IL 60631
Ph: (773)594-9292
URL: http://www.dhs.state.il.us/page.aspx?item=73553
Description: Advises Illinois companies on procurement opportunities and keeps them abreast of changes in the procurement process at the federal, State of Illinois, and local municipal levels. Technical expertise and assistance are offered in proposal preparation, the procurement process, and contract administration. NORBIC also offers assistance with small business preference programs, including Small Women Owned Businesses, Small Disadvantaged Businesses, Veteran, and 8(a) Certification Assistance.

39392 ■ Illinois Procurement Technical Assistance Center-South Suburban College (SSC)
15800 S State St.
South Holland, IL 60473
Ph: (708)596-2000
Co. E-mail: succeed@ssc.edu
URL: http://www.ssc.edu
Contact: Dr. Lynette D. Stokes, President
Facebook: www.facebook.com/SouthSuburbanCollege
X (Twitter): x.com/south_suburban
YouTube: www.youtube.com/user/ssc360
Description: Provides free counseling and technical assistance to Illinois firms pursuing government contracts.

39393 ■ Illinois Procurement Technical Assistance Center - U.S. General Services Administration - Great Lakes
230 S Dearborn St.
Chicago, IL 60604
URL: http://www.gsa.gov/about-us/regions/welcome-to-the-great-lakes-region-5/about-the-great-lakes-region
Contact: John C. Kluczynski, Contact
Description: Serve its federal agency customers in Illinois, Indiana, Michigan, Minnesota, Ohio, and Wisconsin. **Founded:** 1949.

39394 ■ Illinois Procurement Technical Assistance Center - Women's Business Development Center (WBDC)
8 S Michigan Ave., 4th Fl.
Chicago, IL 60603
Ph: (312)853-3477
Free: 800-526-0857
Fax: (312)853-0145
Co. E-mail: wbdc@wbdc.org
URL: http://www.wbdc.org/en
Contact: Emilia DiMenco, President
E-mail: edimenco@wbdc.org
Facebook: www.facebook.com/thewbdc
Linkedin: www.linkedin.com/company/women's-business-development-center-chicago
X (Twitter): x.com/WBDC
YouTube: www.youtube.com/user/wbdc1
Description: Works with women to launch new businesses and strengthen existing businesses in the Chicago area. **Founded:** 1986.

39395 ■ Quincy Business & Technology Center (QBTC)
301 Oak St.
Quincy, IL 62301
Ph: (217)228-5500
Co. E-mail: qbtc@adams.net
URL: http://qbtc.org
Contact: William M. McCleery, Jr., Contact
Facebook: www.facebook.com/QuincyBusinessAndTechnologyCenter
Description: Nurtures the development of entrepreneurial companies helping them to service and grow during their start up period.

INCUBATORS/RESEARCH AND TECHNOLOGY PARKS

39396 ■ 1871
222 W Merchandise Mart Plz., Ste. 1212
Chicago, IL 60654
Ph: (312)239-0310
Co. E-mail: contact@1871.com
URL: http://1871.com
Contact: Betsy Ziegler, Chief Executive Officer
Facebook: www.facebook.com/1871Chicago
Linkedin: www.linkedin.com/company/1871-com
X (Twitter): x.com/1871Chicago
Instagram: www.instagram.com/1871chicago
YouTube: www.youtube.com/user/1871chicago
Description: Consulting and investment firm that provide funds, networking, and co-working office space for startups and entrepreneurs. Provides support via mentors, service providers, investor referrals, programs, and fellow founders to help businesses grow. **Founded:** 2012.

39397 ■ America's Central Port
1635 W First St.
Granite City, IL 62040
Ph: (618)877-8444
Co. E-mail: contact@americascentralport.com
URL: http://www.americascentralport.com
Contact: Dennis Wilmsmeyer, Executive Director
E-mail: dwilmsmeyer@americascentralport.com
Facebook: www.facebook.com/AmericasCentralPort
Linkedin: www.linkedin.com/company/america
Description: Firm provides industrial development and transportation projects. **Founded:** 1959.

39398 ■ Chicago Technology Park (CTP)
2201 W Campbell Park Dr. Ste. 1
Chicago, IL 60612
URL: http://resources.istcoalition.org/the-chicago-technology-park
Description: A small business incubator serving as a ground for technology companies in early development, as well as expansion facilities for those companies that are growing their operations. **Scope:** Seeks to coordinate industry, university, and government partnerships to stimulate the formation of science-based companies and economic development in the Chicago area. Provides access to university and hospital resources, offers assistance in the creation of new venture companies, and provides space in an incubator building. **Founded:** 1984.

39399 ■ DePaul University Coleman Entrepreneurship Center
1 E Jackson Blvd.
Chicago, IL 60604
Ph: (312)362-6480
Fax: (312)476-3240
Co. E-mail: cec@depaul.edu
URL: http://business.depaul.edu/about/centers-institutes/coleman-entrepreneurship-center/Pages/default.aspx
Contact: Bruce Leech, Executive Director
E-mail: b.leech@depaul.edu
Facebook: www.facebook.com/ColemanCenter
Linkedin: www.linkedin.com/company/colemancenter
X (Twitter): x.com/ColemanCenter
Instagram: www.instagram.com/coleman_center
YouTube: www.youtube.com/channel/UCUk8Gb_6Liz5Ke7YXvDt0Sw
Description: Provides a hub for building, connecting, and launching a business for our students and alumni. **Founded:** 2003.

39400 ■ doejo
444 N Wabash 5th Fl.
Chicago, IL 60611
Ph: (312)888-6473
Co. E-mail: ideas@doejo.com
URL: http://doejo.com

Contact: Philip Tadros, Founder
X (Twitter): x.com/doejo

Description: An innovation studio passionate about creating brands, platforms, products and experiences that people love. Strives to solve problems for established companies in all industries and helps funded startups get off the ground. **Founded:** 2008.

39401 ■ Dream Kitchen
51 S Grove Ave.
  Elgin, IL 60120
Ph: (847)380-6802
Co. E-mail: info@dreamhubinc.com
URL: http://dreamhallco.com
Contact: Kevin Echevarria, Co-Founder
Facebook: www.facebook.com/dreamhallat51
Instagram: www.instagram.com/dreamhallat51

Description: Culinary incubator that works with food startups and entrepreneurs. Provides kitchen space for those looking to start, grow, or expand their food business. **Founded:** 2012.

39402 ■ EIGERlab
304 Main St., Ste. 115C
  Rockford, IL 61101
Ph: (815)965-3522
Fax: (815)316-6345
URL: http://www.eigerlab.org
Contact: Mike Cobert, Director
E-mail: mcobert@eigerlab.org

Description: A state-of-the-art, mixed-use incubator. It serves the region with leading edge business and engineering support services.

39403 ■ EnterpriseWorks
60 Hazelwood Dr.
  Champaign, IL 61820
URL: http://researchpark.illinois.edu/locate-here/enterpriseworks-incubator
Contact: Roger West, Contact
E-mail: rwest@illinois.edu

Description: An incubator facility and resource center for science and technology focused entrepreneurs. **Founded:** 2003.

39404 ■ EnterpriseWorks Chicago (EWC)
2242 W Harrison St., Ste. 201
  Chicago, IL 60612
Ph: (312)996-9671
Co. E-mail: ewchicago@uillinois.edu
URL: http://resources.istcoalition.org/enterpriseworks-chicago
Contact: Kapila Viges, Contact

Description: University-based operation is engaged in creating a robust entrepreneurial community to nurture commercialization and accelerate viable high technology startups throughout the Chicago land community, the firm provides entrepreneurs with access to resources for creating viable startups. **Founded:** 2013.

39405 ■ Greater Sterling Development Corp. (GSDC)
c/o Heather Sotelo, Executive Director
  1741 Industrial Dr.
  Sterling, IL 61081
Ph: (815)625-5255
Fax: (815)625-5094
Co. E-mail: hsotelo@sterlingdevelopment.org
URL: http://sterlingdevelopment.org
Contact: Heather Sotelo, Executive Director
E-mail: hsotelo@sterlingdevelopment.org

Description: Provides a variety of business development and relocation assistance services. **Geographic Preference:** Local.

39406 ■ The Incubator
2510 Green Bay Rd.
  Evanston, IL 60201
URL: http://www.theincubator.com
Contact: Tim Lavengood, Executive Director
E-mail: t-lavengood@theincubator.com

Description: Incubator providing assistance and resources to new science and technology-based companies. **Founded:** 1986.

39407 ■ Industrial Council of Nearwest Chicago (ICNC)
320 N Damen Ave. 1st Fl.
  Chicago, IL 60612
Ph: (312)421-3941
Fax: (312)421-1871
Co. E-mail: info@industrialcouncil.com
URL: http://www.industrialcouncil.com
Contact: Robert Carmody, President
Facebook: www.facebook.com/ICNCChicago
Linkedin: www.linkedin.com/company/icncchicago
X (Twitter): x.com/ICNCChicago

Description: One of the oldest and largest business incubators in the world houses over 110 new and growing companies across a diverse set of industries including food and beverage, manufacturing, professional services and apparel. **Founded:** 1967.

39408 ■ Joliet City Center Partnership (CCP)
203 N Ottawa St., Ste. 100
  Joliet, IL 60432
Ph: (815)774-6067
URL: http://jolietccp.com
Contact: Priscilla Cordero, Executive Director
E-mail: priscilla.cordero@jolietdowntown.com
Facebook: www.facebook.com/JolietCityCenterPartnershipLlc
Linkedin: www.linkedin.com/company/joliet-city-center-partnership
X (Twitter): x.com/JolietCCP
Instagram: www.instagram.com/jolietccp

Description: Firm provides financial assistance to small business and property owners.

39409 ■ Joseph Business Center
7600 W Roosevelt Rd.
  Forest Park, IL 60130
Ph: (708)697-6200
Co. E-mail: info@josephbusinessservices.com
URL: http://www.josephcenter.org/home
Contact: Dr. Deloris S. Thomas, President

Description: Part of a statewide network of resource providers for emerging businesses. Provides business consulting, networking opportunities, and training programs to assist entrepreneurs in improving business performance, productivity and profitability.

39410 ■ Justice Entrepreneurs Project (JEP)
321 S Plymouth Ct., Ste. 3B
  Chicago, IL 60604
Ph: (312)546-3282
URL: http://chicagobarfoundation.org/apply-to-the-jep-program
Facebook: www.facebook.com/jepchicago

Description: An incubator for newer lawyers to start innovative, socially conscious law practices in the Chicago area that provide affordable services to low and moderate-income people.

39411 ■ Kitchen Chicago
324 N Leavitt
  Chicago, IL 60612
Ph: (312)455-0863
Co. E-mail: info@kitchenchicago.com
URL: http://www.kitchenchicago.com
Facebook: www.facebook.com/KitchenChicago
X (Twitter): x.com/kitchenchicago
Instagram: www.instagram.com/kitchen_chicago

Description: Culinary incubator providing affordable kitchen space for food startups.

39412 ■ Lake County Tech Hub Business and Technology Incubator
13 N Genessee St.
  Waukegan, IL 60085
Ph: (224)990-4884
Free: 800-775-1168
Co. E-mail: eddie@thehublc.org
URL: http://thehublc.org
Contact: Eddie Soto, Director
Facebook: www.facebook.com/LakeCountyTechHub
Linkedin: www.linkedin.com/company/lake-county-tech-hub-and-business-incubator
X (Twitter): x.com/lakecntytechub
YouTube: www.youtube.com/channel/UCdeT7IZKHqXiEhy55Cr7EnA

Description: Supports the successful development of entrepreneurial companies.

39413 ■ Macomb Area Economic Development Corp. (MAEDCO)
1406 E Carroll St.
  Macomb, IL 61455
Ph: (309)837-4684
Fax: (309)837-4684
URL: http://www.maedco.org
Contact: Kim Pierce, Executive Director
Facebook: www.facebook.com/MAEDCO

Description: The Macomb Area Economic Development Corporation (MAEDCO) is a not-for-profit corporation dedicated to the economic growth of the Macomb region. We have crafted an environment that can foster long-term growth, success, and profits for your business. We are capable of arranging a business package tailored to meet your individual requirements. **Founded:** 1983. **Publications:** *The Journal of Developing Areas* (Quarterly); *Western Courier* (3/week). **Geographic Preference:** Local.

39414 ■ Matter
222 W Merchandise Mart Plz., Ste. 1230
  Chicago, IL 60654
Ph: (312)374-8243
Co. E-mail: info@matter.health
URL: http://matter.health
Contact: Steven Collens, Chief Executive Officer
Facebook: www.facebook.com/MATTER
X (Twitter): x.com/MATTERHealth

Description: Healthcare startup incubator and corporate innovation accelerator. **Founded:** 2015.

39415 ■ mHUB
965 W Chicago Ave.
  Chicago, IL 60642
Ph: (312)248-8701
Co. E-mail: info@mhubchicago.com
URL: http://www.mhubchicago.com
Contact: Haven Allen, Chief Executive Officer
Facebook: www.facebook.com/mHUBChicago
Linkedin: www.linkedin.com/company/mhub-chicago
X (Twitter): x.com/mHUBChicago
Instagram: www.instagram.com/mhubchicago
YouTube: www.youtube.com/c/mHUBofficial

Description: A coworking community of product designers, developers, entrepreneurs, engineers, and manufacturers working to ensure that Chicago's manufacturing industry continues to accelerate, grow, and thrive.

39416 ■ MyKitchens L.L.C.
9416 W Irving Pk. Rd.
  Schiller Park, IL 60176
Ph: (708)714-7151
Co. E-mail: admin@mykitchensllc.com
URL: http://www.mykitchensllc.com
Contact: Suzana Stoltz, Manager
Instagram: www.instagram.com/mykitchenst
YouTube: www.youtube.com/channel/UCAYH5FN9Bd9N_Vy2WJLO_ng

Description: A shared-use kitchen/kitchen incubator with affordable kitchen space for food startups.

39417 ■ National Foodworks Services (NFS)
575 Brush College Rd.
  Decatur, IL 62521
Ph: (217)330-8512
Co. E-mail: info@nationalfoodworks.com
URL: http://www.nationalfoodworks.com
Contact: Ernie Beckman, President

Description: Incubator offering a variety of services for food entrepreneurs and food organizations including marketing services, financial services, and developmental services.

39418 ■ New Venture Challenge (NVC)
Polsky Center at Chicago Booth
  5807 S Woodlawn Ave., Ste. 207
  Chicago, IL 60637
URL: http://polsky.uchicago.edu/programs-events/new-venture-challenge

Description: A business accelerator. **Founded:** 1996.

39419 ■ Peoria NEXT Innovation Center
801 W Main St.
Peoria, IL 61606
Ph: (309)495-7238
URL: http://www.bradley.edu/sites/pnic
Contact: Dr. Stephen Standifird, President
Description: A small business incubator designed to enable leadership in discovery, innovation and commercialization.

39420 ■ Performance Improvement Institute (PII)
201 W Grand Ave., Apt 503
Chicago, IL 60654-7345
Ph: (312)952-0719
URL: http://www.piionline.org
Contact: Mariano L. Bernardez, Manager
Description: A small business incubator focusing on developing and graduating new companies through an incubation process under the leadership of PhD candidates and the supervision of an international faculty. **Founded:** 2005.

39421 ■ Quincy Business & Technology Center (QBTC)
301 Oak St.
Quincy, IL 62301
Ph: (217)228-5500
Co. E-mail: qbtc@adams.net
URL: http://qbtc.org
Contact: William M. McCleery, Jr., Contact
Facebook: www.facebook.com/QuincyBusinessAndTechnologyCenter
Description: Nurtures the development of entrepreneurial companies helping them to service and grow during their start up period.

39422 ■ REach
430 N Michigan Ave., 9th Fl.
Chicago, IL 60611
Ph: (312)329-8524
Co. E-mail: hello@narreach.com
URL: http://nar-reach.com
Contact: Ashley Stinton, Executive Director
Linkedin: www.linkedin.com/company/nar-reach-
X (Twitter): x.com/narREach
Description: Real estate accelerator providing mentorship, venture capital, and education to help navigate the market and optimize your reach. **Founded:** 2012.

39423 ■ Research Park & Enterprise Works
60 Hazelwood Dr.
Champaign, IL 61820
Ph: (217)333-8324
Co. E-mail: research-park@illinois.edu
URL: http://researchpark.illinois.edu
Contact: Laura Appenzeller, Executive Director
E-mail: lfrerich@illinois.edu
Facebook: www.facebook.com/uiresearchpark
Linkedin: www.linkedin.com/company/university-of-illinois-research-park
X (Twitter): x.com/UIResearchPark
Instagram: www.instagram.com/uiresearchpark
YouTube: www.youtube.com/user/researchparkuiuc
Description: A small business incubator providing an environment where technology-based businesses can work with the research faculty and students at UIUC to take advantage of opportunities for collaborative research and easy access to university labs, equipment and services. **Founded:** 1999.

39424 ■ Rev3 Innovation Center
Rev3 Innovation Center
1120 E Diehl Rd.
Naperville, IL 60563
Ph: (630)486-7948
Co. E-mail: info@rev3dupage.com
URL: http://rev3dupage.com
Facebook: www.facebook.com/Rev3DuPage
Description: Operator of an innovation center that is engaged in helping people and companies design, build and launch software and technology. **Founded:** 2013.

39425 ■ River Forest Kitchen (RFK)
349 Ashland Ave.
River Forest, IL 60305
URL: http://www.rfkitchen.com
Contact: Alec Olson, Contact
X (Twitter): x.com/RFKitchen
Pinterest: www.pinterest.com/rfkitch
Description: Provides the platform for artisan chefs to grow their business without the steep learning curve and the start up costs normally incurred for expensive real estate and culinary equipment.

39426 ■ Robert & Carolyn Turner Center for Entrepreneurship
1501 W Bradley Ave.
Peoria, IL 61625
Ph: (309)677-4321
URL: http://bradley.edu/academic/colleges/fcba/centers/turner
Contact: James F. Foley, Director
E-mail: jff@bradley.edu
Description: Assists entrepreneurs and tech-based companies in developing innovative products and services.

39427 ■ Serendipity Labs
1 S Wacker Dr.
Chicago, IL 60606
Free: 800-226-3604
Co. E-mail: info@serendipitylabs.com
URL: http://serendipitylabs.com
Contact: John P. Arenas, Chief Executive Officer
X (Twitter): x.com/SerendipityLabs
Instagram: www.instagram.com/serendipity_labs
YouTube: www.youtube.com/user/SerendipityLabsTV
Description: Coworking space in the Chicago loop offering private offices, workstations, and team rooms for startups and entrepreneurs.

39428 ■ Share A Kitchen
1020 W Devon Ave.
Elk Grove Village, IL 60007
Ph: (323)543-5437
Co. E-mail: info@shareakitchen.com
URL: http://www.shareakitchen.com
Description: Culinary incubator with kitchen space for new start up food businesses.

39429 ■ Shetland Properties L.P.
225 S Highland Ave.
Aurora, IL 60506
Ph: (773)921-5400
Fax: (773)921-6680
Co. E-mail: slate@shetland.com
URL: http://shetland.com
Contact: Mark Slakter, Manager
E-mail: slate@shetland.com
Facebook: www.facebook.com/Shetland-Properties-121848414802
Linkedin: www.linkedin.com/company/shetland-properties
Description: Firm engages in development of real-estate properties. **Founded:** 1986.

39430 ■ Solo & Small Practice Incubator (SSPI)
565 W Adams St.
Chicago, IL 60661
URL: http://kentlaw.iit.edu/law/alumni/solo-and-small-practice-incubator
Contact: Jackie Russell, Contact
E-mail: jrussell5@kentlaw.iit.edu
Description: A one-year program designed to offer a select group of entrepreneurial-minded recent IIT Chicago-Kent graduates with valuable experience and ongoing training to help build their professional careers as solo or small firm legal practitioners.

39431 ■ Southern Illinois University Small Business Incubator
150 E Pleasant Hill Rd.
Carbondale, IL 62901
Co. E-mail: incubator@siu.edu
URL: http://incubator.siu.edu
Description: Helps to accelerate the startup and expansion of small businesses in southerin Illinois. Services include business coaching, business planning, startup/expansion assistance, resource networks, meeting room space, mentoring, and flexible leasing. **Founded:** 1990.

39432 ■ Sterling Small Business Technology Center
c/o Heather Sotelo, Executive Director
1741 Industrial Dr.
Sterling, IL 61081
URL: http://sterlingdevelopment.org/sterling-small-business-and-technology-center
Description: Helps with startup and expansion of small businesses. Offers resources such as affordable space, help with business plans and an effective way to network with other businesses.

39433 ■ Suite Spotte
21 S La Grange Rd., Ste. 200
La Grange, IL 60525
Ph: (708)665-8050
Co. E-mail: info@suitespotte.com
URL: http://suitespotte.com
Contact: Sue Reardon, Founder
Facebook: www.facebook.com/SuiteSpotte
Linkedin: www.linkedin.com/company/suite-spotte-coworking
X (Twitter): x.com/SuiteSpotte
Instagram: www.instagram.com/suitespotte
Description: A suburban coworking and shared office space for startups and entrepreneurs. **Founded:** 2014.

39434 ■ Sustainable Business Center (SBC)
2900 W Main St.
Galesburg, IL 61401
Ph: (309)343-1191
URL: http://www.sustainablebusinesscenter.com/homepage_items/index
Description: Incubator for businesses focused on environmental sustainability and responsibility through innovation. Offers work space, manufacturing space, land for organic agriculture production, business support resources, and a FDA-certified commercial kitchen. Promotes the idea that people, planet, and profit are all equally important to the prosperity of a growing enterprise. **Founded:** 2011.

39435 ■ TechNexus
20 N Upper Wacker Dr., 12th Fl.
Chicago, IL 60606
Ph: (312)435-1000
Co. E-mail: collaborate@technexus.com
URL: http://technexus.com
Contact: Terry Howerton, Chief Executive Officer
Facebook: www.facebook.com/technexus
Linkedin: www.linkedin.com/company/technexus
X (Twitter): x.com/technexus
Description: Company is engaged in providing funds and accelerates technology ventures for entrepreneurs and enterprises.

39436 ■ Technology Entrepreneur Center, Inc. (TEC)
351 Coordinated Science Lab, MC-228
1308 W Main St.
Urbana, IL 61801
Ph: (217)244-3124
Co. E-mail: tec@illinois.edu
URL: http://tec.illinois.edu
Contact: Jed L. Taylor, Executive Director
E-mail: jedt@illinois.edu
Facebook: www.facebook.com/technologyentrepreneurcenter
Linkedin: www.linkedin.com/company/technology-entrepreneur-center
X (Twitter): x.com/tecenter
Instagram: www.instagram.com/TECenter
YouTube: www.youtube.com/user/TECIllinois
Description: A small business incubator assisting technology start-up companies in St. Louis to increase their likelihood of success through access to highly qualified mentors, assistance with business planning and strategies, and office services. **Founded:** 2000.

STATE LISTINGS   Illinois ■ 39451

39437 ■ TechStars Chicago
706 W 15th St.
  Chicago, IL 60607
URL: http://www.techstars.com/accelerators/chicago
Contact: Anthony Alepra, Program Manager
Description: An intensive summer accelerator for startups driven by proven entrepreneurs and investors.

39438 ■ Turner Center for Entrepreneurship
1501 W Bradley Ave.
  Peoria, IL 61625
Ph: (309)676-7611
URL: http://www.bradley.edu/turnercenter
Contact: Stephen Standifird, President
Description: A not-for-profit program located at Bradley University providing business counseling, technical assistance, training, and educational activities for individuals interested in owning their own businesses.

39439 ■ The University of Chicago - Polsky Center for Entrepreneurship and Innovation
5807 S Woodlawn, Ste. 207
  Chicago, IL 60637
Ph: (773)834-4526
Co. E-mail: polsky@uchicago.edu
URL: http://polsky.uchicago.edu
Contact: Camille Andres, Executive Assistant Head
E-mail: candres@uchicago.edu
Facebook: www.facebook.com/PolskyCenter
Linkedin: www.linkedin.com/company/polsky-center
X (Twitter): x.com/polskycenter
Instagram: www.instagram.com/polskycenter
YouTube: www.youtube.com/user/PolskyCenter
Description: Drives the creation of new businesses and partnerships. Runs a business accelerator, operates a co-working space, and offers an innovation fund. **Founded:** 1998.

39440 ■ University Technology Park at Illinois Institute of Technology (UTP)
3440 S Dearborn St.
  Chicago, IL 60616
Ph: (312)567-3060
URL: http://www.iit.edu/utp
Contact: Joshua H. Siegel, Director
E-mail: jsiegel2@iit.edu
Description: Technology park established to serve technology-based companies in the early product and customer-development stages that require lab and office space as well as convenient access to business development and university-based services. **Founded:** 2005.

EDUCATIONAL PROGRAMS

39441 ■ Black Hawk College, Quad-Cities Campus
6600 34th Ave.
  Moline, IL 61265
Ph: (309)796-5000
URL: http://www.bhc.edu
Contact: Tim Wynes, President
Description: Two-year college offering a small business management program. **Founded:** 1946.

39442 ■ Chicago State University Office of Continuing Education
Chicago State University
  Jacoby Dickens Athletic Center (JDC), Rm. 201
  Chicago, IL 60628
Ph: (773)995-4466
Co. E-mail: continuinged@csu.edu
URL: http://www.csu.edu/continuingeducation
Description: Offers mature students career-updating and business-related courses, seminars, and workshops for degree, nondegree, credit, or noncredit status. Conducts course work in advanced business, management, human relations, and small business management. Also provides on-site training and development for employees of small businesses involved in computer operation, budgeting, marketing, and personnel management. Additional courses are presented through the College of Business Administration.

39443 ■ Loyola University Chicago School of Continuing and Professional Studies (SCPS)
820 N Michigan Ave. Lewis Towers 401
  Chicago, IL 60611
Ph: (312)915-8900
Co. E-mail: scps@luc.edu
URL: http://www.luc.edu/scps
Facebook: www.facebook.com/LoyolaSCPS
Linkedin: www.linkedin.com/school/lucscps
X (Twitter): x.com/LoyolaSCPS
Description: Sponsors several programs of interest to small business professionals: The Weekend College is a concentrated program for men and women who wish to attend college while working full time. The Continuing Education Program serves women interested in beginning or continuing their college careers through day classes. Other courses of study are offered through the Business Administration Department.

39444 ■ Rend Lake College (RLC)
468 N Ken Gray Pky.
  Ina, IL 62846
Ph: (618)437-5321
Fax: (618)437-5677
Co. E-mail: appliedscience@rlc.edu
URL: http://www.rlc.edu
Contact: Terry Wilkerson, President
E-mail: wilkersont@rlc.edu
Linkedin: www.linkedin.com/company/rend-lake-college
X (Twitter): x.com/rendlakecollege
Description: Two-year college offering a small business management program. **Founded:** 1956.

39445 ■ Rock Valley College (RVC)
3301 N Mulford Rd.
  Rockford, IL 61114
Ph: (815)921-7821
Free: 800-973-7821
Co. E-mail: rvc-admissions@rockvalleycollege.edu
URL: http://www.rockvalleycollege.edu
Contact: Jarid Funderburg, Chairperson
Facebook: www.facebook.com/rvcgoldeneagles
X (Twitter): x.com/rvcgoldeneagles
Instagram: www.instagram.com/rockvalleycollege
YouTube: www.youtube.com/user/rockvalleycollege1
Description: Two-year college offering a small business management program. **Founded:** 1964.

39446 ■ Sauk Valley Community College (SVCC)
173 IL Rte. 2
  Dixon, IL 61021
Ph: (815)288-5511
Fax: (815)456-4238
Co. E-mail: support@svcc.edu
URL: http://www.svcc.edu
Contact: Dr. Dave Hellmich, President
Facebook: www.facebook.com/saukvalleycc
Linkedin: www.linkedin.com/school/saukvalleycc
X (Twitter): x.com/saukvalleycc
YouTube: www.youtube.com/user/saukvalleycc
Description: Two-year college offering small business management classes. **Founded:** 1965.

CONSULTANTS

39447 ■ Healthbox L.L.C.
350 N Orleans St., Ste. S10000
  Chicago, IL 60654
Co. E-mail: info@healthbox.com
URL: http://www.himss.org
Description: Healthcare-focused accelerator programs, with the goal of helping entrepreneurs navigate the complex industry to grow successful businesses. **Founded:** 2010.

39448 ■ Phoenix Business Consulting, Inc. (PBC)
18888 N Woodale Tr.
  Lindenhurst, IL 60046
Ph: (847)265-3779
Free: 800-655-0422
Fax: (847)265-3780
URL: http://www.phoenixbusinessconsulting.com

Contact: Larry A. Bauman, President
E-mail: larry@bauman.biz
Description: Provider of business consulting services and solutions. **Scope:** Provider of business consulting services and solutions. **Publications:** "Contingency Planning - Expect the Unexpected"; "The Hedge"; "Segmentation Strategies"; "The Scepter of Influence".

PUBLICATIONS

39449 ■ *Chicago Business*
Edward H. Levi Hall, 5801 S Ellis Ave.
  Chicago, IL 60637
Ph: (773)702-1234
Co. E-mail: infocenter@uchicago.edu
URL: http://www.uchicago.edu
Contact: John W. Boyer, Dean
URL(s): www.chibus.com

Ed: David Antos, Jesus Badiola, Disha Malik. **Released:** Biweekly **Description:** Collegiate business school publication. **Availability:** Print; Online.

39450 ■ *Crain's Chicago Business*
1155 Gratiot Ave.
  Detroit, MI 48207-2732
Ph: (313)446-6000
Co. E-mail: info@crain.com
URL: http://www.crain.com
Contact: Barry Asin, President
URL(s): www.chicagobusiness.com
Facebook: www.facebook.com/crainschicago
X (Twitter): x.com/crainschicago
Instagram: www.instagram.com/crainschicago

Released: Weekly **Price:** $20, for print and online 4 week; $225, for print & online annual; $18, for digital per month; $199, for digital annual; $499, for premium access; $399, for health pulse. **Description:** Newspaper covering news stories about various aspects of business and labor activity in the Chicago market. **Availability:** Print; Online. **Type:** Full-text.

PUBLISHERS

39451 ■ Institute of Real Estate Management (IREM)
430 N Michigan Ave., Ste. 500
  Chicago, IL 60611
Ph: (312)329-6000
Free: 800-837-0706
Fax: (800)338-4736
Co. E-mail: getinfo@irem.org
URL: http://www.irem.org
Contact: Libby Ekre, President
Facebook: www.facebook.com/InstituteofRealEstateManagement
Linkedin: www.linkedin.com/company/institute-of-real-estate-management
X (Twitter): x.com/IREM_info
YouTube: www.youtube.com/user/IREMinfo
Description: Professional organization of real property and asset managers. Awards professional designation Certified Property Manager (CPM) to qualifying individuals, Accredited Management Organization (AMO) to qualifying management firms and also awards Accredited Residential Manager (ARM) accreditation to qualifying individuals who are primarily residential site managers. Monitors legislation affecting real estate management. Offers management courses and seminars; conducts research and educational programs, publishes books and reports; maintains formal code of ethics; compiles statistics; maintains employment Website for real estate management industry. **Founded:** 1933. **Publications:** *Journal of Property Management* (Bimonthly); *Real Estate Income/Expense Analysis National Summary*. **Awards:** IREM Academy of Authors (Annual); Lloyd D. Hanford Sr. Distinguished Instructor Award (Annual); IREM Foundation Diversity Outreach Scholarship (Annual); Paul H. Rittle, Sr. Scholarship; Donald M. Furbush Scholarship (Annual); J. Wallace Paletou Award (Annual); Paul H. Rittle Sr. Memorial Scholarship Award (Quarterly); George M. Brooker, CPM Diversity Collegiate Schol-

arship (Semiannual); Donald M. Furbush Professional Development Grants; Paul H. Rittle Sr. Professional Development Grants. **Geographic Preference:** National.

39452 ■ PivotPoint Press
8725 W Higgins Rd., Ste. 700
Chicago, IL 60631
Ph: (847)866-0500
URL: http://www.pivot-point.com
Contact: Robert Passage, Chief Executive Officer
Description: Publishes nonfiction books on business, economics and family. **Founded:** 2005.

39453 ■ Productivity Press
Informa UK Ltd.
2427 Bond St.
University Park, IL 60466-3101
Ph: 44 20 8052 0400
Co. E-mail: info@informa.com
URL: http://www.informa.com
Facebook: www.facebook.com/ProductivityPress
Description: Publishes materials on lean manufacturing and business improvement.

EXPANSION AND GROWTH FINANCING

39454 ■ 13i Capital Corp.
2021 Midwest Rd., Ste. 200
Oak Brook, IL 60523
Ph: (630)620-2255
Fax: (800)849-4183
Co. E-mail: info@13icapital.com
URL: http://13icapital.com
Contact: Jay Thukkaram, Vice President
E-mail: jaythukkaram@13icapital.com
Description: Offer private equity to lower middle-market companies throughout the world. **Founded:** 1993.

39455 ■ Accord CapX LLC [CapX Partners]
800 W fulton market, Ste.725
Chicago, IL 60607
Contact: Alexandra L. Park, Manager
Description: Offers debt financing to small and medium growing companies. Also maintains offices in New York and Boston. **Founded:** 1999. **Industry Preferences:** Aerospace; consumer products; energy; food and beverage; healthcare; manufacturing; technology; transportation.

VENTURE CAPITAL FIRM

39456 ■ Central Illinois Angels Inc. (CIA)
801 W Main St.
Peoria, IL 61606
URL: http://www.centralillinoisangels.com
Contact: Kenneth R. Eathington, Contact
Description: Membership-based angel investment organization. **Founded:** 2009.

39457 ■ Dunrath Capital
641 Courtland Cir.
Western Springs, IL 60558
Ph: (312)546-4782
Co. E-mail: info@dunrath.com
URL: http://www.dunrath.com/index.asp
Contact: John I. Abernethy, Co-Founder Managing Director
E-mail: john@dunrath.com
Description: Venture capital firm for early- and growth-stage companies delivering infrastructure security products and services.

39458 ■ Hyde Park Angels (HPA)
222 W Merchandise Mart Plz., Ste. 1212
Chicago, IL 60654
URL: http://hpa.vc
Contact: Ann Deters, Chairman
Facebook: www.facebook.com/HydeParkAngels
Linkedin: www.linkedin.com/company/hpa-vc
X (Twitter): x.com/hpa_vc
Description: Early stage investment firm for companies in the Midwest. **Founded:** 2007. **Industry Preferences:** IT; financial services; consumer and industrial products.

39459 ■ Hyde Park Venture Partners (HPVP)
415 N LaSalle St., 502
Chicago, IL 60654
URL: http://www.hydeparkvp.com
Contact: Alisa Vass, Chief Administrative Officer Partner
Linkedin: www.linkedin.com/company/hyde-park-venture-partners
X (Twitter): x.com/hydeparkvp
Description: Early-stage venture capital firm for high-growth, mid-continent technology start-ups. Also works out of Indianapolis. **Founded:** 2011. **Investment Policies:** Exceptional founding team, fast-growth potential, and looking for first or second round of capital.

39460 ■ Impact Engine
350 W Wolf Point Plz., No., 9000 N
Chicago, IL 60654
Co. E-mail: funds@theimpactengine.com
URL: http://www.theimpactengine.com
Contact: Jessica Droste Yagan, Chief Executive Officer
Facebook: www.facebook.com/TheImpactEngine
Linkedin: www.linkedin.com/company/theimpactengine
X (Twitter): x.com/TheImpactEngine
Description: A venture fund that invests financial and human capital in early-stage, for-profit businesses that are improving education, health, economic empowerment, and resource efficiency. **Founded:** 2012.

39461 ■ Matthew Pritzker Company LLC
900 N Michigan Ave., Ste. 1730
Chicago, IL 60611
Ph: (312)564-8800
Co. E-mail: info@matthewpritzkercompany.com
URL: http://www.matthewpritzkercompany.com
Description: Venture capital firm for early- and mid-stage companies.

39462 ■ Origin Ventures (OV)
1 E Erie St., Ste. 525-2649
Chicago, IL 60611
Co. E-mail: inquire@originventures.com
URL: http://originventures.com
Contact: Alex Meyer, Managing Partner
Linkedin: www.linkedin.com/company/origin-ventures
X (Twitter): x.com/originventures
Description: Offers venture capital at the seed and Series A stages. Also works out of Salt Lake City. **Founded:** 1999. **Preferred Investment Size:** $500,000 to $4,000,000. **Industry Preferences:** Software; marketplaces; B2B; B2C.

39463 ■ Red Rocket Ventures
Chicago, IL
Co. E-mail: contact@redrocketvc.com
URL: http://www.redrocketvc.com
Contact: George Deeb, Managing Partner
E-mail: george@redrocketvc.com
Facebook: www.facebook.com/RedRocketVC
Linkedin: www.linkedin.com/company/red-rocket-ventures
X (Twitter): x.com/redrocketvc
Description: Consulting and financial advisory firm. Assists B2C and B2B companies with growth strategy and financing needs.

Indiana

ASSOCIATIONS AND OTHER ORGANIZATIONS

39464 ■ Association of Fundraising Professionals IN, Michiana Chapter
c/o Charmaine Torma, President Charmaine Torma Consulting LLC
1605 E Jefferson Blvd.
South Bend, IN 46617
Co. E-mail: afpmichianachapter@gmail.com
URL: http://community.afpglobal.org/afpinmichianachapter/aboutus23/about672
Contact: Charmaine Torma, President
E-mail: ctorma@charmainetorma.com
URL(s): www.afpmichiana.org
Facebook: www.facebook.com/AfpMichiana
X (Twitter): x.com/AFPMichiana
Instagram: www.instagram.com/AFPMichiana
Founded: 1998. **Geographic Preference:** Regional.

39465 ■ Association of Fundraising Professionals Indiana Chapter (AFP-IC)
17437 Carey Rd., No. 265
Westfield, IN 46074
Ph: (317)824-0940
Co. E-mail: afpic@nashams.com
URL: http://community.afpglobal.org/afpinindianachapter/home
Contact: Bethany Warner, President
URL(s): afpglobal.org/chapters/afp-indiana-chapter
Linkedin: www.linkedin.com/company/afpglobal
Founded: 1982. **Geographic Preference:** State.

39466 ■ Business Network International Indiana [BNI Indiana]
PO Box 19827
Indianapolis, IN 46219
Ph: (317)891-0355
Fax: (317)845-8117
URL: http://bni-indiana.com/en-US/index
Contact: Hazel Walker, Executive Director
Facebook: www.facebook.com/BNIIndiana
Description: Provides both men and women a structured environment for the development and exchange of quality business referrals. Offers members the opportunity to share ideas and contacts. **Geographic Preference:** State.

39467 ■ Business Network International Northern Indiana [BNI Northern Indiana]
2302 Dierdorff Rd.
Goshen, IN 46526
Ph: (574)533-3509
Fax: (574)533-2792
Co. E-mail: mdbotts@aol.com
URL: http://bni-ni.com
Contact: Mark Botts, Executive Director
Linkedin: www.linkedin.com/company/bni-northern-indiana

Description: Provides both men and women a structured environment for the development and exchange of quality business referrals. Offers members the opportunity to share ideas and contacts. **Founded:** 1995. **Geographic Preference:** Local.

39468 ■ Entrepreneurs' Organization - Indianapolis Chapter (EO)
12400 Reynolds Dr.
Fishers, IN 46038
URL: http://www.eonetwork.org/indianapolis
Contact: Tony Zammar, Treasurer
Description: Seeks to help entrepreneurs achieve their full potential in their business and personal lives through networking, shared experiences, and collaborative learning.

39469 ■ Indiana Grocery & Convenience Store Association (IGCSA)
PO Box 2186
Indianapolis, IN 46206-2186
Ph: (317)878-4231
Free: 800-222-4742
Co. E-mail: igcsa@igcsa.net
URL: http://www.igcsa.net
Contact: Joseph A. Lackey, President
Geographic Preference: State.

SMALL BUSINESS DEVELOPMENT CENTERS

39470 ■ Central Indiana Small Business Development Center (CISBDC)
Lacy School of Business., 625 Butler Way, Ste. 130
Indianapolis, IN 46208
Ph: (317)940-3919
Co. E-mail: central@isbdc.org
URL: http://isbdc.org/locations/central-indiana-sbdc
Contact: Dan Drexler, Regional Director
Description: Represents and promotes the small business sector. Provides management assistance to current and prospective small business owners. Helps to improve management skills and expand the products and services of members. **Geographic Preference:** Local.

39471 ■ East Central Indiana Small Business Development Center (SBDC)
1208 W White River Blvd., Ste. 129
Muncie, IN 47303
Ph: (765)282-9950
Free: 866-596-7232
Fax: (765)286-0565
Co. E-mail: eastcentral@isbdc.org
URL: http://isbdc.org/locations/east-central-isbdc
Contact: Peggy Cenova, Regional Director
E-mail: pcenova@isbdc.org
Description: Represents and promotes the small business sector. Provides management assistance to current and prospective small business owners. Helps to improve management skills and expand the products and services of members. **Geographic Preference:** Local.

39472 ■ Hoosier Heartland Small Business Development Center
1400 W State St., Ste. J
West Lafayette, IN 47906
Ph: (765)454-7922
Co. E-mail: hoosierheartland@isbdc.org
URL: http://isbdc.org/locations/hoosier-heartland-indiana-sbdc
Description: Provides management assistance to current and prospective small business owners in Hoosier Heartland. **Geographic Preference:** Local.

39473 ■ Indiana Small Business Development Center (ISBDC)
One North Capitol Ave., Ste., 700
Indianapolis, IN 46204
Free: 888-472-3244
Co. E-mail: leadcenter@isbdc.org
URL: http://isbdc.org
Contact: Andrew Carty, Director
E-mail: ancarty@iedc.in.gov
Facebook: www.facebook.com/isbdc
Linkedin: www.linkedin.com/company/indiana-small-business-development-center-isbdc
X (Twitter): x.com/indiana_sbdc
Description: Providing entrepreneurs with the education, information and tools necessary to build successful businesses. **Scope:** Small business development. **Founded:** 1985. **Geographic Preference:** State.

39474 ■ North Central ISBDC
Judd Leighton School of Business and Economics at Indiana University S Bend
1700 W Mishawaka Ave.
South Bend, IN 46615
Ph: (574)520-4126
Co. E-mail: northcentral@isbdc.org
URL: http://isbdc.org/locations/north-central-indiana-sbdc
Contact: Alan Steele, Regional Director
E-mail: asteele@isbdc.org
Description: Represents and promotes the small business sector. Provides management assistance to current and prospective small business owners. Helps to improve management skills and expand the products and services of members. **Geographic Preference:** Local.

39475 ■ Northeast ISBDC
2101 E Coliseum Blvd.
Fort Wayne, IN 46805
Ph: (260)481-0500
Fax: (260)481-0499
Co. E-mail: northeast@isbdc.org
URL: http://isbdc.org/locations/northeast-isbdc
Contact: Wesley Shie, Regional Director
E-mail: wshie@isbdc.org
Description: Represents and promotes the small business sector. Provides management assistance to current and prospective small business owners. Helps to improve management skills and expand the products and services of members. **Geographic Preference:** Local.

39476 ■ Northwest Indiana Small Business Development Center (NISBDC)
9800 Connecticut Dr.
Crown Point, IN 46307
Ph: (219)644-3513
Fax: (219)644-3682
Co. E-mail: northwest@isbdc.org
URL: http://isbdc.org/locations/northwest-indiana-sbdc
Contact: Lorri Feldt, Regional Director
E-mail: lfeldt@isbdc.org
Description: Represents and promotes the small business sector. Provides management assistance to current and prospective small business owners. Helps to improve management skills and expand the products and services of members. **Geographic Preference:** Local.

39477 ■ Southeast Indiana Small Business Development Center (SBDC)
303 Scribner Dr., Ste. 202
New Albany, IN 47150
Ph: (812)952-9765
Co. E-mail: southeast@isbdc.org
URL: http://isbdc.org/locations/southeast-indiana-sbdc
Contact: Jon Myers, Regional Director
E-mail: jmyers@isbdc.org
Description: Provides management assistance to current and prospective small business owners in Southeastern Indiana. **Geographic Preference:** Local.

39478 ■ Southwest Indiana Small Business Development Center
318 Main St., Ste. 401
Evansville, IN 47708
Ph: (812)425-7232
Fax: (812)421-5883
Co. E-mail: southwest@isbdc.org
URL: http://isbdc.org/locations/southwest-indiana-sbdc
Contact: Dominic Poggi, Regional Director
Description: Represents and promotes the small business sector. Provides management assistance to current and prospective small business owners. Helps to improve management skills and expand the products and services of members. **Geographic Preference:** Local.

39479 ■ West Central Indiana Small Business Development Center
ISU Scott College of Business
30 N 7th St.
Terre Haute, IN 47809
Ph: (812)237-7676
Free: 800-227-7232
Fax: (812)237-7675
Co. E-mail: westcentral@isbdc.org
URL: http://isbdc.org/locations/west-central-indiana-sbdc
Contact: Courtney Richey-Chipol, Regional Director
E-mail: crichey@isbdc.org
Description: Represents and promotes the small business sector. Provides management assistance to current and prospective small business owners. Helps to improve management skills and expand the products and services of members. **Geographic Preference:** Local.

SMALL BUSINESS ASSISTANCE PROGRAMS

39480 ■ Growth Alliance for Greater Evansville (GAGE)
318 Main St., Ste. 500
Evansville, IN 47708
Ph: (812)401-4243
Co. E-mail: info@evvregion.com
URL: http://www.growthallianceevv.com
Contact: Stephanie El Tawil, Director
E-mail: stephanie@growthallianceevv.com
Facebook: www.facebook.com/GrowthAlliance
X (Twitter): twitter.com/GrowthAlliance
YouTube: www.youtube.com/user/EvansvilleGAGE

Pinterest: www.pinterest.com/growth_allliance_evansville
Founded: 2007.

39481 ■ Indiana Department of Commerce (IEDC) - International Development
1 N Capitol Ave., Ste. 700
Indianapolis, IN 46204
Ph: (317)232-8800
Free: 800-463-8081
Fax: (317)232-4146
Co. E-mail: iedc@iedc.in.gov
URL: http://iedc.in.gov
Contact: Eric Holcomb, Chairman
Facebook: www.facebook.com/IndianaEDC
X (Twitter): x.com/indiana_edc
Description: Helps businesses interested in foreign trade to establish contacts and leads. Organizes trade missions.

39482 ■ Indiana Economic Development Corp. (IEDC)
1 N Capitol Ave., Ste. 700
Indianapolis, IN 46204
Ph: (317)232-8800
Free: 800-463-8081
Fax: (317)232-4146
Co. E-mail: iedc@iedc.in.gov
URL: http://www.iedc.in.gov
Contact: Eric Holcomb, Chairman Governor
Facebook: www.facebook.com/IndianaEDC
Linkedin: www.linkedin.com/company/indiana-economic-development-corporation
X (Twitter): x.com/Indiana_EDC
Description: Coordinates business services offered by the Department of Commerce and other agencies. Serves as a switchboard for access to those services, such as export promotion, defense procurement, minority business development, and regulatory assistance. **Founded:** 2005. **Geographic Preference:** State.

39483 ■ Indiana Institute of Technology - McMillen Productivity and Design Center
1600 E Washington Blvd.
Fort Wayne, IN 46803
Ph: (260)422-5561
Free: 800-937-2448
Co. E-mail: admissions@indianatech.edu
URL: http://www.indianatech.edu
Contact: Karl W. Einolf, President
Facebook: www.facebook.com/indianatech
Linkedin: www.linkedin.com/school/indiana-tech
X (Twitter): x.com/indianatech
Instagram: www.instagram.com/indianatech
YouTube: www.youtube.com/user/IndianaTechFW
Description: Offers industrial-quality production-level hardware and software, and staff expertise. Provides consulting and seminars in computer-aided design.

39484 ■ Indiana State University Small Business Development Center
30 N 7th St.
Terre Haute, IN 47809
Ph: (812)237-7676
Free: 800-227-7232
Fax: (812)237-7675
Co. E-mail: westcentral@isbdc.org
URL: http://www.indstate.edu/business/SBDC
Contact: Courtney Richey, Regional Director
Description: Provides consulting, seminars, training, and access to economic databases. **Geographic Preference:** State.

39485 ■ Indiana University - Indiana Molecular Biology Institute
Simon Hall MSB1
212 S Hawthorne Dr.
Bloomington, IN 47405-7003
URL: http://biochemistry.indiana.edu/labs-facilities/iu-facilities/imbi.html
Contact: Matt Bochman, Director
Description: Offers expertise and use of its facilities for industrial research in molecular and cellular biology. **Founded:** 1983.

39486 ■ Indiana University - Kelley School of Business - Indiana Business Research Center (IBRC)
1309 E 10th St.
Bloomington, IN 47405
Co. E-mail: ibrc@iu.edu
URL: http://ibrc.kelley.iu.edu
Contact: Carol O. Rogers, Director
E-mail: rogersc@iu.edu
Facebook: www.facebook.com/IUibrc
Linkedin: www.linkedin.com/company/indiana-business-research-center
X (Twitter): x.com/IUibrc
Description: Collects and analyses business and economic data in the state. Information is accessible through the Indiana Information Retrieval System at libraries, universities, and public agencies. Puts out two bimonthly publications. Presents a Business Outlook Panel annually in several cities. **Scope:** Indiana's economic development, population trends, state and local economic indicators, and information technology. **Founded:** 1925. **Publications:** *Indiana Business Review* (Quarterly); *InContext* (Bimonthly); *Indiana Business Review (IBR)* (Quarterly).

39487 ■ Purdue University Technical Assistance Program (TAP)
2550 NW Ave., Ste. 1300
West Lafayette, IN 47906-4158
Ph: (765)494-9188
Fax: (765)496-6990
Co. E-mail: tap@purdue.edu
URL: http://tap.purdue.edu
Contact: Mat Trampski, Executive Director
E-mail: mtrampsk@purdue.edu
Description: Provides technology transfers to businesses free of charge. **Founded:** 1986.

SCORE OFFICES

39488 ■ Greater Wabash Valley SCORE
8000 S Education Dr.
Terre Haute, IN 47802
Ph: (812)298-2452
Co. E-mail: ch.admin0661@scorevolunteer.org
URL: http://greaterwabashvalley.score.org
Contact: Chris Fitzgerald, Founder
X (Twitter): x.com/ScoreWabash
Description: Promotes business and community development in the Terre Haute, IN area. Conducts business education seminars and workshops to those wanting to start a business. **Geographic Preference:** Local.

39489 ■ Indianapolis SCORE
PO Box 40192
Indianapolis, IN 46240
Ph: (317)934-0056
Co. E-mail: indyscore@scorevolunteer.org
URL: http://www.score.org/indianapolis
Contact: Douglas Willard, Contact
Facebook: www.facebook.com/SCOREIndianapolis
Linkedin: www.linkedin.com/company/scorementorsindianapolis
YouTube: www.youtube.com/channel/UCJ4c7JQzH7ZCxq_e_0Bd9gw
Description: Consults those who want to start a new business or grow an existing business. **Founded:** 1964. **Geographic Preference:** Local.

39490 ■ Northwest Indiana SCORE
162 W Lincolnway
Valparaiso, IN 46383
Ph: (219)654-2630
Co. E-mail: help@score.org
URL: http://nwindiana.score.org
Contact: Scott Harkins, Chairman of the Board
Facebook: www.facebook.com/SCORENWIndiana
Instagram: www.instagram.com/score_mentors
YouTube: www.youtube.com/user/SCORESmallBusiness
Pinterest: www.pinterest.com/scorementors
Founded: 1964.

STATE LISTINGS

Indiana ■ 39510

39491 ■ SCORE - Anderson
1303 E 5th St.
Anderson, IN 46012
Ph: (765)641-3063
Co. E-mail: indyscore@scorevolunteer.org
URL: http://indianapolis.score.org/contact-in
dianapolis-score
Description: Provides professional guidance and information to maximize the success of existing and emerging small businesses. Offers business counseling and workshops.

39492 ■ SCORE - Angola
Trine University Innovation One Bldg.
One University Ave.
Angola, IN 46703
URL: http://www.score.org/northeastindiana
Description: Provides professional guidance and information to maximize the success of existing and emerging small businesses. Offers business counseling and workshops.

39493 ■ *Score eNews*
URL: http://www.score.org/node/145651
Contact: Mr. Bob Straub, Chairman
URL(s): www.score.org/newsletters/archive
Released: Monthly **Price:** free. **Description:** Offers latest trends and resources to help small business succeed. **Availability:** Print; Online.

39494 ■ SCORE - Evansville
318 Main St., Ste. 223
Evansville, IN 47708
Ph: (812)426-6144
Fax: (812)492-4301
Co. E-mail: help@score.org
URL: http://evansville.score.org
Contact: Kim Howard, Regional Director
E-mail: khoward@isbdc.org
Linkedin: www.linkedin.com/company/score-mentors
-evansville
X (Twitter): x.com/SCOREEvansville
Description: Provides professional guidance and information to maximize the success of existing and emerging small businesses. Offers business counseling and workshops. **Geographic Preference:** Local.

39495 ■ *SCORE ExpertAnswers*
URL: http://www.score.org/node/145651
Contact: Mr. Bob Straub, Chairman
URL(s): www.score.org/expertanswers
Released: Monthly **Price:** free. **Description:** Brings marketplace trends and advice from small business experts and industry leaders. **Availability:** Print; Online.

39496 ■ SCORE - Fishers
10305 Allisonville Rd.
Fishers, IN 46038
Ph: (317)226-7264
Co. E-mail: indyscore@scorevolunteer.org
URL: http://indianapolis.score.org/contact-in
dianapolis-score
Description: Provides professional guidance and information to maximize the success of existing and emerging small businesses. Offers business counseling and workshops.

39497 ■ SCORE - Greater Wabash Valley
8000 S Education Dr.
Terre Haute, IN 47802
Ph: (812)298-2452
Co. E-mail: scorechapter661@aol.com
URL: http://www.score.org/greaterwabashvalley
Contact: William Carper, Contact
X (Twitter): x.com/ScoreWabash
Description: Provides professional guidance and information to maximize the success of existing and emerging small businesses. Offers business counseling and workshops.

39498 ■ SCORE - Greenwood
65 Airport Pky., Ste. 140
Greenwood, IN 46143
Ph: (317)886-8601
Co. E-mail: indyscore@gmail.com

URL: http://indianapolis.score.org/contact-in
dianapolis-score
Description: Provides professional guidance and information to maximize the success of existing and emerging small businesses. Offers business counseling and workshops.

39499 ■ SCORE - Hammond
5233 Hohman Ave.
Hammond, IN 46320
Ph: (219)654-2630
URL: http://nwindiana.score.org/find-location?state
=IN
Description: Provides professional guidance and information to maximize the success of existing and emerging small businesses. Offers business counseling and workshops.

39500 ■ SCORE - Huntington, Indiana
305 Warren St.
Huntington, IN 46750
Ph: (260)356-5300
URL: http://www.score.org/northeastindiana/about/
mentoring-locations
Description: Provides professional guidance and information to maximize the success of existing and emerging small businesses. Offers business counseling and workshops.

39501 ■ SCORE - Indianapolis
1484 Evenstar Blvd.
Indianapolis, IN 46280
Ph: (317)934-0056
Co. E-mail: indyscore@scorevolunteer.org
URL: http://indianapolis.score.org
Contact: Bridget Weston, Chief Executive Officer
Facebook: www.facebook.com/SCOREIndianapolis
Linkedin: www.linkedin.com/company/scorementorsin
dianapolis
YouTube: www.youtube.com/channel/UCJ
4c7JQzH7ZCxq_e_0Bd9gw
Description: Provides professional guidance and information to maximize the success of existing and emerging small businesses. Offers business counseling and workshops.

39502 ■ SCORE - Kendallville
122 S Main St.
Kendallville, IN 46755
Ph: (260)347-1554
URL: http://www.score.org/northeastindiana/content/
contact-score-northeast-indiana
Description: Provides professional guidance and information to maximize the success of existing and emerging small businesses. Offers business counseling and workshops.

39503 ■ SCORE - Merrillville
440 W 84th Dr.
Merrillville, IN 46410
Ph: (219)654-2630
Co. E-mail: help@score.org
URL: http://nwindiana.score.org
Description: Provides professional guidance and information to maximize the success of existing and emerging small businesses. Offers business counseling and workshops.

39504 ■ SCORE - Northeast Indiana [SCORE - Fort Wayne]
Inside NIIC Center - Rm. C 104
3201 Stellhorn Rd.
Fort Wayne, IN 46802
Ph: (260)422-2601
Co. E-mail: ch.admin0050@scorevolunteer.org
URL: http://www.score.org/northeastindiana
Facebook: www.facebook.com/SCORENortheastIn
diana
Linkedin: www.linkedin.com/company/score-mentors
-northeast-indiana
Description: Provides professional guidance and information to maximize the success of existing and emerging small businesses. Offers business counseling and workshops. **Founded:** 1976. **Geographic Preference:** Local.

39505 ■ SCORE - Northwest Indiana [SCORE - Valparaiso]
162 W Lincolnway
Valparaiso, IN 46383
Ph: (219)654-2630
Co. E-mail: nwinscore@gmail.com
URL: http://www.score.org/nwindiana
Contact: Maria J. Rojas, Contact
Facebook: www.facebook.com/SCORENWIndiana
Linkedin: www.linkedin.com/company/score-mentors
-northwest-indiana-score
Description: Provides professional guidance and information to maximize the success of existing and emerging small businesses. Offers business counseling and workshops. **Founded:** 1964.

39506 ■ SCORE - South Central Indiana
500 Franklin St.
Columbus, IN 47201
Ph: (812)379-4457
Fax: (812)378-7308
Co. E-mail: help@score.org
URL: http://www.score.org/southcentralindiana
Contact: Marcos A. Prata, Contact
Facebook: www.facebook.com/ScoreSouthCentralIn
diana
Linkedin: www.linkedin.com/company/score-mentors
-south-central-indiana
X (Twitter): x.com/ScoreEast
Description: Provides professional guidance and information to maximize the success of existing and emerging small businesses. Offers business counseling and workshops. **Founded:** 1977. **Geographic Preference:** Local.

39507 ■ SCORE - South Central Indiana [SCORE - Bloomington]
Ivy Tech Life Sciences Bldg.
501 N Profile Pkwy.
Bloomington, IN 47404
Ph: (812)379-4457
Fax: (812)378-7308
Co. E-mail: ch.admin0419@scorevolunteer.org
URL: http://southcentralindiana.score.org/contact-sou
th-east-indiana-score
Facebook: www.facebook.com/ScoreSouthCentralIn
diana
Linkedin: www.linkedin.com/company/score-mentors
-south-east-indiana
X (Twitter): twitter.com/ScoreEast
Description: Provides professional guidance and information to maximize the success of existing and emerging small businesses. Offers business counseling and workshops.

39508 ■ SCORE - South East Indiana [Bloomington SCORE]
501 N Profile Pky.
Bloomington, IN 47404
Ph: (812)379-4457
URL: http://southeastindiana.score.org
Description: Serves a wide range of clients from the central Indiana area. Conducts business education seminars and workshops to those wanting to start a business. **Geographic Preference:** Local.

39509 ■ SCORE - Warsaw
523 S Buffalo St.
Warsaw, IN 46580
Ph: (574)267-6311
URL: http://www.score.org/northeastindiana/about/
mentoring-locations
Contact: Michelle Goble, Contact
URL(s): www.score.org/find-location
Description: Provides professional guidance and information to maximize the success of existing and emerging small businesses. Offers business counseling and workshops.

BETTER BUSINESS BUREAUS

39510 ■ Better Business Bureau of Central Indiana [Better Business Bureau]
2601 Fortune Cir., Dr. E, No. 103A
Indianapolis, IN 46241
Ph: (317)488-2222

39511 ■ Indiana

Free: 855-833-1173
Fax: (317)488-2224
Co. E-mail: info@indybbb.org
URL: http://www.bbb.org/local-bbb/bbb-serving-central-indiana
Contact: Tim Maniscalo, President
E-mail: tmaniscalo@indybbb.org
Facebook: www.facebook.com/BBBCentralIN
Linkedin: www.linkedin.com/company/better-business-bureau-of-central-indiana
X (Twitter): x.com/BBBCentralIN
Instagram: www.instagram.com/bbbcentralin
YouTube: www.youtube.com/channel/UCJcMgh6nbPeYU9CEo-oM8EQ

Description: Seeks to promote and foster the highest ethical relationship between businesses and the public through voluntary self-regulation, consumer and business education, and service excellence. Provides information to help consumers and businesses make informed purchasing decisions and avoid costly scams and frauds; settles consumer complaints through arbitration and other means. **Founded:** 1916. **Geographic Preference:** Local.

39511 ■ Better Business Bureau of Northern Indiana
4011 Parnell Ave.
 Fort Wayne, IN 46805
Free: 800-552-4631
Fax: (260)423-3301
Co. E-mail: info@northernindiana.bbb.org
URL: http://www.bbb.org/local-bbb/bbb-serving-northern-indiana
Facebook: www.facebook.com/BBBNIN
Linkedin: www.linkedin.com/company/bbbnorthernin
X (Twitter): x.com/bbbnorthernin
Instagram: www.instagram.com/northernindianabbb
YouTube: www.youtube.com/user/BBBNorthernIndiana

Description: Strives to establish a relationship between businesses and the public through self-regulation, service, and consumer and business education. **Founded:** 1920. **Geographic Preference:** Local.

39512 ■ Tri-State Better Business Bureau
3101 N Green River Rd., Ste. 410
 Evansville, IN 47715
Ph: (812)473-0202
Fax: (812)473-3080
URL: http://www.bbb.org/evansville
Contact: Cathryn E. Eichele, President
Facebook: www.facebook.com/tristatebbb
Linkedin: www.linkedin.com/company/ti-state-better-business-bureau
X (Twitter): x.com/tristatebbb
Instagram: www.instagram.com/tristatebbb
YouTube: www.youtube.com/user/tristatebbb
Pinterest: www.pinterest.com/tristateb

Description: Seeks to promote and foster the highest ethical relationship between businesses and the public through voluntary self-regulation, consumer and business education, and service excellence. Provides information to help consumers and businesses make informed purchasing decisions and avoid costly scams and frauds; settles consumer complaints through arbitration and other means. **Geographic Preference:** Regional.

CHAMBERS OF COMMERCE

39513 ■ Angola Area Chamber of Commerce (AACC)
907 S Wayne St., Bldg. A, Ste. 110
 Angola, IN 46703
Ph: (260)665-3512
Co. E-mail: officeadmin@angolachamber.org
URL: http://www.angolachamber.org
Contact: Eric Yoder, Vice President
Facebook: www.facebook.com/angolachamber
Linkedin: www.linkedin.com/in/angola-chamber-of-commerce
X (Twitter): x.com/AngolaChamber
Instagram: www.instagram.com/angolainchamber

Description: Promotes business and community development in Angola, IN. Maintains industrial committee. **Founded:** 1937. **Publications:** *Business to Business* (Monthly); *Industrial Directory*. **Geographic Preference:** Local.

39514 ■ Avon Chamber of Commerce (ACOC)
8244 E US Hwy. 36, Ste. 140
 Avon, IN 46123
Ph: (317)272-4333
Co. E-mail: info@avonchamber.org
URL: http://www.avonchamber.org
Contact: Melissa Yetter, President
Facebook: www.facebook.com/AvonChamber
X (Twitter): x.com/avonindiana
Instagram: www.instagram.com/avonchamber

Description: Promotes the continuous improvement of the quality of life in the Avon community through the pursuit of new business, cultural, social and economic education of the citizen by providing accurate and timely assistance to the business community. **Geographic Preference:** Local.

39515 ■ Batesville Area Chamber of Commerce
301 Shopping Village
 Batesville, IN 47006
Ph: (812)934-3101
URL: http://batesvillein.com
Contact: Tricia Miller, Executive Director
E-mail: tmiller@batesvillein.com
Facebook: www.facebook.com/BatesvilleAreaChamber

Description: Provides its members with networking, marketing and advertising opportunities, and business counseling and referral services. **Geographic Preference:** Local.

39516 ■ *The Beacon*
200 E Michigan Blvd.
 Michigan City, IN 46360
Ph: (219)874-6221
Co. E-mail: info@mcachamber.com
URL: http://mcachamber.com
Contact: Katie Eaton, President
E-mail: keaton@mcachamber.com
URL(s): mcachamber.com/the-beacon

Released: Weekly **Description:** Contains information, hot topics, current projects and deadlines. **Availability:** Online.

39517 ■ Bedford Area Chamber of Commerce
1116 16th St.
 Bedford, IN 47421
Ph: (812)275-4493
Co. E-mail: bedford@bedfordchamber.com
URL: http://bedfordchamber.com
Contact: Shance Sizemore, Chief Executive Officer
E-mail: shance@bedfordchamber.com

Description: Promotes business and community development in the Bedford, IN area. **Founded:** 1916. **Publications:** *Chamber Advantage* (Monthly). **Geographic Preference:** Local.

39518 ■ Berne Chamber of Commerce (BCC)
205 E Main St.
 Berne, IN 46711
Ph: (260)589-8080
Fax: (260)589-8384
Co. E-mail: info@bernein.com
URL: http://bernein.com
Contact: Susan Buckingham, Executive Director
Facebook: www.facebook.com/BerneChamber

Description: Represents industries, professional service firms, and retailers interested in promoting business and community development in Berne, IN. Sponsors Swiss Day Festival. Conducts tours and provides tourist information for sites throughout the U.S. and Switzerland. **Founded:** 1914. **Publications:** *Swiss Days*; *Briefs*. **Awards:** Berne Chamber of Commerce Business of the Year (Annual); Berne Chamber of Commerce Citizen of the Year (Annual); Berne Chamber of Commerce Lifetime Achievement Award (Annual). **Geographic Preference:** Local.

39519 ■ *BizVoice*
115 W Washington St., Ste. 850 S
 Indianapolis, IN 46204
Ph: (317)264-3110
Fax: (317)264-6855
Co. E-mail: info@indianachamber.com
URL: http://www.indianachamber.com
Contact: Kevin Brinegar, President
E-mail: kbrinegar@indianachamber.com
URL(s): www.bizvoicemagazine.com

Ed: Tom Schuman. **Released:** Quarterly **Price:** $25. 20, Nonmembers. **Description:** Features the Indiana business environment. **Availability:** Print; Online.

39520 ■ Boone County Chamber of Commerce
221 N Lebanon St.
 Lebanon, IN 46052
Ph: (765)482-1320
URL: http://www.boonechamber.org
Contact: Don Barrett, Co-President
Facebook: www.facebook.com/boonecountychamberofcommerce

Description: Promotes business and community development in Boone County, IN. **Founded:** 1919. **Publications:** *C of C News* (Bimonthly). **Geographic Preference:** Local.

39521 ■ Brown County Chamber of Commerce
211 S Van Buren St.
 Nashville, IN 47448
Ph: (812)988-0234
Co. E-mail: info@thebrowncountychamber.org
URL: http://thebrowncountychamber.org
Contact: Greg Fox, President
E-mail: greg@nashvillespicecompany.com
Facebook: www.facebook.com/browncountychamberofcommerce

Description: Promotes business and community development in Brown County, IL. **Geographic Preference:** Local.

39522 ■ Brownsburg Chamber of Commerce
1411 S Green St., Ste. 230
 Brownsburg, IN 46112
Ph: (317)852-7885
Co. E-mail: chamber@brownsburg.com
URL: http://www.brownsburg.com
Contact: Rhonda Wiles, Executive Director
Facebook: www.facebook.com/BrownsburgChamber
Linkedin: www.linkedin.com/company/brownsburg-chamber-of-commerce
X (Twitter): x.com/BBurgChamber
Instagram: www.instagram.com/brownsburgchamber

Description: Promotes business and community development in the Brownsburg, IN area. Sponsors annual Olde Fashioned Fall Festival and annual golf tournament. **Founded:** 1982. **Geographic Preference:** Local.

39523 ■ *Chamber Check*
105 N Market St.
 Rockville, IN 47872
Ph: (765)569-5565
Co. E-mail: pcchamberdirector@gmail.com
URL: http://parkecountychamber.com
Contact: Donna McVay, President
URL(s): parkecountychamber.wordpress.com
Availability: Print.

39524 ■ Chamber of Commerce of Harrison County
111 W Walnut St.
 Corydon, IN 47112
Ph: (812)738-0120
Co. E-mail: llong@harrisonchamber.org
URL: http://www.harrisonchamber.org
Contact: Lisa Long, President
E-mail: llong@harrisonchamber.org
Facebook: www.facebook.com/CCofHC

Description: Promotes business and community development in Harrison County, IN. **Founded:** 1933. **Publications:** *Directory/Business Profile Booklet* (Annual). **Awards:** Harrison County Chamber of Commerce Chairman's Award (Annual). **Geographic Preference:** Local.

39525 ■ *Chamber Page in the Versailles Republican*
220 E US Hwy. 50, Ste. A
Versailles, IN 47042
Ph: (812)689-6654
Co. E-mail: ripleycc@ripleycountychamber.org
URL: http://ripleycountychamber.org
Contact: Justin Smith, President
URL(s): ripleycountychamber.org/membership-benefits
Released: Quarterly **Availability:** Print; Online.

39526 ■ *Chamber Scene*
40 E Franklin St., Ste. 121
Huntington, IN 46750
Ph: (260)356-5300
Fax: (260)200-1222
Co. E-mail: info@huntington-chamber.com
URL: http://www.huntington-chamber.com
Contact: Steve Kimmel, Executive Director
E-mail: skimmel@huntington-chamber.com
URL(s): www.huntington-chamber.com/news/chamber-newsletters
Released: Monthly **Availability:** PDF.

39527 ■ Clinton County Chamber of Commerce
62 N Main St.
Frankfort, IN 46041
Ph: (765)654-5507
Fax: (765)654-9592
URL: http://discoverclintoncounty.com
Contact: Shan Sheridan, Chief Executive Officer
Facebook: www.facebook.com/ccchamberofcommerce
X (Twitter): x.com/cc_chamber1914
Instagram: www.instagram.com/clintonco_chamber
Description: Promotes business and community development in Clinton County, IN. **Founded:** 1830. **Geographic Preference:** Local.

39528 ■ Columbus Area Chamber of Commerce, Inc. (CACC)
500 Franklin St.
Columbus, IN 47201-6214
Ph: (812)379-4457
Co. E-mail: info@columbusareachamber.com
URL: http://business.columbusareachamber.com
Contact: Cindy Frey, President
E-mail: cfrey@columbusareachamber.com
Description: Promotes business and community development in the Columbus, IN area. **Founded:** 1890. **Publications:** *Chamber Connection* (Monthly). **Geographic Preference:** Local.

39529 ■ Crawfordsville & Montgomery County Chamber of Commerce (CMCCC)
101 W Main st., Ste. 412
Crawfordsville, IN 47933
Ph: (765)362-6800
Co. E-mail: info@crawfordsvillechamber.com
URL: http://www.crawfordsvillechamber.com
Contact: Jill Knowling, Secretary
Description: Businesses promoting economic development, tourism, and community and political involvement in Montgomery County, IN. **Founded:** 1918. **Publications:** *Chamber Newsletter* (Weekly); *Community Information Directory* (Biennial). **Geographic Preference:** Local.

39530 ■ Crossroads Regional Chamber of Commerce
440 W 84th Dr.
Merrillville, IN 46410
Ph: (219)769-8180
Co. E-mail: chamberinfo@crossroadschamber.org
URL: http://www.crossroadschamber.org
Contact: Deann Patena, President
E-mail: deann@crossroadschamber.org
Facebook: www.facebook.com/crossroadschamber
Linkedin: www.linkedin.com/company/crossroads-regional-chamber-of-commerce
X (Twitter): x.com/crossroadschamb
Instagram: www.instagram.com/crossroadsregionalchamber
Description: Promotes business and economic development in Merrillville, IN. **Founded:** 1954. **Geographic Preference:** Local.

39531 ■ Culver Chamber of Commerce
Culver, IN
Ph: (574)842-5253
Co. E-mail: culverchamberofcommerce@gmail.com
URL: http://culverchamber.org
Contact: Becky Furry, President
Facebook: www.facebook.com/culverindianachamber
Description: Promotes business and community development in the Culver, IN area. **Founded:** 1925. **Publications:** *Destination Culver* (Semiannual). **Geographic Preference:** Local.

39532 ■ Dearborn County Chamber of Commerce (DCC)
320 Walnut St.
Lawrenceburg, IN 47025
Ph: (812)537-0814
Free: 800-322-8198
Fax: (812)537-0845
URL: http://dearborncountychamber.org
Contact: Eric Kranz, Executive Director
E-mail: ekranz@dearborncountychamber.org
Facebook: www.facebook.com/DearbornCountyChamber
X (Twitter): x.com/Dc3Info
YouTube: www.youtube.com/channel/UCBP_oz8s1IDzatAhPLMv0kw
Description: Promotes business and community development in Dearborn County, IN. **Founded:** 1987. **Publications:** *Chamber Express* (Monthly). **Geographic Preference:** Local.

39533 ■ Decatur Chamber of Commerce (DCC)
125 E Monroe St.
Decatur, IN 46733
Ph: (260)724-2604
Co. E-mail: info@decaturchamber.org
URL: http://www.decaturchamber.org
Contact: Dane Wheeler, President
Facebook: www.facebook.com/Decatur-Chamber-of-Commerce-247044823536
Description: Promotes business, economic, workforce development, and community in Decatur, IN. Sponsors Callithumpian parade, community smorgasbord, Riverside Festival, city-wide sidewalk sale, golf outing, and Holiday Open House. **Founded:** 1903. **Publications:** *Chamber Charger* (Monthly); *Community Service Directory* (Periodic); *Industrial Directory*. **Geographic Preference:** Local.

39534 ■ Demotte Chamber of Commerce
327 N Halleck St.
Demotte, IN 46310
Ph: (219)987-5800
Fax: (219)987-5800
Co. E-mail: info@demottechamber.org
URL: http://demottechamber.org
Contact: Mitch Mullen, President
Description: Promotes business and community development in DeMotte, IN. **Founded:** 1981. **Geographic Preference:** Local.

39535 ■ Duneland Chamber of Commerce
220 Broadway
Chesterton, IN 46304
Ph: (219)926-5513
Co. E-mail: info@dunelandchamber.org
URL: http://www.dunelandchamber.org
Contact: Maura Mundell, President
E-mail: maura@dunelandchamber.org
Facebook: www.facebook.com/DunelandChamber
Linkedin: www.linkedin.com/company/duneland-chamber-of-commerce/about
X (Twitter): x.com/DunelandChamb8r
Description: Serves its members and foster innovative businesses, educational, cultural and government environment. Represents vibrant business organization of small and large businesses, professionals, and interested individuals, whose focus is to market the Duneland area, encourage new growth and assist existing and expanding businesses. Joining the Chamber is an economical and effective way to make new contacts and market your business. **Founded:** 1957. **Publications:** *Duneland Today* (Quarterly). **Geographic Preference:** Local.

39536 ■ *Duneland Today*
220 Broadway
Chesterton, IN 46304
Ph: (219)926-5513
Co. E-mail: info@dunelandchamber.org
URL: http://www.dunelandchamber.org
Contact: Maura Mundell, President
E-mail: maura@dunelandchamber.org
URL(s): www.dunelandchamber.org/membership-benefits
Released: Quarterly **Availability:** Print; PDF.

39537 ■ *Embrace the Pace*
302 W Market St.
Nappanee, IN 46550
Ph: (574)773-7812
Fax: (574)773-4691
Co. E-mail: info@nappaneechamber.com
URL: http://www.nappaneechamber.com
Contact: Jeff Kitson, Executive Director
E-mail: jeff@nappaneechamber.com
URL(s): www.nappaneechamber.com/about-1
Availability: Print.

39538 ■ Franklin Chamber of Commerce (FCC)
120 E Jefferson St.
Franklin, IN 46131
Ph: (317)736-6334
Co. E-mail: franklincoc@franklincoc.org
URL: http://www.franklincoc.org
Contact: Rosie Chambers, Executive Director
Facebook: www.facebook.com/FranklinCoC
Linkedin: www.linkedin.com/company/franklin-chamber-of-commerce
X (Twitter): x.com/FranklinChamber
Instagram: www.instagram.com/franklininchamber
Description: Promotes business and community development in the Franklin, IN area. Sponsors Heritage Festival. **Founded:** 1920. **Publications:** *Depot Signal* (Monthly); *Franklin Chamber of Commerce Directory* (Annual). **Geographic Preference:** Local.

39539 ■ French Lick West Baden Chamber of Commerce
8102 W State Rd., 56
West Baden Springs, IN 47469
Ph: (812)936-3418
Co. E-mail: info@visitfrenchlickwestbaden.com
URL: http://www.visitfrenchlickwestbaden.com
Facebook: www.facebook.com/VisitFrenchLick
X (Twitter): x.com/visitfrenchlick
Instagram: www.instagram.com/visitfrenchlickwestbaden
Pinterest: www.pinterest.com/myfrenchlick
Description: Promotes business and community development in French Lick, IN. **Founded:** 2013. **Geographic Preference:** Local.

39540 ■ Gary Chamber of Commerce (GCC)
504 Broadway, Ste. 328
Gary, IN 46402
Ph: (219)885-7407
Co. E-mail: garychamber@garychamber.com
URL: http://garychamber.com
Contact: Charles Hughes, President
E-mail: chughes@garychamber.com
Facebook: www.facebook.com/GaryChamberofCommerce
X (Twitter): x.com/GaryChamber
Description: Promotes business and community development in the Gary, IN area. **Founded:** 1907. **Publications:** *Potential* (Quarterly). **Geographic Preference:** Local.

39541 ■ Goshen Chamber of Commerce
232 S Main St.
Goshen, IN 46526
Ph: (574)533-2102
Fax: (574)533-2103
Co. E-mail: goshenchamber@goshen.org
URL: http://goshen.org

39542 ■ Indiana

Contact: Nick Kieffer, President
E-mail: nkieffer@goshen.org
Facebook: www.facebook.com/
goshenchamberofcommerce
X (Twitter): x.com/goshenchamber
Description: Promotes business and community development in Goshen, IN. **Founded:** 1954. **Publications:** *Image*. **Geographic Preference:** Local.

39542 ■ The Greater Bloomington Chamber of Commerce
421 W 6th St., Ste. A
Bloomington, IN 47404
Ph: (812)336-6381
Co. E-mail: info@chamberbloomington.org
URL: http://www.chamberbloomington.org
Contact: Eric Spoonmore, President
E-mail: espoonmore@chamberbloomington.org
Linkedin: www.linkedin.com/company/chamberbloom
X (Twitter): x.com/ChamberBloom
Description: Promotes business and community development in the Bloomington, IN area. **Founded:** 1915. **Geographic Preference:** Local.

39543 ■ Greater Danville Chamber of Commerce
49 N Wanye St., Ste. 100
Danville, IN 46122
Ph: (317)745-0670
Fax: (317)745-0682
URL: http://www.danvillechamber.org
Contact: Kelly DiBenedetto, Executive Director
E-mail: kelly@danvillechamber.org
Facebook: www.facebook.com/DanvilleCOC
X (Twitter): x.com/DanvChamberIN
Description: Promotes business and community development in Danville, IN. Holds monthly board meeting. **Founded:** 1991. **Geographic Preference:** Local.

39544 ■ Greater Elkhart County Chamber of Commerce (GECC)
418 S Main St.
Elkhart, IN 46516
Ph: (574)293-1531
Fax: (574)294-1859
Co. E-mail: info@elkhart.org
URL: http://www.elkhart.org
Contact: Levon Johnson, President
Facebook: www.facebook.com/ElkhartChamber
Linkedin: www.linkedin.com/company/greater-elkhart-chamber
X (Twitter): x.com/ElkhartChamber
YouTube: www.youtube.com/channel/UCdTuo5wgdJikIBT_ogb7-Tg
Description: Represents the business community in problem solving, promoting economic development, transportation issues, and downtown development. **Founded:** 1926. **Publications:** *Business Resource Guide*; *Elkhart County Manufacturers Directory*; *Elkhart County Major Employers Directory*; *Elkhart County Manufacturers Labels*; *Elkhart County Recreational Vehicle Directory*. **Awards:** Eartha Awards (Annual); Fairbanks Award (Annual); Greater Elkhart Chamber of Commerce Not for Profit of the Year (Annual); Greater Elkhart Chamber of Commerce Business of the Month (Annual); Greater Elkhart Chamber of Commerce Small Business of the Year (Annual). **Geographic Preference:** Local.

39545 ■ Greater Fort Wayne Chamber of Commerce
200 E Main St., Ste. 800
Fort Wayne, IN 46802
Ph: (260)420-6945
Fax: (260)240-4280
Co. E-mail: info@greaterfortwayneinc.com
URL: http://www.greaterfortwayneinc.com
Contact: Brenda Gerber Vincent, Officer
E-mail: bgerbervincent@gfwinc.com
Facebook: www.facebook.com/GreaterFortWayneInc
Linkedin: www.linkedin.com/company/greater-fort-wayne-inc
X (Twitter): x.com/GreaterFWInc
Instagram: www.instagram.com/greaterfortwayneinc

Description: Promotes business and community development in the Ft. Wayne, IN area. **Publications:** *Update* (Biweekly); *Emphasis* (Quarterly; Bimonthly). **Geographic Preference:** Local.

39546 ■ Greater Greencastle Chamber of Commerce
2 S Jackson St.
Greencastle, IN 46135
Ph: (765)653-4517
Co. E-mail: gchamber@gogreencastle.com
URL: http://goputco.com/message-from-the-director
Description: Promotes and stimulates business, increasing the value of chamber membership to create more opportunities through economic growth and the improved quality of life in the Greencastle, IN area. **Founded:** 1954. **Publications:** *Chamber Chimes* (Monthly). **Geographic Preference:** Local.

39547 ■ Greater Kokomo Economic Development Alliance
Greater Kokomo Economic Development Alliance
700 E Firmin St., Ste. 200
Kokomo, IN 46902
Ph: (765)457-2000
URL: http://www.greaterkokomo.com
Contact: Charles Sparks, Co-President Co-Chief Executive Officer
E-mail: csparks@greaterkokomo.com
Facebook: www.facebook.com/greaterkokomoalliance
Linkedin: www.linkedin.com/company/greater-kokomo-economic-development-alliance
X (Twitter): x.com/greaterkokomo
Description: Promotes business and community development in Howard County, IN. **Founded:** 2009. **Geographic Preference:** Local.

39548 ■ Greater Martinsville Chamber of Commerce
464 S Main St.
Martinsville, IN 46151
Ph: (765)342-8110
Co. E-mail: info@martinsvillechamber.com
URL: http://www.martinsvillechamber.com
Contact: Jamie Taylor, Co-President Co-Chief Executive Officer
Facebook: www.facebook.com/MartinsvilleChamber.IN
X (Twitter): x.com/ChamberMville
YouTube: www.youtube.com/channel/UCYPg5BW3ny89iYkGNDZsRHw
Description: Promotes business and community development in Martinsville, IN. **Geographic Preference:** Local.

39549 ■ Greater Monticello Chamber of Commerce & White County Visitors Bureau
c/o James Mann, Clerk
Treasurer
225 N Main St.
Monticello, IN 47960
Ph: (574)583-5712
Fax: (574)583-9244
Co. E-mail: clerktreasurer@monticelloin.gov
URL: http://www.monticelloin.gov
Contact: James Mann, Treasurer
E-mail: clerktreasurer@monticelloin.gov
Facebook: www.facebook.com/GreaterMonticelloChamber
Description: Strives to build a favorable business government and community environment to enhance the quality of life in Greater Monticello, IN. **Founded:** 1972. **Geographic Preference:** Local.

39550 ■ Greater Scott County Chamber of Commerce
90 N Main St.
Scottsburg, IN 47170
Ph: (812)752-4080
Co. E-mail: scottcom@c3bb.com
URL: http://www.scottchamber.org
Contact: Syd Whitlock, President
E-mail: swhitlock@newwashbank.com
Facebook: www.facebook.com/ScottCountyChamberofCommerce
X (Twitter): x.com/ScottCoChamber1

YouTube: www.youtube.com/channel/UCW-86dybvoMT0bplrxXzbow
Description: Promotes business, industry, and agriculture through the advancement of education, quality of life, environmental awareness, and tourism in Scott County, IN. **Founded:** 1991. **Publications:** *Chamber Exchange* (Monthly). **Geographic Preference:** Local.

39551 ■ Greater Seymour Chamber of Commerce (GSCC)
105 S Chestnut St.
Seymour, IN 47274
Ph: (812)522-3681
Co. E-mail: info@seymourchamber.com
URL: http://www.jacksoncochamber.com
Contact: Dan Robison, Director
Description: Promotes business and community development in the Seymour, IN area. Sponsors art show. **Founded:** 1931. **Geographic Preference:** Local.

39552 ■ Greater Valparaiso Chamber of Commerce (GVCC)
162 W Lincolnway
Valparaiso, IN 46383
Ph: (219)462-1105
Co. E-mail: info@valpochamber.org
URL: http://www.valpochamber.org
Contact: Rex G. Richards, President
E-mail: rex@valpochamber.org
Facebook: www.facebook.com/valpochamber
Instagram: www.instagram.com/valpochamber
Description: Promotes business and community development in the Valparaiso, IN area. **Founded:** 1912. **Publications:** *Valpo Chamber Membership Directory*; *Valpo Chamber's U-Guide*; *Valparaiso Magazine* (Quarterly). **Geographic Preference:** Local.

39553 ■ Greater Zionsville Chamber of Commerce
1475 W Oak St.
Zionsville, IN 46077
Ph: (317)873-3836
Co. E-mail: info@zionsvillechamber.org
URL: http://www.zionsvillechamber.org
Contact: Erica Carpenter, President
Facebook: www.facebook.com/ZvilleChamber
Linkedin: www.linkedin.com/company/zionsville-chamber-of-commerce
X (Twitter): x.com/zvillechamber
Instagram: www.instagram.com/zionsvillechamber
Description: Promotes business and community development in the Zionsville, IN area. Sponsors annual country market, street dance, and village tour of homes. **Founded:** 1961. **Publications:** *Greater Zionsville Chamber of Commerce Newsletter*; *Membership Directory and Research Guide*. **Geographic Preference:** Local.

39554 ■ Greenfield Area Chamber of Commerce
1 Courthouse Plz.
Greenfield, IN 46140
Ph: (317)477-4188
Fax: (317)477-4189
Co. E-mail: info2@greenfieldcc.org
URL: http://www.greenfieldcc.org
Contact: Retta Livengood, President
Description: Promotes business and community development in the Greenfield, IN area. **Founded:** 1951. **Publications:** *Connection* (Monthly). **Educational Activities:** Awards Dinner (Annual). **Awards:** Greenfield Area Chamber of Commerce Non-Profit Community Service of the Year Award. **Geographic Preference:** Local.

39555 ■ Greensburg Decatur County Chamber of Commerce (GDC)
314 W Washington St.
Greensburg, IN 47240
Ph: (812)663-2832
Fax: (812)663-4275
Co. E-mail: info@greensburgchamber.com
URL: http://www.greensburgchamber.com
Contact: Barb Bohman, Treasurer

E-mail: bbohman@rbskpartners.com
Facebook: www.facebook.com/gdcchamber
Description: Local businesses and individuals united to promote economic and community development in the Greensburg, IN area. **Founded:** 1906. **Publications:** *Annual Business Directory* (Annual). **Geographic Preference:** Local.

39556 ■ HighlandGriffith Chamber of Commerce
8536 Kennedy Ave.
Highland, IN 46322
Ph: (219)923-3666
Fax: (219)923-3704
Co. E-mail: info@highlandgriffithchamber.com
URL: http://highlandgriffithchamber.com
Contact: Gina Ribota, President
X (Twitter): x.com/highlandin_coc
Description: Promotes business and community development in Highland, IN. **Publications:** *The Chamber News* (Monthly). **Geographic Preference:** Local.

39557 ■ Hobart Chamber of Commerce
1001 Lillian St.
Hobart, IN 46342
Ph: (219)942-5774
Co. E-mail: info@hobartchamber.com
URL: http://hobartchamber.com
Contact: Jorge Gutierrez, President
E-mail: jorgegutierrez@allstate.com
Facebook: www.facebook.com/HobartChamber
Description: Strives to support and advance the best interests, commercial and industrial, of the members of this organization; to promote trade; to further industrial, professional and other worthy activities; and to serve constructively for the public welfare of the city, county, state and nation; and for these purposes to cooperate with other agencies and organizations. **Publications:** *Business Directory*; *Hobart Horizons* (Monthly); *Hobart Business Directory* (Annual); *Hobart Business Directory*. **Geographic Preference:** Local.

39558 ■ Huntington County Chamber of Commerce
40 E Franklin St., Ste. 121
Huntington, IN 46750
Ph: (260)356-5300
Fax: (260)200-1222
Co. E-mail: info@huntington-chamber.com
URL: http://www.huntington-chamber.com
Contact: Steve Kimmel, Executive Director
E-mail: skimmel@huntington-chamber.com
Facebook: www.facebook.com/HuntingtonCountyChamber
Linkedin: www.linkedin.com/company/huntington-county-chamber-of-commerce/about
Description: Promotes community, economic and industrial development in Huntington, IN. Works to retain and improve present business and industry. Sponsors A. B.I.G. Day (golf tournament), annual Heritage Days, Scholarship Recognition, Administrative Assistants Day, and Huntington County EXPO. Works to recruit new business along with partners such as HCUED, and Venture Works. **Publications:** *Chamber Scene* (Monthly); *Civic and Organization Guide* (Annual); *Huntington City and County Map* (Biennial); *Industrial Guide* (Annual); *Personnel Management Association: Wage and Benefit Study* (Annual); *Program of Action* (Annual); *Visions of Huntington County, Indiana* (Biennial). **Geographic Preference:** Local.

39559 ■ Indiana Chamber of Commerce (ICC) - Library
115 W Washington St., Ste. 850 S
Indianapolis, IN 46204
Ph: (317)264-3110
Fax: (317)264-6855
Co. E-mail: info@indianachamber.com
URL: http://www.indianachamber.com
Contact: Kevin Brinegar, President
E-mail: kbrinegar@indianachamber.com
Facebook: www.facebook.com/indianachamber
Linkedin: www.linkedin.com/company/indiana-chamber-of-commerce

X (Twitter): x.com/IndianaChamber/with_replies
Instagram: www.instagram.com/indianachamber
YouTube: www.youtube.com/user/INChamber
Description: Businesses and other organizations. Promotes free enterprise, and the preservation and advancement of the business climate. Monitors legislative activity. Holds seminars and workshops. **Scope:** Indiana business, economic development and management issues. **Services:** Library open to members of Indiana Chamber of Commerce. **Founded:** 1922. **Holdings:** Figures not available. **Publications:** *BizVoice* (Quarterly); *Indiana Chamber of Commerce--Business Directory & Resource Guide* (Annual); *Indiana General Assembly Legislative Directory*; *Executive Quickline* (Monthly); *Outlook* (Bimonthly); *Indiana Chamber of Commerce--Business Directory & Resource Guide*. **Geographic Preference:** State.

39560 ■ *Indianapolis Monthly City Guide*
111 Monument Cir., Ste. 1950
Indianapolis, IN 46204
Ph: (317)464-2200
Co. E-mail: communications@indychamber.com
URL: http://indychamber.com
Contact: Michael Huber, Officer
E-mail: mhuber@indychamber.com
URL(s): www.indianapolismonthly.com
Facebook: www.facebook.com/IndianapolisMonthly
X (Twitter): x.com/IndyMonthly
Instagram: www.instagram.com/IndyMonthly
Released: Monthly **Price:** $60, for print only 36 issue; $42, for print only 24 issue; $24, for print only 12 issue; $5.95, Single issue. **Availability:** Print; Online.

39561 ■ *Industrial and Business Directory*
210 S Wabash St.
Wabash, IN 46992-3132
Ph: (260)563-1168
Fax: (260)563-6920
URL: http://www.wabashchamber.org
Contact: Jason Callahan, Chairman of the Board
Released: Periodic **Availability:** Print; Online.

39562 ■ Indy Chamber
Indy Chamber
111 Monument Cir., Ste. 1950
Indianapolis, IN 46204
Ph: (317)464-2200
Co. E-mail: communications@indychamber.com
URL: http://indychamber.com
Contact: Michael Huber, Officer
E-mail: mhuber@indychamber.com
X (Twitter): x.com/ButlerCountyCDC
Instagram: www.instagram.com/indychamber
Description: Promotes business and community development in Indianapolis, IN. **Founded:** 1890. **Publications:** *Catalyst* (Semiannual); *Greater Indianapolis Metropolitan Manufacturers* (Triennial); *Indianapolis Chamber of Commerce Membership Directory* (Annual); *Indianapolis City Guide* (Annual); *FYI Local Government Directory and Issues Agenda*; *Greater Indianapolis Not-For-Profit Directory* (Semiannual); *Coalition for Minority Business Development Resource Directory* (Annual); *Indianapolis Monthly City Guide* (Monthly); *Manufacturers Directory CD*; *Newcomer Booklet*. **Geographic Preference:** Local.

39563 ■ Jasper Chamber of Commerce (JCC)
302 W 6th St.
Jasper, IN 47547-0307
Ph: (812)482-6866
URL: http://jasperin.org
Contact: Christian Blome, Co-President
Description: Promotes business and community development in Jasper, IN. Sponsors annual Strassenfest. **Founded:** 1954. **Publications:** *Jasper Fact Book/Membership Directory* (Periodic); *Manufacturing and Business Directory* (Periodic). **Geographic Preference:** Local.

39564 ■ Kendallville Area Chamber of Commerce
122 S Main St.
Kendallville, IN 46755-1716
Ph: (260)347-1554
Co. E-mail: membership@kendallvillechamber.com

URL: http://kendallvillechamber.com
Contact: Sharon Montoya, Executive Director
Facebook: www.facebook.com/KendallvilleAreaChamberOfCommerce
Description: Promotes business and community development in Kendallville, IN. **Founded:** 1925. **Publications:** *Chamber Connection* (Bimonthly). **Geographic Preference:** Local.

39565 ■ Knightstown Indiana Chamber of Commerce
120 E Main St.
Knightstown, IN 46148
URL: http://www.knightstown.in/business_in_knightstown/knightstown_chamber_of_commerce.php
Description: Promotes business and community development in Knightstown, IN area. **Founded:** 1950. **Geographic Preference:** Local.

39566 ■ Knox County Chamber of Commerce (KCCC)
702 Main St.
Vincennes, IN 47591
Ph: (812)882-6440
Co. E-mail: info@knoxcountychamber.com
URL: http://www.knoxcountychamber.com
Contact: Jamie Neal, President
Facebook: www.facebook.com/KnoxCountyChamberOfCommerce
Linkedin: www.linkedin.com/company/knox-county-chamber
YouTube: www.youtube.com/channel/UCLc1dqBx0kQ9pfTirILRO8g
Description: Promotes business and community development in Knox County, IN. **Founded:** 1916. **Geographic Preference:** Local.

39567 ■ Kosciusko Chamber of Commerce
523 S Buffalo St.
Warsaw, IN 46580
Ph: (574)267-6311
Co. E-mail: info@kchamber.com
URL: http://www.kchamber.com
Contact: Rob Parker, President
E-mail: rparker@kchamber.com
X (Twitter): x.com/KosciuskoCOC
Description: Promotes business and community development in Warsaw, IN area. **Founded:** 1911. **Publications:** *The Kosciusko Business Insights* (Monthly). **Geographic Preference:** Local.

39568 ■ La Porte Economic Advancement Partnership (GLCC)
605 Michigan Ave.
La Porte, IN 46350
Ph: (219)324-8584
URL: http://laportepartnership.com
Contact: Bert Cook, Executive Director
Facebook: www.facebook.com/LaPortePartnership
X (Twitter): x.com/GLPCC
Instagram: www.instagram.com/explore/locations/775922045/la-porte-economic-advancement-partnership
Description: Businesses, professional firms, and individuals who promote business and economic development in La Porte, IN. Seeks to retain and expand business and industry in the area. **Founded:** 1930. **Publications:** *LaPorte Area Industrial Directory*; *Business Today* (Semiannual); *LaPorte Business Resource Guide* (Annual). **Geographic Preference:** Local.

39569 ■ LaGrange County Chamber of Commerce
901 S Detroit St.
LaGrange, IN 46761
Ph: (260)463-2443
Fax: (260)463-2683
URL: http://www.lagrangechamber.org
Contact: Andy Linder, President
Description: Provides leadership for the promotion and advancement of economic vitality and quality of life in LaGrange County. **Publications:** *Chamber News*. **Geographic Preference:** Local.

39570 ■ Lakeshore Chamber of Commerce (LCC)
7120 Indianapolis Blvd.
  Hammond, IN 46324-2221
Ph: (219)931-1000
Fax: (219)937-8778
Co. E-mail: info@lakeshorechamber.com
URL: http://www.lakeshorechamber.com
Contact: Dave Ryan, Executive Director
E-mail: dryan@lakeshorechamber.com
Description: Enhances the economic environment of its local business community. **Founded:** 1912. **Publications:** *News and Views* (Quarterly); *Community Directory and Buyers Guide* (Biennial); *Greater Hammond Community Map*; *Greater Hammond Transit Map*; *Summer Events Tabloid* (Annual). **Geographic Preference:** Local.

39571 ■ Ligonier Chamber of Commerce (LCC)
PO Box 121
  Ligonier, IN 46767-0121
Ph: (260)894-9909
Co. E-mail: chamber@ligtel.com
URL: http://www.ligonierindianachamber.org
Description: Promotes business and community development in Ligonier, IN. Helps sponsor Ligonier festival. **Founded:** 1935. **Geographic Preference:** Local.

39572 ■ Linton-Stockton Chamber of Commerce (LSCC)
159 NW 1st St.
  Linton, IN 47441
Ph: (812)847-4846
Fax: (812)847-0246
Co. E-mail: info@lintonchamber.org
URL: http://lintonchamber.org
Contact: Jathan Wright, President
Facebook: www.facebook.com/lintonstocktonchamber
Description: Businesses, civic clubs, fraternal organizations, and interested individuals. Promotes business and community development in Stockton Township, IN. Sponsors Linton Freedom Festival. **Founded:** 1929. **Publications:** *Chamber of Commerce Newsletter* (Monthly). **Geographic Preference:** Local.

39573 ■ Logansport - Cass County Chamber of Commerce
311 S 5th St.
  Logansport, IN 46947
Ph: (574)753-6388
Co. E-mail: info@logan-casschamber.com
URL: http://www.logan-casschamber.com
Contact: Bill Cuppy, Executive Director
E-mail: bill@logan-casschamber.com
Facebook: www.facebook.com/logansportcasschamber
Description: Promotes business and community development in Cass County, IN. **Founded:** 1938. **Publications:** *On Target* (Monthly). **Geographic Preference:** Local.

39574 ■ Madison Area Chamber of Commerce (MACC)
301 E Main St.
  Madison, IN 47250
Ph: (812)265-3135
Co. E-mail: info@madisonindiana.com
URL: http://www.madisonindiana.com
Contact: Lindsay Bloos, Executive Director
E-mail: lbloos@madisonindiana.com
Description: Retail businesses, educational and professional organizations, and clubs. Promotes business and community development in the area. Sponsors annual expos, fairs, and festivals. **Founded:** 1924. **Publications:** *Chamber Insight* (Monthly); *Community Information Directory* (Annual). **Geographic Preference:** Local.

39575 ■ Madison County Chamber (MCC)
1106 Meridian St., Ste. 109
  Anderson, IN 46016
Ph: (765)642-0264
Co. E-mail: info@getlinkedmadison.com
URL: http://www.madisoncochamber.com
Contact: Clayton Whitson, President
E-mail: clayton@getlinkedmadison.com
Facebook: www.facebook.com/GetLinkedMadison
X (Twitter): x.com/GetLinkdMadison
Description: Represents retail, commercial, manufacturing, and professional firms promoting community and economic development in the Anderson, IN area. **Founded:** 1914. **Publications:** *The Business Edge* (Monthly). **Geographic Preference:** Local.

39576 ■ Marion-Grant County Chamber of Commerce
217 S Adams St.
  Marion, IN 46952
Ph: (765)664-5107
Fax: (765)668-5443
Co. E-mail: rhonda@marionchamber.org
URL: http://www.marionchamber.org
Contact: Kylie Jackson, President
E-mail: kylie@marionchamber.org
Facebook: www.facebook.com/mariongrantcountychamberofcommerce
X (Twitter): x.com/MarionChamber
YouTube: www.youtube.com/user/marionchamber
Description: Promotes business and community development in Grant County, IN. **Founded:** 1909. **Publications:** *Momentum* (Monthly). **Educational Activities:** Business Trade Fair. **Awards:** Marion-Grant County Chamber of Commerce Chairman's Award (Annual); Marion-Grant County Chamber of Commerce ATHENA Award (Annual). **Geographic Preference:** Local.

39577 ■ Martin County Chamber of Commerce (MCCC)
210 N Line St.
  Loogootee, IN 47553
Contact: Noel Harty, President
Description: Serves as a voice of the business community in Martin County, IN. Supports business development and growth. Provides statistics, historical data and recommendations regarding the climate of business and business trends. **Geographic Preference:** Local.

39578 ■ Mentone Chamber of Commerce
105 E Main St.
  Mentone, IN 46539
Ph: (574)353-7417
Co. E-mail: valleyrs11@rtcol.com
URL: http://www.mentoneeggcity.com
Contact: Rita Simpson, President
Facebook: www.facebook.com/Mentone-Chamber-of-Commerce-159211237476586
Description: Promotes business and community development in the Mentone, IN area. **Geographic Preference:** Local.

39579 ■ Miami County Chamber of Commerce (MCCC)
13 E Main St.
  Peru, IN 46970
Ph: (765)472-1923
Fax: (765)472-7099
Co. E-mail: info@miamicochamber.com
URL: http://www.miamicochamber.com
Contact: Sandy Chittum, President
Description: Promotes business, community development, and tourism in the Miami County, IN area. **Founded:** 1916. **Publications:** *Chamber News Connection* (Monthly); *Directory of Clubs and Organizations*; *Industrial Directory*. **Educational Activities:** Board Retreat. **Geographic Preference:** Local.

39580 ■ Michigan City Area Chamber of Commerce
200 E Michigan Blvd.
  Michigan City, IN 46360
Ph: (219)874-6221
Co. E-mail: info@mcachamber.com
URL: http://mcachamber.com
Contact: Katie Eaton, President
E-mail: keaton@mcachamber.com
X (Twitter): x.com/michamber
Description: Promotes business and community development in the Michigan City, IN area. **Founded:** 1918. **Publications:** *The Beacon* (Weekly); *Lakeview* (Bimonthly). **Geographic Preference:** Local.

39581 ■ Muncie-Delaware County Chamber of Commerce
401 S High St.
  Muncie, IN 47308
Ph: (765)288-6681
Co. E-mail: info@muncie.com
URL: http://www.muncie.com
Facebook: www.facebook.com/MuncieDelawareCountyChamber
Linkedin: www.linkedin.com/company/muncie-delaware-county-chamber-of-commerce
X (Twitter): x.com/munciecoc
Description: Promotes business and community development in Delaware County, IN. **Founded:** 1894. **Publications:** *Community Profile* (Biennial); *Horizons* (Monthly); *Manufacturer Directory for Muncie-Delaware County* (Annual); *Quality of Life*. **Geographic Preference:** Local.

39582 ■ Munster Chamber of Commerce
1005 Ridge Rd.
  Munster, IN 46321
Ph: (219)836-5549
Fax: (219)836-5551
Co. E-mail: info@chambermunster.org
URL: http://www.munsterchamber.org
Contact: Brad Hemingway, Chairman of the Board
E-mail: joseph.hemingway@hdvest.net
Facebook: www.facebook.com/pages/Munster-Chamber-of-Commerce/122753254409072
Description: Business, industry, and professional individuals interested in promoting business and community development in Munster, IN. Sponsors annual Breakfast with Santa, Blues, Jazz and Arts on the Ridge Festival. **Founded:** 1955. **Publications:** *Chamber Newsletter* (Weekly); *Munster Business Handbook* (Annual). **Awards:** Munster Chamber of Commerce Beautification Award (Annual). **Geographic Preference:** Local.

39583 ■ Nappanee Area Chamber of Commerce
302 W Market St.
  Nappanee, IN 46550
Ph: (574)773-7812
Fax: (574)773-4691
Co. E-mail: info@nappaneechamber.com
URL: http://www.nappaneechamber.com
Contact: Jeff Kitson, Executive Director
E-mail: jeff@nappaneechamber.com
Facebook: www.facebook.com/NappaneeChamberOfCommerce
Description: Promotes business, community, and industrial development in the Nappanee, IN area. Sponsors Apple Festival. **Founded:** 1880. **Publications:** *Embrace the Pace*. **Geographic Preference:** Local.

39584 ■ New Castle-Henry County Chamber of Commerce
100 S Main St., Ste. 108
  New Castle, IN 47362
Ph: (765)529-5210
Fax: (765)521-7408
Co. E-mail: info@nchcchamber.com
URL: http://www.nchcchamber.com
Contact: Cindi Kiner, President
Facebook: www.facebook.com/nchcchamber
X (Twitter): x.com/nchcchamber
Description: Promotes business and community development in the New Castle and Henry County, IN area. **Founded:** 1889. **Publications:** *Chamber Commentary* (Monthly). **Awards:** New Castle-Henry County Chamber of Commerce Business of the Year (Annual); New Castle-Henry County Chamber of Commerce Citizen of the Year (Annual). **Geographic Preference:** Local.

39585 ■ New Palestine Area Chamber of Commerce (NPACC)
42 E Main St.
  New Palestine, IN 46163

Ph: (317)861-2345
Co. E-mail: info@newpalestinechamber.org
URL: http://www.newpalestinechamber.org
Contact: Steve Harris, President
URL(s): newpalchamber.org
X (Twitter): x.com/newpalchamber
Instagram: www.instagram.com/newpalchamber
Description: Promotes business and community development in the New Palestine, IN area. **Founded:** 1955. **Geographic Preference:** Local.

39586 ■ Noblesville Chamber of Commerce (NCC)
PO Box 2015
Noblesville, IN 46061
Ph: (317)773-0086
Co. E-mail: info@noblesvillechamber.com
URL: http://www.noblesvillechamber.com
Contact: Bob Dubois, President
E-mail: bob@noblesvillechamber.com
Facebook: www.facebook.com/
noblesvillechamberofcommerce
Description: Represents businesses, organizations, industries, and individuals promoting business and community development in the Noblesville, IN area. **Founded:** 1935. **Publications:** *The Chamber Enterprise* (Monthly); *Community Information Directory* (Biennial); *Monthly Memo*. **Geographic Preference:** Local.

39587 ■ North Manchester Chamber of Commerce (NMCC)
North Manchester, IN
Ph: (987)654-3210
Co. E-mail: email@northmanchesterchamber.com
URL: http://www.northmanchesterchamber.com
Contact: Sebrena Cline, Chairman
Description: Serves as a community leader fostering projects and programs that will promote the economic health, welfare and development of business in North Manchester area. **Founded:** 1948. **Publications:** *Chamber Notes*. **Awards:** North Manchester Chamber of Commerce Business of the Year (Annual); North Manchester Chamber of Commerce Citizen of the Year (Annual); North Manchester Chamber of Commerce Industry of the Year (Annual). **Geographic Preference:** Local.

39588 ■ North Webster Tippecanoe Township Chamber of Commerce (NWTT)
102 S Morton St.
North Webster, IN 46555
Ph: (574)834-7076
Co. E-mail: nwttchamber@gmail.com
URL: http://nwtt-chamber.square.site
Contact: Emily Shipley, President
Facebook: www.facebook.com/NWTTChamber
Instagram: www.instagram.com/nwttchamber
Description: Promotes business and community development in the North Webster, IN area. **Founded:** 1974. **Geographic Preference:** Local.

39589 ■ Northern Hamilton County Chamber of Commerce
70 N Byron St.
Cicero, IN 46034-5019
URL: http://northernhamiltoncountychamber.com
Description: Promotes business and community development in Hamilton County. **Founded:** 1981. **Geographic Preference:** Local.

39590 ■ One Southern Indiana Chamber and Economic Development
4100 Charlestown Rd.
New Albany, IN 47150
Ph: (812)945-0266
Fax: (812)948-4664
Co. E-mail: info@1si.org
URL: http://1si.org
Contact: Wendy Dant Chesser, President
E-mail: wendy@1si.org
Facebook: www.facebook.com/OneSouthernIndiana
X (Twitter): x.com/1SI_Chamber
Description: Promotes economic and community development in Clark and Floyd counties, IN. **Founded:** 1985. **Publications:** *Report from the Chamber* (Monthly). **Geographic Preference:** Local.

39591 ■ OneZone
8770 N St., Ste. 100B
Fishers, IN 46038
Ph: (317)436-4653
Co. E-mail: info@onezonecommerce.com
URL: http://www.onezonechamber.com
Contact: Jack Russell, President
E-mail: jack@onezonecommerce.com
Facebook: www.facebook.com/OneZoneChamber
Linkedin: www.linkedin.com/company/one-zone
-chamber
X (Twitter): x.com/onezonechamber
Instagram: www.instagram.com/onezonechamber
Description: Enhances members' success, fosters economic growth and contributes to community's quality of life. Sponsors monthly luncheons, networking breakfasts and business after hours events, Taste of the Chamber, Autumn Faire and Golf Classic. **Founded:** 2015. **Publications:** *Business to Business Connection* (Monthly); *Guide to Carmel* (Annual); *Business Bulletin* (Monthly); *Community Directory* (Biennial). **Geographic Preference:** Local.

39592 ■ Orleans Chamber of Commerce (OCC)
PO Box 9
Orleans, IN 47452
Ph: (812)865-9930
Fax: (812)865-3413
URL: http://historicorleans.com
Contact: Lisa Simundson, Executive Director
E-mail: lsimundson@orleanscapecod.o
Description: Promotes business and community development in the area. **Founded:** 1815. **Geographic Preference:** Local.

39593 ■ Owen County Chamber of Commerce and Economic Development Corp.
119 S Main St.
Spencer, IN 47460
Ph: (812)829-3245
Co. E-mail: marce@myowencountychamber.com
URL: http://www.myowencountychamber.com
Contact: Kim Hodges, Co-President
Facebook: www.facebook.com/owenchamberedc
Description: Promotes existing businesses, community & economic development and tourism in Owen County, Indiana. **Publications:** *Business Life* (Quarterly); *News Letter*; *Owen County Business Directory*. **Geographic Preference:** Local.

39594 ■ Paoli Chamber of Commerce
200 W Ct., Ste.
Paoli, IN 47454
Ph: (812)723-4769
Co. E-mail: info@paolichamber.com
URL: http://paolichamber.com
Contact: Gretchen Anderson, Contact
Description: Promotes business and industry in and around Paoli, IN. **Founded:** 1816. **Geographic Preference:** Local.

39595 ■ Parke County Chamber of Commerce
105 N Market St.
Rockville, IN 47872
Ph: (765)569-5565
Co. E-mail: pcchamberdirector@gmail.com
URL: http://parkecountychamber.com
Contact: Donna McVay, President
Facebook: www.facebook.com/ParkeCoun
tyChamberOfCommerce
Description: Promotes business and community development in the Parke County, IN area. **Founded:** 1946. **Publications:** *Chamber Check*. **Geographic Preference:** Local.

39596 ■ Pike County Chamber of Commerce
801 E Main St.
Petersburg, IN 47567
Ph: (812)354-8155
Co. E-mail: chamber@pikecounty.in.gov
URL: http://www.pikecountyin.org
Description: Promotes business and community development in the Pike County, IN. **Geographic Preference:** Local.

39597 ■ Plainfield Chamber of Commerce
101 W Main St.
Plainfield, IN 46168
Ph: (317)839-3800
Fax: (317)839-9670
Co. E-mail: chamber@town.plainfield.in.us
URL: http://www.plainfield-in.com
Contact: Brad DuBois, President
Description: Promotes continuous improvement of commerce in Plainfield by taking leadership in community development through actively supporting and promoting social, economic, cultural, and educational activities. **Founded:** 1967. **Geographic Preference:** Local.

39598 ■ Plymouth Area Chamber of Commerce
120 N Michigan St.
Plymouth, IN 46563
Ph: (574)936-2323
Co. E-mail: plychamber@plychamber.org
URL: http://www.plychamber.org
Contact: Amanda Petrucelli, Co-President
Facebook: www.facebook.com/PlyChamber
X (Twitter): x.com/PlyChamber
Description: Promotes business and community development in the Plymouth, IN area. **Publications:** *Industrial Directory*; *NewsMonth* (Monthly). **Geographic Preference:** Local.

39599 ■ *Program of Action*
40 E Franklin St., Ste. 121
Huntington, IN 46750
Ph: (260)356-5300
Fax: (260)200-1222
Co. E-mail: info@huntington-chamber.com
URL: http://www.huntington-chamber.com
Contact: Steve Kimmel, Executive Director
E-mail: skimmel@huntington-chamber.com
URL(s): www.huntington-chamber.com/membership/
reasons-to-join
Released: Annual **Availability:** Print; PDF.

39600 ■ *Quality of Life*
401 S High St.
Muncie, IN 47308
Ph: (765)288-6681
Co. E-mail: info@muncie.com
URL: http://www.muncie.com
URL(s): muncie.com/site-selection-data/strategic-a
dvantages
Availability: Print.

39601 ■ Ripley County Chamber of Commerce
220 E US Hwy. 50, Ste. A
Versailles, IN 47042
Ph: (812)689-6654
Co. E-mail: ripleycc@ripleycountychamber.org
URL: http://ripleycountychamber.org
Contact: Justin Smith, President
Facebook: www.facebook.com/ripleycountychamber
Description: Promotes business and community development in Ripley County Versailles, IN area. **Founded:** 1992. **Publications:** *Chamber Page in the Versailles Republican* (Quarterly); *Chamber Page in the Versailles Republican* (Quarterly). **Geographic Preference:** Local.

39602 ■ Rush County Chamber of Commerce
315 N Main St.
Rushville, IN 46173
Ph: (765)932-2880
Fax: (765)932-5610
Co. E-mail: rushcountychamber@gmail.com
URL: http://rushcounty.com
Contact: Deborah Ripberger, Contact
Description: Promotes business and community development in Rush County, IN. **Publications:** *Chamber Made* (Quarterly). **Geographic Preference:** Local.

39603 ■ St. John Chamber of Commerce (SJCOC)
9495 Keilman St.
Saint John, IN 46373
Ph: (219)365-4686

Fax: (219)365-4602
Co. E-mail: office@stjohndyerchamber.com
URL: http://stjohndyerchamber.com
Contact: Samantha Alberico, President
Facebook: www.facebook.com/StJohnDyerChamber
Description: Promotes business and community development in the St. John, IN area. **Geographic Preference:** Local.

39604 ■ Schererville Chamber of Commerce
122 E Joliet St.
 Schererville, IN 46375
Ph: (219)322-5412
Fax: (219)322-0598
Co. E-mail: scherervillechamberin@gmail.com
URL: http://scherervillechamber.com
Contact: Mark Jonas, President
Facebook: www.facebook.com/
 TheScherervilleChamber
Description: Promotes business and economic development in Schererville, IN. **Geographic Preference:** Local.

39605 ■ Shelby County Chamber of Commerce (SCCC)
501 N Harrison St.
 Shelbyville, IN 46176
Ph: (317)398-6647
Free: 800-318-4083
Fax: (317)392-3901
Co. E-mail: chamberinfo@shelbychamber.net
URL: http://shelbychamber.net
Contact: Nathan Runnebohm, President
Facebook: www.facebook.com/
 ShelbyCoChamberofCommerce
Linkedin: www.linkedin.com/company/shelby-county
 -chamber-of-commerce-indiana-
X (Twitter): x.com/ShelbyCoC_IN
Instagram: www.instagram.com/shelbycochamberin
YouTube: www.youtube.com/channel/UC6VzLA1Jp
 2XIQS87Ku9zu3g
Description: Promotes business and community development in Shelby County, IN. **Founded:** 1948. **Publications:** *Industrial Directory*. **Geographic Preference:** Local.

39606 ■ South Bend Regional Chamber (SBRC)
101 N Michigan St., Ste. 300
 South Bend, IN 46601
Ph: (574)234-0051
Co. E-mail: info@sbrchamber.com
URL: http://www.sbrchamber.com
Contact: Jeff Rea, President
E-mail: jrea@sbrchamber.com
Facebook: www.facebook.com/southbendchamber
X (Twitter): x.com/southbendchmbr
YouTube: www.youtube.com/channel/UCTjLw_bCjtK
 2C--cPmUQyPQ
Description: Seeks to serve the interests of member businesses through progressive leadership, advocacy and services. **Founded:** 1909. **Publications:** *Book for Business* (Annual); *Chamber@Work* (Monthly). **Geographic Preference:** Local.

39607 ■ Spencer County Regional Chamber of Commerce
2792 N US Hwy. 231., Ste. 100
 Rockport, IN 47635
Ph: (812)649-2186
Co. E-mail: kathy@spencercountychamber.org
Contact: Kathy Reinke, Director
E-mail: kathy@spencercountychamber.org
Facebook: www.facebook.com/SpencerCoun
 tyChamber
Description: Consists of regional businesses in Spencer County, IN dedicated to the progress and growth of the area. **Geographic Preference:** Local.

39608 ■ Starke County Chamber of Commerce
400 N Heaton St.
 Knox, IN 46534
Ph: (574)772-5548
Co. E-mail: info@starkecountychamber.com
URL: http://starkecountychamber.com
Contact: Jerry Gurrado, President
Facebook: www.facebook.com/starkecountychamber
Linkedin: www.linkedin.com/company/starke-county
 -chamber-of-commerce
Description: Promotes business and community development in the Knox, IN area. Sponsors annual Business fair. Maintains Starke County Fine Arts Commission. Conducts Harvest Days Festival and Harvest Day Parade. **Founded:** 1863. **Awards:** Henry F. Schricker Award (Annual). **Geographic Preference:** Local.

39609 ■ *Swiss Days*
205 E Main St.
 Berne, IN 46711
Ph: (260)589-8080
Fax: (260)589-8384
Co. E-mail: info@bernein.com
URL: http://bernein.com
Contact: Susan Buckingham, Executive Director
URL(s): swissdaysberne.com
Released: Latest Issue 2023 . **Availability:** PDF.

39610 ■ Syracuse-Wawasee Chamber of Commerce
207 N Huntington St.
 Syracuse, IN 46567
Ph: (574)457-5637
Co. E-mail: info@swchamber.com
URL: http://www.swchamber.com
Contact: Renea Salyer, Contact
E-mail: renea@swchamber.com
Facebook: www.facebook.com/swchamberoc
Instagram: www.instagram.com/swchamber
YouTube: www.youtube.com/channel/UCdE9
 5mWqCGEqiwmpCYjWS5g/videos
Description: Promotes business and community development in Syracuse, IN. Sponsors annual Syracuse Days and Holiday Magic. **Geographic Preference:** Local.

39611 ■ Terre Haute Chamber of Commerce (THCC)
630 Wabash Ave., Ste. 105
 Terre Haute, IN 47807
Ph: (812)232-2391
Co. E-mail: memberinfo@terrehautechamber.com
URL: http://www.terrehautechamber.com
Contact: Bernice Helman, Chairman
X (Twitter): x.com/THCofC
Description: Businesses, individuals, and professionals. Promotes business and community development in Wabash Valley, including west central Indiana and east central Illinois. **Founded:** 1913. **Publications:** *Valley Business Review* (Monthly); *Terre Haute Chamber of Commerce--Guide to Regional Manufacturers*. **Geographic Preference:** Local.

39612 ■ Tipton Chamber of Commerce (TCC)
119 W Madison St. St.
 Tipton, IN 46072
Ph: (765)675-7533
URL: http://tiptonchamber.org
Contact: Summer Tilley, President
X (Twitter): x.com/tiptonchamber
YouTube: www.youtube.com/channel/UCJv
 t8TWMiYoagT1jhObzBSw
Description: Promotes business and community development in the area. Sponsors parades and festivals. **Founded:** 1928. **Geographic Preference:** Local.

39613 ■ Tipton County Chamber of Commerce (TCCC)
119 W Madison St.
 Tipton, IN 46072
Ph: (765)675-7533
URL: http://www.tiptonchamber.org
Contact: Summer Tilley, President
Facebook: www.facebook.com/tiptoncountychamber
X (Twitter): x.com/tiptonchamber
Instagram: www.instagram.com/tiptoncountychamber
YouTube: www.youtube.com/channel/UCJv
 t8TWMiYoagT1jhObzBSw
Description: Businesses and individuals organized to promote economic and community development in Tipton County, IN. **Founded:** 1889. **Publications:** *Tipton County News and Views* (Quarterly). **Geographic Preference:** Local.

39614 ■ *Valparaiso Magazine*
162 W Lincolnway
 Valparaiso, IN 46383
Ph: (219)462-1105
Co. E-mail: info@valpochamber.org
URL: http://www.valpochamber.org
Contact: Rex G. Richards, President
E-mail: rex@valpochamber.org
URL(s): www.valpochamber.org/valparaiso-magazine
 .html
Released: Quarterly; winter, fall, summer and spring. **Description:** Features community highlights, people, community event calendar and chamber information. **Availability:** Download; Online.

39615 ■ Wakarusa Chamber of Commerce
100 W Waterford St.
 Wakarusa, IN 46573
Ph: (574)862-4344
Fax: (574)862-2245
Co. E-mail: chamber@wakarusachamber.com
URL: http://wakarusachamber.com
Contact: Deb Shively, Contact
Description: Strives to render constructive services for the promotion of the welfare of the community and citizens of Wakarusa, Indiana. **Publications:** *Chamber News*. **Geographic Preference:** Local.

39616 ■ Walkerton Area Chamber of Commerce (WACC)
612 Roosevelt Rd.
 Walkerton, IN 46574
Ph: (574)586-3100
Fax: (574)586-3469
URL: http://www.walkerton.org/business/chamber
Contact: Lisa Patton, President
E-mail: msrec.lp@gmail.com
Description: Promotes business and community development in Walkerton, IN. **Founded:** 1925. **Geographic Preference:** Local.

39617 ■ Warrick County Chamber of Commerce
224 W Main St., Ste. 203
 Boonville, IN 47601
Ph: (812)897-2340
Co. E-mail: info@warrickchamber.org
URL: http://www.warrickchamber.org
Contact: Shari Sherman, Executive Director
E-mail: ssherman@warrickchamber.org
Description: Promotes business and community development in Warrick County, IL. **Geographic Preference:** Local.

39618 ■ Wayne County Area Chamber of Commerce (WCACC)
33 S 7th St., Ste. 2
 Richmond, IN 47374
Ph: (765)962-1511
Co. E-mail: chamber@wcareachamber.org
URL: http://www.wcareachamber.org
Contact: Melissa Vance, President
E-mail: melissa@wcareachamber.org
Facebook: www.facebook.com/wcacc
X (Twitter): x.com/WCACC
YouTube: www.youtube.com/channel/UCnugBCz
 drCWMyA4QiKJsvIg
Description: Promotes business, industrial, civic, and community development in the Richmond-Wayne County IN area. Maintains small business development, regional manufacturing extension, and export assistance centers; sponsors professional women's network. **Founded:** 1955. **Publications:** *Chamber NewsLink* (Monthly). **Geographic Preference:** Local.

39619 ■ Wells County Chamber of Commerce
211 Water St.
 Bluffton, IN 46714
Ph: (260)824-0510
URL: http://wellscoc.com
Contact: Erin Prible, Executive Director

E-mail: eprible@wellscoc.com
Facebook: www.facebook.com/WellsCountyChamber
X (Twitter): x.com/WellsChamber
Description: Promotes the civic and economic development in Wells County. **Geographic Preference:** Local.

39620 ■ Whiting - Robertsdale Chamber of Commerce
1417 119th St.
  Whiting, IN 46394
Ph: (219)659-0292
Co. E-mail: wrchamber@wrchamber.com
URL: http://www.wrchamber.com
Contact: John Sopo, President
Facebook: www.facebook.com/wrchamber7
Description: Promotes business and community development in Whiting-Robertsdale, IN area. **Publications:** *Write Stuff* (Monthly). **Geographic Preference:** Local.

39621 ■ Whitley County Chamber of Commerce & Visitors Center
128 W Van Buren St.
  Roanoke, IN 46783
Ph: (260)248-8131
Co. E-mail: office@whitleychamber.com
URL: http://whitleychamber.org/newmember
Contact: Gary Parrett, President
Facebook: www.facebook.com/WhitleyCountyINChamber
Description: Promotes business and community development in the Columbia City, IN area. **Founded:** 1919. **Publications:** *The Chamber Impact* (Monthly). **Geographic Preference:** Local.

MINORITY BUSINESS ASSISTANCE PROGRAMS

39622 ■ Fort Wayne's Woman's Bureau - Women's Enterprise
2417 Fairfield Ave.
  Fort Wayne, IN 46807
URL: http://womensbureau.org/who-we-are/history-highlights
Description: Provides business counseling, mentoring, training, and other assistance to promote the growth of women-owned businesses.

39623 ■ Indiana Department of Administration (IDOA) - Minority & Women's Business Enterprises Div.
402 W Washington St., Rm. W462
  Indianapolis, IN 46204
Ph: (317)232-3061
Fax: (317)233-6921
Co. E-mail: mwbe@idoa.in.gov
URL: http://www.in.gov/idoa/mwbe/minority-and-womens-business-enterprises
Contact: Graham Melendez, Director, Business Development
E-mail: gmelendez@idoa.in.gov
Description: Supports minority and women's businesses in Indiana. **Founded:** 1983.

39624 ■ Indiana Department of Transportation - Economic Opportunity Division - Disadvantaged Business Enterprise Program
100 N Senate IGCN 925
  Indianapolis, IN 46204
URL: http://www.in.gov/indot/doing-business-with-indot/equity-initiative-services/dbe-acdbe-related/what-is-the-dbe-acdbe-program
Description: Promotes the securing of Department of Highways contracts by minority and women-owned businesses. Provides certification for these companies.

39625 ■ Indiana Small Business Development Center (ISBDC)
One North Capitol Ave., Ste., 700
  Indianapolis, IN 46204
Free: 888-472-3244
Co. E-mail: leadcenter@isbdc.org
URL: http://isbdc.org
Contact: Andrew Carty, Director
E-mail: ancarty@iedc.in.gov
Facebook: www.facebook.com/isbdc
Linkedin: www.linkedin.com/company/indiana-small-business-development-center-isbdc
X (Twitter): x.com/indiana_sbdc
Description: Providing entrepreneurs with the education, information and tools necessary to build successful businesses. **Scope:** Small business development. **Founded:** 1985. **Geographic Preference:** State.

39626 ■ Mid-States Minority Supplier Development Council
2126 N Meridian St.
  Indianapolis, IN 46202
Ph: (317)923-2110
Co. E-mail: info@midstatesmsdc.org
URL: http://www.midstatesmsdc.org
Contact: Carolyn E. Mosby, Chief Executive Officer
E-mail: cmosby@midstatesmsdc.org
Facebook: www.facebook.com/MidStatesMSDC
X (Twitter): x.com/midstatesmsdc
Instagram: www.instagram.com/midstatesmsdc
Description: Promotes purchases by corporations from minority businesses through training programs, a Business Opportunity Fair, meetings, and supplier and purchaser directories. **Founded:** 1976. **Publications:** *Directory of Minority Suppliers* (Annual). **Geographic Preference:** State.

FINANCING AND LOAN PROGRAMS

39627 ■ 1st Source Capital Corp.
1st Source Bank
  100 N Michigan St.
  South Bend, IN 46601
Ph: (574)235-2000
Free: 800-513-2360
Co. E-mail: 1stsource@1stsource.com
URL: http://www.1stsource.com
Contact: Andrea Short, President
Description: Firm provides personal and business banking services. **Founded:** 1863. **Preferred Investment Size:** $200,000 to $750,000. **Industry Preferences:** Communications and media, computer hardware and software, semiconductors and other electronics, medical and health, consumer related, industrial and energy, and transportation.

39628 ■ Cambridge Capital Management Corp.
4181 E 96th St., Ste. 200
  Indianapolis, IN 46240
Ph: (317)843-9704
Fax: (317)844-9815
URL: http://www.cambridgecapitalmgmt.com
Contact: Charles Kennedy, Contact
E-mail: ckennedy@cambridgecapitalmgmt.com
Linkedin: www.linkedin.com/company/cambridgecapitalmgmt
YouTube: www.youtube.com/channel/UChwvcgGdySTIF0cU6wCVOKg
Description: Firm are a managers of non-traditional sources of financing. **Founded:** 1983. **Preferred Investment Size:** $100,000 to $1,000,000.

39629 ■ CID Capital (CID)
10201 N Illinois St., Ste. 200
  Carmel, IN 46290
Ph: (317)818-5030
Fax: (317)644-2914
Co. E-mail: adam@cidcap.com
URL: http://cidcap.com
Contact: Cory Heck, Managing Director
E-mail: cory@cidcap.com
Description: Private equity firm for lower- to middle-market companies.

39630 ■ Elevate Ventures
50 E 91st St., Ste. 213
  Indianapolis, IN 46240
Ph: (317)975-1901
URL: http://elevateventures.com
Contact: Chris LaMothe, Chief Executive Officer
E-mail: clamothe@elevateventures.com
X (Twitter): x.com/elevatein
Description: Hybrid venture capital fund and entrepreneurial development partner. Creates sustainable cultures and infrastructure for entrepreneurs in Indiana. **Founded:** 2011.

39631 ■ Heron Capital Equity Partners
9245 N Meridian St., Ste. 101
  Indianapolis, IN 46260
Ph: (317)686-1950
Fax: (317)686-1954
URL: http://www.heroncap.com
Contact: Greg Maurer, Managing Director
E-mail: greg@heroncap.com
Description: Equity investment firm. **Investment Policies:** Experienced management teams; North American headquarters (with a preference for the Midwest); margin potential greater than 35%. **Industry Preferences:** Manufacturing; healthcare.

39632 ■ IU Angel Network
642 N Madison St., Ste. 113
  Bloomington, IN 47404
URL: http://iuventures.com/investors
Contact: Tedd Green, Co-Founder Chief Operating Officer
Description: Facilitates connections between high-potential startups and investors among Indiana University's community of alumni, faculty, staff, and students to foster an entrepreneurial culture the world.

39633 ■ VisionTech Angels
1220 Waterway Blvd., Ste. H108
  Indianapolis, IN 46202
Ph: (317)701-1711
URL: http://visiontech-partners.com
Contact: Ben Pidgeon, President
E-mail: bpidgeon@visiontech-partners.com
Facebook: www.facebook.com/VisionTechPartners
Linkedin: www.linkedin.com/company/visiontech-partners
X (Twitter): x.com/visiontechangel
Description: Delivers financial and strategic support to promising early-stage and early-growth technology-based startups in the Midwest. Offers business plan evaluation, strategic planning, marketing support, interim executive management, and other services. **Founded:** 2009. **Preferred Investment Size:** $200,000 to $500,000. **Investment Policies:** Large or rapidly growing market; strong management team; proprietary or innovative product/service with a scalable business model that addresses an industry or societal issue; market-ready platform technology or product; ability to attract future funding; credibly exit potential. **Industry Preferences:** Healthcare; information technology; agriculture; manufacturing.

39634 ■ VisionTech Partners, LLC
1220 Waterway Blvd., Ste. H108
  Indianapolis, IN 46202
Ph: (317)701-1711
URL: http://visiontech-partners.com
Contact: Ben Pidgeon, Executive Director
E-mail: bpidgeon@visiontech-partners.com
Facebook: www.facebook.com/VisionTechPartners
X (Twitter): x.com/visiontechangel
Description: Delivers financial and strategic support to promising early-stage and early-growth technology-based startups in the Midwest. **Founded:** 2009. **Preferred Investment Size:** $200,000 to $500,000. **Investment Policies:** Large or rapidly growing market; strong management team; proprietary or innovative product/service with a scalable business model that addresses an industry or societal issue; market-ready platform technology or product; ability to attract future funding; credibly exit potential. **Industry Preferences:** Healthcare; information technology; agriculture; manufacturing.

PROCUREMENT ASSISTANCE PROGRAMS

39635 ■ Indiana APEX Accelerator (PTAC)
5209 Hohman Ave.
  Indianapolis, IN 46204

URL: http://inapex.org
Linkedin: www.linkedin.com/company/indiana-apex-accelerator
Description: Provides marketing and technical assistance and workshop training assisting with all aspects of marketing to the federal, state and local governments. **Founded:** 1984.

INCUBATORS/RESEARCH AND TECHNOLOGY PARKS

39636 ■ CookSpring Shared Kitchen
1025 W Rudisill Blvd. Door N
Fort Wayne, IN 46807
Ph: (260)446-3226
Co. E-mail: info@cookspringfw.com
URL: http://www.cookspringfw.com
Instagram: www.instagram.com/cookspringfw
Description: Culinary incubator offering commercial kitchen space for culinary entrepreneurs so that they have a space to launch their businesses.

39637 ■ DeveloperTown
5255 Winthrop Ave.
Indianapolis, IN 46220
Free: 855-338-8696
Co. E-mail: info@developertown.com
URL: http://developertown.com
Contact: Alex Billingsley, Vice President, Engineering
E-mail: abillingsley@developertown.com
Facebook: www.facebook.com/developertown
X (Twitter): x.com/developertown
YouTube: www.youtube.com/channel/UCrYLOFF7nFpGKDXAA-KR9Yg
Description: Corporate innovators work with us to explore software solutions to support core business needs. By leveraging experience with startups, they help companies successfully understand the viability of potential software solutions and quickly bring them to market.

39638 ■ Evansville Regional Economic Partnership, Inc. (EREP)
318 Main St., Ste. 400
Evansville, IN 47708
URL: http://members.evansvilleregion.com/contact
Contact: Brandon McClish, Executive Director
Description: A small business incubator providing affordable office space, shared services, and business support necessary to create an atmosphere to greatly increase an emerging company's chances for success. Formerly Evansville Small Business Center. **Founded:** 1915. **Publications:** *Regional Industrial Directory* (Biennial).

39639 ■ Flagship Enterprise Center (FEC)
2705 Enterprise Dr.
Anderson, IN 46013
Ph: (765)622-0100
Co. E-mail: marketingadmin@flagshipenterprise.org
URL: http://www.flagshipenterprise.org
Contact: Terry Truitt, President
Facebook: www.facebook.com/flagshipenterprisecenter
Description: A facility supporting the needs of incubator graduates and qualified early stage companies that are transitioning to a permanent location within Anderson and Madison County. **Founded:** 2003.

39640 ■ Hammond INnovation Center (HIC)
5209 Hohman Ave.
Hammond, IN 46320
Ph: (219)750-1200
Fax: (219)750-1211
Co. E-mail: info@hicnwi.org
URL: http://hammonddevelopment.wordpress.com/hammond-innovation-center
Contact: Sue Anderson, Program Director
Facebook: www.facebook.com/pages/Hammond-INnovation-Center/107270085976764
X (Twitter): x.com/HICInnovates
Description: Firm focuses on fostering the growth and success of small business startups and offers competitively priced office space with built-in infrastructure.

39641 ■ Innovation Connector (IC)
1208 W White River Blvd.
Muncie, IN 47303
Ph: (765)285-4900
URL: http://innovationconnector.com
Contact: Ronald K. Fauquher, President
Facebook: www.facebook.com/innovationconnector
Linkedin: www.linkedin.com/company/muncie-innovation-connector-inc
X (Twitter): x.com/innovatemuncie
Description: Firm provides financial services, business consulting and coaching, networking and training services.

39642 ■ Inventrek Technology Park
Greater Kokomo Economic Development Alliance
700 E Firmin St., Ste. 200
Kokomo, IN 46902
Ph: (765)457-2000
URL: http://www.greaterkokomo.com
Contact: Charles Sparks, President
E-mail: csparks@greaterkokomo.com
Facebook: www.facebook.com/greaterkokomoalliance
Linkedin: www.linkedin.com/company/greater-kokomo-economic-development-alliance
X (Twitter): x.com/greaterkokomo
Description: Small business incubator focusing on long-term economic growth for Kokomo and Howard counties by creating new high-tech companies and supporting the development of new technologies for our existing companies. The company is a subsidiary of Greater Kokomo Economic Development Alliance, a non-profit organization.

39643 ■ Kurz Purdue Technology Center
1281 Win Hentschel Blvd.
West Lafayette, IN 47906
Ph: (765)588-3470
Co. E-mail: help@prf.org
URL: http://www.prf.org/researchpark
Contact: Brian E. Edelman, President
Facebook: www.facebook.com/PurdueResFound
X (Twitter): x.com/PurdueRP
YouTube: www.youtube.com/user/PurdueResearchPark
Description: Incubation complex participating in the commercialization and economic development in Indiana.

39644 ■ Mid-America Science Park (MASP)
821 S Lake Rd. S
Scottsburg, IN 47170
Ph: (812)752-9521
URL: http://maspark.org
Contact: Linda Gilray, Director, Development
E-mail: lgilray@maspark.org
Facebook: www.facebook.com/MidAmericaSciencePark
Linkedin: www.linkedin.com/company/mid-america-science-park
X (Twitter): x.com/MidAmericaSP
YouTube: www.youtube.com/channel/UCuq64dt3_el0Nf0ATYq60Tg
Description: Offers entrepreneurs and startups access to office space and shared administrative services, customized labs and training facilities, conference and event space, advanced technology and communication systems, and first-class amenities. **Founded:** 2011.

39645 ■ Nana Clare's Kitchen
3907 Calumet Ave., Ste. No. 106
Valparaiso, IN 46383
Ph: (219)286-3645
Co. E-mail: nanaclares@gmail.com
URL: http://nanaclares.com
Facebook: www.facebook.com/nanaclareskitchenValpo
Description: Provides an affordable way to take your home-based business out of your kitchen and into a commercial kitchen.

39646 ■ Northeast Indiana Innovation Center (NIIC)
3201 Stellhorn Rd.
Fort Wayne, IN 46815
Ph: (260)407-6442
Co. E-mail: info@niic.net
URL: http://niic.net
Contact: Mike Fritsch, President
E-mail: mfritsch@niic.net
Facebook: www.facebook.com/NIIC.NortheastIndianaInnovationCenter
Linkedin: www.linkedin.com/company/northeast-indiana-innovation-center-fort-wayne-indiana
Instagram: www.instagram.com/theniic
YouTube: www.youtube.com/channel/UCBAsuflRHodhPkGxV67Lhdw
Description: A small business incubator dedicated to developing ideas and growing businesses by fostering an environment of innovation and providing a wealth of essential business resources to accelerate growth. **Founded:** 1999.

39647 ■ One World KitchenShare
c/o Jay Burton
2361 W Rappel Ave.
Bloomington, IN 47404
Ph: (812)339-2256
Co. E-mail: jburton@bloomington.com
URL: http://www.kitchenshare.net
Contact: Jay Burton, Contact
E-mail: jburton@bloomington.com
Description: A 24/7 rental kitchen designed to offer new and experienced food businesses a commercial kitchen in which to work without the cost and headaches of creating your own. Our goal is to provide the tools you need to create a successful food business.

39648 ■ Perry County Development Corp. (PCDC)
601 Main St., Ste. A.
Tell City, IN 47586
Ph: (812)547-8377
Fax: (812)547-8378
Co. E-mail: erin@pickperry.com
URL: http://www.pickperry.com
Contact: Erin Emerson, President
E-mail: erin@pickperry.com
Facebook: www.facebook.com/Strong-FamiliesStrong-Community-of-Perry-County-828638497513110
Instagram: www.instagram.com/pickperrycounty
Description: Supports business incubation services to help business startups and entrepreneurs. **Founded:** 1991. **Geographic Preference:** Local.

39649 ■ Purdue Research Park (PRP)
Kurtz Purdue Technology Ctr.
1281 Win Hentschel Blvd.
West Lafayette, IN 47906
Ph: (765)588-3470
Fax: (765)463-3501
URL: http://www.prf.org/researchpark
Contact: Brian E. Edelman, President
X (Twitter): x.com/PurdueRP
YouTube: www.youtube.com/user/PurdueResearchPark
Description: A small business incubator providing a climate that encourages the development of new high-tech ventures and the growth of established technology firms. **Scope:** Provides facilities and University research and technical support services to research and development tenants. **Founded:** 1961. **Publications:** *Purdue Research Park Newsletter/Startup Express Newsletter* (Monthly).

39650 ■ Purdue Technology Center
1281 Win Hentschel Blvd.
West Lafayette, IN 47906
Ph: (765)588-3470
Fax: (765)463-3501
URL: http://www.prf.org
Contact: David Cooper, Chief Investment Officer
Description: Firm engages in funding research programs and managing intellectual properties.

39651 ■ SproutBox Management Inc.
642 N Madison No. 109
Bloomington, IN 47404
Free: 888-417-9341
Co. E-mail: info@sproutbox.com

URL: http://sproutbox.com
Contact: Brad Wisler, Co-Founder
E-mail: brad@sproutbox.com
Facebook: www.facebook.com/sproutbox
X (Twitter): x.com/sproutbox
Description: Product developers, creatives, and business experts who invest in startup companies with high growth potential in exchange for equity.

39652 ■ Uptown Kitchen
7225 Heritage Sq., Dr.
Granger, IN 46530
Ph: (574)968-3030
Co. E-mail: ukquestions@qdi.com
URL: http://www.theuptownkitchen.com
Facebook: www.facebook.com/uptownkitchengranger
Instagram: www.instagram.com/uptownkitchengranger
Description: Supports startups and entrepreneurs in the food industry by providing commercial kitchen space in which to work and grow your business.

39653 ■ Venture Out Business Center (VOBC)
975 Industrial Dr.
Madison, IN 47250
Ph: (812)273-6510
URL: http://www.ventureoutbusinesscenter.com
Contact: Devon Sharpe, President
Facebook: www.facebook.com/venture.out.969
Linkedin: www.linkedin.com/company/venture-out-business-center
Instagram: www.instagram.com/ventureoutbusinesscenter
YouTube: www.youtube.com/channel/UCy97-CZqclJ4xw2cCgaSwrg
Description: Firm provides supporting services for small business. **Founded:** 1995.

39654 ■ WestGate Technology Hub
13598 E WestGate Dr.
Odon, IN 47562
Ph: (812)863-2756
URL: http://www.westgate-academy.com
Facebook: www.facebook.com/PurdueWestGate
Linkedin: www.linkedin.com/company/purduewestgate
X (Twitter): x.com/PurdueWestGate
Instagram: www.instagram.com/wg_academy
Description: Offers training, workshop, and start-up assistance. **Founded:** 1930.

EDUCATIONAL PROGRAMS

39655 ■ Ball State University Entrepreneurship Center
Whitinger Business Bldg., Rm. 207
Muncie, IN 47306
Ph: (765)285-9002
Fax: (765)285-9003
Co. E-mail: entrepreneur@bsu.edu
URL: http://www.bsu.edu/academics/centersandinstitutes/entrepreneurship
Contact: Kimberly Ferguson, Director
E-mail: kimberly.ferguson@bsu.edu
Facebook: www.facebook.com/BallStateENT
Description: Entrepreneurship learning and guidance center for students and alumni. **Founded:** 1983.

39656 ■ Ball State University-Small Business Entrepreneurship Program
Dept. of Management
2000 W University Ave.
Muncie, IN 47306
URL: http://www.bsu.edu
Description: Offers a degree program, courses, seminars, and conferences for entrepreneurs and small business professionals. Covers financial and legal aspects of business ownership as well as small business assistance. **Founded:** 1918.

39657 ■ Ivy Tech Community College of Indiana - Columbus
4475 Central Ave.
Columbus, IN 47203
Ph: (812)372-9925
URL: http://www.ivytech.edu/locations
Contact: Stacy Jo Adams, Contact
Description: Trade and technical college offering a business administration program, and a small business management program. **Founded:** 1963.

39658 ■ Ivy Tech Community College of Indiana-Fort Wayne
3800 N Anthony Blvd.
Fort Wayne, IN 46835
Ph: (260)480-4100
Free: 888-489-5463
Co. E-mail: askfortwayne@ivytech.edu
URL: http://www.ivytech.edu/locations/fort-wayne
Facebook: www.facebook.com/ivytechfortwayne
Linkedin: www.linkedin.com/school/ivytechfortwayne
X (Twitter): x.com/ivytechfw
Instagram: www.instagram.com/ivytechfortwayne
Description: Trade and technical school offering a program in small business management. 1-888-489-5463. **Founded:** 1962.

39659 ■ Ivy Tech Community College of Indiana-Gary
3491 Broadway
Gary, IN 46409
Free: 888-489-5463
Co. E-mail: asklakecounty@ivytech.edu
URL: http://www.ivytech.edu/locations/lake-county/lake-county-at-gary
Description: Trade and technical school offering a program in small business management.

LEGISLATIVE ASSISTANCE

39660 ■ Indiana Senate Committee on Agriculture and Natural Resources
200 W Washington St.
Indianapolis, IN 46204-2786
Ph: (317)232-9600
Free: 800-382-9842
URL: http://iga.in.gov/legislative/2014/committees/agriculture_and_natural_resources_3100

CONSULTANTS

39661 ■ Argona Partners
1125 E Brookside Ave., Ste. B3
Indianapolis, IN 46202
Ph: (510)731-7270
Co. E-mail: team@argonapartners.com
URL: http://www.argonapartners.com
Contact: Amadin Agho, President
Facebook: www.facebook.com/ArgonaPartners
Linkedin: www.linkedin.com/company/argonapartners
X (Twitter): x.com/ArgonaPartners
YouTube: www.youtube.com/channel/UCKcHwB-T-ZPz03jsLTc72eg
Description: Speicalizes in new business consulting. Offers acceleration services. Also operates out of Silicon Valley.

39662 ■ Rose-Hulman Ventures
100 S Campus Dr.
Terre Haute, IN 47802
Ph: (812)244-4000
Co. E-mail: info@rhventures.org
URL: http://www.rhventures.org
Contact: Brian Dougherty, Sr., Senior Director
E-mail: brian.dougherty@rhventures.org
X (Twitter): x.com/RHITVentures
Description: A successful product design, rapid prototyping and development firm that develops innovative technology-based solutions. Serves a diverse mix of clients—from entrepreneurial startups to established companies with global operations.

PUBLICATIONS

39663 ■ *Business People Magazine*
7729 Westfield Dr.
Fort Wayne, IN 46825
Ph: (260)497-0433
Fax: (260)497-0822
URL: http://www.businesspeople.com
Contact: Danielle Hoelle, Art Director
E-mail: dhoelle@businesspeople.com
Facebook: www.facebook.com/BusinessPeople
Linkedin: www.linkedin.com/company/michiana-business-publications
Instagram: www.instagram.com/businesspeoplem
Released: Monthly **Price:** $31.99, Two years; $89.99, for lifetime; $19.99, for 1 year. **Description:** Consumer magazine covering business for Northeast Indiana. **Availability:** Online.

39664 ■ *Crain's Indianapolis*
1155 Gratiot Ave.
Detroit, MI 48207-2732
Ph: (313)446-6000
Co. E-mail: info@crain.com
URL: http://www.crain.com
Contact: Barry Asin, President
URL(s): www.crain.com/?portfolio=angie-hicks
Description: Covers business news in the Indianapolis area. **Availability:** Online.

39665 ■ *Indiana Business Bulletin*
2000 W University Ave.
Muncie, IN 47306
Ph: (765)285-5926
Co. E-mail: cber@bsu.edu
URL: http://www.bsu.edu/academics/centersandinstitutes/cber
Contact: Michael Joseph Hicks, Director
E-mail: mhicks@bsu.edu
URL(s): www.bsu.edu/academics/centersandinstitutes/cber/data-center
Released: Weekly **Availability:** Print.

39666 ■ *Michiana Business*
1700 Mishawaka Ave.
South Bend, IN 46615
URL: http://business.iusb.edu/academic-centers/bureau-of-business-and-economic-research.html
Released: Quarterly **Description:** Quarterly newsletter presented by the Bureau of Business and Economic Research. **Availability:** PDF.

PUBLISHERS

39667 ■ Xlibris L.L.C.
1663 Liberty Dr., Ste. 200
Bloomington, IN 47403
Free: 844-714-8691
Co. E-mail: info@xlibris.com
URL: http://www.xlibris.com
Facebook: www.facebook.com/XlibrisPublisher
Linkedin: www.linkedin.com/company/xlibris
X (Twitter): x.com/xlibrispub
Description: Publishes publishing kits to help the authors for publishing their works. Accepts unsolicited manuscripts. Reaches market through commission reps, direct mail, reviews, listings, telephone sales and wholesalers and distributors, including Amazon, BFN, borders, Ingram, books in print and lightning source. **Scope:** Provides the tools needed to publish using print-on-demand technology. Offers a variety of design, production and publishing services as well as online distribution availability and marketing products for self-publishing authors. **Founded:** 1997. **Publications:** "The Vineyard on Mulberry Street"; "Another Kind of Love Story"; "Dating Nightmares of A Single Woman".

VENTURE CAPITAL FIRM

39668 ■ Allos Ventures
38 W Main St.
Carmel, IN 46032
Ph: (317)275-6800
URL: http://allosventures.com
Contact: David Kerr, Managing Director
Linkedin: www.linkedin.com/company/allos-ventures
X (Twitter): x.com/Allosvc
Description: Venture capital firm for tech companies in the Midwest. Also maintains an office in Cincinnati.

Iowa

ASSOCIATIONS AND OTHER ORGANIZATIONS

39669 ■ Business Network International Heartland--Nebraska, Wyoming, South Dakota, Western Iowa
3430 Toringdon Way
 Charlotte, NC 28277
Free: 855-264-2673
Co. E-mail: info@bniheartland.com
URL: http://bniheartland.com/en-US/index
Contact: Nellie Nutting, Managing Director
E-mail: nellienutting@bni.com

Description: Provides a structured environment for the development and exchange of quality business referrals. Offers members the opportunity to share ideas and contacts in Nebraska, Wyoming, South Dakota and Iowa. **Founded:** 1985. **Geographic Preference:** State.

39670 ■ Business Network International Iowa
1231 SW Hardwicke Ln.
 Ankeny, IA 50023
Ph: (515)865-3862
URL: http://bniiowa.com/en-US/index

Description: Provides both men and women a structured environment for the development and exchange of quality business referrals. Offers members the opportunity to share ideas and contacts. **Geographic Preference:** State.

39671 ■ Entrepreneurs' Organization - Iowa Chapter (EO)
IA
URL: http://www.eonetwork.org/iowa
Contact: Tammy Michaelson, Manager
E-mail: michaelson.tammy@gmail.com

Description: Provides local resources to members which includes networking events, mentorship, live forums, and leadership development. **Founded:** 2000.

SMALL BUSINESS DEVELOPMENT CENTERS

39672 ■ America's SBDC Iowa for Mid Iowa
6500 University Ave., Ste. 100
 Windsor Heights, IA 50324
Ph: (515)331-8954
Co. E-mail: jenica@iastate.edu
URL: http://iowasbdc.org/locations/mid
Contact: Jenica Johnson, Regional Director
E-mail: jenica@iastate.edu

Description: Represents and promotes the small business sector. Provides management assistance to current and prospective small business owners. Helps to improve management skills and expand the products and services of members. **Founded:** 1982. **Geographic Preference:** Local.

39673 ■ America's SBDC Iowa at Southeastern Community College
15330 Truman St.
 Ottumwa, IA 52501
Co. E-mail: iowasbdc@iastate.edu
URL: http://iowasbdc.org/regional-center/ottumwa
Contact: Kelly Prickett, Contact
E-mail: kelly.prickett@indianhills.edu

Description: Represents and promotes the small business sector. Provides management assistance to current and prospective small business owners. Helps to improve management skills and expand the products and services of members. **Founded:** 1981. **Geographic Preference:** Local.

39674 ■ America's SBDC at North Iowa Area Community College
c/o Brook BoehmlerRegional Director
 500 College Dr., Ste. 120A
 Mason City, IA 50401
Ph: (641)422-4342
Co. E-mail: brook.boehmler@niacc.edu
URL: http://iowasbdc.org/locations/nia
Contact: Brook Boehmler, Regional Director
E-mail: brook.boehmler@niacc.edu

Description: Represents and promotes the small business sector. Provides management assistance to current and prospective small business owners. Helps to improve management skills and expand the products and services of members. **Founded:** 1985. **Geographic Preference:** Local.

39675 ■ Eastern Iowa Small Business Development Center
Urban Campus E, Rm. 161
 101 W 3rd St.
 Davenport, IA 52801
Ph: (563)336-3401
Fax: (563)336-3479
URL: http://www.eicc.edu/businesses/small-business-development-center
Contact: Joel Youngs, Regional Director
E-mail: jeyoungs@eicc.edu

Description: Represents and promotes the small business sector. Provides management assistance to current and prospective small business owners. Helps to improve management skills and expand the products and services of members. **Founded:** 1985. **Geographic Preference:** Local.

39676 ■ Indian Hills Small Business Development Center
c/o Kelly Prickett :Regional Director 15330 Truman St.
 Ottumwa, IA 52501
Ph: (641)683-5188
Co. E-mail: kelly.prickett@indianhills.edu
URL: http://iowasbdc.org/tag/ihsbdc
Contact: Kelly Prickett, Regional Director
E-mail: kelly.prickett@indianhills.edu

Description: Represents and promotes the small business sector. Provides management assistance to current and prospective small business owners. Helps to improve management skills and expand the products and services of members. **Founded:** 1981. **Geographic Preference:** Local.

39677 ■ Iowa Small Business Development Center Lead Office (SBDC)
1805 Collaboration Pl., Ste. 1331
 Ames, IA 50010
Ph: (515)294-2030
Fax: (515)294-6522
Co. E-mail: iowasbdc@iastate.edu
URL: http://www.iowasbdc.org
Contact: Lisa Shimkat, Director
E-mail: lshimkat@iastate.edu
Facebook: www.facebook.com/IowaSBDC
Linkedin: www.linkedin.com/company/iowa-sbdc
X (Twitter): x.com/iowasbdc
Instagram: www.instagram.com/iowasbdc
YouTube: www.youtube.com/user/IowaSBDC

Description: Provides management assistance to current and prospective small business owners in Iowa. **Founded:** 1981. **Geographic Preference:** State.

39678 ■ Iowa State University (SBDC) - Small Business Development Center
1805 Collaboration Pl., Ste. 1330
 Ames, IA 50010
Ph: (515)294-2030
Co. E-mail: iowasbdc@iastate.edu
URL: http://iowasbdc.org
Contact: Leah Locke, Regional Director
E-mail: llocke@iastate.edu
Facebook: www.facebook.com/IowaSBDC
Linkedin: www.linkedin.com/company/iowa-sbdc
X (Twitter): x.com/IowaSBDC
Instagram: www.instagram.com/iowasbdc
YouTube: www.youtube.com/user/IowaSBDC

Founded: 1981. **Publications:** *Innovation in Iowa*; *Starting a Small Business in Iowa*.

39679 ■ Iowa State University Small Business Development Center Ames
c/o Leah Locke
 1805 Collaboration Pl., Ste. 1330
 Ames, IA 50010
Ph: (515)296-7828
Fax: (515)294-6522
Co. E-mail: dbieden@iastate.edu
URL: http://iowasbdc.org/locations/isu
Contact: Leah Locke, Regional Director
E-mail: ljhansen@iastate.edu

Description: Represents and promotes the small business sector. Provides management assistance to current and prospective small business owners. Helps to improve management skills and expand the products and services of members. **Geographic Preference:** Local.

39680 ■ Kirkwood Community College Small Business Development Center
101 50th Ave. SW
 Cedar Rapids, IA 52404
URL: http://iowasbdc.org/locations/kirkwood

Contact: Michael Wampler, Regional Director
E-mail: michael.wampler@kirkwood.edu
Description: Represents and promotes the small business sector. Provides management assistance to current and prospective small business owners. Helps to improve management skills and expand the products and services of members. **Founded:** 1988. **Geographic Preference:** Local.

39681 ■ North Central Iowa Small Business Development Center
c/o Justin Faiferlick, Regional Director
2031 Quail Ave.
Fort Dodge, IA 50501
Ph: (515)574-1995
Co. E-mail: kimberlyt@ncisbdc.com
URL: http://iowasbdc.org/locations/nci
Contact: Justin Faiferlick, Regional Director
E-mail: faiferlick@iowacentral.edu
Description: Represents and promotes the small business sector. Provides management assistance to current and prospective small business owners. Helps to improve management skills and expand the products and services of members. **Geographic Preference:** Local.

39682 ■ Northeast Iowa Small Business Development Center
c/o Jay Wickham, Regional Director
900 Jackson St., Ste. 110
Dubuque, IA 52001
Ph: (563)588-3350
Co. E-mail: wickhamja@nicc.edu
URL: http://iowasbdc.org/locations/ne
Contact: Jay Wickham, Regional Director
E-mail: wickhamja@nicc.edu
Description: Represents and promotes the small business sector. Provides management assistance to current and prospective small business owners. Helps to improve management skills and expand the products and services of members. **Founded:** 1985. **Geographic Preference:** Local.

39683 ■ Northwest Iowa Small Business Development Center
Iowa Lakes Community College
1900 Grand Ave., Ste. B-1
Spencer, IA 51301
Ph: (712)262-4213
Co. E-mail: mwampler@iowalakes.edu
URL: http://iowasbdc.org/2013/10/06/spencer
-convenient-healthcare-llc-spencer
Contact: Michael Wampler, Director
E-mail: mwampler@iowalakes.edu
Description: Represents and promotes the small business sector. Provides management assistance to current and prospective small business owners. Helps to improve management skills and expand the products and services of members. **Geographic Preference:** Local.

39684 ■ South Central Iowa Small Business Development Center
Southwestern Community College
1501 W Townline St.
Creston, IA 50801
URL: http://iowasbdc.org/locations/sci
Contact: Jamie David, Regional Director
E-mail: david@swcciowa.edu
Description: Represents and promotes the small business sector. Provides management assistance to current and prospective small business owners. Helps to improve management skills and expand the products and services of members. **Founded:** 2006. **Geographic Preference:** Local.

39685 ■ University of Iowa (SBDC) - Small Business Development Center
c/o Paul Heath, Regional Director
W140 BioVentures Ctr.
2500 Crosspark Rd.
Coralville, IA 52241
Ph: (319)335-3742
Co. E-mail: iowasbdc@iastate.edu
URL: http://iowasbdc.org
Contact: Paul Heath, Regional Director
E-mail: paul-heath@uiowa.edu

X (Twitter): x.com/iowasbdc
Description: Provides services and support to small business owners. **Scope:** Small business development. **Founded:** 1981. **Educational Activities:** Small Business Development Center Workshops.

39686 ■ University of Iowa Small Business Development Center
IOWA Centers for Enterprise
W140 BioVentures Ctr.
2500 Crosspark Rd.
Coralville, IA 52241
Ph: (319)335-3742
Fax: (319)467-4550
Co. E-mail: paul-heath@uiowa.edu
URL: http://iowasbdc.org/locations/uoi
Contact: Paul Heath, Regional Director
E-mail: paul-heath@uiowa.edu
Description: Represents and promotes the small business sector. Provides management assistance to current and prospective small business owners. Helps to improve management skills and expand the products and services of members. **Founded:** 1982. **Geographic Preference:** Local.

39687 ■ University of Northern Iowa Small Business Development Center
8120 Jennings Dr., Ste. 13
Cedar Falls, IA 50613
URL: http://iowasbdc.org/locations/uni
Contact: Amy Dutton, Regional Director
E-mail: amy.dutton@uni.edu
Description: Represents and promotes the small business sector. Provides management assistance to current and prospective small business owners. Helps to improve management skills and expand the products and services of members. **Geographic Preference:** Local.

39688 ■ Western Iowa Tech Small Business Development Center (SBDC)
c/o Todd Rausch, Regional Director
4647 Stone Ave., Rm. B113
Sioux City, IA 51102
Ph: (712)317-3406
Co. E-mail: todd.rausch@witcc.edu
URL: http://iowasbdc.org/locations/wit
Contact: Todd Rausch, Regional Director
E-mail: todd.rausch@witcc.edu
Description: Represents and promotes the small business sector. Provides management assistance to current and prospective small business owners. Helps to improve management skills and expand the products and services of members. **Founded:** 1999. **Geographic Preference:** Local.

SMALL BUSINESS ASSISTANCE PROGRAMS

39689 ■ Iowa Department of Economic Development (IDED) - Business Development
1963 Bell Ave., Ste. 200
Des Moines, IA 50315
URL: http://www.iowaeda.com/expand-your-business
Description: Works with the private sector to promote policies and implement programs that will expand the economy and increase job opportunities for Iowans.

39690 ■ Iowa Department of Economic Development - Targeted Small Business Program (TSB)
1963 Bell Ave., Ste. 200
Des Moines, IA 50315
Co. E-mail: tsbcert@iowaeda.com
URL: http://www.iowaeda.com/small-business/targete
d-small-business
Contact: Kym Stevenson, Contact
Description: Strives to further the economic well being of Iowa small business and to provide them with growth opportunities by offering services and coordinating efforts with existing programs.

39691 ■ VentureNet Iowa
400 E Ct. Ave., Ste. 122
Des Moines, IA 50309

Ph: (515)471-1300
URL: http://www.venturenetiowa.com
Contact: George Wilson, Principal
E-mail: geo@gwiii.com
Description: Acts as a nexus to connect companies to the resources appropriate for its stage of development.

SCORE OFFICES

39692 ■ Des Moines SCORE
RE/MAX Complex 6600 University Ave., Rm. 156
Des Moines, IA 50324
Ph: (515)274-8593
URL: http://www.score.org/desmoines
Contact: Bridget Weston, Chief Executive Officer
Facebook: www.facebook.com/SCOREDesMoines
Linkedin: www.linkedin.com/company/score-mentors
-des-moines
Description: Offers counseling to educate entrepreneurs and help small businesses start, grow and succeed nationwide. Organizes volunteers who are working or retired business owners, executives and corporate leaders who wish to share their wisdom and lessons learned in business. **Founded:** 1964. **Geographic Preference:** Local.

39693 ■ Dubuque Area SCORE
Cedar Rapids, IA
Ph: (563)690-9209
URL: http://eastcentraliowa.score.org/about-score
-dubuque-area
Founded: 1964.

39694 ■ Muscatine SCORE
Muscatine, IA
Ph: (309)797-0082
URL: http://www.score.org/quadcities/about
Contact: Liz Sara, President
Description: Non-profit organization dedicated to the formation, growth, and success of small businesses. **Geographic Preference:** Local.

39695 ■ Quad Cities SCORE
331 W 3rd St.
Davenport, IA 52801
Ph: (309)797-0082
Co. E-mail: help@score.org
URL: http://quadcities.score.org
Contact: Rieva Lesonsky, Contact
Facebook: www.facebook.com/SCOREQuadCities
Description: Provides professional guidance and information to maximize the success of existing and emerging small businesses. Develops business plans and evaluate financial projections. Promotes entrepreneur education in the western Illinois/eastern Iowa Quad Cities area including Moline and Rock Island IL and Davenport and Bettendorf, IA. **Founded:** 1978. **Publications:** *Quad Cities SCORE Newsletter* (Bimonthly). **Geographic Preference:** Local.

39696 ■ SCORE - Davenport
331 W 3rd St.
Davenport, IA 52801
Ph: (309)797-0082
URL: http://quadcities.score.org
Description: Provides professional guidance and information to maximize the success of existing and emerging small businesses. Offers business counseling and workshops.

39697 ■ SCORE - Decorah
703 Valley View Dr.
Decorah, IA 52101
Ph: (563)382-3796
URL: http://eastcentraliowa.score.org
Description: Provides professional guidance and information to maximize the success of existing and emerging small businesses. Offers business counseling and workshops.

39698 ■ SCORE - Des Moines
6600 University Ave., Rm. 157
DSM Score RE/MAX Complex
Des Moines, IA 50324
Ph: (515)274-8593
URL: http://desmoines.score.org

39699 ■ Iowa

Contact: Bridget Weston, Chief Executive Officer
Linkedin: www.linkedin.com/company/score-mentors-des-moines
Description: Provides professional guidance and information to maximize the success of existing and emerging small businesses. Offers business counseling and workshops.

39699 ■ SCORE - Dubuque
2205 Key Way Dr.
Dubuque, IA 52002
Ph: (563)690-9209
URL: http://eastcentraliowa.score.org/about-score-dubuque-area
Description: Provides professional guidance and information to maximize the success of existing and emerging small businesses. Offers business counseling and workshops.

39700 ■ SCORE - East Central Iowa [SCORE - Cedar Rapids]
2750 1st Ave. NE, Ste. 350
Cedar Rapids, IA 52402
Ph: (319)362-6943
Co. E-mail: crexecs@scorevolunteer.org
URL: http://eastcentraliowa.score.org
Contact: Dawn Jones, Contact
Linkedin: www.linkedin.com/company/score-mentors-east-central-iowa
X (Twitter): x.com/SCORE_ECIowa
Description: Provides professional guidance and information to maximize the success of existing and emerging small businesses. Offers business assistance to develop business idea or plan and identify problems and potential solutions. Promotes entrepreneur education in Cedar Rapids area. **Founded:** 1966. **Geographic Preference:** Local.

39701 ■ SCORE - Elkader
132 S Main St.
Elkader, IA 52043
Ph: (563)880-2873
URL: http://eastcentraliowa.score.org
Description: Provides professional guidance and information to maximize the success of existing and emerging small businesses. Offers business counseling and workshops.

39702 ■ SCORE - Fairfield, Iowa
101 N Ct., St.
Fairfield Economic Development Association
Fairfield, IA 52556
URL: http://southcentraliowa.score.org/mentors/joshua-laraby
Contact: Joshua Laraby, Contact
Description: Provides professional guidance and information to maximize the success of existing and emerging small businesses. Offers business counseling and workshops.

39703 ■ SCORE - Manchester, Iowa
200 E Main St.
Manchester, IA 52057
Ph: (563)927-3325
URL: http://eastcentraliowa.score.org
URL(s): pittsburgh.score.org/find-location
Description: Provides professional guidance and information to maximize the success of existing and emerging small businesses. Offers business counseling and workshops.

39704 ■ SCORE - Muscatine
100 W 2nd St.
Muscatine, IA 52761
Ph: (563)263-8895
URL: http://quadcities.score.org/SCORE-Muscatine
Description: Provides professional guidance and information to maximize the success of existing and emerging small businesses. Offers business counseling and workshops.

39705 ■ SCORE - Quad Cities
Davenport Chamber of Commerce
331 W 3rd St.
Davenport, IA 52801
Ph: (309)797-0082
Fax: (309)757-5435
Co. E-mail: score0432@scorevolunteer.org
URL: http://quadcities.score.org
Contact: Frank W. Lyons, Contact
Facebook: www.facebook.com/SCOREQuadCities
Description: Provides professional guidance and information to maximize the success of existing and emerging small businesses. Offers business counseling and workshops. **Founded:** 1978.

39706 ■ SCORE - Sioux City
101 Pierce St.
Sioux City, IA 51101
URL: http://desmoines.score.org/mentors/heidi-reinking
Contact: Heidi Reinking, Contact
Description: Provides professional guidance and information to maximize the success of existing and emerging small businesses. Promotes entrepreneur education in Sioux area, Iowa. **Geographic Preference:** Local.

39707 ■ SCORE - South Central Iowa [South Central Iowa SCORE]
217 E Main
Ottumwa, IA 52501
Ph: (641)814-5907
Co. E-mail: help@score.org
URL: http://southcentraliowa.score.org
Contact: Bridget Weston, Chief Executive Officer
Description: Provides professional guidance and information to maximize the success of existing and emerging small businesses. Offers business counseling and workshops. **Geographic Preference:** Local.

BETTER BUSINESS BUREAUS

39708 ■ Better Business Bureau of Greater Iowa - Quad Cities and Siouxland Region
2625 Beaver Ave.
Des Moines, IA 50310
Ph: (515)243-8137
Fax: (515)243-2227
Co. E-mail: info@dm.bbb.org
URL: http://www.bbb.org/local-bbb/bbb-serving-greater-iowa-quad-cities-and-siouxland-region
Facebook: www.facebook.com/IowaBBB
X (Twitter): x.com/IowaBBB
Description: Seeks to promote and foster the highest ethical relationship between businesses and the public through voluntary self-regulation, consumer and business education, and service excellence. Provides information to help consumers and businesses make informed purchasing decisions and avoid costly scams and frauds; settles consumer complaints through arbitration and other means. **Geographic Preference:** Local.

CHAMBERS OF COMMERCE

39709 ■ Adel Partners Chamber of Commerce
301 S 10th St.
Adel, IA 50003
Ph: (515)993-5472
Fax: (515)993-3384
Co. E-mail: chamber@adelpartners.org
URL: http://www.adelpartners.org
Contact: Deb Bengtson, President
E-mail: chamber@adelpartners.org
Facebook: www.facebook.com/AdelPartnersChamberOfCommerce
Instagram: www.instagram.com/adelpartnerschamber
Description: Promotes business and community development in Adel, IA. **Geographic Preference:** Local.

39710 ■ Algona Area Chamber of Commerce
123 E State St.
Algona, IA 50511-2735
Ph: (515)295-7201
Fax: (515)295-5920
Co. E-mail: info@algona.org
URL: http://www.algona.org
Contact: Shannon Goche, President
Facebook: www.facebook.com/AlgonaChamber

Linkedin: www.linkedin.com/company/algona-area-chamber-of-commerce
Instagram: www.instagram.com/explore/tags/algona
Description: Promotes business and community development in the Algona, IA area. **Founded:** 1936. **Geographic Preference:** Local.

39711 ■ Altoona Area Chamber of Commerce (AACC)
119 2nd St. SE, Ste. A
Altoona, IA 50009
Ph: (515)967-3366
Fax: (515)967-3346
Co. E-mail: info@altoonachamber.org
URL: http://www.altoonachamber.org
Contact: Josh Dunwoody, President
Facebook: www.facebook.com/altoonachamber
X (Twitter): x.com/Altoona_Chamber
Instagram: www.instagram.com/altoonachamber
Description: Promotes business and community development in Altoona, IA. Sponsors Altoona Home Show, Pride Day, retail promotions, Christmas lighting contest and community auction. **Founded:** 1970. **Publications:** *Connecticut River Valley Chamber of Commerce Business Directory*. **Geographic Preference:** Local.

39712 ■ Ames Chamber of Commerce (ACC)
304 Main St.
Ames, IA 50010
Ph: (515)232-2310
URL: http://www.ameschamber.com
Contact: Dan Culhane, President
Facebook: www.facebook.com/AmesChamber
Linkedin: www.linkedin.com/company/ames-chamber-of-commerce
X (Twitter): x.com/AmesChamber
Instagram: www.instagram.com/chamberames
Description: Strives to strengthen the long-term economic vitality of its members and the community. Offers a variety of networking and educational opportunities to help businesses grow and thrive. **Founded:** 1944. **Publications:** *Chamber Update*. **Educational Activities:** Golf Day (Annual). **Geographic Preference:** Local.

39713 ■ Anamosa Area Chamber of Commerce
213 E Main St.
Anamosa, IA 52205
Ph: (319)462-4879
Co. E-mail: director@anamosachamber.org
URL: http://www.anamosachamber.org
Contact: Shannon Frink, President
Facebook: www.facebook.com/AnamosaChamber
Description: Promotes business and community development in Anamosa, IA. **Geographic Preference:** Local.

39714 ■ Ankeny Area Chamber of Commerce
1631 SW Main St., Ste. 204/205
Ankeny, IA 50023
Ph: (515)964-0685
URL: http://www.ankeny.org
Contact: Melisa Cox, President
E-mail: mcox@ankeny.org
Facebook: www.facebook.com/AnkenyAreaChamber
X (Twitter): x.com/AnkenyChamber
YouTube: www.youtube.com/channel/UCTnQhj1R5n6h-wN22FqYJ_Q
Description: Promotes business and community development in Ankeny, IA. **Publications:** *Chamber Action* (Monthly). **Geographic Preference:** Local.

39715 ■ Atlantic Area Chamber of Commerce (AACC)
102 Chestnut St.
Atlantic, IA 50022
Ph: (712)243-3017
Free: 877-283-2124
Fax: (712)243-4404
Co. E-mail: chamber@atlanticiowa.com
URL: http://www.atlanticiowa.com/chamber
Contact: Kent Hanson, President
Description: Promotes business and community development in the Atlantic, IA area. Sponsors Southwest Iowa Focus on Agriculture, Atlantic Fest,

STATE LISTINGS

Coca-Cola Days, and City Wide Christmas Grand Lighting. **Founded:** 1941. **Publications:** *Discover the Chamber* (Monthly). **Educational Activities:** Atlanticfest (Annual). **Geographic Preference:** Local.

39716 ■ **Belmond Area Chamber of Commerce**
223 E Main St.
  Belmond, IA 50421
Ph: (641)444-3386
URL: http://belmondiowa.com
Contact: Darrel Steven Carlyle, Officer
E-mail: dcarlyle@co.wright.ia.us
Description: Promotes business and community development in the Belmond, IA area. **Founded:** 1856. **Geographic Preference:** Local.

39717 ■ **Britt Chamber of Commerce (BCC)**
170 Main Ave., S
  Britt, IA 50423
Ph: (641)843-4433
Co. E-mail: brittchamber@gmail.com
URL: http://brittiowa.com
Description: Promotes business and community development in Britt, IA. Sponsors draft horse show. **Founded:** 1881. **Publications:** *Hobo Guide* (Annual). **Educational Activities:** National Hobo Convention (Annual). **Geographic Preference:** Local.

39718 ■ *Business Directory*
818 Washington St.
  Pella, IA 50219
Ph: (641)628-2626
Fax: (641)628-9697
Co. E-mail: info@pella.org
URL: http://pella.org
Contact: Mark Putnam, President
E-mail: president@central.edu
URL(s): members.pella.org/list
Availability: Print.

39719 ■ **Carroll Chamber of Commerce (CCC)**
407 W 5th St.
  Carroll, IA 51401
Ph: (712)792-4383
Fax: (712)792-4834
Co. E-mail: chamber@carrolliowa.com
URL: http://www.carrolliowa.com
Contact: Kimberly Tiefenthaler, Executive Director
Facebook: www.facebook.com/CarrollChamber
Description: Promotes business and community development in Carroll, IA. **Founded:** 1942. **Geographic Preference:** Local.

39720 ■ **Cedar Rapids Metro Economic Alliance**
501 1st St. SE
  Cedar Rapids, IA 52401
Ph: (319)398-5317
Fax: (319)398-5228
Co. E-mail: economicalliance@cedarrapids.org
URL: http://www.cedarrapids.org
Contact: Doug Neumann, Executive Director
E-mail: dneumann@cedarrapids.org
Facebook: www.facebook.com/
  CRMEconomicAlliance
Linkedin: www.linkedin.com/company/cedar-rapids
  -metro-economic-alliance
X (Twitter): x.com/EconomicAllianc
Instagram: www.instagram.com/crmeconomicalliance
Description: Promotes business and community development in the Cedar Rapids, IA area. **Founded:** 1918. **Publications:** *Area Chamber* (Monthly); *Business and Professional Directory* (Annual). **Geographic Preference:** Local.

39721 ■ **Centerville Area Chamber of Commerce**
128 N 12th St.
  Centerville, IA 52544
Ph: (641)437-4102
Free: 800-611-3800
Co. E-mail: chamber@centervilleia.com
URL: http://www.centervilleia.com
Contact: Brett Mihalovich, President

Description: Promotes business and community development in the Centerville, IA area. **Geographic Preference:** Local.

39722 ■ **Chamber-Main Street Sac City**
302 E Main.
  Sac City, IA 50583
Ph: (712)662-7593
Fax: (712)662-7448
Co. E-mail: city.admin@saccity.city
URL: http://saccity.city/chamber-main-street
Description: Promotes business and community development in Sac City, IA. **Geographic Preference:** Local.

39723 ■ **Chariton Area Chamber/Main Street**
104 N Grand St.
  Chariton, IA 50049
Ph: (641)774-4059
URL: http://www.charitonareachambermainstreet.com
Contact: Alicia McGee, Executive Director
Description: Seeks to promote tourism, economic development, community betterment, retail development and retention and industrial recruitment and retention. **Founded:** 1986. **Geographic Preference:** Local.

39724 ■ **Cherokee Chamber of Commerce**
201 W Main St.
  Cherokee, IA 51012
Ph: (712)225-6414
Co. E-mail: info@cherokeeiowachamber.com
URL: http://cherokeeiowa.com/cherokee-chamber
Contact: Jessica Kannegieter, President
Facebook: www.facebook.com/
  CherokeeIowaChamber
Description: Promotes business and community development in Cherokee, IA area. **Publications:** *Chamber News*. **Geographic Preference:** Local.

39725 ■ **Clarinda Economic Development Corporation (CEDC)**
200 S 15th St.
  Clarinda, IA 51632
Ph: (712)542-2160
URL: http://www.developiowa.net
Contact: Amy McQueen, Contact
Facebook: www.facebook.com/developclarinda
Description: Promotes economic development and community planning in Clarinda, IA. **Founded:** 2001. **Publications:** *CEDC News* (Quarterly); *Chamber Connection* (Bimonthly). **Geographic Preference:** Local.

39726 ■ **Clear Lake Area Chamber of Commerce (CLACC)**
205 Main Ave.
  Clear Lake, IA 50428
Ph: (641)357-2159
Free: 800-285-5338
Co. E-mail: info@clearlakeiowa.com
URL: http://clearlakeiowa.com
Contact: Stacy Doughan, President
E-mail: stacy@clearlakeiowa.com
Facebook: www.facebook.com/ClearLakeIowa
Instagram: www.instagram.com/clearlakeiowa
YouTube: www.youtube.com/channel/UCIJRBY
  2zBMbOUN-yrrz8aIQ
Description: Promotes business and community development in the Clear Lake, IA area. **Founded:** 1943. **Publications:** *At the Lake* (Monthly). **Geographic Preference:** Local.

39727 ■ **Clinton Area Chamber of Commerce (CACC)**
721 S 2nd St.
  Clinton, IA 52733-1024
Ph: (563)242-5702
Fax: (563)242-5803
Co. E-mail: chamber@clintonia.com
URL: http://www.clintonia.com
Contact: Jennifer Boysen, Treasurer

Description: Promotes business and community development in Clinton, IA. Gathers and disseminates information about the community. **Founded:** 1872. **Publications:** *Chamber Update* (Monthly). **Geographic Preference:** Local.

39728 ■ **Council Bluffs Area Chamber of Commerce (CBACC)**
149 W Broadway
  Council Bluffs, IA 51503
Ph: (712)325-1000
Fax: (712)322-5698
Co. E-mail: cbchamber@councilbluffsiowa.com
URL: http://www.councilbluffsiowa.com
Contact: Kim Buthe, Director
Facebook: www.facebook.com/
  CouncilBluffsChamber
Linkedin: www.linkedin.com/company/council-bluffs
  -area-chamber-of-commerce
X (Twitter): x.com/CBchamber
YouTube: www.youtube.com/channel/UCf4iIwEqIYg
  -dUBUBeQqaKg
Description: Promotes business and community development in Council Bluffs, IA. **Founded:** 1916. **Publications:** *Commerce Today* (Monthly). **Geographic Preference:** Local.

39729 ■ **Creston Chamber of Commerce (CCC)**
208 W Taylor St.
  Creston, IA 50801
Ph: (641)782-7021
Fax: (641)782-7022
Co. E-mail: chamber@crestoniowachamber.com
URL: http://www.crestoniowachamber.com
Contact: Karen Berry, President
Facebook: www.facebook.com/Creston-Chamber-of
  -Commerce-161462436462
X (Twitter): x.com/CrestonChamber
Description: Promotes business and community development in Creston, IA. **Publications:** *Chamber Highlights* (Monthly). **Geographic Preference:** Local.

39730 ■ **Decorah Area Chamber of Commerce (DACC)**
507 W Water St.
  Decorah, IA 52101
Ph: (563)382-3990
Co. E-mail: info@decorahareachamber.com
URL: http://www.decorahareachamber.com
Contact: Sara Thomas, President
Facebook: www.facebook.com/decorahchamber
Description: Promotes business and community development in Decorah, IA. Sponsors annual Nordic Fest. **Founded:** 1924. **Geographic Preference:** Local.

39731 ■ *Digest*
709 S Center St.
  Marshalltown, IA 50158
Ph: (641)753-6645
Co. E-mail: office@marshalltown.org
URL: http://www.marshalltown.org
Contact: John Hall, President
E-mail: jhall@marshalltown.org
URL(s): www.marshalltown.org/partnership-publication
Released: Monthly **Availability:** PDF.

39732 ■ *Discover the Chamber*
102 Chestnut St.
  Atlantic, IA 50022
Ph: (712)243-3017
Free: 877-283-2124
Fax: (712)243-4404
Co. E-mail: chamber@atlanticiowa.com
URL: http://www.atlanticiowa.com/chamber
Contact: Kent Hanson, President
URL(s): www.atlanticiowa.com
Released: Monthly **Availability:** Print.

39733 ■ **Dubuque Area Chamber of Commerce**
300 Main St., Ste. 200
  Dubuque, IA 52001
Ph: (563)557-9200
Co. E-mail: office@dubuquechamber.com

URL: http://www.dubuquechamber.com
Contact: Molly Grover, President
E-mail: mgrover@dubuquechamber.com
Facebook: www.facebook.com/dubuquechamber
Linkedin: www.linkedin.com/company/1514711
X (Twitter): x.com/dubuquechamber
Instagram: www.instagram.com/dubuquechamber
YouTube: www.youtube.com/channel/UCcUwUDSffY_leUDsgObAbjw
Description: Promotes business and community development in Dubuque, IA area. **Founded:** 1916. **Publications:** *ChamberEdge* (Monthly). **Geographic Preference:** Local.

39734 ■ Dyersville Area Chamber of Commerce (DACC)
1100 16th Ave., Ct. SE
Dyersville, IA 52040
Ph: (563)875-2311
Co. E-mail: dyersvillechamber@dyersville.org
URL: http://www.dyersville.org
Contact: Karla Thompson, Executive Director
E-mail: kthompson@dyersville.org
Facebook: www.facebook.com/DyersvilleChamber
Instagram: www.instagram.com/dyersvillechamber
Description: Promotes business and community development in Dyersville, IA area. **Publications:** *The Communicator* (Quarterly). **Geographic Preference:** Local.

39735 ■ Eagle Grove Area Chamber of Commerce
212 W Broadway
Eagle Grove, IA 50533
Ph: (515)448-4821
Fax: (515)603-6119
Co. E-mail: chamber@eaglegrove.com
URL: http://www.eaglegrove.com
Contact: Missie Niederhauser, President
Facebook: www.facebook.com/eaglegrove.commerce
X (Twitter): x.com/eg_chamber
YouTube: www.youtube.com/channel/UCXNx7cJ0l5_N7JP7G_WrKfg
Description: Promotes business and community development in Eagle Grove, IA. **Founded:** 1927. **Geographic Preference:** Local.

39736 ■ Eldora Area Chamber of Commerce (EACC)
1442 Washington St.
Eldora, IA 50627
Ph: (641)939-2393
Co. E-mail: eldoraecondev@heartofiowa.net
URL: http://www.eldoraiowa.com
Description: Promotes business and community development in the Eldora, IA area. **Founded:** 1990. **Publications:** *Outlook* (Monthly); *Echo* (Quarterly). **Geographic Preference:** Local.

39737 ■ Elkader Area Chamber of Commerce (EACC)
207 N Main St.
Elkader, IA 52043
Ph: (563)245-2857
Co. E-mail: elkader@alpinecom.net
URL: http://www.elkader-iowa.com
Contact: Amanda Schneider, President
Facebook: www.facebook.com/IAEACC
Instagram: www.instagram.com/elkaderchamber
Description: Promotes business, community development, and tourism in the Elkader, Iowa area. **Founded:** 1964. **Geographic Preference:** Local.

39738 ■ Emmetsburg Chamber of Commerce (ECC)
2021 Main St.
Emmetsburg, IA 50536
Ph: (712)852-4030
Co. E-mail: contact@emmetsburg.com
URL: http://www.emmetsburg.com
Contact: Deb Hite, Executive Director
E-mail: eburgchamber@kemb.org
Facebook: www.facebook.com/cityofemmetsburg
X (Twitter): x.com/emmetsburg3tv
Description: Promotes business and community development in Emmetsburg, IA. Sponsors Summerfest. **Publications:** *Catalyst* (Monthly). **Geographic Preference:** Local.

39739 ■ Estherville Area Chamber of Commerce
620 1st Ave., S
Estherville, IA 51334-2349
Ph: (712)362-3541
Fax: (712)362-7742
Co. E-mail: echamber@gmail.com
URL: http://www.estherville.org
Contact: Lexie Ruter, Executive Director
X (Twitter): x.com/esthervilleiowa
Description: Promotes business and community development in the Estherville, IA area. **Founded:** 1881. **Geographic Preference:** Local.

39740 ■ Fairfield Area Chamber of Commerce (FACC)
204 W Broadway Ave.
Fairfield, IA 52556
Ph: (641)472-2111
Co. E-mail: info@fairfieldiowa.com
URL: http://www.fairfieldiowa.com
Contact: Jason Davis, President
Facebook: www.facebook.com/fairfieldareachamberofcommerce
Description: Promotes business and community development in the Fairfield, IA area. **Founded:** 1927. **Publications:** *Chamber Week* (Weekly). **Educational Activities:** 1St Fridays Art Walk. **Geographic Preference:** Local.

39741 ■ Fort Madison Area Chamber of Commerce
614 7th St.
Fort Madison, IA 52627
Ph: (319)372-5471
Co. E-mail: chamber@fortmadison.com
URL: http://www.fortmadison.com/chamber
Contact: Tim Gobble, Director
E-mail: tgobble@fortmadison.com
Facebook: www.facebook.com/fortmadisonchamberofcommerce
Description: Seeks to provide an environment conducive to community growth and prosperity designed to promote opportunities that will improve the overall economic strength of the membership. **Geographic Preference:** Local.

39742 ■ Garner Chamber of Commerce (GCC)
485 State St.
Garner, IA 50438
Ph: (641)923-3993
Co. E-mail: chamber@comm1net.net
URL: http://www.chambergarneria.com
Contact: Herman Robinson, President
Facebook: www.facebook.com/GarnerIAChamber
Description: Promotes business and community development in Garner, IA. Sponsors festival. **Founded:** 1890. **Geographic Preference:** Local.

39743 ■ Greater Cedar Valley Chamber of Commerce-Cedar Falls
360 Westfield Ave., Ste. 200
Waterloo, IA 50701
Ph: (319)232-1156
Co. E-mail: info@growcedarvalley.com
URL: http://www.growcedarvalley.com
Contact: Cary Darrah, President
E-mail: cary@growcedarvalley.com
Facebook: www.facebook.com/growcedarvalley
Linkedin: www.linkedin.com/company/grow-cedar-valley
X (Twitter): x.com/growcedarvalley
Instagram: www.instagram.com/explore/locations/206579835353/grow-cedar-valley
YouTube: www.youtube.com/user/GreaterCedarValley
Description: Promotes business and community development in Cedar Falls, IA and metropolitan area. **Founded:** 1907. **Publications:** *Waterloo-Cedar Falls Business Directory* (Annual). **Geographic Preference:** Local.

39744 ■ Greater Des Moines Partnership (DSM)
700 Locust St., Ste. 100
Des Moines, IA 50309
Ph: (515)286-4950
Co. E-mail: info@dsmpartnership.com
URL: http://www.dsmpartnership.com
Contact: Jay Byers, Chief Executive Officer
E-mail: jbyers@dsmpartnership.com
Facebook: www.facebook.com/DSMpartnership
Linkedin: www.linkedin.com/company/greater-des-moines-partnership
X (Twitter): x.com/DSMPartnership
Instagram: www.instagram.com/dsmpartnership
YouTube: www.youtube.com/c/GreaterDesMoinesPartnership
Description: Promotes business and community development in the greater Des Moines, IA area. **Founded:** 1888. **Publications:** *Association Directory* (Annual); *Member Directory*; *Media Guide* (Quarterly). **Geographic Preference:** Local.

39745 ■ Greater Fort Dodge Growth Alliance (GFDGA)
24 N 9th St., Ste. A
Fort Dodge, IA 50501
Ph: (515)955-5500
Fax: (515)955-3245
Co. E-mail: info@greaterfortdodge.com
URL: http://ww.greaterfortdodge.com
Contact: Dennis Plautz, Chief Executive Officer
Facebook: www.facebook.com/GreaterFortDodgeGrowthAlliance
Linkedin: www.linkedin.com/company/greater-fort-dodge-growth-alliance
X (Twitter): x.com/Growth_Alliance
YouTube: www.youtube.com/user/GreaterFortDodge
Description: Promotes business and community development in the Ft. Dodge, IA area. **Founded:** 2012. **Geographic Preference:** Local.

39746 ■ Greater Muscatine Chamber of Commerce and Industry (GMCCI)
100 W Second St.
Muscatine, IA 52761
Ph: (563)263-8895
URL: http://muscatine.com
Contact: Gage Huston, Chairman
Facebook: www.facebook.com/GMCCI
X (Twitter): x.com/gmcci_muscatine
Instagram: www.instagram.com/gmcci_muscatine
Description: Promotes business and community development in Muscatine, IA. **Founded:** 1944. **Publications:** *Pearl City Progress* (Monthly). **Geographic Preference:** Local.

39747 ■ Greenfield Chamber/Main Street and Development Office
202 S First St.
Greenfield, IA 50849
Ph: (641)743-8444
URL: http://www.greenfieldiowa.com/chamber-mainstreet
Contact: Stacie Eshelman, Executive Director
E-mail: director@greenfieldiowa.com
Description: Seeks to promote business and community development in and for Greenfield. Activities include Easter Party/Egg Hunt, Wings, Wheels and Whistles Weekend Celebration, the Fall Festival/Pancake Supper, Pre-Holiday Open House, Golden Dollar Night, Numbered Newspaper Contest, Senior Citizen Day, Santa Visit and Daddy Shopping Days. **Founded:** 1995. **Geographic Preference:** Local.

39748 ■ Grinnell Area Chamber of Commerce
833 4th Ave.
Grinnell, IA 50112
Ph: (641)236-6555
URL: http://www.grinnellchamber.org
Contact: Rachael Kinnick, Director
E-mail: rachael@getintogrinnell.com
Facebook: www.facebook.com/GrinnellChamber
X (Twitter): x.com/getintogrinnell
Instagram: www.instagram.com/grinnelliowa
YouTube: www.youtube.com/user/IowaGrinnell
Pinterest: www.pinterest.com/getintogrinnell

STATE LISTINGS

Description: Promotes business and community development in the Grinnell, IA area. **Geographic Preference:** Local.

39749 ■ Grow Cedar Valley (GCVAC)
360 Westfield Ave., Ste. 200
Waterloo, IA 50701
Ph: (319)232-1156
URL: http://www.growcedarvalley.com
Contact: Cary Darrah, President
E-mail: cary@growcedarvalley.com
Facebook: www.facebook.com/growcedarvalley
X (Twitter): x.com/growcedarvalley
Description: Promotes business and community development in Waterloo, IA. Conducts educational and community service projects. **Founded:** 1928. **Educational Activities:** Business After Hours. **Awards:** Harold Brock Innovation Award (Annual); John Deere-Treating Capital Well Award (Annual); Fulfilling the Vision of One Award (Annual); Cedar Valley Partner Award (Annual); Greater Cedar Valley Alliance and Chamber Business of the Year (Annual). **Geographic Preference:** Local.

39750 ■ Grundy Center Chamber of Commerce and Development
703 F Ave., Ste. 2
Grundy Center, IA 50638
Ph: (319)825-6118
Fax: (319)825-6471
Co. E-mail: cityclerk@gcmuni.net
URL: http://grundycenter.com
Facebook: www.facebook.com/people/City-of-Grundy-Center/100064388241538
Description: Promotes business and community development in Grundy Center, IA. **Founded:** 1877. **Geographic Preference:** Local.

39751 ■ Guthrie Center Chamber of Commerce (GCCC)
Becky Benton at State St. Insurance, 316 State St.
Guthrie Center, IA 50115
Ph: (641)332-2190
Co. E-mail: gcchamberofcommerce@gmail.com
URL: http://www.guthriecenter.com/guthriecenterchamber.html
Contact: Kristen Crouthamel, Advisor
E-mail: kristen@investgcsb.com
Description: Promotes business and community development in Guthrie Center, IA. Conducts charitable activities. **Founded:** 1937. **Geographic Preference:** Local.

39752 ■ Hartley Chamber of Commerce
56 2nd St. SE
Hartley, IA 51346
Ph: (712)928-4278
Co. E-mail: hartleychamber@tcaexpress.net
URL: http://www.hartleyiowa.com/chamber-of-commerce/about-the-chamber
Contact: Kent Billings, Vice President
Facebook: www.facebook.com/Hartleychamber
Description: Promotes business and community development in Hartley, IA. **Founded:** 2012. **Geographic Preference:** Local.

39753 ■ Hawarden Chamber and Economic Development Inc.
1150 Central Ave.
Hawarden, IA 51023
URL: http://www.guidestar.org/profile/42-1516190
Description: Promotes business and community development in Hawarden, IA. Conducts annual Labor Day weekend celebration. **Founded:** 2001. **Geographic Preference:** Local.

39754 ■ Humboldt & Dakota City Chamber of Commerce
29 5th St. S
Humboldt, IA 50548
Ph: (515)332-1481
Fax: (515)332-1453
Co. E-mail: chamber@hdcchamber.com
URL: http://www.cityofhumboldt.org
Contact: Mitch Nielsen, President
E-mail: humboldtspine@gmail.com

Description: Promotes business and community development in the Humboldt/Dakota City, IA area. Sponsors 4th of July festival. **Publications:** *Business Growth, Community Progress* (Monthly). **Geographic Preference:** Local.

39755 ■ Independence Area Chamber of Commerce
112 1st St. E
Independence, IA 50644
Ph: (319)334-7178
Fax: (319)334-7394
Co. E-mail: indychamber@indytel.com
URL: http://www.indeecommerce.com
Contact: Jeremy Hahn, President
Facebook: www.facebook.com/indeecommerce
Description: Promotes business and community development in the Independence, IA area. Sponsors festival. **Founded:** 1847. **Publications:** *The Promoter* (Annual). **Geographic Preference:** Local.

39756 ■ Indianola Chamber of Commerce (ICC)
111 N Buxton, Ste. 117
Indianola, IA 50125
Ph: (515)961-6269
Fax: (515)961-9753
Co. E-mail: chamber@indianolachamber.com
URL: http://www.indianolachamber.com
Contact: Brenda Easter, President
E-mail: brenda@indianolachamber.com
Facebook: www.facebook.com/IndianolaChamberOfCommerce
Instagram: www.instagram.com/indianolachamber
YouTube: www.youtube.com/channel/UCKIThREeYpYJ1zQDfyIDU7g
Description: Enhances business environment and contributes to the overall economic well-being and quality of life in Indianola, MS. **Founded:** 1849. **Publications:** *Business and Industry Insight* (Monthly). **Geographic Preference:** Local.

39757 ■ Iowa City Area Business Partnership
136 S Dubuque St.
Iowa City, IA 52240
Ph: (319)337-9637
Co. E-mail: info@iowacityarea.com
URL: http://www.iowacityarea.com
Contact: Kim Casko, President
Facebook: www.facebook.com/icareabusinesspartnership
Linkedin: www.linkedin.com/company/iowa-city-area-chamber-of-commerce
X (Twitter): x.com/icareabusiness
Instagram: www.instagram.com/icareabusinesspartnership
YouTube: www.youtube.com/channel/UCpYVKCm5W3suTt17JXCaqzw
Description: Promotes business and community development in Iowa City and Coralville and Johnson counties, IA. Sponsors Iowa Festival. **Founded:** 1921. **Publications:** *Envision* (Monthly); *Reflections* (Monthly). **Geographic Preference:** Local.

39758 ■ Iowa Falls Chamber of Commerce - Main Street
520 Rocksylvania Ave.
Iowa Falls, IA 50126
Ph: (641)648-5549
Co. E-mail: chamber@iowafallschamber.com
URL: http://iowafallschamber.com
Contact: Diana Thies, Director
Description: Area businesses and organizations. Seeks to promote the community of Iowa Falls and enhance the quality of life in the community. Activities include seasonal events, business retention and recruitment efforts, and community promotion activities. **Founded:** 1993. **Geographic Preference:** Local.

39759 ■ Iowa Great Lakes Area Chamber of Commerce (IGLACC)
565 S Hwy. 71, Ste. 4
Arnolds Park, IA 51331
Ph: (712)332-2107
Co. E-mail: blain@okobojichamber.com
URL: http://okobojichamber.com

Contact: Nick Staus, President
Facebook: www.facebook.com/OkobojiChamber
Linkedin: www.linkedin.com/company/iowa-great-lakes-area-chamber-of-commerce
X (Twitter): x.com/OkobojiChamber
Instagram: www.instagram.com/okobojichamber
YouTube: www.youtube.com/channel/UCpkhzt_Vn_TvzIaAUaFGvBg
Description: Promotes business, community development, and tourism in the Iowa Great Lakes area of northwestern Iowa. Conducts charitable activities. Sponsors festival. **Publications:** *Okoboji Spirit* (Annual). **Geographic Preference:** Local.

39760 ■ Jesup Chamber of Commerce
791 6th St.
Jesup, IA 50648-0592
Ph: (319)827-3100
Co. E-mail: jesupchamber827@gmail.com
URL: http://www.jesupiowa.com
Contact: Michael Fettkether, Director
Description: Promotes business and community development in Jesup, IA. **Geographic Preference:** Local.

39761 ■ Kalona Area Chamber of Commerce (KACC)
514 B Ave.
Kalona, IA 52247
Ph: (319)656-2660
Co. E-mail: info@kalonachamber.com
URL: http://www.kalonachamber.com
Contact: Lyndon Hershberger, President
Facebook: www.facebook.com/KalonaAreaChamberOfCommerce
Instagram: www.instagram.com/kalonachamberofcommerce
Description: Promotes business and community development in Kalona, IA area. **Founded:** 1846. **Geographic Preference:** Local.

39762 ■ Keokuk Area Chamber of Commerce
511 Blondeau St., Ste. 3
Keokuk, IA 52632
Ph: (319)524-5055
Co. E-mail: officemanager@keokukchamber.com
URL: http://keokukchamber.com
Contact: Shelley Oltmans, Executive Director
E-mail: director@keokukchamber.com
X (Twitter): x.com/KeokukChamber
Description: Promotes business and community development in Keokuk, IA. **Founded:** 1920. **Educational Activities:** Chamber's Board of Directors Meeting. **Geographic Preference:** Local.

39763 ■ Knoxville Chamber of Commerce
107 E Main St.
Knoxville, IA 50138
Ph: (641)828-7555
Co. E-mail: info@knoxvilleiachamber.com
URL: http://www.knoxvilleiachamber.com
Contact: Emma Skahill, Executive Director
Description: Strives to create new wealth and growth in the area. Supports businesses and community outreach. **Founded:** 1942. **Publications:** *Community Insight* (Monthly); *Visitors Guide and Economic Development Directory* (Annual). **Geographic Preference:** Local.

39764 ■ Lake City Betterment Association (LCBA)
105 N Center St.
Lake City, IA 51449
Ph: (712)464-3111
Co. E-mail: betterment@lakecityiowa.com
URL: http://www.lakecityiowa.com
Contact: Jim Luhring, President
E-mail: jim.luhring@gmail.com
Facebook: www.facebook.com/LakeCityBetterment
Description: Promotes business and community development in Lake City, IA. Sponsors Western Days July 4th Festival. **Geographic Preference:** Local.

39765 ■ LINK
URL(s): www.keokukchamber.wildapricot.org/page-1656289

Released: Quarterly **Availability:** Print; PDF; Online.

39766 ■ Madison County Chamber of Commerce
73 Jefferson St.
Winterset, IA 50273-1540
Ph: (515)462-1185
Co. E-mail: chamber@madisoncounty.com
URL: http://www.madisoncounty.com
Contact: Amara Huffine, Executive Director
E-mail: exec.dir@madisoncounty.com
Facebook: www.facebook.com/madisoncountyiowa
X (Twitter): x.com/MadisonCountyIA
Instagram: www.instagram.com/madisoncountyiowa
YouTube: www.youtube.com/channel/UCXaEwjUQ8Zgwl12uX0OEobw
Pinterest: www.pinterest.com/madisoncountyia
Description: Promotes business, community development, and tourism in the Winterset, IA area. **Founded:** 1975. **Geographic Preference:** Local.

39767 ■ Manchester Area Chamber of Commerce
200 E Main St.
Manchester, IA 52057
Ph: (563)927-4141
Co. E-mail: macc@manchesteriowa.org
URL: http://www.manchesteriowa.org
Contact: Kurt Heims, President
Facebook: www.facebook.com/ManchesterAreaChamber
X (Twitter): x.com/macciowa
Description: Promotes business and community development in the Manchester, IA area. **Founded:** 1944. **Publications:** *MACC Business News* (Monthly); *Community Resource Guide.* **Awards:** Manchester Area Chamber of Commerce Meritorious Service (Annual); Manchester Area Chamber of Commerce Chamber Person of the Year (Annual). **Geographic Preference:** Local.

39768 ■ Manning Chamber of Commerce (MCC)
321 Ctr. St.
Manning, IA 51455
Ph: (712)210-6929
Co. E-mail: chamber@manningia.com
URL: http://www.manningia.com/pview.aspx?catid=25&id=21030
Contact: Kristina Lupardus, President
Facebook: www.facebook.com/manningiachamber
Description: Promotes business and community development in Manning, IA. **Founded:** 1921. **Geographic Preference:** Local.

39769 ■ Maquoketa Area Chamber of Commerce
124 S Main St., Ste. 2.
Maquoketa, IA 52060
Ph: (563)652-4602
Free: 800-989-4602
Fax: (563)652-3020
Co. E-mail: info@maquoketachamber.com
URL: http://maquoketachamber.com
Contact: Tim Cottle, President
Facebook: www.facebook.com/MaquoketaAreaChamber
Linkedin: www.linkedin.com/company/maquoketa-area-chamber-of-commerce
Description: Promotes business and community development in the Maquoketa, IA area. **Founded:** 1942. **Publications:** *News In Brief* (Bimonthly). **Awards:** Maquoketa Area Chamber of Commerce Friends of Agriculture Awards. **Geographic Preference:** Local.

39770 ■ Marshalltown Area Chamber of Commerce (MACC)
709 S Center St.
Marshalltown, IA 50158
Ph: (641)753-6645
Co. E-mail: office@marshalltown.org
URL: http://www.marshalltown.org
Contact: John Hall, President
E-mail: jhall@marshalltown.org
Facebook: www.facebook.com/mtownchamber
Instagram: www.instagram.com/mtownchamber
Description: Promotes business and community development in the Marshalltown, IA area. Operates the Marshalltown Convention and Visitors Bureau. Convention/Meeting: none. **Founded:** 1898. **Publications:** *Digest* (Monthly); *Marshalltown Works* (Monthly). **Geographic Preference:** Local.

39771 ■ Mason City Area Chamber of Commerce
9 N Federal Ave.
Mason City, IA 50401
Ph: (641)423-5724
Fax: (641)423-5725
Co. E-mail: chamber@masoncityia.com
URL: http://masoncityia.com
Contact: Colleen Frein, President
Facebook: www.facebook.com/MasonCityChamber
Linkedin: www.linkedin.com/company/mason-city-chamber-of-commerce
X (Twitter): x.com/ChamberMC
YouTube: www.youtube.com/channel/UC0zRnw-7dW-ZONI7qPGMPgA
Description: Promotes business and community development in the Mason City, IA area. Sponsors North Iowa Band Festival. **Founded:** 1916. **Geographic Preference:** Local.

39772 ■ McGregor/Marquette Chamber of Commerce
146 Main St.
McGregor, IA 52157
Ph: (563)873-2186
Co. E-mail: mcgregormarquettechamber@gmail.com
URL: http://www.mcgreg-marq.org
Contact: Katie Ruff, President
Description: Promotes business and community development in McGregor and Marquette, IA. Sponsors art shows. **Geographic Preference:** Local.

39773 ■ *Member Directory*
700 Locust St., Ste. 100
Des Moines, IA 50309
Ph: (515)286-4950
Co. E-mail: info@dsmpartnership.com
URL: http://www.dsmpartnership.com
Contact: Jay Byers, Chief Executive Officer
E-mail: jbyers@dsmpartnership.com
URL(s): members.dsmpartnership.com/list
Description: Contains business trends and Chamber news. **Availability:** Online.

39774 ■ Missouri Valley Chamber of Commerce
100 S 4th St.
Missouri Valley, IA 51555
Ph: (712)642-2553
Fax: (712)642-3771
Co. E-mail: movalleychamber@gmail.com
URL: http://missourivalleychamber.org
Contact: Megan Zimmer, President
Facebook: www.facebook.com/MissouriValleyChamberOfCommerce
X (Twitter): x.com/chambervalley
Description: Promotes business and community development in Missouri Valley, IA. Sponsors Loess Hills Indian Market, Cultural Exchange, and Harrison County Fair Parade. **Publications:** *Caboose on the Loose* (Monthly). **Educational Activities:** Chamber Fair Parade. **Awards:** Missouri Valley Chamber of Commerce Business of the Year; Missouri Valley Chamber of Commerce Adult Volunteer of the Year. **Geographic Preference:** Local.

39775 ■ Monticello Area Chamber of Commerce (MACC)
204 E 1st St.
Monticello, IA 52310
Ph: (319)465-5626
Fax: (319)465-3527
Co. E-mail: chamber@macc-ia.us
URL: http://www.macc-ia.us
Contact: Chris Brokaw, President
Facebook: www.facebook.com/MonticelloIowaChamberOfCommerce
X (Twitter): x.com/MonticelloIACC
Description: Promotes business and community development in the area of Monticello in the state of Iowa. **Founded:** 1923. **Geographic Preference:** Local.

39776 ■ Mount Pleasant Area Chamber Alliance
124 S Main St.
Mount Pleasant, IA 52641
Ph: (319)385-3101
Co. E-mail: info@mpiowa.org
URL: http://www.mountpleasantiowa.org
Contact: Meg Richtman, President
Facebook: www.facebook.com/MountPleasantACA
X (Twitter): x.com/MtPleasantIOWA
YouTube: www.youtube.com/channel/UCHIRR5Oip_fXTI3Z8-Qws7A
Description: Promotes business and community development in the Mt. Pleasant, IA area. **Founded:** 1939. **Publications:** *Newsline* (Monthly). **Awards:** MPACC Expansion Award (Annual). **Geographic Preference:** Local.

39777 ■ Northwood Area Chamber of Commerce (NACC)
714 Central Ave.
Northwood, IA 50459
Contact: Teresa George, President
Description: Promotes business and community development in the Northwood, IA area. **Geographic Preference:** Local.

39778 ■ Norwalk Area Chamber of Commerce (NACC)
1043 Sunset Dr., Ste. 3
Norwalk, IA 50211
Ph: (515)981-0619
Co. E-mail: info@norwalkchamber.org
URL: http://www.norwalkchamber.org
Contact: Benjamin Pearson, President
URL(s): member.iowachamber.net/list/member/norwalk-area-chamber-of-commerce-143
Facebook: www.facebook.com/NorwalkChamberIowa
X (Twitter): x.com/norwalkchamber1
YouTube: www.youtube.com/channel/UCVsTppMyzx3Yk1IYThiTv3A
Description: Provides leadership for the advancement of economic development, promotion of members, and enhances the quality of life for the Norwalk area. **Geographic Preference:** Local.

39779 ■ Oelwein Chamber and Area Development (OCAD)
6 S Frederick
Oelwein, IA 50662
Ph: (319)283-1105
Fax: (319)283-2890
Co. E-mail: ocad@oelwein.com
URL: http://www.oelwein.com
Contact: Deb Howard, Executive Director
E-mail: dhoward@oelwein.com
Facebook: www.facebook.com/oelweinchamber
Description: Promotes business and community development in Oelwein, IA. **Founded:** 1918. **Publications:** *Oelwein Outlook* (Monthly). **Geographic Preference:** Local.

39780 ■ Onawa Chamber of Commerce (OCC)
707 Iowa Ave.
Onawa, IA 51040
Ph: (712)423-1801
Co. E-mail: chamber@onawa.com
URL: http://www.onawachamber.com
Contact: Jenn Collison, Contact
E-mail: chamber@onawa.com
Facebook: www.facebook.com/OnawaChamberofCommerce
Description: Promotes business and community development in Onawa, IA. Sponsors Onawa Lewis and Clark Festival. **Publications:** *Chamber News.* **Geographic Preference:** Local.

39781 ■ Orange City Chamber of Commerce
125 Central Ave. SE
Orange City, IA 51041
Ph: (712)707-4885

STATE LISTINGS   Iowa ■ 39798

Co. E-mail: occhmbr@gmail.com
URL: http://orangecityiowa.com/business/chamber
Contact: Mike Hofman, Executive Director
Facebook: www.facebook.com/cityoforangecityia
X (Twitter): x.com/OrangeCityIA
Instagram: www.instagram.com/orangecityia
Description: Seeks to advance the economic, professional, industrial, cultural and civic welfare of the Orange City area. **Geographic Preference:** Local.

39782 ■ Osage Chamber of Commerce
704 Main St.
 Osage, IA 50461
Ph: (641)732-3163
Co. E-mail: chamber@osage.net
URL: http://www.osagechamber.com
Contact: Harlan Bisbee, Treasurer
X (Twitter): x.com/OsageChamber
Description: Promotes business and community development in Osage, IA. **Founded:** 1935. **Geographic Preference:** Local.

39783 ■ Osceola Chamber-Main Street
115 E Washington St.
 Osceola, IA 50213
Ph: (641)342-4200
Co. E-mail: ocms@iowatelecom.net
URL: http://www.osceolachamber.com
Contact: Dave Opie, President
Facebook: www.facebook.com/OCMS06
Description: Promotes business and community development in Osceola, IA. **Geographic Preference:** Local.

39784 ■ Pella Chamber of Commerce (PCC)
818 Washington St.
 Pella, IA 50219
Ph: (641)628-2626
Fax: (641)628-9697
Co. E-mail: info@pella.org
URL: http://pella.org
Contact: Mark Putnam, President
E-mail: president@central.edu
Facebook: www.facebook.com/pacealliance
Description: Promotes business and community development in Pella, IA. Sponsors Fall Festival; bestows annual Community Service Award. **Publications:** *Business Directory*; *Nieuwsbrief* (Monthly). **Geographic Preference:** Local.

39785 ■ Pocahontas Chamber of Commerce
324 N Main St.
 Pocahontas, IA 50574
Ph: (712)335-0900
Co. E-mail: pocahontaschamber@gmail.com
URL: http://www.pokychamber.com
Contact: Parker Aden, Executive Director
Facebook: www.facebook.com/pokychamber
Instagram: www.instagram.com/pocahontasiowa
YouTube: www.youtube.com/channel/UCF7iW
 t5xwkoNNEuESGjiiMQ
Description: Promotes business and community development in Pocahontas, IA. **Geographic Preference:** Local.

39786 ■ Quad Cities Chamber of Commerce
331 W 3rd St.
 Davenport, IA 52801
Ph: (563)322-1706
URL: http://www.quadcitieschamber.com
Contact: A. J. Loss, Chairman
Facebook: www.facebook.com/quadcitieschamber
Linkedin: www.linkedin.com/company/quad-cities
 -chamber-of-commerce
X (Twitter): x.com/chamberqc
YouTube: www.youtube.com/channel/UCjIA
 dSIfpgaFAEtNmjq-SfQ
Description: Promotes business and community development in the area. **Founded:** 2010. **Publications:** *Illinois Quad City Chamber of Commerce--Membership Directory* (Annual); *Business News In Depth* (Bimonthly); *QC Direct* (Annual); *Business News Quarterly* (Quarterly). **Geographic Preference:** Local.

39787 ■ Red Oak Chamber and Industry Association (ROCIA)
307 E Reed St.
 Red Oak, IA 51566
Ph: (712)623-4821
Co. E-mail: info@redoakiowa.com
URL: http://www.redoakiowa.com
Contact: Elaine Carlson, Director
Facebook: www.facebook.com/RedOakChamber
Instagram: www.instagram.com/redoakchamber
YouTube: www.youtube.com/channel/UCCFqoz
 _wv70PmPpppIEaU2g
Description: Promotes business and community development in Red Oak, IA. **Publications:** *Red Oak Chamber of Commerce ChamberGram* (Monthly). **Geographic Preference:** Local.

39788 ■ Rock Rapids Chamber of Commerce [Rock Rapids Community Affairs Corp.]
411 1st Ave.
 Rock Rapids, IA 51246
Ph: (712)472-3456
Co. E-mail: chamber@rockrapids.com
Contact: Shannon Monson, President
Facebook: www.facebook.com/people/Rock-Rapids
 -Chamber-of-Commerce/100064746724456
Description: Promotes social and economic development in Rock Rapid, IA. **Publications:** *Chamber Affairs* (Monthly). **Geographic Preference:** Local.

39789 ■ Rock Valley Chamber of Commerce (RVCC)
PO Box 89
 Rock Valley, IA 51247
Ph: (712)476-9300
Fax: (712)476-9116
Co. E-mail: info@rockvalleychamber.com
URL: http://www.rockvalleychamber.com/web
Contact: Spencer Gort, President
Facebook: www.facebook.com/
 RockValleyIAChamber
X (Twitter): x.com/rvchamberrec
Description: Promotes business and community development in Rock Valley, IA. Sponsors yearly basketball tournament. Publications: none. **Geographic Preference:** Local.

39790 ■ Rockwell City Chamber & Development - Rockwell City Public Library
1219 High St.
 Rockwell City, IA 50579
Ph: (712)297-8874
Co. E-mail: chamber@rockwellcity.com
URL: http://www.rockwellcity.com
Contact: Jason Shaver, President
Description: Promotes business and community development in Rockwell City, IA. **Scope:** Genealogy. **Services:** inter library loan; copying. **Holdings:** 800 books; magazines; newspapers. **Geographic Preference:** Local.

39791 ■ Shelby County Chamber of Commerce & Industry (SCCCI)
1901 Hawkeye Ave., Ste. 101
 Harlan, IA 51537
Ph: (712)755-2114
Fax: (712)755-2115
Co. E-mail: info@exploreshelbycounty.com
URL: http://www.exploreshelbycounty.com
Contact: Steve Ineson, President
E-mail: steve@4seasonstrav.com
Facebook: www.facebook.com/ExploreShelbyCounty
Description: Promotes business and community development in Harlan, IA. **Geographic Preference:** Local.

39792 ■ Sheldon Chamber and Development Corp. (SCDC)
416 9th St.
 Sheldon, IA 51201
Ph: (712)324-4651
URL: http://sheldoniowa.com
Contact: Justin Jonas, President
Facebook: www.facebook.com/SheldonChamber
Description: Promotes business and tourism in Sheldon, IA. **Geographic Preference:** Local.

39793 ■ Shenandoah Chamber and Industry Association (SCIA)
500 W Clarinda Ave.
 Shenandoah, IA 51601
Ph: (712)246-3455
Co. E-mail: chamber@shenandoahiowa.net
URL: http://shenandoahiowa.net
Description: Promotes business and community development in Shenandoah, IA. Sponsors Master Growers Contest, Shen Fest, Business Horizons program, Teacher Appreciation breakfast, Agriculture Banquet, Administration Staff Luncheon, Legislative Coffees, Industry Coffees, Teen Art Show, Spring Craft Fair, CABA Tournament, and Christmas Parade. **Founded:** 1941. **Publications:** *Chamber Report* (3/year). **Geographic Preference:** Local.

39794 ■ Sibley Chamber of Commerce (SCC)
808 3rd Ave.
 Sibley, IA 51249
Co. E-mail: chamber2@premieronline.net
URL: http://www.sibleyiowa.net/sibley/chamber
Contact: Travis Ten Napel, President
Description: Promotes business and community development in Sibley, IA. Sponsors annual Good Ole Summertime festival. **Founded:** 1915. **Geographic Preference:** Local.

39795 ■ Sioux Center Chamber of Commerce (SCCC)
14 3rd St. NW
 Sioux Center, IA 51250
Ph: (712)722-3457
Fax: (712)722-3465
Co. E-mail: admin@siouxcenterchamber.com
URL: http://www.siouxcenterchamber.com
Contact: Barbara Den Herder, Chief Executive Officer
E-mail: barbdh@siouxcenterchamber.com
Facebook: www.facebook.com/siouxcenterchamber
Instagram: www.instagram.com/siouxcenterchamber
Description: Promotes business and community development in Sioux Center, IA. **Founded:** 1967. **Geographic Preference:** Local.

39796 ■ Siouxland Chamber of Commerce (SCC)
101 Pierce St.
 Sioux City, IA 51101
Ph: (712)255-7903
Fax: (712)258-7578
Co. E-mail: chamber@siouxlandchamber.com
URL: http://siouxlandchamber.com
Contact: Chris McGowan, President
Facebook: www.facebook.com/Siouxlan
 dChamberofCommerce
Linkedin: www.linkedin.com/company/siouxlan
 d-chamber-of-commerce
X (Twitter): x.com/SiouxIndChamber
YouTube: www.youtube.com/user/SiouxlandChamber
Description: Promotes business and community development in Sioux City, IA. **Founded:** 1874. **Publications:** *Siouxland Business* (Weekly). **Educational Activities:** Siouxland Chamber of Commerce Dinner (Annual). **Awards:** W. Edwards Deming Business Leadership and Entrepreneurial Excellence Award (Annual). **Geographic Preference:** Local.

39797 ■ Spencer Chamber of Commerce
1805 Hwy. Blvd.
 Spencer, IA 51301
Ph: (712)262-5680
Co. E-mail: info@spenceriowachamber.org
URL: http://spenceriowachamber.org
Contact: Patty Schulz, President
Facebook: www.facebook.com/SpencerChamber
X (Twitter): x.com/explorespencer
Description: Promotes business and community development in Spencer, Clay County and Northwest IA. **Founded:** 1890. **Publications:** *The Spencer Chamber Monthly* (Monthly). **Geographic Preference:** Local.

39798 ■ Storm Lake United (SLU)
119 W 6th St.
 Storm Lake, IA 50588
Ph: (712)732-3780

Free: 888-752-4692
Fax: (712)732-1511
Co. E-mail: info@stormlakeunited.com
URL: http://visitstormlake.com
Contact: Breanna Horsey, Executive Director
Facebook: www.facebook.com/stormlakeunited
X (Twitter): x.com/StormLakeUnited
Instagram: www.instagram.com/stormlakeunited
YouTube: www.youtube.com/channel/
 UCUVmUUlm9bhfVwuFz64knyw
Description: Promotes business and community development and tourism in the Storm Lake, IA area. **Publications:** *Shore Line* (Monthly). **Geographic Preference:** Local.

39799 ■ Story City Greater Chamber Connection
524 Broad St.
 Story City, IA 50248
Ph: (515)733-4214
Co. E-mail: director@storycitygcc.com
URL: http://storycitygcc.org
Contact: Shannon McKinley, Contact
Pinterest: www.pinterest.com/storycitycarousel
Description: Promotes business and community development in Story City, IA. Sponsors Scandinavian Days. **Founded:** 1908. **Geographic Preference:** Local.

39800 ■ Tama/Toledo Area Chamber of Commerce
PO Box 367
 Toledo, IA 52342
Ph: (641)484-6661
Co. E-mail: tama.toledochamber@yahoo.com
URL: http://www.tamatoledochamber.com
Description: Promotes business and community development in Toledo, IA. **Geographic Preference:** Local.

39801 ■ Urbandale Chamber of Commerce
2830 100th St., Ste. 110
 Urbandale, IA 50322
Ph: (515)331-6855
Co. E-mail: info@urbandalechamber.com
URL: http://uniquelyurbandale.com
Contact: Tiffany Menke, President
E-mail: tmenke@urbandalechamber.com
Facebook: www.facebook.com/UrbandaleChamber
X (Twitter): x.com/Urbandalechmbr
Instagram: www.instagram.com/urbandalechamber
YouTube: www.youtube.com/user/Urban
 daleChamber
Description: Promotes business and community development in Urbandale, IA. **Publications:** *Urbandale Chamber Annual Report* (Annual); *Urbandale Restaurant Guide* (Annual); *Urbandale Buyers Guide* (Annual). **Geographic Preference:** Local.

39802 ■ Walcott Chamber of Commerce (WCC)
Walcott City Hall, 128 W Lincoln St.
 Walcott, IA 52773
Ph: (563)284-6571
Fax: (563)284-6984
Co. E-mail: info@cityofwalcott.com
URL: http://cityofwalcott.com
Contact: Wendy J. Minnick, Officer
Founded: 1854. **Geographic Preference:** Local.

39803 ■ Waukon Chamber of Commerce
101 W Main St.
 Waukon, IA 52172
Ph: (563)568-4110
Fax: (563)568-6990
Co. E-mail: waukonchamber@gmail.com
URL: http://www.waukon.org
Contact: Kristen Wilke, President
Facebook: www.facebook.com/waukonchamber
X (Twitter): x.com/WaukonChamber
Description: Promotes business and community development in Waukon, IA. **Publications:** none. **Founded:** 1952. **Geographic Preference:** Local.

39804 ■ Waverly Chamber of Commerce
118 E Bremer Ave.
 Waverly, IA 50677
Ph: (319)352-4526
Co. E-mail: waverly@waverlychamber.com
URL: http://www.waverlyia.com/chamber-of
 -commerce
Contact: Don Meyer, Chairman of the Board
Facebook: www.facebook.com/
 WaverlyChamberofCommerce
Description: Encompasses Chamber of Commerce, Main Street, tourism and quality of life. **Founded:** 1859. **Geographic Preference:** Local.

39805 ■ West Bend Chamber of Commerce
PO Box 366
 West Bend, IA 50597
Ph: (515)887-2181
Co. E-mail: info@westbendchamber.com
URL: http://westbendiowa.com
Contact: Kenneth Bollig, Contact
Description: Serves the members and community by preserving and encouraging growth and development in the West Bend area. **Founded:** 1856. **Geographic Preference:** Local.

39806 ■ West Des Moines Chamber of Commerce (WDMCC)
650 S Prairie View Dr., Ste. 110
 West Des Moines, IA 50265
Ph: (515)225-6009
Co. E-mail: info@wdmchamber.org
URL: http://wdmchamber.org
Contact: Katherine Harrington, President
Facebook: www.facebook.com/wdmchamber
Linkedin: www.linkedin.com/company/wdmchamber
X (Twitter): x.com/wdmchamber
Instagram: www.instagram.com/wdmchamber
YouTube: www.youtube.com/channel/UCa_JRb5lrs
 tucNNZJfBLLsg
Description: Promotes business and community development in West Des Moines, IA. Sponsors Valley Arts Festival. **Founded:** 1938. **Publications:** *Premier Living Guide* (Annual); *West Side Story* (Monthly); *Premier Living Guide* (Annual). **Educational Activities:** West Des Moines Chamber of Commerce Dinner; West Des Moines Chamber of Commerce Membership Luncheon. **Awards:** West Des Moines Chamber of Commerce Citizen of the Year (Annual). **Geographic Preference:** Local.

39807 ■ West Union Chamber of Commerce (WUCC)
101 N Vine St.
 West Union, IA 52175
Ph: (563)422-3070
URL: http://www.westunion.com
Contact: Jason Knox, President
Facebook: www.facebook.com/westunionchamber
Description: Promotes business and community development in the West Union, IA area. **Founded:** 2013. **Publications:** *Chamber of Commerce News*. **Awards:** West Union Chamber of Commerce Citizen of the Year (Annual). **Geographic Preference:** Local.

39808 ■ Williamsburg Chamber of Commerce
210 W State St.
 Williamsburg, IA 52361
Ph: (319)668-1500
Co. E-mail: wburgchamber@gmail.com
URL: http://williamsburgiowa.gov
Facebook: www.facebook.com/wburgchamber
Description: Promotes business and community development in Williamsburg, IA. Sponsors annual Kids Day. Provides seasonal promotions for area merchants. **Founded:** 1854. **Geographic Preference:** Local.

39809 ■ Wilton Chamber of Commerce
104 E 4th St.
 Wilton, IA 52778
Ph: (563)732-2330
Fax: (563)732-2332
URL: http://wiltoniowa.org/chamber
Contact: Becky Brisker, President
URL(s): wiltonchamber.com
Facebook: www.facebook.com/wiltoniowa
X (Twitter): x.com/wiltoniowa
Description: Strives to make Wilton a better place to live and do business. Seeks to promote commercial, industrial and civic development. Activities include a smorgasbord in May; Wilfundy, a golf day for members and their customers, in June; Founders Day in August; Christmas Activities in December. **Publications:** *Chamber Connection* (Weekly). **Geographic Preference:** Local.

FINANCING AND LOAN PROGRAMS

39810 ■ AAVIN Private Equity (AAVIN)
1245 First Ave. SE
 Cedar Rapids, IA 52402
Ph: (319)247-1072
URL: http://www.aavin.com
Contact: Thies Kolln, Partner
E-mail: tkolln@aavin.com
Linkedin: www.linkedin.com/company/aavin-equity-a
 dvisors-llc-
Description: Provider of late stage and expansion stage financings, buyouts and recapitalizations. **Founded:** 1999. **Preferred Investment Size:** $500,000 to $3,000,000. **Investment Policies:** Early, first, second, and third stage, buyouts, recapitalization, and late stage. **Industry Preferences:** Medical devices and services, telecommunications, financial services, manufacturing and distribution, industrial products and services, and computer and software.

39811 ■ Allsop Venture Partners / AAVIN
1245 First Ave. SE
 Cedar Rapids, IA 52402
URL: http://www.aavin.com
Contact: James Thorp, Managing Partner
E-mail: jthorp@aavin.com
Linkedin: www.linkedin.com/company/aavin-equity-a
 dvisors-llc-
Description: Firm provides buyouts and growth capital investments services. **Founded:** 1999. **Preferred Investment Size:** $500,000 to $3,000,000. **Industry Preferences:** communications and media, computer hardware and software, semiconductors and other electronics, medical and health, consumer related, industrial and energy, transportation, financial services, business service, and manufacturing.

39812 ■ Berthel Fisher & Company Planning Inc. (BFCP)
Berthel Fisher and Co. (BFC)
 4201 42nd St. NE, Ste. 100
 Cedar Rapids, IA 52402-7101
Ph: (319)447-5700
Free: 800-356-5234
Fax: (319)447-4250
Co. E-mail: independence@berthel.com
URL: http://www.berthel.com
Contact: Thomas J. Berthel, President
E-mail: tberthel@berthel.com
Description: Provider of investment brokerage, wealth management and investment banking services. **Founded:** 1985.

39813 ■ Corridor Angel Investors
The Geonetric Bldg.,
 415 12th Ave. SE
 Cedar Rapids, IA 52401
Ph: (319)382-5128
URL: http://newbo.co/eastern-iowa-corridor-angel
 -investors
Description: Accredited angel investors funding early-stage companies in (or connected to) Iowa. **Preferred Investment Size:** Up to $50,000. **Investment Policies:** For-profit, scalable business in Iowa. **Industry Preferences:** Education; finance; healthcare; aging; food; manufacturing; transportation; agriculture.

39814 ■ Plains Angels
700 Locust St., Ste. 100
 Des Moines, IA 50309
URL: http://www.dsmpartnership.com/growing
 -business-here/business-resources/plains-angels
Contact: Mike Colwell, Manager
E-mail: mcolwell@dsmpartnership.com

Description: Invests in high-potential emerging companies. **Founded:** 2012.

PROCUREMENT ASSISTANCE PROGRAMS

39815 ■ Iowa Procurement Technical Assistance Center - Iowa State University Extension Office - Center for Industrial Research and Service (CIRAS)
1805 Collaboration Pl., Ste. 2300.
Ames, IA 50010
Ph: (515)294-3420
Co. E-mail: ciras@iastate.edu
URL: http://www.ciras.iastate.edu
Linkedin: www.linkedin.com/company/ciras-iowastateuniversity
X (Twitter): x.com/ciras_isu
YouTube: www.youtube.com/channel/UCJDRwpBeTkCEsotoZTfY8bw
Description: Provides assistance to business in marketing products and services to the Federal, state and local governments. **Founded:** 1963.

39816 ■ Iowa State University of Science & Technology - Center For Industrial Research & Service (CIRAS) - Iowa Procurement Technical Assistance Center
1805 Collaboration Pl., Ste. 2300
Ames, IA 50010
Ph: (515)294-3420
URL: http://www.aptac-us.org/find-a-ptac/?state=IA
Contact: Mary Zimmerman, Specialist
E-mail: maryz@iastate.edu
URL(s): www.ciras.iastate.edu/government-contracting
Description: Provide assistance to business in marketing products and services to the federal, state and local governments.

INCUBATORS/RESEARCH AND TECHNOLOGY PARKS

39817 ■ Entrepreneurial Development Center Inc. (EDC)
230 2nd St. SE, Ste. 212
Cedar Rapids, IA 52401
Ph: (319)369-4955
Fax: (319)832-1481
Co. E-mail: info@edcinc.org
URL: http://www.edcinc.org
Contact: Curt Nelson, Chief Executive Officer
Facebook: www.facebook.com/EDCinc
Linkedin: www.linkedin.com/company/entrepreneurial-development-center
X (Twitter): x.com/edcinc123
Instagram: www.instagram.com/edc_inc_iowa
Description: A small business incubator who pioneered business development and entrepreneurial education programs to accelerate business growth for entrepreneurs in emerging businesses without using public funding. **Founded:** 2003.

39818 ■ Global Insurance Accelerator (GIA)
321 E Walnut St., Ste. 130
Des Moines, IA 50309
Co. E-mail: hello@globalinsuranceaccelerator.com
URL: http://www.globalinsuranceaccelerator.com
Contact: Dan Israel, Managing Director
Linkedin: www.linkedin.com/company/global-insurance-accelerator
Description: Mentor-driven business accelerator designed to foster innovation in the insurance industry by supporting startups targeting the global insurance industry. **Founded:** 2014.

39819 ■ Iowa Startup Accelerator (ISA)
415 12th Ave. SE
Cedar Rapids, IA 52401
Ph: (319)382-5128
Co. E-mail: hello@newbo.co
URL: http://newbo.co
Facebook: www.facebook.com/NewBoCo
X (Twitter): x.com/newboco
Instagram: www.instagram.com/newboco

Description: Firm offers variety of business accelerator. **Founded:** 2014.

39820 ■ Iowa State University Pappajohn Center for Entrepreneurship
1805 Collaboration Pl., Ste. 1300
Ames, IA 50010
Ph: (515)296-6532
Co. E-mail: info@isupjcenter.org
URL: http://www.isupjcenter.org
Contact: Judi Eyles, Director
E-mail: eyles@iastate.edu
Facebook: www.facebook.com/isuentrepreneurship
Linkedin: www.linkedin.com/company/isu-pappajohn-center-for-entrepreneurship
X (Twitter): x.com/ISU_JPEC
Instagram: www.instagram.com/isu_jpec
YouTube: www.youtube.com/channel/UCnViOgIJYv7MEB47SLxWl8Q
Description: Offers tools for building and improving Iowa's businesses; creates a culture that encourages entrepreneurship and innovation. **Founded:** 1997.

39821 ■ Iowa State University Research Park (ISURP)
1805 Collaboration Pl. Ste. 1250
Ames, IA 50010
Ph: (515)296-7275
Fax: (515)296-9924
Co. E-mail: isupark@iastate.edu
URL: http://www.isupark.org
Facebook: www.facebook.com/ISUResearchPark
Linkedin: www.linkedin.com/company/isu-research-park
X (Twitter): x.com/isuresearchpark
Instagram: www.instagram.com/isurpark
YouTube: www.youtube.com/embed/HbR8nbEM0Pc
Description: A small business incubator which identifies technology-based concepts and businesses at early stages of development and provides an environment for their growth. **Scope:** 195-acre site on the University's South Campus facilitating interaction between corporate research laboratories and the University research community. **Founded:** 1988.

39822 ■ John Papajohn Entrepreneurial Center (JPEC)
500 College Dr.
Mason City, IA 50401
Ph: (641)422-4111
Free: 888-466-4222
Co. E-mail: pappajohn@niacc.edu
URL: http://www.pappajohncenter.com
Contact: John Pappa, President
E-mail: pappajohn@niacc.edu
URL(s): iowajpec.org
Facebook: www.facebook.com/NIACCPappajohn
Linkedin: www.linkedin.com/company/pappajohn-center
X (Twitter): x.com/NiaccPappajohn
Description: On the North Iowa Area Community College Campus, provides a nurturing environment where new businesses can develop and grow during those challenging first few years of existence. **Founded:** 1997.

39823 ■ John Pappajohn Entrepreneurial Center (JPEC)
500 College Dr., Ste. 120
Mason City, IA 50401
Ph: (641)422-4111
Co. E-mail: pappajohn@niacc.edu
URL: http://www.pappajohncenter.com/entrepreneurs/start-a-business
Facebook: www.facebook.com/NIACCPappajohn
Linkedin: www.linkedin.com/company/pappajohn-center
X (Twitter): x.com/NiaccPappajohn
Description: Provides business consulting, access to capital, networking events, business acceleration services, and a variety of educational opportunities. **Founded:** 1997.

39824 ■ New Bohemian Innovation Collaborative (NEW)
415 12th Ave. SE
Cedar Rapids, IA 52401

Ph: (319)382-5128
URL: http://newbo.co
Facebook: www.facebook.com/NewBoCo
X (Twitter): x.com/newboco
Instagram: www.instagram.com/newboco
Description: Iowa based tech-based startup accelerator fostering a diverse and inclusive community, supporting and encouraging people with big ideas.

39825 ■ Regional Entrepreneurship, Leadership, and Innovation Center (RELI)
c/o Kelly Prickett, Director, Entrepreneurship & Economic Development Initiative
15330 Truman St.
Ottumwa, IA 52501
Ph: (641)683-5188
Free: 800-726-2585
Co. E-mail: kelly.prickett@indianhills.edu
URL: http://www.indianhills.edu/businessrelations/reli.php
Contact: Kelly Prickett, Director
E-mail: kelly.prickett@indianhills.edu
Description: Designed to help interested communities spur new business growth in their own town or county. To participate, a community must have a group of local citizens who are interested in overseeing the project. Staff will collaborate with the group by offering assistance in the areas of strategic project planning and business recruitment/selection.

39826 ■ Small Business and Startup Stories
700 locust St., Ste.100
Des Moines, IA 50309
URL: http://www.dsmpartnership.com
Contact: Dannie Patrick, President
E-mail: president@ypcdsm.com
Description: Helps startups and entrepreneurs maximize success by providing advice, connections and mentoring. **Founded:** 2007.

39827 ■ SoCo Nexus
209 3rd St. SE
Cedar Rapids, IA 52401
URL: http://www.soconexus.org
Contact: Darian Pennington, Contact
Description: A non-profit organization providing space, support, and mentoring to local technology startups and entrepreneurs.

39828 ■ University of Iowa Research Park - Business Incubation Program
2500 Crosspark Rd.
Coralville, IA 52241-4710
URL: http://researchpark.uiowa.edu/business-incubation
Description: A small business incubator fostering the development of new business ventures that make use of advanced technology, offering services and facilities to start-up businesses and established companies eager to initiate new endeavors. Comprised of the BioVentures Center Facility and the Technology Innovation Center.

39829 ■ University of Iowa Technology Innovation Center
2660 UCC
Iowa City, IA 52242
Co. E-mail: research-webmaster@uiowa.edu
URL: http://now.uiowa.edu/keywords/technology-innovation-center
Description: An incubator for new business ventures that make use of advanced technology. It offers services and facilities to start-up businesses and established companies eager to initiate new endeavors. **Founded:** 1984.

EDUCATIONAL PROGRAMS

39830 ■ Des Moines Area Community College - Urban Campus (DMACC)
1100 7th St.
Des Moines, IA 50314
Ph: (515)244-4226
Free: 800-362-2127
Fax: (515)248-7216
Co. E-mail: ucstudentservicesofc@dmacc.edu

URL: http://www.dmacc.edu/urban/Pages/welcome.aspx
Facebook: www.facebook.com/DMACCUrban
X (Twitter): x.com/dmaccurban
Description: A wide variety of courses and workshops are offered to the working student wishing to develop or update specific occupational skills. Programs emphasize both fundamental concepts and practical experience to assure thorough competence in the chosen field. The Small Business Management Education Program offers a number of courses for credit and noncredit status--designed to meet the educational needs of the small business owner. **Founded:** 1966.

39831 ■ Iowa Lakes Community College
300 S 18th St.
Estherville, IA 51334
Free: 800-242-5106
Co. E-mail: info@iowalakes.edu
URL: http://www.iowalakes.edu
Contact: Tammy Prochnow, Contact
E-mail: tprochnow@iowalakes.edu
Facebook: www.facebook.com/IowaLakesCommunityCollege
X (Twitter): x.com/iowalakes
Instagram: www.instagram.com/iowalakescc
YouTube: www.youtube.com/user/iowalakescommcollege
Pinterest: www.pinterest.com/iowalakescc
Description: Two-year college offering a small business management program. **Founded:** 1970.

39832 ■ Marshalltown Community College (MCC)
3700 S Center St.
Marshalltown, IA 50158
Ph: (641)752-7106
Free: 866-622-4748
Co. E-mail: mccinfo@iavalley.edu
URL: http://mcc.iavalley.edu
Contact: Angie Redmond, Dean
E-mail: angie.redmond@iavalley.edu
Facebook: www.facebook.com/marshalltowncommunitycollege
X (Twitter): x.com/marshalltownCC
Instagram: www.instagram.com/marshalltowncc
YouTube: www.youtube.com/user/ivccd
Description: Two-year college offering a small business course through the continuing education program. **Founded:** 1927.

LEGISLATIVE ASSISTANCE

39833 ■ Iowa Senate Committee on Small Business, Economic Development and Tourism
State Capitol Bldg.
E 12th and Grand
Des Moines, IA 50319
URL: http://test.legis.iowa.gov/DOCS/GA/76GA/Senate/Comm/SmallBus.html
Contact: Steven Hansen, Chairman

CONSULTANTS

39834 ■ Kremer Kehe Inc.
110 S Vine St.
West Union, IA 52175
Contact: Jared Kremer, President
Description: Offers financial solutions to small businesses, including consulting, strategic planning support, tax preparation, accounting, payroll, and marketing.

PUBLICATIONS

39835 ■ *Corridor Business Journal (CBJ)*
845 Quarry Rd., Ste. 125
Coralville, IA 52241
URL: http://www.corridorbusiness.com
Contact: John Lohman, President
URL(s): corridorbusiness.com
Facebook: www.facebook.com/CorridorBusinessJournal
Linkedin: www.linkedin.com/company/corridor-business-journal
X (Twitter): twitter.com/CBJournal
Ed: Gigi Wood. **Released:** Weekly **Price:** $7, for print + online. **Description:** Contains business information on the Cedar Rapids/Iowa City corridor. **Availability:** Print; Online.

39836 ■ *Iowa Business & Technology Resource Guide*
Contact: Janette Larkin, Director, Sales and Marketing
E-mail: janettelarkin@bpcdm.com
URL(s): www.dmbusinessdaily.com/
Released: Annual **Price:** Free. **Description:** Trade magazine covering small business. **Availability:** Print.

VENTURE CAPITAL FIRM

39837 ■ AAVIN Private Equity Advisors
1245 First Ave. SE
Cedar Rapids, IA 52402
Ph: (319)247-1072
URL: http://www.aavin.com
Contact: Gina Milroy, Chief Financial Officer
E-mail: gmilroy@aavin.com
Linkedin: www.linkedin.com/company/aavin-equity-advisors-llc
Description: Venture capital firm investing in late-stage and expansion-stage companies. **Founded:** 1999.

Kansas

ASSOCIATIONS AND OTHER ORGANIZATIONS

39838 ■ Kansas Agribusiness Retailers Association (KARA)
816 SW Tyler, Ste. 100
Topeka, KS 66612
Ph: (785)234-0463
Fax: (785)234-2930
Co. E-mail: membership@kansasag.org
URL: http://www.ksagretailers.org
Contact: Ron Seeber, President
E-mail: ron@kansasag.org
Description: Agribusiness firms that supply fertilizers, crop protection chemicals, seed, petroleum products, and agronomic expertise to Kansas farmers. Aims to foster professional development and business viability for the plant nutrient and crop protection retail industry in Kansas. **Educational Activities:** Kansas Agri Business Expo (Annual). **Geographic Preference:** State.

SMALL BUSINESS DEVELOPMENT CENTERS

39839 ■ Kansas Small Business Development Center at Fort Hays State University (KSBDC)
600 Pk. St., Custer Hall 110
Hays, KS 67601
Ph: (785)628-5615
Fax: (785)628-4163
Co. E-mail: ksbdc@fhsu.edu
URL: http://www.fhsu.edu/ksbdc
Contact: Rick Feltenberger, Regional Director
E-mail: rkfeltenberger2@fhsu.edu
Description: Represents and promotes the small business sector. Provides management assistance to current and prospective small business owners. Helps to improve management skills and expand the products and services of members. **Geographic Preference:** Local.

39840 ■ Kansas Small Business Development Center - Lead Center (KSBDC)
800 SW Jackson St., Ste. 900
Topeka, KS 66612
Ph: (785)296-6514
Fax: (785)357-5210
Co. E-mail: jordan@ksbdc.net
URL: http://www.kansassbdc.net
Contact: Greg Jordan, Director
E-mail: jordan@ksbdc.net
Description: Provides free, one-on-one counseling designed to find practical solutions to business problems. **Founded:** 2017. **Geographic Preference:** State.

SMALL BUSINESS ASSISTANCE PROGRAMS

39841 ■ Business and Technology Institute Small Business Development Center
1701 South Broadway St.
Pittsburg, KS 66762
Ph: (620)231-7000
URL: http://www.btikansas.com/home/SBDC
Description: Provides one-stop managerial, financial, and technical assistance to new and expanding businesses in Southeast Kansas, Missouri, Oklahoma, and Arkansas.

39842 ■ Kansas Department of Commerce - Agriculture Marketing Division
1000 SW Jackson St., Ste. 100
Topeka, KS 66612
Ph: (785)296-3481
Fax: (785)296-3665
Co. E-mail: kdc_marketing@ks.gov
URL: http://www.kansascommerce.gov
Description: Provides marketing assistance through food shows, seminars, and media promotions.

39843 ■ Kansas Department of Commerce - Business and Community Development Div.
1000 SW Jackson., Ste. 100
Topeka, KS 66612
URL: http://www.kansascommerce.gov/about/meet-the-team/community-development
Contact: Kayla Savage, Director
E-mail: kayla.savage@ks.gov
Description: Promotes the growth, diversification, and retention of business and industry in Kansas. Advocates on behalf of small businesses. Act as a clearinghouse for information on permits and licenses. Maintains six regional offices to provide assistance to small businesses.

39844 ■ Kansas Department of Commerce - Trade Development Div.
1000 SW Jackson St., Ste. 100
Topeka, KS 66612
Ph: (913)296-4027
Fax: (913)296-5263
URL: http://www.kansascommerce.com
Description: Provides information and assistance to businesses interested in international trade. Services offered include identifying agents and distributors worldwide, assisting in market development, providing technical information, offering world trade statistical data, and trade lead information services.

39845 ■ NetWork Kansas
PO Box 877
Andover, KS 67002-0877
Free: 877-521-8600
Fax: (316)425-7596
Co. E-mail: info@networkkansas.com
URL: http://www.networkkansas.com
Contact: Erik Pedersen, President
E-mail: epedersen@networkkansas.com
Facebook: www.facebook.com/networkkansas
X (Twitter): x.com/networkkansas
Description: Connects startups and small businesses to resources they need to grow. Provides free assistance to anyone operating or starting a business in Kansas. **Founded:** 2006.

39846 ■ Professional Association of Small Business Accountants (PASBA)
4919 Lamar Ave.
Shawnee Mission, KS 66202
Free: 866-296-0001
Co. E-mail: director@pasba.org
URL: http://www.smallbizaccountants.com
Contact: Kim Bryant, President
Description: Represents certified public accountants, public accountants, and enrolled agents who provide accounting services to small businesses throughout the United States. Aims to improve the business management and marketing skills of its members. Strives to uphold and maintain high standards of good accounting practices. **Founded:** 1982. **Educational Activities:** Spring Marketing Conference (Annual). **Geographic Preference:** National.

39847 ■ Wichita State University College of Applied Studies Technology Center
1845 Fairmount St.
Wichita, KS 67260
URL: http://www.wichita.edu/academics/applied_studies/Deans_Office/About/index.php
Description: Provides training, seminars, and technical information to engineers, managers, and other employees.

SCORE OFFICES

39848 ■ Hutchinson SCORE
Quest Ctr., 1 E 9th Ave.
Hutchinson, KS 67501
URL: http://www.score.org/greaterwichita/contributor/david-inskeep
Contact: David Inskeep, Contact
Description: Provides professional guidance and information to America's small businesses. **Geographic Preference:** Local.

39849 ■ SCORE - Hutchinson
Quest Center
1 E 9th Ave.
Hutchinson, KS 67501
URL: http://wichita.score.org/hutchinson-branch
Contact: Bridget Weston, Chief Executive Officer
Description: Provides professional guidance and information to maximize the success of existing and emerging small businesses. Offers business counseling and workshops.

39850 ■ SCORE - Phillipsburg
205 F St., Ste. 150
Phillipsburg, KS 67661
Ph: (785)540-4110
URL: http://wichita.score.org
Facebook: www.facebook.com/SCOREWichita
X (Twitter): x.com/SCOREWichita
Description: Provides professional guidance and information to maximize the success of existing and emerging small businesses. Offers business counseling and workshops.

39851 ■ SCORE - Topeka
120 SE 6th Ave., Ste. 110
Topeka, KS 66603
Ph: (785)550-5793
Co. E-mail: karlwatson@hotmail.com
URL: http://topeka.score.org
Contact: Mike Welch, Chairman
Facebook: www.facebook.com/SCORETopeka
Linkedin: www.linkedin.com/company/score-mentors-topeka
Description: Provides professional guidance and information to maximize the success of existing and emerging small businesses. Offers business counseling and workshops.

39852 ■ SCORE - Wichita
220 W Douglas, Ste. 450
Wichita, KS 67202
Ph: (316)239-1131
Co. E-mail: score143@sbcglobal.net
URL: http://wichita.score.org
Linkedin: www.linkedin.com/company/score-wichita
X (Twitter): x.com/SCOREWichita
Description: Unites active and retired business management professionals with men and women who are considering starting a small business, encountering problems with their business, or expanding their business. **Founded:** 1976.

39853 ■ Topeka SCORE
120 SE 6th Ave., Ste. 110
Topeka, KS 66603
Ph: (785)550-5793
Co. E-mail: karlwatson@hotmail.com
URL: http://topeka.score.org
Contact: Mike Welch, Chairman
Facebook: www.facebook.com/SCORETopeka
Linkedin: www.linkedin.com/company/score-mentors-topeka
X (Twitter): x.com/SCORE_Topeka
Description: Helps people in planning small business operations. **Founded:** 1964. **Geographic Preference:** Local.

39854 ■ Wichita SCORE Chapter
220 W Douglas, Ste. 450
Wichita, KS 67202
Ph: (316)239-1131
Co. E-mail: score143@sbcglobal.net
URL: http://wichita.score.org
Facebook: www.facebook.com/SCOREWichita
Linkedin: www.linkedin.com/company/score-wichita
X (Twitter): x.com/SCOREWichita
Description: Provides professional guidance and information to America's small businesses. **Founded:** 1976. **Geographic Preference:** Local.

BETTER BUSINESS BUREAUS

39855 ■ *The BBB Bulletin*
345 N Riverview St., Ste. 720
Wichita, KS 67203
Ph: (316)263-3146
Free: 800-856-2417
Fax: (316)263-3063
Co. E-mail: info@kansasplains.bbb.org
URL: http://www.bbb.org/nebraska
Released: Quarterly **Availability:** Print; PDF.

39856 ■ Better Business Bureau of Midwest Plains [BBB of Midwest Plains]
10985 Cody St., Ste. 210
Lenexa, KS 66210
Ph: (816)421-7800
URL: http://www.bbb.org/local-bbb/bbb-of-midwest-plains
Description: Seeks to promote and foster the highest ethical relationship between businesses and the public through voluntary self-regulation, consumer and business education, and service excellence. Provides information to help consumers and businesses make informed purchasing decisions and avoid costly scams and frauds; settles consumer complaints through arbitration and other means. **Geographic Preference:** Local.

39857 ■ Better Business Bureau of Midwest Plains - Wichita Falls [BBB of Midwest Plains - Wichita Falls]
PO Box 75622
Wichita, KS 67275
Ph: (316)263-3542
Fax: (402)391-7535
URL: http://www.bbb.org/local-bbb/bbb-of-midwest-plains
Description: Seeks to promote and foster the highest ethical relationship between businesses and the public through voluntary self-regulation, consumer and business education, and service excellence. Provides information to help consumers and businesses make informed purchasing decisions and avoid costly scams and frauds; settles consumer complaints through arbitration and other means. **Geographic Preference:** Local.

CHAMBERS OF COMMERCE

39858 ■ Anthony Chamber of Commerce
227 W Main
Anthony, KS 67003
Ph: (620)842-5456
Co. E-mail: info@anthonychamber.com
URL: http://www.anthonychamber.com
Contact: Beth Farmer, Executive Director
Facebook: www.facebook.com/AnthonyKSChamber
Description: Promotes business and community development in Anthony, KS. **Geographic Preference:** Local.

39859 ■ Arkansas City Area Chamber of Commerce [Ark City Chamber]
106 S Summit St.
Arkansas City, KS 67005
Ph: (620)442-0230
Co. E-mail: ceo@arkcitychamber.org
URL: http://www.arkcitychamber.com
Contact: Eric Rice, Chairman of the Board
E-mail: erice7168@yahoo.com
URL(s): www.arkansascityks.gov/businesses/chamber_of_commerce.php
Description: Works to promote economic and community development in the city and the region. **Founded:** 1912. **Geographic Preference:** Local.

39860 ■ Ashland Chamber of Commerce
PO Box 37
Ashland, KS 67831
Co. E-mail: ashlandks@gmail.com
URL: http://www.ashlandks.com
Contact: Kelsey Henderson, President
Description: Promotes business and community development in Ashland, KS area. **Geographic Preference:** Local.

39861 ■ Atchison Area Chamber of Commerce (AACC)
200 S 10th
Atchison, KS 66002
Ph: (913)367-2427
Co. E-mail: marketing@atchisonkansas.net
URL: http://www.atchisonkansas.net
Contact: Dianna Kruger, Office Manager
E-mail: dkruger@atchisonkansas.net
Facebook: www.facebook.com/AtchisonChamber
Description: Promotes business and community development in the Atchison, KS area. Sponsors local festivals and community activities. **Founded:** 1919. **Publications:** *Atchison Area Chamber of Commerce--Member Directory*; *Weekly Enews* (Weekly). **Geographic Preference:** Local.

39862 ■ Atwood Chamber of Commerce (ACC)
416 Main St.
Atwood, KS 67730-1826
Ph: (785)626-9630
URL: http://www.uschamber.com/co/chambers/kansas/atwood
Description: Promotes business and community development in Atwood, KS. Issues publications. **Publications:** *Chamber Update*. **Geographic Preference:** Local.

39863 ■ Baldwin City Chamber of Commerce
719 High
Baldwin City, KS 66006
Ph: (785)594-3200
Co. E-mail: info@baldwincitychamber.com
URL: http://www.baldwincitychamber.com
Contact: Cody Anno, President
Facebook: www.facebook.com/baldwincitychamber
X (Twitter): x.com/getbaldwincity
Instagram: www.instagram.com/baldwincitychamber
Description: Promotes business and community development in Baldwin City, KS. **Geographic Preference:** Local.

39864 ■ Baxter Springs Chamber of Commerce
1004 Military Ave.
Baxter Springs, KS 66713
Ph: (620)856-3131
Co. E-mail: chamberinfo.baxtersprings@gmail.com
Contact: Charlene L. Hunley, Contact
Facebook: www.facebook.com/baxterchamber
Description: Promotes business and community development in Baxter Springs, KS. Sponsors annual Cowtown Days festival and Christmas festivities. **Founded:** 1947. **Geographic Preference:** Local.

39865 ■ Belle Plaine Area Chamber of Commerce
PO Box 721
Belle Plaine, KS 67013
Co. E-mail: belleplainechamber@gmail.com
URL: http://belleplainechamber.com
Contact: Allison Everhart, President
Description: Promotes business and community development in the Belle Plaine, KS area. Sponsors Tulip Time Festival in April. **Founded:** 1955. **Geographic Preference:** Local.

39866 ■ Belleville Chamber of Commerce and Main Street
1205 18th St.
Belleville, KS 66935
Ph: (785)527-5524
Co. E-mail: bellevilleccms@gmail.com
URL: http://www.bellevilleks.org
Contact: Bethany Swafford, Co-President
Facebook: www.facebook.com/bellevillechambermainstreet
Description: Advances the commercial, industrial, civic and general interests of the city of Belleville and the surrounding area. **Founded:** 1869. **Geographic Preference:** Local.

39867 ■ Beloit Area Chamber of Commerce (BACC)
209 E Main, No. 104
Beloit, KS 67420
Ph: (785)738-2717
Co. E-mail: beloitchamber@nckcn.com
URL: http://beloitchamber.com
Contact: Gretchin Staples, President
Description: Promotes business and community development in Mitchell County, KS. Conducts annual Consumer and Farm Show. **Founded:** 1902. **Geographic Preference:** Local.

39868 ■ Bonner Springs/Edwardsville Area Chamber of Commerce
309 Oak st.
Bonner Springs, KS 66012
Ph: (913)422-5044
Fax: (913)441-1366
Co. E-mail: info@bsedwchamber.org
URL: http://www.bsedwchamber.org
Contact: Zack Daniel, President
Facebook: www.facebook.com/BSEDWChamber
X (Twitter): x.com/BSEDWChamber
Instagram: www.instagram.com/BSEDWChamber
Pinterest: www.pinterest.com/bsedwchamber
Description: Promotes business and community development in the Bonner Springs and Edwardsville, KS areas. Sponsors annual Tiblow Days and Autumn Fest celebrations. **Founded:** 1972. **Geographic Preference:** Local.

STATE LISTINGS

Kansas ■ 39886

39869 ■ Briefings
700 SW Jackson, Ste. 209
Topeka, KS 66603
Ph: (785)233-3945
Co. E-mail: tba@topekabar.com
URL: http://www.topekabar.com
Contact: Gregory A. Lee, President
URL(s): www.topekabar.com/Advertising
Ed: Chris Gunn. **Released:** Monthly **Availability:** Print.

39870 ■ Business Perspective
9001 W 110th St., No. 150
Overland Park, KS 66210
Ph: (913)491-3600
Co. E-mail: opcc@opchamber.org
URL: http://www.opchamber.org
Contact: Tracey Osborne Oltjen, President
E-mail: tosborne@opchamber.org
URL(s): www.opchamber.org/media-center
Released: Monthly **Description:** Features Overland Park and member businesses. **Availability:** PDF.

39871 ■ The Chamber Outlook
117 N Walnut St.
Hutchinson, KS 67504
Ph: (620)662-3391
Free: 800-691-4262
Fax: (620)662-2168
Co. E-mail: debrat@hutchchamber.com
URL: http://www.hutchchamber.com
Contact: Debra Teufel, President
E-mail: debrat@hutchchamber.com
URL(s): www.hutchchamber.com/membership/benefits-and-value/marketing
Released: Monthly **Availability:** Print.

39872 ■ The Chamber Vision
719 Commercial St.
Emporia, KS 66801
Ph: (620)342-1600
Free: 800-279-3730
Fax: (620)342-3223
Co. E-mail: chamber@emporiakschamber.org
URL: http://emporiakschamber.org
Contact: Jeanine McKenna, President
E-mail: jmckenna@emporiakschamber.org
URL(s): emporiakschamber.org/become-a-member
Released: Monthly **Availability:** Print; PDF.

39873 ■ Chanute Area Chamber of Commerce & Office of Tourism
21 N Lincoln Ave.
Chanute, KS 66720
Ph: (620)431-3350
Co. E-mail: information@chanutechamber.com
URL: http://www.chanutechamber.com
Contact: Jane Brophy, Executive Director
E-mail: director@chanutechamber.com
Facebook: www.facebook.com/Get-Chanute-154598253369
Description: Supports the development of the business and community industry within the area of Chanute in the state of Kansas. **Geographic Preference:** Local.

39874 ■ Cheney Chamber of Commerce
Cheney City Hall, 131 N Main
Cheney, KS 67025
Ph: (316)542-3622
Fax: (316)542-0185
Co. E-mail: cheneychamber@gmail.com
URL: http://www.cheneyks.org
Contact: Ryan Runnells, President
Facebook: www.facebook.com/cityofcheney
Description: Promotes business and community development in Cheney, KS. Sponsors Spring Fling and Coming Home for Christmas festivals. Publications: none. **Geographic Preference:** Local.

39875 ■ Clay Center Area Chamber of Commerce
517 Ct., St.
Clay Center, KS 67432
Ph: (785)632-5674
Co. E-mail: claycenterchamber@gmail.com
URL: http://www.claycenterchamber.com
Contact: Shannon Stark, Executive Director
Description: Promotes business and community development in Clay Center, KS area. **Geographic Preference:** Local.

39876 ■ Coffey County Chamber of Commerce
305A Neosho St.
Burlington, KS 66839
Contact: Sarah J. J. Stockwell, Contact
Description: Promotes business and community development in the Burlington, KS area. **Founded:** 1990. **Publications:** Whistle Stop (Monthly). **Geographic Preference:** Local.

39877 ■ Coffeyville Area Chamber of Commerce (CCC)
807 S Walnut St.
Coffeyville, KS 67337
Ph: (620)251-2550
Free: 800-626-3357
Co. E-mail: chamber@coffeyville.com
URL: http://coffeyvillechamber.org
Contact: Candi Westbrook, President
Facebook: www.facebook.com/coffeyvilleareachamberofcommerce
X (Twitter): x.com/CoffeyvilleCOC
Description: Promotes business and community development in Coffeyville, KS. **Founded:** 1901. **Geographic Preference:** Local.

39878 ■ Colby - Thomas County Chamber of Commerce
350 S Range Ave.
Colby, KS 67701
Ph: (785)460-3401
Co. E-mail: info@colbychamber.com
URL: http://colbychamber.com
Facebook: www.facebook.com/ColbyChamber
Linkedin: www.linkedin.com/colbychamber
X (Twitter): x.com/colbychamber
Description: Promotes business and community development in the Colby, KS area. Sponsors local festivals. **Publications:** Coby Chamber Communicator (Monthly). **Geographic Preference:** Local.

39879 ■ Concordia Area Chamber of Commerce
207 W 6th St.
Concordia, KS 66901
Ph: (785)243-4290
Co. E-mail: info@concordiakansaschamber.com
URL: http://www.concordiakansaschamber.com
Contact: Annie Bergmann, Executive Director
Facebook: www.facebook.com/concordiakschamber
X (Twitter): x.com/conKSchamber
Instagram: www.instagram.com/info_concordiakansaschamber
Description: Promotes business and community development in Concordia, MO area. **Founded:** 1926. **Geographic Preference:** Local.

39880 ■ Decatur County Area Chamber of Commerce
104 S Penn Ave., Ste. 1
Oberlin, KS 67749
Ph: (785)475-3441
Co. E-mail: o-daedc@oberlinkansas.gov
URL: http://decaturcountytennessee.org
Contact: Ginger Teague, President
Description: Promotes business and community development in Decatur County, KS. **Geographic Preference:** Local.

39881 ■ Derby Chamber of Commerce (DCC)
611 N Mulberry St., Ste. 200
Derby, KS 67037
Ph: (316)788-3421
Fax: (316)788-6861
Co. E-mail: info@derbychamber.com
URL: http://www.derbychamber.com
Contact: Mark Staats, President
E-mail: mark@derbychamber.com
Facebook: www.facebook.com/DerbyChamber
X (Twitter): x.com/derbychamber
Instagram: www.instagram.com/derbychamber
YouTube: www.youtube.com/channel/UC_N2932znjEb6ggyG_aGD9w
Description: Promotes business and community development in Derby, KS. Helps sponsor Christmas parade. Participates in organizing Derby Days celebration. **Founded:** 1957. **Publications:** News. **Geographic Preference:** Local.

39882 ■ Dodge City Area Chamber of Commerce, Inc. (DCACC)
101 E Wyatt Earp Blvd.
Dodge City, KS 67801
Ph: (620)227-3119
Fax: (620)227-2957
Co. E-mail: info@dodgechamber.com
URL: http://www.dodgechamber.com
Contact: Anna Bjerken, Co-Chief Executive Officer Co-President
Facebook: www.facebook.com/dodgecitychamberofcommerce
Linkedin: www.linkedin.com/company/dodge-city-area-chamber-of-commerce
YouTube: www.youtube.com/channel/UC0PpODCFzn5Yx7L61ZzxY7g
Description: Promotes business and community development in the Dodge City, KS area. **Founded:** 1917. **Publications:** The Business Advantage. **Geographic Preference:** Local.

39883 ■ Doniphan County Chamber of Commerce (DCCC)
PO Box 250
Troy, KS 66087
Ph: (785)985-2235
Co. E-mail: chamber.commerce@dpcountyks.com
URL: http://dpcountyks.com/directory/doniphan-county-chamber-of-commerce
Contact: Marty Allen, Contact
Description: Promotes business and community development in Doniphan County, KS. **Geographic Preference:** Local.

39884 ■ Douglass Chamber of Commerce (DCC)
PO Box 401
Douglass, KS 67039
Ph: (316)746-3135
URL: http://www.chamber-commerce.net/dir/6265/Douglass-Chamber-of-Commerce-in-Douglass
Description: Promotes business and community development in Douglass, KS. **Geographic Preference:** Local.

39885 ■ El Dorado Chamber of Commerce (EDCC)
201 E Central Ave.
El Dorado, KS 67042
Ph: (316)321-3150
Co. E-mail: reception@eldoradochamber.com
URL: http://www.eldoradochamber.com
Contact: Billy Jackson, President
Facebook: www.facebook.com/ElDoradoChamber
Linkedin: www.linkedin.com/in/el-dorado-chamber-of-commerce-8661a68b
X (Twitter): x.com/ChamberDorado
Instagram: www.instagram.com/eldorado_chamber
YouTube: www.youtube.com/channel/UC1M311wlqwhx6bMLeZTqgFQ/videos
Description: Promotes business and community development in El Dorado, KS. Sponsors El Dorado Prairie Port Festival. **Founded:** 1921. **Geographic Preference:** Local.

39886 ■ Ellinwood Chamber of Commerce
110 1/2 N Main St.
Ellinwood, KS 67526
Ph: (620)566-7353
Co. E-mail: info@ellinwoodchamber.com
URL: http://www.ellinwoodchamber.com
Contact: Jordan Waite, Executive Director
Facebook: www.facebook.com/EllinwoodChamberofCommerce
X (Twitter): x.com/EllinwoodKS
Description: Promotes business and community development in the Ellinwood, KS area. **Founded:** 1980. **Geographic Preference:** Local.

39887 ■ Ellsworth-Kanopolis Area Chamber of Commerce
114 1/2 N Douglas
Ellsworth, KS 67439
Ph: (785)472-4071
URL: http://www.uschamber.com/co/chambers/kansas/ellsworth
Description: Promotes business and community development in the Ellsworth/Kanopolis, KS area. **Founded:** 1947. **Publications:** *Chamber Updates* (Monthly); *Chamber Updates* (Annual). **Awards:** Ellsworth-Kanopolis Area Chamber of Commerce Citizen of the Year Award. **Geographic Preference:** Local.

39888 ■ Emporia Area Chamber and Visitors Bureau
719 Commercial St.
Emporia, KS 66801
Ph: (620)342-1600
Free: 800-279-3730
Fax: (620)342-3223
Co. E-mail: chamber@emporiakschamber.org
URL: http://emporiakschamber.org
Contact: Jeanine McKenna, President
E-mail: jmckenna@emporiakschamber.org
X (Twitter): x.com/eaco
YouTube: www.youtube.com/channel/UCyPA534t3CSmZdjnw1CcWKw
Description: Promotes business and community development in the Emporia, KS area. **Publications:** *The Chamber Vision* (Monthly). **Geographic Preference:** Local.

39889 ■ Fort Scott Area Chamber of Commerce (FSACC)
231 E Wall St.
Fort Scott, KS 66701
Ph: (620)223-3566
Fax: (620)223-3574
Co. E-mail: information@fortscott.com
URL: http://fortscott.com
Contact: Lindsay Madison, President
E-mail: lindsay.madison@fortscott.com
Facebook: www.facebook.com/fortscottchamber
X (Twitter): x.com/ftscottchamber
Instagram: www.instagram.com/fortscottchamber
YouTube: www.youtube.com/user/FortScottChamber
Pinterest: www.pinterest.com/ftscottchamber
Description: Promotes business and community development in the Ft. Scott, KS area. **Founded:** 1842. **Publications:** *The Bugle Call* (Monthly). **Geographic Preference:** Local.

39890 ■ Fredonia Area Chamber of Commerce [Fredonia Chamber of Commerce]
716 Madison St.
Fredonia, KS 66736
Ph: (620)378-3221
Co. E-mail: fredoniachamber@fredoniaks.org
URL: http://www.fredoniakschamber.org
Facebook: www.facebook.com/fredonia.chamber
Description: Promotes business and community development in Fredonia, KS. Sponsors the Fredonia Homecoming Festival. **Geographic Preference:** Local.

39891 ■ Garden City Area Chamber of Commerce (GCACC)
1509 E Fulton Terr.
Garden City, KS 67846
Ph: (620)276-3264
Co. E-mail: chamber@gardencitychamber.net
URL: http://www.gardencitychamber.net
Contact: Janene Radke, Director
E-mail: jradke@gardencitychamber.net
Facebook: www.facebook.com/GCKSChamber
X (Twitter): x.com/gckschamber
Description: Promotes business and community development in the Garden City, KS area. **Founded:** 1888. **Publications:** *News & Views* (Semimonthly). **Geographic Preference:** Local.

39892 ■ Gardner Edgerton Chamber of Commerce
109 E Main St.
Gardner, KS 66030
Ph: (913)856-6464
Co. E-mail: info@gardneredgerton.org
URL: http://gardneredgerton.org/?__cf_chl_managed_tk__=pmd_78ecd2e354bac019cffb8cf81eccf5318ea01c73-1626833302-0-gqNtZGzNAqKjcnBszQai
Contact: Jason Leib, President
Description: Promotes business and community development in Gardner, KS. **Founded:** 1975. **Geographic Preference:** Local.

39893 ■ Garnett Area Chamber of Commerce (GACC)
131 W 5th Ave.
Garnett, KS 66032
Ph: (785)448-6767
Co. E-mail: director@garnettchamber.org
URL: http://www.garnettchamber.org
Contact: Helen Norman, President
Facebook: www.facebook.com/GarnettChamber
X (Twitter): x.com/garnettchamber
Instagram: www.instagram.com/garnettchamber
Description: Promotes business and community development in the Garnett, KS area. **Founded:** 1970. **Geographic Preference:** Local.

39894 ■ Glasco Chamber Pride (GCP)
PO Box 572
Glasco, KS 67445
Ph: (785)568-2515
URL: http://www.chamber-commerce.net/dir/6877/Glasco-Chamber-Pride-in-Glasco
Description: Promotes business and community development in Glasco, KS. **Founded:** 1920. **Geographic Preference:** Local.

39895 ■ Grant County Chamber of Commerce (GCCC)
113B S Main St.
Ulysses, KS 67880
Ph: (620)356-4700
Fax: (620)424-2437
Co. E-mail: uchamber@pld.com
URL: http://www.ulysseschamber.org
Contact: Galen Pelton, President
Facebook: www.facebook.com/UlyssesChamberofCommerceandTourism
Description: Promotes business and community development in the Grant County, KS area. Sponsors Home Products Dinner and annual Spring Fling. **Founded:** 1954. **Publications:** *Chamberline* (Monthly). **Geographic Preference:** Local.

39896 ■ Great Bend Chamber of Commerce & Economic Development (GBCF)
1125 Williams St.
Great Bend, KS 67530
Ph: (620)792-2401
Fax: (620)792-2404
Co. E-mail: marketing@greatbend.org
URL: http://www.greatbend.org
Contact: Megan Barfield, President
Facebook: www.facebook.com/gbcoc
X (Twitter): x.com/gbcoc
YouTube: www.youtube.com/channel/UC9FF9QB631NIXDiWZ-1bO3w
Description: Promotes programs and projects designed to retain businesses and improve the quality of life in Barton County, KS. Sponsors special events and expositions. **Founded:** 1921. **Publications:** *Outlook Business Journal* (Monthly). **Geographic Preference:** Local.

39897 ■ Greater Topeka Chamber of Commerce
719 S Kansas Ave., Ste. 100
Topeka, KS 66603
URL: http://topekapartnership.com/topeka-chamber
Contact: Curtis Sneden, Contact
Facebook: www.facebook.com/topekachamber
X (Twitter): x.com/TopekaChamber
Description: Promotes business and community development in the Topeka, KS area. **Publications:** *Topeka Business* (Monthly). **Awards:** Greater Topeka Chamber of Commerce Small Business Award (Annual). **Geographic Preference:** Local.

39898 ■ Halstead Chamber of Commerce (HCC)
PO Box 328
Halstead, KS 67056
Ph: (316)247-2397
Co. E-mail: halsteadkschamber@gmail.com
URL: http://halsteadks.com/2221/Chamber-of-Commerce
Contact: Dr. Ron Barry, President
Facebook: www.facebook.com/HalsteadKSChamber
Description: Promotes business and community development in Halstead, KS. **Geographic Preference:** Local.

39899 ■ Hays Area Chamber of Commerce
2700 Vine St.
Hays, KS 67601
Ph: (785)628-8201
Co. E-mail: hayscc@hayschamber.com
URL: http://hayschamber.com
Contact: Sarah Wasinger, President
E-mail: sarah@hayschamber.com
X (Twitter): x.com/hayschamber
Instagram: www.instagram.com/hayschamber
Description: Promotes business and community development in the Hays, KS area. **Founded:** 1917. **Publications:** *Chamber News*. **Geographic Preference:** Local.

39900 ■ Haysville Chamber of Commerce
210 S Main
Haysville, KS 67060
Ph: (316)529-2461
Co. E-mail: haysvillechamber@gmail.com
URL: http://haysvillechamber.com
Contact: Deanna Straub, President
Facebook: www.facebook.com/HaysvillKsChamber
Description: Promotes business and community development in Haysville, KS. **Geographic Preference:** Local.

39901 ■ Hesston Community Chamber of Commerce
115 E Smith
Hesston, KS 67062
Ph: (620)327-4412
Fax: (620)327-4595
Co. E-mail: chamber@hesstonks.org
URL: http://www.hesstonks.org
Contact: Megan Smith, Executive Director
Description: Promotes economic development, tourism, and community development in the Hesston, Kansas community. **Founded:** 1966. **Publications:** *Chamber Bulletin* (Periodic). **Geographic Preference:** Local.

39902 ■ Hoisington Chamber of Commerce (HCC)
123 N Main St.
Hoisington, KS 67544
Ph: (620)653-4311
Co. E-mail: hoisingtoncofc@outlook.com
URL: http://www.hoisingtonkansas.com
Contact: Eric Schoendaler, Treasurer
Facebook: www.facebook.com/HoisChamber
Description: Promotes business and community development in Hoisington, KS. Sponsors annual Labor Day celebration. Makes charitable contributions to Hoisington Main St., Inc. Along with the City of Hoisington, forms the nucleus of local economic development group. Publications: none. **Geographic Preference:** Local.

39903 ■ Holton/Jackson County Chamber of Commerce
104 W 5th St.
Holton, KS 66436
Ph: (785)364-3963
Co. E-mail: chamber@exploreholton.com
URL: http://www.exploreholton.com
Contact: Laura Golden, President
E-mail: lgolden@dsjc.com
Description: Promotes business and community development in Holton, KS. **Geographic Preference:** Local.

STATE LISTINGS

Kansas ■ 39920

39904 ■ Horton Chamber of Commerce (HCC)
205 E 8th St.
  Horton, KS 66439
Ph: (785)486-3321
Co. E-mail: hortonchamber@rainbowtel.net
URL: http://www.cityofhorton.com/chamber
Contact: Glen Obbards, President
Description: Promotes business and community development in Horton, KS. **Founded:** 1925. **Geographic Preference:** Local.

39905 ■ Hutchinson/Reno County Chamber of Commerce
117 N Walnut St.
  Hutchinson, KS 67504
Ph: (620)662-3391
Free: 800-691-4262
Fax: (620)662-2168
Co. E-mail: debrat@hutchchamber.com
URL: http://www.hutchchamber.com
Contact: Debra Teufel, President
E-mail: debrat@hutchchamber.com
Facebook: www.facebook.com/HutchChamber
X (Twitter): x.com/hutchchamber
Instagram: www.instagram.com/hutchchamber
Description: Promotes business and community development in the Hutchinson, KS area. **Founded:** 1892. **Publications:** The Chamber Outlook (Monthly). **Geographic Preference:** Local.

39906 ■ Independence Chamber of Commerce (ICC)
616 N Pennsylvania Ave.
  Independence, KS 67301
Ph: (620)331-1890
Co. E-mail: chamber@indkschamber.org
URL: http://indkschamber.org
Contact: Lisa Wilson, President
E-mail: lwilson@indkschamber.org
Description: Promotes business and community development in Independence, KS. **Founded:** 1914. **Geographic Preference:** Local.

39907 ■ Iola Area Chamber of Commerce
10 W Jackson Ave.
  Iola, KS 66749
Ph: (620)365-5252
Co. E-mail: chamber@iolachamber.org
URL: http://www.iolachamber.org
Contact: Miles Mentzer, President
Facebook: www.facebook.com/IolaAreaChamber
Instagram: www.instagram.com/iola_area_chamber
Description: Promotes business and community development in Iola, KS. **Publications:** Chamber News (Monthly). **Educational Activities:** Iola Area Chamber of Commerce Board meeting. **Geographic Preference:** Local.

39908 ■ *Issue*
500 N Main St. No. 101
  Newton, KS 67114
Ph: (316)283-2560
URL: http://newtonchamberks.org
Contact: Dyan Roberson, Director
E-mail: dyan@thenewtonchambe.com
URL(s): newtonchamberks.org/newsletter
Released: Monthly **Availability:** Online.

39909 ■ Junction City Area Chamber of Commerce (JCACC)
222 W 6th St.
  Junction City, KS 66441
Ph: (785)762-2632
Co. E-mail: info@jcacc.org
URL: http://www.junctioncitychamber.org
Contact: Mark Claussen, Chairman
Linkedin: www.linkedin.com/company/junction-city
  -area-chamber-of-commerce
X (Twitter): x.com/jckschamber
YouTube: www.youtube.com/channel/UCmmOY
  4X9H0PRm_7h1CymuwA
Description: Promotes business and community development in the Junction City, KS area. **Founded:** 1934. **Publications:** E-Post (Weekly); Signpost. **Geographic Preference:** Local.

39910 ■ Kansas Chamber of Commerce
835 SW Topeka Blvd.
  Topeka, KS 66612
Ph: (785)357-6321
URL: http://www.kansaschamber.org
Contact: Alan Cobb, President
Facebook: www.facebook.com/kansaschamber
X (Twitter): x.com/kansaschamber
Description: Promotes business and community development in Kansas. **Publications:** Business Advocate. **Geographic Preference:** Local.

39911 ■ Kansas City Kansas Area Chamber of Commerce
727 Minnesota Ave.
  Kansas City, KS 66101
Ph: (913)371-3070
Fax: (913)371-3732
Co. E-mail: info@kckchamber.com
URL: http://www.kckchamber.com
Contact: Daniel Silva, President
E-mail: daniel@kckchamber.com
Linkedin: www.linkedin.com/company/kansas-city
  -kansas-area-chamber-of-commerce
X (Twitter): x.com/KCKChamber
Instagram: www.instagram.com/kckchamber
Description: Promotes business and community development in the Kansas City, KS area. **Founded:** 1898. **Publications:** Chamber Linc (Quarterly); KCK Business Report (Monthly). **Geographic Preference:** Local.

39912 ■ Kingman Area Chamber of Commerce (KACC)
111 S Main St.
  Kingman, KS 67068
Ph: (620)532-1853
Co. E-mail: thekingmanareachamber@gmail.com
URL: http://www.kingmancc.com
Contact: Ashley Keimig, President
Facebook: www.facebook.com/
  KingmanAreaChamberofCommerce
Instagram: www.instagram.com/
  kingmanareachamber
Description: Promotes business and community development in Kingman County, KS. **Geographic Preference:** Local.

39913 ■ Larned Area Chamber of Commerce
502 Broadway St.
  Larned, KS 67550
Ph: (620)285-6916
Co. E-mail: larnedcofc@gbta.net
URL: http://www.larnedks.org
Contact: Brock Miller, President
Facebook: www.facebook.com/larnedchamber
X (Twitter): x.com/LarnedChamber
YouTube: www.youtube.com/channel/
  UCqWmWvBVbp1SFpw7Sbg-dHg
Description: Promotes business and community development in Pawnee County, KS. Sponsors local festivals. **Founded:** 1947. **Geographic Preference:** Local.

39914 ■ Lawrence Chamber of Commerce
718 New Hampshire St.
  Lawrence, KS 66044
Ph: (785)865-4411
Co. E-mail: info@lawrencechamber.com
URL: http://lawrencechamber.com
Contact: Bonnie Lowe, President
E-mail: blowe@lawrencechamber.com
Facebook: www.facebook.com/LawrenceChamber
X (Twitter): x.com/LawrenceChamber
Instagram: www.instagram.com/lawrencechamber
YouTube: www.youtube.com/user/
  LawrenceKSChambe
Description: Works to promote and enhance the economic vitality of Lawrence and Douglas County and to be the leading advocate of issues that affect the economic well-being of the members and customers. **Founded:** 1878. **Publications:** Community Profile and Relocation Guide (Annual). **Geographic Preference:** Local.

39915 ■ Leavenworth-Lansing Area Chamber of Commerce (LLACC)
518 Shawnee St.
  Leavenworth, KS 66048
Ph: (913)682-4112
Fax: (913)682-8170
Co. E-mail: info@llchamber.com
URL: http://www.llchamber.com
Contact: Jen Anders, President
Facebook: www.facebook.com/llchamberofcommerce
Instagram: www.instagram.com/lvlchamber
YouTube: www.youtube.com/channel/UCdtp_ixn_p
  1vMnINEnIrByQ
Description: Promotes business and community development in Leavenworth County, KS. **Founded:** 1916. **Geographic Preference:** Local.

39916 ■ Leawood Chamber of Commerce (LCC)
13451 Briar Dr., Ste. 201
  Leawood, KS 66209
Ph: (913)498-1514
Co. E-mail: chamber@leawoodchamber.org
URL: http://leawoodchamber.org
Contact: Kevin Jeffries, Co-President Co-Chief Executive Officer
E-mail: kevinj@leawoodchamber.org
Facebook: www.facebook.com/leawoodchamber
Linkedin: www.linkedin.com/company/leawoo
  d-chamber-of-commerce
X (Twitter): x.com/leawoodchamber
Instagram: www.instagram.com/leawoodchamber
Description: Promotes business and community development in Leawood, KS area. **Founded:** 1996. **Geographic Preference:** Local.

39917 ■ Lenexa Chamber of Commerce (LCC)
11180 Lackman Rd.
  Lenexa, KS 66219
Ph: (913)888-1414
Co. E-mail: staff@lenexa.org
URL: http://www.lenexa.org
Contact: Sarah Dietz, Director
E-mail: sdietz@lenexa.org
Facebook: www.facebook.com/LenexaChamber
Linkedin: www.linkedin.com/company/lenexachamber
X (Twitter): x.com/LenexaChamber
Description: Promotes business and community development in Lenexa, KS. **Founded:** 1925. **Geographic Preference:** Local.

39918 ■ Liberal Chamber of Commerce
4 Rock Island Rd.
  Liberal, KS 67905
Ph: (620)624-3855
Fax: (620)624-8851
Co. E-mail: info@liberalkschamber.com
URL: http://www.liberalkschamber.com
Contact: Rozelle Webb, Chief Executive Officer
E-mail: rozelle@liberalkschamber.com
Facebook: www.facebook.com/Liberal-Chamber-of
  -Commerce-147523398899
X (Twitter): x.com/LiberalChamber
Description: Aims to enhance the business climate and to improve the quality of life in Liberal, KS area. **Founded:** 1927. **Geographic Preference:** Local.

39919 ■ Louisburg Chamber of Commerce (LCC)
215 S Broadway
  Louisburg, KS 66053
Ph: (913)837-2826
Co. E-mail: chamber@louisburgkansas.com
URL: http://www.louisburgkansas.com
Contact: Joel Viterna, President
Facebook: www.facebook.com/LouisburgKSChamber
Description: Promotes business and community development in the Louisburg, KS area. **Geographic Preference:** Local.

39920 ■ Lucas Area Chamber of Commerce (LACC)
135 S Main St.
  Lucas, KS 67648
Ph: (785)525-6288
Co. E-mail: lucascoc@wtciweb.com

URL: http://lucaskansas.com
Contact: Mary Ann Steinle, President
Description: Promotes business and community development in Lucas, KS. Sponsors charitable functions and festivals. **Founded:** 1970. **Geographic Preference:** Local.

39921 ■ Manhattan Area Chamber of Commerce
501 Poyntz Ave.
 Manhattan, KS 66502
Ph: (785)776-8829
Co. E-mail: chamber@manhattan.org
URL: http://www.manhattan.org
Contact: Jason Smith, President
E-mail: jason@manhattan.org
Facebook: www.facebook.com/ManhattanAreaChamberofCommerce
X (Twitter): x.com/MHKChamber
Instagram: www.instagram.com/manhattan_ks_chamber
YouTube: www.youtube.com/user/ManhattanAreaChamber
Description: Promotes business and community development in Manhattan, KS. **Founded:** 1925. **Publications:** *Little Apple Business Review* (Monthly). **Geographic Preference:** Local.

39922 ■ Mankato Chamber of Commerce (MCC)
514 W S St.
 Mankato, KS 66956
Co. E-mail: mankatochamber@gmail.com
URL: http://www.mankatoks.com/chamber-of-commerce
Contact: Kenny Walker, Owner
Description: Promotes business and community development in Mankato, KS. **Geographic Preference:** Local.

39923 ■ Marysville Chamber of Commerce
101 N 10th St.
 Marysville, KS 66508
Description: Consists of sole proprietors to large manufacturers. Serves as a voice for the business community, offering programs and activities to foster the continued success of the members. Through specific members' services and community events, the Chamber strives to meet its goals. These include: developing and enhancing the marketing of the Marysville area, and recognizing and promoting excellence in education to ensure a sound foundation of human resources for a healthy local economy. **Founded:** 1987. **Publications:** *Bi-Annual Member Directory* (Semiannual); *Bi-Annual Member Directory* (Semiannual); *Marysville Chamber News* (Quarterly). **Geographic Preference:** Local.

39924 ■ McPherson Chamber of Commerce
306 N Main
 McPherson, KS 67460
Ph: (620)241-3303
Co. E-mail: chamber@mcphersonks.org
URL: http://www.mcphersonchamber.org
Contact: Lauren Hughes, President
Facebook: www.facebook.com/McPherson-Chamber-of-Commerce-105348722716
X (Twitter): x.com/Mac_chamber
Description: Promotes business and community development in McPherson, KS. **Founded:** 1921. **Publications:** *The Outlook* (Monthly). **Geographic Preference:** Local.

39925 ■ Meade Chamber of Commerce (MCC)
Meade, KS
URL: http://www.meadechamber.com
Description: Promotes business and community development in Meade, KS. **Founded:** 1885. **Publications:** *The Chamber Forum* (Quarterly). **Geographic Preference:** Local.

39926 ■ Medicine Lodge Area Chamber of Commerce (MLACC)
Medicine Lodge, KS 67104
Ph: (620)886-1786
Co. E-mail: medicinelodgechamber@gmail.com
URL: http://www.mlcoc.net
Contact: Julie Warner, President
Facebook: www.facebook.com/medicinelodgechamber
Description: Promotes business and community development in the Medicine Lodge, KS area. Sponsors Indian Summer Days festival. **Founded:** 1988. **Geographic Preference:** Local.

39927 ■ Minneapolis Area Chamber of Commerce
200 W 2nd St.
 Minneapolis, KS 67467
Ph: (785)392-3068
Co. E-mail: mplschamber@eaglecom.net
URL: http://www.ottawacountykansas.com/about-our-chamber.html
Contact: Elizabeth Lockhart, Executive Director
Description: Promotes business and community development in Minneapolis, KS. **Geographic Preference:** Local.

39928 ■ Mound City Area Chamber of Commerce
112 S 2nd St.
 Mound City, KS 66056
Ph: (913)795-2220
URL: http://www.moundcity.org/chamber
Contact: Al Hurt, President
Founded: 1849. **Geographic Preference:** Local.

39929 ■ Mound City Chamber of Commerce
112 2nd St.
 Mound City, KS 66056
Ph: (913)795-2202
Co. E-mail: info@moundcity.org
URL: http://www.moundcity.org/chamber
Contact: Al Hurt, President
Facebook: www.facebook.com/MoundCity
Description: Promotes business and community development in the area. **Geographic Preference:** Local.

39930 ■ Moundridge Community Chamber of Commerce
PO Box 312
 Moundridge, KS 67107-0312
Ph: (620)345-8246
Co. E-mail: mmcgee@moundridge.com
URL: http://www.moundridge.com/182/Chamber-of-Commerce
Contact: Sommer Smith, President
Description: Promotes business and community development in the Moundridge, KS area. **Geographic Preference:** Local.

39931 ■ Mulvane Chamber of Commerce
104 Prather
 Mulvane, KS 67110
Ph: (316)777-4850
URL: http://www.mulvanechamber.com
Contact: Angela Fox, Treasurer
E-mail: angela.fox.ha1n@statefarm.com
Facebook: www.facebook.com/mulvanechamber
Description: Promotes business and community development in Mulvane, KS. **Founded:** 1879. **Geographic Preference:** Local.

39932 ■ Ness City Chamber of Commerce (NCCC)
PO Box 262
 Ness City, KS 67560
Ph: (785)798-2413
Co. E-mail: nccofc@gbta.net
URL: http://www.nesscountychamber.com
Description: Promotes business and community development in Ness City, KS. **Publications:** *Ness Chamber* (Monthly). **Geographic Preference:** Local.

39933 ■ News
611 N Mulberry St., Ste. 200
 Derby, KS 67037
Ph: (316)788-3421
Fax: (316)788-6861
Co. E-mail: info@derbychamber.com
URL: http://www.derbychamber.com
Contact: Mark Staats, President
E-mail: mark@derbychamber.com
URL(s): www.globalmarshallplan.org/subscribe
Availability: Online.

39934 ■ News & Views
1509 E Fulton Terr.
 Garden City, KS 67846
Ph: (620)276-3264
Co. E-mail: chamber@gardencitychamber.net
URL: http://www.gardencitychamber.net
Contact: Janene Radke, Director
E-mail: jradke@gardencitychamber.net
URL(s): www.gardencitychamber.net/pages/Marketing
Released: Semimonthly **Availability:** Online.

39935 ■ Newton Area Chamber of Commerce (NACC)
500 N Main St. No. 101
 Newton, KS 67114
Ph: (316)283-2560
URL: http://newtonchamberks.org
Contact: Dyan Roberson, Director
E-mail: dyan@thenewtonchambe.com
Facebook: www.facebook.com/newtonareachamberofcommerce
Instagram: www.instagram.com/newtonchamberks
YouTube: www.youtube.com/channel/UCGxLtEoJn8yqbpnKwhjeuaw
Description: Works to promote and develop the civic, commercial, industrial, agricultural and professional interest of the City of Newton, Kansas and its vicinity. **Publications:** *Issue* (Monthly); *Membership Directory and Newcomer's Guide* (Annual). **Geographic Preference:** Local.

39936 ■ Northeast Johnson County Chamber of Commerce (NEJC)
5115 Roe Blvd., Ste. 100
 Roeland Park, KS 66205
Ph: (913)262-2141
Co. E-mail: info@nejcchamber.com
URL: http://nejcchamber.com
Contact: Deb Settle, President
E-mail: dsettle@nejcchamber.com
Facebook: www.facebook.com/nejcchamber
LinkedIn: www.linkedin.com/company/nejcchamber
X (Twitter): x.com/nejcchamber
Instagram: www.instagram.com/nejcchamber
Description: Promotes business and community development in Northeast Johnson County, KS area. **Publications:** *News-Voice* (Annual). **Awards:** Northeast Johnson County Small Business of the Year (Annual); Northeast Johnson County Volunteer of the Year (Annual). **Geographic Preference:** Local.

39937 ■ Norton Area Chamber of Commerce
205 S State St.
 Norton, KS 67654
Ph: (785)877-2501
Co. E-mail: nortoncc@ruraltel.net
URL: http://www.discovernorton.com
Contact: Donna Eastman Liddle, Chief Executive Officer
E-mail: nortoncc@ruraltel.net
Facebook: www.facebook.com/NortonChamberOfCommerce
X (Twitter): x.com/DiscoverNorton
Description: Promotes business and community development in the Norton, KS area. Sponsors charitable events. Conducts educational programs and competitions. **Founded:** 1905. **Geographic Preference:** Local.

39938 ■ Oakley Area Chamber of Commerce
415 W 2nd St.
 Oakley, KS 67748
URL: http://www.discoveroakley.com/144/Find
Description: Promotes business and community development in Oakley, KS. Sponsors State Corn Husking Festival. **Publications:** *Chamber Communique* (Bimonthly). **Geographic Preference:** Local.

39939 ■ Olathe Chamber of Commerce (OCC)
18103 W 106th St. S 100
 Olathe, KS 66061

Ph: (913)764-1050
Fax: (913)782-4636
Co. E-mail: chamber@olathe.org
URL: http://www.olathe.org
Contact: Tim McKee, Chief Executive Officer
E-mail: tmckee@olathe.org
Facebook: www.facebook.com/OlatheChamber
Linkedin: www.linkedin.com/in/olathechamber
X (Twitter): x.com/OlatheChamber
Instagram: www.instagram.com/olathechamber
Description: Promotes business and community development in the Olathe, KS area. Sponsors annual Olathe Expo and Olathe Night at the Royals. **Founded:** 1921. **Publications:** *Olathe Business Report* (Weekly (Fri.)). **Educational Activities:** Blazing New Trails; Chamber Coffee at Santa Marta Senior Living Community. **Awards:** Bartlett-Olson Membership Achievement Award (Annual); Olathe Chamber of Commerce Ambassador of the Year (Annual); Olathe Chamber of Commerce Citizen of the Year (Annual); Olathe Chamber of Commerce Corporate Citizen of the Year (Annual); Olathe Chamber of Commerce Volunteer of the Year (Annual). **Geographic Preference:** Local.

39940 ■ Osage City Chamber of Commerce
PO Box 56
Osage City, KS 66523
Ph: (785)219-2510
Co. E-mail: osagecitychamber@gmail.com
URL: http://www.osagecitychamber.com
Contact: Adam Burnett, President
Facebook: www.facebook.com/Osage-City-Chamber-of-Commerce-136005343076480
Description: Promotes business and community development in Osage City, KS. **Founded:** 1920. **Geographic Preference:** Local.

39941 ■ Osawatomie Chamber of Commerce
509 5th St.
Osawatomie, KS 66064
Ph: (913)755-4114
Co. E-mail: chamber@osawatomiechamber.org
URL: http://www.osawatomiechamber.org
Contact: Kari Bradley, Executive Director
Facebook: www.facebook.com/osawatomiechamber
Description: Promotes business and community development in Osawatomie, KS. **Founded:** 1948. **Geographic Preference:** Local.

39942 ■ Osborne Area Chamber of Commerce (OACC)
128 N First St.
Osborne, KS 67473
Ph: (785)346-5611
Fax: (785)346-2522
URL: http://www.discoverosborne.com
Contact: Keri Thornton, President
Facebook: www.facebook.com/OsborneChamber
Description: Promotes business and community development in the Osborne, KS area. Convention/Meeting: none. Publications: none. **Founded:** 1925. **Geographic Preference:** Local.

39943 ■ Ottawa Area Chamber of Commerce
109 E 2nd St.
Ottawa, KS 66067
Ph: (785)242-1000
Fax: (785)242-4792
Co. E-mail: chamber@ottawakansas.org
URL: http://ottawakansas.org
Contact: John Coen, President
E-mail: john@ottawakansas.org
Facebook: www.facebook.com/OttawaKansas
X (Twitter): x.com/ottawakschamber
Instagram: www.instagram.com/ottawakschamber
Description: Promotes business and community development in the Franklin County, KS area. **Awards:** Ottawa Area Chamber of Commerce - Entrepreneur Award (Annual). **Geographic Preference:** Local.

39944 ■ *Outlook Business Journal*
1125 Williams St.
Great Bend, KS 67530
Ph: (620)792-2401
Fax: (620)792-2404
Co. E-mail: marketing@greatbend.org
URL: http://www.greatbend.org
Contact: Megan Barfield, President
URL(s): www.greatbend.org/businessjournals
Released: Monthly **Availability:** PDF; Online.

39945 ■ Overland Park Chamber of Commerce (OPCC)
9001 W 110th St., No. 150
Overland Park, KS 66210
Ph: (913)491-3600
Co. E-mail: opcc@opchamber.org
URL: http://www.opchamber.org
Contact: Tracey Osborne Oltjen, President
E-mail: tosborne@opchamber.org
Facebook: www.facebook.com/opchamber
Linkedin: www.linkedin.com/company/overland-park-chamber-of-commerce
X (Twitter): x.com/opchamber
Instagram: www.instagram.com/opchamber
YouTube: www.youtube.com/channel/UCqEMbMHW-xm1UVDAo6YYT5g
Description: Promotes business and community development in Johnson County, KS. **Founded:** 1967. **Publications:** *Business Intelligence Report* (Monthly); *Business Perspective* (Monthly); *Growing a Business in Johnson County* (Periodic). **Geographic Preference:** Local.

39946 ■ Paola Chamber of Commerce
6 W Peoria St.
Paola, KS 66071
Ph: (913)294-4335
Co. E-mail: info@paolachamber.org
URL: http://www.paolachamber.org
Contact: Michelle Kaiser, President
Facebook: www.facebook.com/paolachamber
X (Twitter): x.com/paolakansas
YouTube: www.youtube.com/channel/UCpcel7HGXFBdp4V5iveCPhw
Pinterest: www.pinterest.com/visitpaola
Description: Seeks to promote the commercial, industrial and civic interests of the Paola area. Sponsors six promotions per year. **Founded:** 1920. **Publications:** *Business Courier* (Weekly); *Paola's Business* (Monthly). **Educational Activities:** Leadership; Legislative Breakfast. **Geographic Preference:** Local.

39947 ■ Parsons Chamber of Commerce
506 Main St.
Parsons, KS 67357
Ph: (620)421-6500
Co. E-mail: chamber@parsonschamber.org
URL: http://www.parsonschamber.org
Contact: Toby Johnston, President
Description: Promotes business and community development in Parsons, KS. **Founded:** 1871. **Geographic Preference:** Local.

39948 ■ Phillipsburg Area Chamber of Commerce
270 State St.
Phillipsburg, KS 67661-0326
Ph: (785)543-2321
Fax: (785)543-2321
Co. E-mail: cvbcham@ruraltel.net
URL: http://www.chamber-commerce.net/dir/9667/Phillipsburg-Area-Chamber-of-Commerce-in-Phillipsburg
Contact: Jackie Swatzell, Contact
Description: Promotes business and community development in the Phillipsburg, KS area. **Geographic Preference:** Local.

39949 ■ Pittsburg Area Chamber of Commerce
117 W 4th St.
Pittsburg, KS 66762
Ph: (620)231-1000
URL: http://pittsburgareachamber.com
Contact: Blake Benson, President
Facebook: www.facebook.com/PittsburgAreaCoC
YouTube: www.youtube.com/channel/UC1DZUqLi3qjZC2k6uJW8g7g
Description: Promotes business and community development in the Pittsburg, KS area. **Founded:** 1897. **Publications:** *Keeping PACE* (Monthly); *The Morning Sun*. **Geographic Preference:** Local.

39950 ■ Pratt Area Chamber of Commerce
211 S Main St.
Pratt, KS 67124
Ph: (620)672-5501
Co. E-mail: info@prattkansas.org
URL: http://www.prattkansas.org
Contact: Ashley Smith, Chief Executive Officer
Facebook: www.facebook.com/PrattAreaChamberofCommerce
Description: Promotes business and community development in Pratt County, KS. **Founded:** 1929. **Geographic Preference:** Local.

39951 ■ Russell Area Chamber of Commerce (RACC)
507 N Main St.
Russell, KS 67665
Ph: (785)483-6960
Co. E-mail: russellkschamber@gmail.com
URL: http://russellchamber.org
Contact: Linda Crowder, President
Facebook: www.facebook.com/russellareachamberofcommerce
Instagram: www.instagram.com/russellareachamberofcommerce
Description: Promotes business, tourism, and community development in Russell County, KS. Serves as an information center. Sponsors business after hours, ambassador calls, legislative coffees, secretary's day luncheon, agricultural appreciation dinner, ribbon cuttings, rental and employment listings, and greeter service. **Founded:** 1949. **Publications:** *News Briefs From the Chamber* (Monthly). **Geographic Preference:** Local.

39952 ■ Sabetha Chamber of Commerce
805 Main St.
Sabetha, KS 66534-1826
Ph: (785)285-2139
Co. E-mail: info@sabethachamber.com
URL: http://www.sabethachamber.com
Contact: Cindy Alderfer, President
Description: Promotes business and community development in Sabetha, KS. **Founded:** 1857. **Geographic Preference:** Local.

39953 ■ Salina Area Chamber of Commerce (SACC)
120 W Ash St.
Salina, KS 67401
Ph: (785)827-9301
Co. E-mail: info@salinakansas.org
URL: http://www.salinakansas.org
Contact: Eric Brown, President
E-mail: ebrown@salinakansas.org
Facebook: www.facebook.com/salinachamber
X (Twitter): x.com/SalinaCofC
YouTube: www.youtube.com/user/SalinaAreaChamberofC/videos
Description: Promotes business and community development in the Salina, KS area. **Founded:** 1911. **Educational Activities:** Mid-America Farm Exposition (Annual). **Geographic Preference:** Regional.

39954 ■ Seneca Chamber of Commerce
523 Main St.
Seneca, KS 66538
Ph: (785)336-1313
Co. E-mail: senecaimpact@gmail.com
URL: http://senecakansas.com/chamber/contact-the-chamber
Contact: Darrel Kohlman, President
E-mail: dkohlman@usd115.org
Geographic Preference: Local.

39955 ■ Shawnee Chamber of Commerce (SCC)
15100 W 67th St., Ste. 202
Shawnee, KS 66217-9344
Ph: (913)631-6545
Co. E-mail: info@shawneekschamber.com
URL: http://www.shawnee-ks.com

Contact: Ann Smith-Tate, President
E-mail: asmithtate@shawneekschamber.com
X (Twitter): x.com/shawneechamber
YouTube: www.youtube.com/channel/
UCQEeQrCpRjnzn-Ti9ZsXsyA

Description: Promotes business and community development in the Shawnee, KS area. **Founded:** 1946. **Publications:** *Chamberline* (Monthly). **Geographic Preference:** Local.

39956 ■ Smith Center Chamber of Commerce
119 W Ct.
  Smith Center, KS 66967
Ph: (785)282-3895
URL: http://www.smithcenterks.com
Contact: Mary Ann Schemm, Contact

Description: Promotes business and community development in Smith Center, KS. **Founded:** 1938. **Geographic Preference:** Local.

39957 ■ Sterling Chamber of Commerce
PO Box 56
  Sterling, KS 67579
Ph: (620)278-3727
Co. E-mail: mishleraccounting@lrmutual.com
URL: http://www.sterlingkschamber.com
Contact: Cheryl Buckman, Treasurer

Description: Promotes business and community development in Sterling, KS. **Geographic Preference:** Local.

39958 ■ Wamego Chamber of Commerce
529 Lincoln Ave.
  Wamego, KS 66547
Ph: (785)456-7849
Co. E-mail: info@visitwamego.com
URL: http://www.wamegochamber.com
Contact: Casie Hartwich, Group President
Facebook: www.facebook.com/WamegoChamber

Description: Promotes agriculture, business, and community development in Wamego, KS. Sponsors area festivals. **Geographic Preference:** Local.

39959 ■ *Weekly Enews*
200 S 10th
  Atchison, KS 66002
Ph: (913)367-2427
Co. E-mail: marketing@atchisonkansas.net
URL: http://www.atchisonkansas.net
Contact: Dianna Kruger, Office Manager
E-mail: dkruger@atchisonkansas.net
URL(s): www.atchisonkansas.net/index.php/
  businesses/how-the-chamber-can-help-your
  -business

Released: Weekly **Availability:** Print; Online.

39960 ■ Wellsville Chamber of Commerce
c/o Susan Stueve, President
  PO Box 472
  Wellsville, KS 66092
Ph: (785)816-0406
Co. E-mail: wellsvillechamberofcommerce@hotmail
  .com
URL: http://wellsvillechamber.org
Contact: Susan Stueve, President
Facebook: www.facebook.com/
  WellsvilleChamberOfCommerce

Description: Promotes business and community development in Wellsville, KS. **Geographic Preference:** Local.

39961 ■ Wichita Regional Chamber of Commerce (WRCC)
350 W Douglas Ave.
  Wichita, KS 67202
Ph: (316)265-7771
Co. E-mail: info@wichitachamber.org
URL: http://www.wichitachamber.org
Contact: John Rolfe, President
Facebook: www.facebook.com/ChamberWichita
Linkedin: www.linkedin.com/company/
  chamberwichita
X (Twitter): x.com/ChamberWichita
Instagram: www.instagram.com/chamberwichita
YouTube: www.youtube.com/user/WichitaMe
  troChamber

Description: Promotes business and community development in the Wichita, KS area. **Founded:** 1917. **Publications:** *Wichita Metro Directory of Major Employers* (Biennial); *Impact* (Weekly); *Business Intelligence Report* (Monthly); *Images of the Greater Wichita Area* (Annual). **Geographic Preference:** Local.

39962 ■ Winfield Chamber of Commerce (WCC)
123 E 9th Ave.
  Winfield, KS 67156
Ph: (620)221-2420
Fax: (620)221-2958
Co. E-mail: win@winfieldchamber.org
URL: http://winfieldchamber.org
Contact: Sarah Werner, Chief Executive Officer
E-mail: ceo@winfieldpartners.org
Facebook: www.facebook.com/winfieldareachamber

Description: Promotes business and community development in the area. **Founded:** 1870. **Geographic Preference:** Local.

39963 ■ Woodson County Chamber of Commerce
110 N Main St.
  Yates Center, KS 66783
Ph: (620)625-3235
Co. E-mail: wocochamber2019@gmail.com
URL: http://www.woodsoncountychamber.org
Facebook: www.facebook.com/woodson.chamber

Description: Promotes business, community development, and tourism in Woodson County, KS. **Founded:** 1951. **Geographic Preference:** Local.

MINORITY BUSINESS ASSISTANCE PROGRAMS

39964 ■ Kansas Department of Commerce - Office of Minority and Women Business Development
1000 SW Jackson, Ste. 100
  Topeka, KS 66612
URL: http://www.kansascommerce.gov/program/business-incentives-and-services/mw-development
Contact: Rhonda Harris, Director
E-mail: rhonda.harris@ks.gov

Description: Provides counseling, technical assistance, and procurement counseling. Conducts low-cost business seminars, workshops, and conferences. Offers business reference materials. **Publications:** *Kansas Business Assistance Resource Directory* (Quarterly); *Kansas Companies Who Export Directory* (Annual); *Kansas Aerospace Resource Directory*; *Kansas Agribusiness Directory*; *Directory of Kansas Job Shops* (Irregular); *Directory of Kansas Warehouse and Distribution Centers*; *Kansas International Trade Resource Directory* (Annual); *Fortune 500 Facilities in Kansas*; *Firms Headquartered in Kansas* (Annual); *Kansas Association Directory*; *Kansas New and Expanding Manufacturers*; *Kansas Minority & Women Business Directory* (Annual).

FINANCING AND LOAN PROGRAMS

39965 ■ iiM, LLC [Innovation in Motion]
8500 Shawnee Mission Pkwy., Ste. 150
  Merriam, KS 66202

Description: Investment group funds early-stage companies. Offers connections to experts and resources, business plan development, and marketing strategy, communication, and intellectual property assistance. **Founded:** 2013. **Preferred Investment Size:** $50,000-$300,000. **Industry Preferences:** Animal health; human health; agribusiness.

39966 ■ Kansas Venture Capital Inc. (KVCI)
10601 Mission Rd., Ste. 250
  Leawood, KS 66206
Contact: Brian Lueger, Contact

Description: Provider of investment services. **Founded:** 1976. **Preferred Investment Size:** $500,000 to $260,000,000. **Industry Preferences:** Communications and media, computer related, semiconductors and other electronics, medical and health, consumer related, industrial and energy, business service, and manufacturing.

39967 ■ Openair Equity Partners
6701 W 64th S, Bldg. 5, Ste. 320
  Overland Park, KS 66202
Co. E-mail: info@openairep.com
URL: http://www.openairep.com
Contact: Holly O'Keefe, General Counsel
E-mail: hollyo@octobercapital.com

Description: Equity investment firm. Connects people and things for transformational results.

39968 ■ Women's Capital Connection (WCC)
6405 Metcalf Ave., Bldg. No. 3, Ste. 318
  Overland Park, KS 66202
Ph: (913)492-5922
URL: http://womenscapitalconnection.com
Contact: Sherry Turner, Founder
E-mail: sturner@onekcforwomen.com

Description: Region group of accredited angel investors who identify and fund startups in the Midwest. **Founded:** 2008.

INCUBATORS/RESEARCH AND TECHNOLOGY PARKS

39969 ■ The Center for Entrepreneurship at Wichita State University (WSU)
1845 Fairmount St.
  Wichita, KS 67260
Ph: (316)978-3000
Co. E-mail: cfe@wichita.edu
URL: http://www.wichita.edu/academics/innovation
  _and_new_ventures/cfe/index.php
Contact: Nancy Kersenbrock, Associate Director
E-mail: nancy.kersenbrock@wichita.edu
Facebook: www.facebook.com/wsucfe
Linkedin: www.linkedin.com/in/wsucfe
X (Twitter): x.com/wsucfe

Description: Academic center that promotes entrepreneurial thinking through academic and community programs. **Founded:** 1977.

39970 ■ Center For Advanced Professional Studies (CAPS)
7501 W 149th Ter.
  Overland Park, KS 66223
Ph: (913)239-5900
URL: http://yourcapsnetwork.org
Contact: Corey Mohn, President
E-mail: cmohn@bluevalleyk12.org
Facebook: www.facebook.com/capsnetwork
Linkedin: www.linkedin.com/company/caps-network
X (Twitter): x.com/networkcaps
Instagram: www.instagram.com/capsnetwork

Description: Business incubator striving to revitalize education by creating an innovative environment where businesses, education and community collaborate to become a global learning community.

39971 ■ Enterprise Center of Johnson County (ECJC)
6405 Metcalf Ave., Ste. 318
  Overland Park, KS 66202
Ph: (913)438-2282

Description: A small business incubator providing high-growth potential companies with office space, consulting and advisory services, and financing resources in order to help them grow and succeed.

39972 ■ The Enterprise Center in Johnson County (ECJC)
6405 Metcalf Ave., Ste. 318
  Overland Park, KS 66202
Ph: (913)438-2282
Fax: (913)888-6928
Co. E-mail: info@ecjc.com
URL: http://www.ecjc.com
Contact: Jeff Shackelford, President
Facebook: www.facebook.com/ECJCKS
X (Twitter): x.com/ECJC_KS

Description: Connects entrepreneurs to the resources they need to grow and scale early-stage businesses. **Founded:** 1995.

39973 ▪ Glacial Hills Food Center (GHFC)
1730 1st Ave. W
 Horton, KS 66439
Ph: (785)608-8801
URL: http://ghfoodcenter.com
Facebook: www.facebook.com/GHFoodCenter
Description: A shared-use, incubator kitchen available to rent to the public. New entrepreneurs can use the food center to get their food business off the ground.

39974 ▪ Hodgeman County Culinary Incubator
203 N W St., Ste. 100A
 Hanston, KS 67849
Ph: (620)357-8831
Co. E-mail: hanston@ucom.net
URL: http://hodgemancountyks.com
Contact: Sarah Scott, Treasurer
Description: Culinary incubator supporting food startups.

39975 ▪ KU Innovation Park (BTBC)
2029 Becker Dr.
 Lawrence, KS 66047
Ph: (785)832-2110
Co. E-mail: info@kuinnovationpark.com
URL: http://kuinnovationpark.com
Contact: Adam Courtney, President
Facebook: www.facebook.com/kuinnovationpark
Linkedin: www.linkedin.com/company/bioscience-an
 d-technology-business-center
X (Twitter): x.com/KuInnovation
Instagram: www.instagram.com/btbc_ku
Description: Its mission is to provide business development assistance to early-stage businesses that have spun off from the University of Kansas, as well as to local entrepreneurs who would like to create their own high-technology firms. **Founded:** 2010.

39976 ▪ The Labor Party
216 N Mosley
 Wichita, KS 67202
Ph: (316)712-4623
Co. E-mail: hello@labor-party.com
URL: http://labor-party.com
Contact: Kenton Hansen, Contact
Facebook: www.facebook.com/thelaborparty
X (Twitter): x.com/thelaborparty
Instagram: www.instagram.com/thelaborparty

Description: A coworking space where startups, creative freelancers, independent professionals, and small companies can work together to tackle problems.

39977 ▪ South Central Kansas Economic Development District (SCKEDD)
9730 E 50th St. N
 Bel Aire, KS 67226
Ph: (316)262-7035
Fax: (316)262-7062
Co. E-mail: sckeddonline@gmail.com
URL: http://www.sckedd.org
Description: Helps entrepreneurs and small business owners find financing solutions and strategies to assist their startups to grow. Also offer business and industry guaranteed loan programs, intermediary relending program, revolving loan, rural business development program and the rural microenterprise assistance program. **Founded:** 1972.

39978 ▪ Wichita Technology Corp. (WTC)
550 N 159th St. E , Ste. No 208
 Wichita, KS 67230
Contact: Patricia Brasted, Contact
Description: Provides capital and value added services to well-managed companies with superior growth potential. **Founded:** 1994.

EDUCATIONAL PROGRAMS

39979 ▪ Coffeyville Community College (CCC)
400 W 11th St.
 Coffeyville, KS 67337
Ph: (620)251-7700
Free: 877-51R-AVEN
URL: http://www.coffeyville.edu
Contact: Dr. Marlon Thornburg, President
E-mail: thornburg.marlon@coffeyville.edu
Facebook: www.facebook.com/CCCRedRavens
X (Twitter): x.com/cccredravens
Instagram: www.instagram.com/cccredravens
Description: Two-year college offering a small business management program. **Founded:** 1923. **Publications:** *The Collegian.*

39980 ▪ Labette Community College - Advanced Respiratory Therapist Program
200 S 14th St.
 Parsons, KS 67357
URL: http://www.labette.edu/respiratory/index.html
Contact: Susan Stolte, Director
E-mail: susans@labette.edu

Description: Two-year college offering a small business management program. **Founded:** 1984.

39981 ▪ Wichita State University Center for Entrepreneurship
1845 Fairmount St.
 Wichita, KS 67260-0062
Ph: (316)978-3456
Co. E-mail: cfe@wichita.edu
URL: http://www.wichita.edu/academics/business/en
 trepreneurship
Contact: Nancy Kersenbrock, Assistant Director
E-mail: mark.torline@wichita.edu
Facebook: www.facebook.com/wsucfe
Linkedin: www.linkedin.com/in/wsucfe
X (Twitter): x.com/wsucfe
Description: Offers degreed courses for entrepreneurs and small business management. **Founded:** 1977.

LEGISLATIVE ASSISTANCE

39982 ▪ Kansas House Standing Committee on Economic Development and Tourism (LAS)
300 SW 10th St.
 Topeka, KS 66612
URL: http://www.kslegislature.org/li

PUBLICATIONS

39983 ▪ Wichita Business Journal (WBJ)
121 N Mead, Ste. 100
 Wichita, KS 67202
Ph: (316)267-6406
Fax: (316)267-8570
Co. E-mail: wichita@bizjournals.com
URL: http://www.bizjournals.com
Contact: Brittany Schowalter, Director
E-mail: bschowalter@bizjournals.com
Facebook: www.facebook.com/ICTBizJournal
Linkedin: www.linkedin.com/company/wichita
 -business-journal
X (Twitter): x.com/ICTBizJournal
Instagram: www.instagram.com/ictbizjournal
Description: Publisher of journals. **Founded:** 1986.
Publications: *Wichita Business Journal--Book of Lists* (Annual).

VENTURE CAPITAL FIRM

39984 ▪ Midwest Venture Alliance (MVA)
245 N Waco, Ste. 230A
 Wichita, KS 67202
URL: http://www.avpict.com
Contact: Trish Brasted, Chief Executive Officer
Description: Network of accredited investors committed to investing in high-growth seed and early-stage technology companies in Kansas and surrounding states. **Founded:** 2005.

Kentucky

ASSOCIATIONS AND OTHER ORGANIZATIONS

39985 ■ AgriBusiness Association of Kentucky (ABAK)
340 Democrat Dr.
Frankfort, KY 40601
Ph: (502)226-1122
Fax: (502)875-1595
URL: http://www.kyagbusiness.org
Contact: Jeff Pendleton, President
Facebook: www.facebook.com/kyagbusiness
X (Twitter): x.com/KyAgBusiness

Description: Represents professionals engaged in business of supplying inputs for agriculture production throughout the state of Kentucky. Provides support, resources, and opportunities in Kentucky agriculture. **Founded:** 1962. **Geographic Preference:** State.

39986 ■ Association of Fundraising Professionals Bluegrass Chapter - Lexington Public Library Resources
1600 Old Frankfort Pke.
Lexington, KY 40504
Co. E-mail: afpbluegrasschapter@gmail.com
URL: http://afpglobal.org/chapters/afp-ky-kentucky-bluegrass-chapter
Contact: Carrie Thayer Cardwell, President
URL(s): community.afpglobal.org/afpkybluegrasschapter

Description: Supports fundraising professionals who work for a wide variety of charitable organizations throughout central and eastern Kentucky. **Scope:** Philanthropy. **Geographic Preference:** Local.

39987 ■ Association of Fundraising Professionals Greater Louisville Chapter
Louisville, KY
Co. E-mail: afpgreaterlouisville@gmail.com
URL: http://community.afpglobal.org/afpkygreaterlouisvillechapter/career/center
Contact: Lena Iwu, Coordinator

Description: Fosters the development and growth of fundraising professionals. Promotes high ethical standards in the fundraising profession. Provides training opportunities for fundraising professionals. **Geographic Preference:** Local.

39988 ■ Business Network International - Southwest Kentucky Northern Ohio (BNI)
639 Philadelphia St.
Covington, KY 41011
Ph: (859)655-9434
Fax: (859)655-9697
URL: http://bniswonky.com/en-US/index
Contact: Katie Scanlon, Executive Director
Facebook: www.facebook.com/bniswonky

Description: Provides both men and women a structured environment for the development and exchange of quality business referrals. Offers members the opportunity to share ideas and contacts. **Geographic Preference:** Local.

39989 ■ National Association of Women Business Owners Louisville
614 W Main St., Ste. 6000
Louisville, KY 40202
Co. E-mail: assistant@nawbokentucky.org
URL: http://nawbokentucky.org
Contact: Basha Roberts, President
Linkedin: www.linkedin.com/company/nawbo-ky
X (Twitter): x.com/LouisvilleNAWBO
Instagram: www.instagram.com/nawbokentucky
YouTube: www.youtube.com/channel/UCfJjYeOl4Njk67D9_Rzc7zg

Description: Support female business owners in Kentucky and southern Indiana. **Founded:** 1992. **Geographic Preference:** Local.

SMALL BUSINESS DEVELOPMENT CENTERS

39990 ■ Bluegrass Small Business Development Center
330 E Main St., Ste. 210
Lexington, KY 40507-1525
Ph: (859)257-7666
Free: 888-475-7232
Fax: (859)257-1751
Co. E-mail: bluegrass@ksbdc.org
URL: http://www.ksbdc.org/lexington
Contact: Becky Marefat, Coordinator

Description: Represents and promotes the small business sector. Provides management assistance to current and prospective small business owners. Helps to improve management skills and expand the products and services of members. **Geographic Preference:** Local.

39991 ■ Eastern Kentucky University Small Business Development Center (EKU SBDC)
342 2nd St.
Paintsville, KY 41240
Ph: (606)769-2121
URL: http://kentuckysbdc.com/easternky
Contact: Michelle Spriggs, Director
E-mail: michelle.spriggs@uky.edu
Facebook: www.facebook.com/ekusbdc

Description: Represents and promotes the small business sector. Provides management assistance to current and prospective small business owners. Helps to improve management skills and expand the products and services of members. **Geographic Preference:** Local.

39992 ■ Hopkinsville Small Business Development Center
2800 Ft. Campbell Blvd.
Hopkinsville, KY 42240-4943
URL: http://kentuckysbdc.com
Contact: Anne Wingrove, President
Facebook: www.facebook.com/ksbdc
Linkedin: www.linkedin.com/company/kentucky-small-business-development-center
X (Twitter): x.com/kysbdc
Instagram: www.instagram.com/ksbdc
YouTube: www.youtube.com/user/kysmallbiz

Description: Represents and promotes the small business sector. Provides management assistance to current and prospective small business owners. Helps to improve management skills and expand the products and services of members. **Geographic Preference:** Local.

39993 ■ Kentucky Small Business Development Center (kSBDC) [Elizabethtown Small Business Development Center]
1105 Juliana Ct., No. 6
Elizabethtown, KY 42701
Ph: (270)209-6060
Fax: (270)769-5095
Co. E-mail: hello@kentuckysbdc.com
URL: http://kentuckysbdc.com
Contact: Patricia Krausman, Director
E-mail: patricia.krausman@uky.edu
Facebook: www.facebook.com/ksbdc
Linkedin: www.linkedin.com/company/kentucky-small-business-development-center
X (Twitter): x.com/kysbdc
Instagram: www.instagram.com/ksbdc
YouTube: www.youtube.com/user/kysmallbiz

Description: Promotes the small business sector. Provides management assistance to small business owners. Helps to improve management skills and expand the products and services of members. **Geographic Preference:** Local.

39994 ■ Kentucky Small Business Development Center at Eastern Kentucky University Richmond
521 Lancaster Ave.
Richmond, KY 40475
URL: http://www.eku.edu/azindex/s

Description: Provides management assistance to current and prospective small business owners in Eastern Kentucky. **Geographic Preference:** Local.

39995 ■ Kentucky Small Business Development Center Lead Office (KSBDC)
343 Waller Ave., Ste. 205
Lexington, KY 40504
Ph: (859)257-7668
Free: 888-414-7232
Co. E-mail: hello@kentuckysbdc.com
URL: http://kentuckysbdc.com
Contact: Kristina Joyce, Director
E-mail: kjoyce@uky.edu
Facebook: www.facebook.com/ksbdc
Linkedin: www.linkedin.com/company/kentucky-small-business-development-center
X (Twitter): x.com/kysbdc
Instagram: www.instagram.com/ksbdc
YouTube: www.youtube.com/user/kysmallbiz

Description: Provides management assistance to current and prospective small business owners in Kentucky. **Founded:** 1981. **Geographic Preference:** State.

STATE LISTINGS

Kentucky ■ 40013

39996 ■ Louisville Small Business Development Center
614 W Main St., Ste. 6000
Louisville, KY 40202
Ph: (502)625-0123
Fax: (502)625-0010
URL: http://kentuckysbdc.com/louisville
Contact: David Oetken, Director
E-mail: david.oetken@uky.edu
Facebook: www.facebook.com/louisvillesbdc
Linkedin: www.linkedin.com/in/louisvillesbdc
Description: Represents and promotes the small business sector. Provides management assistance to current and prospective small business owners. Helps to improve management skills and expand the products and services of members. **Geographic Preference:** Local.

39997 ■ Morehead Small Business Development Center
102 W First St.
Morehead, KY 40351
Ph: (606)610-2123
Fax: (606)783-5020
URL: http://ksbdc.org/morehead
Contact: Rachel Bowling, Director
E-mail: rtbowling@moreheadstate.edu
Description: Provides management assistance to current and prospective small business owners in Morehead. **Geographic Preference:** Local.

39998 ■ Murray State SBDC
330 E Main St. Ste. 210
Lexington, KY 40507
Ph: (859)257-7668
Free: 888-414-7232
Fax: (859)323-1907
URL: http://kentuckysbdc.com
Contact: Kristina Joyce, Director
E-mail: kjoyce@uky.edu
Facebook: www.facebook.com/ksbdc
Linkedin: www.linkedin.com/company/kentucky-small-business-development-center
X (Twitter): twitter.com/kysbdc
Instagram: www.instagram.com/ksbdc
YouTube: www.youtube.com/user/kysmallbiz
Description: Represents and promotes the small business sector. Provides management assistance to current and prospective small business owners. Helps to improve management skills and expand the products and services of members. **Geographic Preference:** Local.

39999 ■ Northern Kentucky University Small Business Development Center (NKU SBDC)
330 E Main St., Ste. 210
Lexington, KY 40507
Free: 888-414-7232
Co. E-mail: hello@kentuckysbdc.com
URL: http://kentuckysbdc.com
Facebook: www.facebook.com/ksbdc
Linkedin: www.linkedin.com/company/kentucky-small-business-development-center
X (Twitter): x.com/kysbdc
Instagram: www.instagram.com/ksbdc
YouTube: www.youtube.com/user/kysmallbiz
Description: Represents and promotes the small business sector. Provides management assistance to current and prospective small business owners. Helps to improve management skills and expand the products and services of members. **Founded:** 1981. **Geographic Preference:** Local.

40000 ■ Owensboro Small Business Development Center
200 E 3rd St., Ste. 200
Owensboro, KY 42303
Ph: (270)574-9990
URL: http://kentuckysbdc.com/owensboro
Contact: Jamie Johnson, Contact
E-mail: jamie.johnson@uky.edu
Description: Represents and promotes the small business sector. Provides management assistance to current and prospective small business owners. Helps to improve management skills and expand the products and services of members. **Geographic Preference:** Local.

40001 ■ Paintsville Small Business Development Center
342 2nd St.
Paintsville, KY 41240
Ph: (606)769-2121
URL: http://kentuckysbdc.com/easternky
Contact: Michelle Spriggs, Director
E-mail: michelle.spriggs@uky.edu
Description: Provides management assistance to current and prospective small business owners in Paintsville. **Geographic Preference:** Local.

40002 ■ Pikeville Small Business Development Center
3455 N Mayo Trl., No. 4
Pikeville, KY 41501
URL: http://www.moreheadstate.edu/pikevillesbdc
Description: Provides management assistance to current and prospective small business owners in Pikeville. **Geographic Preference:** Local.

40003 ■ Small Business Development Center at Western Kentucky University
2413 Nashville Rd., Ste. 208
Bowling Green, KY 42101
Ph: (270)745-1905
URL: http://www.wku.edu/sbdc
Contact: Timothy C. Caboni, President
Description: Represents and promotes the small business sector. Provides management assistance to current and prospective small business owners. Helps to improve management skills and expand the products and services of members. **Geographic Preference:** Local.

40004 ■ Southeast Small Business Development Center
100 College Rd.
Middlesboro, KY 40965
Ph: (606)896-2300
URL: http://kentuckysbdc.com/middlesboro
Facebook: www.facebook.com/SoutheastKYSBDC
Description: Represents and promotes the small business sector. Provides management assistance to current and prospective small business owners. Helps to improve management skills and expand the products and services of members. **Geographic Preference:** Local.

SMALL BUSINESS ASSISTANCE PROGRAMS

40005 ■ Kentucky Cabinet for Economic Development - International Trade Div.
Old Capitol Annex
300 W Broadway
Frankfort, KY 40601
URL: http://ced.ky.gov/International/Exports
Description: Preserves and increases employment opportunities through foreign investment within the state, and increased export of Kentucky's manufactured products. Operates a Far East office in Japan and a European office in England.

40006 ■ Kentucky Cabinet for Economic Development (SBSD) - Small Business Services Div.
Old Capital Annex
300 W Broadway
Frankfort, KY 40601
Ph: (502)564-7140
Free: 800-626-2250
Fax: (502)564-3256
Co. E-mail: cedsbsd@ky.gov
URL: http://ced.ky.gov
Contact: Jack Mazura, Executive Director
Description: Serves as an advocate and ombudsman for small business. Works with the Legislative Small Business Task Force, provides information on programs of interest, and provides information on specialized resource assistance. **Founded:** 1976.

40007 ■ Women's Business Center of Kentucky (WBC)
c/o Community Ventures
1450 N Broadway
Lexington, KY 40505
Ph: (859)231-0054
Co. E-mail: wbckentucky@cvky.org
URL: http://www.wbckentucky.org
Contact: Devanny King, Director
Facebook: www.facebook.com/WomensBusinessCenterOfKentucky
X (Twitter): x.com/wbckentucky
Description: Helps women-owned businesses start and grow. Offers free business coaching, support, and other resources. **Founded:** 2011.

SCORE OFFICES

40008 ■ Lexington SCORE
389 Waller Ave., Ste. 130
Lexington, KY 40504
Ph: (859)231-9902
Fax: (859)253-3190
Co. E-mail: scorelex@gmail.com
URL: http://lexington.score.org
Contact: Larry Corum, Contact
E-mail: scorelex@gmail.com
Facebook: www.facebook.com/scorelexington
Linkedin: www.linkedin.com/company/score-mentors-lexington
Description: Provides professional guidance and information to America's small businesses. **Founded:** 1972. **Geographic Preference:** Local.

40009 ■ Louisville SCORE
614 W Main St., Ste. 6000
Louisville, KY 40202
Ph: (502)888-4543
Co. E-mail: help@score.org
URL: http://louisville.score.org
Linkedin: www.linkedin.com/company/score-mentors-louisville
X (Twitter): x.com/SCORELouisvill
Description: Provides professional guidance, mentoring services and financial assistance to maximize the success of existing and emerging small businesses. **Founded:** 1964. **Geographic Preference:** Local.

40010 ■ SCORE - Bowling Green
710 College St.
Bowling Green, KY 42102
Ph: (502)582-5976
Fax: (502)582-5819
Co. E-mail: 75score@score-louisville.org

40011 ■ SCORE - Lexington, Kentucky
389 Waller Ave., Ste. 130
Lexington, KY 40504
Ph: (859)231-9902
Fax: (859)253-3190
Co. E-mail: help@score.org
URL: http://lexington.score.org
Linkedin: www.linkedin.com/company/score-mentors-lexington
Description: Provides professional guidance and information to maximize the success of existing and emerging small businesses. Offers business counseling and workshops. **Founded:** 1972.

40012 ■ SCORE - Louisville
614 W Main St., Ste. 6000
Louisville, KY 40202
Ph: (502)888-4543
URL: http://www.score.org/kentuckiana
Description: Provides professional guidance and information to maximize the success of existing and emerging small businesses. Offers business counseling and workshops. **Founded:** 1964.

BETTER BUSINESS BUREAUS

40013 ■ Better Business Bureau of Central and Eastern Kentucky
1390 Olivia Ln.
Lexington, KY 40511

40014 ■ Kentucky

Ph: (859)259-1008
Fax: (859)259-1639
Co. E-mail: info@bluegrass.bbb.org
URL: http://www.bbb.org/local-bbb/bbb-of-central-an
 d-eastern-kentucky
Facebook: www.facebook.com/BBBservingCentralan
 dEasternKY
X (Twitter): x.com/bbbbluegrassky
Description: Promotes and fosters the highest ethical relationship between businesses and the public through voluntary self-regulation, consumer and business education and service excellence. **Founded:** 1957. **Publications:** *Give But Give Wisely* (Quarterly); *Taking Care of Business* (Quarterly). **Geographic Preference:** Local.

40014 ■ Better Business Bureau of Louisville, Southern Indiana and Western Kentucky
844 S 4th St.
 Louisville, KY 40203
Ph: (502)583-6546
Fax: (502)589-9940
Co. E-mail: info@bbbkyin.org
URL: http://www.bbb.org/local-bbb/bbb-of-louisville
 -southern-indiana-and-western-kentucky
Contact: Reanna Smith-Hamblin, President
E-mail: rsmith-hamblin@louisville.bbb.org
Facebook: www.facebook.com/bbbkyin
Linkedin: www.linkedin.com/company/better-business
 -bureau-louisville
X (Twitter): x.com/bbblouisville
Instagram: www.instagram.com/bbblouisville
YouTube: www.youtube.com/user/BBBLouisville
Description: Promotes ethics in the marketplace, assists businesses and consumers in resolving disputes and provides reliability reports about businesses and charities to help the public make informed decisions on buying and giving. **Founded:** 1916. **Publications:** *Business Beat* (Monthly). **Geographic Preference:** Regional.

CHAMBERS OF COMMERCE

40015 ■ Anderson County Chamber of Commerce (ACCOC)
1090 Glensboro Rd., Ste. 6A
 Lawrenceburg, KY 40342
Ph: (502)839-5564
URL: http://www.andersonchamberky.org
Contact: Jamie Hicks, Chairman
Facebook: www.facebook.com/AndersonCoun
 tyChamberOfCommerce
Description: Promotes business and community development in Anderson County, KY. Conducts annual 4th of July celebration. **Founded:** 1959. **Geographic Preference:** Local.

40016 ■ Ashland Alliance
1730 Winchester Ave.
 Ashland, KY 41105-0830
Ph: (606)324-5111
Fax: (606)325-4607
Co. E-mail: info@ashlandalliance.com
URL: http://ashlandalliance.com
Contact: Tim Gibbs, President
E-mail: tim@ashlandalliance.com
Facebook: www.facebook.com/AshlandAlliance
Description: Promotes business and community development in Boyd and Greenup counties, KY. **Geographic Preference:** Local.

40017 ■ Bell County Chamber of Commerce
189 N 20th St.
 Middlesboro, KY 40965
Ph: (606)248-1075
Fax: (606)248-8851
Co. E-mail: chamber@bellcountychamber.com
URL: http://www.bellcountychamber.org
Contact: Alex Barnett, President
Facebook: www.facebook.com/bellcountykychamber
X (Twitter): x.com/bellcochamber
Description: Promotes business and community development in Bell County Middlesboro, KY area. **Geographic Preference:** Local.

40018 ■ *Bowling Green*
710 College St.
 Bowling Green, KY 42101
Ph: (270)781-3200
Co. E-mail: info@bgchamber.com
URL: http://www.bgchamber.com
Contact: Ron Bunch, President
E-mail: ron@bgchamber.com
URL(s): www.bgchamber.com/marketing
Ed: Brad Golliher. **Released:** Annual **Description:** Magazine of the Bowling Green Area Chamber of Commerce. **Availability:** Print; Online.

40019 ■ Bowling Green Area Chamber of Commerce
710 College St.
 Bowling Green, KY 42101
Ph: (270)781-3200
Co. E-mail: info@bgchamber.com
URL: http://www.bgchamber.com
Contact: Ron Bunch, President
E-mail: ron@bgchamber.com
Facebook: www.facebook.com/bgareachamber
Linkedin: www.linkedin.com/company/
 bgareachamberofcommerce
X (Twitter): x.com/BGChamber
Instagram: www.instagram.com/bgchamber
Description: Promotes business and community development in Warren County, KY. **Founded:** 1935. **Publications:** *Chamber Connection*; *Bowling Green* (Annual). **Awards:** Bowling Green Area Chamber of Commerce ATHENA Award (Annual); ATHENA Young Professional Award (Annual); Bart Hagerman Leadership Award (Annual); Bowling Green Area Chamber of Commerce Small Business Person of the Year (Annual). **Geographic Preference:** Local.

40020 ■ Bullitt County Chamber of Commerce
147 Combs Ct.
 Shepherdsville, KY 40165
Ph: (502)543-6727
URL: http://bullittchamber.org
Contact: Anita Stump, Executive Director
E-mail: anita@bullittchamber.org
Facebook: www.facebook.com/Bulli
 ttChamberofCommerce
Linkedin: www.linkedin.com/company/bullitt-county
 -chamber-of-commerce
X (Twitter): x.com/BullittChambe
Instagram: www.instagram.com/bullitt_county_chamber
Description: Promotes business and community development in Bullitt County, KY. Issues publications. **Founded:** 1979. **Geographic Preference:** Local.

40021 ■ *The Business Bulletin*
116 E Union St.
 Munfordville, KY 42765
Ph: (270)524-2892
Fax: (270)524-1127
Co. E-mail: hart_co@scrtc.com
URL: http://hartcountyky.org
Contact: Fran Bowsher, President
URL(s): hartcountyky.org/membership/membership
 -benefits
Released: Monthly **Description:** Contains business information and updates on community events. **Availability:** Print.

40022 ■ *Business Call*
178 College St.
 Pikeville, KY 41501
Ph: (606)432-5504
Co. E-mail: info@sekchamber.com
URL: http://www.sekchamber.com
Contact: Jordan Gibson, President
E-mail: jordan.gibson@sekchamber.com
URL(s): www.sekchamber.com/sponsor
Released: Monthly **Availability:** Print.

40023 ■ Cadiz-Trigg County Chamber of Commerce
5748 Hopkinsville Rd.
 Cadiz, KY 42211
Ph: (270)522-0259

Co. E-mail: info@triggchamber.com
URL: http://www.triggchamber.com
Contact: Ashley Johnson, Co-Chairman of the Board
Description: Promotes business and community development in Trigg County, KY. **Awards:** Cadiz-Trigg County Chamber of Commerce Educator of the Year (Annual); Cadiz-Trigg County Chamber of Commerce Small Business of the Year (Annual). **Geographic Preference:** Local.

40024 ■ Campbellsville - Taylor County Chamber of Commerce
205 N Columbia Ave.
 Campbellsville, KY 42718
Ph: (270)465-8601
Co. E-mail: info@campbellsvillekychamber.com
URL: http://campbellsvillechamber.com
Contact: John B. Jessie, President
Facebook: www.facebook.com/
 campbellsvillechamber
X (Twitter): x.com/chamber42718
Instagram: www.instagram.com/chamber42718
Description: Promotes business and community development in Campbellsville, KY area. **Founded:** 1987. **Publications:** *Chamber Investment Matters* (Monthly). **Geographic Preference:** Local.

40025 ■ Cave City Area Chamber of Commerce
PO Box 460
 Cave City, KY 42127
Ph: (270)773-5159
Fax: (270)773-7446
Co. E-mail: cavecitychamber@gmail.com
URL: http://www.cavecitychamber.com
Facebook: www.facebook.com/caveci
 tychamberofcommerce
Description: Promotes business and community development in Cave City, AR. Participates in charitable programs; sponsors beauty pageants and Yard-of-the-Month competitions; conducts Watermelon Festival. Convention/Meeting: none. **Founded:** 1930. **Geographic Preference:** Local.

40026 ■ *Chamber Connection*
710 College St.
 Bowling Green, KY 42101
Ph: (270)781-3200
Co. E-mail: info@bgchamber.com
URL: http://www.bgchamber.com
Contact: Ron Bunch, President
E-mail: ron@bgchamber.com
URL(s): www.bgchamber.com/marketing
Description: Includes updates on the latest Chamber activities and upcoming events. **Availability:** PDF; Online.

40027 ■ *Chamber Connection*
300 S 3rd St.
 Paducah, KY 42002-0810
Ph: (270)443-1746
Fax: (270)442-9152
Co. E-mail: info@paducahchamber.org
URL: http://www.paducahchamber.org
Contact: Sandra Wilson, President
E-mail: swilson@paducahchamber.org
URL(s): www.paducahchamber.org/membership/
 member-benefits
Released: Weekly **Availability:** PDF; Online.

40028 ■ *Chamber Newsletter*
201 E Main St.
 Richmond, KY 40475
Ph: (859)623-1720
Co. E-mail: communications@richmondchamber.com
URL: http://www.richmondchamber.com
Contact: Greg Gerard, President
URL(s): www.richmondchamber.com/benefits-an
 d-plans.html
Released: Weekly **Availability:** Online.

40029 ■ *The Chamber Report*
201 S Main St.
 Franklin, KY 42134
Ph: (270)586-7609
URL: http://franklinsimpsonchamber.com
Contact: Mary Pat Bly, President

STATE LISTINGS   Kentucky ■ 40045

URL(s): franklinsimpsonchamber.com/membership-application
Released: Weekly **Availability:** Print; Online.

40030 ■ Christian County Chamber of Commerce
2800 Fort Campbell Blvd.
Hopkinsville, KY 42240
Ph: (270)885-9096
Free: 800-842-9959
Fax: (270)886-2059
Co. E-mail: chamber@christiancountychamber.com
URL: http://www.christiancountychamber.com
Contact: Taylor Hayes, President
E-mail: thayes@christiancountychamber.com
Facebook: www.facebook.com/hccchamber
X (Twitter): x.com/hccchamber
Instagram: www.instagram.com/hccchamber
Description: Promotes business and community development in Christian County, KY. **Founded:** 1888. **Publications:** *Chamberletter* (Monthly); *Chamber Connection* (Monthly); *Chamber Membership Directory*; *Chamberletter* (Monthly). **Geographic Preference:** Local.

40031 ■ Crittenden County Chamber of Commerce, Inc.
Fosh Hall, Walker St.
Marion, KY 42064
Co. E-mail: crittendencountychamber@gmail.com
URL: http://crittendencountychamber.org
Contact: Shanna West, President
E-mail: shanna.hhsupply@outlook.com
Facebook: www.facebook.com/Crittenden-County-Chamber-of-Commerce-Marion-KY-98000 2148789041
Description: Promotes business and community development in Crittenden County, KY. Sponsors festivals. **Founded:** 1973. **Geographic Preference:** Local.

40032 ■ Cumberland County Chamber of Commerce
111 Hill Ste.
Burkesville, KY 42717
Ph: (270)864-5890
Co. E-mail: info@explorecumberlandcounty.com
URL: http://www.explorecumberlandcounty.com/chamber-of-commerce/board-of-directors
Contact: Dr. Elijah Wilson, President
Description: Promotes business and community development in Cumberland County, KY. **Geographic Preference:** Local.

40033 ■ Cynthiana-Harrison County Chamber of Commerce
141 E Pke. St., Ste. 3
Cynthiana, KY 41031
Ph: (859)234-5236
Co. E-mail: cynchamber@gmail.com
URL: http://www.cynthianakychamber.com
Contact: Todd Brown, President
Facebook: www.facebook.com/cynthianaharrisoncountychamberofcommerce
X (Twitter): x.com/cynkychamber
Description: Promotes business and community development in Harrison County, KY. **Founded:** 1794. **Publications:** *Chamber Update*. **Geographic Preference:** Local.

40034 ■ Danville-Boyle County Chamber of Commerce
105 E Walnut St.
Danville, KY 40422
Ph: (859)236-2361
Co. E-mail: info@danvilleboylechamber.com
URL: http://danvilleboylechamber.com
Contact: Dalton Southerland, Chairman of the Board
Facebook: www.facebook.com/danvilleboylechamber
Description: Promotes business and community development in Boyle County, KY. **Founded:** 1919. **Publications:** *IMAGES Magazine* (Annual); *Foresight* (Monthly); *Danville Boyle County Images Magazine* (Annual). **Awards:** School Bell Award (Annual). **Geographic Preference:** Local.

40035 ■ Dawson Springs Chamber of Commerce
301 W Arcadia Ave.
Dawson Springs, KY 42408
Contact: Jenny Sewell, President
Description: Promotes business and community development in Dawson Springs, KY. Sponsors annual city-wide barbecue and annual Industry Appreciation Banquet. Convention/Meeting: none. **Publications:** *Chamber News* (Monthly). **Geographic Preference:** Local.

40036 ■ Edmonton - Metcalfe County Chamber of Commerce
109 E Stockton St.
Edmonton, KY 42129
Ph: (270)432-3222
Co. E-mail: metchamb@scrtc.com
URL: http://www.metcalfechamber.com
Contact: Gaye Shaw, Executive Director
Facebook: www.facebook.com/edmontonmetcalfe.chamber
Description: Promotes business and community development in Metcalfe County, KY. **Geographic Preference:** Local.

40037 ■ Estill County 21st Century, Inc. [Estill Development Alliance (EDA)]
177 Broadway St.
Irvine, KY 40336
Ph: (606)723-2450
URL: http://www.estill.org
Contact: Ethan Moore, President
Description: Works to improve the quality of life for citizens of Estill County through conducting, promoting, and supporting civic, cultural, economic, educational, and social activities and programs that maximize citizen and community involvement. **Founded:** 1995. **Geographic Preference:** Local.

40038 ■ Fleming County Chamber of Commerce (FCCC)
165 W Water St.
Flemingsburg, KY 41041
Ph: (606)845-1223
Fax: (606)845-1213
Co. E-mail: info@flemingkychamber.com
URL: http://www.flemingkychamber.com
Contact: Crystal Ruark, Executive Director
E-mail: crystal@flemingkychamber.com
Facebook: www.facebook.com/flemingkychamber
X (Twitter): x.com/flemingkychmbr
Description: Seeks to promote and encourage the entire business environment of the area. Works with all groups to stimulate the quality of growth of the economy. Activities include member meetings, Business After Hours, Leadership Class and business classes. **Founded:** 1958. **Geographic Preference:** Regional.

40039 ■ *Floyd County*
313 Westminster St.,Ste. 210
Prestonsburg, KY 41653
Ph: (606)886-0364
Fax: (606)889-6574
Co. E-mail: floydchamber@setel.com
URL: http://www.floydcountykentucky.com
Contact: Kathy King Allen, Executive Director
Released: Annual **Price:** Included in membership.
Description: Contains membership directory, relocation packet, conferences, events and visitors information guide. **Availability:** Print.

40040 ■ Frankfort Area Chamber of Commerce
229 W Main St., Ste. 102
Frankfort, KY 40601
Ph: (502)223-8261
Fax: (502)223-5942
Co. E-mail: office@frankfortky.info
URL: http://frankfortky.info
Contact: Jason Hart, Chairman
Facebook: www.facebook.com/FrankfortKYChamber
Linkedin: www.linkedin.com/in/frankfort-area-chamber-of-commerce-b303a045
X (Twitter): x.com/FrankfortCofC

Description: Promotes business and community development in Franklin County, KY. **Founded:** 1921. **Geographic Preference:** Local.

40041 ■ Franklin-Simpson Chamber of Commerce
201 S Main St.
Franklin, KY 42134
Ph: (270)586-7609
URL: http://franklinsimpsonchamber.com
Contact: Mary Pat Bly, President
Facebook: www.facebook.com/FranklinSimpsonChamberOfCommerce
Description: Promotes business and community development in Franklin and Simpson counties, KY. Sponsors charitable activities. Holds competition. **Founded:** 1937. **Publications:** *The Chamber Report* (Weekly). **Geographic Preference:** Local.

40042 ■ Garrard County Chamber of Commerce (GCCOC)
308 W Maple Ave.
Lancaster, KY 40444
Ph: (859)792-2282
Co. E-mail: garrardchamber@gmail.com
URL: http://garrardchamber.com
Contact: Kalem Grasham, President
Linkedin: www.linkedin.com/company/garrard-county-chamber-of-commerce/about
X (Twitter): x.com/garrardchamber
Description: Promotes business, community development and tourism in Garrard County. **Geographic Preference:** Local.

40043 ■ Georgetown-Scott County Chamber of Commerce
160 E Main St.
Georgetown, KY 40324
Ph: (502)863-5424
Co. E-mail: info@gtown.org
URL: http://www.gtown.org
Contact: Kris Castle, President
Facebook: www.facebook.com/GtownScottCountyYoungProfessionals
X (Twitter): x.com/GTSCCHAMBER
Instagram: www.instagram.com/gtscchamber
Description: Promotes business and community development in Scott County, KY. **Founded:** 1959. **Publications:** *Quality of Life*. **Geographic Preference:** Local.

40044 ■ Glasgow-Barren County Chamber of Commerce (GBCCC)
118 E Public Sq.
Glasgow, KY 42141
Ph: (270)651-3161
Free: 800-264-3161
Fax: (270)651-3122
Co. E-mail: chamber@glasgowbarrenchamber.com
URL: http://glasgowbarrenchamber.com
Contact: Ernie Myers, Chief Operating Officer Executive Vice President
E-mail: emyers@glasgow-ky.com
Description: Promotes business and community development in Barren County, KY. Maintains 4 divisions and 20 committees. Houses the Glasgow/Barren County Tourist and Convention Commission, and the Glasgow/Barren County Community Foundation. **Founded:** 1921. **Geographic Preference:** Local.

40045 ■ Grand Rivers Tourism Commission
1858 JH O'Bryan Ave.
Grand Rivers, KY 42045
Ph: (270)362-0152
Co. E-mail: info@grandrivers.org
URL: http://grandrivers.org
Facebook: www.facebook.com/grandriversky
X (Twitter): x.com/GrandRiversKY
Instagram: www.instagram.com/grandriversky
YouTube: www.youtube.com/channel/UCrSm7wlk_D_RrnRBF3kWQKg
Description: Promotes Grand Rivers as a tourist destination. Provides visitor services. **Founded:** 1890. **Geographic Preference:** Local.

Small Business Sourcebook • 42nd Edition

40046 ■ Grant County Chamber of Commerce (GCCC)
1350 N Main St.
Williamstown, KY 41097
Ph: (859)824-3322
Fax: (859)824-7082
Co. E-mail: businessmatters@grantcommerce.com
URL: http://www.grantcommerce.com
Contact: Jamie S. Baker, Executive Director
E-mail: jbaker@grantcommerce.com

Description: Promotes business and community development in Grant County, KY. **Founded:** 1978. **Geographic Preference:** Local.

40047 ■ Grayson Area Chamber of Commerce (GACC)
302 E Main St.
Grayson, KY 41143
Ph: (606)474-4401
Co. E-mail: graysonchamber41143@gmail.com
URL: http://www.graysonchamber.com
Contact: Jill York, President
Facebook: www.facebook.com/GraysonAreaChamberOfCommerce

Description: Promotes business and community development in the Grayson, KY area. **Founded:** 1978. **Geographic Preference:** Local.

40048 ■ Greater Breckinridge County Chamber of Commerce
224 S Main St.
Hardinsburg, KY 40143
Ph: (270)756-0268
Co. E-mail: breckcountychamber@bbtel.com
URL: http://breckinridgecountychamber.com/chamber-of-commerce
Contact: Bob Miller, President
Facebook: www.facebook.com/BreckCoChamber

Description: Strives to create and actively represent a positive business environment for the economic well-being and growth of business, industry, and agriculture in Greater Breckinridge County. **Founded:** 1799. **Publications:** *Chamber Wired* (Monthly). **Geographic Preference:** Local.

40049 ■ Greater Louisville Inc. - the Metro Chamber of Commerce (GLI) - Library
614 W Main St.
Louisville, KY 40202
Ph: (502)625-0000
Co. E-mail: info@greaterlouisville.com
URL: http://www.greaterlouisville.com
Contact: Kent Oyler, President
E-mail: koyler@glidev.wpengine.com
Facebook: www.facebook.com/GLIchamber
Linkedin: www.linkedin.com/company/greater-louisville-inc
X (Twitter): x.com/GLIChamber
Instagram: www.instagram.com/glichamber

Description: Promotes business and community development in Louisville, KY. **Scope:** Business. **Founded:** 1950. **Holdings:** Figures not available. **Publications:** *Greater Louisville Ink* (Monthly); *Louisville Fact Book* (Annual); *Major Employers Directory*. **Geographic Preference:** National; Local.

40050 ■ Greater Owensboro Chamber of Commerce
200 E 3rd St.
Owensboro, KY 42303
Ph: (270)926-1860
Fax: (270)926-3364
Co. E-mail: chamber@owensboro.com
URL: http://chamber.owensboro.com
Contact: Candance Castlen Brake, President
E-mail: cbrake@owensboro.com
Facebook: www.facebook.com/GOChamber
Linkedin: www.linkedin.com/company/2503013
X (Twitter): x.com/GOchamber
Instagram: www.instagram.com/gochamber
YouTube: www.youtube.com/user/ChamberOwensboro

Description: Promotes business and community development in Daviess County, KY. **Founded:** 1913. **Publications:** *Buyers' Guide* (Annual); *The Enterprise* (Monthly); *Owensboro-Daviess County Magazine*. **Geographic Preference:** Local.

40051 ■ Hancock County Chamber of Commerce
1605 US Hwy. 60 W
Hawesville, KY 42348
Ph: (270)922-0729
Fax: (270)927-9043
URL: http://www.hancockky.us/Commerce/chamber.htm
Contact: Shanna Nugent, President

Description: Promotes business and community development in Hancock County, KY. Issues publications. **Founded:** 1925. **Geographic Preference:** Local.

40052 ■ Hardin County Chamber of Commerce (HCCC)
111 W Dixie Ave.
Elizabethtown, KY 42701
Ph: (270)765-4334
Co. E-mail: info@hardinchamber.com
URL: http://hardinchamber.com
Contact: Margy Poorman, President
Facebook: www.facebook.com/hardinchamberky
Linkedin: www.linkedin.com/company/hardinchamberky
X (Twitter): x.com/HardinChamber

Description: Promotes business and community development in the Radcliff, KY area. **Founded:** 1965. **Publications:** *Chamber Action* (Monthly). **Geographic Preference:** Local.

40053 ■ Hart County Chamber of Commerce
116 E Union St.
Munfordville, KY 42765
Ph: (270)524-2892
Fax: (270)524-1127
Co. E-mail: hart_co@scrtc.com
URL: http://hartcountyky.org
Contact: Fran Bowsher, President
Facebook: www.facebook.com/hartcountykychamber
X (Twitter): x.com/CountyHart
Instagram: www.instagram.com/hartcountychamber

Description: Promotes business and community development in Hart County, KY. **Founded:** 1986. **Publications:** *The Business Bulletin* (Monthly). **Geographic Preference:** Local.

40054 ■ Hopkins County Regional Chamber of Commerce
15 E Center St.
Madisonville, KY 42431
Ph: (270)821-3435
Co. E-mail: office@hopkinschamber.com
URL: http://www.hopkinschamber.com
Contact: Lisa Miller, President
E-mail: membership@hopkinschamber.com
Facebook: www.facebook.com/hopkinschamber
Linkedin: www.linkedin.com/company/madisonville-hopkins-county-chamber-of-commerce
Instagram: www.instagram.com/hopkinschamber

Description: Promotes business and community development in the Madisonville, KY area. **Founded:** 1928. **Geographic Preference:** Local.

40055 ■ Jeffersontown Chamber of Commerce
10434 Watterson Trl.
Jeffersontown, KY 40299
Ph: (502)267-1674
Fax: (502)267-2070
Co. E-mail: info@jtownchamber.com
URL: http://www.jtownchamber.com
Contact: Deana Karem, President
E-mail: deana@jtownchamber.com
Linkedin: www.linkedin.com/company/the-chamber-jeffersontown
X (Twitter): x.com/chamberjtown
YouTube: www.youtube.com/channel/UCPkNI7aIDVUaXUkIHbBJ_Pg

Description: Promotes business and community development in Jeffersontown, KY. **Founded:** 1963. **Publications:** *Element* (Bimonthly); *Newsline*. **Educational Activities:** Jeffersontown Gaslight (Annual). **Geographic Preference:** Local.

40056 ■ Jessamine County Chamber of Commerce
116 S Main St.
Nicholasville, KY 40356
Ph: (859)887-4351
Co. E-mail: info@jessaminechamber.org
URL: http://www.jessaminechamber.com
Contact: Jonna Perdue, President

Description: Promotes business and community development in Jessamine County, KY. Conducts Jessamine Jamboree. **Founded:** 1798. **Publications:** *Chamber of Commerce Newsletter* (Periodic); *Jessamine Journal*. **Geographic Preference:** Local.

40057 ■ *Jessamine Journal*
116 S Main St.
Nicholasville, KY 40356
Ph: (859)887-4351
Co. E-mail: info@jessaminechamber.org
URL: http://www.jessaminechamber.com
Contact: Jonna Perdue, President
URL(s): jessaminechamber.org/membership-benefits
Availability: Print.

40058 ■ Kentucky Chamber of Commerce (KCC)
464 Chenault Rd.
Frankfort, KY 40601
Ph: (502)695-4700
Fax: (502)695-5051
Co. E-mail: info@kychamber.com
URL: http://www.kychamber.com
Contact: Ashli Watts, President
X (Twitter): x.com/KyChamber
YouTube: www.youtube.com/user/kychamber

Description: Promotes business and community development in Kentucky. **Founded:** 1946. **Publications:** *Kentucky Chamber News* (6/year); *Chamber Direct Weekly* (Weekly); *Chamber of Commerce Statewide*; *Kentucky Chamber of Commerce--Chamber Directory*. **Geographic Preference:** Local.

40059 ■ *Kentucky Chamber News*
464 Chenault Rd.
Frankfort, KY 40601
Ph: (502)695-4700
Fax: (502)695-5051
Co. E-mail: info@kychamber.com
URL: http://www.kychamber.com
Contact: Ashli Watts, President
URL(s): www.kychamber.com/news
Released: 6/year **Availability:** Print; PDF; Online.

40060 ■ LaRue County Chamber of Commerce - LaRue County Public Library
60 Lincoln Sq.
Hodgenville, KY 42748
Ph: (270)358-3411
URL: http://laruecountychamber.org
Contact: Natilea Boyd, President
Facebook: www.facebook.com/laruecountychamber
X (Twitter): x.com/laruechamber

Description: Promotes business and community development in LaRue County, KY. **Services:** Copying. **Founded:** 1970. **Publications:** *Chamber Notes* (Monthly). **Educational Activities:** General Membership Meeting. **Geographic Preference:** Local.

40061 ■ Liberty-Casey County Chamber of Commerce
c/o Nicki Johnson, Chamber Director
The Bedford Inn 579 Wallace Wilkinson Blvd.
Liberty, KY 42539
Ph: (606)706-9694
Fax: (606)787-0146
Co. E-mail: libertycaseychamber@gmail.com
URL: http://libertycaseychamber.org
Contact: Nicki Johnson, Director
E-mail: 1987dnjohnson@gmail.com
Facebook: www.facebook.com/Liberty-Casey-County-Chamber-of-Commerce-242586112918

Description: Promotes business and community development in Casey County, KY. **Founded:** 1984. **Geographic Preference:** Local.

40062 ■ Lincoln County Chamber of Commerce
201 E Main St. No. 8.
Stanford, KY 40484
Ph: (606)365-4118
Co. E-mail: director@lincolncountychamberof.live-website.com
URL: http://lincolncountychamber.com
Contact: Andrea Miller, Executive Director
Description: Promotes business and community development in Lincoln County, KY. Encourages industrial development, tourism, and improved education. Conducts charitable activities. Sponsors Parade, and Snow Queen and Snow Princess Contests during Christmas Season. **Founded:** 1780. **Geographic Preference:** Local.

40063 ■ Logan County Chamber of Commerce (LCCC)
116 S Main St.
Russellville, KY 42276
Ph: (270)726-2206
Co. E-mail: logancountychamber@gmail.com
URL: http://loganchamber.com
Contact: Keith Batchelor, President
Facebook: www.facebook.com/LoganChamberofCommerce
Linkedin: https://www.linkedin.com/in/logan-county-chamber-of-commerce-1b68aa18b
X (Twitter): x.com/ChamberLogan
Instagram: www.instagram.com/loganchamberky
Description: Promotes business and community development in Logan County, KY. Sponsors local festival. **Founded:** 1939. **Publications:** *Logan County Newsline* (Monthly); *Promoting Preservation and Progress*. **Geographic Preference:** Local.

40064 ■ London-Laurel County Chamber of Commerce
409 S Main St.
London, KY 40741
Ph: (606)864-4789
Fax: (606)864-7300
Co. E-mail: info@londonlaurelchamber.com
URL: http://londonlaurelchamber.com
Contact: Deanna Herrmann, Executive Director
E-mail: deanna@londonlaurelchamber.com
Facebook: www.facebook.com/londonlaurelchamber
X (Twitter): x.com/londonkychamber
Description: Promotes business and community development in Laurel County, KY. **Founded:** 1980. **Publications:** *Chamber Spotlight* (Monthly). **Educational Activities:** Membership Meeting. **Geographic Preference:** Local.

40065 ■ *Major Employers Directory*
614 W Main St.
Louisville, KY 40202
Ph: (502)625-0000
Co. E-mail: info@greaterlouisville.com
URL: http://www.greaterlouisville.com
Contact: Kent Oyler, President
E-mail: koyler@glidev.wpengine.com
URL(s): www.greaterlouisville.com/talent-old/major-employers
Availability: Online.

40066 ■ Marion County Chamber of Commerce
239 N Spalding Ave., Ste. 201
Lebanon, KY 40033
Ph: (270)692-9594
Co. E-mail: info@marioncountykychamber.com
URL: http://www.lebanon-ky.com
Contact: Donnie Brockman, President
Description: Promotes business and community development in Marion County, KY. **Publications:** *Chamber Connection* (Bimonthly). **Educational Activities:** Marion County Country Ham Days (Annual). **Geographic Preference:** Local.

40067 ■ Marshall County Chamber of Commerce
93 Carroll Rd.
Benton, KY 42025
Ph: (270)527-7665
Co. E-mail: chamber@marshallcounty.net
URL: http://www.marshallcounty.net
Contact: Stephanie Donohoo, Contact
Facebook: www.facebook.com/KentuckyLakeChamber
Description: Promotes business and community development in Marshall County, KY. Ensures orderly and progressive economic development. **Founded:** 1950. **Geographic Preference:** Local.

40068 ■ Mayfield-Graves County Chamber of Commerce (MG)
201 E College St.
Mayfield, KY 42066
Ph: (270)247-6101
Fax: (270)247-6110
Co. E-mail: info@mayfieldgraveschamber.com
URL: http://www.mayfieldgraveschamber.com
Contact: Jason Lemle, President
E-mail: jason@gravescountyed.com
Facebook: www.facebook.com/mayfieldgraveschamber
X (Twitter): x.com/mgcchamber
Instagram: www.instagram.com/mgcchamber
Description: Promotes business and community development in Graves County, KY. **Founded:** 1962. **Geographic Preference:** Local.

40069 ■ Maysville-Mason County Area Chamber of Commerce
201 E 3rd St.
Maysville, KY 41056
Ph: (606)564-5534
Co. E-mail: chamber@maysvilleky.net
URL: http://maysvillechamber.com
Contact: Lori Ulrich, Chairman
Facebook: www.facebook.com/MaysvilleMasonCoChamber
Instagram: www.instagram.com/maysvillechamber
YouTube: www.youtube.com/channel/UCysQt0ToE64JDvbu6MKXCGw
Description: Promotes business and community development in Mason County, KY. **Founded:** 1961. **Geographic Preference:** Local.

40070 ■ McCreary County Chamber of Commerce
PO Box 548
Whitley City, KY 42653
Ph: (502)628-3537
Co. E-mail: mccrearycommerce@gmail.com
URL: http://mccrearychamber.com
Contact: Kristina McFeeters, President
Facebook: www.facebook.com/McCrearyChamber
Description: Promotes business and community development in McCreary County, KY. **Founded:** 1979. **Geographic Preference:** Local.

40071 ■ Mercer County Chamber of Commerce (MCCC)
101 S Main St., Ste. 1
Harrodsburg, KY 40330
Ph: (859)734-2365
Co. E-mail: info@mercerchamber.com
URL: http://www.mercerchamber.com
Contact: Sam Carr, President
Facebook: www.facebook.com/Mercer-County-Chamber-of-Commerce-118190561533873
Description: Promotes business and community development in the Harrodsburg, KY area. Conducts annual Pioneer Days Festival. **Founded:** 1951. **Publications:** *County Business Directory*; *New Directions* (Periodic). **Educational Activities:** Pioneer Days (Annual); Mercer County Chamber of Commerce Banquet. **Geographic Preference:** Local.

40072 ■ Monticello/Wayne County Chamber of Commerce
120 S Main St., Ste. 3
City Hall
Monticello, KY 42633
Ph: (606)348-3064
Co. E-mail: info@monticellokychamber.com
URL: http://www.monticellokychamber.com
Contact: Brittany Guffey, President
Facebook: www.facebook.com/MonticelloWayneCountyChamberofCommerce
Instagram: www.instagram.com/monticellokychamberofcommerce
Description: Promotes business and community development in Wayne County, KY. **Founded:** 1967. **Publications:** *Chamber Courier* (Quarterly). **Geographic Preference:** Local.

40073 ■ Morehead-Rowan County Chamber of Commerce
150 E 1st St.
Morehead, KY 40351
Ph: (606)784-6221
Co. E-mail: info@moreheadchamber.com
URL: http://www.moreheadchamber.com
Contact: Jason Slone, President
Facebook: www.facebook.com/moreheadchamber
X (Twitter): x.com/moreheadchamber
Description: Promotes business and community development in Rowan County, KY. **Founded:** 1955. **Publications:** *It's Your Business*. **Awards:** Morehead-Rowan County Chamber of Commerce Business Beautification Award (Annual); Morehead-Rowan County Chamber of Commerce Educator of the Year (Annual); Manufacturer/Industry of the Year (Annual); Morehead-Rowan County Chamber of Commerce New Business of the Year (Annual); Ora L. Cline Award (Annual); Service Above Self (Annual). **Geographic Preference:** Local.

40074 ■ Morgantown-Butler County Chamber of Commerce
112 S Main St.
Morgantown, KY 42261
Ph: (270)526-6827
Co. E-mail: morgantownbutlercochamber@gmail.com
URL: http://morgantowncoc.com
Contact: Tristan Evans Klein, President
Facebook: www.facebook.com/MorgantownButlerCountyChamberofCommerce
Description: Promotes business and community development in Butler County, KY. Sponsors annual Green River Catfish Festival. Promotes area tourism. Publications: none. **Founded:** 1980. **Geographic Preference:** Local.

40075 ■ Mount Sterling-Montgomery County Chamber of Commerce
124 N Maysville Rd.
Mount Sterling, KY 40353
Ph: (859)498-5343
Co. E-mail: contact@mtsterlingchamber.com
URL: http://www.mtsterlingchamber.com
Contact: Tammy Henderson, President
Facebook: www.facebook.com/mtsterlingchamberofcommerce
Description: Promotes business and community development in Montgomery County, KY. **Founded:** 1792. **Geographic Preference:** Local.

40076 ■ Murray-Calloway County Chamber of Commerce
805 N 12th St.
Murray, KY 42071
Ph: (270)753-5171
URL: http://www.mymurray.com
Contact: Michelle Bundren, President
E-mail: michelle@mymurray.com
Facebook: www.facebook.com/murraychamber
X (Twitter): x.com/MurrayChamber
Description: Promotes business, tourism, and community development in Calloway County, KY. **Founded:** 1927. **Publications:** *Murray-Calloway County Magazine* (Annual). **Geographic Preference:** Local.

40077 ■ *The Northern Kentucky Business Journal*
300 Buttermilk Pke., Ste. 330
Fort Mitchell, KY 41017
Ph: (859)578-8800
Fax: (859)578-8802

URL: http://www.nkychamber.com
Contact: Brent Cooper, President
E-mail: bcooper@nkychamber.com
Released: Bimonthly **Description:** Provides area businesses with information on the latest networking events and legislative issues that may impact the business community. **Availability:** PDF; Online.

40078 ■ Northern Kentucky Chamber of Commerce
300 Buttermilk Pke., Ste. 330
 Fort Mitchell, KY 41017
Ph: (859)578-8800
Fax: (859)578-8802
URL: http://www.nkychamber.com
Contact: Brent Cooper, President
E-mail: bcooper@nkychamber.com
Facebook: www.facebook.com/nkychamberofcommerce
Linkedin: www.linkedin.com/company/northern-kentucky-chamber-of-commerce
X (Twitter): x.com/nkychamber
Instagram: www.instagram.com/nkychamber
YouTube: www.youtube.com/user/NKYChamber1
Description: Strives to develop strong businesses and vibrant economy through business advocacy and leadership. **Founded:** 1969. **Publications:** *The Northern Kentucky Business Journal* (Bimonthly); *Northern Kentucky Industrial Directory* (Annual); *Northern Kentucky Public Officials Directory*; *Northern Kentucky Education Guide* (Annual); *Northern Kentucky Local Government Directory* (Annual); *Northern Kentucky: Business Directory*. **Geographic Preference:** Local.

40079 ■ Oldham Chamber & Economic Development (OCED)
204 S 1st Ave.
 La Grange, KY 40031
Ph: (502)222-1635
Fax: (502)222-3159
URL: http://www.oldhamcountychamber.com
Contact: David Bizianes, President
E-mail: david@oldhamcountychamber.com
Facebook: www.facebook.com/oldham.chamber1
X (Twitter): x.com/OldhamChamber
Description: Promotes business and community development in Oldham County, KY. Supports community activities. **Founded:** 1962. **Publications:** *NewsChamber* (Monthly); *Oldham County Kentucky* (Periodic). **Educational Activities:** Networking @ Noon. **Geographic Preference:** Local.

40080 ■ Paducah Area Chamber of Commerce
300 S 3rd St.
 Paducah, KY 42002-0810
Ph: (270)443-1746
Fax: (270)442-9152
Co. E-mail: info@paducahchamber.org
URL: http://www.paducahchamber.org
Contact: Sandra Wilson, President
E-mail: swilson@paducahchamber.org
Facebook: www.facebook.com/paducahchamber
Description: Promotes business and community development in McCracken County, KY. **Founded:** 1938. **Publications:** *Chamber Connection* (Weekly). **Awards:** Paducah Area Chamber of Commerce Business of the Year (Annual); Paducah Area Chamber of Commerce Summit Award (Annual); Paducah Area Chamber of Commerce Volunteer of the Year (Periodic). **Geographic Preference:** Local.

40081 ■ Paris-Bourbon County Chamber of Commerce
806 Main St.
 Paris, KY 40361
Ph: (859)987-3205
Co. E-mail: chamber@parisky.com
URL: http://parisbourbonchamber.com
Contact: Lauren Biddle, Executive Director
E-mail: dhamelback@parisky.com
Facebook: www.facebook.com/ParisBourbonChamber
Instagram: www.instagram.com/parisbourbonchamber
YouTube: www.youtube.com/channel/UCSWESeH6LUIzlCg6hH74D0g
Description: Promotes business and community development in Bourbon County, KY. Provides governmental liaison. Conducts community social and promotional activities. **Founded:** 1941. **Publications:** *Paris-Bourbon County Chamber Directory* (Annual). **Educational Activities:** Business after Hours. **Geographic Preference:** Local.

40082 ■ Prospect Area Chamber of Commerce
9509 US Hwy. 42, Ste. 107
 Prospect, KY 40059
Ph: (502)228-7493
Co. E-mail: info@prospectareachamber.org
URL: http://www.prospectareachamber.org
Contact: Meredith Hensley, President
E-mail: meredith@klaschools.com
Facebook: www.facebook.com/ProspectAreaChamber
Linkedin: www.linkedin.com/company/prospect-area-chamber-of-commerce
Instagram: www.instagram.com/prospectareachamberofcommerce
YouTube: www.youtube.com/channel/UCEhDsea6tiXqGMk0X-EUGQA
Description: Promotes business development in Prospect, CT. **Founded:** 2004. **Publications:** *Prospect Chamber News* (Monthly). **Geographic Preference:** Local.

40083 ■ Richmond Chamber of Commerce
201 E Main St.
 Richmond, KY 40475
Ph: (859)623-1720
Co. E-mail: communications@richmondchamber.com
URL: http://www.richmondchamber.com
Contact: Greg Gerard, President
Facebook: www.facebook.com/richmondkychamber
X (Twitter): x.com/RichKYChamber
Instagram: www.instagram.com/richmondchamber
Description: Promotes business and community development in Richmond, KY. **Founded:** 2013. **Publications:** *Chamber Newsletter* (Weekly). **Geographic Preference:** Local.

40084 ■ Russell County Chamber of Commerce
650 S Hwy. 127
 Russell Springs, KY 42642
Ph: (270)866-4303
Co. E-mail: info@russellcountychamber.com
URL: http://russellcountychamber.com
Contact: Marisa Ramsey, President
Facebook: www.facebook.com/russellcountychamberofcommerce
X (Twitter): x.com/RCKYCHAMBER
Description: Promotes business and community development in Russell County, KY. **Geographic Preference:** Local.

40085 ■ Scottsville-Allen County Chamber of Commerce
110 S Ct., St.
 Scottsville, KY 42164
Ph: (270)237-4782
Fax: (270)237-5498
Co. E-mail: chamber@scottsvilleky.info
URL: http://www.scottsvilleky.info
Contact: Brian Carter, President
Description: Promotes business and community development in Allen County, KY. Collects and disseminates information. Conducts local festivals. **Founded:** 1815. **Publications:** *Chamber Briefings* (Monthly). **Geographic Preference:** Local.

40086 ■ Somerset Pulaski County Chamber of Commerce
236 E Mt. Vernon St.
 Somerset, KY 42501
Ph: (606)679-7323
Co. E-mail: info@somersetpulaskichamber.com
URL: http://somersetpulaskichamber.com
Contact: Bobby Clue, Executive Director
E-mail: bobby.clue@somersetpulaskichamber.com
Facebook: www.facebook.com/somersetpulaskichamber
X (Twitter): x.com/spcchamber
Instagram: www.instagram.com/spcchamber
YouTube: www.youtube.com/user/shoplocalsomerset
Description: Promotes business and community development in Pulaski County, KY. **Founded:** 1925. **Publications:** *Business Gazette* (Periodic). **Educational Activities:** Chamber Membership Luncheon. **Geographic Preference:** Local.

40087 ■ Southeast Kentucky Chamber of Commerce
178 College St.
 Pikeville, KY 41501
Ph: (606)432-5504
Co. E-mail: info@sekchamber.com
URL: http://www.sekchamber.com
Contact: Jordan Gibson, President
E-mail: jordan.gibson@sekchamber.com
Facebook: www.facebook.com/sekchamber
X (Twitter): x.com/sekchamber
Instagram: www.instagram.com/sekchamber
YouTube: www.youtube.com/user/sekchamber
Description: Promotes business and community development in Pike County, KY. **Publications:** *Business Call* (Monthly). **Geographic Preference:** Local.

40088 ■ Tompkinsville - Monroe County Chamber of Commerce
202 N Magnolia St.
 Tompkinsville, KY 42167
Ph: (270)487-1314
Co. E-mail: monroecountyedc@gmail.com
URL: http://www.visitmonroecountyky.com/chamber-of-commerce.html
Contact: Bart Rowland, President
Facebook: www.facebook.com/people/Tompkinsville-Monroe-County-Chamber-of-Commerce/100068862234126
Description: Promotes business and community development in the Tompkinsville, KY area. **Geographic Preference:** Local.

40089 ■ Winchester-Clark County Chamber of Commerce (WCCC)
2 S Maple St.
 Winchester, KY 40391
Ph: (859)744-6420
Co. E-mail: info@winchesterkychamber.com
URL: http://www.winchesterkychamber.com
Contact: Cindy Banks, Executive Director
E-mail: cindybanks@winchesterkychamber.com
X (Twitter): x.com/CCChamberofComm
Instagram: www.instagram.com/winchester_ky_chamber
YouTube: www.youtube.com/channel/UCyq_x7Z_ila7yeBPbxC1PdQ
Description: Promotes business and community development in Clark County, KY. Conducts golf tournament and annual Daniel Boone Pioneer Festival; bestows annual Citizen of the Year and Business of the Year awards. **Founded:** 1941. **Publications:** *Community Profile*. **Educational Activities:** Business Enhancement. **Geographic Preference:** Local.

40090 ■ Woodford County Chamber of Commerce
126 S Main St.
 Versailles, KY 40383
Ph: (859)873-5122
URL: http://www.woodfordcountyinfo.com
Contact: Emily Downey, President
E-mail: emkdowney@gmail.com
Facebook: www.facebook.com/woodfordchamber2
Linkedin: www.linkedin.com/company/woodford-county-chamber-of-commerce
X (Twitter): x.com/ChamberofComKY
Instagram: www.instagram.com/woodfordcountychamber
YouTube: www.youtube.com/channel/UC0oE_2oxbhDgPhW_KLmaXrQ/featured
Description: Promotes business, tourism, and community development in Woodford County, KY. **Founded:** 1928. **Geographic Preference:** Local.

MINORITY BUSINESS ASSISTANCE PROGRAMS

40091 ■ Kentucky Cabinet for Economic Development - Small & Minority Business Div.
Old Capitol Annex, 300 W Broadway
Frankfort, KY 40601
Ph: (502)564-7140
Free: 800-626-2930
Fax: (502)564-3256
Co. E-mail: econdev@ky.gov
URL: http://ced.ky.gov
Contact: Katie Smith, Deputy Secretary Commissioner
E-mail: katie.smith@ky.gov
Facebook: www.facebook.com/CEDkygov
Linkedin: www.linkedin.com/company/cedkygov
X (Twitter): x.com/CEDkygov
Description: The cabinet is responsible for encouraging job creation and retention. The programs administered by the cabinet are designed to support and promote economic development for local small, minority, and women-owned businesses.

40092 ■ Tri-State Minority Supplier Development Council Regional Office Kentucky (TSMSDC)
401 W Main St., Ste. 1706
Louisville, KY 40202
Ph: (502)365-9762
Fax: (502)365-9450
Co. E-mail: info@tsmsdc.net
URL: http://tsmsdc.com
Contact: Susan A. L. Marston, Regional Vice President
Description: Provides a variety of business development and referral services to minority business owners in Kentucky, West Virginia, and parts of Indiana.

FINANCING AND LOAN PROGRAMS

40093 ■ Appalachian Development Alliance (ADA)
362 Old Whitley Rd.
London, KY 40743-1738
Contact: Lynn Littrell, President
Description: Works to facilitate accessing capital and the sharing of best practices for developmental lending in Appalachian Kentucky. **Founded:** 2000. **Geographic Preference:** Regional.

40094 ■ Bluegrass Angels (BGA)
330 E Main St., No. 100
Lexington, KY 40507
Co. E-mail: admin@bluegrassangels.com
URL: http://bluegrassangels.com
Contact: Brian Luftman, President
Facebook: www.facebook.com/BluegrassAngelsInvestors
Linkedin: www.linkedin.com/company/bluegrassangels
X (Twitter): x.com/BluegrassAngels
Description: Angel investors for Kentucky startups. Creates new jobs and provides strong financial returns to its members. **Founded:** 2004. **Investment Policies:** Innovative high-tech startups with a scalable business model.

40095 ■ Chrysalis Ventures
333 E Main St., Ste. No. 304
Louisville, KY 40202
Ph: (502)583-7644
Co. E-mail: businessplans@chrysalisventures.com
URL: http://www.chrysalisventures.com
Contact: Charlie Crawford, Vice President
E-mail: ccrawford@chrysalisventures.com
Description: Investment firm provides of fund deployment, early stage and growth investments services for healthcare and technology sectors. **Founded:** 1993. **Preferred Investment Size:** $2,000,000 to $15,000,000. **Industry Preferences:** Internet specific, medical and health, computer software and services, other products, communications and media, consumer related, and biotechnology.

40096 ■ eLink Ventures, LLC
eLink Design
400 E Vine St.
Lexington, KY 40507
Ph: (859)927-3811
Co. E-mail: info@elinkdesign.com
URL: http://www.elinkdesign.com
Contact: Andrew Chiles, Partner
Description: Offers venture capital and service-based investments for forward-thinking companies, including B2B or B2C environments. **Founded:** 2001.

40097 ■ Iceberg Ventures
1715 Spring Dr.
Louisville, KY 40205
Contact: Gregory E. Fischer, Member
Description: Provider of financial and intellectual capital, venture capital advisory counsel services including finance, recruiting and team building for early stage companies. **Founded:** 1999. **Investment Policies:** Early stage.

40098 ■ Kentucky Highlands Investment Corp. (KHIC)
362 Old Whitley Rd.
London, KY 40743-1738
Ph: (606)864-5175
Fax: (606)864-5194
Co. E-mail: info@khic.org
URL: http://www.khic.org
Contact: Jerry Rickett, President
Description: Investment corporation provides debt and equity investments, business loans, business training and business coaching services. **Founded:** 1952. **Preferred Investment Size:** $500 to $10,000,000. **Investment Policies:** Start-up, second stage, and special situation. **Industry Preferences:** Manufacturing.

PROCUREMENT ASSISTANCE PROGRAMS

40099 ■ Kentucky & Tennessee Procurement Center
600 Dr. Martin Luther King Jr Pl., Rm. 188
Louisville, KY 40202
Ph: (502)582-5971
URL: http://www.sba.gov/offices/district/ky/louisville
Contact: Robert Coffey, Director
Description: Covers activities for Army Corps of Engineers (Louisville, KY), Fort Knox (Fort Knox, KY), Fort Campbell (Fort Campbell, KY), and Army Corps of Engineers (Nashville, TN).

INCUBATORS/RESEARCH AND TECHNOLOGY PARKS

40100 ■ Aging2
201 E Jefferson St., Ste. 214
Louisville, KY 40202
Co. E-mail: info@aging2.com
URL: http://www.aging2.com
Contact: Tammy York Day, President
Facebook: www.facebook.com/Aging2
Linkedin: www.linkedin.com/company/aging2
X (Twitter): x.com/aging20
Instagram: www.instagram.com/_aging2.0
YouTube: www.youtube.com/agingtoo
Description: Volunteer-run network accelerates innovation to address the challenges and opportunities in aging. Offers networking and education; identifies startups, innovative providers, and industry organization; shares innovation best practices and insights. **Founded:** 2011.

40101 ■ Ashland Community & Technical College - The Entrepreneur Center
4700 college Dr.
Ashland, KY 41101
URL: http://www.stateuniversity.com/universities/KY/Ashland_Community_and_Technical_College.html
Description: A small business incubator helping local people start local businesses. Provides an affordable start to any individual or group of individuals that may possess the desire to start a business thus contributing to the growth of economic development in the Tri-State area.

40102 ■ Awesome Inc.
348 E Main St.
Lexington, KY 40507
Ph: (859)960-4600
Co. E-mail: info@awesomeinc.org
URL: http://www.awesomeinc.org
Contact: Brian Raney, Contact
E-mail: brian@awesomeinc.org
Facebook: www.facebook.com/awesomeinclex
Linkedin: www.linkedin.com/school/awesome-inc
X (Twitter): x.com/awesomeinclex
Instagram: www.instagram.com/awesomeinclex
YouTube: www.youtube.com/c/AwesomeincOrgLex
Description: Accelerator offering workspace, web development, video, graphic design, legal and accounting services. **Founded:** 2009.

40103 ■ BE NKY Growth Partnership [Northern Kentucky Tri-Ed]
300 Buttermilk Pke., Ste. 332
Fort Mitchell, KY 41017
Ph: (859)344-0040
Free: 888-874-3365
URL: http://be-nky.com
Contact: Lee Crume, President
E-mail: lcrume@be-nky.com
Description: Offers public and private funds to foster regional cooperation and enhance the business climate in Boone, Campbell, and Kenton counties. **Founded:** 1987.

40104 ■ Eastern Kentucky University Business and Technology Accelerator (EKU)
521 Lancaster Ave.
Business & Technology Ctr., Rm. 041
Richmond, KY 40475
Ph: (859)622-8577
Fax: (859)622-6274
Co. E-mail: bizaccelerator@eku.edu
URL: http://bizaccelerator.eku.edu
Description: Business incubator. Offers low-cost office space, coaching, and other resources to assist entrepreneurs in Kentucky.

40105 ■ Eastern Kentucky University - Center for Economic Development, Entrepreneurship and Technology (CEDET)
521 Lancaster Ave.
Richmond, KY 40475
Ph: (859)622-2334
Fax: (859)622-6274
URL: http://cedet.eku.edu
Facebook: www.facebook.com/EKUCEDET
X (Twitter): twitter.com/eku_cedet
Description: A small business incubator providing assistance to businesses, organizations, industries, and communities to aid in their development. **Scope:** Economic and technological development.

40106 ■ The Entrepreneur Center
4700 Roberts Dr.
Ashland, KY 41102
Ph: (606)326-2129
URL: http://ashland.kctcs.edu/Workforce_Solutions/Entrepreneur_Center
Facebook: www.facebook.com/AshlandCTC
X (Twitter): twitter.com/actc
YouTube: www.youtube.com/user/ashlandctc123
Description: A small business incubator helping local people start local businesses. It provides an affordable start to any individual or group of individuals that may possess the desire to start a business thus contributing to the growth of economic development in the Tri-State area.

40107 ■ Kentucky Innovation Network (KIN)
300 W Broadway
Frankfort, KY 40601

Kentucky

Ph: (502)564-7670
Co. E-mail: info@kyinnovation.com
URL: http://www.kyinnovation.com
Contact: Terry Samuel, President
Facebook: www.facebook.com/KentuckyInnovation
Linkedin: www.linkedin.com/company/ky-innovation
X (Twitter): x.com/kyinnovation
Description: A network of business leaders and mentors that encourage relationships, grow new and existing companies and create jobs. **Founded:** 2001.

40108 ■ Kentucky Science & Technology Corporation (KSTC)
380 S Mill St., Ste. 300
Lexington, KY 40508
Ph: (859)233-3502
Fax: (859)259-0986
URL: http://www.kstc.org
Contact: Terry Samuel, President
E-mail: tsamuel@kstc.com
Linkedin: www.linkedin.com/company/kentucky-science-and-technology-corporation
X (Twitter): x.com/kstc_ky
Description: An entrepreneurial company dedicated to enhancing the capacity of people, companies and organizations to develop and apply science and technology and compete responsibly in the global marketplace. **Founded:** 1987.

40109 ■ University of Kentucky Office of Commercialization and Development - Advanced Science and Technology Commercialization Center (ASTeCC)
A152 ASTeCC Bldg., 145 Graham Ave.
University of Kentucky
Lexington, KY 40506-0286
Ph: (859)218-6563
URL: http://astecc.uky.edu
Contact: Tanya Floyd, Manager
E-mail: tanya.floyd@uky.ed
Description: A faculty research facility and commercialization center established for multidisciplinary research, technology transfer, and new business startups. **Founded:** 1994.

40110 ■ Western Kentucky University - Small Business Accelerator (SBA) [WKU Small Business Accelerator]
2413 Nashville Rd., Ste. B8
Bowling Green, KY 42101
Ph: (270)901-3490
Co. E-mail: accelerator@wku.edu
URL: http://www.wku.edu/accelerator
Contact: Jeff Hook, Director
E-mail: william.hook@wku.edu
Facebook: www.facebook.com/wkuaccelerator
X (Twitter): x.com/wku_accelerator
Description: Business incubator offers cost-controlled office and light manufacturing spaces to knowledge-based startups and early-stage companies. Services include business development consulting, training, mentors and networking, connections to funding options, and access to rapid prototyping. **Founded:** 2004.

40111 ■ XLerateHealth (XLH)
204 S Floyd St.
Louisville, KY 40202
URL: http://www.xleratehealth.com
Contact: Kathy Weaver, Director
Facebook: www.facebook.com/xleratehealth
Linkedin: www.linkedin.com/company/xleratehealth
X (Twitter): x.com/XLerateHealth
Description: Helps early stage healthcare companies build out their commercialization strategy, which includes their intersection with payers, providers, and customers. Helps these early stage startup companies prepare their product/service for commercialization and connects them with beta site partners in the healthcare eco-system so that the startup companies obtain real-time "customer discovery" feedback from actual potential customers. **Founded:** 2012.

EDUCATIONAL PROGRAMS

40112 ■ Bowling Green Community College of Western Kentucky University
1906 College Heights Blvd.
Bowling Green, KY 42101-3576
URL: http://www.wku.edu/wkuhistory
Description: Two-year college offering a small business management program. **Founded:** 1986.

40113 ■ Morehead State University (MSU)
150 University Blvd.
Morehead, KY 40351
Ph: (606)783-2000
Free: 800-585-6781
Co. E-mail: social@moreheadstate.edu
URL: http://www.moreheadstate.edu
Contact: Dr. Jay Morgan, President
E-mail: president@moreheadstate.edu
Facebook: www.facebook.com/MoreheadStateUniversity
Linkedin: www.linkedin.com/school/moreheadstate
X (Twitter): x.com/moreheadstate
Instagram: www.instagram.com/moreheadstate
YouTube: www.youtube.com/c/MSUeaglevideo
Description: Provides training programs that benefit the small business community. **Founded:** 1887.

CONSULTANTS

40114 ■ eLink Design
eLink Design
400 E Vine St.
Lexington, KY 40507
Ph: (859)927-3811
Co. E-mail: info@elinkdesign.com
URL: http://www.elinkdesign.com
Contact: Andrew Land Chiles, Director
Facebook: www.facebook.com/eLinkDesign
Description: Offers marketing, web design, and consulting services. Builds marketing plans. Helps set the direction for, prioritize, and review business plans. **Founded:** 2001.

40115 ■ Makarios Consulting
2900 Cir. Crest Ct.
Prospect, KY 40059
Ph: (610)380-8735
URL: http://makariosconsulting.com
Contact: Rip Tilden, Partner
Facebook: www.facebook.com/MakariosConsulting
Linkedin: www.linkedin.com/in/timothyithomas
X (Twitter): x.com/makariosconsult
Description: Business management consultants. Offers strategic planning, business plan execution, leadership development, executive coaching, and small business consulting.

PUBLICATIONS

40116 ■ *Louisville Business First: The Weekly Business Newspaper of Greater Louisville*
120 W Morehead St.
Charlotte, NC 28202
Co. E-mail: circhelp@bizjournals.com
URL: http://www.acbj.com
Contact: Mike Olivieri, Executive Vice President
URL(s): www.bizjournals.com/louisville
Linkedin: www.linkedin.com/company/business-first-of-louisville
X (Twitter): x.com/BFLouisville
Instagram: www.instagram.com/bflouisville
Ed: Lisa Benson. **Released:** Weekly **Price:** $950, for Nationwide + BOL; $220, for print + online; $380, for 52 weeks; $210, for online. **Description:** Weekly Business Newspaper. **Availability:** Print; Online.

PUBLISHERS

40117 ■ Kentucky Cabinet for Economic Development - Small & Minority Business Div.
Old Capitol Annex, 300 W Broadway
Frankfort, KY 40601
Ph: (502)564-7140
Free: 800-626-2930
Fax: (502)564-3256
Co. E-mail: econdev@ky.gov
URL: http://ced.ky.gov
Contact: Katie Smith, Deputy Secretary Commissioner
E-mail: katie.smith@ky.gov
Facebook: www.facebook.com/CEDkygov
Linkedin: www.linkedin.com/company/cedkygov
X (Twitter): x.com/CEDkygov
Description: The cabinet is responsible for encouraging job creation and retention. The programs administered by the cabinet are designed to support and promote economic development for local small, minority, and women-owned businesses.

VENTURE CAPITAL FIRM

40118 ■ Connetic Ventures
910 Madison Ave.
Covington, KY 41011
Co. E-mail: info@connetic.ventures
URL: http://conneticventures.com
Contact: Kyle Schlotman, Chief Executive Officer
Facebook: www.facebook.com/conneticusa
Linkedin: www.linkedin.com/company/connetic-ventures
X (Twitter): x.com/conneticVC
Instagram: www.instagram.com/connetic.ventures
Description: Helps startups and entrepreneurs succeed by providing investment strategies and funding. **Founded:** 2014.

Louisiana

ASSOCIATIONS AND OTHER ORGANIZATIONS

40119 ■ Association of Fundraising Professionals Greater Baton Rouge Chapter
PO Box 87504
Baton Rouge, LA 70893
Ph: (337)501-5696
Co. E-mail: afpbatonrouge@gmail.com
URL: http://community.afpnet.org/greaterbatonrouge
Contact: Danielle Mack, President
X (Twitter): x.com/afpbatonrouge
Description: Supports professional fundraisers in the Baton Rouge area. **Geographic Preference:** Local.

40120 ■ Business Network International Louisiana
3500 N Cswy., Blvd., Ste. 1460
Metairie, LA 70002
Ph: (504)834-5264
Fax: (504)267-6058
Co. E-mail: info@louisianabni.com
URL: http://bnilouisiana.com/en-US/index
Contact: Tim Paulin, Executive Director
Facebook: www.facebook.com/lamsbni
X (Twitter): x.com/BNILouisiana
Description: Provides both men and women a structured environment for the development and exchange of quality business referrals. Offers members the opportunity to share ideas and contacts. **Geographic Preference:** State.

40121 ■ Entrepreneurs' Organization - Louisiana Chapter (EO)
LA
URL: http://www.eonetwork.org/louisiana
Description: Provides local resources to members which includes networking events, mentorship, live forums, and leadership development. **Founded:** 1987.

40122 ■ International Association of Women New Orleans Chapter
New Orleans, LA
URL: http://www.iawomen.com/chapters/new-orleans-chapter
Facebook: www.facebook.com/iawomen
Linkedin: www.linkedin.com/company/iawomenhq
X (Twitter): twitter.com/iawomenHQ
Description: Serves as a network for businesswomen to promote their product or service.

SMALL BUSINESS DEVELOPMENT CENTERS

40123 ■ Innovation Enterprise
Louisiana Tech University
Ruston, LA 71272
URL: http://www.latech.edu
Description: Supports entrepreneurs, business innovators, and corporate partners.

40124 ■ Louisiana Small Business Development Center Greater New Orleans Region
909 S Jefferson Davis Parkwy. Xavier S Rm. 203
New Orleans, LA 70125
Ph: (504)831-3730
Co. E-mail: lsbdc.gnor@louisianasbdc.org
URL: http://www.louisianasbdc.org/lsbdc-greater-new-orleans-region
Contact: Carmen Sunda, Director
X (Twitter): x.com/LSBDCGNOR
Description: Represents and promotes the small business sector. Provides management assistance to current and prospective small business owners. Helps to improve management skills and expand the products and services of members. **Geographic Preference:** Local.

40125 ■ Louisiana Small Business Development Center - Lead Center (LSBDC)
8000 Innovation Pk. Dr.
Baton Rouge, LA 70820
Ph: (225)578-7555
Co. E-mail: bgreenwood@louisianasbdc.org
URL: http://www.LouisianaSBDC.org
Contact: Bryan Greenwood, Director
E-mail: bgreenwood@louisianasbdc.org
Description: Works to provide broad-based management and technical assistance to existing and potential Louisiana businesses through coordinated use of local, state, and federal programs, private sector assets, and resources available at member organizations. Also offers specialized services in technology and international trade. **Geographic Preference:** Local.

40126 ■ Louisiana Small Business Development Center at Louisiana State University in Shreveport
4646 Hilry Huckaby Ave.
Shreveport, LA 71107
Ph: (318)670-9700
Free: 866-782-4159
Co. E-mail: lsbdc.susla@louisianasbdc.org
URL: http://www.louisianasbdc.org
Facebook: www.facebook.com/lsbdcsouthernshreveport
X (Twitter): x.com/LSBDCSUSLA
Description: Provides management assistance to current and prospective small business owners in Shreveport. **Founded:** 1983. **Geographic Preference:** Local.

40127 ■ Louisiana Small Business Development Center at McNeese State University (LSBDC MSU)
SEED Ctr.
4310 Ryan St., Ste. 162
Lake Charles, LA 70605
Ph: (337)475-5529
Co. E-mail: lsbdc.msu@louisianasbdc.org
URL: http://www.lsbdc.org/msu
Contact: Susan Thibodeaux, Director
Facebook: www.facebook.com/LSBDCMSU
X (Twitter): x.com/LSBDCMSU
Description: Represents and promotes the small business sector. Provides management assistance to current and prospective small business owners. Helps to improve management skills and expand the products and services of members. **Geographic Preference:** Local.

40128 ■ Louisiana Small Business Development Center at Northwestern State University (LSBDC)
310 Sam Sibley Dr.
Natchitoches, LA 71457
Ph: (318)678-6142
Co. E-mail: lsbdc.nwcr@lsbdc.org
URL: http://www2.lsbdc.org/center.aspx
Contact: Caspari Hall, President
Description: Represents and promotes the small business sector. Provides management assistance to current and prospective small business owners. Helps to improve management skills and expand the products and services of members. **Geographic Preference:** Local.

40129 ■ Louisiana Small Business Development Center at Southeastern Louisiana University
1514 Martens Dr.
Hammond, LA 70402
Ph: (985)549-3831
Fax: (985)549-2127
Co. E-mail: lsbdc.slu@lsbdc.org
URL: http://www.southeastern.edu/admin/sbdc/index.html
Contact: William Joubert, Director
Description: Represents and promotes the small business sector. Provides management assistance to current and prospective small business owners. Helps to improve management skills and expand the products and services of members. **Founded:** 1984. **Geographic Preference:** Local.

40130 ■ Louisiana Small Business Development Center at Southern University
616 Harding Blvd.
Baton Rouge, LA 70807
Ph: (225)771-2891
Co. E-mail: lsbdc.subr@louisianasbdc.org
URL: http://www.louisianasbdc.org/lsbdc-at-southern-university
Facebook: www.facebook.com/lsbdcsubr
X (Twitter): x.com/LSBDCSUBR
Description: Provides management assistance to current and prospective small business owners in Louisiana. **Founded:** 1986. **Geographic Preference:** Local.

40131 ■ Louisiana Small Business Development Center at University of Louisiana at Lafayette
537 Cajundome Blvd., Ste. 236
Lafayette, LA 70506
Ph: (337)482-6312
Co. E-mail: lsbdc.ull@louisianasbdc.org

40132 ■ Louisiana

URL: http://www.louisianasbdc.org/lsbdc-university-of-louisiana-at-lafayette
Contact: Heidi Melancon, Director
Facebook: www.facebook.com/lsbdcull
X (Twitter): x.com/lsbdcull
Description: Represents and promotes the small business sector. Provides management assistance to current and prospective small business owners. Helps to improve management skills and expand the products and services of members. **Founded:** 1983. **Geographic Preference:** Local.

40132 ■ University of Louisiana at Lafayette - Louisiana Small Business Development Center (LSBDC)
537 Cajundome Blvd., Ste. 236
Lafayette, LA 70506
Ph: (337)482-6312
Co. E-mail: lsbdc.ull@louisianasbdc.org
URL: http://www.louisianasbdc.org
Contact: Dr. Heidi Melancon, Director
Facebook: www.facebook.com/lsbdc
Linkedin: www.linkedin.com/company/louisiana-small-business-development-center
X (Twitter): x.com/lsbdc
YouTube: www.youtube.com/user/LSBDC
Description: Offers services to small businesses including business plans, financing, financial analysis, sales and marketing, management, taxes and accounting, human resources, and international trade. **Scope:** Small business development. **Founded:** 1983. **Educational Activities:** LSBDC Seminars.

40133 ■ University of Louisiana at Monroe (ULM) - Small Business Development Center (SBDC)
700 University Ave.
Monroe, LA 71209
Ph: (318)342-1224
Co. E-mail: lsbdc.ulm@louisianasbdc.org
URL: http://www.louisianasbdc.org
Contact: Virendra Chhikara, Director
E-mail: chhikara@ulm.edu
Facebook: www.facebook.com/lsbdculm
Linkedin: www.linkedin.com/company/louisiana-small-business-development-center
X (Twitter): x.com/LSBDCULM
YouTube: www.youtube.com/user/LSBDC
Description: Offers a variety of services to help you grow your business. Services include business plans, financing, financial analysis, sales, marketing, management, accounting, human resources, risk management, and technology. **Scope:** Assists potential and existing small business people, especially with women/minority/disadvantage microenterprise development. **Founded:** 1983.

SCORE OFFICES

40134 ■ Baton Rouge Area SCORE
7515 Jefferson Hwy., Ste. 159
Baton Rouge, LA 70806
Ph: (225)215-0080
Co. E-mail: scorebr@scorebr.org
URL: http://www.score.org/batonrougearea
Contact: Robert Shaver, Chairman
Facebook: www.facebook.com/SCOREBatonRouge
Linkedin: www.linkedin.com/company/score-mentors-baton-rouge
X (Twitter): x.com/SCOREMentors
Description: Provides professional guidance and information to maximize the success of existing and emerging small businesses. Offers business counseling and workshops. **Founded:** 1964. **Geographic Preference:** Local.

40135 ■ Lafayette SCORE
c/o opportunity Machine., 537 Conjundome Blvd.
Lafayette, LA 70501
URL: http://batonrougearea.score.org
Description: Provides public service to America by offering small business advice and training. **Geographic Preference:** Local.

40136 ■ Northshore SCORE
200 Buras Ranch Rd.
Covington, LA 70433
Ph: (985)520-0929
Fax: (207)680-4510
Co. E-mail: scorens@scorens.org
URL: http://northshore.score.org
Contact: Benjamin Joseph Patterson, Contact
Facebook: www.facebook.com/ScoreNorthshore
YouTube: www.youtube.com/watch?v=F5oPjBZ2vFc
Founded: 2009.

40137 ■ Northwest Louisiana SCORE
400 Edwards St.
Shreveport, LA 71101
URL: http://www.score.org/find-location?state=LA
Description: Provides professional guidance and information to America's small businesses. **Founded:** 1964. **Geographic Preference:** Local.

40138 ■ SCORE - Acadiana
537 Cajundome Blvd.
Lafayette, LA 70506
Ph: (337)541-2778
Co. E-mail: scorebr@scorebr.org
URL: http://acadiana.score.org/find-location
X (Twitter): twitter.com/SCOREAcadiana
Description: Provides professional guidance and information to maximize the success of existing and emerging small businesses. Offers business counseling and workshops.

40139 ■ SCORE - New Orleans
500 Poydras St., Ste. 828, Rm. 105
New Orleans, LA 70130
Ph: (504)475-7602
Co. E-mail: ch.admin0044@scorevolunteer.org
URL: http://www.score.org/neworleans
Facebook: www.facebook.com/SCORENewOrleans
Linkedin: www.linkedin.com/company/scorenola
Instagram: www.instagram.com/scorementors_neworleans
YouTube: www.youtube.com/channel/UCRFrDwlejC3YA5vlKhXeqxA
Description: Provides professional guidance and information to maximize the success of existing and emerging small businesses. Offers business counseling and workshops.

40140 ■ SCORE - Northeast Louisiana
1810 Auburn Ave., Ste. 104
Monroe, LA 71201
Ph: (318)677-2535
Co. E-mail: help@score.org
URL: http://nela.score.org
URL(s): www.score.org/find-location
Description: Provides professional guidance and information to maximize the success of existing and emerging small businesses. Offers business counseling and workshops. **Founded:** 1998. **Geographic Preference:** Local.

40141 ■ SCORE - Northwest Louisiana
400 Edwards St.
Shreveport, LA 71101
Ph: (318)677-2535
Fax: (318)677-2541
Co. E-mail: toniaaskins@gmail.com
URL: http://northwestlouisiana.score.org
X (Twitter): x.com/SCORE279
YouTube: www.youtube.com/channel/UCGnfcFZpqcacFxCSe6iMbYw
Description: Provides professional guidance and information to maximize the success of existing and emerging small businesses. Offers business counseling and workshops.

40142 ■ SCORE - Southwest Louisiana
4310 Ryan St.
Lake Charles, LA 70605
Ph: (337)433-3632
Fax: (337)436-3727
URL: http://www.score.org/find-location
Description: Seeks to educate entrepreneurs and help small businesses start, grow and succeed nationwide. Organizes volunteers who are working or retired business owners, executives and corporate leaders who wish to share their wisdom and lessons learned in business. **Geographic Preference:** Local.

40143 ■ Southwest Louisiana SCORE
Lake Charles, LA 70605
URL: http://www.score.org/find-location?page=2
Contact: Bridget Weston, Chief Executive Officer

BETTER BUSINESS BUREAUS

40144 ■ Better Business Bureau of Central Louisiana and the Ark-La-Tex
1900 N 18th St., Ste. 411
Monroe, LA 71201
Ph: (318)797-1330
URL: http://www.bbb.org/local-bbb/bbb-serving-northeast-and-central-louisiana-and-the-ark-la-tex
Contact: Bob Davis, President
Facebook: www.facebook.com/bbbnortheastcentrallouisianaarklatex
Linkedin: www.linkedin.com/company/bbb-ar-la-tx
Description: Seeks to promote and foster the highest ethical relationship between businesses and the public through voluntary self-regulation, consumer and business education, and service excellence. Provides information to help consumers and businesses make informed purchasing decisions and avoid costly scams and frauds; settles consumer complaints through arbitration and other means. **Founded:** 1912. **Geographic Preference:** State.

40145 ■ Better Business Bureau of Northeast Louisiana
2006 E 70th St.
Shreveport, LA 71105
URL: http://www.bbb.org/local-bbb/bbb-serving-northeast-and-central-louisiana-and-the-ark-la-tex
Description: Seeks to promote and foster the highest ethical relationship between businesses and the public through voluntary self-regulation, consumer and business education, and service excellence. Provides information to help consumers and businesses make informed purchasing decisions and avoid costly scams and frauds; settles consumer complaints through arbitration and other means. **Geographic Preference:** Local.

40146 ■ Better Business Bureau Serving Acadiana
4003 W Congress St.
Lafayette, LA 70506
Ph: (337)981-3497
Fax: (337)981-7559
URL: http://www.bbb.org
YouTube: www.youtube.com/channel/UCevbxvMU7Qmefv-mkRZJKgQ
Description: Seeks to promote and foster the highest ethical relationship between businesses and the public through voluntary self-regulation, consumer and business education, and service excellence. Provides information to help consumers and businesses make informed purchasing decisions and avoid costly scams and frauds; settles consumer complaints through arbitration and other means. **Founded:** 1975. **Geographic Preference:** Local.

40147 ■ Better Business Bureau of South Central Louisiana
748 Main St.
Baton Rouge, LA 70802
Ph: (225)346-5222
Fax: (225)346-1029
URL: http://www.bbb.org
Facebook: www.facebook.com/BatonRougeBBB
Linkedin: www.linkedin.com/company/better-business-bureau-of-south-central-louisiana
Description: Seeks to promote and foster the highest ethical relationship between businesses and the public through voluntary self-regulation, consumer and business education, and service excellence. Provides information to help consumers and businesses make informed purchasing decisions and avoid costly scams and frauds; settles consumer complaints through arbitration and other means. **Founded:** 1950. **Geographic Preference:** Local.

STATE LISTINGS

40148 ■ Better Business Bureau of Southwest Louisiana
4040 Lake St.
Lake Charles, LA 70605
Ph: (337)478-6253
Fax: (337)474-8981
URL: http://www.bbb.org/local-bbb/bbb-of-southwest-louisiana
Contact: Angela Guth, President
Facebook: www.facebook.com/BBBSWLA
Linkedin: www.linkedin.com/company/better-business-bureau-of-southwest-louisiana
X (Twitter): x.com/BBBSWLA
Instagram: www.instagram.com/bbbswla
Description: Seeks to promote and foster the highest ethical relationship between businesses and the public through voluntary self-regulation, consumer and business education, and service excellence. Provides information to help consumers and businesses make informed purchasing decisions and avoid costly scams and frauds; settles consumer complaints through arbitration and other means. **Founded:** 1950. **Geographic Preference:** Local.

CHAMBERS OF COMMERCE

40149 ■ Ascension Chamber of Commerce
1006 W Hwy. 30
Gonzales, LA 70737
Ph: (225)647-7487
Fax: (225)647-5124
Co. E-mail: info@ascensionchamber.com
URL: http://www.ascensionchamber.com
Contact: David Alexander, President
Facebook: www.facebook.com/AscensionChamber
X (Twitter): x.com/AscenChamber
Instagram: www.instagram.com/ascenchamber
Description: Promotes business and economic development in Ascension Parish. **Founded:** 1949. **Geographic Preference:** Local.

40150 ■ Assumption Area Chamber of Commerce
PO Box 718
Napoleonville, LA 70390
Ph: (985)513-2770
Co. E-mail: assumptionchamberofcommerce@gmail.com
URL: http://www.assumption-chamber.org
Contact: Jennifer Rivere, Treasurer
Description: Aims to advance, promote, and improve the civic, commercial, industrial, agricultural, trade, educational, and general interests of the Parish of Assumption. **Geographic Preference:** Local.

40151 ■ Baton Rouge Black Chamber of Commerce (BRBCC)
7516 Bluebonnet Blvd., Ste. 127
Baton Rouge, LA 70810
Description: Represents Black owned businesses. Seeks to empower and sustain African American communities through entrepreneurship and capitalistic activity. Provides advocacy, training and education to Black communities. **Geographic Preference:** Local.

40152 ■ Bogalusa Chamber of Commerce
608 Willis Ave.
Bogalusa, LA 70427
Ph: (985)735-5731
URL: http://www.bogalusa.org
Contact: David Merlin Duke, Contact
Description: Promotes business and community development in Bogalusa, LA. Sponsors Festival in the Park. **Founded:** 1920. **Publications:** *Facts, Festivals, Annual events, History, places of interest for Bogalusa and Washington Parish*; *Looking Up* (Bimonthly); *Newcomer's Guide* (Annual). **Geographic Preference:** Local.

40153 ■ Bossier Chamber of Commerce (BCC)
710 Benton Rd.
Bossier City, LA 71111
Ph: (318)746-0252
Co. E-mail: info@bossierchamber.com
URL: http://www.bossierchamber.com
Contact: Lisa Johnson, President
E-mail: ljohnson@bossierchamber.com
Facebook: www.facebook.com/BossierChamber
Linkedin: www.linkedin.com/company/bossier-chamber-of-commerce
X (Twitter): x.com/bossierchamber
Instagram: www.instagram.com/bossierchamber
YouTube: www.youtube.com/user/bossierchamber
Description: Promotes business and community development in Bossier, LA. **Founded:** 1947. **Publications:** *Chamber Update* (Weekly). **Geographic Preference:** Local.

40154 ■ Breaux Bridge Area Chamber of Commerce
314 E Bridge St.
Breaux Bridge, LA 70517
Ph: (337)332-5406
Co. E-mail: info@breauxbridgeacc.com
URL: http://breauxbridgeacc.com
Facebook: www.facebook.com/BreauxBridgeACC
Description: Promotes business and community development in Breaux Bridge, LA. **Founded:** 1972. **Geographic Preference:** Local.

40155 ■ Central Louisiana Chamber of Commerce
1118 3rd St.
Alexandria, LA 71301
Ph: (318)442-6671
Co. E-mail: info@cenlachamber.org
URL: http://www.cenlachamber.org
Contact: Deborah Randolph, President
Facebook: www.facebook.com/CentralLouisianaChamberofCommerce
Linkedin: www.linkedin.com/company/central-louisiana-regional-chamber-of-commerce
Description: Promotes economic development in the region. **Founded:** 1914. **Publications:** *Cenla Magazine* (Bimonthly); *Chamber Connection* (Biweekly). **Geographic Preference:** Local.

40156 ■ *Chamber*
160 W Pine St.
Ponchatoula, LA 70454
Ph: (985)386-2536
Fax: (985)386-2537
Co. E-mail: chamber@ponchatoulachamber.com
URL: http://ponchatoulachamber.com
Contact: Sean Benoit, President
URL(s): ponchatoulachamber.com/about-the-chamber
Description: Includes information on upcoming events and local news regarding business. **Availability:** Print; Online.

40157 ■ Chamber of Commerce of Lafourche and the Bayou Region
107 W 26th St.
Larose, LA 70373
Ph: (985)693-6700
Fax: (985)693-6702
URL: http://lafourchechamber.com
Contact: Lin Kiger, President
Description: Promotes business and community development in Larose, LA area. **Founded:** 1994. **Publications:** *The Chamber Matters* (Quarterly). **Awards:** Lafourche and Bayou Region Chamber Business Person of the Year (Annual). **Geographic Preference:** Local.

40158 ■ *Chamber Connection*
Released: Annual **Availability:** Print; Online.

40159 ■ *Chamber Insight*
PO Box 467
Thibodaux, LA 70302
Ph: (985)446-1187
Fax: (985)446-1191
Co. E-mail: info@thibodauxchamber.com
URL: http://www.thibodauxchamber.com
Contact: Sarah Daigle, Chairman of the Board
URL(s): www.thibodauxchamber.com/chamber-insight
Released: Monthly **Availability:** PDF.

40160 ■ *Chamber News Updates*
610 Hollycrest Blvd.
Covington, LA 70433
Ph: (985)892-3216
Co. E-mail: info@sttammanychamber.org
URL: http://sttammanychamber.org
Contact: Lacey Osborne, President
URL(s): sttammanychamber.org/sttammanystrong
Released: Weekly; Last edition 2022. **Availability:** Online.

40161 ■ Chamber Southwest Louisiana (SWLA)
4310 Ryan St.
Lake Charles, LA 70605
URL: http://www.allianceswla.org
Contact: George Swift, President
Description: Strives to develop Southwest Louisiana by creating economic opportunity, and demanding responsible government and quality education. **Founded:** 2006. **Publications:** *Clubs and Organizations Directory*; *Major Employer's of SWLA Directory*; *SWLA Business Directory*. **Geographic Preference:** Local.

40162 ■ Claiborne Chamber of Commerce
519 S Main St.
Homer, LA 71040
Ph: (318)927-3271
Co. E-mail: clairbornecoc@gmail.com
URL: http://claibornechamber.com
Contact: Pat Abshire, Executive Director
Facebook: www.facebook.com/claibornechamberofcommerce
Description: Strives to promote, assist, and encourage the advancement of the material prosperity and commercial, industrial, and civic progress of Claiborne Parish, Louisiana. **Founded:** 1965. **Geographic Preference:** Local.

40163 ■ Concordia Chamber Of Commerce, Inc.
1401 Carter St.
Vidalia, LA 71373
URL: http://www.vidaliala.com
Contact: Jeannie Archer, Officer
Description: Promotes business and community development in Vidalia, LA. **Founded:** 2011. **Geographic Preference:** Local.

40164 ■ Coushatta-Red River Chamber of Commerce
2010 Red Oak Rd.
Coushatta, LA 71019
Ph: (318)932-3289
Fax: (318)932-6311
Co. E-mail: redriverchamber@bellsouth.net
URL: http://redriverparish.org
Contact: Karen Squires, President
Facebook: www.facebook.com/coushattaredriver.chamber
Description: Promotes business and community development in the Red River Parish Coushatta, LA area. Supports local charities; conducts political and business networking forums. **Founded:** 1969. **Geographic Preference:** Local.

40165 ■ Donaldsonville Chamber of Commerce
714 Railroad Ave.
Donaldsonville, LA 70346
Ph: (225)473-4814
Co. E-mail: dvillecoc@bellsouth.net
URL: http://donaldsonvillechamber.org
Facebook: www.facebook.com/donaldsonvillechamberofcommerce
Description: Promotes business and community development in the Donaldsonville, LA area. Sponsors festival. **Founded:** 1946. **Publications:** *Chamber Voice* (Bimonthly); *Chamber Voice* (Monthly). **Geographic Preference:** Local.

40166 ■ East St. Tammany Chamber of Commerce
1808 Front St.
Slidell, LA 70458
Ph: (985)643-5678

URL: http://www.uschamber.com/co/chambers/louisiana/slidell

Description: Promotes business and community development in the Slidell, LA area. Sponsors annual Business Day. **Founded:** 1962. **Geographic Preference:** Local.

40167 ■ Eunice Chamber of Commerce
c/o Francine Hughes
200 S CC Duson
Eunice, LA 70535
Ph: (337)457-2565
Fax: (337)546-0278
Co. E-mail: director@eunicechamber.com
URL: http://www.eunicechamber.com/home
Contact: Nickie Toups, President
E-mail: president@eunicechamber.com

Description: Promotes business and community development in Eunice, LA. **Geographic Preference:** Local.

40168 ■ French - American Chamber of Commerce - Gulf Coast Chapter (GC)
PO Box 57255
New Orleans, LA 70157-7255
Ph: (504)458-3528
Co. E-mail: info@facc-gc.com
URL: http://www.facc-gc.com
Contact: Eric Belin, President
Facebook: www.facebook.com/FACCGC
Linkedin: www.linkedin.com/company/french-american-chamber-of-commerce---gulf-coast-chapter
X (Twitter): x.com/FACCGC

Description: Dedicated to promoting and developing trade and investment between France and the Gulf Coast. **Founded:** 1876. **Geographic Preference:** State.

40169 ■ *Gateway News*
23520 Eden St.
Plaquemine, LA 70764
Ph: (225)687-3560
Fax: (225)687-3575
Co. E-mail: jslandry@ibervillechamber.com
URL: http://www.ibervillechamber.com
Contact: McKenzie Wille, Chairman of the Board Treasurer
URL(s): www.ibervillechamber.com/newsletters
Released: Bimonthly **Availability:** PDF.

40170 ■ Greater Hammond Chamber of Commerce
400 NW Railroad Ave.
Hammond, LA 70404
Ph: (985)345-4457
Fax: (985)345-4749
Co. E-mail: info@tangipahoachamber.org
URL: http://greaterhammondchamber.org
Contact: Melissa Bordelon, President
YouTube: www.youtube.com/user/hammondchamber
Pinterest: www.pinterest.com/tangipahoachamber

Description: Promotes business and community development in Hammond, LA. **Founded:** 1950. **Publications:** *The Chamber ADVANTAGE* (Monthly). **Geographic Preference:** Local.

40171 ■ Greater Minden Chamber (GMC)
110 Sibley Rd.
Minden, LA 71055
Ph: (318)377-4240
Fax: (318)377-4215
Co. E-mail: info@mindenchamber.com
URL: http://greatermindenchamber.com
Contact: Jana Morgan, Co-President Co-Chief Executive Officer
E-mail: president@mindenchamber.com
Facebook: www.facebook.com/greatermindenchamber
Instagram: www.instagram.com/greatermindenchamber

Description: Promotes business and community development in South Webster Parish, LA. Sponsors annual Caney-Dorcheat Triathlon. **Founded:** 1942. **Publications:** *Chamber ROI* (Quarterly). **Geographic Preference:** Local.

40172 ■ Greater Pointe Coupee Chamber of Commerce
500 Main St.
New Roads, LA 70760
Contact: Aamand Mcduff, Treasurer

Description: Promotes business and community development in the Pointe Coupee Parish, LA area. **Founded:** 1985. **Geographic Preference:** Local.

40173 ■ Greater Vernon Chamber of Commerce
PO Box 1228
Leesville, LA 71496
Ph: (337)238-0349
Fax: (337)238-0340
Co. E-mail: chambervernonparish@hotmail.com
URL: http://www.chambervernonparish.com
Contact: Logan Morris, Officer
Facebook: www.facebook.com/chamber.ofcommerce.7
X (Twitter): x.com/vernon_chamber

Description: Promotes business, community development, and tourism in the Leesville-Vernon Parish, LA area. **Founded:** 1871. **Geographic Preference:** Local.

40174 ■ Houma-Terrebonne Chamber of Commerce (HTCC)
6133 Hwy. 311
Houma, LA 70360
Ph: (985)876-5600
Fax: (985)876-5611
Co. E-mail: info@houmachamber.com
URL: http://houmachamber.com
Contact: Nicol Montiville, Chief Executive Officer
E-mail: nicol@houmachamber.com
Facebook: www.facebook.com/htchamber
Linkedin: www.linkedin.com/company/houma-terrebonne-chamber-of-commerce
X (Twitter): x.com/houmachamber
YouTube: www.youtube.com/channel/UCtWyBlk4zxfRMAAd8eJMaqg
Pinterest: www.pinterest.com/HTChamber

Description: Promotes business and community development in Terrebonne Parish, LA. **Founded:** 1918. **Geographic Preference:** Local.

40175 ■ Iberville Chamber of Commerce
23520 Eden St.
Plaquemine, LA 70764
Ph: (225)687-3560
Fax: (225)687-3575
Co. E-mail: jslandry@ibervillechamber.com
URL: http://www.ibervillechamber.com
Contact: McKenzie Wille, Chairman of the Board Treasurer
X (Twitter): x.com/Ibervillecoc

Description: Promotes business and community development in Plaquemine, LA area. **Founded:** 1946. **Publications:** *Gateway News* (Bimonthly). **Geographic Preference:** Local.

40176 ■ Jefferson Chamber of Commerce
3421 N Cswy., Blvd., Ste. 203
Metairie, LA 70002
Ph: (504)835-3880
Fax: (504)835-3828
Co. E-mail: amandah@jeffersonchamber.org
URL: http://jeffersonchamber.org
Contact: Ruth Lawson, President
Facebook: www.facebook.com/jeffersonchamber
Linkedin: www.linkedin.com/company/jefferson-chamber-of-commerce
X (Twitter): x.com/jeffersoncoc
Instagram: www.instagram.com/jefferson_chamber
YouTube: www.youtube.com/user/thejeffersonchamber

Description: Works to improve the quality of life and the economic, civic, and cultural environment in Jefferson Parish. **Founded:** 1997. **Geographic Preference:** Local.

40177 ■ Kentwood Area Chamber of Commerce
909 Ave., G
Kentwood, LA 70444
Contact: Beryl Billiott, President

Description: Promotes business and community development in Kentwood, LA. **Geographic Preference:** Local.

40178 ■ Livingston Parish Chamber of Commerce (LPC)
248 Veterans Blvd.
Denham Springs, LA 70726
Ph: (225)665-8155
Co. E-mail: staff@livingstonparishchamber.org
URL: http://www.livingstonparishchamber.org
Contact: April Wehrs, President
Facebook: www.facebook.com/livingstonparishchamberofcommerce
X (Twitter): x.com/LivingChamber
YouTube: www.youtube.com/channel/UCD8SGwow2kMaELcGK2HyXbQ

Description: Businesses, clergy, and other individuals interested in advancing the general welfare and prosperity of Livingston Parish, LA. Conducts charitable activities. **Founded:** 1966. **Publications:** *Chamber News*. **Educational Activities:** Business Expo. **Geographic Preference:** Local.

40179 ■ Marksville Chamber of Commerce (MCC)
PO Box 767
Marksville, LA 71351
Ph: (318)253-8599
Co. E-mail: marksvillechamber@gmail.com
URL: http://www.marksvillechamber.org
Contact: Chad Dauzat, President
Facebook: www.facebook.com/MarksvilleChamber

Description: Promotes business, community development, and tourism in Marksville, LA. **Founded:** 1952. **Publications:** *Chaucer News* (Monthly). **Educational Activities:** Marksville Chamber of Commerce General assembly. **Geographic Preference:** Local.

40180 ■ *Money Magazine*
PO Box 467
Thibodaux, LA 70302
Ph: (985)446-1187
Fax: (985)446-1191
Co. E-mail: info@thibodauxchamber.com
URL: http://www.thibodauxchamber.com
Contact: Sarah Daigle, Chairman of the Board
URL(s): www.thibodauxchamber.com/about-us
Availability: Print; Online.

40181 ■ Monroe Chamber of Commerce (MCC)
1811 Auburn Ave., Ste. 01
Monroe, LA 71201
Ph: (318)323-3461
URL: http://www.monroe.org
Contact: Roy Heatherly, President
Facebook: www.facebook.com/monroechamberofcommercela
Linkedin: www.linkedin.com/in/monroe-chamber-a551a8215
X (Twitter): x.com/monroe_chamber
YouTube: www.youtube.com/channel/UCdPX1997XJWejOSRiRjUlbQ

Description: Promotes business and community development in the Ouachita Parish, LA area. Sponsors annual Riverfest in the spring, annual Winterfest in December, and annual Boat Flotilla, Crabfest, and fireworks display. **Founded:** 1921. **Publications:** *Economic Review* (Annual); *Images* (Monthly); *Inside the Chamber* (Quarterly). **Geographic Preference:** Local.

40182 ■ Natchitoches Area Chamber of Commerce
373 2nd St.
Natchitoches, LA 71457
Ph: (318)352-6894
Co. E-mail: info@natchitocheschamber.com
URL: http://www.natchitocheschamber.com
Contact: Laura Lyles, President
E-mail: laura.lyles@natchitocheschamber.com
Facebook: www.facebook.com/NatchitochesChamber
X (Twitter): x.com/natchchamber

YouTube: www.youtube.com/user/natchi
toucheschamber
Pinterest: www.pinterest.com/natchchamber
Description: Promotes business, community development, and tourism in Natchitoches, LA. Sponsors Festival of Lights. **Founded:** 1714. **Publications:** *The Front Door* (Monthly). **Geographic Preference:** Local.

40183 ■ One Acadiana
804 E St. Mary Blvd.
Lafayette, LA 70503
Ph: (337)233-2705
Fax: (337)234-8671
Co. E-mail: contact@oneacadiana.org
URL: http://www.oneacadiana.org
Contact: Troy Wayman, President
Facebook: www.facebook.com/oneacadiana
Linkedin: www.linkedin.com/company/lafchamber
X (Twitter): x.com/oneacadiana
Description: Promotes business and community development in the Lafayette, LA area. **Founded:** 1935. **Publications:** *Inforum* (Bimonthly). **Geographic Preference:** Local.

40184 ■ Opelousas-St. Landry Chamber of Commerce (OSLCC)
109 W Vine St.
Opelousas, LA 70570
Ph: (337)942-2683
Co. E-mail: chamber@stlandrychamber.com
URL: http://www.stlandrychamber.com
Contact: Raquella Manuel, President
Description: Promotes business and community development in the St. Landry Parish, LA area. **Founded:** 1919. **Geographic Preference:** Local.

40185 ■ Ponchatoula Chamber of Commerce
160 W Pine St.
Ponchatoula, LA 70454
Ph: (985)386-2536
Fax: (985)386-2537
Co. E-mail: chamber@ponchatoulachamber.com
URL: http://ponchatoulachamber.com
Contact: Sean Benoit, President
Facebook: www.facebook.com/PonchatoulaChamber
X (Twitter): x.com/PonchChamber
Description: Promotes business and community development in Ponchatoula, LA. **Publications:** *Chamber*. **Geographic Preference:** Local.

40186 ■ Rayne Chamber of Commerce
107 Oak St.
Rayne, LA 70578
Ph: (337)334-2332
Fax: (337)334-8341
URL: http://www.raynechamber.com
Contact: Marietta Sikat, President
Description: Promotes business and community development in Rayne, LA. **Founded:** 1972. **Geographic Preference:** Local.

40187 ■ Ruston - Lincoln Chamber of Commerce
2111 N Trenton St.
Ruston, LA 71270
Ph: (318)255-2031
Fax: (318)255-3481
Co. E-mail: info@rustonlincoln.org
URL: http://www.rustonlincoln.org
Contact: Judy Copeland, President
E-mail: jcopeland@rustonlincoln.org
Facebook: www.facebook.com/RustonChamber
X (Twitter): x.com/RustonChamber
Instagram: www.instagram.com/rustonchamber
Description: Promotes business and community development in the Ruston, LA area. Sponsors annual Louisiana Peach Festival. **Founded:** 1919. **Publications:** *Chamber Checklist* (Weekly). **Geographic Preference:** Local.

40188 ■ Sabine Parish Chamber of Commerce
1601 Texas Hwy.
Many, LA 71449
Ph: (318)256-3523
Co. E-mail: spchamber@cp-tel.net
URL: http://sabineparishchamber.com
Contact: Pollie Brandon, Officer
Description: Promotes business and community development in Sabine Parish, LA. **Founded:** 1947. **Geographic Preference:** Local.

40189 ■ St. Tammany Chamber of Commerce
610 Hollycrest Blvd.
Covington, LA 70433
Ph: (985)892-3216
Co. E-mail: info@sttammanychamber.org
URL: http://sttammanychamber.org
Contact: Lacey Osborne, President
Facebook: www.facebook.com/sttammanywestchamber
Linkedin: www.linkedin.com/company/st--tammany-west-chamber-of-commerce
X (Twitter): x.com/stwcc
Instagram: www.instagram.com/sttammanychamber
YouTube: www.youtube.com/user/sttammanychamber
Description: Promotes business and community development in Abita Springs, Covington, Folsom, Madisonville, and Mandeville, LA areas. **Founded:** 1963. **Publications:** *Chamber News Updates* (Weekly). **Geographic Preference:** Regional.

40190 ■ Shreveport Chamber of Commerce [Greater Shreveport Chamber of Commerce (GSCC)]
400 Edwards St.
Shreveport, LA 71101
Ph: (318)677-2500
Co. E-mail: info@shreveportchamber.org
URL: http://shreveportchamber.org
Contact: Dr. Timothy J. Magner, President
E-mail: tim.magner@shreveportchamber.org
Facebook: www.facebook.com/ShreveportChamber
X (Twitter): x.com/shrevechamber
Description: Promotes business and community development in Shreveport/Bossier City, LA area. Convention/Meeting: none. **Founded:** 1910. **Publications:** *Northwest Louisiana Manufacturers Directory* (Biennial); *Investor's Update*; *Shreveport Chamber of Commerce--Directory of Manufacturers* (Biennial). **Awards:** Shreveport Chamber of Commerce Athena Award (Annual); Shreveport Chamber of Commerce Forum Small Business of the Year Award (Annual); J. Pat Beaird Industry of the Year (Annual); Very Important Volunteer Awards (Quarterly); Walk of Stars Award (Annual). **Geographic Preference:** Local.

40191 ■ *Slidell City Map*
Released: Periodic **Price:** Free. **Availability:** Print; Online.

40192 ■ *Slidell Connection*
Released: Monthly **Price:** Free. **Availability:** Print; Online.

40193 ■ Springhill - North Webster Chamber of Commerce
400 N Giles
Springhill, LA 71075
Ph: (318)539-4717
Co. E-mail: manager@nwebsterchamber.com
URL: http://www.springhillla.com
Contact: Ronda Taylor, Manager
E-mail: manager@nwebsterchamber.com
Facebook: www.facebook.com/northwebsterchamber
Description: Promotes business and community development in the Springhill, LA area. **Geographic Preference:** Local.

40194 ■ *SWLA Business Directory*
4310 Ryan St.
Lake Charles, LA 70605
URL: http://www.allianceswla.org
Contact: George Swift, President
URL(s): swlachamber.chambermaster.com/list
Availability: Online.

40195 ■ Thibodaux Chamber of Commerce
PO Box 467
Thibodaux, LA 70302
Ph: (985)446-1187
Fax: (985)446-1191
Co. E-mail: info@thibodauxchamber.com
URL: http://www.thibodauxchamber.com
Contact: Sarah Daigle, Chairman of the Board
X (Twitter): x.com/ThibChamber
Description: Promotes business and community development in Thibodaux, LA. Sponsors local festival. Holds forums and legislative breakfast. Promotes annual business expo. **Founded:** 1966. **Publications:** *Chamber Insight* (Monthly); *Money Magazine*. **Awards:** Thibodaux Chamber of Commerce Teenager of the Year (Annual). **Geographic Preference:** Local.

40196 ■ Union Parish Chamber of Commerce (UPCC)
116 N Main St.
Farmerville, LA 71241
Ph: (318)368-3947
Fax: (318)368-3945
URL: http://www.unionparishchamber.org
Contact: Jon McKinnie, II, President
E-mail: econ.dev.upcc@gmail.com
Facebook: www.facebook.com/Union.Chamber
Instagram: www.instagram.com/unionparishchamber
Description: Promotes business and community development in Union Parish. **Founded:** 1996. **Publications:** *Union Parish Community Guide* (Annual; Semiannual); *Chamber Newsletter*. **Educational Activities:** General Membership. **Geographic Preference:** Local.

40197 ■ Vermilion Chamber of Commerce
1907 Veterans Memorial Dr.
Abbeville, LA 70510
Ph: (337)893-2491
Co. E-mail: lynn@vermilionchamber.org
URL: http://www.vermilionchamber.org
Contact: Angelle Broussard, President
Facebook: www.facebook.com/VermilionParishChamber
X (Twitter): x.com/VermChamber
Description: Promotes business and community development in the Abbeville, LA area. Sponsors workshops and seminars. Conducts French Market Festival. **Founded:** 1920. **Geographic Preference:** Local.

40198 ■ West Baton Rouge Chamber of Commerce (WBRCC)
7520 Hwy. 1 S
Addis, LA 70710
Ph: (225)383-3140
Fax: (225)685-1044
Co. E-mail: info@wbrchamber.org
URL: http://wbrchamber.org
Contact: Anna Johnson, Executive Director
E-mail: anna@wbrchamber.org
Facebook: www.facebook.com/WBRchamber
X (Twitter): x.com/WestBRChamber
Description: Promotes business and community development in Port Allen, LA area. **Publications:** *Point West* (Monthly). **Geographic Preference:** Local.

40199 ■ West Monroe-West Ouachita Chamber of Commerce [The Louisville Avenue Bridge or Lee Joyner Bridge]
112 Professional Dr.
West Monroe, LA 71291
Ph: (318)325-1961
Co. E-mail: lstrode@westmonroechamber.org
URL: http://www.westmonroechamber.org
Contact: Kristopher Kelley, Executive Director
E-mail: kkelley@westmonroechamber.org
Facebook: www.facebook.com/WestMonroeChamber
X (Twitter): x.com/WMWOChamberofCo
Instagram: www.instagram.com/WMWOchamber
Description: Promotes business and community development in West Monroe, LA. **Founded:** 1955. **Publications:** *Compass Point* (Monthly). **Awards:** A.O. Evans Award (Annual). **Geographic Preference:** Local.

40200 ■ Winnsboro-Franklin Parish Chamber of Commerce (WFPCC)
513 Prairie St.
Winnsboro, LA 71295

Ph: (318)435-4488
Co. E-mail: contact@winnsborochamber.com
URL: http://www.winnsborochamber.com
Contact: Scott Perkins, President
Facebook: www.facebook.com/winnsborochamberofcommerce

Description: Promotes business and community development in Franklin Parish, LA. Sponsors annual Catfish Festival in April. **Founded:** 1949. **Geographic Preference:** Local.

40201 ▪ Zachary Chamber of Commerce (ZCC)
4633 Main St.
Zachary, LA 70791
Ph: (225)654-6777
Co. E-mail: members@zacharychamber.com
URL: http://www.zacharychamber.com
Contact: Russell Blanchard, Officer
Facebook: www.facebook.com/Zachary-Chamber-of-Commerce-106847926062332
X (Twitter): x.com/zachary_chamber

Description: Promotes business and community development in Zachary, LA. **Founded:** 1968. **Publications:** *Monthly ZNews* (Monthly). **Geographic Preference:** Local.

MINORITY BUSINESS ASSISTANCE PROGRAMS

40202 ▪ Southern Region Minority Supplier Development Council (SRMSDC)
400 Poydras St., Ste. 15
New Orleans, LA 70130
Ph: (504)293-0400
Co. E-mail: info@srmsdc.org
URL: http://www.srmsdc.org
Contact: Alvin-O Williams, President
Facebook: www.facebook.com/SRMSDC
X (Twitter): x.com/SouthernRMSDC

Description: Assists corporations in developing and expanding minority vendor programs. **Founded:** 1973.

40203 ▪ Urban League of Greater New Orleans Women's Business Resource Center
4640 S Carrollton Ave., Ste. 210
New Orleans, LA 70119
Ph: (504)620-2332
URL: http://urbanleaguela.org/wbrc
Facebook: www.facebook.com/urbanleaguela
X (Twitter): twitter.com/urbanleaguela
Instagram: www.instagram.com/urbanleaguela

Description: Provides women business owners with formalized business planning for business expansion. **Founded:** 2001.

FINANCING AND LOAN PROGRAMS

40204 ▪ Acadiana Angels
935 Camellia Blvd., Ste. 200
Lafayette, LA 70508
Contact: Jess Fike, President

Description: Early-stage investor group. Offers educational opportunities to members so they can make informed investment decisions; fosters economic development and job creation in Louisiana; encourages members to contribute to the early-stage entrepreneurial ecosystem in the area. **Investment Policies:** Dynamic growth markets; strong value propositions; sound business plan; scalable companies; clear exit strategy. **Industry Preferences:** Analytics/big data; energy; biotech; digital media; education technology; food/beverage; water management; healthcare; shipping; manufacturing; materials; logistics; SaaS; hospitality.

40205 ▪ Advantage Capital
909 Poydras St., Ste. 2230
New Orleans, LA 70112
Ph: (504)522-4850
URL: http://www.advantagecap.com
Contact: Mary Beth Maygarden, Director
E-mail: mmaygarden@advantagecap.com
Facebook: www.facebook.com/AdvantageCapitalPartners
Linkedin: www.linkedin.com/company/advantage-capital-partners
X (Twitter): x.com/ACPImpact

Description: Investment capital firm for businesses underserved by traditional sources. Includes insurance companies and banks. Provides equity and debt capital, along with strategic and operational counsel. **Founded:** 1992. **Industry Preferences:** Communication; information technology; life science; business services; manufacturing; energy.

40206 ▪ BVM Capital Partners LLC
820 Garrett Dr.
Bossier City, LA 71111
Ph: (318)746-8430
URL: http://bvmcap.com
Contact: Ross P. Barrett, Managing Partner

Description: Finances early- and expansion-stage companies with proprietary technology platforms or unique products for the treatment of cancer. Works closely with the MD Anderson Cancer Center and the LSU Feist Weiller Cancer Center.

40207 ▪ Voodoo Ventures, LLC
2912 Mcilhenny Dr.
Baton Rouge, LA 70809
Contact: John Mckearn, Manager

Description: Offers capital to startups with disruptive business models.

PROCUREMENT ASSISTANCE PROGRAMS

40208 ▪ Louisiana Procurement Technical Assistance Center (LA PTAC)
537 Cajundome Blvd., Ste. 232
Lafayette, LA 70506
Ph: (337)482-6422
URL: http://www.aptac-us.org/news/louisiana-missouri-montana-procurement-counselors-recognized-national-certification
Contact: Peggy Sammons, Consultant
E-mail: peggy.sammons@louisiana.edu

Description: Works to help local businesses compete successfully in the government marketplace. **Founded:** 1989.

40209 ▪ Louisiana Procurement Technical Assistance Center at Lafayette Economic Development Authority (LEDA)
211 E Devalcourt St.
Lafayette, LA 70506
Ph: (337)593-1400
Free: 800-810-7771
Fax: (337)234-3009
Co. E-mail: information@lafayette.org
URL: http://lafayette.org
Contact: Mandi D. Mitchell, President
E-mail: nikkib@lafayette.org
Facebook: www.facebook.com/lafayettela
Linkedin: www.linkedin.com/company/lafayette-economic-development-authority
X (Twitter): x.com/ledalafayettela
YouTube: www.youtube.com/channel/UC9WK01Ro1bzg-8Kgnmc4tKg

Description: Businesses and individuals interested in learning about government contracting and subcontracting, and/or are actively seeking or currently performing under government contracts and subcontracts with the Department of Defense, federal state and local governments, contact the procurement specialists below covering Acadia, Evangeline, Iberia, Lafayette, St. Landry, St. Martin, St. Mary and Vermilion Parishes.

40210 ▪ Louisiana Procurement Technical Assistance Center - University of Louisiana - LAPTAC State Administrative Office
537 Cajundome Blvd., Ste. 232
Lafayette, LA 70506
Ph: (337)482-6422
Free: 800-206-3545
Fax: (337)482-5837
Co. E-mail: la-ptac@louisiana.edu
URL: http://ptac.louisiana.edu
Contact: Cynthia Carrier, Program Manager
E-mail: cynthia.carrier@louisiana.edu

Description: Generates employment and improve the general economy of Louisiana by assisting business firms in obtaining and performing under the U.S. Department of Defense, other federal agencies, state and local government contracts. **Founded:** 1985.

40211 ▪ Northwest Louisiana Government Procurement Center
400 Edwards St.
Shreveport, LA 71101
Ph: (318)677-2500
Co. E-mail: apex@shreveportchamber.org
URL: http://nwlaptac.org
Contact: Dr. Gayle Flowers, Director
E-mail: gayle@shreveportchamber.org

Description: Increases the number of federal, state, and local government contract award dollars being awarded to businesses thus creating and retaining jobs.

INCUBATORS/RESEARCH AND TECHNOLOGY PARKS

40212 ▪ Arts Council of New Orleans - Arts Business Program
1307 Oretha Castle Haley Blvd., Ste. 100
New Orleans, LA 70113
URL: http://www.artscouncilofneworleans.org/article.php?story=about.whoweare
Contact: Amanda Winstead, President

Description: A small business incubator created as an arts management resource center and a professional business environment, serving the creative and administrative growth of individuals and organizations in the arts community; it is a place where individuals and organizations can learn and where they can come together for an exchange of ideas and creative energy.

40213 ▪ Biomedical Research Foundation (BRF)
2031 Kings Hwy.
Shreveport, LA 71103
Ph: (318)716-4100
URL: http://www.brfla.org
Contact: John F. George, Jr., President
Facebook: www.facebook.com/BRFLouisiana
Linkedin: www.linkedin.com/company/brf-louisiana
X (Twitter): x.com/brf_louisiana
YouTube: www.youtube.com/channel/UCONzk0OgGQC5HiQ7aEPjYyA

Description: Operates as a catalyst to expand and develop research, entrepreneurship and high-growth businesses in our region. **Founded:** 1986.

40214 ▪ Central Louisiana Business Incubator
1501 Wimbledon Blvd.
Alexandria, LA 71301
Ph: (318)561-2299
URL: http://www.clbi.org
Contact: Alainna Mire, Executive Director
Facebook: www.facebook.com/pages/Central-La-Business-Incubator/106659429479605
Linkedin: www.linkedin.com/company/central-louisiana-business

Description: A not-for-profit corporation created as an economic tool designed to accelerate the growth and success of entrepreneurial companies through an array of business support resources and services.

40215 ▪ The Coordinating and Development Corporation Division of Entrepreneurial Development (CDC)
PO Box 37005
Shreveport, LA 71133-7005
Co. E-mail: info@cdconline.org
URL: http://cdconline.org
Contact: Jack Skaggs, President
Facebook: www.facebook.com/TheCoordinatingandDevelopmentCorp
Linkedin: www.linkedin.com/company/thecdc-nwla

STATE LISTINGS   Louisiana ▪ 40232

Description: Established to foster the success of the area's small businesses and entrepreneurs. Provides expert assistance to entrepreneurs and existing small businesses to help them start a new business or grow or save an existing business. Founded: 1954.

40216 ▪ Dixie Business Center (DBC)
c/o John Ware, Executive Director
1810 S Range Ave.
Denham Springs, LA 70726
Ph: (225)665-0809
Fax: (225)665-8171
Co. E-mail: info@dixiebusinesscenter.org
URL: http://www.dixiebusinesscenter.org
Contact: John Ware, Executive Director

Description: A nonprofit business incubator program dedicated to helping new and emerging businesses develop, grow, and succeed.

40217 ▪ Go.Be.
2016 Oretha Castle Haley Blvd.
New Orleans, LA 70113
Ph: (504)309-2073
Fax: (504)309-2090
URL: http://gobe.org
Contact: Yolanda Brumfield, Executive Director (Acting)
E-mail: yolanda@gobe.org
Facebook: www.facebook.com/gobeorg
Linkedin: www.linkedin.com/company/gobeorg
X (Twitter): x.com/GoBeOrg
Instagram: www.instagram.com/gobeorg
YouTube: www.youtube.com/channel/UCabqvRwf8ySaNpvPgPdVWFQ

Description: Provides business development services to startup minority- and women-owned businesses throughout Southeast Louisiana.

40218 ▪ InterTech Science Park
2031 Kings Hwy.
Shreveport, LA 71103
URL: http://www.brfla.org/intertech-science-park

Description: An 800-acre urban science and technology park created to develop the region's human, financial and physical infrastructure required for technology companies to flourish. It provides its tenants with access to academic facilities, researchers, core equipment laboratories, animal care, multi-tenant wet lab and office space, land for building, venture capital, business planning assistance. and financial incentives. Founded: 1997.

40219 ▪ JEDCO Enterprise Center (JEDCO)
700 Churchill Pky.
Avondale, LA 70094
Ph: (504)875-3908
Fax: (504)875-3923
Co. E-mail: info@jedco.org
URL: http://www.jedco.org
Contact: Jerry Bologna, President
E-mail: jbologna@jedco.org
Facebook: www.facebook.com/JeffersonParishEconomicDevelopment
X (Twitter): x.com/jedco_news

Description: Supports local startups and entrepreneurs by providing small business financing, business workshops, an innovation center, and startup information. Founded: 1987.

40220 ▪ Jefferson Parish Economic Development Commission (JEDCO) - Business Innovation Center
700 Churchill Pky.
Avondale, LA 70094
URL: http://www.jedco.org

Description: A small business incubator offering affordable services designed to help new businesses grow and thrive. Founded: 1972.

40221 ▪ Legal Innovators for Tomorrow (LIFT)
601 St. Charles Ave.
New Orleans, LA 70130
URL: http://www.lsba.org/LIFT/default.aspx

Description: A two-year pilot program operated by the Louisiana State Bar Association. Provides new attorneys with the resources necessary to develop an innovative, public interest-oriented solo or small law firm.

40222 ▪ Louisiana Business Incubation Association (LBIA)
7117 Florida Blvd.
Baton Rouge, LA 70806
Ph: (225)218-1100
URL: http://www.louisianaincubation.org
Facebook: www.facebook.com/louisiana-business-incubation-association-266312240196156

Description: Seeks to advance business incubation and entrepreneurship. Educates businesses and investors on incubator benefits. Provides information, research and networking resources to help members develop and manage successful business incubation programs. Founded: 1990. Geographic Preference: State.

40223 ▪ Louisiana Business & Technology Center (LBTC)
Vc For Fas 330 Thomas Boyd
Baton Rouge, LA 70803
URL: http://calendar.lsu.edu/department/louisiana_business_technology_center

Description: A small business incubator located on the campus of Louisiana State University providing space for new business start-ups within its 25,000 square-foot incubator. Companies located in the incubator can concentrate on production and marketing, which directly affects success and profits, while leaving the day-to-day administrative details and overhead problems to the LBTC staff.

40224 ▪ Louisiana State University AgCenter Food Incubator
101 Efferson Hall
Baton Rouge, LA 70803
Ph: (225)578-4161
Co. E-mail: gsandoz@agcenter.lsu.edu
URL: http://www.lsuagcenter.com/portals/our_offices/departments/food-science/extension_outreach/incubator
Contact: Gaye Sandoz, Director
E-mail: gsandoz@agcenter.lsu.edu
Facebook: www.facebook.com/LSUFoodInnovationInstitute
X (Twitter): x.com/LSUfoodincubat
Instagram: www.instagram.com/lsu_agcenter_foodii

Description: One-stop resource center for people looking to break into the food business, the incubator puts within reach of entrepreneurs the tools to test, produce, package and market foods.

40225 ▪ Louisiana State University (LSU) - LSU Research and Technology Foundation (RTF) - Louisiana Emerging Technology Center (LETC)
206 Louisiana Emerging Technology Center
Baton Rouge, LA 70808
URL: http://www.lsu.edu/americanway/index.php

Description: Designed specifically as an incubator for companies with wet-lab needs, serves small and start-up businesses developing and commercializing university technologies. Founded: 2002.

40226 ▪ LSU Innovation Park
8000 Innovation Pk. Dr.
Baton Rouge, LA 70820
Ph: (225)578-7555
Co. E-mail: innovationpark@lsu.edu
URL: http://www.lsu.edu/innovation/innovation-park/index.php
Contact: Kristy Elliott, Director, Operations
E-mail: kbarlo2@lsu.edu

Description: A technology-based, university research complex that offers a community for businesses and entrepreneurs to develop, foster, and enhance innovation in Louisiana utilizing LSU's vast network of resources. Founded: 1988.

40227 ▪ LSU Student Incubator
8000 Innovation Pk. Dr.
Baton Rouge, LA 70820

URL: http://www.lsu.edu/innovation

Description: A supportive environment where students' new entrepreneurial start-up businesses are nurtured. Students receive use of fully-equipped office space and office equipment, on-going training and coaching, technical assistance, access to capital, use of meeting rooms, and professional help in launching their own business.

40228 ▪ New Orleans BioInnovation Center
1441 Canal St.
New Orleans, LA 70112
Ph: (504)680-2973
Co. E-mail: info@neworleansbio.com
URL: http://neworleansbio.com
Contact: Kris Khalil, Executive Director
Facebook: www.facebook.com/neworleansbio
Linkedin: www.linkedin.com/in/neworleansbio
X (Twitter): x.com/neworleansbio

Description: A technology business incubator created to foster entrepreneurship within the New Orleans bioscience community by assisting companies commercializing biotechnologies from New Orleans-based universities.

40229 ▪ Nexus Louisiana
7117 Florida Blvd.
Baton Rouge, LA 70806
Ph: (225)218-1100
Co. E-mail: hello@nexusla.org
URL: http://nexusla.org
Contact: Stephen Loy, Executive Director
Facebook: www.facebook.com/nexuslouisiana
Linkedin: www.linkedin.com/company/nexusla
X (Twitter): x.com/latechpark
Instagram: www.instagram.com/nexuslouisiana
YouTube: www.youtube.com/channel/UCtZt-8rs_9E_ioFxK-olqVw

Description: Firm provides business services such as data center, internet connectivity, tenant space, advance phone and communication equipment. Founded: 1994.

40230 ▪ Northeast Louisiana Business and Community Development Center (NLBCDC)
700 University Ave., Stubbs 204
Monroe, LA 71209
Ph: (318)342-1143
Co. E-mail: nlbcdc@ulm.edu
URL: http://www.ulm.edu/nlbcdc
Contact: Susan Duggins, Executive Director
E-mail: duggins@ulm.edu

Description: Offers shared space, services and equipment to help firms as they establish or grow their businesses. Provide affordable shared services, access to office equipment and technology, flexible leases, and room for expansion. Founded: 2009.

40231 ▪ Small, Women, and Minority Owned Business Incubator [Southern University Small, Women and Minority-Owned Business Incubator]
4646 Hilary Huckaby Ave.
Shreveport, LA 71107
Ph: (318)670-9700
URL: http://www.susla.edu
Contact: Jacoby Tubbs, Executive Director

Description: Offers an environment where entrepreneurs learn effective business practices and engage in business operations. Founded: 2004.

40232 ▪ Southeast Louisiana Business Center (SLBC)
1514 Martens Dr.
Hammond, LA 70402
Ph: (985)549-3199
Co. E-mail: wjoubert@southeastern.edu
URL: http://www.southeastern.edu/admin/slbc
Contact: Starlyn Nickens, Administrative Assistant
E-mail: starlyn.nickens@southeastern.edu

Description: A small business incubator whose goal is to extend a nurturing environment to start-up and expanding small businesses in the area. The Center houses area economic development agencies, business counseling resources, and incubator space.

40233 ■ Louisiana

40233 ■ Southern University at Shreveport Small, Women and Minority-Owned Business Incubator (SUSLA)
3050 Martin Luther King Jr. Dr.
 Shreveport, LA 71107
Ph: (318)670-6000
URL: http://www.susla.edu/page/our-campuses
Description: Provides an environment in which a business can learn effective business practices, while actually engaging in business operations. Business incubator includes flexible affordable rental space, marketing assistance, technical assistance, office equipment, and financial planning.

40234 ■ Southwest Louisiana Economic Development Alliance
4310 Ryan St., 3rd Fl.
 Lake Charles, LA 70605
Ph: (337)433-3632
Fax: (337)436-3727
Co. E-mail: donotreply@allianceswla.org
URL: http://www.allianceswla.org
Contact: George Swift, President
E-mail: gswift@allianceswla.org
Facebook: www.facebook.com/AllianceSWLA
Linkedin: www.linkedin.com/company/the-southwest-louisiana-economic-development-alliance
X (Twitter): x.com/swlaalliance
YouTube: www.youtube.com/channel/UCgAWxdTHOMN1gkeeTPNoHIg
Description: An alliance established to strengthen the business recruiting and retention efforts for Allen, Beauregard, Calcasieu, Cameron, and Jeff Davis parishes. **Founded:** 1913. **Geographic Preference:** Local.

40235 ■ Southwest Louisiana Entrepreneurial & Economic Development Center (SEED)
4310 Ryan St.
 Lake Charles, LA 70605
Ph: (337)433-3632
Co. E-mail: sseemion@allianceswla.org
URL: http://seedcenterswla.com
Facebook: www.facebook.com/SEED-Center-Business-Incubator-641195042564902
Linkedin: www.linkedin.com/company/seed-center-business-incubator
Description: Offers startups a place where you can learn how to do business while you conduct businesses. Provides access to additional resource partners.

40236 ■ SUNO Inc. [Small Business Development and Management Institute; SUNO Small Business Incubator]
6400 Press Dr.
 New Orleans, LA 70126
Ph: (504)286-5000
Co. E-mail: service@suno.edu
URL: http://www.suno.edu
Contact: Dennis J. Shields, President
Facebook: www.facebook.com/SouthernUniversityAtNewOrleans
X (Twitter): x.com/SUNOKnights
Instagram: www.instagram.com/southernuniversityatneworleans
Description: Serves the local community in successful development of start-up and fledgling companies by providing entrepreneurs with an array of targeted resources and services. **Founded:** 1959.

EDUCATIONAL PROGRAMS

40237 ■ Louisiana State University Stephenson Entrepreneurship Institute (LSUSEI)
3000 Business Education Complex
 501 S Quad Dr.
 Baton Rouge, LA 70803
Ph: (225)578-0313
Co. E-mail: sei@lsu.edu
URL: http://www.lsu.edu/business/sdeis/sei.php
Facebook: www.facebook.com/LSUSEI
Linkedin: www.linkedin.com/company/stephenson-entrepreneurship-institute
X (Twitter): x.com/lsuentrepreneur
Instagram: www.instagram.com/lsuentrepreneurship
Description: Promotes and fosters entrepreneurial practices through education, outreach, and research. Serves the University and the community working closely with partners to assist economic development and small business development in the community. **Founded:** 2007.

40238 ■ Louisiana Tech University Innovation Enterprise
509 W Alabama
 Ruston, LA 71272
URL: http://www.latech.edu/research-innovation-enterprise/innovation-entrepreneurship-resources
Description: A hotbed of ideas, entrepreneurship, creativity, and new partnerships created through collaborations involving students, faculty, and our business partners. Brings forward the resources and capabilities of a world-class university to support entrepreneurs, business innovators, and corporate partners in pursuing new opportunities for growth and prosperity in north Louisiana.

PUBLICATIONS

40239 ■ *New Orleans City Business*
7025 Albert Pick Rd.
 Greensboro, NC 27409
Ph: (612)317-9420
Free: 877-615-9536
Co. E-mail: customerservice@bridgetowermedia.com
URL: http://www.bridgetowermedia.com
Contact: Adam Reinebach, President
URL(s): neworleanscitybusiness.com
Facebook: www.facebook.com/NewOrleansCityBusiness
Linkedin: www.linkedin.com/company/new-orleans-citybusiness
X (Twitter): x.com/City_Business
Instagram: www.instagram.com/city_business
Ed: Natalie Chandler. **Released:** Biweekly; daily online. **Price:** $10, for plans start at monthly online; $399, for annual leads & data + print; $139, for print and online annual; $11, for print and online; $369, for leads & data; $129, for annual; $2, Single issue. **Description:** Business newspaper (Tabloid). **Availability:** Print; Online. **Type:** Full-text.

RESEARCH CENTERS

40240 ■ Louisiana State University in Shreveport College of Business Administration - Center for Business and Economic Research (CBER)
c/o Douglas White
 One University Pl., BE 120
 Shreveport, LA 71115
Ph: (318)797-5146
Co. E-mail: cber@lsus.edu
URL: http://www.lsus.edu/community/center-for-business-and-econ-research
Contact: Douglas White, Director
E-mail: douglas.white@lsus.edu
Description: Integral unit of College of Business Administration, Louisiana State University in Shreveport. **Scope:** New business recruitment and existing business expansion for the Shreveport/Bossier metro area. **Founded:** 1982. **Publications:** *Monthly reports* (Monthly). **Educational Activities:** Economic Outlook Conference (Annual).

40241 ■ Southeastern Louisiana University - Business Research Center (BRC)
1514 Martens Dr.
 Hammond, LA 70401
Ph: (985)549-3199
Fax: (985)549-2127
Co. E-mail: brc@southeastern.edu
URL: http://www.southeastern.edu/admin/sbrc/index.html
Contact: William Joubert, Director
E-mail: william.joubert@southeastern.edu
Description: Integral unit of College of Business, Southeastern Louisiana University. **Scope:** Economic indicators of southeastern Louisiana parishes. **Founded:** 1984.

Maine

ASSOCIATIONS AND OTHER ORGANIZATIONS

40242 ■ National Federation of Independent Business Maine
PO Box 4629
   Portland, ME 04112-4629
Ph: (207)807-4900
URL: http://www.nfib.com/maine
Contact: David R. Clough, Director
E-mail: dclough2@maine.rr.com
X (Twitter): twitter.com/nfib_me
Description: Represents small and independent businesses. Aims to promote and protect the rights of members to own, operate and grow their businesses. **Geographic Preference:** State.

SMALL BUSINESS DEVELOPMENT CENTERS

40243 ■ Maine Small Business Development Centers - Lead Center
96 Falmouth St.
   Portland, ME 04104
Ph: (207)780-4420
Fax: (207)780-4810
Co. E-mail: mainesbdc@usm.maine.edu
URL: http://www.mainesbdc.org
Contact: Mark Delisle, Director
E-mail: mark.delisle@maine.edu
Description: Provides business management assistance, training and information services to Maine's micro and small business community. Focus is to assist in the creation and maintenance of viable micro and small businesses and the jobs these businesses provide. **Founded:** 1977. **Geographic Preference:** Local.

SMALL BUSINESS ASSISTANCE PROGRAMS

40244 ■ Maine Department of Economic and Community Development
Burton M. Cross Bldg., 3rd Fl.
   111 Sewall St.
   Augusta, ME 04330-6830
Ph: (207)624-9800
URL: http://www.maine.gov/decd
Contact: Heather Johnson, Commissioner
Facebook: www.facebook.com/MaineDECD
X (Twitter): x.com/MEDECD
Description: Provides business planning, financing, information, and networking assistance to existing Maine businesses that need financing for expansion purposes. Utilizes programs offered through the Maine WEET and JTPA offices. Assists in identifying funding sources, including federal, state, and private. Also runs the Job Opportunity Zone Program which focuses attention on four designated depressed areas.

40245 ■ Maine Department of Economic and Community Development - Office of Business Development
Burton Cross Bldg., 3rd Fl.
   111 Sewall St.
   Augusta, ME 04330-6830
URL: http://www.maine.gov/decd/business-development
Contact: Charlotte Mace, Director
E-mail: charlotte.mace@maine.gov
Description: Encourages investment in new Maine businesses and provides technical assistance to businesses in labor training, financing, site selection, and state licenses, and permits. Includes Maine Products Marketing Program which promotes regional and national awareness of Maine's products.

40246 ■ Maine Development Foundation (MDF)
2 Beech St., Ste. 203
   Hallowell, ME 04347
Ph: (207)622-6345
Fax: (207)622-6346
Co. E-mail: mdf@mdf.org
URL: http://www.mdf.org
Contact: Yellow Light Breen, President
E-mail: yellow@mdf.org
Facebook: www.facebook.com/MaineDevelopmentFoundation
YouTube: www.youtube.com/channel/UCwYfrHJvN5f_bTIVLYxtRYg
Description: Nonprofit corporation that assists Maine businesses. Services include coordination of joint public-private projects; research and long-range planning for future economic development; and economic education. **Founded:** 1978.

40247 ■ Maine International Trade Center (MITC)
2 Portland Fish Pier, Ste. 204
   Portland, ME 04101
Ph: (207)541-7400
Co. E-mail: info@mitc.com
URL: http://www.mitc.com
Contact: Wade Merritt, President
E-mail: merritt@mitc.com
Facebook: www.facebook.com/MaineInternationalTradeCenter
Linkedin: www.linkedin.com/company/maine-international-trade-center
X (Twitter): x.com/MEIntlTradeCtr
Description: A private, nonprofit organization offering extensive export services to Maine businesses. Also includes a library of information on world trade. **Founded:** 1996.

SCORE OFFICES

40248 ■ Augusta SCORE
68 Sewall St.
   Augusta, ME 04330
Ph: (207)782-3708
Co. E-mail: scoremaine@gmail.com
URL: http://centralmaine.score.org/augusta
Description: Provides entrepreneur education and the formation, growth and success of small business nationwide. Provides free counseling and low-cost workshops. **Geographic Preference:** Local.

40249 ■ Downeast Maine SCORE
202 Harlow St.
   Bangor, ME 04401
URL: http://www.score.org/northernmaine
Founded: 1964.

40250 ■ Oxford Hills SCORE
125 Manley Rd.
   Auburn, ME 04210
Ph: (207)782-3708
Co. E-mail: scoremaine@gmail.com
URL: http://centralmaine.score.org
Contact: William T. Webster, Jr., Chairman
Facebook: www.facebook.com/SCORECentralMaine
Linkedin: www.linkedin.com/in/scoremaine
Instagram: www.instagram.com/scoremaine
Description: Serves as volunteer program in which working and retired business management professionals provide free business counseling to men and women who are considering starting a small business, encountering problems with their business, or expanding their business. Offers free one-on-one counseling, online counseling and low cost workshops on a variety of business topics. **Founded:** 1964. **Geographic Preference:** Local.

40251 ■ Portland Maine SCORE
100 Middle St. Fl. 2
   Portland, ME 04101
Ph: (207)772-1147
Co. E-mail: scoremaine@gmail.com
URL: http://southernmaine.score.org
Contact: Jonathan Trumper, Director
Linkedin: www.linkedin.com/in/scoremaine
YouTube: www.youtube.com/channel/UCygqa_WOIk2ohXvLqfJaD5Q
Description: Delivers expertise and resources to maximize the success of existing and emerging small businesses. Offers 3-hour workshops in how to start own business, writing a business plan, marketing and sales, face to face or email counseling at no cost. **Geographic Preference:** Local.

40252 ■ SCORE - Androscoggin County
125 Manley Rd.
   Auburn, ME 04210
Ph: (207)782-3708
URL: http://business.lametrochamber.com/list/member/score-androscoggin-county-185
Contact: Jon Anderson, Chairman
YouTube: www.youtube.com/channel/UCygqa_WOIk2ohXvLqfJaD5Q
Description: Provides professional guidance and information to maximize the success of existing and emerging small businesses. Offers business counseling and workshops.

40253 ■ SCORE - Augusta
68 Sewall St., Rm. 512
Augusta, ME 04330
Ph: (207)743-0499
URL: http://oxfordhills.score.org/augusta
Contact: David Brush, Contact

Description: Provides professional guidance and information to maximize the success of existing and emerging small businesses. Offers business counseling and workshops. **Founded:** 1964.

40254 ■ SCORE - Bangor
202 Harlow St., Fed Office Bldg., Rm. 20700
Bangor, ME 04401
Ph: (207)772-1147
Fax: (207)326-4548
Co. E-mail: scorebangor@gmail.com
URL: http://bangor.score.org
Facebook: www.facebook.com/SCOREBangor
Instagram: www.instagram.com/scoremaine

Description: Provides professional guidance and information to maximize the success of existing and emerging small businesses. Offers business counseling and workshops. **Founded:** 1964.

40255 ■ SCORE - Belfast
14 Main St.
Belfast, ME 04915
Ph: (207)772-1147
Co. E-mail: scoremaine@gmail.com
URL: http://bangor.score.org/belfast
Founded: 1964.

40256 ■ SCORE - Downeast Maine
Ellsworth, ME
Ph: (207)536-1143
Co. E-mail: scoremaine@gmail.com
URL: http://bangor.score.org/downeastmaine

Description: Provides professional guidance and information to maximize the success of existing and emerging small businesses. Offers business counseling and workshops.

40257 ■ SCORE - Oxford Hills
125 Manley Rd.
Auburn, ME 04210
Ph: (207)743-0499
Co. E-mail: oxfordhillsscore@gmail.com
URL: http://oxfordhills.score.org
Facebook: www.facebook.com/SCOREOxfordHills

Description: Provides professional guidance and information to maximize the success of existing and emerging small businesses. Offers business counseling and workshops.

40258 ■ SCORE - Portland, Maine
100 Middle St., Fl2
Portland, ME 04101
Ph: (207)772-1147
Co. E-mail: scoremaine@gmail.com
URL: http://portlandme.score.org
Facebook: www.facebook.com/scoremaine
Linkedin: www.linkedin.com/in/scoremaine
Instagram: www.instagram.com/scoremaine
YouTube: www.youtube.com/channel/UCygqa_WOlk2ohXvLqfJaD5Q

Description: Provides professional guidance and information to maximize the success of existing and emerging small businesses. Offers business counseling and workshops. **Founded:** 1965.

40259 ■ SCORE - Rumford [SCORE - Oxford Hills]
60 Lowell St.
Rumford, ME 04276
Ph: (207)743-0499
Co. E-mail: scoremaine@gmail.com
URL: http://oxfordhills.score.org/find-location
Contact: George L. Kimball, Contact

Description: Provides professional guidance and information to maximize the success of existing and emerging small businesses. Offers business counseling and workshops.

CHAMBERS OF COMMERCE

40260 ■ *Area Guide*
263 Main St., Ste. 2
Bridgton, ME 04009
Ph: (207)647-3472
Fax: (207)647-8372
Co. E-mail: info@gblrcc.org
URL: http://www.gblrcc.org
Contact: Heidi Edwards, President
E-mail: hedwards@norwaysavingsbank.com
URL(s): www.gblrcc.org/area-guide
Released: Annual **Availability:** PDF; Online.

40261 ■ Bangor Regional Chamber of Commerce (BRCC)
2 Hammond St., Ste. One
Bangor, ME 04401
Ph: (207)947-0307
Fax: (207)990-1427
Co. E-mail: admin@bangorregion.com
URL: http://www.bangorregion.com
Contact: Deb Neuman, President
Facebook: www.facebook.com/bangorregion
Linkedin: www.linkedin.com/company/bangor-region-chamber-of-commerce
X (Twitter): x.com/bangorchamber
Instagram: www.instagram.com/bangorchamber

Description: Seeks to sustain and promote economic vitality in the Bangor region. **Founded:** 1911. **Publications:** *Chamber News*; *Bangor Region Visitors Guidebook* (Annual). **Educational Activities:** Early Bird Breakfast (Monthly). **Awards:** Norbert X. Dowd Award (Annual). **Geographic Preference:** Local.

40262 ■ Bar Harbor Chamber of Commerce (BHCC)
2 Cottage St.
Bar Harbor, ME 04609
Ph: (207)288-5103
Co. E-mail: info@visitbarharbor.com
URL: http://www.barharborinfo.com
Contact: Stephanie Clement, Secretary
Facebook: www.facebook.com/barharborcc
X (Twitter): x.com/VisitBarHarbor
Instagram: www.instagram.com/visitbarharbor
Pinterest: www.pinterest.com/visitbarharbor

Description: Businesses, organizations, and interested individuals. Promotes economic development and tourism in Bar Harbor, ME. **Founded:** 1969. **Publications:** *Bar Harbor Visitors' Guide*. **Geographic Preference:** Local.

40263 ■ *Bar Harbor Visitors' Guide*
2 Cottage St.
Bar Harbor, ME 04609
Ph: (207)288-5103
Co. E-mail: info@visitbarharbor.com
URL: http://www.barharborinfo.com
Contact: Stephanie Clement, Secretary
URL(s): www.visitbarharbor.com/info
Price: $14.95, Individuals for US only. **Availability:** PDF; Download; Online.

40264 ■ Belfast Area Chamber of Commerce (BACC)
14 Main St.
Belfast, ME 04915
Ph: (207)338-5900
Co. E-mail: chamberoffice@belfastmaine.org
URL: http://www.belfastmaine.org
Contact: Alex Hawthorne, Co-President
E-mail: ahawthorne@mathewsbrothers.com
Facebook: www.facebook.com/Belfast-Area-Chamber-of-Commerce-595052753844186
Linkedin: www.linkedin.com/company/belfast-area-chamber-of-commerce
X (Twitter): x.com/belfastchamber
Instagram: www.instagram.com/belfastareachamber

Description: Promotes business and community development in the Belfast, ME area. Conducts lobbying activities. Sponsors annual fishing contest, 4th of July and downtown Christmas celebrations, Chamber Bay cruise, and historic home tour. **Founded:** 1979. **Publications:** *Belfast Booklet* (Annual). **Geographic Preference:** Local.

40265 ■ Bethel Area Chamber of Commerce (BACC)
8 Station Pl.
Bethel, ME 04217
Ph: (207)824-2282
Free: 800-442-5826
Fax: (207)824-7123
Co. E-mail: connect@bethelmaine.com
URL: http://www.bethelmaine.com
Contact: Jessie Perkins, Executive Director
E-mail: jessie@bethelmaine.com
Facebook: www.facebook.com/bethelarea
X (Twitter): x.com/bethelmaine
Instagram: www.instagram.com/bethelmaine
YouTube: www.youtube.com/user/bethelmaine/videos

Description: Businesses, industries, and interested individuals. Promotes business and community development. Provides legislative advocacy. Acts as information center; hosts approximately 15 major local, area, and regional events; offers free lodging reservation service. **Founded:** 1920. **Awards:** Bethel Area Chamber of Commerce Business of the Year Award (Annual); Bethel Area Chamber of Commerce Student Citizenship Awards; Bethel Area Chamber of Commerce Employee of the Year (Annual). **Geographic Preference:** Local.

40266 ■ Biddeford Saco Chamber of Commerce and Industry (BSCCI)
28 Water St., Ste. 1
Biddeford, ME 04005
Ph: (207)282-1567
Co. E-mail: info@biddefordsacochamber.org
URL: http://biddefordsacochamber.org
Contact: Jim LaBelle, Executive Director
E-mail: jim@biddefordsacochamber.org
Facebook: www.facebook.com/BiddeforddSacoChamber

Description: Promotes business and community development in the Biddeford-Saco, ME area. **Founded:** 1927. **Publications:** *Chamber News*; *Guide Book* (Annual). **Geographic Preference:** Local.

40267 ■ Blue Hill Peninsula Chamber of Commerce (BHPCoC)
16 S St., Ste. B
Blue Hill, ME 04614
Ph: (207)374-3242
Co. E-mail: chamber@bluehillpeninsula.org
URL: http://www.bluehillpeninsula.org
Contact: Beth Dickens, President
Facebook: www.facebook.com/bluehillpeninsula
Instagram: www.instagram.com/blue_hill_peninsula

Description: Individuals interested with the Blue Hill Peninsula and the civic, economic, cultural, commercial, industrial, environmental, and educational position of it. **Founded:** 2000. **Geographic Preference:** Local.

40268 ■ Boothbay Harbor Region Chamber of Commerce
192 Townsend Ave.
Boothbay Harbor, ME 04538
Ph: (207)633-2353
Co. E-mail: seamaine@boothbayharbor.com
URL: http://www.boothbayharbor.com
Contact: Douglas Goldhirsch, President
Facebook: www.facebook.com/boothbayharbor

Description: Promotes business and community development in Boothbay Harbor, ME area. **Publications:** *Boothbay Harbor Region Guide* (Annual); *Official Boothbay Harbor Region Guide* (Annual). **Geographic Preference:** Local.

40269 ■ *Capital Area Guide*
URL(s): www.augustamaine.com/chamber_membership.asp
Released: Biennial **Price:** Included in membership. **Availability:** Print.

40270 ■ Caribou Information Book and Chamber of Commerce & Industry Membership Directory: Caribou Map and Guide (Maine)
URL(s): www.cariboumaine.netwww.cariboumaine.net/members.html; www.cariboumaine.net/aboutus/benefits/76-mapandguide.html
Released: Irregular; Biennial; latest edition 2004. **Price:** Free. **Description:** Covers approximately 265 member businesses in Caribou, Maine. **Entries include:** Business name, address, phone, products or services. **Arrangement:** Classified by product or service. **Availability:** Diskette; Print; Online.

40271 ■ Chamber Connections
8 Venture Ave.
Brunswick, ME 04011
Ph: (207)725-8797
Co. E-mail: admin@midcoastmaine.com
URL: http://www.midcoastmaine.com
Contact: Cory R. King, Executive Director
E-mail: executivedirector@midcoastmaine.com
URL(s): www.midcoastmaine.com/chamber-info/membership-application
Description: Includes business and community information as well as updates about chamber events and members. **Availability:** Online.

40272 ■ Damariscotta Region Chamber of Commerce (DRCC)
277 Main St.
Damariscotta, ME 04543
Ph: (207)563-8340
Co. E-mail: info@damariscottaregion.com
URL: http://damariscottaregion.com
Contact: Jane Oliver Gravel, Vice President Co-President
Facebook: www.facebook.com/DamaricottaRegionChamber
Description: Seeks to promote business and community development and enhance the relationship between local businesses and professionals with the public. **Geographic Preference:** Local.

40273 ■ Deer Isle - Stonington Chamber of Commerce
114 Little Deer Isle Rd.
Deer Isle, ME 04627
Ph: (207)385-0042
Co. E-mail: deerisle@deerisle.com
URL: http://www.deerisle.com
Contact: Dean Haskell, Co-President
Facebook: www.facebook.com/DISChamber
Description: Promotes business and community development in Deer Isle, ME. **Geographic Preference:** Local.

40274 ■ Destination Moosehead Lake (DML)
480 Moosehead Lake Rd.
Greenville, ME 04441
Ph: (207)695-2702
Co. E-mail: destinationmooseheadlake@gmail.com
URL: http://destinationmooseheadlake.com
Contact: Jennifer Aucoin, President
Facebook: www.facebook.com/mooseheadlake
X (Twitter): x.com/MHLinfo
Description: Promotes business and community development in the Moosehead Lake, ME region. Sponsors 4th of July celebration, annual "Moosemainea" in the spring, and annual Winter Festival. **Geographic Preference:** Local.

40275 ■ Eastport Area Chamber of Commerce (EACC)
141 Water St.
Eastport, ME 04631
Ph: (207)853-4644
Co. E-mail: contact@eastportchamber.net
URL: http://eastportchamber.net
Contact: Don Dunbar, President
Facebook: www.facebook.com/eastportchamber
Description: Promotes business and community development in the Eastport, ME area. **Founded:** 1924. **Geographic Preference:** Local.

40276 ■ Ellsworth Area Chamber of Commerce
151 High St., Ste. 6
Ellsworth, ME 04605
Ph: (207)667-5584
Fax: (207)667-2617
Co. E-mail: info@ellsworthchamber.org
URL: http://www.ellsworthchamber.org
Contact: Jack Frost, Co-President
YouTube: www.youtube.com/channel/UCzV3PgcmUUKrShGzSi_Cs7w
Description: Promotes tourism and economic development in the Ellsworth, ME area. Sponsors home and garden show, craft show, Autumn Gold Retail Sale, and business after hours program. Holds monthly board meeting. **Founded:** 1956. **Awards:** Ellsworth Area Top Drawer Award (Annual). **Geographic Preference:** Local.

40277 ■ Fort Fairfield Chamber of Commerce
18 Community Center Dr.
Fort Fairfield, ME 04742
Ph: (207)472-3800
Fax: (207)472-3810
URL: http://fortfairfield.org
Contact: Darren Hanson, Director
Facebook: www.facebook.com/townoffortfairfield
Description: Seeks to advance business and economic growth of Fort Fairfield community. **Geographic Preference:** Local.

40278 ■ Franklin County Chamber of Commerce
615 Wilton Rd.
Farmington, ME 04938
Ph: (207)778-4215
Fax: (207)778-2438
Co. E-mail: director@franklincountymaine.org
URL: http://www.franklincountymaine.org
Contact: Scott Lavertu, President
Facebook: www.facebook.com/franklincountymaine
Instagram: www.instagram.com/franklincountymaine
Description: Seeks to promote business community and individual's interests in Franklin, ME. **Geographic Preference:** Local.

40279 ■ FreeportUSA
115 Main St.
Freeport, ME 04032
Ph: (207)865-1212
Co. E-mail: info@visitfreeport.com
URL: http://www.visitfreeport.com
Contact: Kelly Edwards, Executive Director
Facebook: www.facebook.com/FreeportMaine
Linkedin: www.linkedin.com/company/freeportusa
X (Twitter): x.com/visitfreeport
Instagram: www.instagram.com/visitfreeport
YouTube: www.youtube.com/channel/UCWkyz6LSA6SrSldYbCP3Kmg
Pinterest: www.pinterest.com/freeportusa
Description: Promotes Freeport area to viable markets, and maximizing beneficial partnerships on a local, state, national and international level. **Founded:** 1977. **Geographic Preference:** Local.

40280 ■ Greater Bridgton Lakes Region Chamber of Commerce (GBLRCC)
263 Main St., Ste. 2
Bridgton, ME 04009
Ph: (207)647-3472
Fax: (207)647-8372
Co. E-mail: info@gblrcc.org
URL: http://www.gblrcc.org
Contact: Heidi Edwards, President
E-mail: hedwards@norwaysavingsbank.com
Facebook: www.facebook.com/GBLRCC
Instagram: www.instagram.com/gblrcc
Description: Promotes business and community development in Bridgton, ME. **Publications:** *Area Guide* (Annual); *The Chamber Chatter* (Weekly). **Geographic Preference:** Local.

40281 ■ Greater Fort Kent Area Chamber of Commerce (GFKCC)
291 W Main St.
Fort Kent, ME 04743
Ph: (207)834-5354
Co. E-mail: fortkentchamber@gmail.com
URL: http://www.fortkentchamber.com
Contact: Dawn Daigl, President
X (Twitter): x.com/GFKArea_Chamber
YouTube: www.youtube.com/channel/UCebrFqVPYIJ4KWA_H1ap-iQ
Description: Promotes business and community development in Fort Kent, ME. Sponsors area festivals and competitions. Holds Can Am Sled Dog Race. **Founded:** 1946. **Geographic Preference:** Local.

40282 ■ Greater Houlton Chamber of Commerce (HCC)
109 Main St.
Houlton, ME 04730
Ph: (207)532-4216
Co. E-mail: chamber@greaterhoulton.com
URL: http://www.greaterhoulton.com
Contact: Devon Cote, President
Facebook: www.facebook.com/HoultonChamber
X (Twitter): x.com/HoultonChamber
Instagram: www.instagram.com/houltonchamber
Description: Promotes business and community development in the Greater Houlton, ME area. Sponsors Potato Feast Days. **Founded:** 1914. **Geographic Preference:** Local.

40283 ■ Greater Van Buren Chamber of Commerce
51 Main St., Ste. 101
Van Buren, ME 04785
Ph: (207)868-2886
Fax: (207)868-2222
Co. E-mail: vbtownmanager@gmail.com
URL: http://www.vanburenmaine.com/chamber.html
Contact: Theodore Smith, Chairman
Facebook: www.facebook.com/Greater-Van-Buren-Chamber-of-Commerce-391509684260683
Description: Promotes business and community development in Van Buren, ME. **Geographic Preference:** Local.

40284 ■ Guide Book
28 Water St., Ste. 1
Biddeford, ME 04005
Ph: (207)282-1567
Co. E-mail: info@biddefordsacochamber.org
URL: http://biddefordsacochamber.org
Contact: Jim LaBelle, Executive Director
E-mail: jim@biddefordsacochamber.org
URL(s): biddefordsacochamber.org/info
Released: Annual **Availability:** Print.

40285 ■ In Touch
50 Elm St.
Waterville, ME 04901
Ph: (207)873-3315
Fax: (207)877-0087
URL: http://midmainechamber.com/cms
Contact: Kimberly Lindlof, President
E-mail: kimberly@midmainechamber.com
URL(s): www.midmainechamber.com/member-center/news-communication-publications
Released: Monthly **Description:** Mid-maine chamber of commerce newsletter. Includes message from the President, list of new members, up coming events, location for business after hour socials, membership news and other items of interest to our members. **Availability:** Print; PDF; Online.

40286 ■ Katahdin Area Chamber of Commerce
1029 Central St.
Millinocket, ME 04462
Ph: (207)723-4443
Co. E-mail: info@katahdinmaine.com
URL: http://www.katahdinmaine.com
Contact: Gail Fanjoy, President
Facebook: www.facebook.com/katahdinchamber
Instagram: www.instagram.com/katahdinchamber
Description: Promotes business and community development in the Katahdin region. **Founded:** 1995. **Geographic Preference:** Local.

40287 ■ Maine

40287 ■ Kennebec Valley Chamber of Commerce (KVCC)
269 W Ave.
  Augusta, ME 04330
Ph: (207)623-4559
Fax: (207)626-9342
Co. E-mail: info@kennebecvalleychamber.com
URL: http://www.augustamaine.com
Contact: Katie L. Dohert, President
E-mail: kld@kennebecvalleychamber.com
Facebook: www.facebook.com/
  KVChamberofCommerce
X (Twitter): x.com/kennebecchamber
Instagram: www.instagram.com/kennebecchamber
Description: Businesses. Promotes economic development and tourism in the Augusta, ME area. Holds seminars. Sponsors Issues Breakfasts and Whatever Week and Race. **Founded:** 1932. **Educational Activities:** Whatever Festival. **Awards:** Kennebec Valley Business of the Year (Annual); Kennebec Valley Business Person of the Year (Annual); Kennebec Valley Community Service Award (Annual); Kennebec Valley Lifetime Achievement Award (Annual); Kennebec Valley President's Award (Annual); Kennebec Valley Special Service Award (Annual). **Geographic Preference:** Local.

40288 ■ Kennebunk-Kennebunkport-Arundel Chamber of Commerce
16 Water St.
  Kennebunk, ME 04043
Ph: (207)967-0857
Co. E-mail: members@gokennebunks.com
URL: http://gokennebunks.com
Contact: Laura Dolce, Executive Director
E-mail: director@gokennebunks.com
Facebook: www.facebook.com/gokennebunks
X (Twitter): x.com/TheKennebunks
Instagram: www.instagram.com/gokennebunks
Description: Businesses. Promotes business and community development in Kennebunk and Kennebunkport, ME. Sponsors Wedding Expo of the Kennebunks, February is for Lovers, annual Home and Food Show, B&B Inn and Garden Tour, Chamber Golf Tournament, concert and picnic on the green, Kennebearport Teddy Bear Show, Hole in One Contest, annual holiday auction and Downtown Decadence. **Publications:** Chamber News (Monthly); Experience Kennebunk-Kennebunkport (Annual); Guide to the Kennebunks (Annual). **Geographic Preference:** Local.

40289 ■ Lewiston Auburn Metropolitan Chamber of Commerce
415 Lisbon St., Ste. 100
  Lewiston, ME 04240
Ph: (207)783-2249
Co. E-mail: info@lametrochamber.com
URL: http://lametrochamber.com
Contact: Shanna Cox, President
E-mail: president@lametrochamber.com
Facebook: www.facebook.com/LAMetroChamber
Linkedin: www.linkedin.com/company/lewiston
  -auburn-metropolitan-chamber-of-commerce
X (Twitter): x.com/LAMetroChamber
Instagram: www.instagram.com/lametrochamber
YouTube: www.youtube.com/channel/UCfaDIlr5TIWj
  6ziTBjhPp8A
Description: Promotes business and community development in Androscoggin County area. **Founded:** 1887. **Awards:** Androscoggin County Chamber of Commerce Adult Scholarships (Annual). **Geographic Preference:** Local.

40290 ■ Limestone Chamber of Commerce
93 Main St.
  Limestone, ME 04750
Ph: (207)325-4704
Fax: (207)325-3330
Co. E-mail: tm@limestonemaine.org
URL: http://limestonemaine.org
Contact: Michelle Albert, Officer
E-mail: mmalbert@yahoo.com
Facebook: www.facebook.com/wearelimestone
Description: Promotes business and community development in Limestone area. **Founded:** 1997. **Geographic Preference:** Local.

40291 ■ Maine State Chamber of Commerce (MSCC)
128 State St., Ste. 101
  Augusta, ME 04330
Ph: (207)623-4568
Fax: (207)622-7723
URL: http://www.mainechamber.org
Contact: Peter Gore, Consultant
E-mail: pgore@mainechamber.org
Facebook: www.facebook.com/MaineChamber
Linkedin: www.linkedin.com/company/mainechamber
X (Twitter): x.com/MaineChamber
Instagram: www.instagram.com/mainechamber
YouTube: www.youtube.com/user/MaineChamber
Description: Promotes business and community development in Maine. Provides legislative advocacy. Holds seminars. **Founded:** 1889. **Publications:** Impact (Weekly). **Geographic Preference:** State.

40292 ■ Mid-Maine Chamber of Commerce
50 Elm St.
  Waterville, ME 04901
Ph: (207)873-3315
Fax: (207)877-0087
URL: http://midmainechamber.com/cms
Contact: Kimberly Lindlof, President
E-mail: kimberly@midmainechamber.com
Facebook: www.facebook.com/MidMaineChamber
X (Twitter): x.com/midmainechamber
Description: Promotes business and community development in the mid-Maine area. Sponsors monthly Business After Hours program and monthly business forum. **Founded:** 1912. **Publications:** In Touch (Monthly); Newsline (Semimonthly). **Educational Activities:** Annual Awards Dinner (Annual). **Awards:** Mid-Maine Chamber Business of the Year (Annual); Mid-Maine Chamber Business Person of the Year (Annual); Mid-Maine Chamber Distinguished Community Service Award (Annual). **Geographic Preference:** Local.

40293 ■ Mount Desert Chamber of Commerce
41 Harbor Dr.
  Northeast Harbor, ME 04662
Ph: (207)276-5040
Co. E-mail: info@mtdesertchamber.org
URL: http://mtdesertchamber.org
Contact: Lisa Lyn Parsons, Co-President
Facebook: www.facebook.com/EnjoyMtDesert
Instagram: www.instagram.com/enjoymtdesert
Description: Promotes business and community development in Mount Desert, ME. Sponsors seasonal Information Bureau and Yachtman's Reading Room at St. Sea Marina. **Founded:** 1963. **Publications:** Northeast Harbor Port Directory (Periodic). **Educational Activities:** Christmas Festival (Annual). **Geographic Preference:** Local.

40294 ■ Ogunquit Chamber of Commerce (OCC)
36 Main St.
  Ogunquit, ME 03907
Ph: (207)646-1279
Co. E-mail: e_inquiry@ogunquit.org
URL: http://www.ogunquit.org
Contact: Scott Vogel, Chairman
Facebook: www.facebook.com/OgunquitMaine
X (Twitter): x.com/ogunquitchamber
YouTube: www.youtube.com/channel/UCKE6KI
  56pAsQjSls4C9u6Qw
Description: Promotes business and community development in Ogunquit, ME. Sponsors events such as art shows, fireworks displays, Christmas by the Sea festival, and Patriot's Day celebration. **Founded:** 1966. **Geographic Preference:** Local.

40295 ■ Old Orchard Beach Chamber of Commerce (OOBCC)
11 1st St.
  Old Orchard Beach, ME 04064
Ph: (207)934-2500
Co. E-mail: info@oldorchardbeachmaine.com
URL: http://oldorchardbeachmaine.com
Contact: Kim Howard, Executive Director
Facebook: www.facebook.com/oldorchar
  dbeachchamberofcommerce
Description: Promotes business and community development in Old Orchard Beach, ME. Sponsors Beach Olympics to benefit Special Olympics and Adopt a Family Christmas program. **Founded:** 2015. **Geographic Preference:** Local.

40296 ■ Oxford Hills Chamber of Commerce (OHCC)
4 W Ave.
  South Paris, ME 04281
Ph: (207)743-2281
Fax: (207)743-0687
Co. E-mail: info@oxfordhillsmaine.com
URL: http://www.oxfordhillsmaine.com
Contact: John Emerson, President
Description: Promotes business and community development in Oxford Hills, ME. Sponsors seminars and workshops. Operates year-round visitor's information center. **Founded:** 1971. **Publications:** Chamber Bullet (Quarterly); E-Message Board (Weekly); Explore Maine's Oxford Hills (Annual; 9/year). **Awards:** Oxford Hills Chamber of Commerce Community Service Award (Annual); Oxford Hills Chamber of Commerce Employee of the Year (Annual). **Geographic Preference:** Local.

40297 ■ Penobscot Bay Regional Chamber of Commerce (PBRCC)
25 Pk. St., Ste. 2
  Rockland, ME 04841
Ph: (207)596-0376
Co. E-mail: info@camdenrockland.com
URL: http://penbaychamber.com
Contact: Eric Belley, Co-President Co-Chief Executive Officer
E-mail: eric@camdenrockland.com
Facebook: www.facebook.com/Penobsco
  tBayRegionalChamber
Description: Strives to promote and support members and the economic well being of the area community. **Founded:** 2011. **Publications:** Chamber Newsletter (Quarterly; Weekly (Fri.)). **Educational Activities:** Business After Hours (Monthly); Penobscot Bay Regional Chamber of Commerce Annual Dinner (Annual). **Geographic Preference:** Local.

40298 ■ Piscataquis Chamber of Commerce (PCCC)
1033 S St.
  Dover Foxcroft, ME 04426
Ph: (207)564-7533
Co. E-mail: info@piscataquischamber.com
URL: http://www.piscataquischamber.com
Contact: Matt Spooner, President
Facebook: www.facebook.com/piscataquischamber
X (Twitter): x.com/SeePiscataquis
Description: Promotes business and community development in the Southern Piscataquis County, ME. **Geographic Preference:** Local.

40299 ■ Portland Regional Chamber of Commerce (PRCC) [Greater Portland Chamber of Commerce]
93 Exchange St.
  Portland, ME 04101
Ph: (207)772-2811
Fax: (207)772-1179
Co. E-mail: chamber@portlandregion.com
URL: http://www.portlandregion.com
Contact: Quincy Hentzel, II, President
E-mail: qhentzel@portlandregion.com
X (Twitter): x.com/PortlandChamber
YouTube: www.youtube.com/c/PortlandRegion
Description: Promotes business and community development in the Portland, ME area. **Founded:** 1853. **Publications:** Chamber Membership Directory; Business Perspectives (Monthly). **Educational Activities:** Maine Business Expo. **Geographic Preference:** Local.

STATE LISTINGS Maine ■ 40315

40300 ■ Rangeley Lakes Region Chamber of Commerce
6 Pk. Rd.
Rangeley, ME 04970
Ph: (207)864-5571
Fax: (207)864-5366
Co. E-mail: info@rangeleymaine.com
URL: http://www.rangeleymaine.com
Contact: Joanne Dunlap, President
Facebook: www.facebook.com/RangeleyLakesChamber
Description: Promotes economic development and tourism in the Rangeley, ME area. **Founded:** 1955. **Geographic Preference:** Local.

40301 ■ River Valley Chamber of Commerce
10 Bridge St.
Rumford, ME 04276
Ph: (207)364-3241
Co. E-mail: info@rivervalleychamber.com
URL: http://rivervalleychamber.com
Contact: Patti Daigle, President
Facebook: www.facebook.com/RiverValleyChamber
Description: Promotes business and community development in the Rumford, Mexico, Dixfield, Peru, Canton, Hanover, Andover, Byron and Roxbury areas of Maine. **Founded:** 1912. **Publications:** *River Valley Voice* (Weekly). **Educational Activities:** River Valley Chamber of Commerce Dinner (Annual). **Geographic Preference:** Local.

40302 ■ St. Croix Valley Chamber of Commerce
39 Union St.
Calais, ME 04619
Ph: (207)454-2308
Co. E-mail: visitstcroixvalley@gmail.com
URL: http://visitstcroixvalley.com
Contact: Tammi Smith, Contact
Facebook: www.facebook.com/StCroixValleyChamberofCommerce
Description: Business and professional membership organization working to make the St. Croix Valley, ME area a better place to live, work and to raise a family. **Founded:** 1947. **Geographic Preference:** Local.

40303 ■ St. John Valley Chamber of Commerce
356 Main St.
Madawaska, ME 04756
Ph: (207)728-7000
Co. E-mail: info@stjohnvalleychamber.org
URL: http://www.stjohnvalleychamber.org
Contact: Gail Beaupre, President
Description: Promotes business and community development in Madawaska, ME. Sponsors Top O'Maine Trade Show and is home to the Acadian Festival. **Founded:** 1980. **Publications:** *LeCoeur de la Val Lee* (Quarterly). **Geographic Preference:** Local.

40304 ■ Schoodic Area Chamber of Commerce
PO Box 381
Winter Harbor, ME 04693
Co. E-mail: schoodic.chamber.commerce@gmail.com
URL: http://schoodicchamber.com
Contact: Cheryl Bracket, President
E-mail: cgbrackett18@gmail.com
Facebook: www.facebook.com/SchoodicAreaChamber
Description: Promotes business and community development in on the Schoodic Peninsula, ME. Bestows scholarships. Sponsors annual summer Lobster Festival and annual Trade Day (town-wide yard sale). **Geographic Preference:** Local.

40305 ■ Sebago Lakes Region Chamber of Commerce (SLRCC)
909A Roosevelt Trl.
Windham, ME 04062
Ph: (207)892-8265
Fax: (207)893-0110
Co. E-mail: info@sebagolakeschamber.com
URL: http://www.sebagolakeschamber.com
Contact: Robin Mullins, Executive Director
Facebook: www.facebook.com/SebagoLakesRegionChamberOfCommerce
Description: Hosts legislative forums and business programs. Promotes tourism region and supports community events. **Subscriptions:** artwork business records clippings maps photographs reports (includes research). **Publications:** *Annual Business and Pleasure Guide* (Annual); *Soundings* (Quarterly); *Greater Windham Chamber of Commerce--Annual Business and Pleasure Guide* (Annual). **Educational Activities:** Chamber Business Break (Monthly); Director's Meeting (Monthly). **Awards:** Frank Koenig Business Person of the Year Award (Annual); Sebago Lakes Region Community Service Leadership Award (Annual); Sebago Lakes Region Volunteer of the Year Award (Annual). **Geographic Preference:** Local.

40306 ■ Skowhegan Area Chamber of Commerce (SACC)
23 Commercial St.
Skowhegan, ME 04976
Ph: (207)474-3621
Fax: (207)474-3306
URL: http://www.somersetcounty-me.org/non-profit-community-agencies/88-skowhegan-area-chamber-of-commerce-sacc.html
Description: Promotes business, commercial, manufacturing, and civic interests of Greater Skowhegan area. **Founded:** 1940. **Geographic Preference:** Local.

40307 ■ Southern Midcoast Maine Chamber (SMMC)
8 Venture Ave.
Brunswick, ME 04011
Ph: (207)725-8797
Co. E-mail: admin@midcoastmaine.com
URL: http://www.midcoastmaine.com
Contact: Cory R. King, Executive Director
E-mail: executivedirector@midcoastmaine.com
Facebook: www.facebook.com/southernmidcoastmainechamber
Linkedin: www.linkedin.com/e/vgh/1860180
Description: Promotes business and community development in the Bath and Brunswick, ME areas. Operates seasonal tourist information center. **Publications:** *Bath/Brunswick Visitor's Guide* (Annual); *Bath-Brunswick Region Map* (Annual); *Chamber Connections*; *Community Resource Directory*. **Educational Activities:** Award Ceremony. **Awards:** Southern Midcoast Maine Chamber Small Business of the Year Award (Annual); Southern Midcoast Maine Chamber Citizen of the Year Award (Annual); Southern Midcoast Maine Chamber Volunteer of the Year Award (Annual). **Geographic Preference:** Local.

40308 ■ *Visitor's Guide*
URL(s): www.mooseheadlake.org/page/962-733/vacation-planner
Availability: Print; PDF.

40309 ■ Wells Chamber of Commerce
PO Box 356
Wells, ME 04090
Ph: (207)646-2451
Co. E-mail: wellschamber@wellschamber.org
URL: http://www.wellschamber.org
Contact: Eleanor J. Vadenais, President
E-mail: eleanor@wellschamber.org
Facebook: www.facebook.com/WellsMaineChamberOfCommerce
X (Twitter): x.com/wells_chamber
Instagram: www.instagram.com/visitwellsmaine
Description: Promotes business and community development in Wells, ME. Sponsors local festivals and annual Christmas parade. **Geographic Preference:** Local.

40310 ■ Winthrop Lakes Region Chamber of Commerce (WLRCC)
17 Highland Ave.
Winthrop, ME 04364
Ph: (207)377-8020
Fax: (207)377-7201
Co. E-mail: info@winthropchamber.org
URL: http://www.winthropchamber.org
Contact: Kim Vandermeulen, President
E-mail: kvandermeulen@amiems.com
Facebook: www.facebook.com/WinthropChamber
Description: Promotes business in Winthrop. **Geographic Preference:** Local.

40311 ■ *The Yarmouth Chamber*
305 Main St.
Yarmouth, ME 04096
Ph: (207)846-3984
Fax: (207)846-5419
Co. E-mail: info@yarmouthmaine.org
URL: http://yarmouthmaine.org
Contact: Chrissy Mann, Co-President
URL(s): yarmouthmaine.org/join
Released: Weekly **Availability:** Print.

40312 ■ Yarmouth Chamber of Commerce
305 Main St.
Yarmouth, ME 04096
Ph: (207)846-3984
Fax: (207)846-5419
Co. E-mail: info@yarmouthmaine.org
URL: http://yarmouthmaine.org
Contact: Chrissy Mann, Co-President
Facebook: www.facebook.com/yarmouthchamber
Linkedin: www.linkedin.com/company/yarmouth-chamber-of-commerce--maine
X (Twitter): x.com/YMEchamber
Description: Promotes business and community development in Yarmouth, ME. **Founded:** 1956. **Publications:** *The Yarmouth Chamber* (Weekly). **Educational Activities:** Yarmouth Clam Festival (Annual). **Geographic Preference:** Local.

MINORITY BUSINESS ASSISTANCE PROGRAMS

40313 ■ The CEI Women's Business Center (WBC)
2 Portland Fish Pier, Ste. 201
Portland, ME 04101
Ph: (207)504-5899
Co. E-mail: wbc@ceimaine.org
URL: http://www.ceimaine.org/advising/business/womens-business-center/wbcsouth
Contact: Grace Mo-Phillips, Program Director
Description: A provider of business counseling, workshops and events tailored for women in business. The organization offers business plan development, financing, marketing and financial management skills, training seminars, business purchasing and selling advisory, and networking opportunities. **Publications:** "Open door on Haystack Mountain School of Crafts". **Training:** First-Time Homebuyer (HOE-7634), May 2012; Healthy Food Finance Initiative Luncheon, Feb 2012; What is Development Finance?; Workforce Development; Natural Resource Development.

FINANCING AND LOAN PROGRAMS

40314 ■ CEI Ventures Inc.
30 Federal St., Ste. 400
Brunswick, ME 04011
Ph: (207)504-5900
Fax: (207)882-7308
URL: http://www.ceimaine.org
Contact: Chandler Jones, Principal
E-mail: chandler.jones@ceimaine.org
Description: Provider of investment solutions. **Founded:** 1994. **Preferred Investment Size:** $1,000,000 to $4,000,000.

40315 ■ Maine Angels (MA)
414 Danforth St.
Portland, ME 04102
Co. E-mail: contact@maineangels.org
URL: http://www.maineangels.org
Contact: Bill Thomas, Chairman
Linkedin: www.linkedin.com/company/maine-angels

Description: Private equity investors for promising early-stage companies in New England. **Founded:** 2003.

40316 ▪ North Atlantic Capital Corp.
Two City Ctr., 5th Fl.
  Portland, ME 04101
Ph: (207)772-4470
Fax: (207)772-3257
Co. E-mail: mark@northatlanticcapital.com
URL: http://www.northatlanticCapital.com
Contact: Barbara Williams, Coordinator
E-mail: bwilliams@northatlanticcapital.com
Linkedin: www.linkedin.com/company/north-atlantic-capital

Description: Firm is a provider of free research and strategic M and A services along with executive education programs to help entrepreneurs. **Scope:** Firm is a provider of free research and strategic M and A services along with executive education programs to help entrepreneurs. **Founded:** 1986. **Preferred Investment Size:** $4,000,000 $8,000,000. **Industry Preferences:** Internet specific, computer hardware, other products, consumer related, industrial and energy, computer software and services, communications and media, medical and health, semiconductors and other electronics, and biotechnology.

PROCUREMENT ASSISTANCE PROGRAMS

40317 ▪ Eastern Maine Development Corp. (EMDC)
40 Harlow St.
  Bangor, ME 04401
Ph: (207)942-6389
Fax: (207)942-3548
Co. E-mail: info@emdc.org
URL: http://www.emdc.org
Contact: Lee Umphrey, President
E-mail: lumphrey@emdc.org
Facebook: www.facebook.com/EMDCMaine
Linkedin: www.linkedin.com/company/emdcmaine
X (Twitter): x.com/EMDCMaine
Instagram: www.instagram.com/emdcmaine
YouTube: www.youtube.com/channel/UCjYlwAyw8RHKEHJoLxIXPqQ

Description: Helps businesses and communities in Maine to develop and grow. **Founded:** 1967. **Geographic Preference:** Regional.

40318 ▪ Maine Procurement Technical Assistance Center Bangor (PTAC)
40 Harlow St.
  Bangor, ME 04401
Ph: (207)942-6389
Co. E-mail: maineptac@emdc.org
URL: http://www.maineptac.org
Contact: Ken Bloch, Director
E-mail: kbloch@emdc.org
Facebook: www.facebook.com/ptacmaine
Linkedin: www.linkedin.com/company/emdcmaine
X (Twitter): x.com/MainePTAC
Instagram: www.instagram.com/emdcmaine
YouTube: www.youtube.com/channel/UCjYlwAyw8RHKEHJoLxIXPqQ

Description: Helps Maine small businesses obtain government contracts with the Department of Defense, other federal agencies, state/local governments, and prime contractors.

40319 ▪ Maine Procurement Technical Assistance Center (Maine PTAC) - Outreach Center
40 Harlow St.
  Bangor, ME 04401
Ph: (207)942-6389
Co. E-mail: maineptac@emdc.org
URL: http://www.maineptac.org
Contact: Ken Bloch, Director
E-mail: kbloch@emdc.org

Description: Helps Maine small businesses obtain government contracts with the Department of Defense, other federal agencies, state/local governments, and prime contractors.

INCUBATORS/RESEARCH AND TECHNOLOGY PARKS

40320 ▪ Anchorspace
337 Main St.
  Bar Harbor, ME 04609
Ph: (207)613-5344
Co. E-mail: info@anchorspace.com
URL: http://anchorspace.com
Contact: Jill Lee, Contact

Description: Provides coworking space for startups and entrepreneurs.

40321 ▪ Fork Food Lab (FFL)
72 Parris St.
  Portland, ME 04101
Ph: (207)558-0881
Co. E-mail: info@forkfood.com
URL: http://www.forkfoodlab.com
Contact: Bill Seretta, Executive Director

Description: Culinary incubator whose goal is to give food entrepreneurs the tools they need to create a successful business.

40322 ▪ Maine Center for Entrepreneurs (MCED)
68 Commercial St., Bldg. C
  Portland, ME 04101
Co. E-mail: info@mced.biz
URL: http://www.mced.biz
Contact: Tom Rainey, Executive Director
E-mail: tomrainey@mced.biz
Facebook: www.facebook.com/maineentrepreneurs
Linkedin: www.linkedin.com/company/maine-center-for-entrepreneurs
Instagram: www.instagram.com/mainecenterforentrepreneurs

Description: A small business incubator providing business incubation services for innovative start-ups. **Founded:** 1997.

40323 ▪ Midcoast Regional Redevelopment Authority (MRRA)
15 Terminal Rd., Ste. 200
  Brunswick, ME 04011
Ph: (207)798-6512
Fax: (207)798-6510
Co. E-mail: info@mrra.us
URL: http://mrra.us
Contact: Kristine Logan, Executive Director
Facebook: www.facebook.com/MidcoastRegionalRedevelopmentAuthority
Linkedin: www.linkedin.com/company/midcoast-regional-redevelopment-authority
X (Twitter): x.com/mrramaine
Instagram: www.instagram.com/brunswicklanding
YouTube: www.youtube.com/channel/UC_Ps-acnXPhVy8xTM6dUz2A

Description: Mission is to manage the transition of base properties from military to civilian uses, redevelop base properties, and create new high-quality jobs for Maine. **Founded:** 2006.

40324 ▪ O'Maine Studios
54 Danforth St.
  Portland, ME 04101
Ph: (617)510-0546
Co. E-mail: info@omainestudios.com
URL: http://omainestudios.com
Contact: Rory Strunk, Chief Executive Officer
E-mail: rory@omainestudios.com
Facebook: www.facebook.com/omainestudios
Instagram: www.instagram.com/omainestudios

Description: Culinary incubator working with food and beverage businesses to share their food with the world.

40325 ▪ TechPlace
74 Orion St.
  Brunswick, ME 04011
Ph: (207)607-4195
URL: http://techplacemaine.us
Facebook: www.facebook.com/techplacemaine
X (Twitter): x.com/techplaceme

Description: Supports the small business development needs of early-stage companies in a collaborative environment. Gives entrepreneurs a place to network with other innovators, research and develop ideas, build prototypes, test products, assemble, grow, learn, and become successful manufacturing and technology companies.

40326 ▪ Union River Center for Innovation
415 Water St.
  Ellsworth, ME 04605
Free: 800-930-5313
Co. E-mail: info@unionriverinnovation.com
URL: http://unionriverinnovation.com
Facebook: www.facebook.com/unionrivercenterforinnovation
Linkedin: www.linkedin.com/company/unionrivercenterforinnovation
X (Twitter): x.com/UnionRiverCI
Instagram: www.instagram.com/unionrivercenterforinnovation

Description: A startup incubator and coworking space working with Maine's most prestigious institutions and business development organizations to provide entrepreneurs with the services and amenities they need to achieve rapid growth and sustained success. Offers business coaching, super high speed internet access, workshops and seminars, modern equipment, and private offices.

40327 ▪ UpStart Center for Entrepreneurship
20 Godfrey Dr.
  Orono, ME 04473
Ph: (207)866-2406
Co. E-mail: info@upstartcentermaine.com
URL: http://www.upstartcentermaine.com
Contact: Rod McKay, Executive Director
E-mail: rodneygmckay@gmail.com
Facebook: www.facebook.com/UpStartCenterMaine
X (Twitter): x.com/UpStartCenter

Description: A small business incubator providing information technology companies expertise, tools, resources, and networks. **Founded:** 2002.

EDUCATIONAL PROGRAMS

40328 ▪ University of Maine at Machias (UMM)
116 O'Brien Ave.
  Machias, ME 04654
Ph: (207)255-1200
Co. E-mail: ummadmissions@maine.edu
URL: http://machias.edu
Contact: Joan Ferrini-Mundy, President
Facebook: www.facebook.com/UMaineMachias
X (Twitter): x.com/UMaineMachias
Instagram: www.instagram.com/umainemachias
YouTube: www.youtube.com/user/UMaineMachiasPR

Description: Offers programs in small business management.

CONSULTANTS

40329 ▪ Innovation Policyworks
135 Maine St., Ste. A-183
  Brunswick, ME 04011
Ph: (207)522-9028
URL: http://www.innovationpolicyworks.com
Contact: Catherine Renault, Owner Principal
E-mail: crenault@innovationpolicyworks.com

Description: Enables economic development officials at state, regional and local levels make better, data-driven decisions by providing expert research, analysis and recommendations.

Maryland

ASSOCIATIONS AND OTHER ORGANIZATIONS

40330 ■ Association of Fundraising Professionals Maryland Chapter
PO Box 25
Fort Howard, MD 21052
Ph: (443)640-1047
Co. E-mail: info@afpmaryland.org
URL: http://afpmd.memberclicks.net
Contact: Kimberly Weiner, President
Facebook: www.facebook.com/AFPMarylandChapter
Linkedin: www.linkedin.com/company/afpmarylandchapter
Geographic Preference: State.

40331 ■ Business Network International Maryland - East - BNI 4 Shore
Annapolis, MD 21403
URL: http://bni4shore.com/en-US/index
Contact: Querin Hamilton, President
Description: Provides both men and women a structured environment for the development and exchange of quality business referrals. Offers members the opportunity to share ideas and contacts. **Geographic Preference:** State.

40332 ■ Entrepreneurs' Organization - Baltimore Chapter (EO Baltimore)
1212 E 25th St., Lower Level
Baltimore, MD 21218
Co. E-mail: membership@eobaltimore.org
URL: http://www.eobaltimore.org
Contact: Donna Weitz, Director
E-mail: director@eobaltimore.org
Facebook: www.facebook.com/EOBaltimore
X (Twitter): x.com/eo_baltimore
Instagram: www.instagram.com/eo_baltimore
YouTube: www.youtube.com/channel/UC4kmL6Qv0LWknULUaSM4olw
Description: Provides local resources to members which includes networking events, mentorship, live forums, and leadership development.

40333 ■ International Association of Women Annapolis Chapter
Annapolis, MD
URL: http://www.iawomen.com/chapters/annapolis-chapter
Description: Serves as network of accomplished women united to achieve professional goals. Provides a forum for sharing ideas and experiences of professional women regarding career success. Promotes an active business and networking community from all industries. **Geographic Preference:** Local.

40334 ■ National Federation of Independent Business Maryland
60 W St., Ste. 101
Annapolis, MD 21404
Free: 866-247-9103
URL: http://www.nfib.com
Contact: Mike O'Halloran, Director
E-mail: mikea.ohalloran@nfib.org
X (Twitter): x.com/nfib_md
Description: Represents small and independent businesses. Aims to promote and protect the rights of members to own, operate and grow their businesses. **Geographic Preference:** State.

SMALL BUSINESS DEVELOPMENT CENTERS

40335 ■ Baltimore City Small Business Resource Center (SBRC)
3000 Druid Park Dr., Ste. 3000B
Baltimore, MD 21215
Ph: (443)451-7160
Fax: (410)396-5136
Co. E-mail: mombd@baltimorecity.gov
URL: http://mwbd.baltimorecity.gov
Contact: Paul E. E. Taylor, Contact
E-mail: p.taylor@baltimorecity.gov
Facebook: www.facebook.com/SBRCbaltimore
Description: Represents and promotes the small business sector. Provides management assistance to current and prospective small business owners. Helps to improve management skills and expand the products and services of members. **Geographic Preference:** Local.

40336 ■ Baltimore County Small Business Development Center
University of Maryland Baltimore
620 W Lexington St., 4th Fl.
Baltimore, MD 21201
URL: http://www.marylandsbdc.org/locations/baltimore-region/baltimore-resource-partners
Contact: Jennifer Funn, Regional Director
E-mail: jsmithfu@umd.edu
Description: Represents and promotes the small business sector. Provides management assistance to current and prospective small business owners. Helps to improve management skills and expand the products and services of members. **Founded:** 1988. **Geographic Preference:** Local.

40337 ■ Howard County Small Business Development Center
6751 Columbia Gateway Dr., Ste. 500
Columbia, MD 21045
URL: http://www.marylandsbdc.org/locations/corridor-region
Contact: Brandon Mason, Consultant
E-mail: bwmason@umd.edu
Description: Represents and promotes the small business sector. Provides management assistance to current and prospective small business owners. Helps to improve management skills and expand the products and services of members. **Geographic Preference:** Local.

40338 ■ Maryland Small Business Development Center - Capital Region
7761 Diamondback Dr.
College Park, MD 20742
Co. E-mail: pbardack@umd.edu
URL: http://www.mdsbdc.umd.edu
Contact: Paul Bardack, Executive Director
E-mail: pbardack@umd.edu
Description: Provides assistance to small business owners and free one-on-one counseling services for a variety of business needs. **Geographic Preference:** State.

40339 ■ Maryland Small Business Development Center - Eastern Region
Perdue School of Business
Salisbury University
215 E Campus Complex
corner of Power & Wayne St. s
Salisbury, MD 21801-6860
Ph: (410)548-4419
Fax: (410)548-5389
URL: http://www.marylandsbdc.org/locations/eastern-region
Contact: Vanette Seals, Administrator
Description: Represents and promotes the small business sector. Provides management assistance to current and prospective small business owners. Helps to improve management skills and expand the products and services of members. **Geographic Preference:** Local.

40340 ■ Maryland Small Business Development Center Northern Region
401 Thomas Run Rd.
Bel Air, MD 21015
URL: http://www.marylandsbdc.org/locations/northern-region
Contact: Amy Yingling, Regional Director
E-mail: ayingling5@carrollcc.edu
Description: Represents and promotes the small business sector. Provides management assistance to current and prospective small business owners. Helps to improve management skills and expand the products and services of members. **Founded:** 1988. **Geographic Preference:** State; Local.

40341 ■ Maryland Small Business Development Center - Southern Region
8730 Mitchell Rd.
La Plata, MD 20646
Ph: (301)934-7583
URL: http://www.sbdchelp.com
Contact: Wynne Briscoe, Regional Director
E-mail: wsbriscoe@csmd.edu
URL(s): www.marylandsbdc.org/locations/southern-region
Facebook: www.facebook.com/SOMDSBDC
Linkedin: www.linkedin.com/company/somdsbdc
X (Twitter): x.com/somdSBDC
Description: Provides management assistance to current and prospective small business owners in Maryland. **Founded:** 1988. **Geographic Preference:** Local.

40342 ■ Northern Region Small Business and Technology Development Center at Harford Community College
7761 Diamondback Dr.
College Park, MD 20742

URL: http://www.marylandsbdc.org/locations/northern-region
Contact: Amy Yingling, Regional Director
E-mail: ayingling5@carrollcc.edu
Description: Represents and promotes the small business sector. Provides management assistance to current and prospective small business owners. Helps to improve management skills and expand the products and services of members. **Geographic Preference:** Local.

40343 ■ Venture Access Inc.
108 S Bond St.
Bel Air, MD 21014
Co. E-mail: info@ventureaccess.org
URL: http://ventureaccess.org
Facebook: www.facebook.com/VentureAccess
Linkedin: www.linkedin.com/company/venture-access-inc
Instagram: www.instagram.com/ventureaccessinc
YouTube: www.youtube.com/channel/UChNQnjkuNbr5bqouXfiJmtg
Description: Regional economic development partner for entrepreneurs in Northeastern Maryland.

SMALL BUSINESS ASSISTANCE PROGRAMS

40344 ■ The American Small Business Coalition, LLC (ASBC)
PO Box 2786
Columbia, MD 21045
Ph: (410)381-7378
Co. E-mail: support@govcon.club
URL: http://www.theasbc.org
Contact: Margaret Timberlake, President
Facebook: www.facebook.com/TheASBC
Linkedin: www.linkedin.com/company/theasbc2022
Instagram: www.instagram.com/the_asbc
Description: Supports stakeholders of U.S. government contracting. Empowers small businesses to find and win government contracts. **Founded:** 2004. **Publications:** *American Small Business Coalition--Membership Directory.* **Geographic Preference:** National.

40345 ■ CDER Small Business and Industry Assistance (SBIA)
10001 New Hampshire Ave.
Hillandale Bldg., 4th Fl.
Silver Spring, MD 20993
Ph: (301)796-6707
Free: 866-405-5367
Co. E-mail: cdersbia@fda.hhs.gov
URL: http://www.fda.gov/drugs/development-approval-process-drugs/cder-small-business-industry-assistance-sbia?utm_medium=email&utm_source=govdelivery
Linkedin: www.linkedin.com/showcase/cder-small-business-and-industry-assistance
Description: Helps small pharmaceutical companies navigate the FDA and provides assistance in understanding the regulation of human drug producs. Offers seminars, webinars, conferences, and a newsletter.

40346 ■ Maryland Department of Business and Economic Development - Business Development Div.
401 E Pratt St.
Baltimore, MD 21202
URL: http://commerce.maryland.gov/careers
Description: attracts new businesses to the state, expands global commerce, cultivates important industry clusters and raises awareness of Maryland as a leader in technology and innovation.

40347 ■ Maryland Economic Development Corporation (MEDCO)
7 Saint Paul St., Ste. 940
Baltimore, MD 21202
Ph: (410)625-0051
URL: http://medco-corp.com
Contact: Thomas Sadowski, Executive Director
E-mail: t_sadowski@medco-corp.com

Description: Develops vacant or under-utilized industrial sites and other facilities and economic resources that would serve the public interest. Assists in the expansion, modernization, and retention of existing Maryland businesses. Provides marketing, financing, and networking information. **Founded:** 1984. **Geographic Preference:** State.

40348 ■ Small Business Network
11436 Cronhill Dr., Ste. 4B
Owings Mills, MD 21117
Ph: (410)363-6980
Description: Small business networking services. **Publications:** *Small Business Network--National Directory* (Annual).

40349 ■ U.S. Department of Health and Human Services - National Institutes of Health - National Institute of Mental Health - Division of AIDS Research - Small Business Innovation Research Program (NIH)
c/o Dr. Vasudev Rao
Division of AIDS Research, NIMH
5601 Fishers Ln.
Rockville, MD 20852
Ph: (240)669-5609
Co. E-mail: vasudev.rao@nih.gov
URL: http://www.nimh.nih.gov/about/organization/dar/small-business-innovation-research-sbir-program-and-the-small-business-technology-transfer-sttr-program
Contact: Vasudev Rao, Contact
E-mail: vasudev.rao@nih.gov
Description: Supports research by small businesses to develop innovative technologies with high potential to succeed commercially or to provide significant societal benefit. **Scope:** Supports research on small businesses' innovative technologies that have the potential to achieve commercial success or provide societal benefits.

40350 ■ U.S. Department of Health and Human Services - National Institutes of Health - National Institute of Mental Health - Division of AIDS Research - Small Business Technology Transfer Program
Dr. Vasudev Rao
5601 Fishers Ln.
Rockville, MD 20852
Ph: (240)669-5609
Co. E-mail: vasudev.rao@nih.gov
URL: http://www.nimh.nih.gov/about/organization/dar/small-business-innovation-research-sbir-program-and-the-small-business-technology-transfer-sttr-program
Contact: Dr. Vasudev Rao, Contact
E-mail: vasudev.rao@nih.gov
Description: Supports research by small businesses to develop innovative technologies with high potential to succeed commercially or to provide significant societal benefit. **Scope:** Supports research aimed at facilitating the validation and commercialization of new methods of assessing psychopathology.

SCORE OFFICES

40351 ■ Greater Baltimore SCORE
Columbia, MD
Ph: (410)962-6195
Fax: (410)962-1805
Co. E-mail: baltimorescore@verizon.net
URL: http://www.score.org/greaterbaltimore
Facebook: www.facebook.com/SCOREGreaterBaltimore
Linkedin: www.linkedin.com/company/score-mentors-greater-baltimore
Description: Serves as volunteer program in which working and retired business management professionals provide free business counseling to men and women who are considering starting a small business, encountering problems with their business, or expanding their business. Offers free one-on-one counseling, online counseling and low cost workshops on a variety of business topics. **Founded:** 1965. **Geographic Preference:** Local.

40352 ■ Mid-Shore SCORE
101 Marlboro Ave., Talbot County Chamber of Commerce
Easton, MD 21601
Free: 877-572-0735
URL: http://www.score.org/content/contact-mid-shore-score
Description: Seeks to educate entrepreneurs and help small businesses start, grow and succeed nationwide. Organizes volunteers who are working or retired business owners, executives and corporate leaders who wish to share their wisdom and lessons learned in business. **Geographic Preference:** Local.

40353 ■ SCORE - Belair
401 Thomas Run Rd.
Bel Air, MD 21015
Ph: (410)836-4237
URL: http://www.score.org/find-location?state=MD
Description: Provides professional guidance and information to maximize the success of existing and emerging small businesses. Offers business counseling and workshops.

40354 ■ SCORE - Gaithersburg
9841 Washingtonian Blvd., Ste. 200
Gaithersburg, MD 20878
Ph: (301)291-5776
URL: http://washingtondc.score.org/maryland-mentor-locations
Contact: David Westreich, Contact
Description: Provides professional guidance and information to maximize the success of existing and emerging small businesses. Offers business counseling and workshops.

40355 ■ SCORE - Greater Baltimore
100 S Charles St. Ste. 1201
Baltimore, MD 21201
Ph: (410)962-6195
Free: 800-634-0245
Co. E-mail: baltimorescore@verizon.net
URL: http://www.score.org/greaterbaltimore
Facebook: www.facebook.com/SCOREGreaterBaltimore
Linkedin: www.linkedin.com/company/score-mentors-greater-baltimore
Description: Provides professional guidance and information to maximize the success of existing and emerging small businesses. Offers business counseling and workshops. **Founded:** 1964.

40356 ■ SCORE - Largo
1801 McCormick Dr., 3rd Fl.
Largo, MD 20774
Ph: (301)583-4650
URL: http://washingtondc.score.org
Contact: Alverta Lopez, Contact
Description: Provides professional guidance and information to maximize the success of existing and emerging small businesses. Offers business counseling and workshops.

40357 ■ SCORE - Mid-Maryland
4539 Metropolitan Ct.
Frederick, MD 21704
Ph: (240)215-4757
Co. E-mail: score@scorefrederick.org
URL: http://www.score.org/mid-maryland
Facebook: www.facebook.com/scoremidmaryland
Linkedin: www.linkedin.com/company/score-midmaryland
Description: Seeks to educate entrepreneurs and help small businesses start, grow and succeed nationwide. Organizes volunteers who are working or retired business owners, executives and corporate leaders who wish to share their wisdom and lessons learned in business. **Geographic Preference:** Local.

40358 ■ SCORE - Mid-Shore
101 Marlboro Ave.
Talbot County Chamber of Commerce
Easton, MD 21601
Free: 877-572-0735
URL: http://www.score.org/content/contact-mid-shore-score

STATE LISTINGS

Description: Provides professional guidance and information to maximize the success of existing and emerging small businesses. Offers business counseling and workshops.

40359 ■ SCORE - Silver Spring Library
900 Wayne Ave.
Silver Spring, MD 20910
Ph: (240)773-9420
URL: http://washingtondc.score.org/score-washington-dc-mentoring-locations
Description: Provides professional guidance and information to maximize the success of existing and emerging small businesses. Offers business counseling and workshops.

40360 ■ SCORE - Southern Maryland
1521 Ritchie Hwy., Ste. 206
Arnold, MD 21012
Ph: (410)266-9553
Free: 800-634-0245
Co. E-mail: info.gcp@scorevolunteer.org
URL: http://www.score.org/somd
Contact: Steve Platte, Contact
Facebook: www.facebook.com/scoresouthernmaryland
Linkedin: www.linkedin.com/company/score-mentors-southern-maryland
Description: Provides no cost business counseling and workshops on starting and growing small businesses to entrepreneurs and individuals interested to start a small business in Anne Arundel, Calvert, Charles, and St. Mary's Counties in Maryland. **Founded:** 1987. **Geographic Preference:** Local.

40361 ■ SCORE - Upper Shore [Upper Shore SCORE]
122 N Cross St.
Chestertown, MD 21620
Ph: (410)810-2969
Fax: (410)778-1406
Co. E-mail: help@score.org
URL: http://townofchestertown.com/businesses-2/score-upper-shore
Contact: Bridget Weston, Chief Executive Officer
URL(s): marylandentrepreneurhub.com/resource-profile/upper-shore-score-mentoring
Description: Provides professional guidance and information to maximize the success of existing and emerging small businesses. Offers business counseling and workshops. **Founded:** 1964. **Geographic Preference:** Local.

40362 ■ SCORE - Washington DC
11701 Georgia Ave.
Silver Spring, MD 20906
URL: http://www.score.org/washingtondc
Description: Provides professional guidance and information to maximize the success of existing and emerging small businesses. Offers business counseling and workshops.

BETTER BUSINESS BUREAUS

40363 ■ Better Business Bureau of Greater Maryland
502 S Sharp St.
Baltimore, MD 21201-2445
Ph: (410)347-3990
Fax: (410)347-3936
Co. E-mail: info@greatermd.bbb.org
URL: http://www.bbb.org/local-bbb/bbb-of-greater-maryland
Contact: Angie Barnett, President
E-mail: abarnett@greatermd.bbb.org
Facebook: www.facebook.com/bbbgreatermd
Linkedin: www.linkedin.com/company/bbbgreatermd
X (Twitter): x.com/bbbgreatermd
Instagram: www.instagram.com/bbbgreatermd
YouTube: www.youtube.com/user/BBBGreaterMD
Description: Promotes and fosters ethical relationships between businesses and the public through voluntary self-regulation, consumer and business education and service excellence. **Founded:** 1917. **Geographic Preference:** Local.

CHAMBERS OF COMMERCE

40364 ■ Aberdeen Chamber of Commerce (ACC)
18 Howard St.
Aberdeen, MD 21001
Ph: (410)272-2580
Co. E-mail: director@aberdeencc.org
URL: http://www.aberdeencc.org
Contact: Sheryl Davis Kohl, President
Description: Seeks to promote the city of Aberdeen and the businesses within. Activities include fund raisers, raffles, carnivals, Business Card Exchanges, monthly meetings and mailings promoting Aberdeen. **Founded:** 1950. **Publications:** *Chamber News* (Bimonthly). **Geographic Preference:** Local.

40365 ■ Allegany County Chamber of Commerce (ACCC)
Bell Tower Bldg.
24 Frederick St.
Cumberland, MD 21502
Ph: (301)722-2820
Co. E-mail: info@alleganycountychamber.com
URL: http://alleganycountychamber.com
Contact: Jeffery D. O'Neal, Chairman
Facebook: www.facebook.com/alleganycountychamber
Linkedin: www.linkedin.com/company/allegany-county-chamber-of-commerce
Instagram: www.instagram.com/alleganycountychamber
Description: Promotes business and community development in Allegany County, MD. Sponsors workshops. **Founded:** 1914. **Publications:** *Chamber News* (Monthly); *Allegany County Map* (Annual); *Know Your Chamber*; *Membership Directory and Community Profile*. **Geographic Preference:** Local.

40366 ■ Annapolis and Anne Arundel County Chamber of Commerce, Inc.
1910 Towne Ctr., Blvd., Ste. 250
Annapolis, MD 21401
Ph: (410)266-3960
Fax: (410)266-8270
Co. E-mail: info@aaaccc.org
URL: http://annearundelchamber.org
Contact: Mark Kleinschmidt, President
E-mail: mark@aaaccc.org
Facebook: www.facebook.com/AAACChamber
Linkedin: www.linkedin.com/company/anne-arundel-county-chamber-of-commerce
X (Twitter): x.com/aaacochamber
Instagram: www.instagram.com/annearundelchamber
Description: Promotes business and community development in Anne Arundel County and Annapolis, MD. Sponsors annual relocation tour, annual trade show, and monthly business mixers and networking breakfasts. Hosts cable television show "It's Good Business". **Founded:** 1918. **Publications:** *Chamber News*. **Awards:** AAACCC Business Leader of the Year (Annual). **Geographic Preference:** Local.

40367 ■ Baltimore City Chamber of Commerce
400 E Pratt St., 8th Fl.
Baltimore, MD 21202
Ph: (443)860-2020
Co. E-mail: info@baltimorecitychamber.org
URL: http://baltimorecitychamber.org
Contact: Teresa Evans, Chairman
Facebook: www.facebook.com/BaltimoreCityChamberOfCommerce
Linkedin: www.linkedin.com/company/baltimorecitychamber
Instagram: www.instagram.com/baltimorecitychamber
Description: Promotes business prosperity by nurturing partnerships and identifying resources that maximizes business and economic development in Baltimore City, MD. **Founded:** 1992. **Geographic Preference:** Local.

40368 ■ Baltimore County Chamber of Commerce (BCCC)
102 W Pennsylvania Ave., Ste. 305
Towson, MD 21204
Ph: (410)825-6200
Fax: (410)821-9901
URL: http://www.baltcountychamber.com
Contact: Brent Howard, President
E-mail: bhoward@baltcountychamber.com
Facebook: www.facebook.com/BaltCountyChamber
Linkedin: www.linkedin.com/company/baltimore-county-chamber-of-commerce
X (Twitter): x.com/baltcochamber
Description: Promotes business and community development in Baltimore County, MD. **Founded:** 1966. **Publications:** *Membership Directory and Resource Guide*; *Sound Business* (Quarterly); *Baltimore Shipping Services* (Annual). **Awards:** Baltimore County Chamber of Commerce Excellence in Education (Annual). **Geographic Preference:** Local.

40369 ■ Berlin Chamber of Commerce (BCC)
14 S Main St.
Berlin, MD 21811
Ph: (410)641-4775
Co. E-mail: berlinmdchamber@gmail.com
URL: http://berlinchamber.org
Contact: Mike Poole, President
Facebook: www.facebook.com/BerlinChamber
Instagram: www.instagram.com/berlinchamber
Description: Promotes business and community development in Berlin, Maryland. Conducts various programs to assist small businesses to compete successfully. **Founded:** 1984. **Publications:** *Chamber Channel*; *CommUNITY* (Quarterly); *Visitor's Guide*. **Educational Activities:** Berlin Chamber of Commerce Meeting (Annual). **Geographic Preference:** Local.

40370 ■ Calvert County Chamber of Commerce (CCCC)
120 Dares Beach Rd.
Prince Frederick, MD 20678-0009
Ph: (410)535-2577
Fax: (443)295-7213
Co. E-mail: calvertchamber@calvertchamber.org
URL: http://www.calvertchamber.org
Contact: Kathryn Maney, President
E-mail: kathy@calvertchamber.org
Facebook: www.facebook.com/CalvertCountyChamber
Linkedin: www.linkedin.com/company/calvert-county-chamber-of-commerce
Instagram: www.instagram.com/calvertchamber
Description: Promotes business and community development in Calvert County, MD. **Founded:** 1982. **Publications:** *The Navigator* (Monthly). **Geographic Preference:** Local.

40371 ■ Carroll County Chamber of Commerce (CCCC)
9 E Main St., Ste. 105
Westminster, MD 21157
Ph: (410)848-9050
Fax: (410)876-1023
Co. E-mail: info@carrollcountychamber.org
URL: http://carrollcountychamber.org
Contact: Mike McMullin, President
E-mail: mmcmullin@carrollcountychamber.org
Facebook: www.facebook.com/CarrollCountyChamber
Linkedin: www.linkedin.com/company/carroll-county-chamber-of-commerce-maryland
YouTube: www.youtube.com/channel/UC8PMFsw6gnHSvn8w4xZ62HQ/featured
Description: Promotes a sound economic environment and business community development in Carroll County, MD. **Founded:** 1924. **Publications:** *Carroll County Chamber of Commerce Membership Directory and Buyer's Guide* (Annual); *Chamber Works* (Monthly). **Educational Activities:** Carroll County Chamber of Commerce Meeting. **Geographic Preference:** Local.

40372 ■ *Carroll County Chamber of Commerce Membership Directory and Buyer's Guide*
9 E Main St., Ste. 105
Westminster, MD 21157
Ph: (410)848-9050
Fax: (410)876-1023

Co. E-mail: info@carrollcountychamber.org
URL: http://carrollcountychamber.org
Contact: Mike McMullin, President
E-mail: mmcmullin@carrollcountychamber.org
URL(s): members.carrollcountychamber.org/member directory
Released: Annual **Description:** Covers businesses in Carroll County, MD. **Availability:** Print; Online.

40373 ■ Cecil County Chamber of Commerce
216 E Pulaski Hwy., Ste. 120
 Elkton, MD 21921
Ph: (410)392-3833
Co. E-mail: info@cecilchamber.com
URL: http://www.cecilchamber.com
Contact: Debbie Brown, Executive Director
E-mail: dbrown@cecilchamber.com
Facebook: www.facebook.com/cecilcoun tychamberofcommerce
Description: Promotes business and community development in Cecil County. **Founded:** 1920. **Publications:** *Chamber Matters* (Bimonthly); *Outlook*. **Geographic Preference:** Local.

40374 ■ *The Chamber*
1 S Potomac St.
 Hagerstown, MD 21740
Ph: (301)739-2015
Co. E-mail: info@hagerstown.org
URL: http://www.hagerstown.org
Contact: Paul Frey, President
E-mail: paul@hagerstown.org
URL(s): www.hagerstown.org/contact-us
Released: Monthly **Availability:** Print.

40375 ■ *Chamber of Commerce Business Directory*
122 N Cross St.
 Chestertown, MD 21620
Ph: (410)810-2968
Co. E-mail: admin@kentchamber.org
URL: http://www.kentchamber.org
Contact: Barbara Foster, President
URL(s): www.kentchamber.org/member-benefits
Released: Annual **Availability:** Online.

40376 ■ Chamber of Commerce of Frederick County (CCFC)
118 N Market St., Ste. 200
 Frederick, MD 21701
Ph: (301)662-4164
Co. E-mail: info@frederickchamber.org
URL: http://www.frederickchamber.org
Contact: Rick Weldon, President
E-mail: rweldon@frederickchamber.org
Facebook: www.facebook.com/fredcochamber
X (Twitter): x.com/fredcochamber
Instagram: www.instagram.com/fredcochamber
Description: Promotes business and community development in Frederick County, MD. **Founded:** 1912. **Publications:** *Member Directory*. **Geographic Preference:** Local.

40377 ■ *Chamber News*
Bell Tower Bldg.
 24 Frederick St.
 Cumberland, MD 21502
Ph: (301)722-2820
Co. E-mail: info@alleganycountychamber.com
URL: http://alleganycountychamber.com
Contact: Jeffery D. O'Neal, Chairman
URL(s): alleganycountychamber.com/news/monthly -newsletter
Released: Monthly **Description:** Consists of news and updates on advocacy issues, events and members. **Availability:** PDF.

40378 ■ *Chamber Works*
Released: Quarterly **Description:** Includes information about the chamber and upcoming events and programs. **Availability:** Print.

40379 ■ Charles County Chamber of Commerce (CCCOC)
303 Charles St., Ste. 100
 La Plata, MD 20646
Ph: (301)932-6500

Co. E-mail: info@charlescountychamber.org
URL: http://www.charlescountychamber.org
Contact: Bonnie Grady, President
Facebook: www.facebook.com/CCMDChamber
Linkedin: www.linkedin.com/in/charles-county-cham ber-of-commerce-81204851
X (Twitter): x.com/CCCOC
Description: Promotes business and community development in Charles County, MD. **Founded:** 1956. **Publications:** *Business* (Bimonthly). **Geographic Preference:** Local.

40380 ■ Chesapeake Gateway Chamber of Commerce
405 Williams Ct., Ste. 108
 Baltimore, MD 21220
Ph: (443)317-8763
Co. E-mail: info@chesapeakechamber.org
URL: http://www.chesapeakechamber.org
Contact: Sophia Montgomery, President
E-mail: sophia.montgomery@countryinn.com
Facebook: www.facebook.com/ChesapeakeGa tewayChamber
Description: Seeks to promote an economic environment in the Baltimore, MD area and to attract new business while allowing established business to prosper. Works for the enhancement of the quality of life in the region by reinvesting resources in all phases of community life. **Founded:** 1956. **Publications:** *Shore Line* (Quarterly). **Geographic Preference:** Local.

40381 ■ Crisfield Area Chamber of Commerce
906 W Main St.
 Crisfield, MD 21817
Ph: (410)968-2500
Co. E-mail: office@crisfieldchamberofcommerce.com
URL: http://www.crisfieldchamber.org
Contact: William Buttrill, Contact
Facebook: www.facebook.com/CrisfieldChamber
Description: Promotes business and community development in the Crisfield, MD area. **Founded:** 1975. **Geographic Preference:** Local.

40382 ■ Dorchester Chamber of Commerce
306 High St.
 Cambridge, MD 21613
Ph: (410)228-3575
Fax: (410)228-6848
Co. E-mail: info@dorchesterchamber.org
URL: http://www.dorchesterchamber.org
Contact: Bill Christopher, President
E-mail: bill@dorchesterchamber.org
Facebook: www.facebook.com/Dorches terChamberOfCommerce
Linkedin: www.linkedin.com/company/dorchester -chamber-of-commerce
Description: Advocacy organization. Seeks to provide quality leadership and facilitate economic growth through responsive member services, political activity and regional partnerships. **Founded:** 1921. **Publications:** *Chamber News*. **Geographic Preference:** Local.

40383 ■ Elkton Chamber and Alliance
101 E Main St.
 Elkton, MD 21921
Ph: (410)398-5076
URL: http://www.elktonalliance.org
Contact: Brad Carrillo, President
Description: Promotes business and community development in the Elkton, MD area. **Founded:** 1998. **Publications:** *Minutes and Memorandum*. **Geographic Preference:** Local.

40384 ■ Gaithersburg-Germantown Chamber of Commerce (GGCC)
910 Clopper Rd., Ste. 205N
 Gaithersburg, MD 20878
Ph: (301)840-1400
Fax: (240)261-6395
Co. E-mail: info@ggchamber.org
URL: http://www.ggchamber.org
Contact: Dr. John Compton, Vice Chairman of the Board

Linkedin: www.linkedin.com/company/gaithersburg -germantown-chamber
X (Twitter): x.com/ggccnews
YouTube: www.youtube.com/channel/UCtU1AC 2KMIgLSW8C5IXsWoQ
Description: Promotes business and community development in Gaithersburg, Maryland. **Publications:** *The e-Resource* (Quarterly). **Geographic Preference:** Local.

40385 ■ Garrett County Chamber of Commerce
15 Visitors Center Dr.
 McHenry, MD 21541
Ph: (301)387-4386
Free: 888-387-5237
Fax: (301)387-2080
Co. E-mail: info@garrettchamber.com
URL: http://www.visitdeepcreek.com
Contact: Patty Manown Mash, Secretary
E-mail: pmanownmash@gmail.com
Facebook: www.facebook.com/deepcreeklakemd
X (Twitter): x.com/visitdeepcreek
Instagram: www.instagram.com/visitdeepcreek
YouTube: www.youtube.com/user/GarrettChamber#p
Pinterest: www.pinterest.com/deepcreekgroups/garre tt-co-chamber-events
Description: Strives to provide supports for small businesses and the tourism industry. **Geographic Preference:** Local.

40386 ■ Greater Baltimore Chamber of Commerce (GBCC)
7 Church Ln., Ste. 6
 Pikesville, MD 21208
Ph: (410)484-2337
Fax: (410)484-4151
Co. E-mail: info@greaterbaltimorechamber.org
URL: http://greaterbaltimorechamber.org
Contact: Beth Rheingold, President
Facebook: www.facebook.com/greaterbal timorechamber
Linkedin: www.linkedin.com/company/greaterbal timorechamber
X (Twitter): x.com/greaterbaltcc
Instagram: www.instagram.com/greaterbal timorechamber
Description: Strives to maintain the quality of life in both residential and commercial areas, draw new businesses, maintain schools, social and religious institutions and enhance the village Pikesville. **Founded:** 1977. **Geographic Preference:** Local.

40387 ■ Greater Bethesda-Chevy Chase Chamber of Commerce
7910 Woodmont Ave., Ste. 1204
 Bethesda, MD 20814
Ph: (301)652-4900
Fax: (301)657-1973
URL: http://www.greaterbethesdachamber.org
Contact: Allie Williams, President
Facebook: www.facebook.com/TGBChamber
Linkedin: www.linkedin.com/company/the-greater-be thesda-chamber-of-commerce
X (Twitter): x.com/tgbchamber
Instagram: www.instagram.com/tgbchamber
YouTube: www.youtube.com/user/bccchamber
Description: Promotes business and community development in the Bethesda - Chevy Chase communities within Maryland. **Founded:** 1926. **Publications:** *ChamberNews* (Monthly); *Membership Directory and Business Referral* (Annual). **Geographic Preference:** Local.

40388 ■ Greater Bowie Chamber of Commerce (GBCC)
2614 Kenhill Dr., No. 117
 Bowie, MD 20715
Ph: (301)262-0920
Co. E-mail: info.bowiechamber@gmail.com
URL: http://greaterbowiechamberofcommerce.org
Contact: Michael Oleru, President
Facebook: www.facebook.com/people/Greater-Bowie -Chamber-of-Commerce/100086138863444
Linkedin: www.linkedin.com/company/bowie-chamber
X (Twitter): x.com/chamberBowie

Description: Promotes business and community development in Bowie, MD. **Founded:** 1983. **Publications:** *Greater Bowie Chamber of Commerce--Business Directory* (Weekly). **Geographic Preference:** Local.

40389 ■ Greater Crofton Chamber of Commerce (GCCC)
2126 Espey Ct., Ste. A
Crofton, MD 21114
Ph: (410)721-9131
Co. E-mail: info@croftonchamber.com
URL: http://croftonchamber.com
Contact: Gary Heldt, President
Facebook: www.facebook.com/croftoncommerce
Linkedin: www.linkedin.com/company/croftonchamber
X (Twitter): x.com/croftonchamber
Instagram: www.instagram.com/croftonchamber
Description: Promotes business and community development in Crofton, MD area. **Founded:** 1989. **Publications:** *Business and Community Guide* (Annual). **Geographic Preference:** Local.

40390 ■ Greater Severna Park and Arnold Chamber of Commerce (GSPACC)
1 Holly Ave.
Severna Park, MD 21146
Ph: (410)647-3900
Co. E-mail: info@gspacc.com
URL: http://www.gspacc.com
Contact: Liz League, Chief Executive Officer
E-mail: ceo@gspacc.com
Facebook: www.facebook.com/GSPAChamber
Linkedin: www.linkedin.com/company/greater-severna-park-arnold-chamber-of-commerce
Instagram: www.instagram.com/gspacctoday
Description: Promotes business and community development in the Severna Park, MD area. **Founded:** 1957. **Publications:** *Business Directory*; *Getting Down to Business* (Monthly). **Geographic Preference:** Local.

40391 ■ Greater Silver Spring Chamber of Commerce (GSSCC)
8601 Georgia Ave., Ste. 203
Silver Spring, MD 20910
Ph: (301)565-3777
Fax: (301)565-3377
Co. E-mail: info@gsscc.org
URL: http://www.gsscc.org
Contact: Stewart Zemil, Contact
Facebook: www.facebook.com/gsschamber
Linkedin: www.linkedin.com/company/gsscc
X (Twitter): x.com/GSSChamber
Description: Members benefit from advocacy efforts, access to information, business development and networking events, members-only marketing opportunities, and business services and discounts, including an energy purchasing co-operative. **Founded:** 1993. **Publications:** *Business Directory and Buyers' Guide* (Annual); *Business E-News* (Weekly); *Weekly Update* (Weekly). **Awards:** GSSCC Small Business of the Year (Annual). **Geographic Preference:** Local.

40392 ■ Hagerstown-Washington County Chamber of Commerce (HWCCC)
1 S Potomac St.
Hagerstown, MD 21740
Ph: (301)739-2015
Co. E-mail: info@hagerstown.org
URL: http://www.hagerstown.org
Contact: Paul Frey, President
E-mail: paul@hagerstown.org
Facebook: www.facebook.com/WashCountyChamber
Linkedin: www.linkedin.com/company/washingtoncountychamberofcommercemd
X (Twitter): x.com/WashCoChamber
Instagram: www.instagram.com/washcochamber
YouTube: www.youtube.com/channel/UCKu6KXEWSjmmWrd6Oa6NGJA
Description: Promotes business and community development in Washington County, MD. Conducts legislative activities and promotes leadership development. **Founded:** 1919. **Publications:** *The Chamber* (Monthly); *Chamber Spotlight*; *ChamberLink*; *Washington County Business Directory* (Annual). **Awards:** Chamber Small Business Person of the Year (Annual); Hagerstown-Washington County Chamber of Commerce Teacher of the Year (Annual); Washington County Business Awards (Annual). **Geographic Preference:** Local.

40393 ■ Harford County Chamber of Commerce (HCCC)
108 S Bond St.
Bel Air, MD 21014
Ph: (410)838-2020
Co. E-mail: info@harfordchamber.org
URL: http://harfordchamber.org
Contact: Angela Rose, President
E-mail: angela@harfordchamber.org
Facebook: www.facebook.com/harfordchamber
Linkedin: www.linkedin.com/company/1759222
X (Twitter): x.com/harford_chamber
Instagram: www.instagram.com/harford_chamber
YouTube: www.youtube.com/channel/UCpzdRVcUb6Cul7oj500nHZQ
Description: Promotes business and community development in Harford County, MD. Maintains 18 committees. Holds business expos and card exchanges. **Founded:** 1976. **Publications:** *Chamber Voice* (Monthly); *Spokesman* (Monthly). **Awards:** Harford County Chamber of Commerce Member of the Year (Annual); Harford Awards (Annual); Harford County Chamber of Commerce Hall of Fame (Annual). **Geographic Preference:** Local.

40394 ■ Havre de Grace Chamber of Commerce
450 Pennington Ave.
Havre de Grace, MD 21078
Ph: (410)939-3303
Fax: (410)939-3490
URL: http://www.hdgchamber.com
Contact: Mike Mullahey, President
Facebook: www.facebook.com/pages/Chamber-of-Commerce/162791820406258
X (Twitter): x.com/havredegrace
Instagram: www.instagram.com/havredegracemd
YouTube: www.youtube.com/user/havredegracemd
Description: Promotes business and community development in Havre De Grace, MD. **Founded:** 1928. **Geographic Preference:** Local.

40395 ■ Howard County Chamber of Commerce (HCCC)
6240 Old Dobbin Ln.
Columbia, MD 21045
Ph: (410)730-4111
Fax: (410)730-4584
Co. E-mail: info@howardchamber.com
URL: http://www.howardchamber.com
Contact: Leonardo McClarty, President
E-mail: lmcclarty@howardchamber.com
Facebook: www.facebook.com/HowardChamber
Linkedin: www.linkedin.com/company/howard-county-chamber-of-commerce
X (Twitter): x.com/HoCoChamber
Instagram: www.instagram.com/hocochamber
YouTube: www.youtube.com/user/HoCoChamber
Description: Promotes business and community development in Howard County, MD. **Founded:** 1969. **Awards:** Howard County Chamber of Commerce Business Person of the Year (Annual). **Geographic Preference:** Local.

40396 ■ Kent County Chamber of Commerce (KCCC)
122 N Cross St.
Chestertown, MD 21620
Ph: (410)810-2968
Co. E-mail: admin@kentchamber.org
URL: http://www.kentchamber.org
Contact: Barbara Foster, President
Facebook: www.facebook.com/kentcountychamberofcommerce
YouTube: www.youtube.com/channel/UCSfRzVYJo10ABep8Ja_wCH
Description: Promotes business and community development in Kent County, MD. **Founded:** 1928. **Publications:** *The Casey Three Chamber Report* (Monthly); *Chamber of Commerce Business Directory* (Annual). **Geographic Preference:** Local.

40397 ■ *Legislative Report*
60 W St., Ste. 100
Annapolis, MD 21401
Ph: (410)269-0642
Co. E-mail: info@mdchamber.org
URL: http://mdchamber.org
Contact: Mary D. Kane, President
E-mail: mkane@mdchamber.org
URL(s): www.mdchamber.org/2024/04/25/2024-session-recap
Availability: Print; PDF; Download.

40398 ■ Maryland Chamber of Commerce (MCC)
60 W St., Ste. 100
Annapolis, MD 21401
Ph: (410)269-0642
Co. E-mail: info@mdchamber.org
URL: http://mdchamber.org
Contact: Mary D. Kane, President
E-mail: mkane@mdchamber.org
Facebook: www.facebook.com/mdchamber
Linkedin: www.linkedin.com/company/maryland-chamber-of-commerce
X (Twitter): x.com/mdchamber
Description: Promotes business and community development in the state of Maryland. **Founded:** 1968. **Publications:** *Guide to Maryland Government* (Annual); *Maryland Guide to Government*; *Business Advocate* (Biweekly); *Business Directory* (Annual); *Legislative Report*; *Maryland Manual On-Line: Guide to Maryland Government* (Quarterly). **Geographic Preference:** State.

40399 ■ *Member Directory*
118 N Market St., Ste. 200
Frederick, MD 21701
Ph: (301)662-4164
Co. E-mail: info@frederickchamber.org
URL: http://www.frederickchamber.org
Contact: Rick Weldon, President
E-mail: rweldon@frederickchamber.org
URL(s): web.frederickchamber.org/search
Availability: Print.

40400 ■ *Membership Directory and Community Profile*
Bell Tower Bldg.
24 Frederick St.
Cumberland, MD 21502
Ph: (301)722-2820
Co. E-mail: info@alleganycountychamber.com
URL: http://alleganycountychamber.com
Contact: Jeffery D. O'Neal, Chairman
URL(s): alleganycountychamber.com/membership-levels
Description: Contains categorical listing of the best businesses in Allegany County. **Availability:** Print.

40401 ■ Montgomery County Chamber of Commerce (MCCC)
51 Monroe St., Ste. 1800
Rockville, MD 20850
Ph: (301)738-0015
Fax: (301)738-8792
Co. E-mail: marketing@mccmd.com
URL: http://www.mccmd.com
Contact: Gigi Godwin, President
Facebook: www.facebook.com/MCCCMD
Linkedin: www.linkedin.com/company/montgomery-county-chamber-of-commerce
X (Twitter): x.com/MCCCMD
YouTube: www.youtube.com/channel/UCLh4IvHQ8gaXqVD9kQvKowQ
Description: Promotes business and community development in Montgomery County, MD. **Founded:** 1959. **Geographic Preference:** Local.

40402 ■ North East Chamber of Commerce
PO Box 609
North East, MD 21901

Ph: (814)725-4262
Co. E-mail: info@northeastchamber.org
URL: http://northeastchamber.org
Contact: Tracy Reynolds, President
Facebook: www.facebook.com/TheNorthEastChamber
Description: Supports the business and community industry within the area of North East in the state of Maryland. **Founded:** 1850. **Geographic Preference:** Local.

40403 ■ Northern Anne Arundel County Chamber of Commerce (NAACCC)
7439 Baltimore Annapolis Blvd.
Glen Burnie, MD 21061
Ph: (410)766-8282
Co. E-mail: info@naaccc.com
URL: http://www.naaccc.com
Contact: Adrian Cox, President
Facebook: www.facebook.com/naaccc
X (Twitter): x.com/NAACCCMD
Description: Works with other community resources to promote local tourism, create jobs, and recruit new businesses in Northern Anne Arundel County, MD area. **Founded:** 1947. **Geographic Preference:** Local.

40404 ■ Northwest Chamber of Commerce (ROMG)
PO Box 336
Reisterstown, MD 21136
Ph: (410)702-7073
Fax: (410)702-7075
Co. E-mail: nw@northwestchambermd.com
URL: http://northwestchambermd.com
Contact: Emily Winters, Executive Director
E-mail: emily@northwestchambermd.com
Facebook: www.facebook.com/NorthwestChamber
Instagram: www.instagram.com/nwchambermd
YouTube: www.youtube.com/channel/UCe 1hfPUU7miasK_pshSQbNQ
Description: Works to serve as a primary business resource and to promote community development. **Founded:** 1949. **Publications:** *Chamber News*. **Geographic Preference:** Local.

40405 ■ Ocean City Chamber of Commerce
Eunice Q. Sorin Visitor & Conference Ctr
12320 Ocean Gateway
Ocean City, MD 21842
Ph: (410)213-0552
Co. E-mail: info@oceancity.org
URL: http://oceancity.org
Facebook: www.facebook.com/Oceancitychamber
Instagram: www.instagram.com/ocmd_chamber_of _commerce
Description: Works to provide community leadership in fostering and supporting economic development and the continued growth of tourism in Ocean City. **Founded:** 2010. **Publications:** *Voice for Business*. **Awards:** Ocean City Outstanding Citizen of The Year Award (Annual). **Geographic Preference:** Local.

40406 ■ Ocean Pines Area Chamber of Commerce
11047 Racetrack Rd.
Berlin, MD 21811
Ph: (410)641-5306
Fax: (410)641-6176
Co. E-mail: info@oceanpineschamber.org
URL: http://www.oceanpineschamber.org
Contact: Kerrie Bunting, President
Facebook: www.facebook.com/OceanPinesChamber
X (Twitter): x.com/OceanPinesCC
Instagram: www.instagram.com/oceanpineschamber
Description: Represents local business professionals, merchants & services in and around Ocean Pines and the surrounding areas of the Delmarva Peninsula. **Founded:** 1975. **Geographic Preference:** Local.

40407 ■ Olney Chamber of Commerce (OCC)
PO Box 550
Olney, MD 20830
Ph: (301)774-7117
Fax: (301)774-4944
Co. E-mail: chamber@olneymd.org
URL: http://www.olneymd.org
Contact: Fred Silver, President
Facebook: www.facebook.com/OlneyChamberMD
X (Twitter): x.com/olneycommerce
Instagram: www.instagram.com/olneychamber
Description: Promotes business and community development in Montgomery County, MD. Sponsors Community Night. **Founded:** 1964. **Geographic Preference:** Local.

40408 ■ Pocomoke Area Chamber of Commerce
129 Market St.
Pocomoke City, MD 21851
Ph: (410)957-1919
Co. E-mail: pocomokechamber@gmail.com
URL: http://www.pocomokechamber.com
Contact: Jamie Bailey, President
Facebook: www.facebook.com/PocomokeChamber
Linkedin: www.linkedin.com/company/pocomoke -area-chamber-of-commerce
Description: Promotes business and community development in Pocomoke City, MD. Sponsors festival, parade, and bowl-a-thons and Great Pocomoke Fair in August. **Founded:** 1952. **Publications:** *Pep Talk* (Quarterly). **Educational Activities:** General Membership (Monthly). **Awards:** Pocomoke Area Chamber of Commerce Business Person of the Year (Annual). **Geographic Preference:** Local.

40409 ■ Poolesville Area Chamber of Commerce (PACC)
PO Box 256
Poolesville, MD 20837
URL: http://www.poolesvillechamber.com
Contact: Tom Kettler, President
Facebook: www.facebook.com/poolesvillechamber
Description: Promotes business and community development in Poolesville, MD area. **Founded:** 1979. **Geographic Preference:** Local.

40410 ■ Potomac Chamber of Commerce (PCC)
PO Box 59160
Potomac, MD 20859-9160
Ph: (301)299-2170
Fax: (301)983-9828
Co. E-mail: pcc@potomacchamber.org
URL: http://www.potomacchamber.org
Contact: Adam Greenberg, President
E-mail: adam@potomacpizza.com
Description: Promotes business and community development in Potomac, MD. **Geographic Preference:** Local.

40411 ■ Prince George's Chamber of Commerce (PGCOC)
4640 Forbes Blvd., Ste. 130
Lanham, MD 20706
Ph: (301)731-5000
Fax: (301)731-8015
Co. E-mail: dstaples@pgcoc.org
URL: http://pgcoc.org
Contact: Denise Staples, Director, Operations
Facebook: www.facebook.com/ pgchamberofcommerce
Linkedin: www.linkedin.com/company/prince-george's -chamber-of-commerce/about
X (Twitter): x.com/PGCOC
Description: Promotes business and community development in Prince George's County, MD. **Founded:** 1924. **Publications:** *Membership Directory and Quality of Life Guide* (Annual). **Geographic Preference:** Local.

40412 ■ Queen Anne's County Chamber of Commerce (QACCC)
1561 Postal Rd.
Chester, MD 21619
Ph: (410)643-8530
Fax: (410)643-8477
Co. E-mail: linda@qacchamber.com
URL: http://www.qacchamber.com
Contact: Linda Friday, President
E-mail: linda@qacchamber.com
Facebook: www.facebook.com/qacchamber
X (Twitter): x.com/qacchamber
Instagram: www.instagram.com/qacchamber
Description: Promotes business and community development in Queen Annes County, MD. **Geographic Preference:** Local.

40413 ■ Rockville Chamber of Commerce (RCC)
1 Research Ct., Ste. 450
Rockville, MD 20850
Ph: (301)424-9300
Fax: (301)762-7599
Co. E-mail: dawn@rockvillechamber.org
URL: http://www.rockvillechamber.org
Contact: Marji Graf, President
E-mail: marji@rockvillechamber.org
X (Twitter): x.com/chamberrock
Description: Promotes business and community development in Rockville, MD. **Founded:** 1957. **Geographic Preference:** Local.

40414 ■ St. Mary's County Chamber of Commerce Inc.
22738 Maple Rd., Ste. 104
Lexington Park, MD 20653
Ph: (301)737-3001
Co. E-mail: info@smcchamber.com
URL: http://smcchamber.com
Contact: Dr. Christine L. Bergmark, President
E-mail: cbergmark@smcchamber.com
Facebook: www.facebook.com/st.mary.county.chamber.of.commerce
X (Twitter): x.com/StMarysCountyC1
Description: Promotes business and community development in St. Mary's County, MD. **Founded:** 1634. **Publications:** *Business and Community Services Directory* (Annual). **Geographic Preference:** Local.

40415 ■ Salisbury Area Chamber of Commerce (SACC) - Library
200 E Church St.
Salisbury, MD 21801
Ph: (410)749-0144
Fax: (410)860-9925
Co. E-mail: chamber@salisburyarea.com
URL: http://salisburyarea.com
Contact: Bill Chambers, President
E-mail: bchambers@salisburyarea.com
Facebook: www.facebook.com/salisburychamber
Linkedin: www.linkedin.com/company/salisbury-area -chamber-of-commerce
X (Twitter): x.com/SBYChamber
YouTube: www.youtube.com/channel/UCp8Hk tBCrwfp8KG6y4YzHcA
Description: Promotes business and community development in Salisbury, MD. **Scope:** small business planning; management; business plans; business law; financing. **Services:** open to the public. **Founded:** 1920. **Holdings:** Book; magazine. **Publications:** *Salisbury Business Journal* (Monthly). **Geographic Preference:** Local.

40416 ■ *Salisbury Business Journal*
200 E Church St.
Salisbury, MD 21801
Ph: (410)749-0144
Fax: (410)860-9925
Co. E-mail: chamber@salisburyarea.com
URL: http://salisburyarea.com
Contact: Bill Chambers, President
E-mail: bchambers@salisburyarea.com
URL(s): sbybiz.org
Facebook: www.facebook.com/sbybizjournal
X (Twitter): x.com/SBYBizJournal
Released: Monthly **Availability:** Online.

40417 ■ Snow Hill Area Chamber of Commerce
PO Box 176
Snow Hill, MD 21863
Ph: (410)334-0104
Co. E-mail: snowhillchamber@gmail.com
URL: http://www.snowhillchamber.com
Contact: Michael Franklin, President
Facebook: www.facebook.com/SHChamber176
Description: Promotes business and community development in Snow Hill, MD. **Geographic Preference:** Local.

STATE LISTINGS

Maryland ■ 40433

40418 ■ *Voice for Business*
Eunice Q. Sorin Visitor & Conference Ctr
12320 Ocean Gateway
Ocean City, MD 21842
Ph: (410)213-0552
Co. E-mail: info@oceancity.org
URL: http://oceancity.org
URL(s): oceancity.org/the-chamber
Availability: Print.

40419 ■ *Washington County Business Directory*
1 S Potomac St.
Hagerstown, MD 21740
Ph: (301)739-2015
Co. E-mail: info@hagerstown.org
URL: http://www.hagerstown.org
Contact: Paul Frey, President
E-mail: paul@hagerstown.org
URL(s): www.hagerstown.org/membership-benefits
Released: Annual **Availability:** Print; Online.

40420 ■ *Weekly Update*
8601 Georgia Ave., Ste. 203
Silver Spring, MD 20910
Ph: (301)565-3777
Fax: (301)565-3377
Co. E-mail: info@gsscc.org
URL: http://www.gsscc.org
Contact: Stewart Zemil, Contact
URL(s): www.gsscc.org/why-join-gsscc.html
Released: Weekly **Description:** Contains electronic update for members only. **Availability:** Print.

MINORITY BUSINESS ASSISTANCE PROGRAMS

40421 ■ Capital Region Minority Supplier Development Council (CRMSDC)
10750 Columbia Pke., Ste. 200
Silver Spring, MD 20901
Ph: (301)593-5860
Co. E-mail: crmsdc@crmsdc.org
URL: http://crmsdc2.wpengine.com
Contact: Sharon R. Pinder, President
E-mail: sharon.pinder@crmsdc.org
Facebook: www.facebook.com/CRMSDC
Linkedin: www.linkedin.com/company/capitalregionmsdc
X (Twitter): x.com/crmsdc
Instagram: www.instagram.com/crmsdc
YouTube: www.youtube.com/channel/UCRuQ-5o8jfd_o43jXwnmuzg
Description: Provides a direct link between corporate America and minority-owned businesses. Increases procurement and business opportunities for minority businesses of all sizes. **Founded:** 1972. **Geographic Preference:** Regional.

40422 ■ Mayor's Office of Baltimore - Minority & Women-Owned Business Development
3000 Druid Pk. Dr. -, Ste. 3000B.
Baltimore, MD 21215
URL: http://smba-d.baltimorecity.gov
Description: Works to improve the opportunites for minority and women-owned businesses to do business with the city of Baltimore.

40423 ■ Prince George's Community College - Center for Minority Business Development
301 Largo Rd.
Largo, MD 20774
Ph: (301)546-7422
URL: http://www.pgcc.edu
Facebook: www.facebook.com/pgccnews
Linkedin: www.linkedin.com/school/prince-george's-community-college
X (Twitter): x.com/pgccnews
Instagram: www.instagram.com/pgccnews
YouTube: www.youtube.com/pgcctv
Description: Provides business development, educational programs, assessment tools, counseling, and mentoring programs to local minority businesses.

FINANCING AND LOAN PROGRAMS

40424 ■ ABS Capital Partners
201 International Cir., Ste. 150
Hunt Valley, MD 21030
Ph: (410)246-5600
Co. E-mail: abscapital@abscapital.com
URL: http://www.abscapital.com
Contact: Bion Ludwig, Partner
E-mail: bludwig@abscapital.com
Facebook: www.facebook.com/ABSCapital
Linkedin: www.linkedin.com/company/abs-capital-partners
X (Twitter): x.com/abscapital
Description: Venture capital firm. **Founded:** 1990. **Investment Policies:** Companies with break-even or profitable EBIDTA; at least 25% profitable growth. **Industry Preferences:** Health care; business and tech-enabled services.

40425 ■ Boulder Ventures Ltd.
5425 Wisconsin Ave., Ste. 704
Chevy Chase, MD 20815
Ph: (301)913-0213
Co. E-mail: info@boulderventures.com
URL: http://www.boulderventures.com
Contact: Kishen Mangat, Partner
Description: Venture capital firm investing in companies. **Preferred Investment Size:** $5,000,000 to $10,000,000. **Industry Preferences:** Communications and media, Internet specific, computer software and services, consumer related, semiconductors and other electronics, other products, consumer related, biotechnology, and medical and health.

40426 ■ Epidarex Capital
7910 Woodmont Ave., Ste. 1210
Bethesda, MD 20814
Ph: (301)298-5455
Co. E-mail: info@epidarex.com
URL: http://epidarex.com
Contact: A. Sinclair Dunlop, Managing Partner
X (Twitter): x.com/epidarex
Description: Invests in early-stage, high-growth companies in under-ventured markets with the UK and US. **Industry Preferences:** Life sciences; health technology.

40427 ■ Global Environment Fund (GEF)
4800 Hampden Ln., Ste. 200
Bethesda, MD 20814
Co. E-mail: info@globalenvironmentfund.com
URL: http://www.globalenvironmentfund.com
Contact: Katie Vasilescu, Chief Communications Officer Chief Operating Officer
Linkedin: www.linkedin.com/company/global-environment-fund
Description: Invests in businesses around the world that offer cost-effective solutions to environmental and energy challenges. Manages private equity dedicated to clean technology, emerging markets, and sustainable forestry. **Founded:** 1990. **Industry Preferences:** Renewable energy and environmental infrastructure.

40428 ■ Grotech Ventures
9722 Groffs Mill Dr., Ste. 856
Owings Mills, MD 21117-6341
Ph: (703)637-9555
URL: http://www.grotech.com
Contact: Steve Fredrick, Partner
E-mail: sfredrick@grotech.com
Linkedin: www.linkedin.com/company/grotech-capital-group
Description: Provides investment services. **Founded:** 1984. **Preferred Investment Size:** $500,000 to $5,000,000. **Industry Preferences:** Internet specific, consumer related, communications and media, other products, computer software, and services, and semiconductors and other electronics, and other products.

40429 ■ Kinetic Ventures L.L.C.
Two Wisconsin Cir., Ste. 700
Chevy Chase, MD 20815
Ph: (301)652-8066
URL: http://kineticventures.com
Contact: William T. Heflin, Managing Director
Description: Firm provides venture capital investment services. **Founded:** 1985. **Preferred Investment Size:** $2,000,000 to $7,000,000. **Industry Preferences:** Internet specific, communications and media, computer software and services, industrial and energy, semiconductors and other electronics, and computer hardware.

40430 ■ New Enterprise Associates, Inc. (NEA)
5425 Wisconsin Ave., Ste. 800
Chevy Chase, MD 20815
Ph: (301)272-2300
Fax: (301)272-1700
Co. E-mail: lprelations@nea.com
URL: http://www.nea.com
Contact: Peter Barris, Chairman
Linkedin: www.linkedin.com/company/new-enterprise-associates
X (Twitter): twitter.com/NEA
Instagram: www.instagram.com/neavc
YouTube: www.youtube.com/user/NEAYVideos
Description: Provider of venture capital, private equity and other financial services. **Founded:** 1977. **Preferred Investment Size:** $200,000 to $20,000,000. **Industry Preferences:** Communications and media, Internet specific, medical and health, computer software and services, semiconductors and other electronics, biotechnology, computer hardware, other products, consumer related, industrial and energy.

40431 ■ New Market Venture Partners (NMVP)
8161 Maple Lawn Blvd., Ste. 350
Fulton, MD 20759
Ph: (301)362-5511
URL: http://newmarketsvp.com
Contact: Donald Spero, Co-Founder
E-mail: dspero@newmarketsvp.com
Facebook: www.facebook.com/newmarkets
Linkedin: www.linkedin.com/company/new-markets-venture-partners
X (Twitter): x.com/newmarketsvp
Description: Education technology venture firm for early- and growth-stage companies. **Founded:** 2003. **Industry Preferences:** Education; information technology; business services.

40432 ■ Novak Biddle Venture Partners L.P. (NBVP)
PO Box 341877
Bethesda, MD 20827
Ph: (240)497-1910
Co. E-mail: info@novakbiddle.com
URL: http://www.novakbiddle.com
Contact: A. G. W. Biddle, III, Partner
Description: Provider of equity financing, investments and assistance services. **Founded:** 1997. **Preferred Investment Size:** $100,000 to $10,000,000. **Industry Preferences:** Internet specific, communications and media, computer software and services, semiconductors and other electronics, computer hardware, other products, and medical and health.

40433 ■ Questmark Partners
2850 Quarry Lake Dr., Ste. 301
Baltimore, MD 21209
URL: http://questm.com
Contact: Ben Schapiro, Partner Founder
X (Twitter): x.com/QuestMarkVC
Description: Expansion-stage investment firm. **Founded:** 1998. **Preferred Investment Size:** $5,000,000-$15,000,0000. **Investment Policies:** Strong recurring revenue; market strategy; potential for standalone success. **Industry Preferences:** Enterprise software; mobile software; tech-enabled business services; security; financial technology; consumer internet; vertically-focused cloud software; healthcare IT.

40434 ■ Spring Capital Partners L.P. (SCP)
The Foxleigh Bldg., Ste. 340
2330 W Joppa Rd.
Lutherville, MD 21093
Ph: (410)685-8000
Fax: (410)545-0015
URL: http://springcap.com
Contact: Jonathan T. Howe, Director

Description: Company providing financing solutions to businesses. **Founded:** 1999. **Preferred Investment Size:** $2,000,000 to $7,000,000. **Industry Preferences:** Communications and media, computer related, semiconductors and other electronics, medical and health, consumer related, industrial and energy, transportation, and manufacturing.

40435 ■ Sterling Partners (SP)
167 N Green St. 4th Fl.
Chicago, IL 60607
Ph: (312)465-7000
Fax: (312)465-7001
URL: http://sterlingpartners.com
Contact: Michelle Shuster, Director
Linkedin: www.linkedin.com/company/sterling-partners

Description: Firm is engaged in business and healthcare services. **Founded:** 1983. **Preferred Investment Size:** Up to $200,000,000. **Industry Preferences:** Communications and media, computer software, medical and health, consumer related, business service, and manufacturing.

40436 ■ T. Rowe Price Group, Inc.
T. Rowe Price Group, Inc.
100 E Pratt St.
Baltimore, MD 21202
Ph: (410)345-2000
Free: 800-638-7890
URL: http://www.troweprice.com
Contact: Robert W. Sharps, President
Facebook: www.facebook.com/troweprice
Linkedin: www.linkedin.com/company/t--rowe-price
X (Twitter): twitter.com/troweprice
Instagram: www.instagram.com/t._rowe_price/
YouTube: www.youtube.com/user/TRowePriceGroup

Description: A financial services holding company that provides global investment management services to individual and institutional investors in company-sponsored mutual funds distributed in the United States and other investment portfolios. **Founded:** 1937.

40437 ■ Telecommunications Development Fund (TDF)
2 Wisconsin Cir., Ste. 920
Chevy Chase, MD 20815
Ph: (240)483-4286
URL: http://www.tdfventures.com
Contact: Andrew Pereyra, Office Manager

Description: Venture capital firm provides investment services. **Preferred Investment Size:** $500,000 to $5,000,000. **Industry Preferences:** Computer software and services, Internet specific, computer hardware, communications and media, semiconductors and other electronics.

PROCUREMENT ASSISTANCE PROGRAMS

40438 ■ Maryland APEX Accelerator (MD PTAC)
5825 University Research Ct., Ste. 1300
College Park, MD 20740
Ph: (301)405-6550
Fax: (301)314-6550
Co. E-mail: ptapadmn@umd.edu
URL: http://www.marylandapex.org
Contact: Denise Warner, Director
E-mail: dwarner1@umd.edu
Facebook: www.facebook.com/MarylandPtac
YouTube: www.youtube.com/channel/UC0kzwL-8pKma34MDcAnRE0Q

Description: Provides marketing, contractual and technical assistance to Maryland small business owners who are interested in marketing their products and services to federal, state and local government agencies. **Founded:** 2002.

INCUBATORS/RESEARCH AND TECHNOLOGY PARKS

40439 ■ Anne Arundel Economic Development Corporation (AAEDC)
2660 Riva Rd., Ste. 200
Annapolis, MD 21401
Ph: (410)222-7410
Co. E-mail: info@aaedc.org
URL: http://www.aaedc.org
Contact: Jeff Armiger, President
Facebook: www.facebook.com/AnneArundelEDC
Linkedin: www.linkedin.com/company/anne-arundel-economic-development-corporation
X (Twitter): x.com/AAEDC
Instagram: www.instagram.com/myarundelbizpodcast
YouTube: www.youtube.com/user/TheAAEDC

Description: Works with business agencies, business people and local economic developers and educators in pursuing economic growth and expansion. Provides support and resources for business development needs and programs. Assists in the retention and expansion of existing firms and the attraction of new businesses. **Geographic Preference:** Local.

40440 ■ B-More Kitchen
5609 HESS Ave.
Baltimore, MD 21212
URL: http://www.bmorekitchen.com
Instagram: www.instagram.com/bmorekitchen

Description: A food incubator dedicated to helping small food businesses launch or grow.

40441 ■ Betamore
101 W Dickman St., Ste. 1000
Baltimore, MD 21230
Ph: (410)861-0534
Co. E-mail: hello@betamore.com
URL: http://www.betamore.com/en
Contact: Greg Cangialosi, Chairman Co-Founder
Facebook: www.facebook.com/morebeta
Linkedin: www.linkedin.com/company/betamore
X (Twitter): x.com/betamore
Instagram: www.instagram.com/betamore

Description: A campus for technology and entrepreneurship provding coworking space for startups. **Founded:** 2012.

40442 ■ BioHealth Innovation Inc. (BHI)
1 Church St., Ste. 801
Rockville, MD 20850
Ph: (301)637-7950
Co. E-mail: info@biohealthinnovation.org
URL: http://www.biohealthinnovation.org
Contact: Richard Bendis, President
E-mail: rbendis@biohealthinnovation.org
Facebook: www.facebook.com/BioHealthInnovation
Linkedin: www.linkedin.com/company/biohealth-innovation-inc-
X (Twitter): x.com/BioHealthInnov

Description: Distributor of medical products. **Founded:** 2011.

40443 ■ Bowie Business Innovation Center (BIC)
14000 Jericho Pk. Rd., ELLC A-131
Bowie, MD 20715
Ph: (301)383-1550
Co. E-mail: info@bowiebic.com
URL: http://bowiebic.com
Contact: June Evans, Executive Director
Facebook: www.facebook.com/bowie.bic
Linkedin: www.linkedin.com/in/bowiebic
X (Twitter): x.com/BowieBIC
Instagram: www.instagram.com/bowiebic

Description: Business incubator providing business support services and facilities that help companies survive and grow during their startup period.

40444 ■ Brewers Hill Hub
3700 O'Donnell St., Ste. 200
Baltimore, MD 21224
Ph: (410)327-4040
Co. E-mail: info@brewershillhub.com
URL: http://www.brewershillhub.com

Description: Coworking space supporting Baltimore startups and entrepreneurs by providing desks, cubicles, private offices and suites.

40445 ■ bwTech@UMBC Research and Technology Park
5520 Research Pk. Dr., Ste. 100
Baltimore, MD 21228
Ph: (443)543-5047
URL: http://bwtech.umbc.edu
Contact: Aaron Miscenich, Executive Director
Facebook: www.facebook.com/bwtechumbc
Linkedin: www.linkedin.com/company/bwtechumbc
X (Twitter): x.com/bwtechrpc

Description: Provides office space for technology park. **Founded:** 1989.

40446 ■ Charles Village Exchange
2526 St. Paul St.
Baltimore, MD 21218
Ph: (443)708-8490
Co. E-mail: info@charlesvillageexchange.com
URL: http://charlesvillageexchange.com
Facebook: www.facebook.com/charlesvillageexchange

Description: A contemporary shared work space for startups and entrepreneurs, providing focus and communal areas for collaboration and socialization.

40447 ■ The CO-OP
12 W Madison St.
Baltimore, MD 21201
Ph: (443)436-2667
Co. E-mail: info@co-opworks.com
URL: http://co-opworks.com

Description: Hosts emerging businesses and organizations who are ready to take success to the next level. Offers convenience, design, community, and amenities to startups and entrepreneurs.

40448 ■ CoLab
2209 Maryland Ave.
Baltimore, MD 21218
Ph: (443)388-9904
URL: http://www.colabbaltimore.com
Facebook: www.facebook.com/mdavcolab
X (Twitter): x.com/mdavcolab
Instagram: www.instagram.com/co_labbaltimore

Description: A coworking space for startups and entrepreneurs that is equal parts creative and business.

40449 ■ Common Kitchen (CK)
12250 Clarksville Pke., Ste. A
Clarksville, MD 21029
Ph: (443)535-1252
Co. E-mail: lsteele@thecommonkitchen.com
URL: http://thecommonkitchen.com
Facebook: www.facebook.com/thecommonkitchenclarksville
Instagram: www.instagram.com/thecommonkitchenclarksville

Description: Affordable shared commercial kitchen for new businesses. Offers locally made food and products.

40450 ■ CorLyst L.L.C.
7380 Coca Cola Dr., Ste. 106
Hanover, MD 21076
Ph: (443)445-3605
Fax: (443)288-4420
URL: http://corlyst-llc.com
Contact: Dr. David Young, President

Description: Firm provides business and technical expertise in multiple areas including product development, drug, device development, potential patent application, marketing and data management.

40451 ■ Cyber Incubator
5520 Research Pk. Dr., Ste. 100
Baltimore, MD 21228

STATE LISTINGS

Ph: (443)543-5047
Co. E-mail: incubator@bwtech.com
URL: http://bwtech.umbc.edu
Facebook: www.facebook.com/bwtechumbc
Linkedin: www.linkedin.com/company/bwtechumbc
X (Twitter): x.com/bwtechrpc
Description: Firm provides cyber security-related products and services.

40452 ■ Dorchester County Economic Development Department (DCED)
104 Tech Pk. Dr., Ste. 41
  Cambridge, MD 21613
Ph: (410)228-0155
Fax: (410)228-9518
Co. E-mail: info@choosedorchester.org
URL: http://choosedorchester.org
Contact: Susan Banks, Director
E-mail: sbanks@choosedorchester.org
Facebook: www.facebook.com/DorchesterCountyEconomicDevelopment
X (Twitter): x.com/DorchesterEcon
YouTube: www.youtube.com/choosedorchester
Description: A public agency focused on developing and implementing strategic initiatives, to promote economic growth and stability by supporting existing businesses and attracting new industry. **Founded:** 1980.

40453 ■ Dorchester County Economic Development Office - Eastern Shore Innovation Center (ESIC)
104 Tech Pk. Dr.
  Cambridge, MD 21613
URL: http://choosedorchester.org/dorchester-economic-development/innovation-center
Contact: Susan Banks, Contact
E-mail: sbanks@choosedorchester.org
Description: Full-service business incubator helping business owners and operators successfully navigate the financial, regulatory and workforce landscapes. **Founded:** 2016.

40454 ■ Emerging Technology Centers (ETC)
101 N Haven St., Ste. 301
  Baltimore, MD 21224
Ph: (443)451-7000
Co. E-mail: info@etcbaltimore.com
URL: http://www.etcbaltimore.com
Contact: Deb Tillett, President
E-mail: dtillett@etcbaltimore.com
Facebook: www.facebook.com/etcbaltimore
X (Twitter): x.com/etcbaltimore
Instagram: www.instagram.com/etcbaltimore
Description: A non-profit business incubator program focused on growing early-stage technology and biotechnology companies in Baltimore City. It offers fully wired offices and space for participating companies at below market rates, with flexible leases, shared basic services and equipment, tech support, and on-site management. **Founded:** 1999.

40455 ■ Energetics Technology Center (ETC)
4445 Indian Head Hwy.
  Indian Head, MD 20640
Ph: (301)645-6637
Co. E-mail: contactus@etcmd.com
URL: http://www.etcmd.com
Contact: Matthew McCulloh Riordan, Contact
Facebook: www.facebook.com/ETCMD
Linkedin: www.linkedin.com/company/energetics-technology-center
Description: Provides research and engineering services, and policy development capabilities to government, academia, and private industry clients. Supports technology startups. **Founded:** 2006.

40456 ■ Frederick Innovative Technology Center (FITCI)
4539 Metropolitan Ct.
  Frederick, MD 21704
Ph: (301)694-2999
Co. E-mail: info@fitci.org
URL: http://www.fitci.org
Contact: Kathie Callahan Brady, President
E-mail: kathie@fitci.org
Facebook: www.facebook.com/FITCI

Linkedin: www.linkedin.com/company/frederick-innovative-technology-center-inc
X (Twitter): x.com/FITCInc
Instagram: www.instagram.com/fitciinc
YouTube: www.youtube.com/channel/UCHvKF3rMe8l7sHnWIFd60QQ
Description: A small business incubator offering local entrepreneurs facilities, services, and an environment in which they can prosper. **Founded:** 2004.

40457 ■ Germantown Innovation Center
20271 Goldenrod Ln., 2nd Fl.
  Germantown, MD 20876
Ph: (301)528-4001
URL: http://www.mcinnovationnetwork.com/facilities-tenants/germantown-innovation-center
Description: Business incubator and accelerator, aiding emerging businesses by offering convenient locations in close proximity to business assets, turnkey office space, shared conference rooms, and resource and support services.

40458 ■ hotDesks
8737 Brooks Dr., Ste. 101
  Easton, MD 21601
Ph: (410)770-9330
URL: http://hotdesks.org
Contact: Tina Thompson, Manager
E-mail: tthompson@docogonet.com
Description: Offers a way for startups and entrepreneurs to connect and network with mentor and fellow entrepreneurs in the region. hotDekss is a network of co-working spaces and a calendar of events and activities targeted to entrepreneurs. **Founded:** 2013.

40459 ■ Impact Hub Baltimore
10 E N Ave.
  Baltimore, MD 21202
Ph: (443)821-7482
URL: http://baltimore.impacthub.net
Contact: Brain Howe, Governor
Facebook: www.facebook.com/impacthubbalt
X (Twitter): x.com/impacthubbalt
Description: A membership-based community space that connects entrepreneurs and startups to accelerators.

40460 ■ Innovative Partners Incubation (IPI)
Annapolis, MD
Ph: (908)789-3424
URL: http://www.innovativepartners.com
Contact: Jeffrey C. Milanette, President
E-mail: jeffm@innovativepartners.com
Facebook: www.facebook.com/IPIncubation
Description: Specializes in economic development and job creation using business incubation to accelerate the successful development of technology entrepreneurship and their companies. Delivers full-service incubation assistance from feasibility study to best practice application. **Founded:** 1986.

40461 ■ Maryland Center for Entrepreneurship's Innovation Catalyst
6751 Columbia Gateway Dr., Ste. 500
  Columbia, MD 21046
Ph: (410)313-6550
Fax: (410)313-6525
URL: http://www.hceda.org/maryland-center-for-entrepreneurship/icat.aspx
Facebook: www.facebook.com/HoCoEDA
X (Twitter): twitter.com/HCEDA
YouTube: www.youtube.com/user/howardcountyeda
Description: Provides emerging technology and IP-based companies with new and innovative programs providing them access to an ever-expanding set of resources and growing community of entrepreneurs, investors, service providers, and mentors.

40462 ■ Maryland International Incubator (MI2)
7809 Regents Dr.
  College Park, MD 20742
URL: http://energy.umd.edu/incubators
Description: Connects Maryland and International companies for successful joint ventures through a targeted array of business services, state-of-the-art facilities, and world-class resources.

40463 ■ Montgomery County Department of Economic Development - Business Innovation Network (BIN)
20271 Goldenrod Ln., 2nd Fl.
  Germantown, MD 20876
URL: http://www.montgomerycountymd.gov/business/expand-move/incubators.html
Description: A small business incubator and accelerator offering fertile ground for innovations in bioscience, information technology, education, and the arts. Its goal is to nurture and grow young, enterprising businesses into smart and successful companies through its Business Innovation Network.

40464 ■ Mtech Technology Advancement Program
4467 Technology Dr., 1105 Herbert Rabin Technology Advancement Building University of Maryland
  College Park, MD 20742-3371
URL: http://www.mtechventures.umd.edu
Contact: Scott Christensen, Manager
E-mail: schris14@umd.edu
Description: Operator of restaurant.

40465 ■ North Star Innovation Partners
1601 Ballenger Creek Pke.
  Point of Rocks, MD 21777
Ph: (301)524-5654
Fax: (301)576-5065
Co. E-mail: info@northstarinnovation.com
URL: http://www.northstarinnovation.com
Contact: Lisa S. Smith, President
Description: Works with diverse communities to develop and implement practical innovation ecosystem strategies, and tools such as business incubation/business acceleration programs and access to early stage capital initiatives to drive innovation and increased entrepreneurship in those communities.

40466 ■ Open Works (OW)
1400 Greenmount Ave.
  Baltimore, MD 21202
Ph: (410)862-0424
Co. E-mail: frontdesk@openworksbmore.com
URL: http://www.openworksbmore.org
Contact: Will Holman, Executive Director
Facebook: www.facebook.com/OpenWorksBmore
Linkedin: www.linkedin.com/company/open-works-baltimore
X (Twitter): x.com/OpenWorksBmore
Instagram: www.instagram.com/open_works_bmore
Description: Provides tools, technology, and knowledge to startups and entrepreneurs through low cost space, memberships, and classes. **Founded:** 2016.

40467 ■ Rockville Innovation Center
155 Gibbs St. 4th Fl.
  Rockville, MD 20850
URL: http://montgomerycountymd.gov/business/expand-move/incubators.html
Description: A small business incubator providing space and support for approximately 30 start-up technology companies to grow. **Founded:** 2007.

40468 ■ The Rural Development Center
University of Maryland, E Shore
Richard E Henson Ctr., Rm. 2147
  Princess Anne, MD 21853
URL: http://skipjacknews.net/mdhawk
Description: Firm engages in community-based incubator serving the needs of people in rural communities.

40469 ■ Silver Spring Innovation Center (SSIC)
8070 Georgia Ave.
  Silver Spring, MD 20910
Ph: (301)589-9442
URL: http://silverspringdowntown.com/go/silver-spring-innovation-center
Description: Provides a creative atmosphere to grow advanced technology companies.

40470 ■ Startup Maryland
101 W Dickman St.
  Baltimore, MD 21230
URL: http://startupmd.org

40471 ■ Maryland

Contact: Mike Binko, President
X (Twitter): x.com/startupmd
Instagram: www.instagram.com/startupmaryland
Description: Helps startups in Maryland to achieve the next level of success. Provides support such as curation, capital, and coaching. **Founded:** 2012.

40471 ■ TechFire
4185 Indian Head Hwy.
 Indian Head, MD 20640
Ph: (301)645-6637
URL: http://www.techfirenetwork.com
Contact: Robert Kavetsky, President
Facebook: www.facebook.com/techfire
Linkedin: www.linkedin.com/company/energetics-technology-center
YouTube: www.youtube.com/iframe_api
Description: Provides useful business solutions to technology startups and entrepreneurs. Has a special focus to support women, minority and veteran entrepreneurs, in order for them to become successful and sustainable companies that fuels Maryland economy.

40472 ■ Towson University Incubator
Towson University 8000 York Rd.
 Towson, MD 21252-0001
Ph: (410)704-4444
Co. E-mail: incubator@towson.edu
URL: http://www.towson.edu
Contact: David Cross, Assistant Director
E-mail: dcross@towson.edu
Facebook: www.facebook.com/TUincubator
Linkedin: www.linkedin.com/company/tuincubator
X (Twitter): x.com/TowsonU
YouTube: www.youtube.com/TowsonUniversity
Description: Serves as an entrepreneurial resource and activity hub inside and outside of Towson University. Committed to innovation, values practice over theory, and continually looks for ways to redefine and grow entrepreneurship.

40473 ■ University of Maryland Bio Park (UMB)
801 W Baltimore St.
 Baltimore, MD 21201
Co. E-mail: info@umbiopark.com
URL: http://www.umbiopark.com
Contact: James L. Hughes, President
E-mail: jhughes@umaryland.edu
Facebook: www.facebook.com/umbiopark
Linkedin: www.linkedin.com/company/university-of-maryland-biopark
X (Twitter): x.com/UMBioPark
Description: Laboratory and office space for emerging high-growth life science companies.

40474 ■ University of Maryland at College Park - Maryland Technology Enterprise Institute (Mtech)
4467 Technology Dr., 1105 Herbert Rabin Technology Advancement Bldg.
 College Park, MD 20742-3371
Ph: (301)405-3906
Co. E-mail: mtech@umd.edu
URL: http://www.mtech.umd.edu/index.html
Contact: Dr. William E. Bentley, Director
E-mail: bentley@umd.edu
Facebook: www.facebook.com/mtechumd
Linkedin: www.linkedin.com/company/maryland-technology-enterprise-institute-mtech-university-of-maryland
X (Twitter): x.com/mtechumd
Description: Assists in problem identification, provides support, and formulates solutions. Also performs information searches. Reviews and critiques new ideas, products, and designs. **Scope:** Engineering, science and technology enterprise. **Founded:** 1983. **Publications:** Mtech Impact Report (Annual); Mtech News, Opportunities and Events e-newsletter (Biweekly). **Educational Activities:** Biotechnology Research and Education Program (BREP), Offers bioprocessing and biopharmaceutical facilities and services, graduate degree programs, training and consulting for Maryland companies.; Hillman Entrepreneurs Program, A scholarship program targeted to students who have an interest in entrepreneurship and an enthusiasm for starting a business venture or leading a company.; Maryland International Incubator, Connects Maryland and international companies for successful joint ventures through a targeted array of business services, state-of-the-art facilities, and world-class resources.; Technology Advancement Program incubator, Helps entrepreneurs build some of the most successful technology companies by providing business advice and support, market intelligence, introductions, access to funding and other critical assistance.; TERP Startup Laboratory, Early stage technology incubation program for University of Maryland faculty, students, and regional entrepreneurs.; University of Maryland Technology Startup Boot Camp (Annual), An intensive, one-day workshop about how to launch and grow new ventures, taught by regional leaders in entrepreneurship.

40475 ■ Wheaton Business Innovation Center
11002 Veirs Mill Rd., 7th Fl.
 Wheaton, MD 20902
URL: http://www.mcinnovationnetwork.com/facilitiesandtenants/facilities/wheaton-ic
Facebook: www.facebook.com/BINMCMD
Description: A small business incubator created for current, locally-based business service, government contracting, and/or professional trade businesses looking to grow. **Founded:** 1986.

EDUCATIONAL PROGRAMS

40476 ■ University of Baltimore (MSB) - Merrick School of Business
11 W Mt. Royal Ave.
 Baltimore, MD 21201
Ph: (410)837-4955
Co. E-mail: merrickschool@ubalt.edu
URL: http://www.ubalt.edu/merrick
Contact: Murray M. Dalziel, Dean
E-mail: mdalziel@ubalt.edu
Facebook: www.facebook.com/UBaltBusiness
Linkedin: www.linkedin.com/school/ubaltbusiness
X (Twitter): x.com/UBaltBusiness
Instagram: www.instagram.com/UBaltBusiness
Description: Undergraduate and graduate business courses, institutes, and conferences are offered in flexible evening and weekend schedules. Programs are designed for persons already in positions of executive responsibility, as well as for those about to enter into managerial positions. **Founded:** 1925.

CONSULTANTS

40477 ■ Facility Logix
3901 National Dr., Ste. 270
 Burtonsville, MD 20866
Ph: (240)560-5588
URL: http://flgx.com
Contact: Patricia Larrabee, President
E-mail: patl@flgx.com
Linkedin: www.linkedin.com/company/facility-logix-llc
Description: Provides strategic insight for clients seeing a competitive edge in growing life science clusters and developing lab and bio-manufacturing spaces. **Founded:** 2004.

40478 ■ Idea Age Consulting
5004 Honeygo Blvd., No. 201
 Westminster, MD 21158
Ph: (303)900-9264
Co. E-mail: gogo@askcoachgogo.com
URL: http://www.ideaageconsulting.com
Contact: Gogo Erekosima, Co-Founder
E-mail: gogo@askcoachgogo.com
Facebook: www.facebook.com/businessconsultants
X (Twitter): x.com/IdeaAgePeople
Description: Consulting firm offers sales and small business coaching. Creates social media content and marketing strategies.

PUBLICATIONS

40479 ■ *The Daily Record: Business*
7025 Albert Pick Rd.
 Greensboro, NC 27409
Ph: (612)317-9420
Free: 877-615-9536
Co. E-mail: customerservice@bridgetowermedia.com
URL: http://www.bridgetowermedia.com
Contact: Adam Reinebach, President
URL(s): nydailyrecord.com
Facebook: www.facebook.com/nydailyrecord
Linkedin: www.linkedin.com/company/the-daily-record-rochester-ny
X (Twitter): x.com/nydailyrecord
Instagram: www.instagram.com/rbjdaily
YouTube: www.youtube.com/user/MDDailyRecord1
Released: Daily **Price:** $16, for online plans start at monthly; $249, for digital + print annual; $199, for plans start at annual; $26, for digital + print month; $319, for annual print + online; $299, for annual premium only; $24, for digital only month; $20, for digital + online. **Description:** Daily Business newspaper reporting news and features on business, real estate, technology, healthcare and law. **Availability:** Print; Online.

40480 ■ *South Carroll Business Association--Directory (Sykesville, Maryland)*
PO Box 1401
 Sykesville, MD 21784
Ph: (410)861-0506
Co. E-mail: info@southcarroll.org
URL: http://www.southcarroll.org
Contact: Ben Cook, President
URL(s): www.southcarroll.org/directory
Description: Covers local business owners and managers in South Caroll county. **Entries include:** Company name, address, contact information, contact person, e-mail, and website. **Availability:** Print.

EARLY STAGE FINANCING

40481 ■ Angel Venture Forum (AVF)
Baltimore, MD
Ph: (202)618-2025
URL: http://www.angelventureforum.com
Contact: Valerie S. Gaydos, President
X (Twitter): x.com/AngelVentures
Description: Consortium of early-stage angel investors for companies with fast growth potential. **Preferred Investment Size:** Less than $3,000,000. **Investment Policies:** ROI of at least 30% with a projected exit in 3-5 years; potential economic development and job creation; experienced management team; well-defined market; justifiable valuation.

VENTURE CAPITAL FIRM

40482 ■ Baltimore Angels
100 S Charles St.
 Baltimore, MD 21202
Description: Angel capital investment and mentorship firm supporting startups and entrepreneurs in the Mid-Atlantic.

40483 ■ Capital Growth Inc. (CGI)
Baltimore, MD
Ph: (202)618-2025
URL: http://capitalgrowth.com
Contact: Valerie Gaydos, Principal

STATE LISTINGS

Description: Angel investor who specializes in venture intelligence, business building, capital formation, and interim management. **Founded:** 1994.

40484 ■ New Enterprise Associates, Inc. (NEA)
5425 Wisconsin Ave., Ste. 800
 Chevy Chase, MD 20815
Ph: (301)272-2300
Fax: (301)272-1700
Co. E-mail: lprelations@nea.com
URL: http://www.nea.com
Contact: Peter Barris, Chairman
Linkedin: www.linkedin.com/company/new-enterprise-associates
X (Twitter): twitter.com/NEA
Instagram: www.instagram.com/neavc
YouTube: www.youtube.com/user/NEAYVideos

Description: Provider of venture capital, private equity and other financial services. **Founded:** 1977. **Preferred Investment Size:** $200,000 to $20,000,000. **Industry Preferences:** Communications and media, Internet specific, medical and health, computer software and services, semiconductors and other electronics, biotechnology, computer hardware, other products, consumer related, industrial and energy.

Massachusetts

ASSOCIATIONS AND OTHER ORGANIZATIONS

40485 ■ **Boston Harbor Angels**
Joy St.
Boston, MA 02114
Co. E-mail: info@bostonharborangels.com
URL: http://www.bostonharborangels.com
Contact: Ziad Moukheiber, President
Facebook: www.facebook.com/ziad.boston
Linkedin: www.linkedin.com/company/boston-harbor-angels
Description: Angel investor group for early-stage high-growth companies. **Founded:** 2005. **Investment Policies:** Clear and defensible competitive advantage; capital-efficient companies that can reach profitability with less than $5,000,000 of equity investment; can offer a tenfold return on investment within five years.

40486 ■ **Business Network International, Greater Boston Region**
111 Boston Post Rd.
Sudbury, MA 01776
Ph: (978)443-6800
Fax: (978)443-4171
Contact: Jennifer Tolley, Regional Director
Facebook: www.facebook.com/pg/bnimass
Description: Provides both men and women a structured environment for the development and exchange of quality business referrals. Offers members the opportunity to share ideas and contacts. **Geographic Preference:** Local.

40487 ■ **Entrepreneurs' Organization - Boston Chapter (EO)**
Boston, MA
URL: http://www.eonetwork.org/boston
Description: Provides local resources to members which includes networking events, mentorship, live forums, and leadership development. **Founded:** 1994.

40488 ■ **The Indus Entrepreneurs Boston**
One Broadway, 14th Fl.
Cambridge, MA 02142
Ph: (617)225-0419
Co. E-mail: info@boston.tie.org
URL: http://www.tieboston.org
Contact: Anu Chitrapu, President
Facebook: www.facebook.com/tieboston
Linkedin: www.linkedin.com/company/tieboston
X (Twitter): x.com/tieboston
Description: Advocates for the advancement of entrepreneurship and exchange of ideas. Works in fostering entrepreneurship and nurturing entrepreneurs, providing a networking platform for members and helping members integrate with the mainstream community. **Founded:** 1997. **Geographic Preference:** Local.

40489 ■ **International Association of Women Boston Chapter**
Boston, MA
Free: 888-852-1600
Co. E-mail: memberservices@iawomen.com
Facebook: www.facebook.com/IAWomenBoston
Description: Serves as network of accomplished women united to achieve professional goals. Provides a forum for sharing ideas and experiences of professional women regarding career success. Promotes an active business and networking community from all industries. **Geographic Preference:** Local.

40490 ■ **New England Business Brokers Association (NEBBA)**
11 Robert Toner Blvd.
Suite 5, PMB 233
North Attleboro, MA 02760
Ph: (978)263-5559
Co. E-mail: administrator@nebba.com
URL: http://www.nebba.com
Contact: Jennife Fox, President
E-mail: jfox@tworldma.com
Description: Disseminates industry information; encourages growth of sales; assists in new industry developments. Represents members in legislative matters and lobbies for recognition of the industry. Coordinates activity among business brokerages and cooperates with other types of brokerages. Conducts educational and promotional programs for members. **Founded:** 1993. **Geographic Preference:** Regional.

40491 ■ **New England Business Travel Association (NEBTA)**
PO Box 276
Boston, MA 02215
URL: http://nebta.org
Contact: Kristen Reeves, President
E-mail: kristen.reeves@mksinst.com
X (Twitter): x.com/NEWENGLANDBTA
Description: Promotes the value of business travel management by representing corporate travel managers and travel service providers. Monitors developments in the business travel field and provides current, critical industry information. **Founded:** 1969.

40492 ■ **New England Venture Capital Association (NEVCA)**
545 Boylston
Boston, MA 02116
Co. E-mail: info@newenglandvc.org
URL: http://newenglandvc.org
Contact: Ari Fine Glantz, Executive Director
Linkedin: www.linkedin.com/company/new-england-venture-capital-association_2
X (Twitter): x.com/NewEnglandVC
Description: Promotes venture capital investing and entrepreneurship in New England.

SMALL BUSINESS DEVELOPMENT CENTER LEAD OFFICE

40493 ■ **Massachusetts Small Business Development Center Network**
University of Massachusetts
Tillson House
23 Tillson Farm Rd.
Amherst, MA 01003-9346
Ph: (202)670-4886
Co. E-mail: cconroy@msbdc.umass.edu
URL: http://www.msbdc.org
Contact: Liora Stone, President
Description: Provides one-to-one free comprehensive and confidential services focusing on, business growth and strategies, financing and loan assistance as well as strategic, marketing and operational analysis. **Geographic Preference:** Local; State.

SMALL BUSINESS DEVELOPMENT CENTERS

40494 ■ **Massachusetts Small Business Development Center Network**
University of Massachusetts
Tillson House
23 Tillson Farm Rd.
Amherst, MA 01003-9346
Ph: (202)670-4886
Co. E-mail: cconroy@msbdc.umass.edu
URL: http://www.msbdc.org
Contact: Liora Stone, President
Description: Provides one-to-one free comprehensive and confidential services focusing on, business growth and strategies, financing and loan assistance as well as strategic, marketing and operational analysis. **Geographic Preference:** Local; State.

40495 ■ **Massachusetts Small Business Development Center Network Berkshire Regional Office**
33 Dunham Mall, Ste. 103
Pittsfield, MA 01201
Ph: (413)499-0933
Fax: (413)499-3005
URL: http://www.msbdc.org/berkshire
Contact: Keith Girouard, Director
E-mail: kgirouard@msbdc.umass.edu
Description: Represents and promotes the small business sector. Provides management assistance to current and prospective small business owners. Helps to improve management skills and expand the products and services of members. **Geographic Preference:** Local.

40496 ■ **Massachusetts Small Business Development Center Network Central Office**
23 Tillson Farm Rd.
Amherst, MA 01003
Ph: (413)545-6301
Fax: (413)545-1273
URL: http://www.msbdc.org
Facebook: www.facebook.com/sbdcatclark
Description: Represents and promotes the small business sector. Provides management assistance to current and prospective small business owners. Helps to improve management skills and expand the products and services of members.

STATE LISTINGS Massachusetts ■ 40512

40497 ■ Massachusetts Small Business Development Center Network Northeast Regional Office
71 Loring Ave., Rm. CC156
 Salem, MA 01970
Ph: (978)542-6343
Fax: (978)542-6345
URL: http://sbdc.salemstate.edu
Contact: Nancy Gerardi, Regional Director
E-mail: ngerardi@salemstate.edu
Description: Represents and promotes the small business sector. Provides management assistance to current and prospective small business owners. Helps to improve management skills and expand the products and services of members. **Founded:** 1980. **Geographic Preference:** Local.

40498 ■ Massachusetts Small Business Development Center Network Southeast Regional Office
200 Pocasset St.
 Fall River, MA 02721
Ph: (508)673-9783
Fax: (508)674-1929
URL: http://www.msbdc.org/semass
Contact: Anne Fenton, Coordinator
E-mail: amfenton@msbdc.umass.edu
Description: Represents and promotes the small business sector. Provides management assistance to current and prospective small business owners. Helps to improve management skills and expand the products and services of members. **Founded:** 1982. **Geographic Preference:** Local.

40499 ■ Massachusetts Small Business Development Center Network Western Regional Office (WRO)
Scibelli Enterprise Ctr.
 1 Federal St., Bldg. 101
 Springfield, MA 01105
Ph: (413)577-1768
Fax: (413)737-2312
URL: http://www.msbdc.org/wmass
Contact: Anita Eliason, Advisor
E-mail: aeliason@msbdc.umass.edu
Facebook: www.facebook.com/msbdcwro
X (Twitter): x.com/msbdc_wro
Description: Represents and promotes the small business sector. Provides management assistance to current and prospective small business owners. Helps to improve management skills and expand the products and services of members. **Founded:** 1980. **Geographic Preference:** Local.

40500 ■ Small Business Service Bureau, Inc. (SBSB)
38 Austin St.
 Worcester, MA 01615-0014
Free: 800-472-7199
Co. E-mail: info@sbsbhealth.com
URL: http://www.sbsb.com
Contact: Lisa M. Carroll, President
Facebook: www.facebook.com/SBSBinc
Linkedin: www.linkedin.com/company/small-business-service-bureau
Description: A national membership organization serving the small business communityfamily businesses, home-based businesses, small companies, military veterans turned entrepreneurs, and the self-employed. **Founded:** 1967. **Publications:** *Legislative News* (Bimonthly). **Geographic Preference:** National.

40501 ■ Worcester Business Development Corp. (WBDC)
89 Shrewsbury St., Ste. 300
 Worcester, MA 01604
Ph: (508)755-5734
Fax: (508)755-9639
Co. E-mail: info@worcesterbdc.com
URL: http://www.thewbdc.com
Contact: Craig L. Blais, President
Facebook: www.facebook.com/worcesterbdc
Linkedin: www.linkedin.com/company/the-worcester-business-development-corporation
X (Twitter): x.com/WorcesterBDC

Instagram: www.instagram.com/worcesterbdc
YouTube: www.youtube.com/channel/UC9PRn8gEYQPXU3ngyXsBb2A
Description: Firm engages in economic development services. **Founded:** 1965. **Geographic Preference:** Local.

SMALL BUSINESS ASSISTANCE PROGRAMS

40502 ■ Massachusetts Executive Office of Housing and Economic Development (MA EOHED)
1 Ashburton Pl., Rm. 2101
 Boston, MA 02108
Ph: (617)788-3610
Fax: (617)788-3605
URL: http://www.mass.gov/orgs/executive-office-of-economic-development
Contact: Meggie Quackenbush, Director, Communications
E-mail: margaret.m.quackenbush@mass.gov
Linkedin: www.linkedin.com/showcase/executive-office-of-housing-and-economic-development-eohed-
X (Twitter): x.com/MassEOED
Instagram: www.instagram.com/masseoed
Description: Promotes economic opportunity, collaborative leadership, job creation, and business growth.

40503 ■ Massachusetts Export Center
Mount Ida Campus of UMass Amherst, Campus Ctr., Ste. 207
 100 Carlson Ave.
 Newton, MA 02459-3326
Ph: (617)973-6610
URL: http://www.msbdc.org/export
Contact: Paula Murphy, Director
Description: Provides assistance in market analysis, training, advice on export practices and financing for participation in foreign trade missions, export counseling, and market research. Also identifies foreign contacts for exporting firms and organizes and conducts trade events.

40504 ■ Massachusetts Office of Housing and Economic Development
1 Ashburton Pl., Ste. 2101
 Boston, MA 02108
Ph: (617)788-3610
Fax: (617)788-3605
URL: http://www.mass.gov/orgs/executive-office-of-economic-development
Contact: Meggie Quackenbush, Director, Communications
E-mail: margaret.m.quackenbush@mass.gov
X (Twitter): x.com/MassEOED
Description: Provides assistance and information on relocating and expanding businesses in Massachusetts.

40505 ■ Massachusetts Office of International Trade and Investment (MOITI)
1 Ashburton Pl., Rm. 2101
 Boston, MA 02108
URL: http://www.mass.gov/orgs/massachusetts-office-of-international-trade-and-investment
Contact: Jeevan Ramapriya, Executive Director
Description: Oversees the state's international trade activities. Also monitors the degree of foreign investment in Massachusetts.

SCORE OFFICES

40506 ■ Boston SCORE
10 Cswy., St.
 Boston, MA 02222
Ph: (617)565-5591
Co. E-mail: ch.admin0020@scorevolunteer.org
URL: http://www.score.org/boston
Facebook: www.facebook.com/SCOREBoston
Linkedin: www.linkedin.com/company/score-boston
X (Twitter): x.com/SCOREBoston

Description: Volunteer program in which working and retired business management professionals provide free business counseling to men and women who are considering starting a small business, encountering problems with their business, or expanding their business. **Founded:** 1964. **Geographic Preference:** Local.

40507 ■ Cape Cod and the Islands SCORE
5 Patti Page Way.
 Centerville, MA 02632
Ph: (508)775-4884
Fax: (508)790-2540
Co. E-mail: capecodscore@verizon.net
URL: http://capecod.score.org
Facebook: www.facebook.com/SCORECapeCod
Linkedin: www.linkedin.com/company/score-mentors-cape-cod
Description: Serves as volunteer program in which working and retired business management professionals provide free business counseling to men and women who are considering starting a small business, encountering problems with their business, or expanding their business. Offers free one-on-one counseling, online counseling and low cost workshops on a variety of business topics. **Founded:** 1964. **Geographic Preference:** Local.

40508 ■ Northeast Massachusetts SCORE
583 Chestnut St.
 Lynn, MA 01904
Ph: (781)592-2900
Co. E-mail: help@score.org
URL: http://nemassachusetts.score.org
Contact: David Conley, Manager
Facebook: www.facebook.com/SCORENorthEastMassachusetts
Description: Serves as volunteer program in which working and retired business management professionals provide free business counseling to men and women who are considering starting a small business, encountering problems with their business, or expanding their business. Offers free one-on-one counseling, online counseling and low cost workshops on a variety of business topics. **Geographic Preference:** Local.

40509 ■ SCORE - Amherst
243 Triangle St.
 Amherst, MA 01002
URL: http://westernmassachusetts.score.org
Description: Provides professional guidance and information to maximize the success of existing and emerging small businesses. Offers business counseling and workshops.

40510 ■ SCORE - Beverly [SCORE - Northeast Massachusetts]
181 Eliot St., 100 Cummings Center, Ste. 101M
 Beverly, MA 01915
Ph: (978)922-9441
URL: http://nemassachusetts.score.org/content/branch-locator-and-counseling-schedule
Contact: David Conley, Contact
Description: Provides professional guidance and information to maximize the success of existing and emerging small businesses. Offers business counseling and workshops.

40511 ■ SCORE - Boston [SCORE - Lexington Chamber of Commerce]
10 Cswy., St.
 Boston, MA 02222
Ph: (617)565-5591
Co. E-mail: ch.admin0020@scorevolunteer.org
URL: http://www.score.org/boston
Facebook: www.facebook.com/SCOREBoston
Linkedin: www.linkedin.com/company/score-boston
X (Twitter): x.com/SCOREBoston
Description: Provides professional guidance and information to maximize the success of existing and emerging small businesses. Offers business counseling and workshops. **Founded:** 1964.

40512 ■ SCORE - Burlington, Massachusetts
140 Middlesex Tpke.
 Burlington, MA 01803

Small Business Sourcebook • 42nd Edition

Ph: (978)317-8893
Co. E-mail: contactus@score.org
URL: http://www.score.org/nemassachusetts/content/about/northeast-massachusetts-score-branches
Contact: Bill Feingold, Branch Manager
Facebook: www.facebook.com/SCORENorthEastMassachusetts

Description: Provides professional guidance and information to maximize the success of existing and emerging small businesses. Offers business counseling and workshops.

40513 ■ SCORE - Cape Cod & the Islands
5 Patti Page Way
Centerville, MA 02632
Ph: (508)775-4884
Fax: (508)790-2540
Co. E-mail: capecodscore@scorevolunteer.org
URL: http://www.score.org/capecod
Contact: Susan Chandler, Chairman
E-mail: susan.chandler@scorevolunteer.org
Facebook: www.facebook.com/SCORECapeCod
Linkedin: www.linkedin.com/company/score-mentors-cape-cod

Description: Provides professional guidance and information to maximize the success of existing and emerging small businesses. Offers business counseling and workshops. **Founded:** 1964.

40514 ■ SCORE - Dorchester
594 Columbia Rd.
Dorchester, MA 02125
URL: http://www.score.org/somd/success-story/absolute-pressure-cleaning

Description: Provides professional guidance and information to maximize the success of existing and emerging small businesses. Offers business counseling and workshops.

40515 ■ SCORE - Eastham
3 Main St. Mercantile, Unit 8
Eastham, MA 02642
Ph: (508)240-7873
URL: http://www.score.org/find-location?state=MA

Description: Provides professional guidance and information to maximize the success of existing and emerging small businesses. Offers business counseling and workshops.

40516 ■ SCORE - Falmouth
679 Davis Straits, Unit A
Falmouth, MA 02540
Ph: (508)775-4884
Fax: (508)790-2540
Co. E-mail: capecodscore@verizon.net
URL: http://capecod.score.org
Facebook: www.facebook.com/SCORECapeCod
Linkedin: www.linkedin.com/company/score-mentors-cape-cod
X (Twitter): x.com/SCOREMentors
YouTube: www.youtube.com/user/SCORESmallBusiness/featured
Pinterest: www.pinterest.com/marcgoldberg777/cape-cod-score-mentors-board

Description: Provides professional guidance and information to maximize the success of existing and emerging small businesses. Offers business counseling and workshops.

40517 ■ SCORE - Fitchburg
860 S St.
Fitchburg, MA 01420
Ph: (978)353-7600
URL: http://www.score.org/worcester/about/our-regional-offices

Description: Provides professional guidance and information to maximize the success of existing and emerging small businesses. Offers business counseling and workshops.

40518 ■ SCORE - Framingham
860 Worcester Rd.
Framingham, MA 01702
Co. E-mail: covid19@scoreboston.org
URL: http://boston.score.org

Description: Provides professional guidance and information to maximize the success of existing and emerging small businesses. Offers business counseling and workshops.

40519 ■ SCORE - Framingham Public Library
49 Lexington St.
Framingham, MA 01702
Ph: (617)565-5591
URL: http://boston.score.org
Contact: Rieva Lesonsky, President
Linkedin: www.linkedin.com/company/score-boston
X (Twitter): x.com/SCOREBoston

Description: Provides professional guidance and information to maximize the success of existing and emerging small businesses. Offers business counseling and workshops.

40520 ■ SCORE - Greenfield
395 Main St.
Greenfield, MA 01301
Ph: (413)785-0314
Co. E-mail: ch.admin0228@scorevolunteer.org
URL: http://westernmassachusetts.score.org/content/find-mentor-71

Description: Provides professional guidance and information to maximize the success of existing and emerging small businesses. Offers business counseling and workshops.

40521 ■ SCORE - Haverhill
2 Merrimack St.
Haverhill, MA 01830
Ph: (978)270-8827
URL: http://www.score.org/nemassachusetts/content/about/northeast-massachusetts-score-branches
Contact: David Brush, Branch Manager

Description: Provides professional guidance and information to maximize the success of existing and emerging small businesses. Offers business counseling and workshops.

40522 ■ SCORE - Hopkinton
13 Main St.
Hopkinton, MA 01748
Ph: (508)497-9777
URL: http://worcester.score.org
URL(s): pittsburgh.score.org/find-location

Description: Provides professional guidance and information to maximize the success of existing and emerging small businesses. Offers business counseling and workshops.

40523 ■ SCORE - Jamaica Plain
30 South St.
Jamaica Plain, MA 02130
Co. E-mail: help@score.org
URL: http://boston.score.org/greater-boston-mentoring-locations
Contact: Jack Lester, Contact

Description: Provides professional guidance and information to maximize the success of existing and emerging small businesses. Offers business counseling and workshops.

40524 ■ SCORE - Kirstein Business Library
700 Boylston St.
Boston, MA 02116
Ph: (617)565-5591
URL: http://boston.score.org/kirstein-business-library

Description: Provides professional guidance and information to maximize the success of existing and emerging small businesses. Offers business counseling and workshops.

40525 ■ SCORE - Lawrence
500A Merrimack St.
Lawrence, MA 01843
Ph: (978)922-9441
URL: http://nemassachusetts.score.org/content/branch-locator-and-counseling-schedule

Description: Provides professional guidance and information to maximize the success of existing and emerging small businesses. Offers business counseling and workshops.

40526 ■ SCORE - Lynn
583 Chestnut St.
Lynn, MA 01904
Ph: (978)922-9441
Co. E-mail: help@score.org
URL: http://nemassachusetts.score.org
Facebook: www.facebook.com/SCORENorthEastMassachusetts
Linkedin: www.linkedin.com/company/score-mentors
X (Twitter): x.com/scorementors
Instagram: www.instagram.com/score_mentors
YouTube: www.youtube.com/user/SCORESmallBusiness

Description: Provides professional guidance and information to maximize the success of existing and emerging small businesses. Offers business counseling and workshops.

40527 ■ SCORE - Milford, Massachusetts
311 Main St., Ste. 200
Worcester, MA 01608
Ph: (508)753-2929
Co. E-mail: info@scoreworcester.org
URL: http://worcester.score.org
Linkedin: www.linkedin.com/company/score-worcester-chapter

Description: Provides professional guidance and information to maximize the success of existing and emerging small businesses. Offers business counseling and workshops.

40528 ■ SCORE - Nantucket
0 Main St.
Nantucket, MA 02554
URL: http://www.score.org/capecod?set-location=28&consent=all

Description: Provides professional guidance and information to maximize the success of existing and emerging small businesses. Offers business counseling and workshops.

40529 ■ SCORE - Natick
14 East Central St.
Natick, MA 01760
Ph: (617)565-5591
Co. E-mail: help@score.org
URL: http://www.score.org/find-location?state=MA

Description: Provides professional guidance and information to maximize the success of existing and emerging small businesses. Offers business counseling and workshops.

40530 ■ SCORE - Newburyport
38R Merrimac St.
Newburyport, MA 01950
Ph: (978)462-6680
URL: http://nemassachusetts.score.org/content/branch-locator-and-counseling-schedule
Contact: Adrian Leighton, Branch Manager

Description: Provides professional guidance and information to maximize the success of existing and emerging small businesses. Offers business counseling and workshops.

40531 ■ SCORE - Newton, Massachusetts
330 Homer St.
Newton, MA 02459
Ph: (617)565-5591
URL: http://boston.score.org/greater-boston-mentoring-locations

Description: Provides professional guidance and information to maximize the success of existing and emerging small businesses. Offers business counseling and workshops.

40532 ■ SCORE - Northampton
99 Pleasant St.
Northampton, MA 01060
URL: http://www.score.org/westernmassachusetts/content/western-massachusetts-score-counseling-locations

Description: Provides professional guidance and information to maximize the success of existing and emerging small businesses. Offers business counseling and workshops.

STATE LISTINGS

40533 ■ SCORE - Orleans
44 Main St.
Orleans, MA 02653
URL: http://capecod.score.org
Contact: Bob Stein, Contact
Description: Provides professional guidance and information to maximize the success of existing and emerging small businesses. Offers business counseling and workshops.

40534 ■ SCORE - Pittsfield
66 Allen St.
Pittsfield, MA 01201
URL: http://westernmassachusetts.score.org/western-massachusetts-score-counseling-locations
Description: Provides professional guidance and information to maximize the success of existing and emerging small businesses. Offers business counseling and workshops.

40535 ■ SCORE - Plymouth, Massachusetts
100 Armstrong Rd., Ste. 204
Plymouth, MA 02360
Ph: (508)830-1620
URL: http://www.score.org/sema/content/counseling-locations-contact
Contact: Robert R. R. Kursmark, Contact
Description: Provides professional guidance and information to maximize the success of existing and emerging small businesses. Offers business counseling and workshops.

40536 ■ SCORE - Quincy
669 Hancock St.
Quincy, MA 02170
Ph: (781)682-3241
URL: http://www.score.org/sema/content/counseling-locations-contact
Facebook: www.facebook.com/SCORESEMassachusetts
Linkedin: www.linkedin.com/company/scoresema
X (Twitter): x.com/SCOREMentors
Pinterest: www.pinterest.com/scorementors
Description: Provides professional guidance and information to maximize the success of existing and emerging small businesses. Offers business counseling and workshops.

40537 ■ SCORE - Revere
126 Squire Rd.
Revere, MA 02151
Ph: (978)922-9441
URL: http://nemassachusetts.score.org/content/branch-locator-and-counseling-schedule
Contact: Ben DeWinter, Branch Manager
Description: Provides professional guidance and information to maximize the success of existing and emerging small businesses. Offers business counseling and workshops.

40538 ■ SCORE - Rockland
1050 Hingham St.
Rockland, MA 02370
Ph: (617)479-1111
URL: http://www.score.org/sema/content/counseling-locations-contact
Description: Provides professional guidance and information to maximize the success of existing and emerging small businesses. Offers business counseling and workshops. **Founded:** 1964.

40539 ■ SCORE - Rockport
247 Main St.
Rockport, MA 01966
Ph: (978)922-9441
URL: http://nemassachusetts.score.org
Description: Provides professional guidance and information to maximize the success of existing and emerging small businesses. Offers business counseling and workshops.

40540 ■ SCORE - SE Massachusetts
170 Dean St.
Taunton, MA 02780
Ph: (508)824-4068
URL: http://score.org/sema
Contact: John L. Seguin, Contact

Description: Provides professional guidance and information to maximize the success of existing and emerging small businesses. Offers business counseling and workshops.

40541 ■ SCORE - Shirley, Massachusetts
2 Shaker Rd., Ste. B200
Shirley, MA 01464
Ph: (978)425-5761
URL: http://www.score.org/worcester/about/our-regional-offices
Description: Provides professional guidance and information to maximize the success of existing and emerging small businesses. Offers business counseling and workshops.

40542 ■ SCORE - Somerville FabVille Design Lab
10 Tyler St.
Boston, MA 02119
Ph: (617)565-5591
URL: http://boston.score.org/somerville-artisans-asylum
Facebook: www.facebook.com/SCOREBoston
Linkedin: www.linkedin.com/company/score-boston
X (Twitter): twitter.com/SCOREBoston
Description: Provides professional guidance and information to maximize the success of existing and emerging small businesses. Offers business counseling and workshops.

40543 ■ SCORE - Somerville Public Library
79 Highland Ave.
Somerville, MA 02143
URL: http://boston.score.org/greater-boston-mentoring-locations
Description: Provides professional guidance and information to maximize the success of existing and emerging small businesses. Offers business counseling and workshops.

40544 ■ SCORE - Southeast Massachusetts
Metro S Chamber of Commerce
60 School St.
Brockton, MA 02301
Ph: (508)587-2673
URL: http://sema.score.org
Facebook: www.facebook.com/SCORESEMassachusetts
Linkedin: www.linkedin.com/company/scoresema
X (Twitter): x.com/SCOREMentors
Description: Provides professional guidance and information to maximize the success of existing and emerging small businesses. Offers business counseling and workshops. **Founded:** 1978. **Geographic Preference:** Local.

40545 ■ SCORE - Stoneham
80 Montvale Ave.
Stoneham, MA 02180
Ph: (203)913-0173
URL: http://www.score.org/find-mentor
Contact: Bill McLeod, Branch Manager
Description: Provides professional guidance and information to maximize the success of existing and emerging small businesses. Offers business counseling and workshops.

40546 ■ SCORE - Sturbridge
311 Main St., Ste. 200
Worcester, MA 01608
Ph: (508)753-2929
Co. E-mail: info@scoreworcester.org
URL: http://worcester.score.org
Facebook: www.facebook.com/SCOREWorcester
Description: Provides professional guidance and information to maximize the success of existing and emerging small businesses. Offers business counseling and workshops.

40547 ■ SCORE - West Massachusetts
1 Federal St., Bldg. 101
Springfield, MA 01105
Ph: (413)785-0314
Co. E-mail: contact.0228@scorevolunteer.org
URL: http://westernmassachusetts.score.org

Linkedin: www.linkedin.com/company/score-mentors-western-massachusetts
Description: Provides professional guidance and information to maximize the success of existing and emerging small businesses. Offers business counseling and workshops.

40548 ■ SCORE - West Tisbury
PO Box 913
West Tisbury, MA 02575
URL: http://capecod.score.org
Description: Provides professional guidance and information to maximize the success of existing and emerging small businesses. Offers business counseling and workshops.

40549 ■ SCORE - Westborough
30 Lyman St., 2nd Fl., Ste. 6
Westborough, MA 01581
Ph: (508)836-4444
URL: http://www.score.org/find-location?state=MA
Description: Provides professional guidance and information to maximize the success of existing and emerging small businesses. Offers business counseling and workshops.

40550 ■ SCORE - Whitinsville
670 Linwood Ave., Bldg. A, Ste. 105
Whitinsville, MA 01588
Ph: (508)234-9090
URL: http://www.score.org/worcester/about/our-regional-offices
Description: Provides professional guidance and information to maximize the success of existing and emerging small businesses. Offers business counseling and workshops.

40551 ■ SCORE - Worcester
311 Main St., Ste. 200
Worcester, MA 01608
Ph: (508)753-2929
Co. E-mail: info@scoreworcester.org
URL: http://worcester.score.org
Linkedin: www.linkedin.com/company/score-worcester-chapter
Description: Provides professional guidance and information to maximize the success of existing and emerging small businesses. Offers business counseling and workshops. **Founded:** 1967.

40552 ■ SCORE - Worcester Public Library
311 Main St., Ste. 200
Worcester, MA 01608
Co. E-mail: info@scoreworcester.org
URL: http://worcester.score.org
Contact: William C. McLeod, Contact
Description: Provides professional guidance and information to maximize the success of existing and emerging small businesses. Offers business counseling and workshops.

40553 ■ Worcester SCORE
311 Main St., Ste. 200
Worcester, MA 01608
Ph: (508)753-2929
Co. E-mail: info@scoreworcester.org
URL: http://worcester.score.org
Facebook: www.facebook.com/scoreworcester
Linkedin: www.linkedin.com/company/score-worcester-chapter
Description: Works to facilitate the formation, success and growth of small business. Provides free, confidential business counseling to individuals just starting a business and to existing small businesses. Offers low cost educational workshops on business topics. **Founded:** 1964. **Geographic Preference:** Local.

BETTER BUSINESS BUREAUS

40554 ■ Better Business Bureau Serving Central and Western Massachusetts and Northeastern Connecticut
400 Grove St.
Worcester, MA 01605
Ph: (508)755-3340

40555 ■ Massachusetts

URL: http://www.bbb.org/local-bbb/bbb-serving-central-and-western-ma-and-northeastern-ct
X (Twitter): x.com/BBB_CNE
Instagram: www.instagram.com/bbbcentralnewengland
Description: Seeks to promote and foster the highest ethical relationship between businesses and the public through voluntary self-regulation, consumer and business education, and service excellence. Provides information to help consumers and businesses make informed purchasing decisions and avoid costly scams and frauds; settles consumer complaints through arbitration and other means. **Founded:** 1940. **Awards:** Better Business Bureau of Central New England Torch Award for Marketplace Ethics (Annual). **Geographic Preference:** Regional.

40555 ■ Better Business Bureau Serving Eastern Massachusetts, Maine, Rhode Island and Vermont (BBB)
5 Mt. Royal Ave. Ste. 100
  Marlborough, MA 01752-1927
Ph: (508)652-4800
Fax: (508)652-4820
URL: http://www.bbb.org/local-bbb/better-business-bureau-serving-eastern-ma-me-ri-and-vt
Description: Fosters and promotes the highest ethical relationship between businesses and the public through voluntary self-regulation, consumer and business education, and service excellence. **Founded:** 1912. **Geographic Preference:** Regional.

CHAMBERS OF COMMERCE

40556 ■ Amherst Area Chamber of Commerce (AACC)
35 S Pleasant St.
  Amherst, MA 01002
Ph: (413)253-0700
Co. E-mail: info@amherstarea.com
URL: http://www.amherstarea.com
Contact: Lynn Gray, Manager
E-mail: president@amherstarea.com
Facebook: www.facebook.com/AmherstAreaChamberofCommerce
Linkedin: www.linkedin.com/company/amherstareacc
X (Twitter): x.com/AmherstAreaCC
Instagram: www.instagram.com/amherstareacc
YouTube: www.youtube.com/channel/UCmD9jGAVmyCEZdRWCsP1Hyg
Description: Promotes business and community development in Amherst, MA. **Founded:** 1956. **Publications:** *Community Beacon* (Monthly). **Awards:** Amherst Area Chamber of Commerce A+ Awards (Annual). **Geographic Preference:** Local.

40557 ■ Arlington Chamber of Commerce
c/o Beth Locke, Executive Director
  611 Massachusetts Ave.
  Arlington, MA 02474
Ph: (781)643-4600
Co. E-mail: info@arlcc.org
URL: http://arlcc.org
Contact: Beth Locke, Executive Director
Facebook: www.facebook.com/arlcc.org
X (Twitter): x.com/ARLINGTONMACHAM
YouTube: www.youtube.com/channel/UCr3ks9xtKfHSt8-19rYtzAA
Description: Promotes business and community development in Arlington, MA. **Founded:** 1916. **Geographic Preference:** Local.

40558 ■ Assabet Valley Chamber of Commerce
PO Box 575
  Hudson, MA 01749
Ph: (978)568-0360
Co. E-mail: info@assabetvalleychamber.org
URL: http://www.assabetvalleychamber.org
Contact: Sarah Maston, Officer
Facebook: www.facebook.com/assabetvalleychamber
X (Twitter): x.com/asvacc

Description: Promotes business and community development in Hudson, Maynard, Stow, Bolton and Berlin, MA. **Founded:** 1986. **Geographic Preference:** Local.

40559 ■ *Bedford Banner*
12 Mudge Way
  Bedford, MA 01730
URL: http://bedfordchamber.org
Contact: Maria Porto, President
URL(s): bedfordchamber.org/membership
Description: Includes information, updates and other articles concerning Bedford Chamber of Commerce. **Availability:** Print.

40560 ■ Bedford Chamber of Commerce
12 Mudge Way
  Bedford, MA 01730
URL: http://bedfordchamber.org
Contact: Maria Porto, President
Facebook: www.facebook.com/bedfordmachamber
Linkedin: www.linkedin.com/in/bedford-area-chamber-of-commerce-6641a038
X (Twitter): x.com/BEDFORDMCHAMBER
Instagram: www.instagram.com/explore/locations/1015398737/bedford-chamber-of-commerce
Description: Seeks to promote business and community interests of Bedford area. **Publications:** *Bedford Banner*. **Geographic Preference:** Local.

40561 ■ Blackstone Valley Chamber of Commerce (BVCC)
670 Linwood Ave., No. 5
  Whitinsville, MA 01588
Ph: (508)234-9090
Fax: (508)234-5152
Co. E-mail: bvadmin@blackstonevalley.org
URL: http://www.blackstonevalley.org
Contact: Jeannie Hebert, President
E-mail: jhebert@blackstonevalley.org
Facebook: www.facebook.com/BVChamberofCommerce
Linkedin: www.linkedin.com/company/blackstone-valley-chamber-of-commerce
Instagram: www.instagram.com/the_bvcc
Description: Promotes business and community development in Whitinsville, MA. **Founded:** 1979. **Publications:** *Valley Focus*. **Geographic Preference:** Regional.

40562 ■ Bristol County Chamber of Commerce, Inc.
200 Pocasset St.
  Fall River, MA 02721
Contact: Brian Lecomte, President
Description: Promotes business and community development in the Fall River, MA area. **Founded:** 1911. **Geographic Preference:** Regional.

40563 ■ Brookline Chamber of Commerce
251 Harvard St.
  Brookline, MA 02446
Ph: (617)739-1330
Fax: (617)739-1200
Co. E-mail: info@brooklinechamber.com
URL: http://www.brooklinechamber.com
Contact: David Gladstone, President
E-mail: dgladstone@brkl.com
Facebook: www.facebook.com/BrooklineChamber
Linkedin: www.linkedin.com/company/brookline-chamber-of-commerce
X (Twitter): x.com/BrooklineChmbr
Instagram: www.instagram.com/BrooklineChamber
Description: Acts as a resident and business advocate, provides marketing and networking opportunities, and is focused on improving Brookline and its surroundings. Sponsors an arts and crafts festival; holds seminars, receptions, and networking events. **Founded:** 1917. **Publications:** *Brookline Business Directory: Business Directory*; *Brookline Business Directory* (Annual); *Brookline Business Report* (Quarterly); *Business, Tourist and Shopping Directory* (Annual). **Educational Activities:** Breakfast and Networking. **Geographic Preference:** Local.

40564 ■ Cambridge Chamber of Commerce (CCC)
One Kendall Sq.
  Cambridge, MA 02139
Ph: (617)876-4100
Co. E-mail: ccinfo@cambridgechamber.org
URL: http://www.cambridgechamber.org
Contact: David Maher, President
E-mail: dmaher@cambridgechamber.org
Facebook: www.facebook.com/cambridgechamber
Linkedin: www.linkedin.com/company/cambridge-chamber-of-commerce
X (Twitter): x.com/CambridgeChambr
Instagram: www.instagram.com/cambridgechambr
YouTube: www.youtube.com/channel/UCfNMTZhfq58ZCGirJaMF4gg
Description: Promotes business and community development in Cambridge, MA area. **Founded:** 1923. **Publications:** *Cambridge Chamber of Commerce Business Directory*. **Geographic Preference:** Local.

40565 ■ Cape Ann Chamber of Commerce
24 Harbor Loop
  Gloucester, MA 01930
Ph: (978)283-1601
Co. E-mail: info@capeannchamber.com
URL: http://capeannchamber.com
Contact: Caitlin Pszenny, President
Facebook: www.facebook.com/capeannchamber
Instagram: www.instagram.com/capeannchamber
YouTube: www.youtube.com/user/CapeAnnChamber
Description: Promotes business and community development in Essex, Gloucester, Manchester, and Rockport, MA. **Founded:** 1922. **Publications:** *Soundings* (Monthly). **Geographic Preference:** Local.

40566 ■ Cape Cod Canal Region Chamber of Commerce
70 Main St.
  Buzzards Bay, MA 02532
Ph: (508)759-6000
Co. E-mail: info@capecodcanalchamber.org
URL: http://www.capecodcanalchamber.org
Contact: Marie Oliva, President
E-mail: moliva@capecodcanalchamber.org
Facebook: www.facebook.com/capecodcanalchamber
Linkedin: www.linkedin.com/company/cape-cod-canal-region-chamber-of-commerce
X (Twitter): x.com/canalcapecod
Description: Promotes business and community development in the region. **Founded:** 1978. **Publications:** *Chamber E-Connection* (Monthly). **Geographic Preference:** Local.

40567 ■ *The Chamber Report*
100 Armstrong Rd., Ste. 204
  Plymouth, MA 02360
Ph: (508)830-1620
Fax: (508)830-1621
Co. E-mail: info@plymouthchamber.com
URL: http://plymouthchamber.com
Contact: Amy Naples, Executive Director
E-mail: amy@plymouthchamber.com
URL(s): plymouthchamber.com/membership
Released: Monthly **Availability:** Online.

40568 ■ *The Chamber Speaks*
355 Main St., Ste. 202
  Stoneham, MA 02180
Ph: (781)438-0001
Fax: (781)438-0007
Co. E-mail: ed@stonehamchamber.org
URL: http://stonehamchamber.org
Contact: Jeff Buxton, President
E-mail: jeffreylbuxton@gmail.com
URL(s): stonehamchamber.org/members/advertise-with-us
Released: Bimonthly; January, March, May, July, September and November. **Availability:** Print; PDF; Online.

40569 ■ Chatham Chamber of Commerce
2377 Main St.
  South Chatham, MA 02659

STATE LISTINGS   Massachusetts ■ 40583

Ph: (508)945-5199
Free: 800-715-5567
Co. E-mail: chamber@chathaminfo.com
URL: http://www.chathaminfo.com
Contact: Gary Thulander, President
Facebook: www.facebook.com/chatham.chamber
X (Twitter): x.com/chathamchamber2
Instagram: www.instagram.com/cha
 thamchambercapecod
YouTube: www.youtube.com/channel/UC9m2O
 5oPqlQjxv6tj9Azw9g
Description: Promotes business and community development in Chatham, MA. **Founded:** 1942. **Geographic Preference:** Local.

40570 ■ Cohasset Chamber of Commerce
13 Elm St.
 Cohasset, MA 02025
Ph: (781)383-2200
Co. E-mail: lawrencecorthell@hinghamsavings.com
URL: http://www.cohassetchamber.org
Contact: Sean Cunning, Contact
Facebook: www.facebook.com/cohasse
 tchamberofcommerce
X (Twitter): x.com/CohassetChamber
Instagram: www.instagram.com/cohassetchamber
Description: Promotes business and community development in Cohasset, MA. Sponsors parade; conducts charitable activities. **Founded:** 1775. **Geographic Preference:** Local.

40571 ■ Concord Chamber of Commerce
32 Main St.
 Concord, MA 01742
Ph: (978)369-3120
Co. E-mail: info@concordchamberofcommerce.org
URL: http://www.concordchamberofcommerce.org
Contact: Marie Foley, President
E-mail: president@concordchamberofcommerce.org
Facebook: www.facebook.com/concord.chamber
Linkedin: www.linkedin.com/in/concord-chamber
 -136716223
Description: Promotes business and community development in Concord, MA. Conducts charitable programs; sponsors festival. **Publications:** *Concord Chamber of Commerce Directory*; *Cultural Events Calendar*; *The Grapevine* (Monthly); *Guide Map*; *Lexington Concord Battleroad*; *Women's Group Newsletter* (Periodic). **Geographic Preference:** Local.

40572 ■ Cranberry Country Chamber of Commerce (CCCC)
9 Clayton Rd.
 Middleboro, MA 02346
Ph: (508)947-1499
Fax: (508)947-1446
Co. E-mail: info@cranberrycountry.org
URL: http://cranberrycountry.org
Contact: Valerie Glynn, President
E-mail: valerie@cranberrycountry.org
Linkedin: www.linkedin.com/company/cranberry-coun
 try-chamber-of-commerce
X (Twitter): x.com/cranchamber
YouTube: www.youtube.com/channel/UCf
 5tCXBqVTl9g8CRQeyAVgA
Description: Seeks to enhance business community and economic environment of Middleboro, MA. **Geographic Preference:** Local.

40573 ■ East Boston Chamber of Commerce (EBCC)
464 Bremen St., Ste., 1
 East Boston, MA 02128
Ph: (617)569-5000
Co. E-mail: eastbostonchamberofcommerce@gmail
 .com
URL: http://eastbostonchamberofcommerce.com
Contact: Shirley Fabbo, President
Facebook: www.facebook.com/eastbostonchamber
Description: Promotes business and community development in East Boston, MA. **Founded:** 1960. **Publications:** *Chronicle Newsletter* (Monthly). **Geographic Preference:** Local.

40574 ■ Eastham Chamber of Commerce on Cape Cod
1700 Rte. 6
 Eastham, MA 02642
Co. E-mail: info@easthamchamber.com
URL: http://easthamchamber.com
Contact: Elizabeth Aldred, Director
Description: Promotes and encourages the spirit of fair trade and good business through activities and programs designed to benefit the commercial, cultural, and civic welfare of Eastham, MA. **Founded:** 1644. **Geographic Preference:** Local.

40575 ■ Falmouth Chamber of Commerce (FCC)
20 Academy Ln.
 Falmouth, MA 02540
Ph: (508)548-8500
Co. E-mail: info@falmouthchamber.com
URL: http://www.falmouthchamber.com
Contact: Michael Kasparian, President
E-mail: mkasparian@falmouthchamber.com
Facebook: www.facebook.com/FalmouthChamber
X (Twitter): x.com/FalmouthChamber
YouTube: www.youtube.com/user/FalmouthChamber
Description: Promotes business and community development in Falmouth, MA. Seeks to preserve and support the aesthetic integrity and character of the area by encouraging cultural, civic, and educational interest in the town. Also organizes Christmas by the Sea weekend and holiday parade during the first weekend of December; conducts annual Cape Cod Antique Market and Show and Sale. **Founded:** 1914. **Publications:** *Annual Directory and Guidebook* (Annual); *Coastlines* (Monthly); *Falmouth Brochure* (Annual). **Educational Activities:** Falmouth Chamber of Commerce Meeting (Annual). **Awards:** Falmouth Chamber of Commerce Citizen of the Year (Annual). **Geographic Preference:** Local.

40576 ■ *Flagship*
55 Elm Ave.
 Hyannis, MA 02601
Ph: (508)775-7778
Co. E-mail: info@hyannis.com
URL: http://hyannis.com
Contact: Marty Bruemmel, President
URL(s): business.hyannis.com/list/member/puritan
 -cape-cod-hyannis-771
Released: Weekly **Description:** Contains the latest news and events. **Availability:** Print.

40577 ■ Franklin County Chamber of Commerce (FCCC)
79 Old Main St.
 Deerfield, MA 01342
Ph: (413)773-5463
Co. E-mail: fccc@franklincc.org
URL: http://www.franklincc.org
Contact: Diana Szynal, Co-President
E-mail: diana@franklincc.org
Facebook: www.facebook.com/FranklinCoun
 tyChamberofCommerce
Instagram: www.instagram.com/franklincoun
 tymachamber
YouTube: www.youtube.com/channel/UC7m9g
 tBMnVy5vdQmmt_H18g
Description: Promotes business and community development in Franklin County, MA. Promotes local tourism. Sponsors music festival, and Home and Leisure Expo. **Founded:** 1919. **Publications:** *County Lines* (Monthly); *Major Employees*. **Geographic Preference:** Local.

40578 ■ Greater Beverly Chamber of Commerce (GBCC)
100 Cummings Ctr., Ste. 107K
 Beverly, MA 01915
Ph: (978)232-9559
Fax: (978)232-9372
Co. E-mail: info@greaterbeverlychamber.com
URL: http://greaterbeverlychamber.com
Contact: Kelly DeFelice, President
Facebook: www.facebook.com/beverlychamber
Linkedin: www.linkedin.com/company/grea
 terbeverlychamber/about
Description: Promotes business and community development in Beverly, MA. **Geographic Preference:** Local.

40579 ■ Greater Boston Chamber of Commerce (GBCC)
265 Franklin St., Ste. 1701
 Boston, MA 02110
Ph: (617)227-4500
Co. E-mail: chamberprograms@bostonchamber.com
URL: http://www.bostonchamber.com
Contact: James E. Rooney, President
E-mail: ceo@bostonchamber.com
Facebook: www.facebook.com/pages/Greater-Boston
 -Chamber-of-Commerce/89430334806
Linkedin: www.linkedin.com/company/greater-boston
 -chamber-of-commerce
X (Twitter): x.com/bostonchamber
YouTube: www.youtube.com/user/GreaterBos
 tonChamber
Description: Promotes business and community development in Boston, MA area. **Publications:** *Greater Boston Directory of Associations* (Biennial); *Greater Boston Chamber of Commerce--Business Directory*; *Major Employers in Greater Boston*. **Geographic Preference:** Local.

40580 ■ Greater Chicopee Chamber of Commerce
48 Center St.
 Chicopee, MA 01013
Ph: (413)594-2101
Fax: (413)594-2103
Co. E-mail: admin@chicopeechamber.org
URL: http://www.chicopeechamber.org
Contact: Mim Zayas, Chairman
Facebook: www.facebook.com/ChicopeeChamber
X (Twitter): x.com/ChamberChicopee
Description: Promotes business and community development in Chicopee, MA. **Founded:** 1962. **Publications:** *The Chamber Exchange* (Monthly). **Awards:** Business of the Year (Annual); Citizen of the Year (Annual); Volunteer of the Year (Annual). **Geographic Preference:** Local.

40581 ■ Greater Gardner Chamber of Commerce (GGCC)
29 Parker St.
 Gardner, MA 01440-6381
Ph: (978)632-1780
Fax: (978)630-1767
Co. E-mail: info@gardnerma.com
URL: http://gardnerma.com
Contact: Micheal Gerry, Co-President Co-Chief
 Executive Officer
Description: Promotes economic development and tourism in Worcester County, MA. Sponsors Experience Gardner Summer Festival, annual Golf Tournament, and Northeast Clambake. **Founded:** 1889. **Publications:** *Business Calendar*; *Business Voice* (Monthly). **Geographic Preference:** Local.

40582 ■ Greater Haverhill Chamber of Commerce
2 Merrimack St., 3rd Fl.
 Haverhill, MA 01830
Ph: (978)373-5663
Fax: (978)373-8060
Co. E-mail: info@haverhillchamber.com
URL: http://haverhillchamber.com
Contact: Alex Eberhardt, President
E-mail: president@haverhillchamber.com
Facebook: www.facebook.com/Grea
 terHaverhillChamber
Linkedin: www.linkedin.com/company/grea
 terhaverhillchamber
X (Twitter): x.com/GrHavChamber
Instagram: www.instagram.com/grhaverhillchamber
Description: Promotes business and community development in Haverhill, MA. **Founded:** 1888. **Geographic Preference:** Local.

40583 ■ Greater Holyoke Chamber of Commerce (GHC)
177 High St.
 Holyoke, MA 01040
Ph: (413)534-3376

Small Business Sourcebook • 42nd Edition

Co. E-mail: hello@holyokechamber.com
URL: http://www.holyokechamber.com
Contact: Barry Feingold, President
Facebook: www.facebook.com/growholyoke
Description: Aims to strengthen the economy of Greater Holyoke by representing and involving the business community in public policy decisions affecting the business climate, by helping individual businesses to prosper, and by creating a community environment conducive to economic opportunity and a positive quality of life. **Founded:** 1890. **Geographic Preference:** Local.

40584 ■ Greater Hyannis Area Chamber of Commerce
55 Elm Ave.
  Hyannis, MA 02601
Ph: (508)775-7778
Co. E-mail: info@hyannis.com
URL: http://hyannis.com
Contact: Marty Bruemmel, President
Facebook: www.facebook.com/hyannischamber
Linkedin: www.linkedin.com/company/hyannis-area
  -chamber-of-commerce
X (Twitter): x.com/hyachamber
Description: Promotes business and community development in the Hyannis, MA area. **Founded:** 1982. **Publications:** *Flagship* (Weekly). **Geographic Preference:** Local.

40585 ■ Greater Lowell Chamber of Commerce (GLCC)
133 Merrimack St., 2nd Fl.
  Lowell, MA 01852
Ph: (978)459-8154
Fax: (978)452-4145
Co. E-mail: dmcfadden@greaterlowellchamber.org
URL: http://greaterlowellcc.org
Contact: Danielle McFadden, President
E-mail: dmcfadden@greaterlowellchamber.org
Facebook: www.facebook.com/greaterlowellchamber
X (Twitter): x.com/greaterlowellcc
Instagram: www.instagram.com/grea
  terlowellchamber
YouTube: www.youtube.com/channel/UCG2EmFRu
  6RRn51Aat8RetNA
Description: Seeks to enhance the business community and quality of life of Lowell, MA area. Supports local charities; conducts political and business networking forums. **Geographic Preference:** Local.

40586 ■ Greater Lynn Chamber of Commerce (LACC)
583 Chestnut St.
  Lynn, MA 01904
Ph: (781)592-2900
Fax: (781)592-2903
Co. E-mail: info@greaterlynnchamber.com
URL: http://greaterlynnchamber.com
Contact: Colin Codner, Executive Director
E-mail: colin@greaterlynnchamber.com
Facebook: www.facebook.com/GreaterLynnChamber
X (Twitter): x.com/GreaterLynnCC
Instagram: www.instagram.com/greaterlynnchamber
Description: Represents the interests of the Lynn area business community at the local, state, and federal levels of government. Provides community programs and public advocacy in the area. **Founded:** 1912. **Geographic Preference:** Local.

40587 ■ Greater Newburyport Chamber of Commerce and Industry
38R Merrimac St.
  Newburyport, MA 01950
Ph: (978)462-6680
Co. E-mail: info@newburyportchamber.org
URL: http://www.newburyportchamber.org
Contact: Frank G. Cousins, Jr., President
Facebook: www.facebook.com/nbptchamber
Linkedin: www.linkedin.com/company/nbptchamber
Instagram: www.instagram.com/nbptchamber
YouTube: www.youtube.com/user/nbptchamber
Description: Seeks to address member needs and to be a leader in economic development. **Founded:** 1966. **Publications:** *Navigator* (Monthly). **Geographic Preference:** Local.

40588 ■ Greater Northampton Chamber of Commerce (GNCC)
99 Pleasant St.
  Northampton, MA 01060
Ph: (413)584-1900
Co. E-mail: info@explorenorthampton.com
URL: http://www.northamptonchamber.com
Contact: Richard Horton, President
Facebook: www.facebook.com/GreaterNorthamp
  tonChamberofCommerce
Linkedin: www.linkedin.com/company/greater-nor
  thampton-chamber-of-commerce
Instagram: www.instagram.com/greaternorthamp
  tonchamber
YouTube: www.youtube.com/channel/
  UChYlZEOljFDxbQsYBN_Dvhg
Description: Promotes business and community development in the Northampton, MA area. **Publications:** *Greater Northampton Chamber of Commerce--Membership Directory* (Annual). **Geographic Preference:** Local.

40589 ■ Guide
860 S St.
  Fitchburg, MA 01420
Ph: (978)353-7600
Fax: (978)353-4896
Co. E-mail: chamber@northcentralmass.com
URL: http://www.northcentralmass.com
Contact: Roy M. Nascimento, President
E-mail: rnascimento@northcentralmass.com
URL(s): www.northcentralmass.com/news/publica
  tionswww.visitnorthcentral.com
Released: Semiannual; spring/summer and fall/winter editions. **Availability:** Print; Online.

40590 ■ Hanover Chamber of Commerce
PO Box 68
  Hanover, MA 02339
Co. E-mail: chamber@hanovermachamber.com
URL: http://www.hanovermachamber.com
Contact: Erin Richardson, President
Description: Promotes business and community development in Hanover, MA. **Founded:** 1964. **Publications:** *Anchor News Bulletin* (Monthly). **Geographic Preference:** Local.

40591 ■ Harwich Chamber of Commerce (HCC)
1 Schoolhouse Rd.
  Harwich Port, MA 02646
Ph: (508)430-1165
Co. E-mail: cyndi@harwichcc.com
URL: http://harwichcc.com/cape-cod-vacation
Contact: Rich Hristov, President
Facebook: www.facebook.com/HarwichCapeCod
Pinterest: www.pinterest.com/harwichcapecod
Description: Promotes business and community development in Harwich Port, MA. Sponsors events. **Publications:** *Map and Guide* (Biennial); *Notice*. **Geographic Preference:** Local.

40592 ■ Lenox Chamber of Commerce (LCC)
4 Housatonic St.
  Lenox, MA 01240
Ph: (413)637-3646
Co. E-mail: info@lenox.org
URL: http://lenox.org
Contact: Sheila O'Riley, Contact
Facebook: www.facebook.com/LenoxChamber
X (Twitter): x.com/LenoxChamber
Instagram: www.instagram.com/visitlenox
Description: Promotes member businesses and community development in Lenox, MA. **Founded:** 1975. **Publications:** *An Official Guide To Lenox* (Annual). **Geographic Preference:** Local.

40593 ■ Lexington Chamber of Commerce (LCC)
1620 Massachusetts Ave.
  Lexington, MA 02420
Ph: (781)862-2480
Co. E-mail: director@lexingtonchamber.org
URL: http://www.lexingtonchamber.org
Contact: Erin Sandler-Rathe, Executive Director
Facebook: www.facebook.com/Lexing
  tonMAChamber
Linkedin: www.linkedin.com/company/lexington
  -chamber-of-commerce
Instagram: www.instagram.com/lexing
  tonchamberofcommerce
YouTube: www.youtube.com/channel/UCnJEK
  64ZGlF4ElRlPdjc2-A
Description: Promotes business and community development in Lexington, MA. Sponsors annual Discovery Day Festival, annual Oktoberfest, 10K road race, and other social and promotional activities. **Founded:** 1939. **Publications:** *Visitor's Guide* (Annual). **Geographic Preference:** Local.

40594 ■ Malden Chamber of Commerce (MCC)
PO Box 639
  Malden, MA 02148
Ph: (781)322-4500
Co. E-mail: info@maldenchamber.org
URL: http://www.maldenchamber.org
Contact: Hilda Torres, President
Facebook: www.facebook.com/MaldenChamber
X (Twitter): x.com/MaldenMAChamber
Instagram: www.instagram.com/maldenchamber
Description: Promotes business and community development in Malden, MA. **Founded:** 1891. **Publications:** *View Points* (Bimonthly); *Business Review* (Bimonthly). **Awards:** Malden Chamber of Commerce Business of the Year (Annual). **Geographic Preference:** Local.

40595 ■ Marblehead Chamber of Commerce
62 Pleasant St.
  Marblehead, MA 01945
Ph: (781)631-2868
Fax: (781)639-8582
Co. E-mail: info@marbleheadchamber.org
URL: http://www.marbleheadchamber.org
Contact: Dan Brothers, President
Facebook: www.facebook.com/marbleheadchamber
X (Twitter): x.com/visitmarblehead
Description: Promotes business and community development in Marblehead, MA. Sponsors Christmas Walk and festival. **Publications:** *Marblehead Chamber of Commerce Business Directory*. **Educational Activities:** Business Breakfast Forums. **Geographic Preference:** Local.

40596 ■ Marlborough Regional Chamber of Commerce (MRCC)
11 Florence St.
  Marlborough, MA 01752-2822
Ph: (508)485-7746
Co. E-mail: marlcham@marlboroughchamber.org
URL: http://www.marlboroughchamber.org
Contact: Robert Schlacter, Co-President Co-Chief Executive Officer
E-mail: rschlacter@marlboroughchamber.org
Facebook: www.facebook.com/MarlboroughChamber
X (Twitter): x.com/MarlboroChamber
Instagram: www.instagram.com/marlboroughchamber
YouTube: www.youtube.com/channel/UCwQppZldow
  _Wd6fNjDf8gBA
Description: Promotes and advocates for business and civic interests in the Marlborough, MA area and collaborates with the community for the overall economic benefit of the region. **Founded:** 1924. **Publications:** *It's Your Business*. **Educational Activities:** MERC Annual Conference (Annual). **Geographic Preference:** Local.

40597 ■ Martha's Vineyard Chamber of Commerce (MVCC)
24 Beach Rd.
  Vineyard Haven, MA 02568
Ph: (508)693-0085
Fax: (508)693-7589
Co. E-mail: info@mvy.com
URL: http://www.mvy.com
Contact: Greg Orcutt, Executive Director
Facebook: www.facebook.com/visitmv
X (Twitter): x.com/VisitMV
Description: Promotes tourism, business, and community development on the island of Martha's Vineyard, MA. **Founded:** 1978. **Publications:** *The Visitors Guide*. **Geographic Preference:** Local.

STATE LISTINGS

40598 ■ Medford Chamber of Commerce
1 Shipyard Way, Ste. 302
Medford, MA 02155
Ph: (781)396-1277
URL: http://medfordchamberma.com
Contact: Maury Carroll, President
Facebook: www.facebook.com/medfordmachamber
X (Twitter): x.com/medchamberma
YouTube: www.youtube.com/watch

Description: Promotes business and community development in Medford, MA. **Founded:** 1926. **Geographic Preference:** Local.

40599 ■ Melrose Chamber of Commerce
1 W Foster St.
Melrose, MA 02176
Ph: (781)665-3033
Co. E-mail: info@melrosechamber.org
URL: http://www.melrosechamber.org
Contact: Louis P. Izzi, President
Facebook: www.facebook.com/MelroseChamber
X (Twitter): x.com/melrosechamber2

Description: Seeks to enhance the professional and business communities of Melrose, MA through programs, publicity, and public relations strategies. **Geographic Preference:** Local.

40600 ■ Merrimack Valley Chamber of Commerce (MVCC)
264 Essex St.
Lawrence, MA 01840-1496
Ph: (978)686-0900
Co. E-mail: office@merrimackvalleychamber.com
URL: http://merrimackvalleychamber.com
Contact: Michael Bevilacqua, Vice President
Facebook: www.facebook.com/MERRIMACKVALLEYCHAMBER
X (Twitter): x.com/mv_chamber
Instagram: www.instagram.com/merrimackvalleychamber
YouTube: www.youtube.com/channel/UCyTZurpOtpIV0Jl-nXKnUKw

Description: Promotes business and community development in the Merrimack Valley, MA area. **Founded:** 1888. **Publications:** *Economic Development Promotional Brochure*. **Educational Activities:** Business EXPO/Trade Show (Semiannual). **Awards:** Wilkinson Award (Annual). **Geographic Preference:** Local.

40601 ■ Metro South Chamber of Commerce
60 School St.
Brockton, MA 02301
Ph: (508)586-0500
Fax: (508)587-1340
Co. E-mail: info@metrosouthchamber.com
URL: http://metrosouthchamber.com
Contact: Christopher Cooney, President
E-mail: chris@metrosouthchamber.com
Facebook: www.facebook.com/metrosouthchambercommerce
Linkedin: www.linkedin.com/company/metro-south-chamber-of-commerce
X (Twitter): x.com/MetroSouth
YouTube: www.youtube.com/channel/UC14Oap-wsyVZ6aZ0NQHLvaw/featured

Description: Supports and promotes the local business community through leadership in public advocacy, education, networking, information and community development. **Founded:** 1913. **Geographic Preference:** Local.

40602 ■ MetroWest Chamber of Commerce
860 Worcester Rd.
Framingham, MA 01702
Ph: (508)879-5600
Fax: (508)875-9325
Co. E-mail: info@metrowest.org
URL: http://www.metrowest.org
Contact: Jamie Stafslien, Co-President Co-Chief Executive Officer
Facebook: www.facebook.com/MetroWestChamber
Linkedin: www.linkedin.com/groups/1816646
X (Twitter): x.com/mwcoc
Instagram: www.instagram.com/metrowestchamber

Description: Promotes business and community development in South Middlesex County, MA. **Founded:** 1895. **Publications:** *Member Directory and Buyer's Guide* (Annual); *MetroWest Business* (Bimonthly); *MetroWest Chamber of Commerce--Directory*. **Educational Activities:** Business After Hours (Monthly); Business Networking Breakfasts. **Geographic Preference:** Local.

40603 ■ Middlesex West Chamber of Commerce (MWCOC)
179 Great Rd., Ste. 104B
Acton, MA 01720
Ph: (978)263-0010
Fax: (978)264-0303
Co. E-mail: info@mwcoc.com
URL: http://mwcoc.com
Contact: Jonathan Kerr, Executive Director
Facebook: www.facebook.com/MiddlesexWestChamber
X (Twitter): x.com/MWestChamber/status/740895235799166976

Description: Promotes business and community development in the region. **Geographic Preference:** Regional.

40604 ■ Milford Area Chamber of Commerce (MACC)
258 Main St., Ste. 306
Milford, MA 01757
Ph: (508)473-6700
Fax: (508)473-8467
Co. E-mail: locallaghan@milfordchamber.org
URL: http://milfordchamber.org
Contact: Laura O'Callaghan, President
E-mail: locallaghan@milfordchamber.org
Facebook: www.facebook.com/milfordchamber
X (Twitter): x.com/MACCommerce
Instagram: www.instagram.com/maccommerce
YouTube: www.youtube.com/user/MilfordChamber
Pinterest: www.pinterest.com/MilfordAreaCC

Description: Unites businesses and professionals, and creates central agency to improve business community in Milford area. **Founded:** 1922. **Publications:** *ChamberNEWS* (Monthly). **Geographic Preference:** Local.

40605 ■ Nantucket Island Chamber of Commerce
Zero Main St., 2nd Fl.
Nantucket, MA 02554
Ph: (508)228-1700
Co. E-mail: info@nantucketchamber.org
URL: http://www.nantucketchamber.org
Contact: Robin Kirk, President
Facebook: www.facebook.com/ACKChamber
X (Twitter): x.com/VisitNantucket
Instagram: www.instagram.com/ackchamber
YouTube: www.youtube.com/channel/UC_qo3RjuqsoQNI_hqrUd3Ew
Pinterest: www.pinterest.com/visitnantucket

Description: Promotes business and community development in the Nantucket, MA area. Sponsors festivals, activities, and events to encourage tourism. **Founded:** 1937. **Publications:** *Travel and Lodging Brochure* (Annual); *Nantucket Island Chamber of Commerce--Official Guide*. **Geographic Preference:** Local.

40606 ■ Nashoba Valley Chamber of Commerce (NVCOC)
2 Shaker Rd., Ste. B200
Shirley, MA 01464
Ph: (978)425-5761
Fax: (978)425-5764
Co. E-mail: director@nvcoc.com
URL: http://business.nvcoc.com
Contact: Melissa Fetterhoff, President
Facebook: www.facebook.com/NVCoC
Linkedin: www.linkedin.com/company/nashoba-valley-chamber-of-commerce
X (Twitter): x.com/NashobaVChamber
Instagram: www.instagram.com/nashobavchamber
YouTube: www.youtube.com/user/NashobaValleyChamber
Pinterest: www.pinterest.com/nashobavchamber

Description: Promotes business and community development in Nashoba Valley. **Publications:** *Chamber Connections* (Monthly). **Geographic Preference:** Local.

40607 ■ Neponset River Regional Chamber (NRRC)
83 Morse St., Ste. 6
Norwood, MA 02062
Ph: (781)769-1126
Co. E-mail: info@nrrchamber.com
URL: http://nrrchamber.com
Contact: Thomas J. O'Rourke, President
E-mail: tom@nrrchamber.com
Facebook: www.facebook.com/NeponsetRiverRegionalChamber
Linkedin: www.linkedin.com/company/neponset-river-regional-chamber
X (Twitter): x.com/NV_chamber

Description: Promotes business and community development in Norfolk County, MA. **Founded:** 1894. **Publications:** *Neponset Valley Business Connection* (Monthly). **Educational Activities:** Networking Events-B. **Awards:** Neponset Valley Business of the Year (Annual); Neponset Valley Business Person of Year (Annual); Paul Smith Volunteer of the Year (Annual). **Geographic Preference:** Local.

40608 ■ *Neponset Valley Business Connection*
83 Morse St., Ste. 6
Norwood, MA 02062
Ph: (781)769-1126
Co. E-mail: info@nrrchamber.com
URL: http://nrrchamber.com
Contact: Thomas J. O'Rourke, President
E-mail: tom@nrrchamber.com
URL(s): nrrchamber.com/newsletter.html

Released: Monthly **Description:** Promotes member and business in Neponset Valley. **Availability:** Online.

40609 ■ Newton - Needham Chamber of Commerce [Charles River Regional Chamber]
117 Kendrick st., Ste. 300
Needham, MA 02494
Ph: (617)244-5300
Co. E-mail: info@nnchamber.com
URL: http://www.charlesriverchamber.com
Contact: Greg Reibman, President
E-mail: greibman@charlesriverchamber.com
Facebook: www.facebook.com/crrchamber
Linkedin: www.linkedin.com/company/crrchamber
X (Twitter): x.com/crrchamber
Instagram: www.instagram.com/crrchamber

Description: Promotes business and community development in Newton, Needham and neighboring areas. **Founded:** 1969. **Publications:** *Business*; *IN-Business* (Bimonthly). **Geographic Preference:** Local.

40610 ■ North Central Massachusetts Chamber of Commerce (NCMCC)
860 S St.
Fitchburg, MA 01420
Ph: (978)353-7600
Fax: (978)353-4896
Co. E-mail: chamber@northcentralmass.com
URL: http://www.northcentralmass.com
Contact: Roy M. Nascimento, President
E-mail: rnascimento@northcentralmass.com
Facebook: www.facebook.com/ncmchamber
Linkedin: www.linkedin.com/groups/North-Central-Massachusetts-Chamber-Commerce-8253188
X (Twitter): x.com/ncmchamber

Description: Promotes business and community development in North Central Massachusetts. **Founded:** 1984. **Publications:** *The Guide* (Semiannual); *Manufacturers Directory* (Annual); *Guide* (Semiannual); *NorthCentralMass.com* (Quarterly). **Geographic Preference:** Local.

40611 ■ North Quabbin Chamber of Commerce (NQ)
80 Freedom St.
Athol, MA 01331
Ph: (978)249-3849

Co. E-mail: info@northquabbinchamber.com
URL: http://www.northquabbinchamber.com
Contact: Melissa Eaton, President
E-mail: melissa.eaton@northquabbinchamber.com
Facebook: www.facebook.com/Nor
thQuabbinChamber
Linkedin: www.linkedin.com/north-quabbin-chamber-and-visitors-bureau
X (Twitter): x.com/NQChamber
Instagram: www.instagram.com/nqvisitorsbureau
Description: Promotes business and community development in the North Quabbin region of Massachusetts. **Founded:** 1982. **Geographic Preference:** Local.

40612 ■ North Shore Chamber of Commerce
5 Cherry Hill Dr., Ste. 100
Danvers, MA 01923
Ph: (978)774-8565
Co. E-mail: info@northshorechamber.org
URL: http://www.northshorechamber.org
Contact: Karen Andreas, President
E-mail: karen.andreas@northshorechamber.org
Facebook: www.facebook.com/northshorechamber
X (Twitter): x.com/NSChamber
Instagram: www.instagram.com/northshorechamber
YouTube: www.youtube.com/user/TheNor
thShoreChamber
Description: Shapes public policy and events to ensure business and government decisions to improve the economy and quality of life of North Shore community. **Founded:** 1918. **Publications:** *North Shore Business Journal* (Monthly); *North Shore Chamber of Commerce--Membership Directory*. **Geographic Preference:** Local.

40613 ■ North Suburban Chamber of Commerce
3 Baldwin Green Common, Ste. 204
Woburn, MA 01801
Contact: James A. McCurdy, President
Description: Promotes business and community development in the Woburn, MA area. **Geographic Preference:** Local.

40614 ■ *NorthCentralMass.com*
860 S St.
Fitchburg, MA 01420
Ph: (978)353-7600
Fax: (978)353-4896
Co. E-mail: chamber@northcentralmass.com
URL: http://www.northcentralmass.com
Contact: Roy M. Nascimento, President
E-mail: rnascimento@northcentralmass.com
URL(s): www.northcentralmass,com/news/newsletter
Released: Quarterly **Availability:** PDF; Online.

40615 ■ Peabody Chamber of Commerce
58 Pulaski St., Unit B4-7
Peabody, MA 01960
Ph: (978)531-0384
Co. E-mail: director@peabodychamber.com
URL: http://www.peabodychamber.com
Contact: Matthew Genzale, Chairman
X (Twitter): x.com/PeabodyChamber
Description: Promotes business and community development in the Peabody, MA area. **Founded:** 1932. **Publications:** *Business to Business News* (Monthly); *Local Phone Guide* (Annual). **Educational Activities:** Peabody Chamber of Commerce Luncheon. **Geographic Preference:** Local.

40616 ■ Plymouth Area Chamber of Commerce (PACC)
100 Armstrong Rd., Ste. 204
Plymouth, MA 02360
Ph: (508)830-1620
Fax: (508)830-1621
Co. E-mail: info@plymouthchamber.com
URL: http://plymouthchamber.com
Contact: Amy Naples, Executive Director
E-mail: amy@plymouthchamber.com
Facebook: www.facebook.com/plymou
thareachamberofcommerce
X (Twitter): x.com/pacc1620
Instagram: www.instagram.com/plymou
thareachamberofcommerce

YouTube: www.youtube.com/channel/UCk__-siN_HK
tkqh13MBHuvg
Description: Promotes business and community development in Plymouth County, MA. Holds training sessions, board meetings, committee meetings, and more. **Founded:** 1949. **Publications:** *The Chamber Report* (Monthly); *Guide to Downtown Plymouth* (Annual). **Geographic Preference:** Local.

40617 ■ Provincetown Chamber of Commerce
307 Commercial St., Lopez Sq.
Provincetown, MA 02657
Ph: (508)487-3424
Fax: (508)487-8966
Co. E-mail: info@ptownchamber.com
URL: http://ptownchamber.com
Contact: Radu Luca, Executive Director
Facebook: www.facebook.com/PtownChamber
X (Twitter): x.com/PtownChamber
Instagram: www.instagram.com/PtownChamber
Description: Promotes business and community development in Provincetown, MA. Promotes tourism. **Founded:** 1953. **Publications:** *Provincetown Chamber of Commerce--Visitor's Guide* (Annual); *Provincetown Chamber of Commerce - Winter Visitor Guide*. **Educational Activities:** Board of Directors (Annual). **Geographic Preference:** Local.

40618 ■ *Provincetown Chamber of Commerce--Visitor's Guide*
307 Commercial St., Lopez Sq.
Provincetown, MA 02657
Ph: (508)487-3424
Fax: (508)487-8966
Co. E-mail: info@ptownchamber.com
URL: http://ptownchamber.com
Contact: Radu Luca, Executive Director
URL(s): ptownchamber.com/visitors-guide
Released: Annual; latest issue 2023-2024. **Availability:** Online.

40619 ■ *Provincetown Chamber of Commerce - Winter Visitor Guide*
307 Commercial St., Lopez Sq.
Provincetown, MA 02657
Ph: (508)487-3424
Fax: (508)487-8966
Co. E-mail: info@ptownchamber.com
URL: http://ptownchamber.com
Contact: Radu Luca, Executive Director
URL(s): ptownchamber.com/winter-visitor-guide
Availability: Print.

40620 ■ Quaboag Hills Chamber of Commerce (QHCC)
4 Springfield St., Three Rivers, Ste. 525
Three Rivers, MA 01080
Ph: (413)283-2418
Co. E-mail: info@qhma.com
URL: http://qhma.com
Contact: Renee Niedziela, Treasurer
Facebook: www.facebook.com/QuaboagChamber
Description: Promotes business and community development in Quaboag Valley area of Massachusetts. Sponsors seminars and workshops and annual Legislators' Night and Citizen of the Year dinners. Provides insurance plan. **Publications:** *Your Business*. **Geographic Preference:** Local.

40621 ■ Reading-North Reading Chamber of Commerce (RNRCC)
PO Box 771
Reading, MA 01867
Ph: (978)664-5060
Co. E-mail: legan@rnrchamber.com
URL: http://www.readingnreadingchamber.org
Contact: Jenniffer Rogers, President
Facebook: www.facebook.com/ReadingNorthRea
dingChamberofCommerce
X (Twitter): x.com/townofreadingma
Description: Keeps its members aware of issues concerning them on the state and local levels, or issues that impact the business community as a whole. **Founded:** 1989. **Geographic Preference:** Local.

40622 ■ Revere Chamber of Commerce (RCC)
313 Broadway
Revere, MA 02151
Ph: (781)629-5442
URL: http://www.reverechamber.org
Contact: Patrick Lospennato, President
E-mail: patlospennato@gmail.com
Facebook: www.facebook.com/reverechamber.org
Instagram: www.instagram.com/
reverechamberofcommerce
Description: Businesses, organizations, and interested individuals. Promotes business and community development in Revere, MA. **Founded:** 1915. **Publications:** *Chamber Membership Directory*; *The Revere Chamber Now* (Monthly). **Geographic Preference:** Local.

40623 ■ Salem Chamber of Commerce
265 Essex St.
Salem, MA 01970
Ph: (978)744-0004
Co. E-mail: info@salem-chamber.org
URL: http://www.salem-chamber.org
Contact: Tina Jordan, President
Facebook: www.facebook.com/SalemMaChamber
Linkedin: www.linkedin.com/company/salem-chamber-of-commerce
X (Twitter): x.com/SalemMAChamber
Instagram: www.instagram.com/salemchamber
Pinterest: www.pinterest.co.kr/pin/2221541941049
16867
Description: Represents the interests of member businesses and works to enhance the business environment of Salem, MA. **Founded:** 1912. **Publications:** *Salem Chamber of Commerce--Membership Directory*. **Geographic Preference:** Local.

40624 ■ Sandwich Chamber of Commerce
520 Rte. 130
Sandwich, MA 02563
Ph: (508)681-0918
Co. E-mail: info@sandwichchamber.com
URL: http://www.sandwichchamber.com
Contact: Beverly Comeau, President
Facebook: www.facebook.com/san
dwichchamberofcommerce
Description: Works to provide a favorable business climate by acting as a vehicle to help promote the area's economic progress. Supports the development of the business community and to improve the quality of life for those that live and work in the area. **Founded:** 1979. **Publications:** *Business Connection* (Monthly). **Geographic Preference:** Local.

40625 ■ Scituate Chamber of Commerce
PO Box 401
Scituate, MA 02066
Ph: (781)545-4000
Co. E-mail: info@scituatechamber.org
URL: http://scituatechamber.org
Contact: Susan Fiore, President
E-mail: susan@ksi.design
Facebook: www.facebook.com/Scituate-Chamber-of-Commerce-195754347114770
Description: Works to support and promote the well-being of Scituate's business community. Encourages partnership and collaboration among businesses. Provides opportunities for networking, community involvement and professional growth. **Founded:** 1957. **Geographic Preference:** Local.

40626 ■ Somerville Chamber of Commerce
2 Alpine St.
Somerville, MA 02144
Ph: (617)776-4100
URL: http://somervillechamber.org
Contact: Stephen V. Mackey, President
E-mail: smackey@somervillechamber.org
X (Twitter): x.com/SomervilleChamb
Description: Promotes business and community development in Somerville, MA. **Founded:** 1946. **Geographic Preference:** Local.

STATE LISTINGS

40627 ■ South Hadley and Granby Chamber of Commerce
2 Lyman St.
South Hadley, MA 01075
Ph: (413)532-6451
Co. E-mail: contact@shadleygranbychamber.com
URL: http://www.shgchamber.com
Contact: Regina Zebrowski, President
Facebook: www.facebook.com/shgchamber

Description: Promotes business and community development in South Hadley, MA. **Founded:** 1959. **Geographic Preference:** Local.

40628 ■ South Shore Chamber of Commerce (SSCC)
1050 Hingham St.
Rockland, MA 02370
Ph: (781)421-3900
Co. E-mail: info@southshorechamber.org
URL: http://www.southshorechamber.org
Contact: Peter Forman, President
E-mail: pforman@southshorechamber.org
Facebook: www.facebook.com/sou
thshorechamberofcommerce
Linkedin: www.linkedin.com/company/southshore
-chamber-of-commerce
X (Twitter): x.com/sschamber
Instagram: www.instagram.com/southshorechamber

Description: Seeks to improve the business climate of South Shore region. **Founded:** 2012. **Geographic Preference:** Local.

40629 ■ SouthCoast Chamber
227 Union St., Mezzanine 2
New Bedford, MA 02740
Ph: (508)999-5231
Fax: (508)999-5237
URL: http://onesouthcoast.com
Contact: Eileen Danahey, Chairman
Facebook: www.facebook.com/southcoastchamber
Linkedin: www.linkedin.com/company/new-bedfor
d-area-chamber-of-commerce
X (Twitter): x.com/newbedfordarea

Description: Seeks to enhance business community and quality of life in South Coast region. **Founded:** 1885. **Publications:** *Chamber Focus* (Bimonthly). **Geographic Preference:** Local.

40630 ■ Southern Berkshire Chamber of Commerce (SBCC)
40 Railroad St., Ste. 2
Great Barrington, MA 01230
Ph: (413)528-1510
Fax: (413)528-2200
Co. E-mail: info@southernberkshirechamber.com
URL: http://southernberkshirechamber.com
Contact: Bill Tighe, President
Facebook: www.facebook.com/sou
thernberkshirechamber
X (Twitter): x.com/SBerkChamber
Instagram: www.instagram.com/sberkchamber

Description: Promotes business and community development in the southern Berkshire region. **Founded:** 1920. **Publications:** *Community Guide & Business Directory*; *Speaking For Business* (Monthly). **Geographic Preference:** Regional.

40631 ■ Stockbridge Chamber of Commerce (SCC)
50 Main St.
Stockbridge, MA 01262
Ph: (413)298-5200
Fax: (413)931-3128
Co. E-mail: info@stockbridgechamber.org
URL: http://stockbridgechamber.org
Contact: Pamela L. Boudreau, President
Facebook: www.facebook.com/pages/Stockbridge
-Chamber-of-Commerce/198442233650045

Description: Promotes business and community development in Stockbridge, MA. **Publications:** *Welcome to Stockbridge Massachusetts*. **Educational Activities:** Summer Arts and Crafts in Stockbridge Show (Annual). **Geographic Preference:** Local.

40632 ■ Stoneham Chamber of Commerce
355 Main St., Ste. 202
Stoneham, MA 02180
Ph: (781)438-0001
Fax: (781)438-0007
Co. E-mail: ed@stonehamchamber.org
URL: http://stonehamchamber.org
Contact: Jeff Buxton, President
E-mail: jeffreylbuxton@gmail.com
Facebook: www.facebook.com/StonehamChamber
X (Twitter): x.com/stonehamchamber
Instagram: www.instagram.com/stoneham_chamber

Description: Promotes business and community development in Stoneham, MA. **Founded:** 1984. **Publications:** *Business Directory*; *The Chamber Speaks* (Bimonthly). **Geographic Preference:** Local.

40633 ■ Swedish American Chamber of Commerce New England (SACC-NE)
399 Boylston St., 6th Fl.
Boston, MA 02116
Co. E-mail: info@sacc-ne.org
URL: http://www.sacc-ne.org
Contact: Rasmus Goksor, Chief Executive Officer
Facebook: www.facebook.com/saccne
Linkedin: www.linkedin.com/company/sacc-ne
X (Twitter): x.com/saccne
Instagram: www.instagram.com/saccne

Description: Accelerate trade, commerce, investment relationships and promote entrepreneurship, innovation and business opportunities. **Founded:** 1988. **Geographic Preference:** Regional.

40634 ■ Taunton Area Chamber of Commerce (TACC)
170 Dean St.
Taunton, MA 02780
Ph: (508)824-4068
Co. E-mail: info@tauntonareachamber.org
URL: http://www.tauntonareachamber.org
Contact: Kris Silva, President
E-mail: kris@tauntonareachamber.org
Facebook: www.facebook.com/TauntonAreaChamber
Instagram: www.instagram.com/tauntonareachamber
YouTube: www.youtube.com/channel/UCrO_0YSwK
4uZxn6kWW6QmhA

Description: Promotes business and community development in the Taunton, MA area. **Founded:** 1917. **Publications:** *Chamber Connection* (Weekly). **Geographic Preference:** Local.

40635 ■ Town Map
226 Lowell St.
Wilmington, MA 01887
Ph: (978)657-7211
Fax: (978)657-0139
Co. E-mail: wilmingtonchamber@verizon.net
URL: http://www.wilmingtonbusiness.com
Contact: Mike Champoux, President
URL(s): www.wilmingtonbusiness.com/relo.htm
Availability: Print.

40636 ■ Tri-Town Chamber of Commerce
Bldg. L100
280 School St.
Mansfield, MA 02048
Ph: (508)339-5655
Fax: (508)339-8333
Co. E-mail: office@tri-townchamber.org
URL: http://www.tri-townchamber.org
Contact: Kara Griffin, Executive Director
Linkedin: www.linkedin.com/company/tri-town
-chamber-of-commerce
X (Twitter): x.com/TriTownChamber

Description: Promotes business and community development in Foxborough, Mansfield, and Norton, MA. **Founded:** 1986. **Geographic Preference:** Local.

40637 ■ United Regional Chamber of Commerce
310 S St.
Plainville, MA 02762
Ph: (508)316-0861
URL: http://unitedregionalchamber.org
Contact: Jack Lank, President
Facebook: www.facebook.com/UnitedRegional

Description: Promotes business and community development in the Attleboro, MA area. **Founded:** 1917. **Publications:** *United Regional Chamber of Commerce--Directory*; *Keynotes* (Monthly). **Awards:** United Regional Chamber of Commerce ATHENA Award (Annual); United Regional Chamber of Commerce Person of the Year Award (Annual); United Regional Chamber of Commerce Teacher of the Year Award (Annual). **Geographic Preference:** Local.

40638 ■ Valley Focus
670 Linwood Ave., No. 5
Whitinsville, MA 01588
Ph: (508)234-9090
Fax: (508)234-5152
Co. E-mail: bvadmin@blackstonevalley.org
URL: http://www.blackstonevalley.org
Contact: Jeannie Hebert, President
E-mail: jhebert@blackstonevalley.org
URL(s): blackstonevalley.org/sponsorships

Description: Features chamber events and happenings, local economic development. **Availability:** Print.

40639 ■ Wachusett Area Chamber of Commerce
1174 Main St.
Holden, MA 01520
Ph: (508)829-9220
Co. E-mail: info@wachusettareachamber.org
URL: http://wachusettareachamber.org
Contact: Johnna Carlson, President
E-mail: johnna@controlpointmechanical.com

Description: Promotes business and community development in Holden, Princeton, Paxton and Rutland, MA. **Founded:** 1992. **Publications:** *InTouch* (Quarterly). **Geographic Preference:** Local.

40640 ■ Walpole Chamber of Commerce (WCC)
944 B Main St.
Walpole, MA 02081
Ph: (508)451-5840
Co. E-mail: harry_brousaides@bulfinchgroup.com
URL: http://www.walpolechamber.org
Contact: Harry Brousaides, President
E-mail: harry_brousaides@bulfinchgroup.com
Facebook: www.facebook.com/Walpole-MA-Chamber
-of-Commerce-357197290181

Description: Promotes business and community development in Walpole, MA. **Founded:** 1955. **Publications:** *Walpole Chamber of Commerce--Business and Resource Directory*. **Geographic Preference:** Local.

40641 ■ Waltham Chamber of Commerce
84 S St.
Waltham, MA 02453-3537
Ph: (781)894-4700
Co. E-mail: pgibbons@walthamchamber.com
URL: http://www.walthamchamber.com
Contact: Douglas G. Waybright, President
Facebook: www.facebook.com/WalthamWes
tSuburbanChamber
Linkedin: www.linkedin.com/company/the-waltham
-chamber-of-commerce
X (Twitter): x.com/TheWaltham

Description: Promotes business and community development in the Waltham, MA area. **Founded:** 1917. **Publications:** *Industrial Directory of Waltham*. **Geographic Preference:** Local.

40642 ■ Wellesley Chamber of Commerce
148 Linden St., Ste. 107
Wellesley, MA 02482-4671
URL: http://www.charlesriverchamber.com/alexis
-avila
Contact: Greg Reibman, President
URL(s): members.bostonchamber.com/list/member/
wellesley-chamber-of-commerce-wellesley-10808

Description: Seeks to promote business and community development and enhance the relationship between local businesses and professionals with the public. **Geographic Preference:** Local.

40643 ■ Wellfleet Chamber of Commerce
1410 Rte. 6
Wellfleet, MA 02667

Ph: (508)349-2510
Co. E-mail: info@wellfleetchamber.com
URL: http://www.wellfleetchamber.com
Contact: Bob Morrill, President
Facebook: www.facebook.com/WellfleetChamber
Instagram: www.instagram.com/wellfleetchamber
Description: Promotes business and community development in Wellfleet, MA. **Geographic Preference:** Local.

40644 ■ Williamstown Chamber of Commerce
84 Spring St.
 Williamstown, MA 01267
Ph: (413)458-9077
Co. E-mail: info@williamstownchamber.com
URL: http://williamstownchamber.com/about-us
Contact: Richard Duncan, President
E-mail: rrd5@williams.edu
Facebook: www.facebook.com/williams townchambercommerce
Instagram: www.instagram.com/berkshireou tdoorchallenge
Description: Promotes and supports business and tourism in Williamstown, MA and surrounding region. Fosters economic development, new business development, and cultural tourism. Provides advocacy within the town and to the county and state leadership. **Founded:** 1969. **Publications:** *Fact Finder/Map* (Annual). **Educational Activities:** Membership Meeting. **Geographic Preference:** Local.

40645 ■ Wilmington Chamber of Commerce
226 Lowell St.
 Wilmington, MA 01887
Ph: (978)657-7211
Fax: (978)657-0139
Co. E-mail: wilmingtonchamber@verizon.net
URL: http://www.wilmingtonbusiness.com
Contact: Mike Champoux, President
URL(s): www.wilmingtontewksburychamber.org
Facebook: www.facebook.com/Wilming tonTewksburyChamber
X (Twitter): x.com/WilmTewkChamber
Description: Promotes business and community development in the area. **Founded:** 1853. **Publications:** *Town Map*; *Wilmington Business Directory*; *Chamber Outlook*; *Wilmington Business Online Directory*. **Educational Activities:** Expo - Consumer's Marketplace. **Geographic Preference:** Local.

40646 ■ Winchester Chamber of Commerce
38 Church St., Ste. 3
 Winchester, MA 01890
Ph: (781)729-8870
Co. E-mail: info@winchesterchamber.com
URL: http://winchesterchamber.com
Contact: Craig Rabe, President
Facebook: www.facebook.com/winches terchamberma
Instagram: www.instagram.com/winches terchamberma
Description: Promotes business and community development in the area. **Founded:** 1978. **Geographic Preference:** Local.

40647 ■ Winthrop Chamber of Commerce
207 Hagman Rd.
 Winthrop, MA 02152
Ph: (617)846-9898
Co. E-mail: info@winthropchamber.com
URL: http://winthropchamber.com
Contact: Marc Chapdelaine, Co-President
Facebook: www.facebook.com/win thropchamberofcommerce
YouTube: www.youtube.com/watch
Description: Strives to foster a healthy economic climate in Winthrop. **Founded:** 1852. **Publications:** *Chamber Bulletin*; *Chamber Currents* (Monthly). **Geographic Preference:** Local.

40648 ■ Worcester Regional Chamber of Commerce (WRCC)
311 Main St., Ste. 200
 Worcester, MA 01608
Ph: (508)753-2924
Co. E-mail: info@worcesterchamber.org
URL: http://www.worcesterchamber.org
Contact: Timothy P. Murray, President
E-mail: tmurray@worcesterchamber.org
X (Twitter): x.com/chamberworc
YouTube: www.youtube.com/channel/UChYfQ7DzJD -3CosA8Nc1rCA
Description: Promotes business and community development in the Worcester region. Sponsors festivals and hall of fame; presents business and service awards. Operates county welcome center and tourism development. Promotes economic development in the Worcester region. **Founded:** 1875. **Geographic Preference:** Regional.

40649 ■ *Your Business*
4 Springfield St., Three Rivers, Ste. 525
 Three Rivers, MA 01080
Ph: (413)283-2418
Co. E-mail: info@qhma.com
URL: http://qhma.com
Contact: Renee Niedziela, Treasurer
URL(s): www.qhma.com/sponsorship-opportunities -for-members
Availability: Print; PDF; Online.

MINORITY BUSINESS ASSISTANCE PROGRAMS

40650 ■ Center for Women and Enterprise Administrative Offices & Eastern Massachusetts Center - Boston
44 School St., Ste. 200
 Boston, MA 02108
Ph: (617)536-0700
Co. E-mail: info.easternma@cweonline.org
URL: http://www.cweonline.org
Contact: Susan Rittscher, Chief Executive Officer
Description: Encourages the creation and growth of women-owned businesses through business training, technical assistance, certification, and access to capital.

40651 ■ Greater New England Minority Supplier Development Council Massachusetts Office (GNEMSDC)
101 Huntington Ave., 17th Fl.
 Boston, MA 02119
Ph: (617)578-8900
Fax: (617)578-8902
URL: http://gnemsdc.org
Facebook: www.facebook.com/gnemsdc
Linkedin: www.linkedin.com/company/gnemsdc
Instagram: www.instagram.com/gnemsdc
Description: Aims to advance business opportunities for certified Asian, Black, Hispanic, and Native American business enterprises in Massachusetts, Connecticut, Rhode Island, Maine, New Hampshire, and Vermont. **Founded:** 1975. **Publications:** *Minority Supplier Directory* (Annual).

40652 ■ Massachusetts Small Business Development Center Network Boston Regional Office & Minority Business Center (MSBDC)
University of Massachusetts
 23 Tillson Farm Rd.
 Amherst, MA 01003
Ph: (413)545-6301
Fax: (413)545-1273
URL: http://www.msbdc.org
Description: Committed to helping your business succeed in Massachusetts.

FINANCING AND LOAN PROGRAMS

40653 ■ 20/20 HealthCare Partners (20/20 HCP)
2000 Commonwealth Ave., Ste. 200
 Auburndale, MA 02466
URL: http://2020hcp.com
Contact: Hillel Bachrach, Managing Partner
Description: Early stage investment group. **Industry Preferences:** Technology and life science innovation.

40654 ■ .406 Ventures
Independence Wharf
 470 Atlantic Ave., 12 Fl.
 Boston, MA 02210
Ph: (617)406-3300
Co. E-mail: contact@406ventures.com
URL: http://406ventures.com
Contact: So-June Min, Chief Financial Officer
Facebook: www.facebook.com/people/406-Ventures/ 100064166254939
X (Twitter): x.com/406Ventures
Description: Venture capital firm focused on early-stage technology investments. **Founded:** 2005. **Industry Preferences:** Cybersecurity; digital health; data and cloud.

40655 ■ ABRY Partners, LLC
888 Boylston, Ste. 1600
 Boston, MA 02199
Ph: (617)859-2959
Co. E-mail: information@abryuk.com
URL: http://abry.com
Contact: Rob MacInnis, Partner
Description: A media-focused private-equity investment firm. **Founded:** 1989. **Preferred Investment Size:** $25,000,000 to $150,000,000. **Investment Policies:** Leveraged buyout, expansion, acquisition, recapitalization, roll-ups, and mezzanine. **Industry Preferences:** Communications and media, medical and health, and other products.

40656 ■ ABS Ventures
950 Winter St., Ste. 2600
 Waltham, MA 02451
Co. E-mail: abs@absventures.com
URL: http://www.absventures.com
Contact: Susan Adams, Chief Financial Officer
Description: Firm provides investing strategies for mid-stage technology companies. **Founded:** 1982. **Preferred Investment Size:** $5,000,000 to $15,000,000. **Investment Policies:** Early and later stage, fund of funds, expansion, recapitalization, and special situation. **Industry Preferences:** Computer software and services, medical and health, communications and media, Internet specific, computer hardware, biotechnology, other products, industrial and energy, consumer related, semiconductors and other electronics.

40657 ■ Advanced Technology Ventures (ATV)
500 Boylston St., Ste. 1380
 Boston, MA 02116
URL: http://www.atvcapital.com
Description: Venture capital firm investment management services. **Founded:** 1979. **Preferred Investment Size:** $15,000,000 to $35,000,000. **Industry Preferences:** Internet specific, computer software and services, computer hardware, other products, semiconductors and other electronics, communications and media, medical and health, biotechnology, industrial and energy, and consumer related.

40658 ■ Advancit Capital LLC
846 University Ave.
 Norwood, MA 02062
URL: http://www.advancitcapital.com
Contact: Shari Redstone, Managing Partner
 Co-Founder Partner
Description: Offers capital to early-stage companies at the intersection of media, entertainment, and technology. Also operates out of New York.

40659 ■ Advent International Corporation
Advent International Corporation
 800 Boylston St., Prudential Twr.
 Boston, MA 02199-8069
Ph: (617)951-9400
Co. E-mail: adventinternational-us@fgsglobal.com
URL: http://www.adventinternational.com
Contact: Hakim Ghanem, Director
Linkedin: www.linkedin.com/company/advent-interna tional
Description: Global private equity investors. **Founded:** 1984. **Preferred Investment Size:** $1,000,000 minimum. **Industry Preferences:** Other products, consumer related, communications and

STATE LISTINGS

media, Internet specific, industrial and energy, medical and health, computer software and services, computer hardware, semiconductors and other electronics, and biotechnology.

40660 ■ Alantra
1 Federal St., Fl. 22
Boston, MA 02110
Ph: (617)482-6200
URL: http://www.alantra.com
Contact: María González de Apodaca, Partner Chief Operating Officer
Description: Provider of investment banking solutions. **Preferred Investment Size:** $300,000 to $500,000. **Industry Preferences:** Computer hardware and software, semiconductors and other electronics, medical and health, consumer related, industrial and energy, and manufacturing.

40661 ■ Ampersand Capital Partners
55 William St., Ste. 240
Wellesley, MA 02481
Ph: (781)239-0700
Fax: (781)239-0824
Co. E-mail: info@ampersandcapital.com
URL: http://ampersandcapital.com
Contact: Natalia C. Anderson, Manager
Description: Middle market private equity firm. Funds capital to early- and late-stage healthcare companies. Also maintains an office in the Netherlands. **Founded:** 1988. **Industry Preferences:** Healthcare: laboratory products and testing services; contract manufacturing; pharma services; specialty healthcare services.

40662 ■ Ampersand Ventures Management Corp.
55 William St., Ste. 240
Wellesley, MA 02481
Ph: (781)239-0700
Fax: (781)239-0824
Co. E-mail: info@ampersandcapital.com
URL: http://ampersandcapital.com
Contact: Natalia C. Anderson, Manager
Description: Radio station that broadcast music and other programs. **Founded:** 1988. **Preferred Investment Size:** $5,000,000 to $10,000,000. **Industry Preferences:** Healthcare and industrial.

40663 ■ Arctaris Royalty Partners
1330 Boylston St., Ste. 600
Chestnut Hill, MA 02467
Ph: (617)735-6000
URL: http://www.arctaris.com
Contact: Lee Kimball, Director
E-mail: lee@arctaris.com
Linkedin: www.linkedin.com/company/arctaris-impact-investors-llc
Description: Impact investment fund manager. Provides capital to growth-oriented profitable businesses in underserved regions, particularly inner cities and rural communities, in the United States. Uses a royalty-base loan structure. **Founded:** 2009.

40664 ■ Ascent Venture Partners
PO Box 520
Bedford, MA 01730
Ph: (617)720-9400
URL: http://www.ascentvp.com
Contact: Jason Molfetas, Director, Finance
Linkedin: www.linkedin.com/company/ascent-venture-partners
X (Twitter): x.com/ascentvp
Description: Venture capital firm. **Founded:** 1985. **Preferred Investment Size:** $2,000,000 to $8,000,000. **Industry Preferences:** Internet specific, medical and health, computer software and services, communications and media, medical and health, computer hardware, consumer related, industrial and energy, semiconductors and other electronics.

40665 ■ Barrington Partners
33 Arch St., 17th Fl.
Boston, MA 02110
Ph: (617)407-1782
URL: http://barringtonp.com
Contact: Andrew Hunter, Partner
E-mail: ahunter@barringtonp.com
Description: Provider of investment banking, financial services, intelligence, tailored solutions, transaction advice and consulting services. **Founded:** 1995. **Investment Policies:** Seed and early stage. **Industry Preferences:** Internet specific, other products, communications and media.

40666 ■ Beacon Angels
Boston, MA
URL: http://beaconangels.com
Contact: William F. Swiggart, Manager
Description: Angel group for early-stage fast-growing companies. **Founded:** 2006. **Preferred Investment Size:** $50,000 to $400,000.

40667 ■ Bessemer Venture Partners (BVP)
196 Broadway, 2nd Fl.
Cambridge, MA 02139
Ph: (617)588-1700
URL: http://www.bvp.com/india
Contact: Kent Bennett, Partner
Linkedin: www.linkedin.com/company/bessemer-venture-partners
Description: Firm provides investment services for communications and media, computer software and services, semiconductors and other electronics, consumer related, medical and much more. **Founded:** 1911. **Preferred Investment Size:** $1,000,000 to $10,000,000. **Industry Preferences:** Internet specific, communications and media, computer software and services, semiconductors and other electronics, consumer related, medical and health, industrial and energy, other products and biotechnology.

40668 ■ BioVentures Investors
70 Walnut St., Ste. 302
Wellesley, MA 02481
Contact: Marc Goldberg, Manager
Description: Provider of venture capital, private equity and seed stage investments for healthcare sector, medical devices, diagnostics and other tech. **Preferred Investment Size:** $3,000,000 to $7,000,000. **Investment Policies:** Seed, early, first and second stage, balanced, special situation, and private placement. **Industry Preferences:** Biotechnology, and medical and health.

40669 ■ Boston Financial & Equity Corp. (BFEC)
1330 Beacon St., Ste. 268
Brookline, MA 02446
Ph: (617)267-2900
Co. E-mail: contact@bfec.com
URL: http://www.bfec.com
Contact: Debbie Monosson, President
X (Twitter): x.com/Venturelease
Description: Firm provides financing solutions to non-bankable companies and also leasing and asset-based loans, as well as equipment lease and working capital loans. **Founded:** 1968. **Preferred Investment Size:** $500,000 to $1,000,000. **Industry Preferences:** Diversified.

40670 ■ Boston Millennia Partners (BMP)
30 Rowes Wharf, Ste. 400
Boston, MA 02110
Ph: (617)428-5150
Fax: (617)428-5160
URL: http://www.bostonmillenniapartners.com
Contact: Clodagh Hoey, Manager, Finance
E-mail: clodagh@bmpvc.com
Facebook: www.facebook.com/pages/Boston-Millennia-Partners/282787865120554
Linkedin: www.linkedin.com/company/boston-millennia-partners
X (Twitter): x.com/BostonMillennia
Description: Investment firm provides of private equity financial services for telecommunications, information technology, healthcare and life sciences industries. **Founded:** 1979. **Preferred Investment Size:** $3,000,000 to $10,000,000. **Industry Preferences:** Internet specific, computer software and

Massachusetts ■ 40676

services, biotechnology, communications and media, semiconductors and other electronics, other products, computer hardware, consumer related, medical and health.

40671 ■ Boston Seed Capital
1 Marina Pk. Dr., Ste. 315
Boston, MA 02210
Co. E-mail: info@bostonseed.com
URL: http://bostonseed.com
Contact: Eileen Rocchio, Vice President, Finance Controller
Description: Invests in entrepreneurs seeking to improve work, life, and play through innovative tech companies. **Industry Preferences:** Consumer digital; sports and marketplaces; AI; data; security.

40672 ■ Branch Venture Group
50 Milk St.
Boston, MA 02109
Co. E-mail: info@branchventuregroup.com
URL: http://www.branchventuregroup.com
Contact: Julia Paino, Partner
Description: Offers funding, advice, and educational opportunities to early-stage food companies. **Preferred Investment Size:** $50,000-$100,000. **Investment Policies:** Sustainable competitive advantage; capital efficiency; well-defined exit strategy. **Industry Preferences:** Food and beverage products; digital content and media; e-commerce and marketplace platforms; agriculture technology; industry robotics ; restaurant technology; food-related life sciences.

40673 ■ Breakaway Ventures (BV)
800 S St., Ste. 610
Waltham, MA 02453
Ph: (617)399-0635
URL: http://www.breakaway.com
Contact: Dennis Baldwin, Managing Partner Founder
E-mail: dbaldwin@breakaway.com
Description: Invests in consumer brands to accelerate growth and create value. **Founded:** 2006.

40674 ■ Brook Venture Partners
301 Edgewater Pl., Ste. 425
Wakefield, MA 01880
Ph: (781)295-4000
Fax: (781)295-4007
Co. E-mail: rspencer@brookventure.com
URL: http://www.brookventure.com
Contact: Brennan Mulcahey, Partner
E-mail: bmulcahey@brookventure.com
Facebook: www.facebook.com/BrookVenture
Linkedin: www.linkedin.com/company/brook-venture-partners
Description: Private equity and venture capital firm investing in healthcare, IT and marketing technology industries. **Founded:** 1995. **Preferred Investment Size:** $2,000,000 to $5,000,000. **Industry Preferences:** Communications, computer software, Internet specific, semiconductors and other electronics, medical and health, other products.

40675 ■ Catalyst Health Ventures (CHV)
129 S St., 4th Fl.
Boston, MA 02111
Ph: (781)228-5228
Co. E-mail: info@chv.vc
URL: http://chv.vc
Contact: Darshana Zaveri, Managing Partner Co-Founder
Linkedin: www.linkedin.com/company/chv-vc
Description: Offers financing for early-stage healthcare companies focused on oncology, cardiovascular disease, obesity, and women's health. **Founded:** 2008. **Investment Policies:** Addresses a major unmet clinical need; proprietary technological solutions for reduced treatment costs and improved patient outcomes; minimizes risk through a foundation of engineering and development; capital efficient.

40676 ■ Clean Energy Venture Group (CEVG)
One Broadway
Cambridge, MA 02138
URL: http://cevg.com
Contact: Anne Slaughter Andrew, Partner

Small Business Sourcebook • 42nd Edition

40677 ■ Massachusetts

Linkedin: www.linkedin.com/company/clean-energy-venture-group
X (Twitter): x.com/ceventuregroup
Description: Offers seed capital to early-stage clean energy companies. Also operates out of New York. **Founded:** 2005.

40677 ■ Commonwealth Capital Ventures
400 W Cummings Pk., Ste. 1725-134
  Woburn, MA 01801
Ph: (781)890-5554
URL: http://www.commonwealthvc.com
Contact: Stephen McCormack, Partner
E-mail: jeff@commonwealthvc.com
Description: Venture capital firm that provides early and growth stage investments. **Founded:** 1995. **Preferred Investment Size:** $2,000,000 to $8,000,000. **Industry Preferences:** Computer software and services, Internet specific, communications and media, industrial and energy, medical and health, consumer related, semiconductors and other electronics, biotechnology, and other products.

40678 ■ Cue Ball Capital
1 Faneuil Hall Sq., 7th Fl.
  Boston, MA 02109
Ph: (617)542-0100
Fax: (617)542-0033
Co. E-mail: ping@cueball.com
URL: http://cueball.com
Contact: Tony Tjan, Managing Partner
Linkedin: www.linkedin.com/in/anthony-tjan-4528125a
X (Twitter): x.com/cueballcapital
Description: Purpose- and profit-driven venture capital firm. **Founded:** 2005.

40679 ■ Cutlass Capital LLC
229 Marlborough St.
  Boston, MA 02116
URL: http://cutlasscapital.com
Contact: Jonathan W. Osgood, Co-Founder Member
E-mail: jonosgood@cutlasscapital.com
Description: Venture capital firm for the health care industry. Also maintains an office in San Francisco. **Founded:** 2001. **Industry Preferences:** Medical device and specialty health care services.

40680 ■ Dace Ventures
405 Waltham St., Ste. 140
  Lexington, MA 02421
URL: http://www.daceventures.com
Contact: Dave Andonian, Managing Partner
Investment Policies: Innovation; first mover advantages,. **Industry Preferences:** Digital media; consumer marketing; mobile services.

40681 ■ Data Point Capital
341 Newbury St., 6th Fl.
  Boston, MA 02115
Ph: (617)874-5152
Co. E-mail: info@datapointcapital.com
URL: http://datapointcapital.com
Contact: Colin Angle, Chief Executive Officer
Description: Venture capital firm focused on data-driven businesses. Also helps entrepreneurs identify key performance indicators scale their businesses. **Industry Preferences:** Consumer internet (e-commerce, mobile, media; cloud-based enterprise software; industrial IoT.

40682 ■ Eastward Capital Partners LLC (ECP)
432 Cherry St.
  West Newton, MA 02465
Ph: (617)969-6700
Fax: (617)969-7900
Co. E-mail: contacts@eastwardcp.com
URL: http://eastwardcp.com
Contact: Dennis Cameron, Partner
E-mail: dennis@eastwardcp.com
Linkedin: www.linkedin.com/company/eastward-capital
Description: Offers venture debt and equity financing to technology companies backed by venture capital firms.

40683 ■ Endeavor Capital Management
388 E 8th St.
  Boston, MA 02127
Ph: (617)971-9700
URL: http://endeavour.com
Contact: Anthony Borghi, Contact
E-mail: acborghi@endeavor.com
Description: Provider of private equity and venture capital investments for expansion stage opportunities, buyouts and acquiring expansion stage companies. **Founded:** 1995. **Preferred Investment Size:** $50,000 to $5,000,000. **Industry Preferences:** Other products, communications and media, Internet specific, consumer related, medical and health, computer hardware, computer software and services, and industrial and energy.

40684 ■ F-Prime
1 Main St., 13th Fl.
  Cambridge, MA 02142
Co. E-mail: info@fprimecapital.com
URL: http://fprimecapital.com
Contact: Henry Trapnell, Director
E-mail: htrapnell@fprimecapital.com
Linkedin: www.linkedin.com/company/f-prime-capital-partners
X (Twitter): x.com/fprimecapital
Description: Creates and invests in healthcare and technology companies that improve lives. Also maintains offices in San Francisco and London. **Founded:** 1946. **Industry Preferences:** Health (therapeutics, medtech, health IT/services); technology (enterprise software, fintech, frontier tech).

40685 ■ F.A. Technology Ventures Corp. (FATV)
20 Main St.
  Acton, MA 01720
URL: http://fatechventures.com
Contact: Gregory Hulecki, Partner Co-Founder
Description: Venture capital firm engaged in financial services. **Founded:** 1999. **Preferred Investment Size:** $3,000,000 to $8,000,000. **Investment Policies:** Early stage and expansion. **Industry Preferences:** Communications, computer software, and industrial and energy.

40686 ■ Flagship Pioneering
Flagship Pioneering
  55 Cambridge Pky., Ste. 800E
  Cambridge, MA 02142
Ph: (617)868-1888
Fax: (617)868-1115
URL: http://www.flagshippioneering.com
Contact: Michael Rosenblatt, Chief Executive Officer
Linkedin: www.linkedin.com/company/flagship-pioneering
X (Twitter): x.com/FlagshipPioneer
Founded: 2000. **Preferred Investment Size:** $500,000 to $5,000,000. **Investment Policies:** Start-up, seed, research and development, early and first stage, and balanced. **Industry Preferences:** Computer software and services, communications and media, biotechnology, Internet specific, medical and health, semiconductors and other electronics, other products, computer hardware, and industrial and energy.

40687 ■ Fletcher Spaght Ventures (FSV)
75 State St., Ste. 100
  Boston, MA 02109
Ph: (617)247-6700
Co. E-mail: contact@fletcherspaght.com
URL: http://www.fletcherspaght.com
Contact: Peter Low, Senior Vice President
Linkedin: www.linkedin.com/company/fletcher-spaght
YouTube: www.youtube.com/channel/UC-zBH4g5sIKL2BtZysGcAFg
Description: Venture capital firm investing in growth stage healthcare and technology companies. **Founded:** 2001. **Investment Policies:** Early stage. **Industry Preferences:** Communications, computer hardware and software, Internet specific, semiconductors and other electronics, medical and health, industrial and energy, transportation, and financial services.

STATE LISTINGS

40688 ■ Gemini Investors
20 William St., Ste. 250
  Wellesley, MA 02481
Ph: (781)237-7001
Fax: (781)237-7233
Co. E-mail: chughes@gemini-investors.com
URL: http://www.gemini-investors.com
Contact: James J. Goodman, President
E-mail: jgoodman@gemini-investors.com
Description: Firm provides private investment services in management buyouts, shareholder liquidity, acquisition financing, recapitalizations, mezzanine, SBIC and growth capital transactions in lower middle market companies. **Founded:** 1993. **Preferred Investment Size:** $3,000 to $8,000. **Industry Preferences:** Communications and media, medical and health, computer software and services, Internet specific, other products, computer hardware, industrial and energy, manufacturing, and consumer related.

40689 ■ General Catalyst Partners / General Catalyst Group L.L.C.
20 University Rd., 4th Fl.
  Cambridge, MA 02138
Ph: (617)234-7000
Co. E-mail: info@generalcatalyst.com
URL: http://www.generalcatalyst.com
Contact: Austin McChord, Chief Executive Officer
Description: Provider of venture capital and private equity investments. **Founded:** 2000. **Preferred Investment Size:** $1,000,000 to $25,000,000. **Industry Preferences:** Internet specific, computer software and services, communications and media, other products, industrial and energy, semiconductors and other electronics, and consumer related.

40690 ■ Globespan Capital Partners, Inc.
1 Boston Pl., Ste. 2810
  Boston, MA 02108
Ph: (617)305-2300
URL: http://www.globespancapital.com
Contact: Andy Goldfarb, Executive Director
Facebook: www.facebook.com/globespancapitalpartners
Linkedin: www.linkedin.com/company/globespan-capital-partners
X (Twitter): x.com/GlobespanCap
Description: Venture capital firm. **Founded:** 2003.

40691 ■ Glouston Capital Partners (GCP)
800 Boylston St., Ste. 1325
  Boston, MA 02199-7610
Ph: (617)587-5300
Fax: (617)587-5301
URL: http://www.glouston.com
Contact: Lindsay McNamara, Vice President
E-mail: lmcnamara@glouston.com
Description: Employee-owned private equity investment specialist. **Founded:** 1994.

40692 ■ Great Hill Equity Partners L.L.C.
200 Clarendon St., 29th Fl.
  Boston, MA 02116
Ph: (617)790-9400
Fax: (617)790-9401
URL: http://www.greathillpartners.com
Contact: Heather Fox Ewing, Director
E-mail: hfox@greathillpartners.com
Linkedin: www.linkedin.com/company/great-hill-partners
Description: Venture capital firm provides investments in late venture, late stage, growth capital, buyouts and middle market companies. **Founded:** 1998. **Preferred Investment Size:** $50,000,000 to $150,000,000. **Industry Preferences:** Internet specific, communications and media, computer hardware, software and services, semiconductors and other electronics, and other products.

40693 ■ Grove Street Advisors L.L.C.
2221 Washington St., Ste. 201
  Newton, MA 02462
Contact: Bruce Ou, Manager
Description: Private equity firm invests in lower middle-market buyout, growth equity and venture capital funds. **Founded:** 1998. **Preferred Investment**

Size: $1,000,000 to $7,500,000. **Industry Preferences:** Communications and media, computer software and hardware, Internet specific, semiconductors and other electronics, consumer related, industrial and energy, and business service.

40694 ▪ HarbourVest Partners, LLC
1 Financial Ctr.
  Boston, MA 02111
Ph: (617)348-3707
Fax: (617)350-0305
URL: http://www.harbourvest.com
Contact: Keiko Fuchioka, Director
E-mail: kfuchioka@harbourvest.com
Linkedin: www.linkedin.com/company/harbourvest-partners
Description: Firm provides private equity investors. **Founded:** 1978. **Preferred Investment Size:** $10,000,000 to $100,000,000. **Industry Preferences:** Other products, Internet specific, communications and media, computer software and services, consumer related, computer hardware, semiconductors and other electronics, industrial and energy, biotechnology, medical and health.

40695 ▪ Healthcare Ventures L.L.C. / Healthcare Investments
47 Thorndike St., Ste. B1-1
  Cambridge, MA 02141
Ph: (617)252-4343
Co. E-mail: info@hcven.com
URL: http://www.hcven.com
Contact: Harold Werner, Manager
Description: Provider of private equity and venture capital investments for life science and health care sectors. **Founded:** 1985. **Preferred Investment Size:** $500,000 to $10,000,000. **Industry Preferences:** Biotechnology, medical and health, Internet specific, and consumer related.

40696 ▪ Highland Capital Partners
One Broadway, 14th Fl.
  Cambridge, MA 02142
Contact: Jessica Healey, Contact
Description: Investment firm provides venture capital and private equity investment services for consumer technology, enterprise technology and other. **Founded:** 1987. **Preferred Investment Size:** $100,000 to $20,000,000. **Industry Preferences:** Internet specific, computer software and services, communications and media, medical and health, other products, biotechnology, semiconductors and other electronics, computer hardware, and industrial and energy.

40697 ▪ HLM Venture Partners
800 S St., Ste. 200
  Waltham, MA 02453
Ph: (617)266-0030
URL: http://hlmvp.com
Contact: Ed Cahill, Partner
Linkedin: www.linkedin.com/company/hlm-venture-partners
X (Twitter): x.com/hlmvp
Description: Venture capital firm for healthcare technology companies. **Investment Policies:** Emerging growth companies with proven business success, marketing skills, and innovative products. **Industry Preferences:** Digital health; tech-enabled healthcare services; medical devices and diagnostics.

40698 ▪ Hub Angels Investment Group LLC
Boston, MA
Co. E-mail: info@hubangels.com
URL: http://www.hubangels.com
Contact: Charles Cameron, Managing Director Co-Founder
X (Twitter): x.com/HubAngels
Description: Matches early-stage tech-driven companies with investors in the Northeast U.S. and Canada. **Founded:** 2000. **Industry Preferences:** Healthcare/life sciences; IT; technology.

40699 ▪ Indicator Ventures
22 Boston Wharf Rd. 7th Fl.
  Boston, MA 02210
URL: http://www.indicatorventures.com
Contact: Marissa Grey, Head
Linkedin: www.linkedin.com/company/indicator-ventures
X (Twitter): x.com/indicatorvc
Description: Early-stage venture fund focused on the digital landscape, primarily B2B applications. Also operates out of New York and San Francisco. **Investment Policies:** Capital-efficient businesses solving high-impact problems with the ability to quickly scale.

40700 ▪ Kepha Partners
303 Wyman St., Ste. 300
  Waltham, MA 02451
URL: http://kephapartners.com
Contact: Eric Hjerpe, Partner
Description: Investment firm that focuses on pre-seed, seed, and Series A companies. Also sources and recruits experienced executives from its personal networks. **Founded:** 1998.

40701 ▪ Launchpad Venture Group LLC
19 Hallron Rd.
  Newton, MA 02462-1115
URL: http://www.launchpadventuregroup.com
Contact: Jodi Collier, Executive Director
Linkedin: www.linkedin.com/company/launchpad-venture-group
Description: Angel investor group. **Founded:** 2000.

40702 ▪ LRVHealth
1 Boston Pl., 38th Fl.
  Boston, MA 02108
Ph: (617)326-3770
Co. E-mail: lrvhealth@lrvhealth.com
URL: http://www.lrvhealth.com
Contact: Will Cowen, Co-Founder Partner
Linkedin: www.linkedin.com/company/lrvhealth
X (Twitter): x.com/LRVHealth
Description: Venture capital firm interested in early-stage digital health companies. **Founded:** 2000.

40703 ▪ M/C Partners
53 State St., Ste. 2602
  Boston, MA 02109
Ph: (617)345-7200
Fax: (617)345-7201
Co. E-mail: mcp@mcpartners.com
URL: http://mcpartners.com
Contact: Abhishek Rampuria, Partner
E-mail: arampuria@mcpartners.com
Linkedin: www.linkedin.com/company/m-c-partners
Description: Venture capital firm specializes in early stage, mid stage, later stage, turnarounds and buyouts financing in emerging segments. **Founded:** 1986. **Preferred Investment Size:** $5,000,000 to $50,000,000. **Industry Preferences:** Communications and media, Internet specific, semiconductors and other electronics, computer software and services, and consumer related.

40704 ▪ Massachusetts Capital Resource Co. (MCRC)
Massachusetts Capital Resource Co. (MCRC)
  420 Boylston St.
  Boston, MA 02116
Ph: (617)536-3900
Co. E-mail: businessdevelopment@masscapital.com
URL: http://masscapital.com
Contact: Suzanne L. Dwyer, President
E-mail: sdwyer@masscapital.com
Linkedin: www.linkedin.com/company/massachusetts-capital-resource-company
Description: Firm provides financial services. **Founded:** 1977. **Preferred Investment Size:** $750,000 to $5,000,000. **Industry Preferences:** Industrial and energy, semiconductors and other electronics, computer software, hardware and services, consumer related, communications and media, medical and health, and Internet specific.

40705 ▪ MassVentures (MV)
308 Congress St., 5th Fl.
  Boston, MA 02210
URL: http://www.mass-ventures.com
Contact: Charlie Hipwood, President
Linkedin: www.linkedin.com/company/massventures
X (Twitter): x.com/massventures

YouTube: www.youtube.com/channel/UCTF8j1G5KgFF413DeD-rPoQ/playlists
Description: Venture capital firm provides investment services. **Founded:** 1978. **Preferred Investment Size:** $350,000 to $500,000. **Industry Preferences:** Computer software, hardware and services, semiconductors and other electronics, Internet specific, biotechnology, medical and health, industrial and energy, communications and media.

40706 ▪ Masthead Venture partner, LLC
301 Newbury St., Ste. 241
  Danvers, MA 01923
Ph: (617)621-3000
Co. E-mail: info@mvpartners.com
URL: http://mvpartners.com
Description: Venture capital and private equity investment services. **Preferred Investment Size:** $500,000 to $5,000,000. **Investment Policies:** Seed and early stage. **Industry Preferences:** Communications, computer software, semiconductors and other electronics, biotechnology, and medical and health.

40707 ▪ MIT Alumni Angels of Boston (MITAAB)
Boston, MA
URL: http://www.mitalumniangels.com
Contact: Wan Li Zhu, Co-Founder Managing Director
Description: Connects MIT alumni investors with entrepreneurs in the Boston area. **Founded:** 2014.

40708 ▪ MIT Alumni Life Sceince Angels of Boston
Boston, MA
URL: http://mitlifesciangels.com
Contact: Patrick Rivelli, Co-Founder Managing Director
Description: Connects MIT alumni investors with life science entrepreneurs in the Boston area. **Founded:** 2017.

40709 ▪ MP Healthcare Venture Management, Inc. (MPH)
Mitsubishi Tanabe Pharma Corp. (MTPC)
  33 Arch St.
  Boston, MA 02110
Ph: 81 6 6205-5085
URL: http://www.mt-pharma.co.jp/e
Contact: Dr. Jeffrey Moore, President
Description: Venture capital firm for early-stage biotech companies based in North America and Europe. **Founded:** 2006. **Industry Preferences:** Novel therapeutics; platform technologies; diagnostics; vaccines.

40710 ▪ MPM BioImpact, Inc.
MPM BioImpact, Inc.
  399 Boylston St., Ste. 1100
  Boston, MA 02116
Ph: (617)425-9200
Co. E-mail: info@mpmcapital.com
URL: http://www.mpmcapital.com
Contact: Detlev Biniszkiewicz, Partner
Linkedin: www.linkedin.com/company/mpm-capital
Description: Venture capital firm provides investment services. **Founded:** 2018. **Preferred Investment Size:** $5,000,000 to $50,000,000. **Industry Preferences:** Biotechnology, medical and health, computer software and services, and Internet specific.

40711 ▪ Navigator Technology Ventures (NTV)
Nano Science & Technology Institute
  4 Cambridge Ctr., 2nd Fl.
  Cambridge, MA 02142
Ph: (617)494-0111
Co. E-mail: info@ntven.com
URL: http://www.nsti.org/directory/org.html?i=1709
Contact: Alain Hanover, Manager
Preferred Investment Size: $500,000 to $750,000,000. **Investment Policies:** Early and later stage. **Industry Preferences:** Communications, technology, semiconductors and other electronics, and biotechnology.

40712 ■ New Atlantic Ventures (NAV.VC)
240 Franklin St., No. 1
Cambridge, MA 02139
Contact: Sayem Khan, Manager
Description: Venture capital firm provides investment services. **Preferred Investment Size:** $500,000 to $5,000,000. **Investment Policies:** Start-up, seed, second, early and later stage. **Industry Preferences:** Communications, computer hardware and software, Internet specific, semiconductors and other electronics, consumer related, industrial and energy, and business service.

40713 ■ New Technology Ventures (NTV)
2344 Washington St., No. 620430
Newton, MA 02462
URL: http://www.newtechvc.com
Contact: Hal Chapel, Managing Director Partner
Description: Multi-stage venture capital firm develops, launches, and invests in disruptive solutions addressing meaningful unmet needs in large markets. Seeks to build rapidly growing companies that can dominate markets and generate substantial value. **Investment Policies:** Large market opportunities that address significant unmet needs; risk mitigation; capital efficiency; team relationships. **Industry Preferences:** Cybersecurity; software; healthcare information technology.

40714 ■ NextView Ventures
22 Boston Wharf Rd., 7th Fl.
Boston, MA 02210
URL: http://nextview.vc
Contact: Amanda Tommasino, Director, Finance
Linkedin: www.linkedin.com/company/nextview-ventures
X (Twitter): x.com/nextviewvc
Description: Venture capital firm focused on how the everyday economy (food, housing, apparel, health, transportation) will be overhauled by ubiquitous software, data, and connectivity. Also operates out of New York City. **Founded:** 2010. **Investment Policies:** Companies redesigning the everyday (products that consumers interact with daily or habitually).

40715 ■ North Bridge Venture Partners (NBVP)
150 A St., Ste. 102
Needham, MA 02494
Ph: (781)290-0004
URL: http://www.northbridge.com
Linkedin: www.linkedin.com/company/north-bridge-venture-partners
Description: Firm provides investment management services. **Founded:** 1994. **Preferred Investment Size:** Offers venture capital solutions. **Industry Preferences:** Communications and media, Internet specific, computer software and services, computer hardware, semiconductors and other electronics, medical and health, other products, and biotechnology.

40716 ■ North Hill Ventures
535 Boylston St.6th Fl.
Boston, MA 02116
Ph: (617)835-9719
Co. E-mail: info@northhillventures.com
URL: http://www.northhillventures.com
Contact: Brett J. Rome, Contact
E-mail: brettj.rome@northhillventures.com
Description: Provider of investment services. **Founded:** 1999. **Preferred Investment Size:** $2,000,000 to $5,000,000. **Industry Preferences:** Consumer related, financial services, and business service.

40717 ■ Norwich Ventures
303 Wyman St., Ste. 300
Waltham, MA 02451
Ph: (781)890-2163
URL: http://www.norwichventures.com
Contact: Aaron Sandoski, Co-Founder Managing Director
Description: Early-stage medtech venture capital firm. **Founded:** 2004. **Industry Preferences:** Medical devices; healthcare.

40718 ■ Novartis Venture Fund (NVF)
196 Broadway
Cambridge, MA 02139
URL: http://www.nvfund.com
Contact: Dr. Laura Brass, Managing Director
Description: Venture fund. Invests from seed to commercial stages in therapeutic areas of medical need. Also operates in Switzerland. **Industry Preferences:** Healthcare; medical devices.

40719 ■ One Liberty Ventures
175 Brattle St.
Cambridge, MA 02138
Contact: Edwin M. Kania, Jr., President
Preferred Investment Size: $1,000,000 to $10,000,000. **Industry Preferences:** Communications and media, computer software, hardware and services, Internet specific, biotechnology, medical and health, semiconductors and other electronics, industrial and energy.

40720 ■ PJC
50 Milk St., 16th Fl.
Boston, MA 02109
URL: http://www.pjc.vc
Contact: Matt Hayes, Partner
Linkedin: www.linkedin.com/company/pjcvc
Description: Early-stage venture firm. **Founded:** 2001. **Industry Preferences:** Internet; healthcare; clean technology; software.

40721 ■ Polaris Venture Partners
1 Marina Pk. Dr.
Boston, MA 02210
Ph: (781)290-0770
Co. E-mail: partnership@polarispartners.com
URL: http://polarispartners.com
Contact: Dave Barrett, Partner
Facebook: www.facebook.com/Polaris-Partners-404737049642094
Linkedin: www.linkedin.com/company/polaris-partners
X (Twitter): x.com/polarisvc
Description: Firm provides investments in information technology and healthcare companies. **Founded:** 1996. **Preferred Investment Size:** $250,000 to $15,000,000. **Industry Preferences:** Internet specific, computer software services, computer hardware, biotechnology, communications and media, business services, manufacturing, medical and health, and other products.

40722 ■ PureTech Health PLC
6 Tide St., Ste. 400
Boston, MA 02210
Ph: (617)482-2333
Fax: (617)482-3337
Co. E-mail: info@puretechhealth.com
URL: http://puretechhealth.com
Contact: Eric Elenko, President
Linkedin: www.linkedin.com/company/puretech-health
X (Twitter): twitter.com/PureTechH
Description: Biotechnology company. Invests in companies developing medicines to combat disease.

40723 ■ Raptor Group Holdings
185 Dartmouth St., 7th Fl.
Boston, MA 02116
Ph: (617)772-4600
URL: http://www.raptorgroup.com
Contact: Jim Pallotta, Founder
X (Twitter): x.com/raptorgroup
Description: Private investment company for companies across various stages and asset classes, including early stage venture. Also operates out of New York. **Investment Policies:** Operating and strategic expertise; extensive global network. **Industry Preferences:** Sports; consumer; technology; media; entertainment; financial services; healthcare.

40724 ■ Romulus Capital (RC)
101 Arch St.
Boston, MA 02110
URL: http://romuluscap.com
Contact: Joey Kim, Partner
E-mail: jkim@romuluscap.com
Linkedin: www.linkedin.com/company/romulus-capital
X (Twitter): x.com/romuluscap
Description: Early-stage venture capital fund founded out of MIT with a focus on technology and science-enabled companies. Specialized in technology companies solving problems in large traditional industries (like agriculture or construction) or deep technology companies out of top-tier research groups (like MIT or Harvard). **Founded:** 2008.

40725 ■ Saturn Partners (SP)
75 Federal St., Ste. 1320
Boston, MA 02110
Ph: (617)574-3330
Co. E-mail: saturnasset@saturnpartnersvc.com
URL: http://saturnpartnersvc.com
Contact: Ed Lafferty, Chief Financial Officer Partner
E-mail: elafferty@saturnpartnersvc.com
Description: Venture capital firm for seed- and early-stage companies. **Founded:** 1994. **Investment Policies:** Innovative solution at the leading edge of industry trends; patent-protected (or hard it replicate) disruptive technology changing industry dynamics; addressing a critical market need by alleviating a significant problem.

40726 ■ Seacoast Capital
55 Ferncroft Rd., Ste. 110
Danvers, MA 01923
Ph: (978)750-1300
URL: http://www.seacoastcapital.com
Contact: Phil Curatilo, Principal Chief Marketing Officer
E-mail: pcuratilo@seacoastcapital.com
Facebook: www.facebook.com/seacoastcapitalpartners
Linkedin: www.linkedin.com/company/seacoast-capital
Description: Provider of investment management services. **Scope:** Invests growth capital in small companies led by strong, entrepreneurial management teams. Provides follow-on financing for acquisitions, internal growth or the execution of roll-out strategies. Assists portfolio companies develop and refine strategic plans, recruit additional management or board talent, access debt or equity capital markets, identify and negotiate acquisitions, develop compensation and incentive programs and maximize value for all stakeholders upon exit. **Founded:** 1994. **Preferred Investment Size:** $2,000,000 to $10,000,000. **Industry Preferences:** Other products, Internet specific, consumer related, semiconductors and other electronics, medical and health, industrial and energy, computer software and services.

40727 ■ SideCar Angels, Inc.
90 Brook St.
Westwood, MA 02090
Contact: Jeffrey M. Stoler, President
Description: Investment organization that seeks to ride "sidecar" with top-tier angel groups and venture capital firms to fund early-stage companies. Membership is limited to accredited investors; by invitation only. **Founded:** 2012. **Investment Policies:** Established and experienced teams; potential to achieve sound financial indicators in a reasonable amount of time; competitive advantage with significant growth potential; scalable projects in fast-growing markets.

40728 ■ Sigma Prime Ventures
20 Custom House St.
Boston, MA 02110
Ph: (617)330-7872
URL: http://www.sigmaprime.com
Contact: Robert E. Davoli, Managing Director
Facebook: www.facebook.com/sigmaprimev
Linkedin: www.linkedin.com/company/sigma-prime-ventures
X (Twitter): x.com/sigmaprimev
Description: Invests in early-stage companies, primarily on the East Coast. **Founded:** 2012. **Industry Preferences:** SaaS; cloud; mobile; disruptive technologies; technology-enabled services.

STATE LISTINGS Massachusetts ■ 40744

40729 ■ Solstice Capital
81 Washington St., Ste. 303
 Salem, MA 01970-3547
Ph: (617)523-7733
URL: http://www.solcap.com
Contact: Harry George, Managing Partner
Description: Firm provides venture capital investment services. **Founded:** 1995. **Preferred Investment Size:** $500,000 to $1,000,000. **Industry Preferences:** Computer software and services, industrial and energy, Internet specific, biotechnology, medical and health, semiconductors and other electronics, computer hardware, communications and media, consumer related, and other products.

40730 ■ Spark Capital
200 Clarendon St., Fl. 59
 Boston, MA 02116
Ph: (617)830-2000
Co. E-mail: contactus@sparkcapital.com
URL: http://www.sparkcapital.com
Contact: Chelsea Davis, Director
X (Twitter): x.com/sparkcapital
Description: Venture capital firm funding early-, mid- and late-stage companies. Also maintains offices in New York and San Francisco. **Founded:** 2005. **Industry Preferences:** Advertising; cloud computing; mobile.

40731 ■ Stage 1 Ventures, LLC
890 Winter St., Ste. 208
 Waltham, MA 02451
Ph: (781)772-1010
Co. E-mail: info@stage1ventures.com
URL: http://www.stage1ventures.com
Contact: Jonathan Gordon, Managing Director
E-mail: jgordon@stage1ventures.com
Description: Early-stage venture capital firm. Also operates out of Florida, California, and Taiwan.

40732 ■ Summit Partners L.P.
222 Berkeley St., 18th Fl.
 Boston, MA 02116
Ph: (617)824-1000
Fax: (617)824-1100
URL: http://www.summitpartners.com
Contact: Erin White, Chief Compliance Officer
Linkedin: www.linkedin.com/company/summit-partners
X (Twitter): x.com/summitpartners
Description: Firm provides private equity services for later stage, mezzanine debt, growth capital, middle market, recapitalizations, possession financing and much more. **Founded:** 1984. **Preferred Investment Size:** $5,000,000 to $500,000,000. **Industry Preferences:** Other products, computer software and other services, communications and media, Internet specific, computer hardware, semiconductors and other electronics, medical and health, consumer related, biotechnology, business services, industrial and energy.

40733 ■ SV Health Investors (SV)
One Boston Pl.
 201 Washington St., Ste. 3900
 Boston, MA 02108
Ph: (617)367-8100
URL: http://svhealthinvestors.com
Contact: Paul LaViolette, Chief Operating Officer Managing Partner
Description: Venture capital and growth equity firm investing in life sciences companies. Also maintains an office in London. **Founded:** 1993. **Industry Preferences:** Biotech; medical devices; healthcare services; digital health.

40734 ■ TA Associates Management L.P.
TA Associates Management L.P.
 200 Clarendon St., 56th Fl.
 Boston, MA 02116
Ph: (617)574-6700
URL: http://www.ta.com
Contact: Akshay Srimal, Director
E-mail: asrimal@ta.com
Linkedin: www.linkedin.com/company/ta-associates
X (Twitter): x.com/taassociates
Description: Firm provides private equity and venture capital services in equity and debt capital, mezzanine, management buyouts and many more. **Founded:** 1968. **Preferred Investment Size:** $60,000,000 to $500,000,000. **Industry Preferences:** Computer software and services, other products, communications and media, Internet specific, medical and health, semiconductors and other electronics, consumer related, computer hardware, financial and business services, medical and health.

40735 ■ Third Rock Ventures (TRV)
201 Brookline Ave., Ste. 1401
 Boston, MA 02215
Ph: (617)585-2000
URL: http://www.thirdrockventures.com
Contact: Aaron Arvey, Director
Linkedin: www.linkedin.com/company/third-rock-ventures
X (Twitter): x.com/thirdrockv
Description: Venture capital firm for early-stage life science companies. Also maintains an office in San Francisco. **Founded:** 2007. **Industry Preferences:** Life science; healthcare; biotechnology; medical technology; medical devices.

40736 ■ TiE Boston
One Broadway, 14th Fl.
 Cambridge, MA 02142
Ph: (617)312-3825
Co. E-mail: info@boston.tie.org
URL: http://www.tieboston.org
Contact: Rowena Kay Mascarenhas, Executive Director
E-mail: rowena@tieboston.org
Facebook: www.facebook.com/tieboston
Linkedin: www.linkedin.com/company/tieboston
X (Twitter): x.com/tieboston
Description: Offers funding and advice to early-stage companies. Introduces entrepreneurs to potential investors at monthly business plan presentations. **Founded:** 1997. **Investment Policies:** Innovative, technology-driven startups addressing a significant market opportunity.

40737 ■ TPE Boulder
25 Braintree Hill Pk., Ste. 200
 Braintree, MA 02184
Ph: (781)930-3142
URL: http://www.ticonderogacap.com
Contact: Craig Jones, Partner
E-mail: craig@tpeboulder.com
Description: Firm is engaged in financial investment advisor for software, healthcare and business service companies. **Scope:** Firm is engaged in financial investment advisor for software, healthcare and business service companies. **Founded:** 1997. **Preferred Investment Size:** $2,000,000 to $5,000,000. **Industry Preferences:** Equity firm provides investment management services.

40738 ■ The Venture Capital Fund of New England (VFCNE)
36 Washington St., Ste. 170
 Wellesley, MA 02481
Ph: (781)431-8400
Co. E-mail: inquiries@vcfne.com
URL: http://www.vcfne.com
Contact: Chad Novotny, Managing Director
E-mail: chad.novotny@vcfne.com
Description: Firm providing closed end fund services. **Founded:** 1981. **Preferred Investment Size:** $500,000 to $1,500,000. **Industry Preferences:** Computer software and services, communications and media, medical and health, industrial and energy, semiconductors and other electronics, computer hardware, other products, Internet specific, biotechnology, and consumer related.

40739 ■ Ventures
155 Federal St., Ste.700
 Boston, MA 02110
Description: Services: Provides venture capitals and growth resources to early stage companies. **Preferred Investment Size:** $1,000,000 to $20,000,000. **Investment Policies:** Early and later stage, expansion, generalist PE, industry rollups, recapitalizations, and special situation. **Industry Preferences:** Internet specific, information technology, consumer related, and industrial and energy.

40740 ■ Walnut Ventures
Boston, MA
URL: http://www.walnutventures.com
Contact: Ralph Wagner, Member
Description: Entrepreneurs and executives who invest in and mentor seed and early-stage companies with B2B or B2C products.

PROCUREMENT ASSISTANCE PROGRAMS

40741 ■ Massachusetts APEX Accelerator
UMass Amherst Center at Springfield Tower Sq.,
 1500 Main St.
 Springfield, MA 01115
Ph: (413)545-6303
URL: http://www.msbdc.org/ptac
Description: Helps to guide you through the government procurement process and provide you with information on how to become more competitive in the government marketplace. **Founded:** 1999. **Geographic Preference:** State.

40742 ■ Small Business Administration (SBA)
10 Cswy. St., Rm. 265
 Boston, MA 02222
Ph: (617)565-5590
Co. E-mail: answerdesk@sba.gov
URL: http://www.sba.gov/district/massachusetts
Contact: Robert H. Nelson, Director
Linkedin: www.linkedin.com/company/us-small-business-administration
X (Twitter): x.com/sbagov
Instagram: www.instagram.com/sbagov
YouTube: www.youtube.com/user/sba
Description: Covers activities for Hanscom Air Force Base (Bedford, MA), Army Corps of Engineers (Waltham, MA), Army Soldiers Systems Command (Natick, MA), Transportation Systems Control (Cambridge, MA). **Founded:** 1953.

INCUBATORS/RESEARCH AND TECHNOLOGY PARKS

40743 ■ AccelHUB LLC
10 Hartshorne Rd.
 Wakefield, MA 01880
Contact: Gregory Geehan, Contact
Description: Connects emerging markets, entrepreneurs, and technology ecosystems. Offers open innovation programs, funding, business development assistance, and networking.

40744 ■ Babson College - Arthur M. Blank Center for Entrepreneurship
231 Forest St.
 Babson Park, MA 02457
URL: http://www.babson.edu/academics/centers-and-institutes/the-arthur-m-blank-center-for-entrepreneurship
Contact: Debi Kleiman, Executive Director
E-mail: dkleiman@babson.edu
URL(s): www.babson.edu/entrepreneurship-center/about
Description: Business accelerator providing tailored resources and guidance for new businesses. **Scope:** Entrepreneurship and new and growing businesses, including studies in venture capital, starting and financing new value-creating ventures, family businesses, franchises, and harvesting enterprises through IPO's, merger or sale, and family succession. **Founded:** 1998. **Publications:** *Babson Entrepreneurial Review*; *Frontiers of Entrepreneurship Research* (Annual). **Educational Activities:** Babson College Entrepreneurship Research Conference (Annual). **Awards:** Academy of Distinguished Entrepreneurs (Irregular).

40745 ■ BioSquare
650 Albany St.
Boston, MA 02118
Ph: (617)353-4101
URL: http://www.bu.edu/realestate/biosquare
Contact: Dr. Robert A. Brown, President
E-mail: president@bu.edu
Description: Provides a fully built biotechnology startup space for biotech entrepreneurs.

40746 ■ Cambridge Innovation Center (CIC)
1 Broadway, 14th Fl., Kendall Sq.
Cambridge, MA 02142
Ph: (617)758-4100
URL: http://cic.com
Contact: Brian Dacey, President
E-mail: brian_d@cic.us
Facebook: www.facebook.com/cicnow
X (Twitter): x.com/cicnow
Instagram: www.instagram.com/cicnow
YouTube: www.youtube.com/channel/UCVOGcqfwhN4XamaiPdcx4ig
Description: Helps entrepreneurs and startups as they set up and manage their offices. **Founded:** 1999.

40747 ■ CropCircle Kitchen
196 Quincy St.
Dorchester, MA 02121
Contact: Lesley Delaney-Hawkins, President
Description: Shared use kitchen and culinary business incubator. Supports culinary entrepreneurs by providing technical support, training, oversight, and guidance through the early stages of a new food business. **Founded:** 2009.

40748 ■ Economic Development & Industrial Corporation of Lynn - Office of Economic Development
Lynn City Hall
3 City Hall Sq., Rm. 405
Lynn, MA 01901
URL: http://ediclynn.org/wp
Description: The Economic Development & Industrial Corporation of Lynn (EDIC/Lynn) is a non-profit corporation established under a state mandate in 1977 that functions as the City of Lynn's development bank. **Founded:** 1977.

40749 ■ Edison Business Incubator
60 School St.
Brockton, MA 02301
Ph: (508)586-0500
URL: http://metrosouthchamber.com/resources/incubator
Description: Provides a stepping-stone for fledging businesses wishing to operate in a professional environment but not yet capable of supporting the substantial overhead costs associated with a prime urban location. **Founded:** 1883.

40750 ■ Enterprise Center at Salem State University (SSU)
121 Loring Ave.
Salem, MA 01970
Ph: (978)542-7528
Fax: (978)542-7061
Co. E-mail: lswanson@enterprisectr.org
URL: http://enterprisectr.org
Contact: Laura Swanson, Executive Director
E-mail: lswanson@enterprisectr.org
Facebook: www.facebook.com/EnterpriseCtr
Linkedin: www.linkedin.com/company/the-enterprise-center-business
X (Twitter): x.com/EnterpriseCtr
YouTube: www.youtube.com/channel/UC2zpMqX4Q2rHSSSf0cjXWAA
Description: A business incubator and virtual center for entrepreneurs throughout the North Shore of Boston at every stage of business development. The Center leases office space to start up companies, offers free skill-building workshops to the public, and hosts numerous other programs including one hundred twenty-eight Venture North Networking Breakfasts and an annual Business Plan Competition.

40751 ■ Greentown Labs Inc.
444 Somerville Ave.
Somerville, MA 02143
Free: 888-954-6836
Co. E-mail: hello@greentownlabs.com
URL: http://greentownlabs.com
Contact: Dr. Emily Reichert, Chief Executive Officer
Facebook: www.facebook.com/GreentownLabs
Linkedin: www.linkedin.com/company/greentown-labs
X (Twitter): x.com/greentownlabs
Instagram: www.instagram.com/greentownlabs
Description: Enables entrepreneurs to solve big energy problems by providing space, resources, and funding that allows early stage companies to thrive. **Founded:** 2011.

40752 ■ Institute for Industrial and Applied Life Sciences (IALS)
N510 Life Science Laboratories
240 Thatcher Rd.
Amherst, MA 01003-9364
Ph: (413)545-1710
Co. E-mail: contactials@umass.edu
URL: http://www.umass.edu/ials
Contact: Peter H. Reinhart, Director
E-mail: preinhart@umass.edu
Linkedin: www.linkedin.com/company/umass-ials
X (Twitter): x.com/UMassIALS
Instagram: www.instagram.com/umassials
Description: Incubator supporting businesses in human and animal health and nutrition products and services; basic or applied research; product enhancement, development and/or engineering; and pre-pilot, pilot, or proto-type development.

40753 ■ LearnLaunch (LL)
55 Ct. St.
Boston, MA 02210
Co. E-mail: accelerator@learnlaunch.com
URL: http://learnlaunch.com
Contact: Jean Hammon, Partner
X (Twitter): x.com/LearnLaunchX
Instagram: www.instagram.com/learnlaunch
Description: Offers bootcamps and accelerator programs for educational technology startups. **Founded:** 2012.

40754 ■ Mansfield Bio-Incubator (MBA)
241 Francis Ave.
Mansfield, MA 02048
Co. E-mail: info@bioinc.org
URL: http://www.bioinc.org
Description: Nonprofit organization working to facilitate and assist the creation, growth, and success of the next generation of biotech companies. **Geographic Preference:** State.

40755 ■ Massachusetts Association of Business Incubators (MABI)
c/o Eric Anderson
400 Trade Ctr., Ste. 5900
Woburn, MA 01801
Ph: (781)983-2211
Co. E-mail: info@massincubators.org
URL: http://www.massincubators.org
Contact: Eric S. Anderson, Contact
Description: Supports business incubation programs in Massachusetts. Provides professionals with information, education, and networking opportunities. **Founded:** 2006. **Geographic Preference:** State.

40756 ■ Massachusetts Biomedical Initiatives (MBI)
17 Briden St.
Worcester, MA 01605
Ph: (508)797-4200
Co. E-mail: info@massbiomed.org
URL: http://mbi.bio
Contact: Jon Weaver, President
Facebook: www.facebook.com/massbiomed
Linkedin: www.linkedin.com/company/massbiomed
X (Twitter): x.com/massbiomed
Description: An independent, tax-exempt corporation created to support the growth and expansion of biotechnology and medical device companies throughout the region, enhancing the status of Massachusetts as a world leader in the medical industry. **Founded:** 1984.

40757 ■ Massachusetts Clean Energy Center (MassCEC)
294 Washington St., 11th Fl.
Boston, MA 02108
Ph: (617)315-9300
Fax: (617)315-9356
Co. E-mail: info@masscec.com
URL: http://www.masscec.com
Contact: Jennifer Daloisio, Chief Executive Officer
X (Twitter): x.com/MassCEC
Instagram: www.instagram.com/masscec
YouTube: www.youtube.com/user/MassCEC1/videos
Description: A publicly-funded agency dedicated to accelerating the success of clean energy technologies, companies, and projects in Massachusetts. Provides early-stage investments to startup companies. **Founded:** 2009.

40758 ■ Massachusetts Medical Device Development Center (M2D2)
600 Suffolk St., 2nd Fl.
Lowell, MA 01854
Ph: (978)934-3465
Co. E-mail: m2d2@uml.edu
URL: http://www.uml.edu/Research/M2D2/default.aspx
Contact: Nathaniel Hafer, Director, Operations
E-mail: nathaniel.hafer@umassmed.edu
Description: Offers inventors and executives easy, affordable, and coordinated access to world-class researchers and resources at the Lowell and Worcester campuses of the University of Massachusetts for medical device development.

40759 ■ MassChallenge (MC)
10 Fan Pier Blvd., 3rd Fl.
Boston, MA 02210
Co. E-mail: contact@masschallenge.org
URL: http://masschallenge.org
Contact: Cait Brumme, Chief Executive Officer
X (Twitter): x.com/masschallenge
Description: Helps early-stage entrepreneurs accelerate their growth. **Founded:** 2009.

40760 ■ North Shore InnoVentures (NSIV)
100 Cummings Ctr., Ste. 451C
Beverly, MA 01915
Ph: (978)867-0600
Co. E-mail: info@nsiv.org
URL: http://innoventurelabs.org
Contact: Chris Ilsley, President
Facebook: www.facebook.com/nsinnoventures
Linkedin: www.linkedin.com/company/north-shore-innoventures-beverly-ma
X (Twitter): x.com/NSInnoVentures
YouTube: www.youtube.com/channel/UC4BOP67y7HxKBvF7B8osgqQ
Description: Technology business incubator for biotech and cleantech startups. Promotes entrepreneurship and economic development by fostering life sciences and cleantech companies.

40761 ■ Northeastern University Center for Entrepreneurship Education (NUCEE)
360 Huntington Ave.
Boston, MA 02115
URL: http://entrepreneurship.northeastern.edu
Contact: Marie Meslin, Managing Director
E-mail: m.meslin@northeastern.edu
Description: Empowers students, faculty, and alumni from across the university to innovate, start new companies, and become leaders in the innovation economy. Offers a business incubator providing the tools and resources to support the rapid development of business concepts into self-sustaining or investment-ready ventures. **Founded:** 2010.

40762 ■ Quincy Center for Innovation (QCI)
180 Old Colony Ave., Ste. 300
Quincy, MA 02170
Ph: (617)860-2281
URL: http://www.quincyinno.com

Description: A unique co-operative work environment offering co-working and collaboration to support startups and early phase companies.

40763 ■ Springfield Technical Community College Student Business Incubator
One Armory Sq., Ste.1
  Springfield, MA 01102
URL: http://www.stcc.edu/about-stcc/campus-map-and-directions
Description: Helps bridge the gap between academics and a real world entrepreneurial experience with a supportive environment including individual advisors and mentors. Students receive coaching, information resource referrals, connection to technical assistance and access to potential capital.

40764 ■ Summer@Highland
Boston, MA
URL: http://summer.hcp.com
Description: An entrepreneurship program run by Highland Capital Partners designed to provide student founders with the environment and resources to advance their startups to the next level over the summer. **Founded:** 2007.

40765 ■ Technical Innovation Center (TIC)
100 Barber Ave.
  Worcester, MA 01606
Ph: (508)799-6700
Co. E-mail: tic@triz.org
URL: http://triz.org
Contact: Richard Langevin, Chief Executive Officer
Description: A self-sustaining economic development effort fostering the growth of new and expanding businesses by providing access to advanced technologies, business development resources, and collaborative opportunities. **Founded:** 1995.

40766 ■ TU Incubator
3362 Kovar Rd.
  Cataumet, MA 02534
Ph: (508)563-4331
Co. E-mail: info@tuincubator.com
URL: http://tuincubator.com
Description: Serves as an entrepreneurial resource and activity hub inside and outside of Towson University.

40767 ■ Venture Development Center (VDC)
100 Morrissey Blvd., Wheatley Hall, 3rd Fl.
  Boston, MA 02125-3393
Ph: (617)287-6070
Co. E-mail: vdc@umb.edu
URL: http://www.umb.edu/vdc
Description: Helps entrepreneurs turn their visions into reality.

EDUCATIONAL PROGRAMS

40768 ■ Bunker Hill Community College
250 New Rutherford Ave.
  Boston, MA 02129
Ph: (617)228-2000
Co. E-mail: admissions@bhcc.edu
URL: http://www.bhcc.edu
Contact: Dr. Pam Eddinger, President
E-mail: peddinger@bhcc.edu
Facebook: www.facebook.com/BHCCBoston
Linkedin: www.linkedin.com/school/bunker-hill-community-college
X (Twitter): x.com/BHCCBoston
Instagram: www.instagram.com/bhccboston
YouTube: www.youtube.com/user/bhccboston
Description: Two-year college offering a small business management course. **Founded:** 1973.

40769 ■ Dean College
99 Main St.
  Franklin, MA 02038
Free: 877-TRY-DEAN
Co. E-mail: admissions@dean.edu
URL: http://www.dean.edu
Contact: Kenneth Elmore, President
Facebook: www.facebook.com/DeanDifference
Linkedin: www.linkedin.com/school/dean-college
X (Twitter): x.com/DeanCollege
Instagram: www.instagram.com/deancollege
YouTube: www.youtube.com/user/DeanCollegeOfficial
Description: Two-year college offering a small business management program. **Founded:** 1865. **Geographic Preference:** National.

40770 ■ MassBay Community College
50 Oakland St.
  Wellesley Hills, MA 02481
Ph: (781)239-3000
Co. E-mail: info@massbay.edu
URL: http://www.massbay.edu
Contact: Dr. David Podell, President
Facebook: www.facebook.com/MassBayCommunityCollege
Linkedin: www.linkedin.com/school/massbay-community-college
X (Twitter): x.com/massbaycommcol
Instagram: www.instagram.com/massbayview
YouTube: www.youtube.com/user/MassBayCommCollege
Description: College offering a two-year small business management program. **Founded:** 1961.

40771 ■ Mt. Ida College-Division of Continuing Education
100 Carlson Ave.
  Newton, MA 02459
URL: http://www.umass.edu/profile/pages/continuing_education.html
Description: Offers certificate and/or associate degree programs in business administration and paralegal studies. Also provides noncredit professional development programs to small business owners.

40772 ■ Startup Leadership Program (SLP)
Boylston St.
  Boston, MA 02163
Co. E-mail: info@startupleadership.com
URL: http://www.startupleadership.com
Facebook: www.facebook.com/StartupLeadership
Linkedin: www.linkedin.com/company/startup-leadership-program
X (Twitter): x.com/startlead
Description: A global not-for-profit educational program and professional network for the next generation of founders and entrepreneurs. Offers a highly selective, 6-month world-class education and mentoring program and lifelong network for founders and innovators. **Founded:** 2006.

CONSULTANTS

40773 ■ Ice Glen Associates LLC
11 Elizabeth Rd.
  Hopkinton, MA 01748-2008
Ph: (508)361-6336
Fax: (408)682-0909
Co. E-mail: mmatteodo@iceglen.com
URL: http://iceglen.com
Contact: Maurice Matteodo, Founder Managing Director
Description: Financial advisory firm supporting early-stage tech companies. Offers CFO support, acquisition-related purchase price allocations, Section 409A business valuations, and pre-investment diligence. **Founded:** 2005.

PUBLICATIONS

40774 ■ *Boston Business Journal (BBJ)*
70 Franklin St. 8th Fl.
  Boston, MA 02110
Ph: (617)330-1000
Fax: (617)330-1015
Co. E-mail: boston@bizjournals.com
URL: http://www.bizjournals.com/boston
Contact: Carolyn M. Jones, President
E-mail: cmjones@bizjournals.com
URL(s): www.bizjournals.com/boston
Facebook: www.facebook.com/BostonBusinessJournal
Linkedin: www.linkedin.com/company/boston-business-journal
X (Twitter): x.com/BosBizJournal
Instagram: www.instagram.com/bostonbusinessjournal
Ed: Max Stendahl, Doug Banks. **Released:** Weekly **Price:** $950, for 52 weeks book of Lists; $380, for 52 weeks national wide access; $220, for Digital + Print; $210, for online52 weeks. **Description:** Business newspaper specializing in local and regional business for upper management and CEO's of large and mid-sized businesses. **Availability:** Print; Online. **Type:** Full-text.

40775 ■ Boston Business Journal
70 Franklin St. 8th Fl.
  Boston, MA 02110
Ph: (617)330-1000
Fax: (617)330-1015
Co. E-mail: boston@bizjournals.com
URL: http://www.bizjournals.com/boston
Contact: Carolyn M. Jones, President
E-mail: cmjones@bizjournals.com
Facebook: www.facebook.com/BostonBusinessJournal
X (Twitter): x.com/BosBizJournal
Description: Publisher of newspaper covering news, sports and business information. **Publications:** *Boston Business Journal--Book of Lists* (Weekly); *Boston Business Journal (BBJ)* (Weekly).

40776 ■ *Worcester Business Journal*
Contact: Peter Stanton, Publisher
URL(s): www.wbjournal.com
Facebook: www.facebook.com/wbjournal
X (Twitter): twitter.com/wbjournal
Ed: Brad Kane. **Released:** Biweekly **Price:** $124.95, for 3 Years (87 issues); $94.95, U.S. for 1 Year (29 issues); $89.95, U.S. for 2 Years (58 issues). **Description:** Covers the news, trends, data, politics, and personalities of the Central Massachusetts business community. **Availability:** Print; Online.

PUBLISHERS

40777 ■ Bradford & Bigelow Inc.
3 Perkins Way
  Newburyport, MA 01950
Ph: (978)904-3100
Co. E-mail: sales@bradford-bigelow.com
URL: http://www.bradford-bigelow.com
Contact: Stephen Pompeo, Sr., Manager
E-mail: spompeo@bradford-bigelow.com
Facebook: www.facebook.com/BradfordBigelow
Linkedin: www.linkedin.com/company/bradford-&-bigelow-inc-
X (Twitter): x.com/bradford_biginc
YouTube: www.youtube.com/channel/UCJOpHiA2djYAf2qXGc5xVRg
Description: Publishes health and fitness for self-help, medical care, writing, home improvement, humor, business, travel and fiction for an adult audience. Does not accept unsolicited manuscripts. Reaches market through reviews and listings as well as wholesalers and distributors. **Founded:** 1947.

40778 ■ HRD Press Inc.
22 Amherst Rd.
  Amherst, MA 01002-9709
Ph: (413)253-3488
Free: 800-822-2801
Co. E-mail: info@hrdpress.com
URL: http://www.hrdpress.com
Contact: Mark Snow, Contact
E-mail: mark@hrdpress.com
Description: Publisher of electronic resources, such as workshops and books for consultants, corporate trainers and educators. **Scope:** Publishes print, video, software, and books for consultants, corporate trainers, and educators in the human resource industry. Also provides a wide assortment of administrative, consultative, and technical services. **Founded:** 1972. **Publications:** "The Constant Customer"; "The Manager's Pocket Guide to eCommunication(MPGEC)"; "The Managers Pocket Guide to Emotional Intelligence (MPGEI)"; "Twenty Repro-

ducible Assessment Instruments"; "Establishing the Value of Training". **Training:** Planning for Team Results; Preparing the Future Leader; Problem Solving Process; Supervisory Development Series.

40779 ■ Jeffrey Lant Associates, Inc. (JLA)
50 Follen St., No. 507
 Cambridge, MA 02138
Ph: (617)547-6372
Co. E-mail: drlant@drjeffreylant.com
URL: http://www.drjeffreylant.com
Description: Publishes technical assistance books for nonprofit organizations, consultants, independent professionals and small and home-based businesses. Offers audio cassettes, workshops and consultation services. Also publish twice the monthly Worlgram newsletter. Reaches market through commission representatives, direct mail, telephone sales and the Internet. Accept unsolicited manuscripts. **Founded:** 1997. **Publications:** "E-mail El Dorado," JLA Publications, 1998; "Web Wealth: How to Turn the World Wide Web Into a Cash Hose for Your Business. Whatever You're Selling," 1997; "Multi-Level Money," JLA Publications, 1994; "No More Cold Calls," JLA Publications, 1997; "Cash Copy"; "How to make at least $100000 a year"; "E-Money". **Training:** Business and personal development, including Establishing and Operating Your Successful Consulting Business; Successfully Promoting Your Small Business and Professional Practice; Succeeding in Your Mail Order Business; Successfully Raising Money for Your Nonprofit Organization from Foundations, Corporations and Individuals; Money Making Marketing: Finding the People Who Need What You're Selling and Making Sure They Buy It; Getting Corporations, Foundations, and Individuals to Give You the Money Your Nonprofit Organization Needs.

COMPUTER SYSTEMS/ SOFTWARE

40780 ■ Association for Computing Machinery Stonehill College
320 Washington St.
 North Easton, MA 02356
Ph: (508)565-1000
URL: http://web.stonehill.edu/compsci/acm-student-chapter.htm
Contact: Emily May, President
E-mail: emay@students.stonehill.edu
Geographic Preference: Local.

RESEARCH CENTERS

40781 ■ Massachusetts Institute of Technology - Martin Trust Center for Entrepreneurship
E40-160, 1 Amherst St.
 Cambridge, MA 02142
Ph: (617)253-8653
Co. E-mail: trustcenter@mit.edu
URL: http://entrepreneurship.mit.edu
Contact: Bill Aulet, Managing Director
E-mail: aulet@mit.edu
Facebook: www.facebook.com/EshipMIT
Linkedin: www.linkedin.com/company/martin-trust-center-for-mit-entrepreneurship
X (Twitter): x.com/EshipMIT
Instagram: www.instagram.com/eshipmit
Description: Integral unit of the Sloan School of Management at the Massachusetts Institute of Technology. **Scope:** Entrepreneurship, with emphasis on the dynamic process of high-tech venture development. **Founded:** 1991.

EXPANSION AND GROWTH FINANCING

40782 ■ Coastal Capital Partners
4 Alexander Dr.
 Yarmouthport, MA 02675
Ph: (617)803-3984
Co. E-mail: info@coastalcapitalpartners.com
URL: http://coastalcapitalpartners.com
Contact: Sean Correa, President
Description: Offers alternative commercial financing for small business entrepreneurs in the region.

40783 ■ Volition Capital
177 Huntington Ave., 16th Fl.
 Boston, MA 02115
Ph: (617)830-2100
Co. E-mail: info@volitioncapital.com
URL: http://www.volitioncapital.com
Contact: Kelly Barnum, Manager
Facebook: www.facebook.com/volitioncapital
X (Twitter): x.com/volitioncapital
Description: Growth equity firm. **Founded:** 2010. **Investment Policies:** Solid revenue base of $5-25 million; 25-100% revenue growth; capital efficient. **Industry Preferences:** Software; tech-enabled services; internet; consumer.

VENTURE CAPITAL FIRM

40784 ■ Bolt Innovation Management
292 Newbury St., Ste. 356
 Boston, MA 02115
URL: http://bolt.io
Contact: Axel Bichara, Partner
X (Twitter): x.com/boltvc
Description: A venture capital firm for hardware startups offering seed funding, a high-end prototyping shop, support from a full-time engineering and design staff and assistance with manufacturing and commercialization. **Founded:** 1961.

40785 ■ Founder Collective (FC)
1 Mifflin Pl., Ste. 300
 Cambridge, MA 02138
Co. E-mail: contact@foundercollective.com
URL: http://www.foundercollective.com
Contact: Joe Flaherty, Director
X (Twitter): x.com/fcollective
Description: Seed-stage venture capital firm. Also operates out of New York City.

40786 ■ GrandBanks Capital
1150 Great Plains Ave., No. 920315
 Needham, MA 02492
Ph: (781)997-4300
Fax: (781)997-4301
Co. E-mail: info@grandbankscapital.com
URL: http://www.grandbankscapital.com
Contact: J. J. Healy, Partner
Description: Early-stage investment firm. **Industry Preferences:** Internet infrastructure; software and software services; mobile media; financial technologies and services; wireless technologies and services.

40787 ■ Liberty Mutual Innovation (LMI)
175 Berkeley St.
 Boston, MA 02116
URL: http://www.libertymutualgroup.com/about-lm/corporate-information/overview
Contact: Timothy Sweeney, President
Description: The venture capital arm of Liberty Mutual's U.S. Consumer Markets business. Supports entrepreneurs that are reshaping the insurance industry.

40788 ■ Takeda Ventures Inc. (TVI)
500 Kendall St.
 Cambridge, MA 02142
Contact: Miles Gerson, Chief Executive Officer
Description: Early-stage venture capital arm of Takeda Pharmaceuticals. Supports therapeutic innovation in biopharmaceuticals. **Founded:** 2000.

40789 ■ Windspeed Ventures
561 Virginia Rd., Ste. 222
 Concord, MA 01742
Ph: (781)860-8888
Co. E-mail: info@windspeed.com
URL: http://windspeed.com
Contact: John W. Bullock, Managing Partner
Description: Early state investment firm. **Founded:** 1999. **Industry Preferences:** Telecommunications; software; media; internet services.

Michigan

ASSOCIATIONS AND OTHER ORGANIZATIONS

40790 ■ Accounting Aid Society (AAS)
3031 W Grand Blvd., Ste. 470
Detroit, MI 48202
Ph: (313)556-1920
Fax: (313)556-1941
Co. E-mail: info@accountingaidsociety.org
URL: http://accountingaidsociety.org
Contact: Priscilla Perkins, President
Facebook: www.facebook.com/accountingaidsociety
Linkedin: www.linkedin.com/company/533610
Instagram: www.instagram.com/accountingaidacademy
Description: Expands the financial potential of underserved community members and small businesses in Detroit and Southeast Michigan area. **Scope:** Provider of free income tax assistance programs for low and moderate income families, seniors and others in need. Assists people with local, state and federal tax filings, as well as Property Tax Refunds, Earned Income Credits, Home Heating Credits and Child Credits. Also provides information on tax rights and responsibilities, including help for those who speak English as a second language and offer aid in resolving tax disputes with the IRS. Area served: Michigan. **Founded:** 1972.

40791 ■ Association of Fundraising Professionals - Greater Detroit
PO Box 329
Lake Orion, MI 48361
Ph: (248)579-5004
URL: http://community.afpglobal.org/afpmigreaterdetroitchapter/home
Contact: Melissa Weisse, Vice President
E-mail: mweisse@leaderdog.org
Facebook: www.facebook.com/AFPDetroit
X (Twitter): x.com/AFPDetroit
Description: Fosters the professional development and growth of fundraising professionals in southeast Michigan. **Geographic Preference:** Local.

40792 ■ Association of Fundraising Professionals West Michigan Chapter (AFPWM)
PO Box 6302
Grand Rapids, MI 49516-6302
Co. E-mail: afpwestmichigan@gmail.com
URL: http://afpwm.org
Contact: Ashley Diersch, President
E-mail: adiersch@mowwm.org
URL(s): afpglobal.org/chapters/afp-mi-west-michigan-chapter
Facebook: www.facebook.com/AFPWestMichigan
Linkedin: www.linkedin.com/company/association-of-fundraising-professionals-west-michigan
X (Twitter): x.com/afpwestmichigan
Description: Provides resources to fundraising professionals in western Michigan. **Founded:** 1985. **Geographic Preference:** Local.

40793 ■ Business Network International Michigan
3430 Toringdon Way
Charlotte, NC 28277
Free: 855-264-2673
URL: http://bni-mi.com/en-US/index
Contact: Tonya Acha, Managing Director
E-mail: tonyaacha@bni.com
Facebook: www.facebook.com/bnimichigan
Description: Provides both men and women a structured environment for the development and exchange of quality business referrals. Offers members the opportunity to share ideas and contacts. **Geographic Preference:** State.

40794 ■ Business Network International Wisconsin South & Upper Peninsula Michigan
348 Napoleon Rd.
Michigan Center, MI 49254
Ph: (517)716-1001
URL: http://bniwis.com/en-US/index
Contact: David M. Zemer, Executive Director
Description: Provides both men and women a structured environment for the development and exchange of quality business referrals. Offers members the opportunity to share ideas and contacts. **Founded:** 1985. **Geographic Preference:** Local.

40795 ■ Detroit Association for Business Economics (DABE)
Detroit, MI
URL: http://nabe.com/NABE/Groups/Chapters.aspx
Contact: Andrew King, Co-President
Description: Represents business professionals in the field of business economics. Provides leadership for the use and understanding of economics. **Founded:** 1966. **Geographic Preference:** Local.

40796 ■ Entrepreneurs' Organization - Detroit Chapter (EO)
c/o Anna Longe, Administrator
PO Box 453
Royal Oak, MI 48067
Ph: (248)224-7362
Co. E-mail: admin@eodetroit.com
URL: http://www.eonetwork.org/detroit
Contact: Anna Longe, Administrator
Description: Provides local resources to members which includes networking events, mentorship, live forums, and leadership development. **Founded:** 1994.

40797 ■ Entrepreneurs' Organization - West Michigan Chapter (EO)
MI
URL: http://eonetwork.org/westmichigan
Description: Provides local resources to members which includes networking events, mentorship, live forums, and leadership development. **Founded:** 2016.

40798 ■ Great Lakes Association for Financial Professionals (GLAFP)
1862 Poppleton Dr.
West Bloomfield, MI 48324
Co. E-mail: info@greatlakesafp.org
URL: http://www.greatlakesafp.org
Contact: Richard Moore, President
Linkedin: www.linkedin.com/company/great-lakes-afp
Description: Provides a forum for the exchange of ideas and techniques in the field of financial and treasury management. Promotes the finance and treasury profession through the education and professional development of its members. **Geographic Preference:** Local.

40799 ■ International Association of Women Detroit Chapter
Detroit, MI
URL: http://www.iawomen.com/chapters/detroit-chapter
Description: Serves as network of accomplished women united to achieve professional goals. Provides a forum for sharing ideas and experiences of professional women regarding career success. Promotes an active business and networking community from all industries. **Geographic Preference:** Local.

40800 ■ Michigan Agri Business Association (MABA)
2500 Kerry St., Ste. 102
Lansing, MI 48912
Ph: (517)336-0223
Fax: (866)829-3786
Co. E-mail: maba@miagbiz.org
URL: http://miagbiz.org
Contact: Chuck Lippstreu, President
Facebook: www.facebook.com/michagbiz
X (Twitter): x.com/michagbiz
Description: Businesses producing grain, feed, seed, fertilizer chemicals, and other agricultural products. Conducts legislative, public relations, educational, and member service activities. **Founded:** 1903. **Publications:** *Membership Ag Fax* (Bimonthly); *State Industry Directory* (Annual). **Educational Activities:** Michigan Agri-Business Association Outlook Conference (Annual). **Awards:** Michigan Agri-Business Association Educational Trust Scholarship (Annual). **Geographic Preference:** State.

40801 ■ Michigan Association of Convenience Stores (MACS)
7521 Wetshire Dr., Ste. 200
Lansing, MI 48917
Ph: (517)622-3530
URL: http://www.mpamacs.org
Contact: Mark Griffin, President
E-mail: griffin@mpamacs.org
Facebook: www.facebook.com/MPAMACS
Description: Trade organization representing and advocating for the interests of convenience store operators. **Founded:** 1986. **Geographic Preference:** State.

40802 ■ Michigan Business Innovation Asssociation (MBIA)
4717 Campus Dr., Ste. 100
Kalamazoo, MI 49008
Ph: (269)353-1823
Co. E-mail: michigan.incubation@gmail.com
URL: http://michiganincubation.org
Contact: Sandra Cochrane, President
Facebook: www.facebook.com/MBIAInfo
X (Twitter): x.com/MBIA_Michigan
Description: Offers a supportive entrepreneurial environment in the region. **Founded:** 1985.

40803 ■ Michigan Business Travel Association (MBTA) [Global Business Travel Association - Michigan Chapter]
2757 Maple Ridge
Highland, MI 48356
Co. E-mail: contact@gbtamichigan.org
Contact: Leslee Fritz, President
E-mail: lesleelfritz@yahoo.com
Description: Promotes the value of business travel management by representing corporate travel managers and travel service providers. Monitors developments in the business travel field and provides current, critical industry information. **Founded:** 1967.

40804 ■ Michigan Emu Growers Association (MEGA)
c/o Dennis E Homant, President
2147 Thorntree Ln.
Ortonville, MI 48462
Ph: (248)324-2687
Co. E-mail: dhomant@mi.rr.com
URL: http://michemu.tripod.com
Contact: Dennis E. Homant, President
E-mail: dhomant@mi.rr.com
Description: Association of emu growers in Michigan. **Geographic Preference:** State.

40805 ■ Michigan Plumbing and Mechanical Contractors Association (MPMCA)
PO Box 13100
Lansing, MI 48901
Ph: (517)484-5500
Co. E-mail: info@mpmca.org
URL: http://www.mpmca.org
Contact: Jim Dornbrock, President
Description: Aims to promote and advance the plumbing and mechanical industry in Michigan. **Publications:** *Michigan Master Plumber and Mechanical Contractor* (Quarterly); *Michigan Master Plumber & Mechanical Contractor Magazine* (Quarterly).

40806 ■ Michigan Venture Capital Association (MVCA)
6632 Telegraph Rd., Ste. No. 286
Bloomfield Hills, MI 48301
Free: 844-500-1014
Co. E-mail: info@michiganvca.org
URL: http://michiganvca.org
Contact: Ara Topouzian, Executive Director
E-mail: ara@michiganvca.org
Facebook: www.facebook.com/MichiganVCA
Linkedin: www.linkedin.com/company/michigan-venture-capital-association
X (Twitter): x.com/MichiganVCA
YouTube: www.youtube.com/channel/UCwLM_6KcVaNT1b5bGgOxCiQ
Description: Seeks to grow and sustain a vibrant venture capital community in Michigan. **Founded:** 2002.

40807 ■ National Association of Women Business Owners - Greater Detroit Chapter (NAWBO-GDC)
26677 W 12 Mile Rd.
Southfield, MI 48034
Ph: (313)961-4748
Co. E-mail: admin@nawbogdc.org
URL: http://www.nawbogdc.org
Contact: Nicole Lewis, President
E-mail: nicole@nicolelewisandassociates.com
Facebook: www.facebook.com/NAWBOgdc
Linkedin: www.linkedin.com/company/nawbogdc
X (Twitter): x.com/nawbogdc
Instagram: www.instagram.com/nawbogdc
Description: Women business owners and corporate partners seeking networking opportunities, educational seminars, political and economic influence through an organization with a national presence. **Founded:** 1980. **Publications:** *Vision*. **Educational Activities:** Salute to African American Women Business Owners. **Awards:** NAWBO Top 10 Michigan Business Women Awards - Diversity Champion Award (Irregular); NAWBO Top 10 Michigan Business Women Awards - Giving Spirit Award (Irregular); NAWBO Top 10 Michigan Business Women Awards - Global Business Award (Annual); NAWBO Top 10 Michigan Business Women Awards - Pinnacle Award (Irregular); NAWBO Top 10 Michigan Business Women Awards - Rainmaker Award (Annual); NAWBO Top 10 Michigan Business Women Awards - Red-Tape Buster Award (Annual); NAWBO Top 10 Michigan Business Women Awards - Up-and-Coming Award (Annual); NAWBO Top 10 Michigan Business Women Awards - Warrior Award (Annual); NAWBO Top 10 Michigan Business Women Awards - Words of Wisdom Award (Annual); NAWBO Top 10 Michigan Business Women Awards - Greater Good Award (Irregular); NAWBO Top 10 Michigan Business Women Awards - Breakthrough Award (Annual). **Geographic Preference:** Local.

40808 ■ State Bar of Michigan Business Law Section (SBM BLS)
c/o John T. Schuring, Chairman
200 Ottawa Ave. NW, Ste. 900
Grand Rapids, MI 49503-2427
Ph: (616)336-1023
Co. E-mail: businesslaw@mi.rr.com
URL: http://connect.michbar.org/businesslaw/home
Contact: Kevin T. Block, Director, Communications Director, Development
E-mail: kblock@kerr-russell.com
Facebook: www.facebook.com/SBMBusinessLawSection
Description: Furthers the development and improvement of business law, educating section members in business law and related professional responsibilities. Improves the practice of both in-house and outside business counsel through seminars, practical forums, legislation, and committee activity in a wide variety of areas, such as high technology, small business, bankruptcy, banking, and commercial law. **Awards:** Stephen H. Schulman Outstanding Business Lawyer Award (Annual). **Geographic Preference:** State.

SMALL BUSINESS DEVELOPMENT CENTERS

40809 ■ Michigan Small Business Development Center Capital Region
Lansing Community College
309 N Washington Sq., Ste. 115
Lansing, MI 48933
URL: http://michigansbdc.org
Contact: Laurie Lonsdorf, Regional Director
E-mail: sbdc@lcc.edu
Description: Offers expert assistance at no cost to entrepreneurs looking to start or grow a business. **Geographic Preference:** Local.

40810 ■ Michigan Small Business Development Center Great Lakes Bay Region
7400 Bay Rd., Ste. C300
University Center, MI 48710
URL: http://sbdcmichigan.org/great-lakes-bay-region
Contact: Beth Roszatycki, Officer
E-mail: blroszat@svsu.edu
Facebook: www.facebook.com/MichiganSBDC
X (Twitter): x.com/MichiganSBDC
Description: Provides management assistance to current and prospective small business owners in Center Great Lakes Bay Region. **Geographic Preference:** Local.

40811 ■ Michigan Small Business Development Center Greater Washtenaw Region (SBDC)
Morris Lawrence Bldg., Rm. 104
4800 E Huron River Dr.
Ann Arbor, MI 48105
Ph: (734)477-8762
URL: http://michigansbdc.org/contact-us
Contact: Charlie Penner, Regional Director
Facebook: www.facebook.com/GreaterWashtenawSBDC
Description: Offers expert assistance at no cost to entrepreneurs looking to start or grow a business. **Geographic Preference:** Local.

40812 ■ Michigan Small Business Development Center I-69 Trade Corridor
Kettering University
1700 University Ave., Campus Ctr., 5th Fl.
Flint, MI 48504
URL: http://michigansbdc.org
Contact: Janis Mueller, Regional Director
E-mail: jmueller1@kettering.edu
Description: Provides management assistance to current and prospective small business owners in Center I-69 Trade Corridor. **Geographic Preference:** Local.

40813 ■ Michigan Small Business Development Center Mid Michigan Region
2600 S Summerton Rd.
Mount Pleasant, MI 48858
Ph: (989)317-4623
Co. E-mail: sbdc@midmich.edu
URL: http://michigansbdc.org/contact-us
Contact: Anthony Fox, Regional Director
Facebook: www.facebook.com/MidMichSbdc
Description: Provides management assistance to current and prospective small business owners in Center Mid Michigan Region. **Geographic Preference:** Local.

40814 ■ Michigan Small Business Development Center Northwest Michigan Region
600 E Front St.
Traverse City, MI 49686
Ph: (231)929-5000
Free: 800-692-7774
Fax: (231)929-5012
Co. E-mail: sbdc@networksnorthwest.org
URL: http://www.networksnorthwest.org/data/data.html
Contact: Annie Olds, Regional Director
E-mail: annie.olds@networksnorthwest.org
Facebook: www.facebook.com/networksnorthwest
X (Twitter): x.com/networksnwest
YouTube: www.youtube.com/user/nwmcog/videos
Description: Offers expert assistance at no cost to entrepreneurs looking to start or grow a business. **Geographic Preference:** Local.

40815 ■ Michigan Small Business Development Center Southeast Michigan Region
109 Hill Hall
Ypsilanti, MI 48197
URL: http://michigansbdc.org/contact-us
Contact: Wendy Thomas, Director
E-mail: sdbcsoutheast@emich.edu
Description: Provides management assistance to current and prospective small business owners in Center Southeast Michigan Region. **Geographic Preference:** Local.

40816 ■ Michigan Small Business Development Center Southwest Michigan Region
c/o Tamara Davis, Director
3110 Schneider Hall
Kalamazoo, MI 49008
Co. E-mail: sbdc-kzoo@wmich.edu
URL: http://michigansbdc.org/contact-us
Contact: Tamara Davis, Regional Director
E-mail: sbdc-kzoo@wmich.edu
Facebook: www.facebook.com/MichiganSBDC
X (Twitter): x.com/MichiganSBDC

STATE LISTINGS
Michigan ■ 40835

Description: Offers expert assistance at no cost to entrepreneurs looking to start or grow a business.
Geographic Preference: Local.

40817 ■ Michigan Small Business Development Center West Michigan Region
L. William Seidman Ctr., Ste. 1081
50 Front Ave., SW
Grand Rapids, MI 49504
URL: http://michigansbdc.org/contact-us
Contact: Ed Garner, Regional Director
E-mail: garnered@gvsu.edu
Description: Provides management assistance to current and prospective small business owners in .
Geographic Preference: Local.

40818 ■ Michigan Small Business and Technology Development Center - Lead Center
1020 L. William Seidman Ctr.
50 Front Ave. SW
Grand Rapids, MI 49504
Co. E-mail: sbdcmichigan@gvsu.edu
URL: http://michigansbdc.org/contact-us
Contact: J. D. Collins, Director
Facebook: www.facebook.com/MichiganSBDC
X (Twitter): x.com/MichiganSBDC
Instagram: www.instagram.com/michigansbdc
Description: Offers expert assistance at no cost to entrepreneurs looking to start or grow a business.
Geographic Preference: Local.

40819 ■ Small Business Association of Michigan (SBAM)
120 N Washington Sq., Ste. 1000
Lansing, MI 48933
Free: 800-362-5461
URL: http://www.sbam.org
Contact: Brian Calley, President
E-mail: brian.calley@sbam.org
Facebook: www.facebook.com/
SmallBusinessAssociationofMichigan
Linkedin: www.linkedin.com/company/sbam
X (Twitter): x.com/SBAM
Instagram: www.instagram.com/
smallbusinessassocofmichigan
YouTube: www.youtube.com/channel/UC8RW696tHH
-di8-6Y5qrLmQ
Description: Helps Michigan small businesses succeed by promoting entrepreneurship, leveraging buying power and engaging in political advocacy.
Founded: 1969. Publications: *Journal of Small Business* (Bimonthly); *Small Business Barometer.*
Geographic Preference: State.

SMALL BUSINESS ASSISTANCE PROGRAMS

40820 ■ Michigan Economic Development Corp. (MEDC) - Reference Library
300 N Washington Sq.
Lansing, MI 48913
Ph: (517)241-1400
Free: 888-522-0103
URL: http://www.michiganbusiness.org
Contact: Quentin L. Messer, President
Facebook: www.facebook.com/MEDC
Linkedin: www.linkedin.com/company/medc
X (Twitter): x.com/MEDC
YouTube: www.youtube.com/user/MIAdvantage
Description: Advocate for businesses in Michigan that have a conflict with state agencies or that need assistance in getting attention from state agencies.
Scope: Economics. Founded: 1999. Holdings: Figures not available. Publications: *Michigan Exporters of Wood Products* (Irregular); *Michigan Occupational Information System (MOIS)*; *Michigan Site Network*; *Michigan Manufacturing Technology Export Directory.* Geographic Preference: State.

40821 ■ Midland Business Alliance Foundation (MBA)
300 Rodd St., Ste. 101
Midland, MI 48640
Contact: Brad Kaye, President

SCORE OFFICES

40822 ■ Detroit SCORE
477 Michigan Ave., Ste. 1819
Detroit, MI 48226
Free: 800-634-0425
Co. E-mail: semichigan@scorevolunteer.org
URL: http://semichigan.score.org/score-southeast-michigan-locations
Description: Seeks to provide counseling for new and small business. Founded: 1964. Geographic Preference: State.

40823 ■ SCORE - Ann Arbor Area
1100 N Main St., Ste. 109
Ann Arbor, MI 48104
Ph: (734)929-1121
Co. E-mail: admin.0655@scorevolunteer.org
URL: http://annarborarea.score.org
Contact: Rick W. Scofield, President
Facebook: www.facebook.com/scoreannarbor
Linkedin: www.linkedin.com/company/score-mentors-ann-arbor-area
Description: Provides professional guidance and information to maximize the success of existing and emerging small businesses. Offers business counseling and workshops. Founded: 2000. Geographic Preference: Local.

40824 ■ SCORE - Benton Harbor
80 W Main St.
Benton Harbor, MI 49022
Ph: (269)344-1419
URL: http://swmi.score.org
Facebook: www.facebook.com/
SCOREKalamazooSWMichigan
X (Twitter): x.com/scorementors
Description: Provides professional guidance and information to maximize the success of existing and emerging small businesses. Offers business counseling and workshops.

40825 ■ SCORE - Clawson
416 N Main St.
Clawson, MI 48017
Free: 800-634-0245
Co. E-mail: 18score18@gmail.com
URL: http://semichigan.score.org/score-southeast-michigan-locations
Description: Provides professional guidance and information to maximize the success of existing and emerging small businesses. Offers business counseling and workshops.

40826 ■ SCORE - Detroit
1938 Burdette St.
Ferndale, MI 48220
Ph: (248)313-8863
URL: http://www.score.org/semichigan
Contact: Scott M. Stone, III, Contact
Description: Provides professional guidance and information to maximize the success of existing and emerging small businesses. Offers business counseling and workshops.

40827 ■ SCORE - Flint
McNamara Federal Bldg., Ste. 1819
477 Michigan Ave.
Detroit, MI 48226
Ph: (313)226-7947
URL: http://semichigan.score.org/flint-branch/about-flint-branch
Description: Provides professional guidance and information to maximize the success of existing and emerging small businesses. Offers business counseling and workshops.

40828 ■ SCORE - Grand Blanc
515 Perry Rd.
Grand Blanc, MI 48439
URL: http://detroit.score.org
Description: Provides professional guidance and information to maximize the success of existing and emerging small businesses. Offers business counseling and workshops.

40829 ■ SCORE - Grand Rapids
250 Monroe Ave., NW, No. 150
Grand Rapids, MI 49503
Ph: (616)771-0305
URL: http://www.score.org/grandrapids
Contact: John Rea, Contact
Linkedin: www.linkedin.com/company/score-of-grand-rapids
YouTube: www.youtube.com/user/SCOREofGrandRapids
Description: Provides professional guidance and information to maximize the success of existing and emerging small businesses. Offers business counseling and workshops. Founded: 1964. Geographic Preference: Local.

40830 ■ SCORE - Grandmont Rosedale
19120 Grand River Ave.
Detroit, MI 48223
URL: http://semichigan.score.org/score-southeast-michigan-locations
Description: Provides professional guidance and information to maximize the success of existing and emerging small businesses. Offers business counseling and workshops.

40831 ■ SCORE - Hamtramck
477 Michigan Ave., Ste. 1819
Detroit, MI 48226
Free: 800-634-0245
Co. E-mail: 18score18@gmail.com
URL: http://detroit.score.org
Facebook: www.facebook.com/SCOREDetroit
Linkedin: www.linkedin.com/company/detroitscore
Description: Provides professional guidance and information to maximize the success of existing and emerging small businesses. Offers business counseling and workshops.

40832 ■ SCORE - Hancock
c/o Finlandia University
601 Quincy St.
Hancock, MI 49930
Ph: (715)384-3454
URL: http://centralwisconsin.score.org
Facebook: www.facebook.com/SCORECentralWisconsin
Linkedin: www.linkedin.com/company/score-central-wisconsin-up-michigan
Description: Provides professional guidance and information to maximize the success of existing and emerging small businesses. Offers business counseling and workshops.

40833 ■ SCORE - Incubizo Ferndale
1938 Burdette St.
Ferndale, MI 48220
Ph: (313)226-7947
Co. E-mail: 18score18@gmail.com
URL: http://detroit.score.org
Contact: Karen Thornton, Contact
Linkedin: www.linkedin.com/company/detroitscore
Description: Provides professional guidance and information to maximize the success of existing and emerging small businesses. Offers business counseling and workshops.

40834 ■ SCORE - Kalamazoo
1126 Gull Rd.
Kalamazoo, MI 49048
Ph: (269)344-1419
Co. E-mail: help@score.org
URL: http://swmi.score.org
Facebook: www.facebook.com/
SCOREKalamazooSWMichigan
Linkedin: www.linkedin.com/company/
scorekalamazooswmichigan
X (Twitter): x.com/scorementors
Description: Provides professional guidance and information to maximize the success of existing and emerging small businesses. Offers business counseling and workshops. Founded: 1975.

40835 ■ SCORE - Muskegon
380 W W Ave., Ste. 202
Muskegon, MI 49440
Ph: (231)722-3751

40836 ■ Michigan

Fax: (231)728-7251
Co. E-mail: score@muskegon.org
URL: http://muskegon.score.org
Contact: Bridget Weston, Chief Executive Officer
Linkedin: www.linkedin.com/company/score-muskegon

Description: Serves as volunteer program in which working and retired business management professionals provide free business counseling to men and women who are considering starting a small business, encountering problems with their business, or expanding their business. Offers free one-on-one counseling, online counseling and low cost workshops on a variety of business topics. **Geographic Preference:** Local.

40836 ■ SCORE - Northwest Activities Center
18100 Meyers
  Detroit, MI 48235
URL: http://semichigan.score.org/score-southeast-michigan-locations

Description: Provides professional guidance and information to maximize the success of existing and emerging small businesses. Offers business counseling and workshops.

40837 ■ SCORE - Novi
Novi Library
  45255 W 10 Mile Rd.
  Novi, MI 48375
Ph: (248)349-0720
URL: http://semichigan.score.org/score-southeast-michigan-locations

Description: Provides professional guidance and information to maximize the success of existing and emerging small businesses. Offers business counseling and workshops.

40838 ■ SCORE - Okemos
4515 Dobie Rd.
  Faith Lutheran Church of Meridian Twp.
  Okemos, MI 48864
URL: http://semichigan.score.org/score-southeast-michigan-locations

Description: Provides professional guidance and information to maximize the success of existing and emerging small businesses. Offers business counseling and workshops.

40839 ■ SCORE - Sterling Heights
The Velocity Collaborative Center
  6633 18 Mile Rd.
  Sterling Heights, MI 48314
Ph: (313)226-7947
Co. E-mail: help@score.org
URL: http://detroit.score.org
Facebook: www.facebook.com/SCOREDetroit

Description: Provides professional guidance and information to maximize the success of existing and emerging small businesses. Offers business counseling and workshops.

40840 ■ SCORE - Taylor
20904 Northline Rd.
  Southern Wayne County Regional Chamber
  Taylor, MI 48180
URL: http://semichigan.score.org/score-southeast-michigan-locations

Description: Provides professional guidance and information to maximize the success of existing and emerging small businesses. Offers business counseling and workshops.

40841 ■ SCORE - TechTown Detroit
440 Burroughs St.
  Detroit, MI 48202
Ph: (313)879-5250
Co. E-mail: info@techtowndetroit.org
URL: http://techtowndetroit.org
Contact: Ned Staebler, President
E-mail: nedstaebler@wayne.edu
Facebook: www.facebook.com/techtowndetroit
Linkedin: www.linkedin.com/company/techtown
X (Twitter): x.com/techtowndetroit
Instagram: www.instagram.com/techtowndetroit
YouTube: www.youtube.com/channel/UCgaD9h9E0lv2VckDarf062A

Pinterest: www.pinterest.com/techtowndetroit

Description: Provides professional guidance and information to maximize the success of existing and emerging small businesses. Offers business counseling and workshops. **Founded:** 2000.

40842 ■ SCORE - Tip of the Mitt [SCORE - Petoskey]
401 E Mitchell St.
  Petoskey, MI 49770
Ph: (231)347-4150
Co. E-mail: help@score.org
URL: http://tipofthemitt.score.org
Contact: Andy Hayes, Executive Director
Facebook: www.facebook.com/SCORETipOfTheMittMI

Description: Seeks to educate entrepreneurs and help small businesses start, grow and succeed nationwide. Organizes volunteers who are working or retired business owners, executives and corporate leaders who wish to share their wisdom and lessons learned in business. **Founded:** 1964. **Geographic Preference:** Local.

40843 ■ SCORE - Traverse City - Library
202 E Grandview Pky.
  Traverse City, MI 49684
Ph: (231)947-5075
Free: 888-796-4913
Co. E-mail: help@score.org
URL: http://traversecity.score.org
Facebook: www.facebook.com/SCORETraverseCity

Description: Provides professional guidance and information to maximize the success of existing and emerging small businesses. Offers business counseling and workshops. **Geographic Preference:** Local.

40844 ■ SCORE - Waterford Township
2100 Pontiac Lake Rd.
  Waterford Township, MI 48328
Ph: (248)858-0783
URL: http://semichigan.score.org/score-southeast-michigan-locations

Description: Provides professional guidance and information to maximize the success of existing and emerging small businesses. Offers business counseling and workshops.

40845 ■ SCORE - WeWork Detroit
477 Michigan Ave., Ste. 1819
  Detroit, MI 48226
Free: 800-634-0240
Co. E-mail: 18score18@gmail.com
URL: http://detroit.score.org

Description: Provides professional guidance and information to maximize the success of existing and emerging small businesses. Offers business counseling and workshops.

BETTER BUSINESS BUREAUS

40846 ■ Better Business Bureau of Detroit and Eastern Michigan
20300 W 12 Mile Rd., Ste. 202
  Southfield, MI 48076-6409
Free: 866-788-5706
Fax: (248)356-5135
URL: http://www.bbb.org/local-bbb/bbb-of-detroit-and-eastern-michigan
Contact: Melanie Duquesnel, President
Facebook: www.facebook.com/myBBB
Linkedin: www.linkedin.com/company/better-business-bureau-serving-eastern-michigan-and-the-upper-peninsula
X (Twitter): x.com/BBBEMIUP
Instagram: www.instagram.com/bbbemiup
YouTube: www.youtube.com/channel/UCrjVhqVum3S0ElOuVrqhYLg

Description: Seeks to promote and foster ethical relationship between businesses and the public through voluntary self-regulation, consumer and business education, and service excellence. Provides information to help consumers and businesses make informed purchasing decisions and avoid costly scams and frauds; settles consumer complaints through arbitration and other means. **Founded:** 1917. **Geographic Preference:** Local.

40847 ■ Better Business Bureau - Northwest and West Central Ohio and Southeast Michigan
7668 Kin's Pointe Rd.
  Toledo, OH 43617
Ph: (419)531-3116
Free: 800-743-4222
Fax: (419)578-6001
URL: http://www.bbb.org/local-bbb/bbb-serving-northwest-and-west-central-ohio-and-southeast-michigan
X (Twitter): x.com/BBB_Toledo

Description: Seeks to promote and foster ethical relationship between businesses and the public through voluntary self-regulation, consumer and business education, and service excellence. Provides information to help consumers and businesses make informed purchasing decisions and avoid costly scams and frauds; settles consumer complaints through arbitration and other means. **Geographic Preference:** Regional; Local.

40848 ■ Better Business Bureau of Western Michigan
3330 Claystone St. SE
  Grand Rapids, MI 49546
Ph: (616)774-8236
Fax: (855)581-3777
Co. E-mail: info@westernmichigan.bbb.org
URL: http://www.bbb.org/local-bbb/bbb-serving-western-michigan
Contact: Lisa Frohnapfel, President
Facebook: www.facebook.com/BBBwmi
Linkedin: www.linkedin.com/company/bbb-serving-western-michigan
X (Twitter): x.com/BBBwmi
Instagram: www.instagram.com/bbb_wmi
YouTube: www.youtube.com/user/BBBWesternMichigan

Description: Aims to promote through self-regulation, the highest standards of business ethics, and to instill public confidence in business through programs of education and action that inform, protect and assist. **Founded:** 1937. **Publications:** *Factfinder* (Monthly). **Geographic Preference:** Local.

CHAMBERS OF COMMERCE

40849 ■ Alger County Chamber of Commerce
129 E Munising Ave.
  Munising, MI 49862
Ph: (906)387-2138
Co. E-mail: info@algercountychamber.com
URL: http://algercountychamber.com
Contact: Dr. Katherine Reynolds, Chief Executive Officer
Facebook: www.facebook.com/algercountychamber

Description: Promotes convention business and tourism in the area. **Geographic Preference:** Local.

40850 ■ Allegan Area Chamber of Commerce (AACC)
231 Trowbridge St., Unit 1
  Allegan, MI 49010
Ph: (269)673-2479
URL: http://alleganchamber.com
Contact: Tim Perrigo, Executive Director
E-mail: director@alleganchamber.com
Facebook: www.facebook.com/alleganchamber
X (Twitter): x.com/alleganchamber

Description: Promotes business and community development in the Allegan, MI area. **Geographic Preference:** Local.

40851 ■ Anchor Bay Chamber of Commerce (ABCC)
51180 Bedford St.
  New Baltimore, MI 48047
Ph: (586)725-5148
Co. E-mail: director@anchorbaychamber.com
URL: http://www.anchorbaychamber.com
Contact: Lisa M. Thomas, President

Facebook: www.facebook.com/
AnchorBayChamberofCommerce
Linkedin: www.linkedin.com/company/anchor-bay
-chamber-of-commerce
YouTube: www.youtube.com/channel/UC-PRABEWc
6G0cHsYZQ2SLMw

Description: Promotes business and community development in Anchor Bay area of MI. **Founded:** 1976. **Publications:** *ABCC Newsletter* (Monthly); *Business Directory* (Annual). **Geographic Preference:** Local.

40852 ■ Ann Arbor/Ypsilanti Regional Chamber [A2Y Chamber]
2010 Hogback Rd., Ste. 4
Ann Arbor, MI 48105
Ph: (734)665-4433
Co. E-mail: marketing@a2ychamber.org
URL: http://a2ychamber.org
Contact: Diane Keller, President
Facebook: www.facebook.com/a2ychamber
X (Twitter): x.com/A2YChamber
YouTube: www.youtube.com/user/a
2yregionalchamber

Description: Promotes commerce in the Ann Arbor/Ypsilanti region. **Founded:** 2010. **Publications:** *Ann Arbor Business-to-Business* (Periodic); *Chamber Express e-Newsletter* (Bimonthly); *Directory of Firms, Products, and Services* (Periodic); *Ann Arbor Area Chamber of Commerce--Business Directory*; *Ann Arbor Area Chamber of Commerce--Business Directory*. **Geographic Preference:** Local.

40853 ■ Atlanta Area Chamber of Commerce
12443 State St.
Atlanta, MI 49709
Ph: (989)785-3400
Co. E-mail: atlantamichamber@gmail.com
URL: http://www.atlantamichiganchamber.com
Contact: Clinton Kennedy, President
Facebook: www.facebook.com/atlan
tamichamberofcommerce

Description: Promotes business and community development in Atlanta, MI. **Founded:** 1986. **Geographic Preference:** Local.

40854 ■ Au Gres Area Chamber of Commerce
124 E Huron
Au Gres, MI 48703
Ph: (989)879-8811
Co. E-mail: augresareachamber@gmail.com
URL: http://augresareachamberofcommerce.org
Contact: Allison Wiltse, President
Facebook: www.facebook.com/AuGresChamber
Linkedin: www.linkedin.com/company/au-gres-area
-chamber
X (Twitter): x.com/AuGresChamber

Description: Seeks to promote and foster a positive business environment for the Au Gres area that optimizes and advances the community's prosperity. **Geographic Preference:** Local.

40855 ■ Barry County Area Chamber of Commerce
221 W State St.
Hastings, MI 49058
Ph: (269)945-2454
Fax: (616)974-6087
URL: http://www.mibarry.com
Contact: Jennifer Heinzman, President
E-mail: jennifer@mibarry.com

Description: Promotes business and community development in the Hastings, MI area. **Publications:** *Chamber Directory* (Annual); *Chamber E-Newsletter* (Monthly). **Geographic Preference:** Local.

40856 ■ Battle Creek Area Chamber of Commerce
1 Riverwalk Ctr.
 34 Jackson St. W, Ste. 3A
 Battle Creek, MI 49017
Ph: (269)962-4076
Co. E-mail: office@battlecreek.org
URL: http://battlecreek.org
Contact: Kara E. Beer, President
E-mail: kbeer@battlecreek.org

Facebook: www.facebook.com/battle.c.chamber
Linkedin: www.linkedin.com/company/battle-creek
-area-chamber-of-commerce
X (Twitter): x.com/bcbusinessvoice

Description: Promotes business and community development in the Battle Creek, MI area. **Publications:** *Insight* (Quarterly). **Awards:** Harley Simmons Award (Annual). **Geographic Preference:** Local.

40857 ■ Bay Area Chamber of Commerce (BACC)
812 N Water St.
 Bay City, MI 48708
Ph: (989)893-4567
Fax: (989)895-5594
Co. E-mail: chamber@baycityarea.com
URL: http://www.baycityarea.com
Contact: Jodi LaMont, Specialist
E-mail: jodi@baycityarea.com
Facebook: www.facebook.com/
BayAreaChamberofCommerce
Instagram: www.instagram.com/baychambermi

Description: Promotes business and community development in the Bay City, MI area. **Founded:** 1882. **Publications:** *Bay Area Business Journal* (Bimonthly); *Bay Area Chamber Handbook*. **Awards:** Bay Area Chamber of Commerce Athena Award (Annual); Bay Area Chamber of Commerce Leadership Alumni Community Service Award (Annual). **Geographic Preference:** Local.

40858 ■ Bellaire Chamber of Commerce
308 E Cayuga St.
 Bellaire, MI 49615
Ph: (231)533-6023
Co. E-mail: info@bellairechamber.org
URL: http://www.bellairechamber.org
Contact: Rob Joyce, President
E-mail: robert.joyce@edwardjones.com
Facebook: www.facebook.com/DestinationBellaire
X (Twitter): x.com/BellaireChamber
Instagram: www.instagram.com/destinationbellaire
Pinterest: www.pinterest.com/bellairemi

Description: Promotes business and community development in the Bellaire, MI area. **Geographic Preference:** Local.

40859 ■ Belleville Area Chamber of Commerce (BACC)
248 Main St.
 Belleville, MI 48111
Ph: (734)697-7151
Co. E-mail: info@bellevilleareachamber.org
URL: http://www.bellevilleareachamber.org
Contact: Steve Jones, Director
Facebook: www.facebook.com/
bellevilleareachamberofcommerce

Description: Promotes business and community development in the Belleville, MI area. Participates in annual Strawberry Festival. Holds monthly board meeting. **Founded:** 1950. **Publications:** *Calendar with Directory* (Annual); *Tri-Community Commentator* (Monthly). **Geographic Preference:** Local.

40860 ■ Benzie County Chamber of Commerce
826 Michigan Ave.
 Benzonia, MI 49616
Ph: (231)882-5801
Fax: (231)882-9249
Co. E-mail: chamber@benzie.org
URL: http://www.benzie.org
Contact: Steve Campbell, Chairman
E-mail: stevec@harborlightsresort.net
Facebook: www.facebook.com/BenzieChamber

Description: Promotes business, tourism, and community development in Benzie County, MI. Sponsors festivals. **Founded:** 1981. **Publications:** *Moving Up* (Quarterly). **Geographic Preference:** Local.

40861 ■ Berkley Area Chamber of Commerce
PO Box 72-1253
Berkley, MI 48072
Ph: (248)414-9157
URL: http://berkleychamber.com
Contact: Tim Murad, President
E-mail: tjmurad@kw.com

Facebook: www.facebook.com/BerkleyChamber
Linkedin: www.linkedin.com/company/berkley-area
-chamber-of-commerce
X (Twitter): x.com/BerkleyChamber
Instagram: www.instagram.com/berkleychamber

Description: Promotes and encourages business in Berkley. Creates favorable commercial climate within the City. Acts as a unified voice and liaison between businesses and others. Assists businesses in the City. **Founded:** 1984. **Geographic Preference:** Local.

40862 ■ Birch Run Chamber of Commerce
7971 Main St., Ste. No. 4
Birch Run, MI 48415
Ph: (989)624-9193
Co. E-mail: info@birchrunbridgeportchamber.org
URL: http://www.birchrunchamber.org
Contact: Jamie Antku, Chairman
Facebook: www.facebook.com/BirchRunBridgepor
tCOC

Description: Promotes business and community development in the Birch Run, MI area. **Geographic Preference:** Local.

40863 ■ Birmingham-Bloomfield Chamber of Commerce (BBCC)
725 S Adams Rd., Ste. 130
Birmingham, MI 48009
Ph: (248)644-1700
Fax: (248)644-0286
Co. E-mail: kellyb@bbcc.com
URL: http://www.bbcc.com
Contact: Joe Bauman, President
Facebook: www.facebook.com/BBChamber
Linkedin: www.linkedin.com/company/937191
X (Twitter): x.com/BBChamber

Description: Promotes business and community development in Beverly Hills, Bingham Farms, Birmingham, Bloomfield Hills, and Bloomfield Township, MI. **Founded:** 1948. **Publications:** *Business Insight E-News* (Monthly); *Birmingham Bloomfield Lifestyle* (Annual). **Geographic Preference:** Local.

40864 ■ Blissfield DDA/Main Street
130 S Ln. St.
Blissfield, MI 49228
Ph: (517)486-3642
Co. E-mail: mainstreet@blissfieldmichigan.gov
URL: http://www.blissfieldmainstreet.com
Contact: Tyler Dotson, Director
Facebook: www.facebook.com/downtown.blissfield
X (Twitter): x.com/DTownBlissfield

Description: Promotes business and community development in Blissfield, MI area. **Geographic Preference:** Local.

40865 ■ Boyne Area Chamber of Commerce
115 S Lake St., Ste. A
Boyne City, MI 49712
Ph: (231)582-6222
Co. E-mail: info@boynechamber.com
URL: http://www.boynechamber.com
Contact: Patrick Patoka, Director
Facebook: www.facebook.com/boynechamber
Linkedin: www.linkedin.com/company/boyne-area
-chamber-of-commerce

Description: Works to enhance the economic, industrial, professional, cultural, and civic welfare of the Boyne City Area. **Geographic Preference:** Local.

40866 ■ Brooklyn - Irish Hills Chamber of Commerce
124 S Main St., Ste. A
Brooklyn, MI 49230
Ph: (517)592-8907
Fax: (517)592-8907
Co. E-mail: info@irishhills.com
URL: http://www.irishhills.com
Contact: Cindy Hubbell, President
E-mail: cindy@brooklynmi.com
Facebook: www.facebook.com/
IrishHillsChamberofCommerce
Instagram: www.instagram.com/irishhillschamber

Description: Business owners and professional men and women who invest their time and money in a development program for the entire community.

Works to improve the economic, social, cultural, commercial, industrial and civic welfare of the Brooklyn-Irish Hills area. **Geographic Preference:** Local.

40867 ■ Buchanan Area Chamber of Commerce (BACC)
324 E Dewey St., Ste. 202
Buchanan, MI 49107-0127
Ph: (269)695-3291
Co. E-mail: bacc@buchanan.mi.us
URL: http://www.buchanan.mi.us
Contact: Fran Terry, President
Facebook: www.facebook.com/BuchananChamber
Description: Businesses and individuals promoting economic and community development in the Buchanan, MI area. Conducts annual dinner, area wide promotions, special events and business-related workshops. **Founded:** 1956. **Publications:** *News & Views* (Quarterly); *Redbud Area Directory* (Quarterly); *Redbud Area News* (Monthly). **Geographic Preference:** Local.

40868 ■ *Business Connections*
108 W Pk. St.
Lapeer, MI 48446
Ph: (810)664-6641
Fax: (810)664-4349
Co. E-mail: staff@lapeerareachamber.org
URL: http://www.lapeerareachamber.org
Contact: Wes Smith, President
URL(s): lapeerareachamber.org/business-connection-e-newsletter
Released: Monthly **Description:** Provides information about the community and local businesses. **Availability:** Online.

40869 ■ *Business Directory*
250 Monroe Ave. NW
Grand Rapids, MI 49503
Ph: (616)771-0300
Co. E-mail: info@grandrapids.org
URL: http://www.grandrapids.org
Contact: Rick Baker, President
E-mail: rick@grandrapids.org
URL(s): web.grandrapids.org/search
Availability: Print.

40870 ■ *Business Directory*
215 N Water St.
Owosso, MI 48867
Ph: (989)723-5149
Fax: (989)723-8353
Co. E-mail: customerservice@shiawasseechamber.org
URL: http://www.shiawasseechamber.org
Contact: Char Hebekeuser, Chairman
URL(s): web.shiawasseechamber.org/search
Description: Contains information about Shiawassee county. **Availability:** Online.

40871 ■ *Business Directory*
401 E Mitchell St.
Petoskey, MI 49770
Ph: (231)347-4150
Co. E-mail: chamber@petoskeychamber.com
URL: http://www.petoskeychamber.com
Contact: Nikki Devitt, President
URL(s): www.petoskeychamber.com/list
Availability: Online.

40872 ■ *Business Directory*
228 N Main St., Ste. D
Romeo, MI 48065
Ph: (586)752-4436
Co. E-mail: kelley@rwchamber.com
URL: http://www.rwchamber.com
Contact: Kelley Stephens, Executive Director
E-mail: kelley@rwchamber.com
URL(s): web.rwchamber.com/search
Availability: Print.

40873 ■ *Business Directory and Buying Guide*
317 Union St.
Milford, MI 48381
Ph: (248)685-7129
Co. E-mail: info@huronvcc.com
URL: http://www.huronvcc.com
Contact: Jack Shubitowski, President
URL(s): www.huronvcc.com/our-members/directory-pdf
Released: Annual **Description:** Contains community profiles of Huron Valley and member listing. **Availability:** Online.

40874 ■ *Business News*
113 W Broadway St., Ste. 180
Mount Pleasant, MI 48858
Ph: (989)772-2396
Fax: (989)773-2656
Co. E-mail: jpierson@mt-pleasant.net
URL: http://www.mt-pleasant.net
Contact: Liz Conway, President
E-mail: lconway@mt-pleasant.net
URL(s): www.mt-pleasant.net/why-join
Released: Monthly **Description:** Informs about business updates, special events, announcements and chamber happenings. **Availability:** Online.

40875 ■ *Business Talk*
301 W Michigan Ave., Ste. 101
Ypsilanti, MI 48197-5450
Ph: (734)482-4920
Fax: (734)482-2021
Co. E-mail: info@annarborchamber.org
URL: http://www.ypsichamber.org
Contact: Diane Keller, President
Released: Monthly **Availability:** Print; Online.

40876 ■ *Business and Visitors Guide*
100 Main St., Ste. B
East Jordan, MI 49727
Ph: (231)536-7351
Fax: (231)536-0966
Co. E-mail: info@ejchamber.org
URL: http://www.ejchamber.org
Contact: Mary H. Faculak, President
URL(s): ejchamber.org/chamber-information-membership-benefits
Released: Annual **Availability:** Online.

40877 ■ *Cadillac Area Business Magazine*
222 N Lake St.
Cadillac, MI 49601
Ph: (231)775-9776
Co. E-mail: info@cadillac.org
URL: http://www.cadillac.org
Contact: Kate Dekam, Director
E-mail: kdekam@cadillac.org
URL(s): www.cadillac.org/publications
Released: Quarterly **Availability:** Online; PDF.

40878 ■ Cadillac Area Chamber of Commerce (CACC)
222 N Lake St.
Cadillac, MI 49601
Ph: (231)775-9776
Co. E-mail: info@cadillac.org
URL: http://www.cadillac.org
Contact: Kate Dekam, Director
E-mail: kdekam@cadillac.org
Facebook: www.facebook.com/cadillacchamber
Description: Promotes business and community development in the Cadillac, MI area. **Founded:** 1899. **Publications:** *Cadillac Area Business Magazine* (Quarterly). **Geographic Preference:** Local.

40879 ■ Canton Chamber of Commerce (CCC)
45525 Hanford Rd.
Canton, MI 48187
Ph: (734)453-4040
Fax: (734)453-4503
URL: http://www.cantonchamber.com
Contact: Thomas Paden, President
E-mail: tpaden@cantonchamber.com
Facebook: www.facebook.com/cccmi
X (Twitter): x.com/cantonchmbr
Instagram: www.instagram.com/canton_chamber_mich
Description: Works to advance the economic and civic development of the Canton Community. **Founded:** 1972. **Publications:** *Networker* (Monthly). **Geographic Preference:** State; Local.

40880 ■ Caro Chamber of Commerce
429 N State St., Ste. 101
Caro, MI 48723
Ph: (989)673-5211
Co. E-mail: carochamber101@gmail.com
URL: http://carochamber.com
Contact: Susan Holder, President
Facebook: www.facebook.com/COCbc
Description: Promotes business and community development in the Caro, MI area. Sponsors Cars and Crafts Weekend. **Founded:** 1922. **Publications:** *Action* (Monthly). **Awards:** Caro Chamber of Commerce Merit Award (Annual); Caro Chamber of Commerce Citizen of the Year (Annual). **Geographic Preference:** Local.

40881 ■ Cass City Chamber of Commerce
6506 Main St.
Cass City, MI 48726
Ph: (989)872-4618
Fax: (989)872-4855
Co. E-mail: ccc@casscitychamber.com
URL: http://www.casscitychamber.com
Contact: Mike Rule, President
Facebook: www.facebook.com/CassCityChamber
Description: Promotes business and community development in Cass City, MI. **Founded:** 1951. **Publications:** *Chamber Chat* (Quarterly). **Geographic Preference:** Local.

40882 ■ Central Lake Area Chamber of Commerce
2587 N M-88 Hwy.
Central Lake, MI 49622
Ph: (231)350-9381
Co. E-mail: info@centrallakechamber.com
URL: http://www.centrallakechamber.com
Contact: April Cikity, President
Description: Promotes business and community development in Central Lake, MI area. **Geographic Preference:** Local.

40883 ■ *Chamber Directory*
221 W State St.
Hastings, MI 49058
Ph: (269)945-2454
Fax: (616)974-6087
URL: http://www.mibarry.com
Contact: Jennifer Heinzman, President
E-mail: jennifer@mibarry.com
URL(s): business.mibarry.com/list
Released: Annual **Availability:** Print.

40884 ■ The Chamber of Grand Haven, Spring Lake, Ferrysburg
1 S Harbor Dr.
Grand Haven, MI 49417
Ph: (616)842-4910
Co. E-mail: areainfo@grandhavenchamber.org
URL: http://grandhavenchamber.org
Contact: Joy Gaasch, President
E-mail: jgaasch@grandhavenchamber.org
Facebook: www.facebook.com/GrandHavenSpringLakeFerrysburgChamber
Linkedin: www.linkedin.com/messaging/thread/6476624783843958784
X (Twitter): x.com/GHAChamber
Instagram: www.instagram.com/ghachamberofcommerce
Description: Works to serve the interests of the local business community. **Founded:** 1899. **Publications:** *Business Beacon*; *Clubs and Organizations Directory*; *Industrial Directory*. **Geographic Preference:** Local.

40885 ■ *Chamber Member Directory*
5745 W Maple Rd., Ste. 206
West Bloomfield, MI 48322
Ph: (248)626-3636
Fax: (248)626-4218
Co. E-mail: wbloomfieldchamber@gmail.com
URL: http://westbloomfieldchamber.com
Contact: Suzanne Levine, Executive Director
URL(s): westbloomfieldchamber.com/chamber-member-directory
Availability: Online.

STATE LISTINGS

40886 ■ Chamber News
1116 N Main St.
Three Rivers, MI 49093
Ph: (269)278-8193
Fax: (269)273-1751
Co. E-mail: info@trchamber.com
URL: http://trchamber.com
Contact: Christy Trammell, President
E-mail: christytrammell@trchamber.com
URL(s): trchamber.com/benefits-of-membership
Released: Weekly **Description:** Highlights area business activities, upcoming seminars, workshops and other events of interests to the business community. **Availability:** Mailing list; Online.

40887 ■ Chamber Update
213 N James St.
Grayling, MI 49738
Ph: (989)348-2921
Fax: (989)348-7315
Co. E-mail: info@graylingchamber.com
URL: http://graylingchamber.com
Contact: Traci Cook, Executive Director
E-mail: director@graylingchamber.com
URL(s): www.graylingchamber.com/about-us
Released: Weekly **Availability:** Online.

40888 ■ Charlevoix Area Chamber of Commerce
109 Mason St.
Charlevoix, MI 49720
Ph: (231)547-2101
Fax: (231)547-6633
Co. E-mail: info@charlevoix.org
URL: http://www.charlevoix.org
Contact: Sarah Van Horn, President
E-mail: vanhorn@charlevoix.org
Facebook: www.facebook.com/CVXChamber
Description: Helps businesses to prosper and grow; to increase job opportunities; to encourage an orderly expansion and development of all segments of the community; to contribute to the overall economic stability of the community; to encourage and promote the nation's private enterprise system of competitive marketing. **Geographic Preference:** Regional.

40889 ■ Cheboygan Area Chamber of Commerce (CACC)
124 N Main St.
Cheboygan, MI 49721
Free: 800-968-3302
Co. E-mail: info@cheboygan.com
URL: http://www.cheboygan.com
Contact: J. L. Sumpter, President
Facebook: www.facebook.com/cheboyganchamber
Description: Promotes business and community development in the Cheboygan, MI area. Sponsors Home Show, Parades, Riverfest, AutumnFest and Buffalo Bash. **Founded:** 1943. **Publications:** *Cheboygan Area Chamber of Commerce Membership Directory and Buying Guide* (Annual); *Executive Report* (Monthly). **Geographic Preference:** Local.

40890 ■ Chelsea Area Chamber of Commerce (CACC)
222 S Main St., Ste. B
Chelsea, MI 48118
Ph: (734)475-1145
Co. E-mail: info@chelseamichamber.org
URL: http://www.chelseamichamber.org
Contact: Dr. Jon Curtis, President
E-mail: jonrosscurtis@gmail.com
Description: Promotes business and community development in Chelsea, MI. **Publications:** *Chelsea Area Chamber of Commerce Community Profile & Business Directory* (Annual). **Geographic Preference:** Local.

40891 ■ Chesaning Chamber of Commerce (CCC)
218 N Front St., Ste. B
Chesaning, MI 48616
Ph: (989)845-3055
Co. E-mail: info@chesaningchamber.org
URL: http://www.chesaningchamber.org
Contact: Greg Bruff, President
Facebook: www.facebook.com/ChesaningChamberOfCommerce
Description: Promotes business and community development in Chesaning, MI. **Founded:** 1924. **Geographic Preference:** Local.

40892 ■ Clare Area Chamber of Commerce
201 W 4th St.
Clare, MI 48617
Ph: (989)386-2442
URL: http://www.claremichigan.com
Description: Businesses seeking to promote economic and community development in the Clare, MI area. Sponsors Irish Festival and Summerfest. **Founded:** 1936. **Geographic Preference:** Local.

40893 ■ Clarkston Area Chamber of Commerce
5856 S Main St.
Clarkston, MI 48346
Ph: (248)625-8055
Fax: (248)625-8041
Co. E-mail: info@clarkston.org
URL: http://www.clarkston.org
Contact: Angie Wathen, President
Facebook: www.facebook.com/ClarkstonAreaChamberofCommerce
Linkedin: www.linkedin.com/company/clarkston-area-chamber-of-commerce
X (Twitter): x.com/CACOC
Instagram: www.instagram.com/clarkstonmichamber
Description: Consists of small businesses, community leaders, service clubs and community groups who work together to promote and enhance economic growth and quality of community in the Clarkston Area. **Founded:** 1987. **Geographic Preference:** Local.

40894 ■ Clinton County Chamber of Commerce
1013 S US-27
Saint Johns, MI 48879
Ph: (989)224-7248
Co. E-mail: stjohnsareachamber@gmail.com
URL: http://stjohnsareachamber.wildapricot.org
Contact: Glen Pung, President
Facebook: www.facebook.com/ccchamberofcommerce
Description: Promotes business and community development in the St. Johns, MI area. Sponsors St. Johns Mint Festival, annual Christmas House Decorating Contest and Parade. **Publications:** *Chamber News* (Bimonthly). **Awards:** St. Johns Area Chamber of Commerce/Mint Festival Scholarship (Annual). **Geographic Preference:** Local.

40895 ■ Coldwater Area Chamber of Commerce (CCC)
20 Division St.
Coldwater, MI 49036
Ph: (517)278-5985
Co. E-mail: info@coldwaterchamber.com
URL: http://www.coldwaterchamber.com
Contact: Lori Hunt, Executive Director
Facebook: www.facebook.com/coldwaterareachamber
Linkedin: www.linkedin.com/company/coldwater-area-chamber-of-commerce
Description: Promotes business and community development in the Branch County, MI area. **Founded:** 1975. **Publications:** *Community* (Annual); *The Connection* (Monthly). **Awards:** Coldwater Area Chamber of Commerce Business of the Year (Annual); Coldwater Area Chamber of Commerce Citizen of the Year (Annual); Coldwater Area Chamber of Commerce Educator of the Year (Annual); Coldwater Area Chamber of Commerce Outstanding Community Program (Annual). **Geographic Preference:** Local.

40896 ■ Coloma-Watervliet Area Chamber of Commerce (CWACC)
142 Badt Dr.
Coloma, MI 49038-1028
Ph: (269)468-4430
Co. E-mail: info@coloma-watervliet.org
URL: http://www.coloma-watervliet.org/chamber-of-commerce.php
Contact: Sandra Kraemer, Chairman
Facebook: www.facebook.com/people/Coloma-Watervliet-Area-Chamber-of-Commerce/100064549127870
Description: Promotes businesses in the Coloma-Watervliet area. Organizes Business After Hours, Welcome Baskets to new businesses, ribbon cuttings, ground breakings and offers quarterly newsletters and listing on the website to members. **Founded:** 1895. **Geographic Preference:** Local.

40897 ■ Coopersville Area Chamber of Commerce
182 E St.
Coopersville, MI 49404
Contact: Bill Rozema, President
Description: Promotes business and community development in Coopersville, MI. **Founded:** 1981. **Publications:** *Chamber News*. **Geographic Preference:** Local.

40898 ■ Dearborn Area Chamber of Commerce (DACC)
22100 Michigan Ave.
Dearborn, MI 48124
Ph: (313)584-6100
Fax: (313)584-9818
Co. E-mail: jlovejoy@dearbornareachamber.org
URL: http://www.dearbornareachamber.org
Contact: Jackie Lovejoy, President
E-mail: jlovejoy@dearbornareachamber.org
Facebook: www.facebook.com/DearbornAreaChamber
X (Twitter): x.com/DbnAreaChamber
Description: Aims to promote Dearborn and to help its members to succeed. Promotes business in Dearborn by listing their businesses on the website and on printed directory. Organizes event for networking between members. **Publications:** *Dearborn Business Journal* (Monthly); *Newsbyte* (Bimonthly). **Geographic Preference:** Local.

40899 ■ Delta County Area Chamber of Commerce
1001 N Lincoln Rd.
Escanaba, MI 49829
Ph: (906)786-2192
Co. E-mail: info@deltami.org
URL: http://www.deltami.org
Contact: Vickie Micheau, Executive Director
Facebook: www.facebook.com/DeltaCountyChamber
Description: Promotes business and community development in Delta County, MI. **Founded:** 1921. **Publications:** *Shorelines* (Quarterly). **Geographic Preference:** Local.

40900 ■ Delta County Chamber of Commerce (DCCC)
1001 N Lincoln Rd.
Escanaba, MI 49829
Ph: (906)786-2192
Co. E-mail: info@deltami.org
URL: http://deltami.org
Contact: Vickie Micheau, Executive Director
Facebook: www.facebook.com/DeltaCountyChamber
Description: Promotes fair business practices and fosters a healthy business environment to attract new development to the area. Also promotes community engagement. **Founded:** 1921. **Geographic Preference:** Local.

40901 ■ Detroit Regional Chamber (DRC)
One Woodward Ave., Ste. 1900
Detroit, MI 48232-0840
Ph: (313)964-4000
Free: 866-627-5463
Fax: (313)964-0183
Co. E-mail: members@detroitchamber.com
URL: http://www.detroitchamber.com
Contact: Sandy K. Baruah, President
Facebook: www.facebook.com/detroitchamber
Linkedin: www.linkedin.com/company/detroit-regional-chamber
X (Twitter): x.com/detroitchamber
YouTube: www.youtube.com/c/DetroitRegionalChamber

Description: Promotes business and community development in the southeastern Michigan counties of Lapeer, Livingston, Macomb, Monroe, Oakland, St. Clair, Washtenaw, and Wayne. **Founded:** 1903. **Publications:** *Detroiter* (Quarterly); *Discover, Detroiter: A Publication of the Detroit Regional Chamber*; *Manufacturer's Directory: Manufacturers Directory to Regional Detroit* (Biennial); *Metro Detroit Office Guide* (Annual); *Buyers' Guide* (Annual); *Greater Detroit Manufacturers Directory*; *Greater Detroit Relocation Package*; *Big Business in Metro Detroit: A Major Employers Directory to Regional Detroit* (Biennial); *Passport to International Detroit-Services: A Directory to International Commerce in Regional Detroit* (Biennial); *Michigan Headquartered Companies: Banking, Industrial, Retail & Utilities*; *Fortune 500 Companies Represented in the Metropolitan Detroit Area*; *Manufacturers Directory to Southeast Michigan* (Annual); *Detroit Regional Buyers' Guide* (Annual); *Foreign Companies in Regional Detroit*. **Geographic Preference:** Local.

40902 ■ *Detroiter*
One Woodward Ave., Ste. 1900
Detroit, MI 48232-0840
Ph: (313)964-4000
Free: 866-627-5463
Fax: (313)964-0183
Co. E-mail: members@detroitchamber.com
URL: http://www.detroitchamber.com
Contact: Sandy K. Baruah, President
URL(s): www.detroitchamber.com/detroiter-magazine
Released: Quarterly **Price:** $14, Members; $18, Nonmembers; $4, Single issue. **Availability:** Print; Online.

40903 ■ **DeWitt Area Chamber of Commerce (DACC)**
113 S Bridge St.
DeWitt, MI 48820
Ph: (517)624-2945
Fax: (517)624-2948
URL: http://dewittareacc.org
Contact: Loretta Spinrad, Owner
Description: Promotes business and community development in the area. **Geographic Preference:** Local.

40904 ■ **East Jordan Area Chamber of Commerce (EJACC)**
100 Main St., Ste. B
East Jordan, MI 49727
Ph: (231)536-7351
Fax: (231)536-0966
Co. E-mail: info@ejchamber.org
URL: http://www.ejchamber.org
Contact: Mary H. Faculak, President
Facebook: www.facebook.com/EJChamber
Description: Businesses, churches, service groups, and individuals interested in promoting business and tourism in the East Jordan, MI area. **Founded:** 1961. **Publications:** *Business and Visitors Guide* (Annual); *News Capsule* (Weekly). **Geographic Preference:** Local.

40905 ■ **Eastpointe - Roseville Chamber of Commerce (EACC)**
24840 Gratiot Ave., Ste. C
Eastpointe, MI 48021
Ph: (586)776-5520
Co. E-mail: director@erchamber.com
URL: http://erchamber.com
Contact: Dr. Chris Dyki, President
Facebook: www.facebook.com/erchamber
Description: Promotes business and community development in Eastpointe, MI. **Founded:** 1944. **Publications:** *Newsline* (Monthly). **Geographic Preference:** Local.

40906 ■ **Edwardsburg Area Chamber of Commerce**
Ontwa Twp. Hall
26225 US Hwy. 12
Edwardsburg, MI 49112
Ph: (574)343-3721
URL: http://www.edwardsburgchamber.org
Contact: Roy Smothermon, President
Facebook: www.facebook.com/EdwardsburgChamber
YouTube: www.youtube.com/channel/UCll65hWsaCMGFMYCwQJCUGQ
Description: Promotes business and community development in the Edwardsburg, MI area. **Geographic Preference:** Local.

40907 ■ **Elk Rapids Area Chamber of Commerce (ERACC)**
305 US 31 N
Elk Rapids, MI 49629
Ph: (231)264-8202
Fax: (231)264-6591
Co. E-mail: info@elkrapidschamber.org
URL: http://www.elkrapidschamber.org
Contact: Marcie Earl, Treasurer
Facebook: www.facebook.com/elkrapidschamber
Description: Promotes business and community development in Antrim County, MI. **Founded:** 1965. **Geographic Preference:** Local.

40908 ■ **Farwell Area Chamber of Commerce (FACC)**
221 W Main
Farwell, MI 48622
Ph: (989)588-0580
Fax: (989)588-0580
URL: http://www.farwellareachamber.org
Contact: Eunice Andreas, Chairman
Facebook: www.facebook.com/people/Farwell-Area-Chamber-of-Commerce/100079005162055
Description: Promotes economic development and tourism in the Farwell, MI area. **Geographic Preference:** Local.

40909 ■ **Fenton Regional Chamber of Commerce**
104 S Adelaide St.
Fenton, MI 48430
Ph: (810)629-5447
Fax: (810)629-6608
Co. E-mail: info@fentonchamber.com
URL: http://www.fentonlindenchamber.com
Contact: Shelly Day, Executive Director
E-mail: sday@fentonchamber.com
Facebook: www.facebook.com/fentonlindenchamber
X (Twitter): x.com/fentonChamber
YouTube: www.youtube.com/channel/UCGC1tPXCPnStByp0lgaBxcg
Description: Advocates for member businesses through services and resources, while encouraging a prosperous Fenton Area. **Founded:** 1920. **Publications:** *Business Perspective* (Monthly). **Geographic Preference:** Local.

40910 ■ **Flushing Area Chamber of Commerce (FACC)**
105 E Main St.
Flushing, MI 48433
Ph: (810)659-4141
Co. E-mail: info@flushingchamber.com
URL: http://www.flushingchamber.com
Contact: Leealan Weddel, President
Facebook: www.facebook.com/flushingareachamberofcommerce
Description: Promotes business and community development in the Flushing, MI area. **Founded:** 1948. **Geographic Preference:** Local.

40911 ■ **Frankenmuth Chamber of Commerce and Convention and Visitors Bureau**
635 S Main St.
Frankenmuth, MI 48734
Ph: (989)652-6106
Free: 800-386-8696
Co. E-mail: chamber@frankenmuth.org
URL: http://www.frankenmuth.org/chamber-of-commerce
Contact: Jamie Furbush, President
E-mail: ceo@frankenmuth.org
Facebook: www.facebook.com/frankenmuth
X (Twitter): x.com/frankenmuth
Instagram: www.instagram.com/frankenmuth
YouTube: www.youtube.com/c/FrankenmuthVideos
Description: Promotes business and community development in Frankenmuth, MI. **Founded:** 1902. **Publications:** *Handelskammer* (Monthly). **Geographic Preference:** Local.

40912 ■ **Frankfort - Elberta Area Chamber of Commerce**
517 Main St.
Frankfort, MI 49635
Ph: (231)352-7251
Co. E-mail: fcofc@frankfort-elberta.com
URL: http://www.frankfort-elberta.com
Contact: Andrew Johnson, President
E-mail: andrew@frankfort-insurance.com
Facebook: www.facebook.com/pages/Frankfort-Elberta-Area-Chamber-of-Commerce/196591174454
Description: Supports the livelihood of Frankfort-Elberta and surrounding area. **Geographic Preference:** Local.

40913 ■ **French-American Chamber of Commerce, Michigan Chapter**
c/o Clayton & McKervey
2000 Town Ctr., Ste. 1800
Southfield, MI 48075
Ph: (248)365-0535
Co. E-mail: info@faccmi.org
URL: http://www.faccmi.org
Contact: Cedric Ballarin, President
Linkedin: www.linkedin.com/company/french-american-chamber-of-commerce-michigan-chapter
X (Twitter): x.com/faccmichigan
Description: Strives to contribute to the improvement of economic, commercial and financial relations between France and the United States, particularly the state of Michigan. **Founded:** 1983. **Geographic Preference:** State.

40914 ■ **Gaylord - Otsego County Chamber of Commerce**
319 W Main St.
Gaylord, MI 49734
Ph: (989)732-6333
Fax: (989)732-7990
Co. E-mail: info@gaylordchamber.com
URL: http://www.gaylordchamber.com
Contact: Mike Cwik, Treasurer
Facebook: www.facebook.com/GaylordAreaChamberofCommerce
Linkedin: www.linkedin.com/company/gaylord-area-chamber-of-commerce
Description: Promotes business and community development in Otsego County, MI. Sponsors annual Alpenfest. **Founded:** 1948. **Publications:** *Business to Business Journal* (Quarterly); *Gaylord/Otsego County Chamber of Commerce Membership Directory and Community Profile* (Annual). **Educational Activities:** Alpenfest (Irregular). **Geographic Preference:** Local.

40915 ■ **Grand Blanc Chamber of Commerce (GBCC)**
512 E Grand Blanc Rd.
Grand Blanc, MI 48439
Ph: (810)695-4222
Fax: (810)695-0053
Co. E-mail: gbcc@grandblancchamber.com
URL: http://www.grandblancchamber.com
Contact: Leigh LaForest, President
Facebook: www.facebook.com/grandblancchamber
Linkedin: www.linkedin.com/in/grand-blanc-chamber-of-commerce-06254169
X (Twitter): x.com/gb_chamber
Instagram: www.instagram.com/grandblancchamber
Description: Businesses and organizations dedicated to advancing the commercial, agricultural, industrial, and civic interests of the community. Offers group health insurance and discounts on charge cards; conducts charitable activities, summer festival and golf outing. **Founded:** 1977. **Publications:** *The Business Index* (Monthly); *Chamber Buzz* (Weekly); *Grand Blanc Community Directory and Buyer's Guide*. **Educational Activities:** Ambassadors Meeting (Monthly). **Geographic Preference:** Local.

40916 ■ Grand Ledge Chamber of Commerce (GLACC)
310 Greenwood St., Rm. B-103
Grand Ledge, MI 48837
Ph: (517)627-2383
Co. E-mail: info@grandledgechamber.com
URL: http://www.grandledgechamber.com
Contact: Kevin Skarritt, President
E-mail: kevin@flockmarketing.com
Facebook: www.facebook.com/GrandLedgeChamber

Description: Promotes business and community development in Eaton County, MI. Holds monthly board meeting. **Founded:** 1969. **Geographic Preference:** Local.

40917 ■ Grand Rapids Area Chamber of Commerce
250 Monroe Ave. NW
Grand Rapids, MI 49503
Ph: (616)771-0300
Co. E-mail: info@grandrapids.org
URL: http://www.grandrapids.org
Contact: Rick Baker, President
E-mail: rick@grandrapids.org
Facebook: www.facebook.com/GrandRapidsAreaChamber
Linkedin: www.linkedin.com/company/grand-rapids-area-chamber-of-commerce
X (Twitter): x.com/GRACC
YouTube: www.youtube.com/user/GrandRapidsChamber

Description: Creates opportunities for business success in the Grand Rapids, MI area. **Founded:** 1887. **Publications:** *Business Directory*; *Chamber News*. **Geographic Preference:** Local.

40918 ■ Grandville/Jenison Chamber of Commerce (GJCC)
2939 Wilson Ave. SW, Ste. 106
Grandville, MI 49418
Ph: (616)531-8890
Co. E-mail: gjcc@grandjen.com
URL: http://grandjen.com
Contact: Heather Schaedig, Executive Director
E-mail: heather@grandjen.com

Description: Promotes and stimulates long-term, well-planned economic growth, educational opportunities and community resources of Grandville. **Geographic Preference:** Local.

40919 ■ Gratiot Area Chamber of Commerce (GACC)
110 W Superior St.
Alma, MI 48801
Ph: (989)463-5525
Fax: (989)463-6588
URL: http://gacc.gratiot.org
Contact: Brendan Kelley, Executive Director
X (Twitter): x.com/GratiotChamber

Description: Represents businesses in Gratiot County, MI united to promote the economic growth of the area. **Founded:** 1994. **Publications:** *Chamber Connections* (Monthly); *Gratiot Area Community Guide* (Annual). **Geographic Preference:** Local.

40920 ■ Grayling Regional Chamber of Commerce (GRCC)
213 N James St.
Grayling, MI 49738
Ph: (989)348-2921
Fax: (989)348-7315
Co. E-mail: info@graylingchamber.com
URL: http://graylingchamber.com
Contact: Traci Cook, Executive Director
E-mail: director@graylingchamber.com
Facebook: www.facebook.com/GraylingChamber
X (Twitter): x.com/graylingchamber

Description: Promotes business and community development in Crawford County, MI. Sponsors AuSable River Festival and Canoe Marathon and Grayling's Winter-Fest. **Founded:** 1955. **Publications:** *Chamber Update* (Weekly); *Grayling Community Guide and Membership Directory* (Periodic). **Geographic Preference:** Local.

40921 ■ Greater Albion Chamber of Commerce
PO Box 238
Albion, MI 49224
Ph: (517)629-5533
Co. E-mail: president@greateralbionchamber.org
URL: http://www.greateralbionchamber.org
Contact: Jen Bomba, Chairperson
X (Twitter): x.com/albionchamber

Description: Promotes business and community development in the Albion, MI area. **Founded:** 1923. **Publications:** *Greater Albion Business News* (Monthly). **Geographic Preference:** Local.

40922 ■ Greater Croswell - Lexington Chamber of Commerce
PO Box 142
Lexington, MI 48450
Ph: (810)359-2262
Co. E-mail: croslexchamberofcommerce@gmail.com
URL: http://www.croslexchamber.com
Contact: Carlos Quiroga, President
Facebook: www.facebook.com/croslex

Description: Promotes business and community development in Greater Croswell-Lexington, MI. **Founded:** 1990. **Geographic Preference:** Local.

40923 ■ Greater Dowagiac Area Chamber of Commerce
200 Depot Dr.
Dowagiac, MI 49047
Ph: (269)782-8212
URL: http://www.dowagiacchamber.com
Contact: Kris Soenen, President
E-mail: kris@whoknewconsignment.com

Description: Promotes business and community development in the Dowagiac, MI area. **Publications:** *Dowagiac Event and Festival* (Annual); *Dowagiac Tourist Guide* (Annual); *Looking to the Future* (Monthly). **Geographic Preference:** Local.

40924 ■ Greater Durand Area Chamber of Commerce
109 N Saginaw St.
Durand, MI 48429
Ph: (989)288-3715
Fax: (989)288-5177
Co. E-mail: office@durandchamber.com
URL: http://durandchamber.com
Contact: Darrick Huff, Co-President
X (Twitter): x.com/DurandChamber

Description: Businesses, service groups, industries, and merchants united to promote commerce in the Durand, MI area. Sponsors festival. **Founded:** 1960. **Publications:** *Railnet* (Quarterly). **Geographic Preference:** Local.

40925 ■ Greater Farmington Area Chamber of Commerce (GFACC)
32780 Grand River Ave., Ste. 207A
Farmington, MI 48336
Ph: (248)919-6917
Fax: (248)919-6921
Co. E-mail: info@gfachamber.com
URL: http://www.gfachamber.com
Contact: Geno Grabinski, President
Facebook: www.facebook.com/GFACC
X (Twitter): x.com/GFAChamber

Description: Strives to enhance the economy and business environment in the Greater Farmington-Farmington Hills area. **Founded:** 1963. **Publications:** *The Voice of Business* (Bimonthly). **Geographic Preference:** Local.

40926 ■ *The Greater Mackinaw Area Chamber of Commerce*
707 N Huron Ave.
Mackinaw City, MI 49701
Ph: (231)436-5574
Co. E-mail: info@mackinawchamber.com
URL: http://www.mackinawchamber.com
Contact: Chris Herald, President
URL(s): www.mackinawchamber.com/chamber-membership-services-benefits

Availability: Print; Online.

40927 ■ Greater Niles Chamber of Commerce [Niles Society]
333 N 2nd St., Ste. 302
Niles, MI 49120
Ph: (269)683-1833
Co. E-mail: info@greaternileschamber.com
URL: http://www.greaternileschamber.com
Contact: Jeff Rea, President
E-mail: jrea@greaternileschamber.com
Facebook: www.facebook.com/greaternilescoc
Linkedin: www.linkedin.com/company/greater-niles-chamber-of-commerce
Instagram: www.instagram.com/greaternileschamber

Description: Promotes business and community development in the Niles County, MI area. **Founded:** 1919. **Publications:** *Clubs and Civic Organizations* (Annual); *Manufacturer's Guide* (Periodic); *Niles Renaissance* (Annual). **Geographic Preference:** Local.

40928 ■ Greater Romeo-Washington Chamber of Commerce
228 N Main St., Ste. D
Romeo, MI 48065
Ph: (586)752-4436
Co. E-mail: kelley@rwchamber.com
URL: http://www.rwchamber.com
Contact: Kelley Stephens, Executive Director
E-mail: kelley@rwchamber.com
Facebook: www.facebook.com/romeowashingtonchamberofcommerce
Linkedin: www.linkedin.com/in/kelley-stephens-b4320613
X (Twitter): x.com/ChamberGRW

Description: Promotes business and community development in Macomb County, MI. Sponsors competitions and festival. Conducts charitable activities. **Founded:** 1975. **Publications:** *Business Directory*; *Cornerstone* (Bimonthly). **Educational Activities:** Romeo-Washington Chamber of Commerce Luncheon. **Awards:** Greater Romeo-Washington Chamber of Commerce Lifetime Achievement Award (Annual); Greater Romeo-Washington Chamber of Commerce Member of the Month (Monthly). **Geographic Preference:** Local.

40929 ■ Greater Romulus Chamber of Commerce (GRCC)
1189 Shook Rd.
Romulus, MI 48174
Ph: (734)893-0694
Co. E-mail: admin@romuluschamber.org
URL: http://romuluschamber.org
Contact: Jeff Lowrey, President
Facebook: www.facebook.com/romuluschamber

Description: Small businesses interested in fostering and creating a healthy environment to do business. Works to improve business community by providing various promotional and profitable opportunities. **Geographic Preference:** Local.

40930 ■ Greater West Bloomfield Chamber of Commerce
5745 W Maple Rd., Ste. 206
West Bloomfield, MI 48322
Ph: (248)626-3636
Fax: (248)626-4218
Co. E-mail: wbloomfieldchamber@gmail.com
URL: http://westbloomfieldchamber.com
Contact: Suzanne Levine, Executive Director
Facebook: www.facebook.com/westbloomfieldcc

Description: Promotes business and community development in West Bloomfield, MI. Sponsors West Bloomfield Artfest, Business Person of the Year, Business Beautification Awards, Taste of West Bloomfield, and 6th Annual Golf Classic; conducts charitable activities. **Founded:** 1973. **Publications:** *Chamber Member Directory*; *West Bloomfield Update* (Monthly). **Geographic Preference:** Local.

40931 ■ Greenville Area Chamber of Commerce (GACC)
210 S Lafayette St.
Greenville, MI 48838-1936
Ph: (616)754-5697
Co. E-mail: info@greenvillechamber.net

URL: http://greenvillemi.org
Contact: Andrea Leslie, Chairman of the Board
Description: Promotes business and community development in the Greenville, MI area. **Founded:** 1947. **Publications:** *Business Beat* (Monthly); *Greater Greenville* (Monthly). **Geographic Preference:** Local.

40932 ■ Harbor Beach Chamber of Commerce
PO Box 143
Harbor Beach, MI 48441
Ph: (989)479-6477
Co. E-mail: visitor@harborbeachchamber.com
URL: http://www.harborbeachchamber.com
Contact: Joann Talaski, President
Facebook: www.facebook.com/harborbeachchamber
X (Twitter): x.com/HarborBeachCity
Description: Works to advance businesses within Harbor Beach and the surrounding areas. **Geographic Preference:** Local.

40933 ■ Harbor Country Chamber of Commerce
15311 Three Oaks Rd.
Three Oaks, MI 49128
Ph: (269)469-5409
Fax: (269)469-2257
Co. E-mail: chamber@harborcountry.org
URL: http://www.harborcountry.org
Contact: John Natsis, Secretary
Facebook: www.facebook.com/HarborCountryChamber
X (Twitter): x.com/HarborCountry
Instagram: www.instagram.com/harborcountrymichigan
Pinterest: www.pinterest.com/HarborCountryMI
Description: Promotes convention business and tourism in area. **Founded:** 1980. **Publications:** *Connection* (Monthly); *Harbor Country Guide* (Annual); *Harbor County Guide*. **Geographic Preference:** Local.

40934 ■ *Harbor Country Guide*
15311 Three Oaks Rd.
Three Oaks, MI 49128
Ph: (269)469-5409
Fax: (269)469-2257
Co. E-mail: chamber@harborcountry.org
URL: http://www.harborcountry.org
Contact: John Natsis, Secretary
URL(s): www.harborcountry.org/harbor-country-guide-ads
Released: Annual **Description:** Covers eight communities. **Availability:** Print; PDF; Online.

40935 ■ Harbor Springs Area Chamber of Commerce (HSCC)
118 E Main St.
Harbor Springs, MI 49740
Ph: (231)526-7999
Co. E-mail: info@harborspringschamber.com
URL: http://www.harborspringschamber.com
Contact: Kathie Breighner, President
Facebook: www.facebook.com/harborspringschamber
X (Twitter): x.com/HarborChamber
Instagram: www.instagram.com/harborspringsarea
YouTube: www.youtube.com/channel/UCvYTzfwXEY3_8aRXEmbrA5w
Description: Strives to promote, enhance, and contribute to the well-being of the business community, while preserving the character and traditions of Harbor Springs. **Publications:** *Back to Business* (Bimonthly); *Community Organizations* (Bimonthly); *Visitors Guide* (Annual). **Geographic Preference:** Local.

40936 ■ Harrison Area Chamber of Commerce (HCC)
426 N 1st St., Ste. 103
Harrison, MI 48625
Ph: (989)539-6011
Co. E-mail: office@harrisonareachamber.com
URL: http://ww.harrisonareachamber.com
Contact: Wendy D. Daves, Executive Director
Facebook: www.facebook.com/HarrisonARChamber
Instagram: www.instagram.com/harrison.chamber.9
Description: Promotes businesses in the area and engages with the community by organizing events in the area. Partners with the Economic Development Corporation to strengthen the regions economic viability. **Publications:** *Membership Directory and Relocation Guide* (Annual). **Geographic Preference:** Local.

40937 ■ Hillman Area Chamber of Commerce
14797 State St. S, Ste. 2
Hillman, MI 49746
Ph: (989)742-3739
Co. E-mail: hillmanchamber@yahoo.com
URL: http://hillmanchamber.org
Contact: Jim Paczkowski, Sr., President
Facebook: www.facebook.com/hillmanchamber
Description: Promotes business and community development in the Hillman, MI area. **Geographic Preference:** Local.

40938 ■ Holly Area Chamber of Commerce
300 E St.
Holly, MI 48442
Ph: (248)215-7099
Co. E-mail: thehollychamber@gmail.com
URL: http://www.hollyareachamber.com
Contact: George Kullis, President
Description: Strives to facilitate new business networking, promote communication among existing business and support the development of the community. **Founded:** 1918. **Geographic Preference:** Local.

40939 ■ Houghton Lake Chamber of Commerce (HLCC)
1625 W Houghton Lake Dr.
Houghton Lake, MI 49629
Ph: (989)366-5644
Co. E-mail: hlcc@houghtonlakechamber.org
URL: http://houghtonlakechamber.net
Contact: Amy Langlois, President
Facebook: www.facebook.com/houghtonlake.chamber
X (Twitter): x.com/HLChamber
Description: Promotes business and community development in Houghton Lake, MI area. **Geographic Preference:** Local.

40940 ■ Howell Area Chamber of Commerce (HACC)
123 E Washington St.
Howell, MI 48843
Ph: (517)546-3920
Fax: (517)546-4115
Co. E-mail: admin@howell.org
URL: http://www.howell.org
Contact: Janelle Best, President
Facebook: www.facebook.com/howellchamber
Linkedin: www.linkedin.com/company/howell-area-chamber-of-comm
X (Twitter): x.com/howell_chamber
YouTube: www.youtube.com/channel/UCfP1T-4ICgHMu8ZhxtEOTyw
Description: Works to improve the business community through various programs and services. **Publications:** *Business Views*; *Howell Area Chamber of Commerce--Community Guide and Member Directory*. **Geographic Preference:** Local.

40941 ■ Hudsonville Area Chamber of Commerce (HACC)
3275 Central Blvd.
Hudsonville, MI 49426
Ph: (616)662-0900
Fax: (616)669-2330
Co. E-mail: director@hudsonvillechamber.com
URL: http://www.hudsonvillechamber.com
Contact: Lauren Foley, Executive Director
E-mail: lfoley@hudsonville.org
Facebook: www.facebook.com/HudsonvilleCC
Linkedin: www.linkedin.com/company/hudsonville-area-chamber-of-commerce
X (Twitter): x.com/HudsonvilleCC
Description: Businesses and individuals seeking to promote economic and community development in the Hudsonville, MI area. **Founded:** 1927. **Publications:** *Hudsonville Area Chamber of Commerce Community Profile* (Annual); *Progress Report* (Bimonthly). **Geographic Preference:** Local.

40942 ■ Huron Township Chamber of Commerce (HTCC)
Huron Professional Bldg.
19132 Huron River Dr.
New Boston, MI 48164-0247
Ph: (734)753-4220
Fax: (734)753-4602
Co. E-mail: hurontwpchmbrcomm@yahoo.com
URL: http://www.members.tripod.com/htcc48164
Contact: Ken Moore, President
Description: Strives to bring community and business together. Promotes business and community development within Huron Township, MI. Sponsors annual Chamber Barn Dance, Scholarship Golf Outing (for local H.S.). Participates in the Huron Toys for Tots & Teens program. Holds monthly board meetings. **Founded:** 1981. **Publications:** *Chamber Chips* (Monthly); *Huron Township Business Directory* (Semiannual). **Geographic Preference:** Local.

40943 ■ Huron Valley Chamber of Commerce (HVCC)
317 Union St.
Milford, MI 48381
Ph: (248)685-7129
Co. E-mail: info@huronvcc.com
URL: http://www.huronvcc.com
Contact: Jack Shubitowski, President
Facebook: www.facebook.com/hvchamber
X (Twitter): x.com/hvchamber
YouTube: www.youtube.com/channel/UCIVYyVzB-P9XA7KOT1CJZhQ/featured
Description: Promotes business and community development in the Huron Valley, MI area. **Founded:** 1962. **Publications:** *Business Directory and Buying Guide* (Annual); *Chamber News*. **Awards:** Huron Valley Chamber Business of the Year (Annual); Huron Valley Chamber Citizen of the Year (Annual). **Geographic Preference:** Local.

40944 ■ Indian River Regional Chamber of Commerce
3435 S Straits Hwy.
Indian River, MI 49749
Ph: (231)238-9325
Free: 800-394-8310
Co. E-mail: info@irchamber.com
URL: http://irchamber.com
Contact: Will Mulligan, Executive Director
E-mail: wmulligan@irchamber.com
Facebook: www.facebook.com/IndianRiverChamberOfCommerce
X (Twitter): x.com/irchamber
YouTube: www.youtube.com/channel/UCXTY1Ubz1Lnk2UEzSriZkYA
Description: Promotes business and community development in Indian River, MI. **Founded:** 1933. **Geographic Preference:** Local.

40945 ■ Inkster Chamber of Commerce
PO Box 596
Inkster, MI 48141
Ph: (313)300-1057
Co. E-mail: inksterchamberofcommerce@gmail.com
URL: http://www.inksterchamber.com
Contact: Martha Theis, President
Facebook: www.facebook.com/inksterchamber
Description: Aims to improve businesses operating in Inkster. **Geographic Preference:** Local.

40946 ■ *Insight*
1 Riverwalk Ctr.
34 Jackson St. W, Ste. 3A
Battle Creek, MI 49017
Ph: (269)962-4076
Co. E-mail: office@battlecreek.org
URL: http://battlecreek.org
Contact: Kara E. Beer, President
E-mail: kbeer@battlecreek.org
URL(s): battlecreek.org/insight-newsletters
Released: Quarterly **Availability:** PDF; Online.

40947 ■ Interlochen Area Chamber of Commerce (IACC)
PO Box 13
Interlochen, MI 49643
Co. E-mail: info@interlochenchamber.org
URL: http://www.interlochenchamber.org
Contact: Rory Baker, President
Description: Promotes business and community development in Interlochen, MI area. **Founded:** 1946. **Geographic Preference:** Local.

40948 ■ Ionia Area Chamber of Commerce (IACC)
439 W Main St.
Ionia, MI 48846
Ph: (616)527-2560
Co. E-mail: info@ioniachamber.net
URL: http://www.ioniachamber.org
Contact: Ashley Brownell, President
Facebook: www.facebook.com/ionia.chamber.commerce
Instagram: www.instagram.com/ionia_chamber
YouTube: www.youtube.com/channel/UC6Vx4tAJATbsr1s2EfAHtxQ
Description: Promotes business and community development in the Ionia, MI area. Sponsors festival. **Founded:** 1937. **Publications:** *Chamber News*. **Geographic Preference:** Local.

40949 ■ Ironwood Area Chamber of Commerce (IACC)
150 N Lowell St.
Ironwood, MI 49938
Ph: (906)932-1122
Co. E-mail: chamber@ironwoodchamber.org
URL: http://www.ironwoodchamber.org
Contact: Sam Davey, III, President
Facebook: www.facebook.com/IronwoodChamber
Instagram: www.instagram.com/ironwoodchamber
YouTube: www.youtube.com/channel/UCM4ozcJcvu80rHyePaNXw3A
Description: Businesses and professionals. Promotes business and community development and tourism in the Ironwood, MI area. Conducts annual Jack Frost festival of Lights parade. **Founded:** 1912. **Publications:** *Chamber Chat* (Monthly); *Ironwood - Best of Michigan*. **Geographic Preference:** Local.

40950 ■ Keweenaw Chamber of Commerce (KCC)
902 College Ave.
Houghton, MI 49931
Ph: (906)482-5240
Co. E-mail: info@keweenaw.org
URL: http://www.keweenaw.org
Contact: Mary Myers, Board Member
Description: Promotes business and community development in Houghton and Keweenaw counties, MI. Promotes tourism. **Founded:** 1959. **Publications:** *Chamber Update* (Quarterly); *Keweenaw Peninsula Chamber of Commerce Membership Directory* (Annual); *Keweenaw Street Map & Business Guide* (Semiannual). **Awards:** Keweenaw Peninsula Chamber of Commerce Spark Plug (Annual). **Geographic Preference:** Local.

40951 ■ *Keweenaw Street Map & Business Guide*
902 College Ave.
Houghton, MI 49931
Ph: (906)482-5240
Co. E-mail: info@keweenaw.org
URL: http://www.keweenaw.org
Contact: Mary Myers, Board Member
URL(s): www.keweenaw.org/networking-visibility
Released: Semiannual **Description:** Provides detailed maps of cities in Houghton and Keweenaw Counties. **Availability:** Print; Online.

40952 ■ Lake Gogebic Area Chamber of Commerce
PO Box 114
Bergland, MI 49910
Free: 888-464-3242
Co. E-mail: info@lakegogebicarea.com
URL: http://www.lakegogebicarea.com
Contact: Mary Beth DeFazio, President
Facebook: www.facebook.com/lakegogebicarea
X (Twitter): x.com/areagogebic
Description: Promotes business, tourism and community development in Lake Gogebic, MI area. **Founded:** 1966. **Geographic Preference:** Local.

40953 ■ Lakes Area Chamber of Commerce (LACC)
305 N Pontiac Trl., Ste. A
Walled Lake, MI 48390
Ph: (248)624-2826
Co. E-mail: info@lakesareachamber.com
URL: http://lakesareachamber.com/#!deals
Contact: Laura Bolyard, Executive Director
E-mail: laura@lakesareachamber.com
Facebook: www.facebook.com/lakesareachamberofcommerce
X (Twitter): x.com/LakesAreaCC
Instagram: www.instagram.com/lakesareachamberofcommerce
Description: Promotes business and community development in the townships of Commerce, Waterford, and White Lake, cities of Walled Lake and Wixom, and village of Wolverine, MI. Sponsors golf and bowling tournaments. **Founded:** 1950. **Publications:** *Member Directory*; *Today's Business Choice* (Monthly). **Educational Activities:** Taste of the Lakes. **Geographic Preference:** Local.

40954 ■ Lansing Regional Chamber of Commerce (LRCC)
500 E Michigan Ave., Ste. 200
Lansing, MI 48912
Ph: (517)487-6340
Co. E-mail: info@lansingchamber.org
URL: http://www.lansingchamber.org
Contact: Tim Daman, President
E-mail: tdaman@lansingchamber.org
Facebook: www.facebook.com/LansingChamber
Linkedin: www.linkedin.com/company/lansing-regional-chamber-of-commerce
X (Twitter): x.com/LansingChamber
YouTube: www.youtube.com/channel/UCfXAeBPArw-kB-XWMbcyzTg
Description: Works to facilitate economic development through the support of existing business and the attraction of new businesses for providing business advocacy and offering membership services. **Founded:** 1912. **Publications:** *Focus* (Weekly); *Regional Vision* (Bimonthly); *Lansing Regional Chamber of Commerce--Membership Directory*. **Educational Activities:** Business Lunch Training Seminar Series. **Awards:** Lansing Chamber ATHENA Award (Annual); Lansing Chamber Community Service Award (Annual); Outstanding Small Business Advocate Award (Annual); Outstanding Small Business Award (Annual). **Geographic Preference:** Regional.

40955 ■ Lapeer Area Chamber of Commerce (LACC)
108 W Pk. St.
Lapeer, MI 48446
Ph: (810)664-6641
Fax: (810)664-4349
Co. E-mail: staff@lapeerareachamber.org
URL: http://www.lapeerareachamber.org
Contact: Wes Smith, President
Facebook: www.facebook.com/Lapeerareachamber
YouTube: www.youtube.com/user/lapeerareachamber
Description: Works to promote and foster the business community and enhance the quality of life in the area. **Publications:** *Business Connections* (Monthly). **Geographic Preference:** Local.

40956 ■ Leelanau Peninsula Chamber of Commerce
PO Box 484
Suttons Bay, MI 49682
Ph: (231)252-2880
Co. E-mail: info@leelanauchamber.com
URL: http://www.leelanauchamber.com
Contact: Brayton Farr, President
Facebook: www.facebook.com/LeelanauChamber
Description: Promotes business and community development and tourism in Leelanau County, MI. **Geographic Preference:** Local.

40957 ■ Lewiston Area Chamber of Commerce (LACC)
2946 Kneeland St.
Lewiston, MI 49756
Ph: (989)786-2293
Fax: (989)786-4515
Co. E-mail: lewistonchamberoffice@gmail.com
URL: http://www.lewistonchamber.com
Contact: Autumn Brown, President
Description: Promotes business and community development and tourism in the Lewiston, MI area. Sponsors annual Morel Mushroom and Timberfest events, Car Show, and Arts and Crafts Fairs. **Founded:** 1958. **Publications:** *Communicator* (Quarterly). **Educational Activities:** Ambassadors Formation. **Geographic Preference:** Local.

40958 ■ *Livonia Business Directory*
33300 5 Mile Rd., Ste. 212
Livonia, MI 48154
Ph: (734)427-2122
Fax: (734)427-6055
Co. E-mail: chamber@livonia.org
URL: http://www.livonia.org
Contact: Dan West, President
E-mail: dwest@livonia.org
URL(s): business.livoniawestland.org/list
Released: Annual **Availability:** Online.

40959 ■ Livonia Chamber of Commerce (LCC)
33300 5 Mile Rd., Ste. 212
Livonia, MI 48154
Ph: (734)427-2122
Fax: (734)427-6055
Co. E-mail: chamber@livonia.org
URL: http://www.livonia.org
Contact: Dan West, President
E-mail: dwest@livonia.org
X (Twitter): x.com/LivoniaChamber
Instagram: www.instagram.com/livoniachamber
YouTube: www.youtube.com/user/TheLivoniaChamber
Description: Business association that promotes economic and community development in the city of Livonia, MI. **Founded:** 1950. **Publications:** *Communicator* (Bimonthly); *Industrial Directory*; *Manufacturer's Directory* (Annual); *Livonia Business Directory* (Annual). **Geographic Preference:** Local.

40960 ■ Lowell Area Chamber of Commerce (LACC)
113 Riverwalk Plz.
Lowell, MI 49331
Ph: (616)897-9161
Fax: (616)897-9101
Co. E-mail: info@lowellchamber.org
URL: http://www.lowellchamber.org
Contact: Ian Deming, President
Facebook: www.facebook.com/Lowell-Area-Chamber-of-Commerce-84172814896
Description: Promotes business and community development in the Lowell, MI area. Sponsors semiannual sidewalk sales. Sponsors Riverwalk Arts and Crafts. Christmas festivities, and a golf outing. **Founded:** 1966. **Awards:** Lowell Area Chamber of Commerce Person of the Year (Annual). **Geographic Preference:** Local.

40961 ■ Ludington & Scottville Area Chamber of Commerce
119 S Rath Ave.
Ludington, MI 49431
Ph: (231)845-0324
Fax: (231)845-6857
Co. E-mail: chamberinfo@ludington.org
URL: http://www.ludington.org
Contact: Brandy Henderson Miller, President
E-mail: brandyh@ludington.org
Facebook: www.facebook.com/LudingtonScottvilleChamber

Description: Businesses and individuals interested in promoting business and community development in Ludington area and Mason County, MI. Sponsors Ludington Carferry Festival; Gus Macker 3-on-3 Charity Basketball Tournament; Harbor Festival; Gold Coast Arts and Crafts and Spirit of the Season Parade. **Founded:** 1929. **Publications:** *Area Map*; *Business to Business* (Monthly); *Menu Guide*. **Educational Activities:** Ludington Area Chamber of Commerce Meeting. **Geographic Preference:** Local.

40962 ■ Mackinac Island Tourism Bureau
7274 Main St.
Mackinac Island, MI 49757
Ph: (906)847-3783
Free: 800-454-5227
Co. E-mail: info@mackinacisland.org
URL: http://www.mackinacisland.org
Contact: Tim Hygh, Executive Director
E-mail: timhygh@micvb.com
Facebook: www.facebook.com/mackinacislandtourismbureau
X (Twitter): x.com/mackinacisle
Instagram: www.instagram.com/mackinacisle
YouTube: www.youtube.com/user/mackinacisle
Pinterest: www.pinterest.com/mackinacisle

Description: Promotes business and community development on Mackinac Island, MI. Provides tourism and visitor information. **Geographic Preference:** Local.

40963 ■ Mackinaw City Chamber of Commerce
707 N Huron Ave.
Mackinaw City, MI 49701
Ph: (231)436-5574
Co. E-mail: info@mackinawchamber.com
URL: http://www.mackinawchamber.com
Contact: Chris Herald, President
Facebook: www.facebook.com/MackinawCity
X (Twitter): x.com/mackinawcity
Instagram: www.instagram.com/mackinawchamber

Description: Promotes business and community development and tourism in the Mackinaw City, MI area. Works to create an inviting community dedicated to economic growth and excellence in customer satisfaction. **Publications:** *Community Profile and Membership Directory*; *Fall/Winter/Spring Guide* (Annual); *The Greater Mackinaw Area Chamber of Commerce*; *Summer Visitor's Guide* (Annual); *Mackinaw City Community Guide and Membership Directory*. **Geographic Preference:** Local.

40964 ■ Madison Heights - Hazel Park Chamber of Commerce (MHHPCC)
300 W 13 Mile Rd.
Madison Heights, MI 48071
Ph: (248)542-5010
Co. E-mail: info@madisonheightschamber.com
URL: http://www.madisonheightschamber.com
Contact: Nancy Smith, Executive Director
E-mail: mhhpchamber@gmail.com
Facebook: www.facebook.com/MHHPChamber
Instagram: www.instagram.com/mhhpchamber
YouTube: www.youtube.com/channel/UC2mn5l04xXZBEXcyenda5Zw

Description: Promotes business and community development in Madison Heights, MI. Sponsors annual Bowl-A-Thon and auction. **Founded:** 1994. **Publications:** *Business to Business* (Periodic). **Educational Activities:** Business Expo. **Geographic Preference:** Local.

40965 ■ Mancelona Regional Chamber of Commerce
PO Box 558
Mancelona, MI 49659
Ph: (231)587-5500
Co. E-mail: info@mancelonachamber.org
URL: http://www.mancelonachamber.org
Contact: Joanie Moore, Executive Director
URL(s): www.michigan.org/property/mancelona-regional-chamber-commerce

Description: Promotes business and community development in Mancelona, MI. **Founded:** 1871. **Geographic Preference:** Local.

40966 ■ Manchester Area Chamber of Commerce (MACC)
PO Box 521
Manchester, MI 48158
Ph: (248)605-0626
Co. E-mail: manchester48158@gmail.com
URL: http://48158.com
Contact: Katy Riddle, Executive Director
E-mail: katy@manchestertnchamber.org
Facebook: www.facebook.com/ManchesterChamber48158
Linkedin: www.linkedin.com/company/manchester-chamber-of-commerce
X (Twitter): x.com/MACCTN
Instagram: www.instagram.com/manchestercoc931

Description: Represents businesses and individuals organized to promote economic and community development in the Manchester, MI area. **Founded:** 1984. **Publications:** *Community Resource Guide* (Annual); *MACC Connections* (Bimonthly). **Geographic Preference:** Local.

40967 ■ Manistee Area Chamber of Commerce
400 River St.
Manistee, MI 49660
Ph: (231)723-2575
Co. E-mail: carmen@manisteechamber.com
URL: http://www.manisteechamber.com
Contact: Kelly Tomaszewski, President
Facebook: www.facebook.com/manisteeareachamberofcommerce
Instagram: www.instagram.com/manisteeareachamberofcommerce

Description: Promotes business and community development in Manistee County, MI. Promotes tourism. **Awards:** Manistee Area Chamber of Commerce Ambassador of the Year (Annual); Manistee Area Chamber of Commerce Business of the Year (Annual); Manistee Area Chamber of Commerce Small Business of the Year (Annual); Manistee Area Chamber of Commerce Business Person of the Year (Annual); Manistee Area Chamber of Commerce Action Award for Community Service (Annual). **Geographic Preference:** Local.

40968 ■ Marine City Chamber of Commerce
480 S Water St.
Marine City, MI 48039
Ph: (810)765-4501
Co. E-mail: chamber@visitmarinecity.com
URL: http://www.visitmarinecity.com/chamber-of-commerce
Contact: Laura Merchant, President
Facebook: www.facebook.com/marinecityareachamber

Description: Develops an active organization to promote focus and ensure the economic growth and development of members' business and community at large. **Founded:** 1865. **Geographic Preference:** Local.

40969 ■ Marquette Area Chamber of Commerce - Lake Superior Community Partnership (LSCP)
501 S Front St.
Marquette, MI 49855
Ph: (906)226-6591
Fax: (906)226-2099
Co. E-mail: lscp@marquette.org
URL: http://marquette.org
Contact: Ashley Szczepanski, Director, Marketing
E-mail: ashley@marquette.org

Description: Promotes business, tourism, and community development in the Marquette County, MI area. **Founded:** 1930. **Publications:** *Superior Newsletter* (Monthly); *Marquette Area Chamber of Commerce/Lake Superior Community Partnership-- Directory and Planning Calendar* (Annual); *Directory and Planning Calendar* (Annual). **Geographic Preference:** Local.

40970 ■ Marshall Area Economic Development Alliance (MAEDA)
323 W Michigan Ave.
Marshall, MI 49068

Ph: (269)781-5163
Free: 800-877-5163
Co. E-mail: info@choosemarshall.com
URL: http://choosemarshall.com
Contact: Brad Gruhot, President
E-mail: brad.gruhot@marshallmn.org
Facebook: www.facebook.com/ChooseMarshall
Instagram: www.instagram.com/choosemarshall
YouTube: www.youtube.com/channel/UCUWBPN-4xkBNIZdqF6_6yfg
Pinterest: www.pinterest.com/choosemarshall

Description: Promotes business and community development in the area. Sponsors parades, blood drives, festivals, and other community events. **Publications:** *Community Guide* (Annual); *Chamber News* (Bimonthly); *Marshall Area Chamber Newsletter* (Monthly). **Educational Activities:** Business After Hours (Monthly). **Awards:** Marshall Area Chamber of Commerce Athena Award Program (Annual). **Geographic Preference:** Local.

40971 ■ Mason Area Chamber of Commerce (MACC)
148 E Ash St.
Mason, MI 48854
Ph: (517)676-1046
Fax: (517)676-8504
Co. E-mail: masonchamber@masonchamber.org
URL: http://www.masonchamber.org
Contact: Mark Voss, Director
Facebook: www.facebook.com/masonchamber

Description: Promotes business and community development in the Mason, MI area. **Founded:** 1972. **Publications:** *Mason in Motion Update* (Monthly). **Educational Activities:** Good Morning, Mason! (Irregular). **Awards:** Mason Area Chamber of Commerce Citizen of the Year (Annual); Mason Area Chamber of Commerce Excellence in Business (Annual); Mason Area Chamber of Commerce Excellence in Education (Annual); Mason Area Chamber of Commerce President's Award (Annual). **Geographic Preference:** Local.

40972 ■ Mecosta County Area Chamber of Commerce (MCACC)
127 S State St.
Big Rapids, MI 49307
Ph: (616)780-8208
URL: http://www.mecostacountyareachamber.com
Contact: Michele Albright, President
Linkedin: www.linkedin.com/company/mcacc
X (Twitter): x.com/MecostaChamber
Instagram: www.instagram.com/mecostacountyareachamber

Description: Promotes business and community development in the Mecosta County, MI area. **Founded:** 1937. **Publications:** *Chamber News*. **Educational Activities:** Labor Day Arts and Crafts (Annual). **Geographic Preference:** Local.

40973 ■ Member Directory
305 N Pontiac Trl., Ste. A
Walled Lake, MI 48390
Ph: (248)624-2826
Co. E-mail: info@lakesareachamber.com
URL: http://lakesareachamber.com/#!deals
Contact: Laura Bolyard, Executive Director
E-mail: laura@lakesareachamber.com
URL(s): lakesareachamber.com/members-directory/#!directory
Availability: Online.

40974 ■ Metro Guide
4415 Byron Center Ave., SW
Wyoming, MI 49519
Ph: (616)531-5990
URL: http://www.southkent.org
Contact: Keith Morgan, President
E-mail: keithm@southkent.org
URL(s): business.southkent.org/info
Availability: PDF; Online.

40975 ■ Michigan Chamber of Commerce (MCC)
600 S Walnut St.
Lansing, MI 48933
Ph: (517)371-2100

Free: 800-748-0266
Co. E-mail: info@michamber.com
URL: http://www.michamber.com
Contact: Bob Thomas, Chief Operating Officer
E-mail: bthomas@michamber.com
Facebook: www.facebook.com/michiganchamber
Linkedin: www.linkedin.com/company/michigan
 -chamber-of-commerce
X (Twitter): x.com/michamber
Instagram: www.instagram.com/mi_chamber
Description: Works to represent employer interests in promoting economic development in Michigan. **Founded:** 1959. **Publications:** *Michigan Directory: A Listing of Michigan's Chambers of Commerce & Trade and Professional Associations* (Biennial); *Michigan Forward* (Quarterly). **Geographic Preference:** State.

40976 ■ Michigan West Coast Chamber of Commerce
272 E 8th St.
 Holland, MI 49423
Ph: (616)392-2389
Co. E-mail: info@westcoastchamber.org
URL: http://www.westcoastchamber.org
Facebook: www.facebook.com/WestCoastChamber
Linkedin: www.linkedin.com/company/michigan-wes
 t-coast-chamber-of-commerce
Instagram: www.instagram.com/miwestcoastchamber
YouTube: www.youtube.com/channel/UCkhPNbXKU
 -8IQ7Uwi7iigDw
Description: Promotes business and community development in the Holland, MI area. **Founded:** 1914. **Publications:** *Chamber Newsletter* (Weekly). **Geographic Preference:** Local.

40977 ■ Midland Area Chamber of Commerce (MACC)
300 Rodd St., Ste. 101
 Midland, MI 48640
Ph: (989)839-9522
Fax: (989)835-3701
Co. E-mail: chamber@macc.org
URL: http://mbami.org
Contact: Tony Stamas, President
E-mail: tstamas@mbami.org
Facebook: www.facebook.com/MBAMidland
Linkedin: www.linkedin.com/company/midlan
 dbusinessalliance
X (Twitter): x.com/MBAMidland
Description: Promotes, develop, and support its membership in order to foster a sustainable, prosperous business environment and a high quality, livable community. Supports the vision that Midland can be the best place to work, invest, raise a family and live, in all stages of life. **Awards:** Midland ATHENA Award (Annual); J. Kermit Campbell Award (Annual). **Geographic Preference:** Local.

40978 ■ Milan Area Chamber of Commerce
3 E Main St.
 Milan, MI 48160
Ph: (734)439-7932
Co. E-mail: info@milanchamber.org
URL: http://milanchamber.org
Contact: Carrie Ritchie, President
E-mail: carrie.ritchie@firstmerchants.com
X (Twitter): x.com/MilanMIChamber
Description: Promotes business and commerce in the Milan Area Chamber. **Geographic Preference:** Local.

40979 ■ Missaukee Area Chamber of Commerce
112 S John St.
 Lake City, MI 49651
Ph: (231)839-4969
Co. E-mail: info@missaukeechamber.com
URL: http://www.missaukeechamber.com
Contact: Scott Schryer, President
Facebook: www.facebook.com/
 MissuakeeAreaChamber
Description: Promotes commerce in the region. Sponsors events and community activities. **Publications:** *Lake City Chamber Corner* (Weekly (Fri.)). **Geographic Preference:** Local.

40980 ■ Monroe County Chamber of Commerce (SOCC) - Library
9 Washington
 Monroe, MI 48161
Ph: (734)384-3366
Fax: (734)384-3367
Co. E-mail: chamber@monroecountychamber.com
URL: http://www.monroecountychamber.com
Contact: Michelle Dugan, Executive Director
E-mail: michelle@monroecountychamber.com
Facebook: www.facebook.com/monroemichamber
X (Twitter): x.com/MonroeMIChamber
Instagram: www.instagram.com/monroemichamber
Description: Promotes business and community development in Monroe County, MI. Sponsors festival. **Scope:** Resources - information, education, recreation resources. **Services:** Open to the public. **Founded:** 1974. **Awards:** Monroe County Chamber of Commerce Small Business of the Year (Annual). **Geographic Preference:** Local.

40981 ■ Mount Pleasant Area Chamber of Commerce (MPACC)
113 W Broadway St., Ste. 180
 Mount Pleasant, MI 48858
Ph: (989)772-2396
Fax: (989)773-2656
Co. E-mail: jpierson@mt-pleasant.net
URL: http://www.mt-pleasant.net
Contact: Liz Conway, President
E-mail: lconway@mt-pleasant.net
Facebook: www.facebook.com/MtPleasantChamber
Linkedin: www.linkedin.com/company/mt-pleasan
 t-area-chamber-of-commerce
X (Twitter): x.com/MtPChamber
Description: Promotes business and community development in the Mt. Pleasant, MI area. Participates in area festivals. **Founded:** 1911. **Publications:** *Business News* (Monthly). **Educational Activities:** Business Expo. **Awards:** Mount Pleasant Area Chamber of Commerce Citizen of the Year (Annual); Mount Pleasant Area Chamber of Commerce Eagle Awards (Annual). **Geographic Preference:** Local.

40982 ■ Muskegon Lakeshore Chamber of Commerce (MLCC)
380 W W Ave., Ste. 202
 Muskegon, MI 49440
Ph: (231)722-3751
Fax: (231)728-7251
Co. E-mail: mlcc@muskegon.org
URL: http://www.muskegon.org
Contact: Gary Allore, President
Facebook: www.facebook.com/
 MuskegonLakeshoreChamber
X (Twitter): x.com/MuskegonChamber
Instagram: www.instagram.com/muskegon
 _lakeshore_chamber
Description: Promotes the business community, specifically the members. Uses combined resources to provide high quality benefits at the lowest possible price. **Publications:** *Business Directory*; *Industrial Directory*; *Muskegon Lakeshore Chamber of Commerce--Business Directory*. **Geographic Preference:** Local.

40983 ■ Newberry Area Chamber of Commerce
14150 Co Rd., 428, Ste. B
 Newberry, MI 49868
Ph: (906)293-5562
Co. E-mail: nbychamber@gmail.com
URL: http://newberrymichamber.com
Contact: Benjamin Rahilly, President
URL(s): newberryareachamber.com
Facebook: www.facebook.com/
 newberryareachamber
Description: Promotes business and community development in the Newberry, FL area. **Geographic Preference:** Local.

40984 ■ *News Capsule*
100 Main St., Ste. B
 East Jordan, MI 49727
Ph: (231)536-7351
Fax: (231)536-0966
Co. E-mail: info@ejchamber.org
URL: http://www.ejchamber.org
Contact: Mary H. Faculak, President
URL(s): ejchamber.org/chamber-information-mem
 bership-benefits/membership-benefits
Released: Weekly **Availability:** Online.

40985 ■ Northville Chamber of Commerce (NCC)
195 S Main St.
 Northville, MI 48167
Ph: (248)349-7640
Fax: (248)349-8730
Co. E-mail: douglaswallace@northville.org
URL: http://www.northville.org
Contact: Sara Thompson, Vice Chairman of the Board
X (Twitter): x.com/NorthvilleChamb
Description: Promotes business and community development in the Northville, MI area. **Founded:** 1964. **Geographic Preference:** Local.

40986 ■ Novi Chamber of Commerce (NCC)
41875 W 11 Mile Rd., Ste. 201
 Novi, MI 48375
Ph: (248)349-3743
Fax: (248)349-9719
Co. E-mail: info@novichamber.com
URL: http://www.novichamber.com
Contact: Farah Shammami, Executive Director
E-mail: farah@novichamber.com
Facebook: www.facebook.com/NoviChamber
Description: Businesses, organizations, and individuals interested in promoting business and community development in Novi, MI. Sponsors 50's Festival in July and Art festival in August. **Founded:** 1967. **Publications:** *Novi Chamber of Commerce Newsletter* (Weekly); *Novi Chamber of Commerce-- Business Directory*; *Member Business & Community Directory* (Annual). **Educational Activities:** Novi Chamber of Commerce Meeting. **Geographic Preference:** Local.

40987 ■ *Novi Chamber of Commerce Newsletter*
41875 W 11 Mile Rd., Ste. 201
 Novi, MI 48375
Ph: (248)349-3743
Fax: (248)349-9719
Co. E-mail: info@novichamber.com
URL: http://www.novichamber.com
Contact: Farah Shammami, Executive Director
E-mail: farah@novichamber.com
URL(s): novichamber.com/about-us
Released: Weekly **Availability:** Online.

40988 ■ Ontonagon County Chamber of Commerce
424 E River St.
 Ontonagon, MI 49953
Ph: (906)884-4735
Co. E-mail: ontcofc@up.net
URL: http://www.ontonagonmi.org
Contact: Richard A. Lambert, Officer
Facebook: www.facebook.com/ontonagonchamber
Description: Promotes the county and helps local businesses prosper. **Founded:** 1961. **Geographic Preference:** Local.

40989 ■ Orion Area Chamber of Commerce (OACC)
1335 Joslyn Rd., Ste. 1
 Lake Orion, MI 48360
Ph: (248)693-6300
Co. E-mail: info@orionareachamber.com
URL: http://www.orionareachamber.com
Contact: Garrett Hoffman, President
E-mail: garrett@thehoffagency.com
Facebook: www.facebook.com/
 orionareachamberofcommerce
Linkedin: www.linkedin.com/company/
 orionareachamberofcommerce
X (Twitter): x.com/OrionChamber
Instagram: www.instagram.com/orionchamber
YouTube: www.youtube.com/channel/UC7Ab2ORGg
 __Vn0l-_0bK8RA

Description: Promotes business and community development in the Lake Orion, MI area. **Founded:** 1950. **Publications:** *Chamber Report* (3/year); *Community Profile and Business Directory* (Annual). **Educational Activities:** Annual Community Business Expo (Annual); Women of the Chamber. **Awards:** OACC Education Scholarship (Annual). **Geographic Preference:** Local.

40990 ■ Oxford Area Chamber of Commerce (OACC)
22 W Burdick St.
 Oxford, MI 48371
Ph: (248)628-0410
Co. E-mail: info@oxfordchamber.net
URL: http://oxfordchamber.net
Contact: Amy Desotell, Executive Director

Description: Promotes business and community development in the Oxford, MI area. Conducts business promotions, monthly program, annual golf outing, community awards, and Christmas parade. **Founded:** 1950. **Publications:** *Oxford News* (Monthly). **Educational Activities:** General Membership Meeting. **Geographic Preference:** Local.

40991 ■ Paw Paw Area Chamber of Commerce
206 E Michigan Ave.
 Paw Paw, MI 49079
Ph: (269)657-5395
Fax: (269)655-8755
Co. E-mail: pawpawareachamber@gmail.com
URL: http://www.pawpawchamber.com
Contact: Patrick Bauschke, President
E-mail: patrick@betzlerlifestory.com
Facebook: www.facebook.com/pawpawchamber

Description: Works to promote business interests in the greater Paw area through advocacy and leadership in education, local economic, governmental and community issues. **Founded:** 1921. **Geographic Preference:** Local.

40992 ■ Pentwater Chamber of Commerce
324 S Hancock St.
 Pentwater, MI 49449
Ph: (231)869-4150
Co. E-mail: travelinfo@pentwater.org
URL: http://www.pentwater.org
Contact: Lindsay Blamer, Co-President
Facebook: www.facebook.com/pentchamber
Instagram: www.instagram.com/pentwaterchamber

Description: Promotes business and community development in Pentwater, MI area. **Geographic Preference:** Local.

40993 ■ Petoskey Regional Chamber of Commerce (PRCC)
401 E Mitchell St.
 Petoskey, MI 49770
Ph: (231)347-4150
Co. E-mail: chamber@petoskeychamber.com
URL: http://www.petoskeychamber.com
Contact: Nikki Devitt, President

Description: Promotes business, tourism, and community development in the Petoskey, MI area. **Founded:** 1920. **Publications:** *Petoskey Harbor Springs Community Profile* (Annual); *Business Directory*. **Educational Activities:** Art in the Park (Annual). **Awards:** Petoskey Regional Chamber of Commerce Mission Award (Annual); Petoskey Regional Chamber of Commerce Service Excellence Award (Annual). **Geographic Preference:** Local.

40994 ■ Pigeon Chamber of Commerce
PO Box 618
 Pigeon, MI 48755-5187
Co. E-mail: info@pigeonchamber.com
URL: http://pigeonchamber.com
Contact: Terry Brown, President
E-mail: tbrown@avci.net

Description: Promotes business and community development in Pigeon, MI area. **Founded:** 1903. **Geographic Preference:** Local.

40995 ■ Plymouth Community Chamber of Commerce
850 W Ann Arbor Trl.
 Plymouth, MI 48170
Ph: (734)453-1540
Co. E-mail: admin@plymouthmich.org
URL: http://www.plymouthmich.org
Contact: Wes Graff, President
E-mail: wes@plymouthmich.org
Facebook: www.facebook.com/PlymouthMI
X (Twitter): x.com/Plymouthmich

Description: Promotes business and community development in the Plymouth, MI area. **Founded:** 1950. **Publications:** *News Views* (Monthly). **Geographic Preference:** Local.

40996 ■ Pontiac Regional Chamber (PRC)
402 N Telegraph Rd.
 Pontiac, MI 48341
Ph: (248)335-9600
Co. E-mail: info@pontiacrc.com
URL: http://www.pontiacrc.com
Contact: Regina Campbell, President
Facebook: www.facebook.com/pontiacchamber
Linkedin: www.linkedin.com/company/pontiac-regional-chamber
YouTube: www.youtube.com/channel/UCDetJc6yvETBo_jQBXkJtqA

Description: Promotes growth and development of the business community while contributing to a safe, stable, and prosperous environment. **Founded:** 1904. **Publications:** *Inside Business* (Monthly). **Geographic Preference:** Local.

40997 ■ Redford Township Chamber of Commerce (RTCC)
26050 Five Mile Rd.
 Redford, MI 48239
Ph: (313)535-0960
Co. E-mail: info@redfordchamber.com
URL: http://redfordchamber.com
Contact: Heather Christie, President
Facebook: www.facebook.com/redford.commerce

Description: Promotes business and community development in Redford Township, MI. **Founded:** 1950. **Publications:** *Redford Township Directory* (Annual). **Geographic Preference:** Local.

40998 ■ Reed City Area Chamber of Commerce (RCACC)
200 N Chestnut St.
 Reed City, MI 49677
Ph: (231)832-5431
Co. E-mail: reedcityareachamber@gmail.com
URL: http://www.reedcitychamber.com
Contact: Katie Vincent, President
Facebook: www.facebook.com/ReedCityAreaChamberOfCommerce

Description: Helps the business, industry and tourism of Reed City Area to prosper. **Founded:** 1933. **Geographic Preference:** Local.

40999 ■ River Country Chamber of Commerce of Newaygo County
1 State Rd.
 Newaygo, MI 49337
Ph: (231)652-3068
Fax: (231)452-6512
Co. E-mail: info@rivercountrychamber.com
URL: http://www.rivercountrychamber.com
Contact: Dale Richardson, President
Facebook: www.facebook.com/RiverCountryChamber
Linkedin: www.linkedin.com/company/river-country-chamber-of-commerce-of-newaygo-county

Description: Supports the development business and community interests in the River Country Area of the state of Michigan. **Founded:** 2013. **Geographic Preference:** Local.

41000 ■ Rockford Chamber of Commerce (RCC)
17 S Monroe St.
 Rockford, MI 49341
Ph: (616)866-2000
Fax: (616)866-2141
Co. E-mail: info@rockfordmichamber.com
URL: http://www.rockfordmichamber.com
Contact: Tom Rich, President
Facebook: www.facebook.com/rockfordmichiganchamber
X (Twitter): x.com/RockfordMiCC
YouTube: www.youtube.com/channel/UCNw2TOCz7hfySRYffoKUSXA/featured

Description: Promotes business and community development in the Rockford, MI area. Sponsors annual Start of Summer Celebration and annual Harvest Festival. **Founded:** 1943. **Publications:** *UPdate* (Periodic); *How Your Chamber Works For You!* (Annual); *Rockford Living Magazine*. **Geographic Preference:** Local.

41001 ■ Rogers City Area Chamber of Commerce
292 S Bradley Hwy.
 Rogers City, MI 49779
Ph: (989)734-2535
Co. E-mail: director@rogerscityareachamber.com
URL: http://www.rogerscityareachamber.com
Contact: Christie Klein, Co-President
Facebook: www.facebook.com/RCAreaChamber

Description: Promotes and develops a vital business environment, considering the needs of the community and preserving the unique identity of the Rogers City, MI area. **Geographic Preference:** Local.

41002 ■ Royal Oak Chamber of Commerce (ROCC)
200 S Washington Ave.
 Royal Oak, MI 48067
Ph: (248)547-4000
Co. E-mail: coc@royaloakchamber.com
URL: http://www.royaloakchamber.com
Contact: Alan Kroll, President
Facebook: www.facebook.com/royaloakchamber
X (Twitter): x.com/royaloakchamber
Instagram: www.instagram.com/royaloakchamber
YouTube: www.youtube.com/user/rochamber

Description: Aims to bring business leaders, civic groups and citizens together to improve and enhance the community. **Founded:** 1936. **Geographic Preference:** Local.

41003 ■ Saginaw County Chamber of Commerce
515 N Washington Ave., 3rd Fl.
 Saginaw, MI 48607
Ph: (989)752-7161
Co. E-mail: info@saginawchamber.org
URL: http://www.saginawchamber.org
Contact: Veronica Horn, President
E-mail: veronica@saginawchamber.org
Facebook: www.facebook.com/SaginawChamber
X (Twitter): x.com/saginawcc
YouTube: www.youtube.com/user/saginawcc

Description: Manufacturers, agricultural producers, retail stores, service companies and organizations that share a common vision for the community. Strives to develop the business community in Saginaw County. **Founded:** 1863. **Publications:** *Simply Saginaw: A Guide to Living Local in Saginaw County*; *Saginaw County Chamber of Commerce Business Advocate* (Quarterly). **Awards:** Saginaw County ATHENA Award (Annual); Saginaw County Corporate Community Service Award (Annual); Marsh Princing Leadership Saginaw Alumni Award (Annual); Spirit of Saginaw Award (Irregular). **Geographic Preference:** Local.

41004 ■ *Saginaw County Chamber of Commerce Business Advocate*
515 N Washington Ave., 3rd Fl.
 Saginaw, MI 48607
Ph: (989)752-7161
Co. E-mail: info@saginawchamber.org
URL: http://www.saginawchamber.org
Contact: Veronica Horn, President
E-mail: veronica@saginawchamber.org
URL(s): www.saginawchamber.org/business-advocate.html

Released: Quarterly **Availability:** Online; PDF.

41005 ■ St. Ignace Chamber of Commerce
560 N State St.
Saint Ignace, MI 49781
Ph: (906)643-8717
Free: 800-970-8717
Fax: (906)643-9380
Co. E-mail: info@saintignace.org
URL: http://www.saintignace.org
X (Twitter): x.com/StIgnaceMich
Description: Enhances businesses by building coalitions to build pride and promote the St. Ignace area as a great place to live, work, visit, and do business. **Founded:** 1671. **Publications:** *St. Ignace: Mackinac Area's Premier Vacation Guide.* **Geographic Preference:** Local.

41006 ■ Saline Area Chamber of Commerce (SACC)
101 S Ann Arbor St. No. 301
Saline, MI 48176
Ph: (734)429-4494
Fax: (734)944-6835
Co. E-mail: office@salinechamber.org
URL: http://www.salinechamber.org
Contact: Fred Piercy, President
Facebook: www.facebook.com/SalineChamberMI
YouTube: www.youtube.com/channel/UC9Ib doskZC0rkBHIKILWohw
Description: Works to increase the community's economic progress while preserving the high quality of life that makes Saline so unique through its various community events and projects, members services and activities. **Founded:** 1980. **Publications:** *Saline Business Advocate* (Bimonthly); *Saline Chamber Business Directory & Community Profile* (Annual). **Awards:** Saline Area Chamber Business Enterprise Awards (Annual); Saline Area Chamber Citizen of the Year (Annual); George A. Anderson Vision Award (Annual); Saline Area Chamber Lifetime Achievement Award (Annual). **Geographic Preference:** Local.

41007 ■ Sault Area Chamber of Commerce [Sault Sainte Marie Chamber of Commerce]
2581 I-75 Business Spur
Sault Sainte Marie, MI 49783
Ph: (906)632-3301
Fax: (906)632-2331
Co. E-mail: office@saultstemarie.org
URL: http://saultstemarie.org
Contact: Tony Haller, Executive Director
X (Twitter): x.com/saultchamber
Instagram: www.instagram.com/saultchamber
Description: Business persons, professionals, and individuals interested in promoting business and community development in the Sault Ste. Marie, MI area. Sponsors charitable activities, festivals, and other special events. **Founded:** 1889. **Geographic Preference:** Local.

41008 ■ Schoolcraft County Chamber of Commerce (SCCC)
1000 W Lakeshore Dr.
Manistique, MI 49854
Ph: (906)341-5010
Co. E-mail: info@discovermanistique.com
URL: http://www.discovermanistique.com
Facebook: www.facebook.com/schoolcraf ttourismcommerce
Description: Promotes business and community development in Schoolcraft County, MI. **Geographic Preference:** Local.

41009 ■ Shiawassee Regional Chamber of Commerce (SRCC)
215 N Water St.
Owosso, MI 48867
Ph: (989)723-5149
Fax: (989)723-8353
Co. E-mail: customerservice@shiawasseechamber .org
URL: http://www.shiawasseechamber.org
Contact: Char Hebekeuser, Chairman
Facebook: www.facebook.com/ShiawasseeChamber
Linkedin: www.linkedin.com/company/shiawassee -regional-chamber-of-commerce
Instagram: www.instagram.com/shiawasseechamber

Description: Strives to energize the economic growth of the county through leadership actions. **Founded:** 1902. **Publications:** *Business Directory*; *Shiawassee Business Monthly* (Monthly); *Business Directory*. **Educational Activities:** Shiawassee Regional Chamber of Commerce Dinner. **Awards:** Shiawassee Regional Chamber of Commerce ATHENA Award (Annual); Shiawassee Regional Chamber of Commerce Citizen of the Year (Annual); Shiawassee Regional Chamber of Commerce Chamber Mission Award (Annual); Innovation Award (Annual). **Geographic Preference:** Regional.

41010 ■ Silver Lake Sand Dunes Area Chamber of Commerce
c/o Scott Beal, Executive Director
2388 N Comfort Dr.
Hart, MI 49420
Ph: (231)873-2247
Co. E-mail: marketing@thinkdunes.com
URL: http://thinkdunes.com
Contact: Scott Beal, Executive Director
E-mail: director@thinkdunes.com
Facebook: www.facebook.com/ThinkDunes
X (Twitter): x.com/thinkdunes
Instagram: www.instagram.com/thinkdunes
YouTube: www.youtube.com/user/ThinkDunes
Description: Progressive business people and citizens. Strives to promote the business community and to improve the general welfare and development of Hart, Mears and Silver Lake areas. **Geographic Preference:** Local.

41011 ■ South Haven Area Chamber of Commerce (GSHACC)
606 Phillips St.
South Haven, MI 49090
Ph: (269)637-5171
Fax: (269)639-1570
Co. E-mail: cofc@southhavenmi.com
URL: http://www.southhavenmi.com
Contact: Kathy Wagaman, Director
E-mail: director@southhavenmi.com
Facebook: www.facebook.com/Sou thHavenMIChamberofCommerce
Description: Retail, commercial, industrial, and professional organizations in the South Haven, MI area organized to promote economic and community development. Holds board meetings, luncheons, and annual dinner. **Founded:** 1932. **Publications:** *Chamber Connection* (Weekly). **Geographic Preference:** Local.

41012 ■ Southern Wayne County Regional Chamber (SWCRC)
20904 Northline Rd.
Taylor, MI 48180-4719
Ph: (734)284-6000
Fax: (734)284-0198
URL: http://www.swcrc.com
Contact: Jeffrey Chicoine, II, Chairman of the Board
Facebook: www.facebook.com/SWCRC
Linkedin: www.linkedin.com/company/swcrc
X (Twitter): x.com/swcrc
YouTube: www.youtube.com/user/swcrc
Description: Promotes business and community development in southern Wayne County, MI. Conducts business seminars and legislative forums. Maintains numerous committees. **Founded:** 1966. **Publications:** *Buyer's Guide* (Annual); *Business Connection* (Monthly); *Membership Roster* (Annual); *Business Connection* (Monthly). **Geographic Preference:** Local.

41013 ■ Southfield Area Chamber of Commerce (SACC)
20300 Civic Center Dr., Ste. 1102
Southfield, MI 48076
Ph: (248)557-6661
Co. E-mail: info@southfieldchamber.com
URL: http://www.southfieldchamber.com
Contact: Jasmine Patton, Executive Director
Facebook: www.facebook.com/southfieldchamber
Linkedin: www.linkedin.com/company/southfield-area -chamber-of-commerce
X (Twitter): x.com/SouthfieldCC
Instagram: www.instagram.com/southfieldchamber

Description: Promotes business and community development in the Southfield, MI area. **Founded:** 1953. **Geographic Preference:** Local.

41014 ■ Southwest Michigan First
180 E Water St., Ste. 2690
Kalamazoo, MI 49007
Ph: (269)553-9588
Co. E-mail: tdunham@southwestmichiganfirst.com
URL: http://www.southwestmichiganfirst.com
Contact: Carla Sones, President
E-mail: csones@southwestmichiganfirst.com
Facebook: www.facebook.com/southwestmichiganfirs t
Linkedin: www.linkedin.com/company/southwes t-michigan-first
X (Twitter): x.com/swmfirst
Instagram: www.instagram.com/swmichiganfirst
YouTube: www.youtube.com/user/SWMichiganFirst
Description: Promotes business and community development in Kalamazoo County, MI. Conducts community affairs. **Founded:** 1999. **Publications:** *Kalamazoo County Connection* (Annual); *Enterprise* (Monthly). **Educational Activities:** Business Expo. **Geographic Preference:** Local.

41015 ■ Sterling Heights Regional Chamber of Commerce & Industry
12900 Hall Rd., Ste. 100
Sterling Heights, MI 48313
Ph: (586)731-5400
Co. E-mail: chamberinfo@shrcci.com
URL: http://shrcci.com
Contact: Stacy Ziarko, President
E-mail: sziarko@shrcci.com
Facebook: www.facebook.com/shrcci
X (Twitter): x.com/SHRCCI
YouTube: www.youtube.com/user/shrcci1
Description: Promotes business and community development in Macomb County, Michigan. **Founded:** 1961. **Publications:** *Community Directory* (Annual); *Impact*. **Educational Activities:** Business Expo; Sterling Heights Area Chamber of Commerce Seminar. **Geographic Preference:** Local.

41016 ■ Sturgis Area Chamber of Commerce (SACC)
306 W Chicago Rd.
Sturgis, MI 49091
Ph: (269)651-5758
Co. E-mail: info@sturgischamber.com
URL: http://www.sturgischamber.com
Contact: Matt Scheske, President
Facebook: www.facebook.com/sturgischamber
X (Twitter): x.com/Sturgis_chamber
Instagram: www.instagram.com/sturgis_area _chamberofcommerce
Description: Promotes business and community development in Sturgis, MI. Sponsors Michigan Week Festival and 4th of July celebration. Also sponsors the Sturgis area Business/Education Alliance. **Founded:** 1941. **Publications:** *Chamber Calling* (Monthly). **Geographic Preference:** Local.

41017 ■ Suttons Bay Chamber of Commerce (SBCC)
101 Dame St.
Suttons Bay, MI 49682
URL: http://www.suttonsbayarea.com
Contact: Amy Peterson, President
Facebook: www.facebook.com/su ttonsbaymichamberofcommerce
Instagram: www.instagram.com/su ttonsbaymichamberofcommerce
Description: Represents the interests of business and organizations in Suttons Bay. **Geographic Preference:** Local.

41018 ■ Tawas Area Chamber of Commerce
228 Newman St.
East Tawas, MI 48730
Ph: (989)362-8643
Co. E-mail: info@tawas.com
URL: http://tawas.com
Contact: Ryan Ladley, President

Description: Strives to promote a healthy business climate and build a strong community. **Publications:** *Executive Report* (Monthly). **Geographic Preference:** Local.

41019 ■ Three Rivers Area Chamber of Commerce
1116 N Main St.
Three Rivers, MI 49093
Ph: (269)278-8193
Fax: (269)273-1751
Co. E-mail: info@trchamber.com
URL: http://trchamber.com
Contact: Christy Trammell, President
E-mail: christytrammell@trchamber.com
Facebook: www.facebook.com/TRareaChamber
Description: Works to improve business community and industrial opportunity to enhance the quality of life in the Three River area. **Founded:** 1945. **Publications:** *Chamber News* (Weekly). **Geographic Preference:** Local.

41020 ■ Traverse Connect
202 E Grandview Pky.
Traverse City, MI 49684
Ph: (231)947-5075
Co. E-mail: info@traverseconnect.com
URL: http://traverseconnect.com
Contact: Warren Call, President
E-mail: warren.call@traverseconnect.com
Facebook: www.facebook.com/traverseconnect
Linkedin: www.linkedin.com/company/traverse-connect
Instagram: www.instagram.com/traverseconnect
Description: Strives to develop business community by creating collaborations with community vital partners. **Founded:** 1915. **Publications:** *Traverse Connect News* (Weekly). **Geographic Preference:** Local.

41021 ■ *Traverse Connect News*
202 E Grandview Pky.
Traverse City, MI 49684
Ph: (231)947-5075
Co. E-mail: info@traverseconnect.com
URL: http://traverseconnect.com
Contact: Warren Call, President
E-mail: warren.call@traverseconnect.com
URL(s): traverseconnect.com/about/news
Released: Weekly **Description:** Contains information about chamber activities and programs and health care legislative issues. **Availability:** Online.

41022 ■ Troy Chamber of Commerce
2125 Butterfield, Ste. 100N
Troy, MI 48084
Ph: (248)641-8151
Fax: (248)641-0545
Co. E-mail: theteam@troychamber.com
URL: http://troychamber.com
Contact: Tara Tomcsik-Husak, President
E-mail: tara@troychamber.com
Facebook: www.facebook.com/troychamber
X (Twitter): x.com/TroyChamberMI
Instagram: www.instagram.com/troychamberMI
YouTube: www.youtube.com/user/TroyChamber
Description: Promotes business and community development in Troy, MI. **Founded:** 1959. **Geographic Preference:** Local.

41023 ■ *UPdate*
17 S Monroe St.
Rockford, MI 49341
Ph: (616)866-2000
Fax: (616)866-2141
Co. E-mail: info@rockfordmichamber.com
URL: http://www.rockfordmichamber.com
Contact: Tom Rich, President
URL(s): business.rockfordchamber.com/event-calendar/Details/the-update-1109837?sourceTypeId=Website
Released: Periodic **Availability:** Online.

41024 ■ *Visitors Guide*
118 E Main St.
Harbor Springs, MI 49740
Ph: (231)526-7999

Co. E-mail: info@harborspringschamber.com
URL: http://www.harborspringschamber.com
Contact: Kathie Breighner, President
URL(s): www.harborspringschamber.com/marketing-opportunities
Released: Annual **Availability:** Print; PDF; Online.

41025 ■ Wakefield Chamber of Commerce
PO Box 93
Wakefield, MI 49968
Ph: (906)224-2222
Co. E-mail: support@wakefieldmi.org
URL: http://www.wakefieldmi.org
Description: Promotes business and community development in the area. **Founded:** 1934. **Geographic Preference:** Local.

41026 ■ Waterford Area Chamber of Commerce (WACC)
2309 Airport Rd.
Waterford, MI 48327
Ph: (248)666-8600
Fax: (248)666-3325
Co. E-mail: info@waterfordchamber.org
URL: http://waterfordchamber.org
Contact: Renee Doyle, President
E-mail: rdoyle@michiganunitedcu.org
Facebook: www.facebook.com/WaterfordChamberMI
Linkedin: www.linkedin.com/company/waccchambermi
Instagram: www.instagram.com/waccchambermi
Description: Strives to promote business, tourism and community of the Waterford area through services and representation of the business community. **Founded:** 1998. **Publications:** *Business to Business* (Quarterly). **Geographic Preference:** Local.

41027 ■ Wayne Chamber of Commerce (WCC)
34844 W Michigan Ave., Ste. 1
Wayne, MI 48184
Ph: (734)721-0100
Co. E-mail: info@waynechamber.org
URL: http://www.waynechamber.org
Facebook: www.facebook.com/waynechamber
X (Twitter): x.com/CommerceWayne
Instagram: www.instagram.com/waynechamberofcommerce
Description: Promotes business and community development in Wayne, MI. **Founded:** 1938. **Geographic Preference:** Local.

41028 ■ West Branch Area Chamber of Commerce (WBACC)
422 W Houghton Ave.
West Branch, MI 48661-1224
Ph: (989)345-2821
Fax: (989)345-9075
URL: http://www.wbacc.com
Contact: Heather Neuhaus, Executive Director
Facebook: www.facebook.com/WestBranchAreaChamberofCommerce
Description: Promotes business and community development in West Branch, MI. Sponsors festivals. **Founded:** 1948. **Geographic Preference:** Local.

41029 ■ Westland Chamber of Commerce
36900 Ford Rd.
Westland, MI 48185
Contact: Kiersten Beckwith, President
Description: Promotes business and community development in Westland, MI. **Founded:** 1962. **Publications:** *Commerce Commentary* (Monthly). **Geographic Preference:** Local.

41030 ■ White Lake Area Chamber of Commerce
124 Hanson St.
Whitehall, MI 49461
Ph: (231)893-4585
Free: 800-879-9702
Fax: (231)893-0914
Co. E-mail: info@whitelake.org
URL: http://www.whitelake.org
Contact: Amy VanLoon, Executive Director
E-mail: avanloon@whitelake.org

Facebook: www.facebook.com/whitelakeareachamberofcommerce
Description: Promotes business and community development in Muskegon County, MI. Sponsors festival. **Founded:** 1971. **Publications:** *On Track*. **Educational Activities:** Membership Meeting. **Awards:** White Lake Area Chamber of Commerce El Award (Annual). **Geographic Preference:** Local.

41031 ■ Williamston Area Chamber of Commerce
369 W Grand River Ave.
Williamston, MI 48895
Contact: Brooke Locke, President
Description: Promotes business and community development in Williamston, MI area. **Geographic Preference:** Local.

41032 ■ Wyoming Kentwood Area Chamber of Commerce (WKACC)
4415 Byron Center Ave., SW
Wyoming, MI 49519
Ph: (616)531-5990
URL: http://www.southkent.org
Contact: Keith Morgan, President
E-mail: keithm@southkent.org
Facebook: www.facebook.com/wyomingkentwoodchamber
Instagram: www.instagram.com/wyomingkentwoodchamber
Description: Promotes business and community development in Wyoming, MI. **Founded:** 1980. **Publications:** *Delaware Area Chamber of Commerce Business Directory*; *Metro Guide*; *My Business Advocate* (Monthly). **Awards:** Wyoming Kentwood Area Chamber of Commerce Business of the Year (Annual). **Geographic Preference:** Local.

MINORITY BUSINESS ASSISTANCE PROGRAMS

41033 ■ Grand Valley State University - The Michigan Small Business Development Center (SBDC)
50 Front Ave., SW
Grand Rapids, MI 49504
Ph: (231)929-5060
Co. E-mail: sbdcmichigan@gvsu.edu
URL: http://michigansbdc.org
Contact: J. D. Collins, Executive Director
E-mail: colljaso@gvsu.edu
Facebook: www.facebook.com/MichiganSBDC
Linkedin: www.linkedin.com/company/michigan-sbdc
X (Twitter): x.com/MichiganSBDC
Instagram: www.instagram.com/michigansbdc
YouTube: www.youtube.com/channel/UCFFAuIAXZFvRBHrQpuiLCCA
Description: Provides a full-range of services for a variety of small businesses including: counseling; training; programs for a variety of needs, from how to get started, to financing; effective selling and e-commerce as well as how to develop business plans. Also provides research help and advocacy. **Scope:** Manufacturing, financing, and international business information (particularly the export process) for small businesses. Resources for the export process includes determining and detailing international feasibility, foreign market entry plans, and responding to international inquiries. **Founded:** 1983. **Publications:** *Changing the Face of the American Economy--A Resource Guide for the Michigan Woman Business Owner* (Biennial).

41034 ■ Michigan Economic Development Corp. (MEDC) - Reference Library
300 N Washington Sq.
Lansing, MI 48913
Ph: (517)241-1400
Free: 888-522-0103
URL: http://www.michiganbusiness.org
Contact: Quentin L. Messer, President
Facebook: www.facebook.com/MEDC
Linkedin: www.linkedin.com/company/medc
X (Twitter): x.com/MEDC
YouTube: www.youtube.com/user/MIAdvantage

STATE LISTINGS   Michigan ■ 41052

Description: Advocate for businesses in Michigan that have a conflict with state agencies or that need assistance in getting attention from state agencies. **Scope:** Economics. **Founded:** 1999. **Holdings:** Figures not available. **Publications:** *Michigan Exporters of Wood Products* (Irregular); *Michigan Occupational Information System (MOIS)*; *Michigan Site Network*; *Michigan Manufacturing Technology Export Directory*. **Geographic Preference:** State.

41035 ■ Michigan Economic Development Corp. - Office of Women Business Owners Services
300 N Washington Sq.
 Lansing, MI 48913
Free: 888-522-0103
URL: http://www.michigan.org
Contact: Quentin L. Messer, President
Facebook: www.facebook.com/MEDC
X (Twitter): x.com/MEDC
Instagram: www.instagram.com/michiganbusiness
YouTube: www.youtube.com/user/MIAdvantage
Description: Provides advocacy, technical assistance, and references to outside sources for financial counseling for women entrepreneurs. **Founded:** 1997.

41036 ■ Michigan Minority Supplier Development Council (MMSDC)
100 River Pl., Ste. 300
 Detroit, MI 48207
Ph: (313)873-3200
Fax: (313)873-4783
Co. E-mail: info@minoritysupplier.org
URL: http://minoritysupplier.org
Contact: Michelle Sourie Robinson, President
Facebook: www.facebook.com/MichiganMSDC
Linkedin: www.linkedin.com/company/michiganmsdc
X (Twitter): x.com/MichiganMSDC
Instagram: www.instagram.com/michiganmsdc
YouTube: www.youtube.com/channel/UCsROixorgkNCFMqNI03pLAQ
Description: Aims to foster economic growth within minority communities in Michigan by facilitating business contracts between corporations and certified minority business enterprises (MBEs). **Founded:** 1977.

FINANCING AND LOAN PROGRAMS

41037 ■ Ann Arbor Angels (A2A)
201 S Division St., Ste. 430
 Ann Arbor, MI 48104
Co. E-mail: info@annarborangels.org
URL: http://www.annarborangels.org
Contact: Douglas Finch, President
Description: Angel investors for early-stage innovation-base companies primarily in Southeast Michigan. **Investment Policies:** Potential for apid growth in large markets; revenue potential of $50 million or more; compelling strategy for a significant market share; exit strategy.

41038 ■ Arbor Partners L.L.C.
130 S First St.
 Ann Arbor, MI 48104
Ph: (734)668-9000
Fax: (734)669-4195
Co. E-mail: info@arborpartners.com
URL: http://www.arborpartners.com
Contact: Joshua Beebe, Partner
Description: The company provides investment opportunities in companies in the enterprise software, semiconductors, and advanced materials industries. **Founded:** 1996.

41039 ■ Arboretum Ventures
303 Detroit St., Ste. 301
 Ann Arbor, MI 48104
Ph: (734)998-3688
Co. E-mail: info@arboretumvc.com
URL: http://www.arboretumvc.com
Contact: Amanda Elder, Vice President, Finance
E-mail: aelder@arboretumvc.com
X (Twitter): x.com/ArboretumVC

Description: Provider of venture capital and private equity investment services for healthcare sector. **Founded:** 2002. **Preferred Investment Size:** $1,000,000 to $3,000,000. **Investment Policies:** Seed, early and later stage. **Industry Preferences:** Biotechnology, medical and health.

41040 ■ Belle Capital
PO Box 162
 Douglas, MI 49406
URL: http://www.bellevc.com
Contact: Lauren Flanagan, Managing Director
Description: Early-stage fund investing in high-growth companies in underserved markets, particularly those that are women-owned. **Investment Policies:** At least one female founder of C-level executive and/or be willing to recruit top female talent to the C-suite and Board of Directors. Prefers strong domain expertise, proven commercialization, and entrepreneurial experience. **Industry Preferences:** Digital/mobile/internet; technology-enabled products and services; life sciences/medical devices/digital health; CleanTech.

41041 ■ Belle Impact Fund, LP
217 Lake Shore Rd.
 Grosse Pointe Farms, MI 48236
URL: http://www.bellefunds.com
Contact: Carolyn Cassin, Co-Founder Partner
Description: Invests in early-stage, women-led startups while generating superior returns for investors.

41042 ■ BioStar Capital
206 Bridge St.
 Charlevoix, MI 49720
Ph: (231)437-7622
Co. E-mail: info@biostar.capital
URL: http://www.biostarcapital.com
Contact: Jeremy Touroo, Director
Description: Healthcare investment firm for medical device technologies in cardiovascular and orthopedic medicine. **Founded:** 2003. **Investment Policies:** Seeks medical technology companies that can offer improved quality of life or cost-effectively fill medical needs with clear regulatory pathways and defined reimbursement strategies that are also of interest to large medical companies. **Industry Preferences:** Medical device technologies .

41043 ■ Birmingham Angels
34300 Woodward Ave., Ste. 200
 Birmingham, MI 48009
URL: http://citysideventures.com/birmingham-angels
Contact: Alayna D. Langnas, Bookkeeper
Description: Angel investor group for tech-based early-stage investments.

41044 ■ Cityside Ventures (CSV)
34300 Woodward Ave., Ste. 200
 Birmingham, MI 48009
Ph: (248)605-2028
Co. E-mail: info@citysideventures.com
URL: http://citysideventures.com
Contact: David P. Weaver, President
E-mail: dweaver@citysideventures.com
Facebook: www.facebook.com/citysidevc
Linkedin: www.linkedin.com/company/city-side-ventures
X (Twitter): x.com/CitySideVP
Description: Identifies and funds scalable tech companies at various stages. **Founded:** 2015.

41045 ■ eLab Ventures
206 E Huron St., Ste. 108
 Ann Arbor, MI 48104
Ph: (734)926-5221
Co. E-mail: info@elabvc.com
URL: http://elabvc.com
Contact: Bob Stefanski, Managing Director
Linkedin: www.linkedin.com/company/michigan-elab
X (Twitter): x.com/elabventures
Description: Invests in disruptive technology for autonomous and connected vehicles. Also based in Silicon Valley.

41046 ■ Fontinalis Partners (FP)
1 Woodward Ave., Ste. 1600
 Detroit, MI 48226
Co. E-mail: info@fontinalis.com
URL: http://fontinalis.com
Contact: Laura Petterle, Chief Financial Officer Managing Partner
Linkedin: www.linkedin.com/company/fontinalis-partners-llc
X (Twitter): x.com/fontinalis_fp
Description: Invests exclusively in technology companies that can significantly improve mobility. Also operates out of Boston and San Francisco. **Founded:** 2009. **Industry Preferences:** Advnced mapping; autonomous vehicles; connected vehicles; data and analytics; intelligent infrastructure solutions; location-based services; mobility transactions; smart logistics.

41047 ■ Great Lakes Angels
34300 Woodward Ave., Ste. 200
 Birmingham, MI 48009
Ph: (248)605-2028
Co. E-mail: info@citysideventures.com
URL: http://citysideventures.com/glaf
Contact: Doron York, Chief Executive Officer
E-mail: dyork@citysideventures.com
Linkedin: www.linkedin.com/company/city-side-ventures
X (Twitter): x.com/CitySideVP
Description: Early-stage venture fund for tech-based companies in Michigan. **Founded:** 2015. **Investment Policies:** For-profit entity; fully developed business plan; developed or final stage proof of concept.

41048 ■ Huron River Ventures (HRV)
303 Detroit St., Ste. 105
 Ann Arbor, MI 48104
URL: http://www.huronrivervc.com
Contact: Ryan Waddington, Partner
X (Twitter): x.com/HuronRiverVC
Description: Early-stage venture capital firm. **Founded:** 1976. **Investment Policies:** Disruptors of large markets; customer focused; primarily Midwest-based. **Industry Preferences:** Agriculture; energy; healthcare IT; manufacturing; mobility.

41049 ■ Invest Michigan
235 E Main St., Ste. 105B
 Northville, MI 48167
Co. E-mail: info@investmichigan.org
URL: http://investmichigan.org
Contact: Charlie Moret, President
Description: Invests in early-stage companies for commercializing technology products/services headquartered in Michigan. **Founded:** 2014. **Preferred Investment Size:** $1,000,000. **Investment Policies:** Business, technical, and domain experience; innovative technology; financing plan with 12-18 months of runway. **Industry Preferences:** Manufacturing; life sciences; information technology; advanced manufacturing materials.

41050 ■ Michigan Accelerator Fund 1 (MAF-1)
140 Monroe Ctr. NW, Ste. 300
 Grand Rapids, MI 49503
Ph: (616)235-3555
Co. E-mail: charter@chartercapitalpartners.com
URL: http://www.chartercapitalpartners.com
Contact: John Kerschen, President
E-mail: jkerschen@chartercapitalpartners.com
Description: Invests in high-growth Michigan-based companies.

41051 ■ Michigan Angel Fund (MAF)
Ann Arbor, MI
URL: http://www.miangelfund.com
Contact: Joseph Simms, Managing Partner
Description: Funds capital-efficient early-stage companies in Michigan. **Preferred Investment Size:** $250,000 to $2,000,000. **Industry Preferences:** IT; cleantech; advance manufacturing; life science.

41052 ■ Michigan Venture Fund (VMF)
Detroit, MI
Co. E-mail: venturemichiganfund@gcmlp.com

Small Business Sourcebook • 42nd Edition   2715

41053 ■ Michigan

URL: http://www.venturemichiganfund.com
Description: Venture capital fund for Michigan-based early-stage companies.

41053 ■ North Coast Technology Investors
206 S Fifth Ave., Ste. 250
Ann Arbor, MI 48104
Ph: (734)662-7667
URL: http://www.northcoastvc.com
Contact: Hugo Braun, Co-Founder
Description: Early stage venture capital firm for technology-driven companies in the Midwest US.

41054 ■ Northern Michigan Angels (NMA)
PO Box 1622
Traverse City, MI 49684
URL: http://northernmichiganangels.com
Contact: Jody Trietch, Executive Director
Linkedin: www.linkedin.com/company/northern-michigan-angels
Description: Invests in scalable early-stage companies. Founded: 2012.

41055 ■ Plymouth Growth Partners
555 Briarwood Cir., Ste. 210
Ann Arbor, MI 48108
Ph: (734)747-9401
URL: http://plymouthgp.com
Contact: Chris Frick, Chief Financial Officer
Linkedin: www.linkedin.com/company/plymouth-growth
X (Twitter): x.com/plymouthgp
Description: Invests in growth stage companies with scalable technology in the Great Lakes region. Founded: 2002. Industry Preferences: B2B products and services.

41056 ■ RPM Ventures (RPM)
320 N Main St., Ste. 400
Ann Arbor, MI 48104
Ph: (734)332-1700
Co. E-mail: info@rpmvc.com
URL: http://www.rpmvc.com
Contact: Adam Boyden, Managing Director
Linkedin: www.linkedin.com/company/rpm-ventures
X (Twitter): x.com/rpmvc
Description: Early-stage venture capital firm investing in B2B and B2B2C technology companies. Founded: 2000. Investment Policies: Large, growing market with complex problems; exceptional entrepreneurial teams; industry-changing vision. Industry Preferences: Mobility; automotive; enterprise software; financial services; insurance; real estate.

41057 ■ Sargon Partners Inc.
8230 Goldie St.
Walled Lake, MI 48390
Ph: (248)363-3257
Fax: (248)363-3257
URL: http://sargonpartners.com
Contact: Jeff Golota, Chief Executive Officer
Facebook: www.facebook.com/SargonPartnersInc
Description: Seed- and early-stage venture capital firm. Industry Preferences: Mobile application software; clean technology; community-building software; asset utilization; environmental solutions.

41058 ■ TGap Ventures LLC
7171 Stadium Dr.
Kalamazoo, MI 49009
URL: http://tgapvcfunds.com
Contact: Jack K. Ahrens, II, Partner
E-mail: jahrens620@aol.com
Description: Early-stage venture capital firm. Founded: 1979.

PROCUREMENT ASSISTANCE PROGRAMS

41059 ■ Economic Development Alliance of St. Clair County
100 McMorran Blvd., 4th Fl., Executive, Ste. B
Port Huron, MI 48060
Ph: (810)982-9511
URL: http://edascc.com
Contact: Dan Casey, Chief Executive Officer
E-mail: dcasey@edascc.com
Facebook: www.facebook.com/EDASCC
Linkedin: www.linkedin.com/in/edascc
X (Twitter): x.com/eda_scc
Instagram: www.instagram.com/edaofstclaircounty
YouTube: www.youtube.com/channel/UCPm57 4YIkIfRhKxQH5Rk2BQ
Description: Provides businesses with marketing know-how and technical tools they need to obtain and perform successfully under federal, state and local government contracts. Founded: 1952. Geographic Preference: Local.

41060 ■ Genesee County Metropolitan Planning Commission (GCMPC)
1101 Beach St., Rm. 111
Flint, MI 48502-1470
Ph: (810)257-3010
Fax: (810)257-3185
Co. E-mail: gcmpc@geneseecountymi.gov
URL: http://gcmpc.org
Contact: Derek Bradshaw, Director
E-mail: dbradshaw@geneseecountymi.gov
Facebook: www.facebook.com/GCPlanning
X (Twitter): x.com/gcplanning

41061 ■ Macomb Regional Procurement Technical Assistance Center (PTAC)
Macomb Community College MTEC Bldg.
7900 Tank Ave.
Warren, MI 48092-3936
Ph: (586)498-4122
Co. E-mail: ptac@macomb.edu
URL: http://www.macomb.edu/business/PTAC/index.html
Description: Provides businesses with marketing know-how and technical tools they need to obtain and perform successfully under federal, state and local government contracts.

41062 ■ Michigan Procurement Technical Assistance Center (PTAC)
222 S Westnedge Ave.
Kalamazoo, MI 49007-3737
URL: http://www.ptacsofmichigan.org
Description: Assists businesses in their growth and development.

41063 ■ Michigan Procurement Technical Assistance Center (BDC) - Business Development Center
18600 Haggerty Rd.
Livonia, MI 48152
Ph: (734)462-4438
Fax: (734)462-4673
Co. E-mail: bdc@schoolcraft.edu
URL: http://www.schoolcraft.edu/bdc
Description: Provides businesses with marketing know-how and technical tools they need to obtain and perform successfully under federal, state and local government contracts. Founded: 1963.

41064 ■ Michigan Procurement Technical Assistance Center (DCC) - Downriver Community Conference
15100 Northline Rd., Ste. 101
Southgate, MI 48195
Ph: (734)362-7070
Fax: (734)281-0265
Co. E-mail: helpdesk@dccwf.org
URL: http://dccwf.org
Contact: Jim Perry, Executive Director
E-mail: jim.perry@dccwf.org
Description: Provides businesses with marketing know-how and technical tools they need to obtain and perform successfully under federal, state and local government contracts.

41065 ■ Michigan Procurement Technical Assistance Center (NMC) - Northeast Michigan Consortium
20709 State St.
Onaway, MI 49765
Ph: (989)733-8540
URL: http://www.aptac-us.org/find-a-ptac/?state=MI
Contact: Tamara Moore, Program Manager
E-mail: mooret@nemcworks.org
Description: Offers services including job training, welfare reform, employment service (including America's Talent Bank/Job Bank automated resume system), TAA/NAFTA programs, assistance in securing federal and state procurement contracts and a variety of youth programs.

41066 ■ Michigan Procurement Technical Assistance Center of Saginaw Future Satellite Office
515 N Washington Ave., 3rd Fl.
Saginaw, MI 48607
Ph: (989)754-8222
Co. E-mail: info@saginawfuture.com
URL: http://www.saginawfuture.com
Contact: Joann Crary, President
E-mail: jcrary@saginawfuture.com
Facebook: www.facebook.com/SaginawFuture
X (Twitter): x.com/saginawfuture
Instagram: www.instagram.com/saginawfuture
YouTube: www.youtube.com/user/MarketingSaginaw
Description: Private, non-profit one stop economic development agency helps accomplish business moves and provide a wide array of business services to existing businesses in Saginaw County. Founded: 1992.

41067 ■ Michigan Procurement Technical Assistance Center - West Central Michigan Employment & Training Consortium
14330 Northland Dr.
Big Rapids, MI 49307
Ph: (231)796-0049
URL: http://mwwc.org
Contact: Deborah Smith-Olson, President
Facebook: www.facebook.com/MichiganWorksWestCentral
Linkedin: www.linkedin.com/company/michiganworkswestcentral
X (Twitter): x.com/MiWorksWestCent
Instagram: www.instagram.com/michworkswestcentral
YouTube: www.youtube.com/channel/UCTYeQ87fbbWjwgbKF65_60Q
Description: Provides businesses with marketing know-how and technical tools they need to obtain and perform successfully under federal, state and local government contracts. Founded: 2014.

41068 ■ Procurement Technical Assistance Center of Schoolcraft College (PTAC)
18600 Haggerty Rd.
Livonia, MI 48152
Ph: (734)462-4400
Co. E-mail: ptac@schoolcraft.edu
URL: http://www.schoolcraft.edu
Contact: Dr. Glenn Cerny, President
Facebook: www.facebook.com/SchoolcraftCollege
Linkedin: www.linkedin.com/school/schoolcraft-college
X (Twitter): x.com/schoolcraftnow
Instagram: www.instagram.com/schoolcraftnow
YouTube: www.youtube.com/user/SchoolcraftCollege
Description: Help to locate bidding opportunities for companies and explore what it takes to sell their products and services to the government. Founded: 1961.

41069 ■ Procurement Technical Assistance Center of South Central Michigan - The Enterprise Group of Jackson
100 E Michigan Ave., Ste. 1100
Jackson, MI 49201
Ph: (517)788-4455
Fax: (517)788-4455
Co. E-mail: info@enterprisegroup.com
URL: http://enterprisegroup.org
Contact: Tim Rogers, President
E-mail: trogers@enterprisegroup.org
Facebook: www.facebook.com/theenterprisegroupofjackson
Linkedin: www.linkedin.com/company/the-enterprise-group-of-jackson-inc-
X (Twitter): x.com/jacksoneg

STATE LISTINGS   Michigan ■ 41084

Description: Enhances national defense and economic development of the State of Michigan by assisting Michigan businesses in obtaining and performing on federal, state and local government contracts. **Founded:** 1997.

41070 ■ West Michigan APEX Accelerator (MAFPTAC)
380 W Western, Ste. 202
 Muskegon, MI 49440
Ph: (231)722-7700
URL: http://www.ptacregion3.org
Contact: Kelsey Rhoda, Director
E-mail: krhoda@westmiapex.org
Linkedin: www.linkedin.com/company/muskegon-area-first-ptac
X (Twitter): x.com/MAF_PTAC

Description: Provides businesses with marketing know-how and technical tools they need to obtain and perform successfully under federal, state and local government contracts. **Founded:** 1999.

41071 ■ Western Michigan University - Haworth College of Business
Western Michigan University
 1903 W Michigan Ave.
 Kalamazoo, MI 49008-5457
Ph: (269)387-5050
Fax: (269)387-5710
URL: http://wmich.edu/business
Contact: Stacey Anderson, Director, Marketing Director, Communications
Facebook: www.facebook.com/hcobwmu
Linkedin: www.linkedin.com/school/western-michigan-university---haworth-college-of-b
X (Twitter): x.com/HCOB
Instagram: www.instagram.com/hcobwmu
YouTube: www.youtube.com/hcobwmu

INCUBATORS/RESEARCH AND TECHNOLOGY PARKS

41072 ■ Albion Economic Development Corp.
1002 N Eaton St.
 Albion, MI 49224-0725
Ph: (517)629-3926
URL: http://www.albionedc.org
Contact: Amy Deprez, President
E-mail: adeprez@albionedc.org

Description: Works to improve the economic health of the Albion area. Offers an incubator for new businesses with access to equipment and advice. **Geographic Preference:** Local.

41073 ■ Allen Market Place (AMP)
1611 E Kalamazoo St.
 Lansing, MI 48912
URL: http://allenneighborhoodcenter.org/rentals
Contact: Matt Jones, Contact

Description: Incubator kitchen providing assistance to entrepreneurs to develop successful, micro-businesses that are able to produce high quality, marketable food products through training, marketing, and financial management.

41074 ■ Altarum Institute
Altarum Institute
 26200 Town Center Dr., Ste., 350
 Novi, MI 48375
Ph: (734)302-4600
Free: 800-879-6505
Fax: (734)302-4991
Co. E-mail: recruiting@altarum.org
URL: http://altarum.org
Contact: Michael Monson, President
E-mail: michael.monson@altarum.org
Facebook: www.facebook.com/altarum
Linkedin: www.linkedin.com/company/altarum
X (Twitter): x.com/altarum

Description: Research and development facility emphasizing electronics, computer sciences, and optics and their applications. Provides analytical and experimental investigations and technical assistance. **Scope:** Services: Research on healthcare and hospice. **Founded:** 1946. **Publications:** "The Role of Partnerships in Community Intervention Programs:

New Insights from Case Studies"; "Issue Briefs: "What Works in Health Care"; "Strategic Innovations for Affordable, Sustainable Health Care: A Model for Health System Reform"; "Accountable care organizations"; "Disease management"; "Electronic medical records"; "Medical tourism"; "Patient centered medical homes Patient centered medical homes"; "Payment models"; "Performance measurement and health care quality"; "WIC and Obesity Policy Round table Presentations," Mar, 2010; "Learning From State Surveillance Of Childhood Obesity," Mar, 2010; "Access to Oral Health Care During the Prenatal Period," Aug, 2008; "Home Health Care during an Influenza Pandemic: Issues and Resources," Jul, 2008; "An Assessment of the Impact of Medicaid Managed Care on WIC Program Coordination With Primary Care Services," Sep, 2007; "Evaluation to Determine the Effectiveness of the Public Assistance Reporting and Information System," Jun, 2007; Child Health USA 2006," Jul, 2007; Diet-Specific Social Support among rural adolescents," Jun, 2007. **Training:** Impact on WIC Participants, Feb, 2011; Impact on WIC Vendors and the Food Environment, Feb, 2011; Special Topics, Feb, 2011; Highlights and Updates on Ongoing WIC Food Package Evaluations, Feb, 2011; Can WIC Play a Role In Stemming the Childhood Obesity Epidemic, Mar, 2010; Altarum policy round table on state approaches to covering the uninsured, Jun, 2006; Medical aspects of disaster management conference.

41075 ■ Ann Arbor SPARK Business Accelerator
330 E Liberty
 Ann Arbor, MI 48104
Ph: (734)761-9317
URL: http://annarborusa.org/spark-services/startup-services
Contact: Paul Krutko, President

Description: Accelerator that enables companies to move quickly through their lifecycle. From an initial idea to business formation, proof of concept, marketability and commercialization, the team is there through all stages of start-up development.

41076 ■ Ann Arbor SPARK Regional Incubator Network (SRIN)
330 E Liberty
 Ann Arbor, MI 48104
URL: http://annarborusa.org/spark-services/startup-services/coworking

Description: A small business incubator committed to advancing the economic development of innovation-based businesses in the Ann Arbor region by offering programs, resources, and proactive support to business at every stage, from start-ups to large organizations looking for expansion opportunities.

41077 ■ Ann Arbor/Ypsilanti Regional Chamber [A2Y Chamber]
2010 Hogback Rd., Ste. 4
 Ann Arbor, MI 48105
Ph: (734)665-4433
Co. E-mail: marketing@a2ychamber.org
URL: http://a2ychamber.org
Contact: Diane Keller, President
Facebook: www.facebook.com/a2ychamber
X (Twitter): x.com/A2YChamber
YouTube: www.youtube.com/user/a2yregionalchamber

Description: Promotes commerce in the Ann Arbor/Ypsilanti region. **Founded:** 2010. **Publications:** *Ann Arbor Business-to-Business* (Periodic); *Chamber Express e-Newsletter* (Bimonthly); *Directory of Firms, Products, and Services* (Periodic); *Ann Arbor Area Chamber of Commerce--Business Directory*; *Ann Arbor Area Chamber of Commerce--Business Directory*. **Geographic Preference:** Local.

41078 ■ Automation Alley
Myron Zucker Inc.
 2675 Bellingham Dr.
 Troy, MI 48083-2044
Ph: (586)979-9955
Fax: (586)979-9484
Co. E-mail: sales@myronzucker.com

URL: http://www.myronzucker.com
Contact: Kurt Saldana, President
Facebook: www.facebook.com/AutomationAlley
Linkedin: www.linkedin.com/company/automation-alley
X (Twitter): x.com/automationalley
Instagram: www.instagram.com/automationalley

Description: A technology business accelerator dedicated to growing the economy of Southeast Michigan. **Founded:** 1999.

41079 ■ Bamboo Detroit
1420 Washington
 Ste. 301
 Detroit, MI 48226
Ph: (313)766-0134
Co. E-mail: info@bamboodetroit.com
URL: http://www.bamboodetroit.com
Contact: Amanda Lewan, Co-Founder
Facebook: www.facebook.com/BambooDetroit
X (Twitter): x.com/BambooDetroit
Instagram: www.instagram.com/bamboodetroit

Description: Supports small business startups and entrepreneurs in Detroit by providing co-working space. **Founded:** 2013.

41080 ■ Byte & Mortar
1301 W Lincoln St.
 Birmingham, MI 48009

Description: Provides flexible workspace as well as skilled reception staff, secure and fast WiFi, exclusive mailing address, professional conference space, full-featured phone, utilities, print/copy services, modern furniture, and cleaning.

41081 ■ Central Michigan University Research Corp. (CMURC)
122 Uptown Dr., Ste. 204
 Bay City, MI 48708
Ph: (989)202-6036
Co. E-mail: cmurc@cmurc.com
URL: http://www.cmurc.com
Contact: Erin Strang, President
Facebook: www.facebook.com/CMUResearchCorporation
Linkedin: www.linkedin.com/company/central-michigan-university-research-corporation
Instagram: www.instagram.com/CMUResearchCorp

Description: A not-for-profit organization established to facilitate innovative research and development opportunities between the university and high technology companies and dedicated to establishing and operating a national center of excellence in the research fields of business intelligence and nanoscale sciences.

41082 ■ CoWharf
336 W First St., Ste. 113
 Flint, MI 48502

Description: Supports entrepreneurs by providing casual, coworking space where collaboration takes place. **Founded:** 2012.

41083 ■ The Culinary Studio
29673 NW Hwy.
 Southfield, MI 48034
Ph: (248)353-2500
Co. E-mail: info@myculinarystudio.com
URL: http://www.myculinarystudio.com
Contact: Jo Coleman, Contact

Description: Shared-use kitchen supporting new and growing culinary businesses.

41084 ■ Design Core Detroit (DC3)
460 W Baltimore Ave., Ste. 100C
 Detroit, MI 48202
Ph: (313)664-1478
Co. E-mail: info@designcore.org
URL: http://designcore.org
Contact: Bonnie Fahoome, Executive Director
Facebook: www.facebook.com/designcoredet
X (Twitter): x.com/designcoredet
Instagram: www.instagram.com/designcoredet

Description: Provides leadership, resources, exposure, data, and analytics to elevate economic output and social impact of Detroit's creative economy. **Founded:** 2010.

41085 ■ Detroit Kitchen Connect (DKC)
Detroit, MI
URL: http://detroitkitchenconnect.com
Contact: Christine Quane, Contact
E-mail: cquane@easternmarket.org

Description: Culinary incubator offering low-cost commercial kitchen space to food entrepreneurs.

41086 ■ Downtown Market Incubator Kitchen
435 Ionia Ave. SW
Grand Rapids, MI 49503
Ph: (616)805-5308
Co. E-mail: info@downtownmarketgr.com
URL: http://downtownmarketgr.com/incubator-kitchen
Contact: Tim Kelly, President
Facebook: www.facebook.com/DowntownMarket
X (Twitter): twitter.com/dtmarketgr
Instagram: www.instagram.com/dtmarketgr

Description: Incubator that provides an inclusive space for food start-ups and entrepreneurs who are seeking resources, support, and technical assistance. **Founded:** 1996.

41087 ■ Facility Kitchens
501 Ottawa
Lowell, MI 49331
Ph: (616)642-6911
Co. E-mail: janet@facilitykitchens.com
URL: http://www.facilitykitchens.com
X (Twitter): twitter.com/FacilityKitchen

Description: Commercial rental kitchen, incubator, and mobile food establishment for licensed food production in West Michigan.

41088 ■ The Factory
77 Monroe Ctr., St. NW
Grand Rapids, MI 49503
Ph: (616)803-9131
Co. E-mail: hello@workthefactory.com
URL: http://workthefactory.com
Contact: Lauren Srmek, Manager
Facebook: www.facebook.com/coFactory
Linkedin: www.linkedin.com/company/coworking-west-michigan
Instagram: www.instagram.com/the_factory_gr
YouTube: www.youtube.com/channel/UClzz5Ec9yCy7VRCrqhIguvA/featured

Description: Supports small businesses and entrepreneurs by providing co-working space where collaboration can take place. **Founded:** 2009.

41089 ■ Flint Food Works
300 E First St.
Flint, MI 48502
URL: http://www.flintfoodworks.net
Contact: Timothy W. Herman, Contact

Description: Culinary business incubator providing a facility for food-based businesses to establish a product, perfect their recipe, and develop a business model that will help them grow.

41090 ■ Grand Circus Detroit (GCD)
1570 Woodward Ave., Level 3
Detroit, MI 48226
Ph: (313)338-2780
Co. E-mail: hello@grandcircus.co
URL: http://www.grandcircus.co
Contact: Damien Rocchi, Chief Executive Officer
Facebook: www.facebook.com/GrandCircusCo
Linkedin: www.linkedin.com/school/grandcircus
Instagram: www.instagram.com/grandcircusco
YouTube: www.youtube.com/c/GrandCircus

Description: Trains people for careers in tech and helps local businesses grow by hiring these local tech folks. Hosts 50+ entrepreneurs in a co-working space and offers educational courses and workshops.

41091 ■ Green Garage
4444 Second Ave.
Detroit, MI 48201
Ph: (313)444-4054
Co. E-mail: greengaragedetroit@gmail.com
URL: http://greengaragedetroit.com
Facebook: www.facebook.com/greengaragedet
X (Twitter): x.com/greengarage
Instagram: www.instagram.com/greengarage

Description: A diverse, supportive, and accountable co-working community and helping triple bottom line businesses grow naturally. **Founded:** 2005.

41092 ■ Grow Benzie Inc.
5885 Frankfort Hwy.
Benzonia, MI 49616
Ph: (231)882-9510
Co. E-mail: info@growbenzie.org
URL: http://www.growbenzie.org
Contact: Betsy Evans, President
Facebook: www.facebook.com/Growbenzie
X (Twitter): x.com/growbenzie
Instagram: www.instagram.com/growbenzie
YouTube: www.youtube.com/channel/UCRv2g5x98GYnvMHcrIJSkgg

Description: Dedicated to helping food startups by providing support services including kitchen rental. **Founded:** 2008.

41093 ■ IncWell
110 Willits St.
Birmingham, MI 48009
Contact: Thomas Lasorda, Contact

Description: Invests in early-stage companies up to $250,000, offers affordable, shared workspace, and works directly with portfolio companies on everything, including marketing, manufactuing, and finance.

41094 ■ Innovation Partnerships
1600 Huron Pkwy., 2nd Fl., Building 520
Ann Arbor, MI 48109-2590
Ph: (734)763-0614
Co. E-mail: innovationpartnerships@umich.edu
URL: http://innovationpartnerships.umich.edu
Contact: Bryce Pilz, Executive Director
E-mail: bpilz@umich.edu
Linkedin: www.linkedin.com/company/51693340
X (Twitter): x.com/INNOVPARTNER
YouTube: www.youtube.com/channel/UCyGBq71lfv7Ne4HfBGujhPg/videos

Description: Works to transfer University technology to the marketplace. Services include start-up assistance, licensing, legal support, and decision support. **Founded:** 2011.

41095 ■ J.L.T. Management Company, L.L.C.
31693 Eight Mile Rd.
Livonia, MI 48152
Contact: Todd Luhtanen, Contact

Description: Supports entrepreneurship by providing a fully managed co-working space and the social experience of a coffee house that anyone can afford.

41096 ■ Kettering University Small Business Development Center (KU SBDC)
1700 University Ave.
Flint, MI 48504
URL: http://www.kettering.edu/campus/community-involvement/mi-sbdc

41097 ■ Lakeshore Advantage
201 W Washington Ave., Ste. 410
Zeeland, MI 49464
Ph: (616)772-5226
Co. E-mail: info@lakeshoreadvantage.com
URL: http://www.lakeshoreadvantage.com
Contact: Jennifer Owens, President
E-mail: jennifer.owens@lakeshoreadvantage.com
Facebook: www.facebook.com/lakeshoreadvantage
Linkedin: www.linkedin.com/company/lakeshoreadvantage
X (Twitter): x.com/lakeshoreadvant
YouTube: www.youtube.com/channel/UCDSmm9WG6JOR5qZ8Vblac7w

Description: Firm provides economic development services. **Founded:** 2003.

41098 ■ Lansing Regional SmartZone (LRSZ)
1000 S Washington Ave., Ste. 201
Lansing, MI 48910
Ph: (517)702-3387
URL: http://www.purelansing.com/smartzone
Contact: Bob Trezise, President
E-mail: bob@purelansing.com

Description: In cooperation with the Michigan Economic Development Corporation (MEDC), stimulates the growth of technology-based businesses in the Lansing region. **Industry Preferences:** Life science; advanced manufacturing; information technology.

41099 ■ LINC Community Revitalization Inc.
1167 Madison Ave. SE
Grand Rapids, MI 49507
Ph: (616)451-9140
Co. E-mail: info@lincrev.org
URL: http://lincup.org
Contact: LaKiya Jenkins, Executive Director
Facebook: www.facebook.com/LINCrev
X (Twitter): x.com/LINCrev

Description: Business incubator working to connect community-organizing efforts with real estate development. Offers a 3-year business incubator training program for existing startups in need of business management guidance. **Founded:** 2000.

41100 ■ Macomb-Oakland University INCubator
6633 Eighteen Mile Rd.
Sterling Heights, MI 48314
URL: http://oakland.edu/ucm/lp/FY18/incubators

Description: Supports economic development in Southeast Michigan by accelerating high-tech businesses, cultivating academic innovation, and encouraging research and development.

41101 ■ Michigan Alternative & Renewable Energy Center (MAREC)
200 Viridian Dr.
Muskegon, MI 49440
URL: http://scholarworks.gvsu.edu/marec

Description: Assists aspiring alternative and renewable energy entrepreneurs and business startups throughout the business development cycle. Helps entrepreneurs to gain the knowledge, expertise and strategies you need to be ready for the risks and rewards of the marketplace. MAREC services are offered to its onsite tenants and its affiliate clients.

41102 ■ Michigan Biotechnology Institute (MBI)
325 E Grand River Ave., Ste. 275
East Lansing, MI 48823
Ph: (517)353-9268
URL: http://www.msufoundation.org/mbi
Contact: Dr. Melissa Woo, President
Facebook: www.facebook.com/michiganstateufoundation
Linkedin: www.linkedin.com/company/msufoundation
X (Twitter): x.com/MSUFound

Description: Coordinates the development of biotechnology research and technology transfer to businesses, provides in-house research and development, and provides technology transfer to biotechnology businesses. **Founded:** 1973.

41103 ■ Michigan Life Science and Innovation Center (MLSIC)
46701 Commerce Center Dr.
Plymouth, MI 48170
URL: http://mlsic.com
Contact: Fredrick Molnar, Executive Director
E-mail: molnarf@michigan.org

Description: A home for innovation-based businesses. Provides state-of-the-art laboratory space and entrepreneurial support. **Founded:** 1991.

41104 ■ Michigan Molecular Institute and Impact Analytical
1940 N Stark Rd.
Midland, MI 48642
Free: 855-615-1215
Fax: (989)486-9429
Co. E-mail: info@impactanalytical.com
URL: http://www.impactanalytical.com
X (Twitter): x.com/IATestingLab

Description: Performs advanced research and development, and graduate-level education in polymer science and composite technology. Provides technical assistance and consulting services. Devel-

STATE LISTINGS Michigan ■ 41122

ops new information on the molecular structure and behavior of non-metallic materials. Also performs proprietary research.

41105 ■ Michigan State University Institute for Food Laws and Regulations (MSU IFLR)
Anthony Hall, Ste. 3385 474 S Shaw Ln., Michigan State University
East Lansing, MI 48824
Ph: (517)355-8295
Fax: (517)432-1492
Co. E-mail: iflr@msu.edu
URL: http://www.canr.msu.edu/iflr
Contact: Neal Fortin, Director
E-mail: fortinne@msu.edu
Linkedin: www.linkedin.com/in/iflrmsuedu
X (Twitter): x.com/IFLR

Description: Provides workshops/seminars.

41106 ■ Michigan State University Product Center
Justin S Morrill Hall of Agriculture
446 W Cir. Dr., Rm. 80
East Lansing, MI 48824
Ph: (517)580-3404
Co. E-mail: product@msu.edu
URL: http://www.canr.msu.edu/productcenter
Contact: Katje Armentrout, Contact
E-mail: arment11@msu.edu
Facebook: www.facebook.com/msuproductcenterfoodagbio
X (Twitter): x.com/MakingItInMich
YouTube: www.youtube.com/user/msuanrvideo14

Description: Helps entrepreneurs develop and commercialize high value products in the food, agricultural, and natural resource sectors.

41107 ■ Michigan Tech Enterprise SmartZone (MTEC)
600 E Lakeshore Dr.
Houghton, MI 49931
Ph: (906)487-7000
Fax: (906)487-9523
Co. E-mail: mtec@mtecsz.com
URL: http://www.mtecsz.com
Contact: David Rowe, Chief Executive Officer
Facebook: www.facebook.com/mtecsmartzone
Linkedin: www.linkedin.com/company/mtec-smartzone
X (Twitter): x.com/mtecsmartzone
YouTube: www.youtube.com/user/MTECSmartStart

Description: A private, non-profit corporation fostering high-tech business incubation and growth by offering programs and services that encourage entrepreneurial development and that help ensure the success of start-ups and small companies. **Founded:** 2001.

41108 ■ Midland Tomorrow Innovation Center (MMIC)
300 Rodd St., Ste. 101
Midland, MI 48640
Contact: Brad Kaye, President

Description: Provider of wide variety of internet and telecommunications services, including calling cards, database solutions, directories and guides, internet access, medical transcription, network solutions, search engine optimization, software development, VoIP services, web hosting and design and wholesale services. **Founded:** 1997.

41109 ■ MTEC SmartZone (MTECSZ)
600 E Lakeshore Dr.
Houghton, MI 49931
Ph: (906)487-7000
Fax: (906)487-9523
Co. E-mail: mtec@mtecsz.com
URL: http://www.mtecsz.com
Contact: Eric Waara, Chairman of the Board
Facebook: www.facebook.com/mtecsmartzone
X (Twitter): x.com/mtecsmartzone
YouTube: www.youtube.com/user/MTECSmartStart

Description: Guides entrepreneurs and helps create high tech jobs in Michigan's Keweenaw Peninsula. Provides office space, training, access to funding, coaching and other resources to help businesses owners develop ideas, patents and innovative opportunities. **Founded:** 2002.

41110 ■ Muskegon Area First
380 W Western Ave., Ste. 202
Muskegon, MI 49440
Contact: Tom Zant, President

Description: Business accelerator in Muskegon, Michigan. **Founded:** 1999.

41111 ■ Niles Entrepreneur and Culinary Incubator
Niles Main St.
Farmers Market
Niles, MI 49120
URL: http://nilesincubator.com

Description: Culinary incubator used by entrepreneurs who are starting food-based businesses. Provides a place for these entrepreneurs to learn via valuable training opportunities.

41112 ■ OU Inc.
Shotwell Pavilion
419 Golf View Ln.
Rochester, MI 48309-4477
Ph: (248)370-2100
Fax: (248)648-4799
Co. E-mail: ouinc@oakland.edu
URL: http://oakland.edu/ouinc
Contact: Dr. Ora Hirsch Pescovitz, President
Facebook: www.facebook.com/OUINC1
Linkedin: www.linkedin.com/company/ou-inc
X (Twitter): x.com/ouinc
Instagram: www.instagram.com/ouincubator

Description: Provides entrepreneurial resources and strategic business solutions for developing business ventures and accelerating ideas to market.Focius is in the energy, medical device, and information technology sectors. **Founded:** 2006.

41113 ■ Ponyride
16500 Tireman St.
Detroit, MI 48228
Co. E-mail: info@ponyride.org
URL: http://www.bgcsm.org/programs/ponyride
Contact: Phil Cooley, Officer
Facebook: www.facebook.com/ponyridedetroit
X (Twitter): x.com/ponyridedetroit
Instagram: www.instagram.com/ponyridedetroit

Description: Supports entrepreneurs by giving them the opportunity for production, community outreach, and education.

41114 ■ SPARK Regional Incubator Network (SRIN)
330 E Liberty
Ann Arbor, MI 48104
URL: http://annarborusa.org/spark-services/startup-services/coworking

Description: A network comprised of two business incubators, which provide physical office space, essential services, and business development guidance.

41115 ■ Start Garden
40 Pearl St. NW, No. 200
Grand Rapids, MI 49503
Co. E-mail: support@startgarden.com
URL: http://startgarden.com
Contact: Jorge Gonzalez, Director
E-mail: jorge@startgarden.com
Facebook: www.facebook.com/StrtGrdn
Linkedin: www.linkedin.com/company/start-garden
X (Twitter): x.com/startgarden
Instagram: www.instagram.com/startgarden

Description: Connects businesses and resources in one place. Offers seed funding to startups of $5,00 for two ideas per week. **Founded:** 2012.

41116 ■ The Starting Block Inc.
1535 Industrial Pk. Dr.
Hart, MI 49420
Ph: (231)873-1432
Co. E-mail: tsbi4@frontier.com
URL: http://www.startingblock.biz
Contact: Bill Small, President
Facebook: www.facebook.com/thestartingblockinc

Description: Culinary incubator providing commercial kitchen space to business startups and businesses who are outgrowing their current facilities. **Founded:** 2006.

41117 ■ Tech Brewery
1327 Jones Dr., Ste. 106
Ann Arbor, MI 48105
Ph: (734)436-1327
Co. E-mail: info@techbrewery.org
URL: http://www.techbrewery.org
Contact: Doug Smith, Owner

Description: A community with shared workspace of technologists, entrepreneurs, and startups. **Founded:** 2009.

41118 ■ TechArb
3350 Duderstadt Ctr., 2281 Bonisteel Blvd.
Ann Arbor, MI 48109
URL: http://cfe.umich.edu/techarb
Contact: Nick Moroz, Program Director
E-mail: nmoroz@umich.edu

Description: A student incubator for University of Michigan students. Empowers student startups, offering perks to early-stage student startups including educational workshops, events, and access to resources to legal counsel and design clinics.

41119 ■ Technology Innovation Center (TIC)
325 E Grand River Ave., Ste. 300
East Lansing, MI 48823
Ph: (517)355-9307
URL: http://www.eastlansingtic.org
Contact: Jeff Smith, Director
Facebook: www.facebook.com/EastLansingInnovation

Description: Business accelerator for technology startups. Provides low-cost office space as well as resources to help startups grow and prosper during their first three years. **Founded:** 2008.

41120 ■ TechTown Detroit
440 Burroughs St.
Detroit, MI 48202
Ph: (313)879-5250
Co. E-mail: info@techtowndetroit.org
URL: http://techtowndetroit.org
Contact: Ned Staebler, President
E-mail: nedstaebler@wayne.edu
Facebook: www.facebook.com/techtowndetroit
X (Twitter): x.com/techtowndetroit
Instagram: www.instagram.com/techtowndetroit
YouTube: www.youtube.com/channel/UCgaD9h9E0Iv2VckDarf062A
Pinterest: www.pinterest.com/techtowndetroit

Description: A small business incubator providing the support and access to capital needed to build high tech companies in Detroit. It is a community of entrepreneurs, investors, mentors, service providers, and corporate partners committed to empowering entrepreneurs to build successful technology businesses to improve the quality of life for people across the country and around the world. **Founded:** 2000.

41121 ■ Tejara Center
12740 WWarren, Ste. 300
Dearborn, MI 48126
Contact: Ahmad Chebbani, President

Description: Provides business incubation and acceleration services to entrepreneurs, targeting the needs of ethnic/minority-owned businesses. Services include business assessments, education and coaching, export support, funding aid, and professional resources.

41122 ■ University of Michigan - The Venture Center
2800 Plymouth Rd., Bldg.18
Ann Arbor, MI 48109-2800
Ph: (734)763-0614
Co. E-mail: venturecenter@umich.edu
URL: http://ncrc.umich.edu/private-public-partnerships/office-tech-transfer/venture-accelerator
Contact: Mike Psarouthakis, Director

Description: Provides a door into the University for entrepreneurs and venture partners interested in start-up venture opportunities with U-M technology. Provides access to technology, expertise, resources, and connections to create new startup ventures based on U-M technology.

41123 ■ Warehaus Business Center
311 S River Ave.
 Holland, MI 49423
Ph: (616)594-0176
Co. E-mail: info@warehausholland.com
URL: http://www.warehausholland.com
Contact: Quin Kelley, Founder

Description: Supports small businesses by offering affordable coworking office space in a social environment that encourages innovation and collaboration.

41124 ■ West Michigan Science & Technology Initiative
Grand Valley State University
 301 Michigan St. NE
 Grand Rapids, MI 49503
Co. E-mail: wmsti@gvsu.edu
Linkedin: www.linkedin.com/company/west-michigan-science-&-technology-initiative-wmsti-

Description: A small business incubator dedicating time, product development tools, amenities, and community assets that innovators, entrepreneurs, or small science and technology entrepreneurs need to commercialize their discoveries.

41125 ■ WMed Innovation Center
Western Michigan University Homer Stryker M.D. School of Medicine
 4717 Campus Dr.
 Kalamazoo, MI 49008

Description: A multi-tenant incubator/accelerator providing space and intensive support for life science startup firms in their early stages. There is also space available for graduates of the incubator and for firms that are at a later stage and no longer need the intensive support services of an incubator. **Founded:** 2003.

EDUCATIONAL PROGRAMS

41126 ■ Alpena Community College (ACC)
665 Johnson St.
 Alpena, MI 49707-1495
Ph: (989)356-9021
Free: 888-468-6222
Co. E-mail: helpdesk@alpenacc.edu
URL: http://discover.alpenacc.edu
Contact: Dr. Don MacMaster, President
E-mail: macmastd@alpenacc.edu
Facebook: www.facebook.com/alpenacc
Linkedin: www.linkedin.com/school/alpenacc
Instagram: www.instagram.com/alpenacc

Description: Two-year college offering a small business management program. **Founded:** 1952.

41127 ■ Baker College - Owosso Campus
1020 S Washington St.
 Owosso, MI 48867
Free: 800-964-4299
Co. E-mail: getenrolled@baker.edu
URL: http://www.baker.edu/campuses/michigan/owosso
Contact: Jacqui Spicer, President
Facebook: www.facebook.com/bakercollege

Description: Vocational school offering a small business management program.

41128 ■ Mid Michigan Community College (MMCC)
1375 S Clare Ave.
 Harrison, MI 48625
Ph: (989)386-6622
Co. E-mail: helpdesk@midmich.edu
URL: http://www.midmich.edu
Contact: Tim Hood, President
Facebook: www.facebook.com/midmichcollege
X (Twitter): x.com/midmichcollege
Instagram: www.instagram.com/midmichcollege

YouTube: www.youtube.com/channel/UCFkLoVfvqfUG8-C5cntP7Ig

Description: Two-year college offering a small business management program. **Founded:** 1965.

41129 ■ Montcalm Community College (MCC)
2800 College Dr.
 Sidney, MI 48885
Ph: (989)328-2111
Co. E-mail: admissions@montcalm.edu
URL: http://www.montcalm.edu
Contact: Jane Anderson Beach, President
Facebook: www.facebook.com/MontcalmCC
Linkedin: www.linkedin.com/school/montcalm-community-college
X (Twitter): x.com/MontcalmCC
YouTube: www.youtube.com/channel/UCIKEXQg7ZA3a16AhE6LClcQ

Description: Two-year college offering a small business management program. **Founded:** 1981.

41130 ■ North Central Michigan College (NCMC)
1515 Howard St.
 Petoskey, MI 49770
Free: 888-298-6605
Fax: (231)348-6625
Co. E-mail: helpdesk@ncmich.edu
URL: http://www.ncmich.edu
Contact: Dr. David Roland Finley, President
Facebook: www.facebook.com/NCMC.Main
Linkedin: www.linkedin.com/school/northcentralmc
X (Twitter): x.com/northcentralmc
Instagram: www.instagram.com/northcentralmc
YouTube: www.youtube.com/channel/UC1xZZuODAY5GlWWYW-weK6Q

Description: Two-year college offering a program in small business management. **Founded:** 1958.

41131 ■ Southwestern Michigan College-Workforce Education and Business Solutions
33890 US Hwy. 12
 Niles, MI 49120
Ph: (269)687-4811
Free: 800-456-8675
Co. E-mail: business@swmich.edu
URL: http://www.swmich.edu
Contact: Dr. Joe Odenwald, President

Description: Offers programs/classes in small business/small business management. **Founded:** 1964.

41132 ■ Wayne State University
Wayne State University-Business Management Office
 42 W Warren Ave.
 Detroit, MI 48202
Ph: (313)577-2424
Co. E-mail: admissions@wayne.edu
URL: http://wayne.edu
Contact: Roy M. Wilson, President
URL(s): wayne.edu

Description: Offer exemplary teaching and training programs. **Audience:** Students. **Principal Exhibits:** Offer exemplary teaching and training programs.

REFERENCE WORKS

41133 ■ "Michigan Governor: Drivers to See More Savings Under Auto Insurance Reform Law" in Insurance Journal (November 16, 2021)

Released: November 16, 2021. **Description:** Michigan's new auto insurance law went into effect in 2019, which reduced rates for drivers. Now, Michigan drivers will see more savings through another piece of legislation that will allow them to choose their level of medical coverage. **Availability:** Online.

CONSULTANTS

41134 ■ MRPR Group, P.C.
1 NW Plz.
 28411 NW Hwy., Ste. 800
 Southfield, MI 48034

Ph: (248)357-9000
Co. E-mail: mrpr@mrpr.com
URL: http://www.mrpr.com
Contact: Jason Baltrip, Manager
E-mail: jbaltrip@mrpr.com
Facebook: www.facebook.com/mrprcpa
Linkedin: www.linkedin.com/company/mrpr-group-p-c-

Description: Accounting and business advisory services.

PUBLICATIONS

41135 ■ *Crain's Detroit Business*
1155 Gratiot Ave.
 Detroit, MI 48207-2732
Ph: (313)446-6000
Co. E-mail: info@crain.com
URL: http://www.crain.com
Contact: Barry Asin, President
URL(s): www.crainsdetroit.com
Facebook: www.facebook.com/CrainsDetroit
Linkedin: www.linkedin.com/company/crain%27s-detroit-business
X (Twitter): x.com/crainsdetroit

Released: Weekly **Price:** $189, for print and digital/year; $20, for print + digital month; $179, for online annual; $499, for all access; $18, for digital. **Description:** Local business tabloid covering Wayne, Macomb, Oakland, Livingston, and Washtenaw counties. **Availability:** Print; PDF; Online. **Type:** Full-text.

PUBLISHERS

41136 ■ Delta Alpha Publishing Ltd.
2555 Busha Hwy.
 Marysville, MI 48040
Ph: (810)388-9500
Fax: (810)388-9502
Co. E-mail: dap@deltaalpha.com
URL: http://www.deltaalpha.com
Contact: Damien Abbott, President

Description: Publishes books on real estate, business and travel and reaches the market through direct mail, exhibitions and the internet. **Founded:** 2000.

41137 ■ Humanergy Inc.
5671 N Westnedge Ave.
 Kalamazoo, MI 49004-3075
Ph: (269)789-0446
Co. E-mail: info@humanergy.com
URL: http://humanergy.com
Contact: John Barrett, Principal
E-mail: john@humanergy.com
Facebook: www.facebook.com/humanergy
Linkedin: www.linkedin.com/company/humanergy
X (Twitter): x.com/humanergy
YouTube: www.youtube.com/channel/UC9CzU3MFIfM8bx8FZyMzP6w

Description: Publisher of books on business and leadership. **Founded:** 2000.

41138 ■ Jenkins Group Inc. (JGI)
1129 Woodmere Ave., Ste. B
 Traverse City, MI 49686
Free: 800-706-4636
Fax: (231)933-0448
URL: http://www.jenkinsgroupinc.com
Contact: James J. Kalajian, President
E-mail: jjk@bookpublishing.com

Description: Publishes on business, motivational and professional improvement, health, fitness, nonfiction and children's titles. **Founded:** 1988. **Publications:** *Publishing Entrepreneur: Profit Strategies for the Information & Publishing Industry* (Bimonthly); *Independent Publisher Online: The Voice of The Independent Publishing Industry*; *Independent Publisher: Leading the World of Book Selling in New Directions* (Monthly). **Awards:** Independent Publisher Book Awards (IPPY) (Annual); Living Now Book Awards (Annual); Moonbeam Children's Book Awards (Annual); Axiom Business Book Awards (Annual).

STATE LISTINGS

Michigan ■ 41145

LIBRARIES

41139 ■ Detroit Public Library Business, Science and Technology Department
5201 Woodward Ave.
Detroit, MI 48202
Ph: (313)481-1300
URL: http://detroitpubliclibrary.org/policies/collection-development
Facebook: www.facebook.com/detroitpubliclibrary
X (Twitter): x.com/detroitlibrary
Instagram: www.instagram.com/detroitpubliclibrary
YouTube: www.youtube.com/user/detroitpubliclibrary
Scope: Business, science and technology. **Services:** Interlibrary loan; copying. **Founded:** 1924. **Holdings:** 70,000 books; e-books; audiobooks ; periodicals; cDs. **Preferred Investment Size:** Business and Finance Department and Technology and Science Department.

VENTURE CAPITAL FIRM

41140 ■ Augment Ventures (AV)
206 S 4th Ave.
Ann Arbor, MI 48104
Co. E-mail: info@augmentventures.com
URL: http://www.augmentventures.com
Contact: David Armstrong, Chief Financial Officer Partner

Description: Venture capital firm for early-stage capital-efficient companies in North America. Works with entrepreneurs to develop new markets, build alliances, and hire employees. **Investment Policies:** Transformational companies and disruptive technologies enhancing the quality of life and global business efficiency. **Industry Preferences:** Software; smart hardware; physical science innovations.

41141 ■ Dow Venture Capital
2211 H. H. Dow Way
Midland, MI 48674
URL: http://corporate.dow.com/en-us.html

Description: Invests in start-ups that enable and accelerate Dow's business growth and value. **Industry Preferences:** Consumer; industrial; infrastructure; packaging.

41142 ■ GM Ventures
GM Tech Center Rd.
Warren, MI 48092
URL: http://www.gmventures.com/site/us/en/gm-ventures/home.html
Contact: Kent Helfrich, President

Description: Invests in advanced technology for GM's vehicles, manufacturing facilities, and operating businesses. Looks to drive innovation and mobility. **Founded:** 2010. **Industry Preferences:** Advanced propulsion and materials; connected vehicles; sensors, processors, and memory; advanced manufacturing technology; value chain and business model.

41143 ■ Hopen Life Science Ventures
3133 Orchard Vista., SE
Grand Rapids, MI 49546
Contact: Mark Olesnavage, Contact

Description: Venture capital firm investing in early- to mid-stage life science opportunities primarily in the Midwest. Also operates out of Ohio.

41144 ■ Renaissance Venture Capital
201 S Main St., 10th Fl.
Ann Arbor, MI 48104
Ph: (734)997-8661
Co. E-mail: info@renvcf.com
URL: http://renvcf.com
Contact: Chris Rizik, Chief Executive Officer
X (Twitter): x.com/renvcf

Description: Invests in venture capital funds in the U.S. Uses those funds for innovative Michigan start-ups.

41145 ■ Wolverine Venture Fund (WVF)
701 Tappan Ave., R3200
Ann Arbor, MI 48109
URL: http://zli.umich.edu/wolverine-venture-fund
Contact: Erik Gordon, Managing Director
E-mail: rmegordo@umich.edu

Description: Student-run venture capital firm for companies at the Series A and Series B stages. Partners with local venture capital firms. **Founded:** 1997. **Preferred Investment Size:** $50,000 to $200,000 . **Investment Policies:** Companies able to attract a priced round of venture capital from and established venture capital firm. **Industry Preferences:** Biomedicine; health IT; advanced materials; internet technologies.

Small Business Sourcebook • 42nd Edition

Minnesota

ASSOCIATIONS AND OTHER ORGANIZATIONS

41146 ■ Association of Fundraising Professionals Minnesota Chapter
6600 City W Pky., Ste. 300
Eden Prairie, MN 55344
Ph: (952)444-6361
Fax: (952)444-6363
Co. E-mail: info@afpminnesota.org
URL: http://www.afpminnesota.org/home
Contact: Michelle Edgerton, President
Facebook: www.facebook.com/AFPMN
Geographic Preference: State.

41147 ■ Association of Fundraising Professionals Southern Minnesota Chapter
PO Box 7042
Rochester, MN 55903-7042
Co. E-mail: afpsouthernmn@gmail.com
URL: http://community.afpglobal.org/afpmnsouthernminnesota/home
Contact: Rebecca Snapp, President
Founded: 2003. **Geographic Preference:** Local.

41148 ■ Business Network International Minnesota & Northern Wisconsin (BNI MN) [BNI Minnesota & Northern Wisconsin]
PO Box 27783
Golden Valley, MN 55427
URL: http://www.bnimn.com
Contact: Nancy Giacomuzzi, Contact
Facebook: www.facebook.com/BNIMinnesotaandNorthernWisconsin
Description: Provides both men and women a structured environment for the development and exchange of quality business referrals. Offers members the opportunity to share ideas and contacts. **Geographic Preference:** State.

41149 ■ Entrepreneurs' Organization - Minnesota Chapter
100 S 5th St, Ste. 1075
Minneapolis, MN 55402
URL: http://www.eominnesota.org
Contact: Patrick Donohue, President
URL(s): www.eonetwork.org/minnesota
Facebook: www.facebook.com/EntrepreneursOrganizationMinnesota
Linkedin: www.linkedin.com/company/entrepreneurs-organization-minnesota
Description: Provides local resources to members which includes networking events, mentorship, live forums, and leadership development. **Founded:** 1987.

41150 ■ International Association of Business Communicators Minnesota (IABC MN)
18 N 12th St., Ste. 3975
Minneapolis, MN 55403
Ph: (612)314-3620
Co. E-mail: info@iabcmn.com
URL: http://iabcmn.com
Contact: Andy Gardner, President
Facebook: www.facebook.com/IABCMN
Linkedin: www.linkedin.com/company/international-association-of-business-communicators-iabc-minnesota
X (Twitter): x.com/iabcmn
YouTube: www.youtube.com/user/iabcmn
Description: Represents and supports business communicators throughout Minnesota, including independent consultants and corporate executives in employee communications, marketing communications, public relations, and public affairs. Provides professional development and networking opportunities for members. **Founded:** 2012. **Geographic Preference:** State.

41151 ■ International Association of Women Minneapolis-St. Paul Chapter
Minneapolis, MN
URL: http://www.iawomen.com/chapters
Description: Serves as network of accomplished women united to achieve professional goals. Provides a forum for sharing ideas and experiences of professional women regarding career success. Promotes an active business and networking community from all industries. **Geographic Preference:** Local.

SMALL BUSINESS DEVELOPMENT CENTERS

41152 ■ Central Lakes College Small Business Development Center
501 W College Dr.
Brainerd, MN 56401
URL: http://www.clcmn.edu/small-business-development-center
Contact: Natalia DePauw, Director
E-mail: natalia.depauw@clcmn.edu
Description: Provides management assistance to current and prospective small business owners in Central Lakes. **Geographic Preference:** Local.

41153 ■ Central Minnesota Small Business Development Center
720 4th Ave. S
Saint Cloud, MN 56301-4498
Ph: (320)308-4842
URL: http://www.stcloudstate.edu
Contact: Robbyn Wacker, President
Description: Represents and promotes the small business sector. Provides management assistance to current and prospective small business owners. Helps to improve management skills and expand the products and services of members. **Geographic Preference:** Local.

41154 ■ Northeast Minnesota's Small Business Development Center
Duluth Technology Bldg.
11 E Superior St., Ste. 210
Duluth, MN 55802
Ph: (218)726-7298
Co. E-mail: info@northlandsbdc.org
URL: http://northlandsbdc.org
Contact: Curt Walczak, Director
E-mail: curt@northlandsbdc.org
YouTube: www.youtube.com/channel/UCoJB5KoQwcuaObOV6mqX4yg
Description: Provides management assistance to current and prospective small business owners in Northeast Minnesota. **Geographic Preference:** Local.

41155 ■ Northwest Small Business Development Center (NWSBDC)
201 3rd St. NW
Bemidji, MN 56601
Ph: (218)755-4255
Co. E-mail: nwsbdc@nwmf.org
URL: http://www.nwmf.org/resources/strategic-partnerships/nwsbdc
Contact: Philip Knutson, Regional Director
E-mail: philipk@nwmf.org
Description: Provides management assistance to current and prospective small business owners in Northwest Minnesota. **Geographic Preference:** Local.

41156 ■ Small Business Development Center University of St. Thomas
Opus College of Business
1000 LaSalle Ave.
Minneapolis, MN 55403
Ph: (651)962-4500
Co. E-mail: smallbusiness@stthomas.edu
URL: http://business.stthomas.edu/centers-institutes/schulze-school/about-schulze/small-business-dev-center/index.html
Contact: Diane Paterson, Director
E-mail: smallbus@stthomas.edu
Facebook: www.facebook.com/USTBusiness
Linkedin: www.linkedin.com/school/university-of-st-thomas-opus-college-of-business
X (Twitter): x.com/USTbusiness
Instagram: www.instagram.com/ustbusiness
Description: Represents and promotes the small business sector. Provides management assistance to current and prospective small business owners. Helps to improve management skills and expand the products and services of members. **Geographic Preference:** Local.

41157 ■ Small Business Development Center West Central Minnesota (WC MN SBDC)
901 8th St. S, Grant Ctr., 220.
Moorhead, MN 56562
Ph: (218)299-3037
Co. E-mail: sbdc@cord.edu
URL: http://westcentralmnsbdc.com
Contact: Bill Schalow, Consultant
E-mail: wschalow@cord.edu
Facebook: www.facebook.com/WCMnSBDC
Linkedin: www.linkedin.com/company/27110292
X (Twitter): x.com/MnSBDC
Instagram: www.instagram.com/wcmnsbdc

YouTube: www.youtube.com/user/WestCentralMnSBDC
Description: Represents and promotes the small business sector. Provides management assistance to current and prospective small business owners. Helps to improve management skills and expand the products and services of members. **Founded:** 1980. **Geographic Preference:** Local.

41158 ■ South Central Minnesota Small Business Development Center
424 N Riverfront Dr., Ste. 101
Mankato, MN 56001
Ph: (507)389-8875
Co. E-mail: info@myminnesotabusiness.com
URL: http://www.myminnesotabusiness.com
Contact: Mike Hahn, Regional Director
E-mail: mike.hahn@mnsu.edu
Facebook: www.facebook.com/SBDCSouthCentralMN
Linkedin: www.linkedin.com/company/small-business-development-center-mankato
X (Twitter): x.com/SBDCMankato
YouTube: www.youtube.com/channel/UCL_a8oAuOsnWLgduczx-hxw
Description: Represents and promotes the small business sector. Provides management assistance to current and prospective small business owners. Helps to improve management skills and expand the products and services of members. **Geographic Preference:** Local.

41159 ■ Southeast Minnesota Small Business Development Center
851 30th Ave., SE
Rochester, MN 55904-4999
URL: http://www.rctc.edu/small-business-development-center-at-rctc-receives-donation
Description: Represents and promotes the small business sector. Provides management assistance to current and prospective small business owners. Helps to improve management skills and expand the products and services of members. **Geographic Preference:** Local.

41160 ■ Southwest Small Business Development Center Minnesota (SBDC)
Southwest Minnesota State University
1501 State St., Science and Technology Building., Rm. 201
Marshall, MN 56258
Ph: (507)537-7386
Co. E-mail: sbdc@smsu.edu
URL: http://www.sbdcassistance.com
Contact: Liz Struve, Consultant
Facebook: www.facebook.com/SwMNSBDC
Description: Provides management assistance to current and prospective small business owners in Southwest Minnesota. **Geographic Preference:** Local.

41161 ■ Twin Cities Small Business Development Center
1000 Lasalle Ave.
Minneapolis, MN 55403
Ph: (651)962-4500
Co. E-mail: smallbusiness@stthomas.edu
URL: http://business.stthomas.edu/centers-institutes/small-business-development/index.html
Contact: Diane Paterson, Director
Description: Represents and promotes the small business sector. Provides management assistance to current and prospective small business owners. Helps to improve management skills and expand the products and services of members. **Founded:** 1981. **Geographic Preference:** Local.

SMALL BUSINESS ASSISTANCE PROGRAMS

41162 ■ Minnesota Department of Employment and Economic Development (MDEED) - Library
1st National Bank Bldg.
332 Minnesota St., Ste. E200
Saint Paul, MN 55101
Ph: (651)259-7114
Free: 800-657-3858
Co. E-mail: deed.customerservice@state.mn.us
URL: http://mn.gov/deed
Contact: Elizabeth Frosch, Chief of Staff
Facebook: www.facebook.com/mndeed
Linkedin: www.linkedin.com/company/minnesota-department-of-employment-and-economic-development
X (Twitter): x.com/mndeed
Instagram: www.instagram.com/minnesota_deed
YouTube: www.youtube.com/deedminnesota
Description: Coordinates state government information and resources available to small businesses. Provides information relating to start-up, operation, and expansion of businesses. Offers several free publications. **Scope:** Economic development; international trade; workforce development. **Services:** Interlibrary loan; copying; library open to the public. **Founded:** 1976. **Holdings:** Figures not available.

41163 ■ Minnesota Department of Employment and Economic Development - Business and Community Development Div. (BCD)
Centennial Office Bldg., 3rd Fl., 658 Cedar St.
Saint Paul, MN 55155
URL: http://www.revisor.mn.gov/rules/4300.0100
Description: Provides grants to cities, townships and counties.

41164 ■ Minnesota Department of Employment and Economic Development (DEED) - Minnesota Trade Office
180 E 5th St., Ste. 1200
Saint Paul, MN 55101
Ph: (651)259-7498
Free: 800-657-3858
Fax: (651)296-3555
Co. E-mail: mto.tradeassistance@state.mn.us
URL: http://mn.gov/deed/business/exporting
Contact: Gabrielle Gerbaud, Executive Director
E-mail: gabrielle.gerbaud@state.mn.us
Description: Promotes Minnesota goods and services through export and attraction of foreign investors. Efforts concentrate on small business through several divisions, including Export Development Division, International Marketing and Investment Division, and Export Finance Division.

SCORE OFFICES

41165 ■ Central Minnesota SCORE
355 5th Ave. S
Saint Cloud, MN 56301
URL: http://twincities.score.org/central-minnesota-score-services
Description: Unites active and retired business management professionals with men and women who are considering starting a small business, encountering problems with their business, or expanding their business. Serves St. Cloud, Alexandria, Park Rapids, and Brainerd Lakes.

41166 ■ SCORE - Alexandria, Minnesota
355 5th Ave. S, Saint Cloud
Alexandria, MN 56308
Ph: (320)240-1332
Co. E-mail: central.mn@scorevolunteer.org
URL: http://centralminnesota.score.org
Description: Provides professional guidance and information to maximize the success of existing and emerging small businesses. Offers business counseling and workshops.

41167 ■ SCORE - Anoka
2021 E Hennepin Ave., Ste. 220
Minneapolis, MN 55413-2724
Ph: (952)938-4570
Co. E-mail: minneapolis.score@gmail.com
URL: http://minneapolis.score.org
Facebook: www.facebook.com/SCOREMinneapolis
Linkedin: www.linkedin.com/company/score-mentors-twin-cities
YouTube: www.youtube.com/channel/UCSEl9Lo2q040hlrn3H77zow
Description: Provides professional guidance and information to maximize the success of existing and emerging small businesses. Offers business counseling and workshops.

41168 ■ SCORE - Austin, Minnesota
329 Main St. S, Ste. 102
Austin, MN 55912
Ph: (507)437-4561
Co. E-mail: score0406@scorevolunteer.org
URL: http://seminnesota.score.org
Contact: Bridget Weston, Chief Executive Officer
Description: Provides professional guidance and information to maximize the success of existing and emerging small businesses. Offers business counseling and workshops.

41169 ■ SCORE - Brainerd
501 W College Dr.
Brainerd, MN 56401
Ph: (218)855-8151
Free: 800-933-4413
URL: http://www.score.org/content/brainerd-lakes-score
Contact: Richard Jordan, Contact
Description: Provides professional guidance and information to maximize the success of existing and emerging small businesses. Offers business counseling and workshops.

41170 ■ SCORE - Brooklyn Park
8500 W Broadway Ave.
Brooklyn Park, MN 55443
URL: http://minneapolis.score.org
Description: Provides professional guidance and information to maximize the success of existing and emerging small businesses. Offers business counseling and workshops.

41171 ■ SCORE - Central Minnesota
7760 France Ave., S Ste. 1100
Bloomington, MN 55435
URL: http://www.score.org/twincities
Description: Provides one-on-one confidential business consultation, at no cost. Offers low-cost workshops to current and potential entrepreneurs on business planning, finance, marketing, and similar topics. **Geographic Preference:** Local.

41172 ■ SCORE - Edina
2021 E Hennepin Ave., Ste. 220
Minneapolis, MN 55413-2724
Ph: (952)938-4570
URL: http://minneapolis.score.org
Facebook: www.facebook.com/SCOREMinneapolis
Linkedin: www.linkedin.com/company/score-mentors-twin-cities
YouTube: www.youtube.com/channel/UCSEl9Lo2q040hlrn3H77zow
Description: Provides professional guidance and information to maximize the success of existing and emerging small businesses. Offers business counseling and workshops.

41173 ■ SCORE - Maple Grove
2021 Hennepin Ave. E Ste. 220
Maple Grove, MN 55311
Ph: (952)938-4570
Co. E-mail: twincities@scorevolunteer.org
URL: http://minneapolis.score.org
Facebook: www.facebook.com/SCOREMinneapolis
Linkedin: www.linkedin.com/company/score-mentors-twin-cities
YouTube: www.youtube.com/channel/UCSEl9Lo2q040hlrn3H77zow
Description: Provides professional guidance and information to maximize the success of existing and emerging small businesses. Offers business counseling and workshops.

41174 ■ SCORE - Minneapolis [SCORE - Twin Cities]
2021 E Hennepin Ave., Ste. 220
Minneapolis, MN 55413-2724
Ph: (952)938-4570
Co. E-mail: twincities@scorevolunteer.org
URL: http://twincities.score.org

Description: Serves as volunteer program in which working and retired business management professionals provide free business counseling to men and women who are considering starting a small business, encountering problems with their business, or expanding their business. Offers free one-on-one counseling, online counseling and low cost workshops on a variety of business topics. **Founded:** 1964. **Geographic Preference:** Local.

41175 ■ SCORE - Minneapolis Central Library
2021 Hennepin Ave., E Ste. 220
Minneapolis, MN 55413
URL: http://www.score.org/twincities/event/intellectual-property-brief-advice-clinic-legalcorps
Description: Provides professional guidance and information to maximize the success of existing and emerging small businesses. Offers business counseling and workshops.

41176 ■ SCORE - Park Rapids
301 Ct., Ave.
Park Rapids, MN 56470
Ph: (218)732-2259
Co. E-mail: central.mn@scorevolunteer.org
URL: http://www.score.org/content/park-rapids-score-0
Description: Provides professional guidance and information to maximize the success of existing and emerging small businesses. Offers business counseling and workshops.

41177 ■ SCORE - Plymouth, Minnesota
15700 36th Ave. N
Plymouth, MN 55446
Ph: (952)938-4570
URL: http://minneapolis.score.org
Facebook: www.facebook.com/SCOREMinneapolis
Description: Provides professional guidance and information to maximize the success of existing and emerging small businesses. Offers business counseling and workshops.

41178 ■ SCORE - St. Paul
2021 Hennepin Ave. E, Ste. 220
Minneapolis, MN 55413
Ph: (952)938-4570
Co. E-mail: minneapolis.score@gmail.com
URL: http://stpaul.score.org
Facebook: www.facebook.com/SCORETwinCities
Linkedin: www.linkedin.com/company/score-mentors-twin-cities
X (Twitter): twitter.com/SCOREstpaul
YouTube: www.youtube.com/channel/UCSEI9Lo2q040hlrn3H77zow
Description: Serves as volunteer program in which working and retired business management professionals provide free business counseling to men and women who are considering starting a small business, encountering problems with their business, or expanding their business. Offers free one-on-one counseling, online counseling and low cost workshops on a variety of business topics. **Geographic Preference:** Local.

41179 ■ SCORE - South Central Minnesota
525 Florence Ave.
Owatonna, MN 55060
Ph: (507)455-3215
Co. E-mail: scmnscore@gmail.com
URL: http://www.score.org/southcentralminnesota
Facebook: www.facebook.com/SCORESouthCentralMN
X (Twitter): x.com/SCORESCMinesota
YouTube: www.youtube.com/channel/UCSEI9Lo2q040hlrn3H77zow
Description: Provides professional guidance and information to maximize the success of existing and emerging small businesses. Offers business counseling and workshops.

41180 ■ SCORE - South Metro
350 W Burnsville Pky., Ste. 629
Burnsville, MN 55337
Ph: (952)890-7020
Co. E-mail: scoresouthmetro@scorevolunteer.org
URL: http://southmetro.score.org

Facebook: www.facebook.com/SCORESMetro
Linkedin: www.linkedin.com/company/score-mentors-south-metro
X (Twitter): x.com/SCORESouthMetro
Description: Serves as volunteer program in which working and retired business management professionals provide free business counseling to men and women who are considering starting a small business, encountering problems with their business, or expanding their business. **Founded:** 1964. **Geographic Preference:** Local.

41181 ■ SCORE - Southeast Minnesota
220 S Broadway, Ste. 100
Rochester, MN 55904
Ph: (507)200-0760
Co. E-mail: score0406@scorevolunteer.org
URL: http://seminnesota.score.org
Facebook: www.facebook.com/SCORESEMinnesota
X (Twitter): x.com/SCORESEMN
YouTube: www.youtube.com/channel/UCSEI9Lo2q040hlrn3H77zow
Description: Provides professional guidance and information to maximize the success of existing and emerging small businesses. Offers business counseling and workshops.

41182 ■ Southeast Minnesota SCORE Chapter 406
c/o Rochester Area Chamber of Commerce
220 S Broadway, Ste. 100
Rochester, MN 55904
Ph: (507)200-0760
Co. E-mail: score0406@scorevolunteer.org
URL: http://seminnesota.score.org/content/about-us-197
Contact: Mehrdad Shabestari, Chairman
Description: Volunteer businessmen and women. Provides free small business management assistance to individuals in the Rochester, MN area. Sponsors workshops. **Founded:** 1974. **Geographic Preference:** Local.

BETTER BUSINESS BUREAUS

41183 ■ Better Business Bureau of Minnesota and North Dakota (BBB)
355 5th Ave. S
Saint Cloud, MN 56301
Ph: (651)646-6222
Co. E-mail: ask@thefirstbbb.org
URL: http://www.bbb.org/minnesota
Linkedin: www.linkedin.com/company/better-business-bureau-of-minnesota-and-north-dakota
X (Twitter): x.com/thefirstbbb
Instagram: www.instagram.com/thefirstbbb
YouTube: www.youtube.com/user/thefirstbbb
Description: Provides programs and services to assist consumers and businesses. **Founded:** 1912. **Publications:** *BBB Connections* (Quarterly); *Better Pages* (Annual). **Geographic Preference:** Regional.

CHAMBERS OF COMMERCE

41184 ■ *Advantage*
220 S Broadway, Ste. 100
Rochester, MN 55904
Ph: (507)288-1122
Co. E-mail: chamber@rochestermnchamber.com
URL: http://www.rochestermnchamber.com
Contact: Ryan Parsons, President
E-mail: rparsons@rochestermnchamber.com
URL(s): www.rochestermnchamber.com/the-advantage
Released: Monthly **Availability:** Print; Online; Download; PDF.

41185 ■ Aitkin Area Chamber of Commerce (AACC)
301 Minnesota Ave. N, Unit 4
Aitkin, MN 56431
Ph: (218)927-2316
Free: 800-526-8342
Co. E-mail: upnorth@aitkin.com
URL: http://www.aitkin.com

Contact: Jeff Tidholm, Chairman
E-mail: jeff@tidholmproductions.com
Facebook: www.facebook.com/Aitkin-Area-Chamber-of-Commerce-197689433606227
Description: Promotes business and community development in the Aitkin, MN area. Sponsors Riverboat Heritage Days and Festival of Adventures. **Founded:** 1945. **Geographic Preference:** Local.

41186 ■ Albany Chamber of Commerce
400 Railroad Ave.
Albany, MN 56307
Ph: (320)845-7777
Co. E-mail: albanycc@albanytel.com
URL: http://www.albanymnchamber.org
Contact: Kelly Kasner, President
E-mail: kelly@tanidivison.com
Facebook: www.facebook.com/albanymnchamber
Description: Promotes business and community development in Albany, MN. Sponsors annual Albany Heritage Day. **Founded:** 1904. **Publications:** *Chamber Membership Directory*. **Geographic Preference:** Local.

41187 ■ Albert Lea-Freeborn County Chamber of Commerce (ALFCCOC)
132 N Broadway
Albert Lea, MN 56007
Ph: (507)373-3938
Fax: (507)377-1354
Co. E-mail: director@albertlea.org
URL: http://www.albertlea.org
Contact: Shari Jenson, Executive Director
Facebook: www.facebook.com/alfcchamber
X (Twitter): x.com/ALFCCOC
Description: Promotes and develops a healthy and positive business climate and improves the quality of life in the Albert Lea-Freeborn County area. **Publications:** *Business Monthly* (Monthly); *E-Biz* (Weekly). **Geographic Preference:** Local.

41188 ■ Alexandria Lakes Area Chamber of Commerce
206 Broadway St.
Alexandria, MN 56308
Ph: (320)763-3161
Co. E-mail: info@alexandriamn.org
URL: http://www.alexandriamn.org
Contact: Matt Gilbertson, President
Facebook: www.facebook.com/alexlakesareachamber
Linkedin: www.linkedin.com/company/alexandria-lakes-area-chamber-of-commerce
X (Twitter): x.com/VisitAlexMN
Instagram: www.instagram.com/alexlakesareachamber
Description: Promotes business and community development in the Alexandria, MN area. **Founded:** 1907. **Publications:** *Alexandria Lakes Area Visitor and Livability Guide* (Annual); *Runeskriber* (Monthly). **Geographic Preference:** Local.

41189 ■ *Alexandria Lakes Area Visitor and Livability Guide*
206 Broadway St.
Alexandria, MN 56308
Ph: (320)763-3161
Co. E-mail: info@alexandriamn.org
URL: http://www.alexandriamn.org
Contact: Matt Gilbertson, President
URL(s): www.alexandriamn.org/request-a-visitors-guide.html
Released: Annual **Description:** Magazine containing information on lodging and attractions in Alexandria, MN area. **Availability:** PDF; Online.

41190 ■ Anoka Area Chamber of Commerce (AACC)
12 Bridge Sq.
Anoka, MN 55303
Ph: (763)421-7130
Fax: (763)421-0577
Co. E-mail: mail@anokaareachamber.com
URL: http://www.anokaareachamber.com
Contact: Peter Turok, President
E-mail: pete@anokaareachamber.com
Facebook: www.facebook.com/anokaareachamber

STATE LISTINGS

Linkedin: www.linkedin.com/company/anoka-area-chamber-of-commerce
X (Twitter): x.com/AnokaAreaChambr
Description: Promotes business and community development in Andover, Anoka, Champlin, Dayton, and Ramsey, MN. **Founded:** 1952. **Publications:** *Directory and Map* (Annual). **Geographic Preference:** Local.

41191 ■ Apple Valley Chamber of Commerce
14800 Galaxie Ave., Ste. 101
Apple Valley, MN 55124
Ph: (952)432-8422
Co. E-mail: info@applevalleychamber.com
URL: http://applevalleychamber.com
Contact: Edward Kearney, President
X (Twitter): x.com/AVChamber
YouTube: www.youtube.com/channel/UCbUjhBqVjrCtgXU-2DFCzlQ
Description: Businesses interested in prospering and creating a healthy, positive environment in which to conduct business. Strives to enhance the business environment and to build a better community by uniting businesses and professional firms. **Publications:** *Newsline* (Monthly). **Geographic Preference:** Local.

41192 ■ Austin Area Chamber of Commerce
329 N Main St., Ste. 102
Austin, MN 55912
Ph: (507)437-4561
Co. E-mail: info@austincoc.com
URL: http://austincoc.com
Contact: Elaine Hansen, President
E-mail: elaine@austincoc.com
Description: Promotes business and community development in the Austin, MN area. **Founded:** 1940. **Publications:** *Someplace Special*; *Welcome to Austin*. **Educational Activities:** AMIGO Day (Annual); Ladies Night Out (Annual). **Geographic Preference:** Local.

41193 ■ Baudette-Lake of the Woods Chamber of Commerce
PO Box 659
Baudette, MN 56623
Co. E-mail: info@baudettelakeofthewoodschamber.com
URL: http://www.baudettelakeofthewoodschamber.com
Contact: Erica Anderson, President
Description: Promotes business and community development in Lake of the Woods County, MN. **Founded:** 1973. **Publications:** *Minnesota's Lake of the Woods Area Vacation Guide* (Annual). **Geographic Preference:** Local.

41194 ■ Bemidji Area Chamber of Commerce (BACC)
102 1st St. W, Ste. 105
Bemidji, MN 56601
Ph: (218)444-3541
Free: 800-458-2223
Fax: (218)444-4276
Co. E-mail: chamber@bemidji.org
URL: http://www.bemidji.org
Contact: Abby Randall, Executive Director
Facebook: www.facebook.com/BemidjiChamber
Linkedin: www.linkedin.com/company/bemidji-area-chamber-of-commerce
X (Twitter): x.com/bemidjichamber
Instagram: www.instagram.com/bemidjichamber
Description: Promotes business and community development in the Bemidji, MN area. **Founded:** 1907. **Publications:** *Chamber Report* (3/year). **Geographic Preference:** Local.

41195 ■ Big Lake Chamber of Commerce (BLCC)
625 Rose Dr.
Big Lake, MN 55309
Ph: (763)263-7800
Co. E-mail: info@biglakechamber.com
URL: http://biglakechamber.com
Contact: Monica Parrish, President
Facebook: www.facebook.com/BigLakeChamberofCommerce
Description: Promotes business and community development in Big Lake, AK area. **Geographic Preference:** Local.

41196 ■ Big Stone Lake Area Chamber of Commerce (BSLACC)
987 US Hwy. 12
Ortonville, MN 56278
Ph: (320)839-3284
Co. E-mail: chamber@bigstonelake.com
URL: http://bigstonelakechamber.com
Contact: Greg Peterson, President
Facebook: www.facebook.com/BSLAChamber
Description: Promotes tourism and economic development in the Big Stone Lake Area. **Geographic Preference:** Local.

41197 ■ *The Bottom Line*
1411 W St. Germain, Ste. 101
Saint Cloud, MN 56302-0487
Ph: (320)251-2940
Fax: (320)251-0081
Co. E-mail: information@stcloudareachamber.com
URL: http://www.stcloudareachamber.com
Contact: Gail Ivers, Vice President
E-mail: givers@stcloudareachamber.com
URL(s): www.stcloudareachamber.com/the-bottom-line
Released: Bimonthly **Availability:** Online.

41198 ■ Brainerd Lakes Area Chambers of Commerce
224 W Washington St.
Brainerd, MN 56401
Ph: (218)829-2838
Free: 800-450-2838
Fax: (218)829-8199
Co. E-mail: info@explorebrainerdlakes.com
URL: http://brainerdlakeschamber.com
Contact: Matt Kilian, President
Facebook: www.facebook.com/BrainerdLakesChamber
Linkedin: www.linkedin.com/company/brainerd-lakes-chamber-of-commerce
X (Twitter): x.com/BrainerdLakes
Instagram: www.instagram.com/brainerdlakeschamber
YouTube: www.youtube.com/channel/UCMpTuCgd7eB0xOvk9RSf7_Q
Description: Promotes business and community development in the Brainerd, MN area. Sponsors Brainerd Lakes Woods and Irons. **Founded:** 1882. **Publications:** *Indoor/Outdoor Activity and Restaurant Guide* (Annual); *Chamber Connection, Brainerd Lakes Area* (Monthly); *Chamber E-Newsletter* (Weekly (Fri.)); *Vacation Planning Guide* (Annual). **Educational Activities:** Commerce and Industry Show. **Geographic Preference:** Local.

41199 ■ *The Bridge*
202 First Ave., N
Moorhead, MN 56560
Ph: (218)233-1100
Fax: (218)233-1200
Co. E-mail: info@fmwfchamber.com
URL: http://www.fmwfchamber.com
Contact: Shannon Full, President
URL(s): www.fmwfchamber.com/publications
Released: Bimonthly **Availability:** Print; Online; PDF.

41200 ■ Buffalo Area Chamber of Commerce (BACC)
205 Central Ave.
Buffalo, MN 55313
Ph: (763)682-4902
Co. E-mail: info@buffalochamber.org
URL: http://www.buffalochamber.org
Contact: Jeremy Laxen, Chairman of the Board
Facebook: www.facebook.com/buffalochambermn
Linkedin: www.linkedin.com/company/buffalo-mn-chamber-of-commerce
X (Twitter): x.com/BuffaloChamber1
Instagram: www.instagram.com/buffaloareachamber
YouTube: www.youtube.com/channel/UCXDE4NqT0qW2uh3qRJZS6Zg
Description: Promotes business and community development in the Buffalo, MN area. Holds annual Buffalo Days, Sidewalk Art and Craft Festival, and Buffalo P.R.C.A. Rodeo. **Founded:** 1954. **Geographic Preference:** Local.

41201 ■ Burnsville Chamber of Commerce
350 W Burnsville Pky., Ste. No. 629
Burnsville, MN 55337
Ph: (952)435-6000
Fax: (952)435-6972
Co. E-mail: chamber@burnsvillechamber.com
URL: http://burnsvillechamber.com
Contact: Jennifer Harmening, President
E-mail: jharmening@burnsvillechamber.com
Facebook: www.facebook.com/BurnsvilleChamber
Instagram: www.instagram.com/BVchamber
YouTube: www.youtube.com/channel/UC8ERCHy4C6Var-sRsoopwlQ
Description: Promotes business and community development in Burnsville, MN. **Publications:** *At Work* (Monthly); *Chamber Membership Directory* (Annual). **Geographic Preference:** Local.

41202 ■ *Business Brief*
320 Hoffman Dr.
Owatonna, MN 55060
Ph: (507)451-7970
Free: 800-423-6466
Fax: (507)451-7972
Co. E-mail: oacct@owatonna.org
URL: http://www.owatonna.org
Contact: Brad Meier, President
E-mail: bmeier@owatonna.org
URL(s): owatonna.org/business-brief
Released: Latest edition 2024. **Description:** Contains information regarding membership, tourism, economic development, and OACCT happenings. **Availability:** PDF.

41203 ■ *Business Central*
1411 W St. Germain, Ste. 101
Saint Cloud, MN 56302-0487
Ph: (320)251-2940
Fax: (320)251-0081
Co. E-mail: information@stcloudareachamber.com
URL: http://www.stcloudareachamber.com
Contact: Gail Ivers, Vice President
E-mail: givers@stcloudareachamber.com
URL(s): www.businesscentralmagazine.com
Released: 6/year **Price:** $18, for 1 year. **Description:** Contains feature stories, business tips, and news from throughout Central Minnesota. **Availability:** Print; Online.

41204 ■ *Business Directory*
127 W Main St.
Madelia, MN 56062
Ph: (507)642-8822
Co. E-mail: chamber@madeliamn.com
URL: http://www.visitmadelia.com
Contact: Doug Fenske, President
URL(s): www.visitmadelia.com/directory
Availability: Online.

41205 ■ *Business Monthly*
132 N Broadway
Albert Lea, MN 56007
Ph: (507)373-3938
Fax: (507)377-1354
Co. E-mail: director@albertlea.org
URL: http://www.albertlea.org
Contact: Shari Jenson, Executive Director
URL(s): www.albertlea.org/monthly-newsletters
Released: Monthly **Availability:** PDF; Online.

41206 ■ Canby Area Chamber of Commerce
PO Box 115
Canby, MN 56220-0115
Ph: (507)223-7775
URL: http://www.canbychamber.com
Facebook: www.facebook.com/Canby-Chamber-of-Commerce-406037746074584
Description: Provides information on tourist attractions and outdoor activities in the Canby area. **Geographic Preference:** Local.

41207 ■ Cannon Falls Area Chamber of Commerce
103 4th St., N
Cannon Falls, MN 55009
Ph: (507)263-2289
Co. E-mail: tourism@cannonfalls.org
URL: http://www.cannonfalls.org
Facebook: www.facebook.com/cannonfalls.chamber
YouTube: www.youtube.com/channel/UCQ3vwwBy4ctY8M7YXY-4g2Q
Description: Promotes business and community development in the Cannon Falls, MN area. Supports local charities; conducts political and business networking forums. **Publications:** *Discover Cannon Falls* (Annual); *Chamber News* (Monthly). **Geographic Preference:** Local.

41208 ■ *The Chamber*
700 Summit Ave.
Detroit Lakes, MN 56501
Ph: (218)847-9202
URL: http://www.visitdetroitlakes.com
Contact: Carrie Johnston, President
URL(s): visitdetroitlakes.com/chamber/newsletter
Released: Monthly **Price:** $20, Single issue for annual subscriptions. **Availability:** PDF.

41209 ■ *The Chamber of Commerce News*
200 1st St. NW
Little Falls, MN 56345
Ph: (320)632-5155
Fax: (320)632-2122
URL: http://www.littlefallsmnchamber.com
Contact: Debora K. Boelz, President
E-mail: dboelz@littlefallsmnchamber.com
URL(s): www.littlefallsmnchamber.com/pages/Newsletter
Released: Monthly **Availability:** Download; Online; PDF.

41210 ■ *Chamber Edge*
1411 W St. Germain, Ste. 101
Saint Cloud, MN 56302-0487
Ph: (320)251-2940
Fax: (320)251-0081
Co. E-mail: information@stcloudareachamber.com
URL: http://www.stcloudareachamber.com
Contact: Gail Ivers, Vice President
E-mail: givers@stcloudareachamber.com
URL(s): www.stcloudareachamber.com/membership/get-involved/chamber-connectors
Released: Monthly **Availability:** Online.

41211 ■ *Chamber Membership Directory*
350 W Burnsville Pky., Ste. No. 629
Burnsville, MN 55337
Ph: (952)435-6000
Fax: (952)435-6272
Co. E-mail: chamber@burnsvillechamber.com
URL: http://burnsvillechamber.com
Contact: Jennifer Harmening, President
E-mail: jharmening@burnsvillechamber.com
URL(s): members.burnsvillechamber.com/list
Released: Annual **Availability:** Online.

41212 ■ *Chamber News*
4785 Dakota St.
Prior Lake, MN 55372
Ph: (952)440-1000
URL: http://www.priorlakechamber.com
Contact: Sandi Fleck, President
E-mail: sandi@priorlakechamber.com
URL(s): www.priorlakechamber.com/membership-benefits
Released: Monthly **Availability:** Print.

41213 ■ *Chamber Update*
202 S Ct. St.
Fergus Falls, MN 56537
Ph: (218)736-6951
Co. E-mail: chamber@fergusfalls.com
URL: http://www.fergusfalls.com
Contact: Lisa Workman, President
E-mail: lworkman@fergusfalls.com
URL(s): www.fergusfalls.com/chamber-business-services
Availability: Print; Online.

41214 ■ Chisholm Area Chamber of Commerce
223 W Lake St.
Chisholm, MN 55719
Ph: (218)254-7930
Free: 800-422-0806
Co. E-mail: info@chisholmchamber.com
URL: http://www.chisholmchamber.com
Facebook: www.facebook.com/ChisholmAreaChamber
Description: Promotes business and community development in the Chisholm, MN area. Sponsors Christmas lighting competition, annual Polar Bear Days, annual Firedays, and All Class Grand Reunion. **Founded:** 1933. **Geographic Preference:** Local.

41215 ■ Cloquet Area Chamber of Commerce (CACC)
225 Sunnyside Dr.
Cloquet, MN 55720
Ph: (218)879-1551
Free: 800-554-4350
Fax: (218)878-0223
Co. E-mail: chamber@cloquet.com
URL: http://www.cloquet.com
Contact: Jeannie Kermeen, Chairman
Facebook: www.facebook.com/cloquet.chamber
X (Twitter): x.com/cloquetchamber
Description: Promotes business and community development in the Cloquet, MN area. Provides business consulting and business plan preparation. **Founded:** 1952. **Publications:** *Chamber Review* (Monthly); *Membership Directory*. **Geographic Preference:** Local.

41216 ■ Cokato Chamber of Commerce (CCC)
PO Box 819
Cokato, MN 55321
Ph: (320)286-5505
Fax: (320)286-5876
Co. E-mail: chamber@connectwithcokato.com
URL: http://www.connectwithcokato.com/cokato-chamber
Contact: Teresa Martinson, Secretary
Description: Promotes business and community development in Cokato, MN. Supports local charities; conducts political and business networking forums. **Geographic Preference:** Local.

41217 ■ Cook Chamber of Commerce
PO Box 296
Cook, MN 55723
Co. E-mail: cookmnchamber@gmail.com
URL: http://www.cookchamber.com
Facebook: www.facebook.com/CookMn
Description: Works to increase awareness of the area, support events, tourism promotion, support economic and community development and business affairs that will benefit the entire community. **Geographic Preference:** Local.

41218 ■ Cottage Grove Area Chamber of Commerce
8617 W Point Douglas Rd., Ste. 150
Cottage Grove, MN 55016-0016
Ph: (651)458-8334
Fax: (651)458-8383
Co. E-mail: office@cottagegrovechamber.org
URL: http://www.cottagegrovechamber.org
Contact: Laurie Levine, President
Facebook: www.facebook.com/cgareachamber
Linkedin: www.linkedin.com/in/cottage-grove-area-chamber-5b503115
X (Twitter): x.com/cottage_of
YouTube: www.youtube.com/channel/UCWf8PmuQBvBp3rzPgBXI1WQ
Description: Businesses in Cottage Grove, Newport, and St. Paul Park, in South Washington County, Minnesota. Strives to promote economic development and business growth within the Chamber area; develop a strong business-education partnership and identify legislative issues affecting private enterprise. **Founded:** 1990. **Geographic Preference:** Local.

41219 ■ Crookston Chamber and Visitors Bureau
103 South Broadway
Crookston, MN 56716
Ph: (218)281-4320
Co. E-mail: info@visitcrookston.com
URL: http://www.visitcrookston.com
Contact: Mark Landa, Executive Director
E-mail: mlanda@visitcrookston.com
Facebook: www.facebook.com/crookstonareachamber
X (Twitter): twitter.com/croxchamber
Description: Promotes business and community development in Crookston, MN area. **Geographic Preference:** Local.

41220 ■ Dakota County Regional Chamber of Commerce
1895 Plz. Dr.
Eagan, MN 55122
Ph: (651)452-9872
Co. E-mail: info@dcrchamber.com
URL: http://www.dcrchamber.com
Contact: Lisa Franxman, Treasurer
Facebook: www.facebook.com/dcrchamber
Linkedin: www.linkedin.com/company/dcrchamber
X (Twitter): x.com/DCRChamber
Instagram: www.instagram.com/dcrchamber
YouTube: www.youtube.com/channel/UC_Eo7cdIrm989rT9hNC5k1g
Description: Works to unite and strengthen the business community by providing networking, supporting educational opportunities, encouraging business and community development and determining public policy. **Founded:** 1957. **Geographic Preference:** Local.

41221 ■ Delano Area Chamber of Commerce (DACC)
131 Babcock Blvd. W
Delano, MN 55328-0027
Ph: (763)972-6756
Co. E-mail: dacc@delanochamber.com
URL: http://www.delanochamber.com
Contact: Josh Gehlen, President
E-mail: josh.gehlen@mnlb.bank
Facebook: www.facebook.com/DelanoAreaChamberofCommerce
Description: Works to improve the business community of Delano area. **Educational Activities:** Ambassador/Membership Meeting (Monthly). **Geographic Preference:** Local.

41222 ■ Detroit Lakes Regional Chamber of Commerce
700 Summit Ave.
Detroit Lakes, MN 56501
Ph: (218)847-9202
URL: http://www.visitdetroitlakes.com
Contact: Carrie Johnston, President
Facebook: www.facebook.com/DetroitLakesMN
X (Twitter): x.com/DetroitLakesMN
YouTube: www.youtube.com/channel/UCBYl49MfVzO8NlcGFSTyUvg
Description: Promotes business and community development in the Detroit Lakes, MN area. **Founded:** 1906. **Publications:** *The Chamber* (Monthly); *Membership Directory/Buyers Guide*. **Geographic Preference:** Local.

41223 ■ *Discovery Guide*
1204 Pk. Ave., S
Park Rapids, MN 56470
Ph: (218)732-4111
Free: 800-247-0054
Fax: (218)732-4112
Co. E-mail: chamber@parkrapids.com
URL: http://parkrapids.com
Contact: Debbie Tostenson, Chairman
E-mail: debbiet@cnbbank.com
URL(s): parkrapids.com/discovery-guide
Released: Latest issue 2024. **Availability:** PDF; Download; Online.

41224 ■ Duluth Area Chamber of Commerce (DACC)
5 W 1st St., Ste. 101
Duluth, MN 55802
Ph: (218)722-5501
Co. E-mail: inquiry@duluthchamber.com
URL: http://www.duluthchamber.com
Contact: Matt Baumgartner, President
Facebook: www.facebook.com/duluth.chamber
Linkedin: www.linkedin.com/in/duluthchamber
X (Twitter): x.com/duluthchamber
Instagram: www.instagram.com/duluthchamber
YouTube: www.youtube.com/user/DuluthAreaChamber#p

Description: Promotes business and community development in Duluth, MN. Supports local charities; conducts political and business networking forums. **Founded:** 1870. **Publications:** *Xpress* (Monthly); *The Duluthian* (Bimonthly). **Geographic Preference:** Local.

41225 ■ Eden Prairie Chamber of Commerce (EPC)
10925 Valley View Rd.
Eden Prairie, MN 55344
Ph: (952)944-2830
Fax: (952)944-0229
Co. E-mail: communications@epchamber.org
URL: http://www.epchamber.org
Contact: Pat MulQueeny, President
E-mail: pat.mulqueeny@epchamber.org
Linkedin: www.linkedin.com/company/eden-prairie-chamber-of-commerce
X (Twitter): x.com/EPChamber
Instagram: www.instagram.com/epchamber

Description: Provides their members opportunities for community leadership. Acts as an advocate for commerce. Promotes community growth and development. **Founded:** 1969. **Geographic Preference:** Local.

41226 ■ Elk River Area Chamber of Commerce (ERACC)
509 Hwy. 10
Elk River, MN 55330
Ph: (763)441-3110
Fax: (763)441-3409
Co. E-mail: eracc@elkriverchamber.org
URL: http://www.elkriverchamber.org
Contact: Debbi Rydberg, Executive Director
E-mail: debbi@elkriverchamber.org
Facebook: www.facebook.com/ElkRiverAreaChamber
Linkedin: www.linkedin.com/company/elk-river-area-chamber-of-commerce
X (Twitter): x.com/ElkRiverChamber
Instagram: www.instagram.com/elkriverareachamber

Description: Promotes business and community development in the Elk River, MN area. **Founded:** 1968. **Publications:** *City Map*. **Geographic Preference:** Local.

41227 ■ Ely Chamber of Commerce (ECC)
1600 E Sheridan St.
Ely, MN 55731
Ph: (218)365-6123
URL: http://www.ely.org/about-us
Contact: Dafne Caruso, President

Description: Promotes business and tourism in Ely, MN. Sponsors Blueberry Art Festival and Fall Harvest Moon Festival. **Founded:** 1908. **Publications:** *Vacation Guide* (Annual). **Geographic Preference:** Local.

41228 ■ Fairmont Area Chamber of Commerce
323 Blue E Ave.
Fairmont, MN 56031
Ph: (507)235-5547
Co. E-mail: info@fairmontchamber.org
URL: http://fairmontchamber.org
Contact: Kandi Menne, Co-President
Facebook: www.facebook.com/fairmontchamber
Linkedin: www.linkedin.com/company/fairmontchamber
X (Twitter): x.com/fairmontchamber

Description: Promotes business and community development in the Fairmont, MN area. Supports local charities; conducts political and business networking forums. **Founded:** 1926. **Publications:** *Chamber Update* (Monthly). **Geographic Preference:** Local.

41229 ■ Fargo Moorhead West Fargo Chamber of Commerce
202 First Ave., N
Moorhead, MN 56560
Ph: (218)233-1100
Fax: (218)233-1200
Co. E-mail: info@fmwfchamber.com
URL: http://www.fmwfchamber.com
Contact: Shannon Full, President
Facebook: www.facebook.com/fmwfchamber
Linkedin: www.linkedin.com/company/fargo-moorhead-west-fargo-chamber-of-commerce
X (Twitter): x.com/fmwfchamber
Instagram: www.instagram.com/fmwfchamber
YouTube: www.youtube.com/user/FMChamber

Description: Unifies and advances business and community interests in a bi-state, metropolitan community and the surrounding region. **Founded:** 1879. **Publications:** *The Bridge* (Bimonthly); *Building Bridges* (Annual); *Community Profile* (Annual). **Awards:** Fargo Moorhead Chamber Choice Business of the Year (Annual); Fargo Moorhead Chamber Choice Not-for-Profit of the Year (Annual); Fargo Moorhead Chamber Choice Small Business of the Year (Annual). **Geographic Preference:** Regional.

41230 ■ Faribault Area Chamber of Commerce and Tourism
530 Wilson Ave.
Faribault, MN 55021
Ph: (507)334-4381
Co. E-mail: chamber@faribaultmn.org
URL: http://www.faribaultmn.org
Contact: Nort Johnson, President
E-mail: nort@faribaultmn.org

Description: Promotes agricultural, business, and community development in the Faribault, MN area. Promotes tourism. Holds annual Heritage Days festival, Balloon Rally and Business Expo. **Founded:** 1913. **Publications:** *Chamber Members Directory*; *Greater Raleigh Chamber of Commerce--Major Employers Directory*; *Organizational Directory* (Periodic). **Educational Activities:** Business Farm Luncheon (Annual). **Awards:** Faribault Area Chamber Business of the Year (Annual). **Geographic Preference:** Local.

41231 ■ Fergus Falls Area Chamber of Commerce (FFACC)
202 S Ct. St.
Fergus Falls, MN 56537
Ph: (218)736-6951
Co. E-mail: chamber@fergusfalls.com
URL: http://www.fergusfalls.com
Contact: Lisa Workman, President
E-mail: lworkman@fergusfalls.com
X (Twitter): x.com/FergusChamber

Description: Promotes business and community development in the Fergus Falls, MN area. Holds annual Scandinavian and Frostbite Festivals. **Founded:** 1886. **Publications:** *Chamber Update*. **Geographic Preference:** Local.

41232 ■ Forest Lake Area Chamber of Commerce (FLACC)
Town Sq. Bldg.
20 N Lake St., Ste. 204
Forest Lake, MN 55025-0474
Ph: (651)464-3200
Fax: (651)464-3201
Co. E-mail: chamber@flacc.org
URL: http://forestlakechamber.org
Contact: Nannette M. LaNasa, Executive Director
Facebook: www.facebook.com/forestlakechamb
X (Twitter): x.com/forestlakechamb

Description: Promotes business and community development in the Forest Lake, MN area. Sponsors Fun in the Forest festival. **Founded:** 1964. **Publications:** *Chamber Connection* (Monthly). **Geographic Preference:** Local.

41233 ■ Glencoe Area Chamber of Commerce
1107 11th St. E, Ste. 104
Glencoe, MN 55336
Ph: (320)864-3650
Co. E-mail: sally@glencoechamber.com
URL: http://glencoechamber.com
Contact: Sally Custer, President
E-mail: sally@glencoechamber.com
Facebook: www.facebook.com/GACCMN

Description: Strives to create, promote, and enhance the business environment and improve the quality of life in the Glencoe area. **Geographic Preference:** Local.

41234 ■ *Glenwood Chamber of Commerce Newsletter*
7 1st St. NW
Glenwood, MN 56334
Ph: (320)634-3636
Fax: (320)634-3637
Co. E-mail: chamber@glenwoodlakesarea.org
URL: http://www.glenwoodlakesarea.org
Contact: Jordan McMahon, President
URL(s): www.glenwoodlakesarea.org/newsletter
Released: Weekly **Availability:** Online.

41235 ■ Glenwood Lakes Area Chamber of Commerce (GACC)
7 1st St. NW
Glenwood, MN 56334
Ph: (320)634-3636
Fax: (320)634-3637
Co. E-mail: chamber@glenwoodlakesarea.org
URL: http://www.glenwoodlakesarea.org
Contact: Jordan McMahon, President
Facebook: www.facebook.com/glenwoodlakesareachamber
YouTube: www.youtube.com/channel/UC8AohGqVOWXZC6olmAlNltA

Description: Promotes business and community development in Glenwood, MN. Sponsors Waterama festival, Lake Minnewaska Ice Fishing Contest and Physically Limited Golfers Association National Tournament. **Founded:** 1951. **Publications:** *Glenwood Chamber of Commerce Newsletter* (Weekly). **Geographic Preference:** Local.

41236 ■ Grand Marais Chamber of Commerce
PO Box 805
Grand Marais, MN 55604
Ph: (218)370-9665
Co. E-mail: ccchamber@boreal.org
URL: http://www.cookcountychamber.org
Contact: Jennifer Stoltz, Treasurer
Facebook: www.facebook.com/cookcountychamber.MN

Description: Supports member businesses, economic growth, and community events in the Grand Marais Area. **Geographic Preference:** Local.

41237 ■ Grand Rapids Area Chamber of Commerce (GRACC)
1 NW 3rd St.
Grand Rapids, MN 55744
Ph: (218)326-6619
Free: 800-472-6366
Co. E-mail: info@grandmn.com
URL: http://www.grandmn.com
Contact: Mark Rudolph, President
E-mail: mrudolph@grandmn.com
Facebook: www.facebook.com/grchambermn

Description: Promotes business and community development in the Grand Rapids, MN area. **Founded:** 1902. **Publications:** *The Voice of Business* (Monthly). **Geographic Preference:** Local.

41238 ■ Granite Falls Area Chamber of Commerce (GFACC)
676 Prentice St.
Granite Falls, MN 56241
Ph: (320)321-3202
Co. E-mail: granitefallschamberofcommerce@gmail.com
URL: http://www.granitefallschamber.com

Facebook: www.facebook.com/Grani
teFallsAreaChamberOfCommerce
X (Twitter): x.com/GraniteChamber
Pinterest: www.pinterest.com/gfchamber
Description: Promotes business and community development in the Granite Falls, MN area. **Geographic Preference:** Local.

41239 ■ Greater Stillwater Chamber of Commerce
333 N Main St., No. 202
Stillwater, MN 55082
Ph: (651)439-4001
Fax: (651)439-4035
Co. E-mail: info@greaterstillwaterchamber.com
URL: http://greaterstillwaterchamber.com
Contact: Chuck LeRoux, Secretary
Facebook: www.facebook.com/GreaterStillwa
terChamber
Linkedin: www.linkedin.com/company/greater-stillwa
ter-chamber-of-commerce
X (Twitter): x.com/StillwaterCOC
Instagram: www.instagram.com/greaterstillwa
terchamber
Description: Promotes business and community development in Stillwater, MN. **Founded:** 1891. **Geographic Preference:** Local.

41240 ■ Greater Wayzata Area Chamber of Commerce
402 E Lake St.
Wayzata, MN 55391
Ph: (952)473-9595
Co. E-mail: info@wayzatachamber.com
URL: http://wayzatachamber.com
Contact: Becky Pierson, President
E-mail: bpierson@wayzatachamber.com
Facebook: www.facebook.com/Wayza
taChamberofCommerce
Linkedin: www.linkedin.com/company/greater-wayza
ta-area-chamber-of-commerce
Description: Promotes business and community development in Wayzata, MN. Sponsors trolley rides and concerts in the summer, fall and winter golf outing, and annual festival in September. **Founded:** 1939. **Publications:** *Discover Wayzata*; *Whistle Stop* (Monthly). **Educational Activities:** James J. Hill Days (Annual). **Geographic Preference:** Local.

41241 ■ Hastings Area Chamber of Commerce and Tourism Bureau
314 Vermillion St., Ste. 100
Hastings, MN 55033-1211
Ph: (651)437-6775
Co. E-mail: info@hastingsmn.org
URL: http://www.hastingsmn.org
Contact: Kristy Barse, President
E-mail: kristy@hastingsmn.org
Facebook: www.facebook.com/HastingsMN
X (Twitter): x.com/ChamberHastings
Description: Works together to advance the commercial, financial, industrial, and civic interest of the community. **Geographic Preference:** Local.

41242 ■ Hermantown Chamber of Commerce
5094 Miller Trunk Hwy., Ste. 600
Hermantown, MN 55811
Ph: (218)729-6843
Co. E-mail: info@hermantownchamber.com
URL: http://www.hermantownchamber.com
Contact: Kimberly Parmeter, President
E-mail: kim@hermantownchamber.com
Facebook: www.facebook.com/HermantownChamber
Linkedin: www.linkedin.com/company/hermantown
-area-chamber-of-commerce
X (Twitter): x.com/htownchamber
Instagram: www.instagram.com/hermantownchamber
Description: Promotes business and community development in the Hermantown, MN area. Provides leadership for the community, promotes local resources, enhances local programs, and coordinates development efforts. **Geographic Preference:** Local.

41243 ■ Hibbing Area Chamber of Commerce
109 E Howard St.
Hibbing, MN 55746
Ph: (218)262-3895
Free: 800-444-2246
Co. E-mail: hibbcofc@hibbing.org
URL: http://www.hibbing.org
Contact: Shelly Hanson, President
E-mail: s.hanson@hibbing.org
Facebook: www.facebook.com/HibbingAreaChamber
Instagram: www.instagram.com/hibbingareachamber
Description: Promotes business and community development in Hibbing, MN. **Founded:** 1905. **Geographic Preference:** Local.

41244 ■ Houston Area Chamber of Commerce (HACC)
PO Box 3
Houston, MN 55943
Ph: (507)896-4033
Co. E-mail: houstonmnchamber@gmail.com
URL: http://www.houstonmnchamber.com
Contact: Kristie G. G. Miller, Contact
Facebook: www.facebook.com/Hous
tonAreaChamberofCommerce
Description: Promotes business and community development in the Houston area. Sponsors the Emmett Kelly Clown Festival, annual golf tournament, Texas County Fair and Old Settler's Reunion, Heritage Days, the Christmas parade and Christmas promotions. **Founded:** 1906. **Geographic Preference:** Local.

41245 ■ Hutchinson Area Chamber of Commerce and Tourism
2 Main St. S
Hutchinson, MN 55350
Ph: (320)587-5252
Free: 800-572-6689
Fax: (320)587-4752
Co. E-mail: info@explorehutchinson.com
URL: http://explorehutchinson.com
Contact: Mary Hodson, President
E-mail: mary@explorehutchinson.com
Facebook: www.facebook.com/HutchChameran
dTourism
Linkedin: www.linkedin.com/company/hutchinson-mn
-area-chamber-and-tourism
X (Twitter): x.com/HutchChamberMN
Instagram: www.instagram.com/hutchinsonchamber
YouTube: www.youtube.com/channel/UCg_5Ji
3tx8Tb0-EiPG6XWMw
Pinterest: www.pinterest.com/hutchmnchamber
Description: Seeks to promote city of Hutchinson, MN as a place for conventions and business gatherings. **Founded:** 1948. **Publications:** *Hometown Happenings* (Monthly). **Geographic Preference:** Local.

41246 ■ I-94 West Chamber of Commerce
21370 John Milless Dr.
Rogers, MN 55374
Ph: (763)428-2921
Co. E-mail: info@i94westchamber.org
URL: http://www.i94westchamber.org
Contact: Dawn Sperr, Advisor
Facebook: www.facebook.com/pages/I-94-Wes
t-Chamber-of-Commerce/124725567540816
Linkedin: www.linkedin.com/company/i-94-wes
t-chamber-of-commerce
X (Twitter): x.com/I94West
Instagram: www.instagram.com/I94WestChamber
YouTube: www.youtube.com/channel/
UCMziwMuaEqOrl6qJWox3I0Q
Description: Promotes business and community development in Dayton, MN. Supports local charities; conducts political and business networking forums. **Founded:** 1988. **Geographic Preference:** Local.

41247 ■ International Falls Area Chamber of Commerce
301 2nd Ave.
International Falls, MN 56649
Ph: (218)283-9400
Free: 800-325-5766
Fax: (218)283-3572
Co. E-mail: chamberadmin@intlfalls.org
URL: http://www.ifallschamber.com
Contact: Tricia Heibel, President
E-mail: tricia@intlfalls.org
Facebook: www.facebook.com/IFallsChamber
Description: Promotes business and community development in the International Falls, MN area. **Founded:** 1953. **Geographic Preference:** Local.

41248 ■ Jackson Area Chamber of Commerce (JACC)
114 3rd St.
Jackson, MN 56143
Ph: (507)847-3867
Fax: (507)847-3869
Co. E-mail: chamber@jacksonmn.com
URL: http://www.jacksonmn.com
Contact: Corey Christopher, Executive Director
Facebook: www.facebook.com/
JacksonAreaChamberofCommerce
X (Twitter): x.com/JxnChamber
Description: Promotes business and community development in the area. **Founded:** 2011. **Publications:** *Experience the Jackson Area*. **Geographic Preference:** Local.

41249 ■ La Crescent Chamber of Commerce
111 S Walnut St.
La Crescent, MN 55947
Contact: Sarah Danielson, President
Description: Promotes business, community development, and tourism in La Crescent, MN. **Founded:** 1959. **Geographic Preference:** Local.

41250 ■ Lake Benton Area Chamber of Commerce and Convention and Visitors Bureau
106 S Center St.
Lake Benton, MN 56149
Ph: (507)368-9577
Co. E-mail: chamber@lakebenton.us
URL: http://lakebenton.us
Contact: Karen Lichtsinn, Administrator
Facebook: www.facebook.com/lakebentonchamber
Description: Provides information about business opportunities in Lake Benton. **Geographic Preference:** Local.

41251 ■ Lake City Area Chamber of Commerce
100 E Lyon Ave.
Lake City, MN 55041
Ph: (641)345-4123
Co. E-mail: chamberevents@lakecity.org
URL: http://lakecity.org
Contact: Vicki Krage, President
E-mail: vickikrage@gmail.com
Facebook: www.facebook.com/LakeCi
tyChamberofCommerce
X (Twitter): x.com/lakecitychamber
Description: Promotes commerce in the Lake City area. **Founded:** 1953. **Publications:** *Lake City Chamber Corner* (Weekly (Fri.)). **Geographic Preference:** Local.

41252 ■ Lake City Chamber of Commerce
100 E Lyon Ave.
Lake City, MN 55041
Ph: (651)345-4123
Co. E-mail: chamberevents@lakecity.org
URL: http://lakecity.org
Contact: Carolyn Ellingson, President
E-mail: ellingson.carolyn@mayo.edu
Facebook: www.facebook.com/LakeCi
tyChamberofCommerce
X (Twitter): x.com/lakecitychamber
Description: Promotes business and community development in the Lake City, MN area. **Founded:** 1935. **Geographic Preference:** Local.

41253 ■ Lake County Chamber of Commerce
1330 MN-61
Two Harbors, MN 55616
Ph: (218)834-2600
Co. E-mail: info@lakecounty-chamber.com
URL: http://lakecounty-chamber.com
Contact: Warren Miller, Chairman
Facebook: www.facebook.com/
ExperienceLakeCounty
X (Twitter): x.com/LovinLakeCounty
Instagram: www.instagram.com/lovinlakecounty

STATE LISTINGS

Description: Promotes business and community development in the Two Harbors, MN area. **Publications:** *Chamber Outlook* (Weekly). **Geographic Preference:** Local.

41254 ■ Lake Crystal Area Chamber of Commerce
113 S Main St.
  Lake Crystal, MN 56055
Ph: (507)726-6088
Co. E-mail: lcacc56055@gmail.com
URL: http://www.lakecrystalchamber.com
Contact: Annette Farrell, President
Facebook: www.facebook.com/lake.c.chamber
Description: Promotes business and community development in Lake Crystal Area, MN. **Geographic Preference:** Local.

41255 ■ Lake Vermilion Area Chamber of Commerce (LVACC)
PO Box 776
  Tower, MN 55790
Ph: (218)753-2301
Free: 800-869-3766
URL: http://www.madeontherange.com/lake-vermilion-chamber-of-commerce.html
Description: Promotes business and community development in Tower, MN. Holds annual Fourth of July Celebration. **Geographic Preference:** Local.

41256 ■ Laurentian Chamber of Commerce
5465 Mountain Iron Dr.
  Virginia, MN 55792
Ph: (218)741-2717
Co. E-mail: president@laurentianchamber.org
URL: http://laurentianchamber.org
Contact: Teresa Appelwick, President
E-mail: president@laurentianchamber.org
Facebook: www.facebook.com/LaurentianChamber
Linkedin: www.linkedin.com/company/laurentian-chamber-of-commerce
X (Twitter): x.com/LaurentianChamb
Instagram: www.instagram.com/laurentianchamber
Description: Promotes business and community development in Virginia, Eveleth, Mountain Iron, and Gilbert, MN. Educates on the value and importance of a thriving business community and on business issues impacting them; advocates for issues as appropriate; identifies the needs of the business community and becomes aware of its health; fosters participation and involvement in the chambers to build leaders; and serves as an information and referral resource for members. **Founded:** 2003. **Publications:** *Youth Employment Directory* (Periodic). **Geographic Preference:** Local.

41257 ■ Le Sueur Area Chamber of Commerce (LSACC)
PO Box 111
  Le Sueur, MN 56058
Ph: (507)665-2501
Co. E-mail: info@lesueurchamber.org
URL: http://www.lesueurchamber.org
Contact: Steve Thaemert, Executive Director
Linkedin: www.linkedin.com/in/le-sueur-chamber-999716260
Description: Promotes business and community development in the Le Sueur, MN area. Sponsors Legislative Day at the Capitol, garage sales, Farm and Home Show, Giant Celebration, Agriculture Appreciation Affair and Manufacture Expo. **Founded:** 1852. **Publications:** *Chamber Chat* (Weekly). **Educational Activities:** Farm and Home Show. **Geographic Preference:** Local.

41258 ■ Leech Lake Area Chamber of Commerce (LLACC)
201 Minnesota Ave., W
  Walker, MN 56484
Ph: (218)547-1313
Free: 800-833-1118
Co. E-mail: info@leech-lake.com
URL: http://www.leech-lake.com
Contact: Jill Duclos, Secretary
Facebook: www.facebook.com/leechlakechamber
X (Twitter): x.com/leechlakecc
Instagram: www.instagram.com/leechlakechamber

YouTube: www.youtube.com/channel/UCmgfKvhdbYoeKD0LUuLGGKA
Description: Promotes business and community development in the Leech Lake, MN area. **Founded:** 1963. **Publications:** *Chamber Chatter* (Monthly). **Educational Activities:** Ethnic Festival (Annual). **Geographic Preference:** Local.

41259 ■ Litchfield Area Chamber of Commerce
219 N Sibley Ave.
  Litchfield, MN 55355
Ph: (320)693-8184
Co. E-mail: litch@litch.com
URL: http://litch.com
Contact: Judy Hulterstrum, Executive Director
E-mail: judy@litch.com
Facebook: www.facebook.com/LitchfieldChamber
Description: Promotes business and community development in Litchfield, MN. **Founded:** 1955. **Geographic Preference:** Local.

41260 ■ Litchfield Chamber of Commerce
219 N Sibley Ave.
  Litchfield, MN 55355
Ph: (320)693-8184
Co. E-mail: litch@litch.com
URL: http://litch.com
Contact: Judy Hulterstrum, Executive Director
Facebook: www.facebook.com/LitchfieldChamber
X (Twitter): x.com/litchchamber
Instagram: www.instagram.com/litchchamber
Description: Promotes business and community development in Litchfield, MI. **Founded:** 1967. **Geographic Preference:** Local.

41261 ■ Little Falls Area Chamber of Commerce (LFACC)
200 1st St. NW
  Little Falls, MN 56345
Ph: (320)632-5155
Fax: (320)632-2122
URL: http://www.littlefallsmnchamber.com
Contact: Debora K. Boelz, President
E-mail: dboelz@littlefallsmnchamber.com
Description: Promotes business and community development in the Little Falls, MN area. Holds arts and crafts fair. **Founded:** 1888. **Publications:** *The Chamber of Commerce News* (Monthly). **Educational Activities:** Little Falls Arts and Crafts Fair (Annual). **Geographic Preference:** Local.

41262 ■ Long Prairie Area Chamber of Commerce (LPACC)
42 3rd St. N
  Long Prairie, MN 56347
Ph: (320)732-2514
Co. E-mail: chamber@longprairie.org
URL: http://www.longprairie.org
Contact: Josiah Tonder, President
Facebook: www.facebook.com/LongPrairieAreaChamberofCommerce
Description: Promotes business and community development in the Long Prairie, MN area. Sponsors Prairie Days Festival. **Founded:** 1961. **Publications:** *The Voice of Commerce* (Bimonthly). **Geographic Preference:** Local.

41263 ■ Luverne Area Chamber of Commerce (LCC)
213 E Luverne St.
  Luverne, MN 56156
Ph: (507)283-4061
Co. E-mail: luvernechamber@co.rock.mn.us
URL: http://www.luvernechamber.com
Contact: Becky Walgrave, President
Facebook: www.facebook.com/luvchamber
Description: Promotes business and community development in Laverne, OK. **Founded:** 1934. **Geographic Preference:** Local.

41264 ■ Madelia Area Chamber of Commerce
127 W Main St.
  Madelia, MN 56062
Ph: (507)642-8822
Co. E-mail: chamber@madeliamn.com
URL: http://www.visitmadelia.com

Contact: Doug Fenske, President
Facebook: www.facebook.com/madeliachamber
Description: Promotes business and community development in the Madelia, MN area. **Publications:** *Business Directory*; *Madelia Area Chamber Newsletter* (Monthly). **Geographic Preference:** Local.

41265 ■ *Madella Area Chamber Newsletter*
127 W Main St.
  Madelia, MN 56062
Ph: (507)642-8822
Co. E-mail: chamber@madeliamn.com
URL: http://www.visitmadelia.com
Contact: Doug Fenske, President
URL(s): www.visitmadelia.com/news
Released: Monthly **Availability:** Download; PDF.

41266 ■ Marshall Area Chamber of Commerce (MACC)
317 W Main St.
  Marshall, MN 56258
Ph: (507)532-4484
Co. E-mail: chamber@marshallmn.org
URL: http://marshallmn.org
Contact: Brad Gruhot, President
E-mail: brad.gruhot@marshallmn.org
Facebook: www.facebook.com/marshallareachamber
Linkedin: www.linkedin.com/company/marshall-are-chamber-of-commerce
X (Twitter): x.com/ChamberMarshall
Instagram: www.instagram.com/marshallareachamber
Description: Promotes business and community development in the area. **Founded:** 1930. **Publications:** *Community Guide* (Annual); *Chamber News* (Bimonthly); *Marshall Area Chamber Newsletter* (Monthly). **Educational Activities:** Business After Hours (Monthly). **Awards:** Marshall Area Chamber of Commerce Athena Award Program (Annual). **Geographic Preference:** Local.

41267 ■ Melrose Area Chamber of Commerce
223 Main St. E
  Melrose, MN 56352
Ph: (320)256-7174
Co. E-mail: melrosechamber@outlook.com
URL: http://www.melrosemn.org
Contact: Tom Budde, President
Facebook: www.facebook.com/Melrose-Area-Chamber-of-Commerce-220929447918543
Description: Promotes business and community development in Melrose, MN. Sponsors festival and beauty pageant. **Founded:** 1928. **Geographic Preference:** Local.

41268 ■ *Membership Directory*
225 Sunnyside Dr.
  Cloquet, MN 55720
Ph: (218)879-1551
Free: 800-554-4350
Fax: (218)878-0223
Co. E-mail: chamber@cloquet.com
URL: http://www.cloquet.com
Contact: Jeannie Kermeen, Chairman
URL(s): www.cloquet.com/members/member-directory
Availability: Online.

41269 ■ MetroNorth Chamber of Commerce (MNC)
9380 Central Ave. NE, Ste. 320, 21st Century Bank Bldg.
  Blaine, MN 55434
Ph: (763)783-3553
Fax: (763)783-3557
Co. E-mail: chamber@metronorthchamber.org
URL: http://www.metronorthchamber.org
Contact: Lori Higgins, President
E-mail: lori@metronorthchamber.org
Facebook: www.facebook.com/MetroNorthChamber
X (Twitter): x.com/MetroNorthChamb
YouTube: www.youtube.com/user/MetroNorthChamber1
Description: Promotes business and community development in Anoka County, MN. Supports local charities; conducts political and business networking forums. **Founded:** 1968. **Publications:** *Community*

41270 ■ Minnesota

Resource Guide (Annual). **Educational Activities:** Com-Mark Computer and Marketing Expo. **Geographic Preference:** Local.

41270 ■ Milaca Area Chamber of Commerce
255 1st St. E
Milaca, MN 56353
Ph: (320)983-3140
Co. E-mail: info@milacachamber.com
URL: http://www.milacachamber.com/#!directory/ord=rnd
Contact: Carrie Vesel, President
Facebook: www.facebook.com/MilacaAreaChamberOfCommerce
X (Twitter): x.com/MilacaChamber
Instagram: www.instagram.com/milacaareachamberofcommerce
Description: Works to create, protect and enhance the healthy business environment for the benefit of the area. **Founded:** 1886. **Geographic Preference:** Local.

41271 ■ Minneapolis Regional Chamber of Commerce
81 S 9th St., Ste. 200
Minneapolis, MN 55402
Ph: (612)370-9100
Co. E-mail: info@minneapolischamber.org
URL: http://www.mplschamber.com
Contact: Jonathan Weinhagen, President
E-mail: jweinhagen@mplschamber.com
Facebook: www.facebook.com/minneapolischamber
X (Twitter): x.com/MplsChamber
YouTube: www.youtube.com/user/mplschamber1
Description: Promotes business and community development in the Minneapolis, MN area. **Founded:** 1881. **Publications:** *Minneapolis Regional Chamber of Commerce--Membership Directory*. **Awards:** Quality of Life Awards (Annual). **Geographic Preference:** Local.

41272 ■ Minnesota Chamber of Commerce
380 St., Peter St., Ste. 1050
Saint Paul, MN 55102
Ph: (651)292-4650
Free: 800-821-2230
Co. E-mail: mail@mnchamber.com
URL: http://www.mnchamber.com
Contact: Doug Loon, President
E-mail: dloon@mnchamber.com
Facebook: www.facebook.com/MNChamber
Linkedin: www.linkedin.com/company/minnesotachamberofcommerce
X (Twitter): x.com/MN_Chamber
Instagram: www.instagram.com/mnchamberofcommerce
Description: Promotes business and economic growth throughout the state. **Founded:** 1909. **Publications:** *Minnesota Business Views* (Monthly). **Geographic Preference:** State.

41273 ■ Montevideo Area Chamber of Commerce (MACC)
321 S 1st St.
Montevideo, MN 56265
Ph: (320)269-5527
Co. E-mail: generalinfo@montechamber.com
URL: http://montechamber.com
Contact: Kyle TeBeest, President
Facebook: www.facebook.com/montemnchamber
Instagram: www.instagram.com/montemnchamber
Description: Promotes business and community development in the Montevideo, MN area. Administers Convention and Visitors' Bureau. **Founded:** 1905. **Geographic Preference:** Local.

41274 ■ Monticello Area Chamber of Commerce and Industry (MCCI)
118 W 6th St., Ste. B
Monticello, MN 55362
Ph: (763)295-2700
Fax: (763)295-2705
Co. E-mail: info@monticellocci.com
URL: http://www.monticellocci.com
Contact: Lauren Carstens, Chairman

Description: Promotes business and community development in Monticello, MN. **Founded:** 1856. **Awards:** Monticello Area Chamber Business of the Year (Annual). **Geographic Preference:** Local.

41275 ■ Moose Lake Area Chamber of Commerce
4524 S Arrowhead Ln.
Moose Lake, MN 55767
Ph: (218)485-4145
Free: 800-635-3680
Co. E-mail: mooselakechamber@gmail.com
URL: http://www.mooselakechamber.com
Contact: Billie Jo Steen, President
Facebook: www.facebook.com/MooseLakeChamber
Description: Works with other community resources to promote local tourism, create jobs, and recruit new businesses in Moose Lake, IN area. **Geographic Preference:** Local.

41276 ■ Morris Area Chamber of Commerce
4 Atlantic Ave.
Morris, MN 56267
Ph: (320)589-1242
Co. E-mail: morrismnchamber@gmail.com
URL: http://morrismnchamber.org
Contact: Summer Anderson, Director, Administration
Description: Promotes business and community development in the Morris, MN area. Sponsors Prairie Pioneer Days. **Founded:** 1940. **Educational Activities:** Grand Parade of Lights. **Geographic Preference:** Local.

41277 ■ New Prague Chamber of Commerce (NPCC)
101 Main St. E
New Prague, MN 56071
Ph: (952)758-4360
Fax: (952)758-5396
Co. E-mail: info@newprague.com
URL: http://newprague.com
Contact: Brooke Sticha, Executive Director
E-mail: bsticha@newprague.com
Facebook: www.facebook.com/newpraguechamber
X (Twitter): x.com/newpraguecofc
Instagram: www.instagram.com/newpraguechamber
Description: Promotes business and community development in New Prague, MN. Conducts charitable activities. Holds annual New Prague Half-Marathon and 5K, Dozinky Czechoslovakian Harvest Festival and Christmas programs. **Founded:** 1977. **Geographic Preference:** Local.

41278 ■ New Ulm Area Chamber of Commerce
1 N Minnesota St.
New Ulm, MN 56073
Ph: (507)233-4300
Free: 888-463-9856
Fax: (507)354-1504
Co. E-mail: info@newulm.com
URL: http://www.newulm.com
Contact: Sarah Warmka, President
E-mail: sarah@newulm.com
Facebook: www.facebook.com/NewUlm
Linkedin: www.linkedin.com/company/new-ulm-area-chamber-of-commerce
X (Twitter): x.com/newulm
Instagram: www.instagram.com/newulm
YouTube: www.youtube.com/user/newulmcvb
Description: Promotes business and community development in the New Ulm, MN area. Conducts annual Oktoberfest. **Founded:** 1940. **Publications:** *New Ulm Visitors Guide* (Annual); *NU Business Trends* (Monthly); *Program of Work* (Annual). **Geographic Preference:** Local.

41279 ■ Nisswa Chamber of Commerce
25532 S Main St.
Nisswa, MN 56468
Ph: (218)963-2620
Free: 800-950-9610
Fax: (218)963-1420
Co. E-mail: info@nisswa.com
URL: http://www.nisswa.com
Contact: Pam Dorion, President

Facebook: www.facebook.com/pages/Nisswa-Chamber-of-Commerce/111238888912596#!/pages/Nisswa-Chamber-of-Commerce/111238888912596
X (Twitter): x.com/hashtag/nisswa
YouTube: www.youtube.com/channel/UCwghgge1MdqFmU_MxtVscw
Description: Promotes business and community development in Nisswa, MN. Sponsors arts and crafts festival. **Founded:** 1946. **Publications:** *The Pulse* (Quarterly). **Geographic Preference:** Local.

41280 ■ North 65 Chamber of Commerce
2 Enterprise Ave., NE
Isanti, MN 55040-6812
Ph: (763)689-2505
Fax: (763)552-2505
Co. E-mail: info@north65chamber.com
URL: http://www.north65chamber.com
Contact: Melissa Bettendorf, Executive Director
E-mail: melissa@north65chamber.com
Facebook: www.facebook.com/North65Chamber
Linkedin: www.linkedin.com/company/north-65-chamber-of-commerce
Description: Promotes business and community development in the Cambridge, MN area. **Founded:** 2015. **Publications:** *Chamber News Page* (Monthly); *Friday Facts*. **Geographic Preference:** Local.

41281 ■ North Branch Area Chamber of Commerce
6063 Main St.
North Branch, MN 55056
Ph: (651)674-4077
Co. E-mail: contact@northbranchchamber.com
URL: http://northbranchchamber.com
Contact: Christina Huesman, President
Facebook: www.facebook.com/NorthBranchChamber
X (Twitter): x.com/NBAChamber
Description: Promotes local business and organizations. Activities include networking opportunities, publication, community celebrations and festivals. **Founded:** 1964. **Geographic Preference:** Local.

41282 ■ Northfield Area Chamber of Commerce
19 Bridge Sq.
Northfield, MN 55057
Ph: (507)645-5604
Co. E-mail: info@northfieldchamber.com
URL: http://www.northfieldchamber.com
Contact: Penny Carr, Chairman of the Board
Facebook: www.facebook.com/NorthfieldChamberofCommerce
Linkedin: www.linkedin.com/company/northfield-area-chamber-of-commerce-&-tourism
Instagram: www.instagram.com/northfieldchamber
Description: Promotes business and community development in the Northfield, MN area. **Geographic Preference:** Local.

41283 ■ Olivia Area Chamber of Commerce
1310 W Lincoln Ave.
Olivia, MN 56277
Ph: (320)523-1350
Co. E-mail: oliviachamberofcommerce@gmail.com
URL: http://oliviachamber.org
Contact: Scott Tedrick, Contact
Facebook: www.facebook.com/oliviachamberofcommerce
X (Twitter): x.com/oliviamnchamber
Description: Works to create, promote and enhance a healthy business environment and image of the Olivia area. **Founded:** 1976. **Publications:** *Chamber Update*. **Geographic Preference:** Local.

41284 ■ Owatonna Area Chamber of Commerce and Tourism (OACCT)
320 Hoffman Dr.
Owatonna, MN 55060
Ph: (507)451-7970
Free: 800-423-6466
Fax: (507)451-7972
Co. E-mail: oacct@owatonna.org
URL: http://www.owatonna.org
Contact: Brad Meier, President
E-mail: bmeier@owatonna.org

Facebook: www.facebook.com/owatonna
X (Twitter): x.com/owatonnachamber
YouTube: www.youtube.com/user/TheOACCT
Description: Seeks to be the leading partner of the regional center, dedicated to the continuance of its economic prosperity while maintaining community values and pride. Activities include membership, legislative advocacy, communications, information brokering, leadership development, facilitation, networking, cooperative marketing, economic development and tourism promotion. **Founded:** 1924. **Publications:** *Business Brief*; *Chamber Reporter* (Monthly). **Educational Activities:** Business After Hours (Irregular); Good Morning Owatonna. **Geographic Preference:** Local.

41285 ■ Park Rapids Lakes Area Chamber of Commerce (PRLACC)
1204 Pk. Ave., S
Park Rapids, MN 56470
Ph: (218)732-4111
Free: 800-247-0054
Fax: (218)732-4112
Co. E-mail: chamber@parkrapids.com
URL: http://parkrapids.com
Contact: Debbie Tostenson, Chairman
E-mail: debbiet@cnbbank.com
Description: Promotes business and community development in the Park Rapids, MN area. **Publications:** *Discovery Guide*. **Geographic Preference:** Local.

41286 ■ Paynesville Area Chamber of Commerce (PACC)
1105 W Main St.
Paynesville, MN 56362
Ph: (320)243-3233
Co. E-mail: office@paynesvillechamber.org
URL: http://www.paynesvillechamber.org
Contact: Tami Stanger, President
Facebook: www.facebook.com/paynesvilleareachamber
X (Twitter): x.com/PaynesChamber
Description: Promotes business and community development in the Paynesville, MN area. **Geographic Preference:** Local.

41287 ■ Pelican Rapids Area Chamber of Commerce (PRACC)
PO Box 206
Pelican Rapids, MN 56572
Ph: (218)863-4606
Co. E-mail: info@pelicanrapidschamber.com
URL: http://pelicanrapidschamber.com
Facebook: www.facebook.com/PelicanRapidsChamberofCommerce
Description: Promotes business and community development in Pelican Rapids, MN. **Geographic Preference:** Local.

41288 ■ Perham Area Chamber of Commerce
185 E Main St.
Perham, MN 56573
Ph: (218)346-7710
Fax: (218)346-7712
Co. E-mail: chamber@perhamcc.com
URL: http://www.perham.com/contact-us
Contact: Cody Palubicki, President
E-mail: cpalubicki@klnfamilybrands.com
Facebook: www.facebook.com/DiscoverPerham
X (Twitter): x.com/perhamchamber
Instagram: www.instagram.com/discoverperham
YouTube: www.youtube.com/user/turtle1161
Description: Promotes business and community development in the Perham, MN area. Sponsors festival. **Founded:** 1985. **Geographic Preference:** Local.

41289 ■ Pine City Area Chamber of Commerce
315 Main St. S, Ste. 155
Pine City, MN 55063
Ph: (320)322-4040
Co. E-mail: pinecitychamber@gmail.com
URL: http://www.pinecitychamber.com
Contact: Kimberlee Bever, President
Facebook: www.facebook.com/pinecitychamber
Linkedin: www.linkedin.com/company/pine-city-chamber
X (Twitter): x.com/PineCityChamber
Instagram: www.instagram.com/pinecitychamber
YouTube: www.youtube.com/channel/UCMPljbUiGMjw1hWLdXf4ejA
Geographic Preference: Local.

41290 ■ Pipestone Area Chamber of Commerce
117 8th Ave., SE
Pipestone, MN 56164
Ph: (507)825-3316
Fax: (507)825-3317
Co. E-mail: pipecham@pipestoneminnesota.com
URL: http://www.pipestoneminnesota.com
Contact: Erica Volkir, Executive Director
E-mail: erica.pipestonechamber@gmail.com
Facebook: www.facebook.com/pipestonechamber
X (Twitter): x.com/PipestoneMN
Description: Promotes business and community development in Pipestone County, MN. Publications: none. **Founded:** 1927. **Geographic Preference:** Local.

41291 ■ Princeton Area Chamber of Commerce (PACC)
507 1st St.
Princeton, MN 55371
Ph: (763)389-1764
Co. E-mail: pacc@princetonmnchamber.org
URL: http://www.princetonmnchamber.org
Contact: Carrie Vesel, President
Facebook: www.facebook.com/MNPACC
Description: Promotes business and community development in Princeton, MN. Sponsors Rum River Festival. **Founded:** 1926. **Publications:** *Focus* (Weekly). **Geographic Preference:** Local.

41292 ■ Prior Lake Chamber of Commerce
4785 Dakota St.
Prior Lake, MN 55372
Ph: (952)440-1000
URL: http://www.priorlakechamber.com
Contact: Sandi Fleck, President
E-mail: sandi@priorlakechamber.com
Facebook: www.facebook.com/PLChamberMN
X (Twitter): x.com/plchambermn
Instagram: www.instagram.com/plchambermn
Description: Strives to foster business development to enhance the quality of life of the community. **Publications:** *Chamber News* (Monthly). **Geographic Preference:** Local.

41293 ■ Red Wing Area Chamber of Commerce (RWACC)
439 Main St.
Red Wing, MN 55066
Ph: (651)388-4719
Co. E-mail: frontdesk@redwingchamber.com
URL: http://www.redwingchamber.com
Contact: Michelle Larson, President
E-mail: michelle@redwingchamber.com
Description: Promotes business and community development in the Red Wing, MN area. **Publications:** *Chamber Forum* (Bimonthly). **Geographic Preference:** Local.

41294 ■ Redwood Area Chamber and Tourism (RACT)
200 S Mill St.
Redwood Falls, MN 56283
Ph: (507)637-2828
Co. E-mail: chamber@redwoodfalls.org
URL: http://redwoodfalls.org
Contact: Anne Johnson, Executive Director
Facebook: www.facebook.com/redwoodareachamberandtourism
X (Twitter): x.com/redwoodchamber
YouTube: www.youtube.com/user/redwoodareachamber
Description: Promotes business and community development in the Redwood Falls, MN area. **Geographic Preference:** Local.

41295 ■ River Heights Chamber of Commerce (RHCC)
5782 Blackshire Path
Inver Grove Heights, MN 55076
Ph: (651)451-2266
Co. E-mail: info@riverheights.com
URL: http://riverheights.com
Contact: Greg Dennis, Chairman
Facebook: www.facebook.com/RiverHeightsChamber
X (Twitter): x.com/RH_Chamber
Instagram: www.instagram.com/riverheightschamber
YouTube: www.youtube.com/user/RiverHeightsChamber
Description: Promotes business and community development in South St. Paul-Inver Grove Heights, MN. **Founded:** 1903. **Publications:** *Business Perspective* (Monthly). **Educational Activities:** Leadership Conference; Small Business Luncheon (Annual). **Geographic Preference:** Local.

41296 ■ Robbinsdale Chamber of Commerce
PO Box 22646
Robbinsdale, MN 55422
Ph: (763)531-1279
Co. E-mail: dkiser@ccxmedia.org
URL: http://robbinsdalechamber.com
Contact: Annette Coffin, President
E-mail: ac@broadwayawards.net
Facebook: www.facebook.com/Robbinsdale.Chamber
X (Twitter): x.com/RobbinsdaleBIZ
Instagram: www.instagram.com/robbinsdalemnchamber
Description: Promotes business and community development in the Robbinsdale, MN area. **Founded:** 1949. **Geographic Preference:** Local.

41297 ■ Rochester Area Chamber of Commerce (RACC)
220 S Broadway, Ste. 100
Rochester, MN 55904
Ph: (507)288-1122
Co. E-mail: chamber@rochestermnchamber.com
URL: http://www.rochestermnchamber.com
Contact: Ryan Parsons, President
E-mail: rparsons@rochestermnchamber.com
Facebook: www.facebook.com/RochMNChamber
X (Twitter): x.com/rochmnchamber
YouTube: www.youtube.com/user/RochesterChamber
Description: Promotes business and community development in the Rochester/Olmsted County, MN area. **Founded:** 1866. **Publications:** *Rochester Area Chamber of Commerce--Member Directory* (Annual); *Advantage* (Monthly); *Business Reference Guide and Membership Directory* (Annual). **Awards:** Lamp of Knowledge Awards (Annual); Rochester Area Chamber Small Business of the Year (Annual); Rochester Area Chamber Volunteer of the Year (Annual). **Geographic Preference:** Local.

41298 ■ St. Cloud Area Chamber of Commerce (SCACC)
1411 W St. Germain, Ste. 101
Saint Cloud, MN 56302-0487
Ph: (320)251-2940
Fax: (320)251-0081
Co. E-mail: information@stcloudareachamber.com
URL: http://www.stcloudareachamber.com
Contact: Gail Ivers, Vice President
E-mail: givers@stcloudareachamber.com
Facebook: www.facebook.com/SaintCloudAreaChamberofCommerce
Linkedin: www.linkedin.com/company/st-cloud-area-chamber-of-commerce
X (Twitter): x.com/StCldAreaChamb
Instagram: www.instagram.com/stcloudareachamber
YouTube: www.youtube.com/user/StCloudAreaChamber
Description: Promotes business and community development in the St. Cloud, MN area. **Founded:** 1869. **Publications:** *The Bottom Line* (Bimonthly); *Business Central* (6/year); *Chamber Edge* (Monthly). **Educational Activities:** Chamber Connection (Weekly); Chamber Golf Open (Annual). **Geographic Preference:** Local.

41299 ■ St. Joseph Area Chamber of Commerce
PO Box 696
Saint Joseph, MN 56374
Ph: (320)433-1043
Co. E-mail: stjosephchamber@gmail.com
URL: http://www.stjosephchamber.com
Contact: Adam Otteson, President
E-mail: adamo@mycmcu.org
Facebook: www.facebook.com/sjachamber
Description: Promotes business and community development in the eastern and northern suburbs of St. Paul, MN. Convention/Meeting: none. **Geographic Preference:** Local.

41300 ■ Saint Paul Area Chamber of Commerce (SPACC)
401 N Robert St., Ste. 150
Saint Paul, MN 55101
Ph: (651)223-5000
Co. E-mail: info@saintpaulchamber.com
URL: http://www.stpaulchamber.com
Contact: B. Kyle, President
Facebook: www.facebook.com/SaintPaulAreaChamber
Linkedin: www.linkedin.com/company/st-paul-area-chamber
X (Twitter): x.com/spacc
Instagram: www.instagram.com/stpaulchamber
YouTube: www.youtube.com/user/SaintPaulAreaChamber
Description: Voice for business in St. Paul, MN and the east metro area. Strives to influence public policy; provide small business resources; creates economic development; and shapes the future workforce. **Founded:** 1868. **Publications:** *St. Paul Area Chamber of Commerce Directory* (Annual). **Geographic Preference:** Local.

41301 ■ Saint Peter Area Chamber of Commerce
101 S Front St.
Saint Peter, MN 56082
Ph: (507)934-3400
Co. E-mail: spchamb@hickorytech.net
URL: http://www.stpeterchamber.com
Contact: Ed Lee, Executive Director
Description: Strives to provide leadership in order to enhance and promote economic development and quality of life in the St. Peter area. **Geographic Preference:** Local.

41302 ■ Sandstone Area Chamber of Commerce (SACC)
PO Box 23
Sandstone, MN 55072
Ph: (320)630-4477
Co. E-mail: nwemb@copper.net
URL: http://www.sandstonechamber.org
Contact: Pete Spartz, Vice President
Description: Promotes business and community development in Sandstone, MN. Encourages tourism. **Geographic Preference:** Local.

41303 ■ Sauk Centre Area Chamber of Commerce (SCCC)
524 4th St. S
Sauk Centre, MN 56378
Ph: (320)352-5201
Fax: (320)351-5202
Co. E-mail: stacie@saukcentrechamber.com
URL: http://www.saukcentrechamber.com
Contact: Stacie Michels, President
E-mail: stacie@saukcentrechamber.com
Facebook: www.facebook.com/saukcentreareachamber
X (Twitter): x.com/chambersauk
Instagram: www.instagram.com/scchamber
Description: Promotes business and community development in Sauk Centre, MN. Holds festival. **Geographic Preference:** Local.

41304 ■ Savage Chamber of Commerce
6050 McColl Dr.
Savage, MN 55378
Ph: (952)894-8876
Co. E-mail: mail@savagechamber.com
URL: http://www.savagechamber.com
Contact: Anne Masis, President
E-mail: anne@savagechamber.com
Facebook: www.facebook.com/SavageChamber
Description: Strives to unite business and professional people who are dedicated to the ongoing development and support of business activities, industrial opportunities and civic enhancement of the Savage area. **Founded:** 1964. **Awards:** Savage Chamber of Commerce Business Person of the Year (Annual). **Geographic Preference:** Local.

41305 ■ Shakopee Chamber of Commerce
1801 E County Rd. 101
Shakopee, MN 55379
Ph: (952)445-1660
Fax: (952)445-1669
Co. E-mail: chamber@shakopee.org
URL: http://www.shakopee.org
Contact: Tim Zunker, President
E-mail: tzunker@shakopee.org
Facebook: www.facebook.com/ShakopeeChamber
Linkedin: www.linkedin.com/company/shakopee-chamber-of-commerce
X (Twitter): x.com/ShakopeeChamber
Description: Promotes convention business and tourism in Shakopee, MN area. Operates tourist information center. Offers outdoor adventures, water parks, golf courses, and living history museums. **Founded:** 1955. **Publications:** *Chamber Reporter Insert* (Monthly). **Geographic Preference:** Local.

41306 ■ Slayton Area Chamber of Commerce (SACC)
2545 Broadway Ave.
Slayton, MN 56172
Ph: (507)836-6902
Co. E-mail: slaytonchamber@gmail.com
URL: http://www.slaytonareachamber.com
Contact: Loretta Gervais, Contact
Facebook: www.facebook.com/hereandhome
Description: Promotes business and community development in the Slayton, MN area. Conducts charitable activities. **Founded:** 1942. **Geographic Preference:** Local.

41307 ■ Sleepy Eye Area Chamber of Commerce (SEACC)
115 2nd Ave., NE
Sleepy Eye, MN 56085
Ph: (507)794-4731
Co. E-mail: secofc@sleepyeyechamber.com
URL: http://www.sleepyeyechamber.com
Contact: Briar Braulick, President
Facebook: www.facebook.com/SleepyEyeChamber
X (Twitter): x.com/SleepyEyeCofC
YouTube: www.youtube.com/channel/UCG8TD1wecLzPW3R6IKxGJlw
Description: Promotes business and community development in the Sleepy Eye, MN area. **Geographic Preference:** Local.

41308 ■ Swedish American Chamber of Commerce Minnesota (SACCMN)
c/o The American Swedish Institute
2600 Pk. Ave.
Minneapolis, MN 55407
Co. E-mail: info@saccmn.org
URL: http://www.saccmn.org
Contact: Stephan Quie, President
Facebook: www.facebook.com/saccminnesota
Linkedin: www.linkedin.com/company/swedish-american-chamber-of-commerce---minnesota
X (Twitter): x.com/saccmn
Instagram: www.instagram.com/saccmn
Description: Strives to enhance trade, commerce, and investment between Sweden and the Upper Midwestern region of the United States. **Founded:** 1992. **Geographic Preference:** State.

41309 ■ Thief River Falls Chamber of Commerce
102 Main Ave., N
Thief River Falls, MN 56701
Ph: (218)681-3720
Free: 855-873-6466
Fax: (218)681-3739
Co. E-mail: contact@trfchamber.com
URL: http://www.trfchamber.com
Contact: Vanessa Ellefson, Executive Director
E-mail: vanessa.ellefson@trfchamber.com
Facebook: www.facebook.com/trfchamber
X (Twitter): x.com/trfchamber
Description: Works to establish Thief River Falls as the regional center of Northwest Minnesota. Promotes the welfare of all area citizens. **Founded:** 1913. **Geographic Preference:** Local.

41310 ■ Tracy Area Chamber of Commerce
336 Morgan St.
Tracy, MN 56175
Ph: (507)629-5528
URL: http://www.tracymn.org
Contact: Mandy Hoffman, Contact
Facebook: www.facebook.com/CityofTracyMN
YouTube: www.youtube.com/channel/UCbwjBrIKp6gh9Z_mINg10eA/videos
Description: Promotes business and community development in the Tracy, MN area. Sponsors Box Car Days festival every Labor Day. **Founded:** 1910. **Geographic Preference:** Local.

41311 ■ Twin Cities North Chamber of Commerce (TCNCC)
The Reserve 1915 Hwy. 36 W
Roseville, MN 55113
Ph: (763)571-9781
Fax: (763)572-7950
Co. E-mail: info@twincitiesnorth.org
URL: http://www.twincitiesnorth.org
Contact: John Connelly, President
E-mail: john@twincitiesnorth.org
Facebook: www.facebook.com/pages/Twin-Cities-North-Chamber-of-Commerce/143994668947914
X (Twitter): x.com/TwinCitiesNorth
Description: Promotes business and community development in the northern Twin Cities suburbs, specifically Arden Hills, Blaine, Columbia Heights, Fridley, Mounds View, New Brighton, Shoreview and Spring Lake Park. **Founded:** 1958. **Geographic Preference:** Local.

41312 ■ Twin Cities Quorum
18 N 12th St., Ste. 3606
Minneapolis, MN 55403
Ph: (612)460-8153
Co. E-mail: info@twincitiesquorum.com
URL: http://www.twincitiesquorum.com
Contact: Ron Gersdorf, President
Facebook: www.facebook.com/TCQuorum
Founded: 1995. **Geographic Preference:** Local.

41313 ■ TwinWest Chamber of Commerce
10700 Old County Rd. 15, Ste. 170
Minneapolis, MN 55441
Ph: (763)450-2220
Fax: (763)450-2221
URL: http://business.mplschamber.com/list/member/twinwest-chamber-foundation-25135
Description: Promotes business and community development in the areas of Brooklyn Center, Brooklyn Park, Crystal, Golden Valley, Hopkins, Medicine Lake, Minnetonka, New Hope, Plymouth, and St. Louis Park. **Publications:** *TwinWest Chamber of Commerce--Membership Directory & Business Guide*; *TwinWest Directions* (10/year); *TwinWest Membership Directory and Business Resource Guide* (Annual). **Awards:** TwinWest Foundation Scholarships (Annual). **Geographic Preference:** Local.

41314 ■ *Vacation Guide*
1600 E Sheridan St.
Ely, MN 55731
Ph: (218)365-6123
URL: http://www.ely.org/about-us
Contact: Dafne Caruso, President
URL(s): www.ely.org/membership/information-and-benefits
Released: Annual **Availability:** Print.

41315 ■ Waconia Chamber of Commerce
209 S Vine St.
Waconia, MN 55387
Ph: (952)442-5812

STATE LISTINGS   Minnesota ■ 41330

Fax: (952)856-4476
Co. E-mail: request@destinationwaconia.org
URL: http://www.destinationwaconia.org
Contact: Christine Fenner, President
E-mail: cfenner@destinationwaconia.org
Facebook: www.facebook.com/DestinationWaconia
Instagram: www.instagram.com/destinationwaconia
YouTube: www.youtube.com/channel/UCBX
  2eTQajb8cssqFg4m59IQ/featured
Description: Seeks to enhance the economic and social health community by improving the business atmosphere of the area. **Geographic Preference:** Local.

41316 ■ Waseca Area Chamber of Commerce (WACC)
210 N State St.
  Waseca, MN 56093
Ph: (507)835-3260
Fax: (507)835-3267
Co. E-mail: info@wasecachamber.com
URL: http://www.wasecachamber.com
Contact: Nate Bastian, President
Facebook: www.facebook.com/wasecaacc
X (Twitter): x.com/WasecaChamber
Description: Promotes business in Waseca, MN. **Founded:** 1953. **Geographic Preference:** Local.

41317 ■ *Weekly Facts*
4751 Hwy. 61
  White Bear Lake, MN 55110
Ph: (651)429-8593
Fax: (651)429-8592
Co. E-mail: info@whitebearchamber.com
URL: http://www.whitebearchamber.com
Contact: Shari Wilson, Executive Director
E-mail: shari@whitebearchamber.com
URL(s): www.whitebearchamber.com/join-us-today
Released: Weekly **Availability:** Print.

41318 ■ *Welcome to Austin*
329 N Main St., Ste. 102
  Austin, MN 55912
Ph: (507)437-4561
Co. E-mail: info@austincoc.com
URL: http://austincoc.com
Contact: Elaine Hansen, President
E-mail: elaine@austincoc.com
URL(s): www.austincoc.com/maximize-your
  -membership
Availability: Print.

41319 ■ Wells Area Chamber of Commerce
53 1st. SW, Ste. 100
  Wells, MN 56097
Ph: (507)553-6450
Co. E-mail: wellscc@bevcomm.net
URL: http://www.wellsareachamber.com
Contact: Corey Olson, Co-President
Facebook: www.facebook.com/WellsAreaChamber
X (Twitter): x.com/wellsareacc
YouTube: www.youtube.com/channel/UC07v
  6MRpArmUVHKOH9rwL2g
Description: Promotes business and community development in the Wells, MN area. Sponsors Wells Kernel Days. **Founded:** 1869. **Geographic Preference:** Local.

41320 ■ White Bear Area Chamber of Commerce
4751 Hwy. 61
  White Bear Lake, MN 55110
Ph: (651)429-8593
Fax: (651)429-8592
Co. E-mail: info@whitebearchamber.com
URL: http://www.whitebearchamber.com
Contact: Shari Wilson, Executive Director
E-mail: shari@whitebearchamber.com
Facebook: www.facebook.com/whi
  tebeararechamber
X (Twitter): x.com/WhiteBearChambr
Description: Promotes business and community development in the White Bear Lake, MN area. **Founded:** 1923. **Publications:** *Weekly Facts* (Weekly). **Geographic Preference:** Local.

41321 ■ Willmar Lakes Area Chamber of Commerce (WLACC)
2104 Hwy. 12 E
  Willmar, MN 56201
Ph: (320)235-0300
Co. E-mail: chamber@willmarareachamber.com
URL: http://www.willmarareachamber.com
Contact: Ken Warner, President
E-mail: kwarner@willmarareachamber.com
Facebook: www.facebook.com/
  willmarlakesareachamber
Linkedin: www.linkedin.com/company/willmar-lakes
  -area-chamber-of-commerce
Instagram: www.instagram.com/
  willmarlakesareachamber_mn
YouTube: www.youtube.com/channel/UCi
  -rRIAckPEealpRrw8kgjA
Description: Promotes business and community development in the Willmar, MN area. **Founded:** 1929. **Publications:** *City and County Map*. **Geographic Preference:** Local.

41322 ■ Windom Area Chamber of Commerce and Visitors Bureau (WACCVB)
303 9th St.
  Windom, MN 56101
Ph: (507)831-2752
Free: 800-794-6366
URL: http://www.windomchamber.com/convention
  -visitor-bureau
Contact: Amy Leopold, Director
Description: Promotes business and community development in Windom, MN. Serves as a community information center. Sponsors community events including annual summer celebration, Riverfest. **Publications:** *Chamber Update*. **Geographic Preference:** Local.

41323 ■ Winona Area Chamber of Commerce (WACC)
902 E 2nd St., Ste. 120
  Winona, MN 55987
Ph: (507)452-2272
Fax: (507)454-8814
Co. E-mail: info@winonachamber.com
URL: http://www.winonachamber.com
Contact: Christie Ransom, President
E-mail: cransom@winonachamber.com
Facebook: www.facebook.com/winonachamber
Description: Promotes business and community development in the Winona, MN area. **Founded:** 1912. **Geographic Preference:** Local.

41324 ■ Woodbury Area Chamber of Commerce (WACC)
700 Commerce Dr., Ste. 285
  Woodbury, MN 55125
Ph: (651)578-0722
Co. E-mail: chamber@woodburychamber.org
URL: http://www.woodburychamber.org
Contact: Laurie Staiger, President
E-mail: laurie@woodburychamber.org
Facebook: www.facebook.com/woodburymnchamber
Linkedin: www.linkedin.com/pub/woodbury-area
  -chamber-of-commerce/39/950/521
X (Twitter): x.com/woodburychamber
YouTube: www.youtube.com/user/Woo
  dburyChamber
Description: Promotes business and community development in Woodbury, MN. **Founded:** 1985. **Publications:** *The Chamber Connection*; *Directory of Chamber Members*. **Awards:** Woodbury Chamber Business of the Year (Annual); Woodbury Chamber Citizen of the Year (Annual); Woodbury Chamber Educational Team of the Year (Annual); Woodbury Chamber Elementary Educator of the Year (Annual); Woodbury Chamber Secondary Educator of the Year (Annual). **Geographic Preference:** Local.

41325 ■ Worthington Area Chamber of Commerce
1121 3rd Ave.
  Worthington, MN 56187
Ph: (507)372-2919
Co. E-mail: wcofc@worthingtonmnchamber.com
URL: http://worthingtonmnchamber.com

Contact: Stacy Fricke, President
Facebook: www.facebook.com/Worthing
  tonMNChamber
Instagram: www.instagram.com/worthing
  tonmnchamber
Description: Promotes business and community development in the Worthington, MN area. **Geographic Preference:** Local.

MINORITY BUSINESS ASSISTANCE PROGRAMS

41326 ■ Metropolitan Economic Development Association (MEDA)
1256 Penn Ave. N, Ste. 4800
  Minneapolis, MN 55411
Ph: (612)332-6332
Co. E-mail: info@meda.net
URL: http://www.meda.net
Facebook: www.facebook.com/MedaMinnesota
X (Twitter): x.com/Meda_MN
Instagram: www.instagram.com/medaminnesota
YouTube: www.youtube.com/channel/UCdJxvoK
  -88rBAZXCiUHyCuQ
Description: Provides services to BIPOC entrepreneurs in Minnesota. **Scope:** Provider of assistance to businesses owned and managed by BIPOC residents of Minnesota. **Founded:** 1971.

41327 ■ Midwest Minority Supplier Development Council (MMSDC)
111 3rd Ave. S, Ste. 375
  Minneapolis, MN 55401-2579
Contact: Heather N. Olson, President
Description: Provides a direct link between corporate America and minority-owned businesses. Increases procurement and business opportunities for minority businesses of all sizes. **Founded:** 1975. **Geographic Preference:** State.

41328 ■ Women's Business Development Center - Minnesota (WBDCMN)
375 Selby Ave.
  Saint Paul, MN 55102
Ph: (312)853-3477
Co. E-mail: wbdc-mn@wbdc.org
URL: http://www.wbdc.org
Contact: Emilia DiMenco, President
E-mail: edimenco@wbdc.org
Description: Offers certification, training, mentoring, networking, and business development services to women's businesses in Minnesota, North Dakota, South Dakota, and Wisconsin. **Founded:** 2003.

FINANCING AND LOAN PROGRAMS

41329 ■ Arthur Ventures (AV)
80 S 8th St., Ste. 3710
  Minneapolis, MN 55402
URL: http://www.arthurventures.com
Contact: Brittany Patterson, Director
E-mail: brittany@arthurventures.com
Linkedin: www.linkedin.com/company/arthur-ventures
X (Twitter): x.com/arthurventures
Description: Venture capital firm. Offers investment services for seed stage companies in information technology, life sciences, and clean technology services. **Founded:** 2013. **Industry Preferences:** Information technology; life sciences; clean technology services.

41330 ■ Cherry Tree Investments Inc.
301 Carlson Pky., Ste. 103
  Minnetonka, MN 55305
Ph: (952)893-9012
Co. E-mail: info@cherrytree.com
URL: http://cherrytree.com
Contact: Elmer Baldwin, Executive Director
E-mail: ebaldwin@cherrytree.com
Linkedin: www.linkedin.com/company/cherry-tree
Description: Provider of investment banking and wealth management solutions. **Founded:** 1980. **Preferred Investment Size:** $250,000 to $1,000,000.

41331 ■ Minnesota

Industry Preferences: Communications, computer hardware and software, Internet specific, semiconductors and other electronics, biotechnology, medical and health, consumer related, financial services, business service, agriculture, forestry and fishing.

41331 ■ The Collaborative CFO Workgroups
10 S 5th St., Ste. 415
Minneapolis, MN 55402
Ph: (612)338-3828
Co. E-mail: info@collaborative.net
URL: http://www.collaborative.net
Contact: Dan Carr, Founder
Description: A forum of Minnesota finance executives to share, learn, and solve problems.

41332 ■ Coral Group
60 S Sixth St., Ste. 2410
Lake Elmo, MN 55042
Ph: (612)335-8682
URL: http://coralgrp.com
Contact: Yuval Almog, Contact
E-mail: yuval.almog@coralgrp.com
Description: Firm provides indirect, funds and growth capital investment services. **Founded:** 1983. **Preferred Investment Size:** $1,000,000 to $10,000,000. **Industry Preferences:** Communications and media, medical and media, computer software, hardware and services, Internet specific, biotechnology, semiconductors and other electronics, industrial and energy, and consumer related.

41333 ■ Gopher Angels
Minneapolis, MN
Co. E-mail: contact@gopherangels.com
URL: http://gopherangels.com
Contact: Sara Russick, Managing Director
Co-Founder
Description: Angel investor group for seed and Series A companies in the Midwest with a substantial market opportunity. **Founded:** 2012. **Industry Preferences:** Healthcare and health IT; enterprise and SaaS; food and beverage; medical devices; agtech.

41334 ■ Lemhi Ventures
21550 Golfview Cir.
Jordan, MN 55352
URL: http://lemhiventures.com
Contact: Tony Miller, Managing Partner
Description: Invests in disruptive and transformation healthcare companies. **Founded:** 2006.

41335 ■ Mayo Clinic Ventures
Minnesota BioBusiness Ctr. - 4th Fl., 221 First Ave. SW
Rochester, MN 55902
Ph: (507)293-3900
Fax: (507)284-5410
Co. E-mail: mayoclinicsupport@mayoclinic.com
URL: http://businessdevelopment.mayoclinic.org
Contact: Andrew J. Danielsen, Chairman
Facebook: www.facebook.com/MayoClinic
Linkedin: www.linkedin.com/showcase/mayo-clinic-ventures
X (Twitter): x.com/mayoinvents
Instagram: www.instagram.com/mayoclinic
YouTube: www.youtube.com/c/MayoClinic
Pinterest: www.pinterest.com/MayoClinic
Description: Venture capital firm provides seed, startups and early stage investments to healthcare information technology, biopharmaceuticals, diagnostics, biomarker and medical devices. **Preferred Investment Size:** $250,000 to $1,000,000. **Industry Preferences:** Biotechnology, medical and health, Internet specific, industrial and energy.

41336 ■ Norwest Equity Partners (NEP)
80 S 8th St., Ste. 3600
Minneapolis, MN 55402
Ph: (612)215-1600
URL: http://nep.com
Contact: Adam Verhasselt, Vice President
E-mail: averhasselt@nep.com
Description: Holding company that offers investment advisory services. **Founded:** 1961. **Preferred Investment Size:** $30,000,000 to $150,000,000. **Industry Preferences:** Computer software and services, communications and media, consumer related, agriculture, industrial and energy, medical and health, manufacturing and business service.

41337 ■ RAIN Source Capital
419 Bush St.
Red Wing, MN 55066
Ph: (651)632-2140
URL: http://rainsourcecapital.com
Contact: Steve Mercil, Chief Executive Officer
E-mail: smercil@rainsourcecapital.com
Description: Offers capital to companies in Idaho, Iowa, Minnesota, Montana, North Dakota, and South Dakota.

41338 ■ Sherpa Partners L.L.C.
5759 Long Brake Cir.
Edina, MN 55439
Co. E-mail: info@sherpapartners.com
URL: http://www.sherpapartners.com
Contact: Mckenzie C. Lewis, Partner
Description: Venture capital firm focuses on early-stage technology companies. **Founded:** 1997. **Preferred Investment Size:** $250,000 to $1,000,000. **Industry Preferences:** Communications and media, computer software, semiconductors and other electronics.

41339 ■ Sofia Fund
MN
Ph: (651)699-9614
Co. E-mail: info@sofiafund.com
URL: http://sofiafund.com
Contact: Cathy Connett, Chief Executive Officer
X (Twitter): x.com/sofiafund
Description: Invests in women-led growth companies. Prefers gender-diverse teams offering disruptive, scalable business models using technology to solve real problems. **Founded:** 1998. **Industry Preferences:** Information technology; business products and services; health and wellness.

41340 ■ Southeast Minnesota Capital Fund (SMCF)
221 1st Ave. SW, Ste. 600
Rochester, MN 55902
Co. E-mail: exec@semncapital.com
URL: http://semncapital.com
Contact: Xavier Frigola, Executive
E-mail: exec@semncapital.com
Description: Invests in high-growth, high-potential companies, preferably in Southeast Minnesota. **Founded:** 2014.

41341 ■ Taylor Corporation
Taylor Corporation
1725 Roe Crest Dr.
North Mankato, MN 56003
Ph: (507)625-2828
Free: 800-631-7644
Co. E-mail: communications@taylorcorp.com
URL: http://www.taylorcorp.com
Contact: Charlie Whitaker, Chief Executive Officer
URL(s): www.taylor.com/solutions/promotional-marketing
Facebook: www.facebook.com/TaylorCorp
Linkedin: www.linkedin.com/company/taylorcorporation
X (Twitter): twitter.com/TaylorCorp
Instagram: www.instagram.com/taylorcorporation
YouTube: www.youtube.com/channel/UCHp2VMDrSQhdsuRdjQ6WksA
Description: Provider of commercial printing services, including greeting cards, invitations and notes. **Founded:** 1975.

41342 ■ Technology Venture Partners (TVP)
7760 France Ave. S, Ste. 1165
Minneapolis, MN 55435
URL: http://tvp.com
Contact: Bryson D. Hollimon, Managing Partner
Description: Venture capital firm specializing in growth equity investments for high potential companies. **Industry Preferences:** Technology; healthcare.

41343 ■ Two Rivers Angel Network
Thief River Falls, MN
Co. E-mail: contact@tworiversangelnetwork.com
URL: http://www.tworiversangelnetwork.com
Description: Invests in businesses addressing a local market need or solving a problem. **Investment Policies:** Business profitability; ability to provide a return on investment; addressing a strong market need.

41344 ■ U.S. Bancorp Piper Jaffray Private Capital
800 Nicollet Mall, Ste. 900
Minneapolis, MN 55402
Ph: (612)303-6000
URL: http://www.pipersandler.com
Contact: Deb Schoneman, President
Facebook: www.facebook.com/pipersandler
Linkedin: www.linkedin.com/company/pipersandler
X (Twitter): x.com/Piper_Sandler
Description: Firm operates as investment bank and asset management firm. **Founded:** 1895. **Industry Preferences:** Diversified.

PROCUREMENT ASSISTANCE PROGRAMS

41345 ■ APEX Accelerator (MN PTAC)
250 Second Ave. S, Ste. 106
Minneapolis, MN 55401
Co. E-mail: ptac.adm@state.mn.us
URL: http://mn.gov/admin
Contact: John Kilian, Manager
E-mail: john.kilian@state.mn.us
Founded: 1991.

41346 ■ Metropolitan Economic Development Association (MEDA)
1256 Penn Ave. N, Ste. 4800
Minneapolis, MN 55411
Ph: (612)332-6332
Co. E-mail: info@meda.net
URL: http://www.meda.net
Facebook: www.facebook.com/MedaMinnesota
X (Twitter): x.com/Meda_MN
Instagram: www.instagram.com/medaminnesota
YouTube: www.youtube.com/channel/UCdJxvoK-88rBAZXCiUHyCuQ
Description: Provides services to BIPOC entrepreneurs in Minnesota. **Scope:** Provider of assistance to businesses owned and managed by BIPOC residents of Minnesota. **Founded:** 1971.

INCUBATORS/RESEARCH AND TECHNOLOGY PARKS

41347 ■ Dayforce
3311 E Old Shakopee Rd.
Minneapolis, MN 55425-1640
Ph: (952)853-8100
Free: 800-729-7655
URL: http://www.ceridian.com
Contact: Carrie Rasmussen, Chief Information Officer
Linkedin: www.linkedin.com/company/ceridian
X (Twitter): twitter.com/ceridian
YouTube: www.youtube.com/user/ceridian
Description: Supplier of cloud-based human capital management technology solutions that provide control and visibility across human resources, benefits, talent management, workforce management, and payroll services. **Founded:** 1992. **Special Services:** Comdata®.

41348 ■ Genesis Business Centers Ltd.
902 1/2 First St. N
Hopkins, MN 55343
Ph: (612)455-2215
Fax: (612)455-2216
URL: http://www.genesiscenters.com
Contact: Harlan Jacobs, President
Description: Firm engaged in providing programs and business development services. **Founded:** 1993.

41349 ■ GIA Kitchen
955 Mackubin St.
Saint Paul, MN 55117

Co. E-mail: giakitchen@gmail.com
URL: http://www.giakitchen.com
Facebook: www.facebook.com/GiaKitchenMN
Description: An incubator kitchen available for rent to startups and mid-sized food businesses.

41350 ■ The Good Acre (TGA)
1790 Larpenteur Ave. W
Falcon Heights, MN 55113
Ph: (651)493-7158
Co. E-mail: info@thegoodacre.org
URL: http://thegoodacre.org
Contact: Megan Morgan, President
Facebook: www.facebook.com/TheGoodAcreMN
X (Twitter): x.com/TheGoodAcreMN
Instagram: www.instagram.com/thegoodacremn
Description: Commercial kitchen available for use by small food producers who want to source their products from local farmers. **Founded:** 2013.

41351 ■ Greater Mankato Business Accelerator
3 Civic Center Plz., Ste. 100
Mankato, MN 56001
Ph: (507)385-6640
Free: 800-697-0652
Co. E-mail: info@greatermankato.com
URL: http://greatermankato.com
Contact: Jessica Beyer, President
Facebook: www.facebook.com/greatermankatogrowth
Linkedin: www.linkedin.com/company/greater-mankato-growth
X (Twitter): x.com/greatermankato
YouTube: www.youtube.com/user/greatermankatogrowth
Description: Provider of business acceleration and start-up services. **Founded:** 1868.

41352 ■ Harmony's Community Kitchen
302 Irvine Ave. NW
Bemidji, MN 56601
Ph: (218)751-2009
Co. E-mail: customerservice@harmonyfoods.coop
URL: http://www.harmonyfoods.coop/communitykitchen
Contact: Mary Overlie, Director
E-mail: mary.board@harmonyfoods.coop
Facebook: www.facebook.com/harmonycoop
X (Twitter): x.com/HarmonyCoop
Instagram: www.instagram.com/harmonyfoodcoop
YouTube: www.youtube.com/channel/UCpPCbgSjsupAu9EIQ9g4SGQ
Description: A community kitchen providing local food producers with kitchen space in which to help their business grow.

41353 ■ Owatonna Partners For Economic Development (OPED)
120 S Oak Ave.
Owatonna, MN 55060
URL: http://owatonnadevelopment.com
Contact: Brad Meier, President
E-mail: bmeier@owatonna.org
X (Twitter): x.com/developowatonna
Description: A small business incubator providing a facility in which small and start-up businesses can grow, prosper, and contribute to the surrounding community's economic base. **Founded:** 1988. **Geographic Preference:** Local.

41354 ■ Sprout
609 13th Ave. NE, Ste. 8
Little Falls, MN 56345
Ph: (320)412-3081
Co. E-mail: info@sproutmn.com
URL: http://www.sproutmn.com
Contact: Arlene Jones, Executive Director
X (Twitter): x.com/sproutmn
YouTube: www.youtube.com/channel/UCHEWgiXRgQn_a1CnJbzQpsw
Description: Kitchen facility and incubator for local food producers. Provides commercial space for startups. **Founded:** 2012.

41355 ■ University of Minnesota Duluth Center for Economic Development - Small Business Development Center (SBDC)
202 W Superior St., Ste. 800
Duluth, MN 55802
Ph: (218)740-7307
Co. E-mail: info@northlandsbdc.org
URL: http://northlandsbdc.org
Contact: Curt Walczak, Director
E-mail: curt@northlandsbdc.org
Facebook: www.facebook.com/northlandsbdc
Linkedin: www.linkedin.com/company/northlandsbdc
X (Twitter): x.com/northlandsbdc
Instagram: www.instagram.com/northlandsbdc
YouTube: www.youtube.com/c/NorthlandSmallBusinessDevelopmentCenter
Description: An incubator for technology development companies. Offers access to UMD's Center for Economic Development services. **Founded:** 1986.

41356 ■ University of Minnesota - The Venture Center
280 McNamara Alumni Ctr., 200 Oak St. SE
Minneapolis, MN 55455
Co. E-mail: venture@umn.edu
URL: http://research.umn.edu/units/techcomm/startups/venture-center
Description: Works with University researchers, entrepreneurs, and investors in activities essential to the establishment and success of a new company. **Founded:** 2006.

EDUCATIONAL PROGRAMS

41357 ■ Alexandria Technical College (ATC)
1601 Jefferson St.
Alexandria, MN 56308
Ph: (320)762-0221
Co. E-mail: info@alextech.edu
URL: http://www.alextech.edu
Contact: Erin Berns, President
Facebook: www.facebook.com/ATCCMN
Linkedin: www.linkedin.com/school/atccmn
X (Twitter): x.com/ATCCMN
Instagram: www.instagram.com/atccmn
YouTube: www.youtube.com/user/AlexandriaTech
Description: Trade and technical school offering a program in small business management.

41358 ■ Central Lakes College (CLC)
501 W College Dr.
Brainerd, MN 56401
Ph: (218)855-8000
Free: 800-933-0346
Fax: (218)855-8220
Co. E-mail: accessibilityservices@clcmn.edu
URL: http://www.clcmn.edu
Contact: Hara Charlier, President
Facebook: www.facebook.com/centrallakescollege
Linkedin: www.linkedin.com/school/central-lakes-college
X (Twitter): x.com/clcmnedu
YouTube: www.youtube.com/user/centrallakescollege
Description: Trade and technical school offering a program in entrepreneurship and small business management. **Founded:** 1995.

41359 ■ Minnesota State Community and Technical College - Detroit Lakes
900 Hwy. 34 E
Detroit Lakes, MN 56501
Ph: (218)846-3700
Free: 877-450-3322
Fax: (218)736-1706
Co. E-mail: mstatestaffer@minnesota.edu
URL: http://www.minnesota.edu/about/campuses/detroit-lakes
Facebook: www.facebook.com/MStateCollege
Linkedin: www.linkedin.com/school/msctc
X (Twitter): x.com/MStateCollege
Instagram: www.instagram.com/mstatecollege
Description: Trade and technical school offering a program in small business management.

41360 ■ Minnesota State Community and Technical College - Fergus Falls
1414 College Way
Fergus Falls, MN 56537
Ph: (218)736-1500
Free: 877-450-3322
Fax: (218)736-1528
URL: http://www.minnesota.edu/about/campuses/fergus-falls-campus
Description: Two-year college offering a small business management program.

41361 ■ Minnesota West Community and Technical College (MWCTC)
1314 N Hiawatha Ave.
Pipestone, MN 56164
Free: 800-658-2330
Fax: (507)825-4656
URL: http://www.mnwest.edu
Contact: Dr. Terry Gaalswyk, PhD, President
E-mail: terry.gaalswyk@mnwest.edu
X (Twitter): x.com/MinnesotaWest
Description: Vocational school offering a small business management program. **Founded:** 1967.

41362 ■ Normandale Community College (NCC)
9700 France Ave. S
Bloomington, MN 55431
Ph: (952)358-8200
Free: 800-481-5412
Co. E-mail: admissions@normandale.edu
URL: http://www.normandale.edu
Contact: Dr. Joyce Ester, President
E-mail: joyce.ester@normandale.edu
Facebook: www.facebook.com/NormandaleCommunityCollege
X (Twitter): x.com/normandale_cc
YouTube: www.youtube.com/user/normandalevideos
Description: Two-year college offering a business and marketing management program, covering management skills, cash management, and marketing techniques used in business. **Founded:** 1968.

CONSULTANTS

41363 ■ Lumina Consulting Group
2112 Broadway Ave. NE
Minneapolis, MN 55413
Ph: (612)293-7767
URL: http://luminaconsultinggroup.com
Contact: Leary Gates, Chief Executive Officer
Linkedin: www.linkedin.com/company/lumina-consulting
X (Twitter): x.com/luminacg
Description: Consulting firm specializing in growth options for businesses.

PUBLICATIONS

41364 ■ *Minneapolis-Saint Paul Business Journal*
120 W Morehead St.
Charlotte, NC 28202
Co. E-mail: circhelp@bizjournals.com
URL: http://www.acbj.com
Contact: Mike Olivieri, Executive Vice President
URL(s): www.bizjournals.com/twincities
Linkedin: www.linkedin.com/company/minneapolis-st-paul-business-journal
X (Twitter): x.com/mspbjnews
Instagram: www.instagram.com/mspbusinessjournal
Released: Weekly **Price:** $70, for digital only Annual Insights or Annual + Hardcopy; $950, for premium unlimited 52 weeks Nationwide + BOL; $380, for premium elite 52 weeks Nationwide Access; $220, for print + online 52 weeks Premium Plus; $4, for print + online or online 4 weeks; $245, for Nationwide Access 40+ Cities; $21, for digital only 52 weeks. **Description:** Newspaper that covers business in the Minneapolis area. **Availability:** Print.

41365 ■ *Prairie Business Magazine (PB)*
101 5th St. N
Fargo, ND 58102-4826

41366 ■ Minnesota

Ph: (701)235-7311
Co. E-mail: afredrickson@forumcomm.com
URL: http://www.forumcomm.com
URL(s): www.grandforksherald.com/prairie-business
X (Twitter): twitter.com/prairiebiz
Ed: Kris Bevill. **Released:** Monthly **Description:** Magazine featuring business people and companies from North Dakota, Minnesota and South Dakota. **Availability:** Online.

PUBLISHERS

41366 ■ American Institute of Small Business (AISB)
PO Box 124
Excelsior, MN 55331
URL: http://www.ed2go.com/business
Description: Firm engages in the training small business entrepreneurs. **Founded:** 1984.

41367 ■ Thomson Reuters Minneapolis-Saint Paul
Thomson Reuters Corporation
610 Opperman Dr.
Eagan, MN 55123
Ph: (416)687-7500
URL: http://www.thomsonreuters.com
Contact: Steve Hasker, Co-President Co-Chief Executive Officer
Linkedin: www.linkedin.com/company/thomson-reuters
X (Twitter): x.com/thomsonreuters
Instagram: www.instagram.com/thomsonreuters
YouTube: www.youtube.com/thomsonreuters
Description: Publishes on legal information, intellectual property, business. **Founded:** 1872. **Publications:** *Witkin Library-Complete Set, LawDesk® CD-ROM ed.*; *California Criminal Practice Library, LawDesk® CD-ROM*; *Blackacre's RESPA*; *UCCSEARCH Anderson Treatise, LawDesk® CD-ROM ed.*; *AHLA Health Law Digest, LawDesk® CD-ROM ed.*; *AHLA Health Law Practice Law, LawDesk® CD-ROM ed.*; *Handbook on Georgia Practice with Forms*; *Redfearn's Wills & Administration of Estates in Georgia, 7th Forms on CD*; *The Law of Real Estate Financing* (Semiannual); *Trademark Trial and Appeal Board Practice and Procedure* (Annual); *Basic Legal Transactions* (Annual); *Real Estate Leasing Practice Manual*; *Multimedia and Technology Licensing Agreements*; *Daniel's Georgia Criminal Trial Practice Forms* (Annual); *Rise of American Law*; *Arizona Practice Series: Arizona Corporate Practice, 2015-2016 ed.*; *Arkansas Practice Series: Arkansas Model Jury Instructions, Civil*; *Aviation Tort and Regulatory Law, 2014-2015 ed.*; *UCCSEARCH Hawkland Treatise, LawDesk® CD-ROM ed.*; *Advising Small Businesses: Forms* (Annual); *Advising the Elderly Client* (Annual); *AHLA Health Law, LawDesk® CD-ROM ed.*; *AHLA Seminar Pages, LawDesk® CD-ROM ed.*; *Basic Legal Forms with Commentary, 2d*; *Briefing Papers, LawDesk® CD-ROM ed.*; *Business Entities, LawDesk® CD-ROM ed.*; *Business Transactions PowerLink, LawDesk® CD-ROM ed.*; *Business Transactions, LawDesk® CD-ROM ed.*; *California Civil Practice Complete, LawDesk® CD-ROM ed.*; *California Criminal Practice Library, LawDesk® CD-ROM ed.*; *Business and Commercial Litigation in Federal Courts*; *Massachusetts Practice: Business Corporations with Forms, 2014-2015 ed.*; *Powerlink: Employment Coordinator, LawDesk® CD-ROM ed.*; *Social Security Disability Claims Practice and Procedure, LawDesk® CD-ROM ed.*; *Social Security Disability Law and Procedure in Federal Court, LawDesk® CD-ROM ed.*; *The Government Contractor, LawDesk® CD-ROM ed.*; *The Nash and Cibinic Report, LawDesk® CD-ROM ed.*; *Trademark Registration Practice, LawDesk® CD-ROM ed.*; *Trawick's Florida Practice & Procedure Forms* (Annual); *UCC Search, LawDesk® CD-ROM ed.*; *West's® Annotated California Codes, LawDesk® CD-ROM ed.* (Annual); *California Jury Instruction Selector - Criminal*; *A Practical Guide to Document Authentication: Legalization of Notarized and Certified Documents, 2015-2016 ed.*; *Alabama Practice Series: Alabama Family Law*; *Missouri Practice Series: Appellate Practice, 2d*; *eDiscovery & Digital Evidence* (Annual); *E-Commerce and Internet Law: Treatise with Forms* (Annual); *The Law of Juries*; *Antitrust Law Handbook*; *Mergers & Acquisitions (M&A)*; *Baldwin's Ohio Practice Series: Baldwin's Civil Practice, 2d* (Periodic); *Benefits Guide*; *ImmForms Plus*; *Commercial Real Estate Forms, 3d* (Semiannual); *Complete Manual of Criminal Forms, 3d* (Annual); *Estate Planning, LawDesk® CD-ROM ed.*; *Georgia Automobile Insurance Law with Forms* (Annual); *Georgia Law Enforcement Handbook* (Annual); *Brown's Georgia Pleading, Practice, and Legal Forms*; *Housing and Development Reporter: HDRom Search Base, LawDesk® CD-ROM ed.*; *Immigration Research Information Service, LawDesk® CD-ROM ed. (IRIS)*; *Kaplan's Nadler Georgia Corporations, Limited Partnerships, and Limited Liability Companies with Forms*; *La Coe's Pleadings Under the Florida Rules of Civil Procedure*; *Legal Solutions™ Plus California Central District Bankruptcy Forms*; *Legal Solutions™ Plus California Southern District Bankruptcy Forms*; *Legal Solutions™ Plus Federal Bankruptcy Forms*; *McCarthy on Trademarks on CD-ROM*; *McCarthy on Trademarks - Cases Only, LawDesk® CD-ROM ed.*; *Georgia Divorce, Alimony, and Child Custody Forms*; *Miller and Starr California Real Estate, LawDesk® CD-ROM ed.*; *Nichols Electronic Legal Forms, LawDesk® CD-ROM ed.*; *Couch on Insurance, LawDesk® CD-ROM ed.*; *Business Counselor's Law and Compliance Practice Manual, 2014 ed.*; *Michigan Legal Forms: Business Enterprises with Forms*; *California Civil Practice: Business Litigation*; *Baldwin's Ohio Practice Series: Business Organizations, 2d*; *Missouri Practice Series: Business Organizations, 2d*; *Buyout Agreements Line by Line*; *California Criminal Practice, Motions, Jury Instructions and Sentencing, 3d*; *California Desktop Codes: California Education Code, 2016 ed.*; *California Jury Instructions--Civil (CACI)*.

VENTURE CAPITAL FIRM

41368 ■ Omphalos Ventures
100 Fuller St. S, Ste. 140
Shakopee, MN 55379
Ph: (952)657-5561
URL: http://www.omphalosventures.net
Contact: Mark Marlow, President
E-mail: mmarlow@omphalosventures.com
Description: Early-stage investment firm. **Founded:** 2010. **Industry Preferences:** Nano; sensor and environmental technology; medical devices; healthcare services; manufacturing; technology-enabled services; AI; robotics.

Mississippi

ASSOCIATIONS AND OTHER ORGANIZATIONS

41369 ■ National Federation of Independent Business Mississippi
Jackson, MS
Ph: (225)287-4626
URL: http://www.nfib.com/mississippi
Contact: Dawn McVea, Director
E-mail: dawn.mcvea@nfib.org
X (Twitter): x.com/nfib_ms
Description: Represents small and independent businesses. Aims to promote and protect the rights of members to own, operate and grow their businesses. **Geographic Preference:** State.

SMALL BUSINESS DEVELOPMENT CENTERS

41370 ■ East Central Community College Small Business Development Center (SBDC)
Decatur, MS
URL: http://www.eccc.edu/small-business-development-center
Contact: Tony Hisaw, Director
E-mail: tony.hisaw@eccc.edu
Description: Represents and promotes the small business sector. Provides management assistance to current and prospective small business owners. Helps to improve management skills and expand the products and services of members. **Geographic Preference:** Local.

41371 ■ Jackson State University Small Business Development Center (JSU)
3rd Fl., Ste. 332, Campus Map, Building 15
Jackson, MS 39217
Ph: (601)979-1100
URL: http://www.jsums.edu/sbdc
Contact: Rickey Jones, Director
E-mail: rickey.d.jones@jsums.edu
Description: Provides management assistance to current and prospective small business owners in Jacksonville. **Geographic Preference:** Local.

41372 ■ Jones County Junior College Small Business Development Center
900 S Ct., St.
Ellisville, MS 39437
URL: http://www.jcjc.edu
Contact: Dr. Jesse Smith, President
Description: Represents and promotes the small business sector. Provides management assistance to current and prospective small business owners. Helps to improve management skills and expand the products and services of members. **Founded:** 1991. **Geographic Preference:** Local.

41373 ■ Mississippi State University Small Business Development Center (MSUSBDC)
114 McCool Hall 40 Old Main
Mississippi State, MS 39762
Ph: (662)325-8684
Fax: (662)325-2410
Co. E-mail: business@msstate.edu
URL: http://www.business.msstate.edu/faculty-research/research-centers/small-business-development-center
Contact: Chip Templeton, Jr., Director
E-mail: ctempleton@business.msstate.edu
Facebook: www.facebook.com/MSUBusiness
X (Twitter): x.com/MSUBusiness
Instagram: www.instagram.com/msubusiness
YouTube: www.youtube.com/channel/UCpF2oWd7rPl7eFGaCuvkrMQ
Description: Represents and promotes the small business sector. Provides management assistance to current and prospective small business owners. Helps to improve management skills and expand the products and services of members. **Founded:** 1981. **Geographic Preference:** Local.

41374 ■ University of Mississippi - Mississippi Small Business Development Center (MSBDC)
122 Jeanette Phillips Dr.
University, MS 38677-1848
Ph: (662)915-5001
Free: 800-725-7232
Fax: (662)915-5650
Co. E-mail: msbdc@olemiss.edu
URL: http://mississippisbdc.org
Contact: Sharon Nichols, Director
E-mail: sknicho1@olemiss.edu
Facebook: www.facebook.com/mississippiSBDC
Linkedin: www.linkedin.com/company/mississippisbdc
X (Twitter): x.com/mississippiSBDC
Instagram: www.instagram.com/mississippisbdc
Description: Composed of 10 service centers, hosted by five universities and five community colleges in the state of Mississippi. Serves as a one-stop resource center for a variety of counseling, workshops and information for growing businesses and startups. **Scope:** Small business management, including feasibility studies, business law, venture capital, government contracting, and financial, production, and personnel management. **Founded:** 1981. **Publications:** *Going Into Business in Mississippi: An Entrepreneur's Handbook*; *The Mississippi Innovator*; *SBDC Business Beat* (Quarterly). **Educational Activities:** MSBDC Seminars and training on small business development. **Geographic Preference:** State; Local.

41375 ■ University of Mississippi Small Business Development Center (UMSBDC)
122 Jeanette Phillips Dr.
University, MS 38677-1848
Free: 800-725-7232
Fax: (662)915-5650
Co. E-mail: msbdc@olemiss.edu
URL: http://mississippisbdc.org
Contact: Chip Templeton, Director
E-mail: chip@mississippisbdc.org
Facebook: www.facebook.com/mississippiSBDC
Linkedin: www.linkedin.com/company/mississippisbdc
X (Twitter): x.com/mississippiSBDC
Instagram: www.instagram.com/mississippisbdc
Description: Represents and promotes the small business sector. Provides management assistance to current and prospective small business owners. Helps to improve management skills and expand the products and services of members. **Founded:** 1981. **Geographic Preference:** Local.

SMALL BUSINESS ASSISTANCE PROGRAMS

41376 ■ Mississippi Enterprise for Technology (MSET) - Mississippi Technology Transfer Office
1103 Balch Blvd.
Stennis Space Center, MS 39529
URL: http://mset.org/about-mset
Description: Helps advanced technology companies locate or expand in Mississippi. **Founded:** 1994.

41377 ■ Mississippi University for Women Career Services
1100 College St.
Columbus, MS 39701
URL: http://www.muw.edu/careers
Facebook: www.facebook.com/muwcareerservices
Instagram: www.instagram.com/careerservices_thew
Description: Provides employment-related services to students and organizations. **Founded:** 1884.

41378 ■ U.S. Department of Commerce (MDA) - Mississippi Development Authority
501 N W St.
Jackson, MS 39201
Ph: (601)359-3449
Free: 800-360-3323
Co. E-mail: social@mississippi.org
URL: http://mississippi.org
Contact: Laura Hipp, Executive Director
Facebook: www.facebook.com/msdevelopmentauthority
Description: Provides assistance to the state's businesses and industries, including loans and loan guarantees to small businesses, and an outreach program. **Founded:** 1936.

SCORE OFFICES

41379 ■ SCORE - Metro Jackson
PO Box 12085
Jackson, MS 39236
Ph: (601)589-0949
URL: http://jackson.score.org
Linkedin: www.linkedin.com/company/score-mentors-mississippi
Description: Unites active and retired business management professionals with men and women who are considering starting a small business, encounter-

ing problems with their business, or expanding their business. Serves the Mississippi counties of Hinds, Copiah, Madison, Rankin, and Warren.

41380 ■ SCORE - Northeast Mississippi
PO Box 12085
 Jackson, MS 39236
Free: 800-634-0245
Co. E-mail: help@score.org
URL: http://mississippi.score.org
Contact: Darleana McHenry, Contact
Facebook: www.facebook.com/SCOREMississippi
Linkedin: www.linkedin.com/company/score-mentors-mississippi
Description: Provides professional guidance and information to maximize the success of existing and emerging small businesses. Offers business counseling and workshops. **Founded:** 1964.

BETTER BUSINESS BUREAUS

41381 ■ Better Business Bureau of Mississippi
660 Katherine Dr., Ste. 400
 Flowood, MS 39232
Ph: (601)398-1700
Fax: (769)251-1054
Co. E-mail: info@ms.bbb.org
URL: http://www.bbb.org/local-bbb/bbb-serving-mississippi
Contact: John O'Hara, President
E-mail: johara@ms.bbb.org
Facebook: www.facebook.com/BBBMS
X (Twitter): x.com/BBBMississippi
Description: Seeks to promote and foster ethical relationship between businesses and the public through voluntary self-regulation, consumer and business education, and service excellence. Provides information to help consumers and businesses make informed purchasing decisions and avoid costly scams and frauds; settles consumer complaints through arbitration and other means. **Founded:** 1964. **Geographic Preference:** State.

CHAMBERS OF COMMERCE

41382 ■ Area Development Partnership (ADP)
1 Convention Center Plz.
 Hattiesburg, MS 39401
Ph: (601)296-7500
URL: http://www.theadp.com
Contact: Chad Newell, President
E-mail: c.newell@theadp.com
Facebook: www.facebook.com/adphattiesburg
X (Twitter): x.com/adphattiesburg
YouTube: www.youtube.com/channel/UCTSkAcrGJM8VhkYwrKIc-Mg
Pinterest: www.pinterest.com/ADPHattiesburg
Description: Strives to improve the quality of life for citizens of the Greater Hattiesburg Area through community and economic development. **Founded:** 1906. **Publications:** *The Navigator* (Quarterly). **Educational Activities:** Area Development Partnership Accelerate (Monthly). **Geographic Preference:** Local.

41383 ■ Belzoni-Humphreys Development Foundation (BHDF)
110 Magnolia St.
 Belzoni, MS 39038
Ph: (662)247-4838
Fax: (662)247-4805
Co. E-mail: catfish@belzonicable.com
URL: http://www.belzonims.com
Contact: Mark Bellipanni, President
Description: Fosters economic development. Grows all kinds of plants in the Mississippi Delta from cotton, sweet potatoes, and tobacco plants to distribution, manufacturing and processing plants. **Geographic Preference:** Local.

41384 ■ Biloxi Chamber of Commerce
11975 E Seaway Rd.
 Gulfport, MS 39503
Ph: (228)604-0014
Fax: (228)604-0105
Co. E-mail: info@mscoastchamber.com
URL: http://biloxi.org
Contact: Sam Burke, Chairman
Description: Promotes business and community development in Biloxi, MS. Sponsors Biloxi Seafood Festival, Music in May, community activities, and seminars. **Awards:** Biloxi Chamber of Commerce Educator Awards (Annual). **Geographic Preference:** Local.

41385 ■ Brookhaven - Lincoln County Chamber of Commerce
230 S Whitworth Ave.
 Brookhaven, MS 39601
Ph: (601)833-1411
Co. E-mail: info@brookhavenchamber.com
URL: http://brookhavenchamber.org/wp
Contact: Garrick Combs, Executive Director
E-mail: gcombs@brookhavenchamber.com
Facebook: www.facebook.com/brookhavenchamber
Description: Strives to enhance the industrial, commercial, tourism, retiree development, civic and general interests of Lincoln County, MS. **Founded:** 1931. **Publications:** *Lincoln County Manufacturers and Distribution Centers Directory* (Annual); *Brookhaven's Guide to Family Living* (Annual). **Geographic Preference:** Local.

41386 ■ Calhoun City Chamber of Commerce (CCCC)
138 B- Public Sq.
 Calhoun City, MS 38916
Ph: (662)628-6990
Co. E-mail: calhouncitychamber@tds.net
URL: http://calhouneda.com/cities/calhoun-city/calhoun-city-chamber-of-commerce
Contact: Laura Edwards, President
Description: Promotes business and community development in Calhoun County, MS. Sponsors periodic festival. Publications: none. **Founded:** 1969. **Geographic Preference:** Local.

41387 ■ Chamber Chatter
201 Hwy. 11 N
 Picayune, MS 39466
Ph: (601)798-3122
Co. E-mail: picayunechamber@gmail.com
URL: http://greaterpicayunechamber.org
Contact: Kenny McDonald, President
URL(s): greaterpicayunechamber.org/chamber-sponsorships
Availability: Print.

41388 ■ Chamber News
9123 Prigeon Roost Rd.
 Olive Branch, MS 38654
Ph: (662)895-2600
Fax: (662)895-2625
Co. E-mail: info@olivebranchms.com
URL: http://www.olivebranchms.com
Contact: Vickie DuPree, Chief Executive Officer
URL(s): olivebranchms.com/prospective-members/member-benefits
Availability: Print; Online.

41389 ■ City of Ridgeland Chamber of Commerce
754 S Pear Orchard Rd.
 Ridgeland, MS 39157
Ph: (601)991-9996
URL: http://ridgelandchamber.com
Contact: Linda Bynum, Executive Director
X (Twitter): x.com/RidgelandCC
Description: Encourages an economic environment conducive to the continuing development of new and existing business. **Publications:** *Vision* (Monthly); *Images* (Annual). **Geographic Preference:** Local.

41390 ■ Clarke County Chamber of Commerce
100 S Railroad Ave.
 Quitman, MS 39355
Ph: (601)776-5701
Fax: (601)776-5745
Co. E-mail: clarkechamber@att.net
URL: http://clarkcountychamber.com
Facebook: www.facebook.com/Clarke-County-Chamber-of-Commerce-107648882596557
Description: Seeks to unify the citizens of Clarke County, MS to foster growth in leadership, education, and economics. Works to improve the quality of life in the area. **Founded:** 1833. **Geographic Preference:** Local.

41391 ■ Clarksdale - Coahoma County Chamber of Commerce and Industry Foundation (CCCCCIF)
PO Box 160
 Clarksdale, MS 38614-0160
Ph: (662)627-7337
URL: http://www.uschamber.com/co/chambers/mississippi/clarksdale
Description: Promotes business and community development in Coahoma County, MS. Sponsors Sunflower River 10-K Run and Delta Jubilee barbecue contest. **Publications:** *Newcomers Guide*; *On Target* (Quarterly). **Geographic Preference:** Local.

41392 ■ Cleveland-Bolivar County Chamber of Commerce (CBCCC)
101 S Bayou Ave.
 Cleveland, MS 38732
Ph: (662)843-2712
Fax: (662)843-2718
Co. E-mail: info@clevelandmschamber.com
URL: http://www.clevelandmschamber.com
Contact: Cheryl Comans, President
Facebook: www.facebook.com/cleveland.chamber
Description: Promotes business and community development in Bolivar County, MS. Holds monthly board and committee meeting. **Founded:** 1947. **Publications:** *Action Line Newsletter* (Monthly); *Community Data Book* (Periodic). **Geographic Preference:** Local.

41393 ■ Clinton Chamber of Commerce
100 E Leake St.
 Clinton, MS 39056
Ph: (601)924-5912
Fax: (601)925-4009
Co. E-mail: info@clintonchamber.org
URL: http://www.clintonchamber.org
Contact: Gerad Hardy, Contact
Facebook: www.facebook.com/ClintonChamberofCommerce
Linkedin: www.linkedin.com/company/clinton-chamber-of-commerce-clinton-ms
X (Twitter): x.com/39056_Chamber
Instagram: www.instagram.com/39056_chamber
YouTube: www.youtube.com/channel/UCKNAKY2eKM0X8EM-clcC6iQ
Description: Promotes business and community development in Clinton, MS. **Founded:** 1965. **Publications:** *The Chamber Network* (Bimonthly). **Geographic Preference:** Local.

41394 ■ Community Development Foundation (CDF)
398 E Main St.
 Tupelo, MS 38804-4037
Ph: (662)842-4521
Co. E-mail: info@cdfms.org
URL: http://www.cdfms.org
Contact: David P. Rumbarger, President
Facebook: www.facebook.com/cdfms
Linkedin: www.linkedin.com/company/cdfms
X (Twitter): x.com/cdfms
Instagram: www.instagram.com/cdfms
YouTube: www.youtube.com/user/cdfvideo
Description: Strives to improve the civic, economic, and social welfare of people living in Tupelo and Lee County. **Founded:** 1948. **Publications:** *Northeast Mississippi Business Journal* (Monthly). **Geographic Preference:** Local.

41395 ■ Community Development Partnership (CDP) [Philadelphia Community Development Partnership]
256 W Beacon St.
 Philadelphia, MS 39350
Ph: (601)656-1000
URL: http://www.neshoba.org
Contact: Tim Moore, Executive Director

E-mail: mooretim1975@gmail.com
Facebook: www.facebook.com/MississippisPhiladelphia
Description: Promotes business and community development in Neshoba County and Philadelphia, MS. **Founded:** 1954. **Geographic Preference:** Local.

41396 ■ Covington County Chamber of Commerce
500 Komo St.
Collins, MS 39428
Ph: (601)765-6012
URL: http://www.covingtonchamber.com/in/index.php
Contact: Marie Shoemake, Contact
Facebook: www.facebook.com/Covington-County-Chamber-MS-137298526321146
Description: Promotes business and community development in Covington County, MS. Sponsors annual horse show and Day in the Park. **Founded:** 1987. **Publications:** *Chamber News* (Monthly). **Geographic Preference:** Local.

41397 ■ D'Iberville-St. Martin Chamber of Commerce
10491 Lemoyne Blvd., Ste. A
Diberville, MS 39540
Ph: (228)392-2293
Fax: (888)269-9867
Co. E-mail: dsm@dsmchamber.com
URL: http://dsmchamber.com
Contact: Joyce Johnson, President
Facebook: www.facebook.com/people/DIbervilleSt-Martin-Area-Chamber-of-Commerce/100064779700427
Linkedin: www.linkedin.com/in/d'iberville-st-martin-chamber-of-commerce-536600163
X (Twitter): x.com/dsmchamber
Instagram: www.instagram.com/dsmchamber
Pinterest: www.pinterest.com/dsmchamber
Description: Promotes business and community development in D'Iberville and St. Martin, MS area. **Founded:** 1974. **Geographic Preference:** Local.

41398 ■ Greater Jackson Chamber of Commerce (GJCC)
PO Box 22548
Jackson, MS 39225-2548
Ph: (601)948-7575
Fax: (601)352-5539
Co. E-mail: contact@greaterjacksonpartnership.com
URL: http://www.greaterjacksonpartnership.com
Contact: Jeff Rent, President
E-mail: jrent@greaterjacksonms.com
Facebook: www.facebook.com/GreaterJacksonChamberPartnership
X (Twitter): twitter.com/GJCP
Description: Promotes business and community development in the Jackson County, MI area. **Founded:** 1880. **Geographic Preference:** Local.

41399 ■ Greater Jackson Chamber Partnership (GJCP)
212 N Congress St.
Jackson, MS 39201
Ph: (601)948-7575
Facebook: www.facebook.com/GreaterJacksonChamberPartnershipp
Linkedin: www.linkedin.com/company/greater-jackson-chamber-partnership
Description: Promotes business and community development in Jackson, MS. **Founded:** 1880. **Publications:** *Jackson Metropolitan Manufacturers Directory* (Irregular); *Jackson Commerce* (Weekly); *Metro Buyers' Guide* (Annual); *Firms with Major Regional & National Headquarter Facilities in Jackson.* **Geographic Preference:** Regional.

41400 ■ Greater Picayune Area Chamber of Commerce
201 Hwy. 11 N
Picayune, MS 39466
Ph: (601)798-3122
Co. E-mail: picayunechamber@gmail.com
URL: http://greaterpicayunechamber.org
Contact: Kenny McDonald, President
Facebook: www.facebook.com/picayunechamberofcommerce
X (Twitter): x.com/GPACOC
Instagram: www.instagram.com/picayunechamber
Description: Promotes business and community development in the Picayune, MS area. Sponsors festival. **Founded:** 1935. **Publications:** *Chamber Chatter*. **Awards:** Greater Picayune Area Chamber Citizen of the Year (Annual); Greater Picayune Area Chamber Civic Club of the Year (Annual); Greater Picayune Area Chamber Volunteer of the Year (Annual). **Geographic Preference:** Local.

41401 ■ Greenwood-Leflore Chamber of Commerce (GLCC)
402 Hwy. 82 W
Greenwood, MS 38935
Ph: (662)453-4152
Fax: (662)453-8003
Co. E-mail: info@greenwoodms.com
URL: http://greenwoodmschamber.com
Contact: Beth Stevens, Executive Director
Facebook: www.facebook.com/gwdmschamber
X (Twitter): x.com/gwdmschamber
Instagram: www.instagram.com/greenwoodleflorechamber
Description: Promotes business and community development in the Greenwood-Leflore, MS area. **Founded:** 1917. **Publications:** *What's Happening* (Bimonthly). **Geographic Preference:** Local.

41402 ■ Grenada Area Chamber of Commerce
95 SW Frontage Rd.
Grenada, MS 38901
Ph: (662)226-2571
Co. E-mail: info@grenadamississippi.com
URL: http://greatergrenada.com
Contact: Matthew Harrison, Chief Executive Officer
Facebook: www.facebook.com/thegrenadachamber
Description: Promotes business and community development in Grenada County, MS. **Founded:** 1934. **Publications:** *Guide to Grenada*. **Geographic Preference:** Local.

41403 ■ Hancock County Chamber of Commerce (HCCC)
100 S Beach Blvd., Ste. A
Bay Saint Louis, MS 39520
Ph: (228)467-9048
Fax: (228)467-6033
Co. E-mail: info@hancockchamber.org
URL: http://hancockchamber.org
Contact: Tish Haas Williams, Executive Director
E-mail: tish@hancockchamber.org
Facebook: www.facebook.com/hancock.chamber
X (Twitter): x.com/HancockChamber
Instagram: www.instagram.com/hancock_chamber
Description: Promotes business and community development in Hancock County, MS. **Founded:** 1925. **Geographic Preference:** Local.

41404 ■ Hernando Main Street Chamber of Commerce
421 W Commerce St.
Hernando, MS 38632
Ph: (662)429-9055
Fax: (662)429-2909
Co. E-mail: chamber@hernandoms.org
URL: http://www.hernandoms.org
Contact: Sibonie Swatzyna, Executive Director
E-mail: sibonie@hernandoms.org
Facebook: www.facebook.com/HernandoMSChamber
X (Twitter): x.com/HernandoMS
Instagram: www.instagram.com/hernandochamber
Description: Promotes business and community development in Hernando, MS area. **Geographic Preference:** Local.

41405 ■ Horn Lake Chamber of Commerce (HLCC)
3101 Goodman Rd. W
Horn Lake, MS 38637
Ph: (662)393-9897
Fax: (662)393-2942
Co. E-mail: info@hornlakechamber.com
URL: http://www.hornlakechamber.com
Contact: Michael Cobbs, President
Facebook: www.facebook.com/hornlakechamber
X (Twitter): x.com/hornlakechamber
Instagram: www.instagram.com/hornlakechamber
Description: Works to create jobs by recruiting new business to the area. **Publications:** *Business Review* (Monthly). **Geographic Preference:** Local.

41406 ■ Itawamba County Development Council (ICDC)
107 W Wiygul St.
Fulton, MS 38843
Ph: (662)862-4571
URL: http://itawambams.com
Contact: Ann Izard, Executive Assistant
E-mail: aizard@itawambams.com
Facebook: www.facebook.com/VisitItawamba
X (Twitter): x.com/ItawambaCDC
Description: Strives to improve and enhance the quality of life for all citizens and promotes orderly business and economic development in Itawamba County. **Founded:** 1953. **Geographic Preference:** Local.

41407 ■ Jones County Chamber of Commerce
153 Base Dr., Ste. 3
Laurel, MS 39441-0527
Ph: (601)649-3031
Free: 800-392-9629
Fax: (601)428-2047
Co. E-mail: info@edajones.com
URL: http://jonescounty.com
Contact: Ross Tucker, President
E-mail: rosst@edajones.com
Facebook: www.facebook.com/jonescountychamber
X (Twitter): x.com/joneschamberms
Instagram: www.instagram.com/jonescountychamber
YouTube: www.youtube.com/user/jonescountychamber
Pinterest: www.pinterest.com/jonescountyms
Description: Promotes business and economic development in Jones County. **Founded:** 1950. **Publications:** *Directions*. **Geographic Preference:** Local.

41408 ■ Kosciusko-Attala Chamber of Commerce (KACC)
124 N Jackson St.
Kosciusko, MS 39090
Ph: (662)289-2981
URL: http://www.go-mississippi.com/Kosciusko-Attala-Chamber-of-Commerce-MS
Contact: Riley Hudson, Executive Director
E-mail: rileyhudson@kapartnership.org
URL(s): kapartnership.org
Facebook: www.facebook.com/Kosciusko.MS
Description: Promotes business and community development in the Kosciusko-Attala, MS area. Sponsors local festival. **Founded:** 1935. **Publications:** *Highlights* (Periodic). **Geographic Preference:** Local.

41409 ■ Leake County Chamber of Commerce (LCCC)
103 N Pearl St.
Carthage, MS 39051
Ph: (601)267-9231
Co. E-mail: director@leakems.com
URL: http://leakems.com
Description: Promotes business and community development in Leake County, MS. **Founded:** 1833. **Publications:** *News Leakes*. **Educational Activities:** Carthage's Octoberfest. **Geographic Preference:** Local.

41410 ■ Leland Chamber of Commerce
206 N Broad St.
Leland, MS 38756
Ph: (662)379-3764
Co. E-mail: lelandcoc@gmail.com
URL: http://www.lelandchamber.com
Contact: William Powell, Chairman
Description: Promotes business and economic development in Leland, MS. **Founded:** 1968. **Geographic Preference:** Local.

41411 ■ Louisville-Winston County Chamber of Commerce
Winston County Economic Development Partnership
70 W Pk. St.
Louisville, MS 39339
Ph: (662)773-3921
Co. E-mail: amy@winstoncounty.com
URL: http://www.winstoncountyms.com/chamber-of-commerce
Contact: Amy Hillyer, Contact
E-mail: amy@winstoncounty.com
Facebook: www.facebook.com/WinstonCountyChamber
YouTube: www.youtube.com/channel/UCJLyRpsFg7JgkIKL-vk36Nw
Description: Promotes business and community development in Winston County, MS. **Geographic Preference:** Local.

41412 ■ Madison County Chamber of Commerce
1085 Gluckstadt Rd. No. 300, Ste. 101
Madison, MS 39110
Ph: (601)605-2554
Fax: (601)605-2260
URL: http://www.madisoncountychamber.com
Contact: Dr. Delta Stark, President
Description: Promotes business and community development in the London, OH area. **Founded:** 1959. **Geographic Preference:** Local.

41413 ■ Marion County Development Partnership (MCDP)
412 Courthouse Sq.
Columbia, MS 39429
Ph: (601)736-6385
Fax: (601)736-6392
Co. E-mail: info@mcdp.info
URL: http://www.mcdp.info
Contact: Lori Watts, Director
Facebook: www.facebook.com/mcdp.ms
Linkedin: www.linkedin.com/company/mcdp---marion-county-development-partnership
Description: Promotes business and community development in Marion County, MS. **Founded:** 1922. **Publications:** *The Chamber Message* (Quarterly). **Geographic Preference:** Local.

41414 ■ *Membership Directory and Community Guide*
9123 Prigeon Roost Rd.
Olive Branch, MS 38654
Ph: (662)895-2600
Fax: (662)895-2625
Co. E-mail: info@olivebranchms.com
URL: http://www.olivebranchms.com
Contact: Vickie DuPree, Chief Executive Officer
URL(s): olivebranchms.com/prospective-members/member-benefits
Availability: Print.

41415 ■ Mississippi Gulf Coast Chamber of Commerce, Inc.
11975 Seaway Rd., Ste. B120
Gulfport, MS 39503
Ph: (228)604-0014
Fax: (228)604-0105
Co. E-mail: info@mscoastchamber.com
URL: http://mscoastchamber.com
Contact: Adele Lyons, Chief Executive Officer
Facebook: www.facebook.com/MSCoastChamber
Linkedin: www.linkedin.com/in/mississippi-gulf-coast-chamber-of-commerce-inc-3918402a
X (Twitter): x.com/MSCoastChamber
YouTube: www.youtube.com/user/MSCoastChamber
Description: Promotes business and community development in the Gulf Coast area of MS. Sponsors civic clearing house, public relations counseling, legislative representation at all levels of government, information bureau, and research and promotion programs. **Founded:** 2007. **Publications:** *Relocation Guide* (Annual). **Geographic Preference:** Local.

41416 ■ Monroe County Chamber of Commerce
124 W Commerce St.
Aberdeen, MS 39730
Ph: (662)369-6488
Co. E-mail: misty@gomonroe.org
URL: http://gomonroe.org
Contact: Chelsea Baulch, Executive Director
E-mail: chelsea@gomonroe.org
Facebook: www.facebook.com/gomonroeorg
Linkedin: www.linkedin.com/company/monroe-county-chamber-of-commerce
X (Twitter): x.com/gomonroeorg
Instagram: www.instagram.com/gomonroeorg
Description: Promotes business and community development in Aberdeen-South Monroe, MS. Sponsors Christmas at Blue Bluff and outdoor festivals. **Founded:** 1921. **Publications:** *Monroe Messenger*. **Geographic Preference:** Local.

41417 ■ Monroe County Chamber of Commerce
1608 Hwy. 25 S
Amory, MS 38821
Ph: (662)256-7194
Co. E-mail: misty@gomonroe.org
URL: http://gomonroe.org
Contact: Chelsea Baulch, Executive Director
E-mail: chelsea@gomonroe.org
Facebook: www.facebook.com/gomonroeorg
X (Twitter): x.com/gomonroeorg
Instagram: www.instagram.com/gomonroeorg
Description: Promotes business and community development in the Amory, MS area. **Founded:** 1946. **Geographic Preference:** Local.

41418 ■ Natchez-Adams County Chamber of Commerce (NACCC)
211 Main St.
Natchez, MS 39120
Ph: (601)445-4611
Fax: (601)445-9361
Co. E-mail: natchezchamber@natchezchamber.com
URL: http://natchezchamber.com
Contact: Debbie L. Hudson, Co-President Co-Chief Executive Officer
E-mail: debbie@natchezchamber.com
Facebook: www.facebook.com/Natchezchamberofcommerce
Description: Promotes business and community development in Natchez-Adams County, MS. **Founded:** 1908. **Geographic Preference:** Local.

41419 ■ Newton Chamber of Commerce (NCC)
128 S Main St.
Newton, MS 39345
Ph: (601)683-2201
URL: http://newtonchamberms.com
Contact: Donald Vares, President
Facebook: www.facebook.com/chambernewton
YouTube: www.youtube.com/user/newtonmschamber
Description: Promotes business and community development in the Newton, MS area. Sponsors Open Air A'Fair festival. **Founded:** 1952. **Geographic Preference:** Local.

41420 ■ Ocean Springs Chamber of Commerce (OSCC)
1000 Washington Ave.
Ocean Springs, MS 39564
Ph: (228)875-4424
Fax: (228)875-0332
Co. E-mail: mail@oceanspringschamber.com
URL: http://www.oceanspringschamber.com
Contact: Carole Marie Stuart, Co-President
Facebook: www.facebook.com/oceanspringschamberofcommerce
X (Twitter): x.com/OceanSpringsCha
Pinterest: www.pinterest.com/pin/407505466257598971
Description: Promotes business and community development in Ocean Springs, MS. **Founded:** 1947. **Geographic Preference:** Local.

41421 ■ Okolona Area Chamber of Commerce
219 Main St.
Okolona, MS 38860
Ph: (662)447-5913
Fax: (662)447-0254
URL: http://www.okolonams.org
Contact: Nancy Schreck, Executive
Description: Promotes business and community development in Okolona, MS area. **Founded:** 1950. **Geographic Preference:** Local.

41422 ■ Olive Branch Chamber of Commerce (OBCC)
9123 Prigeon Roost Rd.
Olive Branch, MS 38654
Ph: (662)895-2600
Fax: (662)895-2625
Co. E-mail: info@olivebranchms.com
URL: http://www.olivebranchms.com
Contact: Vickie DuPree, Chief Executive Officer
Facebook: www.facebook.com/obchamber
Linkedin: www.linkedin.com/company/olive-branch-chamber-of-commerce
X (Twitter): x.com/OBChamber
Instagram: www.instagram.com/olivebranchchamber
Description: Promotes business and community development in the Olive Branch, MS area. **Founded:** 1973. **Publications:** *Chamber News*; *Membership Directory and Community Guide*. **Educational Activities:** Christmas Parade; During Hours. **Geographic Preference:** Local.

41423 ■ Oxford-Lafayette County Chamber of Commerce (OLCCC)
299 W Jackson Ave.
Oxford, MS 38655
Ph: (662)234-4651
Co. E-mail: info@oxfordms.com
URL: http://oxfordms.com
Contact: Jon Maynard, Contact
Facebook: www.facebook.com/OxfordMSChamber
Description: Promotes business and community development in the Oxford-Lafayette County, MS area. **Founded:** 1940. **Publications:** *LOU View* (Weekly). **Geographic Preference:** Local.

41424 ■ Pearl Chamber of Commerce (PCC)
110 George Wallace Dr.
Pearl, MS 39208
Ph: (601)939-3338
Fax: (601)939-5717
Co. E-mail: pearlchamberofcommerce@pearlms.org
URL: http://www.pearlms.org
Contact: Kathy Deer, Executive Director
Facebook: www.facebook.com/Pearl-Chamber-of-Commerce-150869701646414
Description: Promotes business and community development in Pearl, MS. **Founded:** 1979. **Geographic Preference:** Local.

41425 ■ Pike County Chamber of Commerce
213 Main St.
McComb, MS 39648-3923
Ph: (601)684-2291
URL: http://pikeinfo.com/chamber
Contact: Catherine Sanders, Executive Director
E-mail: csanders@pikeinfo.com
Facebook: www.facebook.com/Pike-Co-Chamber-of-Commerce-162086207152568
X (Twitter): x.com/ChamberPikeCo
Description: Promotes business and community development in Pike County, MS. **Founded:** 1865. **Publications:** *Going Our Way* (Monthly). **Geographic Preference:** Local.

41426 ■ Pontotoc County Chamber of Commerce
109 N Main St.
Pontotoc, MS 38863
Ph: (662)489-5042
Fax: (662)489-5263
Co. E-mail: chamber@pontotocchamber.com
URL: http://pontotocchamber.com
Contact: Nathan White, President
Facebook: www.facebook.com/PontotocCountyChamberMainStreet
Description: Promotes business and community development in Pontotoc County, MS. Sponsors annual Christmas parade and annual Bodock Festival. **Founded:** 1987. **Geographic Preference:** Local.

STATE LISTINGS Mississippi ■ 41445

41427 ■ Port Gibson-Claiborne County Chamber of Commerce
1601 Church St.
Port Gibson, MS 39150
Ph: (601)437-4351
Co. E-mail: portgibsonchamber@att.net
URL: http://portgibsonchamber.wixsite.com/portgibsonchamber
Contact: Lorraine Hunt, President
Description: Promotes business and community development in the Port Gibson-Claiborne County, MS area. Provides tourist information on the area. **Founded:** 1803. **Geographic Preference:** Local.

41428 ■ Rankin County Chamber of Commerce
101 Service Dr.
Brandon, MS 39043-0428
Ph: (601)825-2268
Fax: (601)825-1977
Co. E-mail: information@rankinchamber.com
URL: http://www.rankinchamber.com
Contact: Mandi Arinder, Executive Director
E-mail: marinder@rankinchamber.com
Facebook: www.facebook.com/RankinCountyChamber
X (Twitter): x.com/RankinChamber
Description: Promotes business and community development in Rankin County, MS. Also promotes highway, recreation, agriculture and forestry, and health development. **Founded:** 1994. **Publications:** *Civic Club and Organizational Directory* (Periodic); *Day Care Center Directory* (Periodic); *Manufacturer Directory* (Periodic). **Geographic Preference:** Local.

41429 ■ Southaven
500 Main St.
Southaven, MS 38671
Ph: (662)342-6114
Co. E-mail: info@southavenchamber.com
URL: http://www.southavenchamber.com
Contact: Debbie King, Executive Director
Released: Annual **Description:** Contains community information and business directories. **Availability:** Online.

41430 ■ Southaven Chamber of Commerce
500 Main St.
Southaven, MS 38671
Ph: (662)342-6114
Co. E-mail: info@southavenchamber.com
URL: http://www.southavenchamber.com
Contact: Debbie King, Executive Director
Facebook: www.facebook.com/SouthavenCofC
Linkedin: www.linkedin.com/company/southaven-chamber-of-commerce
X (Twitter): x.com/ShavenChamber
YouTube: www.youtube.com/user/SouthavenCofC
Description: Promotes business and community development in Southaven-Horn Lake, MS. **Founded:** 1969. **Publications:** *Southaven* (Annual); *Chamber Network* (Monthly); *Visitors Guide* (Annual); *Chamber Digest*. **Geographic Preference:** Local.

41431 ■ Tunica County Chamber of Commerce
1371 Main St.
Tunica, MS 38676
Ph: (662)363-2865
URL: http://www.uschamber.com/co/chambers/mississippi/tunica
Contact: John H. Pritchard, Contact
Description: Promotes business and community development in Tunica, MS area. **Founded:** 1956. **Geographic Preference:** Local.

41432 ■ Vicksburg-Warren County Chamber of Commerce (VWCCC)
1622 Washington St., Ste. 201
Vicksburg, MS 39180
Ph: (601)636-1012
URL: http://vicksburgusa.com
Contact: Pablo Diaz, President
E-mail: pablo@vicksburgusa.com
Linkedin: www.linkedin.com/company/vicksburg-chamber
X (Twitter): x.com/vburgchamber
Instagram: www.instagram.com/vicksburgchamber
Description: Promotes business and community development in Vicksburg-Warren County, MS. **Founded:** 1912. **Geographic Preference:** Local.

41433 ■ Walthall County Chamber of Commerce
901 Union Rd.
Tylertown, MS 39667
Ph: (601)876-2680
Co. E-mail: walthallchamber@bellsouth.net
URL: http://www.walthallchamber.com
Contact: Carolyn F. Dillon, Treasurer
Facebook: www.facebook.com/walthallchamber
X (Twitter): x.com/walthallchamber
Description: Promotes business and community development in Walthall County, MS. **Geographic Preference:** Local.

MINORITY BUSINESS ASSISTANCE PROGRAMS

41434 ■ City of Jackson Economic Development Division - Equal Business Opportunity Office
219 S President St.
Jackson, MS 39201
URL: http://www.jacksonms.gov/ebo
Description: Provides assistance in the development of minority entrepreneurs.

41435 ■ Crudup-Ward Women's Business Center (CWAC)
630-656 Longview St.
Forest, MS 39074
Ph: (601)469-3357
Fax: (601)564-7170
Co. E-mail: admin@crudupwardactivitycenter.org
URL: http://www.crudupwardactivitycenter.org/womens-business-center.html
Contact: Annie Ward Lowery, President
E-mail: anniewlowery@gmail.com
Description: Provides business information, counseling, management, and technical assistance to women looking to create or expand a business. **Founded:** 1996.

41436 ■ Mississippi Development Authority (MSD) - Minority and Small Business Development Div.
501 N W St.
Jackson, MS 39201
Ph: (601)359-3448
Co. E-mail: minority@mississippi.org
URL: http://mississippi.org/minority-small-business/grants
Description: Facilitates networking and industry partnerships for minority and women-owned businesses.

41437 ■ Mississippi Minority Business Enterprise Center
501 N W St.
Jackson, MS 39201
URL: http://mississippi.org/minority-small-business
Description: Provider of business development services to minority enterprises, focusing on strategic growth businesses. **Founded:** 1934.

FINANCING AND LOAN PROGRAMS

41438 ■ Bulldog Angel Network! (BAN)
117 Woodrow Balch Dr.
Huntsville, AL 35806
Ph: (256)682-6190
URL: http://ban.clubexpress.com
Contact: Wade C. Patterson, President
E-mail: wadepat123@gmail.com
Description: Network of Mississippi State University alumni and friends offering angel investments to early-stage companies majority owned by MSU students, faculty, or alumni. **Founded:** 2017.

PROCUREMENT ASSISTANCE PROGRAMS

41439 ■ Missisipi Development Authority - Mississippi Procurement Technical Assistance Program (MPTAP)
Woolfolk Bldg. 4th Fl., 501 N W St.
Jackson, MS 39201
Ph: (601)359-3448
URL: http://mscpc.com
Facebook: www.facebook.com/MSPTAP
Linkedin: www.linkedin.com/in/msptac-ms-procurement-tech-assistance-prog-002a3920b
X (Twitter): x.com/askmptap

41440 ■ Mississippi Contract Procurement Technical Assistance Center - East Central Satellite
723 23Rd. Ave.
Meridian, MS 39301
Ph: (601)934-5975
URL: http://www.mscpc.com
Description: Enhances national defense and economic development of the state of Mississippi by assisting Mississippi businesses in obtaining federal, state, local government and commercial contracts serving Clarke, Covington, Jasper, Jones, Kemper, Lauderdale, Leake, Neshoba, Newton, Scott, Smith, and Wayne Counties.

41441 ■ Mississippi Contract Procurement Technical Center, Inc. - Central Mississippi Procurement Center, Inc. (CMPC)
c/o Mississippi Development Authority
501 N W St.
Jackson, MS 39201
URL: http://www.mscpc.com
Description: Enhances national defense and economic development of the state of Mississippi by assisting Mississippi businesses in obtaining federal, state, local government and commercial contracts serving Adams, Claiborne, Copiah, Franklin, Hinds, Jefferson, Jefferson Davis, Lawrence, Lincoln, Madison, Rankin, Simpson, and Warren counties.

41442 ■ Mississippi Development Authority - Mississippi Contract Procurement Center Inc.
PO Box 849
Jackson, MS 39205
URL: http://www.mscpc.com
Description: Provides information and direct assistance to firms wishing to do business with the federal government.

41443 ■ Mississippi Procurement Technical Assistance Program (MPTAP) - Delta Contract Procurement Center (DCPC)
PO Box 849
Jackson, MS 39205
Ph: (601)359-3448
Fax: (601)359-5290
URL: http://www.mscpc.com
Facebook: www.facebook.com/MSPTAP
X (Twitter): x.com/askmptap
Description: Assisting Mississippi businesses in obtaining federal, state, local government and commercial contracts. **Founded:** 1988.

41444 ■ Mississippi Procurement Technical Assistance Program - Mississippi Development Authority - Minority and Small Business Development Div. (MSBDD) (MSBDD)
PO Box 849
Jackson, MS 39205
URL: http://www.mscpc.com
Description: To enhance economic development of the state of Mississippi by assisting Mississippi businesses in obtaining federal, state, local government and commercial contracts.

41445 ■ Northeast Mississippi Procurement Technical Assistance Program
318 7th St. N
Columbus, MS 39703
Ph: (662)329-1077

Small Business Sourcebook • 42nd Edition

Fax: (662)327-6600
URL: http://www.mscpc.com
Description: Assisting Mississippi businesses in obtaining federal, state, local government and commercial contracts.

INCUBATORS/RESEARCH AND TECHNOLOGY PARKS

41446 ■ Coahoma County Business Development Center
CCC Workforce Development Center
510 Sunbelt Dr.
Clarksdale, MS 38614
Ph: (662)627-9139
Fax: (622)627-9171
URL: http://www.coahomacc.edu/programs/workforce/index.html
Contact: Valmadge T. Towner, President
Facebook: www.facebook.com/CCCTigers
X (Twitter): x.com/_TigerNation
Instagram: www.instagram.com/ccctigers
YouTube: www.youtube.com/CCCoahoma
Description: A small business incubator that assists entrepreneurs in the business start-up process and gives aid to new businesses to help ensure their survival. **Founded:** 1949.

41447 ■ Innovate Mississippi
121 N State St., Third Fl., Ste. 500
Jackson, MS 39201
Ph: (601)960-3610
Fax: (601)960-3605
Co. E-mail: info@innovate.ms
URL: http://www.innovate.ms
Contact: Tony Jeff, President
E-mail: tjeff@innovate.ms
Facebook: www.facebook.com/InnovateMS
Linkedin: www.linkedin.com/company/mississippi-technology-alliance
X (Twitter): x.com/innovatems
Instagram: www.instagram.com/innovatems
Description: A non-profit, public-private partnership whose primary mission is to drive science and technology-based economic development efforts throughout the state, with the end goal being wealth creation through higher paying quality jobs; it focuses on creating wealth by leveraging research capacity and supporting technology business development for Mississippi companies. **Founded:** 2001.

41448 ■ The Innovation Center
1636 Popps Ferry Rd., Ste. 100
Biloxi, MS 39532
Co. E-mail: connect@innovatems.com
URL: http://www.innovatems.com
Facebook: www.facebook.com/theinnovationcenter
Description: Assists small businesses in learning the fundamentals for exporting products and services by developing skills in international marketing, trade finance, and global logistics. **Founded:** 1990.

41449 ■ Insight Park
850 Insight Pk. Ave.
University, MS 38677
Ph: (662)915-2526
Co. E-mail: info@insightparkum.com
URL: http://insightpark.olemiss.edu
Contact: William Nicholas, Director
E-mail: williamn@olemiss.edu
Facebook: www.facebook.com/InsightPark
X (Twitter): x.com/UMResearchPark
Description: Helps young companies to survive and grow during the startup phase. Provides hands-on assistance in areas of development, research, marketing, and legal matters.

41450 ■ Jackson State University (JSU) - Mississippi e-Center
1230 Raymond Rd.
Jackson, MS 39204
Ph: (601)979-1246
URL: http://msecenter.com
Contact: Dr. William E. McHenry, Executive Director
E-mail: william.mchenry@msecenter.com
Facebook: www.facebook.com/profile.php?id=100065411832677
YouTube: www.youtube.com/channel/UCVQZaoyv684_G9H2alyFb-g
Description: Business incubator that is a cutting edge information technology center. **Founded:** 2001.

41451 ■ Mississippi Action for Community Education, Inc. (MACE)
119 S Theobald St.
Greenville, MS 38701
Ph: (662)335-3523
Free: 888-812-5837
Fax: (662)335-2943
Co. E-mail: mace03@deltamace.org
URL: http://www.deltamace.org/index.php
Contact: Mable Starks, President
E-mail: mstarks@deltamace.org
Facebook: www.facebook.com/mace.delta
X (Twitter): x.com/MACE_News
Description: A non-profit minority, rural development organization Working to improve the economic situation of minorities and the poor. **Founded:** 1967.

41452 ■ Mississippi Enterprise for Technology (MSET) - Mississippi Technology Transfer Office
1103 Balch Blvd.
Stennis Space Center, MS 39529
URL: http://mset.org/about-mset
Description: Helps advanced technology companies locate or expand in Mississippi. **Founded:** 1994.

41453 ■ Mississippi State University - Center for Entrepreneurship
101 McCool Hall, 40 Old Main
Starkville, MS 39759
Ph: (662)325-3521
Co. E-mail: info@ecenter.msstate.edu
URL: http://ecenter.msstate.edu
Contact: Eric Alan Hill, Director
E-mail: ehill@ecenter.msstate.edu
Facebook: www.facebook.com/msstateecenter
X (Twitter): x.com/msstateecenter
Instagram: www.instagram.com/msstateecenter
YouTube: www.youtube.com/user/ECenterMSState

Description: Business incubator that provides startups and early stage companies with infrastructure, community, and resources designed to help them build stable, fast-growing businesses.

41454 ■ Neshoba Business Enterprise Center
256 W Beacon St.
Philadelphia, MS 39350
Ph: (601)656-1000
URL: http://www.neshoba.org/economic-development/neshoba-business-enterprise-center
Description: Incubator offers office, manufacturing, and warehouse space to start-up businesses for up to three years.

41455 ■ North Mississippi Enterprise Initiative (NMEI)
9 Industrial Pk. Dr., Ste. 104
Oxford, MS 38655
Ph: (662)281-0720
URL: http://www.northmiss.org
Contact: Holly Kelly, Executive Director
E-mail: holly@northmiss.org
Description: A non-profit, public/private regional partnership for entrepreneurial growth. It manages three business incubators - Oxford, Batesville and Grenada - and provides leadership in entrepreneurship within the region.

41456 ■ Renasant Center for IDEAs (RCFI) [Tupelo/Lee County Regional Business Incubator]
398 E Main St.
Tupelo, MS 38804
URL: http://www.cdfms.org/ed/small-business-development
Description: A business incubator helping small businesses grow into global competitors, utilizing a suite of productive services and resources to help design, develop and distribute entrepreneurs and their business goals into the community and global economy.

41457 ■ Winston County Business and Industry Incubator (WCBI)
311 W Pk. St.
Louisville, MS 39339
URL: http://www.winstoncountyms.com
Description: Offers affordable office space, business mentoring, and resource advice.

PUBLICATIONS

41458 ■ *Mississippi Business Journal*
1242 S Green St.
Tupelo, MS 38804
Ph: (662)842-2611
Free: 800-264-6397
Co. E-mail: digital@djournal.com
URL: http://djjournal.com
Contact: Adam Armour, Editor
E-mail: adam.armour@journalinc.com
URL(s): www.djournal.com/mbj
Facebook: www.facebook.com/mbjournal
X (Twitter): x.com/mbjournal
Instagram: www.instagram.com/msbusinessjournal
Ed: Ross Reily. **Released:** Monthly; with one annual issue. **Price:** $99, for print + online; $60, for online.
Description: Journal providing news and analysis of business in Mississippi. **Availability:** Print; PDF; Download; Online.

Missouri

ASSOCIATIONS AND OTHER ORGANIZATIONS

41459 ■ Association of Fundraising Professionals St. Louis Regional Chapter
8050 Watson Rd., Ste. 240
Saint Louis, MO 63119
Ph: (314)222-2811
Co. E-mail: info@afpstl.org
URL: http://afpstl.org
Contact: Theresa Fleck, Vice President
E-mail: president@afpstl.org
Facebook: www.facebook.com/AFPSTL
Linkedin: www.linkedin.com/company/afpglobal
X (Twitter): x.com/AFPSTL
Description: Promotes high ethical standards in the fundraising profession in the St. Louis area. **Geographic Preference:** Regional.

41460 ■ Business Network International Mid America
2082 Quarry Rd.
O'Fallon, IL 62269
Ph: (314)822-1030
URL: http://bnimidamerica.com/en-US/findachapter
Contact: Victor Muzquiz, Executive Director
Description: Provides both men and women a structured environment for the development and exchange of quality business referrals. Offers members the opportunity to share ideas and contacts. **Founded:** 1994. **Geographic Preference:** Regional.

41461 ■ Entrepreneurs' Organization - Kansas City Chapter (EO)
Kansas City, MO
Co. E-mail: membership@eokansascity.com
URL: http://www.eonetwork.org/kansascit
Contact: Christian Arnold, President
Description: Provides local resources to members which includes networking events, mentorship, live forums, and leadership development. **Founded:** 1998.

41462 ■ Entrepreneurs' Organization - St. Louis Chapter
101 W Argonne, Ste. 131
Kirkwood, MO 63122
URL: http://www.eonetwork.org/stlouis
Contact: Jen Auer, Administrator
E-mail: jauer@eostlouis.org
Description: Provides local resources to members which includes networking events, mentorship, live forums, and leadership development. **Founded:** 1993.

41463 ■ International Association of Business Communicators Kansas City (KC IABC)
PO Box 32785
Kansas City, MO 64111
Co. E-mail: kciabcchapter@gmail.com
URL: http://kciabc.com
Contact: Brenda Poor, President
Facebook: www.facebook.com/KCIABC
Linkedin: www.linkedin.com/company/kciabc
X (Twitter): x.com/KCIABC
Instagram: www.instagram.com/kciabc
Description: Represents the interests of communication managers, public relations directors, writers, editors and audiovisual specialists. Encourages establishment of college-level programs in organizational communication. Conducts surveys on employee communication effectiveness and media trends. Conducts research in the field of communication. **Geographic Preference:** Local.

41464 ■ International Association of Business Communicators St. Louis (IABC-St. Louis)
PO Box 430157
Saint Louis, MO 63143
Free: 800-218-8097
Co. E-mail: info@iabcstl.org
URL: http://iabcstl.org
Contact: Elizabeth Sargis, President
E-mail: elizabeth@elizabethsargis.com
Facebook: www.facebook.com/IABCSTL
Linkedin: www.linkedin.com/company/iabc-st-louis
X (Twitter): x.com/iabcstl
Description: Represents the interests of communication managers, public relations directors, writers, editors and audiovisual specialists. Encourages establishment of college-level programs in organizational communication. Conducts surveys on employee communication effectiveness and media trends. Conducts research in the field of communication. **Geographic Preference:** Local.

41465 ■ International Association of Women Kansas City Metro Chapter
Kansas City, MO
Co. E-mail: kansascity@iawomen.com
URL: http://www.iawomen.com/chapters
Contact: Amanda Hahn, President
E-mail: amandahahncoaching@gmail.com
URL(s): community.iawomen.com/kansascity/home
Facebook: www.facebook.com/iawomenkansascity
Description: Serves as a network for businesswomen to promote their service or product.

41466 ■ Missouri Agribusiness Association (MO-AG)
410 Madison St.
Jefferson City, MO 65101
Ph: (573)636-6130
Fax: (573)636-3299
Co. E-mail: info@mo-ag.com
URL: http://www.mo-ag.com
Contact: Steve Taylor, Executive Director
E-mail: staylor@mo-ag.com
Facebook: www.facebook.com/moagribusiness
X (Twitter): x.com/MOAGBIZ
Description: Seeks to strengthen the U.S. agricultural sectors. Facilitates American agribusiness participation in agricultural trade and development programs. Raises public awareness of agriculture's vital importance in national and global economic health. **Founded:** 1969. **Geographic Preference:** State.

41467 ■ Missouri Economic Development Council (MEDC) - Library
c/o Jim Fram, Executive Director
PO Box 105918
Jefferson City, MO 65110
Ph: (573)552-5622
Co. E-mail: jimfram@showme.org
URL: http://www.showme.org
Contact: Scott Sattler, President
E-mail: perryida@perrycountymo.org
Description: Promotes business and economic development. **Scope:** Economy. **Services:** Not open to the public. **Founded:** 1979. **Holdings:** Figures not available. **Geographic Preference:** State.

41468 ■ National Association of Women Business Owners Kansas City (NAWBO-KC)
Kansas City, MO
Co. E-mail: nawbokc@gmail.com
URL: http://www.nawbokc.org
Contact: Kelly Byrnes, President
Facebook: www.facebook.com/NAWBOKC
Description: Supports female entrepreneurs in Kansas City by providing networking, educational programming, and professional mentoring. **Founded:** 1975. **Geographic Preference:** Local.

41469 ■ National Federation of Independent Business Missouri
308 E High St., Ste. 110
Jefferson City, MO 65101
Ph: (573)634-7660
URL: http://www.nfib.com/missouri
Contact: Brad Jones, Director
E-mail: brad.jones@nfib.org
X (Twitter): x.com/nfib_mo
Description: Represents small and independent businesses. Aims to promote and protect the rights of members to own, operate and grow their businesses. **Geographic Preference:** State.

SMALL BUSINESS DEVELOPMENT CENTERS

41470 ■ Jefferson County Small Business and Technology Development Center
MO
URL: http://extension.missouri.edu/counties/jefferson/services
Contact: Mistti Ritter, Officer
Description: provide assistance to those wanting to start, maintain or expand a business through the Missouri small business and technology centers. **Geographic Preference:** Local.

41471 ■ Missouri Small Business and Technology Development Center Audrain County
Courthouse
101 N Jefferson St., Rm. 304
Mexico, MO 65265
Ph: (573)581-3231
Fax: (573)581-2766
URL: http://extension.missouri.edu/counties/audrain
Contact: Jim Crawford, Specialist
Description: Represents and promotes the small business sector. Provides management assistance to current and prospective small business owners. Helps to improve management skills and expand the products and services of members. **Geographic Preference:** Local.

41472 ■ Missouri Small Business and Technology Development Center Barton County
3950 Newman Rd.
Joplin, MO 64801
URL: http://www.mssutraining.com
URL(s): sbdc.missouri.edu/locations/missouri-sbdc-at-missouri-southern-state-university-mssu
Description: Represents and promotes the small business sector. Provides management assistance to current and prospective small business owners. Helps to improve management skills and expand the products and services of members. **Geographic Preference:** Local.

41473 ■ Missouri Small Business and Technology Development Center Camden County
3201 W 16th St., Rm. F255
Sedalia, MO 65301
URL: http://sbdc.missouri.edu/locations/missouri-sbdc-at-state-fair-community-college
Description: Represents and promotes the small business sector. Provides management assistance to current and prospective small business owners. Helps to improve management skills and expand the products and services of members. **Geographic Preference:** Local.

41474 ■ Missouri Small Business and Technology Development Center Cape Girardeau County
c/o SE Missouri State University
920 Broadway
Cape Girardeau, MO 63701
Ph: (573)651-2929
Fax: (573)986-6083
URL: http://sbdc.missouri.edu/locations/missouri-sbdc-at-southeast-missouri-state-university-semo
Description: Provides management assistance to current and prospective small business owners in Cape Girardeau County. **Geographic Preference:** Local.

41475 ■ Missouri Small Business and Technology Development Center Cole County
917 Leslie Blvd.
Jefferson City, MO 65101
Ph: (573)681-5031
Fax: (573)882-1955
Co. E-mail: musbdcadmin@missouri.edu
URL: http://sbdc.missouri.edu
Contact: Leslie Fischer, Specialist
Facebook: www.facebook.com/MissouriSBDC
Linkedin: www.linkedin.com/company/missourisbdc
X (Twitter): x.com/MissouriSBDC
YouTube: www.youtube.com/user/mosbtdc
Description: Helps businesses succeed in every stage from concept to startup, growth to renewal, mature to succession through a variety of programs. **Founded:** 1966. **Geographic Preference:** Local.

41476 ■ Missouri Small Business and Technology Development Center - Holt County
101 E Missouri St.
Oregon, MO 64473
Ph: (660)446-3724
Fax: (660)446-3726
URL: http://extension.missouri.edu/counties/holt
Contact: Annette Deering, Contact
Description: Offers assistance to current and prospective small business owners in Holt County. **Geographic Preference:** Local.

41477 ■ Missouri Small Business and Technology Development Center Howell County
395 E Broadway
West Plains, MO 65775
URL: http://efactory.missouristate.edu/howell
Contact: Janna Pearman Jacobs, Contact
Description: Helps businesses succeed in every stage from concept to startup, growth to renewal, mature to succession through a variety of programs. **Geographic Preference:** Local.

41478 ■ Missouri Small Business and Technology Development Center Macon County
404 N Missouri., Ste. AB
Macon, MO 63552
URL: http://sbdc.missouri.edu/people/mark-christian-99813
Contact: Mark Christian, Contact
Description: Helps businesses succeed in every stage from concept to startup, growth to renewal, mature to succession through a variety of programs. **Geographic Preference:** Local.

41479 ■ Missouri Small Business and Technology Development Center Madison County [MU Extension in Madison County]
137 W Main St.
Fredericktown, MO 63645
Ph: (573)783-3303
Fax: (573)783-5346
URL: http://extension2.missouri.edu/counties/madison
Contact: Stephanie Schindler, Specialist
Description: Represents and promotes the small business sector. Provides management assistance to current and prospective small business owners. Helps to improve management skills and expand the products and services of members. **Geographic Preference:** Local.

41480 ■ Missouri Small Business and Technology Development Center Monroe County
208 N Main St.
Paris, MO 65275
Ph: (660)327-4158
Co. E-mail: extpubs@missouri.edu
URL: http://missouribusiness.net/center/monroe-county-sbtdc
Contact: Charles Holland, Specialist
E-mail: hollandca@missouri.edu
Description: Helps businesses succeed in every stage from concept to startup, growth to renewal, mature to succession through a variety of programs. **Geographic Preference:** Local.

41481 ■ Missouri Small Business and Technology Development Center MSU West Plains
395 E Broadway
West Plains, MO 65775
Ph: (417)255-7966
Co. E-mail: wpsbdc@missouristate.edu
URL: http://efactory.missouristate.edu/west-plains-sbdc
Contact: Chrystal Irons, Director
E-mail: cirons@missouristate.edu
Description: Represents and promotes the small business sector. Provides management assistance to current and prospective small business owners. Helps to improve management skills and expand the products and services of members. **Geographic Preference:** Local.

41482 ■ Missouri Small Business and Technology Development Center Phelps County
30 W Pershing Rd.
Kansas City, MO 64108
URL: http://extension.missouri.edu/counties/phelps/services
Contact: Laura Faherty, Officer
Description: Represents and promotes the small business sector. Provides management assistance to current and prospective small business owners. Helps to improve management skills and expand the products and services of members. **Geographic Preference:** Local.

41483 ■ Missouri Small Business and Technology Development Center St. Charles
5988 Mid Rivers Mall Dr.
Saint Charles, MO 63304
Ph: (636)441-6880
URL: http://sbdc.missouri.edu/locations/missouri-sbdc-at-st.-charles-economic-development-corp.-satellite
Description: Helps businesses succeed in every stage from concept to startup, growth to renewal, mature to succession through a variety of programs. **Geographic Preference:** Local.

41484 ■ Missouri Small Business and Technology Development Center Taney County
122 Felkins Ave.
Forsyth, MO 65653
Ph: (417)546-4431
Fax: (417)546-4457
URL: http://extension.missouri.edu/counties/taney/services
Contact: Willa Williams, Contact
E-mail: williamswl@missouri.edu
URL(s): sbdc.missouristate.edu/missouri-sbdc-at-missouri-state-university-partners-with-taney-county-partnership-tcp-to-expand-services-to-small-businesses
Description: Represents and promotes the small business sector. Provides management assistance to current and prospective small business owners. Helps to improve management skills and expand the products and services of members. **Geographic Preference:** Local.

41485 ■ Missouri Small Business and Technology Development Center University of Missouri, Columbia
Lafferre Hall Rm. E2437N 416 S 6th St.
Columbia, MO 65211
Ph: (573)884-1555
URL: http://sbdc.missouri.edu
Contact: Delia Marin, Contact
Facebook: www.facebook.com/MissouriSBDC
Linkedin: www.linkedin.com/company/missourisbdc
X (Twitter): x.com/MObusinessNet
YouTube: www.youtube.com/user/mosbtdc
Description: Helps businesses succeed in every stage from concept to startup, growth to renewal, mature to succession through a variety of programs. **Geographic Preference:** Local.

41486 ■ Missouri Small Business Technology and Development Centers - Lead Center (MO SBDC)
416 S 6th St., 217 EBN
Columbia, MO 65211
Co. E-mail: musbdcadmin@missouri.edu
URL: http://sbdc.missouri.edu
Contact: Mike Adams, Contact
Geographic Preference: State.

41487 ■ Missouri Southern State University Small Business and Technology Development Center
Plaster Hall, Rm. 107, 3950 Newman Rd.
Joplin, MO 64801
Ph: (417)625-3128
Co. E-mail: sbdc@mssu.edu
URL: http://www.mssutraining.com
Contact: Lisa Robinson, Director
E-mail: robinson-l@mssu.edu
Facebook: www.facebook.com/mssusbdc
YouTube: www.youtube.com/channel/UCOCPFZLq9hBKb7UOATKkPkw

Description: Represents and promotes the small business sector. Provides management assistance to current and prospective small business owners. Helps to improve management skills and expand the products and services of members. **Founded:** 1987. **Geographic Preference:** Local.

41488 ■ Missouri State University Small Business and Technology Development Center (MSU SBDC)
405 N Jefferson Ave.
Springfield, MO 65806
Ph: (417)837-2617
Co. E-mail: sbdc@missouristate.edu
URL: http://sbdc.missouristate.edu
Contact: Chrystal Irons, Director
Linkedin: www.linkedin.com/company/missouri-state
-university-small-business-and-technology
-development-center
X (Twitter): x.com/sbdc_msu
Description: Specializes in providing one-on-one consulting that is comprehensive and individualized to meet the particular needs of business owners and entrepreneurs. **Founded:** 1982. **Geographic Preference:** Local.

41489 ■ Northwest Missouri State University Small Business and Technology Development Center (SBDC)
3003 Frederick Ave.
Saint Joseph, MO 64506
Ph: (816)364-4105
Fax: (816)364-4873
URL: http://www.nwmissouri.edu/services/sbdc
Contact: Rebecca Lobina, Regional Director
E-mail: lobina@nwmissouri.edu
Description: Represents and promotes the small business sector. Provides management assistance to current and prospective small business owners. Helps to improve management skills and expand the products and services of members. **Founded:** 1980. **Geographic Preference:** Local.

41490 ■ Northwest Missouri State University Small Business and Technology Development Center St. Joseph Center (SBDC)
3003 Frederick Ave.
Saint Joseph, MO 64506
Ph: (816)364-4105
Fax: (816)364-4873
URL: http://www.nwmissouri.edu/services/sbtdc/con
tact.htm
Contact: Rebecca Lobina, Regional Director
E-mail: lobina@nwmissouri.edu
Description: Represents and promotes the small business sector. Provides management assistance to current and prospective small business owners. Helps to improve management skills and expand the products and services of members. **Founded:** 1980. **Geographic Preference:** Local.

41491 ■ Southeast Missouri State University Small Business and Technology Development Center (SMSU SBTDC)
920 Broadway
Cape Girardeau, MO 63701
Ph: (573)651-2929
Fax: (573)986-6083
Co. E-mail: contact@semo.edu
URL: http://sbdc.missouri.edu/locations/missouri-sb
dc-at-southeast-missouri-state-university-semo
Contact: Chrystal Irons, Director
Facebook: www.facebook.com/MissouriSBDC
Linkedin: www.linkedin.com/company/missourisbdc
X (Twitter): x.com/MissouriSBDC
YouTube: www.youtube.com/user/mosbtdc
Description: Represents and promotes the small business sector. Provides management assistance to current and prospective small business owners. Helps to improve management skills and expand the products and services of members. **Founded:** 1873. **Geographic Preference:** Local.

41492 ■ Springfield Business Development Corp. (SBDC)
202 S John Q. Hammons Pky.
Springfield, MO 65806
Ph: (417)862-5567
Free: 800-879-7504
URL: http://www.sbdcinvestors.com
Description: Seeks to promote business through economic and community development. Assists businesses in their expansion and financing needs. Enhances the quality of life and fosters the growth of good jobs within the community. **Geographic Preference:** Local.

41493 ■ Truman State University Small Business Technology & Development Center
100 E Normal Ave.
Kirksville, MO 63501
Ph: (660)665-3348
Co. E-mail: sbtdc@truman.edu
URL: http://www.truman.edu/about/our-people/a
dministrative-offices
Contact: Dr. Susan L. Thomas, President
Description: Provides management assistance to current and prospective small business owners in Truman. **Geographic Preference:** Local.

41494 ■ University of Missouri Kansas City Small Business and Technology Development Center (UMKC SBTDC)
4747 Troost Ave., Ste. 103
Kansas City, MO 64110
Ph: (816)235-6063
URL: http://sbtdc.umkc.edu
Contact: Carmen DeHart, Regional Director
Facebook: www.facebook.com/UmkcSBTDC
X (Twitter): twitter.com/UMKCSBTDC
YouTube: http://www.youtube.com/channel/
UCPjHgnjCsIXqA0ioDNa5ntw
Description: Provides management assistance to current and prospective small business owners in Missouri. **Geographic Preference:** Local.

SMALL BUSINESS ASSISTANCE PROGRAMS

41495 ■ Missouri Business Development Program
Columbia, MO 65211
Co. E-mail: ecrd@missouri.edu
URL: http://missouribusiness.net
Description: Provides assistance to company officials and local community leaders in their efforts to retain existing jobs and create additional jobs through business expansion. Provides technical assistance and information. People wanting to start small business.

41496 ■ Missouri Department of Economic Development - Division of Business and Community Services
PO Box 1157
Jefferson City, MO 65101
Ph: (573)751-4539
URL: http://ded.mo.gov/tags/business-and-communi
ty-services
Contact: Amy Berendzen, Director, Communications
E-mail: amy.berendzen@ded.mo.gov
Description: Provides assistance to international firms. Works to stimulate direct foreign investment in the state and develop export possibilities.

41497 ■ University of Central Missouri Small Business and Technology Development Center (SBDC)
Dockery Bldg., Rm. 102
Warrensburg, MO 64093
Ph: (660)543-4402
URL: http://www.ucmo.edu/offices
X (Twitter): x.com/MissouriSBDC
Description: Provides assistance to small business owners from start-up to operation processes. **Geographic Preference:** Local.

SCORE OFFICES

41498 ■ Mid-Missouri SCORE
9506 Olive Blvd., Ste. 217
Saint Louis, MO 63132
Free: 866-726-7340
URL: http://www.score.org/stlouis

41499 ■ SCORE - Florissant
8190 N Lindbergh Blvd.
Florissant, MO 63031
Free: 866-726-7340
URL: http://www.score.org/find-location
Description: Provides professional guidance and information to maximize the success of existing and emerging small businesses. Offers business counseling and workshops.

41500 ■ SCORE - Jefferson City
213 Adams St.
Jefferson City, MO 65101
Ph: (573)634-3616
URL: http://lakeoftheozarks.score.org/content/men
toring-locations-0
Contact: Bridget Weston, Chief Executive Officer
Description: Provides professional guidance and information to maximize the success of existing and emerging small businesses. Offers business counseling and workshops.

41501 ■ SCORE - Kansas City
4747 Troost Ave., Ste. 101
Kansas City, MO 64110
Ph: (816)235-6675
Co. E-mail: help@score.org
URL: http://kansascity.score.org
Contact: Gregory Thomas, Contact
Facebook: www.facebook.com/SCOREKansasCity
Linkedin: www.linkedin.com/company/score-kansas
-city
Description: Provides consulting services to individuals wishing to start a new business or who have problems with established businesses. **Founded:** 1964. **Geographic Preference:** Local.

41502 ■ SCORE - Kirkwood
300 N Kirkwood Rd.
Kirkwood, MO 63122
URL: http://www.score.org/stlouis
Description: Provides professional guidance and information to maximize the success of existing and emerging small businesses. Offers business counseling and workshops.

41503 ■ SCORE - Lake of the Ozarks
739 W US Hwy. 54
Camdenton, MO 65020
Ph: (573)346-5441
Co. E-mail: admin.0493@scorevolunteer.org
URL: http://lakeoftheozarks.score.org
Contact: Bridget Weston, Chief Executive Officer
Facebook: www.facebook.com/SCORELakeof
theOzarks
Linkedin: www.linkedin.com/company/score-mentors
-lake-of-the-ozarks
Description: Serves as volunteer program in which working and retired business management professionals provide free business counseling to men and women who are considering starting a small business, encountering problems with their business, or expanding their business. Offers free one-on-one counseling, online counseling and low cost workshops on a variety of business topics. **Founded:** 1964. **Geographic Preference:** Local.

41504 ■ SCORE - Lebanon
186 N Adams Ave.
Lebanon, MO 65536
Ph: (417)588-3256
URL: http://lakeoftheozarks.score.org/content/men
toring-locations-0
Description: Provides professional guidance and information to maximize the success of existing and emerging small businesses. Offers business counseling and workshops.

41505 ■ SCORE - St. Charles
5988 Mid Rivers Mall Dr. Economic Development
Buliding
Saint Charles, MO 63304
Free: 866-726-7340
URL: http://stlouis.score.org

41506 ■ Missouri

Description: Provides professional guidance and information to maximize the success of existing and emerging small businesses. Offers business counseling and workshops.

41506 ■ SCORE - St. Louis
9506 Olive Blvd., Ste. 217
Saint Louis, MO 63132
Free: 866-726-7340
URL: http://www.score.org/stlouis
Contact: Bridget Weston, Chief Executive Officer
Facebook: www.facebook.com/stlscore
Linkedin: www.linkedin.com/company/score-st-louis-chapter
YouTube: www.youtube.com/user/stlscore
Description: Serves as volunteer program in which working and retired business management professionals provide free business counseling to men and women who are considering starting a small business, encountering problems with their business, or expanding their business. Offers free one-on-one counseling, online counseling and low cost workshops on a variety of business topics. **Founded:** 1964. **Geographic Preference:** Local.

41507 ■ SCORE - Southwest Missouri
405 N Jefferson, Ste. 1040J
Springfield, MO 65806
Ph: (417)986-4730
Co. E-mail: swmo61@scorevolunteer.org
URL: http://swmissouri.score.org
Contact: Robert Headlee, President
Facebook: www.facebook.com/SCORESWMissouri
Linkedin: www.linkedin.com/company/score-mentors-southwest-missouri
X (Twitter): x.com/SCORESWMissouri
Description: Provides professional guidance and information to maximize the success of existing and emerging small businesses. Offers business counseling and workshops.

41508 ■ Southeast Missouri SCORE
405 N Jefferson, No.1040J
Springfield, MO 65806
Ph: (417)986-4730
URL: http://www.score.org/find-location?state=MO

BETTER BUSINESS BUREAUS

41509 ■ Better Business Bureau of Eastern Missouri and Southern Illinois
211 N Broadway, Ste. 2060
Saint Louis, MO 63102
Ph: (314)645-3300
Fax: (314)645-2666
URL: http://www.bbb.org/local-bbb/bbb-of-eastern-and-southwest-missouri-and-southern-illinois
Facebook: www.facebook.com/stlouisbbb
X (Twitter): x.com/stlouisbbb
Instagram: www.instagram.com/stlouisbbb
YouTube: www.youtube.com/bbbstl
Description: Seeks to promote and foster ethical relationship between businesses and the public through voluntary self-regulation, consumer and business education, and service excellence. Provides information to help consumers and businesses make informed purchasing decisions and avoid costly scams and frauds; settles consumer complaints through arbitration and other means. **Geographic Preference:** Regional.

41510 ■ Better Business Bureau of Greater Kansas City
1000 W 46th St.
Kansas City, MO 64114
Ph: (816)421-7800
Fax: (816)359-3174
URL: http://www.bbb.org/local-bbb/bbb-of-greater-kansas-city
Linkedin: www.linkedin.com/company/better-business-bureau-of-greater-kansas-city
X (Twitter): x.com/kcbbb
Pinterest: www.pinterest.com/bbbkansascity
Description: Seeks to promote and foster the highest ethical relationship between businesses and the public through voluntary self-regulation, consumer and business education, and service excellence. Provides information to help consumers and businesses make informed purchasing decisions and avoid costly scams and frauds; settles consumer complaints through arbitration and other means. **Founded:** 1916. **Geographic Preference:** Local.

41511 ■ Better Business Bureau of Midwest Plains - Wichita Falls [BBB of Midwest Plains - Wichita Falls]
PO Box 75622
Wichita, KS 67275
Ph: (316)263-3542
Fax: (402)391-7535
URL: http://www.bbb.org/local-bbb/bbb-of-midwest-plains
Description: Seeks to promote and foster the highest ethical relationship between businesses and the public through voluntary self-regulation, consumer and business education, and service excellence. Provides information to help consumers and businesses make informed purchasing decisions and avoid costly scams and frauds; settles consumer complaints through arbitration and other means. **Geographic Preference:** Local.

41512 ■ Better Business Bureau of Southwest Missouri
948 St. Louis St.
Springfield, MO 65805
URL: http://www.bbb.org/local-bbb/bbb-of-eastern-and-southwest-missouri-and-southern-illinois
Description: Seeks to promote and foster the highest ethical relationship between businesses and the public through voluntary self-regulation, consumer and business education, and service excellence. Provides information to help consumers and businesses make informed purchasing decisions and avoid costly scams and frauds; settles consumer complaints through arbitration and other means. **Geographic Preference:** Local.

CHAMBERS OF COMMERCE

41513 ■ Affton Chamber of Commerce
9815 Mackenzie Rd.
Affton, MO 63123
Ph: (314)631-3100
Co. E-mail: info@afftonchamber.com
URL: http://www.afftonchamber.com
Contact: Lisa Rackley, Executive Director
E-mail: lisa@afftonlemaychamber.com
YouTube: www.youtube.com/channel/UCzk9JOttM53eEGT9z6o8i2g
Description: Strives to advance the commercial, industrial, and general interests of Affton and its adjacent territory. Promotes trade, industry, and public welfare in the community. **Founded:** 1947. **Publications:** *Affton Business Connection* (Monthly). **Educational Activities:** Affton Chamber of Commerce Meeting (Monthly). **Awards:** Affton Chamber of Commerce Business Person of the Year (Annual); Affton Chamber of Commerce Citizen of the Year (Annual). **Geographic Preference:** Local.

41514 ■ Arnold Chamber of Commerce
1314 Jeffco
Arnold, MO 63010
Ph: (636)296-1910
URL: http://www.arnoldchamber.org
Contact: Meredith McCarthy, Secretary
Facebook: www.facebook.com/Arnold-Chamber-364913803382
Description: Promotes business and community development in Arnold, MO. **Geographic Preference:** Local.

41515 ■ Aurora Missouri Chamber of Commerce
121 E Olive St.
Aurora, MO 65605
Ph: (417)678-4150
Fax: (417)678-1387
Co. E-mail: auroracoc@mo-net.com
URL: http://aurorachamber.wordpress.com
Description: Promotes business and community development in Aurora, MO. Sponsors Youth Basketball Tournament, Business Expo, Ye Olde Mining Days, Golf Tournament, Car and Truck Show, Radio Auction, Miss Holly Pageant, Christmas Parade and Santa Train. **Founded:** 1939. **Geographic Preference:** Local.

41516 ■ Ava Area Chamber of Commerce (AACC)
810 Collins Ave.
Ava, MO 65608
Ph: (417)683-4594
Co. E-mail: info@avachamber.org
URL: http://www.avachamber.org
Contact: Anita Madche, Co-President
Facebook: www.facebook.com/Ava-Area-Chamber-315247602186378
Description: Promotes business and community development in the Ava, MO area. Supports local community projects. Sponsors Poke Salad Days, Glade Top Trail, Christmas Parade, and local contests. **Founded:** 1935. **Publications:** *Community Service Directory* (Periodic). **Geographic Preference:** Local.

41517 ■ Barton County Chamber of Commerce
110 W 10th St.
Lamar, MO 64759
Ph: (417)682-3595
URL: http://www.bartoncounty.com
Contact: Astra Ferris, Chief Executive Officer
E-mail: astra@bartoncounty.com
Facebook: www.facebook.com/bartoncountychamber
Linkedin: www.linkedin.com/company/barton-county-chamber-of-commerce
X (Twitter): x.com/BCMOChamber
Instagram: www.instagram.com/barton_county_chamber
YouTube: www.youtube.com/channel/UC0hN7Jh52kIIjZE2gPtlWKA
Description: Promotes business and community development in Lamar and Barton County, MO. **Founded:** 1994. **Geographic Preference:** Local.

41518 ■ Belton Chamber of Commerce (BCOC)
517 Main St.
Belton, MO 64012
Ph: (816)331-2420
Co. E-mail: chamberbelton@gmail.com
URL: http://www.beltonmochamber.org
Contact: Diane Huckshorn, Executive Director
Facebook: www.facebook.com/belton.chamber.7
X (Twitter): x.com/Belton_Chamber
Description: Businesses and individuals in Belton, MO organized to encourage a strong local economy and quality of life by promoting sound government and an informed membership and community. **Founded:** 1945. **Geographic Preference:** Local.

41519 ■ Black Chamber of Commerce of Greater Kansas City (BCCGKC)
5737 Swope Pky.
Kansas City, MO 64130
Ph: (816)336-1435
Co. E-mail: info@bcckc.org
URL: http://bccgkc.org
Contact: Kelvin Perry, President
Facebook: www.facebook.com/bccgkc
Linkedin: www.linkedin.com/company/bccgkc
X (Twitter): x.com/BlackChamberKC
Description: Seeks to provide leadership in promoting African American businesses. **Founded:** 1985. **Geographic Preference:** Local.

41520 ■ Blue Springs Chamber of Commerce
1000 W Main St.
Blue Springs, MO 64015
Ph: (816)229-8558
Fax: (816)229-1244
Co. E-mail: bschamberinfo@bluespringschamber.com
URL: http://www.bluespringschamber.com
Contact: Lara Vermillion, President
E-mail: lvermillion@bluespringschamber.com

STATE LISTINGS

Facebook: www.facebook.com/
BlueSpringsChamberOfCommerce
Linkedin: www.linkedin.com/company/blue-springs
-chamber-of-commerce
X (Twitter): x.com/BlueS_Chamber
Description: Promotes business and community development in Blue Springs, MO. **Publications:** *Directory and New Resident Guide.* **Educational Activities:** Fall Fun Festival Meeting (Annual). **Geographic Preference:** Local.

41521 ▪ Bolivar Area Chamber of Commerce
117A S Main Ave.
Bolivar, MO 65613
Ph: (417)326-4118
Co. E-mail: info@bolivarchamber.com
URL: http://bolivarchamber.com
Contact: Paul Folbre, President
Facebook: www.facebook.com/bolivarchamber
Description: Promotes business and community development in the Bolivar, MO area. Sponsors annual Country Days, Chicken BBQ, Christmas parade and St. Patrick's Day Auction. **Founded:** 1913. **Publications:** *Bolivar Area Chamber of Commerce Visitor's Guide and Membership Directory* (Annual); *Chamber Newsletter* (Monthly); *Community Profile; Bolivar Area Chamber of Commerce--Membership Directory* (Annual). **Geographic Preference:** Local.

41522 ▪ Boonville Area Chamber of Commerce
320 1st St.
Boonville, MO 65233
Ph: (660)882-2721
Co. E-mail: info@boonvillemochamber.com
URL: http://boonvillemochamber.com
Contact: Laura Gramlich, President
E-mail: gramlichjl@hotmail.com
Description: Strives to support businesses, industries and educational entities of Booneville and Prentiss County in order to improve the quality of life of the people. **Geographic Preference:** Local.

41523 ▪ Bowling Green Chamber of Commerce
18047 Business Hwy. 161
Bowling Green, MO 63334
Ph: (573)324-3733
Co. E-mail: info@bgchamber.org
URL: http://bgchamber.org
Contact: Tracy Brookshier, President
Facebook: www.facebook.com/bgchamber
Description: Promotes business and community development in Bowling Green, MO. **Geographic Preference:** Local.

41524 ▪ Branson-Lakes Area Chamber of Commerce (BLACC)
4100 Gretna Rd.
Branson, MO 65616
Ph: (417)334-4084
Free: 800-296-0463
Co. E-mail: info@bransonchamber.com
URL: http://www.bransonchamber.com
Contact: Pam Yancey, Chairman
Facebook: www.facebook.com/BransonChamber
Linkedin: www.linkedin.com/company/branson-lakes
-area-chamber-of-commerce-and-cvb
X (Twitter): x.com/bransonchamber
Instagram: www.instagram.com/bransonchamber
YouTube: www.youtube.com/channel/UCeL2WPV0
17rt-dmNiD2z7aw
Description: Promotes business, tourism, and community development in the Branson/Lakes, MO area. **Founded:** 1947. **Publications:** *Keynotes* (Periodic); *Slip Away to Branson; The Source.* **Awards:** Branson-Lakes Area Chamber Small Business of the Year Award (Annual). **Geographic Preference:** Local.

41525 ▪ Brookfield Chamber of Commerce
207B N Main St.
Brookfield, MO 64628
Ph: (660)258-7255
Co. E-mail: chamber@brookfieldmochamber.com
URL: http://www.brookfieldmochamber.com
Contact: Tawnya McLaury, President

Facebook: www.facebook.com/brookfieldarea
Description: Promotes and protects the commercial, professional, financial, and general business interests of the City of Brookfield, MO. **Geographic Preference:** Local.

41526 ▪ Brunswick Area Chamber of Commerce (BACC)
PO Box 104
Brunswick, MO 65236
Co. E-mail: chamber@brunswickmo.com
URL: http://brunswickmo.com/residents/economic
-development/chamber-of-commerce
Contact: Debbie Boehmke, Contact
Facebook: www.facebook.com/
BrunswickAreaChamberOfCommerce
Description: Businesses, organizations, and individuals interested in promoting the Brunswick, OH area. Holds seminars and social functions. **Founded:** 1931. **Publications:** *Connections* (Monthly). **Geographic Preference:** Local.

41527 ▪ Buckner Chamber of Commerce
PO Box 287
Buckner, MO 64016
Ph: (816)650-3191
Co. E-mail: bucknerchamber@gmail.com
URL: http://sites.google.com/site/bucknerchamber
Contact: Ed Burns, Vice President Co-President
Description: Promotes business and community development in Buckner, MO. **Geographic Preference:** Local.

41528 ▪ Buffalo Area Chamber of Commerce
119 S Maple St., Ste. 105
Buffalo, MO 65622
Ph: (417)345-2852
Co. E-mail: buffalochamber@gmail.com
URL: http://buffaloareachamber.org
Contact: Laura Coots, President
Facebook: www.facebook.com/buffaloareachamber
Description: Strives to improve and enhance the commercial, industrial, and civic interests of Buffalo, Missouri and its trade area. **Publications:** *The Members' Messenger* (Monthly). **Geographic Preference:** Local.

41529 ▪ *Business and Community*
366 S Kirkwood Rd.
Kirkwood, MO 63122
Ph: (314)821-4161
Co. E-mail: info@thechamber.us
URL: http://www.kirkwooddesperes.com
Contact: Peg Weathers, President
E-mail: peg@thechamber.us
URL(s): www.kirkwooddesperes.com/community
Availability: Print.

41530 ▪ *Business Outlook*
320 E 4th St.
Joplin, MO 64801
Ph: (417)624-4150
Co. E-mail: info@joplincc.com
URL: http://www.joplincc.com
Contact: Toby Teeter, President
URL(s): joplinbusinessoutlook.com
Released: Monthly **Description:** Contains chamber events, initiatives, programs, services, and the latest business and community issues. **Availability:** PDF; Online.

41531 ▪ California Chamber of Commerce
500 S Oak St.
California, MO 65018
Ph: (573)796-3040
Co. E-mail: chamber@calmo.com
URL: http://www.calmo.com
Contact: Sharon Campbell, President
Description: Promotes business and community development in California, MO. Sponsors Ozark Ham and Turkey Festival. **Geographic Preference:** State.

41532 ▪ Callaway Chamber of Commerce (CCC)
510 Market St.
Fulton, MO 65251
Ph: (573)642-3055

Fax: (573)642-5182
Co. E-mail: marketing@callawaychamber.net
URL: http://www.callawaychamber.net
Contact: Judy Ebersole, Ambassador
Facebook: www.facebook.com/
CallawayChamberofCommerce
X (Twitter): x.com/CallawayChambe1
Instagram: www.instagram.com/callawaychamber
YouTube: www.youtube.com/channel/UCk790yznVIv
1NWY8rlUR6Hg
Description: Promotes business and community development in Callaway County, MO. Sponsors Kingdom Days. Conducts charitable activities. **Founded:** 1930. **Publications:** *Chamber Communique* (Monthly). **Geographic Preference:** Local.

41533 ▪ Camdenton Area Chamber of Commerce
739 W US Hwy. 54
Camdenton, MO 65020
Ph: (573)346-2227
Free: 800-769-1004
Fax: (573)346-3496
Co. E-mail: info@camdentonchamber.com
URL: http://www.camdentonchamber.com
Contact: Amanda Hayes, President
Facebook: www.facebook.com/camdentonchamber
Linkedin: www.linkedin.com/company/camdenton
-area-chamber-of-commerce
X (Twitter): x.com/CACCLake
Description: Promotes business and community development in the Camdenton, MO area. Sponsors festivals, products and services trade show. Promotes tourism. **Educational Activities:** Lake of the Ozarks Products and Services Show (Annual). **Geographic Preference:** Local.

41534 ▪ Cameron Area Chamber of Commerce
416 N Walnut, Ste. A
Cameron, MO 64429
Ph: (816)632-2005
Co. E-mail: cameronmochamber@gmail.com
URL: http://cameronmochamber.com
Contact: Joshua Strong, President
Facebook: www.facebook.com/Cameronmochamber
Description: Enhances human and economic resources. **Founded:** 1929. **Geographic Preference:** Local.

41535 ▪ Cape Girardeau Area Chamber of Commerce
220 N Fountain St.
Cape Girardeau, MO 63701
Ph: (573)335-3312
Fax: (573)335-4686
Co. E-mail: info@capechamber.com
URL: http://www.capechamber.com
Contact: John Mehner, President
E-mail: jmehner@capechamber.com
Facebook: www.facebook.com/CapeChamber
Instagram: www.instagram.com/capeareachamber
Description: Promotes business and community development in Cape Girardeau, MO. **Founded:** 1917. **Geographic Preference:** Local.

41536 ▪ Carthage Chamber of Commerce (CCC)
402 S Garrison Ave.
Carthage, MO 64836
Ph: (417)358-2373
Fax: (417)358-7479
Co. E-mail: info@carthagechamber.com
URL: http://carthagechamber.com
Contact: Julie A. Reams, President
E-mail: jreams@carthagechamber.com
Facebook: www.facebook.com/CarthageChamber
Linkedin: www.linkedin.com/company/carthage
-chamber-of-commerce
X (Twitter): x.com/carthagechamber
YouTube: www.youtube.com/watch
Description: Promotes business, community development, and tourism in Carthage, MO. **Founded:** 1932. **Publications:** *Spotlight on Carthage* (Monthly). **Geographic Preference:** Local.

41537 ■ Cassville Area Chamber of Commerce
c/o Morgan Williams, Director
504 Main St.
Cassville, MO 65625
Ph: (417)847-2814
Co. E-mail: chamber@cassville.com
URL: http://www.cassville.com/about-us
Contact: Morgan Williams, Director
Facebook: www.facebook.com/CassvilleChamber
X (Twitter): x.com/chamber65625
Instagram: www.instagram.com/chamber65625
Description: Promotes business and community development in Cassville, MO. Conducts annual music/variety show, Christmas parade, semi-annual Trout Derby, industrial golf tournament, and car show. **Geographic Preference:** Local.

41538 ■ Centralia Area Chamber of Commerce (CACC)
PO Box 235
Centralia, MO 65240
Ph: (573)682-2272
Fax: (573)682-1111
URL: http://www.centraliamochamber.com
Contact: Tim Stevens, President
Facebook: www.facebook.com/CentraliaChamberofCommerce
Description: Promotes business and community development in the Centralia, MO area. Sponsors Anchor Festival. **Founded:** 1939. **Geographic Preference:** Local.

41539 ■ *Chamber Business Line*
300 S Providence Rd.
Columbia, MO 65205
Ph: (573)874-1132
Co. E-mail: reception@columbiamochamber.com
URL: http://www.columbiamochamber.com
Contact: Matt McCormick, President
E-mail: mmccormick@columbiamochamber.com
URL(s): comochamber.com/about-our-chamber/member-benefits
Released: Monthly **Availability:** Online.

41540 ■ *Chamber Chatter*
202 S John Q. Hammons Pky.
Springfield, MO 65806
Ph: (417)862-5567
Co. E-mail: info@springfieldchamber.com
URL: http://www.springfieldchamber.com
Contact: Matt Morrow, President
E-mail: matt@springfieldchamber.com
URL(s): springfieldmnchamber.org/chamber-chatter
Released: Monthly **Availability:** PDF.

41541 ■ *Chamber Membership*
5909 Raytown Trafficway
Raytown, MO 64133-3860
Ph: (816)353-8500
Fax: (816)353-8525
Co. E-mail: staff@raytownchamber.com
URL: http://raytownchamber.com
Contact: Pat Erts, Chairman
URL(s): raytownchamber.com/chamber/chamber-benefits
Released: Annual **Availability:** Print; Online.

41542 ■ *Chamber News*
1311 Kingshighway St.
Rolla, MO 65401
Ph: (573)364-3577
Free: 888-809-3817
Co. E-mail: rollacc@rollachamber.org
URL: http://rollachamber.org
Contact: Dominic Deluca, Sr., Chief Executive Officer
URL(s): business.rollachamber.org/news
Availability: Print; Online.

41543 ■ *Chamber Newsletter*
117A S Main Ave.
Bolivar, MO 65613
Ph: (417)326-4118
Co. E-mail: info@bolivarchamber.com
URL: http://bolivarchamber.com
Contact: Paul Folbre, President
URL(s): bolivarchamber.com/august-2022-newsletter
Released: Monthly **Availability:** Online; PDF.

41544 ■ Charleston Chamber of Commerce
110 S Main St.
Charleston, MO 63834
Ph: (573)683-6509
Co. E-mail: chamber@charlestonmo.org
URL: http://www.charlestonmo.org/chamber
Facebook: www.facebook.com/CharlestonARChamber
Description: Promotes business and community development in Charleston, MO. **Founded:** 1962. **Geographic Preference:** Local.

41545 ■ Chesterfield Chamber of Commerce (CCC)
301 Southlake Blvd., Ste. 102, N
Chesterfield, MO 63005
Ph: (804)748-6364
Co. E-mail: info@chesterfieldchamber.com
URL: http://chesterfieldchamber.com
Contact: Danielle Fitz, Co-President Co-Chief Executive Officer
Facebook: www.facebook.com/ChesterfieldChamberVa
Linkedin: www.linkedin.com/company/chesterfieldchamberva
X (Twitter): x.com/ChesterfieldCOC
Instagram: www.instagram.com/chesterfieldchamberva
Description: Promotes business and community development in Chesterfield, MO. **Founded:** 1999. **Publications:** *Out and About* (Quarterly). **Geographic Preference:** Local.

41546 ■ Chillicothe Area Chamber of Commerce (CACC)
514 Washington St.
Chillicothe, MO 64601
Ph: (660)646-4050
Free: 877-224-4554
Co. E-mail: chamber@chillicothemo.com
URL: http://www.chillicothemo.com
Contact: Lauren Horsman, President
Facebook: www.facebook.com/chillicotheareachamber
X (Twitter): x.com/ChilliMoChamber
YouTube: www.youtube.com/user/ChilliMoChamber
Description: Promotes business and community development in the Chillicothe, MO area. **Founded:** 1855. **Publications:** *Chamber Connection* (Monthly). **Awards:** Chillicothe Area Chamber Business of the Year (Annual). **Geographic Preference:** Local.

41547 ■ Clayton Chamber of Commerce (CCC)
225 S Meramec Ave., Ste. 300
Clayton, MO 63105
Ph: (314)726-3033
Fax: (314)726-0637
Co. E-mail: ccc@claytoncommerce.com
URL: http://claytoncommerce.com
Contact: Ellen M. Gale, Executive Director
E-mail: egale@claytoncommerce.com
Description: Promotes business and community development in Clayton, MO. **Founded:** 1952. **Geographic Preference:** Local.

41548 ■ *Clinton*
200 S Main St.
Clinton, MO 64735
Ph: (660)885-8166
Co. E-mail: info@clintonmo.com
URL: http://clintonmo.com
Contact: David Lee, Director
E-mail: david@clintonmo.com
URL(s): www.clintonareachamber.org/town-of-clinton
Availability: Print.

41549 ■ Clinton Area Chamber of Commerce
200 S Main St.
Clinton, MO 64735
Ph: (660)885-8166
Co. E-mail: info@clintonmo.com
URL: http://clintonmo.com
Contact: David Lee, Director
E-mail: david@clintonmo.com
Facebook: www.facebook.com/ClintonMO
X (Twitter): x.com/ChamberClinton
Instagram: www.instagram.com/visitclintonmo
Pinterest: www.pinterest.com/visitclintonmo
Description: Promotes business and community development and tourism in Benton, Henry, and St. Clair counties, MO. **Founded:** 1935. **Publications:** *Clinton*; *Calendar of Events*; *Chamber Update* (Weekly); *Spirit*. **Geographic Preference:** Local.

41550 ■ Columbia Chamber of Commerce
300 S Providence Rd.
Columbia, MO 65205
Ph: (573)874-1132
Co. E-mail: reception@columbiamochamber.com
URL: http://www.columbiamochamber.com
Contact: Matt McCormick, President
E-mail: mmccormick@columbiamochamber.com
Facebook: www.facebook.com/COMOChamber
X (Twitter): x.com/COMOChamber
Instagram: www.instagram.com/comochamber
YouTube: www.youtube.com/user/ColumbiaMOChamber
Description: Promotes business and community development in Columbia, MO. **Founded:** 1905. **Publications:** *Chamber Business Line* (Monthly). **Educational Activities:** Agricultural Recognition Banquet (Annual). **Geographic Preference:** Local.

41551 ■ *Community Guide*
1315 N Hwy. Dr.
Fenton, MO 63099
Ph: (636)717-0200
Fax: (636)717-0214
Co. E-mail: exdir@fentonmochamber.com
URL: http://www.fentonmochamber.com
Contact: Charlie Fischer, President
URL(s): www.fentonmochamber.com/about-us.html
Released: Annual **Description:** Contains area business listing. **Availability:** Print.

41552 ■ Creve Coeur - Olivette Chamber of Commerce
10950 Olive Blvd., Ste. 101
Creve Coeur, MO 63141
Ph: (314)569-3536
Fax: (314)569-3073
Co. E-mail: info@ccochamber.com
URL: http://www.ccochamber.com
Contact: Allen Burnett, President
E-mail: allen.burnett@jbt-stl.com
Facebook: www.facebook.com/CreveCoeurOlivetteChamber
X (Twitter): x.com/CCOChamber
YouTube: www.youtube.com/channel/UCHtLXqZV5aqnkBXu3RKU1dw
Description: Promotes economic development in Creve Coeur and Olivette, MO. Convention/Meeting: none. **Publications:** *Quality of Life Magazine* (Periodic). **Geographic Preference:** Local.

41553 ■ Cuba Chamber of Commerce
71 Hwy. P
Cuba, MO 65453
Ph: (573)885-2531
Co. E-mail: info@cubamochamber.com
URL: http://cubamochamber.com
Contact: Tyler Monda, President
YouTube: www.youtube.com/channel/UCGonKnSb7MGik4sERWbQpBg
Description: Promotes business and community development in the Cuba, MO area. **Founded:** 1953. **Geographic Preference:** Local.

41554 ■ Dexter Chamber of Commerce (DCC)
515 W Market St., Ste. B
Dexter, MO 63841
Ph: (573)624-7458
Fax: (573)624-7459
Co. E-mail: info@dexterchamber.com
URL: http://dexterchamber.com
Contact: Dustin Mayer, Co-President
Facebook: www.facebook.com/dextermochamber

Description: Promotes business, industrial, and community development in Dexter, MO. **Founded:** 1947. **Awards:** Dexter Chamber of Commerce Organization of the Year (Annual). **Geographic Preference:** Local.

41555 ■ East Prairie Chamber of Commerce
106 S Washington St.
East Prairie, MO 63845
Ph: (573)649-5243
Co. E-mail: info@epmochamber.org
URL: http://www.epmochamber.org
Contact: Bryan Mainord, President
Facebook: www.facebook.com/eastprairiechamber
Description: Promotes business and community development in the East Prairie, MO area. **Founded:** 1962. **Geographic Preference:** Local.

41556 ■ El Dorado Springs Chamber of Commerce
1303 S State Hwy. 32
El Dorado Springs, MO 64744
Ph: (417)876-4154
URL: http://www.eldoradospringschamber.com
Contact: Peggy Snodgrass, Contact
Facebook: www.facebook.com/ElDoradoSpringsChamber
YouTube: www.youtube.com/channel/UCzEldKJlvDJHyOpFobQjd9w
Description: Promotes business and community development in El Dorado Springs, MO. **Awards:** El Dorado Springs Chamber Citizen of the Year (Annual); El Dorado Springs Chamber Club/Organization of the Year (Annual); El Dorado Springs Chamber Hall of Fame (Annual). **Geographic Preference:** Local.

41557 ■ Eldon Area Chamber of Commerce (ECC)
210 E Sixth St.
Eldon, MO 65026
Ph: (573)392-3752
Fax: (573)392-0634
Co. E-mail: eldoninfo@eldonchamber.com
URL: http://eldonchamber.com
Contact: Mary Oberreither, Executive Director
Facebook: www.facebook.com/EldonChamber
Description: Promotes business and community development in Eldon, MO. Sponsors Eldon Turkey Festival. **Geographic Preference:** Local.

41558 ■ Ellington Chamber of Commerce
155 W Walnut St.
Ellington, MO 63638
Ph: (573)663-7997
Co. E-mail: chamber@ellingtonmo.com
URL: http://ellingtonmo.com
Contact: Beth Buford, Contact
Facebook: www.facebook.com/EllingtonChamberofCommerce
Description: Promotes business and community development in Ellington, MO area. **Geographic Preference:** Local.

41559 ■ Eureka Chamber of Commerce
113 Hilltop Village Center Dr., Ste. C
Eureka, MO 63025
Ph: (636)938-6062
Co. E-mail: info@eurekachamber.org
URL: http://www.eurekachamber.org
Contact: Chuck Maher, President
Facebook: www.facebook.com/EurekaMoChamber
Instagram: www.instagram.com/eurekamochamber
Description: Promotes businesses and community development in Eureka area. **Founded:** 1954. **Geographic Preference:** Local.

41560 ■ Excelsior Springs Area Chamber of Commerce
426 S Thompson Ave.
Excelsior Springs, MO 64024
Ph: (816)630-6161
Co. E-mail: info@exspgschamber.com
URL: http://exspgschamber.com
Contact: Courtney Cole, Executive Director

Description: Organized to encourage a strong local economy and quality of life by promoting sound government and an informed membership and community. Promotes business and community development in Excelsior Springs, MO. **Founded:** 1927. **Publications:** *Chamber Connection* (Quarterly). **Awards:** Excelsior Springs Area Chamber Member of the Year (Annual); Excelsior Springs Area Citizen of the Year (Annual); Excelsior Springs Area Volunteer of the Year (Annual). **Geographic Preference:** State.

41561 ■ Farmington Regional Chamber of Commerce (FRC)
302 N Washington St.
Farmington, MO 63640-0191
Ph: (573)756-3615
Fax: (573)756-1003
Co. E-mail: chamber@farmingtonregionalchamber.com
URL: http://www.farmingtonregionalchamber.com
Contact: Larry Joseph, Chairman of the Board
Facebook: www.facebook.com/farmingtonchamber
Linkedin: www.linkedin.com/company/farmington-chamber-of-commerce-missouri-
X (Twitter): x.com/FarmingtonChamb
YouTube: www.youtube.com/channel/UCOLaEZWJWOXQL06AVqKt6zw
Description: Promotes business and community development in Farmington, MO. Sponsors Farmington Country Days. **Founded:** 1941. **Publications:** *Your Chamber Connection* (Monthly). **Geographic Preference:** Local.

41562 ■ Fenton Area Chamber of Commerce (FACC)
1315 N Hwy. Dr.
Fenton, MO 63099
Ph: (636)717-0200
Fax: (636)717-0214
Co. E-mail: exdir@fentonmochamber.com
URL: http://www.fentonmochamber.com
Contact: Charlie Fischer, President
Facebook: www.facebook.com/FentonMoChamber
Linkedin: www.linkedin.com/company/fenton-area-chamber-of-commerce
X (Twitter): x.com/fentonmochamber
Instagram: www.instagram.com/fentonmochamber
YouTube: www.youtube.com/user/fentonmochamber
Description: Promotes business and community development in the Fenton, MO area. **Founded:** 1970. **Publications:** *Business to Business* (Monthly); *Community Guide* (Annual); *Fenton Area Chamber of Commerce--Community Guide* (Annual); *Community Guide* (Annual). **Awards:** FACC High School Scholarship Program (Annual). **Geographic Preference:** Local.

41563 ■ Forsyth Area Chamber of Commerce
157 Main St.
Forsyth, MO 65653
Ph: (417)546-2741
Co. E-mail: info@forsythmissouri.org
URL: http://www.forsythmissouri.org
Contact: Charyl E. Soyland, President
X (Twitter): x.com/ForsythAreaCOC
Description: Promotes growth and prosperity of Forsyth and the surrounding communities by leading, attracting, focusing, and encouraging relationships between Chamber members and sponsoring community, civic, and cultural activities. **Founded:** 1861. **Publications:** *Chamber Chat* (Monthly). **Geographic Preference:** Local.

41564 ■ Greater Kansas City Chamber of Commerce
30 W Pershing Rd., Ste. 301
Kansas City, MO 64108-2423
Ph: (816)221-2424
Fax: (816)221-7440
Co. E-mail: info@kcchamber.com
URL: http://www.kcchamber.com
Contact: Joe Reardon, President
Facebook: www.facebook.com/greaterkc
X (Twitter): x.com/kcchamber
YouTube: www.youtube.com/user/greaterkcchamber

Description: Promotes business and community development in the Greater Kansas City, MO area. **Founded:** 1916. **Publications:** *The City Haller* (Weekly); *Economic Forecast* (Annual); *Greater Kansas City Business* (Monthly); *Chamber of Commerce of Greater Kansas City--Membership Directory and Buyer's Guide* (Annual). **Geographic Preference:** Local.

41565 ■ Greater Maryville Chamber of Commerce
408 N Market
Maryville, MO 64468
Ph: (660)582-8643
Fax: (660)582-3071
Co. E-mail: chamber@maryvillechamber.com
URL: http://www.maryvillechamber.com
Contact: David Baker, President
Facebook: www.facebook.com/MaryvilleChamber
X (Twitter): x.com/greaterville
Description: Promotes business and community development in the Maryville, MO area. **Publications:** *Update* (Monthly). **Geographic Preference:** Local.

41566 ■ Greater North County Chamber of Commerce
420 W Washington St.
Florissant, MO 63031
Ph: (314)831-3500
Fax: (314)831-9682
Co. E-mail: info@greaternorthcountychamber.com
URL: http://greaternorthcountychamber.com
Contact: Bret Berigan, Treasurer
E-mail: bret.berigan@bjc.org
X (Twitter): x.com/GreaterNCC
YouTube: www.youtube.com/channel/UC97OxoDNSee45lz_Njcm10w
Description: Promotes business and community development in the Florissant, MO area. **Founded:** 1955. **Publications:** *Our Town* (Quarterly). **Geographic Preference:** Local.

41567 ■ Greater Poplar Bluff Area Chamber of Commerce
1111 W Pine St.
Poplar Bluff, MO 63901
Ph: (573)785-7761
Co. E-mail: info@poplarbluffchamber.org
URL: http://poplarbluffchamber.org
Contact: Steve Halter, President
E-mail: shalter@poplarbluffchamber.org
Facebook: www.facebook.com/poplarbluffchamber
Linkedin: www.linkedin.com/company/poplarbluffchamber
X (Twitter): x.com/pbchamber
Instagram: www.instagram.com/pbchamber
YouTube: www.youtube.com/channel/UCRkHKTIrF82tJ8Soh-sCGmg
Description: Promotes business and community development in the Greater Poplar Bluff, MO area. **Founded:** 1938. **Publications:** *Bluff Business Bulletin* (Monthly). **Awards:** Greater Poplar Bluff Area Citizen of the Year (Annual). **Geographic Preference:** Local.

41568 ■ Greater St. Charles County Chamber of Commerce
5988 mid rivers mall Dr.
Saint Charles, MO 63302
Ph: (636)946-0633
Co. E-mail: info@stcharlesregionalchamber.com
URL: http://www.stcharlesregionalchamber.com
Contact: Scott Tate, President
E-mail: scott@stcharlesregionalchamber.com
Facebook: www.facebook.com/stcharlesregionalchamber
Linkedin: www.linkedin.com/company/stcharlesregionalchamber
X (Twitter): x.com/StCRegChamber
Instagram: www.instagram.com/stcharlesregionalchamber
YouTube: www.youtube.com/GSTCCC
Pinterest: www.pinterest.com/GSTCCC
Description: Promotes business and community development in St. Charles, MO area. **Founded:** 1917. **Awards:** Greater St. Charles County Citizen of

the Year; Greater St. Charles County Recognition of Service Excellence Awards (Annual); Greater St. Charles County Small Business of the Year (Annual). **Geographic Preference:** Local.

41569 ▪ Greater Warrensburg Area Chamber of Commerce and Visitors Center
100 S Holden St.
  Warrensburg, MO 64093
Ph: (660)747-3168
Free: 877-OLD-DRUM
Fax: (660)429-5490
Co. E-mail: chamber@warrensburg.org
URL: http://www.warrensburg.org
Contact: Suzanne Taylor, Executive Director
E-mail: staylor@warrensburg.org
Facebook: www.facebook.com/
  ChamberWarrensburgMO
Linkedin: www.linkedin.com/company/greater-area
  -warrensburg-chamber-of-commerce
X (Twitter): x.com/BurgChamberMO
Instagram: www.instagram.com/burgchambermo
YouTube: www.youtube.com/user/madefreshdaily
  2009
Description: Promotes business and community development in Warrensburg, MO. Sponsors Fall Festival. **Founded:** 1885. **Publications:** *Kaleidoscope* (Monthly). **Geographic Preference:** Local.

41570 ▪ Greater West Plains Area Chamber of Commerce
401 Jefferson Ave.
  West Plains, MO 65775
Ph: (417)256-4433
Co. E-mail: info@wpchamber.com
URL: http://wpchamber.com
Contact: Jessica Collins, IOM, Executive Director
Facebook: www.facebook.com/wpmochamber
Description: Promotes business and community development in the Greater West Plains, MO area. Sponsors annual Fur, Fin, and Feather Festival. **Founded:** 1978. **Publications:** *West Plains Ambassador* (Bimonthly). **Geographic Preference:** Local.

41571 ▪ Hannibal Area Chamber of Commerce
307 Broadway
  Hannibal, MO 63401
Ph: (573)221-1101
Fax: (573)221-3389
Co. E-mail: info@hannibalchamber.org
URL: http://www.hannibalchamber.org
Contact: McKenzie Disselhorst, Executive Director
E-mail: director@hannibalchamber.org
Facebook: www.facebook.com/HannibalChamber
Description: Promotes business and community development in Hannibal, MO. **Founded:** 1919. **Publications:** *Hannibal Area Chamber of Commerce--Community Resource Guide* (Annual). **Geographic Preference:** Local.

41572 ▪ Harrisonville Area Chamber of Commerce (HACC)
106 S Independence St.
  Harrisonville, MO 64701
Ph: (816)380-5271
Co. E-mail: info@harrisonvillechamber.com
URL: http://www.harrisonvillechamber.com
Contact: Monty Kisner, President
Facebook: www.facebook.com/HarrisonvilleChamber
Instagram: www.instagram.com/harrisonvillechamber
Description: Promotes business and community development in the Harrisonville, MO area. **Founded:** 1965. **Geographic Preference:** Local.

41573 ▪ Hermann Area Chamber of Commerce (HACC)
150 Market St.
  Hermann, MO 65041
Ph: (573)486-2313
Co. E-mail: chamber@hermannareachamber.com
URL: http://www.hermannareachamber.com
Contact: Gary Watts, President
Facebook: www.facebook.com/hermannchamber
Description: Promotes business and community development in the Hermann, MO area. **Founded:** 1944. **Geographic Preference:** Local.

41574 ▪ Higginsville Chamber of Commerce (HCC)
1813 N Main St.
  Higginsville, MO 64037
Ph: (660)584-3030
Co. E-mail: chamber@ctcis.net
URL: http://www.higginsvillechamber.com
Contact: Donald Knehans, President
Facebook: www.facebook.com/pg/Higginsville-Chamber-of-Commerce-207442532624029
Description: Promotes business and community development in Higginsville, MO. Sponsors annual Higginsville Country Fair. **Founded:** 1869. **Awards:** Higginsville Chamber Business of the Year (Annual). **Geographic Preference:** Local.

41575 ▪ Holden Chamber of Commerce
124 W 2nd St.
  Holden, MO 64040
Ph: (816)732-6844
Co. E-mail: info@holdenchamber.com
URL: http://www.holdenchamber.com
Contact: Jennifer Smithson, President
Description: Promotes business and community development in Holden, MO. **Founded:** 1946. **Geographic Preference:** Local.

41576 ▪ Houston Chamber of Commerce (HCC)
501 E Walnut St.
  Houston, MO 65483
Ph: (417)217-4399
Co. E-mail: chamberhoustonmo@gmail.com
URL: http://www.houstonmochamber.com
Contact: Kristie Miller, Executive Director
Description: Promotes business and community development in the Houston area. Sponsors the Emmett Kelly Clown Festival, annual golf tournament, Texas County Fair and Old Settler's Reunion, Heritage Days, the Christmas parade and Christmas promotions. **Geographic Preference:** Local.

41577 ▪ Independence Chamber of Commerce
210 W Truman Rd.
  Independence, MO 64050
Ph: (816)252-4745
Co. E-mail: ichamber@ichamber.biz
URL: http://ichamber.biz
Contact: Tom Lesnak, President
E-mail: tom@ichamber.biz
Facebook: www.facebook.com/IndepChamber
X (Twitter): x.com/IndepChamber
Instagram: www.instagram.com/indepchamber
Description: Promotes business and community development in Independence, MO. **Founded:** 1920. **Publications:** *Chamber News*. **Geographic Preference:** Local.

41578 ▪ *Investor Inside*
12 Municipal Dr.
  Park Hills, MO 63601-2065
Ph: (573)431-1051
Fax: (573)431-2327
Co. E-mail: info@phlcoc.net
URL: http://www.phlcoc.net
Contact: Brenda Kimrey, President
URL(s): www.phlcoc.net/chamber-newsletters
Released: Periodic **Availability:** Online.

41579 ▪ Joplin Area Chamber of Commerce (JACC)
320 E 4th St.
  Joplin, MO 64801
Ph: (417)624-4150
Co. E-mail: info@joplincc.com
URL: http://www.joplincc.com
Contact: Toby Teeter, President
Facebook: www.facebook.com/joplinchamber
X (Twitter): x.com/joplinchamber
Instagram: www.instagram.com/joplinchamber
YouTube: www.youtube.com/user/joplinareachamber
Description: Promotes the growth and development of the Joplin, MO area. **Founded:** 1917. **Publications:** *Business Outlook* (Monthly); *Industrial Directory*. **Awards:** Joplin Area Chamber of Commerce Golden Apple Awards (Annual); Joplin Area Chamber of Commerce Business of the Year (Annual). **Geographic Preference:** Local.

41580 ▪ Kennett Chamber of Commerce (KCC)
1601 1st St.
  Kennett, MO 63857
Ph: (573)888-5828
Free: 866-848-5828
Fax: (573)888-9802
Co. E-mail: info@kennettmo.com
URL: http://www.kennettmo.com
Contact: Jeff Dorris, President
Description: Promotes business and community development in Kennett, MO. **Founded:** 1946. **Geographic Preference:** Local.

41581 ▪ Kirksville Area Chamber of Commerce
304 S Franklin St.
  Kirksville, MO 63501
Ph: (660)665-3766
Fax: (660)665-3767
Co. E-mail: info@kirksvillechamber.com
URL: http://www.kirksvillechamber.com
Contact: Sandra Williams, Executive Director
E-mail: sandra.williams@kirksvillechamber.com
Linkedin: www.linkedin.com/company/kirksville-area
  -chamber-of-commerce
Description: Promotes business and community development in the Kirksville, MO area. **Geographic Preference:** Local.

41582 ▪ Kirkwood-Des Peres Area Chamber of Commerce
366 S Kirkwood Rd.
  Kirkwood, MO 63122
Ph: (314)821-4161
Co. E-mail: info@thechamber.us
URL: http://www.kirkwooddesperes.com
Contact: Peg Weathers, President
E-mail: peg@thechamber.us
Facebook: www.facebook.com/kirkwoo
  ddespereschamber
X (Twitter): x.com/kirkwoodchamber
Instagram: www.instagram.com/kirkwoo
  ddespereschamber
Description: Promotes business and community development in the Kirkwood, MO area. **Founded:** 1946. **Publications:** *Business and Community*; *Chamber Advantage* (Monthly); *Chamber Flash* (Monthly); *Kirkwood - Des Peres Area Chamber of Commerce--Community Directory & Visitors' Guide*. **Educational Activities:** Business Advantage. **Awards:** Kirkwood-Des Peres Area Business Person of the Year (Annual); Kirkwood-Des Peres Area Citizen of the Year (Annual); Kirkwood-Des Peres Area Lifetime Achievement Award (Annual). **Geographic Preference:** Local.

41583 ▪ Lake of the Ozarks West Chamber of Commerce
125 Oddo Dr., Right off of N Hwy. 5
  Sunrise Beach, MO 65079
Ph: (573)374-5500
Fax: (573)374-8576
Co. E-mail: info@lakewestchamber.com
URL: http://www.lakewestchamber.com
Contact: Tom McNeill, Board Member
E-mail: tom@decoinsurance.com
Facebook: www.facebook.com/LakeWestChamber
Linkedin: www.linkedin.com/company/lake-wes
  t-chamber-of-commerce
X (Twitter): x.com/lakewestmo
Description: Works with other community resources to promote local tourism, create jobs, and recruit new businesses in Lake of the Ozarks West, MO area. **Founded:** 1987. **Geographic Preference:** Local.

41584 ▪ Lebanon Area Chamber of Commerce
186 N Adams
  Lebanon, MO 65536
Ph: (417)588-3256
Free: 888-588-5710
Fax: (417)588-3251

Co. E-mail: chamber@lebanonmissouri.com
URL: http://lebanonmissouri.com
Contact: Mark Campbell, President
Facebook: www.facebook.com/
lebareachamberofcommerce
Description: Promotes business and community development in the Lebanon, MO area. Sponsors Hillbilly Days Arts and Crafts Festival, and Holiday Festival Parade. **Geographic Preference:** Local.

41585 ■ Lexington Area Chamber of Commerce (LCC)
1016 Main St.
Lexington, MO 64067
Ph: (660)259-3082
Co. E-mail: chamber@historiclexington.com
URL: http://www.historiclexington.com
Contact: Andrew Rice, President
Facebook: www.facebook.com/LexingtonMoChamber
X (Twitter): x.com/lexmochamber
Instagram: www.instagram.com/lexmochamber
Description: Promotes business, industry, and community development in Lexington, MO. Offers free community Christmas dinner. Conducts volleyball competitions. Sponsors River Festival and Farmer Appreciation Dinner. **Founded:** 1938. **Publications:** Chamber News (Monthly). **Educational Activities:** Apple, Arts and Antique. **Geographic Preference:** Local.

41586 ■ Liberty Area Chamber of Commerce
1170 W Kansas St., Ste. H
Liberty, MO 64068
Ph: (816)781-5200
Fax: (816)781-4901
Co. E-mail: info@libertychamber.com
URL: http://libertychamber.com
Contact: Gayle Potter, President
E-mail: gaylep@libertychamber.com
Facebook: www.facebook.com/liberty.chamber
Linkedin: www.linkedin.com/company/liberty-area
-chamber-of-commerce
Instagram: www.instagram.com/libertymochamber
YouTube: www.youtube.com/channel/UC
_WzGTA0TiOdsBph-ynGktw
Description: Volunteer partnership of business, civic and professional people working together to build a healthy economy and improve the quality of life in the greater Liberty, Missouri area. **Founded:** 1951. **Publications:** The Chamber News (Monthly). **Geographic Preference:** Local.

41587 ■ Macon Area Chamber of Commerce
102 Vine St.
Macon, MO 63552
Ph: (660)385-2811
URL: http://www.maconmochamber.com
Contact: Sharon Scott, Executive Director
Description: Promotes business and community development in the Macon, MO area. Sponsors competitions and festival. **Founded:** 1935. **Geographic Preference:** Local.

41588 ■ Madison County Chamber of Commerce
PO Box 181
Fredericktown, MO 63645
Ph: (573)783-2604
Co. E-mail: info@madisoncountycc.com
URL: http://www.madisoncountycc.com
Contact: Beth Simmons, President
Facebook: www.facebook.com/madisoncountycc
Description: Promotes business and community development in the Madison County, MO area. Sponsors seminars. **Founded:** 1946. **Geographic Preference:** Local.

41589 ■ *Mainstreet News*
100 W Jackson St.
Mexico, MO 65265
Ph: (573)581-2765
Fax: (573)581-6226
Co. E-mail: mexicochamber@mexico-chamber.org
URL: http://mexico-chamber.org
Contact: Dana Keller, Executive Director
URL(s): www.mexico-chamber.org/mainstreet-news

Released: Monthly **Description:** Contains upcoming chamber events, activities and latest happenings in the community. **Availability:** Download; PDF.

41590 ■ Malden Chamber of Commerce (MCC)
607 N Douglass St.
Malden, MO
Ph: (573)276-4519
Co. E-mail: denton@maldenchamberofcommerce
.com
URL: http://www.maldenchamber.com
Facebook: www.facebook.com/Malden-Chamber-of
-Commerce-100064251416715
Description: Promotes business and community development in the area. Sponsors events and activities. **Publications:** View Points (Bimonthly); Business Review (Bimonthly). **Awards:** Malden Chamber of Commerce Business of the Year (Annual). **Geographic Preference:** Local.

41591 ■ Marshall Chamber of Commerce (MCC)
214 N Lafayette
Marshall, MO 65340
Ph: (660)886-3324
URL: http://www.marshallmochamber.com
Contact: Sandy Hisle, President
E-mail: sandy@marshalltwerrealty.com
Facebook: www.facebook.com/marshallmochamber
X (Twitter): x.com/marshallmocc
Instagram: www.instagram.com/marshallmocc
YouTube: www.youtube.com/channel/UCjgwfNu4a
15xxlllGi7TlFw
Pinterest: www.pinterest.com/marshallmocc
Description: Promotes business and community development in Marshall and Saline counties, MO. **Founded:** 1921. **Geographic Preference:** Local.

41592 ■ Maryland Heights Chamber of Commerce (MHCC)
11705 Dorsett Rd.
Maryland Heights, MO 63043
Ph: (314)942-2110
URL: http://www.mhcc.com
Contact: Becky Kammeier, Chairman
Linkedin: www.linkedin.com/company/maryland-heigh
ts-chamber-of-commerce
X (Twitter): x.com/ChamberMHCC
Description: Promotes business and community development in Maryland Heights, MO area. **Founded:** 1990. **Awards:** MHCC Business Leader of the Year (Annual). **Geographic Preference:** Local.

41593 ■ Mexico Area Chamber of Commerce (MACC)
100 W Jackson St.
Mexico, MO 65265
Ph: (573)581-2765
Fax: (573)581-6226
Co. E-mail: mexicochamber@mexico-chamber.org
URL: http://mexico-chamber.org
Contact: Dana Keller, Executive Director
Facebook: www.facebook.com/
MexicoAreaChamberOfCommerce
Description: Promotes business and community development in the Mexico, MO area. Focuses on tourism, transportation, and agribusiness. **Founded:** 1917. **Publications:** Mainstreet News (Monthly). **Educational Activities:** Agriculture Appreciation and Commerce & Industry Appreciation. **Geographic Preference:** Local.

41594 ■ Missouri Chamber of Commerce and Industry (MCCI)
428 E Capitol Ave.
Jefferson City, MO 65101
Ph: (573)634-3511
URL: http://mochamber.com
Contact: Brendan Cossette, Chief Operating Officer
Facebook: www.facebook.com/missourichamber
Linkedin: www.linkedin.com/company/
missourichamber
X (Twitter): x.com/MissouriChamber
YouTube: www.youtube.com/channel/UCRpdFSVu
6Ruu-XCwxeJpaXg

Description: Promotes economic vitality and strength in the Jefferson City area. Participates and partners in activities that improve the economy and quality of life. **Founded:** 1923. **Publications:** Image Publication/Membership Directory and Buyer's Guide; Missouri Legislative Directory (Biennial); Chamber Chronicle (Bimonthly). **Educational Activities:** Chamber Connections Mixers. **Geographic Preference:** Local.

41595 ■ Monett Chamber of Commerce
200 E Broadway St.
Monett, MO 65708
Ph: (417)235-7919
Fax: (417)235-4076
URL: http://www.monettchamber.com
Contact: Kellie Moreland, President
Description: Promotes business and community development in Monett, MO. **Publications:** Talk of the Towne (Monthly). **Educational Activities:** Beef Conference. **Geographic Preference:** Local.

41596 ■ Monroe City Chamber of Commerce
PO Box 22
Monroe City, MO 63456
Ph: (573)735-4391
Co. E-mail: monroecitychamber@gmail.com
URL: http://www.monroecitychamber.com
Contact: Janie Neice, President
Facebook: www.facebook.com/Monroe-City-Chamber
-of-Commerce-655752584491900
Description: Promotes business and community development in the Monroe City, MO area. **Geographic Preference:** Local.

41597 ■ Montgomery City Area Chamber of Commerce
PO Box 31
Montgomery City, MO 63361
Co. E-mail: directory@mcchamber.org
URL: http://www.mcchamber.org
Contact: Desiree Peak, President
E-mail: president@mcchamber.org
Description: Promotes business and community development in Montgomery City, MO area. **Geographic Preference:** Local.

41598 ■ Mt. Vernon, MO Chamber of Commerce
425 E Mt. Vernon Blvd.
Mount Vernon, MO 65712
Ph: (417)466-7654
Co. E-mail: chamber@mtvchamber.com
URL: http://www.mtvernonchamber.com
Contact: Jason Prater, President
URL(s): www.mtvchamber.com
Facebook: www.facebook.com/Mt-Vernon-MO-Area
-Chamber-of-Commerce-168447229060
Description: Promotes business and community development in Mt. Vernon, MO. **Geographic Preference:** Local.

41599 ■ Mountain Grove Chamber of Commerce
PO Box 434
Mountain Grove, MO 65711
Ph: (417)926-4135
Co. E-mail: chamber@mountaingrovechamber.com
URL: http://www.mountaingrovechamber.com
Contact: Jim Dickey, Director
E-mail: jdickey@mg.k12.mo.us
Facebook: www.facebook.com/Moun
tainGroveChamber
Description: Promotes business and community development in Mountain Grove, MO. Sponsors Mayfest celebration. **Geographic Preference:** Local.

41600 ■ Nevada-Vernon County Chamber of Commerce (NVCCC)
225 W Austin, Ste. 200
Nevada, MO 64772
Ph: (417)667-5300
Co. E-mail: chamber1@nevada-mo.com
URL: http://www.nevada-mo.com
Contact: Jessica Bland, President
E-mail: jbland@farmersagent.com

41601 ■ Missouri

Facebook: www.facebook.com/NevadaVernonCountyChamberOfCommerce
Description: Promotes business and community development in Nevada-Vernon County, MO. Sponsors Bushwhacker Days. **Founded:** 1890. **Publications:** *Chamber Connections* (Quarterly). **Geographic Preference:** Local.

41601 ■ New Madrid Chamber of Commerce
560 Mott St.
New Madrid, MO 63869
Ph: (573)748-2866
Fax: (573)748-5402
Co. E-mail: chambernm@yahoo.com
URL: http://www.new-madrid.mo.us
Contact: Reagan Baird, President
Facebook: www.facebook.com/NewMadridMissouri
Description: Promotes business and community development in New Madrid, MO area. **Founded:** 1783. **Geographic Preference:** Local.

41602 ■ Nixa Area Chamber of Commerce
106 W Sherman Way, Ste. 6
Nixa, MO 65714
Ph: (417)725-1545
Co. E-mail: info@nixachamber.com
URL: http://www.nixachamber.com
Contact: Chris Russell, Chief Executive Officer
E-mail: chrisrussell@nixachamber.com
Facebook: www.facebook.com/NixaChamber
X (Twitter): x.com/nixachamber
YouTube: www.youtube.com/channel/UC8T-uUCsIqJxD39ZZHJEN_g
Description: Works to provide leadership, to assist growth and development of business, and to enhance the community as a desirable place to live, learn, work, shop and play. **Founded:** 1989. **Geographic Preference:** Local.

41603 ■ Northland Regional Chamber of Commerce (NRCC)
634 NW Englewood Rd.
Kansas City, MO 64118
Ph: (816)455-9911
Fax: (816)455-9933
Co. E-mail: northland@northlandchamber.com
URL: http://www.northlandchamber.com
Contact: Jenny Johnston, President
Facebook: www.facebook.com/NorthlandChamber
X (Twitter): x.com/northlandregion
Instagram: www.instagram.com/northlandchamber
Description: Promotes business and community development in Clay and Platte County, MO. **Founded:** 1992. **Publications:** *The Northland Voice* (Monthly). **Geographic Preference:** Regional.

41604 ■ Oak Grove Chamber of Commerce
PO Box 586
Oak Grove, MO 64075
Ph: (816)690-4147
Co. E-mail: ogchamberboard@gmail.com
URL: http://www.theogchamber.com
Facebook: www.facebook.com/oakgrovechamber
Instagram: www.instagram.com/oakgrovechamber
Description: Strives to advance wholesome commercial aspects and beneficial directives in the business community. **Geographic Preference:** Local.

41605 ■ O'Fallon Chamber of Commerce & Industries
2145 Bryan Valley Commercial Dr.
O Fallon, MO 63366
Ph: (636)240-1818
Fax: (888)349-1897
Co. E-mail: info@ofallonchamber.org
URL: http://www.ofallonchamber.org
Contact: Kathy Duck, President
E-mail: kduck@ofallonchamber.org
Facebook: www.facebook.com/ofallonchamber
X (Twitter): x.com/OFallonChamber
YouTube: www.youtube.com/user/OFallonChamber
Description: Promotes business and community development in O'Fallon, MO. Conducts charitable activities. Sponsors area festival and Person of the Year competition. **Founded:** 1950. **Publications:** *Connections* (Monthly); *O'Fallon Chamber News* (Monthly). **Educational Activities:** Business Luncheon. **Geographic Preference:** Local.

41606 ■ *Out and About*
301 Southlake Blvd., Ste. 102, N
Chesterfield, MO 63005
Ph: (804)748-6364
Co. E-mail: info@chesterfieldchamber.com
URL: http://chesterfieldchamber.com
Contact: Danielle Fitz, Co-President Co-Chief Executive Officer
URL(s): www.chesterfieldmochamber.com/our-publications
Released: Quarterly; January-March, April-June, July-September, October-December. **Availability:** Online; PDF.

41607 ■ Owensville Chamber of Commerce (OCC)
102 S Cuba St.
Owensville, MO 65066
Ph: (573)437-4270
URL: http://owensvillemissouri.com
Contact: Chris Shaul, President
Description: Promotes a healthy climate for business, commerce, and industry in Owensville, MO. **Founded:** 1944. **Geographic Preference:** Local.

41608 ■ Ozark Chamber of Commerce (OCC)
1471 W South St.
Ozark, MO 65721
Ph: (417)581-6139
Fax: (417)581-0639
Co. E-mail: info@ozarkchamber.com
URL: http://ozarkchamber.com
Contact: Chrystal Irons, Contact
Description: Promotes business and community development in Ozark, MO and surrounding areas. Conducts charitable and promotional activities. Sponsors Christmas parade, business education, Adopt-A-School activities, and other community events. **Founded:** 1949. **Publications:** *Chamber Connection* (Monthly); *Ozark Area Chamber of Commerce--Professional Directory and Community Information* (Annual). **Geographic Preference:** Local.

41609 ■ Pacific Area Chamber of Commerce
142 W St. Louis St.
Pacific, MO 63069
Ph: (636)271-6639
Co. E-mail: exdir@pacificchamber.com
URL: http://pacificchamber.com
Contact: Sarah Summers, Vice President
Facebook: www.facebook.com/PacificAreaChamberOfCommerce
Description: Promotes business and community development in Pacific, MO. **Geographic Preference:** Local.

41610 ■ Paris Area Chamber of Commerce (PACC)
225 N Main St.
Paris, MO 65275
Ph: (660)327-3508
Co. E-mail: parismochamber@gmail.com
URL: http://parisareachamber.com
Contact: Jo Reynolds, Contact
Facebook: www.facebook.com/Paris-Area-Chamber-of-Commerce-190199510995735
Description: Promotes business and community development in Paris, MO. **Founded:** 1986. **Geographic Preference:** Local.

41611 ■ Park Hills-Leadington Chamber of Commerce (PHLCOC)
12 Municipal Dr.
Park Hills, MO 63601-2065
Ph: (573)431-1051
Fax: (573)431-2327
Co. E-mail: info@phlcoc.net
URL: http://www.phlcoc.net
Contact: Brenda Kimrey, President
Facebook: www.facebook.com/PHLCOC
Linkedin: www.linkedin.com/company/phlcoc
X (Twitter): x.com/phlcoc
Instagram: www.instagram.com/phlchamber

STATE LISTINGS

YouTube: www.youtube.com/channel/UC2UabSe19-mMl-6oTGriYxA
Description: Promotes business and community development in St. Francois County, MO. Conducts social and promotional events and assists with Economic Development. **Founded:** 1942. **Publications:** *Investor Inside* (Periodic). **Geographic Preference:** Local.

41612 ■ Perryville Chamber of Commerce
2 W, Ste. Maries St.
Perryville, MO 63775
Ph: (573)547-6062
Fax: (573)547-6071
Co. E-mail: jackie@perryvillemo.com
URL: http://www.perryvillemo.com
Contact: Jamie Robinson, Secretary Treasurer
Facebook: www.facebook.com/pvillemochamber
X (Twitter): x.com/pvillemochamber
YouTube: www.youtube.com/channel/UCya64QWiNqyYGC-zZoYw0Lg
Pinterest: www.pinterest.com/visitpvillemo
Description: Promotes business and community development in Perryville, MO. Sponsors annual Mayfest and Mother's Day Weekend celebration. **Geographic Preference:** Local.

41613 ■ Piedmont Area Chamber of Commerce
313 Piedmont Ave.
Piedmont, MO 63957
Ph: (573)223-4046
Co. E-mail: chamberofcommerce@boycomonline.com
URL: http://www.visitpiedmontmo.com
Facebook: www.facebook.com/PiedmontChamberofCommerce
Description: Promotes business and community development in Piedmont, MO. **Geographic Preference:** Local.

41614 ■ Platte City Area Chamber of Commerce and Economic Development Council
620 3rd St.
Platte City, MO 64079
Ph: (816)858-5270
Co. E-mail: info@plattecitymo.com
URL: http://www.plattecitymo.com
Contact: Tricia Friddell, Executive Director
E-mail: tricia@plattecitymo.com
Facebook: www.facebook.com/PlatteCityAreaChamberOfCommerce
Instagram: www.instagram.com/platte_city_area_chamber
Description: Focuses on connecting members with business resources to stimulate growth through retention and expansion. **Geographic Preference:** Local.

41615 ■ Plattsburg Chamber of Commerce (PCC)
PO Box 134
Plattsburg, MO 64477
Ph: (816)539-2649
Co. E-mail: contact@plattsburgchamber.org
URL: http://plattsburgchamber.org
Contact: Sherri Shatto, President
Description: Promotes business and community development in the Plattsburg, MO area. Sponsors fall and Christmas festival. Convention/Meeting: none. Publications: none. **Founded:** 1954. **Geographic Preference:** Local.

41616 ■ Raymore Chamber of Commerce
1000 W Foxwood Dr., Ste. 200
Raymore, MO 64083
Ph: (816)322-0599
Co. E-mail: raymorechamber@sbcglobal.net
URL: http://raymorechamber.com
Contact: Sean Petrie, Treasurer
Facebook: www.facebook.com/raymorechamberofcommerce
Description: Works to improve business community and economic growth through leadership, educational or legislative awareness and community interactions. **Geographic Preference:** Local.

STATE LISTINGS   Missouri ■ 41632

41617 ■ Raytown Area Chamber of Commerce (RACC)
5909 Raytown Trafficway
Raytown, MO 64133-3860
Ph: (816)353-8500
Fax: (816)353-8525
Co. E-mail: staff@raytownchamber.com
URL: http://raytownchamber.com
Contact: Pat Erts, Chairman
Facebook: www.facebook.com/RaytownChamber
X (Twitter): x.com/raytownchamber
Instagram: www.instagram.com/raytownchamber
YouTube: www.youtube.com/channel/UC1Otfvrp-Mb_ihgrHm-X6ow

Description: Promotes business and community development in Raytown, MO and surrounding area. Conducts annual Raytown Roundup Days. **Founded:** 1929. **Publications:** *Chamber Membership* (Annual); *Crossroads Connection* (Monthly). **Educational Activities:** Discover Raytown. **Geographic Preference:** Local.

41618 ■ Republic Area Chamber of Commerce (RACC)
PO Box 682
Republic, MO 65738
Ph: (417)732-5200
Fax: (417)732-2851
Co. E-mail: director@republicchamber.com
URL: http://republicchamber.com
Contact: Britny Fulks, Chairman of the Board
Facebook: www.facebook.com/RACC65738

Description: Assists all members of the community engaged in retail, wholesale, commercial, industrial, tourism, and trade fields, in the professional, educational, and agricultural fields, and in all other fields where interest is evident to solve the mutual or individual problems in the respective fields. Recognizes and promotes the use of the resources of the area and to work for the improvement and protection of those resources through legislation, or other courses of action when deemed necessary. **Geographic Preference:** Local.

41619 ■ Richmond Area Chamber of Commerce (RACC)
104 W N Main St.
Richmond, MO 64085
Ph: (816)776-6916
Fax: (816)776-6917
Co. E-mail: director@richmondchamber.org
URL: http://richmondchamber.org
Facebook: www.facebook.com/RichmondChamberMI

Description: Promotes economic growth and development of Richmond, MI. **Geographic Preference:** Local.

41620 ■ Richmond Chamber of Commerce
104 W N Main St.
Richmond, MO 64085
Ph: (816)776-6916
Fax: (816)776-6917
Co. E-mail: director@richmondchamber.org
URL: http://www.richmondchamber.org
Contact: Felicia Farabee, President
X (Twitter): x.com/chamber_mo

Description: Promotes business and community development in Richmond, MO. **Geographic Preference:** Local.

41621 ■ Ripley County Chamber of Commerce (RCCC)
101 Washington St., Ste. A
Doniphan, MO 63935
Ph: (573)996-2212
Co. E-mail: info@ripleycountymissouri.org
URL: http://www.ripleycountymissouri.org
Contact: Jake Netherland, Secretary
Facebook: www.facebook.com/ripleycountychamberofcommerce

Description: Strives to foster commercial and industrial development in Doniphan, Missouri and the surrounding areas. Provides technical assistance to its business members. **Founded:** 1961. **Geographic Preference:** Local.

41622 ■ Rolla Area Chamber of Commerce
1311 Kingshighway St.
Rolla, MO 65401
Ph: (573)364-3577
Free: 888-809-3817
Co. E-mail: rollacc@rollachamber.org
URL: http://rollachamber.org
Contact: Dominic Deluca, Sr., Chief Executive Officer
Facebook: www.facebook.com/rolla.chamber
YouTube: www.youtube.com/channel/UCyRDXMTuBr8ka9lLsrg_7gQ

Description: Promotes business and community development in the Rolla, MO area. **Founded:** 1928. **Publications:** *Connecticut River Valley Chamber of Commerce Business Directory*; *Chamber News*. **Geographic Preference:** Local.

41623 ■ St. Clair Area Chamber of Commerce
960 Plz. Dr., Ste. H
Saint Clair, MO 63077
Ph: (636)629-6000
Fax: (636)629-5510
Co. E-mail: chamber@stclairmo.com
URL: http://stclairmo.org
Contact: Tim Davis, President
Facebook: www.facebook.com/St-Clair-Area-Chamber-of-Commerce-125130757553218

Description: Promotes business and community development in the St. Clair, MO area. Sponsors festival. **Founded:** 1957. **Awards:** Celebrate St. Clair - Business of the Year (Annual). **Geographic Preference:** Local.

41624 ■ Ste. Genevieve Chamber of Commerce
51 S 3rd St.
Sainte Genevieve, MO 63670
Ph: (573)883-3686
Fax: (573)883-7092
Co. E-mail: info@stegenchamber.org
URL: http://www.stegenchamber.org
Contact: Dena Kreitler, Executive Director
E-mail: dena@stegenchamber.org
Facebook: www.facebook.com/SteGenevieveChamber
Instagram: www.instagram.com/stegenchamber

Description: Offers support and promotion to local businesses. **Founded:** 1924. **Geographic Preference:** Local.

41625 ■ St. James Chamber of Commerce
100 State Rte. B
Saint James, MO 65559
Ph: (573)265-6649
URL: http://stjameschamber.net
Contact: Casey Stuck, President
Facebook: www.facebook.com/STJChamber

Description: Promotes business and community development in St. James, MO area. **Founded:** 2011. **Geographic Preference:** Local.

41626 ■ St. Joseph Chamber of Commerce
3003 Frederick Ave.
Saint Joseph, MO 64506
Ph: (816)232-4461
Free: 800-748-7856
Fax: (816)364-4873
Co. E-mail: bailey@saintjoseph.com
URL: http://saintjoseph.com
Contact: Natalie Redmond, President
E-mail: redmond@saintjoseph.com
Linkedin: www.linkedin.com/company/st.-joseph-area-chamber-of-commerce
X (Twitter): x.com/StJoeChamber
YouTube: www.youtube.com/user/StJoeChamber

Description: Promotes business and community development in the St. Joseph, MO area. **Founded:** 1862. **Publications:** *Business Barometer* (Monthly); *Business Intelligence Report* (Monthly); *Connections*; *21st Century Update* (Quarterly); *Toot Your Horn* (Bimonthly). **Geographic Preference:** Local.

41627 ■ Salem Area Chamber of Commerce (SACC)
1136 S Main St.
Salem, MO 65560
Ph: (573)720-6900
URL: http://www.salemmo.com
Contact: Carlos Lopez, President

Description: Promotes business and community development in the area. **Publications:** *Salem Area Chamber of Commerce Business Directory and Resource Guide* (Annual); *Community & Business Directory*; *Business News* (Monthly). **Awards:** Salem Area Chamber of Commerce Agri-Business of the Year (Annual); Salem Area Chamber of Commerce Business of the Year (Annual); Salem Area Chamber of Commerce Crystal Apple Awards (Irregular); Salem Area Chamber of Commerce Employer of the Year (Annual); Salem Area Chamber of Commerce First Citizen Awards (Annual); Salem Area Chamber of Commerce New Business of the Year (Annual); Salem Area Chamber of Commerce Small Business of the Year (Annual). **Geographic Preference:** Local.

41628 ■ Savannah Area Chamber of Commerce (SACC)
411 Ct., St.
Savannah, MO 64485
Ph: (816)324-3976
Co. E-mail: savannahmochamber@gmail.com
URL: http://www.savannahmochamber.com
Contact: Dr. Eric Kurre, President
Facebook: www.facebook.com/savannahmochamber

Description: Promotes business and community development in the area. **Founded:** 1947. **Geographic Preference:** Local.

41629 ■ Sedalia Area Chamber of Commerce
600 E 3rd St.
Sedalia, MO 65301
Ph: (660)826-2222
URL: http://www.sedaliachamber.com
Contact: Katie Shannon, Co-President
Facebook: www.facebook.com/SedaliaAreaChamberofCommerce
Linkedin: www.linkedin.com/company/sedalia-area-chamber-commerce
X (Twitter): x.com/ChamberSedalia

Description: Promotes business and community development in the Sedalia, MO area. **Founded:** 1913. **Geographic Preference:** Local.

41630 ■ Sikeston Area Chamber of Commerce
128 N New Madrid St.
Sikeston, MO 63801
Ph: (573)471-2498
Co. E-mail: chamber@sikeston.net
URL: http://www.sikeston.net
Contact: Marcie Lawson, Executive Director
E-mail: marcie.lawson@sikeston.net
Facebook: www.facebook.com/sikestonregionalchamber
Instagram: www.instagram.com/sikestonregionalchamber

Description: Promotes business, tourism, and community development in the Sikeston, MO area. **Founded:** 1929. **Publications:** *Images of Sikeston* (Monthly). **Geographic Preference:** Local.

41631 ■ Smithville Area Chamber of Commerce
105 W Main St.
Smithville, MO 64089
Ph: (816)532-0946
URL: http://www.smithvillechamber.org
Contact: Rebecca Pendleton-Meek, Co-President
Facebook: www.facebook.com/SmithvilleAreaChamberOfCommerce

Description: Promotes business and community development in the area. **Founded:** 1989. **Geographic Preference:** Local.

41632 ■ South Kansas City Chamber of Commerce (SKCCC)
406 E Bannister Rd., Ste. F
Kansas City, MO 64131-3028
Ph: (816)761-7660
Fax: (816)761-7340
Co. E-mail: vwolgast@southkcchamber.com
URL: http://southkcchamber.com
Contact: Vickie Wolgast, President

E-mail: vwolgast@southkcchamber.com
Facebook: www.facebook.com/southkcchamber
Linkedin: www.linkedin.com/company/south-kc-chamber
X (Twitter): x.com/SouthKCChamber

Description: Promotes business and community development in southern Kansas City, MO. **Founded:** 1931. **Geographic Preference:** Local.

41633 ■ *Spotlight on Carthage*
402 S Garrison Ave.
  Carthage, MO 64836
Ph: (417)358-2373
Fax: (417)358-7479
Co. E-mail: info@carthagechamber.com
URL: http://carthagechamber.com
Contact: Julie A. Reams, President
E-mail: jreams@carthagechamber.com
URL(s): carthagechamber.com/membership-benefits

Released: Monthly; Monday. **Availability:** Print.

41634 ■ Springfield Area Chamber of Commerce (SACC)
202 S John Q. Hammons Pky.
  Springfield, MO 65806
Ph: (417)862-5567
Co. E-mail: info@springfieldchamber.com
URL: http://www.springfieldchamber.com
Contact: Matt Morrow, President
E-mail: matt@springfieldchamber.com
Facebook: www.facebook.com/springfieldchamber
Linkedin: www.linkedin.com/company/springfield-area-chamber-of-commerce
X (Twitter): x.com/SGFChamber
Instagram: www.instagram.com/sgfchamber

Description: Promotes business and community development in the Springfield, MO area. **Founded:** 1919. **Publications:** *Spirit* (Monthly); *Chamber Chatter* (Monthly). **Geographic Preference:** Local.

41635 ■ Steelville Area Chamber of Commerce
PO Box 956
  Steelville, MO 65565
Ph: (573)775-5533
Co. E-mail: chamber@misn.com
URL: http://chamberofcommerce.steelville.com
Contact: Tiffany Troutt, President
Facebook: www.facebook.com/SteelvilleChamber

Description: Promotes business and community development in Steelville, MO area. **Founded:** 1982. **Geographic Preference:** Local.

41636 ■ Stockton Area Chamber of Commerce (SACC)
3 Public Sq.
  Stockton, MO 65785
Ph: (417)276-5213
Co. E-mail: stocktonchamber@gmail.com
URL: http://www.stocktonmochamber.com
Contact: Woody Kahl, President
E-mail: woodykahl@yahoo.com

Description: Works with other community resources to promote local tourism, create jobs, and recruit new businesses in Stockton, MO area. **Founded:** 1846. **Geographic Preference:** Local.

41637 ■ Sullivan Area Chamber of Commerce
No. 2 W Springfield Rd.
  Sullivan, MO 63080
Ph: (573)468-3314
Fax: (573)860-2313
Co. E-mail: sullivanmochamber@gmail.com
URL: http://www.sullivanmochamber.com
Contact: Johnathon Tripp, Co-President
Facebook: www.facebook.com/SullivanChamber

Description: Promotes business and community development in Sullivan, MO. Participates in charitable programs; sponsors competitions; offers seminars. **Publications:** *Friday Facts* (Weekly (Fri.)); *Newcomer's Guide* (Annual). **Educational Activities:** September Business Showcase. **Geographic Preference:** Local.

41638 ■ Table Rock Lake Chamber of Commerce
PO Box 495
  Kimberling City, MO 65686
Ph: (417)739-2564
Free: 800-595-0393
Co. E-mail: trlchamber@visittablerocklake.com
URL: http://www.visittablerocklake.com
Contact: Sheila Thomas, President
E-mail: sthomas@visittablerocklake.com
Facebook: www.facebook.com/TableRockLakeChamber
Linkedin: www.linkedin.com/in/table-rock-lake-chamber-of-commerce-83772ab6
X (Twitter): x.com/tablerocklakemo
Instagram: www.instagram.com/tablerocklakechamber
YouTube: www.youtube.com/channel/UCfZITtF7OcaAXEmR22pXpsw

Description: Promotes business and community development in the Table Rock Lake area and Stone County. **Founded:** 1974. **Publications:** *Table Rock Lake Vacation Guide* (Annual); *Table Rock Talk* (Monthly). **Awards:** Table Rock Lake Teacher of the Year; Table Rock Lake Community Service Award (Annual). **Geographic Preference:** Local.

41639 ■ *Table Rock Lake Vacation Guide*
PO Box 495
  Kimberling City, MO 65686
Ph: (417)739-2564
Free: 800-595-0393
Co. E-mail: trlchamber@visittablerocklake.com
URL: http://www.visittablerocklake.com
Contact: Sheila Thomas, President
E-mail: sthomas@visittablerocklake.com
URL(s): business.visittablerocklake.com/info

Released: Annual **Description:** Contains information on vacation planning to Table Rock Lake area. **Availability:** Print; PDF; Download; Online.

41640 ■ *Trenton*
1846 E 9th St.
  Trenton, MO 64683
Ph: (660)359-4324
Fax: (660)359-4606
Co. E-mail: trentonchambermo2@gmail.com
URL: http://www.trentonmochamber.com
Contact: Debbie Carman, Executive Director
URL(s): www.trentonmochamber.com/index.php/membership

Released: Monthly **Availability:** Print; Online.

41641 ■ Trenton Area Chamber of Commerce
1846 E 9th St.
  Trenton, MO 64683
Ph: (660)359-4324
Fax: (660)359-4606
Co. E-mail: trentonchambermo2@gmail.com
URL: http://www.trentonmochamber.com
Contact: Debbie Carman, Executive Director

Description: Promotes business and community development in north central Missouri. **Publications:** *Trenton* (Monthly). **Geographic Preference:** Local.

41642 ■ Troy Area Chamber of Commerce (TCC)
850 E Cherry St., Ste. A
  Troy, MO 63379
Ph: (636)462-8769
Fax: (636)528-3731
Co. E-mail: info@troyonthemove.com
URL: http://troyonthemove.com
Contact: Justin Butler, President
E-mail: justin@butlertomko.com
X (Twitter): x.com/TroyChamber

Description: Promotes business and community development in Troy, MO. **Publications:** *Troy on the Move* (Annual). **Awards:** Troy Area Man of the Year; Troy Area Woman of the Year. **Geographic Preference:** Local.

41643 ■ *Troy on the Move*
850 E Cherry St., Ste. A
  Troy, MO 63379
Ph: (636)462-8769
Fax: (636)528-3731

Co. E-mail: info@troyonthemove.com
URL: http://troyonthemove.com
Contact: Justin Butler, President
E-mail: justin@butlertomko.com
URL(s): troyonthemove.com

Released: Annual **Availability:** Print; PDF.

41644 ■ Union Chamber of Commerce
103 S Oak St.
  Union, MO 63084
Ph: (636)583-8979
Co. E-mail: uniorchamberwv@yahoo.com
URL: http://www.unionmochamber.org

Description: Businesses and individuals interested in advancing the civic, cultural, economic, industrial, and professional welfare of the Union, MO area. Sponsors Meet the Candidates Forum. Conducts Founder's Day 10 K Run. **Founded:** 1979. **Geographic Preference:** Local.

41645 ■ Versailles Area Chamber of Commerce (VACC)
109 N Monroe
  Versailles, MO 65084
Ph: (573)378-4401
Fax: (573)378-4401
Co. E-mail: info@versailleschamber.com
URL: http://versailleschamber.com
Contact: Rebekah Wright, President
E-mail: rebekah@print-wright.com
Facebook: www.facebook.com/versaillesareachamberofcommerce

Description: Promotes business and community development in Versailles, MO. Sponsors Olde Tyme Apple Festival and Christmas Lighting and Parade. **Geographic Preference:** Local.

41646 ■ Warrenton Area Chamber of Commerce
PO Box 333
  Warrenton, MO 63383
Ph: (636)456-2530
Co. E-mail: warrentoncoc@socket.net
URL: http://www.warrentoncoc.com
Contact: Katie Joyce, Co-President
Facebook: www.facebook.com/warrentonareachamber

Description: Promotes the general welfare and prosperity of the Warrenton area. **Founded:** 1923. **Geographic Preference:** Local.

41647 ■ Warsaw Area Chamber of Commerce
181 Harrison St.
  Warsaw, MO 65355
Ph: (660)438-5922
Co. E-mail: warsawchamber@outlook.com
URL: http://welcometowarsaw.com/chamber
Contact: Carrie Rieman, President
Facebook: www.facebook.com/WarsawAreaChamber
Instagram: www.instagram.com/warsawmochamberof

Description: Promotes business and community development in the Warsaw, MO area. **Geographic Preference:** Local.

41648 ■ Washington Area Chamber of Commerce
323 W Main St.
  Washington, MO 63090
Ph: (636)239-2715
Co. E-mail: info@washmo.org
URL: http://www.washmochamber.org
Contact: Jennifer Giesike, President
E-mail: jgiesike@washmo.org
Facebook: www.facebook.com/washmochamber
X (Twitter): x.com/washmochamber
Instagram: www.instagram.com/washmochamber
Pinterest: www.pinterest.com/washmochamber

Description: Promotes business and community development in the Washington, MO area. **Founded:** 1923. **Publications:** *Communicator* (Weekly). **Educational Activities:** Chamber Banquet. **Geographic Preference:** Local.

41649 ■ Waynesville-St. Robert Area Chamber of Commerce
137 St. Robert Blvd., Ste. B
  Saint Robert, MO 65584

Ph: (573)336-5121
Fax: (573)336-5472
Co. E-mail: info@wsrchamber.com
URL: http://www.waynesville-strobertchamber.com
Contact: Cecilia Murray, Executive Director
E-mail: chamberdirector@wsrchamber.com
Facebook: www.facebook.com/WaynesvilleStRobertChamber
X (Twitter): x.com/wsrchamber
YouTube: www.youtube.com/channel/UCaTPt2kfc_G7U474qBGLN5Q
Pinterest: www.pinterest.com/wsrchamber

Description: Promotes business and community development in the greater Waynesville-St. Robert, Fort Leonard Wood area. Sponsors summer film festivals, Annual Spring and Fall Golf Tournaments, Annual April Fool's Day Community Trout Fry, and Annual Leader Appreciation Breakfast. **Founded:** 1979. **Publications:** *Voice* (Monthly). **Educational Activities:** Waynesville-St. Robert Area Chamber of Commerce Luncheon (Monthly). **Awards:** Waynesville-St. Robert Area Chamber of Commerce Citizen of the Year (Annual). **Geographic Preference:** Local.

41650 ■ Webb City Area Chamber of Commerce
112 W Broadway St.
  Webb City, MO 64870
Ph: (417)673-1154
URL: http://webbcitymo.org/department/chamber-contact
Contact: Carl Francis, Contact
Facebook: www.facebook.com/webbcitychamber
X (Twitter): x.com/WC_CofC
Instagram: www.instagram.com/wcchamber

Description: Promotes business and community development in Webb City, MO. Conducts educational activities in local schools. Sponsors area festivals and the Christmas Parade in December. Promotes many activities for the young population such as the DARE program, educational activities in local schools and an annual banquet. **Geographic Preference:** Local.

41651 ■ Webster Groves-Shrewsbury-Rock Hill Area Chamber of Commerce (WGSRH)
357 Marshall Ave., Ste. 102
  Webster Groves, MO 63119
Ph: (314)962-4142
Fax: (314)962-9398
Co. E-mail: chamberinfo@go-webster.com
URL: http://www.webstershrewsburychamber.com
Contact: Chris Fowler, President
E-mail: chrisf@amadaseniorcare.com
Facebook: www.facebook.com/WebsterChamber
X (Twitter): x.com/WebsterChamber
YouTube: www.youtube.com/user/WGSAChamber

Description: Promotes business and community development in the Missouri cities of Webster Groves, Shrewsbury and surrounding area. Conducts golf tournament, business expo, community awards banquet and other events to promote its membership and community. **Founded:** 1937. **Publications:** *Business and Community Guide* (Annual); *Chamber Chronicle* (Monthly). **Awards:** Heart of the Community Award (Annual). **Geographic Preference:** Local.

41652 ■ West St. Louis County Chamber of Commerce (WSLCCC)
15965 Manchester Rd., Ste. 102
  Ellisville, MO 63011
Ph: (636)230-9900
Co. E-mail: info@westcountychamber.com
URL: http://westcountychamber.com
Contact: Lori A. Kelling, President
E-mail: lkelling@westcountychamber.com
X (Twitter): x.com/WestCoChamber
YouTube: www.youtube.com/user/westcochamber

Description: Promotes business and community development in western St. Louis County, MO. **Founded:** 1957. **Publications:** *The Enterprise* (Monthly); *West St. Louis County Chamber of Commerce--Membership Directory* (Annual). **Educational Activities:** General Membership (Monthly). **Geographic Preference:** Local.

41653 ■ Willard Area Chamber of Commerce
PO Box 384
  Willard, MO 65781
Ph: (417)742-2442
Co. E-mail: willardchamber@gmail.com
URL: http://www.willardchamber.org
Contact: Jason Knight, Co-President
Facebook: www.facebook.com/WillardAreaChamberofCommerce

Description: Promotes business and community development in the area. **Founded:** 2000. **Geographic Preference:** Local.

41654 ■ Windsor Area Chamber of Commerce
102 N Main St.
  Windsor, MO 65360
Ph: (660)647-2318
URL: http://www.windsormo.org
Contact: Austin Cannon, President

Description: Promotes business and community development in Windsor, MO. Publications: none. **Geographic Preference:** Local.

41655 ■ Wright City Area Chamber of Commerce
PO Box 444
  Wright City, MO 63390
Ph: (636)206-6191
URL: http://new.wrightcityareachamber.org
Contact: Kimberly Arbuthnot, President
Facebook: www.facebook.com/wrightcityarea.chamberofcommerce

Description: Promotes business and community development in Wright City, MO. Sponsors Strassenbash festival. **Founded:** 1857. **Geographic Preference:** Local.

MINORITY BUSINESS ASSISTANCE PROGRAMS

41656 ■ University of Missouri, Kansas City (UMKC) - Small Business and Technology Development Center (SBTDC)
4747 Troost Ave.
  Kansas City, MO 64110
Ph: (816)235-6063
Co. E-mail: sbdc@umkc.edu
URL: http://sbtdc.umkc.edu
Contact: Carmen DeHart, Regional Director
Facebook: www.facebook.com/UmkcSBTDC
X (Twitter): x.com/umkcsbtdc
YouTube: www.youtube.com/channel/UCPjHgnjCsIXqA0ioDNa5ntw

Description: Small business development. **Founded:** 1990.

FINANCING AND LOAN PROGRAMS

41657 ■ Ascension Ventures (AV)
4600 Edmundson Rd.
  Saint Louis, MO 63134
Co. E-mail: info@ascensionventures.org
URL: http://ascensionventures.org
Contact: Jamie Wehrung, Chief Administrative Officer
Linkedin: www.linkedin.com/company/ascension-ventures

Description: Healthcare venture fund focused on early- to late-stage companies. **Founded:** 2001. **Investment Policies:** Prefers companies within three to five years of a liquidating event; sustainable competitive advantage; established management team. **Industry Preferences:** Healthcare information technology and services; medical devices and diagnostics.

41658 ■ BioGenerator (BG)
4340 Duncan Ave., Ste. 100
  Saint Louis, MO 63110
Ph: (314)615-6355
Co. E-mail: info@biogeneratorventures.com
URL: http://www.biogeneratorventures.com

Contact: Allyson Mayer, Principal

Description: Supports new company formation and investment in early-stage bioscience companies in St. Louis.

41659 ■ Capital For Business Inc. (CFB)
Commerce Bancshares, Inc.
11 S Meramec Ave., Ste. 1330
  Saint Louis, MO 63105
Free: 800-453-2265
Fax: (821)234-2479
Co. E-mail: mymoney@commercebank.com
URL: http://www.commercebank.com
Contact: Bill Witzofsky, Senior Vice President
E-mail: bill.witzofsky@cfb.com

Description: Firm provides investment management services. **Founded:** 1959. **Preferred Investment Size:** $500,000 to $5,000,000. **Industry Preferences:** Internet specific, medical and health, consumer related, semiconductors and other electronics, computer hardware, communications and media.

41660 ■ Cultivation Capital
911 Washington Ave., Ste. 801
  Saint Louis, MO 63101
Ph: (314)216-2051
Co. E-mail: info@cultivationcapital.com
URL: http://cultivationcapital.com
Contact: Paul Meier, Principal
Facebook: www.facebook.com/CultivationCapital
Linkedin: www.linkedin.com/company/cultivation-capital
X (Twitter): x.com/CultivationCap

Description: Offers capital and counsel to entrepreneurs. Also operates offices in Chicago, Los Angeles, and Philadelphia. **Founded:** 2012. **Industry Preferences:** Life sciences and health tech; agriculture and food tech; software and IT,.

41661 ■ Prolog Ventures
7733 Forsyth Blvd., Ste. 1100
  Clayton, MO 63105
Co. E-mail: prolog@prologventures.com
URL: http://www.prologventures.com
Contact: Greg Johnson, Managing Director Co-Founder
X (Twitter): x.com/PrologVentures

Description: Early-stage venture capital firm focused on life sciences. Also maintains an office in New Jersey. **Founded:** 2000. **Industry Preferences:** Food and beverages; personal and household care; consumer wellness; hygiene; ag tech; diagnostics.

41662 ■ RiverVest Venture Partners
101 S Hanley Rd., Ste. 1850
  Saint Louis, MO 63105
Ph: (314)726-6700
Co. E-mail: info@rivervest.com
URL: http://www.rivervest.com
Contact: Dr. John McKearn, Managing Director
E-mail: jmckearn@rivervest.com
Linkedin: www.linkedin.com/company/rivervest-venture-partners
X (Twitter): x.com/rivervest

Description: Venture capital firm investing in early-stage life science companies. **Founded:** 2000. **Preferred Investment Size:** $500,000 to $6,000,000. **Industry Preferences:** Biotechnology, medical and health.

41663 ■ St. Louis Arch Angels
155 Carondelet Plz. Unit 902
  Saint Louis, MO 63105-0029
Ph: (314)324-3189
URL: http://www.stlouisarchangels.com
Contact: Brian J. Kinman, Chief Executive Officer
E-mail: bkinman902@gmail.com
Linkedin: www.linkedin.com/company/st-louis-arch-angels
X (Twitter): x.com/StlArchAngels

Description: Invests in high-potential startups in the St. Louis area. **Founded:** 2005.

41664 ■ Missouri

PROCUREMENT ASSISTANCE PROGRAMS

41664 ■ Missouri Procurement Technical Assistance Center (MO PTAC)
228 Gentry Hall
Columbia, MO 65211
Ph: (573)882-8058
URL: http://www.aptac-us.org/find-a-ptac/?state=MO
Contact: Jana Weitkemper, Program Manager
E-mail: weitkemperj@missouri.edu
URL(s): extension.missouri.edu/programs/missouri-procurement-technical-assistance-centers
Description: Assists businesses including small, disadvantaged and women owned firms in obtaining federal, state and local government contracts.

41665 ■ Missouri Procurement Technical Assistance Center Center for Entrepreneurship and Outreach
900 Innovation Dr., Ste. 145
Rolla, MO 65401
URL: http://extension.missouri.edu/programs/creating-entrepreneurial-communities
Description: Assists businesses including small, disadvantaged and women owned firms in obtaining federal, state and local government contracts.

41666 ■ Missouri Southern State University - Heartland Procurement Technical Assistance Center - Institute for Procurement Assistance
3950 Newman Rd.
Joplin, MO 64801
URL: http://www.mssu.edu/business-affairs/purchasing
Contact: Jeff L. Gibson, Director, Operations
E-mail: gibson-j@mssu.edu
Description: Covers activities for Kansas.

41667 ■ St. Louis Economic Development Partnership (STLP)
120 S Central Ave., Ste. 200
Saint Louis, MO 63105
Ph: (314)615-7663
Fax: (314)615-7666
Co. E-mail: info@stlpartnership.com
URL: http://stlpartnership.com
Contact: Rodney Crim, President
Facebook: www.facebook.com/STLPartnership
Linkedin: www.linkedin.com/company/stlpartnership
X (Twitter): x.com/stlpartnership
Description: Promotes business and economic development. **Founded:** 1984.

41668 ■ University of Missouri - Missouri Procurement Technical Assistance Center - Howell County Extension Center
1376 Bill Virdon Blvd.
West Plains, MO 65775
Ph: (417)256-2391
Fax: (573)884-5787
Co. E-mail: howellco@missouri.edu
URL: http://extension.missouri.edu/counties/howell
Contact: Willis Mushrush, Specialist
E-mail: mushrushw@missouri.edu
Facebook: www.facebook.com/HowellCoExt
Description: Assists businesses including small, disadvantaged and women owned firms in obtaining federal, state and local government contracts.

INCUBATORS/RESEARCH AND TECHNOLOGY PARKS

41669 ■ Capital Innovators (CI)
4240 Duncan Ave.
Saint Louis, MO 63110
Ph: (314)669-5832
Co. E-mail: info@capitalinnovators.com
URL: http://capitalinnovators.com
Contact: Judy Sindecuse, Chief Executive Officer
Facebook: www.facebook.com/CapInnovators
Linkedin: www.linkedin.com/company/capital-innovators
X (Twitter): x.com/capinnovators
Instagram: www.instagram.com/capinnovators
Description: Firm engaged of finance investment holding company with subsidiaries engaged in manufacturer of air related ducts and accessories, construction of clean rooms, laboratory, installation of environment-control exhaust systems and bio-fuel production equipment, general contractors for building construction, plumbing and air-conditioning. **Founded:** 2011.

41670 ■ Center for Emerging Technologies (CET)
20 S Sarah St.
Saint Louis, MO 63108
Co. E-mail: info@cetstl.com
URL: http://www.cetstl.org
Contact: Gabriela Ramirez-Arellano, Executive Director
E-mail: gramirezarellano@cortexstl.com
Description: Provides the infrastructure and resources needed for early-stage, high-growth companies that are developing breakthrough technologies. **Founded:** 1998.

41671 ■ Dean L. Hubbard Center for Innovation and Entrepreneurship
800 University Dr.
Maryville, MO 64468
URL: http://www.nwmissouri.edu/ag/about.htm
Description: A service-oriented business incubator connecting industry and academics which offers state-of-the-art research facilities, a commercial analytical lab, and tailored support for business acceleration. **Founded:** 2009.

41672 ■ Economic Development Center of St. Charles County Missouri (EDC)
5988 Mid Rivers Mall Dr.
Saint Charles, MO 63304
Ph: (636)441-6880
Fax: (636)441-6881
Co. E-mail: info@edcscc.com
URL: http://www.edcscc.com
Contact: Scott J. Drachnik, President
E-mail: sdrachnik@edcscc.com
Facebook: www.facebook.com/EDCSCC
Linkedin: www.linkedin.com/company/edcscc
X (Twitter): x.com/edcscc
Description: A state-of-the-art small business incubator for home-based businesses and startups. **Founded:** 1990.

41673 ■ Enactus
444 S Campbell Ave.
Springfield, MO 65806
Ph: (417)831-9505
Co. E-mail: contact@enactus.org
URL: http://enactus.org
Contact: Robyn S. Fehrman, President
Facebook: www.facebook.com/enactus
X (Twitter): x.com/enactus
Instagram: www.instagram.com/enactus
YouTube: www.youtube.com/c/EnactusOrg
Pinterest: www.pinterest.com/enactus
Description: A global non-profit organization active on more than 1,700 college campuses in more than 36 countries and territories consisting of student teams who develop projects to help create economic opportunity by teaching concepts related to free market economics, business ethics, entrepreneurship, and personal finance and success skills. **Founded:** 1975. **Educational Activities:** National Exposition. **Geographic Preference:** National.

41674 ■ The Ennovation Center
201 N Forest Ave.
Independence, MO 64050
Ph: (816)463-3532
Co. E-mail: info@ennovationcenter.com
URL: http://www.ennovationcenter.com
Contact: Danielle DuPree, Executive Director
E-mail: ddupree@inedc.biz
Facebook: www.facebook.com/ennovationcenter
X (Twitter): x.com/in_ennovation
YouTube: www.youtube.com/user/TheEnnovationCenter
Description: A business development incubator housing companies who utilize two distinct start-up specialties -- a commercial kitchen co-working space and a business technologies area with office and lab space. **Founded:** 2010.

41675 ■ Helix Center Biotech Incubator
1100 Corporate Sq.
Saint Louis, MO 63132
Ph: (314)432-2672
URL: http://stlpartnership.com/innovation-entrepreneurship/helix-center
Contact: Fatima Oberoi, Contact
E-mail: foberoi@stlpartnership.com
Description: Incubator helping to accelerate the growth of your startup, technology, or plant and life sciences businesses. Provides mentoring, financing, and collaboration services. **Founded:** 1984.

41676 ■ Hispanic Economic Development Corp. (HEDC)
1722 Holly St.
Kansas City, MO 64108
Ph: (816)221-3442
Fax: (816)221-6458
Co. E-mail: info@kchedc.org
URL: http://www.kchedc.org/hedc
Contact: Pedro Zamora, Executive Director
Facebook: www.facebook.com/kchedc
X (Twitter): x.com/kchedc
Description: HEDC utilizes its designation as a CDC to access various resources and tools that allow the organization to serve as a catalyst for change within the Latino community. **Founded:** 1993.

41677 ■ Innovation Stockyard
4221 Mitchell Ave.
Saint Joseph, MO 64507
Ph: (816)749-4012
URL: http://innovationstockyard.com
Contact: Sara Hagen, Manager
E-mail: sara.hagen@innovationstockyard.com
Description: A one-stop business incubator for those who want to start or grow any business, but specializing in the animal sciences field. Offers business and scientific consulting and facilities to help bring your idea to market.

41678 ■ Joseph Newman Innovation Center
407 S Pennsylvania Ave.
Joplin, MO 64801
Ph: (417)624-4150
Fax: (417)624-4303
Co. E-mail: info@joplincc.com
URL: http://joplincc.com/joseph-newman-innovation-center
Facebook: www.facebook.com/josephnewmaninnovationcenter
Description: Economic development tool designed to accelerate the growth and success of entrepreneurial companies through an array of business support resources and services, the centers main goal is to produce successful firms that will leave the program financially viable and freestanding. **Founded:** 2006.

41679 ■ Life Science Business Incubator at Monsanto Place
1601 S Providence Rd.
Columbia, MO 65211-3460
Ph: (573)884-0496
URL: http://missouriinnovation.com
Description: A small business incubator promoting comprehensive economic development strategy for mid-Missouri by leveraging research and innovation at the University of Missouri-Columbia in order to attract additional life science enterprises to the region and to create new life science ventures around university technologies. **Founded:** 1984.

41680 ■ Midwest Center for Law & Justice
1801 W Norton Rd., Ste. 301
Springfield, MO 65803
Description: Provider of legal services in family, civil, criminal and other segments.

STATE LISTINGS   Missouri ■ 41698

41681 ■ Missouri Enterprise
1426 E State Rte. 72
  Rolla, MO 65401
Free: 800-956-2682
Co. E-mail: info@missourienterprise.org
URL: http://www.missourienterprise.org
Contact: Dusty Cruise, President
E-mail: dcruise@missourienterprise.org
Facebook: www.facebook.com/MissouriEnterprise
Linkedin: www.linkedin.com/company/missouri-en
  terprise
X (Twitter): x.com/moenterprise
YouTube: www.youtube.com/channel/UC5J-vs
  6kPvDEjYd8vqitxxg
Description: Offers business consulting services to mid-sized manufacturing companies. **Founded:** 1989.

41682 ■ Missouri Innovation Center (MIC)
1601 S Providence Rd.
  Columbia, MO 65211-3460
Ph: (573)884-0496
Co. E-mail: mumicincubator@missouri.edu
URL: http://missouriinnovation.com
Contact: Quinten Messbarger, President
Facebook: www.facebook.com/MissouriInnova
  tionCenter
Linkedin: www.linkedin.com/company/missouri
  -innovation-center
YouTube: www.youtube.com/channel/
  UCrzShRVoss7sNENm3Txik5A
Description: Incubator that supports the life science and technology industry in mid-Missouri.

41683 ■ Missouri Rural Enterprise and Innovation Center (MREIC)
315 S Franklin St.
  Kirksville, MO 63501
Ph: (660)665-3348
Fax: (660)785-2530
URL: http://www.mreic.org
Facebook: www.facebook.com/NEMOInnova
  tionCenter
Description: Works to enhance entrepreneurship by providing a supportive infrastructure for entrepreneurs allowing them to enhance their capabilities, broaden their network and successfully grow their companies.

41684 ■ Missouri State University - The eFactory Business Incubator
1110 E Madison St.
  Springfield, MO 65897
URL: http://efactory.missouristate.edu/our-impact
Description: Provides resources, guidance, and assistance with startup activities to help businesses survive and grow during a time when they're most vulnerable.

41685 ■ Nidus Partners L.P.
1005 N Warson Rd., Ste. 401
  Saint Louis, MO 63132
Ph: (314)812-8003
Fax: (314)812-8080
URL: http://www.niduspartners.com
Contact: Mich Hein, Managing Partner
E-mail: mich@niduspartners.com
X (Twitter): x.com/NidusPartners
Description: Venture capital firm provides seed funding.

41686 ■ Northland Center for Advanced Professional Studies
2000 NE 46th St.
  Kansas City, MO 64116
Ph: (816)977-8111
URL: http://www.northlandcaps.org
Contact: Tony Reinhart, President
Facebook: www.facebook.com/NorthlandCAPS
Linkedin: www.linkedin.com/school/northland-caps
X (Twitter): x.com/NorthlandCAPS
Instagram: www.instagram.com/northland_caps

Description: Provides high school students with an innovative and entrepreneurial professional-based educational model that is designed to provide students with the skills needed to succeed in the competitive college environment and global workforce. **Founded:** 2013.

41687 ■ Ozark Foothills Business Incubator
Ozark Foothills Development Association
  3019 Fair St.
  Poplar Bluff, MO 63901
Contact: Alan Lutes, Executive Director
E-mail: alan@ofrpc.org

41688 ■ St. Charles County Economic Development Center (EDC)
5988 Mid Rivers Mall Dr.
  Saint Peters, MO 63304
Ph: (636)441-6880
Fax: (636)441-6881
Co. E-mail: info@edcscc.com
URL: http://www.edcscc.com
Contact: Scott J. Drachnik, President
E-mail: sdrachnik@edcscc.com
Facebook: www.facebook.com/EDCSCC
Linkedin: www.linkedin.com/company/edcsccmo
X (Twitter): x.com/edcscc
Description: A small business incubator working in partnership with local governments, community and business leaders, and other regional organizations to offer business financing programs, job creation, and business recruitment and retention. **Founded:** 1990.

41689 ■ St. Louis Enterprise Centers - Midtown
City of St. Louis, City Hall, 1200 Market St.
  Saint Louis, MO 63103
URL: http://www.stlouis-mo.gov/live-work/community/
  neighborhoods/midtown/index.cfm
Contact: DeAnna Murphy, Contact
Description: A small business incubator providing new and growing small businesses with affordable business space, shared support services, access to expert mentors, and valuable networking opportunities. Maintains five state-of-the-art enterprise centers.

41690 ■ Solo and Small Firm Incubator (UMKC)
500 E 52nd St.
  Kansas City, MO 64110
Ph: (816)235-1603
URL: http://law.umkc.edu/academics/tech-and-law
  -practice.html
Description: Provides hands-on assistance to recent graduates who choose to enter solo or small firm practice.

41691 ■ Southeast Innovation Center for Innovation and Entrepreneurship
SE Missouri State University
  1 University Plz.
  Cape Girardeau, MO 63701
Ph: (573)651-2000
URL: http://semo.edu/colleges-departments/business
  -computing/entrepreneurship
Contact: Alberto Davila, Contact
E-mail: adavila@semo.edu
Description: Offers new businesses access to resources that can assist them with their ideas, business plans, patent searches, marketing studies, financing, training and engineering.

41692 ■ Springfield Innovation Inc.
901 S National Ave., Carr 205
  Springfield, MO 65897
Contact: Allen Kunkel, President
Description: Supports advanced product development with a focus on advancing the competitiveness of Missouri-based industries and supporting technology based entrepreneurs while providing interdisciplinary work experiences for Missouri State University students.

41693 ■ STLVentureWorks-Grand Center
7733 Forsyth Blvd., Ste. 2200
  Saint Louis, MO 63105
Ph: (314)615-7663
Fax: (314)615-7666
URL: http://stlpartnership.com
Description: Offers speciality space for culinary-related companies. Provides office, warehouse, and production space as well as the resources to help companies from virtually any business sector thrive. **Founded:** 1984.

41694 ■ T-REX
911 Washington Ave.
  Saint Louis, MO 63101
Ph: (314)241-7500
URL: http://downtowntrex.org
Facebook: www.facebook.com/trex.stlouis
Linkedin: www.linkedin.com/company/t-rex
  -technology-entrepreneur-center
X (Twitter): x.com/DowntownTREX
Instagram: www.instagram.com/trex.stlouis
YouTube: www.youtube.com/channel/UCKuf0V4fEozl
  5IbfQtQCptA
Description: Provides startup entrepreneurs with low cost and flexible enterprise space as well as programming, mentoring, and business resources. **Founded:** 2011.

41695 ■ Think Big Partners
1712 Main St., 4th Fl.
  Kansas City, MO 64108
Contact: Herb Sih, Contact
X (Twitter): x.com/thinkbigkc
Description: Helps companies grow faster, smarter and more efficiently through a network of in-house services, community members and national partners. **Founded:** 2009.

41696 ■ UMKC Innovation Center
4747 Troost Ave.
  Kansas City, MO 64110
URL: http://umkcinnovates.com
Contact: Callie England, Director, Marketing
E-mail: cengland@umkc.edu
Description: Works with university, community, and global resources to create a hub for commercialization across the Kansas City, MO region. The center is closely aligned with the University of Missouri offices of research and economic development and technology transfer and serves faculty, students and the community in moving commercialization opportunities to market.

EDUCATIONAL PROGRAMS

41697 ■ Jefferson College-Extended Learning
1000 Viking Dr.
  Hillsboro, MO 63050
Ph: (636)481-3000
Co. E-mail: admissions@jeffco.edu
URL: http://www.jeffco.edu
Contact: Blake M. Tilley, Executive Director
Facebook: www.facebook.com/JeffersonCollege
X (Twitter): x.com/GoJeffco
Instagram: www.instagram.com/gojeffco
YouTube: www.youtube.com/user/
  JeffersonCollegeTV
Description: Offers a program/classes in small business/small business management. **Founded:** 1960.

41698 ■ St. Louis Community College Institute for Continuing Education (STLCC CE)
3221 McKelvey Rd., Ste. 250
  Bridgeton, MO 63044
Ph: (314)984-7777
Fax: (314)228-2271
Co. E-mail: cedropbox@stlcc.edu
URL: http://stlcc.edu

Description: Small Business Program offers courses designed for small business owners.

LEGISLATIVE ASSISTANCE

41699 ■ Missouri Department of Economic Development (DED)
301 W High St., Ste. 720
 Jefferson City, MO 65101
Ph: (573)751-4962
Fax: (573)526-7700
Co. E-mail: ecodev@mo.gov
URL: http://ded.mo.gov
Contact: Maggie Kost, Director (Acting)
Facebook: www.facebook.com/MissouriDepartmentofEconomicDevelopment
X (Twitter): x.com/MoEcoDevo
Description: Works to identify and solve problems specific to small business. **Founded:** 1976.

REFERENCE WORKS

41700 ■ "7.7% Workers' Comp Decrease Recommended in Missouri" in Insurance Journal (November 16, 2021)
Released: November 16, 2021. **Description:** The largest decrease in workers' compensation insurance loss costs sine 2009 is being recommended in Missouri. This is due to a decline in loss-time claim frequency since workplaces have increased safety standards. **Availability:** Online.

PUBLICATIONS

41701 ■ *Ingram's: Kansas City's Business Magazine*
2049 Wyandotte
 Kansas City, MO 64108
Ph: (816)842-9994
Fax: (816)474-1111
Co. E-mail: editorial@ingrams.com
URL: http://ingrams.com
Contact: Eric Campbell, President
URL(s): ingrams.com/home-2-2/about
Linkedin: www.linkedin.com/company/ingram%27s-magazine
X (Twitter): x.com/IngramsMagazine
Ed: Jack Cashill. **Released:** Monthly **Price:** $119.95, for print 3 years; $79.95, for print 2 years; $49.45, for print 1 year. **Description:** Business and lifestyle magazine covering Lawrence, Topeka, Overland Park, KS, and Kansas City and St. Joseph, MO. **Availability:** Print; Online.

41702 ■ *Ingram's Magazine*
2049 Wyandotte
 Kansas City, MO 64108
Ph: (816)842-9994
Fax: (816)474-1111
Co. E-mail: editorial@ingrams.com
URL: http://ingrams.com
Contact: Eric Campbell, President
Linkedin: www.linkedin.com/company/ingram%27s-magazine
X (Twitter): x.com/IngramsMagazine
Released: Monthly **Price:** $119.95, for print 3 year; $49.95, for print 1 year; $79.95, for print 2 year; $5, for back issue. **Availability:** Print; PDF; Download; Online.

41703 ■ *Kansas City Business Journal*
120 W Morehead St.
 Charlotte, NC 28202
Co. E-mail: circhelp@bizjournals.com
URL: http://www.acbj.com
Contact: Mike Olivieri, Executive Vice President
URL(s): www.bizjournals.com/kansascity
Linkedin: www.linkedin.com/company/kansas-city-business-journal
X (Twitter): x.com/KCBizjournal
Ed: Chris Curry, Brian Kaberline, Jonna Lorenz. **Released:** Weekly **Price:** $950, for 52 weeks premium unlimited; $4, for 4 weeks digital or print and digital; $220, for 1 year print and online; $380, for premium elite 52 weeks; $245, Members for nationwide access; $9, for Nationwide Access; $70, Members for print and online; $70, Members for 1 year digital; $4, Members for digital trial; $210, for 1 year online. **Description:** Local business newspaper. **Availability:** Print; PDF; Download; Online. **Type:** Full-text.

41704 ■ Kansas City Business Journal (KCBJ)
1100 Main St., Ste. 2450
 Kansas City, MO 64105
Ph: (816)421-5900
Fax: (816)472-4010
Co. E-mail: kansascity@bizjournals.com
URL: http://www.bizjournals.com/kansascity
Contact: Sarah Ventola, Director
E-mail: ventola@bizjournals.com
Facebook: www.facebook.com/KCBizJournal
Linkedin: www.linkedin.com/company/kansas-city-business-journal
X (Twitter): x.com/KCBizjournal
Instagram: www.instagram.com/kcbizjournal
Description: Publisher of journal covering business news, business events, business networking, real estate, financial services, legal services. **Founded:** 1985. **Publications:** *Kansas City Business Journal* (Weekly).

41705 ■ *St. Charles County Business Record*
7025 Albert Pick Rd.
 Greensboro, NC 27409
Ph: (612)317-9420
Free: 877-615-9536
Co. E-mail: customerservice@bridgetowermedia.com
URL: http://www.bridgetowermedia.com
Contact: Adam Reinebach, President
URL(s): molawyersmedia.com/news/st-charles
Facebook: www.facebook.com/Missouri.Lawyers.Media
Linkedin: www.linkedin.com/company/missouri-lawyers-media
Released: Daily; Monday through Sunday. **Price:** $429, Individuals for annual print and online; $35, Individuals for online monthly. **Description:** Serves as the paper of record for the local courts, the legal and business communities, and local citizens of St. Charles County, Missouri. **Availability:** Print; Online.

41706 ■ *St. Louis Business Journal*
120 W Morehead St.
 Charlotte, NC 28202
Co. E-mail: circhelp@bizjournals.com
URL: http://www.acbj.com
Contact: Mike Olivieri, Executive Vice President
URL(s): www.bizjournals.com/stlouis
Facebook: www.facebook.com/stlbj
Linkedin: www.linkedin.com/company/st-louis-business-journal
X (Twitter): x.com/stlouisbiz
Instagram: www.instagram.com/stlouisbiz
Ed: Joe Dwyer, III. **Released:** Weekly **Price:** $950, for Premium Unlimited; $380, for nationwide Access premium elite; $220, for print and online premium plus; $210, for online only premium 52 weeks. **Description:** Business newspaper. **Availability:** Print; Online. **Type:** Full-text.

41707 ■ Saint Louis Business Journal
Old Post Office
 815 Olive St., Ste. 100
 Saint Louis, MO 63101
Ph: (314)421-6200
Fax: (314)621-5031
Co. E-mail: stlouis@bizjournals.com
URL: http://www.bizjournals.com/stlouis
Contact: Robert Bobroff, President
E-mail: rbobroff@bizjournals.com
Facebook: www.facebook.com/stlbj
Linkedin: www.linkedin.com/company/st-louis-business-journal
X (Twitter): x.com/stlouisbiz
Instagram: www.instagram.com/stlouisbiz
Description: Publisher of journal and newspaper about updated and breaking business news. **Founded:** 1980.

41708 ■ Springfield Business Journal (SBJ)
2101 W Chesterfield Blvd., Ste. B105
 Springfield, MO 65807
Ph: (417)831-3238
Fax: (417)864-4901
Co. E-mail: sbj@sbj.net
URL: http://www.sbj.net
Contact: Amy Egger, Manager, Finance
E-mail: aegger@sbj.net
Facebook: www.facebook.com/sbj.net
Linkedin: www.linkedin.com/company/springfield-business-journal
X (Twitter): x.com/sbjnet
Description: Publisher of newspapers. **Founded:** 1980. **Publications:** *Springfield Business Journal: Serving Southwest Missouri* (Weekly).

PUBLISHERS

41709 ■ Michael Edmond Gray
300 Eagle Flight
 Ozark, MO 65721
Free: 800-918-7323
Fax: (888)329-2747
Co. E-mail: info@rollinghillspublishing.com
URL: http://www.autoupkeep.com
Facebook: www.facebook.com/AutoUpkeep
Linkedin: www.linkedin.com/in/michaelegray
X (Twitter): x.com/autoupkeep
Instagram: www.instagram.com/autoupkeep
YouTube: www.youtube.com/user/AutoUpkeep
Description: The company provides book publishing services with focus on non-fiction: automobiles: construction: crafts and hobbies; education; finances; real estate; and marriage and family.

41710 ■ Three House Publishing
490 Hillbrook Dr., Ste. A
 Ballwin, MO 63011
Contact: Jeremy Dennis, Owner
Description: Publishes course materials. It also publishes novels and short stories.

INFORMATION SERVICES

41711 ■ Kauffman Entrepreneurs
4801 Rockhill Rd.
 Kansas City, MO 64110
URL: http://www.entrepreneurship.org
Facebook: www.facebook.com/kauffmaneship
X (Twitter): x.com/eship
Description: Online resource helps develop ideas and start businesses.

RESEARCH CENTERS

41712 ■ Missouri State University - Center for Business and Economic Development (CBED)
901 S National Ave.
 Springfield, MO 65897
URL: http://www.missouristate.edu/21cent/themebus.html
Description: Integral unit of School of Business at Missouri State University. Offers consulting for the state of Missouri; small business development center services and assists inventors and manufacturers and minority manufacturers. **Scope:** Business. Conducts contract research and serves as an umbrella organization in the School for small business development projects, research activities, and

STATE LISTINGS

coordination of educational and training programs.
Educational Activities: CBED Management Development Institute Series; CBED Professional Development Seminars.

EARLY STAGE FINANCING

41713 ■ Centennial Investors (CI)
1601 S Providence Rd.
Columbia, MO 65211-3460
Ph: (573)818-2929
URL: http://www.centennialinvestors.com
Contact: Steve Guthrie, President
Description: Offers early-stage funding for high-potential companies primarily in mid-Missouri. **Founded:** 2006. **Preferred Investment Size:** $150,000 to $500,000. **Investment Policies:** Technology- or science-based companies; prefers mid-Missouri; three- to seven-year exit strategy.

VENTURE CAPITAL FIRM

41714 ■ Five Elms Capital
4801 Main St., Ste. 700
Kansas City, MO 64112
Ph: (913)953-8960
Co. E-mail: ws@fiveelms.com
URL: http://www.fiveelms.com
Contact: Austin Gideon, Partner
Linkedin: www.linkedin.com/company/five-elms-capital
Description: Capital investment firm focusing on small to mid-range B2B software companies. Investment ranges between $10 and $150 million. **Founded:** 2006.

Montana

ASSOCIATIONS AND OTHER ORGANIZATIONS

41715 ■ Association of Fundraising Professionals Montana Chapter (AFP MT)
PO Box 151
Billings, MT 59103
Ph: (406)237-6149
Co. E-mail: afpmontana@gmail.com
URL: http://community.afpnet.org/afpmtmontanachapter/home
Contact: Melissa Dulin, President
Facebook: www.facebook.com/AFPMT
Description: Fosters the development and growth of fundraising professionals. Promotes high ethical standards in the fundraising profession. Provides training opportunities for fundraising professionals. **Geographic Preference:** State.

41716 ■ Montana Agricultural Business Association (MABA)
PO Box 7325
Helena, MT 59604
Ph: (406)227-3523
Fax: (406)227-3745
Co. E-mail: mabamgea@gmail.com
URL: http://www.mtagbiz.org
Contact: Jake Yates, President
Facebook: www.facebook.com/MontanaAgriculturalBusinessAssociation
X (Twitter): x.com/maba_ag
Description: Seeks to strengthen the U.S. agricultural sectors. Facilitates American agribusiness participation in agricultural trade and development programs. Raises public awareness of agriculture's vital importance in national and global economic health. **Geographic Preference:** State.

41717 ■ National Federation of Independent Business Montana
Helena, MT 59601
Ph: (406)899-5659
URL: http://www.nfib.com/montana
Contact: Ronda Wiggers, Director
Description: Represents small and independent businesses. Aims to promote and protect the rights of members to own, operate and grow their businesses. **Geographic Preference:** State.

SMALL BUSINESS DEVELOPMENT CENTERS

41718 ■ Billings Small Business Development Center
222 N 32nd St., Ste. 200
Billings, MT 59101
URL: http://sbdc.mt.gov/Locations/Billingswww.bigskyeconomicdevelopment.org/small-business/sbdc
Description: Represents and promotes the small business sector. Provides management assistance to current and prospective small business owners. Helps to improve management skills and expand the products and services of members. **Geographic Preference:** Local.

41719 ■ Bozeman Small Business Development Center
865 Technology Blvd., Ste. A
Bozeman, MT 59718
URL: http://sbdc.mt.gov/Locations/Bozeman
Contact: Kristi Gee, Regional Director
E-mail: kgee@prosperamt.org
Description: Represents and promotes the small business sector. Provides management assistance to current and prospective small business owners. Helps to improve management skills and expand the products and services of members. **Geographic Preference:** Local.

41720 ■ Great Falls Small Business Development Center
405 3rd St. Northwest, Ste. 203
Great Falls, MT 59404
URL: http://sbdc.mt.gov/Locations/Great-Falls
Contact: Jason Nitschke, Contact
E-mail: jnitschke@growgreatfalls.org
Description: Represents and promotes the small business sector. Provides management assistance to current and prospective small business owners. Helps to improve management skills and expand the products and services of members. **Geographic Preference:** Local.

41721 ■ Havre Small Business Development Center (SBDC)
c/o Joe LaPlante, Director of Small Business Development
48 2nd Ave.
Havre, MT 59501
Ph: (406)265-9226
Co. E-mail: jlaplante@bearpaw.org
URL: http://www.bearpaw.org/sbdc
Contact: Joe LaPlante, Director
E-mail: jlaplante@bearpaw.org
URL(s): sbdc.mt.gov/Locations/Havre
Description: Provides management assistance to current and prospective small business owners in Havre. **Geographic Preference:** Local.

41722 ■ Helena Small Business Development Center
301 S Pk. Ave.
Helena, MT 59601
Fax: (406)447-6376
URL: http://sbdc.mt.gov/Locations/Helena
Contact: Ryan Loomis, Contact
X (Twitter): x.com/mtsbdc
Description: Provides management assistance to current and prospective small business owners in Helena. **Geographic Preference:** Local.

41723 ■ Kalispell Small Business Development Center
777 Grandview Dr.
Kalispell, MT 59901
Ph: (406)756-3836
URL: http://americasbdc.org/find-your-sbdc
Contact: Robert Driscoll, Regional Director
E-mail: rdriscoll@fvcc.edu
Description: Provides management assistance to current and prospective small business owners in Kalispell. **Geographic Preference:** Local.

41724 ■ Missoula Small Business Development Center
32 Campus Dr.
Missoula, MT 59812
Ph: (406)243-4770
URL: http://www.umt.edu/sbdc
Contact: Jennifer Stephens, Director
E-mail: jennifer.stephens@mso.umt.edu
URL(s): sbdc.mt.gov/Locations/Missoula
Facebook: www.facebook.com/MissoulaSBDC
LinkedIn: www.linkedin.com/company/missoulasbdc
X (Twitter): x.com/missoulasbdc
YouTube: www.youtube.com/channel/UCnEwog8EwDM9V3szdLigE1g
Description: Represents and promotes the small business sector. Provides management assistance to current and prospective small business owners. Helps to improve management skills and expand the products and services of members. **Geographic Preference:** Local.

41725 ■ Montana Small Business Development Center (MT)
301 S Pk. Ave.
Helena, MT 59620-0533
Ph: (406)841-2746
Fax: (406)841-2871
Co. E-mail: mtsbdc@mt.gov
URL: http://sbdc.mt.gov
Contact: Julie Jaksha, President
E-mail: jjaksha@ascentbank.com
Facebook: www.facebook.com/MontanaSBDC
X (Twitter): x.com/mtsbdc
Description: Focuses on counseling in areas such as financial analysis, business planning, training and workshops and loan packaging assistance to help small businesses achieve their goals of growth, expansion, innovation and success. **Geographic Preference:** State.

41726 ■ Southeastern Montana Small Business Development Center
301 S Pk. Ave.
Helena, MT 59601
Ph: (406)841-2870
Fax: (406)841-2871
Co. E-mail: mtsbdc@mt.gov
URL: http://sbdc.mt.gov
Facebook: www.facebook.com/MontanaSBDC
X (Twitter): x.com/mtsbdc
Description: Represents and promotes the small business sector. Provides management assistance to current and prospective small business owners. Helps to improve management skills and expand the products and services of members. **Geographic Preference:** Local.

STATE LISTINGS

41727 ■ Wolf Point Small Business Development Center
233 Cascade St.
  Wolf Point, MT 59201-1409
Ph: (406)653-2590
Co. E-mail: sbdc@gndc.org
URL: http://gndc.org/small-business-development-center
Contact: Shandy Hanks, Director
Description: Represents and promotes the small business sector. Provides management assistance to current and prospective small business owners. Helps to improve management skills and expand the products and services of members. **Geographic Preference:** Local.

SMALL BUSINESS ASSISTANCE PROGRAMS

41728 ■ Big Sky Economic Development (BSED) [Montana Procurement Technical Assistance Center]
201 N Broadway
  Billings, MT 59101
Ph: (406)256-6871
Fax: (406)256-6877
Co. E-mail: contact@bigskyeconomicdevelopment.org
URL: http://bigskyeconomicdevelopment.org
Contact: Steve Arveschoug, Executive Director
E-mail: stevea@bigskyeda.org
Facebook: www.facebook.com/bigskyed
Linkedin: www.linkedin.com/company/big-sky-economic-development
Instagram: www.instagram.com/lifeatbsed
YouTube: www.youtube.com/channel/UCYjFV2K9KD3TCGnBqxJ2RNQ/videos
Description: Offers U.S. Customs services, bonded and general warehouse storage, no inventory tax, and licensing brokerage services to shippers, wholesalers, and manufacturers. Access is provided to international and domestic shippers. **Founded:** 1989.

41729 ■ Montana Department of Agriculture - Agricultural Development Div. (ADD)
302 N Roberts
  Helena, MT 59601
Ph: (406)444-2402
Fax: (406)444-9442
Co. E-mail: agr@mt.gov
URL: http://agr.mt.gov/About/Agricultural-Development-Division
Description: Provides market research and other assistance to Montana's agricultural producers through identification, analysis, and direction in development of both foreign and domestic markets.

41730 ■ Montana Department of Commerce - Business Resources Div.
301 S Pk. Ave.
  Helena, MT 59620-0501
URL: http://brand.mt.gov
Description: Publicizes and advertises Montana to firms planning relocations or expansions.

41731 ■ Montana Department of Commerce - Census and Economic Information Center (CEIC)
301 S Pk. Ave.
  Helena, MT 59620-0501
Ph: (406)841-2740
URL: http://ceic.mt.gov
Contact: Mary Craigle, Bureau Chief
E-mail: mcraigle@mt.gov
Description: Provides population and economic information to businesses, government agencies, and the general public for research, planning, and decision-making purposes. **Scope:** Census information. **Founded:** 1970.

41732 ■ Montana Department of Commerce - Community Development Div. (CDD)
301 S Pk. Ave.
  Helena, MT 59620-0523
Ph: (406)841-2770

Fax: (406)841-2771
URL: http://comdev.mt.gov
Description: Provides assistance to cities, towns, counties, and tribal governments in planning and carrying out effective economic development programs specifically designed to meet local needs.

41733 ■ Montana Department of Commerce - Montana Office of Tourism and Business Development - Office of Trade and International Relations
301 S Park Ave.
  Helena, MT 59620-0501
URL: http://business.mt.gov/Business-Assistance/Export-Montana/About
Contact: Angelyn DeYoung, Manager
E-mail: adeyoung@mt.gov
Description: Enhances sales of Montana goods and services in international markets and encourages tourism promotion and reverse investment opportunities. Also offers one-stop technical assistance to businesses wishing to enter foreign markets.

41734 ■ Montana Department of Commerce - Office of Trade & International Relations - Business Resources Division - Made in Montana Program
301 S Pk. Ave.
  Helena, MT 59601
Ph: (406)841-2757
Fax: (406)841-2701
Co. E-mail: madeinmontana@mt.gov
URL: http://www.madeinmontanausa.com
Facebook: www.facebook.com/MadeinMontanaUSA
Instagram: www.instagram.com/madeinmontanausa
Description: Works with individual small businesses to develop and expand outlets for products manufactured or processed in Montana.

41735 ■ University of Montana (UM) - Montana Business Connections
32 Campus Dr.
  Missoula, MT 59812
URL: http://www.umt.edu/research/outreach/researchpubs/MBC.php
Description: Seeks to use the Montana University System to link business owners and entrepreneurs with information, resources, and expertise. **Founded:** 1893.

SCORE OFFICES

41736 ■ Billings SCORE
402 N Broadway
  Billings, MT 59101
Ph: (406)927-7640
Co. E-mail: billings.score@scorevolunteer.org
URL: http://billings.score.org
Facebook: www.facebook.com/SCOREBillings
X (Twitter): x.com/SCOREBillings
Founded: 1964.

41737 ■ Butte SCORE
1000 George St.
  Butte, MT 59701
Ph: (406)723-3177
URL: http://www.score.org/westernmontana/about/mentoring-locations

41738 ■ Great Falls SCORE
100 1st Ave. N
  Great Falls, MT 59401
URL: http://www.score.org/westernmontana

41739 ■ Missoula SCORE
2501 S Catlin St., Ste. 205
  Missoula, MT 59801
Ph: (406)442-4986
URL: http://www.score.org/find-location?state=MT

41740 ■ SCORE - Billings
402 N Broadway.
  Billings, MT 59102
Ph: (406)927-7640
Co. E-mail: billings.score@scorevolunteer.org
URL: http://billings.score.org
Contact: Al Jones, Chairman

Facebook: www.facebook.com/SCOREBillings
Linkedin: www.linkedin.com/company/score-mentors-billings
X (Twitter): x.com/SCOREBillings
Description: Provides professional guidance and information to maximize the success of existing and emerging small businesses. Offers business counseling and workshops. **Founded:** 1964.

41741 ■ SCORE - Bozeman
2000 Commerce Way
  Bozeman, MT 59715
Ph: (406)586-5421
Fax: (406)586-8286
Co. E-mail: scorebozeman@gmail.com
URL: http://bozeman.score.org
Facebook: www.facebook.com/SCOREBozeman
Linkedin: www.linkedin.com/company/score-mentors-bozeman
Description: Serves as volunteer program in which working and retired business management professionals provide free business counseling to men and women who are considering starting a small business, encountering problems with their business, or expanding their business. Offers free one-on-one counseling, online counseling and low cost workshops on a variety of business topics. **Geographic Preference:** Local.

41742 ■ SCORE - Great Falls
225 Cruse Ave., Ste. D
  Helena, MT 59601
Ph: (406)461-9856
URL: http://greatfalls.score.org
Description: Provides professional guidance and information to maximize the success of existing and emerging small businesses. Offers business counseling and workshops.

41743 ■ SCORE - Kalispell
15 Depot Pk.
  Kalispell, MT 59901
Ph: (406)755-2449
URL: http://westernmontana.score.org/kalispell
Description: Provides professional guidance and information to maximize the success of existing and emerging small businesses. Offers business counseling and workshops.

41744 ■ SCORE - Missoula
2501 S Catlin St. Ste. 205
  Missoula, MT 59801
Ph: (406)442-4986
URL: http://westernmontana.score.org/missoula
Description: Provides professional guidance and information to maximize the success of existing and emerging small businesses. Offers business counseling and workshops.

41745 ■ SCORE - Western Montana
225 Cruse Ave., Ste. D
  Helena, MT 59601
Ph: (406)461-9856
Co. E-mail: help@score.org
URL: http://westernmontana.score.org
Facebook: www.facebook.com/SCOREWesternMontana
Linkedin: www.linkedin.com/company/western-montana-score
X (Twitter): x.com/SCOREMentors
YouTube: www.youtube.com/user/SCORESmallBusiness
Pinterest: www.pinterest.com/scorementors
Description: Unites active and retired business management professionals with men and women who are considering starting a small business, encountering problems with their business, or expanding their business. Serves Helena, Butte, Kalispell, Missoula and White Sulphur Springs. **Founded:** 1964.

BETTER BUSINESS BUREAUS

41746 ■ Better Business Bureau Great West + Pacific [BBB Great West + Pacific]
PO Box 191279
  Boise, ID 83719

Ph: (208)342-4649
URL: http://www.bbb.org/local-bbb/bbb-great-west-pacific
Linkedin: www.linkedin.com/company/bbbgwp
Instagram: www.instagram.com/bbbgwp
YouTube: www.youtube.com/bbbgwp
Description: Seeks to promote and foster the highest ethical relationship between businesses and the public through voluntary self-regulation, consumer and business education, and service excellence. Provides information to help consumers and businesses make informed purchasing decisions and avoid costly scams and frauds; settles consumer complaints through arbitration and other means. **Geographic Preference:** State.

CHAMBERS OF COMMERCE

41747 ■ Anaconda Chamber of Commerce
306 E Pk. Ave.
Anaconda, MT 59711
Ph: (406)563-2400
Co. E-mail: info@discoveranaconda.com
URL: http://discoveranaconda.com
Description: Promotes business and community development in Anaconda, MT. Sponsors annual Christmas Stroll, Chocolate Festival, and Wayne Estes Northwest Basketball Championship. **Founded:** 1934. **Geographic Preference:** Local.

41748 ■ Baker Chamber of Commerce and Agriculture
115 S Main St.
Baker, MT 59313
Ph: (406)778-2266
Co. E-mail: bakerchamber@midrivers.com
URL: http://www.bakermt.com
Contact: Melissa Higbee, Executive Director
Facebook: www.facebook.com/bakerchamber
Description: Promotes business and community development in Baker, MT area. **Founded:** 1910. **Geographic Preference:** Local.

41749 ■ Beaverhead Chamber of Commerce
10 W Reeder St.
Dillon, MT 59725
Ph: (406)683-5511
Co. E-mail: info@beaverheadchamber.org
URL: http://www.beaverheadchamber.org
Contact: Roxanne Engellant, President
Facebook: www.facebook.com/BeaverheadChamberofCommerce
Description: Promotes business and community development in Beaverhead County, MT. Sponsors Rancher Roundup festival. **Founded:** 1948. **Publications:** *Beaverhead County, Montana* (Annual); *Recreational Opportunities and Information in Dillon and Beaverhead County, Montana*; *Welcome Guide* (Annual). **Geographic Preference:** Local.

41750 ■ Belgrade Chamber of Commerce (BCC)
10 E Main St.
Belgrade, MT 59714
Ph: (406)388-1616
Co. E-mail: info@belgradechamber.org
URL: http://www.belgradechamber.org
Contact: Andrew Cetraro, Co-President
Facebook: www.facebook.com/BelgradeChamber406
X (Twitter): x.com/BelgradeChamber
Description: Strives to serve its members by promoting business, economic, and community development in Belgrade, MT. **Founded:** 1963. **Publications:** *Belgrade Montana, Community Profile and Chamber News*; *Chamber Update*. **Geographic Preference:** Local.

41751 ■ Bigfork Area Chamber of Commerce (BACC)
PO Box 237
Bigfork, MT 59911
Ph: (406)837-5888
Co. E-mail: info@bigfork.org
URL: http://bigfork.org
Contact: Diane Kautzman, President
E-mail: diane@bigfork.org
Facebook: www.facebook.com/BigforkChamberofCommerce
Instagram: www.instagram.com/bigforkmontana
YouTube: www.youtube.com/channel/UCZK0BNhmt0lnVCJM4_1rmzg
Description: Promotes business and community development in the Bigfork, MT area. Encourages tourism. **Founded:** 1970. **Geographic Preference:** Local.

41752 ■ Billings Area Chamber of Commerce
815 S 27th St.
Billings, MT 59101
Ph: (406)245-4111
Co. E-mail: info@billingschamber.com
URL: http://www.billingschamber.com
Contact: John Brewer, President
E-mail: john@billingschamber.com
Facebook: www.facebook.com/BillingsChamberofCommerceCVB
Instagram: www.instagram.com/billingschamber
YouTube: www.youtube.com/user/BillingsChamberCVB
Description: Promotes business and community development in the Billings, MT area. **Geographic Preference:** Local.

41753 ■ Bitterroot Valley Chamber of Commerce
105 E Main St.
Hamilton, MT 59840
Ph: (406)363-2400
Fax: (406)363-2402
Co. E-mail: localinfo@bvchamber.com
URL: http://bitterrootchamber.com
Contact: Bridger Biggins, President
Facebook: www.facebook.com/Bitterroot-Valley-Chamber-of-Commerce-103451483020846
X (Twitter): x.com/visitbitterroot
Instagram: www.instagram.com/visitbitterrootvalley
Description: Promotes business and community development in the Bitterroot Valley, MT area. Sponsors Microbrew Festival and Winterfest. **Founded:** 1913. **Publications:** *Bitterroot Business News* (Quarterly). **Geographic Preference:** Local.

41754 ■ Bozeman Area Chamber of Commerce (BACC)
2000 Commerce Way
Bozeman, MT 59715
Ph: (406)586-5421
Fax: (406)586-8286
Co. E-mail: info@bozemanchamber.com
URL: http://bozemanchamber.com
Contact: Daryl Schliem, Chief Executive Officer
Facebook: www.facebook.com/bozemanchamberofcommerce
Linkedin: www.linkedin.com/company/bozeman-area-chamber-of-commerce/about
X (Twitter): x.com/BozemanChamber
Instagram: www.instagram.com/bozemanchamberofcommerce
YouTube: www.youtube.com/channel/UCk_4NBBe5d3iKc0X2KIFB9A
Pinterest: www.pinterest.co.uk/pin/422494008768100032
Description: Promotes business and community development in the Bozeman, MT area. Sponsors festival. **Founded:** 1910. **Publications:** *Bozeman Visitor Guide* (Periodic); *Gallatin Valley Business* (Monthly). **Awards:** Bozeman Area Chamber of Commerce Community Excellence Award (Annual). **Geographic Preference:** Local.

41755 ■ Butte-Silver Bow Chamber of Commerce
1000 George St.
Butte, MT 59701
Free: 800-735-6814
Fax: (406)723-1215
Co. E-mail: marketing@buttechamber.org
URL: http://www.buttechambersite.org
Contact: Mark Johnston, President
E-mail: mjohnston@bankofbutte.com
Facebook: www.facebook.com/ButteChamberofCommerce
X (Twitter): x.com/ButteChamber
Description: Promotes business and community development in Silver Bow County, MT. Sponsors competitions. Serves as a Convention and Visitor Bureau for travel in Montana. **Founded:** 1912. **Publications:** *The Progress* (Monthly); *Visitors' Guide* (Annual). **Geographic Preference:** Local.

41756 ■ *Chamber News*
100 1st Ave., N
Great Falls, MT 59401
Ph: (406)761-4434
Fax: (406)761-6129
Co. E-mail: info@greatfallschamber.org
URL: http://www.greatfallschamber.org
Contact: Shane Etzwiler, President
E-mail: setzwiler@greatfallschamber.org
URL(s): www.greatfallschamber.org/publications
Released: Weekly **Availability:** PDF; Online.

41757 ■ Circle Chamber of Commerce and Agriculture
PO Box 321
Circle, MT 59215
Ph: (406)485-4782
Co. E-mail: chamber.circle.montana@gmail.com
URL: http://www.circle-montana.com
Contact: Jana Hance, Contact
Facebook: www.facebook.com/circle.chamber
Description: Promotes business and community development in Circle, MT. **Geographic Preference:** Local.

41758 ■ Conrad Area Chamber of Commerce
12 5th Ave. SE
Conrad, MT 59425
Ph: (406)271-7791
Co. E-mail: chamber@3rivers.net
URL: http://www.conradmt.com
Contact: Barbie Killion, Executive Director
Facebook: www.facebook.com/Conrad-Area-Chamber-of-Commerce-294320643954654
Description: Promotes business and community development and tourism in Conrad, MT. Sponsors Art on Main festival and Farm and Ranch Appreciation Day. Organizes retail promotions. **Founded:** 1965. **Publications:** *Live Wire* (Monthly). **Geographic Preference:** Local.

41759 ■ Culbertson Chamber of Commerce
210 Broadway
Culbertson, MT 59218
Ph: (406)787-5271
URL: http://www.culbertsonmt.com
Facebook: www.facebook.com/townofculbertson
Description: Promotes business and community development in Culbertson, MT area. **Founded:** 1887. **Geographic Preference:** Local.

41760 ■ Cut Bank Area Chamber of Commerce
PO Box 1243
Cut Bank, MT 59427
Ph: (406)873-4041
URL: http://www.cutbankchamber.com
Contact: Stephanie Eney, Vice President
Facebook: www.facebook.com/cutbankchamber
Description: Promotes business and community development in the Cut Bank, MT area. **Geographic Preference:** Local.

41761 ■ Daniels County Chamber of Commerce and Agriculture
120 Main St.
Scobey, MT 59263
Ph: (406)487-2061
Co. E-mail: scobey@nemont.net
URL: http://www.scobeymt.com
Contact: Tim Rask, President
Description: Works to promote a healthy economic environment. **Geographic Preference:** Local.

41762 ■ Ennis Area Chamber of Commerce
201 E Main St.
Ennis, MT 59729
Ph: (406)682-4388
Co. E-mail: info@ennischamber.com
URL: http://www.ennischamber.com

Contact: Bruce Eiting, President
Facebook: www.facebook.com/
EnnisChamberofCommerce
Description: Promotes business and community development in Ennis, MT. **Founded:** 1991. **Geographic Preference:** Local.

41763 ■ Eureka Area Chamber of Commerce (EACC)
11 Dewey Ave.
Eureka, MT 59917
Ph: (406)297-4636
Co. E-mail: eurekachamber01@gmail.com
URL: http://welcome2eureka.com
Contact: Fern Sartori, President
Facebook: www.facebook.com/EurekaMontanaChamber
Description: Promotes business and community development in Eureka, MT area. **Geographic Preference:** Local.

41764 ■ Fort Benton Chamber of Commerce
PO Box 12
Fort Benton, MT 59442
Ph: (406)622-3864
Co. E-mail: info@fortbentonchamber.org
URL: http://www.fortbentonchamber.org
Contact: Bethany DeBorde, Secretary
E-mail: riverpressnews@gmail.com
Facebook: www.facebook.com/FortBentonChamber
Description: Promotes business and community development in Fort Benton, MT area. **Founded:** 1846. **Geographic Preference:** Local.

41765 ■ Gardiner Chamber of Commerce
216 Pk. St.
Gardiner, MT 59030
Ph: (406)848-7971
Co. E-mail: info@gardinerchamber.com
URL: http://www.gardinerchamber.com
Contact: Mike Skelton, President
Description: Promotes business and community development in Gardiner, MT. **Geographic Preference:** Local.

41766 ■ Garfield County Chamber of Commerce and Agriculture
Main St.
Jordan, MT 59337
Contact: Candy Murnion, Contact
Facebook: www.facebook.com/people/Garfield-County-MT/100063547393594
Description: Promotes business and community development in Garfield County, MT area. **Geographic Preference:** Local.

41767 ■ Glasgow Chamber of Commerce Newsletter
54147 US Hwy. 2., Ste. 2
Glasgow, MT 59230
Ph: (406)228-2222
Fax: (406)228-2244
Co. E-mail: chamber@nemont.net
URL: http://www.glasgowchamber.net
Contact: Gregg Hunter, President
URL(s): www.glasgowchamber.net/join-the-chamber.html
Availability: Online.

41768 ■ Glasgow Area Chamber of Commerce and Agriculture
54147 US Hwy. 2., Ste. 2
Glasgow, MT 59230
Ph: (406)228-2222
Fax: (406)228-2244
Co. E-mail: chamber@nemont.net
URL: http://www.glasgowchamber.net
Contact: Gregg Hunter, President
Facebook: www.facebook.com/Glasgow-Area-Chamber-of-Commerce-Agriculture-Inc-216055981302
Description: Promotes agricultural, business, and community development in the Valley County, MT area. Sponsors Montana Governor's Cup Walleye Tournament and longest Dam run. **Founded:** 1887. **Publications:** Glasgow Chamber of Commerce Newsletter. **Geographic Preference:** Local.

41769 ■ Glendive Chamber of Commerce and Agriculture (GCCA)
808 N Merrill Ave.
Glendive, MT 59330
Ph: (406)377-5601
Co. E-mail: chamber@midrivers.com
URL: http://www.glendivechamber.com
Contact: Denny Malone, President
Facebook: www.facebook.com/glendive.chamber
Instagram: www.instagram.com/glendivechamberofficial
Description: Promotes business and community development in Glendive, MT. **Founded:** 1900. **Geographic Preference:** Local.

41770 ■ Great Falls Area Chamber of Commerce
100 1st Ave., N
Great Falls, MT 59401
Ph: (406)761-4434
Fax: (406)761-6129
Co. E-mail: info@greatfallschamber.org
URL: http://www.greatfallschamber.org
Contact: Shane Etzwiler, President
E-mail: setzwiler@greatfallschamber.org
Facebook: www.facebook.com/GreatFallsChamber
Linkedin: www.linkedin.com/company/greatfallschamber
Instagram: www.instagram.com/greatfallschamber
Description: Supports a strong local economy, promotes the community, represents business to government and provides networking and relationship-building opportunities. **Founded:** 1935. **Publications:** Chamber News (Weekly). **Geographic Preference:** Local.

41771 ■ Hardin Area Chamber of Commerce and Agriculture
10 E Railway st.
Hardin, MT 59034
Ph: (406)665-1672
Co. E-mail: hardinchamber@gmail.com
URL: http://www.hardinmtchamber.com
Contact: Violet Hankel, President
Facebook: www.facebook.com/hardinchambermt
Description: Promotes business and community development in Big Horn County, MT. Operates information center for new residents and tourists. Makes available demographic, legislative, and statistical information. Sponsors community programs. Distributes informational materials regarding tourist attractions in the area. Provides legislative advocacy and promotional activities. Supports Operation Sparkle. Sponsors Little Big Horn Days, Fourth of July events, and Christmas decorations. **Geographic Preference:** Local.

41772 ■ Havre Area Chamber of Commerce (HACC)
130 5th Ave.
Havre, MT 59501
Ph: (406)265-4383
URL: http://havrechamber.com
Facebook: www.facebook.com/HavreAreaChamberofCommerce
Description: Promotes business and community development in Havre, MT. **Founded:** 1909. **Geographic Preference:** Local.

41773 ■ Helena Area Chamber of Commerce (HACC)
225 Cruse Ave., Ste. A
Helena, MT 59601
Ph: (406)442-4120
Fax: (406)447-1532
Co. E-mail: info@helenachamber.com
URL: http://www.helenachamber.com
Contact: Katie Nichols, Director, Communications Director, Marketing
Facebook: www.facebook.com/HelenaAreaChamberofCommerce
Instagram: www.instagram.com/helenaareachamberofcommerce
Description: Promotes business and community development in the Helena, MT area. Encourages tourism. **Founded:** 1890. **Publications:** Guide to Helena Living and Business (Annual); Helena Business (Monthly). **Awards:** Helena Area Chamber Business of the Year (Annual); Helena Area Chamber Volunteer of the Year (Annual); Helena Area Chamber Business Person of the Year. **Geographic Preference:** Local.

41774 ■ Kalispell Chamber of Commerce
15 Depot Pk.
Kalispell, MT 59901
Ph: (406)758-2800
Co. E-mail: info@kalispellchamber.com
URL: http://www.kalispellchamber.com
Contact: Joe Unterreiner, Co-President
E-mail: joe@kalispellchamber.com
Facebook: www.facebook.com/kallispellchamber
X (Twitter): x.com/kalispellchambr
Instagram: www.instagram.com/kalispellchamber
YouTube: www.youtube.com/user/kalispellchamber
Description: Free assistance to help Montana businesses obtain city, county, state, or federal government contracts serving Flathead, Lake, Sanders, and Lincoln Counties. **Founded:** 1987. **Publications:** Chamber News. **Geographic Preference:** Local.

41775 ■ Lakeside-Somers Chamber of Commerce
7191 US Hwy. 93 S (within W Shore Community Library)
Lakeside, MT 59922
Co. E-mail: lakesidesomers@gmail.com
URL: http://www.lakesidesomerschamber.org
Contact: David Fetveit, President
E-mail: david@twre.com
Facebook: www.facebook.com/LakesideSomers
Instagram: www.instagram.com/lakesidesomers
Description: Promotes business and community development in Lakeside, MT. Sponsors community fair and Christmas tree lighting/decoration contest. Coordinates winter activities through an event called "Winterfest". **Geographic Preference:** Local.

41776 ■ Laurel Chamber of Commerce
108 E Main
Laurel, MT 59044
Ph: (406)628-8105
Co. E-mail: laurelchamber@laurelmontana.org
URL: http://www.laurelmontana.org
Contact: Karen Black, President
Facebook: www.facebook.com/LaurelMontanaChamberofCommerce
Linkedin: www.linkedin.com/in/laurel-chamber-of-commerce-21696719
Description: Promotes business and community development in Laurel, MT. **Founded:** 1908. **Geographic Preference:** Local.

41777 ■ Lewistown Area Chamber of Commerce
408 E Main St.
Lewistown, MT 59457
Ph: (406)535-5436
Free: 866-912-3980
Co. E-mail: lewchamb@midrivers.com
URL: http://www.lewistownchamber.com
Facebook: www.facebook.com/LewistownChamber
Description: Promotes agriculture, business, and community development in Lewistown and the Central Montana area. **Founded:** 1908. **Publications:** The Heartbeat (Monthly). **Geographic Preference:** Local.

41778 ■ Libby Area Chamber of Commerce (LACC)
905 W 9th St.
Libby, MT 59923
Ph: (406)293-4167
Co. E-mail: info@libbychamber.org
URL: http://www.libbychamber.org
Contact: Bruce Vincent, President
Facebook: www.facebook.com/LibbyAreaChamber
Description: Promotes natural resource, business, and community development in the Libby, MT area. **Founded:** 2019. **Geographic Preference:** Local.

41779 ■ Lincoln Valley Chamber of Commerce (LVCC)
PO Box 985
Lincoln, MT 59639
Ph: (406)362-4949
URL: http://lincolnmontana.com
Contact: Greg Smith, Owner
Facebook: www.facebook.com/Lincoln-Valley-Chamber-of-Commerce-781469521882322
Description: Promotes business and community development in the Lincoln, MT area. **Founded:** 1976. **Geographic Preference:** Local.

41780 ■ Livingston Area Chamber of Commerce (LACC)
303 E Pk. St.
Livingston, MT 59047
Ph: (406)222-0850
Fax: (406)222-0852
URL: http://www.livingston-chamber.com
Contact: Jennifer Estes, Chairman
E-mail: allblingedout@gmail.com
Facebook: www.facebook.com/visitlivingstonmt
Instagram: www.instagram.com/livingstonnjchamber
Description: Promotes business and community development in the Livingston, MT area. **Founded:** 1944. **Publications:** *Chamber Connections* (Monthly). **Geographic Preference:** Local.

41781 ■ Manhattan Area Chamber of Commerce
112 S Broadway
Manhattan, MT 59741
Ph: (406)284-4162
Co. E-mail: chamber@manhattanareachamber.com
URL: http://www.manhattanareachamber.com
Contact: Betsy Mancuso, President
Facebook: www.facebook.com/manhattanareachambermt
Description: Fosters the changing environment for business success that enhances the quality of life in the Manhattan, MT area. **Founded:** 1988. **Geographic Preference:** Local.

41782 ■ Miles City Area Chamber of Commerce
511 Pleasant St.
Miles City, MT 59301
Ph: (406)234-2890
URL: http://milescitychamber.com
Contact: John Laney, Director
Description: Promotes business and community development in Miles City, MT area. **Geographic Preference:** Local.

41783 ■ Mineral County Chamber of Commerce (MCCC)
PO Box 483
Superior, MT 59872-0483
Ph: (406)822-4891
URL: http://www.uschamber.com/co/chambers/montana/superior
Description: Promotes business and community development in Mineral county and its surrounding area. **Geographic Preference:** Local.

41784 ■ Missoula Area Chamber of Commerce
825 E Front St.
Missoula, MT 59807
Ph: (406)543-6623
Co. E-mail: info@missoulachamber.com
URL: http://missoulachamber.com
Contact: Kim Latrielle, President
E-mail: kim@missoulachamber.com
Facebook: www.facebook.com/Missoula.Chamber
X (Twitter): x.com/MissoulaChamber
Description: Promotes business and community development in the Missoula, MT area. **Founded:** 1904. **Geographic Preference:** Local.

41785 ■ Montana Chamber of Commerce (MCC)
616 Helena Ave., Ste. 300
Helena, MT 59624
Ph: (406)431-3248
Co. E-mail: info@montanachamber.com

URL: http://www.montanachamber.com
Contact: Todd O'Hair, President
E-mail: todd@montanachamber.com
Facebook: www.facebook.com/MontanaChamber
Linkedin: www.linkedin.com/company/montana-chamber-of-commerce
X (Twitter): x.com/MontanaChamber
Instagram: www.instagram.com/montanachamber
YouTube: www.youtube.com/channel/UCLZ7D6onWTIquN1MN5j8vfA
Description: Seeks to advocate statewide for business in the Legislature and Congress. **Founded:** 1931. **Publications:** *Eye on Business* (Monthly). **Geographic Preference:** State.

41786 ■ Philipsburg Chamber of Commerce
PO Box 661
Philipsburg, MT 59858
Ph: (406)859-3388
Co. E-mail: chamber@philipsburgmt.com
URL: http://www.philipsburgmt.com/index.php
Facebook: www.facebook.com/Philipsburg-MT-Official-Chamber-of-Commerce-222324830691
Description: Promotes business and community development in Philipsburg, MT. Sponsors Flint Creek Valley Days. **Founded:** 1946. **Geographic Preference:** Local.

41787 ■ Polson Chamber of Commerce (PCC)
402 1st St. E, Ste. 102
Polson, MT 59860
Ph: (406)883-5969
Fax: (406)319-2073
URL: http://www.polsonchamber.com
Contact: Mandy Smith, President
Description: Promotes business and community development in the Port Polson, MT area. **Founded:** 1909. **Publications:** *The Chambergram* (Monthly). **Geographic Preference:** Local.

41788 ■ Powell County Chamber of Commerce
529 Main St.
Deer Lodge, MT 59722
Ph: (406)846-2094
Co. E-mail: powellcountychamber@outlook.com
URL: http://www.powellcountymontana.com/deerlodge
Contact: Bridgett Herrick, President
Facebook: www.facebook.com/PowellCountyChamber
Description: Promotes businesses, community development and tourism in the city of Deer Lodge and Powell County, MT. Sponsors annual BBQ, annual banquet, Territorial Days, Demolition Derby, Pumpkin Sunday and Christmas Stroll. **Publications:** *Deer Lodge Demographics*; *Deer Lodge Visitor's Guide*; *Self Guided Tour of Historic Buildings in Deer Lodge*. **Geographic Preference:** Local.

41789 ■ *The Progress*
1000 George St.
Butte, MT 59701
Free: 800-735-6814
Fax: (406)723-1215
Co. E-mail: marketing@buttechamber.org
URL: http://www.buttechambersite.org
Contact: Mark Johnston, President
E-mail: mjohnston@bankofbutte.com
URL(s): www.buttechambersite.org/information/chamber-news
Released: Monthly **Availability:** Online.

41790 ■ Red Lodge Area Chamber of Commerce (RLACC)
701 N Broadway
Red Lodge, MT 59068
Ph: (406)446-1718
Free: 888-281-0625
URL: http://redlodgechamber.org
Contact: Heather Cope, President
Description: Promotes business and community development in the Red Lodge, MT area. Encourages tourism. **Founded:** 1930. **Publications:** *The Red Lodge Insider* (Quarterly). **Educational Activities:** Beartooth. **Geographic Preference:** Local.

41791 ■ *Self Guided Tour of Historic Buildings in Deer Lodge*
529 Main St.
Deer Lodge, MT 59722
Ph: (406)846-2094
Co. E-mail: powellcountychamber@outlook.com
URL: http://www.powellcountymontana.com/deerlodge
Contact: Bridgett Herrick, President
URL(s): powellcountymontana.com/attractions
Availability: Print.

41792 ■ Shelby Area Chamber of Commerce (SACC)
100 Montana Ave.
Shelby, MT 59474
Ph: (406)434-7184
Co. E-mail: shelbymtcoc@gmail.com
URL: http://www.shelbymtchamber.org
Contact: Shana Lee, President
Facebook: www.facebook.com/shelbymtchamber
Instagram: www.instagram.com/shelbymtchamber
Description: Promotes business and community development in Toole County, MT. **Founded:** 1946. **Geographic Preference:** Local.

41793 ■ Sidney Area Chamber of Commerce and Agriculture (SACCA)
909 S Central Ave.
Sidney, MT 59270
Ph: (406)433-1916
Co. E-mail: admin@sidneymt.com
URL: http://www.sidneymt.com/about/contact-us
Contact: Alli Nelson, President
Facebook: www.facebook.com/SidneyMTChamber
X (Twitter): x.com/SidneyMTChamber
Instagram: www.instagram.com/sidneymtchamber
Pinterest: www.pinterest.com/sidneymtchamber
Description: Promotes business and community development in Sidney, MT. Sponsors Sunrise Festival of the Arts. **Founded:** 1911. **Publications:** *The Advantage* (Monthly). **Geographic Preference:** Local.

41794 ■ Stillwater County Chamber of Commerce
565 9th St., Ste. 50
Columbus, MT 59019
Ph: (406)322-4505
Co. E-mail: admin@stillwatercountychamber.com
URL: http://stillwatercountychamber.com
Contact: Joyce Kelley, President
Facebook: www.facebook.com/StillwaterCountyChamber
Description: Promotes business and community development in Columbus, MT. Sponsors festival. **Geographic Preference:** Local.

41795 ■ Sweet Grass County Chamber of Commerce
PO Box 1012
Big Timber, MT 59011
Ph: (406)932-5131
Co. E-mail: sweetgrasschamber@gmail.com
URL: http://bigtimber.com
Contact: Cathy Radwanski, President
Description: Promotes business and community development in Sweet Grass County, MT. **Founded:** 1919. **Geographic Preference:** Local.

41796 ■ Thompson Falls Chamber of Commerce
PO Box 493
Thompson Falls, MT 59873
Ph: (406)827-4930
Co. E-mail: tfchamber@thompsonfallschamber.com
URL: http://thompsonfalls.org/chamber-of-commerce
Facebook: www.facebook.com/thompsonfallschamberofcommerce
Description: Promotes business and community development in Thompson Falls, MT. Sponsors Pony Express Days festival. **Geographic Preference:** Local.

41797 ■ *Three Fork Telephone Book*
PO Box 1103
Three Forks, MT 59752

STATE LISTINGS

Ph: (406)285-4753
Co. E-mail: tfchamber@gmail.com
URL: http://threeforksmontana.com
Contact: Brooke Leugers, President
URL(s): threeforksmontana.com/membership
Released: Annual; every September. **Description:** Contains telephone number of residents as well as business in Three Forks and Willow Creek area. **Availability:** Online.

41798 ■ Three Forks Chamber of Commerce (TFCC)
PO Box 1103
Three Forks, MT 59752
Ph: (406)285-4753
Co. E-mail: tfchamber@gmail.com
URL: http://threeforksmontana.com
Contact: Brooke Leugers, President
Facebook: www.facebook.com/3forkschamber
X (Twitter): x.com/3ForksChamber
Description: Promotes business and community development in Three Forks, MT. Participates in Rodeo Parade and community picnic. **Founded:** 1964. **Publications:** *Three Fork Telephone Book* (Annual). **Geographic Preference:** Local.

41799 ■ West Yellowstone Chamber of Commerce (WYCC)
30 Yellowstone Ave.
West Yellowstone, MT 59758
Ph: (406)646-7701
Fax: (406)646-9691
Co. E-mail: info@destinationyellowstone.com
URL: http://destinationyellowstone.com
Contact: Katrina Wiese, President
Facebook: www.facebook.com/DestinationYellowstone
X (Twitter): x.com/destyellowstone
Instagram: www.instagram.com/destinationyellowstone
Pinterest: www.pinterest.com/destinationyellowstone
Description: Promotes business and community development in West Yellowstone, MT. **Geographic Preference:** Local.

41800 ■ Whitefish Chamber of Commerce
505 Second St.
Whitefish, MT 59937
Ph: (406)862-3501
Co. E-mail: visit@whitefishchamber.org
URL: http://www.whitefishchamber.org
Contact: Kevin Gartland, Executive Director
E-mail: kevin@whitefishchamber.org
Description: Serves as an information bank which supplies valuable community information. Promotes community events to establish a positive image of Whitefish as a great place to work, live and do business. **Founded:** 1947. **Publications:** *Chamber Newsletter* (Weekly); *Tabloid of Services* (Periodic). **Geographic Preference:** Local.

FINANCING AND LOAN PROGRAMS

41801 ■ Frontier Angels (FA)
PO Box 4781
Bozeman, MT 59772-4781
URL: http://www.frontierangels.com
Contact: Pat LaPointe, Managing Director
Linkedin: www.linkedin.com/company/frontier-angels
Description: Angel investor group for early-stage technology-based companies, primarily in Montana. **Founded:** 2006. **Investment Policies:** Defensible intellectual property; tech-leveraged business model; strong management; market demand. **Industry Preferences:** Software; data/analytics; IoT; edge computing; medical devices; biotech; life sciences; health tech; photonics; ag tech; clean tech; energy tech; consumer tech.

PROCUREMENT ASSISTANCE PROGRAMS

41802 ■ Big Sky Economic Development (BSED) [Montana Procurement Technical Assistance Center]
201 N Broadway
Billings, MT 59101
Ph: (406)256-6871
Fax: (406)256-6877
Co. E-mail: contact@bigskyeconomicdevelopment.org
URL: http://bigskyeconomicdevelopment.org
Contact: Steve Arveschoug, Executive Director
E-mail: stevea@bigskyeda.org
Facebook: www.facebook.com/bigskyed
Linkedin: www.linkedin.com/company/big-sky-economic-development
Instagram: www.instagram.com/lifeatbsed
YouTube: www.youtube.com/channel/UCYjFV2K9KD3TCGnBqxJ2RNQ/videos
Description: Offers U.S. Customs services, bonded and general warehouse storage, no inventory tax, and licensing brokerage services to shippers, wholesalers, and manufacturers. Access is provided to international and domestic shippers. **Founded:** 1989.

41803 ■ Kalispell Chamber of Commerce
15 Depot Pk.
Kalispell, MT 59901
Ph: (406)758-2800
Co. E-mail: info@kalispellchamber.com
URL: http://www.kalispellchamber.com
Contact: Joe Unterreiner, Co-President
E-mail: joe@kalispellchamber.com
Facebook: www.facebook.com/kallispellchamber
X (Twitter): x.com/kalispellchambr
Instagram: www.instagram.com/kalispellchamber
YouTube: www.youtube.com/user/kalispellchamber
Description: Free assistance to help Montana businesses obtain city, county, state, or federal government contracts serving Flathead, Lake, Sanders, and Lincoln Counties. **Founded:** 1987. **Publications:** *Chamber News*. **Geographic Preference:** Local.

41804 ■ Montana Department of Administration - State Procurement Bureau (SPB)
PO Box 200801
Helena, MT 59620-0801
URL: http://spb.mt.gov
Description: Offers current government procurement information to interested small business bidders. Also provides technical assistance.

41805 ■ Montana Procurement Technical Assistance Center - Great Falls Development Authority
405 3rd St. NW, Ste. 203
Great Falls, MT 59404
Ph: (406)564-0957
Fax: (406)454-2995
URL: http://growgreatfallsmontana.org/government-contracting/ptac-faqs
Contact: Brett Doney, President
E-mail: bdoney@gfdevelopment.org

INCUBATORS/RESEARCH AND TECHNOLOGY PARKS

41806 ■ Bozeman Technology Incubator
1320 Manley Rd.
Bozeman, MT 59715
URL: http://bozeman.com
Contact: Greg Gianforte, Founder
Description: Incubator providing free mentoring to all of Montana's high-tech and manufacturing businesses. **Founded:** 1997.

41807 ■ Lake County Community Development Corp. (LCCDC)
407 Main St. SW
Ronan, MT 59864
Ph: (406)676-5901
Co. E-mail: info@missionwestcdp.org
URL: http://missionwestcdp.org
Contact: Jim Thaden, Executive Director
E-mail: jim.thaden@missionwestcdp.org
Description: A small business incubator working with existing companies to develop and expand their businesses and to structure financial resources appropriate to their situation, and helping recruit new companies which may provide additional and higher wage jobs. **Founded:** 1995.

41808 ■ Mission Mountain Food Enterprise Center (LCCDC)
407 Main St. SW
Ronan, MT 59864
URL: http://missionwestcdp.org/mission-mountain-food-enterprise-center
Contact: Jan Tusick, Director
E-mail: jan.tusick@missionwestcdp.org
Description: Food processing, research, and development facility for the incubation of specialty food entrepreneurs and value-added agricultural producers.

41809 ■ Montana Governor's Office of Economic Development (GOED)
1301 E 6th Ave.
Helena, MT 59601
Ph: (406)444-5634
Facebook: www.facebook.com/MTGOED
Description: Assists Montana businesses through all stages of the life cycle.

41810 ■ Montana Technology Enterprise Center (MonTEC)
1121 E Broadway St.
Missoula, MT 59802
Ph: (406)290-9800
Co. E-mail: info@sterlingcmg.com
URL: http://www.montanaenterprisecenter.com/#companies
Contact: Scott Whittenburg, Contact
Description: A technology and business incubator conceived to bolster local start-ups and to encourage the commercialization of university research. Collaborative enterprise between the University of Montana and the Missoula Area Economic Development Foundation.

41811 ■ MonTEC
1121 E Broadway St.
Missoula, MT 59802
Ph: (406)290-9800
Co. E-mail: info@sterlingcmg.com
URL: http://www.montanaenterprisecenter.com
Description: A high-growth, technology focused business incubator that is building a community of high growth enterprises on the Clark Fork River.

Nebraska

ASSOCIATIONS AND OTHER ORGANIZATIONS

41812 ■ American Concrete Institute Nebraska Chapter - Library
1425 W 9th St.
 Fremont, NE 68025
URL: http://www.concrete.org/chapters/findachapter/
 chapterhome.aspx?cid=C0C08000
Contact: Michael L. Willman, Contact
E-mail: michael.willman@gcpat.com

Description: Technical society of engineers, architects, contractors, educators, and others interested in improving techniques of design construction and maintenance of concrete products and structures. **Scope:** Concrete durability; mixture proportioning; construction techniques; concrete structures design. **Services:** Open to the public; documents, reports, and standards cannot be scanned or emailed. **Founded:** 1987. **Holdings:** 400 - standards, codes, committee reports, manuals, symposia, and special documents; publications. **Geographic Preference:** State.

41813 ■ Business Network International Heartland--Nebraska, Wyoming, South Dakota, Western Iowa
3430 Toringdon Way
 Charlotte, NC 28277
Free: 855-264-2673
Co. E-mail: info@bniheartland.com
URL: http://bniheartland.com/en-US/index
Contact: Nellie Nutting, Managing Director
E-mail: nellienutting@bni.com

Description: Provides a structured environment for the development and exchange of quality business referrals. Offers members the opportunity to share ideas and contacts in Nebraska, Wyoming, South Dakota and Iowa. **Founded:** 1985. **Geographic Preference:** State.

41814 ■ Entrepreneurs' Organization - Nebraska Chapter (EO)
NE
Co. E-mail: eonebraskaeo@gmail.com
URL: http://www.eonetwork.org/nebraska
Contact: Ronnie Crowley, Administrator
E-mail: eonebraskaeo@gmail.com

Description: Provides local resources to members which includes networking events, mentorship, live forums, and leadership development. **Founded:** 2001.

41815 ■ International Association of Business Communicators Omaha (IABC) [IABC Omaha]
Omaha, NE
Co. E-mail: iabcomaha.info@gmail.com
URL: http://www.iabc.com/Connect/Chapters
 -Regions
Facebook: www.facebook.com/IABCOmaha

Description: Represents the interests of communication managers, public relations directors, writers, editors and audiovisual specialists. Encourages establishment of college-level programs in organizational communication. Conducts surveys on employee communication effectiveness and media trends. Conducts research in the field of communication. **Geographic Preference:** Local.

41816 ■ National Federation of Independent Business Nebraska
233 S 13th St., Ste. 700
 Lincoln, NE 68501-0008
Ph: (402)474-3570
URL: http://www.nfib.com/nebraska
Contact: Ryan McIntosh, Director

Description: Represents small and independent businesses. Aims to promote and protect the rights of members to own, operate and grow their businesses. **Geographic Preference:** State.

41817 ■ Nebraska Agri-Business Association, Inc.
8700 Executive Woods Dr., Ste. 400
 Lincoln, NE 68512-9612
Ph: (402)476-1528
Co. E-mail: info@na-ba.com
URL: http://na-ba.com
Contact: Scott Merritt, Director

Description: Represents individuals involved in the agricultural chemical and fertilizer industry. **Founded:** 1955. **Publications:** *The Fertilizer and Ag-Chemical Digest* (Quarterly). **Educational Activities:** Nebraska Agri-Business Exposition (Annual). **Geographic Preference:** State.

SMALL BUSINESS DEVELOPMENT CENTERS

41818 ■ Nebraska Small Business Development Center Chadron State College (NBDC)
Burkhiser Technology Complex, Rm. 120
 1000 Main St.
 Chadron, NE 69337
Ph: (308)432-6282
Co. E-mail: nbdc@csc.edu
URL: http://www.csc.edu/business/nbdc
Contact: Gary Dusek, Consultant
E-mail: gdusek@csc.edu

Description: Provides management assistance to current and prospective small business owners in Chadron. **Founded:** 1977. **Geographic Preference:** Local.

41819 ■ Nebraska Small Business Development Center Kearney
c/o Odee Ingersoll, Director
 W Center Bldg., Rm. 127E
 University of Nebraska at Kearney
 1917 W 24th St.
 Kearney, NE 68849-4440
Ph: (308)865-8344

Co. E-mail: ingersollo@unk.edu
URL: http://www.unomaha.edu/nebraska-business
 -development-center/about/consultant-directory/o
 dee-ingersoll.php
Contact: Odee Ingersoll, Director
E-mail: ingersollo@unk.edu

Description: Provides management assistance to current and prospective small business owners in Kearney. **Geographic Preference:** Local.

41820 ■ Nebraska Small Business Development Center Lincoln
SE Community College
 Entrepreneurship Ctr., Ste. 209
 285 S 68th St. Pl.
 Lincoln, NE 68510-2449
URL: http://www.unomaha.edu/nebraska-business
 -development-center/services/business-resiliency
 -resources.php
Contact: Zack Zimmerman, Director
E-mail: zzimmerman@southeast.edu

Description: Provides management assistance to current and prospective small business owners in Lincoln. **Geographic Preference:** Local.

41821 ■ Nebraska Small Business Development Center North Platte
200 Mammel Hall 6708 Pine St.
 Omaha, NE 68182
Ph: (402)554-6232
URL: http://www.unomaha.edu/nebraska-business
 -development-center/business-start-and-growth/sb
 dc-directory.php
Contact: Charlie McPherson, Director
E-mail: cmcpherson@unomaha.edu

Description: Provides management assistance to current and prospective small business owners in North Platte. **Geographic Preference:** Local.

41822 ■ Nebraska Small Business Development Center Omaha (NBDC)
200 Mammel Hall
 6708 Pine St.
 Omaha, NE 68182
Ph: (402)554-6232
Co. E-mail: unonbdc@unomaha.edu
URL: http://www.unomaha.edu/nebraska-business
 -development-center/index.php
Contact: Scott Asmus, Officer
E-mail: sasmus@unomaha.edu
Facebook: www.facebook.com/
 NebraskaBusinessDevelopmentCenter
Linkedin: www.linkedin.com/company/nebraska-busi-
 ness-development-center
X (Twitter): x.com/NBDC_nebraska
YouTube: www.youtube.com/channel/UCmtyKj
 _Zuauvj6bnqqZOalQ

Description: Provides management assistance to current and prospective small business owners in Omaha. **Founded:** 1977. **Geographic Preference:** Local; State.

41823 ■ Nebraska Small Business Development Center Scottsbluff
c/o Spencer Rien, Director
Rm. 108A, 4502 Ave.
Scottsbluff, NE 69361
Ph: (308)635-7513
Co. E-mail: srien@unomaha.edu
URL: http://www.unomaha.edu/nebraska-business-development-center/business-start-and-growth/sbdc-directory.php
Contact: Spencer Rien, Director
E-mail: srien@unomaha.edu
Description: Provides management assistance to current and prospective small business owners in Scottsbluff. **Geographic Preference:** Local.

41824 ■ Nebraska Small Business Development Center Wayne
Gardner Hall
Wayne State College
1111 Main St.
Wayne, NE 68787
URL: http://www.wsc.edu/info/20372/partnerships/114/nebraska_business_development_center
Contact: Loren Kucera, Director
E-mail: lokucer1@wsc.edu
Description: Provides management assistance to current and prospective small business owners in Wayne. **Founded:** 1977. **Geographic Preference:** Local.

SMALL BUSINESS ASSISTANCE PROGRAMS

41825 ■ Nebraska Ombudsman's Office
Centre Ter., Bldg.
1225 L St., Ste. No. 300
Lincoln, NE 68509-4604
URL: http://www.nebraskalegislature.gov
Description: Receives complaints against state agencies.

SCORE OFFICES

41826 ■ SCORE - Blue Springs
285 S 68Th St. Pl. Ste. 208
Lincoln, NE 68510
Ph: (402)437-2409
Co. E-mail: infolincoln@scorevolunteer.org
URL: http://lincoln.score.org
Facebook: www.facebook.com/SCORELincoln
Description: Provides professional guidance and information to maximize the success of existing and emerging small businesses. Offers business counseling and workshops.

41827 ■ SCORE - Columbus & Norfolk [SCORE - Nebraska Route 81; SCORE Mentors Nebraska Route 81]
4860 33rd Ave.
Columbus, NE 68601
Ph: (402)562-1242
URL: http://neroute81.score.org/SCORENorfolk
Facebook: www.facebook.com/NorfolkAreaScore
Linkedin: www.linkedin.com/company/score-nebraska-route81
Description: Seeks to educate entrepreneurs and help small businesses start, grow and succeed nationwide. Organizes volunteers who are working or retired business owners, executives and corporate leaders who wish to share their wisdom and lessons learned in business. **Founded:** 2004. **Geographic Preference:** Local.

41828 ■ SCORE - Grand Island [SCORE - Central Nebraska]
3180 W Hwy. 34 - College Pk.
Grand Island, NE 68801
Ph: (308)380-6915
Co. E-mail: help@score.org
URL: http://centralnebraska.score.org
Contact: Bridget Weston, Chief Executive Officer
X (Twitter): twitter.com/SCORECeNebraska

Description: Provides professional guidance and information to maximize the success of existing and emerging small businesses. Offers business counseling and workshops.

41829 ■ SCORE - Greater Omaha
10675 Bedford Ave., Ste. 100
Omaha, NE 68134
Ph: (402)221-3606
Fax: (402)221-3680
Co. E-mail: help@score.org
URL: http://omaha.score.org
Contact: Pauline Stark, Chairman
Linkedin: www.linkedin.com/company/score-mentors-greater-omaha
X (Twitter): x.com/SCOREOmaha
Description: Provides professional guidance and information to maximize the success of existing and emerging small businesses. Offers business counseling and workshops. **Founded:** 1964. **Geographic Preference:** Local.

41830 ■ SCORE - Lincoln, Nebraska
285 S 68th St. Pl., Ste. 280
Lincoln, NE 68510
Ph: (402)437-2409
Co. E-mail: infolincoln@scorevolunteer.org
URL: http://lincoln.score.org
Contact: Bridget Weston, Chief Executive Officer
Facebook: www.facebook.com/SCORELincoln
Linkedin: www.linkedin.com/company/score-lincoln
Description: Provides professional guidance and information to maximize the success of existing and emerging small businesses. Offers business counseling and workshops. **Geographic Preference:** Local.

41831 ■ SCORE - Scottsbluff
2620 College Park
Western NE Community College - Scottsbluff Campus
Scottsbluff, NE 69361
Ph: (402)221-3606
URL: http://omaha.score.org
Facebook: www.facebook.com/SCOREOmaha
X (Twitter): x.com/SCOREOmaha
Description: Provides professional guidance and information to maximize the success of existing and emerging small businesses. Offers business counseling and workshops.

BETTER BUSINESS BUREAUS

41832 ■ Better Business Bureau of Midwest Plains - Lincoln
PO Box 27806
Ralston, NE 68127
URL: http://www.bbb.org/local-bbb/bbb-of-midwest-plains
Description: Seeks to promote and foster the highest ethical relationship between businesses and the public through voluntary self-regulation, consumer and business education, and service excellence. Provides information to help consumers and businesses make informed purchasing decisions and avoid costly scams and frauds; settles consumer complaints through arbitration and other means. **Geographic Preference:** Local.

41833 ■ Better Business Bureau of Midwest Plains - Omaha [BBB of Midwest Plains - Omaha (BBB)]
11811 P St.
Omaha, NE 68137
Ph: (402)391-7612
Fax: (402)391-7535
URL: http://www.bbb.org/local-bbb/bbb-of-midwest-plains
Description: Marketplace protection agency engaged in promoting the business interest of their members, as well as helping consumers with the various problems that occur daily. **Publications:** *The Business Standard* (Monthly). **Geographic Preference:** Local.

CHAMBERS OF COMMERCE

41834 ■ Ainsworth Area Chamber of Commerce and North Central Development Center (NCDC)
335 N Main St.
Ainsworth, NE 69210
Ph: (402)387-2740
URL: http://visitnebraska.com/ainsworth/north-central-development-center
Description: Promotes business and community development in the Ainsworth Area, NE. **Geographic Preference:** Local.

41835 ■ Albion Chamber of Commerce (ACC)
420 W Market St.
Albion, NE 68620
Ph: (260)403-1795
Co. E-mail: albionin@albionin.org
URL: http://albionne.com/work/chamber-of-commerce
Contact: Makensey Harris, President
Description: Promotes business and community development in Albion, NE. **Founded:** 1954. **Geographic Preference:** Local.

41836 ■ Alliance Chamber of Commerce
305 Box Butte Ave.
Alliance, NE 69301
Ph: (308)762-1520
Free: 800-738-0648
Fax: (308)762-4919
Co. E-mail: chamber@alliancechamber.com
URL: http://www.alliancechamber.com
Contact: Mikayla Randolph-Smith, President
Facebook: www.facebook.com/Alliance-Chamber-of-Commerce-330741423642019
Description: Promotes business and community development in the Alliance, NE area. **Founded:** 1927. **Geographic Preference:** Local.

41837 ■ Arapahoe Chamber of Commerce
PO Box 624
Arapahoe, NE 68922
Ph: (308)962-7777
Co. E-mail: chamber@arapahoe-ne.com
URL: http://www.arapahoe-ne.com
Contact: Angie Moore, President
Facebook: www.facebook.com/arapahoechamber
X (Twitter): x.com/arapahoechamber
Instagram: www.instagram.com/arapahoechamber
Description: Promotes business and community development in Arapahoe, NE. **Founded:** 1991. **Geographic Preference:** Local.

41838 ■ Auburn Chamber of Commerce
1101 J St.
Auburn, NE 68305
Ph: (402)274-3521
Co. E-mail: auburnchamberofcommerce@gmail.com
URL: http://www.auburnechamber.org
Contact: Tonia Greiner, Executive Director
URL(s): auburn.ne.gov/business
X (Twitter): x.com/AuburnNEB
Description: Promotes business and community development in the Auburn area. Sponsors Calvert Sheridan Days, Fall Foliage Festival, Farmer/Merchant Dinner Dance, Christmas on the Square, and Farm and Home Show. **Geographic Preference:** Local.

41839 ■ Aurora Area Chamber and Development (AACD)
1604 L St.
Aurora, NE 68818-2131
Ph: (402)694-6911
Co. E-mail: hello@auroranebraska.com
URL: http://www.auroranebraska.com
Facebook: www.facebook.com/aurorachamberofcommerce
Instagram: www.instagram.com/aurorachamberofcommerce
Description: Promotes business and community development in Aurora, NE. **Founded:** 1923. **Geographic Preference:** Local.

41840 ■ Nebraska   STATE LISTINGS

41840 ■ Beatrice Area Chamber of Commerce (BCC)
218 N 5th St.
 Beatrice, NE 68310
Ph: (402)223-2338
Co. E-mail: info@beatricechamber.com
URL: http://www.beatricechamber.com
Contact: Heath Stewart, Chairman of the Board
E-mail: hstewart@fnni.com
Facebook: www.facebook.com/Bea
 triceAreaChamber
X (Twitter): x.com/beatricechamber
YouTube: www.youtube.com/user/Bea
 triceAreaChamber
Description: Promotes business and community development in the Beatrice, NE area. **Founded:** 1880. **Publications:** *Chamber News.* **Geographic Preference:** Local.

41841 ■ Broken Bow Chamber of Commerce
424 S 8th Ave., Ste. 4
 Broken Bow, NE 68822
Ph: (308)872-5691
Co. E-mail: info@brokenbow-ne.com
URL: http://www.brokenbow-ne.com
Contact: Tania Kreitman, President
E-mail: manager@watchthefox.com
X (Twitter): x.com/bowchamber
Description: Promotes business and community development in Broken Bow, NE. **Geographic Preference:** Local.

41842 ■ Burwell Chamber of Commerce
404 Grand Ave.
 Burwell, NE 68823
Ph: (308)346-5210
Co. E-mail: burwellinformation@nctc.net
URL: http://burwellchamber.com
Contact: Cindy Markvicka, President
Facebook: www.facebook.com/Burwell.NE
Description: Works to promote agricultural, commercial, industrial, educational and civic interests of the City of Burwell and its surrounding area. **Geographic Preference:** Local.

41843 ■ Central City Area Chamber of Commerce
1532 17th Ave.
 Central City, NE 68826
Ph: (308)946-3897
Co. E-mail: ccareachamber@gmail.com
URL: http://www.centralcitychamber.org
Contact: Stephanie Stuhmer, President
Facebook: www.facebook.com/ccareachamber
X (Twitter): x.com/ChamberCCArea
Instagram: www.instagram.com/chamberccarea
Description: Promotes business and community development in Central City, NE area. **Geographic Preference:** Local.

41844 ■ Chadron - Dawes County Area Chamber of Commerce (CDCCC)
706 W 3rd St.
 Chadron, NE 69337
Ph: (308)432-4401
Fax: (308)432-4757
Co. E-mail: chamber@chadron.com
URL: http://www.chadron.com
Contact: Duane Gardener, President
Facebook: www.facebook.com/ChadronChamber
Description: Promotes business and community development in the Chadron, NE area. Sponsors Fur Trade Days. Convention/Meeting: none. **Founded:** 1885. **Geographic Preference:** Local.

41845 ■ *Chamber Newsletter*
918 Washington Ave.
 Plattsmouth, NE 68048
Ph: (402)296-6021
Fax: (402)296-6974
URL: http://www.plattsmouthchamber.com
Contact: Alicia Garbers, President
URL(s): www.plattsmouthchamber.com/about
Released: Weekly **Availability:** Print; Online.

41846 ■ Chappell Chamber of Commerce
749 2nd ST.
 Chappell, NE 69129
Co. E-mail: chappellchamber69129@outlook.com
URL: http://chappellchamber.org
Contact: Cindy Williams, President
Description: Promotes business and community development in Chappell, NE. **Geographic Preference:** Local.

41847 ■ Cheyenne County Chamber of Commerce (CCCC)
740 Illinois St.
 Sidney, NE 69162-1748
Ph: (308)254-5851
Co. E-mail: chamber@cheyennecountychamber.com
URL: http://cheyennecountychamber.com
Contact: McKailie Carnahan-Kuhns, Co-President Co-Chief Executive Officer
E-mail: director@cheyennecountychamber.com
X (Twitter): x.com/Cheycochamber
Pinterest: www.pinterest.com/cheycochamber
Description: Promotes business and community development in Cheyenne County and Sidney, NE. **Founded:** 1920. **Geographic Preference:** Local.

41848 ■ Columbus Area Chamber of Commerce (CACC)
753 33rd Ave.
 Columbus, NE 68601
Ph: (402)564-2769
Fax: (402)564-2026
URL: http://www.thecolumbuspage.com
Contact: Dawson Brunswick, President
Facebook: www.facebook.com/colnechamber
X (Twitter): x.com/colnechamber
YouTube: www.youtube.com/channel/UCC8Eyhpda 5NCZne2YgTTh3Q
Description: Promotes business and community development in the Columbus, NE area. **Geographic Preference:** Local.

41849 ■ Crete Chamber of Commerce
1302 Linden Ave.
 Crete, NE 68333
Ph: (402)826-2136
Co. E-mail: office.cretechamber@gmail.com
URL: http://www.cretechamber.org
Contact: Paul Heath, President
E-mail: paul@heathsports.com
Description: Promotes business and community development in the Crete, NE area. **Founded:** 1925. **Geographic Preference:** Local.

41850 ■ *Direction for Business*
309 W 2nd St.
 Grand Island, NE 68801
Ph: (308)382-9210
Co. E-mail: info@gichamber.com
URL: http://www.gichamber.com
Contact: Cindy Johnson, President
E-mail: cjohnson@gichamber.com
URL(s): www.gichamber.com/business-after-hours
Availability: Online.

41851 ■ *Executive*
3 Landmark Ctre, Ste. 302, 1128 Lincoln Mall
 Lincoln, NE 68508
Ph: (402)474-4422
Co. E-mail: nechamber@nechamber.com
URL: http://www.nechamber.com
Contact: Bryan Slone, President
E-mail: bslone@nechamber.com
URL(s): www.nechamber.com/executive-newsletter .html
Released: Irregular **Availability:** PDF.

41852 ■ Fairbury Chamber of Commerce
518 E St.
 Fairbury, NE 68352
Ph: (402)729-3000
Co. E-mail: fairburychamber@diodecom.net
URL: http://fairburychamber.org
Contact: April Stone, President
Facebook: www.facebook.com/ FairburyChamberOfCommerce
Description: Promotes business and community development in Fairbury, NE. **Founded:** 1919. **Geographic Preference:** Local.

41853 ■ Falls City Area Chamber of Commerce (FCACC)
1705 Stone St.
 Falls City, NE 68355
Ph: (402)245-4228
URL: http://www.fallscityareachamber.com
Contact: Sara Ruiz, President
Facebook: www.facebook.com/FallsCi tyChamberMainStreet
Description: Promotes business and community development in the Falls City, NE area. Conducts charitable activities. Sponsors area festivals. **Founded:** 1930. **Geographic Preference:** Local.

41854 ■ Fremont Area Chamber of Commerce (FACC)
128 E 6th St.
 Fremont, NE 68025
Ph: (402)721-2641
Co. E-mail: info@fremontne.org
URL: http://www.fremontne.org
Contact: Tara Lea, President
E-mail: tara@fremontne.org
Facebook: www.facebook.com/people/City-of -Fremont-NE/100066581297847
X (Twitter): x.com/fremareachamber
YouTube: www.youtube.com/channel/UCNn 4WuGjfGVXi71Cy-MZAgA
Description: Promotes business and community development in the area. Issues periodic publications. **Founded:** 1903. **Publications:** *Community Profile and Business Directory* (Annual); *Pathfinder* (Monthly). **Geographic Preference:** Local.

41855 ■ Gordon Chamber of Commerce
320 N Maple St.
 Gordon, NE 69343
Contact: Cassie L. L. Craven, President
Description: Promotes business and community development in Gordon, NE. Sponsors festival. **Founded:** 1941. **Geographic Preference:** Local.

41856 ■ Gothenburg Area Chamber of Commerce
1001 Lake Ave.
 Gothenburg, NE 69138
Ph: (308)537-3505
Fax: (308)537-2541
Co. E-mail: chamber@gothenburgdelivers.com
URL: http://www.gothenburgdelivers.com/member- ship.html
Contact: Allison Jonas, President
Facebook: www.facebook.com/GothenburgChamber
X (Twitter): x.com/gothenburgcdo
Description: Promotes business and community development in the Gothenburg, NE area. Sponsors annual festival. **Founded:** 1940. **Publications:** *Pony Express Exchange* (Quarterly). **Geographic Preference:** Local.

41857 ■ Grand Island Area Chamber of Commerce (GIACC)
309 W 2nd St.
 Grand Island, NE 68801
Ph: (308)382-9210
Co. E-mail: info@gichamber.com
URL: http://www.gichamber.com
Contact: Cindy Johnson, President
E-mail: cjohnson@gichamber.com
Facebook: www.facebook.com/ gichamberofcommerce
Linkedin: www.linkedin.com/company/grand-islan d-area-chamber-of-commerce
X (Twitter): x.com/gichamber
YouTube: www.youtube.com/user/GIChamber
Description: Promotes business and community development in the Grand Island, NE area. Sponsors festival. **Publications:** *Direction for Business.* **Geographic Preference:** Local.

STATE LISTINGS

41858 ■ Greater Omaha Chamber of Commerce
808 Conagra Dr., Ste. 400
Omaha, NE 68102
Ph: (402)346-5000
Fax: (402)346-7050
URL: http://www.omahachamber.org
Contact: David G. Brown, Co-President Co-Chief Executive Officer
Facebook: www.facebook.com/GreaterOmahaChamber
Linkedin: www.linkedin.com/company/greater-omaha-chamber
X (Twitter): x.com/OmahaChamber
Description: Promotes business and community development in the Omaha, NE area. **Founded:** 1893. **Publications:** *Profile*; *Directory of Omaha Manufacturers* (Biennial); *Major Employers Directory*; *Manufacturer's Directory* (Biweekly). **Geographic Preference:** Local.

41859 ■ Greater York Area Chamber of Commerce
603 N Lincoln Ave.
York, NE 68467
Ph: (402)362-5531
Fax: (402)362-5953
Co. E-mail: info@yorkchamber.org
URL: http://www.yorkchamber.org
Contact: Madonna Mogul, Executive Director
E-mail: madonnam@yorkchamber.org
Facebook: www.facebook.com/yorkchamberofcommerce
X (Twitter): x.com/yorknechamber
Instagram: www.instagram.com/yorknechamber
Description: Promotes business and community development in the York, NE area. Sponsors Yorkfest. **Publications:** *Surveyor* (Monthly). **Geographic Preference:** Local.

41860 ■ Hartington Area Chamber of Commerce
107 W State St.
Hartington, NE 68739
Ph: (402)254-6357
Fax: (402)254-6391
Co. E-mail: devcoor@hartel.net
URL: http://ci.hartington.ne.us/business-chamber
Contact: Chris Miller, President
Facebook: www.facebook.com/HartingtonNebraska
Description: Promotes business, agriculture, education, tourism and community development in Hartington, NE area. **Geographic Preference:** Local.

41861 ■ Hastings Area Chamber of Commerce (HACC)
301 S Burlington Ave.
Hastings, NE 68901
Ph: (402)461-8400
Fax: (402)461-4400
Co. E-mail: info@hastingschamber.com
URL: http://www.hastingschamber.com
Contact: Mikki Shafer, President
E-mail: mshafer@hastingschamber.com
Facebook: www.facebook.com/HastingsAreaChamberOfCommerce
X (Twitter): x.com/HastingsCOC
Description: Promotes business and community development in Hastings, NE. **Founded:** 1903. **Publications:** *Investment Report* (Monthly). **Geographic Preference:** Local.

41862 ■ Holdrege Area Chamber of Commerce (HACC)
504 4th Ave.
Holdrege, NE 68949
Ph: (308)995-4444
Co. E-mail: info@holdregechamber.com
URL: http://www.holdregechamber.com
Contact: Greg Barnes, Contact
Linkedin: www.linkedin.com/company/holdrege-area-chamber-of-commerce
X (Twitter): x.com/HoldregeCoC
Description: Promotes business and community development in the Holdrege, NE area. **Founded:** 1904. **Publications:** *Target* (Monthly). **Geographic Preference:** Local.

41863 ■ Imperial Chamber of Commerce
PO Box 82
Imperial, NE 69033
Ph: (308)882-5444
Co. E-mail: imperialchamberofcommerce@gmail.com
URL: http://imperialchamber.com
Description: Promotes business and community development in Imperial, NE area. **Geographic Preference:** Local.

41864 ■ Kearney Area Chamber of Commerce (KACC)
1007 2nd Ave.
Kearney, NE 68848
Ph: (308)237-3101
URL: http://www.kearneycoc.org
Contact: Derek Rusher, President
E-mail: drusher@kearneycoc.org
Facebook: www.facebook.com/KACCNebraska
Linkedin: www.linkedin.com/company/kearney-area-chamber-of-commerce
X (Twitter): x.com/KACCNebraska
Description: Serves the needs of the greater Kearney area as an advocate in its promotion, growth and quality of life. Works with all segments of the community to facilitate the basic infrastructure by pursuing business and industry, education, agriculture, healthcare, cultural, civic and other common interests. **Founded:** 1918. **Publications:** *Kearney Business Agenda* (Monthly). **Educational Activities:** Cranes Watch. **Geographic Preference:** Local.

41865 ■ *Kearney Business Agenda*
1007 2nd Ave.
Kearney, NE 68848
Ph: (308)237-3101
URL: http://www.kearneycoc.org
Contact: Derek Rusher, President
E-mail: drusher@kearneycoc.org
URL(s): www.kearneycoc.org/newsletter
Released: Monthly; first Tuesday. **Availability:** Online.

41866 ■ Kimball Banner County Chamber of Commerce (KBCCC)
122 S Chestnut St.
Kimball, NE 69145-1208
Ph: (308)235-3782
URL: http://www.uschamber.com/co/chambers/nebraska/kimball
Description: Promotes business and community development in Kimball and Banner counties, NE. **Publications:** *Kimball High Points*. **Geographic Preference:** Local.

41867 ■ La Vista Area Chamber of Commerce
9647 Giles
La Vista, NE 68128
Ph: (402)339-2078
Fax: (402)339-2076
URL: http://www.midamericachamberexecutives.com/list/member/la-vista-area-chamber-of-commerce-la-vista-1686
Contact: Dawson Brunswick, President
Description: Business, individual, and professional people. Works to develop and improve the economic, industrial, professional, cultural, and civic well-being of the La Vista community. **Founded:** 1960. **Publications:** *Briefs*; *Links*; *Pulse*. **Geographic Preference:** Local.

41868 ■ Lincoln Chamber of Commerce (LCOC)
1128 Lincoln Mall, Ste. 100
Lincoln, NE 68508
Ph: (402)436-2350
Co. E-mail: lincchamber@lcoc.com
URL: http://www.lcoc.com
Contact: Jason Ball, President
E-mail: jball@lcoc.com

Nebraska ■ 41873

Facebook: www.facebook.com/LincolnChamber
X (Twitter): x.com/lincolnchamber
YouTube: www.youtube.com/channel/UCujqNAtlfcUKNncnH2Z-8Dg
Description: Promotes business and community development in Lincoln, NE. **Founded:** 2012. **Publications:** *A Directory of Lincoln, Nebraska Manufacturers* (Biennial); *The Chamber Vision*. **Geographic Preference:** Local.

41869 ■ Loup City Chamber of Commerce
833 S 8th St.
Loup City, NE 68853
Ph: (308)745-0430
Co. E-mail: lcchamber@cornhusker.net
URL: http://www.loupcitychamber.org
Contact: Jennifer Smydra, President
E-mail: smydra@cornhusker.net
Facebook: www.facebook.com/loupcitychamber
Description: Promotes business and community development in the Loup City, NE area. **Geographic Preference:** Local.

41870 ■ McCook Chamber of Commerce [McCook Area Chamber of Commerce]
402 Norris Ave., Ste. 320
McCook, NE 69001
Ph: (308)345-3200
Co. E-mail: info@mccookchamber.org
URL: http://www.mccookchamber.org
Contact: Dawson Brunswick, President
Facebook: www.facebook.com/McCookChamberofCommerce
Linkedin: www.linkedin.com/company/mccook-chamber-of-commerce
X (Twitter): x.com/chambermccook
Instagram: www.instagram.com/mccookchamberofcommerce
Description: Promotes business and community development in McCook, NE. Conducts charitable activities. **Founded:** 1925. **Publications:** *Chamber Visions* (Monthly). **Educational Activities:** Heritage Days Parade and Craft Fair (Annual). **Geographic Preference:** Local.

41871 ■ Minden Chamber of Commerce (MCC)
325 N Colorado Ave.
Minden, NE 68959
Ph: (308)832-1811
Co. E-mail: chamberminden20@gmail.com
URL: http://www.mindenne.org
Contact: Angela L. Horine, President
Facebook: www.facebook.com/Minden-Nebraska-Chamber-of-Commerce-45944212649
X (Twitter): x.com/MindenNECoC
Description: Promotes business and community development in Minden, NE. **Geographic Preference:** Local.

41872 ■ Nebraska Chamber of Commerce and Industry (NCCI)
3 Landmark Ctre, Ste. 302, 1128 Lincoln Mall
Lincoln, NE 68508
Ph: (402)474-4422
Co. E-mail: nechamber@nechamber.com
URL: http://www.nechamber.com
Contact: Bryan Slone, President
E-mail: bslone@nechamber.com
Linkedin: www.linkedin.com/company/nebraskachamber
X (Twitter): x.com/NebraskaChamber
YouTube: www.youtube.com/user/NebraskaChamber
Description: Promotes business and community development in Nebraska. **Founded:** 1912. **Publications:** *Executive* (Irregular). **Awards:** Nebraska Business Hall of Fame (Annual); Nebraska Business Hall of Fame Scholarship (Annual). **Geographic Preference:** Local.

41873 ■ Nebraska City Tourism and Commerce (NCTC)
806 1st Ave.
Nebraska City, NE 68410
Ph: (402)873-6654
Co. E-mail: amya@nebraskacity.com
URL: http://nebraskacity.com

Contact: Alex Goering, President
Facebook: www.facebook.com/GoNebraskaCity
X (Twitter): x.com/GoNebraskaCity
Pinterest: www.pinterest.com/pin/801500683397 36187

Description: Promotes business and community development in Nebraska City, NE. Promotes tourism. Sponsors Applejack Festival, Arbor Day Celebration, and promotional events. **Founded:** 1854. **Publications:** *The View* (Monthly). **Educational Activities:** Annual AppleJack Festival (Annual). **Geographic Preference:** Local.

41874 ■ Norfolk Area Chamber of Commerce (NACC)
609 W Norfolk Ave.
Norfolk, NE 68701-5140
Ph: (402)371-4862
Fax: (402)371-0182
Co. E-mail: info@norfolkareachamber.com
URL: http://norfolkareachamber.com
Contact: Austen Hagood, President
E-mail: ahagood@norfolkareachamber.com
X (Twitter): x.com/NorfolkAreaCham

Description: Promotes business and community development in Norfolk, NE. **Founded:** 1885. **Publications:** *The Chamber Advantage* (Monthly). **Geographic Preference:** Local.

41875 ■ North Platte Area Chamber of Commerce & Development Corporation (NPAREA)
502 S Dewey St.
North Platte, NE 69101
Ph: (308)532-4966
Co. E-mail: chamber@nparea.com
URL: http://www.nparea.com
Contact: Gary Person, President
E-mail: gary@nparea.com
Facebook: www.facebook.com/NorthPlatteChamber
X (Twitter): x.com/npchamber

Description: Promotes business and community development in North Platte, NE. **Founded:** 1919. **Publications:** *North Platte Area Chamber of Commerce and Development Newsletter* (Monthly). **Geographic Preference:** Local.

41876 ■ Ogallala - Keith County Chamber of Commerce (OKCCC)
119 E 2nd St.
Ogallala, NE 69153
Ph: (308)284-4066
Free: 800-658-4390
Fax: (308)284-3126
Co. E-mail: info@explorekeithcounty.com
URL: http://www.explorekeithcounty.com
Contact: Jo Brown, President
Facebook: www.facebook.com/OgallalaChamber
X (Twitter): x.com/OgallalaKeithCo
Instagram: www.instagram.com/keithcountychamber

Description: Promotes business and community development in Keith County, NE. **Founded:** 1958. **Geographic Preference:** Local.

41877 ■ O'Neill Area Chamber of Commerce
125 S 4th St.
O'Neill, NE 68763
Ph: (402)336-2355
Co. E-mail: lauri@oneillchamber.com
URL: http://www.oneillchamber.org
Contact: Lauri Havranek, President
E-mail: lauri@oneillchamber.com

Description: Promotes business and community development in the O'Neill, NE area. **Geographic Preference:** Local.

41878 ■ *Ord Area Business*
1514 K St.
Ord, NE 68862
Ph: (308)728-7875
Co. E-mail: info@ordnebraska.com
URL: http://ordnebraska.com
Contact: Dan Vech, President
URL(s): chamber.ordnebraska.com/list
Availability: Print.

41879 ■ Ord Area Chamber of Commerce (OCC)
1514 K St.
Ord, NE 68862
Ph: (308)728-7875
Co. E-mail: info@ordnebraska.com
URL: http://ordnebraska.com
Contact: Dan Vech, President
Facebook: www.facebook.com/ordnebraska
X (Twitter): x.com/OrdNE
Instagram: www.instagram.com/ordnebraska
Pinterest: www.pinterest.com/ordareachamber

Description: Promotes business and community development in the Ord, NE area. **Founded:** 1947. **Publications:** *Extraordinary News* (Monthly); *Ord Area Business*. **Geographic Preference:** Local.

41880 ■ Plattsmouth Chamber of Commerce (PCC)
918 Washington Ave.
Plattsmouth, NE 68048
Ph: (402)296-6021
Fax: (402)296-6974
URL: http://www.plattsmouthchamber.com
Contact: Alicia Garbers, President

Description: Promotes business and community development in Plattsmouth, NE. **Founded:** 1952. **Publications:** *Chamber Newsletter* (Weekly). **Educational Activities:** Kass Kounty King Korn Karnival. **Geographic Preference:** Local.

41881 ■ *Profile*
808 Conagra Dr., Ste. 400
Omaha, NE 68102
Ph: (402)346-5000
Fax: (402)346-7050
URL: http://www.omahachamber.org
Contact: David G. Brown, Co-President Co-Chief Executive Officer
URL(s): www.omahachamber.org/economic-development/target-industries/logistics/thank-you-manufacturing-and-logistics
Availability: Print.

41882 ■ Ralston Area Chamber of Commerce (RACC)
5505 Miller Ave.
Ralston, NE 68127
Ph: (402)339-7737
Fax: (402)339-7954
Co. E-mail: info@ralstonareachamber.org
URL: http://ralstonareachamber.org
Contact: Tim Rexius, President
Facebook: www.facebook.com/RalstonAreaChamberofCommerce
X (Twitter): x.com/RalstonAreaCC
YouTube: www.youtube.com/channel/UCUJb3sRU2D0mpmqHl-3K-ow

Description: Promotes business and community development in Ralston, NE area. **Founded:** 1960. **Geographic Preference:** Local.

41883 ■ Sarpy County Chamber of Commerce (SCCC)
1243 Golden Gate Dr., Ste. 1, Sarpy County
Papillion, NE 68046
Ph: (402)339-3050
Co. E-mail: chamber@sarpychamber.org
URL: http://www.sarpychamber.org
Contact: Karen Gibler, President
E-mail: president@sarpychamber.org
Facebook: www.facebook.com/SarpyChamber
Linkedin: www.linkedin.com/company/sarpy-county-chamber-of-commerce
X (Twitter): twitter.com/sarpycounty

Description: Promotes business and community development in Papillion and the mid-Sarpy County area of Nebraska. Sponsors Papillion Days, Old German Christmas, Business Expo., Monarch Market Place and Grand Give Away Auction. **Founded:** 1995. **Publications:** *Chamber News*. **Geographic Preference:** Local.

41884 ■ Schuyler Area Chamber of Commerce (SACC)
1119 B St.
Schuyler, NE 68661
Ph: (402)352-5472
Co. E-mail: schuylerchamber@gmail.com
URL: http://www.schuylerchamber.net
Contact: JoLynn Ratzlaff, President
Facebook: www.facebook.com/Schuylerareachamberofcommerce

Description: Promotes business and community development in Schuyler, NE. **Founded:** 1932. **Geographic Preference:** Local.

41885 ■ Scottsbluff/Gering United Chamber of Commerce
1517 Broadway, Ste. 104
Scottsbluff, NE 69361
Ph: (308)632-2133
Co. E-mail: office@scottsbluffgering.net
URL: http://www.scottsbluffgering.net
Contact: Karen Anderson, Executive Director
E-mail: karen@scottsbluffgering.net
Facebook: www.facebook.com/ScottsbluffGeringChamber

Description: Promotes business and community development in Scottsbluff and Gering, NE. **Founded:** 1929. **Publications:** *Impact* (Bimonthly). **Awards:** Scottsbluff/Gering United Chamber of Commerce Trailblazer of the Year (Annual); Scottsbluff/Gering United Chamber of Commerce Rising Super Star Award (Annual); Scottsbluff/Gering United Chamber of Commerce Visionary Super Star Award (Annual). **Geographic Preference:** Local.

41886 ■ Tekamah Chamber of Commerce
203 S 13th
Tekamah, NE 68061
Co. E-mail: tekamahchamber@gmail.com
URL: http://www.tekamah.life
Contact: Cami Gregerson, President
Facebook: www.facebook.com/tekamahchamberofcommerce
X (Twitter): x.com/TekamahC

Description: Promotes business and community development in Tekamah, NE. **Geographic Preference:** Local.

41887 ■ Valentine Chamber of Commerce
PO Box 201
Valentine, NE 69201
Ph: (402)376-5138
Co. E-mail: valentinecc66@gmail.com
URL: http://valentinechamber.org
Contact: Chris Hernstrom, President
Facebook: www.facebook.com/Valentine-Chamber-of-Commerce-266952073935

Description: Promotes business and community development in Valentine, NE. **Founded:** 1884. **Geographic Preference:** Local.

41888 ■ Wahoo Chamber of Commerce and Economic Development
605 N Broadway
Wahoo, NE 68066
Ph: (402)443-3222
URL: http://www.wahoo.ne.us
Contact: Theresa Klein, Executive Director
E-mail: tklein@wahoo.ne.us

Description: Promotes business and community development in Wahoo, NE. **Geographic Preference:** Local.

41889 ■ Washington County Chamber of Commerce
1646 Washington St.
Blair, NE 68008
Ph: (402)533-4455
Co. E-mail: jordan@washingtoncountychamberne.com
URL: http://washingtoncountychamberne.com
Contact: Denise Dein, Co-President
E-mail: ddein@fsbtfremont.bank
Facebook: www.facebook.com/WashingtonCountyChamberNE
X (Twitter): x.com/WashCoNECoc
Instagram: www.instagram.com/Wash_Co_NE_CoC

Description: Promotes business and community development in the Blair, NE area. Sponsors Gateway to the West Days. **Founded:** 1958. **Publications:**

STATE LISTINGS

Blair Area Chamber of Commerce--Membership Directory/Buyer's Guide (Annual). **Geographic Preference:** Local.

41890 ■ West Point Chamber of Commerce (WPCC)
200 Anna Stalp Ave.
 West Point, NE 68788
Ph: (402)372-2981
Fax: (402)372-1105
Co. E-mail: info@westpointchamber.com
URL: http://www.westpointchamber.com
Contact: Tina Biteghe Ndong, Executive Director
Facebook: www.facebook.com/WPChamber.NE
Description: Promotes business and community development in West Point, NE. Sponsors Sidewalk Days, Membership Banquet, and Annual Appreciation Barbecue. Holds seminars and workshops. **Publications:** *Update* (Monthly). **Geographic Preference:** Local.

41891 ■ Western Douglas County Chamber of Commerce (WDCCC)
20801 Elkhorn Dr.
 Elkhorn, NE 68022
Ph: (402)289-9560
Co. E-mail: info@westochamber.org
URL: http://www.westochamber.org
Contact: Blake Martin, President
Facebook: www.facebook.com/WestOChamber
Description: Promotes business and community development in the Western Douglas County. **Founded:** 1947. **Geographic Preference:** Local.

PROCUREMENT ASSISTANCE PROGRAMS

41892 ■ Nebraska Procurement Technical Assistance Center (PTAC) - Nebraska Business Development Center - University of Nebraska at Kearney
West Ctr., Bldg., Rm. 127E
 1917 W 24th St.
 Kearney, NE 68849-4440
URL: http://www.unk.edu/academics/nbdc/index.php
Contact: Chuck Beck, Consultant
E-mail: cwbeck@unomaha.edu
Description: Helps Nebraska businesses grow and generate new business by locating opportunities for business with the government.

41893 ■ Procurement Technical Assistance Center at Lincoln - Nebraska Business Development Center (NBDC)
200 Mammel Hall
 6708 Pine St.
 Omaha, NE 68182
Ph: (402)554-6232
Co. E-mail: nbdc@unomaha.edu
URL: http://www.unomaha.edu/nebraska-business -development-center
Contact: Gary Dusek, Director
Facebook: www.facebook.com/ NebraskaBusinessDevelopmentCenter
Linkedin: www.linkedin.com/company/nebraska-busi -ness-development-center
X (Twitter): x.com/NBDC_nebraska
YouTube: www.youtube.com/channel/UCmtyKj _Zuauvj6bnqqZOalQ
Description: Helps Nebraska businesses grow and generate new business by locating opportunities for business with the government. **Founded:** 1977.

INCUBATORS/RESEARCH AND TECHNOLOGY PARKS

41894 ■ NMotion
151 N 8th St., Ste. 518
 Lincoln, NE 68508
Co. E-mail: hello@nmotion.co
URL: http://www.nmotion.co
Contact: Scott Henderson, Principal
Facebook: www.facebook.com/NMotionStartup
Linkedin: www.linkedin.com/company/nmotionstar tups

X (Twitter): x.com/nmotionstartups
Instagram: www.instagram.com/nmotionstartups
Description: Accelerator that helps guide and support founders through the critical stages of startup development from idea to Series A. **Founded:** 2013.

41895 ■ Panhandle Area Development District (PADD)
1620 Broadway, Ste. A-10
 Scottsbluff, NE 69361
Ph: (308)436-6584
Fax: (308)436-6577
URL: http://nepadd.com
Contact: Bryan Venable, Executive Director
E-mail: bryanv@nepadd.com
Description: Committed to developing programs and strategies to make the Nebraska Panhandle a highly desirable place to start a business. Works with startups and entrepreneurs.

41896 ■ Southeast Community College Entrepreneurship Center
285 S 68th St. Pl.
 Lincoln, NE 68510-2449
Ph: (402)323-3383
Free: 800-642-4075
Fax: (402)323-3399
URL: http://www.southeast.edu/about/maps-and-drec tions.php
Description: Business incubator providing access to resources necessary for a startup to grow in its early stages.

41897 ■ University of Nebraska at Omaha (UNO) - Nebraska Business Development Center (NBDC)
200 Mammel Hall., 6708 Pine St.
 Omaha, NE 68182
Ph: (402)554-6232
Co. E-mail: nbdc@unomaha.edu
URL: http://www.unomaha.edu/nebraska-business -development-center/index.php
Contact: Catherine Lang, Executive Director
E-mail: cdlang@unomaha.edu
Facebook: www.facebook.com/ NebraskaBusinessDevelopmentCenter
Linkedin: www.linkedin.com/company/nebraska-busi -ness-development-center
X (Twitter): x.com/NBDC_nebraska
YouTube: www.youtube.com/channel/UCmtyKj _Zuauvj6bnqqZOalQ
Description: Helps Nebraska businesses grow and create new jobs. Experienced certified consultants provide confidential, impartial consulting services and educational opportunities for established and start up businesses, as well as researchers, entrepreneurs and professionals. **Founded:** 1977.

41898 ■ Western Nebraska Community College Business Linkubator (WNCC)
1601 E 27th Str.
 Scottsbluff, NE 69361
Ph: (308)635-3606
Co. E-mail: help@wncc.edu
URL: http://www.wncc.edu/about-wncc/our-cam puses/index
Contact: Dr. Carmen M. Simone, President
E-mail: simonec@wncc.edu
Facebook: www.facebook.com/wncc.edu
Linkedin: www.linkedin.com/school/western-nebraska -community-college
X (Twitter): x.com/wncc
Instagram: www.instagram.com/wnccofficial
YouTube: www.youtube.com/channel/UCMGLj78K 3Reu6MKU6ek4NSw
Description: Provides entrepreneurial development and education to grow and diversify western Nebraska businesses. The Linkubator connects businesses with a wide array of services and resources orchestrated to help entrepreneurs grow their vision.

EDUCATIONAL PROGRAMS

41899 ■ Nebraska Department of Economic Development-Industrial Training Programs (DED)
301 Centennial Mall S
 Lincoln, NE 68509-4666
Free: 800-426-6505
URL: http://www.nebraska.gov/agencies/#gsc.tab=0
Facebook: www.facebook.com/DevelopNebraska
Linkedin: www.linkedin.com/company/nebraska -department-of-economic-development
X (Twitter): x.com/DevelopNebraska
YouTube: www.youtube.com/user/nebraskaded
Description: Customized job training programs. **Founded:** 1967.

41900 ■ University of Nebraska at Lincoln Center for Entrepreneurship (UNLC4E)
730 N 14th St., Ste. 315
 Lincoln, NE 68588-0405
Ph: (402)472-3353
Co. E-mail: entrepreneurship@unl.edu
URL: http://business.unl.edu/academic-programs/cen ter-for-entrepreneurship
Contact: Samuel A. Nelson, Director
E-mail: snelson11@unl.edu
Facebook: www.facebook.com/nebraskaen trepreneurship
Linkedin: www.linkedin.com/showcase/nebraska-cen ter-for-entrepreneurship
X (Twitter): x.com/nebraskaentr
Instagram: www.instagram.com/nebraskaen trepreneurship
Description: Offers a program/classes in small business/small business management. **Founded:** 1981.

PUBLICATIONS

41901 ■ *Business in Nebraska*
730 N 14th St.
 Lincoln, NE 68588-0405
Co. E-mail: businessundergrad@unl.edu
URL: http://business.unl.edu/research/bureau-of -business-research
Contact: Mitch Herian, Director
E-mail: mherian2@unl.edu
URL(s): business.unl.edu/research/bureau-of -business-research/bureau-reports/business-in -nebraska
Released: Quarterly **Availability:** PDF; Online.

41902 ■ *The Omaha Business Journal*
1308 S 119th St.
 Omaha, NE 68144
Ph: (402)330-1760
URL: http://mbj.com
Contact: Savannah Behrends, Assistant Editor
E-mail: news@mbj.com
URL(s): www.mbj.com/about
Description: Business publication covering local start-ups and entrepreneurs. **Availability:** Print.

EARLY STAGE FINANCING

41903 ■ Nebraska Angels
701 P St., Ste. 302
 Lincoln, NE 68501
Co. E-mail: info@nebraskaangels.org
URL: http://www.nebraskaangels.org
Contact: Bart Dillashaw, Member
Linkedin: www.linkedin.com/company/nebraska -angels
Description: Consortium of angel investors. Averages eight deals per year. **Founded:** 2006. **Preferred Investment Size:** $25,000 to $100,000 per transaction or $250,000 to $750,000 as a group. **Investment Policies:** Rapidly growing market opportunity with the potential to provide a 10x+ return on investment within three to five years; unique solution to a market problem; highly experience team; developed revenue model. .

VENTURE CAPITAL FIRM

41904 ■ Dundee Venture Capital
3717 Harney St. 2nd Fl.
Omaha, NE 68131
URL: http://dundeeventurecapital.com
Contact: Greg Beaufait, Partner
Facebook: www.facebook.com/DundeeVentureCapital
Linkedin: www.linkedin.com/company/dundee-venture-capital
X (Twitter): x.com/dundeevc
Instagram: www.instagram.com/dundeevc
Description: Invests in early-stage tech companies in underserved markets across the Midwest. **Founded:** 2010. **Preferred Investment Size:** $250,000 to $750,000. **Investment Policies:** Prefers to see a prototype and early traction with an engaged customer base. **Industry Preferences:** Enterprise software; consumer brands; marketplaces.

Nevada

ASSOCIATIONS AND OTHER ORGANIZATIONS

41905 ■ Association of Fundraising Professionals Las Vegas Chapter
1880 E Warm Springs Rd., Ste. 100
Las Vegas, NV 89119
Ph: (702)798-5156
Fax: (702)796-1109
Co. E-mail: admin@afplasvegas.org
URL: http://afplasvegas.org
Contact: Emma Durant, Co-President
Facebook: www.facebook.com/AFP.LV
Linkedin: www.linkedin.com/company/association-of-fundraising-professionals-afp-las-vegas
X (Twitter): x.com/AFPlasVegas
Instagram: www.instagram.com/afplasvegas
Description: Seeks to advance philanthropy and excellence in the fundraising professional in Las Vegas. **Geographic Preference:** Local.

41906 ■ Association of Fundraising Professionals Sierra Chapter
PO Box 13356
Reno, NV 89507
Ph: (775)220-3993
URL: http://community.afpglobal.org
Contact: Andrea Wright, President
Description: Supports fundraising professionals in Reno, Sparks, Carson City, Lake Tahoe, and the surrounding communities of Nevada. **Founded:** 1988. **Geographic Preference:** Local.

41907 ■ Business Network International, Reno Area
PO Box 34498
Reno, NV 89533
Ph: (775)223-4292
Co. E-mail: info@bninevada.com
URL: http://bninevada.com/en-US/index
Contact: Greg Haupert, Executive Director
Description: Provides both men and women a structured environment for the development and exchange of quality business referrals. Offers members the opportunity to share ideas and contacts. **Geographic Preference:** Local.

41908 ■ National Association of Women Business Owners Southern Nevada (NAWBO SNV)
PO Box 96355
Las Vegas, NV 89193
Co. E-mail: admin@nawbosnv.org
URL: http://nawbosnv.org
Contact: TaChelle Lawson, President
Facebook: www.facebook.com/NAWBOSNV
Linkedin: www.linkedin.com/company/nawbo-southern-nevada
YouTube: www.youtube.com/channel/UCqYhTxVjk54hQOAlO3dlhlA
Founded: 1990. **Geographic Preference:** Local.

SMALL BUSINESS DEVELOPMENT CENTERS

41909 ■ Carson City Nevada Small Business Development Center
111 W Proctor St.
Carson City, NV 89703
Free: 800-240-7094
URL: http://nevadasbdc.org/who-we-are/offices
Contact: Kathy Halbardier, Advisor
Description: Provides management assistance to current and prospective small business owners in Carson City. **Geographic Preference:** Local.

41910 ■ Churchill County Nevada Small Business Development Center
448 W Williams Ave., Ste. 103
Fallon, NV 89406
Ph: (775)423-8587
Fax: (775)423-1759
Co. E-mail: sbdc@ceda-nv.org
URL: http://nevadasbdc.org/who-we-are/centers/fallon
Description: Represents and promotes the small business sector. Provides management assistance to current and prospective small business owners. Helps to improve management skills and expand the products and services of members. **Geographic Preference:** Local.

41911 ■ Elko Nevada Small Business Development Center
Great Basin College
1500 College Pky.
Elko, NV 89801
Ph: (775)327-2191
URL: http://nevadasbdc.org/who-we-are/centers/elko
Contact: George Kleeb, Advisor
E-mail: george.kleeb@gbcnv.edu
Description: Provides management assistance to current and prospective small business owners in Elko Nevada. **Geographic Preference:** Local.

41912 ■ Ely Nevada Small Business Development Center
744 E N Industrial Way
Ely, NV 89301
Free: 800-240-7094
Co. E-mail: admin@nevadasbdc.org
URL: http://nevadasbdc.org
Contact: Caroline McIntosh, Advisor
E-mail: cmcintosh@unr.edu
Description: Represents and promotes the small business sector. Provides management assistance to current and prospective small business owners. Helps to improve management skills and expand the products and services of members. **Geographic Preference:** Local.

41913 ■ Las Vegas Nevada Small Business Development Center
Urban Chamber Business Development Center
1951 Stella Lake St.
Las Vegas, NV 89106
Ph: (702)648-6222
Free: 800-240-7094
Co. E-mail: admin@nevadasbdc.org
URL: http://nevadasbdc.org
Contact: Northern Nevada, Manager
Facebook: www.facebook.com/NevadaSBDC
X (Twitter): x.com/NevadaSBDC
Instagram: www.instagram.com/nevada.sbdc
YouTube: www.youtube.com/channel/UCPHOizGelf4DU8NUhU6eiuA/videos
Description: Represents and promotes the small business sector. Provides management assistance to current and prospective small business owners. Helps to improve management skills and expand the products and services of members. **Geographic Preference:** Local.

41914 ■ Las Vegas Nevada Small Business Development Center Henderson
112 Water St.
Henderson, NV 89015
Ph: (702)606-4711
URL: http://nevadasbdc.org/who-we-are/centers/henderson
Contact: Anabel Navarro, Regional Manager
E-mail: anabelnavarro@unr.edu
Description: Represents and promotes the small business sector. Provides management assistance to current and prospective small business owners. Helps to improve management skills and expand the products and services of members. **Geographic Preference:** Local.

41915 ■ Las Vegas Small Business Development Center
1951 Stella Lake St.
Las Vegas, NV 89106
Ph: (702)648-6222
URL: http://nevadasbdc.org/who-we-are/contact-us
Description: Helps to improve management skills and expand the products and services of members in the area. **Geographic Preference:** Local.

41916 ■ Laughlin Nevada Small Business Development Center
Laughlin Chamber of Commerce
1585 S Casino Dr.
Laughlin, NV 89029
Ph: (702)298-2214
Free: 800-240-7094
Fax: (702)298-5708
URL: http://nevadasbdc.org
Description: Represents and promotes the small business sector. Provides management assistance to current and prospective small business owners. Helps to improve management skills and expand the products and services of members. **Geographic Preference:** Local.

41917 ■ Nevada Small Business Development Center - Lead Office (NSBDC)
1664 North Virginia St.
Reno, NV 89557-0032
Ph: (775)327-2334

41918 ▪ Nevada

Free: 800-240-7094
Fax: (775)784-4337
Co. E-mail: admin@nevadasbdc.org
URL: http://nevadasbdc.org
Contact: Winnie M. Dowling, Director
Facebook: www.facebook.com/NSBDC
X (Twitter): twitter.com/nsbdc
Instagram: www.instagram.com/nevada.sbdc
YouTube: www.youtube.com/channel/UCPHOizGelf4DU8NUhU6eiuA/videos
Description: Enhances economic growth in Nevada through a network of facilities statewide that provide the expertise, knowledge and innovation necessary to assist startup and existing businesses succeed. Services include business counseling, professional training, environmental and safety assistance, research, geographic information, technology development assistance, and disadvantaged business outreach. **Geographic Preference:** State.

41918 ▪ Pahrump Valley Chamber of Commerce (PVCC)
1301 S Hwy. 160, 2nd Fl.
Pahrump, NV 89048
Ph: (775)727-5800
Co. E-mail: info@pahrumpchamber.com
URL: http://pahrumpchamber.com
Contact: Beth Lee, Co-President
Facebook: www.facebook.com/PahrumpValleyChamber
Linkedin: www.linkedin.com/company/pahrumpvalleychamber
Instagram: www.instagram.com/pahrumpvalleychamber
Description: Promotes business and community development in Pahrump, NV. Encourages tourism. Sponsors the annual Chili Cook Off, Biz Expo, Wild West Extravaganza and Pahrump A Pum Pum. **Founded:** 1975. **Geographic Preference:** Local.

41919 ▪ Winnemucca Nevada Small Business Development Center
85 E 5th St.
Winnemucca, NV 89445
Free: 800-240-7094
URL: http://nevadasbdc.org/who-we-are/centers/winnemucca
Contact: Kathy Halbardier, Advisor
E-mail: kathyshalbardier@gmail.com
Description: Represents and promotes the small business sector. Provides management assistance to current and prospective small business owners. Helps to improve management skills and expand the products and services of members. **Geographic Preference:** Local.

SMALL BUSINESS ASSISTANCE PROGRAMS

41920 ▪ Nevada Department of Business and Industry
3300 W Sahara Ave., Ste. 200
Las Vegas, NV 89102
Ph: (702)486-2750
Fax: (702)486-2758
Co. E-mail: biinfo@business.nv.gov
URL: http://business.nv.gov
Contact: Terry Reynolds, Director
Linkedin: www.linkedin.com/company/department-of-business-and-industry
X (Twitter): x.com/NevadaDBI
YouTube: www.youtube.com/channel/UC2w84hVCRNEDhwdBiFuSpMg
Description: Regulates deceptive trade practices in the marketplace through investigations and protects consumers by registering and bonding businesses, clubs, telemarketers, organizations, and sports betting information services. **Founded:** 1996.

41921 ▪ Nevada Governor's Office of Economic Development (GOED)
808 W Nye Ln.
Carson City, NV 89703
Ph: (775)687-9900
Free: 800-336-1600
Fax: (775)687-9924
Co. E-mail: goed@goed.nv.gov
URL: http://goed.nv.gov
Contact: James Humm, Director
E-mail: j.humm@goed.nv.gov
Facebook: www.facebook.com/NevadaGOED
Linkedin: www.linkedin.com/company/nevada-governor's-office-of-economic-development
X (Twitter): x.com/DiversifyNevada
Instagram: www.instagram.com/diversifynevada
YouTube: www.youtube.com/channel/UCnq7jQLnvpfhH02d2dSCbWw
Description: Firm provides economic development services. **Founded:** 2011.

SCORE OFFICES

41922 ▪ SCORE - Henderson
112 Water St.
Henderson, NV 89015
URL: http://lasvegas.score.org/contact-us-30
Contact: Raj Tumber, Contact
Description: Provides professional guidance and information to maximize the success of existing and emerging small businesses. Offers business counseling and workshops.

41923 ▪ SCORE - Las Vegas
300 S 4th St., Ste. 400
Las Vegas, NV 89101
Ph: (702)388-6104
Fax: (702)388-6469
Co. E-mail: info@scorelv.org
URL: http://lasvegas.score.org
Linkedin: www.linkedin.com/company/score-mentors-las-vegas
X (Twitter): x.com/SCORE_LasVegas
Description: Provides professional guidance and information to maximize the success of existing and emerging small businesses. Offers business counseling and workshops. **Founded:** 1964. **Geographic Preference:** Local.

41924 ▪ SCORE - Mesquite
11 W Pioneer Blvd.
Mesquite, NV 89027
Ph: (702)388-6104
URL: http://www.score.org/find-location?state=NV
Description: Provides professional guidance and information to maximize the success of existing and emerging small businesses. Offers business counseling and workshops.

41925 ▪ SCORE - Northern Nevada
450 Sinclair St.
Innevation Ctr., Univ. of Nevada Reno
Reno, NV 89501
Free: 844-232-7227
Co. E-mail: help@score.org
URL: http://northernnevada.score.org
Contact: Bridget Weston, Contact
Facebook: www.facebook.com/SCORENNevada
Linkedin: www.linkedin.com/company/score-northern-nevada-chapter-415
X (Twitter): x.com/ScoreReno
Description: Provides professional guidance and information to maximize the success of existing and emerging small businesses. Offers business counseling and workshops. **Geographic Preference:** Local.

41926 ▪ SCORE - Urban Chamber of Commerce
1951 Stella Lake St., Ste. 30
Las Vegas, NV 89106
Ph: (702)648-6222
Fax: (702)685-4050
URL: http://www.urbanchamber.org
Contact: Jarron Gray, Chairman
Facebook: www.facebook.com/UrbanChamber
Linkedin: www.linkedin.com/company/urban-chamber-of-commerce
X (Twitter): x.com/UrbanChamber
Instagram: www.instagram.com/urbanchamberofcommerce
YouTube: www.youtube.com/channel/UCz7qyzIFT-hSTyd-MveeTaQ
Description: Provides professional guidance and information to maximize the success of existing and emerging small businesses. Offers business counseling and workshops.

BETTER BUSINESS BUREAUS

41927 ▪ Better Business Bureau of Southern Nevada
6040 S Jones Blvd.
Las Vegas, NV 89118
Ph: (702)320-4500
Fax: (702)320-4560
URL: http://www.bbb.org/bbb-directory/us/nv
Description: Seeks to promote and foster ethical relationship between businesses and the public through voluntary self-regulation, consumer and business education, and service excellence. Provides information to help consumers and businesses make informed purchasing decisions and avoid costly scams and frauds; settles consumer complaints through arbitration and other means. **Founded:** 1955. **Publications:** *BB Views* (Quarterly). **Geographic Preference:** Local.

CHAMBERS OF COMMERCE

41928 ▪ Beatty Nevada Chamber of Commerce - The Beatty Library District's goals
119 E Main St.
Beatty, NV 89003
Ph: (775)553-2424
Free: 866-736-3716
Co. E-mail: beattychamber95@gmail.com
URL: http://www.beattynevada.org
Contact: Nicole Altman, President
Description: Strives to improve the economic condition of Beatty, Nevada by promoting its environmental, entertainment and other tourist attractions. **Scope:** Computer Technology. **Holdings:** 15,000 Books; Magazines; Newspapers; Books On Cd; Dvds. **Geographic Preference:** Local.

41929 ▪ Boulder City Chamber of Commerce
100 Nevada Way
Boulder City, NV 89005
Ph: (702)293-2034
Fax: (702)293-0574
Co. E-mail: info@bouldercitychamber.com
URL: http://www.bouldercitychamber.com
Contact: Jill Lagan, Chief Executive Officer
E-mail: jill@bouldercitychamber.com
Facebook: www.facebook.com/bouldercitychamber
X (Twitter): x.com/bcnevadachamber
Instagram: www.instagram.com/bcnevadachamber
Description: Promotes business and community development in Boulder City, NV. Conducts annual spring jamboree and annual Christmas parade and fair. **Founded:** 1932. **Publications:** *Communication Link* (Quarterly). **Geographic Preference:** Local.

41930 ▪ Caliente Chamber of Commerce
100 Eepot St.
Caliente, NV 89008
Ph: (775)726-3129
Fax: (775)726-3447
URL: http://www.chamber-commerce.net/dir/5444/Caliente-Chamber-of-Commerce-in-Caliente
Description: Promotes business and community development in Caliente, NV. Sponsors annual Homecoming Festival on Memorial Day weekend. **Geographic Preference:** Local.

41931 ▪ Carson City Area Chamber of Commerce
1900 S Carson St., Ste. 200
Carson City, NV 89701
Ph: (775)882-1565
Fax: (775)882-4179
Co. E-mail: admin@carsoncitychamber.com
URL: http://www.carsoncitychamber.com
Contact: Ronni Hannaman, Executive Director

Description: Promotes business and community development in Carson City, NV. **Founded:** 1945. **Publications:** *Nevada Manufacturers Register* (Annual); *Nevada Statewide Industrial Directory*; *Carson City Area Chamber of Commerce--Membership Business Directory*; *Membership and Business Directory*; *Voice of Business*; *Carson City Area Chamber of Commerce--Membership Business Directory*. **Geographic Preference:** Local.

41932 ■ Carson Valley Chamber of Commerce
1477 US Hwy. 395, Ste. A
Gardnerville, NV 89410
Ph: (775)782-8144
Fax: (775)782-1025
Co. E-mail: info@carsonvalleynv.org
URL: http://www.carsonvalleynv.org
Contact: Alex Uribe, President
Facebook: www.facebook.com/carsonvalleychamber
Linkedin: www.linkedin.com/company/carsonvalleychamber
Instagram: www.instagram.com/carsonvalleychamber
YouTube: www.youtube.com/channel/UC4UDESRNV4IGQRN8aZDf2PQ

Description: Promotes business, community development and tourism in the Carson Valley area of Nevada. **Founded:** 1945. **Publications:** *Business Directory*; *Chamber Connection* (Weekly). **Geographic Preference:** Local.

41933 ■ Dayton Area Chamber of Commerce
555 US Hwy. 50 E
Dayton, NV 89403
Ph: (775)246-7909
Co. E-mail: daytonnvchamber@gmail.com
URL: http://daytonnvchamber.com
Contact: John Cassinelli, President
Facebook: www.facebook.com/Daytonnvchamberofcommerce

Description: Promotes community and business growth in Dayton, Nevada. **Founded:** 1849. **Publications:** *Dayton Area Chamber of Commerce Newsletter* (Monthly). **Geographic Preference:** Local.

41934 ■ Elko Area Chamber of Commerce
1405 Idaho St. Sherman Station
Elko, NV 89801
Ph: (775)738-7135
Fax: (775)738-7136
Co. E-mail: chamber@elkonevada.com
URL: http://www.elkonevada.com
Contact: Billie Crapo, Chief Executive Officer
Facebook: www.facebook.com/elkoareachamber

Description: Promotes business and community development in Elko County, NV. **Publications:** *Business Roundup* (Monthly); *Elko Directory*. **Geographic Preference:** Local.

41935 ■ *Elko Directory*
1405 Idaho St. Sherman Station
Elko, NV 89801
Ph: (775)738-7135
Fax: (775)738-7136
Co. E-mail: chamber@elkonevada.com
URL: http://www.elkonevada.com
Contact: Billie Crapo, Chief Executive Officer
URL(s): www.elkonevada.com/directory
Availability: Online.

41936 ■ Fallon Chamber of Commerce
85 S Maine St.
Fallon, NV 89406
Ph: (775)423-2544
Fax: (775)423-5555
Co. E-mail: info@fallonchamber.com
URL: http://www.fallonchamber.com
Contact: Cynthia McGarrah, President
Facebook: www.facebook.com/fallonchamber

Description: Promotes business and community development in Churchill County, NV. Encourages tourism. Sponsors annual Hearts of Gold Cantaloupe Festival. **Founded:** 1948. **Geographic Preference:** Local.

41937 ■ Fernley Chamber of Commerce
70 N W St.
Fernley, NV 89408
Ph: (775)575-4459
Co. E-mail: info@fernleychamber.org
URL: http://www.fernleychamber.org
Contact: Shannon Ceresola, President
Facebook: www.facebook.com/FernleyChamberOfCommerce

Description: Promotes business and community development in Fernley, NV. Provides visitors' information and sponsors special events. **Founded:** 1969. **Publications:** *Chamber News*. **Geographic Preference:** Local.

41938 ■ Henderson Chamber of Commerce (HCC)
400 N Green Valley Pky., 2nd Fl.
Henderson, NV 89074
Ph: (702)565-8951
Co. E-mail: info@hendersonchamber.com
URL: http://www.hendersonchamber.com
Contact: Scott Muelrath, President
Facebook: www.facebook.com/HendersonChamber
X (Twitter): x.com/hcc_nevada
YouTube: www.youtube.com/hendersonchamberofcommerce

Description: Promotes business and community development in Henderson, NV. **Founded:** 1945. **Publications:** *Henderson Chamber of Commerce--Membership and Business Directory* (Annual); *Chamber Business Directory*; *Chamber Connection* (Monthly). **Geographic Preference:** Local.

41939 ■ Humboldt County Chamber of Commerce
30 W Winnemucca Blvd.
Winnemucca, NV 89445
Ph: (775)623-2225
Co. E-mail: wmcachamber@gmail.com
URL: http://www.humboldtcountychamber.org
Contact: Alicia Davis-Cramer, President

Description: Promotes business and community development in the area. **Founded:** 1920. **Geographic Preference:** Local.

41940 ■ Incline Village Chamber of Commerce
969 Tahoe Blvd.
Incline Village, NV 89451
Ph: (775)832-1606
URL: http://www.laketahoechambers.com/chambers/incline-village-chamber-of-commerce

Description: Promotes business and community development in the Crystal Bay and Incline Village, NV areas. Encourages quality business practices, hospitable treatment of visitors, and community involvement. Maintains business development center. Sponsors theatrical performances. **Founded:** 1976. **Publications:** *The Village Voice* (Monthly). **Geographic Preference:** Local.

41941 ■ Las Vegas Metro Chamber of Commerce
575 Symphony Pk. Ave., Ste. 100
Las Vegas, NV 89106
Ph: (702)641-5822
Fax: (702)735-2011
URL: http://www.vegaschamber.com
Contact: Mary Beth Sewald, President
X (Twitter): x.com/lvchamber
YouTube: www.youtube.com/user/lasvegaschamber

Description: Promotes business and community development in Las Vegas, NV. **Founded:** 1911. **Publications:** *Las Vegas Metro Chamber of Commerce--Business Directory* (Annual); *The Business Voice* (10/year); *Open Door* (Monthly); *Las Vegas Chamber of Commerce--Business Directory*. **Geographic Preference:** Local.

41942 ■ Latin Chamber of Commerce of Nevada, Inc.
300 N 13th St.
Las Vegas, NV 89101
Ph: (702)385-7367
Co. E-mail: info@lvlcc.com
URL: http://www.lvlcc.com
Contact: Peter Guzman, President
E-mail: peter@lvlcc.com
Facebook: www.facebook.com/lccnv
X (Twitter): x.com/lvlcc

Description: Businesses, corporations, and Hispanic individuals interested in developing economic, political, and social power for the Hispanic community. Provides scholarships and career, employment, and procurement programs. Offers business counseling. Sponsors annual golf tournament, eight luncheons, five cocktail mixers and two banquets a year. **Founded:** 1976. **Publications:** *Comunicacion* (Quarterly). **Educational Activities:** Awards Banquet. **Geographic Preference:** Local.

41943 ■ Laughlin Chamber of Commerce
1585 S Casino Dr.
Laughlin, NV 89029
Ph: (702)298-2214
Co. E-mail: info@laughlinchamber.com
URL: http://www.laughlinchamber.com
Contact: Jackie Mazzeo, President
E-mail: jackie@laughlinchamber.com
Facebook: www.facebook.com/laughlin.chamber
X (Twitter): x.com/laughlinchamber

Description: Businesses and professional men and women. Works to foster the civic, commercial and industrial development in the community. **Geographic Preference:** Local.

41944 ■ *Membership and Business Directory*
1900 S Carson St., Ste. 200
Carson City, NV 89701
Ph: (775)882-1565
Fax: (775)882-4179
Co. E-mail: admin@carsoncitychamber.com
URL: http://www.carsoncitychamber.com
Contact: Ronni Hannaman, Executive Director
URL(s): carsoncitychamber.com/directory
Availability: Online.

41945 ■ Mesquite Chamber of Commerce
840 Pinnacle Ct., Bldg. 11, Unit 101
Mesquite, NV 89027
Ph: (702)346-2902
Fax: (702)346-6138
Co. E-mail: info@mesquitechamber.com
URL: http://www.mesquitenvchamber.com
Contact: Carol Kolson, President
E-mail: carol@mesquitenvchamber.com
Facebook: www.facebook.com/MesquiteChamber
X (Twitter): x.com/mesquitenvchmbr
YouTube: www.youtube.com/channel/UCo2cV-7e_lfXurOd_hqfsCw

Description: Promotes business and community development in the area. **Founded:** 1974. **Publications:** *Voice of Business*. **Geographic Preference:** Local.

41946 ■ Mineral County Chamber of Commerce
PO Box 2250
Hawthorne, NV 89415
Co. E-mail: info@chambermineralcountynv.org
URL: http://chambermineralcountynv.org
Contact: Gloria Lopez, President
Facebook: www.facebook.com/chambermineralcountynv
X (Twitter): x.com/CountyMinera

Description: Encourages tourism; supports education. Sponsors fairs and festivals. Conducts community service activities. Publications: none. **Founded:** 1979. **Geographic Preference:** Local.

41947 ■ Moapa Valley Chamber of Commerce
PO Box 361
Overton, NV 89040
Ph: (702)398-7160
Co. E-mail: moapavalleychamber@gmail.com
URL: http://www.moapavalleychamber.com
Contact: Pam Duvall, Manager
Facebook: www.facebook.com/Moapa-Valley-Chamber-of-Commerce-313214702051435
X (Twitter): x.com/MoapaValley

41948 ■ Nevada   **STATE LISTINGS**

Description: Promotes business and community development in the Moapa Valley area of Nevada. Sponsors Clark County Fair and conducts seminars. **Founded:** 1930. **Publications:** *Moapa Valley City Map* (Monthly). **Geographic Preference:** Local.

41948 ■ Pahrump Valley Chamber of Commerce (PVCC)
1301 S Hwy. 160, 2nd Fl.
Pahrump, NV 89048
Ph: (775)727-5800
Co. E-mail: info@pahrumpchamber.com
URL: http://pahrumpchamber.com
Contact: Beth Lee, Co-President
Facebook: www.facebook.com/PahrumpValleyChamber
Linkedin: www.linkedin.com/company/pahrumpvalleychamber
Instagram: www.instagram.com/pahrumpvalleychamber

Description: Promotes business and community development in Pahrump, NV. Encourages tourism. Sponsors the annual Chili Cook Off, Biz Expo, Wild West Extravaganza and Pahrump A Pum Pum. **Founded:** 1975. **Geographic Preference:** Local.

41949 ■ Pershing County Chamber of Commerce and Visitors Center
1005 W Broadway.
Lovelock, NV 89419
Ph: (775)273-7213
URL: http://web.thechambernv.org/Chambers-Of-Commerce/Pershing-County-Chamber-of-Commerce-Lovelock--2783
Contact: Wendy Nelson, Contact
E-mail: wendy@pershingchamber.com
Instagram: www.instagram.com/pershing_chamber

Description: Promotes business and community development in Pershing County, NV. Conducts charitable events. Sponsors competitions. **Publications:** *The Chamber ADVANTAGE* (Monthly). **Geographic Preference:** Local.

41950 ■ Pioche Chamber of Commerce
644 Main St.
Pioche, NV 89043
Co. E-mail: infopiochechamber@gmail.com
URL: http://piochenevada.com/chamber-of-commerce

Description: Promotes business and community development in Pioche, NV. **Geographic Preference:** Local.

41951 ■ Wells Chamber of Commerce
436 6th St.
Wells, NV 89835
Ph: (775)752-3540
URL: http://sites.google.com/joshnicholes.com/wellsnv
Contact: Mindy Carter, President
E-mail: mindy@wellsnevada.com
Facebook: www.facebook.com/WellsNevada

Description: Promotes business and community development in Wells, NV. Sponsors festival, car shows, chariot races, Jr. rodeo, walk, bike, and run marathon. **Founded:** 1869. **Geographic Preference:** Local.

41952 ■ White Pine Chamber of Commerce
636 Aultman St.
Ely, NV 89301-1555
Ph: (775)289-8877
Fax: (775)289-6144
Co. E-mail: wpcc@whitepinechamber.com
URL: http://www.whitepinechamber.com
Contact: Gayle Bartlett, President
Facebook: www.facebook.com/whitepinechamber89301

Description: Promotes business and community development in the Ely, NV area. **Founded:** 1921. **Geographic Preference:** Local.

MINORITY BUSINESS ASSISTANCE PROGRAMS

41953 ■ Nevada Minority Supplier Development Council
1785 E Sahara Ave., Ste. 360
Las Vegas, NV 89104
URL: http://nmsdc.org/nmsdc-regional-affiliates-list
Contact: Cecil Plummer, President

Description: Provides a direct link between corporate America and minority-owned businesses. Increases procurement and business opportunities for minority businesses of all sizes. **Geographic Preference:** State.

FINANCING AND LOAN PROGRAMS

41954 ■ The Benefit Capital Companies, Inc. (BCC)
3235-3245 N Pioneer Rd.
Logandale, NV 89021
Ph: (702)398-3222
Free: 800-922-3767
Fax: (702)398-3700
Co. E-mail: inquiry@benefitcapital.com
URL: http://www.benefitcapital.com
Contact: Kenneth P. Winslow, President

Description: Firm provides investment and merchant banking services for middle-market companies, financial advisory, and much more. **Founded:** 1984. **Training:** Employee Stock Ownership Plans-New Developments in the Creative Uses of ESOPs. **Preferred Investment Size:** $2,500,000 minimum. **Industry Preferences:** Diversified.

41955 ■ Sierra Angels (SA)
450 Sinclair St.
Reno, NV 89501
URL: http://www.sierraangels.com
Contact: Jeff Saling, President

Description: Investment group offers funding, mentoring, and network for early-stage technology companies in Nevada and California. **Founded:** 1997.

41956 ■ Tahoe Technology & Capital Group Inc. (TTCG)
Incline Village, NV
URL: http://www.tahoetechcapgroup.com

Description: Early-stage venture capital firm for media, technology, and green start-ups. **Founded:** 2005.

41957 ■ VTF Capital
5940 S Rainbow Blvd., Ste. 400 No. 49100
Las Vegas, NV 89118-2507
Co. E-mail: ideas@vtfcapital.com
URL: http://vtfcapital.com
Contact: Patrick Olson, Manager
Facebook: www.facebook.com/vtfcapital
Linkedin: www.linkedin.com/company/vegastechfund
X (Twitter): x.com/vtfcapital

Description: Invests in and solves platform-level problems with companies in commerce technology, digital brand, and pre-consumer logistics at the seed and pre-seed stages. **Founded:** 2012. **Preferred Investment Size:** $200,000-$1,000,000.

PROCUREMENT ASSISTANCE PROGRAMS

41958 ■ Nevada Governor's Office of Economic Development (GOED)
808 W Nye Ln.
Carson City, NV 89703
Ph: (775)687-9900
Free: 800-336-1600
Fax: (775)687-9924
Co. E-mail: goed@goed.nv.gov
URL: http://goed.nv.gov
Contact: James Barrett, President
Facebook: www.facebook.com/NevadaGOED
Linkedin: www.linkedin.com/company/nevada-governor's-office-of-economic-development
X (Twitter): x.com/DiversifyNevada
Instagram: www.instagram.com/diversifynevada
YouTube: www.youtube.com/channel/UCnq7jQLnvpfhH02d2dSCbWw

Description: Government agency aims to promote economic development services in Nevada. **Founded:** 2011.

41959 ■ Nevada Governor's Office of Economic Development - Procurement Outreach Program Southern Nevada Regional Office
3300 West Sahara Ave., Level 1, Ste. 104
Las Vegas, NV 89102
URL: http://goed.nv.gov/programs-incentives/procurement-assistance-outreach
Contact: Joan C. Rueben, Director
E-mail: jrueben@goed.nv.gov

Description: Assists small and disadvantaged businesses in Nevada obtain and complete federal government contracts. Also encourages the expansion of the manufacturing and service sectors into government contracting.

INCUBATORS/RESEARCH AND TECHNOLOGY PARKS

41960 ■ Adams Hub
111 W Proctor St.
Carson City, NV 89703
Ph: (775)222-0001
Co. E-mail: info@adamshub.org
URL: http://www.adamshub.org
Facebook: www.facebook.com/AdamsHubforInnovation
Instagram: www.instagram.com/adamshub

Description: Inspires entrepreneurs and help them turn their big ideas into innovative businesses. Provides a collaborative workspace for knowledge-sharing, networking, and learning. **Founded:** 2014.

41961 ■ Henderson Business Resource Center (HBRC)
112 S Water St.
Henderson, NV 89015
Ph: (702)209-3967
URL: http://www.hendersonchamber.com
Contact: Rich Lyles, Contact
E-mail: rlyles@diversifynevada.com

Description: A small business incubator who develops and supports local businesses and strengthens and diversifies the local economy through entrepreneurship training opportunities, mentoring programs and introductions to potential capital sources.

EDUCATIONAL PROGRAMS

41962 ■ Community College of Southern Nevada-Cheyenne Campus (CSN)
3200 E Cheyenne Ave.
North Las Vegas, NV 89030
Ph: (702)651-4000
URL: http://www.csn.edu

Description: Offers a program/classes in small business/small business management. **Founded:** 1971.

PUBLISHERS

41963 ■ Long & Silverman Publishing Inc. (L&S)
800 N Rainbow Blvd., Ste. 208
Las Vegas, NV 89107-1103
Ph: (509)275-9448
Free: 888-902-2766
Fax: (702)477-9733
Co. E-mail: sales@lspub.com
URL: http://www.lspub.com

Description: Publisher of books on business, economics, finances, inspirational, marketing, motivation, success, real estate, self-help, and taxes. **Founded:** 2003.

STATE LISTINGS

41964 ■ Strategic Press Inc.
1460 Pittman Ave.
Sparks, NV 89431
Free: 800-767-5964
Co. E-mail: info@strategicpress.com
URL: http://www.strategicpress.com
Contact: Derek G. Rowley, Contact
Description: Publisher of business and marketing books and special reports for small business owners and entrepreneurs, it also offers audio cassettes, posters and prints, does not accept unsolicited manuscripts and reaches the market through direct mail. **Founded:** 1998.

RESEARCH CENTERS

41965 ■ University of Nevada, Las Vegas - Lee Business School - Center for Business and Economic Research (CBER)
4505 S Maryland Pkwy
Las Vegas, NV 89154
Ph: (702)895-3011
Co. E-mail: cber@unlv.edu
URL: http://cber.unlv.edu
Contact: Andrew Woods, Director
E-mail: andrew.woods@unlv.edu
URL(s): www.unlv.edu/business/cber
Facebook: www.facebook.com/cberunlv
X (Twitter): x.com/cber_unlv
Description: Integral unit of Lee Business School, University of Nevada, Las Vegas. Offers business and economics research expertise for public and private organizations in support of the development of the Nevada economy. **Scope:** Economic impact analysis, feasibility studies, market analysis, and econometric modeling. **Founded:** 1975. **Publications:** *CBER-LIED Report on Housing-Market Conditions; Southern Nevada Business Confidence Index* (Quarterly); *Nevada Kids Count Data Book* (Annual); *Economic Outlook* (Semiannual). **Educational Activities:** CBER Economic Outlook Conferences, To economic sectors and state and local government officials.

VENTURE CAPITAL FIRM

41966 ■ Redhills Ventures
PO Box 370369
Las Vegas, NV 89137-0369
Ph: (702)233-2160
Co. E-mail: info@redhillsventures.com
URL: http://redhillsventures.com
Contact: Rom E. Hendler, Director
Description: Private family investment firm. **Investment Policies:** Well-conceived business plans; experienced management teams; high-growth potential. **Industry Preferences:** Financial; high-tech; healthcare.

New Hampshire

ASSOCIATIONS AND OTHER ORGANIZATIONS

41967 ■ Business Network International New Hampshire [BNI New Hampshire]
53 stiles Rd. C 201
Salem, NH 03079
Ph: (603)893-5853
Fax: (603)893-6144
URL: http://bninh.com/en-US/index
Contact: Lindsay Roberts, Executive Director
Facebook: www.facebook.com/BNI-New-Hampshire-315095168105
Description: Provides both men and women a structured environment for the development and exchange of quality business referrals. Offers members the opportunity to share ideas and contacts. **Geographic Preference:** State.

41968 ■ International Association of Women Manchester Chapter
Manchester, NH
URL: http://www.iawomen.com/chapters/manchester-chapter
Contact: Jennifer Pendleton, President
E-mail: jmpendleton2007@yahoo.com
Description: Serves as network of accomplished women united to achieve professional goals. Provides a forum for sharing ideas and experiences of professional women regarding career success. Promotes an active business and networking community from all industries. **Geographic Preference:** Local.

SMALL BUSINESS DEVELOPMENT CENTERS

41969 ■ Small Business Development Center (SBDC)
10 Garrison Ave.
Durham, NH 03824
Ph: (603)862-2200
Co. E-mail: nh.sbdc@unh.edu
URL: http://www.nhsbdc.org
Contact: Wendy Hunt, President
Facebook: www.facebook.com/NHSmallBusinessDevelopmentCenter
Linkedin: www.linkedin.com/company/nh-sbdc
X (Twitter): x.com/NHSBDC
YouTube: www.youtube.com/user/nhsbdc
Description: Represents and promotes the small business sector. Provides management assistance to current and prospective small business owners. Helps to improve management skills and expand the products and services of members. **Founded:** 1984. **Geographic Preference:** Local.

41970 ■ Small Business Development Center
88 Commercial St.
Manchester, NH 03101
Ph: (603)862-2200
URL: http://www.nhsbdc.org/about/locations
Contact: Andrea O'Brien, Advisor
E-mail: andrea.obrien@unh.edu
Linkedin: www.linkedin.com/company/nh-sbdc
Description: Represents and promotes the small business sector. Provides management assistance to current and prospective small business owners. Helps to improve management skills and expand the products and services of members. **Founded:** 1984. **Geographic Preference:** Local.

41971 ■ Small Business Development Center Seacoast (SBDC)
c/o Warren Daniel
10 Garrison Ave., No. 270N
Durham, NH 03824
Ph: (603)862-2200
Co. E-mail: warren.daniel@unh.edu
URL: http://www.nhsbdc.org/region/seacoast-region
Contact: Warren Daniel, Advisor
E-mail: warren.daniel@unh.edu
Description: Represents and promotes the small business sector. Provides management assistance to current and prospective small business owners. Helps to improve management skills and expand the products and services of members. **Founded:** 1984. **Geographic Preference:** Local.

SMALL BUSINESS ASSISTANCE PROGRAMS

41972 ■ New Hampshire Department of Resources and Economic Development - Division of Economic Development - Business Resource Center
100 N M Str., Ste. 100.
Concord, NH 03301
Ph: (603)271-2591
Co. E-mail: info@nheconomy.com
URL: http://www.nheconomy.com
Contact: Tina Kasim, Program Manager
E-mail: tina.kasim@livefree.nh.gov
Facebook: www.facebook.com/NHEconomy
Linkedin: www.linkedin.com/company/state-of-new-hampshire
X (Twitter): twitter.com/NHEconomy
YouTube: www.youtube.com/user/NHEconomy
Description: Assists companies considering locating in New Hampshire in their review of staffing and facility requirements, marketing considerations, support services, and other services. Also offers complete, current, and reliable information on those sections of the state best able to support a specific project. Also helps existing businesses.

SCORE OFFICES

41973 ■ SCORE - Lakes Region
383 S Main St.
Laconia, NH 03246
Ph: (603)666-7561
Contact: Nancy Strojny, Secretary
Facebook: www.facebook.com/SCORE-Lakes-Region-267985316676922
Linkedin: www.linkedin.com/company/score-lakes-region-nh
X (Twitter): twitter.com/lr_score
Description: Provides professional guidance and information to maximize the success of existing and emerging small businesses. Offers business counseling and workshops. **Geographic Preference:** Local.

41974 ■ SCORE - Merrimack Valley [SCORE - Lebanon; SCORE - Conway]
20 W Park St.
Lebanon, NH 03766
URL: http://scorenh.org/index.html
Description: Provides professional guidance and information to maximize the success of existing and emerging small businesses. Offers business counseling and workshops. **Founded:** 1967. **Geographic Preference:** Regional; Local.

41975 ■ SCORE - Monadnock
34 Mechanic St.
Keene, NH 03431
Ph: (603)352-0320
URL: http://merrimackvalley.score.org/monadnock-branch
Description: Works to provide quality business counseling without charge to residents and business area. **Founded:** 1969. **Geographic Preference:** Local.

41976 ■ SCORE - Nashua
191 Main St.
Nashua, NH 03060
Ph: (603)666-7561
URL: http://merrimackvalley.score.org/branch/score-nashua-nh
Description: Provides professional guidance and information to maximize the success of existing and emerging small businesses. Offers business counseling and workshops.

41977 ■ SCORE - Plymouth, New Hampshire
SCORE Plymouth NH Enterprise Center One Bridge St.
Plymouth, NH 03264
Ph: (603)666-7561
URL: http://www.score.org/find-location
Contact: Frank Callahan, Contact
Description: Provides professional guidance and information to maximize the success of existing and emerging small businesses. Offers business counseling and workshops.

41978 ■ SCORE - Rochester
230 Commerce Way, Ste. 120
Portsmouth, NH 03801
Ph: (603)433-0575
URL: http://seacoast.score.org/mentors/james-r-andrews
Contact: James R. Andrews, Contact
Description: Provides professional guidance and information to maximize the success of existing and emerging small businesses. Offers business counseling and workshops.

STATE LISTINGS

41979 ■ SCORE - Salem, New Hampshire
Salem, NH
Ph: (603)666-7561
URL: http://merrimackvalley.score.org
Description: Provides professional guidance and information to maximize the success of existing and emerging small businesses. Offers business counseling and workshops.

41980 ■ SCORE - Seabrook
25 Liberty Ln.
Seabrook, NH 03874
Ph: (603)433-0575
Co. E-mail: info@scorehelp.org
URL: http://seacoast.score.org
Facebook: www.facebook.com/SeacoastSCORE
Linkedin: www.linkedin.com/company/seacoast-score
Instagram: www.instagram.com/seacoastscore
Description: Provides professional guidance and information to maximize the success of existing and emerging small businesses. Offers business counseling and workshops.

41981 ■ SCORE - Seacoast
230 Commerce Way, Ste. 120
Portsmouth, NH 03801
Ph: (603)433-0575
Fax: (603)433-0576
Co. E-mail: info@scorehelp.org
URL: http://seacoast.score.org
Facebook: www.facebook.com/SeacoastSCORE
Linkedin: www.linkedin.com/company/seacoast-score
Instagram: www.instagram.com/seacoastscore
Description: Provides professional guidance and information to maximize the success of existing and emerging small businesses. Offers business counseling and workshops.

41982 ■ SCORE - Wolfeboro
7 Center St.
Wolfeboro, NH 03894
URL: http://www.score.org/find-location
Description: Provides professional guidance and information to maximize the success of existing and emerging small businesses. Offers business counseling and workshops.

41983 ■ Seacoast SCORE Chapter 185
NH
Ph: (603)433-0575
Co. E-mail: ch.admin0185@scorevolunteer.org
URL: http://www.score.org/seacoast/profile/david-l-underhill
Contact: David L. Underhill, Contact
Description: Represents the interests of retired business professionals who volunteer their experience and knowledge to help small business owners and potential small business owners achieve success. Provides free business counseling and seminars. **Founded:** 1964. **Geographic Preference:** Local.

BETTER BUSINESS BUREAUS

41984 ■ Better Business Bureau of New Hampshire
48 Pleasant St.
Concord, NH 03301
Ph: (603)224-1991
Fax: (603)228-9035
Co. E-mail: info@bbbnh.org
URL: http://www.bbb.org/local-bbb/bbb-serving-new-hampshire
Contact: Robert Shomphe, President
Linkedin: www.linkedin.com/company/bbb-of-new-hampshire
X (Twitter): x.com/BBBNewHampshire
Description: Seeks to promote and foster ethical relationship between businesses and the public through voluntary self-regulation, consumer and business education, and service excellence. Provides information to help consumers and businesses make informed purchasing decisions and avoid costly scams and frauds; settles consumer complaints through arbitration and other means. **Founded:** 1912. **Geographic Preference:** State.

CHAMBERS OF COMMERCE

41985 ■ Bethlehem Visitors Center
2182 Main St., Rt. 302
Bethlehem, NH 03574
Ph: (603)869-3409
Co. E-mail: visitorcenter@bethlehemnh.org
URL: http://bethlehemnh.org
Description: Promotes business and community development in Bethlehem, NH. **Geographic Preference:** Local.

41986 ■ *The Chamber Advantage*
550 Central Ave.
Dover, NH 03820
Ph: (603)742-2218
Co. E-mail: info@dovernh.org
URL: http://www.dovernh.org
Contact: Margaret Joyce, President
E-mail: margaret@dovernh.org
URL(s): www.dovernh.org/newsletter
Released: Monthly **Availability:** Online.

41987 ■ Exeter Area Chamber of Commerce (EACC)
120 Water St., Ste. B
Exeter, NH 03833-0278
Ph: (603)772-2411
Co. E-mail: info@exeterarea.org
URL: http://www.exeterarea.org
Contact: Jennifer Wheeler, President
E-mail: jennifer@exeterarea.org
Facebook: www.facebook.com/EACofC
Linkedin: www.linkedin.com/company/exeter-area-chamber-of-commerce
X (Twitter): x.com/exeterchambernh
Instagram: www.instagram.com/exeter_area_chamber
Description: Promotes business and community development in the Exeter, NH area. **Founded:** 1959. **Publications:** *Crosswinds* (Semiannual); *Crosswinds* (Biennial). **Awards:** Exeter Area Chamber Business of the Year (Annual). **Geographic Preference:** Local.

41988 ■ Franconia Notch Regional Chamber of Commerce
PO Box 755
Franconia, NH 03580
Ph: (603)823-5661
Co. E-mail: info@franconianotch.org
URL: http://www.franconianotch.org
Contact: Kevin Johnson, Director
E-mail: membership@franconianotch.org
Facebook: www.facebook.com/FranconiaNotchChamber
Description: Promotes business and community development in North Central New Hampshire. **Publications:** *Mountain Country* (Annual). **Geographic Preference:** Local.

41989 ■ Greater Claremont Chamber of Commerce (GCCC)
Moody Bldg.
24 Opera House Sq.
Claremont, NH 03743
Ph: (603)543-1296
Co. E-mail: info@greaterclaremontnh.org
URL: http://www.greaterclaremontnh.org
Contact: Cat Andrews, President
Facebook: www.facebook.com/GreaterClaremontChamber
Linkedin: www.linkedin.com/company/the-greater-claremont-chamber-of-commerce
Description: Promotes business and community development in the Claremont, NH area. Sponsors annual Northern Lights in Broadstreet program, a high school career day, and a retail auction. **Founded:** 1917. **Awards:** GCCC Citizen of the Year (Annual). **Geographic Preference:** Local.

41990 ■ Greater Derry Londonderry Chamber of Commerce
29 W Broadway
Derry, NH 03038
Ph: (603)432-8205
Co. E-mail: info@gdlchamber.org
URL: http://gdlchamber.org
Contact: Ashley Haseltine, Co-President
E-mail: ashley@gdlchamber.org
Description: Promotes business and community development in Derry, Hampstead, and Windham, NH. Sponsors Derry Fest Home Days and community decorations and holiday parades. **Publications:** *Network*. **Geographic Preference:** Local.

41991 ■ Greater Dover Chamber of Commerce (GDCC)
550 Central Ave.
Dover, NH 03820
Ph: (603)742-2218
Co. E-mail: info@dovernh.org
URL: http://www.dovernh.org
Contact: Margaret Joyce, President
E-mail: margaret@dovernh.org
Facebook: www.facebook.com/greaterdoverchamber
Linkedin: www.linkedin.com/company/greaterdover
X (Twitter): x.com/doverchamber
Instagram: www.instagram.com/greaterdoverchamber
Description: Promotes business and community development in the Dover, NH area. Solicits convention and tourism business. Sponsors seminars, workshops, sidewalk sales, summer concerts, street festivals, and other activities. Operates tourist information center. Holds Business After Hours for member businesses. **Founded:** 1920. **Publications:** *The Chamber Advantage* (Monthly); *Dining, Lodging and Visitors' Guide* (Annual); *Explore Dover* (Semiannual); *Greater Dover Chamber of Commerce Business Directory*; *Greater Dover Chamber of Commerce Member Directory*. **Geographic Preference:** Local.

41992 ■ Greater Hillsborough Chamber of Commerce
5 W Main St.
Hillsboro, NH 03244
Ph: (603)464-5858
Co. E-mail: info@hillsboroughnhchamber.org
URL: http://ghcocnh.org
Contact: Keith T. Cobbett, Co-President
E-mail: keith@granitestatecomputers.com
Facebook: www.facebook.com/HillsboroughNhChamberOfCommerce
Instagram: www.instagram.com/explore/locations/341576420/greater-hillsborough-nh-chamber-of-commerce
Description: Represents business people. Promotes business and community development in Hillsborough, NH. **Founded:** 1971. **Publications:** *Chamber Update*. **Geographic Preference:** Local.

41993 ■ Greater Hudson Chamber of Commerce (GHCC)
71 Lowell Rd.
Hudson, NH 03051
Ph: (603)889-4731
Co. E-mail: info@hudsonchamber.com
URL: http://www.hudsonchamber.com
Contact: Kelly Goddu, President
Facebook: www.facebook.com/greaterhudsonchamberofcommerce
X (Twitter): x.com/HudsonChamberNH
Description: Promotes business and community development in Hudson, NH. **Founded:** 1968. **Geographic Preference:** Local.

41994 ■ Greater Manchester Chamber of Commerce (GMCC) - Library
54 Hanover St.
Manchester, NH 03101
Ph: (603)792-4100
Fax: (603)626-0910
Co. E-mail: customerservice@manchester-chamber.org
URL: http://www.manchester-chamber.org
Contact: Heather McGrail, President
URL(s): www.gmchamber.co.uk
Facebook: www.facebook.com/grtrmanchester
X (Twitter): x.com/grtrmanchester
Instagram: www.instagram.com/grtrmanchester
YouTube: www.youtube.com/channel/UC338noF8zCfS806jikHTJDQ

41995 ■ New Hampshire

Description: Businesses. Promotes business and community development in northern Hillsborough County, NH. Sponsors educational programs; provides government affairs services. **Founded:** 1954. **Holdings:** Articles; books; periodicals. **Geographic Preference:** Local.

41995 ■ Greater Nashua Chamber of Commerce (GNCC)
60 Main St., Ste. 200
Nashua, NH 03060
Ph: (603)881-8333
Co. E-mail: info@nashuachamber.com
URL: http://www.nashuachamber.com
Contact: Wendy Hunt, President
Facebook: www.facebook.com/GreaterNashuaChamber
Linkedin: www.linkedin.com/company/greater-nashua-chamber-of-commerce
X (Twitter): x.com/NashuaChamber
Instagram: www.instagram.com/greater_nashua_chamber
YouTube: www.youtube.com/c/GreaterNashuaChamberofCommerce/featured

Description: Promotes business and community development in the Nashua, NH area. Conducts lobbying activities; sponsors public affairs programs, golf tournament, and outlook. **Founded:** 1926. **Publications:** *Chamber Update* (Quarterly); *Gateways Relocation and Quality of Life Magazine* (Annual). **Educational Activities:** Greater Nashua Chamber of Commerce Dinner. **Awards:** Greater Nashua Citizen of the Year Award (Annual). **Geographic Preference:** Local.

41996 ■ Greater Ossipee Area Chamber of Commerce (GOACC)
PO Box 121
West Ossipee, NH 03890
Ph: (603)651-1600
Co. E-mail: info@ossipeevalley.org
URL: http://www.ossipeevalley.org
Contact: Lynn Kearney, President
E-mail: shoyt@purityspring.com
Facebook: www.facebook.com/GreaterOssipeeAreaChamberofCommerce
Instagram: www.instagram.com/goacc_nh

Description: Promotes business and economic development in the Greater Ossipee area. **Founded:** 1993. **Awards:** GOACC Scholarship (Annual). **Geographic Preference:** Local.

41997 ■ Greater Portsmouth Chamber of Commerce (GPCC)
500 Market St.
Portsmouth, NH 03801
Ph: (603)610-5510
Fax: (603)436-5118
Co. E-mail: info@portsmouthcollaborative.org
URL: http://www.portsmouthchamber.org
Contact: Ben VanCamp, President
E-mail: ben@portsmouthcollaborative.org
Facebook: www.facebook.com/PortsmouthChamber
Linkedin: www.linkedin.com/company/greater-portsmouth-chamber-of-commerce
X (Twitter): x.com/portschamber
Instagram: www.instagram.com/portschamber
YouTube: www.youtube.com/channel/UCjJmBw9h7eQgCTo-p4mIGlg

Description: Promotes business and community development in the Portsmouth, New Hampshire area and southwestern Maine. Sponsors annual Chamber Children's Day and Pumpkinfest. **Founded:** 1917. **Publications:** *Dividends* (Monthly); *Guide to the Seacoast*. **Geographic Preference:** Local.

41998 ■ Greater Rochester Chamber of Commerce (GRCC)
18 S Main St.
Rochester, NH 03867
Ph: (603)332-5080
Fax: (603)332-5216
Co. E-mail: memberservices@rochesternh.org
URL: http://www.rochesternh.org
Contact: Laura A. Ring, President
E-mail: lring@rochesternh.org
Facebook: www.facebook.com/RochesterChamber

X (Twitter): x.com/GRCCNH

Description: Promotes business and community development in northern Strafford County, NH. Coordinates annual Holiday parade. Holds annual dinner-dance and annual golf outing. **Founded:** 1928. **Publications:** *Buyer's Guide* (Annual); *Update* (Monthly). **Geographic Preference:** Local.

41999 ■ Greater Somersworth Chamber of Commerce (GSCC)
472 High St.
Somersworth, NH 03878
Ph: (603)749-7175
URL: http://gscdtfc.wildapricot.org
Contact: Michael Muise, Chairman

Description: Promotes business and economic development in Somersworth, NH. **Geographic Preference:** Local.

42000 ■ Hampton Area Chamber of Commerce (HACC)
47 Winnacunnet Rd.
Hampton, NH 03842
Ph: (603)926-8718
Co. E-mail: info@hamptonchamber.com
URL: http://www.hamptonchamber.com
Contact: John B. Nyhan, President
E-mail: john@hamptonchamber.com
Facebook: www.facebook.com/hamptonchamber
Instagram: www.instagram.com/hamptonchamber1

Description: Promotes economic development and tourism in the Hampton, NH area. Operates Visitor Welcome Center. **Founded:** 1915. **Publications:** *Activities Guide* (Annual); *Tidings* (Monthly); *Visitors Guide*. **Geographic Preference:** Local.

42001 ■ Hanover Area Chamber of Commerce (HACC)
Ste. 208
53 S Main St.
Hanover, NH 03755
URL: http://www.uppervalleybusinessalliance.com/list/member/hanover-area-chamber-of-commerce-hanover-3684

Description: Promotes business, tourism, and community relation in Hanover, NH area. Operates information booth in summer. Sponsors annual Street Fest and annual Upper Valley Home and Trade Show. **Publications:** *Map*; *Business Directory*. **Geographic Preference:** Local.

42002 ■ Jaffrey Chamber of Commerce (JCC)
7 Main St.
Jaffrey, NH 03452
Ph: (603)532-4549
Fax: (603)532-8823
Co. E-mail: info@jaffreychamber.com
URL: http://www.jaffreychamber.com
Contact: Cyndy Burgess, President
E-mail: cyndyburgess@gmail.com
Facebook: www.facebook.com/people/Jaffrey-Chamber-of-Commerce/100064633693536
Linkedin: www.linkedin.com/home

Description: Businesses, educational institutions, churches, and interested individuals. Promotes business and community development in the Jaffrey, NH area. Sponsors Festival of Fireworks. **Founded:** 1982. **Geographic Preference:** Local.

42003 ■ *Keene and Cheshire County Profile*
Released: Biennial **Price:** $5. **Availability:** Print; Online.

42004 ■ Lake Sunapee Region Chamber of Commerce (LSRCC)
328 Main St.
New London, NH 03257
Ph: (603)526-6575
Co. E-mail: admin@lakesunapeeregionchamber.com
URL: http://lakesunapeeregionchamber.com
Contact: Ashlee Rowley, Director
Facebook: www.facebook.com/LSRCC
Instagram: www.instagram.com/lakesunapeechamber
YouTube: www.youtube.com/channel/UC0_Q_DYjrt_ATGAf7cjExNQ

Description: Promotes business and community development in the New London, NH area. Operates information booth. **Founded:** 1970. **Geographic Preference:** Regional.

42005 ■ Lakes Region Chamber of Commerce
383 S Main St.
Laconia, NH 03246
Ph: (603)524-5531
Co. E-mail: jhaight@lakesregionchamber.org
URL: http://www.lakesregionchamber.org
Contact: Karmen Gifford, President
E-mail: kgifford@lakesregionchamber.org
Facebook: www.facebook.com/LakesRegionChamberNH
X (Twitter): x.com/LakesRegionCoC
Instagram: www.instagram.com/lakesregionchambernh
YouTube: www.youtube.com/user/LRChamberCommerce/channels

Description: Promotes business and community development in the Laconia, NH area. **Founded:** 1920. **Publications:** *Chamber News*. **Geographic Preference:** Local.

42006 ■ *Lincoln-Woodstock Chamber Newsletter*
Released: Monthly **Availability:** Print.

42007 ■ Littleton Area Chamber of Commerce (LACC)
PO Box 519
Littleton, NH 03561
Ph: (603)444-6561
Co. E-mail: info@littletonareachamber.com
URL: http://littletonareachamber.com
Contact: Andrew Macchione, President
Facebook: www.facebook.com/littletonareachamber
Linkedin: www.linkedin.com/company/littleton-area-chamber-of-commerce
Instagram: www.instagram.com/littletonareachamber

Description: Promotes business and community development in the Littleton, NH area. Maintains hospital, industry, commercial, retail service, and community divisions. Sponsors Business Expo, Home & Trade Show Expo, Frostbite Follies Winter Carnival, Riverfront Art Show, Trout Tournament and Fishing Derby, Taste of Littleton, Concerts in the Park Series, Christmas Parade, Santa Party and Holiday Craft Fair Fourth of July Fireworks, Economic Development Celebration Luncheon. **Founded:** 1922. **Publications:** *Membership Directory and Relocation - Tourism Guide* (Annual). **Educational Activities:** Art Show (Annual). **Awards:** Littleton Area Chamber of Commerce Citizen of the Year (Annual). **Geographic Preference:** Local.

42008 ■ *Map*
Ste. 208
53 S Main St.
Hanover, NH 03755
URL: http://www.uppervalleybusinessalliance.com/list/member/hanover-area-chamber-of-commerce-hanover-3684
URL(s): business.hanoverchamber.com/map
Availability: Print.

42009 ■ Meredith Area Chamber of Commerce
272 Daniel Webster Hwy.
Meredith, NH 03253
Ph: (603)279-6121
Co. E-mail: info@meredithareachamber.com
URL: http://www.meredithareachamber.com
Contact: Wendy Bagley, President
Facebook: www.facebook.com/MeredithAreaChamber
Instagram: www.instagram.com/meredithareachamber

Description: Promotes business and community development in the Centre Harbor, NH area. **Geographic Preference:** Local.

STATE LISTINGS

42010 ■ Newport Area Chamber of Commerce
15 Main St.
Newport, NH 03773
Ph: (603)863-1510
Co. E-mail: chamber@newportnhchamber.org
URL: http://www.newportnhchamber.org
Contact: Shannon MacMichael, President
E-mail: shannon.obey@comcast.net
Facebook: www.facebook.com/NewportArea
Description: Promotes business and community development in the Newport, NH area. Sponsors annual Christmas lighting program and beautification projects. Holds weekly band concert during summer. **Geographic Preference:** Local.

42011 ■ North Country Chamber of Commerce
104 Main St., Ste. 206
Colebrook, NH 03576
Ph: (603)237-8939
Co. E-mail: office@chamberofthenorthcountry.com
URL: http://www.chamberofthenorthcountry.com
Contact: Hannah Campbell, President
Facebook: www.facebook.com/NorthCoun
tryChamberofCommerce
X (Twitter): x.com/NCChamberofC
Description: Promotes business and community development in the northern New Hampshire area. Promotes tourism. **Publications:** *North Country Chamber of Commerce - Membership Directory* (Annual). **Geographic Preference:** Local.

42012 ■ Northern Gateway Regional Chamber of Commerce
PO Box 537
Lancaster, NH 03584
Ph: (603)788-2530
Co. E-mail: northerngatewaychamber@gmail.com
URL: http://www.northerngatewaychamber.org
Contact: Kim Doolan, President
Facebook: www.facebook.com/Northern-Gateway
-Regional-Chamber-of-Commerce-130455749120
Instagram: www.instagram.com/northernga
tewaychamber
Description: Promotes business and community development in Lancaster, NH. **Publications:** *Chamber Buzz* (Bimonthly). **Geographic Preference:** Local.

42013 ■ Southern New Hampshire Chamber of Commerce
81 Main St.
Salem, NH 03079
Ph: (603)893-3177
Fax: (603)894-5158
Co. E-mail: admin@gschamber.com
URL: http://salem.southernnhchamber.com
Contact: Donna Morris, President
E-mail: donna@gschamber.com
Facebook: www.facebook.com/
grsalemchamberofcommerce
X (Twitter): x.com/chamber81main
Description: Promotes business and community development in Salem and the surrounding area. **Founded:** 1898. **Publications:** *Community Profiles* (Annual); *Impact* (Bimonthly). **Geographic Preference:** Local.

42014 ■ *Tidings*
47 Winnacunnet Rd.
Hampton, NH 03842
Ph: (603)926-8718
Co. E-mail: info@hamptonchamber.com
URL: http://www.hamptonchamber.com
Contact: John B. Nyhan, President
E-mail: john@hamptonchamber.com
URL(s): www.hamptonchamber.com/member/
newmemberapp
Released: Monthly **Availability:** Print; Online.

42015 ■ Upper Valley Business Alliance (UVBA)
2 S Pk. St.
Lebanon, NH 03766
Ph: (603)448-1203
Fax: (603)448-6489
Co. E-mail: uvba@uppervalleybusinessalliance.com
URL: http://www.uppervalleybusinessalliance.com
Contact: Tracy Hutchins, Executive Director
E-mail: tracy@uppervalleybusinessalliance.com
Facebook: www.facebook.com/
UpperValleyBusinessAlliance
Linkedin: www.linkedin.com/company/
uppervalleybusinessalliance
X (Twitter): x.com/uvba_nh
Instagram: www.instagram.com/uvbanh
Description: Promotes business and community development in Lebanon, NH. **Founded:** 1916. **Publications:** *The Chamber View* (Monthly); *Lebanon Area Street Map*. **Educational Activities:** Home and Trade Show (Annual). **Geographic Preference:** Local.

42016 ■ *Visitors Guide*
47 Winnacunnet Rd.
Hampton, NH 03842
Ph: (603)926-8718
Co. E-mail: info@hamptonchamber.com
URL: http://www.hamptonchamber.com
Contact: John B. Nyhan, President
E-mail: john@hamptonchamber.com
URL(s): www.hamptonchamber.com/visitor-guide
Released: Latest issue 2024. **Availability:** Download; PDF; Online.

42017 ■ Western White Mountains Chamber of Commerce
159C Main St.
North Woodstock, NH 03262
Ph: (603)745-6621
Co. E-mail: info@westernwhitemtns.com
URL: http://westernwhitemtns.com
Contact: Kate Wetherell, President
E-mail: kwetherell@visitwhitemountains.com
Facebook: www.facebook.com/westernwhitemtns
Instagram: www.instagram.com/westernwhitemtns
YouTube: www.youtube.com/channel/UCNPFU1h
-XXDIsr7FaqD-zEA
Description: Promotes business and community development in Lincoln and Woodstock, NH. Provides referral service and mailing list. Operates Lincoln-Woodstock Central Reservation Service and information booth. **Geographic Preference:** Local.

MINORITY BUSINESS ASSISTANCE PROGRAMS

42018 ■ Women's Rural Entrepreneurial Network (WREN)
PO Box 331
Bethlehem, NH 03574
Ph: (603)869-9736
Co. E-mail: hello@wrenworks.org
Contact: Julie A. Weisman, Chairman of the Board
Facebook: www.facebook.com/wrenworksnh
Description: Provides business development and technical assistance to women who would like to start a business. **Founded:** 1994.

FINANCING AND LOAN PROGRAMS

42019 ■ eCoast Angel Network
Portsmouth, NH
Co. E-mail: info@ecoastangels.net
URL: http://www.ecoastangels.net
Contact: Lynn Marsh, Chairman Executive
E-mail: screening@ecoastangels.com
Description: Angel investor group for early-stage companies in the Northeast. **Founded:** 2000. **Investment Policies:** Credible exit strategy; experienced management team; market understanding and opportunity; unfair competitive advantage; defensible intellectual property; realistic financial projections. **Industry Preferences:** Advanced technology; ecommerce; healthcare; industrial products and services.

42020 ■ Harbor Light Capital Partners, LLC (HLCP)
91 Ct. St.
Keene, NH 03431
Ph: (603)355-9954
URL: http://www.hlcp.com
Contact: Todd E. Warden, Vice President, Marketing and Business Development
Description: Venture capital firms for innovative companies in New England and the Intermountain West. Targets the gap between seed and institutional rounds of funding. Also operates out of Idaho. **Founded:** 1911. **Preferred Investment Size:** $1,000,000 to $5,000,000. **Investment Policies:** Disruptive technology; strong intellectual property; large market opportunity; proven entrepreneurs; solid operating plan. **Industry Preferences:** Information technology; healthcare.

PROCUREMENT ASSISTANCE PROGRAMS

42021 ■ New Hampshire Procurement Technical Assistance Center - New Hampshire Economic Development
100 N Main St., Ste. 100
Concord, NH 03301
URL: http://www.nheconomy.com/division-of-economic-development
Contact: Cynthia Harrington, Deputy Director
E-mail: cynthia.j.harrington@livefree.nh.gov

INCUBATORS/RESEARCH AND TECHNOLOGY PARKS

42022 ■ Alpha Loft
135 McDonough St., Unit 21
Portsmouth, NH 03801
Description: A small business incubator seeking to provide a supportive entrepreneurial environment that stimulates the growth of businesses to ensure economic vitality and encourage job creation by providing affordable office space and technical assistance to early-stage companies.

42023 ■ Dartmouth College - Dartmouth Entrepreneurial Network (DEN)
4 Currier Pl., Ste. 107
Hanover, NH 03755
Ph: (603)646-8888
URL: http://www.dartmouth.edu/oett/den
Description: Helps entrepreneurs succeed with support from the DEN Innovation Center. Offers coworking space, a startup bootcamp series, and financial support.

42024 ■ Dartmouth Regional Technology Center (DRTC)
16 Cavendish Ct.
Lebanon, NH 03766
Ph: (603)643-5174
URL: http://www.thedrtc.com
Contact: Trip Davis, Chairman
Description: A small business incubator focusing on developing businesses with a proven concept and a solid plan. It offers an educational and infrastructure support program aimed at developing promising technology startups by assisting them in refining their business plans, helping them identify and seek sources of investment and expertise, and providing them with basic business infrastructure and support to make them as productive as possible in as short a time as possible. **Founded:** 2004.

42025 ■ Enterprise Center at Plymouth (ECP)
1 Bridge St.
Plymouth, NH 03264
Ph: (603)536-2011
URL: http://www.graftonrdc.org/incubators
Description: A business incubator that supports entrepreneurs, small business owners, and overall economic development.

42026 ■ Hannah Grimes Center for Entrepreneurship
25 Roxbury St.
Keene, NH 03431
Ph: (603)352-5063
Fax: (603)352-5063

Co. E-mail: info@hannahgrimes.com
URL: http://www.hannahgrimes.com
Contact: Terrence Williams, President
Facebook: www.facebook.com/HannahGrimesCenter
Linkedin: www.linkedin.com/company/hannah-grimes-center
Instagram: www.instagram.com/hannahgrimescenter
Description: Educates, supports and assists the development of small businesses, entrepreneurs and community builders in Keene, New Hampshire and throughout the Monadnock region.

PUBLICATIONS

42027 ■ *Business NH Magazine*
80 Canal St.
   Manchester, NH 03101
URL: http://www.businessnhmagazine.com
Contact: Heidi J. Copeland, President
URL(s): www.businessnhmagazine.com
Facebook: www.facebook.com/BusinessNHMag
Linkedin: www.linkedin.com/company/business-nh-magazine
X (Twitter): twitter.com/BusinessNHMag
Released: Monthly **Price:** $28, Individuals for cost; $60, Individuals for three years; $85.95, Individuals for regular one year cover price; $46, Two years for two year. **Description:** Contains timely, accurate and comprehensive information that can help you succeed in business, make informed decisions and stay on top of business trends in the Granite State. **Availability:** Print; Online.

VENTURE CAPITAL FIRM

42028 ■ Borealis Ventures
10 Allen St.
   Hanover, NH 03755
Ph: (603)643-1500
Co. E-mail: team@borealis.vc
URL: http://www.borealis.vc
Contact: Ben Shaw, Partner
E-mail: ben@borealis.vc
Linkedin: www.linkedin.com/company/borealis-ventures
X (Twitter): x.com/BorealisVC
Description: Venture capital firm looking to transform healthcare through digital innovation, new therapies, and other technologies. Invests from early to emerging stages. **Founded:** 2002.

New Jersey

ASSOCIATIONS AND OTHER ORGANIZATIONS

42029 ■ **Association of Fundraising Professionals New Jersey Chapter (AFP-NJ)**
PO Box 4147
Toms River, NJ 08756-4147
Ph: (732)279-4258
Co. E-mail: afpnjchapter@comcast.net
URL: http://community.afpglobal.org/afpnewjerseychapter/home
Contact: Gwen Paxon, President
E-mail: president@afp-nj.org
Facebook: www.facebook.com/afpnjchapter
X (Twitter): x.com/AFPNJChapter
Geographic Preference: State.

42030 ■ **Entrepreneurs' Organization - New Jersey Chapter (EO)**
NJ
URL: http://www.eonetwork.org/newjersey
Facebook: www.facebook.com/eonewjersey
Description: Supports entrepreneurs and business owners in New Jersey. Members must be founders, owners, or controlling shareholders of a company grossing more than $1 million annually. **Founded:** 1998.

42031 ■ **International Association of Business Communicators New Jersey (IABC NJ) [IABC New Jersey]**
45 Park Pl., S
Morristown, NJ 07960
Co. E-mail: info@iabcnj.com
URL: http://iabcnj.com
Contact: Deb Capua, President
Facebook: www.facebook.com/iabcnj
X (Twitter): twitter.com/iabcnj
Description: Represents the interests of communication managers, public relations directors, writers, editors and audiovisual specialists. Encourages establishment of college-level programs in organizational communication. Conducts surveys on employee communication effectiveness and media trends. Conducts research in the field of communication. **Founded:** 1970. **Awards:** New Jersey IRIS Award (Annual). **Geographic Preference:** State.

42032 ■ **National Federation of Independent Business New Jersey**
222 W State St.
Trenton, NJ 08608
Ph: (609)337-1532
Co. E-mail: eileen.kean@nfib.org
URL: http://www.nfib.com/new-jersey
X (Twitter): x.comcom/nfib_nj
Description: Trade association of small business owners. Conducts lobbying activities. Provides information to the public and small businesses. **Founded:** 1943. **Publications:** Capitol Coverage (Quarterly). **Educational Activities:** Small Business Summit (Annual). **Geographic Preference:** State.

42033 ■ **New Jersey Business & Industry Association (NJBIA)**
10 W Lafayette St.
Trenton, NJ 08608-2002
Ph: (609)393-7707
Co. E-mail: info@njbia.org
URL: http://njbia.org
Contact: Michele Siekerka, President
E-mail: msiekerka@njbia.org
Facebook: www.facebook.com/NJBIA
Linkedin: www.linkedin.com/company/new-jersey-business-&-industry-association-njbia
X (Twitter): x.com/njbia
YouTube: www.youtube.com/user/NJBusiness
Description: Works to improve business climate through lobbying. Provides member companies with information and money-saving benefits to help their businesses. Sponsors seminars. **Founded:** 1910. **Publications:** *New Jersey Business: A Publication of the New Jersey Business and Industry Association* (Monthly); *Business Voice* (Monthly); *Directory of Manufacturers* (Periodic); *New Jersey Business* (Monthly); *New Jersey Business--New Jersey Hotels and Motels Issue*; *New Jersey Business--Book of Lists* (Annual); *New Jersey Business--Ad Agency Directory Issue* (Annual); *Directory of the 216th New Jersey Legislature*. **Educational Activities:** Impact Symposium (Annual). **Geographic Preference:** State.

SMALL BUSINESS DEVELOPMENT CENTERS

42034 ■ **Bergen Small Business Development Center**
355 Main St.
Hackensack, NJ 07601
Ph: (201)684-7135
URL: http://www.sbdcbergen.com
Description: Represents and promotes the small business sector. Provides management assistance to current and prospective small business owners. Helps to improve management skills and expand the products and services of members. **Geographic Preference:** Local.

42035 ■ **Centenary College Small Business Development Center (SBDC)**
300 Littleton Rd.
Parsippany, NJ 07054
Ph: (908)852-1400
Co. E-mail: sbdc@centenarycollege.edu
URL: http://centenarycollege.allregistrations.com
Description: Represents and promotes the small business sector. Provides management assistance to current and prospective small business owners. Helps to improve management skills and expand the products and services of members. **Geographic Preference:** Local.

42036 ■ **Monmouth/Ocean Small Business Development Center (MOSBDC)**
c/o Brookdale Community 765 Newman Springs Rd.
ATEC Building, Rm. 111
Lincroft, NJ 07738

Ph: (732)842-8685
Fax: (732)224-2061
Co. E-mail: mosbdc@brookdalecc.edu
URL: http://www.mosbdc.com
Contact: Jackeline Mejias-Fuertes, Regional Director
Facebook: www.facebook.com/MOSBDC
Linkedin: www.linkedin.com/company/mosbdc
X (Twitter): x.com/mosbdc
Instagram: www.instagram.com/mosbdc
YouTube: www.youtube.com/user/MOSBDC765
Description: Provides management assistance to current and prospective small business owners in Monmouth. **Founded:** 1979. **Geographic Preference:** Local.

42037 ■ **New Jersey City University Small Business Development Center (NJCUSBDC)**
285 Westside Ave., Ste. 199
Jersey City, NJ 07305
Ph: (201)200-2156
Co. E-mail: sbdc@njcu.edu
URL: http://www.sbdchudsoncounty.com
Facebook: www.facebook.com/SBDCHudsonCounty
X (Twitter): x.com/Sbdchudson
YouTube: www.youtube.com/channel/UC0NpotEtBGKfu4hnfxOSRbg
Description: Represents and promotes the small business sector. Provides management assistance to current and prospective small business owners. Helps to improve management skills and expand the products and services of members. **Geographic Preference:** Local.

42038 ■ **New Jersey Small Business Development Center - Lead Office (NJSBDC)**
1 Washington Pk., 3rd Fl.
Newark, NJ 07102
Ph: (973)353-1927
Fax: (973)353-1110
Co. E-mail: sbdcinfo@njsbdc.com
URL: http://www.njsbdc.com
Contact: Kelly Brozyna, Director
E-mail: kelly.brozyna@business.rutgers.edu
Facebook: www.facebook.com/NJSBDC
Linkedin: www.linkedin.com/in/njsbdchq
X (Twitter): x.com/njsbdc
YouTube: www.youtube.com/channel/UCsPLK9OBnlikzZodyEOtDEw
Description: Provides management consulting services and training to small business owners and entrepreneurs in every county of New Jersey. **Geographic Preference:** State.

42039 ■ **New Jersey Small Business Development Center at Raritan Valley Community College**
PO Box 3300.
Somerville, NJ 08876
Ph: (908)526-1200
Co. E-mail: sbdc@raritanval.edu
URL: http://njsbdc.com/njsbdc-at-raritan-valley-community-college
Contact: Bill Harnden, Director

Description: Represents and promotes the small business sector. Provides management assistance to current and prospective small business owners. Helps to improve management skills and expand the products and services of members. **Founded:** 2010. **Geographic Preference:** Local.

42040 ■ New Jersey Small Business Development Center at Rutgers University-Camden (NJ SBDC)
419 Cooper St.
 Camden, NJ 08102
Ph: (856)225-6221
Fax: (856)225-6621
Co. E-mail: rsbdc@camden.rutgers.edu
URL: http://rsbdc.org
Contact: Robert Palumbo, Director
Facebook: www.facebook.com/NJSBDCRutgers
Linkedin: www.linkedin.com/company/njsbdc-rutgers-camden
Description: Represents and promotes the small business sector. Provides management assistance to current and prospective small business owners. Helps to improve management skills and expand the products and services of members. **Founded:** 1997. **Geographic Preference:** Local.

42041 ■ Rutgers-Newark Small Business Development Center (RNSBDC)
25 James St.
 Newark, NJ 07102
Ph: (973)353-5950
Fax: (973)353-5950
Co. E-mail: rnsbdc@business.rutgers.edu
URL: http://www.rnsbdc.com
Contact: Dr. Tendai Ndoro, President
E-mail: tndoro@business.rutgers.edu
Facebook: www.facebook.com/rnsbdc
X (Twitter): x.com/rnsbdc
Instagram: www.instagram.com/rnsbdc
Pinterest: www.pinterest.com/rnsbdc
Description: Represents and promotes the small business sector. Provides management assistance to current and prospective small business owners. Helps to improve management skills and expand the products and services of members. **Geographic Preference:** Local.

42042 ■ Rutgers, The State University of New Jersey - Rutgers School of Business - Camden - New Jersey Small Business Development Center (NJ SBDC)
419 Cooper St.
 Camden, NJ 08102
Ph: (856)225-6221
Fax: (856)225-6621
Co. E-mail: rsbdc@camden.rutgers.edu
URL: http://www.rsbdc.org
Contact: Robert Palumbo, Director
Facebook: www.facebook.com/NJSBDCRutgers
Linkedin: www.linkedin.com/company/njsbdc-rutgers-camden
Description: Provides comprehensive consulting services and educational opportunities to small business owners and potential owners throughout the state of New Jersey. **Scope:** Small business development. **Founded:** 1986. **Educational Activities:** New Jersey Small Business Development Center Noncredit continuing education program, Leading to a Small Business Certificate of Training.; Small Business Start-up and Doing Business With the Government.

42043 ■ Small Business Development Center at Kean University (SBDC at Kean University)
1 Washington Pk.
 Newark, NJ 07102
Ph: (973)353-1927
Co. E-mail: sbdcinfo@njsbdc.com
URL: http://www.sbdckean.com
Contact: Kelly Brozyna, Chief Executive Officer
URL(s): www.kean.edu/offices/small-business-development-center
Facebook: www.facebook.com/NJSBDC
X (Twitter): twitter.com/njsbdc
YouTube: www.youtube.com/channel/UCsPLK9OBnlikzZodyEOtDEw

Description: Operates in partnership with the U.S. Small Business Administration (SBA) and the New Jersey Commerce and Economic Growth and Tourism Commission; provides free, professional small business consulting and training services. **Founded:** 1977. **Publications:** *Start Up and Business Plan Guides* (Annual). **Awards:** NJSBDC Small Business Success Award (Irregular). **Geographic Preference:** Local.

42044 ■ Small Business Development Center The College of New Jersey (SBDC)
2000 Pennington Ave.
 Ewing, NJ 08628
Ph: (609)771-2947
Fax: (609)637-5217
Co. E-mail: info@sbdcnj.com
URL: http://www.sbdcnj.com
Contact: Lilian Mauro, Regional Director
E-mail: regionaldirector@sbdcnj.com
Facebook: www.facebook.com/sbdcnjfan
Linkedin: www.linkedin.com/company/nj-small-business-development-center-at-the-college-of-new-jersey
X (Twitter): x.com/SBDCatTCNJ
Description: Represents and promotes the small business sector. Provides management assistance to current and prospective small business owners. Helps to improve management skills and expand the products and services of members. **Founded:** 1981. **Geographic Preference:** Local.

42045 ■ William Paterson University Small Business Development Center
131 Ellison St.
 Paterson, NJ 07505
Ph: (973)321-1378
Co. E-mail: sbdc@wpunj.edu
URL: http://www.wpunj.edu/sbdc/contact-us.html
Contact: Kate Muldoon, Regional Director
E-mail: muldoonk@wpunj.edu
Description: Represents and promotes the small business sector. Provides management assistance to current and prospective small business owners. Helps to improve management skills and expand the products and services of members. **Founded:** 1977. **Geographic Preference:** Local.

SMALL BUSINESS ASSISTANCE PROGRAMS

42046 ■ Ceridian Small Business Solutions Div.
34 Maple Ave.
 Pine Brook, NJ 07058-9394
Free: 800-729-7655
URL: http://www.ceridian.com
Description: Services: Provider of payroll and tax filing services for small and medium-sized businesses. **Founded:** 1969.

42047 ■ New Jersey Business Action Center (NJBAC)
33 W State St., 4th Fl.
 Trenton, NJ 08608
Free: 800-537-7397
Co. E-mail: businessactioncenter@sos.nj.gov
URL: http://www.nj.gov/state/bac/index.shtml
Contact: Melanie Willoughby, Executive Director
Facebook: www.facebook.com/njbusinessactioncenter
Linkedin: www.linkedin.com/company/new-jersey-business-action-center
X (Twitter): x.com/NJ_BAC
YouTube: www.youtube.com/channel/UCdKsnITHINuh5Cp-c2v0rHg
Description: Business advocacy team within the Department of State in New Jersey. Directs business owners to government agencies, officials or contacts. Facilitates meetings with regulatory agencies. **Founded:** 2010.

42048 ■ New Jersey Department of Business and Economic Development
36 W State St.
 Trenton, NJ 08625

Ph: (609)858-6700
Free: 844-965-1125
Co. E-mail: customercare@njeda.com
URL: http://www.njeda.com
Contact: Tim Sullivan, Chief Executive Officer
Facebook: www.facebook.com/NewJerseyEDA
Linkedin: www.linkedin.com/company/njeda
X (Twitter): x.com/NewJerseyEDA
Instagram: www.instagram.com/newjerseyeda
Description: Provides complete assistance packages, including financing, site selection, and construction. Package may also include labor recruitment and training.

42049 ■ New Jersey Economic Development Authority - International Trade and Protocol
36 W State St.
 Trenton, NJ 08625
Ph: (609)858-6700
Co. E-mail: customercare@njeda.com
URL: http://www.njeda.com
Contact: Tim Sullivan, Chief Executive Officer
Facebook: www.facebook.com/NewJerseyEDA
Linkedin: www.linkedin.com/showcase/newjerseyeda
X (Twitter): x.com/newjerseyeda
Instagram: www.instagram.com/newjerseyeda
Description: Helps New Jersey companies in export development and expansion. Also encourages foreign investment in the state.

42050 ■ New Jersey Economic Development Authority - Office of the Business Advocate
33 W State St.
 Trenton, NJ 08625-0820
URL: http://www.nj.gov/state/bac/business-advocates.shtml
Contact: Stephen Milgrom, Manager
E-mail: stephen.milgrom@sos.nj.gov
Description: Certify Minority, women- owned and small businesses. Formerly New Jersey Commerce Commission.

SCORE OFFICES

42051 ■ Central Jersey SCORE
PO Box 5333
 Somerville, NJ 08876
Ph: (908)526-1200
Co. E-mail: scorecentraljersey14@gmail.com
URL: http://centraljersey.score.org
Facebook: www.facebook.com/SCORECentralJersey
Linkedin: www.linkedin.com/company/score-mentors-central-jersey
Description: Unites active and retired business management professionals with men and women who are considering starting a small business, encountering problems with their business, or expanding their business. Serves the New Jersey counties of Somerset, Hunterdon, and Middlesex.

42052 ■ SCORE - Bedminster
468 Hill Dr.
 Bedminster, NJ 07921
URL: http://www.score.org/northeastnj/success-story/connecta-pharma
Description: Provides professional guidance and information to maximize the success of existing and emerging small businesses. Offers business counseling and workshops.

42053 ■ SCORE - Branchburg
118 Lamington Rd.
 Branchburg, NJ 08876
Ph: (732)526-1200
URL: http://centraljersey.score.org
Description: Provides professional guidance and information to maximize the success of existing and emerging small businesses. Offers business counseling and workshops.

42054 ■ SCORE - Bridgewater
1 Vogt Dr.
 Bridgewater, NJ 08807
Ph: (908)526-1200
URL: http://centraljersey.score.org

Description: Provides professional guidance and information to maximize the success of existing and emerging small businesses. Offers business counseling and workshops.

42055 ■ SCORE - Cape May Court House
30 Mechanic St.
Cape May Court House, NJ 08210
Ph: (732)505-6033
Co. E-mail: score150@verizon.net
URL: http://oceancounty.score.org/find-location
Contact: Bridget Weston, Chief Executive Officer
Facebook: www.facebook.com/SCOREOceanCounty
Description: Provides professional guidance and information to maximize the success of existing and emerging small businesses. Offers business counseling and workshops.

42056 ■ SCORE - Central Jersey
PO Box 5333
Somerville, NJ 08876
Free: 800-634-0245
URL: http://www.score.org/centraljersey
Facebook: www.facebook.com/SCORECentralJersey
Linkedin: www.linkedin.com/company/score-mentors-central-jersey
Description: Provides professional guidance and information to maximize the success of existing and emerging small businesses. Offers business counseling and workshops.

42057 ■ SCORE - Cherry Hill
Cherry Hill, NJ
URL: http://princeton.score.org/mentors/david-hoffman
Contact: David Hoffman, Contact
Description: Provides professional guidance and information to maximize the success of existing and emerging small businesses. Offers business counseling and workshops.

42058 ■ SCORE - Clifton
2 Gateway Ctr.
Newark, NJ 07102
Ph: (973)645-3982
Co. E-mail: metronj@scorevolunteer.org
URL: http://metronj.score.org
Linkedin: www.linkedin.com/company/score-metro-nj
X (Twitter): twitter.com/SCORE_Metronj
Description: Provides professional guidance and information to maximize the success of existing and emerging small businesses. Offers business counseling and workshops.

42059 ■ SCORE - Clinton
189 Center St.
Clinton, NJ 08809
Ph: (908)238-1935
URL: http://www.score.org/find-location
Description: Provides professional guidance and information to maximize the success of existing and emerging small businesses. Offers business counseling and workshops.

42060 ■ SCORE - East Brunswick
2 Civic Center Dr.
East Brunswick, NJ 08816
Ph: (609)393-0505
URL: http://princeton.score.org
Description: Provides professional guidance and information to maximize the success of existing and emerging small businesses. Offers business counseling and workshops.

42061 ■ SCORE - East Brunswick Investors Bank
645 Rte. 18
East Brunswick, NJ 08816
Ph: (732)613-5710
URL: http://www.score.org/centraljersey/about/resource-partners
Contact: Bruce van Saun, Chief Executive Officer
URL(s): www.citizensbank.com/homepage.aspx
Description: Provides professional guidance and information to maximize the success of existing and emerging small businesses. Offers business counseling and workshops.

42062 ■ SCORE - Edison
60 Raritan Ctr.
Edison, NJ 08837
Ph: (732)346-1090
URL: http://centraljersey.score.org/our-locations-1
Description: Provides professional guidance and information to maximize the success of existing and emerging small businesses. Offers business counseling and workshops.

42063 ■ SCORE - Flemington
240 US-202
Flemington, NJ 08822
Ph: (908)237-0829
URL: http://centraljersey.score.org/our-locations-1
Description: Provides professional guidance and information to maximize the success of existing and emerging small businesses. Offers business counseling and workshops.

42064 ■ SCORE - Florham Park
325 Columbia Tpke., Ste. 101
Florham Park, NJ 07932
URL: http://www.score.org/northwestnj/about/our-locations
Description: Provides professional guidance and information to maximize the success of existing and emerging small businesses. Offers business counseling and workshops.

42065 ■ SCORE - Galloway Township
306 E Jimmie Leads Rd.
Absecon, NJ 08205
Ph: (732)505-6033
URL: http://oceancounty.score.org/content/find-location
Description: Provides professional guidance and information to maximize the success of existing and emerging small businesses. Offers business counseling and workshops.

42066 ■ SCORE - Hillsborough
Township of Municipal Bldg., 379 S Branch Rd.
Hillsborough, NJ 08844
URL: http://www.score.org/tampa
Description: Provides professional guidance and information to maximize the success of existing and emerging small businesses. Offers business counseling and workshops.

42067 ■ SCORE - Jackson
2 Jackson Dr.
Jackson, NJ 08527
Ph: (732)505-6033
URL: http://www.score.org/find-location
Description: Provides professional guidance and information to maximize the success of existing and emerging small businesses. Offers business counseling and workshops.

42068 ■ SCORE - Jersey City
678 Newark Ave.
Jersey City, NJ 07306
Ph: (973)645-3982
URL: http://www.score.org/metronj/about/our-mentoring-locations
Description: Provides professional guidance and information to maximize the success of existing and emerging small businesses. Offers business counseling and workshops.

42069 ■ SCORE - Lakewood
301 Lexington Ave.
Lakewood, NJ 08701
Ph: (732)505-6033
URL: http://oceancounty.score.org
Description: Provides professional guidance and information to maximize the success of existing and emerging small businesses. Offers business counseling and workshops.

42070 ■ SCORE - Little Egg Harbor
290 Mathistown Rd.
Little Egg Harbor, NJ 08087
Ph: (732)505-6033
URL: http://oceancounty.score.org

Description: Provides professional guidance and information to maximize the success of existing and emerging small businesses. Offers business counseling and workshops.

42071 ■ SCORE - Mahwah
100 Ridge Rd.
Mahwah, NJ 07430
URL: http://www.score.org/find-location?state=NJ
Description: Provides professional guidance and information to maximize the success of existing and emerging small businesses. Offers business counseling and workshops.

42072 ■ SCORE - Manahawkin
33 Washington St.
Toms River, NJ 08753
Ph: (732)505-6033
Fax: (732)505-0331
Co. E-mail: score150@verizon.net
URL: http://oceancounty.score.org
Contact: Bridget Weston, Chief Executive Officer
Facebook: www.facebook.com/SCOREOceanCounty
Linkedin: www.linkedin.com/company/score-mentors-ocean-county
Description: Provides professional guidance and information to maximize the success of existing and emerging small businesses. Offers business counseling and workshops.

42073 ■ SCORE - Metro New Jersey
2 Gateway Center, 10th Fl.
Newark, NJ 07102
Ph: (973)645-3982
Co. E-mail: metronj@scorevolunteer.org
URL: http://www.score.org/metronj/about
Linkedin: www.linkedin.com/company/score-metro-nj
X (Twitter): x.com/SCORE_Metronj
Description: Provides professional guidance and information to maximize the success of existing and emerging small businesses. Offers business counseling and workshops. **Geographic Preference:** Local.

42074 ■ SCORE - Monmouth [SCORE Mentors Monmouth]
765 Newman Springs Rd. Brookdale Community Clg., ATeC Bldg., Rm. 110
Lincroft, NJ 07738
Ph: (732)660-5220
Co. E-mail: monmouthscore@gmail.com
URL: http://www.score.org/monmouth
Facebook: www.facebook.com/MonmouthSCORE
Linkedin: www.linkedin.com/company/score-monmouth
YouTube: www.youtube.com/channel/UCb6Unycd5C0OB-UvVEjXi3g
Description: Provides professional guidance and information to maximize the success of existing and emerging small businesses. Offers business counseling and workshops. **Founded:** 1964. **Geographic Preference:** Local.

42075 ■ SCORE - Monmouth Junction
110 Kingston Ln.
Monmouth Junction, NJ 08852
URL: http://princeton.score.org/princeton-counseling-locations
Description: Provides professional guidance and information to maximize the success of existing and emerging small businesses. Offers business counseling and workshops.

42076 ■ SCORE - Montclair
C3 Workplace
26 Pk. St., Ste. 2000
Montclair, NJ 07042
Ph: (973)509-4650
URL: http://www.score.org/metronj/about/our-mentoring-locations
Contact: Robert Schwartz, Contact
Description: Provides professional guidance and information to maximize the success of existing and emerging small businesses. Offers business counseling and workshops.

42077 ■ SCORE - Morristown
285 Madison Ave., Zen Building, Rm. 241
Madison, NJ 07940
URL: http://www.score.org/northwestnj/about/our-loca tions
Description: Provides professional guidance and information to maximize the success of existing and emerging small businesses. Offers business counseling and workshops.

42078 ■ SCORE - Newton, New Jersey
179 US Highway 46, Ste. 15-245
Rockaway, NJ 07866
URL: http://www.score.org/northwestnj
Description: Provides professional guidance and information to maximize the success of existing and emerging small businesses. Offers business counseling and workshops.

42079 ■ SCORE - Northwest New Jersey
179 Hwy. 46, Ste. 15-245
Rockaway, NJ 07866
URL: http://www.score.org/northwestnj
Description: Provides professional guidance and information to maximize the success of existing and emerging small businesses. Offers business counseling and workshops.

42080 ■ SCORE - Ocean County
33 Washington St.
Toms River, NJ 08753
Ph: (732)505-6033
Fax: (732)505-0331
Co. E-mail: score150@verizon.net
URL: http://oceancounty.score.org
Contact: Bridget Weston, Chief Executive Officer
Facebook: www.facebook.com/scoreoceancounty
Linkedin: www.linkedin.com/company/score-mentors -ocean-county
X (Twitter): twitter.com/SCORE_OceanCty
Description: Provides professional guidance and information to maximize the success of existing and emerging small businesses. Offers business counseling and workshops. **Founded:** 1964. **Geographic Preference:** Local.

42081 ■ SCORE - Old Bridge
Municipal Ctr.
1 Old Bridge Plz.
Old Bridge, NJ 08857
Ph: (732)721-5600
URL: http://centraljersey.score.org/our-locations-1
Description: Provides professional guidance and information to maximize the success of existing and emerging small businesses. Offers business counseling and workshops.

42082 ■ SCORE - Plainsboro
9 Van Doren St.
Plainsboro, NJ 08536
Ph: (609)393-0505
URL: http://princeton.score.org
URL(s): www.score.org/find-location
Description: Provides professional guidance and information to maximize the success of existing and emerging small businesses. Offers business counseling and workshops.

42083 ■ SCORE - Princeton
259 Nassau St., Ste. 2
Princeton, NJ 08542
Ph: (609)393-0505
Free: 800-634-0245
Co. E-mail: admin.0631@scorevolunteer.org
URL: http://www.score.org/princeton
Facebook: www.facebook.com/SCOREmen torsPrinceton
Linkedin: www.linkedin.com/company/score-mentors -princeton
X (Twitter): x.com/PrincetonScore
Instagram: www.instagram.com/scorementors _princeton
Description: Provides professional guidance and information to maximize the success of existing and emerging small businesses. Offers business counseling and workshops. **Founded:** 1964. **Geographic Preference:** Local.

42084 ■ SCORE - Princeton Public Library
65 Witherspoon St.
Princeton, NJ 08542
Ph: (609)924-9529
Fax: (609)924-7937
Co. E-mail: refstaff@princetonlibrary.org
URL: http://princeton.score.org
Contact: Jennifer Podolsky, Executive Director
E-mail: jpodolsky@princetonlibrary.org
Linkedin: www.linkedin.com/company/score-mentors -princeton
X (Twitter): x.com/PrincetonScore
Instagram: www.instagram.com/princetonpl
YouTube: www.youtube.com/c/PrincetonPL
Description: Provides professional guidance and information to maximize the success of existing and emerging small businesses. Offers business counseling and workshops.

42085 ■ SCORE - Randolph
214 Center Grove Rd.
Randolph, NJ 07869
URL: http://www.score.org/northwestnj/about/our-loca tions
Description: Provides professional guidance and information to maximize the success of existing and emerging small businesses. Offers business counseling and workshops.

42086 ■ SCORE - Ridgewood
125 N Maple Ave.
Ridgewood, NJ 07450
Ph: (201)336-6090
URL: http://northeastnj.score.org
Facebook: www.facebook.com/ SCORENENewJersey
Description: Provides professional guidance and information to maximize the success of existing and emerging small businesses. Offers business counseling and workshops.

42087 ■ SCORE - Secaucus
1379 Paterson Plank Rd.
Secaucus, NJ 07094
Ph: (973)645-3982
URL: http://www.score.org/metronj/about/our-men toring-locations
Description: Provides professional guidance and information to maximize the success of existing and emerging small businesses. Offers business counseling and workshops.

42088 ■ SCORE - Somerset
675 Franklin Blvd.
Somerset, NJ 08875
Ph: (732)448-4001
Co. E-mail: help@score.org
URL: http://centraljersey.score.org/our-locations-1
Description: Provides professional guidance and information to maximize the success of existing and emerging small businesses. Offers business counseling and workshops.

42089 ■ SCORE - Southern New Jersey
300 Carnegie Ctr., Ste. 150
Princeton, NJ 08540
Ph: (609)393-0505
Co. E-mail: admin.0631@scorevolunteer.org
URL: http://princeton.score.org
Contact: Amulya K. Garga, Chairman
Linkedin: www.linkedin.com/company/score-mentors -princeton
X (Twitter): x.com/PrincetonScore
Description: Provides professional guidance and information to maximize the success of existing and emerging small businesses. Offers business counseling and workshops. **Founded:** 1964. **Geographic Preference:** Local.

42090 ■ SCORE - Summit
75 Maple St.
Summit, NJ 07901
Ph: (908)273-0350
URL: http://www.score.org/find-location?state=NJ
Description: Provides professional guidance and information to maximize the success of existing and emerging small businesses. Offers business counseling and workshops.

42091 ■ SCORE - Teaneck
Teaneck Public Library
840 Teaneck Rd.
Teaneck, NJ 07666
URL: http://northeastnj.score.org
Description: Provides professional guidance and information to maximize the success of existing and emerging small businesses. Offers business counseling and workshops.

42092 ■ SCORE - Totowa
Totowa Business Ctr.
930 Riverview Dr., Ste. 250
Totowa, NJ 07512
URL: http://northeastnj.score.org/resource/northeas t-nj-score-locations
Description: Provides professional guidance and information to maximize the success of existing and emerging small businesses. Offers business counseling and workshops.

42093 ■ SCORE - Union
355 Chestnut St.
Union, NJ 07083
URL: http://www.score.org/metronj
Description: Provides professional guidance and information to maximize the success of existing and emerging small businesses. Offers business counseling and workshops.

42094 ■ SCORE - Warren, New Jersey
42 Mountain Blvd.
Warren, NJ 07059
URL: http://www.score.org/northwestnj
Description: Provides professional guidance and information to maximize the success of existing and emerging small businesses. Offers business counseling and workshops.

42095 ■ SCORE - Westfield
212 Lenox Ave.
Westfield, NJ 07090
Ph: (973)645-3982
URL: http://www.score.org/metronj
Description: Provides professional guidance and information to maximize the success of existing and emerging small businesses. Offers business counseling and workshops.

42096 ■ SCORE - Woodbridge
91 Main St.
Woodbridge, NJ 07095
Ph: (732)636-4000
URL: http://centraljersey.score.org
Description: Provides professional guidance and information to maximize the success of existing and emerging small businesses. Offers business counseling and workshops.

42097 ■ Southern New Jersey SCORE
259 Nassau St., Ste. 2
Princeton, NJ 08542
Ph: (609)393-0505
Co. E-mail: admin.0631@scorevolunteer.org
URL: http://www.score.org/princeton
Contact: Liz Sara, President
Facebook: www.facebook.com/SCOREmen torsPrinceton
X (Twitter): x.com/PrincetonScore

BETTER BUSINESS BUREAUS

42098 ■ Better Business Bureau of New Jersey (BBB)
1262 Whitehorse-Hamilton Sq. Rd., Bldg. A, Ste. 202
Hamilton Township, NJ 08690
Ph: (609)588-0808
Fax: (609)588-0546
Co. E-mail: info@newjersey.bbb.org
URL: http://www.bbb.org/local-bbb/bbb-serving-new -jersey

STATE LISTINGS

Contact: Melissa Companick, President
Facebook: www.facebook.com/bbbnewjersey
Linkedin: www.linkedin.com/company/bbbnewjersey
X (Twitter): x.com/bbbnewjersey
Description: Promotes and fosters ethical relationships between businesses and the public through voluntary self-regulation, consumer and business education, and service excellence. **Founded:** 1962. **Publications:** *Better Business Bureau of New Jersey Consumer Guide* (Annual). **Geographic Preference:** Local.

CHAMBERS OF COMMERCE

42099 ■ Asbury Park Chamber of Commerce (APCC)
1201 Springwood Ave., Unit 104
Asbury Park, NJ 07712
Ph: (732)775-7676
Fax: (732)775-7675
Co. E-mail: info@asburyparkchamber.com
URL: http://www.asburyparkchamber.com
Contact: Chris Femiano, President
X (Twitter): x.com/AsburyParkChmbr
Description: Professionals, non-profit organizations, services, hotels, restaurants, and others. Promotes business and community development in the Asbury Park, NJ area. Sponsors jazz festival, Easter parade, and Columbus Day Landing. **Founded:** 1971. **Geographic Preference:** Local.

42100 ■ Avalon Chamber of Commerce
2989 Ocean Dr.
Avalon, NJ 08202
Ph: (609)967-3936
Co. E-mail: info@visitavalonnj.com
URL: http://www.visitavalonnj.com/#!event-list
Facebook: www.facebook.com/avalonnewjersey
X (Twitter): x.com/visitavalonnj
Description: Promotes business and community development in Avalon, NJ. **Publications:** *Advertising Brochure* (Annual). **Geographic Preference:** Local.

42101 ■ Brick Township Chamber of Commerce
270 Chambers Bridge Rd., Ste. 6
Brick, NJ 08723
Ph: (732)477-4949
Fax: (732)477-5788
Co. E-mail: info@brickchamber.com
URL: http://www.brickchamber.com
Contact: Scott Greenberg, President
Facebook: www.facebook.com/BrickChamber
Linkedin: www.linkedin.com/company/10090933
Instagram: www.instagram.com/brickchamber
Description: Represents the interests of retailers, businesses, and professionals. Promotes business and community development in Brick Township, NJ. Sponsors monthly educational seminars. **Founded:** 1956. **Publications:** *Brick Lifestyles* (Annual). **Awards:** Brick Township Distinguished Citizens Awards (Annual). **Geographic Preference:** Local.

42102 ■ Bridgeton Area Chamber of Commerce (BACC)
Hopewell Twp. Municipal Bldg., 590 Shiloh Pke.
Bridgeton, NJ 08302
Ph: (856)455-1312
URL: http://www.cumberlandgrows.com/bridgeton-chamber-of-commerce
Contact: Tony Stanzione, Executive Director
Description: Promotes business and economic development in Bridgeton, NJ. **Founded:** 1890. **Geographic Preference:** Local.

42103 ■ Brigantine Beach Chamber of Commerce
1012 W Brigantine Ave.
Brigantine, NJ 08203
Ph: (609)800-2321
Co. E-mail: brigantinechamber@gmail.com
URL: http://brigantinechamber.com
Contact: Ken Schaffer, Contact
E-mail: ken.schaffer@outlook.com
Facebook: www.facebook.com/search/top

Description: Promotes business and community development in Brigantine, NJ. **Founded:** 1926. **Publications:** *Brigantine Beach - Where Mankind and Nature Thrive in Harmony*. **Geographic Preference:** Local.

42104 ■ Burlington County Regional Chamber of Commerce (BCRCC)
520 Fellowship Rd. E502
Mount Laurel, NJ 08054
Ph: (856)439-2520
Co. E-mail: admin@bcrcc.com
URL: http://www.bcrcc.com
Contact: Kristi M. Howell, President
Facebook: www.facebook.com/BCRChamber
Linkedin: www.linkedin.com/groups/698557
X (Twitter): x.com/BCRChamber
Instagram: www.instagram.com/burlingtoncountychamber
Description: Promotes business and community development in Burlington County, NJ. **Founded:** 1964. **Publications:** *The Communicator* (Weekly). **Geographic Preference:** Local.

42105 ■ Burlington Mercer Chamber of Commerce
PO Box 65
Bordentown, NJ 08505
Ph: (609)298-7774
Co. E-mail: info@burlingtonmercerchamber.org
URL: http://burlingtonmercerchamber.org
Contact: William Ryan, President
Facebook: www.facebook.com/BurlingtonMercerChamber
X (Twitter): x.com/burlmerchamber
Description: Promotes business and community development in the Bordentown, NJ area. **Geographic Preference:** Local.

42106 ■ *Business Directory and Buyer's Guide*
429 Hollywood Ave.
Carneys Point, NJ 08069
Ph: (856)351-2245
Co. E-mail: info@salemcountychamber.com
URL: http://salemcountychamber.com
Contact: Jennifer Jones, Executive Director
E-mail: jennifer@salemcountychamber.com
URL(s): salemcountychamber.com/business-directory-shoppers-guide
Description: Contains the complete listing of Chamber members. **Availability:** Print; Online.

42107 ■ *Business Directory and Map*
195 Changebridge Rd.
Montville, NJ 07045
Ph: (973)263-3310
Fax: (973)263-3453
Co. E-mail: info@montvillechamber.org
URL: http://montvillechamber.org
Contact: Danielle Speciale, President
URL(s): www.montvillechamber.org/membership
Availability: Online.

42108 ■ Camden County Regional Chamber of Commerce
1916 Old Cuthbert Rd., Unit B-17
Cherry Hill, NJ 08034
Ph: (856)667-1600
Fax: (856)667-1464
URL: http://camdencountychamber.com
Contact: David P. Mickelson, President
Facebook: www.facebook.com/CamdenCountyRegionalChamber
X (Twitter): x.com/camcochamber
Instagram: www.instagram.com/camden_county_chamber
Description: Promotes business and community development in Cherry Hill, NJ. **Founded:** 1977. **Publications:** *The Commentary* (Monthly). **Geographic Preference:** Local.

42109 ■ Cape May County Chamber of Commerce
13 Crest Haven Rd.
Cape May Court House, NJ 08210
Ph: (609)465-7181

Co. E-mail: info@cmcchamber.com
URL: http://www.capemaycountychamber.com/main/home
Contact: John Kelly, Accountant
E-mail: john@cmcchamber.com
Linkedin: www.linkedin.com/company/cmcchamber
X (Twitter): x.com/CMCChamber
Description: Promotes business and community development in Cape May County, NJ. **Founded:** 1944. **Publications:** *C.M. Co. St. Maps & Guide*; *Jersey Cape Vacation Guide* (Annual); *Jersey Caper* (Bimonthly). **Geographic Preference:** Local.

42110 ■ Chamber of Commerce of Greater Cape May
PO Box 556
Cape May, NJ 08204
Ph: (609)884-5508
Fax: (609)884-2054
Co. E-mail: contact@capemaychamber.com
URL: http://www.capemaychamber.com
Facebook: www.facebook.com/CapeMayChamber
X (Twitter): x.com/VisitCapeMay
Description: Promotes business and community development in the Cape May, NJ area. Sponsors festival and competitions; conducts charitable activities. **Founded:** 1951. **Publications:** *Christmas in Cape May*; *Tulip Festival* (Periodic); *Cape May Visitor's Guide*. **Geographic Preference:** Local.

42111 ■ Chamber of Commerce Serving Old Bridge, Sayreville and South Amboy [Old Bridge, Sayreville & South Amboy Chamber of Commerce]
2695 Rte. 516, Ste. 7
Old Bridge, NJ 08857
Ph: (732)607-6340
Co. E-mail: ccommerceobssa@gmail.com
URL: http://www.chamberofcommerceobssa.org
Contact: David Lee Hernandez, Jr., President
Description: Promotes and advocates for local businesses. **Founded:** 1987. **Geographic Preference:** Local.

42112 ■ Chamber of Commerce Southern New Jersey (CCSNJ)
220 Laurel Rd., Ste. 203
Voorhees, NJ 08043
Ph: (856)424-7776
URL: http://www.chambersnj.com
Contact: Christina M. Renna, President
E-mail: crenna@chambersnj.com
Facebook: www.facebook.com/ChamberofCommerceSouthernNewJersey
X (Twitter): x.com/CCSNJ
Instagram: www.instagram.com/ccsnj
YouTube: www.youtube.com/user/CCSouthernNJ
Description: Provides its members with opportunities to meet each other and network, resources to enhance their positions in the marketplace, and a collective voice on public policy issues that impact on operations and profitability. **Founded:** 1873. **Geographic Preference:** Local.

42113 ■ *Chamber Information Booklet*
URL(s): stoneharborbeach.com/wp-content/uploads/2015/07/StoneHarborVactionGuide.pdf
Availability: Print; PDF.

42114 ■ *Chamberfax*
24 Beechwood Rd., Ste. 229
Summit, NJ 07902-0824
Ph: (908)522-1700
Co. E-mail: info@suburbanchambers.org
URL: http://www.suburbanchambers.org
Contact: Karen Hadley, Executive Director
E-mail: khadley@suburbanchambers.org
URL(s): www.suburbanchambers.org/membership-information
Released: Monthly **Description:** Sent via fax and on-line. **Availability:** Print.

42115 ■ *The Collection*
24 Beechwood Rd., Ste. 229
Summit, NJ 07902-0824
Ph: (908)522-1700
Co. E-mail: info@suburbanchambers.org

URL: http://www.suburbanchambers.org
Contact: Karen Hadley, Executive Director
E-mail: khadley@suburbanchambers.org
URL(s): www.suburbanchambers.org/the-collection-magazine
Ed: Diane Gallo. **Released:** Semiannual **Availability:** Online.

42116 ■ Cranford Chamber of Commerce
8 Springfield Ave.
  Cranford, NJ 07016
Ph: (908)272-6114
Fax: (908)272-3742
Co. E-mail: info@cranford.com
URL: http://www.cranford.com/chamber
Contact: Andis Kalnins, President
Facebook: www.facebook.com/cranfordweb
X (Twitter): x.com/cranfordweb
Description: Promotes business and community development in Cranford, NJ. **Founded:** 1871. **Geographic Preference:** Local.

42117 ■ Delaware River Towns Chamber of Commerce & Visitors Bureau
PO Box 210
  Lambertville, NJ 08530
Ph: (609)397-0055
URL: http://lambertvillechamber.com
Contact: Cindy Kunnas, Director
E-mail: director@lambertvillechamber.com
Description: Small business owners. Promotes business and community development in the Lambertville, NJ area. Sponsors annual Shad Festival and arts and crafts show. **Founded:** 1972. **Geographic Preference:** Local.

42118 ■ East Brunswick Regional Chamber of Commerce (EBRCC)
1 Civic Center Dr.
  East Brunswick, NJ 08816
URL: http://www.ebrcc.org
Contact: Joe Kim, President
Facebook: www.facebook.com/pg/ebchamber
Linkedin: www.linkedin.com/company/ebrcc
Instagram: www.instagram.com/ebrcc08816
Description: Promotes business and community development in the East Brunswick, NJ area. **Founded:** 2017. **Geographic Preference:** Local.

42119 ■ East Orange Chamber of Commerce (EOCC)
PO Box 2418
  East Orange, NJ 07019-2418
Ph: (973)674-0900
URL: http://www.uschamber.com/co/chambers/new-jersey/east-orange
Description: Promotes business and community development in East Orange, NJ. **Founded:** 1924. **Geographic Preference:** Local.

42120 ■ Eastern Monmouth Area Chamber of Commerce (EMACC)
8 Reckless Pl., Ste. 1
  Red Bank, NJ 07701
Ph: (732)741-0055
Co. E-mail: info@emacc.org
URL: http://emacc.org
Contact: Dominic Latorraca, Secretary
Linkedin: www.linkedin.com/company/eastern-monmouth-area-chamber-of-commerce
X (Twitter): x.com/emaccnj
Instagram: www.instagram.com/emaccnj
YouTube: www.youtube.com/channel/UCG0inCwhSfWVMtDnVWWp3VQ
Description: Promotes business and community development in Eastern Monmouth-Red Bank, NJ area. Sponsors festivals and hall of fame; presents business and service awards. Operates county welcome center and tourism development. **Founded:** 1928. **Geographic Preference:** Local.

42121 ■ Edison Chamber of Commerce (ECC)
939 Amboy Ave.
  Edison, NJ 08837
Ph: (732)738-9482
Co. E-mail: admin@edisonchamber.com
URL: http://www.edisonchamber.com
Contact: Joe Coyle, President
Facebook: www.facebook.com/EdisonChamberOfCommerce
X (Twitter): x.com/EdisonChamber
YouTube: www.youtube.com/user/edisonchamber
Description: Promotes business and community development in Edison, NJ. Sponsors business/education week, golf classic, Taste of Middlesex, award dinner and Memorial Day parade. **Founded:** 1952. **Publications:** *Edison Highlights* (Quarterly). **Awards:** Edison Chamber of Commerce Educator of the Year (Annual); Edison Chamber of Commerce Chamber Member of the Year (Annual). **Geographic Preference:** Local.

42122 ■ Englewood Chamber of Commerce (ECC)
PO Box 8161
  Englewood, NJ 07631
Ph: (201)567-2381
URL: http://nnjchamber.com
Contact: Carol Rauscher, President
E-mail: crauscher@nnjchamber.com
Facebook: www.facebook.com/EnglewoodChamberofCommerce
Instagram: www.instagram.com/englewoodchamberofcommerce
Description: Promotes business and community development in Englewood, NJ. Sponsors sidewalk sale. **Publications:** *Shopping Guide* (Biennial). **Geographic Preference:** Local.

42123 ■ Fair Lawn Chamber of Commerce (FL)
8-01 Fair Lawn Ave.
  Fair Lawn, NJ 07410
Ph: (201)796-7050
Co. E-mail: info@fairlawnchamber.org
URL: http://www.fairlawnchamber.org
Facebook: www.facebook.com/fairlawnchamber
Instagram: www.instagram.com/fairlawnchamberofcommerce
Description: Promotes business and community development in Fair Lawn, NJ. **Founded:** 1954. **Publications:** *Fair Lawn Chamber of Commerce Membership Directory and Community Guide* (Biennial); *Fair Lawn Focus* (Monthly). **Geographic Preference:** Local.

42124 ■ Fort Lee Regional Chamber of Commerce (FLRCC)
210 Whiteman St., Ste. 102
  Fort Lee, NJ 07024
Ph: (201)944-7575
Co. E-mail: assistant@fortleechamber.com
URL: http://www.fortleechamber.com
Contact: Jeffrey Ware, President
Facebook: www.facebook.com/flrcc
X (Twitter): x.com/FLRCC
Description: Promotes business and community development in Fort Lee, NJ. **Founded:** 1950. **Publications:** *Community Directory* (Annual); *Fortleenj.com* (Monthly). **Geographic Preference:** Local.

42125 ■ Gateway Regional Chamber of Commerce
135 Jefferson Ave.
  Elizabeth, NJ 07201
Ph: (908)352-0900
Co. E-mail: info@gatewaychamber.com
URL: http://gatewaychamber.com
Contact: James R. Coyle, President
E-mail: jamescoyle@gatewaychamber.com
Description: Promotes business and community development in Central New Jersey. Conducts annual Plainfield Festival of Art. **Geographic Preference:** Local.

42126 ■ Gloucester County Chamber of Commerce (GLOCO)
205 Rowan Blvd.
  Glassboro, NJ 08028
Ph: (856)881-6560
Co. E-mail: lvail@gloucestercountychamber.com
URL: http://gc-chamber.com
Contact: Janet Garraty, Executive Director
E-mail: director@gc-chamber.com
Facebook: www.facebook.com/GCCCNJ
Linkedin: www.linkedin.com/company/gcccnj
X (Twitter): x.com/GCCCNJ
Instagram: www.instagram.com/gcccnj
YouTube: www.youtube.com/user/GCCCNJ
Description: Promotes business and community development in the Gloucester County, VA area. **Founded:** 1965. **Publications:** *Insider* (Monthly). **Geographic Preference:** Local.

42127 ■ Greater Atlantic City Chamber (GACC)
12 S Virginia Ave.
  Atlantic City, NJ 08401
Ph: (609)345-4524
Fax: (609)345-1666
Co. E-mail: info@acchamber.com
URL: http://acchamber.com
Contact: Michael Chait, President
E-mail: mchait@acchamber.com
Facebook: www.facebook.com/ACChamber
Linkedin: www.linkedin.com/company/greater-atlantic-city-chamber
X (Twitter): x.com/ACChamber
Instagram: www.instagram.com/greateracchamber
YouTube: www.youtube.com/user/GreaterACChamber
Description: Promotes business and community development in the Atlantic City, NJ area. **Founded:** 1914. **Geographic Preference:** Local.

42128 ■ Greater Elizabeth Chamber of Commerce (GECC)
456 N Broad St.
  Elizabeth, NJ 07208
Ph: (908)355-7600
URL: http://www.elizabethchamber.com
Contact: Jennifer Costa, President
E-mail: jcosta@goelizabethnj.com
Facebook: www.facebook.com/elizabethnjchamber
Linkedin: www.linkedin.com/company/elizabethchamber
X (Twitter): x.com/ElizNJChamber
Instagram: www.instagram.com/elizabethnjchamber
YouTube: www.youtube.com/channel/UC_0zV8AfkDV8jKwf3UQLQIA/featured
Description: Promotes business and community development in Elizabeth, NJ. **Founded:** 1997. **Publications:** *Chamber News* (Monthly). **Geographic Preference:** Local.

42129 ■ Greater Glassboro Chamber of Commerce (GCC)
PO Box 651
  Glassboro, NJ 08028
Ph: (856)881-7900
Fax: (856)881-2399
Co. E-mail: info@glassborochamber.com
URL: http://chamber-commerce.net/dir/7106/Greater-Glassboro-Chamber-of-Commerce-in-Glassboro
Description: Promotes business and community development in Glassboro, NJ. **Geographic Preference:** Local.

42130 ■ Greater Hammonton Chamber of Commerce
10 S Egg Harbor Rd.
  Hammonton, NJ 08037
Ph: (609)561-9080
Co. E-mail: info@hammontonnj.us
URL: http://www.hammontonnj.us
Facebook: www.facebook.com/GreaterHammontonChamberofCommerce
Description: Promotes business and community development in Hammonton, NJ. Promotes agricultural and cultural interests. Sponsors annual Red, White, and Blueberry Festival. **Founded:** 1926. **Publications:** *Hammonton Business Directory* (Annual). **Geographic Preference:** Local.

42131 ■ Greater Long Branch Chamber of Commerce (GLBCC)
228 Broadway
  Long Branch, NJ 07740
Ph: (732)222-0400

STATE LISTINGS

New Jersey ■ 42148

Co. E-mail: info@longbranchchamber.org
URL: http://www.longbranchchamber.org
Contact: Pauline Poyner, President
Facebook: www.facebook.com/longbranchchamber
Description: Promotes business and community development in the Long Branch, NJ area. Sponsors 4th of July Celebration Festival (Oceanfest), Business Expo, Annual Awards Dinner, Golf Outing & Antique Show. **Founded:** 1933. **Geographic Preference:** Local.

42132 ■ Greater Millville Chamber of Commerce (GMCC)
600 G St., Ste. 540
Millville, NJ 08332
Ph: (856)825-2600
Co. E-mail: chamber@millville-nj.com
URL: http://www.millville-nj.com
Contact: Donald Daigle, President
Facebook: www.facebook.com/millvillechamberofcommerce
X (Twitter): x.com/MillvilleOf
Description: Represents professional, industrial, retail, and civic organizations and individuals. Promotes business and community development in Millville, NJ. Sponsors festival. Conducts charitable activities. **Publications:** *Business Directory*. **Geographic Preference:** Local.

42133 ■ Greater Paterson Chamber of Commerce (GPCC)
100 Hamilton Plz., Ste. 1201
Paterson, NJ 07505
Ph: (973)881-7300
Fax: (973)881-8233
Co. E-mail: info@greaterpatersoncc.org
URL: http://greaterpatersoncc.org
Contact: Orlando Cruz, President
E-mail: ocruz@greaterpatersoncc.org
Facebook: www.facebook.com/greaterpatersonchamber
Description: Promotes business and community development in the Paterson, NJ area. **Founded:** 1918. **Publications:** *News Bulletin* (Bimonthly); *Paterson Independent News* (Bimonthly). **Geographic Preference:** Local.

42134 ■ Greater Spring Lake Area Chamber of Commerce
313 Washington Ave.
Spring Lake, NJ 07762
Ph: (732)449-0577
Co. E-mail: info@springlake.org
URL: http://www.springlake.org
Contact: George D'Amico, Officer
X (Twitter): x.com/greaterspringlk
YouTube: www.youtube.com/channel/UCW3I
dnux0QAyPhVEJNWyS2g
Description: Promotes business and community development in Spring Lake and the surrounding area. **Geographic Preference:** Local.

42135 ■ Greater Toms River Chamber of Commerce (GTRCC)
PO Box 2106
Toms River, NJ 08754
Ph: (732)349-0220
Co. E-mail: info@tomsriverchamber.com
URL: http://tomsriverchamber.com
Contact: Danielle Norcross, Chief Executive Officer
E-mail: danielle@tomsriverchamber.com
Facebook: www.facebook.com/tomsriverchamber
Linkedin: www.linkedin.com/in/tomsriverchamber
X (Twitter): x.com/gtrchamber
Instagram: www.instagram.com/trchamber
YouTube: www.youtube.com/user/TROCCHAMBER
Description: Promotes business development in Ocean County, New Jersey. **Founded:** 1918. **Geographic Preference:** Local.

42136 ■ Greater Vineland Chamber of Commerce (GVCC)
2115 S Delsea Dr.
Vineland, NJ 08360
Ph: (856)691-7400
Co. E-mail: info@vinelandchamber.org
URL: http://www.vinelandchamber.org

Contact: Dawn S. Hunter, Executive Director
X (Twitter): x.com/vinelandchamber
Instagram: www.instagram.com/vinelandchamber
Description: Promotes business and community development in the Vineland, NJ area. Sponsors Dandelion Festival. **Founded:** 1919. **Publications:** *Vineland* (Periodic); *Area Info Guide*; *News and Views* (Monthly). **Geographic Preference:** Local.

42137 ■ Greater Westfield Area Chamber of Commerce (GWACC)
212 Lenox Ave.
Westfield, NJ 07090
Ph: (908)233-3021
Co. E-mail: info@gwaccnj.com
URL: http://www.gwaccnj.com
Contact: Darielle Walsh, President
E-mail: dariellewalsh@comcast.net
Facebook: www.facebook.com/GWACC
Linkedin: www.linkedin.com/company/gwacc
X (Twitter): x.com/GWACC_NJ
Instagram: www.instagram.com/gwaccnj212
Description: Promotes business and community development in the Westfield, NJ area. Sponsors charitable events. Holds Westfield Spring Fling & FestiFall street fairs. **Founded:** 1948. **Publications:** *Business Directory*; *In Town* (Semimonthly). **Educational Activities:** GWACC Networking Happy Hour. **Geographic Preference:** Local.

42138 ■ Greater Wildwood Chamber of Commerce (GWCOC)
3306 Pacific Ave.
Wildwood, NJ 08260
Ph: (609)729-4000
Co. E-mail: info@gwcoc.org
URL: http://www.gwcoc.org
Contact: Angel Daniels, President
Facebook: www.facebook.com/theWildwoodsNJ
X (Twitter): x.com/theWildwoodsNJ
Description: Promotes tourism and economic development in the Wildwood, NJ area. **Founded:** 1938. **Geographic Preference:** Local.

42139 ■ Hackensack Regional Chamber of Commerce (HRCC)
66 Moore St., Ste. 301
Hackensack, NJ 07601
Ph: (201)489-3700
Fax: (201)489-1741
Co. E-mail: info@hackensackchamber.org
URL: http://www.hackensackchamber.org
Contact: Ana Suarez, President
Facebook: www.facebook.com/HackensackRegionalChamber
Linkedin: www.linkedin.com/in/hackensack-regional-chamber-of-commerce-a9b20897
X (Twitter): x.com/HackensackCC
Description: Promotes business and community development in Hackensack, NJ. **Founded:** 1933. **Publications:** *Guide to Hackensack* (Annual); *Hackensack Commerce* (Quarterly). **Geographic Preference:** Local.

42140 ■ *Hackettstown Area Living Magazine*
Released: Biennial **Availability:** Print.

42141 ■ *Hammonton Information Guide*
Released: Periodic **Price:** free.

42142 ■ Hawthorne Chamber of Commerce (HCC)
471 Lafayette Ave.
Hawthorne, NJ 07506
Ph: (973)427-5078
Fax: (973)427-6066
Co. E-mail: info@hawthornechamber.org
URL: http://www.hawthornechamber.org
Contact: Robert Meier, Treasurer
E-mail: robert@whiteandshauger.com
Description: Promotes business and community development in Hawthorne, CA. Sponsors Video Public Information Program. **Founded:** 1919. **Publications:** *The Hawthorne Hotline* (Monthly). **Geographic Preference:** Local.

42143 ■ Howell Chamber of Commerce
PO Box 196
Howell, NJ 07731-0196
Ph: (732)363-4114
Co. E-mail: info@howellchamber.com
URL: http://www.howellchamberofcommerce.wildapricot.org
Contact: Steve Friedeman, President
Facebook: www.facebook.com/HowellChamberNJ
YouTube: www.youtube.com/channel/UCwG
1mHCLYqOrCW0fLnttfMA
Description: Aims to stimulate economic growth and to enhance the quality of life in the Howell, NJ area. **Founded:** 1957. **Awards:** Howell Chamber of Commerce Education Foundation Scholarships (Annual). **Geographic Preference:** Local.

42144 ■ Hudson County Chamber of Commerce (HCCC)
185 Hudson St., Ste. 2730
Jersey City, NJ 07311
Ph: (201)386-0699
Co. E-mail: info@hudsonchamber.org
URL: http://www.hudsonchamber.org
Contact: Daryl Harrison Rand, Co-President
Co-Chief Executive Officer
Facebook: www.facebook.com/HudsonChamberPage
Linkedin: www.linkedin.com/company/hudson-county-chamber-of-commerce
X (Twitter): x.com/GOHudsonChamber
Instagram: www.instagram.com/hudsoncountychamber
YouTube: www.youtube.com/channel/UCv1XQFGo
6XHolvby7wet-kg
Description: Promotes business and community development in Hudson County, NJ. **Founded:** 1888. **Publications:** *Hudson County Business* (Bimonthly). **Geographic Preference:** Local.

42145 ■ Hunterdon County Chamber of Commerce
119 Main St.
Flemington, NJ 08822
Ph: (908)782-7115
Co. E-mail: info@hunterdon-chamber.org
URL: http://www.hunterdon-chamber.org
Contact: Christopher J. Phelan, President
Facebook: www.facebook.com/hunterdonchamber
X (Twitter): x.com/hccoc
YouTube: www.youtube.com/user/HunterdonChamber
Description: Strives to promote a favorable business climate, to support member companies, and to provide business leadership throughout the Hunterdon County. **Founded:** 1916. **Geographic Preference:** Local.

42146 ■ Irvington Chamber of Commerce (ICC)
PO Box 323
Irvington, NJ 07111-0323
Ph: (973)673-0205
Fax: (973)673-5828
Co. E-mail: firsteamgt@aol.com
URL: http://www.irvington-nj.com/ICC.html
Contact: A. Roscoe Coleman, President
Description: Promotes business and community development in Irvington, NJ. **Geographic Preference:** Local.

42147 ■ *Jersey Cape Vacation Guide*
13 Crest Haven Rd.
Cape May Court House, NJ 08210
Ph: (609)465-7181
Co. E-mail: info@cmcchamber.com
URL: http://www.capemaycountychamber.com/main/home
Contact: John Kelly, Accountant
E-mail: john@cmcchamber.com
URL(s): www.jerseycapevacationguide.com
Facebook: www.facebook.com/JerseyCapeVacation
Released: Annual **Availability:** Online.

42148 ■ *Jersey Caper*
13 Crest Haven Rd.
Cape May Court House, NJ 08210

Small Business Sourcebook • 42nd Edition   2789

Ph: (609)465-7181
Co. E-mail: info@cmcchamber.com
URL: http://www.capemaycountychamber.com/main/home
Contact: John Kelly, Accountant
E-mail: john@cmcchamber.com
URL(s): www.jerseycapevacationguide.com
Released: Bimonthly **Availability:** Online.

42149 ■ Jersey Shore Chamber of Commerce (JSCC)
1856 Hwy. 35
Wall, NJ 07719
Ph: (732)280-8800
Fax: (732)280-8505
Co. E-mail: info@jsccnj.com
URL: http://www.jerseyshorechambernj.com
Contact: Greg Hunt, President
Facebook: www.facebook.com/JerseyShoreChamberofCommerce
Linkedin: www.linkedin.com/company/jerseyshorechamberofcommerce
X (Twitter): x.com/JSCCNJ
Instagram: www.instagram.com/jerseyshorechambernj
Description: Promotes business and community development in southern Monmouth County, NJ. Sponsors after-work business card exchanges. Holds business expo, golf outing, and general membership meetings. **Founded:** 1979. **Publications:** *Southern Exposure* (Quarterly); *Southern Monmouth Chamber of Commerce Map and Guide* (Biennial). **Educational Activities:** Business Exposition (Annual); Jersey Shore Chamber of Commerce Tradeshow. **Awards:** Jersey Shore Golden Osprey Awards (Annual). **Geographic Preference:** Local.

42150 ■ Lakewood Chamber of Commerce
1771 Madison Ave., Ste. 5
Lakewood, NJ 08701
Ph: (732)363-0012
Fax: (732)367-4453
Co. E-mail: staff@mylakewoodchamber.com
URL: http://mylakewoodchamber.com
Contact: Justin Flancbaum, President
E-mail: justinf@lakewoodmua.com
Linkedin: www.linkedin.com/company/lakewood-chamber-of-commerce-new-jersey
Description: Promotes business and community development in Lakewood, NJ. Sponsors Staff Appreciation and Secretary's Day luncheon. **Founded:** 1917. **Publications:** *The Business Network* (Monthly). **Educational Activities:** Lakewood Chamber of Commerce Annual Meeting. **Geographic Preference:** Local.

42151 ■ Livingston Chamber of Commerce (LCC)
250 S Livingston Ave.
Livingston, NJ 07039
Ph: (973)992-4343
Co. E-mail: info@livingstonchambernj.com
URL: http://livingstonchambernj.com
Facebook: www.facebook.com/livingstonnjchamberofcommerce
Description: Promotes business and community development in the area. **Publications:** *Chamber Connections* (Monthly). **Geographic Preference:** Local.

42152 ■ Madison Chamber of Commerce
PO Box 152
Madison, NJ 07940
Ph: (973)377-7830
Fax: (973)822-0451
Co. E-mail: madisonchamber@gmail.com
URL: http://www.madisonnjchamber.org
Facebook: www.facebook.com/ilovemadisonnj
X (Twitter): x.com/ilovemadisonnj
Instagram: www.instagram.com/ilovemadisonnj
Description: Aims to support, preserve, and enhance the thriving commercial district of Madison, New Jersey. **Founded:** 1943. **Publications:** *The Madison Marketplace* (Bimonthly). **Geographic Preference:** Local.

42153 ■ Mahwah Regional Chamber of Commerce (MRCC)
1 International Blvd., Ste. 211
Mahwah, NJ 07495-0025
Ph: (201)529-5566
Co. E-mail: info@mahwah.com
URL: http://www.mahwah.com
Contact: Benjamin Mills, President
E-mail: benm@glcpas.com
Facebook: www.facebook.com/MahwahChamber
Linkedin: www.linkedin.com/company/mahwah-regional-chamber-of-commerce
X (Twitter): x.com/themrcc
Instagram: www.instagram.com/the_mrcc
YouTube: www.youtube.com/user/MahwahChamber
Description: Works to promote and serve the business community of New Jersey and New York State. **Founded:** 1957. **Geographic Preference:** Regional.

42154 ■ *Map of Hammonton, NJ*

42155 ■ Maplewood Chamber of Commerce
PO Box 423
Maplewood, NJ 07040
URL: http://www.maplewoodchamber.org
Contact: Ellen Donker, President
Description: Promotes business and community development in Maplewood area, NJ. **Geographic Preference:** Local.

42156 ■ Matawan - Aberdeen Chamber of Commerce (MACOC)
201 Broad St.
Matawan, NJ 07747
Ph: (732)290-1125
Co. E-mail: info@macocnj.com
URL: http://macocnj.com
Contact: Jeffrey Pantelas, President
Facebook: www.facebook.com/macocnj
X (Twitter): x.com/macocnj
Description: Serving its community and in its outreach to new businesses in the area. **Founded:** 1968. **Geographic Preference:** Local.

42157 ■ Meadowlands Regional Chamber of Commerce (MRCC)
1099 Wall St. W, Ste. 100
Lyndhurst, NJ 07071
Ph: (201)939-0707
Co. E-mail: office@meadowlands.org
URL: http://www.meadowlands.org/mrcc
Contact: Elisse Glennon, Contact
Facebook: www.facebook.com/MeadowlandsNJ
Linkedin: www.linkedin.com/company/meadowlands-regional-chamber
X (Twitter): x.com/MR_Chamber
Instagram: www.instagram.com/meadowlands_chamber
YouTube: www.youtube.com/user/MeadowlandsChamber
Description: Promotes business and community development in Bergen and Hudson counties, NJ. Hosts a Job Bank for member companies help cope with Workforce needs. Conducts educational programs, festivals, and shows. **Founded:** 1974. **Publications:** *Economic Update* (Monthly); *Meadowlands/USA* (Quarterly). **Geographic Preference:** Local.

42158 ■ *Meadowlands/USA*
1099 Wall St. W, Ste. 100
Lyndhurst, NJ 07071
Ph: (201)939-0707
Co. E-mail: office@meadowlands.org
URL: http://www.meadowlands.org/mrcc
Contact: Elisse Glennon, Contact
URL(s): local.meadowlands.org/Marketing-ServicesCommunicationsInternet-Marketing/Greer-Enterprises,-Inc-52
Released: Quarterly **Availability:** Print; Online.

42159 ■ *Metroline*
Released: Monthly **Availability:** Print.

42160 ■ Metuchen Area Chamber of Commerce
323 Main St., Ste. B
Metuchen, NJ 08840
Ph: (732)548-2964
Co. E-mail: metuchen.chamber@verizon.net
URL: http://metuchenareachamber.com
Contact: Jacquie Zuvich, President
Facebook: www.facebook.com/MetuchenChamber
Linkedin: www.linkedin.com/company/metuchen-area-chamber
YouTube: www.youtube.com/channel/UC4D9RJv6BMVz6LWK0siWmSw
Description: Promotes business and community development in Metuchen, NJ. **Publications:** *Chamber Connection* (Weekly). **Geographic Preference:** Local.

42161 ■ Middle Township Chamber of Commerce (MTCC)
PO Box 6
Cape May Court House, NJ 08210
Ph: (609)463-1655
Co. E-mail: mtcc4u@gmail.com
URL: http://mtcc4u.com
Contact: Mary P. P. Farrell, President
Facebook: www.facebook.com/mtcc4u
Instagram: www.instagram.com/middletownshipchamber
Description: Business people. Promotes business and community development in Middle Township, NJ. **Founded:** 1982. **Geographic Preference:** Local.

42162 ■ Middlesex County Regional Chamber of Commerce (MCRCC)
109 Church St.
New Brunswick, NJ 08901
Ph: (732)745-8090
Co. E-mail: info@mcrcc.org
URL: http://www.mcrcc.org
Contact: James Berg, Treasurer
Facebook: www.facebook.com/MCRCC
X (Twitter): x.com/GoCentralJersey
Description: Provides opportunities for business growth and prosperity in Middlesex County, New Jersey. **Founded:** 1910. **Geographic Preference:** Local.

42163 ■ Millburn-Short Hills Chamber of Commerce
PO Box 55
Millburn, NJ 07041
Ph: (973)379-1198
Co. E-mail: info@millburnshorthillschamber.org
URL: http://www.millburnshorthillschamber.org
Contact: Jimmy Joseph, President
Facebook: www.facebook.com/mshchamber
Description: Promotes business and community development in the Millburn-Short Hills, NJ area. Includes activities such as economic development, special events, trade shows, networking, school-business partnership, and retail promotions. **Founded:** 1960. **Publications:** *Townscape* (Annual). **Geographic Preference:** Local.

42164 ■ Monmouth Regional Chamber of Commerce (MRCC)
330 Mounts Corner Dr., No. 423
Freehold, NJ 07728
Ph: (732)462-3030
Co. E-mail: info@monmouthregionalchamber.com
URL: http://www.monmouthregionalchamber.com
Contact: Sherilyn Przelomski, President
E-mail: tbusinessenhancementservicesnj@gmail.com
Facebook: www.facebook.com/MonmouthRegionalChamberofCommerce
Linkedin: www.linkedin.com/company/mrcc
X (Twitter): x.com/MRCCNJ
Instagram: www.instagram.com/monmouthregionalchambermrcc
YouTube: www.youtube.com/channel/UCc5GfhFVYgN_ooR5_OXY77w
Description: Promotes business and community development in the Middletown, NJ area. Sponsors annual Christmas tree lighting ceremony. Sponsors monthly lecture. **Publications:** *Actionline* (Monthly); *Area Guide*; *e-Chatter* (Monthly). **Educational Activities:** Business Expo. **Geographic Preference:** Local.

STATE LISTINGS

42165 ■ Montville Township Chamber of Commerce
195 Changebridge Rd.
Montville, NJ 07045
Ph: (973)263-3310
Fax: (973)263-3453
Co. E-mail: info@montvillechamber.org
URL: http://montvillechamber.org
Contact: Danielle Speciale, President
Facebook: www.facebook.com/montvillechamber

Description: Promotes business and community development in Montville Township, NJ. **Founded:** 1962. **Publications:** *Business Directory and Map*. **Educational Activities:** Golf Outing. **Geographic Preference:** Local.

42166 ■ Morris County Chamber of Commerce
325 Columbia Tpke., Ste. 101
Florham Park, NJ 07932
Ph: (973)539-3882
Co. E-mail: chamberworks@morrischamber.org
URL: http://www.morrischamber.org
Contact: Meghan Hunscher, President
E-mail: meghan@morrischamber.org
Facebook: www.facebook.com/morrischamber
Linkedin: www.linkedin.com/company/morriscoun tychamberofcommerce
X (Twitter): x.com/morrischambernj
Instagram: www.instagram.com/morrischambernj
YouTube: www.youtube.com/user/MorrisChamber
Pinterest: www.pinterest.com/pin/10808645978 2662806

Description: Promotes business and community development in Morris County, NJ. **Founded:** 1921. **Geographic Preference:** Local.

42167 ■ Mount Olive Area Chamber of Commerce (MOACC)
PO Box 192
Budd Lake, NJ 07828
Ph: (908)509-1744
Co. E-mail: info@mountolivechambernj.com
URL: http://mountolivechambernj.com
Contact: Charles Aaron, President
E-mail: charles@jerseygirlbrewing.com
Facebook: www.facebook.com/MtOliveChamber

Description: Promotes business and community development in Morris County, NJ. Sponsors monthly conventions. **Publications:** *Mt. Olive Today* (Quarterly). **Awards:** MOACC Business Person of the Year (Annual); Tom Klecka Humanitarian Award (Annual). **Geographic Preference:** Local.

42168 ■ New Jersey Chamber of Commerce (NJCC)
216 W State St.
Trenton, NJ 08608
Ph: (609)989-7888
URL: http://www.njchamber.com
Contact: Michael Egenton, Vice President
Facebook: www.facebook.com/njchamber
Linkedin: www.linkedin.com/company/new-jersey -chamber-of-commerce
X (Twitter): x.com/njchamber

Description: A business advocacy organization that actively supports legislation, regulation, and initiatives that will lead to economic growth, job creation, and prosperity throughout the state of New Jersey. Works to improve New Jersey's business climate and provide its members with opportunities to promote and grow their businesses. **Founded:** 1911.

42169 ■ *News and Views*
2115 S Delsea Dr.
Vineland, NJ 08360
Ph: (856)691-7400
Co. E-mail: info@vinelandchamber.org
URL: http://www.vinelandchamber.org
Contact: Dawn S. Hunter, Executive Director
URL(s): www.vinelandchamber.org/marketing-oppor tunities

Released: Monthly **Description:** Features articles from members and information about the community. **Availability:** Print; Online.

42170 ■ North Essex Chamber of Commerce (NECC)
26 Pk. St., Ste. 2062
Montclair, NJ 07042
Ph: (973)226-5500
Fax: (973)783-4407
Co. E-mail: email@northessexchamber.com
URL: http://www.northessexchamber.com
Contact: Desiree L. Burgos, President
Facebook: www.facebook.com/northessexchamber
Linkedin: www.linkedin.com/company/necc
YouTube: www.youtube.com/channel/UC-twF_sChA 4KIxb2XYv5tFw
Pinterest: www.pinterest.com/northessexchamber

Description: Promotes business and community development in northern Essex County, NJ. Sponsors golf outing. Operates foundation. Holds business shows. **Founded:** 1969. **Publications:** *North Essex Report* (Bimonthly). **Educational Activities:** BIZ Expo (Annual). **Geographic Preference:** Regional.

42171 ■ North Jersey Chamber of Commerce (NJCC)
341 Broad Str.
Clifton, NJ 07013
Ph: (973)470-9300
Co. E-mail: hello@northjerseychamber.org
URL: http://www.northjerseychamber.org
Contact: Michelle Vernuccio, President
E-mail: michelle@northjerseychamber.org
Facebook: www.facebook.com/northjerseychamber
Linkedin: www.linkedin.com/company/north-jersey -chamber-of-commerce
X (Twitter): x.com/NorthNJChamber
Instagram: www.instagram.com/northjerseychamber
YouTube: www.youtube.com/channel/UCVKNc 3BHwnNAhKhrtWt2AoA

Description: Promotes business and community development in Clifton and Passaic, NJ and surrounding communities. **Founded:** 1980. **Publications:** *Mindful Business Matters*; *Chamber Challenge* (11/year); *Products and Services Guide* (Annual). **Geographic Preference:** Local.

42172 ■ Nutley Chamber of Commerce
PO Box 208
Nutley, NJ 07110
Ph: (973)667-5300
Fax: (973)667-5300
Co. E-mail: chamber@nutleychamber.com
URL: http://nutleychamber.com
Contact: Jim McGuire, President
Facebook: www.facebook.com/ nuleychamberofcommerce
Linkedin: www.linkedin.com/in/nutleychamber
X (Twitter): x.com/NutleyChamber
Instagram: www.instagram.com/nutleychamber

Description: Promotes business and community development in Nutley, NJ. Holds monthly board of directors meeting. Sponsors Sidewalk Sale Days and Santa's arrival. Conducts annual Business After Hours show. **Founded:** 1953. **Geographic Preference:** Local.

42173 ■ Ocean City Regional Chamber of Commerce (OCRCC)
PO Box 1706
Ocean City, NJ 08226
Ph: (609)399-1412
Free: 800-232-2465
Fax: (609)398-3932
Co. E-mail: info@oceancitychamber.com
URL: http://www.oceancityvacation.com
Contact: David Allegretto, President
Facebook: www.facebook.com/OceanCityNJVacation
X (Twitter): x.com/ocnjvacation
Instagram: www.instagram.com/oceancityvacation
YouTube: www.youtube.com/user/oceancitychamber
Pinterest: www.pinterest.com/ocnjvacation

Description: Promotes business and community development in the greater Ocean City, NJ area. Bestows beautification and outstanding citizen awards. Sponsors Night in Venice, job fest, and welcome night. Operates information/welcome centers. **Founded:** 1897. **Publications:** *Minutes*; *Ocean City Relocation Information*; *Ocean City Visitors Guide* (Annual). **Geographic Preference:** Local.

42174 ■ *Ocean City Visitors Guide*
PO Box 1706
Ocean City, NJ 08226
Ph: (609)399-1412
Free: 800-232-2465
Fax: (609)398-3932
Co. E-mail: info@oceancitychamber.com
URL: http://www.oceancityvacation.com
Contact: David Allegretto, President
URL(s): oceancityvacation.com/about-the-island/free -visitors-guide

Released: Annual **Availability:** PDF; Online.

42175 ■ Ocean Grove Chamber of Commerce
81 Main Ave.
Ocean Grove, NJ 07756
Ph: (732)774-1391
Co. E-mail: info@oceangrovechamber.org
URL: http://www.oceangrovenj.com

Description: Promotes business and community development in Ocean Grove, NJ. **Founded:** 1869. **Publications:** *The Teammate* (Quarterly). **Geographic Preference:** Local.

42176 ■ Paramus Regional Chamber of Commerce
PO Box 325
Paramus, NJ 07653-0325
Ph: (201)261-3344
Fax: (201)261-3346
Co. E-mail: info@paramuschamber.org
URL: http://paramuschamber.org
Contact: Frederick Rohdieck, President
Facebook: www.facebook.com/paramuschamber

Description: Promotes business and community development in Paramus, NJ. **Founded:** 1951. **Publications:** *Bergen County Economic Development Book* (Biennial). **Geographic Preference:** Local.

42177 ■ Parsippany Area Chamber of Commerce (PACC)
90 E Halsey Rd., Ste. 322
Parsippany, NJ 07054
Ph: (973)402-6400
Co. E-mail: robertpeluso@parsippanychamber.org
URL: http://parsippanychamber.org
Contact: Robert J. Peluso, President
E-mail: robertpeluso@parsippanychamber.org

Description: Promotes business and community development in the Parsippany, NJ area. **Geographic Preference:** Local.

42178 ■ Perth Amboy Chamber of Commerce (PACC)
214 Smith St., No. 210
Perth Amboy, NJ 08861-4334
Ph: (732)442-7400
Fax: (732)442-7450
URL: http://www.chamber-commerce.net/dir/9642/ Perth-Amboy-Chamber-of-Commerce-in-Perth -Amboy

Description: Promotes business and community development in Perth Amboy, NJ. Sponsors Waterfront Festival, retail sales days, annual Easter and Christmas parades, annual golf/tennis outing and dinner, business expos, after hours and excursions, and seminars. Monitors legislative action. Maintains research and data center. Offers business referrals and tourist information. **Founded:** 1957. **Geographic Preference:** Local.

42179 ■ Phillipsburg Area Chamber of Commerce (PACC)
120 Filmore St.
Phillipsburg, NJ 08865
Ph: (610)349-9760
Fax: (908)454-7899
URL: http://www.lehighvalleychamber.org/phillipsburg .html
Facebook: www.facebook.com/PhillipsburgChamber

Description: Promotes business and community development in the Phillipsburg, NJ area. Co-hosts Phillipsburg Ole Towne Festival. Sponsors business expo; seminars; networking functions; informative speaker presentations. **Publications:** *Member Service Directory* (Annual). **Geographic Preference:** Local.

42180 ■ Point Pleasant Beach Chamber of Commerce
517A Arnold Ave.
Point Pleasant Beach, NJ 08742
Ph: (732)899-2424
Co. E-mail: info@pointpleasantbeachnj.com
URL: http://www.pointpleasantbeachchamber.com
Contact: Roger Faulkenberry, President
Facebook: www.facebook.com/PointBeachChamber
X (Twitter): x.com/ptbeachchamber

Description: Represents business owners. Promotes business and community development in the Point Pleasant, NJ area. Promotes tourism; sponsors Festival of the Sea. **Founded:** 1947. **Publications:** *Guide Book* (Periodic). **Geographic Preference:** Local.

42181 ■ Princeton Regional Chamber of Commerce
619 Alexander Rd., Ste. 101
Princeton, NJ 08540
Ph: (609)924-1776
Co. E-mail: info@princetonmercer.org
URL: http://princetonmercerchamber.org
Contact: Hal English, President
E-mail: hal@princetonmercer.org
Facebook: www.facebook.com/princetonmercer
Linkedin: www.linkedin.com/company/princeton-regional-chamber-of-commerce
X (Twitter): x.com/princetonmercer
Instagram: www.instagram.com/princetonmercer
YouTube: www.youtube.com/channel/UCK7R7 4SKDY_ZNnWRzIhfZiA

Description: Represents corporations, small businesses, and independent companies. Promotes business and community development in the Princeton, NJ area. **Founded:** 1959. **Publications:** *Membership and Business Directory* (Annual); *Princeton Area Life* (Annual); *Princeton Area Map*; *Visitor's Guide* (Periodic). **Educational Activities:** Business Council Breakfast Meeting (Monthly); Children's Holiday Show; General Membership Meeting. **Geographic Preference:** Local.

42182 ■ Randolph Area Chamber of Commerce (RACC)
PO Box 391
Mount Freedom, NJ 07970
Ph: (973)361-3462
Co. E-mail: info@randolphchamber.org
URL: http://randolphchamber.org
Contact: Lisa Natoli, President

Description: Promotes the interests and welfare of its members by fostering and encouraging the advancement of the commercial, industrial, civic, and general interests of the Township of Randolph and its trade area. Serves as a liaison between local businesses and the township government. **Geographic Preference:** Local.

42183 ■ *The Review*
URL(s): www.chambersnj.com/CCSNJ/About_Us/News_Page/Newsletter/The_Review_Archives.aspx
Released: Monthly **Availability:** Print; PDF; Online.

42184 ■ Ridgewood Chamber of Commerce (RCC)
27 Chestnut St.
Ridgewood, NJ 07450
Ph: (201)445-2600
Co. E-mail: info@ridgewoodchamber.com
URL: http://www.ridgewoodchamber.com
Contact: Gary Kolesair, President
Facebook: www.facebook.com/RidgewoodCOC
Instagram: www.instagram.com/ridgewoodnjcoc

Description: Promotes business and community development in Ridgewood, NJ. Sponsors Christmas "Downtown for the Holidays". Holds monthly board and committee meetings. **Founded:** 1927. **Geographic Preference:** Local.

42185 ■ Ringwood Chamber of Commerce
PO Box 62
Ringwood, NJ 07456
Ph: (973)962-0300
Co. E-mail: president@ringwoodchamber.net
URL: http://www.ringwoodchamber.net
Contact: Neil McDonald, President
E-mail: president@ringwoodchamber.com
Facebook: www.facebook.com/Ringwoo dChamberOfCommerce

Description: Promotes economic development and represents business professionals, products and services. **Founded:** 1974. **Geographic Preference:** Local.

42186 ■ Roxbury Area Chamber of Commerce (RACC)
PO Box 436
Ledgewood, NJ 07852
Ph: (973)770-0740
Co. E-mail: info@roxburynjchamber.org
URL: http://roxburynjchamber.org
Contact: Linda Smith, President
Facebook: www.facebook.com/RoxburyNJChamber
Linkedin: www.linkedin.com/company/roxbury-area-chamber-of-commerce
X (Twitter): x.com/RoxburyChamber

Description: Promotes business and community development in Roxbury area, NJ. **Founded:** 1980. **Geographic Preference:** Local.

42187 ■ Rutherford Chamber of Commerce
PO Box 216
Rutherford, NJ 07070
Ph: (201)203-4753
URL: http://rutherfordchamberofcommerce.rutherfor dnj.town
Facebook: www.facebook.com/rutherfor dchamberofcommerce
Instagram: www.instagram.com/rutherfordchamber

Description: Promotes business and community development in Rutherford, NJ. Convention/Meeting: none. **Founded:** 1927. **Geographic Preference:** Local.

42188 ■ Salem County Chamber of Commerce
429 Hollywood Ave.
Carneys Point, NJ 08069
Ph: (856)351-2245
Co. E-mail: info@salemcountychamber.com
URL: http://salemcountychamber.com
Contact: Jennifer Jones, Executive Director
E-mail: jennifer@salemcountychamber.com
Facebook: www.facebook.com/salemnjchamber

Description: Works to promote the member's businesses; to advocate in government agencies; and to provide services to benefit the members. **Founded:** 1943. **Publications:** *Membership Directory and Buyer's Guide*; *It's Your Business*; *Business Directory and Buyer's Guide*; *Welcome to Historic Salem County*. **Geographic Preference:** Local.

42189 ■ Southern Ocean County Chamber of Commerce
265 W 9th St.
Ship Bottom, NJ 08008
Ph: (609)494-7211
Co. E-mail: info@sochamber.com
URL: http://visitlbiregion.com
Contact: Jeremy Defilippis, President

Description: Aims to foster positive growth, development, and tourism in the Southern Ocean County region. **Founded:** 1915. **Geographic Preference:** Local.

42190 ■ *Spotlight*
256 Broad St., Rm. 2F
Bloomfield, NJ 07003
Ph: (973)748-2000
Fax: (973)748-2450
URL: http://www.suburbanessexchamber.com
Contact: Cecelia Polizzi, Vice President
URL(s): www.suburbanessexchamber.com/membership-options
Released: Semiannual **Availability:** Print; Online.

42191 ■ Stone Harbor Chamber of Commerce
212 96th St.
Stone Harbor, NJ 08247
Ph: (609)368-6101
URL: http://stoneharborchamber.com
Facebook: www.facebook.com/stoneharborbeach
X (Twitter): x.com/stone_harbor_nj
Instagram: www.instagram.com/explore/tags/s toneharborchamberofcommerce

Description: Promotes business and community development in Stone Harbor, NJ. Sponsors July 4th celebration, annual Merchants Day Sale, annual Boat Show, annual Sail Into Summer Festival, and Christmas At Its Best celebration. **Founded:** 1944. **Publications:** *Stone Harbor* (Periodic). **Educational Activities:** Stone Harbor Chamber of Commerce Dinner. **Geographic Preference:** Local.

42192 ■ Suburban Chamber of Commerce
24 Beechwood Rd., Ste. 229
Summit, NJ 07902-0824
Ph: (908)522-1700
Co. E-mail: info@suburbanchambers.org
URL: http://www.suburbanchambers.org
Contact: Karen Hadley, Executive Director
E-mail: khadley@suburbanchambers.org

Description: Promotes business and community development in the Summit, New Providence, and Berkeley Heights, NJ area. **Founded:** 1917. **Publications:** *Chamberfax* (Monthly); *The Collection* (Semiannual). **Geographic Preference:** Local.

42193 ■ Suburban Essex Chamber of Commerce (SECC)
256 Broad St., Rm. 2F
Bloomfield, NJ 07003
Ph: (973)748-2000
Fax: (973)748-2450
URL: http://www.suburbanessexchamber.com
Contact: Cecelia Polizzi, Vice President
Facebook: www.facebook.com/ SuburbanEssexChamberofCommerce

Description: Promotes business and community development in Bloomfield, NJ. **Founded:** 1917. **Publications:** *Spotlight* (Semiannual). **Geographic Preference:** Local.

42194 ■ Sussex County Chamber of Commerce
120 Hampton House Rd.
Newton, NJ 07860
Ph: (973)579-1811
Fax: (973)579-3031
Co. E-mail: mail@sussexcountychamber.org
URL: http://www.sussexcountychamber.org
Contact: Tammie Horsfield, President
Facebook: www.facebook.com/Sussex-County-Chamber-of-Commerce-126733587391411
X (Twitter): x.com/sussexnj

Description: Association is engaged in the promotion of business and community development through economic development and tourism. **Founded:** 1970. **Publications:** *Success* (Quarterly); *Sussex County Magazine* (Annual). **Geographic Preference:** Local.

42195 ■ *Sussex County Magazine*
120 Hampton House Rd.
Newton, NJ 07860
Ph: (973)579-1811
Fax: (973)579-3031
Co. E-mail: mail@sussexcountychamber.org
URL: http://www.sussexcountychamber.org
Contact: Tammie Horsfield, President
URL(s): www.sussexcountychamber.org/sussex _county_magazine.php

Released: Annual **Availability:** Print; PDF; Online.

STATE LISTINGS

New Jersey ■ 42211

42196 ■ Teaneck Chamber of Commerce (TCC)
802 Cedar Ln.
Teaneck, NJ 07666
Ph: (201)801-0012
Co. E-mail: info@teaneckchamber.org
URL: http://www.teaneckchamber.org
Contact: Larry Bauer, President
E-mail: larry@teaneckchamber.org
Facebook: www.facebook.com/TeaneckCoC
Linkedin: www.linkedin.com/company/teaneck-chamber-of-commerce
Description: Seeks to foster economic growth and development for the business districts of Teaneck, NJ. **Founded:** 1972. **Geographic Preference:** Local.

42197 ■ Union Township Chamber of Commerce
355 Chestnut St., 2nd Fl.
Union, NJ 07083
Ph: (908)688-2777
Co. E-mail: info@unionchamber.com
URL: http://unionchamber.com
Contact: Marie Maguire, President
Facebook: www.facebook.com/UnionNJChamber
Instagram: www.instagram.com/unionnjchamber
Description: Works to unite, strengthen, represent and promote business growth for the members. **Founded:** 1956. **Geographic Preference:** Local.

42198 ■ Vernon Chamber of Commerce (VCC)
PO Box 308
Vernon, NJ 07462
Ph: (973)764-0764
Co. E-mail: info@vernonchamber.com
URL: http://www.vernonchamber.com
Contact: Jennifer Hopper, President
E-mail: jhopper@lakelandbank.com
Description: Promotes business and community development in Vernon, NJ. **Founded:** 1792. **Geographic Preference:** Local.

42199 ■ West Milford Chamber of Commerce (WMCC)
1614 - O Union Valley Rd.
West Milford, NJ 07480
Co. E-mail: info@westmilford.com
URL: http://westmilford.com
Contact: Stu Feldman, President
Facebook: www.facebook.com/WestMilfordChamberOfCommerce
Description: Promotes business and community development in West Milford, NJ. **Geographic Preference:** Local.

42200 ■ Woodbridge Metro Chamber of Commerce
91 Main St.
Woodbridge, NJ 07095
Ph: (732)636-4040
URL: http://www.woodbridgechamber.com
Contact: Bernadette Sohler, Vice Chairman of the Board
Facebook: www.facebook.com/WoodbridgeChamberofCommerce
Linkedin: www.linkedin.com/company/woodbridge-metro-chamber-of-commerce
X (Twitter): x.com/WdgeChamber
YouTube: www.youtube.com/channel/UCWzFzkUtqClioCkkeE3U5gQ
Description: Promotes business and community development in Woodbridge, NJ. **Founded:** 1964. **Geographic Preference:** Local.

42201 ■ Wyckoff Chamber of Commerce
PO Box 2
Wyckoff, NJ 07481
Ph: (201)468-1999
Co. E-mail: wyckoffchamber@gmail.com
URL: http://wyckoffchamber.com
Contact: Barbara Petruccelli, Administrator
Facebook: www.facebook.com/WyckoffChamberOfCommerce
X (Twitter): x.com/wyckoffchamber
Instagram: www.instagram.com/wyckoffchamberofcommerce

YouTube: www.youtube.com/channel/UCuQaa-0E6hN_YBAt4T-3soQ
Description: Promotes business and community development in Wyckoff, NJ. Provides information and sponsors social functions. **Founded:** 1926. **Geographic Preference:** Local.

MINORITY BUSINESS ASSISTANCE PROGRAMS

42202 ■ New Jersey Division of Revenue & Enterprise Services - Small Business Set-Aside Program
33 W State St. - 4th Fl.
Trenton, NJ 08625
URL: http://business.nj.gov/pages/sbe
Description: Responsible for administering the Set-Aside Act for small, women-, and minority-owned businesses. Also helps these businesses compete for government contracts.

FINANCING AND LOAN PROGRAMS

42203 ■ 180 Degree Capital Corp.
7 N Willow St., Ste. 4B
Montclair, NJ 07042
Ph: (973)746-4500
Free: 833-746-4500
Fax: (973)746-4508
Co. E-mail: ir@180degreecapital.com
URL: http://www.180degreecapital.com
Contact: Daniel B. Wolfe, PhD, President
Linkedin: www.linkedin.com/company/180dc/
X (Twitter): twitter.com/180DegreeCap
Description: Non-diversified management investment company, operating as a business development company that specializes in making investments in companies commercializing and integrating products enabled by disruptive technologies predominantly in the life sciences industry. **Founded:** 1981. **Preferred Investment Size:** $100,000 to $2,500,000. **Investment Policies:** Early stage. **Industry Preferences:** An internally managed investment company.

42204 ■ AWT Private Investments
49 Wexford Way
Basking Ridge, NJ 07920
Ph: (908)766-2207
Fax: (908)221-9282
URL: http://www.tamarelli.com
Contact: Wayne Tamarelli, Chief Executive Officer
E-mail: wayne@tamarelli.com
Description: Private equity firm for early-stage technology companies. Also operates out of Palo Alto. **Investment Policies:** Achieved proof of concept; sustainable competitive advantage; alignment with special needs; geographic proximity to either Baking Ridge or Palo Alto; sound business plans.

42205 ■ BaseCamp Ventures
1 Executive Dr., Ste. 8
Moorestown, NJ 08057
Ph: (856)813-1100
URL: http://basecampventures.com
Contact: Mel Baiada, Managing Partner
E-mail: mel@basecampventures.com
Description: Provider of investment services for technology companies. **Preferred Investment Size:** $500,000 to $2,500,000. **Investment Policies:** Early and first stage. **Industry Preferences:** Communications, computer software, and Internet specific.

42206 ■ BD Ventures / Becton, Dickinson and Co.
1 Becton Dr.
Franklin Lakes, NJ 07417-1880
Ph: (201)847-6800
URL: http://www.bd.com
Contact: Dave Hickey, President
Facebook: www.facebook.com/BectonDickinsonandCo
Linkedin: www.linkedin.com/company/bd1
X (Twitter): x.com/BDandCo

YouTube: www.youtube.com/channel/UCPGmutY43EjP_3ijOugNGnA
Description: Manufacturer and distributor of medical devices, instrument systems and reagents. **Industry Preferences:** Biotechnology.

42207 ■ Cardinal Partners / Cardinal Health Partners
230 Nassau St.
Princeton, NJ 08542
Ph: (609)924-6452
Fax: (609)683-1074
Co. E-mail: info@cardinalpartners.com
URL: http://cardinalpartners.com
Contact: Kent Marquardt, Partner
Description: Firm providing investment in new healthcare companies. **Founded:** 1996. **Preferred Investment Size:** $6,000,000 to $12,000,000. **Industry Preferences:** Computer software and services, medical and health, Internet specific, biotechnology, computer hardware, semiconductors and other electronics, communications and media, industrial and energy, other products, and consumer related.

42208 ■ Casabona Ventures LLC
2 Keil Ave., Ste. 244
Kinnelon, NJ 07405
Co. E-mail: info@casabonaventures.com
URL: http://casabonaventures.com
Contact: Mario Casabona, Founder Managing Director
Description: Micro-VC firm for post-seed-stage companies in the mid-Atlantic region. **Founded:** 2006. **Investment Policies:** Valuations less than $5,000,000 supporting the Internet of Things (IoT).

42209 ■ CIT Group / Venture Capital
One CIT Dr.
Livingston, NJ 07039
Ph: (973)740-5000
Fax: (973)740-5087
Co. E-mail: custserv@cit.com
URL: http://www.cit.com
Contact: David Harnisch, President
Facebook: www.facebook.com/CITGroup
Linkedin: www.linkedin.com/company/citgroup
X (Twitter): x.com/citgroup
Instagram: www.instagram.com/citgroup
YouTube: www.youtube.com/citgroup
Description: Provider of lending, leasing and advisory solutions. **Founded:** 1908. **Preferred Investment Size:** $3,000,000 minimum. **Industry Preferences:** Diversified.

42210 ■ Domain Associates L.L.C.
103 Carnegie Ctr., Ste. 300
Princeton, NJ 08540
URL: http://www.domainvc-history.com
Contact: Jim Blair, Partner
X (Twitter): x.com/domainvc
Description: Venture capital firm invest in the life sciences sector. **Founded:** 1985. **Preferred Investment Size:** $1,000,000 to $20,000,000. **Industry Preferences:** Biotechnology, medical and health, Internet specific, computer software and services, industrial and energy, semiconductors and other electronics, and consumer related.

42211 ■ Edelson Technology Partners (ETP)
180 Summit Ave., Ste. 205
Montvale, NJ 07645
Ph: (201)930-9898
Fax: (201)930-8899
URL: http://www.edelsontech.com
Contact: Harry Edelson, Partner
E-mail: harry@edelsontech.com
Description: Firm provides financial services, investment and banking services. **Founded:** 1984. **Preferred Investment Size:** $1,000,000 to $3,000,000. **Industry Preferences:** Communications and media, industrial and energy, computer software and services, consumer related, computer hardware, semiconductors and other electronics, other products, medical and health, Internet specific, and biotechnology.

42212 ■ Edison Partners
281 Witherspoon St.
Princeton, NJ 08540
Ph: (609)896-1900
URL: http://www.edisonpartners.com
Contact: Chris Sugden, Managing Partner
E-mail: csugden@edisonpartners.com
Facebook: www.facebook.com/EdisonPartners
Linkedin: www.linkedin.com/company/edison-partners
X (Twitter): x.com/edisonventure
YouTube: www.youtube.com/channel/UCD2F1lsJpd7VGHgBLZAMfeA
Description: Growth equity investment firm. **Founded:** 1986.

42213 ■ Investors Collaborative (IC)
46 Forshee Cir.
Montvale, NJ 07645
URL: http://naic2.net
Contact: Joseph Puglisi, Manager
E-mail: jpuglisi@naic2.com
Description: Group of angel investors and entrepreneurs. Offers equity capital and mentoring to innovative, early-stage companies in the northeastern part of the United States. **Founded:** 2011. **Preferred Investment Size:** $50,000-$200,000. **Industry Preferences:** IT (data center, mobile, apps/software, analytics); clean technology/energy; healthcare; business and financial services; consumer services and hardware; communications; enterprise software.

42214 ■ Johnston Associates Inc. (JAI)
155 Lambert Dr.
Princeton, NJ 08540
Ph: (609)924-2575
Fax: (609)924-3135
Co. E-mail: info@jaivc.com
URL: http://www.jaivc.com
Contact: Robert F. Johnston, Founder
Description: Provider of venture capital to emerging companies. **Founded:** 1968. **Preferred Investment Size:** $300,000 to $3,000,000. **Industry Preferences:** Biotechnology, medical and health.

42215 ■ Jumpstart New Jersey Angel Network
New Brunswick, NJ 08901
Ph: (856)813-1440
Co. E-mail: info@jumpstartnj.org
URL: http://www.jumpstartnj.org
Contact: Sharon Waters, Managing Director
E-mail: swaters@jumpstartnj.org
Facebook: www.facebook.com/jumpstartnjangelnetwork
Linkedin: www.linkedin.com/company/jumpstart-nj-angel-network
X (Twitter): x.com/jumpstartangels
Description: Member-led angel investor group for early-stage technology ventures in the mid-Atlantic region. **Founded:** 2002.

42216 ■ New Jersey Technology Council/NJTC Venture Fund
101 Jefferson St., No. 1
Hoboken, NJ 07030
Ph: (732)456-5700
Co. E-mail: info@njtc.org
URL: http://techunited.co
Contact: Aaron Price, President
URL(s): techcouncilventures.com
Facebook: www.facebook.com/WeAreTechUnited
Linkedin: www.linkedin.com/company/wearetechunited
X (Twitter): x.com/WeAreTechUnited
Instagram: www.instagram.com/wearetechunited
Description: Organization focuses on business development, education, networking and recognition opportunities as well as advocacy for state and region's technology companies. **Founded:** 1996. **Preferred Investment Size:** $1,000,000 to $10,000,000. **Industry Preferences:** Communications, computer software, Internet specific, semiconductors and other electronics, biotechnology, medical and health, and financial services.

42217 ■ New Venture Partners L.L.C. (NVP)
PO Box 881
New Providence, NJ 07974
Ph: (908)464-1900
Fax: (908)655-9142
Co. E-mail: info@nvpllc.com
URL: http://www.nvpllc.com
Contact: Marc Rappoport, Partner Chief Financial Officer
Description: Investment firm provides venture capital, corporate spinouts, incubation, seed, early and mid stage investments. **Founded:** 2001. **Investment Policies:** Seed and early stage. **Industry Preferences:** Communications and media, computer software, and semiconductors and other electronics.

42218 ■ Newark Venture Partners (NVP)
1 Washington Pk., 7th Fl.
Newark, NJ 07102
Co. E-mail: info@newark.vc
URL: http://www.newarkventurepartners.com
Contact: Vaughn Crowe, Managing Partner
Linkedin: www.linkedin.com/company/newark-venture-partners
X (Twitter): x.com/NewarkVc
Description: Early-stage venture capital fund for B2B technology companies. Also offers accelerator programs. **Founded:** 2015.

42219 ■ Origin Partners
5 Slater Ct.
Hillsborough, NJ 08844
Ph: (908)595-9100
Fax: (908)281-6831
URL: http://www.originpartners.com
Contact: Scott T. Jones, Managing Director
E-mail: jones@originpartners.com
Description: Provider of venture capital investment services for information technologies, communications and medical technologies. **Founded:** 1999. **Preferred Investment Size:** $3,000,000 to $5,000,000. **Investment Policies:** Start-up, seed, early and first stage. **Industry Preferences:** Communications and media, computer software, Internet specific, semiconductors and other electronics, and medical and health.

42220 ■ Ridgewood Capital Management L.L.C.
14 Philips Pky.
Montvale, NJ 07645
Fax: (201)447-0474
URL: http://www.ridgewoodcapital.com
Description: Finance: Early stage, mid stage, late stage and growth capital investments in companies. **Preferred Investment Size:** $2,000,000 to $5,000,000. **Industry Preferences:** Internet specific, semiconductors and other electronics, communications and media, computer software and services, computer hardware, other products, industrial and energy, and biotechnology.

42221 ■ SOSV Invesments LLC
174 Nassau St., Ste. 3000
Princeton, NJ 08542
URL: http://sosv.com
Contact: Sean O'Sullivan, Managing Partner
Linkedin: www.linkedin.com/company/sosv
X (Twitter): x.com/sosv
YouTube: www.youtube.com/channel/UCr3_edKFdOwK6I5L081Zy5Q
Description: Venture capital firm and accelerator. Offers seed, venture, and growth-stage funding. Also operates in Asia and Europe. **Founded:** 1995. **Industry Preferences:** Hardware; life sciences; internet/mobile; food; blockchain.

42222 ■ SoundBoard Venture Fund
105 Grove St.
Montclair, NJ 07042
URL: http://www.soundboardventurefund.com
Contact: Jon Brandt, Partner Member
Description: Collaborative fund investing in early-stage companies.

42223 ■ Threshold Partners
300 Carnegie Center St., Ste. 150
Princeton, NJ 08540
Ph: (412)951-7110
URL: http://www.thresholdpartners.com
Contact: Swami Nathan, Contact
E-mail: snathan@thresholdpartners.com
Linkedin: www.linkedin.com/company/threshold-partners
Description: Investment group for early-stage companies in the U.S. and India. **Founded:** 2001.

42224 ■ TigerLabs
300 Witherspoon St., Ste. 201
Princeton, NJ 08542
Ph: (609)285-3420
Co. E-mail: info@tigerlabs.co
URL: http://tigerlabs.co
Facebook: www.facebook.com/tigerlabs
Instagram: www.instagram.com/tigerlabsco
Description: Offers investment funds for early-stage software companies. Offers co-working space. **Industry Preferences:** Digital health; financial services; internet of things; advertising and media; education.

42225 ■ The Vertical Group (TVG)
PO Box 218
Berkeley Heights, NJ 07922
Ph: (908)277-3737
Co. E-mail: info@vertical-group.com
URL: http://www.vertical-group.com
Contact: Jack W. Lasersohn, Partner
Linkedin: www.linkedin.com/company/the-vertical-group
Description: Provider of venture capital investment services for medical technology. **Founded:** 1988. **Preferred Investment Size:** $250,000 to $10,000,000. **Industry Preferences:** Medical and health, biotechnology, Internet specific, semiconductors and other electronics, computer software and services, communications and media, and industrial and energy.

PROCUREMENT ASSISTANCE PROGRAMS

42226 ■ Atlantic Cape Community College Procurement Technical Assistance Center (PTAC)
391 Dr. Martin Luther King Blvd.
Newark, NJ 07102
Co. E-mail: ptac@njit.edu
URL: http://www.njit.edu/ptac/contacts
Contact: Raul Mercado, Director
E-mail: raul.mercado@njit.edu
Description: Provides contractual and technical assistance to small-established New Jersey businesses, who are interested in marketing their products, services to federal, state and local government agencies.

42227 ■ New Jersey Air Services Development Office (NJASDO)
Bldg. No. 80
Newark Liberty International Airport
Port Authority
1 Conrad Rd
Newark, NJ 07114
Ph: (973)961-4278
Co. E-mail: njasdo@asdoonline.com
URL: http://www.asdoonline.com/NJAPPS/NJ.htm
Contact: Helene M. Gibbs, Program Manager
Description: A procurement facility funded by the Port Authority of New York and New Jersey to assist small firms in Essex, Hudson, and Union counties in obtaining contracts with airlines and other businesses at Newark International Airport. **Founded:** 1988.

42228 ■ New Jersey Institute of Technology - Procurement Technical Assistance Center (PTAC)
COMET Center, 360 N Frontage Rd.
Landing, NJ 07850
Co. E-mail: apex-group@njit.edu
URL: http://www.njit.edu/apex

STATE LISTINGS

Contact: Hailey Hyeri Park, Director
E-mail: hyeri.park@njit.edu

Description: Provides contractual and technical assistance to small-established New Jersey businesses, who are interested in marketing their products, services to federal, state and local government agencies.

42229 ■ Union County Economic Development Corp. (UCEDC)
75 Chestnut St.
Cranford, NJ 07016-2937
Ph: (908)527-1166
Fax: (908)527-1207
Co. E-mail: info@ucedc.com
URL: http://ucedc.com
Contact: Adam Farrah, President
E-mail: afarrah@ucedc.com
Facebook: www.facebook.com/UCEDCNJ
Linkedin: www.linkedin.com/company/ucedc
X (Twitter): x.com/UCEDC
Instagram: www.instagram.com/ucedcnj

Description: providing financial, technical, and community assistance to new and existing businesses with emphasis on benefiting under-served people and communities. **Founded:** 1977.

INCUBATORS/RESEARCH AND TECHNOLOGY PARKS

42230 ■ BD Technologies and Innovation (BDTI)
1 Becton Dr.
Franklin Lakes, NJ 07417-1880
URL: http://www.bd.com/en-us/company/bd-technologies-and-innovation
Contact: Tom Polen, President

Description: Accelerates the development of early-stage life sciences companies working with our company via collaboration, licensing or incubation. **Founded:** 1972.

42231 ■ Bergen Community College Regional Accelerator
1280 Wall St.
Lyndhurst, NJ 07071
Ph: (201)612-5360
URL: http://bergen.edu/ce/bergen-for-business/business-accelerator
Contact: Shirley Pachon, Coordinator
E-mail: spachon@bergen.edu

Description: Provides early stage businesses the support services, guidance and networking opportunities that are critical to changing an idea, product, technology or service into a successful business. **Founded:** 1965.

42232 ■ The Business Development Incubator at New Jersey City University (BDI)
285 W Side Ave. Rm. 254
Jersey City, NJ 07305
Ph: (201)200-3525
Co. E-mail: bdi@njcu.edu
URL: http://www.njcu.edu/student-life/campus-services-resources/frequently-asked-questions-about-campus-life

Description: Facilitates the formation and development of technology-based entrepreneurial ventures with higher-skill, higher-wage jobs, helping them survive and grow during their critical start-up period.

42233 ■ Combustion Group (CG)
28 Valley Rd.
Montclair, NJ 07042
Ph: (973)200-0765
Co. E-mail: concierge@combustiongroup.com
URL: http://combustion.com
Facebook: www.facebook.com/CombustionGroup
X (Twitter): x.com/CombustionGroup
Instagram: www.instagram.com/combustiongroup

Description: Works with mobile web startups to accelerate success quickly.

42234 ■ Commercialization Center for Innovative Technologies (CCIT)
675 US Hwy. One
North Brunswick, NJ 08902
Ph: (732)839-1880
URL: http://www.njeda.com

Description: Business incubator for life sciences and biotechnology !!br0ken!! affordable and customization office, production, and "plug-in ready" wet and dry laboratory space to qualified tenants.

42235 ■ The Incubator/Business One Stop Service (BOSS)
320 Park Ave.
Plainfield, NJ 07060
Ph: (908)757-5155
Fax: (908)757-8398
Co. E-mail: info@thebusinessonestopshop.com
URL: http://thebusinessonestopshop.com
Contact: Jeffery Dunn, Executive Director

Description: A small business incubator with the resources and solutions to help businesses achieve their short-and long-term goals.

42236 ■ Institute for Entrepreneurial Leadership (IFEL)
550 Broad St., Ste. 702
Newark, NJ 07102
Ph: (973)353-0611
Fax: (973)353-0650
Co. E-mail: info@ifelnj.org
URL: http://www.weareifel.org
Contact: Jill Johnson, Chief Executive Officer
Facebook: www.facebook.com/weareifel
Linkedin: www.linkedin.com/company/weareifel
X (Twitter): x.com/weareifel

Description: A small business incubator that takes a holistic, hands-on approach to helping entrepreneurs grow their business. Companies with a strong vision and viable business model can be helped to create wealth for themselves and their community by building a strong foundation for the long-term success of their business. **Founded:** 2002.

42237 ■ Institute for Life Science Entrepreneurship (ILSE)
1000 Morris Ave.
STEM Bldg.
Union, NJ 07083
Ph: (908)737-1922
Fax: (908)737-7205
Co. E-mail: info@ilsebio.com
URL: http://ilsebio.com
Contact: Egda M. Veloz, Director, Finance
X (Twitter): x.com/ilse_bio

Description: Accelerator and business incubator working in partnership with innovators and affiliated academic/biomedical institutions.

42238 ■ JuiceTank
220 Davidson Ave.
Somerset, NJ 08873
Ph: (732)584-6102
Co. E-mail: info@juicetank.com
URL: http://www.juicetank.com
Facebook: www.facebook.com/juicetank
X (Twitter): x.com/juicetank

Description: Start-up accelerator and incubator. Also offers co-working space.

42239 ■ Le Gourmet Factory (LGF)
176A S Van Brunt St.
Englewood, NJ 07631
Ph: (201)408-5471
Co. E-mail: info@legourmetfactory.com
URL: http://www.legourmetfactory.com
Contact: Nick Prastos, Founder Officer
Facebook: www.facebook.com/LeGourmetFactory
X (Twitter): x.com/legourmetcook
YouTube: www.youtube.com/user/LeGourmetFactory

Description: Culinary incubator offering commercial kitchen space for food entrepreneurs. **Founded:** 2013.

42240 ■ New Jersey City University Business Development Incubator
285 W Side Ave., Rm., 254
Jersey City, NJ 07305
Ph: (201)200-3525
URL: http://www.njcu.edu/student-life/campus-services-resources/frequently-asked-questions-about-campus-life

Description: A small business incubator created to assist young, small companies to commercialize their products, processes and services by providing access to marketing, technical, finance, accounting, sales, legal and management assistance.

42241 ■ New Jersey Institute of Technology - Enterprise Development Center (NJIT)
University Hts.
Newark, NJ 07102
URL: http://www.njit.edu/studentsuccess/gallery-image/enterprise-development-center

Description: Supports businesses and innovators as they develop, launch, and commercialize their ideas.

42242 ■ NJIT Enterprise Development Center
211 Warren St.
Newark, NJ 07103
URL: http://www.engineere.com/US/Newark/150412685027440/NJIT-Enterprise-Development-Center?__cf_chl_captcha_tk__=pmd_IGRjCw3HG1jt790x.JWlhA_fe3tNuahkpy.qaiicyho-1634873332-0-gqNtZGzNA2WjcnBszQi9

Description: A program committed to the long-term economic vitality and growth of life science and high tech entrepreneurial ventures in the State of New Jersey. The incubator exists to increase the rate of small business formations and to decrease the failure rate of start-ups.

42243 ■ Organic Food Incubator (OFI)
38 Davey St.
Bloomfield, NJ 07003
Ph: (973)748-0111
Co. E-mail: info@organicfoodincubator.com
URL: http://organicfoodincubator.com
Facebook: www.facebook.com/OrganicFoodIncubator
X (Twitter): x.com/OrganicFoodInc
Instagram: www.instagram.com/OrganicFoodIncubator
YouTube: www.youtube.com/channel/UCr2dcD-HACpSYL7Bg8DxagA
Pinterest: www.pinterest.com/organicfoodinc

Description: Organic food incubator provides solutions to growing food and beverage companies. Provides kitchen space, contract manufacturing, education, and coaching services.

42244 ■ Rutgers Camden Technology Campus (RCTC)
303 Cooper St.
Camden, NJ 08102
Ph: (856)225-1766
Co. E-mail: andradea@camden.rutgers.edu
URL: http://camden.rutgers.edu
Contact: Antonio D. Tillis, Chancellor
Facebook: www.facebook.com/RutgersCamden
Linkedin: www.linkedin.com/school/rutgers-university-camden
X (Twitter): x.com/Rutgers_Camden
Instagram: www.instagram.com/rutgers_camden
YouTube: www.youtube.com/user/RutgersCamdenCampus

Description: A non-profit, mixed-use, small business incubator encouraging entrepreneurs to locate their businesses in Camden by assisting them with low-cost office and conference space, technical support services and mentoring for successful startup. The incubator provides the safety net needed during a new company's most critical and vulnerable period.

42245 ■ Rutgers EcoComplex
1200 Florence Columbus Rd.
Bordentown, NJ 08505
Ph: (609)499-3600
Co. E-mail: ecocomplex@njaes.rutgers.edu
URL: http://ecocomplex.rutgers.edu
Contact: Dr. Serpil Guran, Director

E-mail: serpil.guran@rutgers.edu
Facebook: www.facebook.com/RutgersEcoComplex
Description: Incubator moves inventions from the lab to real-world applications. Promotes New Jersey as a center for alternative energy and environmental innovations and enterprises.

42246 ■ **Rutgers Food Innovation Center (RFIC)**
450 E Broad St.
Bridgeton, NJ 08302
Ph: (856)391-7603
Co. E-mail: accessibility@rutgers.edu
URL: http://foodinnovation.rutgers.edu
Contact: Peggy Brennan-Tonetta, Executive Director
Facebook: www.facebook.com/FoodInnovationCenter
Linkedin: www.linkedin.com/company/rutgersfic
X (Twitter): x.com/RutgersFIC
Instagram: www.instagram.com/Rutgers_FIC
Description: A unique business incubation and economic development accelerator program providing business and technology expertise to startup and established food companies in the mid-Atlantic region, and utilizes its outreach capacity to reach food and agribusinesses throughout the world. **Founded:** 2000.

42247 ■ **Rutgers, The State University of New Jersey - EcoComplex Business Incubator**
1200 Florence Columbus Rd.
Bordentown, NJ 08505
URL: http://ecocomplex.rutgers.edu/incubator-businesses.html
Contact: Lorraine Raider, Contact
E-mail: lorraine.raider@rutgers.edu
Description: A comprehensive business development program and facility for companies in the clean energy, environmental and controlled environment agriculture industries.

42248 ■ **Stevens Venture Center (SVC)**
221 River St., 9th Fl.
Hoboken, NJ 07030
URL: http://www.stevens.edu/directory?letter=s
Description: Offers technology support, training, networking, and other resources to Stevens-affiliated entrepreneurs.

42249 ■ **TechLaunch, LLC (TL)**
2 Kiel Ave., Ste. 244
Kinnelon, NJ 07405
Free: 877-776-5850
Co. E-mail: norma@techlaunch.com
URL: http://www.techlaunch.com
Contact: Mario Casabona, Founder Managing Director
Facebook: www.facebook.com/techlaunch
Linkedin: www.linkedin.com/company/techlaunch-llc
X (Twitter): x.com/techlaunchnj
Description: Technology accelerator. Offers co-working space, workshops, coaching, and seed capital. **Founded:** 2012.

42250 ■ **Technology Centre of New Jersey**
North Brunswick, NJ
Description: A small business incubator offering young, growing firms, as well as large established companies, a way to afford modern laboratory and production facilities that are customized to fit their specific research and development needs. Stand-alone facilities from 5,000 to 60,000 square feet can accommodate state-of-the-art clean rooms and wet labs.

EDUCATIONAL PROGRAMS

42251 ■ **Bergen Community College (BCC)**
400 Paramus Rd.
Paramus, NJ 07652
Ph: (201)447-7100
Co. E-mail: admissions@bergen.edu
URL: http://bergen.edu
Contact: Eric M. Friedman, President
Facebook: www.facebook.com/bergencommunitycollege
Linkedin: www.linkedin.com/school/bergen-community-college
X (Twitter): x.com/bergencc
YouTube: www.youtube.com/BergenCommCollege
Description: Two-year college offering a small business management program. **Founded:** 1963.

42252 ■ **Brookdale Community College**
765 Newman Springs Rd.
Lincroft, NJ 07738-1599
Ph: (732)224-2345
URL: http://www.brookdalecc.edu
Contact: David M. Stout, President
X (Twitter): x.com/BrookdaleCCNews
Instagram: www.instagram.com/brookdaleccnews
YouTube: www.youtube.com/user/brookdaleccnews
Description: Two-year college offering a program in small business management. **Founded:** 1967.

42253 ■ **Fairleigh Dickinson University Rothman Institute of Innovation & Entrepreneurship**
1000 River Rd.
Teaneck, NJ 07666
URL: http://www.fdu.edu/academics/centers-institutes/rothman
Contact: Dr. Dale G. Caldwell, Executive Director
Description: Supports entrepreneurship and innovation in the academic, business and nonprofit communities. In addition, provides outreach programs that help people succeed in their new or growing ventures as well as in their corporations or organizations. **Founded:** 1989.

42254 ■ **Monmouth University Center for Entrepreneurship (MUCE)**
400 Cedar Ave.
West Long Branch, NJ 07764
Ph: (732)263-5360
Co. E-mail: agilbert@monmouth.edu
URL: http://www.monmouth.edu/entrepreneurship
Contact: Alison Gilbert, Director
E-mail: agilbert@monmouth.edu
Description: Mission is to nurture entrepreneurial thinking through a community of business partners committed to achieving social and economic progress.

42255 ■ **Rider University Center for Entrepreneurial Studies**
2083 Lawrenceville Rd.
Lawrenceville, NJ 08648
Co. E-mail: entrepreneurshipctr@rider.edu
URL: http://www.rider.edu/academics/centers-institutes/center-entrepreneurial-studies
Description: Seeks to provide individuals with tools to help them achieve their entrepreneurial potential through experiential learning. Through the Seed Venture Fund, provides seed money for students to create their own ventures while they earn their undergraduate degree.

42256 ■ **Rowan College at Burlington County (RCBC)**
900 College Cir.
Mount Laurel, NJ 08054
Ph: (856)222-9311
Co. E-mail: admissions@rcbc.edu
URL: http://www.rcbc.edu
Facebook: www.facebook.com/RowanCollegeAtBurlingtonCounty
Linkedin: www.linkedin.com/school/rowan-college-at-burlington-county
X (Twitter): x.com/RowanBurlington
YouTube: www.youtube.com/c/RowanCollegeatBurlingtonCounty
Description: Two-year college offering a certificate in small business management. **Founded:** 1969.

42257 ■ **Rutgers Business School - Center for Urban Entrepreneurship & Economic Development (CUEED)**
1 Washington Pk.
Newark, NJ 07102
URL: http://www.business.rutgers.edu/cueed
Contact: Lyneir Richardson, Executive Director
E-mail: lrichardson@business.rutgers.edu
Description: Integrates scholarly works with private capital, government, and non-profit sectors to develop citywide resources and bring renewed economic growth and vitality through urban entrepreneurship. Provides various types of assistance to entrepreneurs in different industries.

REFERENCE WORKS

42258 ■ *"The Best Bar in N.J. is a Semi-Swanky Cocktail Lounge That Serves Some of the Best Food in the Region"* in *NJ.com (June 27. 2019)*
URL(s): www.nj.com/entertainment/2019/06/the-best-bar-in-nj-is-a-semi-swanky-cocktail-lounge-that-serves-some-of-the-best-food-in-the-region.html
Ed: Peter Genovese. **Released:** June 27, 2019.
Description: Profile of Verve, voted as the best bar in New Jersey. What made this bar stand out from the rest was the food, which rivals it's cocktails in quality. **Availability:** Online.

CONSULTANTS

42259 ■ **3Pe Consulting**
10 Knolltop Ct.
Denville, NJ 07834
Co. E-mail: 3peconsulting@gmail.com
Facebook: www.facebook.com/3PeConsulting
Description: Offers services to retailers that range in size from start-ups to multi-billion-dollar businesses. Specialized in turnaround management, merchandising, product development, marketing, and team development. **Founded:** 2009.

42260 ■ **Eagle Strategy Group, LLC.**
726 Rte. 202 S, Ste. 320-177
Bridgewater, NJ 08807
Ph: (908)458-6415
Co. E-mail: sales@eaglestrategygroup.com
URL: http://eaglestrategygroup.com
Facebook: www.facebook.com/EagleStrategy
Linkedin: www.linkedin.com/company/eagle-strategy-group-llc
X (Twitter): x.com/SMBStrategy
Description: Offers coaching and staff support for small and medium-sized businesses. . **Founded:** 2005.

42261 ■ **Venstrat LLC**
252 Nassau St.,2nd Fl.
Princeton, NJ 08542
Ph: (917)887-0914
Fax: (609)681-5034
URL: http://www.venstrat.com
Contact: Dr. William Bassin, Contact
Description: Offers strategic and financial advisory services to small and midsized companies. Also provides economic and financial analysis services for securities litigation. **Founded:** 2006.

PUBLICATIONS

42262 ■ *New Jersey Business*
10 W Lafayette St.
Trenton, NJ 08608-2002
Ph: (609)393-7707
Co. E-mail: info@njbia.org
URL: http://njbia.org
Contact: Michele Siekerka, President
E-mail: msiekerka@njbia.org
URL(s): njbmagazine.com
Facebook: www.facebook.com/njbmagazine
Linkedin: www.linkedin.com/company/new-jersey-business-magazine
X (Twitter): x.com/NJBmagazine
Released: Monthly **Price:** $52, for 3 years; $24, for per year.; $3, Single issue for single issue; $39, Two years for 2 year. **Description:** Provides up-to-date business news and information about the state of the Garden State. **Availability:** Print; Online.

42263 ■ **New Jersey Business Magazine**
310 Passaic Ave.
Fairfield, NJ 07004

Ph: (973)882-5004
Fax: (973)882-4648
Co. E-mail: info@njbmagazine.com
URL: http://www.njbmagazine.com
Contact: Doug Prefach, Manager, Advertising
E-mail: d.prefach@njbmagazine.com
Facebook: www.facebook.com/njbmagazine
Linkedin: www.linkedin.com/company/new-jersey
 -business-magazine
X (Twitter): x.com/NJBmagazine

Description: Publisher of magazine that provides timely news and information to help businesses succeed. **Founded:** 1910.

42264 ■ *New Jersey Monthly*
62 Elm St.
  Morristown, NJ 07960-4110
Ph: (973)539-8230
Free: 888-419-0419
Fax: (973)538-2953
Co. E-mail: research@njmonthly.com
URL: http://njmonthly.com
Contact: Deborah Carter, Managing Editor
E-mail: dcarter@njmonthly.com
URL(s): njmonthly.com/about
Facebook: www.facebook.com/njmonthly
X (Twitter): x.com/njmonthly

Instagram: www.instagram.com/njmonthly
Pinterest: www.pinterest.com/njmonthly

Released: Monthly **Price:** $4.99, for back issue; $19.95, for print - 12 issues; $12, for digital - 12 issues; $1, for Instant access anytime and anywhere an issue; $34.95, for 24 issue print. **Availability:** Print; Online.

PUBLISHERS

42265 ■ **Passaic County, New Jersey - Planning and Economic Development Department**
c/o Andras Holzmann
  Director 401 Grand St., Ste. 417
  Paterson, NJ 07505
Ph: (973)569-4040
Co. E-mail: andrash@passaiccountynj.org
URL: http://www.passaiccountynj.org/departments/
  planning-economic-development
Contact: Andras Holzmann, Director
E-mail: andrash@passaiccountynj.org

Description: A county government department for Passaic County, New Jersey, that handles planning, GIS, community and economic development, the county historian, and public housing. **Founded:** 1978.

42266 ■ **Prentice Hall Business Publishing (PHBP)**
Upper Saddle River, NJ 07458
URL: http://phbusiness.prenhall.com
Description: Publisher of business books.

42267 ■ **PubEasy**
630 Central Ave.
  New Providence, NJ 07974
Free: 888-269-5372
Co. E-mail: help@pubeasy.com
URL: http://beta.pubeasy.com
Contact: David Walter, Director

Description: Publishes online services to facilitate, speed and connect publishers, booksellers, distributors and wholesalers.

VENTURE CAPITAL FIRM

42268 ■ **Rein Capital LLC**
111 Madison Ave.
  Lakewood, NJ 08701
Co. E-mail: info@reincapital.com
URL: http://reincapital.com
Contact: David M. Rein, Managing Partner Founder

Description: Early-stage venture capital firm.

New Mexico

ASSOCIATIONS AND OTHER ORGANIZATIONS

42269 ■ Association of Fundraising Professionals New Mexico Chapter (AFPNM)
PO Box 37408
Albuquerque, NM 87176-7408
Co. E-mail: staff@afp-nm.org
URL: http://community.afpglobal.org/afpnmnewmexicochapter/home
Contact: Jessie Calero, Associate
E-mail: jessie@mandysfarm.org
Geographic Preference: State.

42270 ■ Business Network International, New Mexico
3430 Toringdon Way
Charlotte, NC 28277
Free: 855-264-2673
URL: http://bninewmexico.com/en-US/index
Contact: Debbie Ruiz, Officer
E-mail: debbieruiz@bni.com
Description: Provides both men and women a structured environment for the development and exchange of quality business referrals. Offers members the opportunity to share ideas and contacts. **Geographic Preference:** State.

42271 ■ International Association of Women Albuquerque Chapter (ABQ NOW)
NM
URL: http://now.org/chapter/albuquerque-now
X (Twitter): twitter.com/NOWABQ
Description: Serves as network of accomplished women united to achieve professional goals. Provides a forum for sharing ideas and experiences of professional women regarding career success. Promotes an active business and networking community from all industries. **Founded:** 2013. **Geographic Preference:** Local.

SMALL BUSINESS DEVELOPMENT CENTERS

42272 ■ Alamogordo Small Business Development Center
2400 N Scenic Dr.
Alamogordo, NM 88310-3722
Ph: (575)439-3660
Fax: (575)439-3819
URL: http://www.nmsbdc.org/locations/alamogordo
Contact: Trish Livingston, Officer
E-mail: pmliving@nmsu.edu
Description: Represents and promotes the small business sector. Provides management assistance to current and prospective small business owners in Alamogordo. **Geographic Preference:** Local.

42273 ■ Albuquerque Small Business Development Center
CNM Workforce Training Ctr.
5600 Eagle Rock Ave., NE
Albuquerque, NM 87113
Ph: (505)224-5250
URL: http://www.nmsbdc.org/locations/albuquerque
Contact: Fran Fernandez, Director
E-mail: ffernandez10@cnm.edu
Description: Represents and promotes the small business sector. Provides management assistance to current and prospective small business owners. Helps to improve management skills and expand the products and services of members. **Geographic Preference:** Local.

42274 ■ Albuquerque South Valley Small Business Development Center
1309 4th St., SW
Albuquerque, NM 87102
Ph: (505)224-5250
URL: http://www.nmsbdc.org/locations/albuquerque
Description: Provides management assistance to current and prospective small business owners in South Valley. **Geographic Preference:** Local.

42275 ■ Carlsbad Small Business Development Center
221 S Canyon St.
Carlsbad, NM 88220-5734
Ph: (575)885-9352
Co. E-mail: info@nmsbdc.org
URL: http://www.nmsbdc.org/carlsbad.aspx
Contact: Della Bedingfield, Director
E-mail: dellab@nmsu.edu
Description: Represents and promotes the small business sector. Provides management assistance to current and prospective small business owners. Helps to improve management skills and expand the products and services of members. **Geographic Preference:** Local.

42276 ■ Clovis Small Business Development Center
c/o Clovis Community College
417 Schepps Blvd., Rm. 152
Clovis, NM 88101-8381
Ph: (575)769-4136
Co. E-mail: sbdc@clovis.edu
URL: http://www.nmsbdc.org/clovis.aspx
Contact: Sandra Taylor-Sawyer, Director
E-mail: sandra.sawyer@clovis.edu
Description: Provides management assistance to current and prospective small business owners in Clovis. **Geographic Preference:** Local.

42277 ■ Farmington Small Business Development Center
San Juan College
5101 College Blvd.
Farmington, NM 87402
Ph: (505)566-3528
Fax: (505)566-3698
URL: http://www.nmsbdc.org/locations/farmington
Contact: Carmen Martinez, Director
E-mail: martinezc@sanjuancollege.edu
Facebook: www.facebook.com/SBDCFarmington
Description: Represents and promotes the small business sector. Provides management assistance to current and prospective small business owners. Helps to improve management skills and expand the products and services of members. **Geographic Preference:** Local.

42278 ■ Las Cruces Small Business Development Center
2345 E Nevada Ave., Ste. 101
Las Cruces, NM 88001-3902
Ph: (575)527-7676
Fax: (575)528-7432
Co. E-mail: sbdcinfo@nmsu.edu
URL: http://www.nmsbdc.org/las-cruces.aspx
Contact: Jo Ann Garay, Director
E-mail: jomgaray@nmsu.edu
Description: Represents and promotes the small business sector. Provides management assistance to current and prospective small business owners. Helps to improve management skills and expand the products and services of members. **Geographic Preference:** Local.

42279 ■ Los Alamos Small Business Development Center
4000 University Dr.
Los Alamos, NM 87544
Ph: (505)662-0337
URL: http://www.nmsbdc.org/locations/los-alamos
Contact: Monther Jubran, Director
E-mail: mjubran@unm.edu
Description: Represents and promotes the small business sector in Los Alamos. **Geographic Preference:** Local.

42280 ■ Los Lunas Small Business Development Center
Student Community Center Bldg, 2nd Fl. Rm. 239 & 236
University of New Mexico-Valencia
280 La Entrada Rd.
Los Lunas, NM 87031
Ph: (505)219-5202
URL: http://www.nmsbdc.org/locations/los-lunas
Contact: Vernon Mulanix, Director
E-mail: vernon22@unm.edu
Description: Represents and promotes the small business sector. Provides management assistance to current and prospective small business owners. Helps to improve management skills and expand the products and services of members. **Geographic Preference:** Local.

42281 ■ Mesalands Community College Small Business Development Center
911 S 10th St.
Tucumcari, NM 88401
Ph: (575)461-6600
URL: http://www.nmsbdc.org/locations/tucumcari
Contact: Nathan Kerkula, Director
E-mail: nathank@mesalands.edu

Description: Represents and promotes the small business sector. Provides management assistance to current and prospective small business owners. Helps to improve management skills and expand the products and services of members. **Geographic Preference:** Local.

42282 ■ **New Mexico Small Business Development Center - Lead Office**
6401 Richards Ave.
Santa Fe, NM 87508-4887
Ph: (505)428-1362
Free: 800-281-7232
Fax: (505)428-1469
Co. E-mail: russell.wyrick@sfcc.edu
URL: http://www.nmsbdc.org
Contact: Debbi Moore, Co-President Co-Chief Executive Officer
E-mail: dmoore@lascruces.org
Linkedin: www.linkedin.com/company/new-mexico-small-business-development-center
X (Twitter): x.com/NMSBDCNetwork
Description: Provides quality direct assistance, entrepreneurial education and resource links to small businesses to strengthen the economy of New Mexico. **Publications:** *NMSBDC Network News* (Quarterly). **Geographic Preference:** State.

42283 ■ **New Mexico State University-Grants Small Business Development Center**
701 E Roosevelt Ave.
Grants, NM 87020-2113
Ph: (505)287-6688
Fax: (505)287-2125
URL: http://www.nmsbdc.org/grants.aspx
Contact: Clemente Sanchez, President
Description: Represents and promotes the small business sector. Provides management assistance to current and prospective small business owners. Helps to improve management skills and expand the products and services of members. **Geographic Preference:** Local.

42284 ■ **Roswell Small Business Development Center**
Eastern New Mexico University - Roswell
20 W Mathis
Roswell, NM 88203
Ph: (575)624-7133
Fax: (575)624-7132
Co. E-mail: sbdc@roswell.enmu.edu
URL: http://www.nmsbdc.org/locations/roswell
Contact: Scott Bucher, Director
E-mail: scott.bucher@roswell.enmu.edu
Facebook: www.facebook.com/SBDCRoswell
Description: Represents and promotes the small business sector. Provides management assistance to current and prospective small business owners. Helps to improve management skills and expand the products and services of members. **Geographic Preference:** Local.

42285 ■ **Sandoval County Small Business Development Center**
2601 Campus Blvd., NE
Rio Rancho, NM 87144
URL: http://www.nmsbdc.org/locations/albuquerque
Description: Represents and promotes the small business sector. Provides management assistance to current and prospective small business owners. Helps to improve management skills and expand the products and services of members. **Founded:** 1989. **Geographic Preference:** Local.

42286 ■ **Santa Fe Small Business Development Center**
1950 Siringo Rd.
Santa Fe, NM 87505
Ph: (505)428-1343
Co. E-mail: sbdc@sfcc.edu
URL: http://www.nmsbdc.org/locations/santa-fe
Contact: Deborah Collins, Assistant Director
E-mail: deborah.collins@sfcc.edu
Description: Represents and promotes the small business sector. Provides management assistance to current and prospective small business owners. Helps to improve management skills and expand the products and services of members. **Geographic Preference:** Local.

42287 ■ **Silver City Small Business Development Center at Western New Mexico University (SBDC)**
Watts Hall-Cor. of Swan & Hwy. 180
500 18th St.
Silver City, NM 88062-2672
Ph: (575)538-6320
URL: http://www.nmsbdc.org/locations/silver-city
Contact: Kelli McGhiey, Director
E-mail: kelli.mcghiey@wnmu.edu
Description: Represents and promotes the small business sector. Provides management assistance to current and prospective small business owners. Helps to improve management skills and expand the products and services of members. **Geographic Preference:** Local.

42288 ■ **Small Business Development Center at Northern New Mexico College (NMSBDC)**
1027 N Railroad Ave.
Espanola, NM 87532
Ph: (505)747-2236
URL: http://www.nmsbdc.org/locations/espanola
Contact: Julianna Barbee, Director
E-mail: jbarbee@nnmc.edu
Description: Represents and promotes the small business sector. Provides management assistance to current and prospective small business owners. Helps to improve management skills and expand the products and services of members. **Geographic Preference:** Local.

42289 ■ **University of New Mexico-Gallup Small Business Development Center**
705 Gurley Ave.
Gallup, NM 87301
Ph: (505)863-7500
URL: http://www.nmsbdc.org/locations/gallup
Contact: Cynthia Jarvison, Officer
E-mail: cjarvison@unm.edu
Description: Represents and promotes the small business sector. Provides management assistance to current and prospective small business owners. Helps to improve management skills and expand the products and services of members. **Geographic Preference:** Local.

SMALL BUSINESS ASSISTANCE PROGRAMS

42290 ■ **New Mexico Department of Agriculture - Marketing and Development Div.**
1050 Stewart St.
Las Cruces, NM 88003
URL: http://nmdeptag.nmsu.edu/marketing-and-development.html
Contact: Jason New, Director
E-mail: ddmd@nmda.nmsu.edu
Description: Provides technical assistance to agricultural producers and processors who export both domestically and internationally.

42291 ■ **New Mexico Economic Development Department (EDD)**
Joseph M. Montoya Bldg., 1100 S St. Francis Dr.
Santa Fe, NM 87505-4147
Ph: (505)827-0300
Fax: (505)827-0328
URL: http://edd.newmexico.gov
Contact: Mark Roper, Director
E-mail: mark.roper@state.nm.us
Facebook: www.facebook.com/NewMexicoEconomicDevelopment
Linkedin: www.linkedin.com/company/new-mexico-economic-development-department
X (Twitter): x.com/NMecondev
YouTube: www.youtube.com/channel/UCEVKlfuuLNl4R0VH6GsxZRQ
Description: Firm provides marketing and consulting services. **Publications:** *New Mexico International Trade Directory* (Annual).

42292 ■ **New Mexico General Services Department**
PO Box 6850
Santa Fe, NM 87502
Ph: (505)827-2000
URL: http://www.generalservices.state.nm.us
Description: Promotes and assists small, minority-owned, and women-owned businesses in marketing their goods and services to government, especially to the state of New Mexico.

42293 ■ **New Mexico Small Business Assistance (NMSBA)**
NM
URL: http://www.nmsbaprogram.org
Contact: Mariann Johnston, Program Manager
E-mail: mjohnston@lanl.gov
Description: Offers access to Los Alamos and Sandia national laboratories to small business facing technical challenges. **Founded:** 2000.

42294 ■ **New Mexico State University - Arrowhead Center**
3655 Research Dr.
Las Cruces, NM 88003-8001
Ph: (575)646-6120
Co. E-mail: arrowheadcenter@nmsu.edu
URL: http://arrowheadcenter.nmsu.edu
Contact: Kathy Hansen, Chief Executive Officer
E-mail: hansen@ad.nmsu.edu
Facebook: www.facebook.com/ArrowheadCenterNMSU
Linkedin: www.linkedin.com/in/arrowhead-center-at-nmsu-652b604b
X (Twitter): x.com/ATI_Arrowhead
Instagram: www.instagram.com/arrowheadcenter
YouTube: www.youtube.com/c/ArrowheadCenter
Description: Provides research services and a data bank for economic and business related information. Also provides business and economic research to public and private sectors. **Publications:** *Directory of New Mexico Manufacturers* (Biennial); *Directory of Grant Support and Technical Assistance for Native American Initiatives* (Annual).

SCORE OFFICES

42295 ■ **SCORE - Albuquerque**
4801 Lang Ave., Ste. 110
Albuquerque, NM 87109
Ph: (505)717-4058
Fax: (505)248-8246
Co. E-mail: admin.0067@scorevolunteer.org
URL: http://albuquerque.score.org
Facebook: www.facebook.com/SCOREAlbuquerque
Linkedin: www.linkedin.com/company/albuquerque-score
X (Twitter): x.com/ABQScore
YouTube: www.youtube.com/channel/UC2dAuFm4B_D-2B-24yeyalw
Description: Seeks to educate entrepreneurs and help small businesses start, grow and succeed nationwide. Organizes volunteers who are working or retired business owners, executives and corporate leaders who wish to share their wisdom and lessons learned in business. **Geographic Preference:** Local.

42296 ■ **SCORE - Las Cruces**
505 S Main St., Ste. 125
Las Cruces, NM 88001
Ph: (575)523-5627
Fax: (575)524-2101
Co. E-mail: score.397@scorelascruces.org
URL: http://lascruces.score.org
Facebook: www.facebook.com/Las-Cruces-Score-Chapter-397-883976164969134
Description: Provides professional guidance and information to maximize the success of existing and emerging small businesses. Offers business counseling and workshops. **Geographic Preference:** Local.

42297 ■ **SCORE - Santa Fe and Northern New Mexico**
3900 Paseo del Sol Ste. A320
Santa Fe, NM 87507
Free: 800-634-0245

Co. E-mail: sfnnm.contact-us@scorevolunteer.org
URL: http://www.score.org/santafe
Contact: Cheryl Ancell, Chairman
Facebook: www.facebook.com/SCORESantaFeandNNewMexico
Linkedin: www.linkedin.com/company/score-mentors-sante-fe-and-northern-new-mexic
Instagram: www.instagram.com/score_santafe
Description: Provides professional guidance and information to maximize the success of existing and emerging small businesses. Offers business counseling and workshops. **Founded:** 1964. **Geographic Preference:** Local.

BETTER BUSINESS BUREAUS

42298 ■ **Better Business Bureau Serving New Mexico and Southwestern Colorado**
7007 Jefferson St. NE, Ste. A
Albuquerque, NM 87109
Ph: (505)346-0110
Fax: (505)346-0696
URL: http://www.bbb.org/new-mexico-southwest-colorado
Contact: Brian Baca, President
E-mail: bbaca@bbbsw.org
Description: Seeks to promote and foster ethical relationship between businesses and the public through voluntary self-regulation, consumer and business education, and service excellence. Provides information to help consumers and businesses make informed purchasing decisions and avoid costly scams and frauds; settles consumer complaints through arbitration and other means. **Founded:** 1941. **Geographic Preference:** State.

CHAMBERS OF COMMERCE

42299 ■ **Alamogordo Chamber of Commerce (ACC)**
1301 N White Sands Blvd.
Alamogordo, NM 88310
Ph: (575)437-6120
Free: 800-826-0294
Fax: (575)437-6334
Co. E-mail: chamber@alamogordo.com
URL: http://www.alamogordo.com
Contact: G. B. Oliver, Executive Director
E-mail: dir@alamogordo.com
Facebook: www.facebook.com/AlamogordoCenterofCommerce
Linkedin: www.linkedin.com/company/accgem
X (Twitter): x.com/alamogordocofc
Instagram: www.instagram.com/alamogordocenterofcommerce
YouTube: www.youtube.com/channel/UCwmlcZNES70qU48_M4LRzUg
Description: Promotes business and community development in Alamogordo, NM. Sponsors Cottonwood Festival, arts and crafts, Frontier Village (county fair), and White Sands Balloon Fiesta. **Founded:** 1942. **Publications:** *ChamberChat* (Weekly); *Business Directory*; *Living in Alamogordo* (Periodic). **Awards:** Alamogordo Chamber of Commerce Citizen of the Year (Annual). **Geographic Preference:** Local.

42300 ■ **Angel Fire Chamber of Commerce**
Centro Plz.
3407 Mountain View Blvd.
Angel Fire, NM 87710
Ph: (575)377-6353
Co. E-mail: info@angelfirechamber.org
URL: http://www.angelfirechamber.org/home-2.htm
Contact: Cindy Ward, Chairman of the Board
Facebook: www.facebook.com/AngelFireChamberOfCommerce
Pinterest: www.pinterest.com/pin/335940453432323363
Description: Promotes business and community development in Angel Fire and northern New Mexico. **Founded:** 1982. **Publications:** *Chamber In-House*. **Educational Activities:** Angel Fire Balloon (Irregular). **Geographic Preference:** Local.

42301 ■ **Aztec Chamber of Commerce**
108 S Main Ave.
Aztec, NM 87410
Ph: (505)334-7646
URL: http://aztecchamber.com
Contact: Debbie Klein, Co-President
Facebook: www.facebook.com/Aztec-Chamber-of-Commerce-349191185923
Description: Promotes business and community development in Aztec, NM. **Publications:** *Aztec Etchings* (Monthly). **Geographic Preference:** Local.

42302 ■ **Bloomfield Chamber of Commerce**
224 W Broadway
Bloomfield, NM 87413
Ph: (505)632-0880
Fax: (505)634-1431
Co. E-mail: askus@bloomfieldchamber.info
URL: http://www.bloomfieldchamber.info
Contact: Janet Mackey, President
Description: Promotes business and community development in Bloomfield, NM area. **Geographic Preference:** Local.

42303 ■ *Bottom Line*
150 E Lohman Ave.
Las Cruces, NM 88001
Ph: (575)524-1968
Co. E-mail: chamber@lascruces.org
URL: http://www.lascruces.org
Contact: Debbi Moore, President
E-mail: dmoore@lascruces.org
URL(s): www.lascruces.org/membership/value-without-involvement
Released: Monthly **Availability:** Print.

42304 ■ *Business Directory*
1301 N White Sands Blvd.
Alamogordo, NM 88310
Ph: (575)437-6120
Free: 800-826-0294
Fax: (575)437-6334
Co. E-mail: chamber@alamogordo.com
URL: http://www.alamogordo.com
Contact: G. B. Oliver, Executive Director
E-mail: dir@alamogordo.com
URL(s): www.alamogordo.com/join
Availability: Print; Online.

42305 ■ **Carrizozo Chamber of Commerce**
PO Box 567
Carrizozo, NM 88301
URL: http://carrizozochamber.org
Facebook: www.facebook.com/carrizozochamber
Instagram: www.instagram.com/carrizozochamber
Description: Promotes business and community development in Carrizozo, NM. **Geographic Preference:** Local.

42306 ■ **Chama Valley Chamber of Commerce**
Junction of Hwy. 64 & 17
Chama, NM 87520
Ph: (575)756-2306
Free: 800-477-0149
Co. E-mail: info@chamavalley.com
URL: http://chamavalley.com
Contact: Roseann Talamante, President
Facebook: www.facebook.com/chamavalleychamber
Instagram: www.instagram.com/visitchamanm
Description: Promotes business and community development in Chama, NM. Sponsors festival. **Founded:** 1963. **Geographic Preference:** Local.

42307 ■ *Chamber Voice*
712 Dalies Ave.
Belen, NM 87002
Ph: (505)864-8091
URL: http://belenchamber.com
Contact: John T. Ivey, President
URL(s): belenchamber.com/newsletters
Released: Monthly **Availability:** PDF.

42308 ■ *ChamberChat*
1301 N White Sands Blvd.
Alamogordo, NM 88310
Ph: (575)437-6120
Free: 800-826-0294
Fax: (575)437-6334
Co. E-mail: chamber@alamogordo.com
URL: http://www.alamogordo.com
Contact: G. B. Oliver, Executive Director
E-mail: dir@alamogordo.com
URL(s): www.alamogordo.com/join
Released: Weekly **Availability:** Print.

42309 ■ **Cimarron Chamber of Commerce**
104 N Lincoln Ave.
Cimarron, NM 87714
Ph: (575)376-2417
Free: 888-376-2417
Co. E-mail: cimarronnm@gmail.com
URL: http://www.cimarronnm.com
Contact: Melissa Warner, President
Facebook: www.facebook.com/CimarronNM
Description: Promotes business and community development in the Cimarron, NM area. **Geographic Preference:** Local.

42310 ■ **Clayton-Union County Chamber of Commerce**
1103 S 1st St.
Clayton, NM 88415-2101
Ph: (575)374-9253
Co. E-mail: admin@discoverclaytonnewmexico.org
URL: http://www.uschamber.com/co/chambers/new-mexico/clayton
Contact: David Drumm, President
Facebook: www.facebook.com/ClaytonNewMexicoChamber
Description: Promotes business and community development in Clayton, NM. **Founded:** 1920. **Geographic Preference:** Local.

42311 ■ **Cloudcroft Chamber of Commerce (CCC)**
PO Box 1291
Cloudcroft, NM 88317
Ph: (575)682-2733
Fax: (575)682-6028
Co. E-mail: chamber@coolcloudcroft.com
URL: http://coolcloudcroft.com
Contact: Karen Sonnenfelt, President
Facebook: www.facebook.com/CloudcroftChamber
Linkedin: www.linkedin.com/company/cloudcroft-chamber-of-commerce
Description: Promotes business, community development, and tourism in the Cloudcroft-Alamogordo, NM area. **Founded:** 1900. **Geographic Preference:** Local.

42312 ■ **Clovis/Curry County Chamber of Commerce**
105 E Grand Ave.
Clovis, NM 88101
Ph: (575)763-3435
Free: 800-261-7656
Fax: (575)763-7266
Co. E-mail: info@clovisnm.org
URL: http://www.clovisnm.org
Contact: Ernie Kos, Executive Director
E-mail: ernie@clovisnm.org
Facebook: www.facebook.com/ClovisChamberofCommerce
Instagram: www.instagram.com/clovis_chamber
YouTube: www.youtube.com/channel/UCfb56vfl8chwmOJk8ensUsw
Description: Promotes business and community development in Curry County, NM. **Founded:** 1929. **Geographic Preference:** Local.

42313 ■ **Deming-Luna County Chamber of Commerce**
800 E Pine St.
Deming, NM 88030
Ph: (575)567-3928
Co. E-mail: demingchamber@gmail.com
URL: http://demingchamber.net
Contact: Eric Roach, President
Facebook: www.facebook.com/demingchamberofcommerce
Instagram: www.instagram.com/demingchamber

Description: Promotes business and community development in Deming, NM. Sponsors Great American Duck Race, Rockhound Day, assists with Old Timers' Day. **Founded:** 1910. **Geographic Preference:** Local.

42314 ■ Eagle Nest Chamber of Commerce (ENCC)
PO Box 322
Eagle Nest, NM 87718-0322
Ph: (575)613-8484
Co. E-mail: eaglenestchambernm@gmail.com
URL: http://www.eaglenestchamber.com
Contact: Patrick Espie, President
E-mail: president@eaglenestchamber.org
Facebook: www.facebook.com/eaglenest.chamber
Description: Promotes business, community development, and tourism in Eagle Nest, NM. **Publications:** Members & Services Directory; Northern New Mexico's Lakeside Playground (Periodic). **Educational Activities:** Fish Fest (Annual). **Geographic Preference:** Local.

42315 ■ Elephant Butte Chamber of Commerce
402 Butte Blvd., Hwy. 195
Elephant Butte, NM 87935
Ph: (575)744-4708
Co. E-mail: ebnmchamber@gmail.com
URL: http://www.ebnmchamber.org
Contact: William Dooley, President
Facebook: www.facebook.com/EBcocNM
Instagram: www.instagram.com/elephantbuttechamber
YouTube: www.youtube.com/watch
Description: Seeks to advance the general welfare and prosperity of the Elephant Butte Lake area so that its citizens and all areas of its business community shall prosper. Operates a visitor's center. **Founded:** 1999. **Geographic Preference:** Local.

42316 ■ Espanola Valley Chamber of Commerce (EVCC)
1 Calle De Las Espanolas, Ste. F and G
Espanola, NM 87532
Ph: (505)753-2831
Fax: (505)753-1252
Co. E-mail: info@espanolanmchamber.com
URL: http://www.espanolanmchamber.com
Contact: David Valdez, President
Facebook: www.facebook.com/evcoc
Description: Promotes business and community development in the Espanola, NM area. **Founded:** 1937. **Publications:** Espanola Valley Visitors Guide (Annual); Noticias Del Valle (Monthly). **Geographic Preference:** Local.

42317 ■ Farmington Chamber of Commerce (FCC)
5101 College Blvd., Quality Center for Business
Farmington, NM 87402
Ph: (505)325-0279
Co. E-mail: chamber@gofarmington.com
URL: http://www.gofarmington.com
Contact: Jamie Church, President
Facebook: www.facebook.com/Farmington-Chamber-of-Commerce-138781216275105
X (Twitter): x.com/GoFarmington
Description: Works businesses and the community to advance the economic and civic development in the area. **Founded:** 1953. **Geographic Preference:** Local.

42318 ■ Fort Sumner Chamber of Commerce
c/oKristine Souza,4605 5th ST. NW
Las Cruces, NM 88001
Ph: (575)355-7705
Co. E-mail: fortsumnerchamber@hotmail.com
URL: http://www.fortsumnernewmexico.com
Contact: Kim McCullum, President
Facebook: www.facebook.com/DeBacaChamber
X (Twitter): x.com/chamber_fort
Instagram: www.instagram.com/fortsumnerchamber
Description: Promotes business and community development in the De Baca County, NM area. **Geographic Preference:** Local.

42319 ■ Greater Albuquerque Chamber of Commerce
400 Tijeras Ave.
Albuquerque, NM 87102
Ph: (505)764-3700
Co. E-mail: info@greaterabq.com
URL: http://greaterabq.com
Contact: Terri Cole, President
E-mail: tcole@greaterabq.com
Facebook: www.facebook.com/abqchamber
Linkedin: www.linkedin.com/company/greater-albuquerque-chamber-of-commerce
X (Twitter): x.com/abqchamber
Instagram: www.instagram.com/abqchamber
Description: Promotes business and community development in Albuquerque, NM. **Founded:** 1917. **Publications:** The Business Buzz (Monthly); Economic Profile (Annual); Images of Albuquerque (Annual). **Geographic Preference:** Local.

42320 ■ Greater Artesia Chamber of Commerce
107 N 1st St.
Artesia, NM 88210
Ph: (575)746-2744
Fax: (575)746-2745
URL: http://www.artesiachamber.com/the-chamber
Contact: Hayley Klein, Executive Director
E-mail: hklein@artesiachamber.com
Description: Promotes business and community development in Artesia, NM. **Founded:** 1924. **Geographic Preference:** Local.

42321 ■ Greater Belen Chamber of Commerce
712 Dalies Ave.
Belen, NM 87002
Ph: (505)864-8091
URL: http://belenchamber.com
Contact: John T. Ivey, President
Facebook: www.facebook.com/GreaterBelenChamberofCommerce
Description: Promotes business and community development in Belen, NM. **Publications:** Chamber Voice (Monthly). **Awards:** Greater Belen Chamber Business of the Month (Monthly). **Geographic Preference:** Local.

42322 ■ Greater Las Cruces Chamber of Commerce (GLCCC)
150 E Lohman Ave.
Las Cruces, NM 88001
Ph: (575)524-1968
Co. E-mail: chamber@lascruces.org
URL: http://www.lascruces.org
Contact: Debbi Moore, President
E-mail: dmoore@lascruces.org
Facebook: www.facebook.com/GreaterLasCrucesChamberofCommerce
Linkedin: www.linkedin.com/company/greater-las-cruces-chamber-of-commerce
X (Twitter): x.com/GLCChamber
Instagram: www.instagram.com/glcchamber
YouTube: www.youtube.com/user/LasCrucesChamber
Description: Promotes business and community development in Las Cruces, NM. Assists with the Whole Enchilada Fiesta. **Founded:** 1952. **Publications:** Bottom Line (Monthly). **Awards:** Greater Las Cruces Chamber Business of the Month (Monthly); Greater Las Cruces Chamber Business of the Year (Annual). **Geographic Preference:** Local.

42323 ■ Hobbs Chamber of Commerce (HCC)
400 N Marland
Hobbs, NM 88240
Ph: (575)397-3202
Fax: (575)397-1689
Co. E-mail: welcome@hobbschamber.org
URL: http://www.hobbschamber.org
Contact: Patty Collins, President
E-mail: executive@hobbschamber.org
Facebook: www.facebook.com/hobbschamber
Linkedin: www.linkedin.com/company/hobbs-chamber-of-commerce
X (Twitter): x.com/hobbschamber
Description: Dedicated to the promotion of the free enterprise system and business in general. Activities include EXPO in the Desert, business fair and Christmas in the Desert, holiday lighting and exhibits throughout the city. Offers relocation packets and information regarding the area. **Founded:** 1930. **Geographic Preference:** Local.

42324 ■ Las Cruces Hispanic Chamber of Commerce (LCHCC)
277 E Amador Ave., Ste. 305
Las Cruces, NM 88001
Ph: (575)524-8900
Fax: (575)532-9255
Co. E-mail: office@lascruceshispanicchamber.com
URL: http://www.lascruceshispanicchamber.com
Contact: Curtis Rosemond, President
X (Twitter): x.com/LCHispanicChamb
Description: Promotes economic and social development in the Hispanic community of Las Cruces, NM. **Founded:** 1991. **Geographic Preference:** Local.

42325 ■ Las Vegas-San Miguel Chamber of Commerce (LVSMCC)
500 Railroad Ave.
Las Vegas, NM 87701
Ph: (505)425-3707
Free: 800-832-5947
Co. E-mail: lvsmchamberofcommerce@gmail.com
URL: http://www.lasvegasnm.com
Contact: Phillip Martinez, President
Facebook: www.facebook.com/lvsmchamberofcommerce
Description: Promotes business and community development in Las Vegas, NM. **Founded:** 1945. **Publications:** Chamberline (Bimonthly). **Geographic Preference:** Regional.

42326 ■ Los Alamos Chamber of Commerce
190 Central Pk. Sq.
Los Alamos, NM 87544
Ph: (505)661-4816
Fax: (505)662-0099
Co. E-mail: ryn@losalamos.org
URL: http://www.losalamoschamber.com
Contact: Ryn Herrmann, Director
E-mail: ryn@losalamos.org
Facebook: www.facebook.com/LosAlamosChamber
X (Twitter): x.com/losalamoschmbr
Description: Promotes business and community development in the Los Alamos County, NM area. **Founded:** 1983. **Geographic Preference:** Local.

42327 ■ Los Alamos Commerce & Development Corp. (LACDC)
190 Central Pk. Sq.
Los Alamos, NM 87544
Ph: (505)662-0001
Co. E-mail: reception@losalamos.org
URL: http://losalamosdevelopment.com
Contact: Lauren McDaniel, Executive Director
E-mail: lauren@losalamos.org
Facebook: www.facebook.com/LosAlamosCDC
Linkedin: www.linkedin.com/company/los-alamos-commerce-&-development-corporation
X (Twitter): x.com/LosAlamosCDC
Pinterest: www.pinterest.com/losalamoscdc
Description: Operates the Los Alamos Chamber of Commerce. Acts as a community economic development and business assistance organization in the Los Alamos area. **Founded:** 1983. **Geographic Preference:** Local.

42328 ■ Lovington Chamber of Commerce
114 E Central
Lovington, NM 88260
Ph: (575)396-5311
URL: http://www.lovingtonchamber.org
Contact: David Munoz, Co-President
Facebook: www.facebook.com/lovingtonchamber
X (Twitter): x.com/lvt_chamber
Instagram: www.instagram.com/lovingtonchamber
YouTube: www.youtube.com/watch
Pinterest: www.pinterest.com/lovingtonchamberofcommerce

Description: Promotes business and community development in Lovington, NM. Sponsors Lovington Auto Expo, Southeastern New Mexico Fourth of July Celebration, Lea County Fair and Rodeo, Southeastern New Mexico Arts and Crafts Show, and Electric Light Parade. Awards Miss Lovington Scholarship. Holds directors meeting. **Founded:** 1952. **Awards:** Lovington Chamber of Commerce Citizen of the Year (Annual). **Geographic Preference:** Local.

42329 ■ Magdalena Chamber of Commerce
902 W 1st St., on Rt. 60
Magdalena, NM 87825
Ph: (575)854-3310
Free: 866-854-3217
Co. E-mail: info@magdalena-nm.com
URL: http://magdalena-nm.com/trails-end/chamber_of_commerce.html
Contact: Catherine DeMaria, President
Facebook: www.facebook.com/Magdalena.Chamber.New.Mexico.87825
Description: Seeks to promote business and community development and enhance the relationship between local businesses and professionals with the public. **Geographic Preference:** Local.

42330 ■ *The Noisy Water Gazette*
720 Sudderth Dr.
Ruidoso, NM 88345
Ph: (575)257-7395
Fax: (575)257-4693
Co. E-mail: info@ruidosonow.com
URL: http://www.ruidosonow.com
Contact: Deborah Douds, Director
URL(s): www.ruidosonow.com/marketing
Released: Monthly **Description:** Features information to assist their members in every facet of the business. **Availability:** Print.

42331 ■ Red River Chamber of Commerce
200 W River St.
Red River, NM 87558
Ph: (575)754-2366
Co. E-mail: rrinfo@redriverchamber.org
URL: http://www.redriverchamber.org
Contact: David Wilcox, President
Description: Promotes business and community development in Red River, NM. **Founded:** 1985. **Publications:** *Red River Visitors Guide* (Annual). **Geographic Preference:** Local.

42332 ■ *Regional Business Directory*
URL(s): www.moriartychamber.com/directory.html
Released: Periodic **Availability:** Print; Online.

42333 ■ Rio Rancho Regional Chamber of Commerce (RRRCC)
4001 S Blvd. SE
Rio Rancho, NM 87124
Ph: (505)892-1533
Fax: (505)892-6157
Co. E-mail: riochamber@rrrcc.org
URL: http://www.rrrcc.org
Contact: Jerry Schalow, President
E-mail: jerry@rrrcc.org
Facebook: www.facebook.com/RioRanchoRegionalChamber
Linkedin: www.linkedin.com/company/rio-rancho-chamber-of-commerce
X (Twitter): x.com/RRRchamber
Instagram: www.instagram.com/rioranchochamber
YouTube: www.youtube.com/channel/UCdppwXgVPD8MmnDagFjDYXA
Description: Promotes business and community development in Rio Rancho, NM. Sponsors Springfest, athletic tournaments, soapbox derby competitions, and other community social events. **Founded:** 1980. **Publications:** *Chamber News*. **Geographic Preference:** Local.

42334 ■ Roosevelt County Chamber of Commerce
100 S Ave. A
Portales, NM 88130
Ph: (575)356-8541
Free: 800-635-8036
Fax: (575)356-8542
Co. E-mail: chamber@portales.com
URL: http://www.portales.com
Contact: Chase Gossett, President
Facebook: www.facebook.com/Roosevelt-County-Chamber-of-Commerce-201006536610166
X (Twitter): x.com/rocochamber
YouTube: www.youtube.com/channel/UCXRmnSAghaXLFJxLH-5WF5w
Description: Promotes business and community development in Roosevelt County, NM area. **Founded:** 1934. **Geographic Preference:** Local.

42335 ■ Roswell Chamber of Commerce
131 W 2nd St.
Roswell, NM 88201
Ph: (575)623-5695
Free: 877-849-7679
URL: http://www.roswellnm.org
Contact: Elizabeth Morales, Director, Administration
E-mail: elizabeth@roswellnm.org
Facebook: www.facebook.com/roswell.chamber.20
Description: Promotes business and community development in Roswell, NM. Works with retired senior volunteer program. **Founded:** 1918. **Publications:** *Chamber Report* (3/year); *Roswell Magazine*. **Geographic Preference:** Local.

42336 ■ Ruidoso Valley Chamber of Commerce (RVCC)
720 Sudderth Dr.
Ruidoso, NM 88345
Ph: (575)257-7395
Fax: (575)257-4693
Co. E-mail: info@ruidosonow.com
URL: http://www.ruidosonow.com
Contact: Deborah Douds, Director
Facebook: www.facebook.com/people/Ruidoso-Valley-Chamber-of-Commerce/100063629137907
YouTube: www.youtube.com/channel/UCLA3gex073ZwKh538DtDaag/videos
Description: Fosters development, growth and prosperity of the business community of Ruidoso, Ruidoso Downs and the surrounding area. **Founded:** 1941. **Publications:** *The Noisy Water Gazette* (Monthly). **Educational Activities:** Ruidoso Art and Wine Festival (Annual). **Geographic Preference:** Local.

42337 ■ Santa Fe Chamber of Commerce
1628 St. Michael's Dr.
Santa Fe, NM 87505
Ph: (505)988-3279
Fax: (505)984-2205
Co. E-mail: info@santafechamber.com
URL: http://www.santafechamber.com
Contact: Bridget Dixson, President
E-mail: bridget@santafechamber.com
Facebook: www.facebook.com/santafechamber
X (Twitter): x.com/Santafechamber
Description: Promotes business and community development in Santa Fe, NM. **Founded:** 1882. **Publications:** *Business Advocate* (Monthly); *Business Directory*. **Geographic Preference:** Local.

42338 ■ Silver City-Grant County Chamber of Commerce
3031 Hwy., 180 E
Silver City, NM 88061
Ph: (575)538-3785
Free: 800-548-9378
Fax: (575)597-3790
Co. E-mail: info@silvercity.org
URL: http://www.silvercity.org
Contact: Romeo J. Cruz, Executive Director
E-mail: director@silvercity.org
Facebook: www.facebook.com/Silver-City-Grant-County-Chamber-of-Commerce-and-Conference-Center-103957038768160
Linkedin: www.linkedin.com/in/silver-city-grant-co-chamber-of-commerce-43507379
X (Twitter): x.com/SilverCityOrg
Description: Promotes business and community development in the Old West Country, NM area. **Founded:** 1870. **Publications:** *Group Tours*. **Geographic Preference:** Local.

42339 ■ Taos County Chamber of Commerce (TCCC)
PO Box 3649
Taos, NM 87571
Ph: (575)751-8800
URL: http://www.taoschamber.com
Contact: Larry Mapes, Chairman
Facebook: www.facebook.com/TaosCountyChamberOfCommerce
YouTube: www.youtube.com/channel/UCm3yu8G0pSLM_fUNlek_9Rw
Description: Promotes business, tourism, and community development in the Taos County, NM area. Conducts community holiday celebrations; holds annual Taos Arts Festival and annual Taste of Taos food event. **Founded:** 1962. **Publications:** *Taos County Vacation Guide* (Periodic). **Geographic Preference:** Local.

42340 ■ Tucumcari-Quay County Chamber of Commerce (TQCCC)
404 W Rte. 66
Tucumcari, NM 88401
Ph: (575)461-1694
Fax: (575)461-3884
Co. E-mail: chamber@tucumcarinm.com
URL: http://tucumcarinm.com
Contact: Lee Judd, President
Facebook: www.facebook.com/TucumcariQuayCountyCoC
Description: Promotes business and community development in Quay County, NM. Sponsors annual Pinata Festival. **Founded:** 1909. **Publications:** *Chamber Chat* (Quarterly); *E-Newsletter*. **Geographic Preference:** Local.

MINORITY BUSINESS ASSISTANCE PROGRAMS

42341 ■ WESST
609 Broadway Blvd., NE
Albuquerque, NM 87102
Ph: (505)246-6900
Free: 800-GOW-ESST
Fax: (505)243-3035
Co. E-mail: info@wesst.org
URL: http://www.wesst.org
Contact: Agnes Noonan, President
Facebook: www.facebook.com/WESST.NM
Linkedin: www.linkedin.com/company/wesst
X (Twitter): x.com/GoWESST
Instagram: www.instagram.com/wesstnm
Description: Provides statewide small business development and training in New Mexico. Serves all people, but focus is on women and minorities. **Founded:** 1989.

FINANCING AND LOAN PROGRAMS

42342 ■ Flywheel Ventures
369 Montezuma Ave., No. 564
Santa Fe, NM 87501
Ph: (505)225-1618
Fax: (505)672-7053
URL: http://www.flywheelventures.com
Contact: Paula L. Marez, General Manager
E-mail: paula@flywheelventures.com
X (Twitter): x.com/flywheelvc
Description: Provider of venture capital investments for seed and early-stage companies. **Founded:** 1999. **Preferred Investment Size:** $100,000 to $1,000,000. **Investment Policies:** Seed and early stage. **Industry Preferences:** Communications, computer software, and semiconductors and other electronics.

42343 ■ Technology Ventures Corp. (TVC)
1900 Wyoming Blvd. SE Bldg. 20602
Albuquerque, NM 87116
URL: http://www.techventures.org
Founded: 1993. **Industry Preferences:** Diversified.

INCUBATORS/RESEARCH AND TECHNOLOGY PARKS

42344 ■ Arrowhead Center, New Mexico State University
3655 Research Dr.
 Las Cruces, NM 88003-8001
Ph: (575)646-6120
Co. E-mail: arrowheadcenter@nmsu.edu
URL: http://arrowheadcenter.nmsu.edu
Contact: Kathryn Hansen, Chief Executive Officer
Facebook: www.facebook.com/ArrowheadCenterNMSU
X (Twitter): x.com/ATI_Arrowhead
Instagram: www.instagram.com/arrowheadcenter
YouTube: www.youtube.com/c/ArrowheadCenter
Description: Helps small businesses at all stages start and grow through our services, resources, connections, and expertise.

42345 ■ City of Las Cruces - Economic Development Office
700 N Main St.
 Las Cruces, NM 88001
Ph: (575)541-2286
Co. E-mail: econdev@las-cruces.org
URL: http://www.las-cruces.org/1526/Business-Tools
Contact: Elizabeth Teeters, Director
E-mail: eteeters@lascruces.gov
Description: Business incubator aiding startups and entrepreneurs as they start their business in Las Cruces. **Founded:** 1849.

42346 ■ Economic Development Corporation of Lea County (EDCLC)
200 E Broadway St., Ste. A201
 Hobbs, NM 88240
Ph: (575)397-2039
Co. E-mail: edclc@edclc.org
URL: http://edclc.org
Contact: Jennifer Grassham, President
E-mail: jennifer@edclc.org
Facebook: www.facebook.com/EDCofleacounty
Linkedin: www.linkedin.com/company/economic-development-corporation-of-lea-county
X (Twitter): x.com/edclc
Description: Works to improve the economic condition of Lea County through business expansion, relocation, and retention. **Founded:** 1963.

42347 ■ IOTA
c/o Russell V. Combs Sr, President
 3167 San Mateo NE, Ste. 195
 Albuquerque, NM 87110
URL: http://www.iotasite.com
Contact: Russell V. Combs, Sr., President
E-mail: russc@iotasite.com
Description: Provides incubation, operations, training, and applications.

42348 ■ Keshet Ideas and Innovation Center (KIIC)
4121 Cutler Ave., NE
 Albuquerque, NM 87110
URL: http://keshetarts.org/ideas-and-innovation/#Kiic
Description: Business resource center for arts entrepreneurs. Supports and strengthens arts entrepreneurs on their path for sustainability by championing the value of the artist and the arts economy, by equipping creative industry businesses with the tools for success. **Founded:** 2012.

42349 ■ Los Alamos Research Park (LARP)
190 Central Pk. Sq.
 Los Alamos, NM 87544
Ph: (505)662-0001
Co. E-mail: reception@losalamos.org
URL: http://losalamosdevelopment.com/property
Description: Provides a research and development focused research park. **Founded:** 1983.

42350 ■ Mixing Bowl Kitchen
c/o S Valley Economic Development Center
 318 Isleta Blvd. SW
 Albuquerque, NM 87105
URL: http://www.svedc.org

Description: A multi-purpose small business incubator supporting culinary entrepreneurs. **Founded:** 2005.

42351 ■ Quality Center for Business (QCB)
4601 College Blvd.
 Farmington, NM 87402
Ph: (505)326-3311
Co. E-mail: admissions@sanjuancollege.edu
URL: http://www.sanjuancollege.edu/community/enterprise-center
Contact: Dr. Toni Hopper Pendergrass, President
Description: Services: Integrated approach to assisting area businesses, management training, assistance in business planning, technical support, space and office support solutions.

42352 ■ San Juan College - Enterprise Center
5101 College Blvd.
 Farmington, NM 87402
Ph: (505)566-3700
Co. E-mail: enterprisecenter@sanjuancollege.edu
URL: http://www.sanjuancollege.edu/community/departments/enterprise-center
Facebook: www.facebook.com/SJCEnterpriseCenter
Description: A certified business incubator providing turnkey offices and production space in combination with the business resources needed to turn your idea into a successful business. **Founded:** 1956.

42353 ■ Sandia Science & Technology Park (SS&TP)
1611 Innovation Pkwy. SE
 Albuquerque, NM 87123
Ph: (505)844-5795
Fax: (505)844-1389
URL: http://sstp.org
Contact: Sherman McCorkle, Chief Executive Officer
E-mail: sherman@smccorkle.org
X (Twitter): x.com/sandiatechpark
Description: Provides startups and existing companies with access to world-class facilities, technologies, scientists, and engineers. **Founded:** 1998.

42354 ■ Santa Fe Business Incubator (SFBI)
3900 Paseo del Sol
 Santa Fe, NM 87507
Ph: (505)424-1140
Fax: (505)424-1144
Co. E-mail: info@sfbi.net
URL: http://sfbi.net
Contact: Marie Longserre, President
E-mail: mariel@sfbi.net
X (Twitter): x.com/SantaFeInc
Instagram: www.instagram.com/santafeinc
Description: Firm provides economic development and business management consulting services. **Founded:** 1997.

42355 ■ South Valley Economic Development Center (SVEDC)
318 Isleta Blvd. SW
 Albuquerque, NM 87102
Ph: (505)877-0373
Fax: (505)877-0873
Co. E-mail: info@svedc.org
URL: http://www.svedc.org
Contact: Camille Vasquez, Manager
YouTube: www.youtube.com/channel/UCurhyQPrcOj0oKCD3f0JE5w
Description: A small business incubator with processes that accelerate the successful development of start-up and fledgling companies by providing entrepreneurs with an array of targeted resources and services. **Founded:** 1996.

42356 ■ Supporting Technology Transfer and Catalyzing Economic Development at the University of New Mexico
101 Broadway Blvd. NE, Ste. 1100
 Albuquerque, NM 87102
Ph: (505)272-7900
Co. E-mail: info@innovations.unm.edu
URL: http://innovations.unm.edu
Contact: Elizabeth J. Kuuttila, Chief Executive Officer

E-mail: kuuttila@stc.unm.edu
Facebook: www.facebook.com/unminnovations
X (Twitter): x.com/unminnovations
Instagram: www.instagram.com/unminnovations
YouTube: www.youtube.com/channel/UCvSGf0aK1KNJ358sYJ8_IRQ/featured
Description: Supports technology startups and entrepreneurs.

42357 ■ WESST Enterprise Center (WEC)
609 Broadway Blvd. NE
 Albuquerque, NM 87102
Ph: (505)246-6900
Free: 800-469-3778
Co. E-mail: info@wesst.org
URL: http://www.wesst.org
Contact: Agnes Noonan, President
Facebook: www.facebook.com/WESST.NM
Linkedin: www.linkedin.com/company/wesst
X (Twitter): x.com/GoWESST
Description: A mixed-use small business incubator for up to 20 light manufacturing, service, and technology enterprises. **Founded:** 1989.

EDUCATIONAL PROGRAMS

42358 ■ Central New Mexico Community College (CNM)
900 University Blvd. SE
 Albuquerque, NM 87106
Ph: (505)224-3000
Free: 888-453-1304
Fax: (505)224-4400
Co. E-mail: contactcenter@cnm.edu
URL: http://www.cnm.edu
Contact: Kathie W. Winograd, President
Facebook: www.facebook.com/CNMonline
X (Twitter): x.com/cnmonline
Instagram: www.instagram.com/cnmonline
YouTube: www.youtube.com/user/cnmonline
Description: Trade and technical school offering a program in entrepreneurship. **Founded:** 1965. **Geographic Preference:** National.

42359 ■ Eastern New Mexico University-Roswell (ENMU-Roswell)
52 University Blvd.
 Roswell, NM 88203
Free: 800-243-6687
Co. E-mail: advising.center@roswell.enmu.edu
URL: http://www.roswell.enmu.edu
Contact: Dr. Shawn Powell, President
E-mail: shawn.powell@roswell.enmu.edu
Facebook: www.facebook.com/enmuroswell
X (Twitter): x.com/enmur
Instagram: www.instagram.com/enmuroswell
YouTube: www.youtube.com/channel/UCedb_38DM08pR_kZOZwu_Ng
Description: Part of a small business assistance center system that provides a variety of training programs, including self-paced, evening, and business courses. 1800-243-6687. **Founded:** 1958.

42360 ■ New Mexico Junior College Small Business Development Center (NMJCSBDC)
1 Thunderbird Cir.
 Hobbs, NM 88240
Ph: (575)492-4700
URL: http://www.nmjc.edu/community/sbdc/index.aspx
Contact: Brandon E. Hunt, Director
E-mail: bhunt@nmjc.edu
URL(s): www.nmsbdc.org/locations/hobbs
Description: Part of a small business system that provides a variety of training, including self-paced, and business courses. 1-800-657-6260. **Founded:** 1965.

PUBLICATIONS

42361 ■ *Albuquerque Business First*
120 W Morehead St.
 Charlotte, NC 28202
Co. E-mail: circhelp@bizjournals.com
URL: http://www.acbj.com

42362 ■ New Mexico

Contact: Mike Olivieri, Executive Vice President
URL(s): www.bizjournals.com/albuquerque
Linkedin: www.linkedin.com/company/albuquerque
 -business-first
X (Twitter): x.com/ABQBizFirst
Released: Weekly **Price:** $245, for 52 week nationwide access; $4, for 4 weeks Digital Trial; $70, for digital 52 weeks; $70, for digital & print. **Description:** Local business newspaper. **Availability:** Print; PDF; Download; Online. **Type:** Full-text.

PUBLISHERS

42362 ■ Sun Books - Sun Publishing
PO Box 5588
 Santa Fe, NM 87502-5588
Ph: (505)471-5177
Free: 877-849-0051
Fax: (505)473-4458
Co. E-mail: info@sunbooks.com
URL: http://www.sunbooks.com
Contact: James Allen, Contact
Description: Publisher of self-help, motivational, astrology, business, history, art, philosophy and art books. **Founded:** 1973.

42363 ■ Via Media Publishing Co.
Santa Fe, NM
Ph: (505)470-7842
Co. E-mail: contact@viamediapublishing.com
URL: http://www.viamediapublishing.com
Facebook: www.facebook.com/viamediapublishing
X (Twitter): x.com/ViaMediaPub
Instagram: www.instagram.com/via.media.publishing
Description: Publishes fiction and nonfiction about martial arts. Accepts unsolicited manuscripts. Reaches market through direct mail, reviews, listings and distributors including Bibliog. **Founded:** 1992.
Publications: *The Journal of Asian Martial Arts.*

EARLY STAGE FINANCING

42364 ■ New Mexico Angels
1451 Innovation Pkwy. SE, Ste. 600
 Albuquerque, NM 87123
Ph: (505)931-6435
Co. E-mail: info@nmangels.com
URL: http://nmangels.com
Contact: Drew Tulchin, President
E-mail: drew@nmangels.com
Linkedin: www.linkedin.com/company/new-mexico
 -angels-inc
X (Twitter): x.com/newmexicoangels
Description: Invests in early-stage companies in the Southwest. **Founded:** 1999. **Preferred Investment Size:** $100,000 to $500,000. **Investment Policies:** Companies with an unfair advantage, such as patented/proprietary technologies or processes; potential to penetrate or create global markets; multiple exit strategies.

VENTURE CAPITAL FIRM

42365 ■ Cottonwood Technology Funds (CTF)
422 Old Santa Fe Trl.
 Santa Fe, NM 87501
Ph: (505)412-8537
Co. E-mail: info@cottonwood.vc
URL: http://www.cottonwood.vc
Contact: Dave Blivin, Founder Managing Director
E-mail: dave@cottonwood.vc
X (Twitter): x.com/cottonwoodVC
YouTube: www.youtube.com/c/Cottonwoo
 dTechnologyFund

Description: Seed and pre-seed-stage technology commercialization funds. Provides venture services and capital to tech transfer opportunities with strong commercial potential. **Founded:** 2010.

42366 ■ New Mexico Community Capital (NMCC)
301 Gold Ave. SW, Ste. 102
 Albuquerque, NM 87102
Ph: (505)924-2820
Co. E-mail: info@nmccap.org
URL: http://nmccap.org
Contact: Elizabeth Gamboa, Executive Director
E-mail: liz@nmccap.org
Facebook: www.facebook.com/NMCommunityCapital
Linkedin: www.linkedin.com/company/new-mexico
 -community-capital
X (Twitter): x.com/NMCCAP
Instagram: www.instagram.com/nmccap
YouTube: www.youtube.com/channel/UCLk5HelKrs
 5a9bHOV8KOgWA/videos
Description: Provides capital and knowledge for New Mexico's high-potential businesses in emerging or under-served markets. **Founded:** 2004.

42367 ■ Verge Fund
317 Commercial St. NE
 Albuquerque, NM 87102
Ph: (505)247-1038
Fax: (505)244-8040
Co. E-mail: info@vergefund.com
URL: http://www.vergefund.com
Contact: Chris Gregory, Director, Finance
Description: Supports entrepreneurs in New Mexico with investors, founders, managers, and advisors to develop world class companies.

New York

ASSOCIATIONS AND OTHER ORGANIZATIONS

42368 ■ Association of Fundraising Professionals Long Island Chapter (AFPLI)
223 Wall St., Ste. 246
Huntington, NY 11743
Ph: (631)249-5008
Co. E-mail: info@afpli.org
URL: http://community.afpglobal.org/afpli/home
Contact: Katherine M. Fritz, Co-President
Facebook: www.facebook.com/afpli
Linkedin: www.linkedin.com/in/afp-long-islan d-5a87951a
X (Twitter): x.com/afpli
Founded: 1960. **Geographic Preference:** Local.

42369 ■ Association of Fundraising Professionals New York City Chapter (AFPNY)
555 Eighth Ave., Ste. 1902
New York, NY 10018
Ph: (646)846-3896
Co. E-mail: nycafp@nycafp.org
URL: http://nycafp.org
Contact: Jill Scibilia, Vice President, Development
Facebook: www.facebook.com/nycafp
Linkedin: www.linkedin.com/company/nycafp
X (Twitter): x.com/nycafp
Geographic Preference: Local.

42370 ■ Association of Fundraising Professionals New York, Finger Lakes Chapter
PO Box 194
Ithaca, NY 14851-0194
Co. E-mail: secretary@afpflny.com
URL: http://community.afpnet.org/afpnyfingerlakeschapter/home
Contact: Marianne Pelletier, President
Facebook: www.facebook.com/AFPFingerLakesChapter
Description: Fosters the development and growth of fundraising professionals. Promotes high ethical standards in the fundraising profession. Provides training opportunities for fundraising professionals. **Geographic Preference:** Local.

42371 ■ Association of Fundraising Professionals NY, Mid-Hudson Valley Chapter (AFPMHV)
30 Scott's Corners Dr., Ste. 203
Montgomery, NY 12549
Ph: (845)769-9393
Co. E-mail: mhvafp@gmail.com
URL: http://community.afpnet.org/mhvafp
Contact: Sarah Kimball, President
Facebook: www.facebook.com/AFPMHV
X (Twitter): x.com/MidHudsonAFP
Founded: 2006. **Geographic Preference:** Local.

42372 ■ Association of Fundraising Professionals Western New York Chapter (AFP WNY)
c/o Emily Knapic, Manager
PO Box 535
Buffalo, NY 14209
Ph: (716)887-2655
Fax: (716)887-2770
Co. E-mail: afpwny@afpwnychapter.org
URL: http://community.afpglobal.org/afpwny/home
Contact: Emily Knapic, Manager
Description: Provides professional and volunteer fundraisers in western New York with opportunities to connect with colleagues, engage in creative thinking, and network with new friends. **Geographic Preference:** Local.

42373 ■ Business Development Corporation for a Greater Massena (BDC)
34 Andrews St.
Massena, NY 13662
Ph: (315)769-8484
Co. E-mail: jamesmurphy52@me.com
URL: http://massena.us/240/Business-Development-Corporation-Board
Contact: Jim Murphy, Executive Director
E-mail: jamesmurphy52@me.com
Facebook: www.facebook.com/people/Business-Development-Corp-for-a-Greater-Massena/100051250331684
Description: Seeks to promote business through economic and community development. Assists businesses in their expansion and financing needs. Enhances the quality of life and fosters the growth of good jobs within the community. **Geographic Preference:** Local.

42374 ■ Business Network International, Buffalo Region
Buffalo, NY
URL: http://bninewyork.com/ny-buffalo-bni-downtowners/en-US/index
Description: Provides both men and women a structured environment for the development and exchange of quality business referrals. Offers members the opportunity to share ideas and contacts. **Geographic Preference:** Local.

42375 ■ Business Network International New York
3430 Toringdon Way
Charlotte, NC 28277
Free: 855-264-2673
Co. E-mail: regionaloffice@bni.com
URL: http://bni-newyork.com/en-US/index
Description: Provides both men and women a structured environment for the development and exchange of quality business referrals. Offers members the opportunity to share ideas and contacts. **Geographic Preference:** Local.

42376 ■ Business Network International - Staten Island Area
921 Richmond Ave.
Staten Island, NY 10314
Ph: (718)983-9286
URL: http://bni-newyork.com/ny-staten-island-bni-prefer-to-refer/en-US/index
Contact: Amanda Drucker, President
Description: Provides both men and women a structured environment for the development and exchange of quality business referrals. Offers members the opportunity to share ideas and contacts. **Geographic Preference:** Local.

42377 ■ Business Network International Upstate New York
PO Box 3137
Schenectady, NY 12303
Ph: (518)280-8752
Co. E-mail: bnioffice@bniupstateny.com
URL: http://bniupstateny.com/en-US/index
Contact: Lesley Shimer, Executive Director
E-mail: lesley@bniupstateny.com
Description: Provides both men and women a structured environment for the development and exchange of quality business referrals. Offers members the opportunity to share ideas and contacts. **Geographic Preference:** Local.

42378 ■ Entrepreneurs' Organization - Capital District New York (EO)
18 Durham Ct.
Delmar, NY 12054
URL: http://www.eonetwork.org/capitaldistrictnewyork
Description: Provides local resources to members which includes networking events, mentorship, live forums, and leadership development. **Founded:** 2000.

42379 ■ Entrepreneurs' Organization - New York Long Island Chapter (EO)
125 Froehlich Farm Blvd.
Woodbury, NY 11797
Co. E-mail: hello@eolongisland.org
URL: http://eolongisland.org
Contact: Garrett Taylor, President
URL(s): www.eonetwork.org/ny-longisland
Facebook: www.facebook.com/EOLongIsland
Linkedin: www.linkedin.com/company/eo-long-island
Description: Supports entrepreneurs and business owners in Connecticut. Members must be founders, owners, or controlling shareholders of a company grossing more than $1 million annually. **Founded:** 2018.

42380 ■ Entrepreneurs' Organization - Western New York Chapter (EO)
Rochester, NY
URL: http://www.eonetwork.org/westernnewyork
Contact: Larry Brown, Membership Chairperson
E-mail: lbrown@bridgemarksolutions.com

Description: Provides local resources to members which includes networking events, mentorship, live forums, and leadership development. **Founded:** 2003.

42381 ■ Global Business Travel Association - Upstate New York Chapter
5325 Sheridan Dr.
Williamsville, NY 14231
Co. E-mail: info@gbta-upstatenewyork.org
URL: http://gbta-upstatenewyork.org
Contact: Terri J. B. Moreno, President
Facebook: www.facebook.com/GBTAUpstateNewYorkChapter
X (Twitter): x.com/GBTA_UpstateNY
Instagram: www.instagram.com/bgtaupstatenewyork

Description: Represents travel managers and providers. Promotes the value of the travel manager in meeting corporate travel needs and financial goals. Cultivates a positive public image of the corporate travel industry. Protects the interests of members and their corporations in legislative and regulatory matters. Promotes safety, security, efficiency and quality travel. Provides a forum for the exchange of information and ideas among members. **Founded:** 1990. **Geographic Preference:** State.

42382 ■ The Indus Entrepreneurs New York (TiE NY)
New York, NY
Ph: (646)580-0843
Co. E-mail: ed@tienyc.org
URL: http://ny.tie.org
Contact: Richa Naujoks, Secretary
Facebook: www.facebook.com/tienewyork
Linkedin: www.linkedin.com/company/tienewyork
X (Twitter): x.com/TiENewYork
YouTube: www.youtube.com/channel/UCMCUHkycNeroof81qKVtxXg

Description: Advocates for the advancement of entrepreneurship and exchange of ideas. Works in fostering entrepreneurship and nurturing entrepreneurs, providing a networking platform for members and helping members integrate with the mainstream community. **Founded:** 1998. **Geographic Preference:** Regional.

42383 ■ International Association of Business Communicators New York (NY IABC)
New York, NY
Co. E-mail: admin@iabcny.com
URL: http://www.iabcnewyork.com
Contact: Audra Hession, President
X (Twitter): x.com/IABCNY
YouTube: www.youtube.com/channel/UCBL5ufGU71nmgcdiH_lv4MA

Description: Public relations and communication professionals. Committed to improve the effectiveness of organizations through strategic, interactive and integrated business communication management. Provides products, services, and networking activities to help people and organizations excel in public relations, employee communication, marketing communication, public affairs and other forms of communication. **Founded:** 1972. **Geographic Preference:** State.

42384 ■ International Association of Women New York City Chapter
New York, NY
Co. E-mail: memberservices@iawomen.com
Facebook: www.facebook.com/IAWomenNYC

Description: Serves as a network for professional women seeking to promote their business, product, or service.

42385 ■ National Association of Women Business Owners Long Island Chapter (NAWBO/LI)
244 5th Ave., 2nd Fl., Ste. D60
New York, NY 10001
URL: http://www.nawbo.org/about/people
Geographic Preference: Local.

42386 ■ New York State Agribusiness Association (NYSABA)
PO Box 268
Macedon, NY 14502
Ph: (315)986-9320
Fax: (315)986-8534
Co. E-mail: nysaba@rochester.rr.com
URL: http://www.nysaba.com
Contact: Gregg Sargis, Director

Description: Promotes educational, research, legislative and regulatory activities, which will provide sound business practices and working environment for its members. Works to improve agricultural production efficiency through scientifically sound agronomic practices. **Geographic Preference:** State.

42387 ■ Rochester Angel Network (RAN)
c/o NextCorps Inc.
260 E Main, Ste. 6000
Rochester, NY 14604
URL: http://www.rochesterangels.com
Contact: James S. Senall, Contact
E-mail: james.senall@nextcorps.org

Description: Angel group investing in early-stage high-growth startups. **Founded:** 2005.

42388 ■ Upstate Capital Association of New York
42 N Chestnut St., Ste. 101
New Paltz, NY 12561
Ph: (845)204-8090
Co. E-mail: info@upstatecapital.org
URL: http://upstatecapital.org
Contact: Noa Conger Simons, President
E-mail: noa@upstatecapital.org
Facebook: www.facebook.com/UpstateCapital
Linkedin: www.linkedin.com/company/upstate-capital-association-of-new-york
X (Twitter): x.com/UpstateCapital

Description: Advances venture capital and private equity investments. Focuses on seed capital, venture capital, and private equity sources. **Founded:** 2003.

42389 ■ Western New York Venture Association (WNYVA)
683 Northland Ave.
Buffalo, NY 14211
Ph: (716)636-3626
Fax: (716)845-6418
Co. E-mail: info@wnyventure.com
URL: http://www.wnyventure.com
Contact: Jack McGowan, Executive Director
Facebook: www.facebook.com/WNY-Venture-Association-336101443103346
X (Twitter): x.com/wnyva

Description: Looks to increase growth in the region by increasing the size and sophistication of the angel investor base and the quality of investment opportunities in Western New York. **Founded:** 1989.

SMALL BUSINESS DEVELOPMENT CENTERS

42390 ■ Albany Small Business Development Center
U Albany ETEC, Ste. 146Harriman Campus Rd.
Albany, NY 12222
Ph: (518)442-7232
URL: http://www.nysbdc.org/centers/centerappointment.aspx?centid=10
Contact: Katherine Baker, Director
E-mail: kbaker@albany.edu

Description: Represents and promotes the small business sector. Provides management assistance to current and prospective small business owners. Helps to improve management skills and expand the products and services of members. **Founded:** 1984. **Geographic Preference:** Local.

42391 ■ Baruch College Lawrence N. Field Center for Entrepreneurship
55 Lexington Ave., Ste. 2-140
New York, NY 10010
Ph: (646)312-4780
Co. E-mail: field.center@baruch.cuny.edu
URL: http://blogs.baruch.cuny.edu/fieldcenter
Contact: Marlene Leekang, Executive Director
Facebook: www.facebook.com/BaruchEntrepreneurs
X (Twitter): x.com/eshipbaruch
Instagram: www.instagram.com/baruchentrepreneurs
YouTube: www.youtube.com/user/EShipBaruch

Description: Supports small business owners, entrepreneurs, and startups by offering a variety of services and workshops.

42392 ■ Binghamton Small Business Development Center (SBDC)
120 Hawley St., Ste. 294
Binghamton, NY 13901
Ph: (607)777-4024
Fax: (607)777-4029
Co. E-mail: sbdc@binghamton.edu
URL: http://www.binghamton.edu/centers/small-business-development
Contact: Rochelle Layman, Regional Director
E-mail: rlayman@binghamton.edu
Facebook: www.facebook.com/binghamtonSBDC
Linkedin: www.linkedin.com/company/sbdcbu
X (Twitter): x.com/sbdcbinghamton

Description: Represents and promotes the small business sector. Provides management assistance to current and prospective small business owners. Helps to improve management skills and expand the products and services of members. **Founded:** 1984. **Geographic Preference:** Local.

42393 ■ Brockport Small Business Development Center
College of Brockport
350 New Campus Dr. Hartwell 101
Brockport, NY 14420
Ph: (585)395-8410
Fax: (585)395-8674
Co. E-mail: sbdc@brockport.edu
URL: http://www.nysbdc.org/centers/centers.aspx?centid=22
Contact: Chantz Miles, Director
Facebook: www.facebook.com/SBDCBrockport
X (Twitter): x.com/BrockportSBDC

Description: Represents and promotes the small business sector. Provides management assistance to current and prospective small business owners. Helps to improve management skills and expand the products and services of members. **Founded:** 1987. **Geographic Preference:** Local.

42394 ■ Bronx Small Business Development Center
Lehman College Campus
250 Bedford Pk. Blvd. W
Bronx, NY 10468-1589
Ph: (718)960-8806
Fax: (718)960-7340
Co. E-mail: sbdc.bronx@lehman.cuny.edu
URL: http://www.nysbdc.org/centers/centers.aspx?centid=52
Contact: Jackeline Rosero, Director
Facebook: www.facebook.com/LehmanSBDC
X (Twitter): x.com/nysbdc

Description: Represents and promotes the small business sector. Provides management assistance to current and prospective small business owners. Helps to improve management skills and expand the products and services of members. **Founded:** 1987. **Geographic Preference:** Local.

42395 ■ Buffalo State College Small Business Development Center (SBDC)
Buffalo State College
Cleveland Hall 206
1300 Elmwood Ave.
Buffalo, NY 14222
Ph: (716)878-4030
Fax: (716)878-4067
Co. E-mail: smallbus@buffalostate.edu
URL: http://sbdc.buffalostate.edu
Contact: Susan A. McCartney, Director
E-mail: mccartsa@buffalostate.edu

Description: Represents and promotes the small business sector. Provides management assistance to current and prospective small business owners.

STATE LISTINGS

Helps to improve management skills and expand the products and services of members. **Founded:** 1871. **Geographic Preference:** Local.

42396 ■ Canton Small Business Development Center
c/o Dale Rice, Director
34 Cornell Dr., French Hall
Canton, NY 13617-1098
Ph: (315)386-7312
Fax: (315)379-3814
Co. E-mail: sbdc@canton.edu
URL: http://www.nysbdc.org/centers/centercontact/centerdirect.aspx?centid=47
Contact: Dale Rice, Director
X (Twitter): x.com/cantonsbdc
Description: Represents and promotes the small business sector. Provides management assistance to current and prospective small business owners. Helps to improve management skills and expand the products and services of members. **Geographic Preference:** Local.

42397 ■ College of Staten Island Small Business Development Center
2800 Victory Blvd., Bldg. 3A Rm. 105
Staten Island, NY 10314-9806
Ph: (718)982-2560
Fax: (718)982-2323
Co. E-mail: sbdc@csi.cuny.edu
URL: http://www.sisbdc.org
Contact: Angela Chuppe, Office Manager
URL(s): www.csi.cuny.edu/alumni-community/community/small-business-development-center
Facebook: www.facebook.com/sisbdc
X (Twitter): x.com/sisbdc
Instagram: www.instagram.com/sisbdc
Description: Represents and promotes the small business sector. Provides management assistance to current and prospective small business owners. Helps to improve management skills and expand the products and services of members. **Founded:** 1993. **Geographic Preference:** Local.

42398 ■ Farmingdale Small Business Development Center
2350 Broadhollow Rd.
Farmingdale, NY 11735-1021
Ph: (934)420-2765
URL: http://www.farmingdale.edu/small-business-development-center
Contact: Erica Chase-Gregory, Director
Description: Represents and promotes the small business sector. Provides management assistance to current and prospective small business owners. Helps to improve management skills and expand the products and services of members. **Geographic Preference:** Local.

42399 ■ *Fifty-Forty-Ten-News*
101 S Salina St. No. 10, Ste. 1030
Syracuse, NY 13202-4303
Ph: (315)373-0348
Fax: (315)373-0921
URL: http://www.gsbdc.com
Contact: Kenneth Gardiner, President
E-mail: kgardiner@dmcpas.com
URL(s): gsbdc.com/news
Released: Quarterly **Availability:** Online; PDF.

42400 ■ Greater Syracuse Business Development Corp. (GSBDC)
101 S Salina St. No. 10, Ste. 1030
Syracuse, NY 13202-4303
Ph: (315)373-0348
Fax: (315)373-0921
URL: http://www.gsbdc.com
Contact: Kenneth Gardiner, President
E-mail: kgardiner@dmcpas.com
Description: Seeks to promote business through economic and community development. Assists businesses in their expansion and financing needs. Enhances the quality of life and fosters the growth of good jobs within the community. **Founded:** 1964. **Publications:** *Fifty-Forty-Ten-News* (Quarterly). **Geographic Preference:** Local.

42401 ■ Jamestown Small Business Development Center
Jamestown Community College
525 Falconer St.
Jamestown, NY 14702-0020
Ph: (716)338-1024
Fax: (716)338-1456
Co. E-mail: sbdc@mail.sunyjcc.edu
URL: http://www.nyssbdc.org/centers/centers.aspx?centid=23
Contact: Courtney Curatolo, Director
E-mail: courtneycuratolo@mail.sunyjcc.edu
Facebook: www.facebook.com/NYSSBDCatJCC
Linkedin: www.linkedin.com/company/sbdc-at-jcc
X (Twitter): x.com/nysbdc
YouTube: www.youtube.com/channel/UC4ZkaRBeW589am_5DHeHHxA
Description: Represents and promotes the small business sector. Provides management assistance to current and prospective small business owners. Helps to improve management skills and expand the products and services of members. **Founded:** 1986. **Geographic Preference:** Local.

42402 ■ Lewis County Small Business Development Center
Corporate Woods Bldg., 3rd Fl.
State University Plz.
Albany, NY 12246
Ph: (514)443-5398
URL: http://www.nyssbdc.org/locations/multiplecounties/lewis.html
Description: Represents and promotes the small business sector. Provides management assistance to current and prospective small business owners. Helps to improve management skills and expand the products and services of members. **Geographic Preference:** Local.

42403 ■ Manhattan Small Business Development Center at Pace University
1 Pace Plz., Rm. W501
New York, NY 10038
Ph: (212)618-6655
Co. E-mail: sbdc@pace.edu
URL: http://www.pacesbdc.org
Contact: Andrew Flamm, Director
E-mail: aflamm@pace.edu
Linkedin: www.linkedin.com/company/pace-university-sbdc
X (Twitter): x.com/PaceSBDC
Instagram: www.instagram.com/pacesbdc
Description: Represents and promotes the small business sector. Provides management assistance to current and prospective small business owners. Helps to improve management skills and expand the products and services of members. **Founded:** 1986. **Geographic Preference:** Local.

42404 ■ Mid-Hudson Small Business Development Center
SUNY Ulster Kingston Ctr., 94 Mary's Ave.
Kingston, NY 12401
Ph: (845)802-9150
Co. E-mail: sbdc@sunyulster.edu
URL: http://www.nyssbdc.org/centers/centers.aspx?centid=94
Facebook: www.facebook.com/midhudsonsbdc
X (Twitter): x.com/mid_small
Description: Represents and promotes the small business sector. Provides management assistance to current and prospective small business owners. Helps to improve management skills and expand the products and services of members. **Founded:** 1985. **Geographic Preference:** Local.

42405 ■ Midtown Manhattan Small Business Development Center at Baruch College
Baruch College, Field Ctr., Rm. 2-140
55 Lexington Ave.
New York, NY 10010-2318
Ph: (646)312-4790
Fax: (646)312-4781
URL: http://www.nyssbdc.org/centers/centers.aspx?centid=36
Contact: Ulas Neftci, Director

E-mail: sbdc@baruch.cuny.edu
Description: Represents and promotes the small business sector. Provides management assistance to current and prospective small business owners. Helps to improve management skills and expand the products and services of members. **Founded:** 1993. **Geographic Preference:** Local.

42406 ■ Mohawk Valley Small Business Development Center
Mohawk Valley Community College
326 Broad St.
Utica, NY 13501
Ph: (315)792-5400
Co. E-mail: sbdc@mvcc.edu
URL: http://www.mvcc.edu/sbdc
Contact: Paul Arvantides, Director
E-mail: parvantides@mvcc.edu
Facebook: www.facebook.com/MVSBDC
X (Twitter): x.com/MVSmalBizDevCtr
Description: Represents and promotes the small business sector in Las Vegas. **Founded:** 1986. **Geographic Preference:** Local.

42407 ■ New York State Small Business Development Center (NYS SBDC) - Library
353 Broadway
Albany, NY 12246
Ph: (518)944-2840
Free: 800-732-SBDC
Co. E-mail: sonya.smith@nysbdc.org
URL: http://www.nysbdc.org
Contact: Jim Conroy, President
E-mail: jconroy@nybdc.com
Facebook: www.facebook.com/nysbdc
Linkedin: www.linkedin.com/company/422102
X (Twitter): x.com/nysbdc
YouTube: www.youtube.com/c/NewYorkSmallBusinessDevelopmentCenter
Pinterest: www.pinterest.com/nyssbdc
Description: Provides expert management and technical assistance to start-up and existing businesses across the state of New York. **Scope:** Small Business Development. **Services:** Library open to members only. **Founded:** 1984. **Holdings:** Figures not available. **Geographic Preference:** State.

42408 ■ Niagara Small Business Development Center (SBDC)
3111 Saunders Settlement Rd.
Sanborn, NY 14132
Ph: (716)210-2515
Co. E-mail: sbdc@niagaracc.suny.edu
URL: http://www.niagaracc.suny.edu/sbdc
Contact: Maureen Henderson, Director
E-mail: mhenderson@niagaracc.suny.edu
Facebook: www.facebook.com/niagarasbdc
X (Twitter): x.com/niagarasbdc
Instagram: www.instagram.com/niagarasbdc
Description: Aims to promote small businesses. **Founded:** 1984. **Geographic Preference:** Local.

42409 ■ North Country Small Business Development Center (SBDC)
NY
URL: http://www.plattsburgh.edu/about/centers/small-business-center.html
Description: Focuses on promoting small businesses in North County. **Geographic Preference:** Local.

42410 ■ Onondaga Small Business Development Center
Mulroy Hall
Onondaga Community College
4926 Onondaga Rd.
Syracuse, NY 13215
Ph: (315)498-6070
Co. E-mail: sbdc@sunyocc.edu
URL: http://www.onondagasbdc.org
Contact: Robert Griffin, Director
E-mail: r.d.griffin@sunyocc.edu
URL(s): www.nysbdc.org/centers/centers.aspx?centid=14
Facebook: www.facebook.com/onondagaSBDC
X (Twitter): x.com/onondagaSBDC
Instagram: www.instagram.com/onondagasbdc

42411 ■ Orleans Economic Development (OEDA)
121 N Main St.
Albion, NY 14411
Ph: (585)589-7060
URL: http://www.orleansdevelopment.org
Facebook: www.facebook.com/OrleansEDA
X (Twitter): x.com/OrleansEda
Description: Through the Orleans Microenterprise Program, helps small buinesses and entrepreneurial candidates with business startup assistance.

42412 ■ Queens-York Small Business Development Center
City University of New York, York College
94-50 159th St.
Jamaica, NY 11451-9902
Ph: (718)262-2880
Co. E-mail: sbdc@york.cuny.edu
URL: http://www.nysbdc.org/locations/Queens/queens.html
Contact: Harry Wells, Director
Description: Represents and promotes the small business sector. Provides management assistance to current and prospective small business owners. Helps to improve management skills and expand the products and services of members. **Founded:** 1988. **Geographic Preference:** Local.

42413 ■ Rockland Small Business Development Center
Brucker Hall
Rockland Community College
145 College Rd.
Suffern, NY 10901-3699
Ph: (845)356-6065
Fax: (845)230-7309
URL: http://www.nysbdc.org/centers/centers.aspx?centid=25
Contact: Thomas Morley, Director
E-mail: tmorley@sunyrockland.edu
Facebook: www.facebook.com/NYSSBDC.Rock
X (Twitter): x.com/SBDC_RockWest
Description: Represents and promotes the small business sector. Provides management assistance to current and prospective small business owners. Helps to improve management skills and expand the products and services of members. **Founded:** 1987. **Geographic Preference:** Local.

42414 ■ Stony Brook Small Business Development Center
Stony Brook University, Research & Development Prk
Stony Brook, NY 11794-6016
Ph: (631)632-9070
Fax: (631)632-7176
Co. E-mail: sbdc@stonybrook.edu
URL: http://www.nysbdc.org/centers/centerappointment.aspx?centid=27
Contact: Bernard Ryba, Director
URL(s): www.stonybrook.edu/sbdc
Facebook: www.facebook.com/StonyBrookSmallBusinessDevelopmentCenter
Linkedin: www.linkedin.com/in/stony-brook-small-business-development-center-1b0043b6
X (Twitter): x.com/StonybrookSbdc
Description: Represents and promotes the small business sector. Provides management assistance to current and prospective small business owners. Helps to improve management skills and expand the products and services of members. **Founded:** 1985. **Geographic Preference:** Local.

42415 ■ Stony Brook University - Small Business Development Center (SBDC)
Research and Development Pk., Bldg.17
Saint James, NY 11780
Ph: (631)632-9837
Fax: (631)632-7176
Co. E-mail: sbdc@stonybrook.edu
URL: http://www.stonybrook.edu/commcms/sbdc
Contact: Bernie Ryba, Regional Director
Facebook: www.facebook.com/StonyBrookSmallBusinessDevelopmentCenter
Linkedin: www.linkedin.com/in/stony-brook-small-business-development-center-1b0043b6
X (Twitter): x.com/StonybrookSbdc
YouTube: www.youtube.com/channel/UCsYG_u53HPrnoWBAH0tIX_w
Description: Helps new and existing businesses leads to their increased productivity and profitability. **Scope:** Solutions to problems of small businesses and assistance to entrepreneurs, business and industry leading to increased productivity and profitability. **Founded:** 1988. **Educational Activities:** SBDC Dare to Risk Entrepreneurship - DARE Competition, With the most promising and persuasively developed business ideas.; SBDC Workshops (Irregular).

42416 ■ Watertown Small Business Development Center
Jefferson Community College
1220 Coffeen St.
Watertown, NY 13601-1897
Ph: (315)782-9262
Fax: (315)782-0901
Co. E-mail: sbdc@sunyjefferson.edu
URL: http://americassbdc.org/home/find-your-sbdc
Contact: Elizabeth Lonergan, Director
URL(s): www.nysbdc.org/centers/centers.aspx?centid=12
Facebook: www.facebook.com/WatertownSBDC
Description: Provides management assistance to current and prospective small business owners in Watertown. **Geographic Preference:** Local.

SMALL BUSINESS ASSISTANCE PROGRAMS

42417 ■ Fiducial Century Small Business Solutions Inc.
55 E 59th St., 9th Fl.
New York, NY 10022
Free: 866-343-8242
Co. E-mail: contact@fiducial.com
URL: http://fiducial.com
Contact: Christian Latouche, Founder Chairman
Facebook: www.facebook.com/FiducialNorthAmerica
Linkedin: www.linkedin.com/company/fiducial-north-america
X (Twitter): x.com/Fiducial_NAM
Description: Provides services to small businesses including financial reporting, bookkeeping, tax services, payroll services, and business counseling. **Founded:** 1970.

42418 ■ Invest Buffalo Niagara
257 W Genesee St., Ste. 600
Buffalo, NY 14202
Free: 800-916-9073
Co. E-mail: info@buffaloniagara.org
URL: http://buffaloniagara.org
Contact: Thomas A. Kucharski, President
Facebook: www.facebook.com/InvestBN
Linkedin: www.linkedin.com/company/investbuffaloniagara
X (Twitter): x.com/Invest_BN
Instagram: www.instagram.com/investbuffaloniagara
Description: Economic development and business attraction organization for Western New York. Supports entrepreneurs. Offers project management and other services for businesses looking to expand or relocate.

42419 ■ New York Department of Economic Development (DED) - Division of Minority and Women's Business Development
633 3rd Ave. -Fl. 37
New York, NY 10017
Ph: (646)846-7364
URL: http://esd.ny.gov/doing-business-ny/mwbe
Contact: Jason Myles Clark, Executive Vice President
Description: Certify minority and women owned businesses. Monitor the compliance of state agencies. Meet the goals that the agency sets for the utility of minority and women owned businesses.

42420 ■ New York State's Empire State Development - Division of Science, Technology and Innovation
625 Broadway
Albany, NY 12245
URL: http://www.esd.ny.gov/doing-business-ny/innovation-development-support
Contact: Steven M. Cohen, Chairman
Description: Provides major services, including conducting special training programs, awarding research and development grants for university-based research, encouraging high technology, and providing grants and other services to the Centers for Advanced Technology. **Geographic Preference:** State.

42421 ■ New York State's Empire State Development - Division for Small Business - Small Business Ombudsman
633 3rd Ave., 36th Fl.
New York, NY 10017
URL: http://esd.ny.gov/small-business-environmental-ombudsman-sbeo
Description: Assists businesses in resolving red tape difficulties with all levels of government.

SCORE OFFICES

42422 ■ Dutchess SCORE
1 Civic Ctr. Plz., Rm. 400
Poughkeepsie, NY 12601
Ph: (845)454-1700
URL: http://www.score.org/mid-hudsonvalley
Description: Provides resources and expertise to maximize the success of existing and emerging small businesses. Offers business counseling and workshops. **Founded:** 1964. **Geographic Preference:** Local.

42423 ■ Greater Binghamton SCORE
120 Hawley St., Ste. 301
Binghamton, NY 13901
Ph: (315)616-3544
URL: http://www.score.org/centralny/about/our-locations
Founded: 1964.

42424 ■ Greater Rochester SCORE
Keating Fed Bldg., Rm. 410
100 State St.
Rochester, NY 14614
Ph: (585)263-6473
URL: http://greaterrochester.score.org
Contact: Bridget Weston, Chief Executive Officer
Facebook: www.facebook.com/SCOREGreaterRochester
Linkedin: www.linkedin.com/company/score-greater-rochester
X (Twitter): x.com/ScoreROC23
Description: Provides business owners with information, resources and tools vital to their success. Offers business counseling. **Founded:** 1964. **Geographic Preference:** Local.

42425 ■ Northeast SCORE
1 Computer Dr. S
Albany, NY 12205
Ph: (518)446-1118
Co. E-mail: scorechapter127@gmail.com
URL: http://www.score.org/northeastny
Contact: Bridget Weston, Chief Executive Officer
Facebook: www.facebook.com/SCORENENewYork
Description: Strives for the formation, growth, and success of small businesses. Promotes entrepreneur education in Albany area, New York. **Founded:** 1964. **Geographic Preference:** Local.

STATE LISTINGS

42426 ■ Putnam SCORE
110 Old Rte. 6, Donald B Smith Cty Gov't Campus
  Carmel, NY 10512
Ph: (845)225-6030
Co. E-mail: putnam.score.ny@scorevolunteer.org
URL: http://putnam.score.org
Facebook: www.facebook.com/SCOREPu
  tnamCounty
Linkedin: www.linkedin.com/company/score-mentors
  -putnam
Founded: 1964.

42427 ■ Rockland SCORE
Daniel T. Brucker Hall, 145 College Rd., 6102G
  Suffern, NY 10901
Ph: (845)426-1206
Co. E-mail: contactus@score.org
URL: http://rockland.score.org
Contact: Bridget Weston, Chief Executive Officer
Facebook: www.facebook.com/SCORERocklan
  dCounty
Linkedin: www.linkedin.com/company/16212327
Founded: 1964.

42428 ■ SCORE - Albion
458 W Ave.
  Albion, NY 14411
Ph: (585)589-5335
Co. E-mail: buffaloniagara45@gmail.com
URL: http://buffaloniagara.score.org/find-location?sta
  te=NY
Contact: John Vitale, Chairman
Description: Provides professional guidance and information to maximize the success of existing and emerging small businesses. Offers business counseling and workshops.

42429 ■ SCORE - Armonk
19 Whipporwill Rd. E
  Armonk, NY 10504
Ph: (914)948-3907
URL: http://westchester.score.org/contact-score-wes
  tchester
Description: Provides professional guidance and information to maximize the success of existing and emerging small businesses. Offers business counseling and workshops.

42430 ■ SCORE - Auburn
2 State St.
  Auburn, NY 13021
Ph: (315)616-3544
URL: http://www.score.org/centralny/about/our-loca
  tions
Description: Provides professional guidance and information to maximize the success of existing and emerging small businesses. Offers business counseling and workshops.

42431 ■ SCORE - Batavia
687 E Main St., Ste. 100
  Batavia, NY 14020
Ph: (585)344-2042
URL: http://buffaloniagara.score.org/branch/genesee
  -county-career-center-batavia
Description: Provides professional guidance and information to maximize the success of existing and emerging small businesses. Offers business counseling and workshops.

42432 ■ SCORE - Belmont
c/o, Allegany County Crossroads Conference Center
  6087 St. Rt. 19 N
  Belmont, NY 14813
Ph: (716)307-3225
URL: http://buffaloniagara.score.org/content/find-men
  tor-279
Description: Provides professional guidance and information to maximize the success of existing and emerging small businesses. Offers business counseling and workshops.

42433 ■ SCORE - Brightwaters
1 S County Rd.
  Brightwaters, NY 11718
Ph: (631)665-4350
URL: http://longisland.score.org

Description: Provides professional guidance and information to maximize the success of existing and emerging small businesses. Offers business counseling and workshops.

42434 ■ SCORE - Bronx
851 Grand Concourse, Rm. 123
  Bronx, NY 10451
Ph: (718)590-6252
URL: http://newyorkcity.score.org/contact-nyc-score
Description: Provides professional guidance and information to maximize the success of existing and emerging small businesses. Offers business counseling and workshops.

42435 ■ SCORE - Brooklyn Borough Hall Branch
10 Grand Army Plz.
  Brooklyn, NY 11238
URL: http://newyorkcity.score.org/contact-nyc-score
Description: Provides professional guidance and information to maximize the success of existing and emerging small businesses. Offers business counseling and workshops.

42436 ■ SCORE - Brooklyn Center
10 Grand Army Plz.
  Brooklyn, NY 11238
Ph: (718)623-7000
URL: http://www.score.org/find-location
Description: Provides professional guidance and information to maximize the success of existing and emerging small businesses. Offers business counseling and workshops.

42437 ■ SCORE - Brooklyn Central Library Branch
10 Grand Army Plz.
  Brooklyn, NY 11238
URL: http://newyorkcity.score.org/score-new-york-city
  -mentoring-locations
Contact: Irene Rivera, Contact
Description: Provides professional guidance and information to maximize the success of existing and emerging small businesses. Offers business counseling and workshops.

42438 ■ SCORE - Buffalo Niagara
130 S Elmwood Ave., Ste. 540
  Buffalo, NY 14202
Ph: (716)551-4301
Fax: (716)551-4301
Co. E-mail: buffaloniagara45@gmail.com
URL: http://www.score.org/buffaloniagara
Contact: Brian Loucks, Contact
Facebook: www.facebook.com/
  SCOREBuffaloNiagara
Linkedin: www.linkedin.com/company/16212311
X (Twitter): x.com/SCORE_Buffalo
Description: Provides professional guidance and information to maximize the success of existing and emerging small businesses. Offers business counseling and workshops. **Founded:** 1964. **Geographic Preference:** Regional.

42439 ■ SCORE - Centereach
101 Eastwood Blvd.
  Centereach, NY 11720
URL: http://longisland.score.org/branch/centereach
  -%E2%80%93-miller-business-center-middle-coun
  try-public-library-tuesday-4-5-and-6-pm
Description: Provides professional guidance and information to maximize the success of existing and emerging small businesses. Offers business counseling and workshops.

42440 ■ SCORE - Clarence
8899 Main St., Ste. 4
  Buffalo, NY 14221
Ph: (716)631-3888
URL: http://www.score.org/find-location?state=NY
Description: Provides professional guidance and information to maximize the success of existing and emerging small businesses. Offers business counseling and workshops.

42441 ■ SCORE - Clinton, Franklin, Essex (SCORE-CFE)
7061 Rte. 9
  Plattsburgh, NY 12901
Ph: (802)764-5899
Co. E-mail: scorevermont@scorevolunteer.org
URL: http://vermont.score.org/about-clinton-franklin
  -essex-branch
Description: Provides professional guidance and information to maximize the success of existing and emerging small businesses. Offers business counseling and workshops. **Founded:** 1954.

42442 ■ SCORE - Cortlandt Manor
110 Old Rte. 6, Rm. 8, Bldg 3
  Cortland, NY 13045
Ph: (845)225-6030
URL: http://putnam.score.org
Facebook: www.facebook.com/SCOREPu
  tnamCounty
Description: Provides professional guidance and information to maximize the success of existing and emerging small businesses. Offers business counseling and workshops.

42443 ■ SCORE - Dix Hills
600 S Service Rd.
  Dix Hills, NY 11746
Ph: (631)421-4530
URL: http://longisland.score.org/content/long-islan
  d-chapter-locations
Description: Provides professional guidance and information to maximize the success of existing and emerging small businesses. Offers business counseling and workshops.

42444 ■ SCORE - Dutchess
1 Civic Center Plz. Chamber of Commerce, Rm. 400
  Poughkeepsie, NY 12601
Ph: (845)454-1700
URL: http://www.score.org/mid-hudsonvalley
Description: Provides professional guidance and information to maximize the success of existing and emerging small businesses. Offers business counseling and workshops.

42445 ■ SCORE - East Aurora
300 Gleed St., Ste. 160
  East Aurora, NY 14052
Ph: (716)652-8444
URL: http://buffaloniagara.score.org/content/find-men
  tor-279
Contact: Brian Loucks, Contact
Description: Provides professional guidance and information to maximize the success of existing and emerging small businesses. Offers business counseling and workshops.

42446 ■ SCORE - Eden
8226 N Main St., Smith Bldg.
  Eden, NY 14057
Ph: (716)992-4799
URL: http://buffaloniagara.score.org/branch/eden
  -chamber-commerce
Description: Provides professional guidance and information to maximize the success of existing and emerging small businesses. Offers business counseling and workshops.

42447 ■ SCORE - Elmont
700 Hempstead Tpke.
  Elmont, NY 11003
Ph: (516)354-5280
URL: http://longisland.score.org/content/long-islan
  d-chapter-locations
Contact: Bridget Weston, Chief Executive Officer
Description: Provides professional guidance and information to maximize the success of existing and emerging small businesses. Offers business counseling and workshops.

42448 ■ SCORE - Farmingville
1 Independence Hill
  Farmingville, NY 11738
Ph: (631)451-6563
URL: http://longisland.score.org

Description: Provides professional guidance and information to maximize the success of existing and emerging small businesses. Offers business counseling and workshops.

42449 ■ SCORE - Flushing [SCORE - Queens]
Cep Hall 2, 65-30 Kissena Blvd.
Flushing, NY 11367
Ph: (347)470-4890
Co. E-mail: help@score.org
URL: http://queens.score.org

Description: Provides professional guidance and information to maximize the success of existing and emerging small businesses. Offers business counseling and workshops.

42450 ■ SCORE - Garden City
1225 Franklin Ave., Ste. 325
Garden City, NY 11530
Ph: (516)512-8978
Co. E-mail: help@score.org
URL: http://longisland.score.org/content/long-island-chapter-locations

Description: Provides professional guidance and information to maximize the success of existing and emerging small businesses. Offers business counseling and workshops.

42451 ■ SCORE - Glens Falls
136 Glen St.
Adirondack Regional Chamber of Commerce
Glens Falls, NY 12801
URL: http://www.score.org/northeastny

Description: Provides professional guidance and information to maximize the success of existing and emerging small businesses. Offers business counseling and workshops.

42452 ■ SCORE - Greater Binghamton
Koffman Incubator, 120 Hawley St., Ste. 301
Binghamton, NY 13901
Ph: (607)772-8860
Free: 800-634-0245
URL: http://greaterbinghamtonchamber.com
Contact: Jack Fitzgerald, Chairman

Description: Provides professional guidance and information to maximize the success of existing and emerging small businesses. Offers business counseling and workshops.

42453 ■ SCORE - Greater Rochester
100 State St., Rm. 410 Keating Fed Bldg.
Rochester, NY 14614
Ph: (585)263-6473
URL: http://greaterrochester.score.org
Facebook: www.facebook.com/SCOREGreaterRochester
Linkedin: www.linkedin.com/company/score-greater-rochester

Description: Provides professional guidance and information to maximize the success of existing and emerging small businesses. Offers business counseling and workshops.

42454 ■ SCORE - Hamburg
5200 S Pk. Ave.
Hamburg, NY 14075
URL: http://www.score.org/annarborarea/content/about-us

Description: Provides professional guidance and information to maximize the success of existing and emerging small businesses. Offers business counseling and workshops.

42455 ■ SCORE - Hampton Bays
Hampton Bays Library
52 Ponquogue Ave.
Hampton Bays, NY 11946
Ph: (631)728-6241
URL: http://longisland.score.org

Description: Provides professional guidance and information to maximize the success of existing and emerging small businesses. Offers business counseling and workshops.

42456 ■ SCORE - Harlem Community Development Corporation
163 W 125th St., 17th Fl.
New York, NY 10027
Ph: (212)961-4005
URL: http://newyorkcity.score.org/score-new-york-city-mentoring-locations

Description: Provides professional guidance and information to maximize the success of existing and emerging small businesses. Offers business counseling and workshops.

42457 ■ SCORE - Harrison
2 Bruce Ave.
Harrison, NY 10528
Ph: (914)267-6570
URL: http://westchester.score.org

Description: Provides professional guidance and information to maximize the success of existing and emerging small businesses. Offers business counseling and workshops.

42458 ■ SCORE - Haverstraw
37 West Broad St., RCC Ext., 2nd Fl.
Haverstraw, NY 10927
Ph: (845)426-1206
Co. E-mail: help@score.org
URL: http://www.score.org/find-location?state=NY

Description: Provides professional guidance and information to maximize the success of existing and emerging small businesses. Offers business counseling and workshops.

42459 ■ SCORE - Huntington Station
145 Pidgeon Hill Rd.
Huntington Station, NY 11746
Ph: (631)549-4411
URL: http://longisland.score.org/content/long-island-chapter-locations

Description: Provides professional guidance and information to maximize the success of existing and emerging small businesses. Offers business counseling and workshops.

42460 ■ SCORE - Jamaica
Greater Jamaica Development Corp.
90-04 161st St., 7th Fl.
Jamaica, NY 11432
URL: http://queens.score.org

Description: Provides professional guidance and information to maximize the success of existing and emerging small businesses. Offers business counseling and workshops.

42461 ■ SCORE - Kenmore
3411 Delaware Ave.
Kenmore, NY 14217
URL: http://buffalonigara.score.org

Description: Provides professional guidance and information to maximize the success of existing and emerging small businesses. Offers business counseling and workshops.

42462 ■ SCORE - Long Beach
780 Long Beach Blvd.
Long Beach, NY 11561
Ph: (516)766-5624
URL: http://longisland.score.org/content/long-island-chapter-locations

Description: Provides professional guidance and information to maximize the success of existing and emerging small businesses. Offers business counseling and workshops.

42463 ■ SCORE - Long Island
350 Motor Pky., Ste. 109
Hauppauge, NY 11788
Ph: (631)454-0771
Co. E-mail: help@score.org
URL: http://longisland.score.org
Contact: Bridget Weston, Chief Executive Officer
Linkedin: www.linkedin.com/company/score-mentors-long-island
X (Twitter): x.com/scorelongisland

Description: Provides professional guidance and information to maximize the success of existing and emerging small businesses. Offers business counseling and workshops.

42464 ■ SCORE - Long Island
998C Old Country Rd., No. 116
Plainview, NY 11803
Ph: (631)454-0771
URL: http://www.score.org/longisland/about-score-long-island/our-locations

Description: Provides professional guidance and information to maximize the success of existing and emerging small businesses. Offers business counseling and workshops.

42465 ■ SCORE - Malta
HVCC TEC-SMART
345 Hermes Rd.
Malta, NY 12020
Ph: (518)893-7364
Co. E-mail: scorechapter127@gmail.com
URL: http://northeastny.score.org/content/score-northeast-ny-counseling-locations
Facebook: www.facebook.com/SCORENENewYork

Description: Provides professional guidance and information to maximize the success of existing and emerging small businesses. Offers business counseling and workshops.

42466 ■ SCORE - Massapequa
977 Hicksville Rd.
Massapequa, NY 11758
URL: http://longisland.score.org/mentors/patrick-meehan
Contact: Patrick Meehan, Contact

Description: Provides professional guidance and information to maximize the success of existing and emerging small businesses. Offers business counseling and workshops.

42467 ■ SCORE - Mid-Hudson Valley
1 Civic Center Plaza, Ste. 400
Poughkeepsie, NY 12601
Ph: (845)454-1700
URL: http://www.score.org/mid-hudsonvalley/about

Description: Provides professional guidance and information to maximize the success of existing and emerging small businesses. Offers business counseling and workshops.

42468 ■ SCORE - Monticello
198 Bridgeville Rd.
Monticello, NY 12701
Ph: (845)343-1515
Co. E-mail: finerty@aol.com
URL: http://nymetroareascore.org

Description: Provides professional guidance and information to maximize the success of existing and emerging small businesses. Offers business counseling and workshops.

42469 ■ SCORE - Mount Vernon, New York
Roosevelt Sq. Professional Bldg., 11 W Prospect Ave., 3rd Fl.
Mount Vernon, NY 10550
Ph: (914)267-6570
URL: http://westchester.score.org

Description: Provides professional guidance and information to maximize the success of existing and emerging small businesses. Offers business counseling and workshops.

42470 ■ SCORE - New City
200 Congers Rd.
New City, NY 10956
URL: http://rockland.score.org

Description: Provides professional guidance and information to maximize the success of existing and emerging small businesses. Offers business counseling and workshops.

42471 ■ SCORE - New Rochelle
145 Huguenot St.
New Rochelle, NY 10801
URL: http://westchester.score.org/contact-score-westchester

Description: Provides professional guidance and information to maximize the success of existing and emerging small businesses. Offers business counseling and workshops.

42472 ■ SCORE - New York City
26 Federal Plz., Rm. 3100
New York, NY 10278
Ph: (212)264-4507
Fax: (212)264-4963
Co. E-mail: score-nyc-marketing@scorevolunteer.org
URL: http://newyorkcity.score.org
Contact: Debrah Lee Charatan, President
Linkedin: www.linkedin.com/company/scorenyc
-counselors-to-america's-small-business
YouTube: www.youtube.com/channel/UCpRV_Ebl
4ywFnGg8QrnbL8A
Pinterest: www.pinterest.com/scorenyc
Description: Seeks to educate entrepreneurs and help small businesses start, grow and succeed nationwide. Organizes volunteers who are working or retired business owners, executives and corporate leaders who wish to share their wisdom and lessons learned in business. **Founded:** 1964. **Geographic Preference:** Local.

42473 ■ SCORE - New York Public Library
188 Madison Ave.
New York, NY 10016
URL: http://newyorkcity.score.org/contact-nyc-score
Description: Provides professional guidance and information to maximize the success of existing and emerging small businesses. Offers business counseling and workshops.

42474 ■ SCORE - North Tonawanda
North Tonawanda Library
505 Meadow Dr.
North Tonawanda, NY 14120
Ph: (716)693-4132
URL: http://buffaloniagara.score.org
Description: Provides professional guidance and information to maximize the success of existing and emerging small businesses. Offers business counseling and workshops.

42475 ■ SCORE - Northeast New York
1 Computer Dr. S
Albany, NY 12205
Ph: (518)446-1118
Fax: (518)446-1228
Co. E-mail: scorechapter127@gmail.com
URL: http://northeastny.score.org
Contact: Bridget Weston, Chief Executive Officer
Linkedin: www.linkedin.com/company/score-mentors
-northeast-ny
X (Twitter): x.com/SCORE_NENewYork
Description: Provides professional guidance and information to maximize the success of existing and emerging small businesses. Offers business counseling and workshops. **Founded:** 1964.

42476 ■ SCORE - Olean
301 N Union St.
Olean, NY 14760
Ph: (716)307-4433
URL: http://buffaloniagara.score.org
Description: Provides professional guidance and information to maximize the success of existing and emerging small businesses. Offers business counseling and workshops.

42477 ■ SCORE - Pearl River
80 franklin Ave.
Pearl River, NY 10965
URL: http://rockland.score.org
Description: Provides professional guidance and information to maximize the success of existing and emerging small businesses. Offers business counseling and workshops.

42478 ■ SCORE - Perry
6470 Route 20A
Perry, NY 14530
Ph: (585)237-0230
URL: http://buffaloniagara.score.org/branch/wyoming
-county-chamber-commerce

Description: Provides professional guidance and information to maximize the success of existing and emerging small businesses. Offers business counseling and workshops.

42479 ■ SCORE - Plainview
999 Old Country Rd.
Plainview, NY 11803
Ph: (516)433-5446
URL: http://www.score.org/longisland/about-score
-long-island/our-locations
Description: Provides professional guidance and information to maximize the success of existing and emerging small businesses. Offers business counseling and workshops.

42480 ■ SCORE - Poughkeepsie
1 Civic center Plaza chamber of commerce rm. 400
Poughkeepsie, NY 12601
Ph: (845)454-1700
Co. E-mail: help@score.org
URL: http://dutchess.score.org
Linkedin: www.linkedin.com/company/score-mentors
-dutchess-county
X (Twitter): twitter.com/SCOREDutchess
Description: Provides professional guidance and information to maximize the success of existing and emerging small businesses. Offers business counseling and workshops. **Founded:** 1964.

42481 ■ SCORE - Putnam County
110 Old Rte. 6, Rm. 8, Bldg. 3
Donald B Smith City Govt. Campus
Carmel, NY 10512
Ph: (845)225-6030
Fax: (845)216-9305
Co. E-mail: putnamscore@yahoo.com
URL: http://putnam.score.org
Linkedin: www.linkedin.com/company/score-mentors
-putnam
YouTube: www.youtube.com/channel/UCtrlCCD
dMDQrLpWORRSajUA
Description: Provides professional guidance and information to maximize the success of existing and emerging small businesses. Offers business counseling and workshops.

42482 ■ SCORE - Richmond County Savings Bank
2875 Veteran's Rd. W
Staten Island, NY 10309
Ph: (718)727-1221
Co. E-mail: info@scoresi.org
URL: http://statenisland.score.org/locations-1
Description: Provides professional guidance and information to maximize the success of existing and emerging small businesses. Offers business counseling and workshops.

42483 ■ SCORE - Riverhead
330 Ct., St.
Riverhead, NY 11901
URL: http://longisland.score.org
Description: Provides professional guidance and information to maximize the success of existing and emerging small businesses. Offers business counseling and workshops.

42484 ■ SCORE - Rockland County
Brucker Hall, 6102G
145 College Rd.
Suffern, NY 10901
Ph: (845)426-1206
Co. E-mail: help@score.org
URL: http://rockland.score.org
Contact: Scott Harkins, Chairman of the Board
Facebook: www.facebook.com/SCORERocklan
dCounty
Linkedin: www.linkedin.com/company/score-mentors
-rockland
X (Twitter): x.com/SCORE_Rockland
Description: Provides professional guidance and information to maximize the success of existing and emerging small businesses. Offers business counseling and workshops.

42485 ■ SCORE - Rockville Centre
1120 Woodfield Rd.
Rockville Centre, NY 11570
Ph: (516)536-3071
URL: http://www.score.org/longisland/about-score
-long-island/our-locations
Description: Provides professional guidance and information to maximize the success of existing and emerging small businesses. Offers business counseling and workshops.

42486 ■ SCORE - Saratoga Springs
28 Clinton St.
Saratoga County Chamber of Commerce
Saratoga Springs, NY 12866
Ph: (518)893-7364
URL: http://northeastny.score.org/content/score-nor
theast-ny-counseling-locations
Facebook: www.facebook.com/SCORENENewYork
Description: Provides professional guidance and information to maximize the success of existing and emerging small businesses. Offers business counseling and workshops.

42487 ■ SCORE - Schenectady
306 State St.
The Chamber of Schenectady County
Schenectady, NY 12305
Ph: (518)446-1118
URL: http://northeastny.score.org/content/score-nor
theast-ny-counseling-locations
Description: Provides professional guidance and information to maximize the success of existing and emerging small businesses. Offers business counseling and workshops.

42488 ■ SCORE - Shirley, New York
407 William Floyd Pky.
Shirley, NY 11967
Ph: (631)399-1511
URL: http://www.longisland.score.org/content/long
-island-chapter-locations
Description: Provides professional guidance and information to maximize the success of existing and emerging small businesses. Offers business counseling and workshops.

42489 ■ SCORE - Southampton
91 Coopers Farm Rd.
Southampton, NY 11968
Ph: (631)727-3228
URL: http://longisland.score.org/content/long-islan
d-chapter-locations
Description: Provides professional guidance and information to maximize the success of existing and emerging small businesses. Offers business counseling and workshops.

42490 ■ SCORE - Staten Island
1855 Victory Blvd.
Staten Island, NY 10314
Ph: (718)727-1221
Co. E-mail: info@scoresi.org
URL: http://statenisland.score.org
Contact: John J. Amodio, Chairman
Linkedin: www.linkedin.com/company/score-mentors
-staten-island
Description: Seeks to educate entrepreneurs and help small businesses start, grow and succeed nationwide. Organizes volunteers who are working or retired business owners, executives and corporate leaders who wish to share their wisdom and lessons learned in business. **Founded:** 2018. **Geographic Preference:** Local.

42491 ■ SCORE - Station Island
1855 Victory Blvd.
Staten Island, NY 10314
Ph: (718)727-1221
Co. E-mail: info@scoresi.org
URL: http://statenisland.score.org
Facebook: www.facebook.com/SCOREofSta
tenIsland
Description: Provides professional guidance and information to maximize the success of existing and emerging small businesses. Offers business counseling and workshops.

42492 ■ SCORE - Syracuse
224 Harrison St., Ste. 506
Syracuse, NY 13202
Ph: (315)616-3544
Fax: (315)471-9288
Co. E-mail: syr.info@scorevolunteer.org
URL: http://syracuse.score.org
Contact: Frank R. Williams, Contact
Linkedin: www.linkedin.com/company/score-syracuse-chapter
Description: Provides professional guidance and information to maximize the success of existing and emerging small businesses. Offers business counseling and workshops.

42493 ■ SCORE - Tarrytown
121 N Broadway
Tarrytown, NY 10591
Ph: (914)948-3907
URL: http://westchester.score.org/contact-score-westchester
Description: Provides professional guidance and information to maximize the success of existing and emerging small businesses. Offers business counseling and workshops.

42494 ■ SCORE - Troy, New York
255 River St.
Rensselaer County Regional Chamber of Commerce
Troy, NY 12180
Ph: (518)446-1118
URL: http://northeastny.score.org/content/score-northeast-ny-counseling-locations
Description: Provides professional guidance and information to maximize the success of existing and emerging small businesses. Offers business counseling and workshops.

42495 ■ SCORE - Ulster
SUNY Ulster, 94 Marys Ave.
Kingston, NY 12401
URL: http://www.score.org/mid-hudsonvalley
Facebook: www.facebook.com/SCOREUlster
Description: Provides professional guidance and information to maximize the success of existing and emerging small businesses. Offers business counseling and workshops.

42496 ■ SCORE - Utica
520 Seneca St., Ste. 102
Utica, NY 13502
Ph: (315)616-3544
URL: http://www.score.org/centralny/about/our-locations
Description: Provides professional guidance and information to maximize the success of existing and emerging small businesses. Offers business counseling and workshops.

42497 ■ SCORE - Walt Whitman Mall
160 Walt Whitman Rd.
Huntington Station, NY 11746
Ph: (631)454-0771
URL: http://longisland.score.org
Description: Provides professional guidance and information to maximize the success of existing and emerging small businesses. Offers business counseling and workshops.

42498 ■ SCORE - Westchester
100 Martine Ave.
White Plains, NY 10605
Ph: (914)267-6570
Co. E-mail: scoreinfo@scorewestchester.com
URL: http://westchester.score.org
Instagram: www.instagram.com/scorewestchester
Description: Provides professional guidance and information to maximize the success of existing and emerging small businesses. Offers business counseling and workshops. **Founded:** 2012.

42499 ■ SCORE - White Plains
100 Martine Ave.
White Plains, NY 10601
Ph: (914)267-6570
URL: http://www.score.org/westchester
Description: Provides professional guidance and information to maximize the success of existing and emerging small businesses. Offers business counseling and workshops.

42500 ■ SCORE - Yonkers
55 Main St., 2nd Fl.
Yonkers, NY 10701
Ph: (914)267-6570
URL: http://westchester.score.org/contact-score-westchester
URL(s): www.score.org/find-location
Description: Provides professional guidance and information to maximize the success of existing and emerging small businesses. Offers business counseling and workshops.

42501 ■ SCORE - Yonkers Riverfront Library
One Larkin Ctr.
Yonkers, NY 10701
URL: http://westchester.score.org
Description: Provides professional guidance and information to maximize the success of existing and emerging small businesses. Offers business counseling and workshops.

42502 ■ Syracuse SCORE
224 Harrison St., Ste. 506
Syracuse, NY 13202
Ph: (315)616-3544
Co. E-mail: centralny.info@scorevolunteer.org
URL: http://centralny.score.org
Contact: Bridget Weston, Chief Executive Officer
Description: Provides free business education and mentorship to entrepreneurs in the New York counties of Onondaga, Oswego, Oneida, Madison, and Cortland. **Founded:** 1964. **Geographic Preference:** Local.

42503 ■ Utica SCORE
520 Seneca St., Ste. 102
Utica, NY 13502
Ph: (315)616-3544
URL: http://www.score.org/centralny/about/our-locations

42504 ■ Westchester SCORE
100 Martine Ave.
White Plains, NY 10601
Ph: (914)267-6570
URL: http://www.score.org/westchester
Facebook: www.facebook.com/ScoreWestchester
Linkedin: www.linkedin.com/company/score-westchester
Instagram: www.instagram.com/scorewestchester
Description: Strives for the formation, growth, and success of small businesses. Promotes entrepreneur education in Westchester area, New York. **Founded:** 1964. **Geographic Preference:** Local.

BETTER BUSINESS BUREAUS

42505 ■ Better Business Bureau of Metropolitan New York
30 E 33rd St., 12th Flr.
New York, NY 10016
Ph: (212)533-6200
Fax: (212)477-4912
Co. E-mail: inquiry@newyork.bbb.org
URL: http://www.bbb.org/local-bbb/bbb-serving-metropolitan-new-york
Contact: Lary Scott Blackmon, Chairman
Facebook: www.facebook.com/NewYorkBBB
Linkedin: www.linkedin.com/company/better-business-bureau-serving-metropolitan-new-york
X (Twitter): x.com/NewYorkBBB
Description: Seeks to promote and foster ethical relationship between businesses and the public through voluntary self-regulation, consumer and business education, and service excellence. Provides information to help consumers and businesses make informed purchasing decisions and avoid costly scams and frauds; settles consumer complaints through arbitration and other means. **Founded:** 1922. **Geographic Preference:** Local.

42506 ■ Better Business Bureau of New York - Long Island Office
300 Broadhollow Rd., Ste. 110W
Melville, NY 11747
Ph: (631)493-3000
Fax: (631)499-2194
Co. E-mail: info@longislandassociation.org
URL: http://www.longislandassociation.org
Contact: Matt Cohen, President
Facebook: www.facebook.com/LIAssociation
Linkedin: www.linkedin.com/company/the-long-island-association
X (Twitter): x.com/LongIslandAssoc
Instagram: www.instagram.com/longislandassoc
YouTube: www.youtube.com/channel/UCzzNUdB5OTxvwnlaANQ_Jfg
Description: Seeks to promote and foster ethical relationship between businesses and the public through voluntary self-regulation, consumer and business education, and service excellence. Provides information to help consumers and businesses make informed purchasing decisions and avoid costly scams and frauds; settles consumer complaints through arbitration and other means. **Founded:** 1926. **Geographic Preference:** Local.

42507 ■ Better Business Bureau of New York - Mid-Hudson Region Office
30 E 33rd St., 12th Flr
New York, NY 10016
Ph: (212)533-6200
URL: http://www.bbb.org/local-bbb/bbb-serving-metropolitan-new-york
Description: Seeks to promote and foster ethical relationship between businesses and the public through voluntary self-regulation, consumer and business education, and service excellence. Provides information to help consumers and businesses make informed purchasing decisions and avoid costly scams and frauds; settles consumer complaints through arbitration and other means. **Geographic Preference:** Local.

42508 ■ Better Business Bureau of Upstate New York (BBB)
100 Bryant Woods S
Amherst, NY 14228
Ph: (716)881-5222
Free: 800-828-5000
Fax: (716)883-5349
Co. E-mail: info@upstatenybbb.org
URL: http://www.bbb.org/us/ny/buffalo
Contact: Katarina Schmieder, Director
Facebook: www.facebook.com/BBBUpstateNY
Linkedin: www.linkedin.com/company/bbbupstateny
X (Twitter): x.com/BBBUpstateNY
Instagram: www.instagram.com/bbbupstateny
Description: Promotes and fosters ethical relationships between businesses and the public. **Geographic Preference:** Local.

CHAMBERS OF COMMERCE

42509 ■ *1000 Island Clayton Visitor Guide*
517 Riverside Dr.
Clayton, NY 13624
Ph: (315)686-3771
Free: 800-252-9806
Co. E-mail: info@1000islands-clayton.com
URL: http://www.1000islands-clayton.com
Contact: Christopher Bogenschutz, President
URL(s): www.1000islands-clayton.com/contact/visitor-guide-request
Released: Annual **Availability:** Print; Online.

42510 ■ 1000 Islands Area Clayton Chamber of Commerce
517 Riverside Dr.
Clayton, NY 13624
Ph: (315)686-3771
Free: 800-252-9806
Co. E-mail: info@1000islands-clayton.com
URL: http://www.1000islands-clayton.com
Contact: Christopher Bogenschutz, President
Facebook: www.facebook.com/clayton1000islands
X (Twitter): x.com/claytonchamber

Description: Promotes business, community development, and tourism in the Thousand Island area of New York. **Founded:** 1926. **Publications:** *1000 Island Clayton Visitor Guide* (Annual). **Geographic Preference:** Local.

42511 ■ Adirondack Regional Chamber of Commerce (ARCC)
68 Warren St.
  Glens Falls, NY 12801
Ph: (518)798-1761
Fax: (518)792-4147
Co. E-mail: info@adirondackchamber.org
URL: http://www.adirondackchamber.org
Contact: Michael Bittel, Co-President Co-Chief Executive Officer
E-mail: mbittel@adirondackchamber.org
Facebook: www.facebook.com/adirondackchamber
Linkedin: www.linkedin.com/company/adirondack-regional-chamber-of-commerce
X (Twitter): x.com/adkchamber
Instagram: www.instagram.com/adirondack_regional_chamber
Description: Promotes business and community development in northern Essex, Hamilton, Saratoga, Warren, and Washington counties, NY. **Founded:** 1914. **Publications:** *ARCC Regional Report* (Monthly); *Quality of Life Guide* (Annual). **Geographic Preference:** Local.

42512 ■ Adirondacks-Speculator Region Chamber of Commerce
[Adirondacks-Spectacular Region Chamber of Commerce]
2960 NY-30
  Speculator, NY 12164
Ph: (518)548-4521
Co. E-mail: info@speculatorchamber.com
URL: http://www.speculatorchamber.com
Contact: Sue Montgomery Corey, President
Facebook: www.facebook.com/SpeculatorChamber
X (Twitter): x.com/asrchamber
Instagram: www.instagram.com/speculatorchamber
Description: Promotes business and community development in Speculator, NY area. **Geographic Preference:** Local.

42513 ■ African American Chamber of Commerce of Westchester and Rockland Counties
11 Prospect Ave.
  Mount Vernon, NY 10550
URL: http://usblackchambers.org/usbc-chambers
Contact: Robin L. Douglas, Contact
E-mail: robinlisadouglas@cs.com
Description: Promotes business and community development in Westchester and Rockland counties. **Founded:** 1996. **Geographic Preference:** Local.

42514 ■ Alexandria Bay Chamber of Commerce
7 Market St.
  Alexandria Bay, NY 13607
Ph: (315)482-9531
Fax: (315)482-5434
Co. E-mail: info@alexbay.org
URL: http://www.visitalexbay.org
Contact: Ronald Thomson, Treasurer
Facebook: www.facebook.com/Alexandria-Bay-Chamber-of-Commerce-82504121853
X (Twitter): x.com/MeetMeAtTheBay
Instagram: www.instagram.com/meet_me_at_the_bay
YouTube: www.youtube.com/channel/UCSJ2YAapD9w3rYhDKgp9GeA
Description: Promotes business and community development in Alexandria Bay, NY. **Geographic Preference:** Local.

42515 ■ Amherst Chamber of Commerce (ACC)
400 Essjay Rd., Ste. 150
  Williamsville, NY 14221
Ph: (716)632-6905
Fax: (716)632-0548
Co. E-mail: info@amherst.org
URL: http://amherst.org
Contact: A. J. Baynes, Jr., President
E-mail: ajbaynes@amherst.org
Facebook: www.facebook.com/amherstcoc
Linkedin: www.linkedin.com/company/amherst-chamber-of-commerce
X (Twitter): x.com/Amherst_Chamber
Instagram: www.instagram.com/amherstchamberofcommerce
YouTube: www.youtube.com/channel/UCa4DUZvqzZ_SZW0pJqe6yOA
Description: Aims to create and maintain a positive economic, political, and social climate in Amherst. **Founded:** 1957. **Publications:** *The Agenda* (Monthly). **Geographic Preference:** Local.

42516 ■ Arcade Area Chamber of Commerce
228 Main St.
  Arcade, NY 14009
Ph: (585)492-2114
Fax: (585)492-5103
Co. E-mail: office@arcadechamber.org
URL: http://www.arcadeareachamber.org
Contact: Travis Sick, President
Facebook: www.facebook.com/arcadechamber
Description: Promotes business and community development in the Arcade, NY area. **Publications:** *The Business Advocate* (Irregular). **Geographic Preference:** Local.

42517 ■ Bainbridge Chamber of Commerce
PO Box 2
  Bainbridge, NY 13733
Ph: (607)967-8700
Co. E-mail: bainbridge.chamber@yahoo.com
URL: http://www.bainbridgecofc.com/chamber-of-commerce
Contact: John Payne, President
Facebook: www.facebook.com/Bainbridge-Chamber-of-Commerce-161450047326632
Description: Promotes business and community development in Bainbridge, NY. Sponsors the General Clinton Canoe Regatta. **Founded:** 1829. **Geographic Preference:** Local.

42518 ■ Baldwin Chamber of Commerce (BCC)
2485 Grand Ave.
  Baldwin, NY 11510
Ph: (516)246-5625
Co. E-mail: baldwinchamberofcommerce@gmail.com
URL: http://www.baldwinchamber.com
Facebook: www.facebook.com/BaldwinChamberOfCommerce
Description: Promotes business and community development in Baldwin, NY. **Founded:** 1982. **Geographic Preference:** Local.

42519 ■ Baldwin Park Chamber of Commerce (BOC)
2485 Grand Ave.
  Baldwin, NY 11510
Ph: (516)246-5625
Co. E-mail: baldwinchamberofcommerce@gmail.com
URL: http://baldwinchamber.com
Facebook: www.facebook.com/BaldwinChamberOfCommerce
Instagram: www.instagram.com/baldwinchamberofcommerce
Description: Promotes business and community membership, action oriented, responsive, and demonstrate outstanding leadership. **Founded:** 1906. **Publications:** *Baldwin Park NOW* (Monthly). **Geographic Preference:** Local.

42520 ■ Bedford Hills Chamber of Commerce
PO Box 162
  Bedford Hills, NY 10507-0162
Ph: (914)381-3356
URL: http://www.uschamber.com/co/chambers/new-york/bedford-hills
Description: Promotes business and community development in Bedford Hills, NY. Sponsors "Community Day" sidewalk sales. Convention/Meeting: none. **Founded:** 1966. **Geographic Preference:** Local.

42521 ■ Bethlehem Chamber of Commerce
318 Delaware Ave., Ste. 27
  Delmar, NY 12054
Ph: (518)439-0512
Co. E-mail: info@bethlehemchamber.com
URL: http://www.bethlehemchamber.com
Contact: Jayne Maloney, Board Member
Facebook: www.facebook.com/bethlehemnychamber
Linkedin: www.linkedin.com/company/bethlehem-chamber-of-commerce
X (Twitter): x.com/BethlehemChambr
Instagram: www.instagram.com/bethlehemnychamber
YouTube: www.youtube.com/channel/UC8ZNEBWXmdKpU3yxGIn9oDA
Description: Aims to promote good business practices, favorable business environment and community prosperity. **Founded:** 1957. **Publications:** *In Business for Business* (Monthly); *Welcome to the Town of Bethlehem*. **Geographic Preference:** Local.

42522 ■ Boonville Area Chamber of Commerce
46 Schylyer St.
  Boonville, NY 13309
Ph: (315)942-5112
Co. E-mail: boonvillenyareachamber@gmail.com
URL: http://www.boonvilleareachamber.com
Contact: Laura Gramlich, President
E-mail: gramlichjl@hotmail.com
Description: Assists businesses, organizations and individuals by providing programs and services that enhance the economic climate and the quality of life for the citizens of the community. **Founded:** 1961. **Geographic Preference:** Local.

42523 ■ *The Bottom Line*
1 Civic Center Plz., Ste. 400
  Poughkeepsie, NY 12601
Ph: (845)454-1700
Fax: (845)454-1702
Co. E-mail: office@dcrcoc.org
URL: http://www.dcrcoc.org
Contact: Gregory White, Chairperson
URL(s): www.dcrcoc.org/member/newmemberapp
Availability: Print; Online.

42524 ■ Brewster Chamber of Commerce
16 Mt. Ebo Rd. S, Ste. 12A
  Brewster, NY 10509
Ph: (845)279-2477
Co. E-mail: info@brewsterchamber.com
URL: http://www.brewsterchamber.com
Contact: Kate Corsitto, President
Facebook: www.facebook.com/brewsternychamber
Instagram: www.instagram.com/brewsterchamber
Description: Promotes business and community development in Brewster, NY. **Founded:** 1957. **Geographic Preference:** Local.

42525 ■ Bronx Chamber of Commerce (BCC)
1200 Waters Pl., Ste. 106
  Bronx, NY 10461
Ph: (718)828-3900
Fax: (716)815-7333
Co. E-mail: helpdesk@bronxchamber.org
URL: http://www.bronxchamber.org
Contact: Lisa Sorin, President
Facebook: www.facebook.com/TheNewBronxChamberofCommerce
Linkedin: www.linkedin.com/company/the-new-bronx-chamber-of-commerce
X (Twitter): x.com/thenewbxcc
Instagram: www.instagram.com/thenewbxcc
YouTube: www.youtube.com/channel/UC1XxD-1xNa389eFDO59MklQ
Description: Promotes business and community development in Bronx, NY. Sponsors special events. **Founded:** 1894. **Publications:** *Industrial Directory*; *Bronx Industrial Directory and Yearbook* (Annual). **Geographic Preference:** Local.

42526 ■ Bronxville Chamber of Commerce
51 Pondfield Rd., Ste. 6
  119 Pondfield Rd.
  Bronxville, NY 10708
Ph: (914)337-6040

42527 ■ New York

Co. E-mail: info@bronxvillechamber.org
URL: http://www.bronxvillechamber.org
Contact: Leah Caro, President
Facebook: www.facebook.com/Bronxville-Chamber-of-Commerce-115215478527444
Instagram: www.instagram.com/bronxvillechamber
Description: Promotes business and community development in Bronxville, NY. **Founded:** 1944. **Geographic Preference:** Local.

42527 ■ Brooklyn Chamber of Commerce (BCC)
253 36th, Bldg., 3, 4th Fl. (Industry City)
Brooklyn, NY 11232
Ph: (718)875-1000
Fax: (718)222-0781
Co. E-mail: info@brooklynchamber.com
URL: http://www.brooklynchamber.com
Contact: Randy Peers, President
E-mail: rpeers@brooklynchamber.com
Facebook: www.facebook.com/brooklynchamberofcommerce
Linkedin: www.linkedin.com/company/brooklyn-chamber-of-commerce
X (Twitter): x.com/brooklynchamber
Instagram: www.instagram.com/brooklynchamber
Description: Promotes business and community development in Brooklyn, NY. **Founded:** 1918. **Publications:** *Brooklyn Chamber of Commerce--Membership Directory*. **Geographic Preference:** Local.

42528 ■ Buffalo Niagara Partnership (BNP)
257 W Genesee St., Ste. 600
Buffalo, NY 14202
Ph: (716)852-7100
Free: 844-308-9165
Fax: (716)852-2761
Co. E-mail: connect@thepartnership.org
URL: http://www.thepartnership.org
Contact: Dottie Gallagher, President
Facebook: www.facebook.com/BuffaloNiagaraPartnership
Linkedin: www.linkedin.com/company/buffalo-niagara-partnership
X (Twitter): x.com/BNPartnership
Instagram: www.instagram.com/bnpartnership
YouTube: www.youtube.com/user/BNPartnership
Description: Promotes business and community development in West Seneca, NY. Holds seminars. **Founded:** 1993. **Publications:** *The Focus* (Monthly); *Western New York Magazine* (Monthly); *Public Officials Directory*; *Western New York Business Directory* (Annual). **Geographic Preference:** Local.

42529 ■ *Business to Business*
Released: Periodic **Price:** for members. **Availability:** Print; Online.

42530 ■ Business Council of Westchester (BCW)
800 Weschester Ave., Ste. S-310
Rye Brook, NY 10573
Ph: (914)948-2110
Fax: (914)948-0122
Co. E-mail: info@thebcw.org
URL: http://thebcw.org
Contact: Dr. Marsha Gordon, President
E-mail: mgordon@thebcw.org
Facebook: www.facebook.com/TheBusinessCouncilofWestchester
X (Twitter): x.com/westchesterbiz
YouTube: www.youtube.com/user/WestchesterBiz
Description: Promotes business and community development in Westchester-White Plains, NY area. **Founded:** 1904. **Geographic Preference:** Local.

42531 ■ *Business Directory/Buyer's Guide*
1241 Coffeen St.
Watertown, NY 13601
Ph: (315)788-4400
Fax: (315)788-3369
Co. E-mail: chamber@watertownny.com
URL: http://www.watertownny.com
URL(s): business.watertownny.com/list
Availability: Online.

42532 ■ Cairo Chamber of Commerce
PO Box 515
Cairo, NY 12413
Co. E-mail: cairochamberinfo@gmail.com
URL: http://cairochamberofcommerce.weebly.com
Linkedin: www.linkedin.com/company/cairo-chamber-of-commerce
Description: Promotes goodwill, publicity and development of the commercial welfare of the Cairo area; strives to create a better community spirit among all types of businesses through advancement of activities. **Founded:** 1967. **Geographic Preference:** Local.

42533 ■ *Calendar of Events*
94 Montcalm St., Ste. 1
Ticonderoga, NY 12883
Ph: (518)585-6619
Fax: (518)585-9184
Co. E-mail: chamberinfo@ticonderogany.com
URL: http://www.ticonderogany.com
Contact: Matthew Courtright, President
E-mail: mcourtright@ticonderogany.com
URL(s): ticonderogany.com/tacc-upcoming-events
Availability: Download; Online.

42534 ■ Camden Area Chamber of Commerce (CACC)
PO Box 134
Camden, NY 13316-0134
Ph: (315)245-5000
Co. E-mail: contact@camdennychamber.com
URL: http://www.camdennychamber.com
Contact: Michael Takacs, President
Description: Promotes business and community development in the Camden, AR area. **Publications:** *Chamber News*. **Geographic Preference:** Local.

42535 ■ Canton Chamber of Commerce (CCC)
1 Main St., Ste. 101
Canton, NY 13617
Ph: (315)386-8255
Co. E-mail: cantonchamberny@gmail.com
URL: http://cantonny.gov
Contact: Derek Hetu, President
Facebook: www.facebook.com/Canton-New-York-226200548308
Description: Promotes business and community development in Canton, NY. Holds annual events including Dairy Princess Parade, Peter Rabbit in the Park, Phantoms in the Park, Farmers Market in Village Park, and Winterfest. **Founded:** 1965. **Geographic Preference:** Local.

42536 ■ *Cape Vincent*
173 N James St.
Cape Vincent, NY 13618
Ph: (315)654-2481
Co. E-mail: thecape@tds.net
URL: http://www.capevincent.org
Contact: Kristie Stumpf Rork, Executive Director
URL(s): www.capevincent.org/more-info/contact-the-chamber
Released: Annual **Description:** Contains calendar of events and information about area restaurants, accommodations, services, and marinas. **Availability:** Print.

42537 ■ Cape Vincent Chamber of Commerce
173 N James St.
Cape Vincent, NY 13618
Ph: (315)654-2481
Co. E-mail: thecape@tds.net
URL: http://www.capevincent.org
Contact: Kristie Stumpf Rork, Executive Director
Facebook: www.facebook.com/capevincentchamberofcommerce
Description: Promotes business, community development, and tourism in Cape Vincent, NY. Sponsors festivals, art shows, fishing contest, tennis tournaments, bike and running races. **Founded:** 1853. **Publications:** *Cape Vincent* (Annual); *What's Happening in CV, 13618* (Monthly). **Geographic Preference:** Local.

42538 ■ Carthage Area Chamber of Commerce
120 S Mechanic St.
Carthage, NY 13619
Ph: (315)493-3590
Co. E-mail: carthagenychamber@gmail.com
Facebook: www.facebook.com/carthageareachamberofcommerce
X (Twitter): x.com/carthage_NY
Description: Strives to promote civic, economic, and social welfare in Carthage, NY area. **Founded:** 1921. **Geographic Preference:** Local.

42539 ■ Cayuga County Chamber of Commerce (CCCOC)
2 State St.
Auburn, NY 13021
Ph: (315)252-7291
Fax: (315)255-3077
Co. E-mail: admin@cayugacountychamber.com
URL: http://www.cayugacountychamber.com
Contact: Amy Fuller, Executive Director
E-mail: afuller@cayugacountychamber.com
Facebook: www.facebook.com/Chamber13021
Linkedin: www.linkedin.com/company/5060840
X (Twitter): x.com/chamber13021
Instagram: www.instagram.com/chamber13021
YouTube: www.youtube.com/channel/UCMV0g_eYZkD2PyFDpFhrrSA
Description: Strives to improve economic vitality and quality of life in Cayuga County. **Founded:** 1908. **Geographic Preference:** Local.

42540 ■ CenterState Corporation for Economic Opportunity (CENTERSTATE CEO)
115 W Fayette St.
Syracuse, NY 13202
Ph: (315)470-1800
Fax: (315)471-8545
Co. E-mail: ceo@centerstateceo.com
URL: http://www.centerstateceo.com
Contact: Robert Simpson, President
E-mail: rsimpson@centerstateceo.com
Facebook: www.facebook.com/centerstate
Linkedin: www.linkedin.com/company/centerstate-corporation-for-economic-opportunity
X (Twitter): x.com/CenterStateCEO
Instagram: www.instagram.com/centerstateceo
YouTube: www.youtube.com/user/CenterStateCEO
Description: Promotes business and community development in the Syracuse, NY area. **Founded:** 1889. **Geographic Preference:** Local.

42541 ■ Chamber of Commerce of the Bellmores
2700 Pettit Ave.
Bellmore, NY 11710
Ph: (516)679-1875
Fax: (516)409-0544
Co. E-mail: info@bellmorechamber.com
URL: http://www.bellmorechamber.com
Contact: Jim Spohrer, President
Facebook: www.facebook.com/BellmoreChamber
Description: Promotes business and community development in Bellmore and North Bellmore, NY. **Founded:** 1948. **Publications:** *Business and Professional Directory* (Annual); *Chamber of Commerce of the Bellmores Business and Professional Directory*; *Chamber of Commerce of the Bellmores--Business and Professional Directory* (Annual). **Educational Activities:** General Membership Meeting (Monthly). **Geographic Preference:** Local.

42542 ■ Chamber of Commerce of Greater Bay Shore
77 E Main St.
Bay Shore, NY 11706
Ph: (631)665-7003
Co. E-mail: bayshorecofcbid@optonline.net
URL: http://chamberofcommerceofgreaterbayshore.com
Facebook: www.facebook.com/bayshorechamberofcomm
Description: Promotes business and community development in the Greater Bay Shore, NY area. **Founded:** 1708. **Geographic Preference:** Local.

STATE LISTINGS New York ■ 42557

42543 ■ Chamber of Commerce of the Greater Ronkonkoma
PO Box 2546
Ronkonkoma, NY 11779
Ph: (631)963-2796
Co. E-mail: info@ronkonkomachamber.com
URL: http://www.ronkonkomachamber.com
Contact: Edward McNamara, President
E-mail: emcnamara@ft.newyorklife.com
Facebook: www.facebook.com/RonkonkomaChamber
X (Twitter): x.com/RonkChamber
Description: Promotes business and community development in Ronkonkoma, NY. **Geographic Preference:** Local.

42544 ■ Chamber of Commerce of the Mastics and Shirley
PO Box 4
Mastic, NY 11950
Ph: (631)399-2228
Co. E-mail: mschamber11950@gmail.com
URL: http://masticshirleychamber.org
Contact: Beth Wahl, President
Facebook: www.facebook.com/MasticShirleyChamber
X (Twitter): x.com/MSChamber11950
Description: Seeks to promote business and community development and enhance the relationship between local businesses and professionals with the public. **Founded:** 1951. **Geographic Preference:** Local.

42545 ■ Chamber of Commerce of the Tonawandas
254 Sweeney St.
North Tonawanda, NY 14120
Ph: (716)692-5120
Fax: (716)692-1867
URL: http://the-tonawandas.com
Contact: Robert Pecoraro, President
Facebook: www.facebook.com/ChamberoftheTonawandas
X (Twitter): x.com/TonawandasChamb
Description: Highlights and identifies problems, to help develop solutions to better its communities and business climate and to work toward creating the governmental and public support necessary to promote needed improvements and changes. **Geographic Preference:** Local.

42546 ■ Chamber of Commerce of the Willistons (CCW)
PO Box 207
Williston Park, NY 11596
Ph: (516)739-1943
Co. E-mail: willistonchamberofcommerce@gmail.com
URL: http://www.chamberofthewillistons.com
Contact: Barbara Baur-Rizzo, Secretary
Facebook: www.facebook.com/PattersonLiamE
Description: Promotes business and community development in Williston, NY. Sponsors annual festival and competitions. Conducts charitable activities. **Founded:** 1949. **Geographic Preference:** Local.

42547 ■ Chamber of Southern Saratoga County (CSSC)
58 Clifton Country Rd., Ste. 102
Clifton Park, NY 12065
URL: http://capitalregionchamber.com
Description: Promotes business and community development in Southern Saratoga County, NY. Provides opportunities for networking, education, personal and professional development, and member benefits. **Publications:** *Southern Saratoga County Community Guide* (Annual); *The Bottom Line*; *Chamber Report* (Annual); *Economic Review*. **Educational Activities:** Business After Hours (Annual). **Awards:** Southern Saratoga County Southern Star Awards (Annual). **Geographic Preference:** Local.

42548 ■ Chamber Vision
7061 Rte. 9
Plattsburgh, NY 12901
Ph: (518)563-1000
Fax: (518)563-1028
Co. E-mail: info@northcountrychamber.com
URL: http://northcountrychamber.com
Contact: Garry Douglas, President
E-mail: garry@northcountrychamber.com
URL(s): www.northcountrychamber.com/Chamber/Benefits-of-Membership
Released: Monthly **Availability:** Print.

42549 ■ ChamberGram
904 E Shore Dr.
Ithaca, NY 14850
Ph: (607)273-7080
Fax: (607)272-7617
Co. E-mail: info@tompkinschamber.org
URL: http://www.tompkinschamber.org
Contact: Jennifer Tavares, President
E-mail: jtavares@tompkinschamber.org
URL(s): tompkinschamber.org/category/chambergram
Released: Weekly; 1st Wednesday. **Availability:** Online.

42550 ■ Chautauqua County Chamber of Commerce
300 N Main St.
Jamestown, NY 14701
Ph: (716)484-1101
Fax: (716)366-6200
Co. E-mail: info@chautauquachamber.org
URL: http://www.chautauquachamber.org
Contact: Daniel Heitzenrater, President
E-mail: dheitzenrater@chautauquachamber.org
X (Twitter): x.com/ChautauquaChamb
YouTube: www.youtube.com/channel/UC-_4ExpsNZV_4-nksH1clDA
Description: Aims to provide strong and effective regional leadership and representation which will unify and promote the interests of Chautauqua County. **Founded:** 2000. **Publications:** *Chautauqua Chamber of Commerce--Business Directory*; *The Voice* (Monthly). **Geographic Preference:** Local.

42551 ■ Cheektowaga Chamber of Commerce (CCC)
2875 Union Rd., Ste. 7A
Cheektowaga, NY 14227
Ph: (716)684-5838
Fax: (716)684-5571
URL: http://www.cheektowaga.org
Contact: Kristina Groff, President
E-mail: kgroff@cheektowaga.org
Facebook: www.facebook.com/cheektowagachamber
Linkedin: www.linkedin.com/company/cheektowaga-chamber-of-commerce
X (Twitter): x.com/CheektowagaC
Description: Promotes business and community development in Cheektowaga, NY. Offers health insurance for small businesses. Sponsors Food Fest. **Founded:** 1939. **Geographic Preference:** Local.

42552 ■ Chemung County Chamber of Commerce
400 E Church St.
Elmira, NY 14901-2803
Ph: (607)734-5137
Fax: (607)734-4490
Co. E-mail: info@chemungchamber.org
URL: http://www.chemungchamber.org
Contact: Jennifer Herrick-McGonigal, President
E-mail: jennifer@chemungchamber.org
Facebook: www.facebook.com/ChemungChamber
X (Twitter): x.com/chemungchamber
Description: Promotes business and community development in Chemung County, NY. **Founded:** 1905. **Publications:** *Chemung County Chamber of Commerce--Community Profile and Membership Directory*; *Today's Chamber* (Monthly). **Geographic Preference:** Local.

42553 ■ Clarence Chamber of Commerce
8899 Main St., Ste. 4 & Shimerville Rd.
Clarence, NY 14031-0177
Ph: (716)631-3888
Fax: (716)631-3946
Co. E-mail: info@clarence.org
URL: http://www.clarencechamber.org
Contact: Amy Engler, Executive Director
Facebook: www.facebook.com/Clarence-Chamber-of-Commerce-375012172637294
Description: Aims to support and strengthen the businesses in Clarence, NY area. **Founded:** 1954. **Publications:** *Chamber Connections* (Monthly). **Awards:** Clarence Chamber of Commerce Business of the Year (Annual); Clarence Chamber of Commerce Citizen of the Year (Annual); Clarence Chamber of Commerce Organization of the Year (Annual). **Geographic Preference:** Local.

42554 ■ Clifton Springs Area Chamber of Commerce (CSCOC)
2 E Main St.
Clifton Springs, NY 14432
Ph: (315)462-8200
Co. E-mail: info@cliftonspringschamber.com
URL: http://www.cliftonspringschamber.com
Contact: Jeff Criblear, President
E-mail: jcriblear@hotmail.com
Facebook: www.facebook.com/cliftonspringsnychamber
Description: Promotes business and community development in Clifton Springs, NY. **Geographic Preference:** Local.

42555 ■ Clinton Chamber of Commerce (CCC)
21 W Pk. Row
Clinton, NY 13323
Ph: (315)853-1735
Co. E-mail: info@clintonnychamber.org
URL: http://clintonnychamber.org
Contact: Colleen Furmanski, Co-President
Facebook: www.facebook.com/clintonnychamber
Linkedin: www.linkedin.com/company/clinton-chamber-of-commerce
X (Twitter): x.com/ClintonCCNY
Instagram: www.instagram.com/clintonnychamber
YouTube: www.youtube.com/channel/UCrWh4IJZuQp6UqDeMwHA53w
Description: Promotes business and community development in Clinton, NY. **Founded:** 1953. **Geographic Preference:** Local.

42556 ■ Cold Spring Area Chamber of Commerce
PO Box 36
Cold Spring, NY 10516
Ph: (845)265-3992
Co. E-mail: info@coldspringnychamber.com
URL: http://www.coldspringnychamber.com
Contact: Eliza Starbuck, President
Facebook: www.facebook.com/explorecoldspringny
Description: Promotes business and community development in Cold Spring, NY area. **Founded:** 1910. **Geographic Preference:** Local.

42557 ■ Colonie Chamber of Commerce
950 New Loudon Rd.
Latham, NY 12110
Ph: (518)785-6995
Fax: (518)785-7173
Co. E-mail: info@coloniechamber.org
URL: http://www.coloniechamber.org
Contact: Tom Nolte, President
E-mail: tom@coloniechamber.org
Facebook: www.facebook.com/coloniechamber
Linkedin: www.linkedin.com/company/colonie-chamber-of-commerce
X (Twitter): x.com/coloniechamber
Instagram: www.instagram.com/coloniechamber
YouTube: www.youtube.com/channel/UCSm8Y-OKMw6ECNJNKqR7S_Q
Pinterest: www.pinterest.com/ColonieCC
Description: Offers members' health insurance, dental insurance, cellular phone service and other discounted services. Hosts monthly networking mixers, a golf tournament, Office Appreciation Luncheon on National Secretaries Day and annual dinner. **Founded:** 1985. **Publications:** *Inside Colonie* (Quarterly). **Geographic Preference:** Local.

42558 ■ Columbia County Chamber of Commerce
1 N Front St.
Hudson, NY 12534
Ph: (518)828-4417
Co. E-mail: mail@columbiachamber-ny.com
URL: http://columbiachamber-ny.com
Contact: Bill Gerlach, President
E-mail: wgerlach@columbiachamber-ny.com
Facebook: www.facebook.com/ccchamberny
X (Twitter): x.com/ccchamberny
Instagram: www.instagram.com/ccchamberny
Description: Promotes tourism and economic development in Columbia County, NY. Provides health insurance. Sponsors on-the-job training, seminars, and other events. **Founded:** 1978. **Geographic Preference:** Local.

42559 ■ Cooperstown Chamber of Commerce (CCC)
31 Chestnut St.
Cooperstown, NY 13326
Ph: (607)547-9983
Co. E-mail: office@cooperstownchamber.org
URL: http://www.wearecooperstown.com
Contact: Jess Lanza, President
Facebook: www.facebook.com/cooperstownchamber
Linkedin: www.linkedin.com/company/cooperstownchamber
Instagram: www.instagram.com/wearecooperstown
Description: Promotes business and community development in Cooperstown, NY. Provides tourist information. **Founded:** 1917. **Publications:** *Cooperstown Chamber Visitors Guide* (Annual). **Geographic Preference:** Local.

42560 ■ Corning Area Chamber of Commerce (CACC)
1 W Market St.
Corning, NY 14830
Ph: (607)936-4686
Fax: (607)936-4685
Co. E-mail: info@corningny.com
URL: http://www.corningny.com
Contact: Colleen M. Coro, Co-President
E-mail: cmcoro@corningny.com
Facebook: www.facebook.com/corningnychamber
X (Twitter): x.com/corningchamber
Description: Promotes business, cultural, community development, and tourism in the Corning, NY area. **Founded:** 1914. **Publications:** *Buyer's Guide* (Annual); *The Link* (Monthly). **Geographic Preference:** Local.

42561 ■ Cortland County Chamber of Commerce
83 Main St.
Cortland, NY 13045
Ph: (607)756-2814
Co. E-mail: info@cortlandareachamber.com
URL: http://www.cortlandareachaber.com
Contact: Bob Haight, President
E-mail: bob@cortlandareachamber.com
X (Twitter): x.com/CortlandChamber
Instagram: www.instagram.com/cortlandchamber
Description: Aims to promote the free enterprise system in Cortland, NY area. **Founded:** 1903. **Geographic Preference:** Local.

42562 ■ Dansville Chamber of Commerce (DCC)
126 Main St.
Dansville, NY 14437
Ph: (585)335-6920
Free: 800-949-0174
Co. E-mail: dansvillechamber@frontier.com
URL: http://dansvillechamber.com
Contact: Barry Haywood, President
E-mail: bhaywood14437@yahoo.com
Facebook: www.facebook.com/discoverdansville
X (Twitter): x.com/DansvilleMainSt
Description: Works to build a vibrant economy and quality of life in the community. Serves as an umbrella organization that also includes the NY State Festival of Balloons, the Dansville Economic Development Corporation and the Dansville Business Association. **Founded:** 1845. **Geographic Preference:** Local.

42563 ■ Deposit Chamber of Commerce
PO Box 222
Deposit, NY 13754
Co. E-mail: dma21@aol.com
Facebook: www.facebook.com/DepositChamberofCommerce
Description: Promotes business and community development in the Deposit, NY area. Sponsors festivals and hall of fame; presents business and service awards. Operates county welcome center and tourism development. **Geographic Preference:** Local.

42564 ■ Dutchess County Regional Chamber of Commerce
1 Civic Center Plz., Ste. 400
Poughkeepsie, NY 12601
Ph: (845)454-1700
Fax: (845)454-1702
Co. E-mail: office@dcrcoc.org
URL: http://www.dcrcoc.org
Contact: Gregory White, Chairperson
Facebook: www.facebook.com/dcrcoc
X (Twitter): x.com/dcrcoc
Instagram: www.instagram.com/dcrcoc
YouTube: www.youtube.com/user/DutchessChamber
Description: Promotes economical growth for business and community development in the Dutchess County area. **Founded:** 1907. **Publications:** *Bed and Breakfast Guide*; *The Bottom Line*; *Guide to Government*. **Geographic Preference:** Local.

42565 ■ East Hampton Chamber of Commerce (EHCC)
PO Box 1991
East Hampton, NY 11937
Description: Promotes business and community development in East Hampton, NY. **Founded:** 1648. **Geographic Preference:** Local.

42566 ■ Eastchester Tuckahoe Chamber of Commerce
Tuckahoe Village Hall
65 Main St., Ste. 202
Tuckahoe, NY 10707
Ph: (914)779-7344
Co. E-mail: etcocm@gmail.com
URL: http://www.etcoc.com
Contact: Loretta De Simone, Executive Director
Founded: 1947. **Geographic Preference:** Local.

42567 ■ Ellenville / Wawarsing Chamber of Commerce (EWCOC)
124 Canal St.
Ellenville, NY 12428-1404
Ph: (845)647-4620
Co. E-mail: info@ewcoc.com
URL: http://www.ewcoc.com
Contact: Dan Couse, President
E-mail: dan@dancouse.net
Description: Promotes business and community development in Town of Wawarsing, Ulster County, NY. **Founded:** 1806. **Publications:** *Membership Brochure* (Annual). **Geographic Preference:** Local.

42568 ■ Ellicottville Chamber of Commerce
9 W Washington St.
Ellicottville, NY 14731
Ph: (716)699-5046
Free: 800-349-9099
Fax: (716)699-5636
Co. E-mail: info@ellicottvilleny.com
URL: http://www.ellicottvilleny.com
Contact: Arleen Solly, President
Facebook: www.facebook.com/Ellicottville
Instagram: www.instagram.com/visitellicottville
YouTube: www.youtube.com/user/weareellicottville
Description: Promotes economic development in Ellicottville, NY area. **Geographic Preference:** Local.

42569 ■ Fair Haven Area Chamber of Commerce (FHACC)
PO Box 13
Fair Haven, NY 13064
Co. E-mail: info@fairhavenny.org
URL: http://www.fairhavenny.org
Facebook: www.facebook.com/fairhavenny
Description: Promotes business and community development in the Fair Haven, NY area. Sponsors Oktoberfest, Fourth of July festival and Arts and Crafts Fair. **Founded:** 1970. **Geographic Preference:** Local.

42570 ■ Fort Edward Chamber of Commerce
11 Rogers Island Dr.
Fort Edward, NY 12828-1759
Ph: (518)747-3000
URL: http://www.uschamber.com/co/chambers/new-york/fort-edward
Description: Promotes businesses in Fort Edward. **Geographic Preference:** Local.

42571 ■ Fulton County Regional Chamber of Commerce and Industry
2 N Main St.
Gloversville, NY 12078
Ph: (518)725-0641
Fax: (518)725-0643
Co. E-mail: info@fultoncountyny.org
URL: http://www.fultonmontgomeryny.org
Contact: Mark Kilmer, President
E-mail: president@fultonmontgomeryny.org
Facebook: www.facebook.com/fultonmontgomerychamberny
X (Twitter): x.com/FMChamberNY
Instagram: www.instagram.com/fmchamberny
Description: Promotes business and community development in the Fulton County, NY area. Sponsors winter festival, First Night, and home and business expo. Holds seminars. **Founded:** 1919. **Publications:** *Newsline* (Monthly). **Geographic Preference:** Local.

42572 ■ Garden City Chamber of Commerce (GCCC)
230 7th St.
Garden City, NY 11530
Ph: (516)746-7724
Fax: (516)746-7725
Co. E-mail: info@gardencitychamber.org
URL: http://www.gardencitychamber.org
Contact: Sean Martens, President
E-mail: mventre@windsorcre.com
Facebook: www.facebook.com/GCChamberofCommerce
Description: Promotes business and community development in Garden City, NY. **Founded:** 1926. **Geographic Preference:** Local.

42573 ■ Genesee County Chamber of Commerce
8276 Pk. Rd.
Batavia, NY 14020
Ph: (585)343-7440
Co. E-mail: chamber@geneseeny.com
URL: http://geneseeny.com
Contact: Brian Cousins, Co-President
Facebook: www.facebook.com/GeneseeCountyChamberofCommerce
X (Twitter): x.com/GeneseeChamber
Instagram: www.instagram.com/geneseechamber
YouTube: www.youtube.com/channel/UCejgsz9TLb5xdZTSX-q-1RQ
Description: Strives to lead in the pursuit of creating an environment for business success that will enhance the quality of life for the citizens of Genesee County. Sponsors the Wing Ding Weekend Block Party, Annual Business/Citizen Awards Dinner, Annual Golf Outing and other community events. Official tourism promotion agency for Genesee County. **Founded:** 1972. **Publications:** *Genesee County, Greater Niagara Region Guide* (Annual); *Chamberline* (Monthly); *Membership Directory* (Annual). **Geographic Preference:** Local.

STATE LISTINGS

42574 ■ Geneva Area Chamber of Commerce
537 Exchange St., One Franklin Sq. Bldg., Ste. 202
Geneva, NY 14456
Ph: (315)789-1776
Fax: (315)789-3993
Co. E-mail: info@genevany.com
URL: http://genevany.com
Contact: Miranda Odell, President
Facebook: www.facebook.com/GenevaAreaChamber
X (Twitter): x.com/geneva_chamber
Description: Promotes business and community development in the Geneva, NY area. **Publications:** *Business to Business* (Monthly). **Geographic Preference:** Local.

42575 ■ Glen Cove Chamber of Commerce - Library
30A Glen St., Ste. 207
Glen Cove, NY 11542
Ph: (516)676-6666
Fax: (516)676-6666
Co. E-mail: info@glencovechamber.org
URL: http://www.glencovechamber.org
Contact: Lisa Cohn, Officer
Facebook: www.facebook.com/glencovechamber
Linkedin: www.linkedin.com/company/glen-cove-chamber-of-commerce
X (Twitter): x.com/glencovechamber
Instagram: www.instagram.com/glencovechamber
YouTube: www.youtube.com/channel/UC1-_5hVgwbyJAC3TLPPjiFg
Description: Promotes business and community development in Glen Cove, NY. **Founded:** 1920. **Holdings:** 130,000 books; many videos; DVDs; music CDs. **Geographic Preference:** Local.

42576 ■ Gowanda Area Chamber of Commerce (GACC)
15 S Water St.
Gowanda, NY 14070
Co. E-mail: gowandachamber@yahoo.com
URL: http://gowandachamber.com
Contact: Nicholas Crassi, Jr., President
Facebook: www.facebook.com/Gowanda-Area-Chamber-of-Commerce-110478698976045
Description: Promotes a healthy local economy within Gowanda area by influencing business success, public policy and community development. **Geographic Preference:** Local.

42577 ■ Grand Island Chamber of Commerce (GICC)
2680 Grand Island Blvd., Ste. 9
Grand Island, NY 14072
Ph: (716)773-3651
Fax: (716)773-3316
Co. E-mail: info@gichamber.org
URL: http://gichamber.org
Contact: Eric Fieblekorn, President
Facebook: www.facebook.com/GIChamber
X (Twitter): x.com/GI_Chamber
Description: Promotes business and community development in Grand Island, NY. Sponsors Citizen of the Year award and bicycle race. **Founded:** 1948. **Publications:** *Telephone Directory*. **Geographic Preference:** Local.

42578 ■ Great Neck Chamber of Commerce
Kiosk Information Ctr.
1 Middle Neck Rd.
Great Neck, NY 11021
Ph: (516)487-2000
Co. E-mail: info@greatneckchamber.org
URL: http://greatneckchamber.org
Contact: Hooshang Nematzadeh, First Vice President
Facebook: www.facebook.com/GreatNeckChamber
Instagram: www.instagram.com/greatneckchamber
Description: Promotes business and community development in Great Neck, NY. **Geographic Preference:** Local.

42579 ■ Greater Baldwinsville Chamber of Commerce
12 Oswego St., Ste. 108
Baldwinsville, NY 13027
Ph: (315)638-0550
Co. E-mail: baldwinsvillechamber@gmail.com
URL: http://www.baldwinsvillechamber.com
Contact: Matt Hunt, President
Facebook: www.facebook.com/baldwinsvillechamber
Linkedin: www.linkedin.com/company/greater-baldwinsville-chamber-of-commerce
X (Twitter): x.com/GBvilleChamber
Instagram: www.instagram.com/bvillechamber
Description: Promotes business and community development in the Baldwinsville, NY area. **Founded:** 1961. **Publications:** *News and Views* (Monthly). **Geographic Preference:** Local.

42580 ■ Greater Bath Area Chamber of Commerce
10 W Pulteney Sq.
Bath, NY 14810
Ph: (607)776-7122
URL: http://www.americantowns.com/place/greater-bath-area-chamber-of-commerce-bath-ny.html
Description: Promotes business and community development in the Bath, NY area. **Founded:** 1924. **Publications:** *Greater Bath Area Chamber of Commerce--Business Directory* (Quadrennial). **Geographic Preference:** Local.

42581 ■ Greater Binghamton Chamber of Commerce
5 S College Dr., Ste. 101
Binghamton, NY 13905
Ph: (607)772-8860
Fax: (607)722-4513
Co. E-mail: chamber@greaterbinghamtonchamber.com
URL: http://greaterbinghamtonchamber.com
Contact: Stacey Duncan, President
E-mail: sduncan@greaterbinghamtonchamber.com
X (Twitter): x.com/BingChamber
Description: Promotes business and community development in Binghamton, NY. **Founded:** 1964. **Publications:** *The Broome Chamber--Membership Directory* (Annual); *Greater Binghamton Travel Guide* (Annual); *Planners Guide* (Annual); *Quality of Life Resource Guide* (Annual). **Awards:** Greater Binghamton Chamber Volunteer of the Year (Annual); Greater Binghamton Chamber Civic Leader of the Year (Annual); Greater Binghamton Chamber Community Advocate Of The Year Award (Annual); Greater Binghamton Chamber Small Business Advocate of the Year (Annual); Greater Binghamton Chamber Small Business Person of the Year (Annual). **Geographic Preference:** Local.

42582 ■ Greater Brockport Chamber of Commerce (GBCC)
PO Box 119
Brockport, NY 14420-0119
Ph: (716)637-8684
URL: http://www.uschamber.com/co/chambers/new-york/brockport
Description: Promotes business and community development in the Brockport, NY area. Conducts charitable activities. **Founded:** 1972. **Geographic Preference:** Local.

42583 ■ Greater Cazenovia Area Chamber of Commerce (GCACC)
95 Albany St., Ste. C
Cazenovia, NY 13035
Ph: (315)655-9243
Fax: (315)655-9244
URL: http://cazenovia.com
Facebook: www.facebook.com/cazchamber
Instagram: www.instagram.com/cazchamber
Description: Works to advance and maintain a healthy economic environment in Greater Cazenovia area. **Founded:** 1997. **Publications:** *GCACC News* (Monthly). **Educational Activities:** Membership Meeting (Annual). **Geographic Preference:** Local.

42584 ■ Greater East Aurora Chamber of Commerce (GEACC)
652 Main St.
East Aurora, NY 14052
Ph: (716)652-8444
Co. E-mail: eanycc@verizon.net
URL: http://www.eanycc.com
Contact: Gary D. Grote, Executive Director
E-mail: ggrote@eanycc.com
Facebook: www.facebook.com/EastAuroraChamber
YouTube: www.youtube.com/user/GreaterEastAuroraTV
Description: Promotes business and community development in the East Aurora, NY area. Sponsors area events, including: Roycroft Festival of Arts and Crafts; Toyfest; Business Expo. **Founded:** 1945. **Publications:** *The Chamber* (Annual). **Geographic Preference:** Local.

42585 ■ Greater Gouverneur Chamber of Commerce
53 Herm Towne Rd.
Gouverneur, NY 13642
Ph: (315)287-0331
Fax: (315)287-4926
URL: http://www.gouverneurchamber.net
Contact: Tim Reddick, President
Facebook: www.facebook.com/governeurchamber
Description: Promotes business and community development in Gouverneur, NY. Sponsors flea market, farmer's market, and other social and promotional events. **Founded:** 1908. **Geographic Preference:** Local.

42586 ■ Greater Greenwich Chamber of Commerce (GGCC)
6 Academy St.
Greenwich, NY 12834
Ph: (518)692-7979
Co. E-mail: info@greenwichchamber.org
URL: http://www.greenwichchamber.org
Contact: Liv Thygesen, President
E-mail: livathin@yahoo.com
Facebook: www.facebook.com/GreenwichChamber
Linkedin: www.linkedin.com/company/greenwichnychamber
X (Twitter): x.com/ggreenwichcc
Instagram: www.instagram.com/greenwichnychamber
Description: Promotes business and community development in Greenwich, NY. **Founded:** 1990. **Geographic Preference:** Local.

42587 ■ Greater Harlem Chamber of Commerce (GHCC)
200a W 136th St.
New York, NY 10030
Ph: (212)862-7200
Co. E-mail: ecausey@harlemdiscover.com
URL: http://www.greaterharlemchamber.com
Contact: Lloyd A. Williams, President
E-mail: lwilliams@harlemdiscover.com
Description: Promotes business and community development in the Greater Harlem, NY area. **Founded:** 1896. **Geographic Preference:** Local.

42588 ■ Greater Liverpool Chamber of Commerce (GLC)
314 2nd St.
Liverpool, NY 13088
Ph: (315)457-3895
Co. E-mail: chamber@liverpoolchamber.com
URL: http://liverpoolchamber.com
Contact: Lucretia Hudzinski, Executive Director
E-mail: chamber@liverpoolchamber.com
Description: Promotes business and community development in the Liverpool, NY area. **Founded:** 1927. **Geographic Preference:** Local.

42589 ■ Greater Mahopac-Carmel Chamber of Commerce
692 Rte. 6
Mahopac, NY 10541
Ph: (845)628-5553
Co. E-mail: info@mahopaccarmelchamber.com
URL: http://www.mahopaccarmelchamber.com
Contact: Christine Picone, Chairman
Facebook: www.facebook.com/mahopaccarmelchamber
Instagram: www.instagram.com/gmccc10541
YouTube: www.youtube.com/user/mahopaccarmelonline

42590 ■ Greater Massena Chamber of Commerce
16 Church St.
Massena, NY 13662
Ph: (315)769-3525
Co. E-mail: info@massenachamber.com
URL: http://www.massenachamber.com
Contact: Eowyn Hewey, President
Facebook: www.facebook.com/massenachamber

Description: Promotes business and community development in Massena, NY. Holds monthly board meeting. **Founded:** 1931. **Geographic Preference:** Local.

42591 ■ Greater New York Chamber of Commerce (GNYCC)
20 W 44th St., 4 Fl.
New York, NY 10036
Ph: (212)686-7220
Co. E-mail: info@chamber.nyc
URL: http://chamber.nyc
Contact: Mark Jaffe, President
Facebook: www.facebook.com/NYChamber
Linkedin: www.linkedin.com/company/greater-new-york-chamber-of-commerce
X (Twitter): x.com/nychamber
Instagram: www.instagram.com/nychamber

Description: Seeks to promote business and community development and enhance the relationship between local businesses and professionals with the public. **Geographic Preference:** Local.

42592 ■ Greater Newark Chamber of Commerce
199 Van Buren St.
Newark, NY 14513
Ph: (315)331-2705
Co. E-mail: support@newarknychamber.org
URL: http://newarknychamber.org
Contact: Steven Hasseler, President (Acting)
Facebook: www.facebook.com/Newarknychamberofcommerce

Description: Represents business and community to further the interests of business within the community. Acts as a clearinghouse of business and community information; interacts with government; sponsors community events; and works with economic development. **Founded:** 1924. **Publications:** *Clubs and Organizations List* (10/year); *Community Profile*; *Industry List* (Annual). **Geographic Preference:** Local.

42593 ■ Greater North Syracuse Chamber of Commerce
201 S Main St.
North Syracuse, NY 13212
Ph: (315)458-4181
Co. E-mail: info@plankroadchamber.com
URL: http://www.plankroadchamber.com

Description: Seeks to promote business and community development and enhance the relationship between local businesses and professionals with the public. **Geographic Preference:** Local.

42594 ■ Greater Ogdensburg Chamber of Commerce
318 Ford St.
Ogdensburg, NY 13669
Ph: (315)393-3620
Co. E-mail: info@ogdensburgny.com
URL: http://ogdensburgny.com
Contact: Laura Pearson, Contact
Facebook: www.facebook.com/ogdensburgny

Description: Seeks to promote business and community development and enhance the relationship between local businesses and professionals with the public. **Geographic Preference:** Local.

42595 ■ Greater Olean Area Chamber of Commerce (GOACC)
301 N Union St.
Olean, NY 14760
Ph: (716)372-4433
Fax: (716)372-7912
Co. E-mail: info@oleanny.com
URL: http://oleanny.com
Contact: Jason Crisafulli, President

Description: Provide business and community development assistance, regional tourism information, and membership benefits. **Founded:** 1906. **Publications:** *Community Economic Profile*; *Greater Olean Area Chamber of Commerce Member's Directory*. **Geographic Preference:** Local.

42596 ■ Greater Oneida Chamber of Commerce
136 Lenox Ave.
Oneida, NY 13421
Ph: (315)363-4300
Co. E-mail: office@oneidachamberny.org
URL: http://www.oneidachamberny.org/page/page/8868157.htm
Contact: Rachel Siderine, President
Facebook: www.facebook.com/oneidachamber

Description: Promotes business and community development in Oneida, NY area. **Founded:** 1893. **Geographic Preference:** Local.

42597 ■ Greater Ossining Chamber of Commerce
109 Croton Ave., Ste. 250
Ossining, NY 10562
Ph: (914)941-0009
Fax: (914)941-0812
Co. E-mail: info@ossiningchamber.org
URL: http://www.ossiningchamber.org
Contact: Dr. Gayle Marchica, President
Facebook: www.facebook.com/ossiningchamber
X (Twitter): x.com/OssiningChamber

Description: Promotes business and community development in the Ossining, NY area. Sponsors village fair and holiday activities, business expos, and educational programs. Produces monthly television show. **Founded:** 1945. **Publications:** *Chamber Letter* (Bimonthly). **Geographic Preference:** Local.

42598 ■ Greater Oswego-Fulton Chamber of Commerce (GOFCC)
121 E First St.
Oswego, NY 13126
Ph: (315)343-7681
Fax: (315)342-0831
URL: http://www.oswegofultonchamber.com
Contact: Katie Toomey, Executive Director
E-mail: ktoomey@oswegofultonchamber.com
Facebook: www.facebook.com/GOFCC
Linkedin: www.linkedin.com/company/greater-oswego-fulton-chamber-of-commerce
X (Twitter): x.com/GOFCC

Description: Promotes business and community development in the Oswego, NY area. **Founded:** 1915. **Publications:** *Greater Oswego-Fulton Business Directory* (Annual). **Geographic Preference:** Local.

42599 ■ Greater Patchogue Chamber of Commerce
15 N Ocean Ave.
Patchogue, NY 11772
Ph: (631)207-1000
Fax: (631)475-1599
Co. E-mail: info@patchogue.com
URL: http://patchogue.com
Contact: Dawn Turnbull, President
Facebook: www.facebook.com/patchoguechamber
Linkedin: www.linkedin.com/company/greater-patchogue-chamber-of-commerce-inc-
X (Twitter): x.com/Patchogue
Instagram: www.instagram.com/patchoguechamber

Description: Promotes business and community development in the Patchogue, NY area. Provides transportation, lodging, and recreation information for the Suffolk county and surrounding area. **Founded:** 1923. **Publications:** *Patchogue Chamber Business Letter* (Monthly). **Geographic Preference:** Local.

42600 ■ Greater Port Jefferson Chamber of Commerce
118 W Broadway
Port Jefferson, NY 11777
Ph: (631)473-1414
Fax: (631)474-4540
Co. E-mail: info@portjeffchamber.com
URL: http://portjeffchamber.com
Contact: Mary Joy Pipe, President
Facebook: www.facebook.com/PortJeffChamber
X (Twitter): x.com/PortJeffChamber
Instagram: www.instagram.com/portjeffchamber
YouTube: www.youtube.com/channel/UCDJdYyirmRwtN3B_Dk_400Q

Description: Promotes business and community development in the Port Jefferson, NY area. **Geographic Preference:** Local.

42601 ■ Greater Rochester Chamber of Commerce, Women's Council
c/o Greater Rochester Chamber of Commerce
150 State St., Ste. 400
Rochester, NY 14614
Ph: (585)256-4665
Co. E-mail: cassidy.franklin@greaterrochesterchamber.com
URL: http://rocwomenscouncil.org
Contact: Kate Pellett, President
Facebook: www.facebook.com/weare4women
X (Twitter): x.com/weare4women

Description: Enhances the opportunities and knowledge of business and professional women in the civic, commercial, cultural and educational interests of the Greater Rochester Area. **Founded:** 1932. **Awards:** Rochester Business Alliance, Women's Council - The ATHENA Award(r) (Annual); Rochester Business Alliance, Women's Council - Young Women of Distinction Award (Annual). **Geographic Preference:** Local.

42602 ■ Greater Seaford Chamber of Commerce
PO Box 1634
Seaford, NY 11783
Ph: (516)330-7404
URL: http://www.seafordchamberofcommerce.com
Contact: Margaret Grub, President

Description: Promotes the economic health of the Seaford area and contributes to the civic, economic, and social welfare of the people in the surrounding communities. **Founded:** 1925. **Publications:** *Take Five* (Bimonthly). **Awards:** GSCC Businessperson of the Year (Annual). **Geographic Preference:** Local.

42603 ■ Greater Sleepy Hollow Tarrytown Chamber of Commerce
1 Neperan Rd.
Tarrytown, NY 10591
Co. E-mail: info@sleepyhollowchamber.com
URL: http://www.sleepyhollowtarrytownchamber.com
Contact: Laura Rey Iannarelli, President
URL(s): greatersleepyhollowtarrytown.com
Facebook: www.facebook.com/SleepyHollowTarrytownChamberOfCommerce
Instagram: www.instagram.com/sleepyhollowtarrytownchamber

Description: Promotes business and community development in Tarrytown and North Tarrytown, NY. Provides tour information. Holds monthly board of directors meeting. **Founded:** 1927. **Publications:** *The Chamber Room* (Monthly). **Geographic Preference:** Local.

42604 ■ Greater Smithtown Chamber of Commerce
79 E Main St., Ste. E
Smithtown, NY 11787
Ph: (631)979-8069
Fax: (631)979-2206
URL: http://smithtownchamber.com
Contact: Ayman Awad, President
Facebook: www.facebook.com/smithtownchamber

Description: Promotes business and community development in Smithtown, NY area. **Geographic Preference:** Local.

42605 ■ Greater Utica Chamber of Commerce
520 Seneca St., Ste. 102
Utica, NY 13502
Ph: (315)724-3151
Co. E-mail: info@greateruticachamber.org
URL: http://greateruticachamber.org
Contact: Kari Puleo, Executive Director
E-mail: kpuleo@greateruticachamber.org
Facebook: www.facebook.com/greaterutica315
Instagram: www.instagram.com/uticachamber
Description: Promotes business and community development in Utica, NY. **Founded:** 1896. **Publications:** *Almanac* (Annual); *Chamber Action* (Monthly). **Geographic Preference:** Local.

42606 ■ Greater Warsaw Chamber of Commerce
104 W Buffalo St.
Warsaw, NY 14569
Free: 855-492-7729
Co. E-mail: info@warsawchamber.com
URL: http://warsawchamber.com
Contact: Brenda Kelly, President
Facebook: www.facebook.com/
 WarsawChamberOfCommerce
Instagram: www.instagram.com/
 warsawchamberofcommerce
YouTube: www.youtube.com/user/Grea
 terWarsawChamber
Description: Promotes business and community development in Warsaw, NY. **Geographic Preference:** Local.

42607 ■ Greater Watertown - North Country Chamber of Commerce (GWNC)
1241 Coffeen St.
Watertown, NY 13601
Ph: (315)788-4400
Fax: (315)788-3369
Co. E-mail: chamber@watertownny.com
URL: http://www.watertownny.com
Facebook: www.facebook.com/gwncchamber
Linkedin: www.linkedin.com/company/gwnc-chamber
 -of-commerce
Instagram: www.instagram.com/gwncchamber
Description: Promotes business, community development, and tourism in the Jefferson County, NY area. **Founded:** 1903. **Publications:** *Business Directory/Buyer's Guide*; *Clubs and Organization Listings* (Annual); *Community Audit* (Periodic); *News and Views* (Monthly). **Geographic Preference:** Local.

42608 ■ Greater Westhampton Chamber of Commerce
7 Glovers Ln.
Westhampton Beach, NY 11978
Ph: (631)288-3337
Fax: (631)288-3322
Co. E-mail: info@whbcc.org
URL: http://www.westhamptonchamber.org
Contact: Marlene Brill, President
Facebook: www.facebook.com/gwhcc11978
Instagram: www.instagram.com/westhamp
 tonchamberofcommerce
Description: Organized for the purpose of advancing business relations in the communities of Westhampton, Westhampton Beach, Quiogue, Quogue, East Quogue and Remsenburg-Speonk. Works to improve business within this area, as well as the general economic and cultural welfare of the community. **Founded:** 1948. **Geographic Preference:** Local.

42609 ■ Greene County Chamber of Commerce (GCCC)
327 Main St.
Catskill, NY 12414
Ph: (518)943-4222
Co. E-mail: info@greenecountychamber.com
URL: http://www.greatnortherncatskillschamber.com
Facebook: www.facebook.com/Greene-County
 -Chamber-of-Commerce-403765606384168

Description: Promotes business and community development in Catskill, NY. **Founded:** 1998. **Publications:** *Chamber News* (Monthly). **Awards:** Greene County Business Woman of the Year (Annual); Greene County Business Man of the Year (Annual). **Geographic Preference:** Local.

42610 ■ Greenvale Chamber of Commerce Inc.
PO Box 123
Greenvale, NY 11548-0123
Ph: (516)621-2110
URL: http://www.uschamber.com/co/chambers/new
 -york/greenvale
Description: Promotes business and community development in Greenvale, NY. **Geographic Preference:** Local.

42611 ■ Greenwich Village-Chelsea Chamber of Commerce (GVCCC)
PO Box 1116
New York, NY 10013
Ph: (646)470-1773
Co. E-mail: info@villagechelsea.com
URL: http://www.villagechelsea.com
Contact: Maria Diaz, Executive Director
Facebook: www.facebook.com/GVCCHAMBER
Linkedin: www.linkedin.com/company/gvcchamber
X (Twitter): x.com/GVCChamber
YouTube: www.youtube.com/channel/UCCwzWsFM7
 6KgsPx8tPcd4tg
Description: Promotes business and community development in Greenwich Village-Chelsea, NY. **Founded:** 1949. **Geographic Preference:** Local.

42612 ■ *Guide to Government*
1 Civic Center Plz., Ste. 400
Poughkeepsie, NY 12601
Ph: (845)454-1700
Fax: (845)454-1702
Co. E-mail: office@dcrcoc.org
URL: http://www.dcrcoc.org
Contact: Gregory White, Chairperson
URL(s): www.dcrcoc.org/government-guide
Availability: Print.

42613 ■ Guilderland Chamber of Commerce (GCC)
Star Plz., No. 201
 2050 W Ave.
Guilderland, NY 12084
Ph: (518)456-6611
Fax: (518)456-6690
Co. E-mail: info@guilderlandchamber.com
URL: http://guilderlandchamber.com
Contact: Danielle Walsh, Executive Director
E-mail: dwalsh@guilderlandchamber.com
Facebook: www.facebook.com/Guilderlan
 dChamberofCommerce
Description: Promotes business and community development in the Guilderland, NY area. Conducts educational programs and seminars. Conducts community programs and special events. **Founded:** 1972. **Publications:** *Community & Business Directory*; *Business Line*. **Geographic Preference:** Local.

42614 ■ Hampton Bays Chamber of Commerce (HBCC)
PO Box 632
Hampton Bays, NY 11946
Ph: (631)728-2211
Co. E-mail: info@hamptonbayschamber.com
URL: http://hamptonbayschamber.com
Contact: Christine Taylor, President
X (Twitter): x.com/HBayChamber
Instagram: www.instagram.com/Hamp
 tonBaysChamber
Description: Promotes business and community development in Hampton Bays, NY. **Founded:** 1972. **Geographic Preference:** Local.

42615 ■ Hicksville Chamber of Commerce (HCC)
PO Box 7
Hicksville, NY 11802
Co. E-mail: hicksvillechamberoc@gmail.com
URL: http://www.hicksvillechamber.com

Contact: Charles Razenson, President
Description: Promotes business and community development in Hicksville, NY. **Founded:** 1926. **Educational Activities:** Hicksville Chamber of Commerce Meeting (Monthly). **Awards:** Hicksville Chamber Citizen of the Year (Annual). **Geographic Preference:** Local.

42616 ■ Hudson Valley Gateway Chamber of Commerce
1 S Division St.
Peekskill, NY 10566
Ph: (914)737-3600
Fax: (914)737-0541
Co. E-mail: info@hvgatewaychamber.com
URL: http://www.hvgatewaychamber.com
Contact: Baked Susan, Co-President
Facebook: www.facebook.com/hvgatewaychamber
Linkedin: www.linkedin.com/company/hudson-valley
 -gateway-chamber-of-commerce
YouTube: www.youtube.com/user/
 HVGChamberofCommerce
Description: Promotes business and community development in the Peekskill and Cortlandt, NY area. **Founded:** 1915. **Publications:** *The Chamber Report* (Quarterly). **Geographic Preference:** Local.

42617 ■ Huntington Township Chamber of Commerce (HTCC)
164 Main St.
Huntington, NY 11743
Ph: (631)423-6100
Fax: (631)351-8276
Co. E-mail: info@huntingtonchamber.com
URL: http://www.huntingtonchamber.com
Contact: Merrill Zorn, President
Facebook: www.facebook.com/Hunting
 tonChamberNY
X (Twitter): x.com/huntingtonbiz
Instagram: www.instagram.com/hunting
 tonchamberny
Description: Promotes business and community development in Huntington, NY. **Founded:** 1925. **Geographic Preference:** Local.

42618 ■ Hyde Park Chamber of Commerce
4389 Albany Post Rd.
Hyde Park, NY 12538
Ph: (845)229-8612
Co. E-mail: info@hydeparkchamber.online
URL: http://www.hydeparkchamber.online
Contact: Dot Chenevert, President
Facebook: www.facebook.com/hydeparkchamber17
Description: Promotes business and community development in Hyde Park, NY. Sponsors annual Easter Egg Hunt and Halloween Parade. **Geographic Preference:** Local.

42619 ■ Inlet Information Office
160 Rte. 28 Arrowhead Pk.
Inlet, NY 13360
Ph: (315)357-5501
Co. E-mail: info@inletny.com
URL: http://www.inletny.com
Facebook: www.facebook.com/inletny
X (Twitter): x.com/inletny
Instagram: www.instagram.com/inletny
Description: Promotes business and community development in Inlet, NY. Sponsors events that draw tourism to the area. Works on economic development issues. Seeks to find a balance between economic development and preservation of the natural surroundings. **Publications:** *Inlet Lamplighter* (Quarterly); *Vacation Planner* (Annual). **Geographic Preference:** Local.

42620 ■ Islip Chamber of Commerce
PO Box 112
Islip, NY 11751
Ph: (631)581-2720
Co. E-mail: info@islipchamberofcommerce.org
URL: http://islipchamberofcommerce.org
Contact: Liz Mayott, President
E-mail: president@islipchamberofcommerce.org
Facebook: www.facebook.com/
 islipchamberofcommerce
X (Twitter): x.com/islipchamber

Instagram: www.instagram.com/islipchamber
Description: Promotes business and economic development in Islip, NY. **Founded:** 1923. **Geographic Preference:** Local.

42621 ■ Kenmore-Town of Tonawanda Chamber of Commerce (KTCC)
3411 Delaware Ave., Ste. 206
Kenmore, NY 14217
Ph: (716)874-1202
Co. E-mail: info@ken-ton.org
URL: http://kentonchamber.org
Contact: Cathy Piciulo, President
Facebook: www.facebook.com/KenTonChamberofCommerce
Linkedin: www.linkedin.com/company/kenmore-town-of-tonawanda-chamber-of-commerce
X (Twitter): x.com/KenTonChamber
Description: Promotes business and community development in the Kenmore/Tonawanda, NY area. **Founded:** 1972. **Geographic Preference:** Local.

42622 ■ Kings Park Chamber of Commerce
PO Box 322
Kings Park, NY 11754
Ph: (631)269-7678
Fax: (631)656-0024
Co. E-mail: info@kingsparkli.com
URL: http://kingsparkli.com
Contact: Tony Tanzi, President
Facebook: www.facebook.com/Kings-Park-Chamber-of-Commerce-545479342201142
Description: Promotes business and community development in Kings Park, NY. **Geographic Preference:** Local.

42623 ■ Lackawanna Area Chamber of Commerce
609 Ridge Rd.
Lackawanna, NY 14218
Description: Promotes business and community development in the Lackawanna, NY area. **Geographic Preference:** Local.

42624 ■ Lake George Regional Chamber of Commerce & CVB
2176 U. S. 9
Lake George, NY 12845
Ph: (518)668-5755
Co. E-mail: info@lakegeorgechamber.com
URL: http://www.lakegeorgechamber.com
Contact: Dennis LaFontaine, President
Facebook: www.facebook.com/VisitLakeGeorge
Linkedin: www.linkedin.com/company/lake-george-regional-chamber-of-commerce-&-cvb
X (Twitter): x.com/visitlakegeorge
YouTube: www.youtube.com/channel/UCIBJIw9Kk2pCRi2XM-2D2Cw
Pinterest: www.pinterest.com/visitlakegeorge
Description: Promotes business, community development, and tourism in Lake George, NY. **Founded:** 1950. **Publications:** Good News Travel Fast (Monthly). **Geographic Preference:** Local.

42625 ■ Lancaster Area Chamber of Commerce (LACC)
11 W Main St., Ste. 100
Lancaster, NY 14086
URL: http://www.wnychamber.com
Description: Promotes business and community development in Depew, Elma, and Lancaster, NY. **Founded:** 1987. **Geographic Preference:** Local.

42626 ■ Lewis County Chamber of Commerce
7551 S St. ate St.
Lowville, NY 13367
Ph: (315)376-2213
Co. E-mail: info@lewiscountychamber.org
URL: http://adirondackstughill.com
Facebook: www.facebook.com/lewiscountychamberofcommerce
X (Twitter): x.com/LewisCoChamber
Description: Promotes business and community development in Lewis County, NY. Promotes tourism. **Founded:** 1945. **Geographic Preference:** Local.

42627 ■ Livingston County Chamber of Commerce
4635 Millennium Dr.
Geneseo, NY 14454
Ph: (585)243-2222
Fax: (585)243-4824
Co. E-mail: laura@livingstoncountychamber.com
URL: http://www.livingstoncountychamber.com
Contact: Dawn Aprile, Chairman
Facebook: www.facebook.com/LivingstonCountyChamber
Linkedin: www.linkedin.com/company/livingston-county-area-chamber-of-commerce
X (Twitter): x.com/ChamberLivCty
Instagram: www.instagram.com/in_livingstoncountyny
Description: Promotes business and community development in Livingston County, NY. **Founded:** 1970. **Publications:** Chamber Community (Semiannual); The Chambergram (Monthly); Livingston County Travel Guide (Annual). **Educational Activities:** Chamber Holiday After Hours & Annual Meeting (Annual). **Geographic Preference:** Local.

42628 ■ Long Beach Chamber of Commerce (LBCC)
350 National Blvd.
Long Beach, NY 11561
Ph: (516)432-6000
Co. E-mail: info@thelongbeachchamber.com
URL: http://thelongbeachchamber.com
Contact: Ian Danby, Treasurer
Facebook: www.facebook.com/LongBeachNYChamberOfCommerce
Description: Promotes business and community development in Long Beach, NY. Sponsors art and crafts festival in July and August. **Founded:** 1880. **Geographic Preference:** Local.

42629 ■ Long Island Association (LIA)
300 Broadhollow Rd., Ste. 110W
Melville, NY 11747
Ph: (631)493-3000
Fax: (631)499-2194
Co. E-mail: info@longislandassociation.org
URL: http://www.longislandassociation.org
Contact: Matt Cohen, President
E-mail: mcohen@longislandassociation.org
Facebook: www.facebook.com/LIAssociation
Linkedin: www.linkedin.com/company/the-long-island-association
X (Twitter): x.com/LongIslandAssoc
Instagram: www.instagram.com/longislandassoc
YouTube: www.youtube.com/channel/UCzzNUdB5OTxvwnIaANQ_Jfg
Description: Seeks to create and retain balanced economic opportunities and jobs in a clean, healthy, and safe environment. **Founded:** 1926. **Publications:** Long Island: Reflections on a Miracle (Monthly). **Geographic Preference:** Regional.

42630 ■ Malone Chamber of Commerce (MCC)
497 E Main St.
Malone, NY 12953
Ph: (518)483-3760
Co. E-mail: director@malonechamberofcommerce.com
URL: http://www.malonechamberofcommerce.com
Contact: Mary Scharf, President
Facebook: www.facebook.com/malonechamberofcommerce
Description: Promotes business and community development in the Malone, NY area. Conducts annual Winter Carnival and annual Spring Festival. **Founded:** 1956. **Publications:** Business Directory. **Geographic Preference:** Local.

42631 ■ Manhasset Chamber of Commerce (MCC)
PO Box 754
Manhasset, NY 11030
Co. E-mail: manhassetcoc@gmail.com
URL: http://www.manhassetchamber.com
Contact: Matthew Donno, President
E-mail: mdonno84@gmail.com
Facebook: www.facebook.com/manhassetchamber
Instagram: www.instagram.com/manhassetchamber
Description: Promotes business and community development in Manhasset, NY. **Founded:** 1935. **Geographic Preference:** Local.

42632 ■ Manhattan Chamber of Commerce (MCC)
12 E 49th St., 11th Fl.
New York, NY 10017
Ph: (212)473-7875
Fax: (212)473-8074
Co. E-mail: info@manhattancc.org
URL: http://www.manhattancc.org/common/11099/default.cfm?clientID=11099&ThisPage=home
Contact: Jessica Walker, President
Facebook: www.facebook.com/ManhattanChamberofCommerce
Linkedin: www.linkedin.com/company/manhattan-chamber-of-commerce
X (Twitter): x.com/manhattancofc
Instagram: www.instagram.com/manhattanchamberofcommerce
YouTube: www.youtube.com/channel/UC2Sf7Jv_kKtT7939HsVbgRg
Description: Promotes business and community development in Manhattan, NY. Sponsors festivals. **Founded:** 1920. **Publications:** Enterprise (Quarterly). **Geographic Preference:** Local.

42633 ■ Massapequa Chamber of Commerce
675 Broadway
Massapequa, NY 11758
Ph: (516)541-1443
Co. E-mail: info@massapequachamber.org
URL: http://massapequachamber.org
Contact: Keith Wilson, President
Description: Promotes business and community development in Massapequa, North Massapequa, and Massapequa Park, NY. **Founded:** 1948. **Publications:** Business Directory; Meeting Notice. **Geographic Preference:** Local.

42634 ■ Mattituck Chamber of Commerce
PO Box 1056
Mattituck, NY 11952
Co. E-mail: info@mattituckchamber.org
URL: http://www.mattituckchamber.org
Contact: William Wickham, Contact
Facebook: www.facebook.com/Mattituckchamber
Instagram: www.instagram.com/mattituck_chamber
Description: Promotes business and community development in the Mattituck and North Fork, NY area. **Founded:** 1961. **Geographic Preference:** Local.

42635 ■ Mayville - Chautauqua Area Chamber of Commerce
300 N Main St.
Jamestown, NY 14701
Ph: (716)366-6200
Co. E-mail: swebster@chautauquachamber.org
URL: http://www.chautauquachamber.org/mayville-chautauqua.html
Contact: Daniel Heitzenrater, President
E-mail: dheitzenrater@chautauquachamber.org
Facebook: www.facebook.com/MayvilleChautauquaChamber
Description: Promotes the area as a desirable place to live, conduct business and visit. **Geographic Preference:** Local.

42636 ■ *Members Buyer's Guide*
7061 Rte. 9
Plattsburgh, NY 12901
Ph: (518)563-1000
Fax: (518)563-1028
Co. E-mail: info@northcountrychamber.com
URL: http://northcountrychamber.com
Contact: Garry Douglas, President
E-mail: garry@northcountrychamber.com
URL(s): www.northcountrychamber.com/Chamber/Advertising-Opportunities
Released: Annual **Availability:** Print.

42637 ■ Mineola Chamber of Commerce
PO Box 62
Mineola, NY 11501

STATE LISTINGS

Ph: (516)319-4465
URL: http://www.mineolachamber.com
Contact: Louis Panacciulli, President
Instagram: www.instagram.com/mineolachamber
Description: Promotes business and community development in Mineola, NY. **Founded:** 1858. **Geographic Preference:** Local.

42638 ■ Mount Kisco Chamber of Commerce (MKCC)
3 N Moger Ave.
Mount Kisco, NY 10549
Ph: (914)666-7525
Co. E-mail: director@mtkiscochamber.com
URL: http://www.mtkiscochamber.com
Contact: Matt Grasso, President
Facebook: www.facebook.com/MountKiscoChamber
X (Twitter): x.com/MtKiscoChamber
Description: Promotes business and community development in Mt. Kisco, NY. Sponsors Sidewalk Sales Days and holiday programs. Issues publications. **Founded:** 1965. **Publications:** *Mt. Kisco Lifestyles* (Annual). **Awards:** Mount Kisco Chamber of Commerce Citizen of the Year (Annual). **Geographic Preference:** Local.

42639 ■ New Hartford Chamber of Commerce
PO Box 372
New Hartford, NY 13413
Ph: (315)796-1520
Co. E-mail: info@newhartfordchamber.com
URL: http://newhartfordchamber.com
Facebook: www.facebook.com/NewHartfordChamber
Linkedin: www.linkedin.com/company/newhartfordchamberofcommerce
Description: Promotes business and community development in New Hartford, NY. **Founded:** 1972. **Geographic Preference:** Local.

42640 ■ New Rochelle Chamber of Commerce (NRCC)
417 N Ave.
New Rochelle, NY 10801
Ph: (914)632-5700
Fax: (914)632-0708
Co. E-mail: info@newrochamber.org
URL: http://newrochellechamber.org
Contact: Robert Hayes, President
Facebook: www.facebook.com/newrochellechamber
Linkedin: www.linkedin.com/company/new-rochelle-chamber-of-commerce
X (Twitter): x.com/newrochamber
Instagram: www.instagram.com/newrochamber
Description: Promotes business and community development in New Rochelle, NY. Sponsors spring and fall festival, annual Thanksgiving Parade, and annual haunted house. **Founded:** 1922. **Publications:** *New Rochelle Chamber of Commerce--Business Directory* (Annual); *Chambernews* (Monthly). **Geographic Preference:** Local.

42641 ■ Newcomb Chamber of Commerce
5639 NY-28N
Newcomb, NY 12852
URL: http://www.adirondack.org/chamberlist
Description: Promotes business and community development in Newcomb, NY. **Founded:** 1828. **Geographic Preference:** Local.

42642 ■ Niagara USA Chamber
6311 Inducon Corporate Dr. No. 2
Sanborn, NY 14132
Ph: (716)285-9141
URL: http://niagarachamber.org
Contact: Kory Schuler, Executive Director
Facebook: www.facebook.com/NiagaraUSAChamber
Linkedin: www.linkedin.com/company/niagara-usa-chamber-of-commerce
X (Twitter): x.com/NiagaraUSAChamb
Instagram: www.instagram.com/niagarausachamber
Description: Promotes business and community development in eastern Niagara County, NY. Provides health insurance. Issues publications. **Founded:** 1913. **Publications:** *Commerce Quotes* (Monthly). **Educational Activities:** Community Expo. **Geographic Preference:** Local.

42643 ■ Oceanside Chamber of Commerce
PO Box 1
Oceanside, NY 11572
Ph: (516)763-9177
Co. E-mail: info@oceansidechamber.com
URL: http://www.oceansidechamber.com
Contact: Scott M. Ashton, President
E-mail: scott@oceansidechamber.com
Linkedin: www.linkedin.com/company/oceanside-chamber-of-commerce
X (Twitter): x.com/osidecachamber
YouTube: www.youtube.com/user/OceansideChamber
Description: Promotes business and community development in Oceanside, NY. **Founded:** 1896. **Geographic Preference:** Local.

42644 ■ Orchard Park Chamber of Commerce
6524 E Quaker St.
Orchard Park, NY 14127
Ph: (716)662-3366
Fax: (716)662-5946
Co. E-mail: opcc@orchardparkchamber.org
URL: http://orchardparkchamber.org
Contact: David N. Even, President
Facebook: www.facebook.com/opnychamber
X (Twitter): x.com/OPNYCofC
Instagram: www.instagram.com/explore/locations/342672099/orchard-park-chamber-of-commerce
Description: Develops and encourages the growth and participation of chamber members through actions beneficial to the Orchard Park, NY business community. **Publications:** *Chamber Review* (Monthly). **Geographic Preference:** Local.

42645 ■ Orleans County Chamber of Commerce (OCCC)
PO Box 501
Medina, NY 14103
Ph: (585)301-8464
Co. E-mail: director@orleanschamber.com
URL: http://www.orleanschamber.com
Contact: Paula Knaak, President
E-mail: pknaak@arcoforleans.org
Facebook: www.facebook.com/OrleansCountychamberofcommerce
Description: Seeks to promote business and community development and enhance the relationship between local businesses and professionals with the public. **Founded:** 1997. **Publications:** *Orleans County Chamber of Commerce--Membership Directory*. **Geographic Preference:** Local.

42646 ■ Otsego County Chamber of Commerce
31 Main St., Ste. 2B
Oneonta, NY 13820
Ph: (607)432-4500
Co. E-mail: info@otsegocc.com
URL: http://otsegocc.com
Facebook: www.facebook.com/TheOtsegoCountyChamber
Linkedin: www.linkedin.com/company/otsegocc
Instagram: www.instagram.com/otsegocc
Description: Promotes business, community development, and tourism in Otsego County, NY. **Founded:** 1986. **Publications:** *Otsego County Travel Guide*. **Geographic Preference:** Local.

42647 ■ Partnership for New York City (PFNYC)
1 Battery Pk. Plz., 5th Fl.
New York, NY 10004
Ph: (212)493-7400
Co. E-mail: press@pfnyc.org
URL: http://www.pfnyc.org
Contact: Kathryn S. Wylde, President
Facebook: www.facebook.com/Partnership4NYC
Linkedin: www.linkedin.com/company/partnership-for-new-york-city
X (Twitter): x.com/Partnership4NYC
Instagram: www.instagram.com/partnership4nyc
Description: Promotes business and community development in New York City, NY. Lobbies local, state, and federal government on legislation affecting the city. Provides information and educational programs to members. **Founded:** 1768. **Publications:** *Chamber Report* (3/year). **Geographic Preference:** Local.

42648 ■ Pawling Chamber of Commerce (PCC)
59 Charles Colman Blvd.
Pawling, NY 12564
Ph: (845)855-0500
URL: http://www.pawlingchamber.org
Contact: Diana Tomassetti, President
Facebook: www.facebook.com/PawlingChamber
Description: Promotes Pawling, New York, as a destination for residents and visitors. Seeks to build and maintain a strong local economy. **Geographic Preference:** Local.

42649 ■ Pittsford Chamber of Commerce (PCC)
PO Box 576
Pittsford, NY 14534
Ph: (585)902-2297
Co. E-mail: info@pittsfordchamber.org
URL: http://pittsfordchamber.org
Contact: John Halldow, President
E-mail: roclandbus@gmail.com
Facebook: www.facebook.com/pittsfordnychamberofcommerce
X (Twitter): x.com/pittsfordchambr
Instagram: www.instagram.com/pittsfordchamber
Description: Promotes business and community development in the Pittsford, NY area. **Founded:** 1996. **Publications:** *Chamber*. **Geographic Preference:** Local.

42650 ■ Plattsburgh - North Country Chamber of Commerce
7061 Rte. 9
Plattsburgh, NY 12901
Ph: (518)563-1000
Fax: (518)563-1028
Co. E-mail: info@northcountrychamber.com
URL: http://northcountrychamber.com
Contact: Garry Douglas, President
E-mail: garry@northcountrychamber.com
Facebook: www.facebook.com/NorthCountryChamber
Linkedin: www.linkedin.com/company/north-country-chamber-of-commerce
Instagram: www.instagram.com/ncountrychamber
Description: Promotes business, community development, and tourism in the northeast New York region. **Founded:** 1912. **Publications:** *Chamber Vision* (Monthly); *Members Buyer's Guide* (Annual). **Educational Activities:** NCBC Mixer. **Geographic Preference:** Local.

42651 ■ Potsdam Chamber of Commerce
6 Market St.
Potsdam, NY 13676
Ph: (315)274-9000
Co. E-mail: info@potsdamchamber.com
URL: http://www.potsdamchamber.com
Contact: Robert Bicknell, President
Facebook: www.facebook.com/potsdam.chamber
X (Twitter): x.com/potsdamchamber
Instagram: www.instagram.com/potsdamchamber
Description: Promotes business and community development in Potsdam, NY area. **Publications:** *The Potsdam Pages* (Bimonthly). **Awards:** Potsdam Chamber of Commerce Pride in Potsdam Community Award (Annual). **Geographic Preference:** Local.

42652 ■ Pulaski - Eastern Shore Chamber of Commerce
4917 Jefferson St.
Pulaski, NY 13142
Ph: (315)298-2213
Co. E-mail: pulaskieasternshore@gmail.com
URL: http://www.pulaskieasternshore.com
Contact: Kate Connell, President
Facebook: www.facebook.com/PulaskiChamber

Description: Seeks to promote business and community development and enhance the relationship between local businesses and professionals with the public. **Founded:** 1981. **Geographic Preference:** Local.

42653 ■ Queens Chamber of Commerce
75-20 Astoria Blvd., Ste. 140
Jackson Heights, NY 11372
Ph: (718)898-8500
Co. E-mail: info@queenschamber.org
URL: http://www.queenschamber.org
Contact: Thomas J. Grech, President
E-mail: tgrech@queenschamber.org
Linkedin: www.linkedin.com/company/queens
-chamber-of-commerce
X (Twitter): x.com/queenschamber
YouTube: www.youtube.com/channel/UCq
tgHhwOsxfv-GuqF2WDQog
Description: Aims to foster economic growth and prosperity in Queens, New York, by promoting the interests of business through advocacy, networking, and education. **Founded:** 1911. **Publications:** *Queensborough* (5/year). **Geographic Preference:** Local.

42654 ■ Red Hook Area Chamber of Commerce
7461 S Broadway.
Red Hook, NY 12571
Co. E-mail: info@redhookchamber.org
URL: http://www.redhookchamber.org
Contact: Agatha Bacelar, Executive Director
Instagram: www.instagram.com/rh.chamber
Description: Promotes business and community development in the Red Hook, NY area. **Founded:** 1960. **Publications:** *Hardscrabble News* (Monthly). **Geographic Preference:** Local.

42655 ■ Rensselaer County Regional Chamber of Commerce (RCRCC)
90 4th St., Ste. 200
Troy, NY 12180
Ph: (518)274-7020
Co. E-mail: info@renscochamber.com
URL: http://www.renscochamber.com
Contact: Kate Manley, Co-President
E-mail: kmanley@renscochamber.com
Facebook: www.facebook.com/Renscochamber
Linkedin: www.linkedin.com/company/rensselaer
-county-regional-chamber-of-commerce
X (Twitter): x.com/RenscoChamber
Instagram: www.instagram.com/renscochamber
Description: Promotes business and community development in Rensselaer County Troy, NY area. **Founded:** 1900. **Publications:** *Insight*. **Geographic Preference:** Local.

42656 ■ Rhinebeck Chamber of Commerce
23F E Market St.
Rhinebeck, NY 12572
Ph: (845)876-5904
Co. E-mail: info@rhinebeckchamber.com
URL: http://rhinebeckchamber.com
Contact: David Tellerday, President
Facebook: www.facebook.com/rhinebeck
Instagram: www.instagram.com/rhinebeckchamber
Description: Promotes business and community development in Rhinebeck, NY. **Founded:** 1957. **Geographic Preference:** Local.

42657 ■ Riverhead Chamber of Commerce
125 E Main St.
Riverhead, NY 11901
Ph: (631)727-7600
Co. E-mail: info@riverheadchamber.com
URL: http://www.riverheadchamber.com
Contact: Connie Lassandro, President
Facebook: www.facebook.com/chamberriverhead
Instagram: www.instagram.com/riverheadchamber
YouTube: www.youtube.com/channel/UC3pJoilKzq
tRNrwTkUTVfoQ
Description: Promotes commercial, industrial, civic and general interests of the Township of Riverhead and outlying communities within the Central School District No. 2 and within Suffolk County. **Founded:** 1959. **Publications:** *Passport Magazine* (Annual). **Educational Activities:** Chamber Board of Directors Meetings. **Geographic Preference:** Local.

42658 ■ Rockville Centre Chamber of Commerce (RVCCC)
PO Box 226
Rockville Centre, NY 11571
Co. E-mail: chamberrvc@gmail.com
URL: http://rockvillecentrechamberofcommerce.com
Contact: Lisa Umansky, President
Facebook: www.facebook.com/RVCChamberofCommerce
Instagram: www.instagram.com/rvcchamberofcommerce
Description: Promotes business and community development in Rockville Centre, NY. Sponsors 10-K run, Health Fair, spring and fall festivals, and high school mentoring program. Senior Day. **Founded:** 1906. **Geographic Preference:** Local.

42659 ■ Rome Area Chamber of Commerce
139 W Dominick St.
Rome, NY 13440
Ph: (315)337-1700
Fax: (315)337-1715
Co. E-mail: info@romechamber.com
URL: http://www.romechamber.com
Contact: Kristen Skobla, Co-President
X (Twitter): x.com/RomeNYChamber
YouTube: www.youtube.com/channel/UCc00RICfs
4ias6dXFAnoUjw
Description: Promotes business and community development in the Rome, NY area. **Founded:** 1912. **Geographic Preference:** Local.

42660 ■ Roscoe Chamber of Commerce
PO Box 443
Roscoe, NY 12776
Co. E-mail: roscoeny@yahoo.com
URL: http://www.roscoeny.com
Facebook: www.facebook.com/ROSCOENY
Description: Promotes business and community development in Roscoe, NY. **Founded:** 1950. **Geographic Preference:** Local.

42661 ■ Rye Chamber of Commerce
PO Box 72
Rye, NY 10580
URL: http://www.ryechamberofcommerce.com
Contact: Brian Jackson, President
Facebook: www.facebook.com/shoprye
Instagram: www.instagram.com/ryechamberofcommerce10580
Description: Promotes business and community development in Rye, NY. **Geographic Preference:** Local.

42662 ■ Sag Harbor Chamber of Commerce
PO Box 2810
Sag Harbor, NY 11963
Ph: (631)725-0011
Co. E-mail: info@sagharborchamber.com
URL: http://sagharborchamber.com
Contact: Ellen Dioguardi, President
E-mail: president@sagharborchamber.com
Facebook: www.facebook.com/SagHarborChamberOfCommerce
X (Twitter): x.com/SagHarborCOC
Instagram: www.instagram.com/sagharborchamberofcommerce
Description: Promotes business and community development in the greater Sag Harbor, New York area, including Sag Harbor Village, Noyack, North Haven, and the surrounding area. Promotes local events sponsored and hosted by members as well as local non-profit organizations through published and online events calendar. **Geographic Preference:** Local.

42663 ■ St. James Chamber of Commerce
PO Box 286
Saint James, NY 11780
Ph: (631)584-8510
Co. E-mail: info@stjameschamber.org
URL: http://stjameschamber.org
Contact: Kathleen Weber, President
E-mail: kathleenw@teachersfcu.org
Facebook: www.facebook.com/St.JamesNYChamberOfCommerce
Description: Promotes business and community development in St. James, NY. **Founded:** 1853. **Geographic Preference:** Local.

42664 ■ St. Lawrence County Chamber of Commerce
101 Main St., 1st Fl.
Canton, NY 13617
Free: 877-228-7810
Fax: (315)379-0134
Co. E-mail: info@slcchamber.org
URL: http://www.visitstlc.com
Contact: Nadia Cutler, President
Facebook: www.facebook.com/VisitSTLC
X (Twitter): x.com/visitstlc_ny
Instagram: www.instagram.com/visitstlc
YouTube: www.youtube.com/channel/UCsz
3SeEZjqrcf-psi5X7eEA
Description: Seeks to develop, coordinate and implement plans and programs to further the economic development and tourism in St. Lawrence county and the North Country region. **Founded:** 1965. **Publications:** *St. Lawrence County Chamber Members' Directory*; *Travel Guide*. **Geographic Preference:** Local.

42665 ■ Saranac Lake Area Chamber of Commerce
39 Main St.
Saranac Lake, NY 12983
Ph: (518)891-1990
Co. E-mail: welcome@slareachamber.org
URL: http://www.slareachamber.org
Contact: Danielle Delaini, President
Facebook: www.facebook.com/SLChamber
Instagram: www.instagram.com/saranaclakeareachamber
Description: Promotes business and community development in the Saranac Lake, NY area. Provides sporting events management and tourism information; sponsors concerts. **Founded:** 1921. **Publications:** *Accommodations Directory* (Periodic); *Business Directory*. **Geographic Preference:** Local.

42666 ■ Saratoga County Chamber of Commerce
28 Clinton St.
Saratoga Springs, NY 12866
Ph: (518)584-3255
Co. E-mail: info@saratoga.org
URL: http://www.saratoga.org
Contact: Todd Shimkus, President
E-mail: tshimkus@saratoga.org
Facebook: www.facebook.com/saratoga.chamber
X (Twitter): x.com/SaratogaChamber
Instagram: www.instagram.com/saratogacoun
tychamber
YouTube: www.youtube.com/user/SaratogaTourism
Pinterest: www.pinterest.com/saratogatourism
Description: Promotes business and community development in Saratoga County, NY area. **Founded:** 1918. **Publications:** *Business Connection* (Annual); *Update* (Monthly). **Geographic Preference:** Local.

42667 ■ Schenectady County Chamber Foundation
1473 Erie Blvd.
Schenectady, NY 12305
URL: http://capitalregionchamber.com/schenectady
-county-chamber-foundation
Description: Seeks to promote business and community development and enhance the relationship between local businesses and professionals with the public. **Geographic Preference:** Local.

42668 ■ Schoharie County Chamber of Commerce (SCCC)
256 Main St.
Schoharie, NY 12157
Ph: (518)295-8824
Fax: (518)295-8826
Co. E-mail: info@schohariechamber.com
URL: http://schohariechamber.com
Contact: Ron Ketelsen, President

Facebook: www.facebook.com/SchoCoChamber
Instagram: www.instagram.com/schocochamber
Description: Seeks to promote business and community development and enhance the relationship between local businesses and professionals with the public. **Founded:** 1989. **Geographic Preference:** Local.

42669 ■ Schroon Lake Chamber of Commerce
1075 US Rte. 9
Schroon Lake, NY 12870
Ph: (518)532-7675
Co. E-mail: chamber@schroonlakechamber.org
URL: http://www.schroonlakechamber.org
Contact: Darren Woods, President
Description: Promotes business and community development in the Schroon Lake, NY area. **Founded:** 1915. **Publications:** *Business Directory*. **Educational Activities:** General Meeting (Monthly). **Geographic Preference:** Local.

42670 ■ Seneca County Chamber of Commerce
One W Main St.
Waterloo, NY 13165
Ph: (315)568-2906
Co. E-mail: info@senecachamber.org
URL: http://www.discoverseneca.com/seneca-chamber
Contact: Jeff Shipley, President
E-mail: jshipley@senecachamber.org
Description: Seeks to promote business and community development and enhance the relationship between local businesses and professionals with the public. **Founded:** 1968. **Awards:** Seneca County Chamber Small Business of the Year (Annual). **Geographic Preference:** Local.

42671 ■ Seneca Salamanca Chamber of Commerce
734 Broad St., Ste. 103
Salamanca, NY 14779
Ph: (716)945-2034
Co. E-mail: info@salamancachamber.org
URL: http://salamancachamber.org
Contact: Steve Scott, Contact
E-mail: stephen.scott@sni.org
Description: Promotes business and community development in the Salamanca, NY area. Maintains Visitors Welcome Center in office and at Interstate 86. Organize member networking events, community events and festivals, and enrichment opportunities. **Founded:** 1923. **Publications:** *Escape to Historic Salamanca* (Quarterly); *Visitors Guide Directory* (Periodic). **Geographic Preference:** Local.

42672 ■ Skaneateles Area Chamber of Commerce
22 Jordan St.
Skaneateles, NY 13152
Ph: (315)685-0552
Co. E-mail: info@skaneateles.com
URL: http://www.skaneateles.com
Contact: Ellen Kluge, President
Facebook: www.facebook.com/skaneateleschamber
X (Twitter): x.com/skaneatelesny
Instagram: www.instagram.com/skaneateleschamber
Description: Promotes a comprehensive, quality, economic environment in the Skaneateles, NY area with planned growth for continued success of its membership and the community. **Founded:** 1965. **Publications:** *Skaneateles Community Directory* (Annual); *Skaneateles Chamber of Commerce--Community Directory*. **Geographic Preference:** Local.

42673 ■ *Skaneateles Community Directory*
22 Jordan St.
Skaneateles, NY 13152
Ph: (315)685-0552
Co. E-mail: info@skaneateles.com
URL: http://www.skaneateles.com
Contact: Ellen Kluge, President
URL(s): www.skaneateles.com/membership/membership-benefits
Released: Annual **Availability:** Print.

42674 ■ Sodus Town Chamber of Commerce
PO Box 187
Sodus, NY 14551
Ph: (315)576-3818
Co. E-mail: chamber14551@yahoo.com
URL: http://www.sodusny.org
Contact: Jim Hopkins, President
Facebook: www.facebook.com/SodusChamber
Description: Promotes business and community development in Sodus, NY. **Awards:** Sodus, NY Chamber of Commerce Citizen of the Year (Annual); Sodus, NY Chamber of Commerce Scholarship Award (Annual). **Geographic Preference:** Local.

42675 ■ Southampton Chamber of Commerce
76 Main St.
Southampton, NY 11968
Ph: (631)283-0402
Co. E-mail: info@southamptonchamber.com
URL: http://www.southamptonchamber.com
Contact: Besim Cukaj, Executive Director
E-mail: besim0215@yahoo.com
Facebook: www.facebook.com/southampton.chamber
Linkedin: www.linkedin.com/company/southamptonchamberofcommerce
X (Twitter): x.com/southamptoncofc
Instagram: www.instagram.com/southamptonchamberofcommerce
Description: Promotes business, community development, and tourism in Southampton, Long Island, NY. Sponsors annual Arts and Crafts Festival, annual Golf Tournament, Rag-A-Muffin Parade, annual Business Showcase and annual Southampton Country Holiday Promotion. **Founded:** 1950. **Geographic Preference:** Local.

42676 ■ *Southern Ulster County Chamber of Commerce Business Directory*
Contact: Bill Farrell, President
URL(s): www.southernulsterchamber.org
Released: Annual **Price:** Included in membership. **Description:** Covers businesses and local organizations in southern Ulster County, NY. **Availability:** Print; Online.

42677 ■ *Southern Ulster County Chamber of Commerce Newsletter*
Released: Monthly **Price:** Included in membership. **Description:** Features chamber events, information, and advertising. **Availability:** Print.

42678 ■ Southtowns Regional Chamber of Commerce
6122 S Pk. Ave.
Hamburg, NY 14075
Ph: (716)649-7917
Free: 877-322-6890
Fax: (716)649-6362
Co. E-mail: cyndi@southtownsregionalchamber.org
URL: http://www.southtownsregionalchamber.org
Contact: James Eiseman, Member
Facebook: www.facebook.com/WNYSouthtowns
Linkedin: www.linkedin.com/company/hamburg-chamber-of-commerce
X (Twitter): x.com/WNYSouthtowns
Instagram: www.instagram.com/wnysouthtowns
Description: Promotes business and community development in Hamburg, NY. **Founded:** 1927. **Publications:** *The Source* (Periodic); *Southtowns Regional Chamber of Commerce--Membership Directory*. **Educational Activities:** Business After Hours. **Geographic Preference:** Local.

42679 ■ Springville Area Chamber of Commerce
23 N Buffalo St.
Springville, NY 14141
Ph: (716)592-4746
URL: http://springvilleareachamber.com
Facebook: www.facebook.com/Springville-Area-Chamber-of-Commerce-115822715127182
Description: Promotes business and community development in the area. **Founded:** 1872. **Geographic Preference:** Local.

42680 ■ Staten Island Chamber of Commerce (SICC)
2555 Richmond Ave., Ste. 240
Staten Island, NY 10314
Ph: (718)727-1900
Co. E-mail: info@sichamber.com
URL: http://www.sichamber.com
Contact: Dom Provenzano, Manager
E-mail: dprovenzano@sichamber.com
Facebook: www.facebook.com/sichamber
Linkedin: www.linkedin.com/company/1256967/admin
Instagram: www.instagram.com/sichamber
YouTube: www.youtube.com/user/SICHAMBER
Description: Promotes business and community development in Staten Island, NY. **Founded:** 1895. **Awards:** Staten Island Chamber of Commerce Building Awards (Annual); Louis R. Miller Business Leadership Awards (Annual). **Geographic Preference:** Local.

42681 ■ Suffern Chamber of Commerce
PO Box 291
Suffern, NY 10901
Co. E-mail: greatersuffernchamber@gmail.com
URL: http://www.suffernchamber.org
Contact: Martina Cinarli, President
Facebook: www.facebook.com/suffernchamber
Instagram: www.instagram.com/suffernchamber
Description: Represents businesses in Greater Suffern. **Founded:** 1971. **Geographic Preference:** Local.

42682 ■ Sullivan County Chamber of Commerce (SCCC)
196 Bridgeville Rd., Ste. 7
Monticello, NY 12701
Ph: (845)791-4200
Fax: (845)791-4220
Co. E-mail: president@catskills.com
URL: http://www.catskills.com
Contact: Jaime Schmeiser, President
Facebook: www.facebook.com/SullivanCountyChamberofCommerce
X (Twitter): x.com/SullivanChamber
Instagram: www.instagram.com/sullivanchamber
Description: Works to assure economic growth in Sullivan County. **Founded:** 1974. **Geographic Preference:** Local.

42683 ■ Sunnyside Chamber of Commerce (SCC)
PO Box 4129
Sunnyside, NY 11104
Ph: (917)309-8003
Co. E-mail: sunnysidechamberofcommerce@gmail.com
URL: http://www.sunnyside-chamber.org
Facebook: www.facebook.com/sunnysidechamberofcommerce
X (Twitter): x.com/sunny_chamber
Instagram: www.instagram.com/sunnysidechamber
Description: Promotes business and community development in Sunnyside, WA. **Founded:** 1947. **Awards:** Sunnyside Chamber of Commerce Outstanding Agri-Business Person (Annual); Sunnyside Chamber of Commerce Outstanding Business Person (Annual); Sunnyside Chamber of Commerce Outstanding Community Beautification (Annual); Sunnyside Chamber of Commerce Outstanding Educator (Annual); Sunnyside Chamber of Commerce Outstanding Health Care Person (Annual); Sunnyside Chamber of Commerce Outstanding Public Official (Annual); Sunnyside Chamber of Commerce Outstanding Senior Citizen (Annual); Sunnyside Chamber of Commerce Outstanding Youth (Annual). **Geographic Preference:** Local.

42684 ■ Syosset Woodbury Chamber of Commerce
338 Jericho Tpke., Ste. 136
Syosset, NY 11791
Ph: (516)265-4357
Co. E-mail: info@syossetchamber.com
URL: http://www.syossetchamber.com
Contact: Russell Green, President
Facebook: www.facebook.com/syossetchamber

Linkedin: www.linkedin.com/company/syosset-woo
dbury-chamber-of-commerce
X (Twitter): x.com/SyossetChamber
Instagram: www.instagram.com/syossetchamber
Description: Business owners/operators in the towns of Syosset, Woodbury, Jericho, Muttontown, and Oyster Bay Cove promoting town beautification, holiday ceremonies, a picnic and golf outing. **Founded:** 1998. **Geographic Preference:** Local.

42685 ■ Ticonderoga Area Chamber of Commerce (TACC)
94 Montcalm St., Ste. 1
Ticonderoga, NY 12883
Ph: (518)585-6619
Fax: (518)585-9184
Co. E-mail: chamberinfo@ticonderogany.com
URL: http://www.ticonderogany.com
Contact: Matthew Courtright, President
E-mail: mcourtright@ticonderogany.com
Facebook: www.facebook.com/TiconderogaNY
Description: Promotes business and community development in the Ticonderoga, NY area. Operates information center. Sponsors bass tournament and newcomers' reception. **Founded:** 1925. **Publications:** *Calendar of Events*; *Ticonderoga, Crown Point, Hague Business Directory* (Annual). **Geographic Preference:** Local.

42686 ■ Tioga County Chamber of Commerce (TCCC)
1 Sheldon Guile Blvd.
Owego, NY 13827
Ph: (607)687-2020
Co. E-mail: business@tiogachamber.com
URL: http://www.tiogachamber.com
Contact: Sabrina Henriques, President
Description: Promotes business, community development, and tourism in Tioga County, NY. Operates tourist information center. Provides insurance plan. Sponsors seminars. **Founded:** 1969. **Publications:** *Chamber Visions* (Bimonthly). **Educational Activities:** Business Show (Annual). **Geographic Preference:** Local.

42687 ■ *Today's Chamber*
400 E Church St.
Elmira, NY 14901-2803
Ph: (607)734-5137
Fax: (607)734-4490
Co. E-mail: info@chemungchamber.org
URL: http://www.chemungchamber.org
Contact: Jennifer Herrick-McGonigal, President
E-mail: jennifer@chemungchamber.org
URL(s): chemungchamber.org/member-center/
newsletters
Released: Monthly **Description:** Contains information about the association. **Availability:** Print; PDF; Online.

42688 ■ Tompkins County Chamber of Commerce
904 E Shore Dr.
Ithaca, NY 14850
Ph: (607)273-7080
Fax: (607)272-7617
Co. E-mail: info@tompkinschamber.org
URL: http://www.tompkinschamber.org
Contact: Jennifer Tavares, President
E-mail: jtavares@tompkinschamber.org
Facebook: www.facebook.com/Tompkinschamber
X (Twitter): x.com/tompkinschamber
Instagram: www.instagram.com/tompkinschamber
Description: Promotes business and community development in Tompkins County, NY. **Founded:** 1968. **Publications:** *ChamberGram* (Weekly); *Tompkins County Chamber of Commerce--Membership Directory*. **Geographic Preference:** Local.

42689 ■ Town of Hunter Chamber of Commerce
PO Box 177
Hunter, NY 12442
Ph: (518)263-4900
Co. E-mail: chamberinfo@hunterchamber.org
URL: http://www.hunterchamber.org

URL(s): townofhuntergov.com/business/chamber-of
-commerce
Facebook: www.facebook.com/hunterchamber
Instagram: www.instagram.com/hunter.chamber
Description: Promotes business and community development in Hunter, NY. **Publications:** *Resource Guide for the Town of Hunter* (Annual). **Geographic Preference:** Local.

42690 ■ *Travel Guide*
101 Main St., 1st Fl.
Canton, NY 13617
Free: 877-228-7810
Fax: (315)379-0134
Co. E-mail: info@slcchamber.org
URL: http://www.visitstlc.com
Contact: Nadia Cutler, President
URL(s): www.visitstlc.com/membership-benefits
Description: Contains travel information and things to do and see in the county. **Availability:** Print.

42691 ■ Tupper Lake Chamber of Commerce (TLCC)
121 Pk. St.
Tupper Lake, NY 12986
Ph: (518)359-3328
Fax: (518)359-3328
Co. E-mail: contact@tupperlake.com
URL: http://www.tupperlake.com/live/tupper-lake
-chamber-of-commerce
Contact: Dan Mcclelland, Co-President
Description: Organized to promote the commercial, recreational, industrial and civic interests of the village of Tupper Lake, town of Altamont and its membership. **Founded:** 1958. **Publications:** *Chamber Communicator* (Quarterly). **Geographic Preference:** Local.

42692 ■ Ulster County Chamber of Commerce (UCCC)
214 Fair St.
Kingston, NY 12401
Ph: (845)338-5100
Fax: (845)338-0968
Co. E-mail: info@ulsterchamber.org
URL: http://www.ulsterchamber.org
Contact: Ward D. Todd, President
E-mail: ward@ulsterchamber.org
Facebook: www.facebook.com/Ulster.Chamber
X (Twitter): x.com/Ulster_Chamber
YouTube: www.youtube.com/channel/UCcheMqj4v
6AjIR3IOni7UvQ
Description: Promotes agriculture, business and community development in Ulster County, NY. Conducts charitable activities. **Founded:** 1903. **Geographic Preference:** Local.

42693 ■ Ulster County Regional Chamber of Commerce
214 Fair St.
Kingston, NY 12401
Ph: (845)338-5100
Fax: (845)338-0968
Co. E-mail: info@ulsterchamber.org
URL: http://www.ulsterchamber.org
Contact: Ward Todd, President
E-mail: ward@ulsterchamber.org
Facebook: www.facebook.com/Ulster.Chamber
X (Twitter): x.com/Ulster_Chamber
Instagram: www.instagram.com/ulstercoun
tychamberofcommerce
YouTube: www.youtube.com/channel/UCcheMqj4v
6AjIR3IOni7UvQ
Description: Promotes business and community development in Ulster County, NY. **Founded:** 1903. **Geographic Preference:** Local.

42694 ■ Waddington Chamber of Commerce
Waddington, NY
Description: Promotes business and community development in Waddington, NY. **Geographic Preference:** Local.

42695 ■ Warrensburg Chamber of Commerce
3839 Main St., Ste. 2
Warrensburg, NY 12885
Ph: (518)623-2161

Co. E-mail: info@warrensburgchamber.com
URL: http://warrensburgchamber.com
Contact: Suzanne Tyler, Director
E-mail: styler@warrensburgchamber.com
Facebook: www.facebook.com/Warrensburg-Chamber-of-Commerce-109078925832426
X (Twitter): x.com/wcocny
Description: Promotes business, community development, and tourism in the Warrensburg, NY area. **Founded:** 1975. **Publications:** *Four Seasons in the Adirondack Mountains*; *4 Seasons in the Adirondack Mountains*. **Educational Activities:** Chamber Meeting (Quarterly). **Geographic Preference:** Local.

42696 ■ Warwick Valley Chamber of Commerce (WVCC)
25 S St.
Warwick, NY 10990
Ph: (845)986-2720
Co. E-mail: info@warwickcc.org
URL: http://www.warwickcc.org
Contact: Elizabeth Cassidy, President
Facebook: www.facebook.com/
WarwickValleyChamber
Instagram: www.instagram.com/
warwickvalleychamber
Description: Fosters cooperative action to advance the common interests of members in the town of Warwick, Orange County, New York and surrounding areas. **Founded:** 1939. **Geographic Preference:** Local.

42697 ■ Watkins Glen Area Chamber of Commerce (WGACC)
214 N Franklin St., Rt. 14
Watkins Glen, NY 14891
Ph: (607)535-4300
Free: 800-607-4552
Fax: (607)535-6243
Co. E-mail: info@watkinsglenchamber.com
URL: http://www.explorewatkinsglen.com
Contact: Nigar Hale, Executive Director
Facebook: www.facebook.com/wa
tkinsglenareachamberofcommerce
X (Twitter): x.com/wgacoc
Instagram: www.instagram.com/wgareachamber
Description: Promotes business and community development in Schuyler County, NY. **Founded:** 1889. **Publications:** *Business Directory*; *Country Travel Guide* (Periodic); *Inside The Chamber* (Bimonthly). **Geographic Preference:** Local.

42698 ■ Webster Chamber of Commerce (WCC)
1110 Crosspoint Ln., Ste. C
Webster, NY 14580
Ph: (585)265-3960
Fax: (585)265-3702
URL: http://www.websterchamber.com
Contact: Barry Howard, President
E-mail: bhoward@websterchamber.com
Facebook: www.facebook.com/Webs
terChamberOfCommerce
Description: Promotes business and community development in Webster, NY. **Founded:** 1932. **Publications:** *Business and Community Services Guide* (Annual). **Geographic Preference:** Local.

42699 ■ Wellsville Area Chamber of Commerce (WCC)
114 N Main St.
Wellsville, NY 14895
Ph: (585)593-5080
Co. E-mail: wacocexec@wellsvilleareachamber.com
URL: http://www.wellsvilleareachamber.com
Contact: Daniel Cordaro, President
Facebook: www.facebook.com/
WellsvilleAreaChamber
Instagram: www.instagram.com/
wellsvilleareachamber
Description: Promotes business and community development in Wellsville, NY. **Founded:** 1909. **Publications:** *Chamber News*. **Geographic Preference:** Local.

STATE LISTINGS   New York ■ 42714

42700 ■ West Seneca Chamber of Commerce
1300 Union Rd.
West Seneca, NY 14224
Ph: (716)674-4900
Co. E-mail: director@westseneca.org
URL: http://westseneca.org
Contact: Zach Armstrong, President
Facebook: www.facebook.com/WestSenecaChamberofCommerce
X (Twitter): x.com/WestSenecaChmbr
Description: Promotes business and community development in West Seneca, NY. **Publications:** FOCUS (Monthly). **Geographic Preference:** Local.

42701 ■ Woodstock Chamber of Commerce and Arts (WCOCA)
10 Rock City Rd.
Woodstock, NY 12498
Ph: (845)679-6234
Co. E-mail: info@woodstockchamber.com
URL: http://woodstockchamber.com
Contact: Kathryn Spata, President
E-mail: kathrynspata@nancysartinsanal.com
Facebook: www.facebook.com/pg/woodstockchamberofcommerceandarts
X (Twitter): x.com/WcocaNy
Instagram: www.instagram.com/woodstocknychamber
Description: Promotes business and community development in Woodstock, NY. Sponsors annual Festival of the Arts, street fairs, and other community events. **Publications:** The Woodstock Guide (Annual). **Geographic Preference:** Local.

42702 ■ Wyoming County Chamber of Commerce (WCCC)
36 Ctr. St., Ste. A
Warsaw, NY 14569
Ph: (585)786-0307
Fax: (585)786-0009
Co. E-mail: info@wycochamber.org
URL: http://www.wycochamber.org
Contact: Scott A. Gardner, President
E-mail: sgardner@wycochamber.org
Facebook: www.facebook.com/WyomingCountyChamberofCommerce
X (Twitter): x.com/wycochamber
Instagram: www.instagram.com/wycochamber
YouTube: www.youtube.com/channel/UCBrj3T4a4Lj7qmkmB_oliXQ
Description: Promotes business and community development in the Perry, NY area. Sponsors Sea Serpent Softball tournament, Sea Serpent Arts festival, and Christmas activities, shuttle to Letchworth Craft Show. **Founded:** 2000. **Publications:** Chamber Gazette (Bimonthly). **Geographic Preference:** Local.

42703 ■ Yonkers Chamber of Commerce
55 Main St., 2nd Fl.
Yonkers, NY 10701
Ph: (914)963-0332
Fax: (914)963-0455
Co. E-mail: info@yonkerschamber.com
URL: http://www.yonkerschamber.com
Contact: Kevin Cacace, President
Facebook: www.facebook.com/yonkerschamber
X (Twitter): x.com/YonkersChamber
Pinterest: www.pinterest.co.kr/pin/yonkers-chamber-of-commerce--146015212893253991
Description: Promotes business and community development in Yonkers, NY area. **Founded:** 1893. **Geographic Preference:** Local.

42704 ■ Yorktown Chamber of Commerce (YCC)
650 Lee Blvd. J02A
Yorktown Heights, NY 10598
Ph: (914)245-4599
Fax: (914)734-7171
Co. E-mail: info@yorktownchamber.org
URL: http://www.yorktownchamber.org
Contact: Karen Trendell, President
E-mail: karent@anchorpays.com
Facebook: www.facebook.com/YorktownChamber
X (Twitter): x.com/yorktownchamber

YouTube: www.youtube.com/channel/UCbfV7KD8ZkhHpjVOiZxAakA
Description: Promotes business and community development in the area. **Founded:** 1848. **Geographic Preference:** Local.

MINORITY BUSINESS ASSISTANCE PROGRAMS

42705 ■ Empire State Development - Minority and Women's Business Development Division (DMWBD)
655 3rd Ave., 3rd Fl.
New York, NY 10017
Ph: (212)803-3130
Fax: (212)803-3131
Co. E-mail: nys-midhudson@esd.ny.gov
URL: http://esd.ny.gov/doing-business-ny/mwbe
Description: Assists in obtaining statewide certification, financing, business development and technical assistance, permit and regulatory assistance, market and sales expansion, and employment and training.

42706 ■ New York and New Jersey Minority Supplier Development Council (NY & NJ MSDC)
65 W 36th St., Ste. 702
New York, NY 10018
Ph: (212)502-5663
Fax: (212)502-5807
Co. E-mail: council@nynjmsdc.org
URL: http://nynjmsdc.org
Contact: Terrence Clark, President
E-mail: terrence.clark@nynjmsdc.org
Facebook: www.facebook.com/NYNJCouncil
Linkedin: www.linkedin.com/company/nynjcouncil
X (Twitter): x.com/NYNJCouncil
Instagram: www.instagram.com/nynjcouncil
YouTube: www.youtube.com/channel/UCxXSCiAy3Maj1be1NYHcscw
Description: Provides a direct link between corporate America and minority-owned businesses. Increases procurement and business opportunities for minority businesses of all sizes. **Founded:** 1973. **Educational Activities:** Business Opportunity Expo (Annual). **Geographic Preference:** Regional.

42707 ■ New York State Office of General Services - Minority and Women-Owned Business and Community Relations
Corning Twr.
Empire State Plz., 29th Fl.
Albany, NY 12242
Ph: (518)486-9284
Fax: (518)486-9285
Co. E-mail: mwbe@ogs.ny.gov
URL: http://www.ogs.ny.gov/MWBE
Contact: Tryphina J. Ramsey, Director
E-mail: tryphina.ramsey@ogs.ny.gov

42708 ■ Women's Business Center (WBC)
Canisius College
2001 Main St.
Buffalo, NY 14208
Ph: (716)888-8280
Fax: (716)888-8284
Co. E-mail: wbcinfo@canisius.edu
URL: http://thewomensbusinesscenter.com
Contact: Sara Vescio, Executive Director
Facebook: www.facebook.com/CanisiusWBC
X (Twitter): x.com/canisiuswbc
Description: Provides business development services, such as financial analysis, market research, loan application assistance, mentoring, and workshops and seminars, to women who wish to begin or expand a business.

42709 ■ Women's Venture Fund (WVF)
902 Broadway, 6th Fl.
New York, NY 10010
Ph: (212)563-0499
Co. E-mail: info@wvf-ny.org
URL: http://womensventurefund.org
Contact: Maria Otero, President
Facebook: www.facebook.com/womensventurefund

Linkedin: www.linkedin.com/company/womens-venture-fund
X (Twitter): x.com/womensvfund
YouTube: www.youtube.com/user/womensventurefund
Description: Provider of business development services for the creation or expansion of women-owned businesses in New York. **Founded:** 1996.

FINANCING AND LOAN PROGRAMS

42710 ■ Activate Venture Partners
509 Madison Ave., Ste. 1006
New York, NY 10022
Ph: (212)223-7400
URL: http://www.activatevp.com
Contact: Avlyn Ashterman-Reece, Director
Description: Firm operating venture capital firm. **Founded:** 1999. **Preferred Investment Size:** $250,000 to $2,000,000. **Industry Preferences:** Communications and media, computer software, and Internet specific.

42711 ■ Advent International Corporation
Advent International Corporation
12 E 49th St., 45th Fl.
New York, NY 10017
Ph: (212)813-8300
Co. E-mail: adventinternational-us@fgsglobal.com
URL: http://www.adventinternational.com
Contact: Jason Karl, Principal
Linkedin: www.linkedin.com/company/advent-international
Description: Private equity firm provides investment services. **Founded:** 1984. **Preferred Investment Size:** $1,000,000 minimum. **Industry Preferences:** Communications and media, consumer related, internet specific, industrial and energy, medical and health, computer software and services, computer hardware, semiconductors and other electronics and biotechnology and other products.

42712 ■ Allegra Partners/Lawrence, Smith & Horey
515 Madison Ave.
New York, NY 10022
Contact: Richard W. Smith, Contact
Preferred Investment Size: $5,000,000 to $20,000,000. **Industry Preferences:** Computer software and services, communications and media, other products, Internet specific, consumer related, medical and health.

42713 ■ Angel Round Capital Fund, LP (ARC)
885 3rd Ave., 20th Fl.
New York, NY 10022
Co. E-mail: arcangelfund1@gmail.com
URL: http://www.arcangelfund.com
Contact: David Freschman, Partner
X (Twitter): x.com/arcangelfund
Description: Member-led angel fund investing in seed- and early-stage companies in the Northeast and mid-Atlantic regions. **Founded:** 2010. **Investment Policies:** Revenue and valuations under $5,000,000. **Industry Preferences:** Software; IT; internet; tech-enabled services; business services; digital media; mobile; healthcare IT.

42714 ■ Apax Partners of New York
601 Lexington Ave. Fl. 53
New York, NY 10022
Ph: (212)753-6300
Fax: (212)319-6155
URL: http://www.apax.com
Contact: Andrew Cavanna, Partner
Linkedin: www.linkedin.com/company/apax-partners
X (Twitter): x.com/apax_partners
Description: Private equity advisory firm provides long-term equity financing. **Founded:** 1981. **Preferred Investment Size:** $500,000 minimum. **Industry Preferences:** Financial and business services, medical and health, communications and media, consumer related, information technology, and other products.

42715 ■ Apple Tree Partners (ATP)
230 Pk. Ave., Ste. 2800
 New York, NY 10169
Ph: (212)468-5800
Co. E-mail: info@appletreepartners.com
URL: http://www.appletreepartners.com
Contact: Seth L. Harrison, Managing Partner Founder
Description: Invests in the next generation of transformative biotechnology companies. Also operates out of Boston and London. **Founded:** 1999.

42716 ■ The Argentum Group
17 State St., 22nd Fl.
 New York, NY 10004
Ph: (212)949-6262
Fax: (212)949-8294
Co. E-mail: tag@argentumgroup.com
URL: http://argentumgroup.com
Contact: Daniel Raynor, Managing Partner
E-mail: draynor@argentumgroup.com
Linkedin: www.linkedin.com/company/argentum-capital-partners
Description: Investment firm provides venture capital and private equity investment services for industrial, environmental services, healthcare, telecommunications, technology. **Founded:** 1988. **Preferred Investment Size:** $2,000,000-$10,000,000. **Industry Preferences:** Internet specific, medical and health, computer software and services, communications and media, industrial and energy, and computer hardware.

42717 ■ Armory Square Ventures (ASV)
211 W Jefferson St., 2nd Fl.
 Syracuse, NY 13202
Co. E-mail: info@armorysv.com
URL: http://www.armorysv.com
Contact: Somak Chattopadhyay, Managing Partner
Linkedin: www.linkedin.com/company/armory-square
 -ventures
X (Twitter): x.com/armorysv
Description: Offers early-stage institutional capital for startups in the largest industries in New York and select cities in the Northeast. Actively involved at all stages of growth, including recruiting and management support. **Founded:** 2014. **Preferred Investment Size:** $500,000 to $2,000,000. **Investment Policies:** Repeatable, recurring, or transaction-based revenue models; emphasis on B2B enterprise solution; addressable markets of at least $500,000; full-time technical leader and sales/marketing leader; deployed prototype; capital efficient. **Industry Preferences:** Software; mobile; technology-enabled services.

42718 ■ Arthur P. Gould & Co.
164 Lyons Rd.
 Scarsdale, NY 10583
Ph: (914)729-9116
Fax: (914)723-1756
Co. E-mail: andrew@gouldco.com
URL: http://www.gouldco.com
Contact: Andrew G. Gould, President
E-mail: andrew@gouldco.com
Description: Provider of investment and merchant banking services. **Founded:** 1968. **Preferred Investment Size:** $5,000,000 minimum. **Industry Preferences:** Communications, computer hardware and software, semiconductors and other electronics, biotechnology, medical and health, consumer related, industrial and energy, transportation, financial services, manufacturing, agriculture, forestry and fishing.

42719 ■ Baker Capital
575 Madison Ave., 10th Fl.
 New York, NY 10022
Contact: John C. Baker, Chief Executive Officer
Description: Firm provides investment management services. **Founded:** 1995. **Industry Preferences:** Internet specific, communications and media, computer software and services, computer hardware, semiconductors and other electronics.

42720 ■ Bedford Capital Corp.
81 Main St., Ste. 515
 White Plains, NY 10601
Ph: (914)948-3840
Fax: (914)285-9282
Co. E-mail: info@bedfordnyc.com
URL: http://www.bedfordnyc.com
Description: Firm provides merchant banking and advisory services. **Founded:** 1993. **Preferred Investment Size:** $100,000 to $300,000. **Industry Preferences:** Internet specific, medical and health, consumer related, industrial and energy, financial services, and manufacturing.

42721 ■ Bedrock Capital
2 5th Ave., Ste. 17E
 New York, NY 10011
Co. E-mail: info@bedrockcap.com
URL: http://www.bedrockcap.com
Contact: Spencer Peterson, Contact
Linkedin: www.linkedin.com/company/bedrockcap
X (Twitter): twitter.com/bedrock
Description: Venture capital firm for underestimated and overlooked companies. **Founded:** 2018.

42722 ■ Bertelsmann Digital Media Investments Inc. (BDMI)
1745 Broadway (between 55th & 56th), 20th fl.
 New York, NY 10019
Co. E-mail: info@bdmifund.com
URL: http://www.bdmifund.com
Contact: Louisa Fruehauf, Manager
Linkedin: www.linkedin.com/company/bdmi
X (Twitter): x.com/BDMIFund
Description: Invests in early-stage innovative technology and media companies . **Founded:** 2006.

42723 ■ Bessemer Venture Partners (BVP)
1865 Palmer Ave., Ste. 104
 Larchmont, NY 10538
Ph: (914)833-5300
Co. E-mail: businessplans@bvp.com
URL: http://www.bvp.com
Contact: Nikki Horn, Director
Linkedin: www.linkedin.com/company/bessemer-venture-partners
X (Twitter): x.com/BessemerVP
Instagram: www.instagram.com/bessemer.venture
 .partners
YouTube: www.youtube.com/c/BessemerVenturePartners
Description: Venture capital firm provides investment services to healthcare, information systems, telecommunications and retailing sectors. **Founded:** 1911. **Preferred Investment Size:** $1,000,000 to $10,000,000. **Industry Preferences:** Internet specific, communications and media, computer software and services, computer hardware, semiconductors and other electronics, consumer related, medical and health, industrial and energy, biotechnology, and other products.

42724 ■ BlueCar Partners
New York, NY
URL: http://bluecarpartners.weebly.com
Contact: Granger Whitelaw, Chief Executive Officer
Facebook: www.facebook.com/BluecarPartners
X (Twitter): x.com/bluecar12
Description: Private investment firm. **Investment Policies:** Seed and early stage. **Industry Preferences:** Communications, Internet specific, biotechnology, medical and health, and transportation.

42725 ■ BoxGroup
New York, NY
Co. E-mail: hello@boxgroup.com
URL: http://www.boxgroup.com
Contact: Brian Aledort, Chief Financial Officer
E-mail: brian@boxgroup.com
Description: Venture capital firm. Invests from the pre-seed round to Series A. **Investment Policies:** Prefers entrepreneurs who value curiosity, integrity, and ambition.

42726 ■ Braemar Energy Ventures
350 Madison Ave.
 New York, NY 10017
Ph: (212)697-0900
URL: http://www.braemarenergy.com
Contact: Dorothea Bersani, Chief Administrative Officer
Linkedin: www.linkedin.com/company/braemar-energy-ventures
X (Twitter): x.com/BraemarEnergy
Description: Exclusively focused on venture capital for venture- and expansion-stage companies in the energy sector; includes both alternative and traditional forms of energy. Also operates out of London. **Founded:** 2003.

42727 ■ Brooklyn Bridge Ventures (BBV)
45 Plz. St. W 6E
 Brooklyn, NY 11217
URL: http://www.brooklynbridge.vc
Contact: Charlie O'Donnell, Partner
E-mail: charlie@brooklynbridge.vc
Linkedin: www.linkedin.com/company/brooklyn-bridge
 -ventures
X (Twitter): x.com/bklynbridgevc
Instagram: www.instagram.com/brooklynbridgevc
Description: Venture capital firm. **Founded:** 2012. **Investment Policies:** Technology entrepreneurs in the New York City area who haven't previously raised $750K.

42728 ■ Clarion Capital Corp.
527 Madison Ave., 10th Fl.
 New York, NY 10022
Ph: (212)821-0111
Fax: (212)371-7597
URL: http://www.clarion-capital.com
Contact: Robert J. Klein, President
E-mail: rklein@clarion-capital.com
Linkedin: www.linkedin.com/company/clarion-capital
 -partners
Founded: 1999. **Industry Preferences:** Private equity firm investing in lower-middle market companies.

42729 ■ CM Equity Partners L.P. (CMEP)
900 3rd Ave., 33rd Fl.
 New York, NY 10022
Ph: (212)909-8400
Fax: (212)829-0553
URL: http://www.cmequity.com
Contact: David Shnitkin, Controller
Facebook: www.facebook.com/people/CM-Equity-Partners/100032558622589
Linkedin: www.linkedin.com/company/cm-equity-partners
Description: Provider of venture capital services. **Founded:** 1995. **Preferred Investment Size:** $2,000,000 minimum. **Industry Preferences:** Communications and media, and Internet specific.

42730 ■ Contour Venture Partners
475 Pk. Ave. S, 6th Fl.
 New York, NY 10016
Co. E-mail: businessplan@contourventures.com
URL: http://www.contourventures.com
Contact: Bob Greene, Managing Partner
E-mail: bob@contourventures.com
Description: Venture capital firm for information technology companies at the seed and early stages in the Northeast region of the United States. **Founded:** 2005. **Industry Preferences:** Information technology in financial services, enterprise SaaS, and digital media sectors.

42731 ■ Corigin Ventures
505 5th Ave.
 New York, NY 10110
Ph: (212)775-1111
URL: http://www.corigin.com
Contact: Greg Gleason, President
Description: Early-stage investors in technology startups. **Founded:** 2010. **Preferred Investment Size:** $500,000-$1,250,000 (seed); $100,000 (pre-seed). **Investment Policies:** Founders with unique insights and outsized advantages. **Industry Preferences:** Consumer, proptech, and marketplace: DNVBs focused on customer experience, personalization and customization, wellness (physical and mental), and luxury products/services made accessible.

42732 ■ Coriolis Ventures
160 Mercer St., 3rd Fl.
New York, NY 10012
Co. E-mail: contact@coriolisventures.com
URL: http://www.coriolisventures.com
Contact: Alan Murray, Co-Founder Co-Chief Executive Officer
Description: Early-stage venture and incubation fund. **Founded:** 2006. **Industry Preferences:** New media; hospitality innovation; medtech.

42733 ■ Cote Capital
22 W 22nd St.
New York, NY 10010
Ph: (212)967-2215
URL: http://www.cotecapital.com
Contact: Rod Robertson, President
Facebook: www.facebook.com/CoteCapitalInvest
Linkedin: www.linkedin.com/company/cote-capital
X (Twitter): x.com/CoteCapital
Instagram: www.instagram.com/cotecapital
YouTube: www.youtube.com/channel/UCybn1ohaNomZSXHjnLzkePQ
Description: Works to meet the long-term growth needs of IP-rich companies. Offers funding for capital expenditures. **Founded:** 2016. **Investment Policies:** Reviews how company's intellectual property aligns with business goals to drive revenue, and if it offers substantial performance, cost advantage, or competitor advantage.

42734 ■ CoVenture
600 Madison Ave., 17th Fl.
New York, NY 10022
Co. E-mail: info@coventure.vc
URL: http://coventure.vc
Contact: Michael Breitstein, Director
Facebook: www.facebook.com/Coventure-273762529418422
X (Twitter): twitter.com/coventurevc
Description: Alternative asset manager across three platforms: venture capital, specialty lending, and cryptocurrency.

42735 ■ DFW Capital Partners Inc.
156 5th Ave., Ste. 1100
New York, NY 10010
Ph: (201)836-6000
Fax: (201)836-5666
Co. E-mail: info@dfwcapital.com
URL: http://dfwcapital.com
Contact: Angela Nobre, Controller
Description: Private equity investment firm, focused exclusively on the lower middle market. **Founded:** 1999. **Preferred Investment Size:** $5,000,000 to $20,000,000. **Industry Preferences:** Private equity firm investing in middle-market companies in the healthcare, business, and industrial services industries.

42736 ■ Eastern New York Angels (ENYA)
Albany, NY
Ph: (518)690-0620
URL: http://easternnyangels.com
Description: Offers seed funding to early stage companies in the Eastern New York. **Founded:** 2010. **Preferred Investment Size:** $50,000 to $250,000.

42737 ■ Easton Hunt Capital Partners L.P.
767 3rd Ave., 7th Fl.
New York, NY 10017
Ph: (212)702-0950
Fax: (212)702-0952
URL: http://www.eastoncapital.com
Contact: Francisco Garcia, Managing Director
E-mail: garcia@eastoncapital.com
Description: Firm provides venture capital funds investment services for healthcare and life sciences sectors. **Preferred Investment Size:** $2,000,000 to $7,500,000. **Industry Preferences:** Computer software, industrial and energy, medical and healthcare devices, business service, and manufacturing.

42738 ■ Empire Angels
New York, NY
Co. E-mail: info@empireangels.com
URL: http://empireangels.com

Contact: Christina Bechhold Russ, Co-Founder Partner
E-mail: christina@empireangels.com
Description: Member-led seed fund and angel group with an emphasis on supporting young entrepreneurs. Also operates out of London. **Founded:** 2012.

42739 ■ Eos Partners, L.P.
437 Madison Ave., 14th Fl.
New York, NY 10022
Ph: (212)832-5800
Fax: (212)832-5815
URL: http://www.eospartners.com
Contact: Matthew Young, Vice President
E-mail: myoung@eospartners.com
Description: Firm operating private equity investment partnership providing capital to businesses. **Founded:** 1994. **Preferred Investment Size:** $3,000,000. **Industry Preferences:** Communications and media, other products, consumer related, medical and health, semiconductors and other electronics, computer software and services, Internet specific, industrial and energy.

42740 ■ Expansion Venture Capital (EVC)
250 W 57th St., Rm. 1301
New York, NY 10107
Ph: (212)265-1220
Fax: (516)882-5307
Co. E-mail: info@expansionvc.com
URL: http://expansionvc.com
Contact: Joseph Melohn, President
Linkedin: www.linkedin.com/company/expansion-venture-capital
X (Twitter): x.com/ExpansionVC
Description: Venture capital firm for early- and growth-stage companies. **Founded:** 2011.

42741 ■ ff Venture Capital [ff Asset Management LLC]
The Emipire State Bldg.
350 5th Ave., Ste. 4215
New York, NY 10018
URL: http://www.ffvc.com
Contact: Alex Katz, Partner
X (Twitter): x.com/ffvc
Description: Technology venture capital firm for companies at the seed and early stages. **Founded:** 2008. **Preferred Investment Size:** $500,000 to $750,000. **Investment Policies:** Using technology to develop new markets, change behaviors, or solve important problems.

42742 ■ FirstMark
100 5th Ave., Third Fl.
New York, NY 10011
Ph: (212)792-2200
Co. E-mail: info@firstmarkcap.com
URL: http://firstmark.com
Contact: Ben Winn, Director
Linkedin: www.linkedin.com/company/firstmark
X (Twitter): x.com/FirstMarkCap
Description: Early stage venture capital firm. **Founded:** 2008.

42743 ■ FirstMark Capital
641 Avenue of the Americas, Fl. 6
New York, NY 10011
URL: http://firstmark.com
Contact: Ben Winn, Director
Linkedin: www.linkedin.com/company/firstmark
X (Twitter): x.com/FirstMarkCap
Description: Early-stage venture capital firm. **Founded:** 2008.

42744 ■ FJ Labs
310 E Houston St., Ph 1
New York, NY 10002
URL: http://www.fjlabs.com
Contact: Arne Halleraker, Partner
Description: Venture capital firm primarily focused on marketplace start-ups with large growth potential in New York and the San Francisco Bay Area. **Industry Preferences:** Marketplace, B2B, B2C, and consumer finance, ecommerce, travel, and mobile.

42745 ■ Flybridge Capital Partners
16 W 23rd St., 5th Fl.
New York, NY 10010
Co. E-mail: hello@flybridge.com
URL: http://flybridge.com
Contact: Jesse Middleton, Partner
E-mail: jesse@flybridge.com
Linkedin: www.linkedin.com/company/flybridge-capital
X (Twitter): x.com/flybridge
Description: Seed and early-stage venture capital firm. Also maintains an office in New York City. **Investment Policies:** Companies with strong teams, substantial market opportunities, novel IP, and capital efficiencies. **Industry Preferences:** Software and next generation hardware markets.

42746 ■ Fountain Healthcare Partners
12 E 49th St., 11th Fl.
New York, NY 10017
Ph: (347)746-3252
Co. E-mail: info@fh-partners.com
URL: http://www.fh-partners.com
Contact: Aidan King, Managing Partner Co-Founder
Description: Venture capital firm for healthcare companies in Europe and North America. Also operates out of Dublin. **Investment Policies:** Potential for strong exit in 4-6 years. **Industry Preferences:** Specialty pharma; biopharmaceuticals; medical devices; diagnostics.

42747 ■ Gabelli Multimedia Partners
c/o Gabelli Securities Inc., Attn. Legal Dept.
1 Corporate Ctr.
Rye, NY 10580
Industry Preferences: Communications and media.

42748 ■ Gefinor Capital
2700 Westchester Ave., Ste. 303
Purchase, NY 10577
Ph: (212)308-1111
Fax: (212)308-1182
Co. E-mail: gcmi.info@gefinor.com
URL: http://www.gefinorcapital.com
Contact: Andre Bernath, Chief Financial Officer
Description: Investment firm specializing in private equity investments, hedge fund and wealth management services. **Preferred Investment Size:** $1,000,000 to $2,000,000. **Investment Policies:** Early, first, second, later stage, and mezzanine. **Industry Preferences:** Communications, computer software, Internet specific, semiconductors and other electronics, medical and health, financial services, consumer products, and manufacturing.

42749 ■ Genesys Partners Inc.
126 5th Ave.
New York, NY 10011
Ph: (212)686-2828
Fax: (212)686-5155
Co. E-mail: info@genesyspartners.com
URL: http://www.genesyspartners.com
Contact: James G. Kollegger, Chief Executive Officer
Linkedin: www.linkedin.com/company/genesys-partners-inc.
Description: Provider of investment banking, venture capital services and much more. **Founded:** 1989. **Industry Preferences:** Internet specific.

42750 ■ Golden Seeds (GS)
PO Box 541473
Flushing, NY 11354
Free: 888-629-6774
Co. E-mail: info@goldenseeds.com
URL: http://goldenseeds.com
Contact: Jo Ann Corkran, Managing Partner Co-Chief Executive Officer
Facebook: www.facebook.com/GoldenSeeds
Linkedin: www.linkedin.com/company/goldenseeds
X (Twitter): x.com/GoldenSeeds
Description: Early-stage investment firm focused on women-led companies. **Founded:** 2004.

42751 ■ Gotham Gal Ventures (GGV)
397 W 12th St.
New York, NY 10014
URL: http://gothamgal.com

Contact: Joanne Wilson, Contact
E-mail: joanne@solomonwilson.com
Description: Angel investor focused on startups owned by women.

42752 ■ Gotham Ventures
44 S Broadway, Ste. 100
White Plains, NY 10601
Ph: (212)279-3980
URL: http://gothamvc.com
Contact: Joann Malejko, Member
E-mail: joann@gothamvc.com
Description: Venture capital firm for early-stage information technology startups, primarily in the New York City area. **Industry Preferences:** Digital and social media; ecommerce; advertising; financial technology; enterprise software and security; health and wellness; education.

42753 ■ Great Oaks Venture Capital
667 Madison Ave., Ste. 17B
New York, NY 10065
Ph: (212)821-1800
Co. E-mail: info@greatoaksvc.com
URL: http://www.greatoaksvc.com
Contact: Andy Boszhardt, Managing Partner Founder
Facebook: www.facebook.com/people/Great-Oaks-Venture-Capital/100063746101255
X (Twitter): x.com/greatoaksvc
Description: Venture capital firm. Invests at the Seed and Series A stages. **Preferred Investment Size:** $50,000-$500,000.

42754 ■ Harvest Partners Inc.
280 Pk. Ave., 26th W,Fl.
New York, NY 10017
Ph: (212)599-6300
Co. E-mail: info@harvestpartners.com
URL: http://www.harvestpartners.com
Contact: Jay Wilkins, President
Description: Private equity firm provides for expansion, generational transitions, public-to-private transactions, corporate carve-outs and industry consolidations. **Founded:** 1981. **Preferred Investment Size:** $40,000,000 to $600,000,000. **Industry Preferences:** Other products, industrial and energy, consumer related, communications and media, and Internet specific.

42755 ■ Holding Capital Group Inc. (HCG)
104 W 40th St., 19th Fl.
New York, NY 10018
Ph: (212)486-6670
Fax: (212)486-0843
Co. E-mail: sleischner@holdingcapital.com
URL: http://www.holdingcapital.com
Contact: Steven Leischner, President
E-mail: sleischner@holdingcapital.com
Description: Firm provides investment management services. **Founded:** 1975. **Preferred Investment Size:** $2,000,000 to $150,000,000.

42756 ■ Hudson Valley Startup Fund (HVSF)
6571 Spring Brook Ln.
Rhinebeck, NY 12572
Co. E-mail: info@hvstartupfund.com
URL: http://www.hvstartupfund.com
Contact: Tony DiMarco, Manager
Description: Member-managed seed capital fund. Offers funding, business planning, and strategy guidance to high-growth companies in the Hudson Valley. Seeks to generate returns for member investors and grow the entrepreneurial ecosystem. . **Founded:** 2015. **Investment Policies:** Scalable business model; addressable market; clear exit strategy; some kind of competitive advantage.

42757 ■ I-Hatch Ventures L.L.C.
270 Lafayette St., Ste. 814
New York, NY 10012
Ph: (212)651-1750
Fax: (212)208-4590
Co. E-mail: info@i-hatch.com
URL: http://www.i-hatch.com
Contact: Chip Austin, Partner

Description: Firm invested in technology companies primarily in mobile and broadband sectors. **Founded:** 1999. **Industry Preferences:** Internet specific, computer software, hardware and services, consumer related, communications and media.

42758 ■ I2BF Global Investments Ltd.
55 Broadway 3rd Fl.
New York, NY 10006
Ph: (212)226-7320
Co. E-mail: info@i2bf.com
URL: http://www.i2bf.com
Facebook: www.facebook.com/I2BFglobalventures
Linkedin: www.linkedin.com/company/i2bf-global-ventures
X (Twitter): x.com/i2bf
Description: Offer multi-stage growth capital for technology companies. Also maintains offices in London, Moscow, and Kazakhstan. **Founded:** 2005.

42759 ■ IA Ventures
920 Braodway, 15th Fl.
New York, NY 10010
URL: http://www.iaventures.com
Description: Early-stage venture capital firm.

42760 ■ IDG Capital
1345 Ave. of Americas 33rd Fl.
New York, NY 10105
Ph: (212)337-5200
URL: http://en.idgcapital.com
Contact: Jun Ning, Chairman
Facebook: www.facebook.com/IDGCapital
Linkedin: www.linkedin.com/company/idgvc
Description: Venture capital and private equity firm for global startups. Also works on branding, marketing, human resources, expansion, and financial management.

42761 ■ Insight Venture Partners / Insight Capital Partners
1114 Avenue of the Americas, 36th Fl.
New York, NY 10036
Ph: (212)230-9200
Fax: (212)230-9272
Co. E-mail: growth@insightpartners.com
URL: http://www.insightpartners.com
Contact: Archie Hunter, Executive Director
E-mail: ahunter@insightpartners.com
Facebook: www.facebook.com/InsightPartnersnyc
Linkedin: www.linkedin.com/company/insight--partners
X (Twitter): x.com/insightpartners
Instagram: www.instagram.com/insightpartnersnyc
YouTube: www.youtube.com/user/InsightPartners
Description: Private equity and venture capital firm investing in growth-stage software, internet and data services companies. **Founded:** 1995. **Preferred Investment Size:** $5,000,000 to $30,000,000. **Industry Preferences:** Internet specific, computer software and services, other products, consumer related, computer hardware, communications and media.

42762 ■ Jegi Capital L.L.C.
150 E 52nd St., 18th Fl.
New York, NY 10022
Ph: (212)754-0710
Co. E-mail: contact@jegiclarity-us.com
URL: http://www.jegiclarity.com
Contact: Wilma Jordan, Chief Executive Officer
E-mail: wilmaj@jegi
Linkedin: www.linkedin.com/company/jegiclarity
Description: Provider of investment banking services. **Founded:** 1987. **Preferred Investment Size:** $5,000,000 to $10,000,000. **Investment Policies:** Early, first and second stage. **Industry Preferences:** Computer hardware and software, Internet specific, and semiconductors and other electronics.

42763 ■ Jerusalem Venture Partners (JVP)
122 Grand St.
New York, NY 10013
Ph: (646)882-7815
Co. E-mail: info@jvpvc.com
URL: http://www.jvpvc.com
Contact: Erel N. Margalit, Founder Executive Chairman of the Board

Facebook: www.facebook.com/JerusalemVenturePartners
X (Twitter): x.com/jvpvc
Description: Provider of venture capital specializing in early stage, late stage, growth capital and startup investments. **Founded:** 1993. **Preferred Investment Size:** $2,000,000 to $35,000,000. **Industry Preferences:** Internet specific, semiconductors and other electronics, communications and media, computer software and services, and computer hardware.

42764 ■ The Jordan Edmiston Group Inc. (JEGI)
150 E 52nd St., 18th Fl.
New York, NY 10022
Ph: (212)754-0710
Co. E-mail: contact@jegiclarity-us.com
URL: http://www.jegiclarity.com
Contact: Wilma Jordan, Chief Executive Officer
E-mail: wjordan@jegiclarity-us.com
Linkedin: www.linkedin.com/company/jegiclarity
Description: Firm provides consulting services. **Scope:** Provides strategic consulting and financial advisory and transaction services to publishing and new media companies. The firm focuses its client services on financial advisory services including acquisitions, divestitures, recapitalizations, valuations and management buyouts and management services which can include direct, operational responsibilities on either an interim or long term basis for a project, division, or an entire company. Industries served: publishing, including magazines, newspapers, books, business press, newsletters, databases and information and new media companies. **Founded:** 1987. **Publications:** "Strategic Publications Has Sold Pennysaver Group to SV Investment Partners," 2006. **Preferred Investment Size:** $5,000,000 to $10,000,000. **Investment Policies:** Early, first and second stage. **Industry Preferences:** Computer hardware and software, Internet specific, and semiconductors and other electronics.

42765 ■ Karlani Capital
New York, NY
URL: http://www.karlani.com
Contact: Donald Volk, Partner
Linkedin: www.linkedin.com/company/karlani-capital
X (Twitter): x.com/karlanicapital
Description: Builds, buys, and invests in fast-growing technology-enabled companies. **Founded:** 2013. **Preferred Investment Size:** $100,000-$2,000,000.

42766 ■ KBL Healthcare Ventures (KBL)
757 Third Ave., 21st Fl.
New York, NY 10017
Ph: (212)319-5555
Fax: (212)319-5591
URL: http://www.kblhealthcare.com
Contact: Sandra Santos, Office Manager
E-mail: ss@kblvc.com
Description: Provider of venture capital investments for startups, early stage, and emerging growth companies. **Founded:** 2007. **Preferred Investment Size:** $110,000,000 to $500,000,000. **Industry Preferences:** Medical and health, biotechnology, Internet specific, communications and media, computer software and services.

42767 ■ KEC Ventures
New York, NY
Co. E-mail: info@kecventures.com
URL: http://www.kecventures.com
X (Twitter): x.com/KECVentures
Description: Early-stage venture capital firm.

42768 ■ Kickstarter, PBC
58 Kent St.
Brooklyn, NY 11222
URL: http://www.kickstarter.com
Contact: Aziz Hasan, Chief Executive Officer
Facebook: www.facebook.com/Kickstarter
X (Twitter): x.com/kickstarter
Instagram: www.instagram.com/kickstarter
YouTube: www.youtube.com/user/kickstarter

Description: Provider of a crowd funding platform focused on creativity including films, music, arts, theaters, games, comics, designs, and photography. **Founded:** 2009.

42769 ■ The Lambda Funds
432 E 84th St.
New York, NY 10028
Ph: (212)774-1812
URL: http://www.lambdafund.com
Contact: Anthony Lamport, Contact
E-mail: alamport@lambdafund.com
Description: Venture capital investments firm. **Founded:** 1979. **Preferred Investment Size:** $100,000 to $1,500,000. **Investment Policies:** First stage and management buyouts. **Industry Preferences:** Biotechnology, computer hardware, computer software and services, industrial and energy, consumer related, other products, semiconductors and other electronics, medical and health, communications and media, Internet specific.

42770 ■ Lazard Technology Partners
30 Rockefeller Plz.
New York, NY 10112
Ph: (212)632-6000
URL: http://www.lazard.com
Contact: Alexander F. Stern, President
Facebook: www.facebook.com/LazardCareers
Linkedin: www.linkedin.com/company/lazard
X (Twitter): x.com/lazard
Instagram: www.instagram.com/lazard
YouTube: www.youtube.com/channel/UC5kvy5orZCGN55qOvoGk7ug
Description: Firm provides venture capital investment service. **Founded:** 1848. **Preferred Investment Size:** $2,000,000 to $8,000,000. **Industry Preferences:** Internet specific, computer software and services, computer hardware, communications and media, semiconductors and other electronics, and consumer related.

42771 ■ Lepercq, de Neuflize & Co
Lepercq, de Neuflize & Co
853 Broadway, Ste. 1109
New York, NY 10003
Ph: (212)698-0700
URL: http://www.lepercq.com
Contact: Thomas Riboud Seydoux, Chief Executive Officer
Description: Provides asset management, real estate and office support services. **Founded:** 1936.

42772 ■ Loeb Partners Corp.
19th Fl. 100 Wall St.
New York, NY 10005
Contact: Bruce L. Lev, Chief Executive Officer
Description: Private equity firm provides investments services. **Founded:** 1931. **Industry Preferences:** Internet specific, biotechnology, medical and health, Internet specific, computer software and services, semiconductors and other electronics.

42773 ■ Magnolia Ventures
61 Broadway, 10th Fl.
New York, NY 10006
Ph: (646)448-6819
Fax: (917)591-1703
Co. E-mail: info@magnoliaventuresllc.com
URL: http://magventuresllc.com
Contact: Graham C. Phillips, Partner
Description: Seed-stage venture capital fund. **Founded:** 2009. **Preferred Investment Size:** $50,000 to $1,000,000. **Investment Policies:** Creates or leverages disruptive technologies; offers solutions for existing markets; clear path to profitability and/or liquidity solutions; headquarters in U.S. or Europe.

42774 ■ McGraw-Hill Ventures /McGraw-Hill Capital Corp.
1221 Avenue of the Americas, 48th Fl
New York, NY 10020
Ph: (212)512-3916
Fax: (212)512-4729
URL: http://www.mheducation.com
Contact: Simon Allen, Chief Executive Officer
Linkedin: www.linkedin.com/company/mcgraw-hill-education
X (Twitter): twitter.com/MHEducation
Instagram: www.instagram.com/mheducation
Description: Finance: Invests in media, business services, financial services, consumer services, education and more. **Founded:** 1888. **Preferred Investment Size:** $500,000 to $5,000,000. **Industry Preferences:** Communications and media, computer software, Internet specific, medical and health, industrial and energy, financial services, business service, and manufacturing.

42775 ■ Metropolitan Venture Partners L.L.C. (MetVP)
588 Broadway, Ste. 1103
New York, NY 10012
Description: Finance: Investment in technology-based businesses. **Founded:** 2008. **Preferred Investment Size:** $500,000 to $5,000,000. **Industry Preferences:** Communications, computer software, semiconductors and other electronics, and Internet specific.

42776 ■ Mid-Atlantic Bio Angels (MABA)
New York, NY
Co. E-mail: info@bioangels.net
URL: http://bioangels.net
Description: Angel investor group for new and emerging life science companies. **Founded:** 2012. **Investment Policies:** Products that will change the standard of care in significant markets; clear exit strategy; proof of concept. **Industry Preferences:** Life sciences: therapeutics, devices, and diagnostics.

42777 ■ MIT Alumni Angels of New York (MITAANY)
New York, NY
URL: http://www.mitalumniangelsny.com
Contact: Wan Li Zhu, Managing Director Founder
Description: Connects MIT alumni investors with entrepreneurs in the New York area. **Founded:** 2018.

42778 ■ Nazem and Co.
600 Madison Ave.
New York, NY 10022
Contact: Fred F. Nazem, Contact
Description: Finance: Venture capital firm. **Founded:** 1976. **Preferred Investment Size:** $1,000,000 minimum. **Industry Preferences:** Computer hardware, computer software and services, medical and health, communications and media, biotechnology, semiconductors and other electronics, Internet specific, industrial and energy, other products, and consumer related.

42779 ■ Needham Asset Management
250 Pk. Ave., 10th Fl.
New York, NY 10177
Description: Services: Provider of asset management solutions. **Founded:** 1985. **Preferred Investment Size:** $2,000,000 to $10,000,000. **Industry Preferences:** Semiconductors and other electronics, computer software and services, communications and media, Internet specific, medical and health, computer hardware, other products, consumer related, industrial and energy.

42780 ■ New Leaf Venture Partners (NLVP)
156 5th Ave., Ste. 820
New York, NY 10010
Ph: (646)871-6400
Fax: (646)871-6450
Co. E-mail: info@nlvpartners.com
URL: http://www.nlvpartners.com/home
Contact: Craig Slutzkin, Chief Operating Officer Chief Financial Officer
E-mail: craig@nlvpartners.com
X (Twitter): x.com/nlvpartners
Description: Venture capital firm. **Founded:** 2005. **Industry Preferences:** Biopharmaceuticals; information convergence; life science tools.

42781 ■ NGEN Partners LLC
733 3rd Ave.
New York, NY 10017
Ph: (212)450-9700
Co. E-mail: submissions@ngenpartners.com
URL: http://www.ngenpartners.com
Contact: Andrea Campisi, Manager
Linkedin: www.linkedin.com/company/ngen-partners
X (Twitter): x.com/ngenpartners
Description: Early-stage growth equity investment firm for B2B and B2C companies. **Founded:** 2001. **Industry Preferences:** Clean energy; green technology; health and wellness; energy.

42782 ■ NGN Capital (NGN)
60 Long Ridge Rd., Ste. 402
Stamford, CT 06902
Ph: (212)972-0077
Fax: (212)972-0080
URL: http://www.ngncapital.com
Contact: Alexander Cuomo, Chief Financial Officer
Description: Venture capital firm focused, primarily for later stage funding, Also operates out of Heidelberg, Germany. **Industry Preferences:** Healthcare.

42783 ■ NYU Innovation Fund
16 Washington Pl.
New York, NY 10003
URL: http://entrepreneur.nyu.edu/resource/innovation-venture-fund
Description: Evergreen seed-stage venture capital fun for startups founded by (or commercializing technologies and intellectual property developed by) current NYU students, faculty, or researchers. **Founded:** 2010.

42784 ■ Onondaga Venture Capital Fund, LLC (OVCF)
241 W Fayette St.
Syracuse, NY 13202
Description: Firm provides venture capital fund and investment services. **Preferred Investment Size:** $50,000 to $300,000. **Industry Preferences:** Communications, computer software, semiconductors and other electronics, biotechnology, medical and health, consumer related, and manufacturing.

42785 ■ Opticality Ventures
584 Broadway ste. 610
New York, NY 10012
Ph: (212)625-8444
Fax: (212)625-3829
URL: http://www.opticality.com
Contact: Michael Diamant, President
Preferred Investment Size: $1,000,000 to $5,000,000. **Investment Policies:** Early stage. **Industry Preferences:** Computer software and Internet specific.

42786 ■ Pomona Management LLC
Voya Financial, Inc.
780 3rd Ave.
New York, NY 10017-7076
Free: 800-992-0180
URL: http://corporate.voya.com
Contact: Michael D. Granoff, Chief Executive Officer
Description: Private equity firm that offers investment and liquidity solutions. **Founded:** 1994. **Preferred Investment Size:** $1,000,000 minimum. **Industry Preferences:** Communications and media, computer hardware and software, biotechnology, medical and health, consumer related, industrial and energy, financial services, and manufacturing.

42787 ■ Primary Venture Partners
386 Pk. Ave. S, 14th Fl.
New York, NY 10016
URL: http://www.primary.vc
Contact: Lisa Lewin, Chief Executive Officer
Linkedin: www.linkedin.com/company/primary-venture-partners
X (Twitter): x.com/PrimaryVC
Instagram: www.instagram.com/primaryventures
Description: Provider of venture capital for seed investments. **Founded:** 2015. **Preferred Investment Size:** $100,000 to $2,000,000. **Industry Preferences:** Communications and media, computer hardware, Internet specific, consumer related, semiconductors and other electronics.

42788 ■ Prospect Street Ventures / Prospect Capital Corp. (PCM)
10 E 40th St., 42nd Fl.
New York, NY 10016
Ph: (212)448-0702
URL: http://www.prospectstreet.com
Contact: Michael Grier Eliasek, President
Description: Provider of private debt and equity capital to middle-market companies. **Founded:** 1988. **Preferred Investment Size:** $5,000,000 to $25,000,000. **Industry Preferences:** Internet specific, computer software and services, other products, communications and media, medical and health.

42789 ■ Radius Ventures LLC
1325 Ave. of the Americas, 27th Fl.
New York, NY 10019
Co. E-mail: ea@radiusventures.com
URL: http://www.radiusventures.com
Contact: Jordan Davis, Managing Partner
Description: Venture capital firm investing in leading-edge expansion-stage health and life sciences companies. **Founded:** 1997. **Industry Preferences:** Health and life sciences; biotechnology; pharmaceuticals; diagnostics; medical devices; healthcare services; healthcare information technology.

42790 ■ Rand Capital Corporation
1405 Rand Bldg.
Buffalo, NY 14203
Ph: (716)853-0802
Fax: (716)854-8480
URL: http://www.randcapital.com
Contact: Daniel P. Penberthy, President
Description: A business development company (BDC) that, as a publicly traded closed-end fund, provides venture capital investments for early or expansion stage companies, or for more mature companies. **Founded:** 1969. **Preferred Investment Size:** $500,000 to $1,500,000. **Industry Preferences:** Investment firm provides publicly traded closed-end management investment and venture capital funds for various industries.

42791 ■ Red Sea Ventures (RSV)
New York, NY 10010
Co. E-mail: hello@redseaventures.com
URL: http://www.redseaventures.com
Contact: Scott Birnbaum, Founder Managing Partner
Linkedin: www.linkedin.com/company/red-sea-ventures
X (Twitter): x.com/RedSeaVentures
Description: Early-stage venture capital firm for technology companies. **Founded:** 2011.

42792 ■ Revel Partners
594 broadway, Ste.1101
New York, NY 10012
URL: http://www.revelpartners.com
Contact: Chris Young, Contact
Description: Venture capital firm for B2B software companies at the post-revenue seed to Series A stage in the US and Western Europe. Also operates out of Germany. **Founded:** 2011. **Preferred Investment Size:** $250,000 to $1,500,000. **Industry Preferences:** B2B SasS; marketplaces.

42793 ■ RK Ventures
888 8th Ave., Ste. 135
New York, NY 10019
Co. E-mail: info@rkventures.com
URL: http://www.rkventures.com
Contact: Charles Rogensburg, Contact
Description: Early-stage venture capital firm. **Preferred Investment Size:** $500,000 to $2,000,000. **Investment Policies:** Well-developed product/service addressing a pressing need with a clear path to market. Provide entrepreneur and customer references. **Industry Preferences:** Financial services; software; healthcare.

42794 ■ Rose Tech Ventures LLC (RTV)
158 W 29th St., 11th Fl.
New York, NY 10001
Ph: (212)228-8770
Fax: (212)228-9911
Co. E-mail: info@rose.vc
URL: http://www.rose.vc
Contact: David S. Rose, Managing Partner
E-mail: david@fiveroses.org
Description: Early-stage angel investment fund. **Founded:** 2001.

42795 ■ RTP Ventures (RTP)
104 Fifth Ave. 17th Fl.
New York, NY 10011
URL: http://rtp.vc
Contact: Leonid Boguslavsky, Co-Founder
Description: Early stage venture capital firm for tech companies on the East Coast of the United States. **Investment Policies:** Companies founded by engineers solving big problems with technology.

42796 ■ Russian Partners
28 Liberty St.
New York, NY 10005
Description: Venture capital firm for startups in Russia. Also maintains an office in Moscow. **Founded:** 1991. **Investment Policies:** Unique markets; low entry valuations. potential for resale to an investor or public offering. **Industry Preferences:** Advertising and publishing; construction materials; consumer products and services; financial services and leasing; IT; logistics; media; pharmaceuticals; real estate; retail telecommunication.

42797 ■ Sandler Capital Management
711 5th Ave., 15th Fl.
New York, NY 10022
Ph: (212)754-8100
Fax: (212)826-0280
URL: http://www.sandlercap.com
Contact: Steven Warshavsky, Managing Director Chief Financial Officer
Description: Finance: Investment advisors, both private equity and hedge funds. **Founded:** 1988. **Preferred Investment Size:** $20,000,000 minimum. **Investment Policies:** Equity. **Industry Preferences:** Internet specific, communications and media, other products, computer software and services, consumer related, medical and health, semiconductors and other electronics.

42798 ■ Scout Ventures
65 N Moore St.
New York, NY 10013
URL: http://www.scout.vc
Contact: Brad Harrison, Managing Partner
Linkedin: www.linkedin.com/company/scout-ventures
X (Twitter): twitter.com/scoutventures
Description: Venture capital firm interested in technology startups. **Investment Policies:** Seeks founders from the military/intelligence communities or leading research universities/national labs with capital-efficient businesses and scalable technologies.

42799 ■ Siguler Guff & Co. (SG)
200 Pk. Ave., 23rd Fl.
New York, NY 10166
Ph: (212)332-5100
Fax: (212)332-5120
URL: http://www.sigulerguff.com
Contact: Shaun Khubchandani, Director
Description: Firm provides investment strategies including distressed and special situations, distressed real estate, small business, emerging markets and secondary investments. **Founded:** 1991. **Industry Preferences:** Communications, computer software and hardware, Internet specific, semiconductors and other electronics, biotechnology, medical and health, consumer related, industrial and energy, transportation, financial services, business service, manufacturing, agriculture, forestry and fishing.

42800 ■ Silas Capital, LLC
1330 6th Ave., 14th Fl.
New York, NY 10019
Co. E-mail: info@silascapital.com
URL: http://www.silascapital.com
Contact: Carter Weiss, Partner
Description: Venture capital firm focused on the underserved "white space" of early-stage consumer businesses with a promising brand. **Investment Policies:** Differentiated products that have the potential to be platforms; lead product that can be expanded and diversified; high gross margins; intellectual property; significant growth potential over the 3 to 5 years. **Industry Preferences:** Specialty consumer; consumable goods; internet; consumer retail.

42801 ■ Silicon Alley Venture Partners L.L.C. (SAVP)
300 Park Ave., 18th Fl., GCP
New York, NY 10022
Co. E-mail: partners@savp.com
URL: http://www.savp.com
Contact: Steve Brotman, Managing Partner Founder
Facebook: www.facebook.com/Alphavp
Description: Firm provides seed and early stage investments services. **Founded:** 1998. **Preferred Investment Size:** $3,000,000 to $6,000,000. **Investment Policies:** Start-up, seed, first, early and second stage. **Industry Preferences:** Computer software, Internet specific, technology, and business services.

42802 ■ Space Angels (SA)
New York, NY
Co. E-mail: info@spaceangels.com
URL: http://www.spaceangels.com
Contact: Chad Anderson, Contact
Facebook: www.facebook.com/TheSpaceAngels
Linkedin: www.linkedin.com/company/spaceangels
X (Twitter): x.com/spaceangels
YouTube: www.youtube.com/channel/UCwVtsVkwrD4ZvlTtmSJ7Vjw
Description: Offers capital for early-stage space ventures. **Founded:** 2007.

42803 ■ Starta Ventures
220 E 23rd St., Ste. 400
New York, NY 10010
Ph: (917)947-9692
Co. E-mail: info@starta.vc
URL: http://starta.vc
Contact: Gabriel Arant, Director
Facebook: www.facebook.com/startavc
Linkedin: www.linkedin.com/company/startavc
X (Twitter): x.com/Starta_vc
Instagram: www.instagram.com/starta_vc
YouTube: www.youtube.com/channel/UC_a0pYu8ncp1Drf3_ieHZ4A
Description: Invests in pre-seed to Round A; provides co-investment opportunities for angel investors; helps founder go global. Also offers a six-month accelerator program. **Founded:** 2011.

42804 ■ Tribeca Early Stage Partners (TESP)
205 Hudson St.
New York, NY 10013
Co. E-mail: info@tribecaesp.com
URL: http://www.tribecaesp.com
Contact: John Berton, General Counsel
Description: Offers early-stage capital for fintech companies. **Founded:** 2014. **Preferred Investment Size:** $50,000-$100,000.

42805 ■ Upstage Ventures LLC
New York, NY
URL: http://www.upstageventures.com
Contact: Mark Wachen, Founder Managing Director
Description: Venture capital firm for early-stage consumer internet and interactive marketing companies. **Founded:** 2009.

42806 ■ Valar Ventures
28 Liberty St.
New York, NY 10005
URL: http://www.valar.com
Contact: Andrew McCormack, Co-Founder Managing Partner
Description: Invests in fast-growing, high-margin technology companies pursuing market opportunities.

42807 ■ Vayner/RSE
10 Hudson Yards
New York, NY 10001
URL: http://vaynerrse.com
Description: Venture capital firm specializing in the first round of institutional financing. **Founded:** 2014.

42808 ■ Vencon Management Inc. (VMI)
301 W 53rd St.
New York, NY 10019
Contact: Irwin Barash, Chief Executive Officer
Description: Venture capital firm and management consultants to corporations and entrepreneurs. Specializes in the areas of mergers and acquisitions evaluation and negotiation and the preparation of marketing and business plans. Assists small or new businesses in expansion plans and financing. **Scope:** Venture capital firm and management consultants to corporations and entrepreneurs. Specializes in the areas of mergers and acquisitions evaluation and negotiation and the preparation of marketing and business plans. Assists small or new businesses in expansion plans and financing. **Training:** Heegaard Knot Diagrams, Sep, 2009; Issues in finite Approximation, Oct, 2009. **Preferred Investment Size:** $500,000 to $3,000,000. **Industry Preferences:** Communications, computer software, Internet specific, semiconductors and other electronics, biotechnology, medical and health.

42809 ■ Venrock
7 Bryant Pk., 23rd Fl.
New York, NY 10018
Ph: (212)444-4100
Fax: (212)444-4101
URL: http://www.venrock.com
Contact: Nick Beim, Partner
E-mail: nick@venrock.com
Facebook: www.facebook.com/venrock
Linkedin: www.linkedin.com/company/venrock
X (Twitter): x.com/Venrock
Description: Provider of venture capital, investment and medical devices. **Founded:** 1969. **Preferred Investment Size:** $5,000,000 to $15,000,000. **Industry Preferences:** Biotechnology, Internet specific, computer software and services, communications and media, medical and health, semiconductors and other electronics, industrial and energy, computer hardware, other products, and consumer related.

42810 ■ Venture Capital Fund of America Inc. (VCFA)
509 Madison Ave.
New York, NY 10022
Ph: (212)838-5577
Fax: (212)838-7614
Co. E-mail: sharris@vcfa.com
URL: http://www.vcfa.com
Contact: Andrew K. Reilly, Managing Director
Description: Investment firm provides investment advisory services, financial planning, consulting and investment management services. **Founded:** 1982. **Preferred Investment Size:** $1,000,000 to $100,000,000.

42811 ■ Warburg Pincus L.L.C.
Warburg Pincus L.L.C.
450 Lexington Ave.
New York, NY 10017
Ph: (212)878-0600
Fax: (212)878-9351
URL: http://warburgpincus.com
Contact: Timothy F. Geithner, President
Description: Private equity firm provides investment services. **Founded:** 1966. **Preferred Investment Size:** $1,000,000 minimum. **Industry Preferences:** Other products, communications and media, medical and health, Internet specific, computer hardware computer software and services, consumer related, industrial and energy, biotechnology, semiconductors and other electronics.

42812 ■ WarnerMedia Investments
30 Hudson Yards
New York, NY 10001
Ph: (212)484-8000
Co. E-mail: recruitadmin@warnermediagroup.com
URL: http://www.warnermedia.com/us
Contact: Gerhard Zeiler, President
Facebook: www.facebook.com/warnermedia
Linkedin: www.linkedin.com/company/warnermedia
X (Twitter): twitter.com/WarnerMedia
Instagram: www.instagram.com/warnermedia
YouTube: www.youtube.com/c/WarnerMedia

Description: Invests in early- to mid-stage companies. **Investment Policies:** Delivery of new services, product enhancement, entry or expansion into a key strategic market, or critical research and development. Demonstrated feasibility of business model. Attractive financial return.

42813 ■ Welsh, Carson, Anderson and Stowe (WCAS)
Welsh, Carson, Anderson and Stowe (WCAS)
599 Lexington Ave., Ste. 1800
New York, NY 10022
Ph: (212)893-9500
URL: http://www.wcas.com
Contact: Renee DeSilva, Chief Executive Officer
Description: Firm provides private equity investment services. **Founded:** 1979. **Preferred Investment Size:** $100,000,000 to $500,000,000. **Industry Preferences:** Medical and health, other products, communications and media, Internet specific, computer software and services, computer hardware, consumer related, semiconductors and other electronics.

42814 ■ Westchester Angels
187 Wolf Rd., Ste. 101
Albany, NY 12205
Description: Angel investment group for early-stage companies. **Founded:** 2015.

42815 ■ Westwood Capital LLC
437 Madison Ave., 24th Fl.
New York, NY 10017
Ph: (212)867-3200
Fax: (212)867-7515
Co. E-mail: info@westwoodcapital.com
URL: http://www.westwoodcapital.com
Contact: Jon Messersmith, Managing Director
Description: Offers real estate advisory services; financial advice for mergers and acquisition; securitization and corporate finance; and restructuring advisory services and litigation support. **Founded:** 1995. **Industry Preferences:** Hospitality; gaming; healthcare.

42816 ■ Willowridge Partners Inc.
122 E 42nd St., 37th Fl.
New York, NY 10017
Ph: (212)369-4700
Fax: (212)369-5661
Co. E-mail: info@willowridge.com
URL: http://willowridge.com
Contact: Angela Qiu, Director, Finance
E-mail: aqiu@willowridge.com
Description: Investment manager. Purchases interests in venture capital, buyout, mezzanine, and other private equity funds from existing investors who want liquidity. **Founded:** 1995.

42817 ■ Winklevoss Capital Management, LLC
30 W 24th St., 4th Fl.
New York, NY 10010
URL: http://winklevosscapital.com
Linkedin: www.linkedin.com/company/winklevoss-capital
X (Twitter): x.com/winklevosscap
Instagram: www.instagram.com/winklevosscap
Description: Offers seed funding and infrastructure to early-stage startups. **Founded:** 2012.

42818 ■ Zelkova Ventures
667 Madison Ave.
New York, NY 10065
URL: http://zelkovavc.com
Contact: Jay Levy, Partner
Description: Early-stage venture capital firm. **Founded:** 2006.

PROCUREMENT ASSISTANCE PROGRAMS

42819 ■ Empire State Development-Division for Small Business-Procurement Assistance Program (ESD)
655 3rd Ave., - 3rd Fl.
New York, NY 10017

Ph: (518)292-5266
URL: http://esd.ny.gov/procurement-assistance-program#objective
Description: Government agency aims to help procurement assistance program for small businesses to identify contracting opportunities with state government agencies.

42820 ■ Monroe County Finger Lakes Procurement Technical Assistance Center (MCFL PTAC)
City Pl. Bldg.
50 W Main St., Ste. 1150
Rochester, NY 14614
Ph: (585)753-2017
URL: http://newyorkphotonics.org/profile/479
Contact: Anna Vulaj, Contact
E-mail: avulaj@monroecounty.gov
Description: Assists members in all facets of selling to the government and military.

42821 ■ New York City Department of Business Services - New York City Procurement Outreach Program
110 William St., 7th Fl.
New York, NY 10038
Co. E-mail: procurementhelpdesk@sbs.nyc.gov
URL: http://www.nyc.gov

42822 ■ New York Procurement Center
26 Federal Pl., Ste. 3100
New York, NY 10278
Ph: (212)264-4354
Co. E-mail: answerdesk@sba.gov
URL: http://www.sba.gov/offices/district/ny/new-york
Contact: Beth L. Goldberg, Director
Description: Covers activities for GSA, Federal Supply Service (New York, NY), GSA, Public Buildings Service (New York, NY), Army Corps of Engineers (New York, NY), U.S. Military Academy (West Point, NY).

42823 ■ New York Procurement Technical Assistance Center - Cattaraugus County
303 Ct. St.
Little Valley, NY 14755
Ph: (716)938-2331
Co. E-mail: ptac@cattco.org
URL: http://cattapex.org
Contact: Lenora Leasure, Program Manager
Facebook: www.facebook.com/CattCoPTAC
Linkedin: www.linkedin.com/company/catt-apex
Description: Assist businesses in marketing goods and services to military, federal, state, and local government agencies. **Founded:** 1987.

42824 ■ New York Procurement Technical Assistance Center - LaGuardia Community College PTAC
31-10 Thomson Ave.
Long Island City, NY 11101
Ph: (718)482-5306
Co. E-mail: apex@lagcc.cuny.edu
URL: http://www.laguardia.edu/ce/business-services/apex-accelerators
Description: Assists Queens and other New York City firms market their goods and services to the federal, state, and local governments. **Founded:** 1999.

42825 ■ New York Procurement Technical Assistance Center - Long Island Development Corp. (LIDC)
175 Engineers Rd., Ste. 200
Hauppauge, NY 11788
Ph: (516)433-5000
Fax: (516)433-5046
Co. E-mail: info@lidc.org
URL: http://www.lidc.org
Description: Assistance to small businesses desiring to win contracts to supply the government, both federal and state. **Founded:** 1980.

42826 ■ Rockland Economic Development Corporation (REDC)
50 Sanatorium Rd., Building A, 8th Fl.
Pomona, NY 10970

Ph: (845)364-2170
URL: http://www.redc.org
Contact: Phyllis W. Tucker, Director, Operations Director, Marketing
E-mail: ptucker@redc.org
Facebook: www.facebook.com/REDCORG
Linkedin: www.linkedin.com/company/rockland-economic-developement-corp
X (Twitter): x.com/redcptac

Description: Provides programs and services to make your relocation and expansion decisions easier and cost effective. **Geographic Preference:** Local.

42827 ■ South Bronx Overall Economic Development Corporation (SoBro)
555 Bergen Ave.
Bronx, NY 10455
Co. E-mail: info@sobro.org
URL: http://www.sobro.org
Contact: Jean Smith, Vice Chairman of the Board
Facebook: www.facebook.com/SoBronxNY
Linkedin: www.linkedin.com/company/sobro-south-bronx-overall-economic-development-corporation
X (Twitter): x.com/sboedc
Instagram: www.instagram.com/sobroedc
YouTube: www.youtube.com/channel/UCuH9alVYdnK-2-e4Y-sP4uQ

Description: Assists local businesses in securing government contracts. **Founded:** 1972. **Geographic Preference:** Local.

INCUBATORS/RESEARCH AND TECHNOLOGY PARKS

42828 ■ 43North (43N)
1 W Seneca St., Fl. 24
Buffalo, NY 14203
Co. E-mail: info@43north.org
URL: http://www.43north.org
Contact: Colleen Heidinger, President
E-mail: colleen@43north.org
Facebook: www.facebook.com/43NorthOrg
Linkedin: www.linkedin.com/company/43north
X (Twitter): x.com/forty3north
Instagram: www.instagram.com/forty3north

Description: Accelerator program investing $5,000,000 through an annual startup competition to attract and cultivate high-growth startups in Buffalo, NY. Offers free incubator space, the opportunity to operate tax-free, and a team with hands-on recruiting and marketing support. **Founded:** 2014. **Investment Policies:** Domain expertise; ready-to-ship product; customer traction.

42829 ■ 1776 New York City
63 Flushing Ave., Bldg. 280, Ste. 814
Brooklyn, NY 11205
Ph: (267)765-2070
Co. E-mail: info@1776.vc
URL: http://www.1776.vc/newyorkcity
Contact: Jennifer Maher, Chief Executive Officer
E-mail: jennifer@1776.vc
Facebook: www.facebook.com/1776vc
Linkedin: www.linkedin.com/company/1776vc
X (Twitter): twitter.com/1776
Instagram: www.instagram.com/1776vc

Description: A global incubator and seed fund that believes startups can change the world.

42830 ■ The Accelerator
4 Crotty Ln., Ste. 100
New Windsor, NY 12553
Ph: (845)234-4449
Co. E-mail: mschouten@the-accelerator.com
URL: http://theaccelerator.business
Facebook: www.facebook.com/TheAccelerator.Business

Description: Works to attract manufacturing-based businesses to the mid-Hudson Valley. Offers reduced-rate occupancy costs, workforce training, and mentoring programs. **Industry Preferences:** Fashion design and production; medical devices; software; personal care products; technology.

42831 ■ ACRE
64 Meserole Ave.
Brooklyn, NY 11222
Ph: (718)954-9074
Co. E-mail: info@acrenyc.com
URL: http://www.acrenyc.com
Instagram: www.instagram.com/acre_nyc

Description: Clean energy incubator providing access to strategic advisement, introductions to industry stakeholders, marketing and branding support, investor networks, and access to a community of like-minded founders.

42832 ■ Adirondack Regional Business Incubator
234 Glen St.
Glens Falls, NY 12801
Description: Distributor of key cases.

42833 ■ AF Ventures
New York, NY 10010
Co. E-mail: info@afventures.vc
URL: http://www.afventures.vc
Linkedin: www.linkedin.com/company/afventures
Instagram: www.instagram.com/afventuresvc

Description: Invests in disruptive food and beverage companies and provides them with industry access, expertise, and infrastructure. Accel is a startup fund for startups. **Founded:** 2014.

42834 ■ Albany Center for Economic Success (ACES)
255 Orange St., Ste. 103
Albany, NY 12210
URL: http://mycommunityloanfund.org/aces-staff-and-board
Contact: Patrick Miller, President

Description: A private, non-profit organization focusing on building local business by providing incubator services and technical assistance programs. It provides below market rate office space and supports tenants through shared clerical staff, general office equipment, conference space, and on-going technical service. **Founded:** 1985.

42835 ■ Alexandria Center for Life Science
430 E 29th St.
New York, NY 10016
URL: http://nyc.are.com
Contact: John Cunningham, Contact
E-mail: jcunningham@are.com

Description: Provides tenants with access to an unmatched concentration of scientific, clinical and entrepreneurial talent; top-tier investment capital; and a diverse and innovative commercial life science industry.

42836 ■ Alexandria Launch Labs
Alexandria Center for Life Science
430 E 29th St., 14th Fl.
New York, NY 10016
Co. E-mail: info@alexandrialaunchlabs.com
URL: http://www.alexandrialaunchlabs.com
Linkedin: www.linkedin.com/company/alexandria-launchlabs

Description: A startup platform designed to satisfy a key unmet need for affordable space for seed-stage life science companies in New York City. **Founded:** 2016.

42837 ■ AngelPad
78 5th Ave.
New York, NY 10013
URL: http://angelpad.co
Contact: Carine Magescas, Founder

Description: On-site business accelerator providing human resource support, office space, and PR assistance. **Founded:** 2010.

42838 ■ Antler - USA
9th Ave. Bldg. 368
New York, NY 10001
Co. E-mail: hello@antler.co
URL: http://www.antler.co/location/us
Contact: Annie Ripp, Manager
Facebook: www.facebook.com/antlerglobal
Linkedin: www.linkedin.com/company/antlerglobal
X (Twitter): twitter.com/AntlerGlobal
Instagram: www.instagram.com/antlerglobal

Description: An early-stage startup accelerator for companies based in North America. **Founded:** 2017.

42839 ■ Audubon Business and Technology Center
3960 Broadway
New York, NY 10032
URL: http://www.facilities.cuimc.columbia.edu/audubon-business-and-technology-center

Description: Designed to house early stage, private research and development companies in the Life Sciences industry.

42840 ■ Binghamton University - Southern Tier High Technology Incubator (STHTI)
4400 Vestal Pky. E
Binghamton, NY 13902
URL: http://www.binghamton.edu/research/innovation/econdev/sthti.html
Contact: Kevin E. Drumm, Director

Description: Business incubator that provides the infrastructure needed for companies focusing on energy, electronics and health. Includes specialized laboratories and other features associated with industry-based R&D, including testing and evaluation and prototyping. The incubator will has business resources, and tenants will be connected to research and educational programming at Binghamton University and SUNY Broome. **Founded:** 1946.

42841 ■ Binghamton University - Start-Up Suite
PO Box 6000
Binghamton, NY 13902-6000
URL: http://www.binghamton.edu/research/division-offices/innovation/incubators/index.html

Description: Provides low-cost space and business support services to spin-off enterprises with roots in faculty research.

42842 ■ Blue Ridge Labs (BRL)
150 Ct. St.
Brooklyn, NY 11201
Co. E-mail: blueridgelabs@robinhood.org
URL: http://labs.robinhood.org
Contact: Sergio Marrero, Managing Director
Linkedin: www.linkedin.com/showcase/blue-ridge-labs-at-robin-hood
X (Twitter): x.com/blueridgelabs

Description: A Brooklyn-based social impact incubator whose programs encourage entrepreneurs, designers, and developers to build products for communities that are often overlooked by technology. **Founded:** 2015.

42843 ■ Blueprint Health
c/o Brad Weinberg
447 Broadway 2nd Fl.
New York, NY 10013
Co. E-mail: info@blueprinthealth.org
URL: http://www.blueprinthealth.org
Contact: Richard Barasch, Chief Executive Officer

Description: A mentorship-driven startup accelerator program supporting companies at the intersection of health and technology. **Founded:** 2011.

42844 ■ Bronx Business Tech Incubator
2501 Grand Concourse, 3rd Fl.
Bronx, NY 10468
Ph: (718)960-8381
Co. E-mail: business.incubator@lehman.cuny.edu
URL: http://www.lehman.edu/techincubator
Contact: Marisa Estrella, President

Description: Startup incubator for local small businesses and freelancers. Helps startups build successful companies to create more jobs and to drive new innovation and technology in the Bronx Supported by the New York City Council and New York City Economic Development Corp.

42845 ■ Bronx Cookspace
50 E 168th St.
Bronx, NY 10452
Ph: (718)839-1105
Co. E-mail: aolivares@whedco.org

URL: http://www.bronxcookspace.org/en
Facebook: www.facebook.com/BronxCookSpace
Instagram: www.instagram.com/bronxcookspace
Description: Incubator kitchen offering affordable shared kitchen space for small food businesses; a program of the Women's Housing and Economic Development Corporation (WHEDco).

42846 ■ Brooklyn Fashion + Design Accelerator (BF+DA)
Brooklyn, NY
Co. E-mail: christine@bkaccelerator.com
URL: http://cfda.com/resources/sustainability-resources/detail/brooklyn-fashion-design-accelerator-bfda
Contact: Christine Billard, Coordinator
E-mail: christine@bkaccelerator.com
Description: A hub for ethical fashion and design that provides designers with the resources they need to transform their ideas into successful businesses.

42847 ■ Brooklyn FoodWorks
URL: http://thebrooklynfoodworks.com
Description: A culinary incubator with commercial kitchen space for food startups.

42848 ■ Broome County Industrial Development Agency (BCIDA)
5 S College Dr.
Binghamton, NY 13905
URL: http://theagency-ny.com/broome-county-economic-development-agency
Description: Provides comprehensive services to companies, including needs assessment, site selection, financial aid, and more.

42849 ■ Center for Social Innovation (CSI)
601 W 26th St., Ste. 325
New York, NY 10001
URL: http://socialinnovation.org
Linkedin: www.linkedin.com/company/csitoronto
YouTube: www.youtube.com/user/centreforSI
Description: A coworking space for startups and entrepreneurs. Provides members with tools necessary to accelerate their success.

42850 ■ Center for Urban Entrepreneurship (CUE)
40 Franklin St.
Rochester, NY 14604
URL: http://www.rit.edu/cue
Contact: Ebony Miller, Director
E-mail: emiller@saunders.rit.edu
Description: Helps to reshape the regional economy and build wealth within the urban community by being the central resource for urban entrepreneurial programs and research.

42851 ■ Center4
420 Lexington Ave., Ste. 2531
New York, NY 10170
Contact: Manabu Takanaka, Contact
Description: Connects health and human service nonprofits with technology to transform how these services are delivered to help more individuals in need, work more efficiently and produce better outcomes.

42852 ■ CFDA Fashion Incubator
1350 Ave. of the Americas, 2nd Fl.
New York, NY 10019
URL: http://cfda.com/programs/designers
Description: A business development program designed to support the next generation of fashion designers in New York City. The mission is to help grow and sustain the businesses of the 10 participating brands over the course of the two year program.

42853 ■ The Clean Tech Center (TTG)
235 Harrison St.
Syracuse, NY 13202
Ph: (315)470-1959
Co. E-mail: info@thetechgarden.com
URL: http://www.thetechgarden.com/cleantechcenter.html
Facebook: www.facebook.com/thetechgarden
Linkedin: www.linkedin.com/company/syracuse-technology-garden
X (Twitter): x.com/thetechgarden
Instagram: www.instagram.com/thetechgarden
Description: Develops emerging businesses and commercializing technologies in the following sectors: renewable energy, alternative fuels, system integration and smart grid technologies, transportation, and buildings and construction technologies. **Founded:** 2005.

42854 ■ CNY Biotech Accelerator (CNYBAC)
841 E Fayette St.
Syracuse, NY 13210
Ph: (315)464-9288
Co. E-mail: cnybac@upstate.edu
URL: http://cnybac.com/about-the-accelerator
Contact: Kathi Durdon, Executive Director
E-mail: durdonk@upstate.edu
Description: Firm is a business incubator that engages in providing wet labs, mentorship and other related services for biotechnology innovation.

42855 ■ Collab
309 Starr St.
New York, NY 10001
Ph: (212)727-3190
URL: http://www.collab-orators.com
X (Twitter): x.com/collabnyc
Instagram: www.instagram.com/collabnyc
Description: A fabrication lab and innovation studio that provides space and shared resources to creative entrepreneurs.

42856 ■ Cooke & Bake Center LLC
360-C Mt. Pleasant Ave.
Mamaroneck, NY 10543
Ph: (914)698-3663
Co. E-mail: info@cookandbakecenter.com
URL: http://cookandbakecenter.com
Contact: Janine Zaidman Goldentaier, Chief Executive Officer
Facebook: www.facebook.com/Cook-Bake-Center-151598008231424
YouTube: www.youtube.com/user/CookandBakeCenter
Description: Commercial kitchen available for food producers, photo shoots, classes, private events, and testing sessions. **Founded:** 2008.

42857 ■ Cornell University Institute of Biotechnology (CIB)
130 Biotechnology Bldg.
Ithaca, NY 14853
Ph: (607)255-2300
Co. E-mail: biotech@cornell.edu
URL: http://www.biotech.cornell.edu
Contact: Tami Magnus, Executive Director
X (Twitter): x.com/CornellBiotech
Description: Seeks to catalyze life science research, stimulate biotechnological innovation and foster entrepreneurship locally, regionally and internationally. Provides a hub for cutting edge scientific facilities, education and training.

42858 ■ Couri Hatchery Student Business Incubator
721 University Ave.
Syracuse, NY 13244-2450
URL: http://whit-www-core.syr.edu/programs-and-academics/centers-and-institutes/falcone/for-students/couri.aspx
Description: Student-centered co-working space and mentorship program. Supports student ventures from idea through start-up. Named for John Couri, the co-founder of Duty Free International.

42859 ■ Court Square Law Project
2 Ct. Sq.
Long Island City, NY 11101
Ph: (718)340-4412
Co. E-mail: info@courtsquarelaw.org
URL: http://www.courtsquarelaw.org
Contact: Tamara A. Steckler, Executive Director
X (Twitter): x.com/CourtSquareLaw
Description: Incubator providing high-quality civil legal services to moderate-income clients and jobs to recent law school graduates. Incubator participants are selected through an annual application process. **Founded:** 2016.

42860 ■ CSI Tech Incubator
60 Bay St., Ste. 902
Staten Island, NY 10301
Ph: (646)766-9554
Fax: (646)766-9558
Co. E-mail: csitechincubator@csi.cuny.edu
URL: http://www.csitechincubator.com
Contact: Jasmine Cardona, Executive Director
Facebook: www.facebook.com/CSITechIncubator
Linkedin: www.linkedin.com/in/csitechnologyincubator
X (Twitter): x.com/techincubatorsi
Instagram: www.instagram.com/techincubatorsi
YouTube: www.youtube.com/channel/UCgEP9RQqzZBFZrwhAlBdWZw/videos
Description: Fosters a community of tech innovators and entrepreneurs that are seeking to advance and grow their startups..

42861 ■ CUNY Startup Accelerator
55 Lexington Ave., 2nd Fl., Field Ctr.
New York, NY 10010
Ph: (646)844-2869
Co. E-mail: hi@cunystartups.com
URL: http://cunystartups.com
Contact: Remy Arteaga, Executive Director
E-mail: remy@cunystartups.com
Facebook: www.facebook.com/CUNYStartups
Linkedin: www.linkedin.com/company/cuny-startups
Instagram: www.instagram.com/cunystartups
YouTube: www.youtube.com/channel/UCLMigctvIE_Ev1W_stO-laA
Description: A 4-month program that enables CUNY students to launch a startup. The program combines the cutting-edge methods in solidifying an idea, building a prototype, getting customer feedback and launching a startup. We invest up to $5,000 per startup. **Founded:** 2014.

42862 ■ CUNY SustainableWorks
205 E 42nd St.
New York, NY 10017
Ph: (646)664-9035
URL: http://www1.cuny.edu/sites/sustainable
Description: Working to leverage a platform to enable the market for cleantech innovations and processes.

42863 ■ Digital Harvest Capital
56 E 11th St., 5th Fl.
New York, NY 10003
Co. E-mail: info@digitalharvestcapital.com
URL: http://www.digitalharvestcapital.com
Facebook: www.facebook.com/digitalharvestcapital
Instagram: www.instagram.com/digitalharvestmedia
YouTube: www.youtube.com/channel/UCAI6XmOfJqoVwFiO5ymt4Jg
Description: A development stage digital media incubator that partners with creative entrepreneurs seeking to engage audiences through exceptional entertainment concepts. **Founded:** 2011.

42864 ■ Dreamit Ventures
33 Irving Pl., 10th Fl.
New York, NY 10003
Co. E-mail: info@dreamit.com
URL: http://www.dreamit.com
Contact: Brittany Gillow, Director
Facebook: www.facebook.com/dreamitventures
Linkedin: www.linkedin.com/company/dreamit-ventures
X (Twitter): x.com/dreamit
YouTube: www.youtube.com/user/DreamItVentures
Description: Business incubator supporting entrepreneurs by providing seed, early venture, and late stage venture investing. **Founded:** 2008.

42865 ■ East Side Business Center L.L.C. (ESBC)
1201 E Fayette St., Ste. 26
Syracuse, NY 13210
Ph: (315)472-3820

42866 ■ New York

Fax: (315)234-5724
URL: http://www.housingvisions.org
Description: A small business incubator offering office and light manufacturing, industrial space to new ventures, entrepreneurs and expanding businesses. **Founded:** 1990.

42866 ■ The Ember Company
530 5th Ave., 9th Fl.
 New York, NY 10036
Co. E-mail: info@embercompany.co
URL: http://www.embercompany.co
Contact: Avani Patel, Co-Founder Managing Partner
Linkedin: www.linkedin.com/company/embercompany
X (Twitter): x.com/TheEmberCompany
Instagram: www.instagram.com/theembercompany
Description: A New York-based, four-month program that gives emerging fashion brands the tools they need to grow their businesses. TrendSeeder will provide a creative professional environment to foster promising fashion talent through mentorship and brand building opportunities with advisors, investors, experts in fashion and PR, editors, and marketing and production professionals. **Founded:** 2012.

42867 ■ The Entrepreneur Space (ES)
36-46 37th St.
 Long Island City, NY 11101-1606
Ph: (718)392-0025
Co. E-mail: info@entrepreneurspace.org
URL: http://entrepreneurspace.org
Facebook: www.facebook.com/EntrepreneurSpace
X (Twitter): x.com/ESpaceNYC
Description: Provides tools and resources to small and startup businesses including a commercial kitchen for rent, free or low cost business counseling.

42868 ■ Entrepreneurs Roundtable Accelerator (ERA)
40 W 25 St., 9th Fl.
 New York, NY 10010
URL: http://www.eranyc.com
Contact: Jeremy Harper, Director
Linkedin: www.linkedin.com/company/1968378
X (Twitter): x.com/eranyc
Description: Early stage fund and technology accelerator in New York City that runs 2 four month programs per year. **Founded:** 2011.

42869 ■ The Entrepreneur's Space (ES)
36-46 37th St.
 Long Island City, NY 11101-1606
Ph: (718)392-0025
Co. E-mail: info@entrepreneurspace.org
URL: http://entrepreneurspace.org
Facebook: www.facebook.com/EntrepreneurSpace
X (Twitter): x.com/ESpaceNYC
Description: A food and business incubator that provides counseling, assists minority-owned businesses, organizes promotional events and offers kitchen space.

42870 ■ Farmingdale State College Broad Hollow Bioscience Park (BHBP)
2350 Broadhollow Rd.
 Farmingdale, NY 11735
Ph: (934)420-2000
Co. E-mail: bhbp@farmingdale.edu
URL: http://www.farmingdale.edu/broad-hollow
 -bioscience-park
Contact: Dan Polner, Executive Director
Description: Supports early-stage companies with a need for wet laboratory space.

42871 ■ Fashion Tech Consortium Advanced Accelerator
25 W 39th Str, Ste. 1400
 New York, NY 10018
Co. E-mail: info@fashiontechco.com
URL: http://www.fashiontechco.com
Contact: Michael B. Reidbord, President
Description: Provide enterprise-ready innovative technology solutions to an industry in crisis. Provides a platform for the fashion industry to come together to collaborate, innovate, test and deploy new solutions that will benefit the entire industry. **Founded:** 2017.

42872 ■ FinTech Innovation Lab
1 Battery Park Plz., 5th Fl.
 New York, NY 10004
Co. E-mail: fil.nyc@accenture.com
URL: http://www.fintechinnovationlab.com/regions/
 new-york
Linkedin: www.linkedin.com/company/fintech-innovation-lab
X (Twitter): x.com/FinTechLab
Description: A 12-week accelerator program un by the New York City Investment Fund and Accenture for early and growth stage companies that have developed cutting edge technology products targeted at financial services customers. **Founded:** 2011.

42873 ■ FOOD-X
255 W 36th St.
 New York, NY 10018
Co. E-mail: food-x@food-x.com
URL: http://food-x.com
Contact: Aki Balogh, Chief Executive Officer
Facebook: www.facebook.com/foodxaccelerator
X (Twitter): x.com/foodXhealth
Instagram: www.instagram.com/foodxaccelerator
Description: Food innovation accelerator helping food entrepreneurs bring their products and services to market at super speed. **Founded:** 2014.

42874 ■ FoodFutureCo (FFC)
New York, NY 10036
Co. E-mail: info@foodfuture.co
URL: http://www.foodfuture.co
Contact: Shen Tong, Managing Partner Founder
Facebook: www.facebook.com/FoodFutureCo
Linkedin: www.linkedin.com/company/foodfutureco
X (Twitter): x.com/FoodFutureCo
Instagram: www.instagram.com/foodfutureco
Description: A scale-up accelerator for established, yet small organizations that are providing unique products and solutions across our food system. Focus areas include: consumer products, local food, plant-based food, sustainable seafood, ag tech, food tech and food waste. **Founded:** 2015.

42875 ■ Fordham University - Fordham Foundry
557 E Fordham Rd., 2nd Fl.
 Bronx, NY 10458
Ph: (718)817-5660
Co. E-mail: info@fordhamfoundry.org
URL: http://www.fordhamfoundry.org
Contact: Albert J. Bartosic, Executive Director
E-mail: abartosic@fordham.edu
Facebook: www.facebook.com/fordhamfoundry
Linkedin: www.linkedin.com/company/fordham
 -foundry
X (Twitter): x.com/FordhamFoundry
Instagram: www.instagram.com/fordhamfoundry
Description: Focused on creating and growing small businesses. An independent, mixed-use business incubator located off-campus that was developed specifically to assist promising entrepreneurs in launching new businesses by providing collaborative workspace, shared office equipment, confidential business consultation, a mentoring program, continuous business education and workshops. **Founded:** 2012.

42876 ■ Founder Labs (F)
San Francisco, NY
Co. E-mail: info@founderlabs.org
URL: http://www.founderlabs.org
Contact: Shaherose Charania, Chief Executive Officer
Facebook: www.facebook.com/founderlabs
X (Twitter): x.com/founderlabs
Description: A 5-week pre-incubator for new mobile ideas that focuses on the first phase of launching a mobile startup. **Founded:** 2010.

42877 ■ Founders Factory New York (FF)
New York, NY
URL: http://foundersfactory.com
Contact: Henry Lane Fox, Chief Executive Officer
Description: Tech incubator and accelerator. Also maintains an office in London, England. **Industry Preferences:** Healthcare.

42878 ■ Geneva Enterprise Development Center (GEDC)
122 N Genesee St.
 Geneva, NY 14456
Ph: (315)781-3241
URL: http://www.genevaedc.com
Facebook: www.facebook.com/GenevaEDC
Description: Production incubator. Offers business assistance, finance direction, strategic business support, and office space.

42879 ■ Grand Central Tech (GCT)
22 Vanderbilt Ave., 3rd Fl.
 New York, NY 10017
URL: http://www.companyventures.co
Instagram: www.instagram.com/grandcentraltech
Description: New York's flagship tech accelerator who partners with the world's most innovative corporations to bring key resources to bear on behalf of our startups including: pilot programs, investment, sales channels, mentorship and more. **Founded:** 2015.

42880 ■ Green Worker Cooperatives (GWC)
1231 Lafayette Ave., 2nd Fl.
 Bronx, NY 10474
Ph: (718)617-7807
URL: http://www.greenworker.coop
Contact: Karen Washington, President
Linkedin: www.linkedin.com/company/green-worker
 -cooperatives
X (Twitter): x.com/GreenWorkerCoop
Description: A non-profit organization that incubates environmentally sustainable worker cooperatives in the South Bronx of New York City. **Founded:** 2003.

42881 ■ Griffiss Institute - Cyber Research Institute (CRI)
725 Daedalian Dr.
 Rome, NY 13441
Description: Offers a venue for research and development; fosters collaboration for new funding sources; creates research partnerships; assists in business creation and expansion. .

42882 ■ Harlem Biospace (Hb)
423 W 127th St.
 New York, NY 10027
Co. E-mail: director@harlembiospace.com
URL: http://www.harlembiospace.com
Contact: Chrisha Nario, Director
E-mail: cn@harlembiospace.com
Facebook: www.facebook.com/Harlembiospace
Linkedin: www.linkedin.com/company/harlem
 -biospace
X (Twitter): x.com/Harlembiospace
Instagram: www.instagram.com/harlembiospace
Description: A biotech incubator offering shared wet-lab space for competitively-selected entrants. **Founded:** 2013.

42883 ■ The Hatchery
447 Broadway, 2Fl., ste.381
 New York, NY 10013
Co. E-mail: curious@hatchery.vc
URL: http://hatchery.vc
Contact: Yao Huang, Founder
X (Twitter): x.com/thehatchery
Description: Venture collaboration forum connecting entrepreneurs, emerging companies, and investors through events, advisory services, and an incubator for tech companies in New York. **Founded:** 2007.

42884 ■ HBK Incubates (HBK)
75 Ninth Ave., Ste. 0610
 New York, NY 10011
URL: http://hotbreadkitchen.org/small-business
Description: A shared commercial kitchen space and business support program for high-growth food enterprises, run by award-winning food business Hot Bread Kitchen. Incubator allows entrepreneurs to mitigate start-up risk and grow their food ventures in a community of business owners. **Founded:** 2011.

42885 ■ HHS Accelerator (HHSA)
255 Greenwich St., 9th Fl.
 New York, NY 10007

URL: http://www.nyc.gov/site/mocs/hhsa/about-hhs-accelerator.page
Description: Accelerator that streamlines and enhances the management of the procurement and financial processes for providers delivering direct services to clients and communities. **Founded:** 2013.

42886 ■ Hudson Valley Center for Innovation
c/o Drake Sommers Loeb Tarshis Catania & Liberth PLLC
1 Corwin Ct.
Newburgh, NY 12550
URL: http://www.hvci.org
Contact: Hugh Schwartz, Chief Executive Officer
Description: A not-for-profit corporation formed to foster the growth and development of emerging high value business and technology development firms, and the creation of high-value jobs throughout the Hudson Valley region of New York State through the implementation, and enhancement, of the cost-effective business incubation model.

42887 ■ iBeeHub Incubator
40 Wall St., Ste. 2832
New York, NY 10005
Ph: (347)514-6849
Co. E-mail: info@ibeehub.org
URL: http://www.ibeehub.org/en
Contact: James Chen, Co-Founder
Facebook: www.facebook.com/ibeehub
X (Twitter): x.com/ibeehubnet
Instagram: www.instagram.com/ibeehub
Description: A New York-based angel investor and incubator providing training, consulting, and seed funding to early-stage startup companies. Builds bridges for startups in the U.S. and venture capitalists in China, helping startups connect with Chinese investors and enter or enlarge Chinese market. **Founded:** 2015.

42888 ■ Incubator 39
142 E 39th St.
New York, NY 10016
Co. E-mail: editor@digital.nyc
URL: http://www.digital.nyc/incubators/incubator-39
Facebook: www.facebook.com/theDigitalNYC
X (Twitter): twitter.com/digitalnyc
Description: A hybrid of incubator, accelerator, and co-working business model focused on technology.

42889 ■ Ingk Labs L.L.C.
101 5th Ave., 8th Fl.
New York, NY 10003
Description: Builds companies leveraging IP focused on commerce, customer service, natural language & machine intelligence, analytics & tracking, reputation management, social data aggregation and social noise reduction.

42890 ■ Innovation Incubator
61-20 220th St.
Bayside, NY 11364
Contact: Antony Satyadas, Chief Executive Officer
X (Twitter): x.com/InnovationIncu
Description: Helps firms go to the next level with an immersive environment designed to foster success and surround your entrepreneurial venture with top-notch university resources and experts. **Founded:** 1981.

42891 ■ Institute of Energy: Sustainability, Environment and Equity (IESEE)
c/o Advanced Energy Research and Technology Center
100 Innovation Rd.
Stony Brook, NY 11794-6044
Ph: (631)632-8364
URL: http://www.stonybrook.edu/commcms/iese
Description: Mission is to attract clean-tech and renewable energy companies. Services include mentoring for startup companies, business development for existing companies, and government grant and incentive support.

42892 ■ Interplay Ventures
New York, NY 10011
URL: http://www.interplay.vc
Contact: Mike Rogers, Partner
Linkedin: www.linkedin.com/company/interplayvc
X (Twitter): x.com/interplay
Description: An American startup studio and venture capital company based in New York City. The company incubates, partners and invests in diverse businesses. **Founded:** 2012.

42893 ■ Jefferson County Economic Development (JCED)
800 Starbuck Ave., Ste. 800
Watertown, NY 13601
Ph: (315)782-5865
Free: 800-553-4111
Fax: (315)782-7915
Co. E-mail: mweir@jcida.com
URL: http://www.jcida.com
Contact: David J. Zembiec, Chief Executive Officer
E-mail: dzembiec@jcida.com
Facebook: www.facebook.com/JeffCoEcDev
Linkedin: www.linkedin.com/company/jefferson-county-local-development-corp
X (Twitter): x.com/jeffersonecdev
YouTube: www.youtube.com/channel/UCaq7peeEG3ArVcEmC71Ehgg
Description: Small business incubator offering a one-stop-shop for business development assistance, from capital financing to low-cost facility options to economic development incentives. **Founded:** 1996.

42894 ■ Kaplan EdTech Accelerator
New York, NY
URL: http://kaplan.com/?fbclid=IwAR1nKGsLUg2NFMIC7QeM-1zE7C0x3_ZzG4YK7BBD86GFvtFpBHB7OiQ52qgc
Description: A three-month intensive, mentor-driven, deep immersion program for twelve education technology startups. **Founded:** 2013.

42895 ■ Lair East Labs L.L.C. (LEL)
900 Third Ave., 29th Fl.
New York, NY 10022
Ph: (413)259-5042
Co. E-mail: info@laireastlabs.com
URL: http://laireastlabs.com
Contact: Jie Li, Director
Facebook: www.facebook.com/laireastlabs
X (Twitter): x.com/laireastlabs
Instagram: www.instagram.com/laireastlabs
Description: A startup accelerator for founders interested in launching businesses in China. Uses a 10-week program for startups to learn from alumni founders of top Silicon Valley style accelerators and gain access to a mentor and investor network with extensive experience navigating the Chinese market. **Founded:** 2017.

42896 ■ Lennox Tech Enterprise Center
150 Lucius Gordon Dr., Ste. 100
West Henrietta, NY 14586
Ph: (585)214-2400
Co. E-mail: info@htr.org
URL: http://nextcorps.org
Contact: Jackie Amigone, Manager
E-mail: jackie.amigone@htr.org
Description: A catalyst for innovators who plan to build high-growth businesses, offering success services for startup entrepreneurs. **Founded:** 1987.

42897 ■ Local Development Corporation of East New York (LDCENY)
80 Jamaica Ave., 3rd Fl.
Brooklyn, NY 11207
Ph: (718)385-6700
Fax: (718)385-7505
Co. E-mail: info@ldceny.org
URL: http://www.ldceny.net
Contact: Priscilla Frey-Incorvaia, Chairman
Description: Works to improve the economic situation of East Brooklyn. Operates four divisions: industry, business development, environment, and housing. **Founded:** 1979. **Geographic Preference:** Local.

42898 ■ Long Island High Technology Incubator (LIHTI)
25 Health Sciences Dr.
Stony Brook, NY 11790-3350
Ph: (631)444-8800
Fax: (631)444-8825
Co. E-mail: info@lihti.org
URL: http://lihti.net
Contact: Ryan Welch, Manager, Operations
X (Twitter): x.com/lihti_sbu
Description: The LIHTI offers tenants a place to start up companies without the difficulties normally associated with emerging businesses. The incubator also provides numerous services through its alliances with both public and private sector organizations. **Founded:** 1992.

42899 ■ Made in New York Media Center
30 John St.
Brooklyn, NY 11201
Ph: (718)729-6677
Co. E-mail: community@nymediacenter.com
URL: http://www.nyc-arts.org
Description: A coworking space, business incubator, and exhibition venue providing workspace for media and tech entrepreneurs, innovators, and artists. Provides industry resources, events, mentorship, and educational opportunities to entrepreneurs.

42900 ■ Made in NY Media Center by IFP
30 John St.
Brooklyn, NY 11201
Ph: (718)729-6677
Co. E-mail: community@nymediacenter.com
URL: http://nymediacenter.com
Contact: Jeffrey Sharp, Executive Director
Facebook: www.facebook.com/NyMediaCenter
Linkedin: www.linkedin.com/company/made-in-ny-media-center-by-ifp
X (Twitter): twitter.com/nymediacenter
Instagram: www.instagram.com/nymediacenter
Description: A collaborative workspace and community designed to support and connect the next generation of media and tech entrepreneurs, innovators, and artists with industry resources, events, mentorship, and educational opportunities.

42901 ■ Mancuso Business Development Group
56 Harvester Ave.
Batavia, NY 14020
Ph: (585)343-2800
Fax: (585)343-7096
Co. E-mail: opportunity@mancusogroup.com
URL: http://mancusogroup.com
Contact: Thomas B. Mancuso, Contact
Facebook: www.facebook.com/MancusoGroup
Instagram: www.instagram.com/mancusogroup
Description: Firm provides commercial and residential real estate development services. **Founded:** 1959.

42902 ■ Manufacturing & Technology Enterprise Center (MTEC)
1 Scobie Dr.
Newburgh, NY 12550
Ph: (845)391-8214
Co. E-mail: info@mfgtec.org
URL: http://mfgtec.org
Contact: Tom Phillips, Executive Director
E-mail: tom.phillips@hvtdc.org
Facebook: www.facebook.com/MFGTEC
Description: Develops strategies to help businesses grow to new heights. **Founded:** 1988.

42903 ■ MetaProp
214 W 39th St., Ste. 705
New York, NY 10018
Ph: (646)504-4482
Co. E-mail: info@metaprop.vc
URL: http://www.metaprop.vc
Contact: Safi Aziz, Director
X (Twitter): x.com/MetaPropNYC
YouTube: www.youtube.com/channel/UCd4clugpYKR57nJ82dP2qxQ

Description: Real estate technology accelerator for early stage companies. The program provides world-renowned corporate partners, over 80 mentors, and widespread media coverage. **Founded:** 2015.

42904 ■ Mi Kitchen es su Kitchen
370 E 76th St., Ste. A2004
New York, NY 10021-2550
Ph: (212)452-1866
Fax: (212)452-1767
Co. E-mail: mikitchen1866@aol.com
URL: http://www.mikitchenessukitchen.com
Contact: Kathrine Gregory, Director
Description: A small business incubator offering a time-share rental facility available to up-and-coming food entrepreneurs. **Founded:** 1996.

42905 ■ NeueHouse L.L.C.
New York
New York, NY 10010
Ph: (212)273-0440
Co. E-mail: infony@neuehouse.com
URL: http://neuehouse.com
Facebook: www.facebook.com/NeueHouse
Linkedin: www.linkedin.com/company/neuehouse
Instagram: www.instagram.com/neuehouse
Description: Supports small businesses and entrepreneurs by offering workspace, including distinct conceptual zones with different functions. **Founded:** 2012.

42906 ■ NEW Inc.
231 Bowery, 2nd Fl.
New York, NY 10002
Ph: (212)219-1222
Co. E-mail: incubator@newinc.org
URL: http://www.newinc.org
Contact: Salome Asega, Director
Facebook: www.facebook.com/newinconbowery
X (Twitter): x.com/NEWINC
Instagram: www.instagram.com/newinc
Description: Museum-led cultural incubator dedicated to supporting innovation, collaboration, and entrepreneurship across art, design, and technology. **Founded:** 2014.

42907 ■ New York Digital Health Innovation Lab
1 Battery Park Plz., 5th Fl.
New York, NY 10004
URL: http://digitalhealth.nyc
Linkedin: www.linkedin.com/company/new-york-digital-health-accelerator
X (Twitter): x.com/nydigitalhealth
Description: A program for early- and growth-stage digital health companies that are developing cutting edge technology products in care coordination, patient engagement, predictive analytics and workflow management for healthcare providers. **Founded:** 2013.

42908 ■ New York Medical College - BioInc
New York Medical College
7 Dana Rd.
Valhalla, NY 10595
Ph: (914)594-1999
Co. E-mail: bioinc@nymc.edu
URL: http://www.bioincny.com
Contact: Margarita Diaz, Contact
URL(s): www.nymc.edu/bioinc
Facebook: www.facebook.com/bioincnymc
Linkedin: www.linkedin.com/company/9501062
X (Twitter): x.com/bioincnymc
Description: Biotechnology incubator offering shared resources, turnkey wet lab space, and sponsored professional services to promising, high-potential entrepreneurs and start-ups. Assists members in refining their business strategies, conserving capital, building strong teams, and achieving development and funding milestones. **Founded:** 2014.

42909 ■ NextCorps
260 E Main St., Ste. 6000
Rochester, NY 14604
Ph: (585)214-2400
Fax: (585)327-7931
Co. E-mail: info@nextcorps.org
URL: http://nextcorps.org
Contact: James S. Senall, President
E-mail: james.senall@nextcorps.org
Facebook: www.facebook.com/nextcorps
Linkedin: www.linkedin.com/company/49092
X (Twitter): x.com/nextcorps
Instagram: www.instagram.com/nextcorps
YouTube: www.youtube.com/channel/UCd8UojVymeA27JokavRXCaw
Description: Helps propel high-tech entrepreneurs as well as established manufacturers toward success. **Founded:** 1987.

42910 ■ NYC ACRE
370 Jay St., 7th Fl.
Brooklyn, NY 11201
Co. E-mail: info@ufl.nyc
URL: http://ufl.nyc
Description: Provides space for innovators to connect and develop new technologies essential to meet city and state energy and environmental goals.

42911 ■ NYC Commercial Kitchen
16-50 Utopia Pky.
Whitestone, NY 11357
Ph: (212)470-2207
Co. E-mail: info@nyccommercialkitchen.com
URL: http://nyccommercialkitchen.com
Description: Culinary incubator serving clients who want to start their own businesses without the expensive overhead that comes from owning and managing a commercial kitchen.

42912 ■ NYC Commercial Kitchen
3480 3rd Ave.
Bronx, NY 10456
Ph: (212)470-2207
Co. E-mail: info@nyccommercialkitchen.com
URL: http://nyccommercialkitchen.com
Description: Runs a network of commercial kitchens in the Tri-State area. Allows small business professionals and food service professionals to operate or start a business without the massive overhead associated with a commercial kitchen. Operates other kitchens in Woodhaven and Whitestone, NY .

42913 ■ NYC Media Lab (NYCML)
370 Jay St., 3rd Fl.
Brooklyn, NY 11201
Co. E-mail: info@nycmedialab.org
URL: http://engineering.nyu.edu/research-innovation/centers/nyc-media-lab
Facebook: www.facebook.com/nycmedialab
Linkedin: www.linkedin.com/company/nyc-media-lab
X (Twitter): x.com/nycmedialab
Instagram: www.instagram.com/nycmedialab
YouTube: www.youtube.com/user/nycmedialab
Description: Connects digital media and technology companies with New York City's universities to drive innovation, entrepreneurship, and talent management. Funds prototyping projects that foster collaboration across a range of disciplines. Also runs an early stage accelerator for emerging media and tech startups. **Founded:** 2010.

42914 ■ NYDesigns
29-10 Thomson Ave., 7th Fl.
Long Island City, NY 11101
Ph: (718)663-8400
Co. E-mail: info@nydesigns.org
URL: http://www.nydesigns.org
Contact: Denise Espinal, Manager, Operations
Facebook: www.facebook.com/nydesigns
X (Twitter): x.com/NYDesigns
Instagram: www.instagram.com/nydesignsfablab
Description: Dedicated to the success of design and hardware tech startups in New York City, providing incubation, fabrication, and coworking amenities. **Founded:** 2006.

42915 ■ NYU Poly Incubators
2 MetroTech Ctr, 10th Fl.
Brooklyn, NY 11201
URL: http://engineering.nyu.edu/news/nyu-poly-incubator
Description: A public-private partnership with New York City tasked with creating a sustainable incubation program focused on increasing the success rate of new ventures and generating positive economic impact. The mission of the incubators is to have a positive economic impact in New York City and it is measured in terms of jobs, capital raised, new products launched, exits and the number of students engaged. **Founded:** 2009.

42916 ■ Operation Oswego County (OOC)
44 W Bridge St.
Oswego, NY 13126
Ph: (315)343-1545
Fax: (315)343-1546
Co. E-mail: ooc@oswegocounty.org
URL: http://www.oswegocounty.org
Contact: L. Michael Treadwell, Executive Director
Facebook: www.facebook.com/OperationOswegoCounty
Linkedin: www.linkedin.com/company/operation-oswego-county-inc-
X (Twitter): x.com/OpOswegoCo
YouTube: www.youtube.com/channel/UCzv8zU2C6xiYk-uWR--pEIA
Description: A small business incubator created to establish and implement sound economic development strategies in order to enhance the economic vitality of Oswego County's businesses, industries and citizens leading to an overall better quality of life; its mission is the creation and retention of job opportunities, diversification and strengthening of the economic base, and developing the local economy in a planned, organized and environmentally-friendly atmosphere. **Founded:** 1953. **Publications:** *Oswego County Economic Development News* (Irregular). **Awards:** OOC Ally Award (Annual); OOC Jobs Award (Annual); OOC Business Excellence Award (Annual). **Geographic Preference:** Local.

42917 ■ Orange County Business Accelerator
4 Crotty Ln., Ste. 100
New Windsor, NY 12553
URL: http://www.ocnyida.com/affiliates
Description: Business incubator that is designed to attract new entrepreneurial investment across various industries by providing businesses with below-market occupancy costs, mentoring programs, easy access to experienced professionals and a high-tech plug-and-play office environment.

42918 ■ Oswego County Business Expansion Center (BEC)
44 W Bridge St.
Oswego, NY 13126
Ph: (315)343-1545
Co. E-mail: ooc@oswegocounty.org
URL: http://oswegocounty.org/edi.php
Description: Fosters and assists new and existing businesses with space requirements for purposes of providing economic gains and employment opportunities in Oswego County.

42919 ■ PresenTense NYC
115 E 23rd St., Ste. 308
New York, NY 10010
URL: http://digital.nyc/incubators/presentense-nyc
Description: A four-month long boot camp for social entrepreneurs. The accelerator is seeking Jewish social entrepreneurs working on high impact, sustainable, scalable ventures that solve core societal issues, enrich community life, and grow local economies.

42920 ■ Quake Capital
303 Spring St.
New York, NY 10013
Co. E-mail: brandon@quake.vc
URL: http://quakecapital.com
Contact: Glenn Argenbright, Founder Partner
Facebook: www.facebook.com/quakecap
X (Twitter): x.com/quakecap
Instagram: www.instagram.com/quakecap

STATE LISTINGS

Description: A business accelerator focused on making seed level investments in new and early stage ventures across a wide range of industries. Provides the capital, tools, access, expertise, and advisers to make your vision a reality. **Founded:** 2016.

42921 ■ R/GA Accelerator
450 W 33rd St.,12th Fl.
  New York, NY 10001
URL: http://ventures.rga.com
Description: Hardware accelerator supporting startups interested in IoT (the Internet of Things), working with hardware, software, and data in compelling ways for consumers and businesses.

42922 ■ Rensselaer Incubation Program
Peoples Ave., Complex J 3rd Fl.
  Troy, NY 12180-3590
Ph: (518)276-6023
URL: http://www.rpi.edu/dept/cct/apps/incubator
Description: This program, located at Rensselaer Polytechnic Institute, seeks to nurture new technological ventures. It offers tenants affordable offices space, laboratories, and light manufacturing space as well as other services. **Founded:** 1980.

42923 ■ Rise New York
43 W 23rd St.2nd - 6th Fl.
  New York, NY 10010
Ph: (212)524-8302
Co. E-mail: nyc@thinkrise.com
URL: http://rise.barclays
Description: Offers a business base for startups and entrepreneurs who are growing and launching their FinTech businesses.

42924 ■ Rochester Institute of Technology - Venture Creations
40 Franklin St.
  Rochester, NY 14604
URL: http://www.rit.edu/facilities/venture-creations
Contact: Cindy Papaleo, Officer
E-mail: cpapaleo@rit.edu
Description: An incubator where mid-seed stage companies can advance their concepts their way to joining the ranks of profitable, viable businesses. **Founded:** 2009.

42925 ■ Rochester Institute of Technology Venture Creations (RIT) [RIT Venture Creations]
40 Franklin St.
  Rochester, NY 14604
Ph: (585)475-7720
Co. E-mail: venturecreations@rit.edu
URL: http://www.rit.edu/incubator
Contact: Johan Klarin, Director
E-mail: jbkvci@rit.edu
Facebook: www.facebook.com/RITVentureCreationsIncubator
X (Twitter): x.com/vc_incubator
Description: A technology business incubator that provides a range of services to seed/mid-seed stage startups to help them advance their businesses. **Founded:** 2003.

42926 ■ Runway Startup Postdoc Program
2 W Loop Rd.
  New York, NY 10044
URL: http://tech.cornell.edu/programs/phd/startup-postdocs
Description: Part business school, part research institution, and part startup incubator. Helps recent PhDs in digital technology fields through the shift from academic mindset to an entrepreneurial outlook. Provides a package including a salary, research budget, housing allowance, space, and more for one year.

42927 ■ Samsung Next LLC
Samsung Electronics Co., Ltd.
  30 W 26th St.
  New York, NY 10010
Ph: 82 2 2225-0144
Co. E-mail: support.india@samsung.com
URL: http://www.samsung.com
Contact: Jonathan Machado, Managing Director

Linkedin: www.linkedin.com/company/samsung-next
Description: Empowers founders and early-stage software startups with funding, domain expertise, co-located work spaces, and resources to build products, launch startups and grow companies ready for scale. **Founded:** 2012.

42928 ■ Schenectady County Community Business Center
620 State St.
  Schenectady, NY 12305
URL: http://schenectadycountyny.gov
Description: A small business incubator offering a one-stop resource center for new, growing and challenged small businesses in Schenectady County, New York by providing whatever an entrepreneur needs to build a business.

42929 ■ South Side Innovation Center (SSIC)
2610 S Salina St.
  Syracuse, NY 13205
Ph: (315)443-8466
Co. E-mail: sbrennan@syr.edu
URL: http://southsideinnovation.org
Contact: El-Java Abdul-Qadir, Consultant
Facebook: www.facebook.com/people/South-Side-Innovation-Center/100040422192822
X (Twitter): x.com/southsideinnova
Description: Mission is to increase the strength and size of the area economy by helping a diverse group of emerging and mature businesses reach their potential size and profitability. **Founded:** 2006.

42930 ■ Spark Labs
833 Broadway
  2nd Fl
  New York, NY 10003
Ph: (201)455-7839
Co. E-mail: space@spark-labs.co
URL: http://www.spark-labs.co
Facebook: www.facebook.com/sparklabscoworking
Linkedin: www.linkedin.com/company/spark-labs-inc-
Description: Provides a network of curated and vetted workspaces in 60+ cities worldwide for startups and entrepreneurs.

42931 ■ Starta Accelerator
220 E 23rd St., Ste. 400
  New York, NY 10010
Ph: (917)947-9692
Co. E-mail: info@starta.vc
URL: http://starta.vc
Contact: Gabriel Arant, Director
Facebook: www.facebook.com/startavc
Linkedin: www.linkedin.com/company/startaventures
X (Twitter): x.com/Starta_vc
Instagram: www.instagram.com/starta_vc
YouTube: www.youtube.com/channel/UC_a0pYu8ncp1Drf3_ieHZ4A
Description: Acceleration program in New York for technology startups with Eastern European R&D roots. Provides a customized program for Eastern European founders aiming to adapt to cultural and business environment in the US, complete and define product/market fit, get traction and become part of local startup and investing ecosystem in the U.S.

42932 ■ StartFast Venture Accelerator
28 Waverly Pl.
  Little Falls, NY 13365
Co. E-mail: myco@startfastventures.com
URL: http://startfastventures.com
Contact: Nasir Ali, Partner
Facebook: www.facebook.com/StartFast
X (Twitter): x.com/Start_Fast
YouTube: www.youtube.com/channel/UCteMwBfwp_qDiE9sUZvTS7w
Description: A mentorship-driven startup accelerator providing startups with the best resources to create and grow their businesses.

42933 ■ Startup Ecology
New York, NY
URL: http://www.startupecology.com
Contact: Bjorn Ahbel, Contact

New York ■ 42938

Description: A new type of accelerator/incubator for startups. Provides everything needed to launch from shared workspaces to online training. Startup Ecology becomes your cofounder.

42934 ■ StartUp Health Academy
28 Liberty St.
  New York, NY 10005
Co. E-mail: info@startuphealth.com
URL: http://www.startuphealth.com
Contact: Unity Stoakes, President
Facebook: www.facebook.com/startuphealth
Linkedin: www.linkedin.com/company/startuphealth
X (Twitter): x.com/startuphealth
Instagram: www.instagram.com/startuphealth
YouTube: www.youtube.com/StartUpHealth
Description: A three-year coaching program and global community designed to multiply your equity value and more rapidly scale your business. **Founded:** 2011.

42935 ■ Startup52
275 Buena visita Rd.
  New City, NY 10956
Contact: Chike Ukaegbu, Contact
Description: A tech and innovation platform to solve global problems through entrepreneurship. Focused on grooming extraordinary startup founders to launch highly successful and profitable ventures.

42936 ■ Startupbootcamp FinTech New York (SCP)
NY
Co. E-mail: fintechnyc@startupbootcamp.org
URL: http://www.startupbootcamp.org/accelerator/fintech-new-york
Facebook: www.facebook.com/startupbootcamp
Linkedin: www.linkedin.com/company/startupbootcamp
X (Twitter): twitter.com/Sbootcamp
Instagram: www.instagram.com/startupbootcamp
YouTube: www.youtube.com/channel/UChzXM1nvKlnDPbsYo5jMisg
Description: Business accelerator focused on innovation for the financial services industry. Supports early-stage tech founders to rapidly scale their companies by providing direct access to an international network of the most relevant mentors, partners, and investors in their industry. **Founded:** 2010.

42937 ■ State University of New York at Fredonia - Fredonia Technology Incubator (FTI)
214 Central Ave., State University of New York at Fredonia
  Dunkirk, NY 14048
Ph: (716)680-6009
Co. E-mail: incubator@fredonia.edu
URL: http://www.fredonia.edu/about/offices/center-innovation-economic-development
Contact: Charles Cornell, Director
Facebook: www.facebook.com/people/Fredonia-Technology-Incubator-FTI/100086319616919
Linkedin: www.linkedin.com/company/fredonia-technology-incubator
X (Twitter): x.com/Tech_Incubator
Description: Promotes economic growth in the Western Southern Tier of New York State by supporting entrepreneurship and the development of new, innovative, arts and technology-based companies into successful business ventures.

42938 ■ Stony Brook University Business Incubator at Calverton
4603 Middle Country Rd.
  Calverton, NY 11933
Co. E-mail: calverton_incubator@stonybrook.edu
URL: http://www.stonybrook.edu/foodbusinessincubator
Instagram: www.instagram.com/foodbusinessincubator
Description: Enhances the economic development on Eastern Long Island. **Founded:** 2012. **Industry Preferences:** Agriculture; aquaculture; environment.

42939 ■ Stony Brook University (CEBIP) - Clean Energy Business Incubator Program
Ste. 235, 25 Health Sciences Dr.
Stony Brook, NY 11790
Ph: (631)444-8800
Co. E-mail: info@cebip.org
URL: http://www.cebip.org
Contact: Heidi Anderson, Executive Director
Facebook: www.facebook.com/CEBIPSBU
Linkedin: www.linkedin.com/company/cebipsbu
X (Twitter): x.com/CEBIP_SBU

Description: Incubates "green" technologies by helping to develop and commercialize them, and to create and sustain growth companies.

42940 ■ Stony Brook University Incubator at Calverton
4603 Middle County Rd.
Calverton, NY 11933
Co. E-mail: calverton_incubator@stonybrook.edu
URL: http://www.stonybrook.edu/foo
dbusinessincubator
Contact: Ronald Stegner, Jr., Director
Instagram: www.instagram.com/foo
dbusinessincubator

Description: The incubator program offers laboratory space, production facilities, and support to technology, science and food start-up companies, helping them grow by providing a variety of support resources and services.

42941 ■ SUNY Fredonia Technology Incubator Inc. (FTI)
214 Central Ave.
Dunkirk, NY 14048
Ph: (716)680-6009
Co. E-mail: incubator@fredonia.edu
URL: http://www.fredonia.edu/about/offices/fredonia
-technology-incubator
Contact: Charles Cornell, Director
Facebook: www.facebook.com/people/Fredonia
-Technology-Incubator-FTI/100086319616919
X (Twitter): x.com/Tech_Incubator
Instagram: www.instagram.com/fredtechincbtr

Description: An incubator supporting technology-based businesses. Entrepreneurs also receive help in getting their ideas and businesses up and running, such as through development of business plans, accounting and legal services, office management, financing/venture capital strategies, and marketing plans. **Founded:** 2007.

42942 ■ Syracuse Student Sandbox
235 Harrison St.
Syracuse, NY 13202
Ph: (315)560-6622
URL: http://syracusestudentsandbox.com
Contact: John Liddy, Executive Director
E-mail: john@liddyenterprises.com
Facebook: www.facebook.com/Syracuse-Studen
t-Sandbox-183996312201
X (Twitter): twitter.com/studentsandbox

Description: An incubator that helps aspiring entrepreneurs push their ventures from idea to company. **Founded:** 2009.

42943 ■ Syracuse University - Center for Advanced Systems and Engineering (CASE)
2-212 Ctr. of Science & Technology, Syracuse University
Syracuse, NY 13244
Ph: (315)443-1060
Fax: (315)443-4745
Co. E-mail: case@syr.edu
URL: http://case.syr.edu
Contact: Dr. Pramod Varshney, Executive Director
E-mail: varshney@syr.edu
Facebook: www.facebook.com/people/CASE-The
-Center-for-Advanced-Systems-and-Engineering
X (Twitter): x.com/CASEatSU

Description: An applied research center for advanced technology, Provides R&D collaboration, networking, incubation services, and more. **Founded:** 1984.

42944 ■ A Taste of Long Island Inc.
159 Smith St.
Massapequa Park, NY 11762
Contact: James M. Thompson, Chief Executive Officer

Description: Helps culinary entrepreneurs start and grow their businesses with lower risks in a healthy, professional and supportive environment. Provides commercial kitchen space designed to meet the needs of small scale and start-up food producers.

42945 ■ The Tech Garden (TTG)
235 Harrison St.
Syracuse, NY 13202
Ph: (315)470-1970
Co. E-mail: info@thetechgarden.com
URL: http://www.thetechgarden.com
Contact: Kara Jones, Director
E-mail: kalheim@centerstateceo.com
Facebook: www.facebook.com/thetechgarden
Linkedin: www.linkedin.com/company/syracuse
-technology-garden
X (Twitter): x.com/thetechgarden

Description: An entrepreneurial ecosystem providing comprehensive support for turning great ideas into high-growth businesses. **Founded:** 2005.

42946 ■ Tech Incubator at Queens College (TIQC)
65-30 Kissena Blvd. CEP, Hall 2
Queens, NY 11367
Ph: (718)570-0573
Co. E-mail: info@techincubatorqc.com
URL: http://techincubatorqc.com
Contact: Muhammad Raza, Contact
Facebook: www.facebook.com/QCTechIncubator
Linkedin: www.linkedin.com/company/tiqc
X (Twitter): x.com/QCTechIncubator
Instagram: www.instagram.com/qctechincubator

Description: A startup incubator for tech freelancers, professional developers, and entrepreneurs. Aims to help startup companies and entrepreneurs to build successful technology companies, which in turn creates more job opportunities and drives new innovation and technology development in New York.

42947 ■ Thomas R. Beecher, Jr. Innovation Center (IC)
640 Ellicott St.
Buffalo, NY 14203
URL: http://bnmc.org/innovation-center
Contact: Kari Bonaro, Contact
E-mail: kbonaro@bnmc-old.local

Description: Incubation space housing more than 100 companies including those in life sciences, biotech and social innovation, as well as businesses offering support services like IP attorneys, talent acquisition, sales, and marketing. The collaborative and entrepreneurial setting provides an environment for businesses to grow and network. **Founded:** 2010.

42948 ■ Tipping Point Partners (TPP)
28 Liberty St.
New York, NY 10005
URL: http://www.tippingpointpartners.com
Contact: Art Chang, Contact
E-mail: art@tippingpointpartners.com
X (Twitter): x.com/TippingPointLLC

Description: Supports software startups that build bridges between new technology and human needs with a particular focus on using disruptive technologies to transform existing industries and government.

42949 ■ Tow-Knight Center for Entrepreneurial Journalism
219 W 40th St.
New York, NY 10018
Ph: (646)758-7700
Co. E-mail: admissions@journalism.cuny.edu
URL: http://www.journalism.cuny.edu/centers/tow
-knight-center-entrepreneurial-journalism
Contact: Jeff Jarvis, Director
X (Twitter): x.com/towknightcenter
Instagram: www.instagram.com/towknightcenter
YouTube: www.youtube.com/user/TowKnightCUNY

Description: Runs educational programs, conducts research, supports startups, and promotes collaboration among media, academic, technology and business leaders. Hosts entrepreneurial journalists from New York and around the globe to work to develop journalism-related startups. **Founded:** 2010.

42950 ■ UB STOR
12 Capen Hall
Buffalo, NY 14260-1611
Ph: (716)645-2000
Co. E-mail: vrp@research.buffalo.edu
URL: http://www.buffalo.edu
Contact: John Della Contrada, Vice President, Communications
E-mail: dellacon@buffalo.edu
Facebook: www.facebook.com/universitya
tbuffaloresearch
Linkedin: www.linkedin.com/school/universityatbuffalo
X (Twitter): x.com/BuffaloResearch
Instagram: www.instagram.com/universityatbuffalo
YouTube: www.youtube.com/channel/UCj76k-eVRwU
39wcFtXkUzXg/feed

Description: Supports the creation of new technology-based businesses by providing affordable business services to entrepreneurs. **Founded:** 1988.

42951 ■ UB Technology Incubator
1576 Sweet Home Rd., Ste. 111, UB Technology Incubator, Baird Research Pk.
Amherst, NY 14228
URL: http://www.buffalo.edu/research/about-us/staff
-directory.a-z-staff-directory.html

Description: A small business incubator supporting the creation of new technology-based businesses by providing affordable business services to entrepreneurs. **Founded:** 1988.

42952 ■ University at Buffalo Technology Incubator
1576 Sweet Home Rd.
Amherst, NY 14228
URL: http://www.buffalo.edu/partnerships/about/cen
ters-facilities-equipment/incubators.html

Description: Guides researchers as their discoveries and inventions become new products and services. Also facilitates contracts related to business-university partnerships.

42953 ■ Urban Future Lab (UFL)
370 Jay St., 7th Fl.
Brooklyn, NY 11201
Co. E-mail: info@ufl.nyc
URL: http://ufl.nyc
Contact: Frederic Clerc, Director
Linkedin: www.linkedin.com/company/urban-future
-lab
X (Twitter): x.com/UrbanFutureLab
Instagram: www.instagram.com/urbanfuturelab

Description: A hub for smart cities, clean energy, and smart grid technology. Programs include ACRE, a business incubator that seed-funds series A startups, and a proof-of-concept center called Power-BridgeNY. **Founded:** 2009.

42954 ■ URBAN-X
19 Morris Ave., Brooklyn Navy Yard Bldg. 128
Brooklyn, NY 11205
Co. E-mail: hello@urban-x.com
URL: http://urban-x.com
Contact: Johan Schwind, Managing Director
Facebook: www.facebook.com/urbanxtech
Linkedin: www.linkedin.com/company/urban-x
X (Twitter): x.com/urbanxtech
YouTube: www.youtube.com/c/urbanxaccel

Description: A business accelerator who invests in and accelerates startups who are focused on intelligent cities, urban hyper-growth, and society-scale challenges. **Founded:** 2016.

42955 ■ Urbantech NYC
New York, NY
URL: http://urbantechnyc.com
X (Twitter): x.com/urbantechnyc
Instagram: www.instagram.com/urbantechnyc

STATE LISTINGS

42956 ■ VentureCrushFG
New York, NY
Co. E-mail: venturecrushfg@lowenstein.com
URL: http://www.venturecrush.com/programs/venturecrushfg
Contact: Ed Zimmerman, Chairman Founder Partner
Description: An accelerator that provides entrepreneurs with a network of support for their growth. Connects startups with venture capitalists, angel investors, mentors, and advisors. Founded: 2009.

42957 ■ VentureOut
25 W 39th St
14th fl.
New York, NY 10018
Ph: (212)729-4278
Co. E-mail: info@ventureoutny.com
URL: http://ventureoutny.com
Contact: Brian Frumberg, Chief Executive Officer
Facebook: www.facebook.com/ventureoutny
Linkedin: www.linkedin.com/company/ventureoutny
X (Twitter): x.com/VentureOutNY
Instagram: www.instagram.com/ventureoutny
YouTube: www.youtube.com/channel/UC7D9onW5edZTgD1fw_Bm5xw
Description: Connects technologies companies with opportunities available to them in the US. Offers programs for startups, corporations, and government. Founded: 2012.

42958 ■ Wall Street Share L.L.C.
16 E 40th St., Ste. 802
New York, NY 10016
URL: http://www.wallstreetshare.com
Contact: Joshua C. Adam, Contact
Description: An exclusive hybrid between a venture capital investment operation and a coworking space located in Midtown Manhattan. Invites promising companies into our space, invest our own capital in compelling deals offered by tenant companies, and assist such companies in accessing resources, including capital, investor introductions, strategic relationships, M&A partners, and influencer relationships.

42959 ■ WAMVentures Group L.L.C.
99 Wall St., 17th Fl.
New York, NY 10005
Co. E-mail: contact@wamventures.com
URL: http://www.wamventures.com
Contact: Veronica Guzman, Founder
Description: Firm mainly serves women and diverse business leaders seeking to move their businesses up-market and reach higher levels of excellence.

42960 ■ WEVE Acceleration
119 W 24th St.
New York, NY 10011
Co. E-mail: hello@weveacceleration.com
URL: http://www.numa.co/new-york
Contact: Frances Simowitz, Chief Executive Officer
Linkedin: www.linkedin.com/company/weve-acceleration
Description: Part of a global network that fosters acceleration and innovation. Startup program is designed by serial entrepreneurs and innovators to help growth stage startups scale in the U.S. through key partnerships with corporations, investors, mentors, and experts. Founded: 2017.

42961 ■ Women's Housing & Development Corp. Kitchen Incubator [WHEDco]
50 E 168th St.
Bronx, NY 10452
URL: http://whedco.org/tag/incubator
Description: Offers emerging food companies affordable space in a fully licensed state-of-the-art 4,000 square foot commercial kitchen. It is available on a per diem or monthly basis and fees are competitive for longer-term rentals. It is ideal for caterers, bakers, and food and beverage manufacturers who would otherwise not be able to afford the commercial kitchen space or equipment they need.

42962 ■ Work-Bench Co-op L.L.C.
915 Broadway, Ste. 1200
New York, NY 10010
URL: http://www.work-bench.com
Contact: Kelley Mak, Partner
E-mail: kelly@work-bench.com
Facebook: www.facebook.com/work.bench.vc
Linkedin: www.linkedin.com/company/work-bench
X (Twitter): x.com/work_bench
YouTube: www.youtube.com/channel/UCj-lhr72zeuQlKAUt7oo9SA
Description: Growth accelerator that invests in category-defining companies early in their go-to-market, helping them secure customers and talent. Founded: 2012.

42963 ■ Z80 Labs
1 News Plz., Ste. 10
Buffalo, NY 14203
Description: Internet-focused technology incubator, providing entrepreneurs the ability to build new and innovative tech companies in Buffalo, New York. Services including office space, education programs, mentorship, amenities and infrastructure from local sponsors, as well as expert advice from renowned industry advisors. Founded: 2012.

EDUCATIONAL PROGRAMS

42964 ■ Board of Cooperative Educational Services - Adult and Continuing Education (BOCES)
c/o Lori Yakawiak, Coordinator
3 Washington Ctr., 1 Fl.
Newburgh, NY 12550
Ph: (845)781-6715
Co. E-mail: lori.yakawiak@ouboces.org
URL: http://www.ouboces.org/contact-us/contact-the-adult-continuing-education-division
Contact: Lori Yakawiak, Coordinator
E-mail: lori.yakawiak@ouboces.org
Description: Offers a ten-session class in small business organization.

42965 ■ Bryant and Stratton College - Buffalo Campus
110 Broadway
Buffalo, NY 14203
Ph: (716)884-9120
Co. E-mail: bufcontactcampus@bryantstratton.edu
URL: http://www.bryantstratton.edu/location/buffalo-ny/buffalo
Linkedin: www.linkedin.com/school/bryant-&-stratton-college---buffalo
Description: Business college offering programs in business management and business operations. Founded: 1854.

42966 ■ Bryant and Stratton College - Syracuse Campus
953 James St.
Syracuse, NY 13203-2502
Ph: (315)472-6603
Co. E-mail: syrcontactcampus@bryantstratton.edu
URL: http://www.bryantstratton.edu/location/syracuse-ny
Facebook: www.facebook.com/BSCSyracuse
Description: Business college offering programs in business management and business operations.

42967 ■ eLab
409 College Ave., Ste. 200
Ithaca, NY 14850
Co. E-mail: e-lab@cornell.edu
URL: http://www.elabstartup.com
Contact: Ken Rother, Managing Director
E-mail: ksr77@cornell.edu
Facebook: www.facebook.com/CornelleLab
Linkedin: www.linkedin.com/company/cornell-elab-accelerator
X (Twitter): x.com/CornellELAB
Description: Dedicated to accelerating the top Cornell University startups. Founded: 2008.

42968 ■ Erie Community College - City Campus
121 Ellicott St.
Buffalo, NY 14203
Ph: (716)851-1322
URL: http://www.ecc.edu
Description: Two-year college offering a certificate in small business management. Founded: 1971.

42969 ■ Fiorello H. LaGuardia Community College of the City University of New York - Division of Adult and Continuing Education - Center for Corporate Education
31-10 Thomson Ave.
Long Island City, NY 11101
Ph: (718)482-7200
Co. E-mail: aceprofessional@lagcc.cuny.edu
URL: http://www.lagcc.cuny.edu/cce
Contact: Kenneth Adams, President
Description: Offers courses in supervisory skills and management, microcomputer applications, communication and interpersonal skills, specialized business workshops, and technical training and workshops in retailing skills for small business owners. Maintains an interest in small business by offering programs at no cost to the community through funding by the New York State Department of Education. Small business courses cover personal selling, customer service, merchandise management, accounting, time and stress management, and microcomputers.

42970 ■ Long Island University - Post
720 N Blvd.
Brookville, NY 11548
Ph: (516)299-2000
Fax: (516)299-2137
Co. E-mail: post-enroll@liu.edu
URL: http://www.liu.edu/post
Description: Offers programs in small business management and entrepreneurship. Founded: 1954.

42971 ■ Rochester Institute of Technology - Albert J. Simone Center for Innovation and Entrepreneurship
One Lomb Memorial Dr. Student Innovation Hall, Rm. 1600
Rochester, NY 14623
Ph: (585)475-2305
Co. E-mail: simonecenter@rit.edu
URL: http://www.rit.edu/simonecenter/overview
Contact: Anthony Testa, Director
E-mail: atesta@saunders.rit.edu
Facebook: www.facebook.com/RITSimoneCenter
Linkedin: www.linkedin.com/company/ritsimonecenter
Instagram: www.instagram.com/ritsimonecenter
YouTube: www.youtube.com/user/RITSimoneCenter
Description: Helps students reach their entrepreneurial goals from start to finish. Through the program, students are shown how to take an idea from the beginning stages all the way through to commercialization. Founded: 2007.

42972 ■ SUNY Canton College
34 Cornell Dr.
Canton, NY 13617
Ph: (315)386-7011
Free: 800-388-7123
Fax: (315)386-7929
Co. E-mail: admissions@canton.edu
URL: http://www.canton.edu
Contact: Zvi Szafran, President
E-mail: president@canton.edu
Facebook: www.facebook.com/suny.canton
Linkedin: www.linkedin.com/edu/school
X (Twitter): x.com/SUNYCantonNews
Instagram: www.instagram.com/sunycantongram
YouTube: www.youtube.com/user/cantonpr
Description: Two-year college offering a small business management program. Founded: 1906.

LEGISLATIVE ASSISTANCE

42973 ■ New York Senate Standing Committee
Legislative Office Bldg., Hearing Rm. B. 2 Flr
Albany, NY 12210
URL: http://www.nysenate.gov/committees/higher-education
Description: Small Business. Founded: 1855.

42974 ■ New York State Assembly Committee on Small Business
LOB 624
Albany, NY 12248
URL: http://www.assembly.state.ny.us/comm/?id=34
Contact: Al Stirpe, Chairman
E-mail: stirpea@nyassembly.gov

REFERENCE WORKS

42975 ■ "The Rise and Fall and Rise of the Old New Jewish Deli" in Haaretz (January 16, 2018)
URL(s): www.haaretz.com/us-news/.premium.MAGAZINE-new-deli-the-rise-and-fall-and-rise-of-the-old-n-y-jewish-deli-1.5730860
Ed: Tzach Yoked. Released: January 16, 2018.
Description: Explores the topic of the disappearing Jewish deli in New York City. Once home to over a thousand delis, there are now only 20 left. Not only was the traditional Jewish deli a place to order kosher food, it was also a place for Jewish people to gather and form a community, something that was especially important for Jewish immigrants earlier in the last century. Availability: Online.

42976 ■ "This Legendary New York Bagel Shop is Finally Going National" in Eat This, Not That (October 10, 2021)
Ed: Krissy Gasbarre. Released: October 10, 2021.
Description: A famous New York City bagel shop, H&H Bagels, is heading out of its comfort zone and announcing franchise opportunities, as it tries to branch out into other states. Availability: Download.

CONSULTANTS

42977 ■ Biz Virtuoso Consulting
315 Madison Ave., 3rd Fl.
New York, NY 10017
Ph: (212)374-1425
Free: 800-383-1148
URL: http://bizvirtuoso.com
Contact: Wanda E. Flowers, Co-Founder
Facebook: www.facebook.com/bizvirtuoso
Linkedin: www.linkedin.com/company/biz-virtuoso-inc
X (Twitter): twitter.com/bizvirtuoso
Description: Consulting and coaching firm helping small businesses develop, launch, and grow their companies and concepts. concepts!. Founded: 2006.

42978 ■ Capacity Consulting
210 E Main St., Ste. 306
Middletown, NY 10940
Ph: (845)430-1347
URL: http://capacityconsultinginc.com
Contact: Eric Egeland, President
Facebook: www.facebook.com/capacityconsulting
Linkedin: www.linkedin.com/company/capacity-consulting-inc-
YouTube: www.youtube.com/user/capacityconsulting
Description: Offers strategic and management consulting services for multiple industries. Consults on start-ups, business plans, feasibility studies, marketing strategy, turnarounds, closures, reorganizations, and grants. Founded: 1999.

42979 ■ GlobalEdgeMarkets (GEM)
222 Broadway
New York, NY 10038
Co. E-mail: info@globaledgemarkets.com
URL: http://globaledgemarkets.com
Contact: Alex Romanovich, Chief Executive Officer
E-mail: alexr@globaledgemarkets.com
Facebook: www.facebook.com/globaledgemarkets
Linkedin: www.linkedin.com/company/globaledgemarkets
X (Twitter): x.com/globaledgemkts
Instagram: www.instagram.com/globaledgemkts
Description: Offers marketing and sales services for small to midsize companies. Founded: 2009.

42980 ■ KAYWEB Angels
Level 23, 1330 Avenue of the Americas
New York, NY 10019
Description: Angel investment group offers development services and mentoring to web and mobile startups in exchange for equity. Also has offices in Sydney, Melbourne, and Manila. Founded: 2011.

42981 ■ Manhattan Innovation Lab, LLC
607 W End Ave., Ste. 3B
New York, NY 10024
Ph: (617)270-9813
Co. E-mail: info@manhattaninnovationlab.com
URL: http://www.manhattaninnovationlab.com/Welcome.html
Contact: Michael M. Archer, Contact
Description: Early-stage business accelerator.

42982 ■ Margolis Advisory Group
Ph: (561)336-3054
URL: http://margolisadv.com
Contact: Jeffrey Margolis, Founder
E-mail: jeff@margolisadv.com
Description: Offers growth and management consulting services to investment management firms.

42983 ■ Modicum Agency
145 W 30th St., 3rd Fl.
New York, NY 10001
Free: 800-906-4646
URL: http://www.modicum.agency
Contact: C. Adriano, Contact
Facebook: www.facebook.com/modicumagency
Linkedin: www.linkedin.com/company/modicumagency
Description: Offers tools that solve problems. Works on branding, marketing, conversion, and growth. Founded: 2002.

42984 ■ NYC Advisors LLC
1 Grand Central Pl.
60 E 42nd St., 46th Fl.
New York, NY 10165
Ph: (914)285-9779
Fax: (914)206-3506
Co. E-mail: getinfo@nycadvisors.com
URL: http://www.nycadvisors.com
Contact: Yoav M. Cohen, Chief Executive Officer
Description: Offers strategic, business, and operational support through the development and execution of innovative business plans and solutions. Also offers executive management services, such as interim and part-time CEO, CFO, and COOs; financial and operational restructuring; and buyouts, mergers, and acquisitions. Founded: 2003.

42985 ■ Sales Schema, LLC
438A Lexington Ave.
Brooklyn, NY 11221
Ph: (212)537-4039
URL: http://www.salesschema.com
Contact: Dan Englander, Chief Executive Officer
Description: Agency-focused new business consulting firm. Founded: 2014.

42986 ■ TechSci Research
420 Lexington Ave., Ste. 300
New York, NY 10170
Ph: (646)360-1656
Co. E-mail: sales@techsciresearch.com
URL: http://www.techsciresearch.com
Facebook: www.facebook.com/TechSciResearch
Linkedin: www.linkedin.com/company/techsci-research
X (Twitter): x.com/TechSciResearch
Description: Research-based management consulting firm. Offers decision-making solutions to customers in a range of industries worldwide.

42987 ■ Tronvig Group
80 Marlborough Rd.
Brooklyn, NY 11232
Ph: (718)522-6326
Co. E-mail: info@tronviggroup.com
URL: http://www.tronviggroup.com
Contact: G. G. LeMere, Creative Director
Facebook: www.facebook.com/TronvigGroup
Linkedin: www.linkedin.com/company/tronviggroup
X (Twitter): x.com/TronvigGroup
Description: Boutique brand strategy and marketing consulting firm. Founded: 1997.

PUBLICATIONS

42988 ■ Albany Business Review
2 Winners Cir., Ste. 104
Albany, NY 12205
Ph: (518)640-6800
Fax: (518)640-6836
Co. E-mail: albany@bizjournals.com
URL: http://www.bizjournals.com/albany
Contact: Cindy Applebaum, President
E-mail: capplebaum@bizjournals.com
Facebook: www.facebook.com/albanybusinessreview/273721998873
Linkedin: www.linkedin.com/company/albany-business-review
X (Twitter): x.com/AlbanyBizReview
Instagram: www.instagram.com/albanybusinessreview
Released: Daily Price: $245, for 52 weeks premium elite; $70, for online one year; $70, Institutions for digital and print one year; $4, for online trial. Description: Business tabloid providing local business news for Capital Region area. Availability: Print; PDF; Download; Online. Type: Full-text.

42989 ■ Buffalo Business First
120 W Morehead St.
Charlotte, NC 28202
Co. E-mail: circhelp@bizjournals.com
URL: http://www.acbj.com
Contact: Mike Olivieri, Executive Vice President
URL(s): www.bizjournals.com/buffalo
Linkedin: www.linkedin.com/company/buffalo-business-first
X (Twitter): x.com/BfloBizFirst
Instagram: www.instagram.com/bflobizfirst
Ed: Jeff Wright. Released: Weekly Price: $245, for nationwide access 52 weeks; $70, for digital & print 52 weeks; $70, for digital access 52 weeks; $4, for digital trial 4 weeks. Description: Contains the full text of Buffalo Business First, a business tabloid covering Buffalo, New York. Availability: Print; PDF; Online; Download. Type: Full-text.

42990 ■ Business First of Buffalo: Western New York's Business Newspaper
120 W Morehead St.
Charlotte, NC 28202
Co. E-mail: circhelp@bizjournals.com
URL: http://www.acbj.com
Contact: Mike Olivieri, Executive Vice President
URL(s): www.bizjournals.com/buffalo
Linkedin: www.linkedin.com/company/buffalo-business-first
X (Twitter): x.com/BfloBizFirst
Ed: Michael Canfield. Released: Weekly Price: $950, for premium unlimited; $220, for print and online premium plus; $210, for 52 weeks online premium; $380, for premium elite. Description: Business Newspaper. Availability: Print; PDF; Download; Online.

42991 ■ The Central New York Business Journal (CNYBJ)
415 W Fayette St.
Syracuse, NY 13204
Ph: (315)579-3927
Co. E-mail: info@cnybj.com
URL: http://www.cnybj.com
Contact: Marny Nesher, President
E-mail: mnesher@cnybj.com
URL(s): www.cnybj.com
Facebook: www.facebook.com/cnybj

Linkedin: www.linkedin.com/company/central-new
-york-business-journal
X (Twitter): twitter.com/cnybj
Instagram: www.instagram.com/cnybj
YouTube: www.youtube.com/user/CNYBJ
Released: Weekly **Price:** $79, for 1 year digital only; $95, for 1 year; $93, for online access per year. **Description:** Contains business information on the region of central New York state. **Availability:** Print; Online.

42992 ■ *Crain's New York Business*
685 3rd Ave.
 New York, NY 10017
Ph: (212)210-0100
Free: 877-824-9379
Co. E-mail: customerservice@crainsnewyork.com
URL: http://crainsnewyork.com
Contact: Jessica Botos, Manager, Marketing
E-mail: jessica.botos@crainsnewyork.com
URL(s): www.crainsnewyork.com
Facebook: www.facebook.com/crainsnewyork
Linkedin: www.linkedin.com/company/crain's-new
-york-business
X (Twitter): x.com/crainsnewyork
Instagram: www.instagram.com/crainsnewyork
Pinterest: www.pinterest.com/crainsnewyork
Ed: Jeremy Smerd. **Released:** Latest issues July 15, 2024. **Price:** $140, for annual print and online; $140, for annually online only; $399, for health pulse 12 month; $16, for print and online month; $499, Individuals for all access 12 month; $16, for monthly online only. **Description:** Regional business tabloid. **Availability:** Print; Download; PDF; Online. **Type:** Full-text.

42993 ■ *Daily Business Review*
150 E 42nd St.
 New York, NY 10017
Ph: (212)457-9400
Free: 877-256-2472
Co. E-mail: customercare@alm.com
URL: http://www.alm.com
Contact: Bill Carter, Chief Executive Officer
URL(s): www.law.com/dailybusinessreviewwww.alm
.com/brands/daily-business-review
Facebook: www.facebook.com/DailyBusinessReview
Linkedin: www.linkedin.com/company/miami-daily
-business-review
X (Twitter): twitter.com/dbreview
Price: $29.99, Individuals monthly; print and digital; $29.99, Individuals monthly; digital. **Availability:** Print; Online.

42994 ■ *Long Island Business News (LIBN)*
7025 Albert Pick Rd.
 Greensboro, NC 27409
Ph: (612)317-9420
Free: 877-615-9536
Co. E-mail: customerservice@bridgetowermedia.com
URL: http://www.bridgetowermedia.com
Contact: Adam Reinebach, President
URL(s): libn.com
Facebook: www.facebook.com/LongIslan
dBusinessNews
Linkedin: www.linkedin.com/company/long-islan
d-business-news
Instagram: www.instagram.com/libusinessnews
Ed: Joe Dowd, Bernadette Starzee, Joe Giametta. **Released:** Weekly **Price:** $369, for month leads & Data; $10, for monthly; $129, for annual. **Description:** Source for local business news and data on business, economic trends and the region's robust entrepreneurial sector. **Availability:** Print; Online.

42995 ■ *Rochester Business Journal*
16 W Main St., Ste. 341
 Rochester, NY 14614
Ph: (585)232-6920
Free: 866-941-4130
Fax: (585)232-2740
Co. E-mail: rbj@rbj.net
URL: http://www.rbj.net
Contact: Suzanne Fischer Huettner, Publisher
E-mail: shuettner@bridgetowermedia.com
URL(s): rbj.net/about-us
Facebook: www.facebook.com/RBJdaily

Linkedin: www.linkedin.com/company/rochester
-business-journal
X (Twitter): x.com/RBJdaily
Instagram: www.instagram.com/rbjdaily
Released: Weekly **Price:** $99, for digital annual; $129, for digital + print; $8, for 1 month digital; $369, for leads & data; $399, for annual data; $10, for monthly. **Availability:** Print; Online.

PUBLISHERS

42996 ■ Allworth Press
307 W 36th St., 11th Fl.
 New York, NY 10018
Ph: (212)643-6816
Free: 800-733-3000
Fax: (212)643-6819
URL: http://www.skyhorsepublishing.com/allworth
-press
Contact: Tad Crawford, Founder
Facebook: www.facebook.com/allworthpressbooks
Description: Publisher and distributor of books and magazines. **Founded:** 1989. **Publications:** *Business and Legal Forms for Authors and Self-Publishers*.

42997 ■ Forum Publishing Co.
383 E Main St.
 Centerport, NY 11721
Free: 800-635-7654
Co. E-mail: forumpublishing@aol.com
URL: http://www.forum123.com
Description: Publisher of weekly newspapers and culture magazines. **Founded:** 1981. **Publications:** *Hobby and Crafts Suppliers' Guide*; *National Sales Rep Directory*; *RN and WPL Encyclopedia*; *Retailers Forum Magazine* (Monthly); *U.S.A. Closeout Directory* (Annual); *Directory of Brand Name Apparel Manufacturers*; *Men's & Boys Wear Buyers*; *Women's & Children's Wear & Fashion Accessories Buyers*; *Chain Store Guide Directory of Leading Chain Tenants*; *Dollar Store Merchandise Guide: Sources for Dollar Store Operators*; *Fabrics, Services and Trims*; *Fine Jewelry Wholesalers*; *Gift, Housewares & Home Textile Buyers Guide*; *Wholesale Sources Directory*; *Swap Meet Magazine* (Monthly); *Venture Capital Directory* (Annual); *Annual Trade Show Directory* (Annual); *Closeout Merchandise Directory*; *Apparel Contractors--Asia Edition*; *Apparel Contractors--U. S. Edition*; *Chain Store Guide Dollar Stores*; *Christmas and Holiday Merchandise Guide*; *ABC Art & Craft Event Directory*; *Chain Store Guide Apparel Specialty Stores (CSGAS)*; *Men's & Boys Wear Buyers*; *Women's & Children's Wear & Fashion Accessories Buyers*; *Chain Store Guide Chain Restaurant Operators (CSGCR)*; *Chain Store Guide Department Store Directory (CSGDSD)*; *Chain Store Guide Directory of Leading Chain Tenants (CSGLCT)*; *Chain Store Guide Discount Stores & Specialty Retailers (CSGD)*; *Chain Store Guide Drug & HBC Stores (CSGDH)*; *Chain Store Guide Home Center Operators & Hardware Chains (CSGHC)*; *Chain Store Guide Home Furnishings Retailers (CSGHFR)*; *Chain Store Guide Supermarket, Grocery & Convenience Stores (CSGSGC)*; *Chain Store Guide Wholesale Grocers (CSGWG)*.

42998 ■ Genesis Society
96-22 67th Ave.
 Rego Park, NY 11374
Description: Publishes health-related hand books. **Founded:** 1999.

42999 ■ International Trademark Association (INTA) - Library
675 3rd Ave., 3rd Fl.
 New York, NY 10017
Ph: (212)642-1700
Fax: (212)768-7796
URL: http://www.inta.org
Contact: Zeeger Vink, President
Facebook: www.facebook.com/GoINTA
Linkedin: www.linkedin.com/company/gointa
X (Twitter): x.com/INTA
Instagram: www.instagram.com/intaglobal
YouTube: www.youtube.com/channel/UCfoSgeal
dEpL1f32YWS5nPw

Description: Trademark owners; associate members are lawyers, law firms, advertising agencies, designers, market researchers, and others in the trademark industries. Seeks to: protect the interests of the public in the use of trademarks and trade names; promote the interests of members and of trademark owners generally in the use of their trademarks and trade names; disseminate information concerning the use, registration, and protection of trademarks in the United States, its territories, and in foreign countries. Maintains job bank and speakers' bureau. **Scope:** Branding; practitioners. **Founded:** 1878. **Holdings:** Figures not available. **Publications:** *International Trademark Association--Membership Directory*; *INTA Bulletin* (Weekly (Wed.)); *The Trademark Report (TMR)* (6/year); *The Trademarker Reporter* (Bi-monthly). **Educational Activities:** INTA Annual Meeting (Annual). **Awards:** The Ladas Memorial Award - Student Category (Annual). **Geographic Preference:** National.

43000 ■ International Wealth Success Inc. (IWS)
PO Box 186
 Merrick, NY 11566-0186
Ph: (516)766-5850
Free: 800-323-0548
Fax: (516)766-5919
URL: http://www.iwsmoney.com
Contact: Tyler G. Hicks, Contact
Facebook: www.facebook.com/InternationalWeal
thSuccessInc
X (Twitter): twitter.com/iwsmoney
Description: Publisher of books, newsletters and self-study courses of business opportunities and real estate. **Founded:** 1966. **Publications:** *Directory of 2,500 Active Real-Estate Lenders* (Annual); *Worldwide Riches Opportunities*; *Small Business Investment Company Directory and Handbook*; *Mideast and North African Banks and Financial Institutions*; *Directory of High-Discount Merchandise and Product Sources for Distributors and Mail-Order Wealth Builders* (Annual); *Directory of Freight Forwarders and Custom House Brokers*; *International Wealth Success Newsletter: The Monthly Newsletter of Worldwide Wealth Opportunities (IWS)* (Monthly).

43001 ■ Knopf Doubleday Publishing Group
Penguin Random House
1745 Broadway
 New York, NY 10019
Ph: (212)782-8812
Free: 800-793-2665
Co. E-mail: customerservice@penguinrandomhouse
.com
URL: http://www.penguinrandomhouse.com
Contact: Nan A. Talese, Contact
E-mail: ddaypub@randomhouse.com
Description: Publisher of books on fiction and non-fiction. **Founded:** 1897. **Publications:** *American Historical Supply Catalogue: A Nineteenth-Century Sourcebook*.

43002 ■ McGraw Hill LLC [McGraw Hill Education (MHE)]
McGraw Hill LLC
1325 Avenue of the Americas
 New York, NY 10019
Free: 800-338-3987
URL: http://www.mheducation.com
Contact: Simon Allen, Chief Executive Officer
Facebook: www.facebook.com/McGrawHillEducation
Linkedin: www.linkedin.com/company/mcgraw-hill-e
ducation
X (Twitter): x.com/MHEducation
Instagram: www.instagram.com/mheducation
Description: Provider of outcome-focused learning solutions through curated content and digital learning tools and platforms to students in the classrooms of higher education instructors, pre-kindergarten through 12th grade school districts, and a variety of academic institutions, professionals, and companies. **Founded:** 1888. **Publications:** *Online Broker and Trading Directory*; *Living with Dying: A Loving Guide for Family and Friends*; *How to Find a Scholarship Online*; *Illustrated Buyer's Guide to Used Airplanes*; *MCTS*

Windows Server 2008 Active Directory Services Study Guide (Exam 70-640); Electronics Buyers' Guide; ENR Directory of Design Firms (Biennial); Business Week--R&D Scoreboard (Annual); Power, Power (Monthly); Metals Daily (Daily); Military/Space Electronic Design (Semimonthly); ENR--Top 400 Contractors (Annual); ENR--Top 250 International Contractors (Annual); ENR--Top 600 Specialty Contractors (Annual); Chemical Engineering Buyers Guide; Business Week--Survey of Labor Union Leaders Compensation Issue; Aerospace and Defense International Product News (Bimonthly); GreenSource; The Guide to Internet Job Searching; Opportunities in Teaching Careers (Irregular); Great Jobs for Psychology Majors (Irregular); Careers in Publishing; Opportunities in Music Careers; Great Jobs for Engineering Majors; Careers for Gourmets and Others Who Relish Food; Business Week International--Top 200 Banking Institutions Issue (Annual); ENR--Top Owners Issue (Annual); ENR--Top 100 Construction Management Firms Issue (Annual); BusinessWeek Guide to the Best Business Schools; New York Construction News (Monthly); Aviation Week & Space Technology (Weekly); BusinessWeek--Corporate Scoreboard Issue (Quarterly); The Online Broker and Trading Directory; Ultimate Start-Up Directory; Online Broker and Trading Directory; Opportunities in Foreign Language Careers (Irregular); Data Communications--Product Selection Guide (Annual); Nursing Experience: Trends, Challenges and Transitions; Aviation Internet Directory: A Guide to the 500 Best Aviation Web Sites; Electric Power International (Quarterly); Industrial Chemical News (Monthly); Computer Support Directory; Business Week (Weekly); Engineering News-Record (ENR); The African American Resource Guide to the Internet and Online Services; Electronics Engineers' Handbook; Modern Plastics Encyclopedia--Directory of Trade Names (Annual); Louisiana Contractor (Annual); Power--Buyers' Guide Issue (Annual); Platt's Oilgram News (Daily); ENR--Top 500 Design Firms (Annual); Career Training Sourcebook: Where to Get Free, Low-Cost, and Salaried Job Training; Modern Plastics Encyclopedia (Annual); Standard Corporation Records (Quarterly); CPI Equipment Reporter (Bimonthly); BusinessWeek Guide to the Best Business Schools; Essentials of Business CD-ROM; Opportunities in Forensic Science; Intermountain Contractor (Weekly); Utah Building Magazine (Monthly); NetWare Technical Journal (6/year); Dodge Construction News Illinois, Indiana, Wisconsin Edition: Voice of the Construction Industry (Daily); Defense Technology International (Bimonthly); My House in the Mountain States (Bimonthly); Business Week--1,000 Issue (Annual); Business Week--Survey of Executive Compensation Issue (Weekly); Electrical World (Monthly); ENR Directory of Contractors (Biennial); A/C FLYER: Best Read Resale Magazine Worldwide (Monthly); Independent Power Report's Avoided-Cost Quarterly (Quarterly). **Awards:** Harold W. McGraw, Jr. Prize in Education (Annual).

43003 ▪ Passion Profit Co.
Church Street Sta.
 New York, NY 10008-0618
Ph: (646)481-4238
Co. E-mail: questions@passionprofit.com
URL: http://passionprofit.systeme.io
Contact: Walt F. J. Goodridge, Founder
Description: Publisher of how-to books primarily. **Founded:** 1990.

43004 ▪ Productivity Press
New York, NY
Free: 800-272-7737
URL: http://www.routledge.com/go/productivity-press
Description: Offers educational materials that support continuous improvement in the manufacturing industry. Covers just-in-time, total quality management and mistake proofing. **Founded:** 1983. **Publications:** "Using Lean for Faster Six Sigma Results - a Synchronized Approach," Jun, 2006; "Maintenance Management is a Viable and Valuable Investment for Any Industry Seeking to Beat the Competition," Jun, 2006; "The Basics of Performance Measurement".

43005 ▪ SelectBooks Inc. (SB)
28 Liberty St.
 New York, NY 10005
Ph: (212)206-1997
Fax: (212)206-3815
Co. E-mail: info@selectbooks.com
URL: http://www.selectbooks.com
Contact: Kenzi Sugihara, Chief Executive Officer
X (Twitter): x.com/selectbooksinc
Description: Publisher of non-fiction in the areas of biography, politics, business administration and alternative medicine. **Founded:** 2001.

43006 ▪ Standard And Poor's Financial Services LLC. (S&P)
S&P Global Inc.
 55 Water St.
 New York, NY 10041
Ph: (212)438-1000
Co. E-mail: index_services@spglobal.com
URL: http://www.spglobal.com
Contact: Douglas L. Peterson, President
X (Twitter): x.com/SPGlobalRatings
YouTube: www.youtube.com/user/SPTVbroadcast
Description: Firm engages in financial information publishing. **Founded:** 1860. **Publications:** Standard & Poor's Register - Corporate; Compustat®, Emerging Markets Data Base (EMDB); International Securities Identification Directory (Annual); Standard & Poor's A.S.E. Stock Reports (Weekly); Directory of Bond Agents (Annual); Standard and Poor's Daily Stock Price Records (Quarterly); Garden Conservancy's Open Days Directory: The Guide To Visiting America's Best Private Gardens (Annual); The Review of Securities & Commodities Regulation (Semimonthly); COMPMARK; MarketScope (Weekly); Standard & Poor's CORPORATE DESCRIPTIONS plus NEWS; Standard & Poor's Register DataBases; Mutual Fund Profiles; Trendline Chart Guide (Monthly); NetAdvantage Stock Guide; Variable Annuities; Advisor Insight®; Asset-Backed Securities (ASB); Bank Loan and Recovery Ratings; Collateralized Debt Obligations/Derivatives; Corporate Action Service; Corporate Credit Ratings; Corporate Governance Evaluations & Scores (CGES); Quantitative Stock Reports; Counterparty Credit Ratings; Credit Risk Assessment Templates; CreditModel™; GICS® Direct; Index Alert®; Standard & Poor's Industry Surveys; Standard & Poor's Insurer Financial Enhancement Ratings; Issuer Credit Ratings; RatingsDirect®; Compustat® Global Data (Daily); Standard & Poor's The Outlook; Standard & Poor's Dividend Record (Daily); OTC Chart Manual (Bimonthly); Standard & Poor's Nasdaq and Regional Exchange Stock Reports (Weekly); CreditWeek; Standard and Poor's Dividend Record; Earnings Guide (Monthly); Standard & Poor's Corporate Descriptions plus News; CFRA MarketScope Advisor; Standard & Poor's Mid-Cap 400 Directory (Annual); Industry Surveys; Bond Guide (Monthly); Corporation Records (Daily); Stock Guide (Monthly); S&P Corporations; S&P Electronic Prospectus; S&P Stock Reports/CD-ROM; Daily News on Dialog; Unit Investment Trusts (UIT); Corporate Registered Bond Interest Record; Standard & Poor's Dividend Record; Standard & Poor's MarketScope (Daily); Security Dealers of North America; ANNA Service Bureau; CDO Manager Focus; ClassicDirect; Compustat® North America; Compustat® Unrestated Quarterly; Consultant eDirectory; Outlook Online Edition; Compustat® Corporate Tracker; NetAdvantage Corporation Records; Credit Risk Tracker; CreditPro; CreditWeek®; CreditWire Japan; CUSIP ISIDPlus Access; CUSIP Master Service; EuroThesys Life and Non-Life; ExecuComp; Fund Advisor; ISID Plus; KennyWeb; Standard & Poor's/Investortools Municipal Bond Indices; Municipal Historical Evaluations Data; Standard & Poor's/Investortools Municipal Yield Curves; NetAdvantage Fund Reports; Portfolio Advisor; RatingsDirect® Asia/Pacific; RatingsDirect® Corporations; RatingsDirect® Financial Institutions; RatingsDirect® Global Issuers; RatingsDirect® U.S. Public Finance; RatingsDirect® Structured Finance; NetAdvantage Register of Corporations, Directors, and Executives; Research Insight on the Web; SMA Evaluator; Dividend Record; Standard & Poor's 500 Directory (Annual); Standard & Poor's Register of Corporations, Directors and Executives (Annual); CreditWeek: The Global Authority on Credit Quality (Weekly); Trendline Current Market Perspectives (Monthly); Trendline Daily Action Stock Charts (Weekly; Biweekly; Monthly); Standard & Poor's N.Y. S.E. Stock Reports (Daily); S & P's Insurance Digest/Life Insurance Edition (Quarterly); S & P's Insurance Digest/Property-Casualty & Reinsurance Edition (Quarterly); S & P's Municipal Bond Book, with Notes, Commercial Paper, & IRBs; Security Owner's Stock Guide; Standard & Poor's Statistical Service. Current Statistics; Standard & Poor's Stock Reports: NASDAQ and Regional Exchanges; Standard & Poor's Stock Reports: New York Stock Exchange; Small Pension Funds Directory (Annual); Analyst's Handbook: Composite Corporate Per Share Data by Industry; Standard & Poor's Corporation Records; Standard & Poor's Directory of Bond Agents (Biennial); Standard & Poor's Stock Reports--American Stock Exchange; Standard & Poor's Stock Reports--New York Stock Exchange, American Stock Exchange, Nasdaq Stock Market and Regional Exchanges; Standard & Poor's Stock Reports--Nasdaq and Regional Exchanges; KENNYBASE® (KDBS); Housing Call Reports; Blue List of Current Municipal and Corporate Offerings (Daily (morn.)); Standard and Poor's Bond Guide; Standard and Poor's Ratings Handbook; Standard & Poor's Semi-Weekly Called Bond Record.

43007 ▪ Tokyo Stock Exchange Inc. (TSE)
45 Broadway, 21st Fl.
 New York, NY 10006
Ph: (212)363-2350
Fax: (212)363-2354
URL: http://www.jpx.co.jp/english
Contact: Koichiro Miyahara, President
Description: Publisher of business and statistics, stocks, and shares. **Founded:** 1870. **Publications:** Tokyo Stock Exchange Fact Book.

EARLY STAGE FINANCING

43008 ▪ Brightstone Capital
630 Fifth Ave., 20th Fl.
 New York, NY 10111
Ph: (212)899-5300
Co. E-mail: info@brightstonecap.com
URL: http://brightstonecap.com
Description: Capital investment firm.

43009 ▪ Greycroft Partners (GP)
292 Madison Ave. 8th Fl.
 New York, NY 10017
Co. E-mail: info@greycroft.com
URL: http://www.greycroft.com
Contact: Meghan Fahy, Director
Description: Early- and growth-stage private equity firm. Also maintains an office in Los Angeles. **Founded:** 2006. **Preferred Investment Size:** $100,000 to $5,000,000 for venture capital; $10,000,000 to $35,000,000 for growth capital.

43010 ▪ Grow VC Group
New York, NY
Co. E-mail: info@growvc.com
URL: http://group.growvc.com
Contact: Jouko Ahvenainen, Co-Founder
Facebook: www.facebook.com/growvc
Linkedin: www.linkedin.com/company/grow-vc-group
X (Twitter): x.com/growvc
Description: Holding and investing company; co-founder in global digital businesses. Offers enabling services, components, instruments, and technology. **Founded:** 2009. **Industry Preferences:** Data; digital finance; digital intelligence.

43011 ▪ New York Angels (NYA)
1216 Broadway, Fl. 2
 New York, NY 10001
URL: http://www.newyorkangels.com
Contact: Liz Lindsey, Executive Director
Linkedin: www.linkedin.com/company/new-york-angels
X (Twitter): x.com/thenyangels

Description: Member-led investment organization committed to funding young companies. **Founded:** 2004. **Investment Policies:** Established proof of concept; poised for growth; solving major problems for large addressable target markets. **Industry Preferences:** Business products and services; digital media; financial services; healthtech; medical devices.

EXPANSION AND GROWTH FINANCING

43012 ■ Greycroft Partners (GP)
292 Madison Ave. 8th Fl.
New York, NY 10017
Co. E-mail: info@greycroft.com
URL: http://www.greycroft.com
Contact: Meghan Fahy, Director
Description: Early- and growth-stage private equity firm. Also maintains an office in Los Angeles. **Founded:** 2006. **Preferred Investment Size:** $100,000 to $5,000,000 for venture capital; $10,000,000 to $35,000,000 for growth capital.

43013 ■ Millenium Technology Value Partners (MTVLP)
60 E 42nd St.
New York, NY 10165
Ph: (646)521-7800
Co. E-mail: info@mtvlp.com
URL: http://www.mtvlp.com
Contact: Barbara O'Connell, Office Manager
Description: Offers alternative liquidity programs to leading technology companies. **Founded:** 2002.

VENTURE CAPITAL FIRM

43014 ■ Betaworks Studio L.L.C.
29 Little W 12th St.
New York, NY 10014
URL: http://www.betaworks.com
Description: Provider of technology incubator and investment services for network-focused consumer-facing media businesses. **Founded:** 2018.

43015 ■ BR Venture Fund [Big Red Ventures (BRV)]
114 E Ave.
Ithaca, NY 14853
URL: http://www.brventurefund.com
Contact: Joseph Aldcowski, Manager
Linkedin: www.linkedin.com/company/brventurefund
X (Twitter): x.com/brventurefund
YouTube: www.youtube.com/channel/UCbfspj tZGPI0DhEpDBNvg3A
Description: Early-stage venture capital fund operated by MBA students. **Founded:** 2001. **Preferred Investment Size:** Up to $25,0000. **Investment Policies:** US-based high-growth companies.

43016 ■ Cayuga Venture Fund (CVF)
15 Thornwood Dr.
Ithaca, NY 14850
Ph: (607)266-9266
Fax: (607)266-9267
Co. E-mail: info@cayugaventures.com
URL: http://cayugaventures.com
Contact: Ryoko Nozawa, Director
X (Twitter): x.com/CayugaVentures
Description: Venture capital firm for start-ups in Ithaca and upstate New York. **Investment Policies:** Strong core value proposition; sustainable competitive advantage; high growth in a substantial market; capital efficiency.

43017 ■ City Light
150 E 52nd St.
New York, NY 10022
Ph: (212)403-9514
Co. E-mail: info@citylight.vc
URL: http://citylight.vc
Contact: Josh Cohen, Founder Partner
Linkedin: www.linkedin.com/company/city-light-capital
X (Twitter): x.com/citylightcap

Description: Venture capital firm for companies with a direct relationship between financial outcomes and social impact. **Founded:** 2004. **Industry Preferences:** Safety; environment; education.

43018 ■ Easton Capital
767 3rd Ave., 7th Fl.
New York, NY 10017
Ph: (212)702-0950
Fax: (212)702-0952
URL: http://www.eastoncapital.com
Contact: Charles B. Hughes, Managing Director General Counsel
E-mail: hughes@eastoncapital.com
Description: Healthcare investment firm. **Investment Policies:** Fundamental innovation; proof of efficacy; strategic interest; capital-efficient business model; early exits. **Industry Preferences:** Life science and healthcare.

43019 ■ Excell Technology Partners
343 State St.
Rochester, NY 14650
Co. E-mail: info@excellny.com
URL: http://excellny.com
Contact: Theresa B. Mazzullo, Chief Executive Officer
Linkedin: www.linkedin.com/company/excell-partners -inc.
X (Twitter): x.com/excellpartners
Description: In partnership with Empire State Development, funds pre-seed and seed start-ups in Upstate New York. **Founded:** 2005. **Investment Policies:** Portfolio companies must remain in New York for at least three years post-investment.

43020 ■ Genacast Ventures
588 Broadway St., Ste. 202
New York, NY 10012
URL: http://www.genacast.com
Contact: Gil Beyda, Founder Managing Partner
Linkedin: www.linkedin.com/company/genacast
Description: Venture capital firm for seed-stage B2B technology start-ups in the Northeast. Also operates out of Philadelphia. Works closely with Comcast/NBCU. **Founded:** 2008. **Investment Policies:** Capital efficiencies; deep technology; effective teams.

43021 ■ Harlem Capital Partners (HCP)
1180 Ave. Of The Americas, 8Th Fl.
New York, NY 10036
Co. E-mail: info@harlem.capital
URL: http://harlem.capital
Contact: Melody Hahm, Director
E-mail: melody@harlem.capital
X (Twitter): x.com/HarlemCapital
Description: Venture capital firm focusing on minority-owned startup companies. **Founded:** 2015.

43022 ■ Inspiring Capital (IC's)
New York, NY 10011
Co. E-mail: hello@inspiringcapital.ly
URL: http://www.inspiringcapital.ly
Contact: Nell Derick Debevoise, Chief Executive Officer
Facebook: www.facebook.com/InspiringCap
Linkedin: www.linkedin.com/company/inspiring -capital
X (Twitter): x.com/InspiringCap
Instagram: www.instagram.com/inspiring_capital
Description: Accelerates the integration of profits and purpose by aligning talented business professionals and high-potential, purpose-driven organizations. Combines consulting and training to help startups reach sustainability by applying business strategies to their operations and marketing. **Founded:** 2013.

43023 ■ Lerer Hippeau (LH)
100 Crosby St., Ste. 201
New York, NY 10012
Co. E-mail: contact@lererhippeau.com
URL: http://www.lererhippeau.com
Contact: Kenneth Lerer, Managing Partner
Linkedin: www.linkedin.com/company/lerer-hippeau -ventures

X (Twitter): x.com/lererhippeau
Instagram: www.instagram.com/lererhippeau
Description: Early stage venture capital firm. **Founded:** 2010.

43024 ■ Mount Royal Ventures (MRV)
Pittsford, NY
Co. E-mail: info@mountroyalventures.com
URL: http://www.mountroyalventures.com
Contact: Jonathan Parker, Director
Description: Invests in early-stage start-ups with high growth potential . **Investment Policies:** Proprietary technology; high growth potential; in need of management expertise. **Industry Preferences:** Materials science.

43025 ■ New York Fashion Tech Lab (NYFTL)
Spring Pl., St. Johns Ln.
New York, NY 10013
Co. E-mail: info@nyftlab.com
URL: http://nyftlab.com
Contact: Mary Alonso, Contact
Linkedin: www.linkedin.com/company/new-york -fashion-tech-lab
X (Twitter): x.com/nyftlab
Instagram: www.instagram.com/nyftlab
YouTube: www.youtube.com/channel/UC4ASP 2MKTxFTXHSlyVCeMNg
Pinterest: www.pinterest.com/nyftlab
Description: Focuses on female founders, fashion and retail technology innovation, and early to growth stage emerging tech companies. **Founded:** 2014.

43026 ■ NYC Seed
6 MetroTech Ctr.
Brooklyn, NY 11201
Ph: (707)469-3669
Co. E-mail: apply@nycseed.com
URL: http://www.nycseed.com
Description: Provides New York City seed stage entrepreneurs with the capital and support they need to move from idea to product launch.

43027 ■ Pfizer Ventures (PV)
235 E 42nd St.
New York, NY 10017
URL: http://www.pfizer.com/about/partners/venture -investments
Contact: Andrew J. Muratore, Vice President Chief Counsel
E-mail: andrew.j.muratore@pfizer.com
Description: Venture capital arm of Pfizer. Primarily invests in early-stage ventures in areas of strategic interest to Pfizer. **Founded:** 2004. **Industry Preferences:** Transformative therapeutics, particularly inflammation and immunology, internal medicine, oncology, rare disease and vaccines; neuroscience; platform technologies;; diagnostics; drug delivery .

43028 ■ Starta Captial
220 E 23rd St., No. 400
New York, NY 10010
Co. E-mail: info@starta.vc
URL: http://starta.vc/capital
Description: Early stage venture capital provider investing in early stage innovative and technological B2B and B2C companies and projects.

43029 ■ StartingPoint Ventures
41 E 11th St., 11th. Fl.
New York, NY 10003
URL: http://startingpointventures.com
Contact: Steven Goldthwaite, Co-Founder Partner
Description: Advises and invests in companies with proven teams, innovative ideas, and scalable business models. **Founded:** 2007.

43030 ■ Wider Wake
5 Great Jones St.
New York, NY 10012
Co. E-mail: enquiries@widerwake.net
URL: http://widerwake.net
Contact: Joseph Gomes, Managing Partner
X (Twitter): x.com/WiderWakeEnt
Description: Angel investment network and business consultancy specializing in digital media advertising startups.

North Carolina

ASSOCIATIONS AND OTHER ORGANIZATIONS

43031 ■ Association of Fundraising Professionals Western North Carolina Chapter (AFP-WNC)
PO Box 546
Asheville, NC 28802
Co. E-mail: chapteradmin@afpwnc.org
URL: http://www.afpwnc.org
Contact: Ben Underwood, Co-President
E-mail: president@afpwnc.org
Facebook: www.facebook.com/afpwnc.org
YouTube: www.youtube.com/channel/UCIRtHvTl2CtkuQeVr-Kma3Q
Description: Professional organization that serves as a resource for all who raise funds to better the western North Carolina community. Offers continuing education, professional support, networking, and local recognition. **Geographic Preference:** Local.

43032 ■ Business Marketing Association Carolinas Chapter
5970 Fairview Rd., Ste. 721
Charlotte, NC 28210
URL: http://www.doggettadvertising.com/portfolio/bma-carolinas
Description: Promotes the development of business-to-business marketing and communications professionals through education, training and networking. **Geographic Preference:** Regional.

43033 ■ Carolinas - Virginia Business Brokers Association (CVBBA)
10911 Raven Ridge Rd., Ste. 103-80
Raleigh, NC 27614
Ph: (646)573-7014
Co. E-mail: admin1@cvbba.com
URL: http://www.cvbba.com
Contact: Joe Santora, President
Facebook: www.facebook.com/carolinasvirginiabba
Description: Represents professionals and firms in business brokerage, mergers and acquisitions. Provides business brokers education, conferences, professional designations, and networking opportunities in North and South Carolina and Virginia. Works to become a leader in the exchange of business referrals, and to create professional relationships with successful business transaction advisors. **Founded:** 2005. **Geographic Preference:** Regional.

43034 ■ Entrepreneurs' Organization - Charlotte Chapter (EO)
809 W Hill St.
Charlotte, NC 28208
Ph: (704)582-9367
Co. E-mail: administrator@eocharlotte.org
URL: http://www.eocharlotte.org
Contact: Andrew Jones, Co-President
URL(s): www.eonetwork.org/charlotte
Facebook: www.facebook.com/eocharlotte
Linkedin: www.linkedin.com/company/eocharlotte
X (Twitter): x.com/EOCharlotte
Instagram: www.instagram.com/eocharlotte
YouTube: www.youtube.com/user/EOCharlotte
Description: Provides local resources to members which includes networking events, mentorship, live forums, and leadership development. **Founded:** 1998.

43035 ■ International Association of Women Greensboro Chapter
Greensboro, NC
URL: http://www.iawomen.com/chapters/greensboro-chapter
Description: Serves as network of accomplished women united to achieve professional goals. Provides a forum for sharing ideas and experiences of professional women regarding career success. Promotes an active business and networking community from all industries. **Geographic Preference:** Local.

43036 ■ International Association of Women Raleigh Durham Chapter
Durham, NC
URL: http://www.iawomen.com/chapters
Description: Serves as network of accomplished women united to achieve professional goals. Provides a forum for sharing ideas and experiences of professional women regarding career success. Promotes an active business and networking community from all industries. **Geographic Preference:** Local.

43037 ■ National Association of Women Business Owners Charlotte [NAWBO Charlotte]
1800 Camden Rd., Ste. 107, No. 44
Charlotte, NC 28203
Ph: (704)900-3067
Co. E-mail: nawbo@nawbocharlotte.org
URL: http://nawbocharlotte.org
Contact: Mindy Mills Hinson, President
Facebook: www.facebook.com/nawboclt
X (Twitter): x.com/NAWBOCharlotte
YouTube: www.youtube.com/channel/UCbWJt6lvBplyLvsgB-jwsbw
Description: Promotes the success of the women-owned businesses in the Charlotte area. **Founded:** 1999. **Geographic Preference:** Local.

43038 ■ National Association of Women Business Owners Greater Raleigh (NAWBOGR)
Raleigh, NC
URL: http://nawbo-raleigh.org
Contact: Emily Parks, Co-President
E-mail: emily@organizeforsuccess.com
Facebook: www.facebook.com/NAWBOGreaterRaleigh
X (Twitter): x.com/NAWBO_GR
Instagram: www.instagram.com/nawbo_gr
Description: Represents as voice and vision of women business owners in the Raleigh area. Encouraged and supported many women as they have built their businesses and expanded their customer base. Facilitates economic prosperity of a diverse membership of women business owners through mentoring, networking education and support. **Founded:** 1978. **Geographic Preference:** Local.

43039 ■ North Carolina Agribusiness Council (NCAg)
2500 Regency Pkwy.
Cary, NC 27518
Ph: (919)782-4063
Co. E-mail: info@ncagribusiness.com
URL: http://ncagribusiness.com
Contact: Leon Troutman, President
Description: Agricultural production, processing, and marketing firms and suppliers of goods and services to the industry. Promotes agribusiness advancement and development. Supports research, education, and extension. Represents industry before the public. **Founded:** 1969. **Publications:** AgNews (Weekly). **Educational Activities:** North Carolina Agribusiness Council Conference (Annual). **Geographic Preference:** State.

43040 ■ North Carolina Retail Merchants Association (NCRMA) - Resource Library
209 Fayetteville St.
Raleigh, NC 27601
Ph: (919)832-0811
Co. E-mail: info@ncrma.org
URL: http://ncrma.org
Contact: Andy Ellen, President
E-mail: andye@ncrma.org
Facebook: www.facebook.com/NCRetail
Linkedin: www.linkedin.com/company/north-carolina-retail-merchants-association
X (Twitter): x.com/NCRMA
Description: Strives to improve the business climate for retail merchants throughout North Carolina. **Scope:** Business practice regulations; customer services resources; e-commerce resources; retail laws and security; inventory management; merchandising and tax. **Services:** Open only to members. **Founded:** 1902. **Holdings:** Articles; tip sheets; documents. **Geographic Preference:** State.

SMALL BUSINESS DEVELOPMENT CENTERS

43041 ■ Cape Fear Small Business and Technology Development Center
502 N Front St., Ste. 530
Wilmington, NC 28401
URL: http://cfcc.edu/small-business-center
Contact: Jerry Coleman, Director
E-mail: jdcoleman338@cfcc.edu
Description: Supports the growth and development of North Carolina's economy by encouraging entrepreneurship, assisting in the creation and expansion of small businesses, and facilitating technology development and transfer. **Geographic Preference:** Local.

STATE LISTINGS   North Carolina ■ 43055

43042 ■ North Carolina Small Business and Technology Development Center - Lead Office (SBTDC)
5 W Hargett St., Ste. 600, 6th Fl.
  Raleigh, NC 27601
Ph: (919)715-7272
Free: 800-258-0862
Fax: (919)715-7777
Co. E-mail: bhicks@sbtdc.org
URL: http://sbtdc.org
Contact: Byron Hicks, Officer
E-mail: bhicks@sbtdc.org
Linkedin: www.linkedin.com/company/sbtdc
X (Twitter): x.com/ncsbtdc
Description: Provides management counseling and educational services to small and mid-sized businesses. **Founded:** 1984. **Geographic Preference:** State.

SMALL BUSINESS ASSISTANCE PROGRAMS

43043 ■ Council for Entrepreneurial Development (CED)
600 Pk. Offices Dr., Ste. 100
  Research Triangle Park, NC 27709
Ph: (919)549-7500
Fax: (919)549-7405
URL: http://cednc.org
Contact: Kelly Rowell, President
Linkedin: www.linkedin.com/company/cednc
YouTube: www.youtube.com/channel/UCs_O3vyETz7Yu1QRiugqlnw
Description: Council of entrepreneurs, business and financial service providers, public policy makers, and university faculty, united to promote the enhancement of entrepreneurial development in North Carolina through monthly programs, newsletters, consultation programs, membership directories, seminars and workshops, and an annual venture capital conference. **Founded:** 1984.

43044 ■ N.C. Rural Center [North Carolina Rural Economic Development Center]
4021 Carya Dr.
  Raleigh, NC 27610
Ph: (919)250-4314
Co. E-mail: info@ncruralcenter.org
URL: http://www.ncruralcenter.org
Contact: Patrick Woodie, President
E-mail: pwoodie@ncruralcenter.org
Facebook: www.facebook.com/ncruralcenter
Linkedin: www.linkedin.com/company/north-carolina-rural-economic-development-center
X (Twitter): x.com/NCRuralCenter
Instagram: www.instagram.com/theruralcenter
YouTube: www.youtube.com/user/RuralCenterNC
Description: Provides and is involved in research and demonstration efforts to identify new ideas, strategies, or programs that will generate economic development in rural North Carolina. **Scope:** Rural issues in North Carolina. **Founded:** 1987. **Publications:** *North Carolina Rural Economic Development Center Fact sheets*; *North Carolina Rural Economic Development Center Newsletters*; *North Carolina Rural Economic Development Center Reports*. **Educational Activities:** North Carolina Rural Economic Development Center Briefings, conferences, meetings; Rural Partners Forum (Annual).

43045 ■ North Carolina Community College System Small Business Center Network (SBCN)
200 W Jones St.
  Raleigh, NC 27603
Ph: (919)807-7100
URL: http://www.nccommunitycolleges.edu/businesses/small-business-center-network
Description: Offers consultations and referrals, including business planning. Operates a resource and information center containing printed and electronic resources. Sponsors business and computer expos in cooperation with business and community organizations. Offers workshops to potential and existing small businesses on business topics, including business plans, basics of business, motivation, management, financial planning, computer and software applications, customer relations, farm recordkeeping, and franchising.

43046 ■ North Carolina Department of Agriculture and Consumers Services (NCDA&CS) - Marketing Div.
2 W Edenton St., Rm. 402
  Raleigh, NC 27601
Ph: (919)707-3100
URL: http://www.ncagr.gov/divisions/marketing
Contact: Peter Thornton, Director
Description: Provides small businesses with information on doing business internationally.

43047 ■ North Carolina Department of Commerce - Business/Industry Development Div.
301 N Wilmington St.
  Raleigh, NC 27601-1058
Ph: (919)814-4600
Co. E-mail: info@nccommerce.com
URL: http://www.nccommerce.com
Contact: Anthony M. Copeland, Secretary
Facebook: www.facebook.com/thrivenc
Linkedin: www.linkedin.com/company/north-carolina-department-of-commerce
X (Twitter): x.com/nccommerce
Description: Assists international, national, and state firms in locating new or expanded facilities in North Carolina.

43048 ■ North Carolina Small Business and Technology Development Center (NCSBTDC)
5 W Hargett St., Ste. 600
  Raleigh, NC 27601
Ph: (919)715-7272
Free: 800-258-0862
Co. E-mail: info@sbtdc.org
URL: http://sbtdc.org
Contact: Byron Hicks, Director
E-mail: bhicks@sbtdc.org
Linkedin: www.linkedin.com/company/sbtdc
X (Twitter): x.com/ncsbtdc
Description: Goals are to increase job opportunities and capital investments; to assist in the creation or retention of jobs; to expand economic opportunities; to reduce the incidence of business failure; to assist in community development efforts; and to assist in the development, growth, and expansion of commercial, industrial, and business activities. **Founded:** 1984.

43049 ■ North Carolina State University Industrial Extension Solutions (NCSU IES)
1005 Capability Dr., Ste. 200
  Raleigh, NC 27606
Ph: (919)515-2358
Free: 800-227-0264
Co. E-mail: iesservices@ncsu.edu
URL: http://www.ies.ncsu.edu
Contact: Phil Mintz, Executive Director
Facebook: www.facebook.com/NCStateIES
Linkedin: www.linkedin.com/company/ncstateies
X (Twitter): x.com/NCStateIES
YouTube: www.youtube.com/user/NCStateIES
Description: Provides assistance to North Carolina industries to help them have a competitive advantage through better utilization of engineering technologies. **Founded:** 1955. **Publications:** *North Carolina Plastics Industry Directory: Directory of Polymer Processors in North Carolina* (Biennial).

43050 ■ University of North Carolina at Chapel Hill - Kenan-Flagler Business School - Frank Hawkins Kenan Institute of Private Enterprise
300 Kenan Dr., Ste. 300
  Chapel Hill, NC 27599
Ph: (919)962-8201
Co. E-mail: unckenaninstitute@gmail.com
URL: http://kenaninstitute.unc.edu
Contact: Kim Allen, Executive Director
E-mail: kim_allen@kenan-flagler.unc.edu
Facebook: www.facebook.com/kenaninstitute
Linkedin: www.linkedin.com/company/kenan-institute-of-private-enterprise
X (Twitter): x.com/kenaninstitute
YouTube: www.youtube.com/user/UNCKenanInstitute
Description: National center for private enterprise research focusing on entrepreneurial development, new venture management, and coursework development. **Scope:** Free enterprise, including job creation, changing labor-force skill needs, factors affecting business competitiveness and employment growth, international trade and privatization, management in the financial services industry, policy issues relating to financial services, financial services markets, offshore sourcing in manufacturing, manufacturing quality, manufacturing forecasting, human resources supervision, team building, compensation, management development, and multidisciplinary research on global economic change and international marketing. **Founded:** 1985. **Educational Activities:** Carolina Challenge Star Program; Carolina Entrepreneurial Initiative; International Executive Series and MBA Enterprise Corps.

SCORE OFFICES

43051 ■ Coastal Carolina SCORE
3615 Arendell St.
  Morehead City, NC 28557
Ph: (252)222-6126
Co. E-mail: help@score.org
URL: http://www.score.org/coastalcarolina
Facebook: www.facebook.com/coastalcarolinascore
Description: Promotes business and community development in Morehead City, NC. Conducts business education seminars and workshops to those wanting to start a business. **Founded:** 1964. **Geographic Preference:** Local.

43052 ■ Durham SCORE
104 S Estes Dr.
  Chapel Hill, NC 27514
Ph: (919)240-7765
Co. E-mail: help@score.org
URL: http://www.score.org/chapelhilldurham
Facebook: www.facebook.com/SCOREChapelHill
Linkedin: www.linkedin.com/company/score-mentors-chapel-hill
X (Twitter): x.com/SCOREChapelHill
Founded: 1981.

43053 ■ Outer Banks SCORE
3615 Arendell St.
  Morehead City, NC 28557
URL: http://www.score.org/coastalcarolina
Contact: Bridget Weston, Chief Executive Officer

43054 ■ SCORE - Apex
220 N Salem St.
  Apex, NC 27502
Ph: (919)869-4151
URL: http://raleigh.score.org
Description: Provides professional guidance and information to maximize the success of existing and emerging small businesses. Offers business counseling and workshops.

43055 ■ SCORE - Asheville
151 Patton Ave.
  Federal Bldg. Rm. 259
  Asheville, NC 28801
Ph: (828)271-4786
Co. E-mail: info@ashevillescore.org
URL: http://asheville.score.org
Contact: Dale Collins, President
Facebook: www.facebook.com/SCOREAsheville
Linkedin: www.linkedin.com/company/score-mentors-asheville
X (Twitter): x.com/SCOREAsheville
Description: Serves as volunteer program in which working and retired business management professionals provide free business counseling to men and women who are considering starting a small business, encountering problems with their business, or expanding their business. Offers free one-on-one

counseling, online counseling and low cost workshops on a variety of business topics. **Founded:** 1964. **Geographic Preference:** Local.

43056 ■ SCORE - Boone
Appalachian Enterprise Center
130 Poplar Grove Connector
Boone, NC 28607
Ph: (828)263-2732
Co. E-mail: info@ashevillescore.org
URL: http://asheville.score.org
Contact: Joanne Kalp, Vice President
Facebook: www.facebook.com/SCOREAsheville
Linkedin: www.linkedin.com/company/score-mentors-asheville
X (Twitter): x.com/SCOREAsheville
Description: Provides professional guidance and information to maximize the success of existing and emerging small businesses. Offers business counseling and workshops.

43057 ■ SCORE - Cameron Village Library
1930 Clark Ave., Rm. 120
Raleigh, NC 27605
URL: http://www.score.org/raleigh/mentoring-locations
Description: Provides professional guidance and information to maximize the success of existing and emerging small businesses. Offers business counseling and workshops.

43058 ■ SCORE - Cape Fear Region
4010 Oleander Dr.
Wilmington, NC 28403
Ph: (910)452-5395
Co. E-mail: scorecapefear@gmail.com
URL: http://capefear.score.org
Facebook: www.facebook.com/SCORECapeFearRegion
Linkedin: www.linkedin.com/company/score-mentors-cape-fear
X (Twitter): x.com/score_ilm
Instagram: www.instagram.com/score_mentors
YouTube: www.youtube.com/user/SCORESmallBusiness
Description: Provides professional guidance and information to maximize the success of existing and emerging small businesses. Offers business counseling and workshops. **Founded:** 1964. **Geographic Preference:** Local.

43059 ■ SCORE - Cary
4000 Louis Stephens Dr.
Cary, NC 27519
URL: http://www.score.org/raleigh/mentoring-locations
Description: Provides professional guidance and information to maximize the success of existing and emerging small businesses. Offers business counseling and workshops.

43060 ■ SCORE - Chapel Hill Durham
103 W Main St.
Durham, NC 27701
Ph: (201)412-8718
Co. E-mail: scorechapelhilldurham@scorevolunteer.org
URL: http://chapelhilldurham.score.org
Contact: Mike Atwood, Contact
Facebook: www.facebook.com/SCOREChapelHill
Linkedin: www.linkedin.com/company/score-mentors-chapel-hill
X (Twitter): x.com/SCOREChapelHill
Instagram: www.instagram.com/score_mentors
Description: Provides professional guidance and information to maximize the success of existing and emerging small businesses. Offers business counseling and workshops. **Founded:** 1981. **Geographic Preference:** Local.

43061 ■ SCORE - Charlotte
6302 Fairview Rd., Ste. 300
Charlotte, NC 28210
Ph: (704)344-6576
Fax: (704)344-6769
Co. E-mail: charlottescore47@cltscore.org
URL: http://charlotte.score.org
Contact: Cora Emmerich Ea, Contact
Facebook: www.facebook.com/SCORECharlotte
Linkedin: www.linkedin.com/company/charlotte-score
X (Twitter): x.com/SCORECharlotte
Pinterest: www.pinterest.com/scorecharlotte
Description: Provides professional guidance and information to maximize the success of existing and emerging small businesses. Offers business counseling and workshops. **Founded:** 1965. **Geographic Preference:** Local.

43062 ■ SCORE - Coastal Carolina
3615 Arendell St.
Morehead City, NC 28557
Ph: (252)222-6126
Co. E-mail: help@score.org
URL: http://www.score.org/coastalcarolina
Facebook: www.facebook.com/coastalcarolinascore
Description: Provides professional guidance and information to maximize the success of existing and emerging small businesses. Offers business counseling and workshops. **Geographic Preference:** Local.

43063 ■ SCORE - Greensboro
1451 S Elm Eugene St., Ste. 2306
Greensboro, NC 27406
Ph: (336)333-5399
Co. E-mail: scoregso@gmail.com
URL: http://piedmonttriad.score.org
Description: Provides professional guidance and information to maximize the success of existing and emerging small businesses. Offers business counseling and workshops. **Geographic Preference:** Local.

43064 ■ SCORE - NC Piedmont Triad
The Nussbaum Center For Entrepreneurship
1451 Elm-Eugene St., Ste. 2306
Greensboro, NC 27406
Ph: (336)333-5399
Co. E-mail: scoregso@gmail.com
URL: http://www.score.org/piedmonttriad
Facebook: www.facebook.com/SCOREPiedmontTriad
Linkedin: www.linkedin.com/company/score-mentors-piedmonttriad
Description: Provides public service to America by offering small business advice and training. **Geographic Preference:** Local.

43065 ■ SCORE - New Bern
233 Middle St.
New Bern, NC 28563
URL: http://coastalcarolina.score.org
Description: Provides professional guidance and information to maximize the success of existing and emerging small businesses. Offers business counseling and workshops.

43066 ■ SCORE - Outer Banks
101 Town Hall Dr.
Kill Devil Hills, NC 27948
Ph: (252)216-1501
Fax: (252)473-2897
Co. E-mail: mentor@scoreobx.org
URL: http://outerbanks.score.org
Contact: Kill Devil Hills, Contact
Facebook: www.facebook.com/SCORE497
Description: Provides professional guidance and information to maximize the success of existing and emerging small businesses. Offers business counseling and workshops.

43067 ■ SCORE - Raleigh
Ste. 306, 300 Fayetteville St.
Raleigh, NC 27601
Ph: (919)869-4151
Co. E-mail: contact.raleigh@scorevolunteer.org
URL: http://www.score.org/raleigh
Contact: Mark Wilson, Chairman
Facebook: www.facebook.com/SCORERaleigh
Linkedin: www.linkedin.com/company/raleigh-score
X (Twitter): x.com/raleigh_score
Description: Provides professional guidance and information to maximize the success of existing and emerging small businesses. Offers business counseling and workshops. **Founded:** 1964. **Geographic Preference:** Local.

43068 ■ SCORE - Raleigh Chamber of Commerce
800 S Salisbury St.
Raleigh, NC 27601
Ph: (919)869-4151
URL: http://www.score.org/raleigh/mentoring-locations
Description: Provides professional guidance and information to maximize the success of existing and emerging small businesses. Offers business counseling and workshops.

43069 ■ SCORE - Reidsville
240 Cherokee Camp Rd., Ste. 2
Reidsville, NC 27320
URL: http://greensboro.score.org
Description: Provides professional guidance and information to maximize the success of existing and emerging small businesses. Offers business counseling and workshops.

43070 ■ SCORE - Rocky Mount
727 N Grace St.
Rocky Mount, NC 27804
Co. E-mail: score@braswell-library.org
URL: http://raleigh.score.org
Description: Provides professional guidance and information to maximize the success of existing and emerging small businesses. Offers business counseling and workshops.

43071 ■ SCORE - Sandhills
95 Cherokee Rd.
Pinehurst, NC 28374
Ph: (910)420-0121
Co. E-mail: scorestaffing0364@gmail.com
URL: http://sandhills.score.org
Facebook: www.facebook.com/Sandhills-SCORE-110163000415420
Description: Provides professional guidance and information to maximize the success of existing and emerging small businesses. Offers business counseling and workshops. **Founded:** 1975. **Geographic Preference:** Local.

43072 ■ SCORE - Wake Forest
102 E Roosevelt Ave.
Wake Forest, NC 27587
URL: http://www.score.org/raleigh/mentoring-locations
Description: Provides professional guidance and information to maximize the success of existing and emerging small businesses. Offers business counseling and workshops.

43073 ■ SCORE - Waynesville
112 Virginia Ave.
Waynesville, NC 28786
Ph: (828)407-7632
URL: http://www.score.org/find-location?state=NC
Description: Provides professional guidance and information to maximize the success of existing and emerging small businesses. Offers business counseling and workshops.

43074 ■ SCORE - Western North Carolina
204 Kanuga Rd.
Hendersonville, NC 28739
Ph: (828)693-8702
Co. E-mail: help@score.org
URL: http://westernnc.score.org
Description: Provides professional guidance and information to maximize the success of existing and emerging small businesses. Offers business counseling and workshops. **Geographic Preference:** Local.

BETTER BUSINESS BUREAUS

43075 ■ Better Business Bureau of Asheville/Western North Carolina
112 Executive Pk.
Asheville, NC 28801
URL: http://www.bbb.org
Contact: Tom Bartholomy, President
E-mail: tbartholomy@charlotte.bbb.org

STATE LISTINGS

Description: Seeks to promote and foster the highest ethical relationship between businesses and the public through voluntary self-regulation, consumer and business education, and service excellence. Provides information to help consumers and businesses make informed purchasing decisions and avoid costly scams and frauds; settles consumer complaints through arbitration and other means. **Geographic Preference:** Local.

43076 ■ **Better Business Bureau of Eastern North Carolina**
NC
Ph: (919)277-4222
Fax: (919)277-4221
Co. E-mail: info@raleigh.bbb.org
URL: http://www.bbb.org/local-bbb/bbb-of-eastern-carolinas
Contact: Mallory Wojciechowski, Contact
Facebook: www.facebook.com/BBBCarolinas
Linkedin: www.linkedin.com/company/better-business-bureau-of-eastern-carolinas
X (Twitter): x.com/bbbcarolinas
Instagram: www.instagram.com/bbbcarolinas
Description: Promotes ethics in the business community. Provides information to consumers regarding the reliability of area businesses. Assists in resolving disputes between businesses and consumers. Encourages adherence to the Code of Advertising. Conducts educational programs. **Founded:** 1912. **Publications:** *BusinessLine* (Monthly). **Geographic Preference:** Local.

43077 ■ **Better Business Bureau of Southern Piedmont**
112 Executive Pk.
Asheville, NC 28801
Ph: (828)253-2392
URL: http://www.bbb.org/local-bbb/bbb-of-southern-piedmont-and-western-nc
Contact: Tom Bartholomy, President
Linkedin: www.linkedin.com/company/better-business-bureau-of-southern-piedmont
Description: Seeks to promote and foster the highest ethical relationship between businesses and the public through voluntary self-regulation, consumer and business education, and service excellence. Provides information to help consumers and businesses make informed purchasing decisions and avoid costly scams and frauds; settles consumer complaints through arbitration and other means. **Geographic Preference:** Local.

CHAMBERS OF COMMERCE

43078 ■ **Alamance County Area Chamber of Commerce**
610 S Lexington Ave.
Burlington, NC 27215
Ph: (336)228-1338
Co. E-mail: info@alamancechamber.com
URL: http://www.alamancechamber.com
Contact: Andrea Fleming, Director
E-mail: andrea@alamancechamber.com
Facebook: www.facebook.com/alamancechamber
Linkedin: www.linkedin.com/company/alamance-chamber
X (Twitter): x.com/alamancechamber
Description: Promotes business and community development in Alamance County, NC. **Founded:** 1849. **Publications:** *Industrial Profile/Directory* (Annual); *Directory of Members & Buyers Guide*. **Geographic Preference:** Local.

43079 ■ **Alleghany County Chamber of Commerce (ACCC)**
58 S Main St.
Sparta, NC 28675
Ph: (336)372-5473
Co. E-mail: info@sparta-nc.com
URL: http://alleghanycountychamber.com
Contact: Lisa Bottomley, Executive Director
Facebook: www.facebook.com/AlleghanyChamber
YouTube: www.youtube.com/user/AlleghanyChamber
Description: Promotes business and community development in Alleghany County, NC and operates visitor center. Sponsors Choose and Cut Christmas Tree Day and Mountain Heritage Festival. **Founded:** 1983. **Publications:** *Alleghany Business Directory* (Periodic); *Chamber Views* (Monthly). **Geographic Preference:** Local.

43080 ■ **Andrews Chamber of Commerce**
955 Main St.
Andrews, NC 28901
Ph: (828)321-3584
URL: http://www.visitandrewsnc.com
Contact: Gayle Horton, President
Facebook: www.facebook.com/AndrewsNCChamber
Instagram: www.instagram.com/visitandrewsnc
YouTube: www.youtube.com/channel/UCmSjxcAbjEQSz2aTYQIDCrQ
Description: Strives to advance the general welfare and prosperity of the Town of Andrews. Works toward the betterment of the community and endeavors to improve the economic, civic, environmental, cultural, industrial, educational, agricultural, commercial, professional, recreational, and travel and tourism interest of the area. **Founded:** 1988. **Geographic Preference:** Local.

43081 ■ **Angier Chamber of Commerce**
24 E Depot St.
Angier, NC 27501
Ph: (919)639-2500
Fax: (919)639-8826
Co. E-mail: angiercc@angierchamber.org
URL: http://www.angierchamber.org
Contact: Rick Gutierrez, President
Facebook: www.facebook.com/angierchamberofcommerce
X (Twitter): x.com/angierchamber2
Description: Promotes business and community development in Angier, NC. **Founded:** 1956. **Publications:** *Chamber Newsletter* (Weekly). **Geographic Preference:** Local.

43082 ■ **Anson County Chamber of Commerce (ACCC)**
107-A E Wade St.
Wadesboro, NC 28170
Ph: (704)694-4181
Fax: (704)694-3830
Co. E-mail: info@ansoncountychamber.org
URL: http://ansoncountychamber.org
Contact: Shelby Emrich, President
E-mail: semrich@ansoncountychamber.org
Description: Seeks to promote and preserve the business climate and quality of life for the general welfare of all citizens of Anson County and members through diverse leadership and a shared vision of excellence. **Publications:** *Anson County Newcomers Guide*; *Chamberlines* (Monthly). **Awards:** Henry W. Little III Community Leadership Award (Annual); W. Dunlap Covington Award for Community Services (Annual). **Geographic Preference:** Local.

43083 ■ **Apex Chamber of Commerce**
220 N Salem St.
Apex, NC 27502
Ph: (919)362-6456
Free: 800-345-4504
URL: http://www.apexchamber.com
Contact: Shannon Flaherty, President
E-mail: sflaherty@apexchamber.com
Facebook: www.facebook.com/ApexChamberofCommerce
X (Twitter): x.com/apex_chamber
Instagram: www.instagram.com/apexchamber
YouTube: www.youtube.com/channel/UCWpXKbpb01g5uva-8HOUVvA
Description: Promotes business and community development in the Apex, NC area. **Founded:** 1958. **Publications:** *The Chamber Express* (Monthly). **Awards:** Citizen of the Year (Annual). **Geographic Preference:** Local.

43084 ■ **Archdale-Trinity Chamber of Commerce (ATCC)**
213 Balfour Dr.
Archdale, NC 27263
Ph: (336)434-2073
Fax: (336)431-5845
URL: http://www.archdaletrinitychamber.com
Contact: Beverly M. Nelson, President
E-mail: beverly@archdaletrinitychamber.com
Facebook: www.facebook.com/Archdale-Trinity-Chamber-of-Commerce-275467749770
Description: Promotes business and community development in Archdale and Trinity, NC. Conducts seminars and training programs. **Founded:** 1982. **Publications:** *Chamber Voice*; *Membership Resources Guide*. **Educational Activities:** Bush Hill Heritage Festival. **Geographic Preference:** Local.

43085 ■ **Ashe County Chamber of Commerce**
1 N Jefferson Ave., Ste. C
West Jefferson, NC 28694
Ph: (336)846-9550
Free: 888-343-2743
Co. E-mail: info@ashechamber.com
URL: http://ashechamber.com
Contact: Kitty Honeycutt, Executive Director
Facebook: www.facebook.com/AsheChamber
X (Twitter): x.com/RealAsheChamber
Instagram: www.instagram.com/ashechamber
YouTube: www.youtube.com/channel/UCyXExVINd67LNCHKnFMzgdg/videos
Pinterest: www.pinterest.com/ashecountychamb
Description: Strives to ensure the economic health of the local community by nurturing business growth and encouraging economic development. **Publications:** *Ashe* (Annual). **Geographic Preference:** Local.

43086 ■ **Asheboro/Randolph Chamber of Commerce**
137 S Fayetteville St.
Asheboro, NC 27203-5762
Ph: (336)626-2626
Fax: (336)626-7077
Co. E-mail: info@ashranchamber.com
URL: http://www.chamber.asheboro.com
Contact: Linda Brown, President
E-mail: lbrown@asheboro.com
Facebook: www.facebook.com/ashranchamber
YouTube: www.youtube.com/channel/UCPeIT9MyqPkjHk43nNJFkEQ
Description: Aims to preserve the competitive enterprise system of business and to promote business and community growth and development. **Founded:** 1926. **Publications:** *Images of Asheboro/Randolph* (Annual); *Update* (Monthly). **Educational Activities:** Business After Hours. **Geographic Preference:** Local.

43087 ■ **Asheville Area Chamber of Commerce**
36 Montford Ave.
Asheville, NC 28801
Ph: (828)258-6101
Fax: (828)251-0926
Co. E-mail: member@ashevillechamber.org
URL: http://www.ashevillechamber.org/chamber
Contact: Kit Cramer, President
E-mail: kcramer@ashevillechamber.org
Facebook: www.facebook.com/ashevillechamber
X (Twitter): x.com/avlchamber
Instagram: www.instagram.com/avlchamber
YouTube: www.youtube.com/user/ashevillechamber
Description: Promotes business and community development in the Asheville, NC area. Conducts local festivals. **Founded:** 1898. **Publications:** *Western North Carolina Industrial Directory*; *Membership Directory*; *Buncombe County Major Employers Directory*; *Asheville Report* (Monthly); *Business and Industry Directory*; *Major Employers' Directory* (Annual). **Awards:** Sky High Growth Award (Annual); Asheville Area Chamber Small Business Leader of the Year (Annual); Asheville Area Chamber Small Business of the Month (Monthly). **Geographic Preference:** Local.

43088 ■ **Ayden Chamber of Commerce**
531 W Third St.
Ayden, NC 28513
Ph: (252)746-2266
Co. E-mail: chamber@ayden.com

URL: http://aydenchamberofcommerce.wildapricot.org
Contact: Gwendy Yiznitsky, Chairman
Facebook: www.facebook.com/aydenchamber
X (Twitter): x.com/aydenchamber
Instagram: www.instagram.com/aydenchamber
Description: Promotes business and community development in Ayden, NC. **Founded:** 1981. **Publications:** *The Chamber ADVANTAGE* (Monthly). **Awards:** Ayden Chamber of Commerce Business of the Year (Annual); Ayden Chamber of Commerce Citizen of the Year (Annual). **Geographic Preference:** Local.

43089 ■ Beech Mountain Chamber of Commerce
PO Box 876
  Banner Elk, NC 28604
Ph: (828)222-4848
Co. E-mail: info@beechchamber.com
URL: http://www.beechchamber.com
Contact: J. Alan Holcombe, Contact
Facebook: www.facebook.com/beechmountainchamber
Instagram: www.instagram.com/beechmountainnc
Description: Promotes business and community development in Beech Mountain, NC area. **Geographic Preference:** Local.

43090 ■ Belhaven Community Chamber of Commerce
265 E Water St., Ste. 101
  Belhaven, NC 27810
Ph: (252)943-3770
Co. E-mail: belhaveninfo@rsnet.org
URL: http://visitbelhavennc.com
Contact: Mark Gnagy, President
Facebook: www.facebook.com/BelhavenChamberofCommerce
Instagram: www.instagram.com/belhaven_chamber
YouTube: www.youtube.com/channel/UCw-Ho4eSpAJYy_nTinTV4eg
Description: Promotes business and community development in Bath, Belhaven, and Pantego, NC. Conducts annual 4th of July celebration. **Founded:** 1952. **Publications:** *Chamber News*. **Geographic Preference:** Local.

43091 ■ Benson Area Chamber of Commerce (BACC)
122 E Main St.
  Benson, NC 27504
Ph: (919)894-3825
Fax: (919)894-1052
Co. E-mail: loretta@benson-chamber.com
URL: http://www.benson-chamber.com
Contact: Loretta Byrd, President
Facebook: www.facebook.com/Benson.Chamber
Description: Promotes the Benson area through different activities for the family. Encourages area businesses to prosper. **Geographic Preference:** Local.

43092 ■ Black Mountain-Swannanoa Chamber of Commerce
201 E State St.
  Black Mountain, NC 28711
Ph: (828)669-2300
Free: 800-669-2301
Fax: (828)669-1407
URL: http://www.exploreblackmountain.com
Contact: Sharon Tabor, Executive Director
Facebook: www.facebook.com/BlackMountainSwannanoaNC
Instagram: www.instagram.com/blackmountainchamber
Description: Promotes business and community development in the Black Mountain, NC area. Sponsors Sourwood Festival. Publications: none. **Founded:** 1923. **Geographic Preference:** Local.

43093 ■ Blowing Rock Chamber of Commerce (BRCC)
132 Pk. Ave.
  Blowing Rock, NC 28605
Ph: (828)295-7851
Fax: (828)295-7651
URL: http://www.blowingrockncchamber.com
Contact: Charles Hardin, President
E-mail: hardince@blowingrock.com
Facebook: www.facebook.com/brncchamber
X (Twitter): x.com/BR_Chamber
Description: Promotes business and community development in Blowing Rock, NC. Sponsors Art in the Park which occurs monthly in the summer. **Founded:** 1927. **Publications:** *Chamber Businesses* (Annual); *Blowing Rock Chamber of Commerce--Chamber Businesses* (Annual). **Educational Activities:** Art in the Park (6/year). **Geographic Preference:** Local.

43094 ■ Boone Area Chamber of Commerce (BACC)
149 Jefferson Rd.
  Boone, NC 28607-4495
Ph: (828)264-2225
Fax: (828)264-6644
Co. E-mail: info@boonechamber.com
URL: http://boonechamber.com
Contact: David Jackson, President
Facebook: www.facebook.com/BooneAreaChamber
Linkedin: www.linkedin.com/company/boone-chamber-of-commerce
X (Twitter): x.com/BooneNCChamber
Instagram: www.instagram.com/boonencchamber
Description: Promotes business and community development in the Boone, NC area. **Founded:** 1949. **Publications:** *eVoice* (Biweekly). **Geographic Preference:** Local.

43095 ■ Brevard - Transylvania Chamber of Commerce
175 E Main St.
  Brevard, NC 28712
Ph: (828)884-8900
Co. E-mail: info@brevardncchamber.org
URL: http://brevardncchamber.org
Contact: Melissa Driver, Executive Director
E-mail: melissa@brevardncchamber.org
Facebook: www.facebook.com/brevardncchamber
Linkedin: www.linkedin.com/company/brevard-transylvania-chamber-of-commerce
X (Twitter): x.com/BrevardChamber
Instagram: www.instagram.com/brevardchamber
Description: Promotes business and community development in the Brevard, NC area. **Founded:** 1923. **Publications:** *E News Brief* (Weekly). **Geographic Preference:** Regional.

43096 ■ Brunswick County Chamber of Commerce
112 Pine St.
  Shallotte, NC 28470
Ph: (910)754-6644
Free: 800-426-6644
Co. E-mail: communications@brunswickcountychamber.org
URL: http://brunswickcountychamber.org
Contact: Susan Freeman, Executive Director
Facebook: www.facebook.com/BrunswickCountyChamber
X (Twitter): x.com/BCChamber
YouTube: www.youtube.com/channel/UC7PGjh7c13IUp5hLMhScf8A
Description: Promotes business and community development in the South Brunswick Islands, NC coastal area. **Founded:** 1976. **Publications:** *Brunswick Bulletin* (Monthly); *Visitors and Business Guide* (Annual). **Educational Activities:** North Carolina Oyster Festival (Annual). **Geographic Preference:** Local.

43097 ■ Burke County Chamber of Commerce
110 E Meeting St.
  Morganton, NC 28655
Ph: (828)437-3021
Co. E-mail: info@burkecounty.org
URL: http://burkecountychamber.org
Contact: Tonia F. Stephenson, President
E-mail: tstephenson@burkecounty.org
Linkedin: www.linkedin.com/company/burke-county-chamber-of-commerce-north-carolina
X (Twitter): x.com/TheBurkeChamber
YouTube: www.youtube.com/channel/UC1glatmT9nyQ0pYlbobvQ2Q
Description: Promotes business and community development in Burke County, GA. **Founded:** 1945. **Publications:** *Burke County Chamber of Commerce--Membership Directory*. **Geographic Preference:** Local.

43098 ■ *Business Directory*
100 Coastline St., No. 200
  Rocky Mount, NC 27804
Ph: (252)446-0323
Co. E-mail: rmacc@rockymountchamber.org
URL: http://www.rockymountchamber.org
Contact: David Farris, President
E-mail: dfarris@rockymountchamber.org
URL(s): web.rockymountchamber.org/search
Availability: Online.

43099 ■ *Business Directory*
28 Walnut St.
  Waynesville, NC 28786
Ph: (828)456-3021
Co. E-mail: info@haywoodchamber.com
URL: http://www.haywoodchamber.com/chamber-commerce
Contact: CeCe Hipps, President
E-mail: chipps@haywoodchamber.com
URL(s): www.haywoodchamber.com/the-chamber/join-the-chamber
Released: Annual **Availability:** Online.

43100 ■ *Business Directory*
678 S Van Buren Rd.
  Eden, NC 27288
Ph: (336)623-3336
Fax: (336)623-8800
Co. E-mail: info@edenchamber.com
URL: http://www.edenchamber.com
Contact: Sandra Meadows, Executive Director
E-mail: director@edenchamber.com
URL(s): business.edenchamber.com/list
Availability: Print.

43101 ■ *Business and Industry Directory*
36 Montford Ave.
  Asheville, NC 28801
Ph: (828)258-6101
Fax: (828)251-0926
Co. E-mail: member@ashevillechamber.org
URL: http://www.ashevillechamber.org/chamber
Contact: Kit Cramer, President
E-mail: kcramer@ashevillechamber.org
URL(s): www.ashevillechamber.org/get-engaged
Price: $75, Members for pdf; $100, Nonmembers for pdf. **Availability:** Online; PDF.

43102 ■ Caldwell County Chamber of Commerce (CCCC)
1909 Hickory Blvd. SE
  Lenoir, NC 28645
Fax: (828)726-0616
Co. E-mail: visitors@caldwellchambernc.com
URL: http://www.caldwellchambernc.com
Contact: Bryan Moore, President
Facebook: www.facebook.com/caldchambernc
Linkedin: www.linkedin.com/company/caldwell-county-chamber-of-commerce-nc-
Instagram: www.instagram.com/caldchambernc
Description: Promotes business and community development in Caldwell County, NC. **Founded:** 1920. **Publications:** *Chamber Action* (Monthly). **Geographic Preference:** Local.

43103 ■ Carolina Foothills Chamber of Commerce
2753 Lynn Rd., Ste. A
  Tryon, NC 28782
Ph: (828)859-6236
Co. E-mail: info@carolinafoothillschamber.com
URL: http://www.carolinafoothillschamber.com
Contact: Catina Gray, President
Facebook: www.facebook.com/CarolinaFoothillsChamber
Linkedin: www.linkedin.com/in/carolina-foothills-chamber-of-commerce-27b963217

STATE LISTINGS

Description: Promotes business and community development in Polk County, NC and surrounding areas. **Founded:** 1927. **Publications:** *A Sense of Heritage: The Tryon Chamber of Commerce, 1991*; *Chamber Notes* (Monthly); *Visitors Guide*. **Awards:** Carolina Foothills Chamber Hall of Fame (Annual); Carolina Foothills Chamber Volunteer of the Year (Annual). **Geographic Preference:** Local.

43104 ■ Carolinas Association of Chamber of Commerce Executives (CACCE)
1622 Tarklin Valley
Knoxville, TN 37920
Ph: (404)312-0524
Co. E-mail: tfulmer@tlfexecutiveservices.com
URL: http://www.cacce.org
Contact: Pamela Christopher, President
Facebook: www.facebook.com/Carolinas-Association-of-Chamber-of-Commerce-Executives-CACCE-115043361908258
X (Twitter): x.com/CACCExecs
Description: Strives to advance comprehensive leadership and professional development for Chambers of Commerce through the efforts of the members of the association and their resources. **Founded:** 1994. **Geographic Preference:** Regional.

43105 ■ Carteret County Chamber of Commerce (CCCC)
3332 Bridges St., Ste. 6
Morehead City, NC 28557
Ph: (252)726-6350
Co. E-mail: cart.coc@nccoastchamber.com
URL: http://nccoastchamber.com
Contact: Tom Kies, President
E-mail: tom@nccoastchamber.com
Facebook: www.facebook.com/nccoastchamber
Linkedin: www.linkedin.com/company/carteret-county-chamber-of-commerce
X (Twitter): x.com/nccoastchamber
Instagram: www.instagram.com/nccoastchamber
Description: Promotes business and community development in Carteret County, NC. **Founded:** 1959. **Publications:** *Vacation Guide/Membership Directory* (Annual); *Carteret County Chamber of Commerce--Directory and Visitors Guide* (Annual). **Geographic Preference:** Local.

43106 ■ Cary Chamber of Commerce
307 N Academy St.
Cary, NC 27513
Ph: (919)467-1016
Free: 800-919-2279
Fax: (919)469-2375
Co. E-mail: info@carychamber.com
URL: http://www.carychamber.com
Contact: Mark Lawson, President
Facebook: www.facebook.com/cary.chamber
X (Twitter): x.com/CaryChamber
Instagram: www.instagram.com/thecarychamber
Description: Promotes business and community development in Cary, NC. Conducts seminars and Business After Hours parties. **Founded:** 1962. **Publications:** *Relocation Guide: Town of Cary Overview & Demographics*; *Cary Chamber of Commerce Membership Directory & Buyers Guide*; *Wake County Directory of Manufacturing Firms*; *Wake County Directory of Major Employers*; *Cary Chamber of Commerce Directory of Major Business*; *Cary Chamber of Commerce Member Directory*; *Business Review* (Monthly); *Buyer's Guide* (Annual); *Program of Work*. **Awards:** Cary Chamber of Commerce Community Service Award (Annual). **Geographic Preference:** Local.

43107 ■ Cashiers Area Chamber of Commerce
202 Hwy. 64 W
Cashiers, NC 28717
Ph: (828)743-5191
Co. E-mail: office@cashiersareachamber.com
URL: http://www.cashiersareachamber.com
Contact: Glenn Ubertino, President
Facebook: www.facebook.com/CashiersAreaChamber
Instagram: www.instagram.com/cashiersareachamber

Description: Promotes business and community development in Cashiers, NC area. **Founded:** 1982. **Geographic Preference:** Local.

43108 ■ Caswell County Chamber of Commerce
142 Main St.
Yanceyville, NC 27379
Ph: (336)694-6106
Co. E-mail: amanda@caswellchamber.org
URL: http://caswellchamber.org
Contact: Emily Buchanan, Chairman of the Board
Facebook: www.facebook.com/CaswellChamber
Linkedin: www.linkedin.com/company/caswell-county-chamber-of-commerce
Instagram: www.instagram.com/caswellchamber
Description: Promotes business and community development in Caswell County, NC. **Founded:** 1982. **Geographic Preference:** Local.

43109 ■ Catawba County Chamber of Commerce
1055 Southgate Corporate Pk. SW
Hickory, NC 28602
Ph: (828)328-6111
Fax: (828)328-1175
Co. E-mail: pmanfredi@catawbachamber.org
URL: http://www.catawbachamber.org
Contact: Lindsay Keisler, President
Facebook: www.facebook.com/CatawbaChamber
X (Twitter): x.com/CatawbaChamber
Instagram: www.instagram.com/catawbachamber
Pinterest: www.pinterest.com/catawbachamber
Description: Promotes business and community development in Catawba County, NC. Sponsors Winterfest and Busch Grand National Race Fan Appreciation. **Publications:** *Catawba County Chamber of Commerce--Member Directory*; *e-Views* (Monthly); *Economic Profile* (Periodic). **Geographic Preference:** Local.

43110 ■ Chamber Connection
1099 Gum Branch Rd.
Jacksonville, NC 28540
Ph: (910)347-3141
Co. E-mail: businessservices@jacksonvilleonline.org
URL: http://www.jacksonvilleonline.org
Contact: Laurette Leagon, President
E-mail: president@jacksonvilleonline.org
URL(s): jacksonvilleonline.org/chamber-connection
Released: Monthly **Availability:** Online; PDF.

43111 ■ Chapel Hill-Carrboro Business Directory
104 S Estes Dr.
Chapel Hill, NC 27514
Ph: (919)967-7075
Co. E-mail: info@carolinachamber.org
URL: http://www.carolinachamber.org
Contact: Aaron Martin Nelson, President
E-mail: anelson@carolinachamber.org
URL(s): business.carolinachamber.org/local-business-directory
Availability: Online.

43112 ■ Chapel Hill - Carrboro Chamber of Commerce
104 S Estes Dr.
Chapel Hill, NC 27514
Ph: (919)967-7075
Co. E-mail: info@carolinachamber.org
URL: http://www.carolinachamber.org
Contact: Aaron Martin Nelson, President
E-mail: anelson@carolinachamber.org
Facebook: www.facebook.com/ChapelHillCarrboroChamber
Linkedin: www.linkedin.com/company/917217
X (Twitter): x.com/carolinachamber
Instagram: www.instagram.com/carolinachamber
YouTube: www.youtube.com/channel/UC71igM6rn0Alfz6EW5NGUvA
Description: Promotes business and community development in Chapel Hill, NC. **Founded:** 1963. **Publications:** *Member Business Directory*; *Chapel Hill-Carrboro Business Directory*; *Business Matters* (Bimonthly); *Business Today* (Monthly); *Perspectives*.

North Carolina ■ 43117

Awards: Chapel Hill - Carrboro Chamber Business of the Year (Annual); Duke Energy Citizenship and Service Award (Annual). **Geographic Preference:** Local.

43113 ■ Charlotte Regional Business Alliance
330 S Tryon St.
Charlotte, NC 28202
Ph: (704)378-1300
Co. E-mail: news@charlotteregion.com
URL: http://charlotteregion.com
Contact: Janet Labar, President
Facebook: www.facebook.com/CharlotteRegionalBusinessAlliance
Linkedin: www.linkedin.com/company/charlotte-regional-business-alliance
X (Twitter): x.com/clt_alliance
Instagram: www.instagram.com/clt_alliance
YouTube: www.youtube.com/c/CharlotteRegionalBusinessAlliance
Description: Promotes business and community development in Charlotte, NC. **Founded:** 1915. **Geographic Preference:** Local.

43114 ■ Chatham County United Chamber of Commerce (CCUCC)
531 E 3rd St.
Siler City, NC 27344
Ph: (919)742-3333
Fax: (919)742-1333
Co. E-mail: info@ccucc.net
URL: http://www.ccucc.net
Contact: Cindy Poindexter, President
E-mail: cindyp@ccucc.net
Facebook: www.facebook.com/ChathamNCChamberofCommerce
Description: Promotes business and community development in Chatham County. Holds Business After Hours mixers. Sponsors Chicken Festival. Conducts seminars. **Founded:** 1947. **Publications:** *Concerning Chatham County* (Monthly); *Membership Directory and Buyer's Guide* (Biennial). **Geographic Preference:** Local.

43115 ■ Cherokee Chamber of Commerce (CCC)
PO Box 1838
Cherokee, NC 28719
Ph: (828)788-0034
Co. E-mail: info@cherokeesmokies.com
URL: http://www.cherokeesmokies.com
Contact: Amy Watkins Parker, Executive Director
Facebook: www.facebook.com/CherokeeSmokies
Pinterest: www.pinterest.com/cherokeecoc
Description: Promotes business and community development in the Cherokee Indian Reservation in Cherokee, NC. Operates Cherokee Visitor Center. **Founded:** 2006. **Publications:** *Cherokee Group Tour Manual* (Annual); *Cherokee Official Vacation Map and Directory* (Annual); *Cherokee Visitor Center Newsletter* (Quarterly). **Geographic Preference:** Local.

43116 ■ Cherokee County Chamber of Commerce (CCCC)
805 US Hwy. 64 W
Murphy, NC 28906
Ph: (828)837-2242
Fax: (828)837-6012
Co. E-mail: info@cherokeecountychamber.com
URL: http://www.cherokeecountychamber.com
Contact: Steven Aft, President
Facebook: www.facebook.com/cherokeecountync
X (Twitter): x.com/ncwelcomecenter
Instagram: www.instagram.com/cherokeecountync
Description: Promotes business and community development in Cherokee County, NC. **Founded:** 1839. **Publications:** *Cherokee County Directory*. **Geographic Preference:** Local.

43117 ■ Cherryville Chamber of Commerce EDC
220 E Main St.
Cherryville, NC 28021
Ph: (704)435-3451
Co. E-mail: chamber@cityofcherryville.com
URL: http://cherryvillechamber.com

Facebook: www.facebook.com/Cherryville-Chamber
-of-Commerce-167150693338125
Linkedin: www.linkedin.com/company/cherryville
-chamber-of-commerce
Description: Promotes business and community development in Cherryville, NC. **Geographic Preference:** Local.

43118 ■ Clay County Chamber of Commerce
96 Sanderson St.
Hayesville, NC 28904
Ph: (828)389-3704
URL: http://www.claychambernc.com
Contact: Chris Morhardt, President
Facebook: www.facebook.com/claychambernc
Instagram: www.instagram.com/claycoun
tyncchamber
Description: Serves the business community by providing leadership and educational support for its members in an effort to preserve the quality of life in Clay County through responsible growth. **Founded:** 1986. **Geographic Preference:** Local.

43119 ■ Clayton Chamber of Commerce (CCC)
301 E Main St.
Clayton, NC 27520
Ph: (919)553-6352
URL: http://claytonchamber.com
Contact: Dana Wooten, President
E-mail: dana@claytonchamber.com
Facebook: www.facebook.com/ClaytonChamberNC
X (Twitter): x.com/CCOC_ClaytonNC
YouTube: www.youtube.com/channel/UCZHRy6OeSf
1H4b76NIKFMXQ
Description: Promotes business and community development in Clayton, NC. Sponsors annual Harvest Festival in October. **Founded:** 1951. **Publications:** *Clayton Chamber of Commerce-- Membership Directory & Buyers Guide* (Annual); *Membership Directory and Buyers' Guide* (Annual). **Geographic Preference:** Local.

43120 ■ Cleveland County Chamber of Commerce
200 S Lafayette St.
Shelby, NC 28150
Ph: (704)487-8521
Fax: (704)487-7458
Co. E-mail: info@clevelandchamber.org
URL: http://clevelandchamber.org
Contact: Christine Cribb, Executive Director
E-mail: christine@clevelandchamber.org
Facebook: www.facebook.com/ClevelandCoun
tyChamber
Linkedin: www.linkedin.com/company/cleveland-coun
ty-chamber
Instagram: www.instagram.com/clevelandcoun
tychamber
Description: Promotes business and community development in Cleveland County, NC. **Founded:** 1948. **Publications:** *Chamber Comments* (Monthly); *Membership Listing*; *Come Closer* (Bimonthly); *InterAction* (Monthly). **Educational Activities:** Business After Hours (Monthly). **Geographic Preference:** Local.

43121 ■ Clinton-Sampson Chamber of Commerce (CACC)
414 Warsaw Rd.
Clinton, NC 28328
Ph: (910)592-6177
Fax: (910)592-5770
Co. E-mail: info@clintonsampsonchamber.org
URL: http://www.clintonsampsonchamber.org
Contact: Jason Smith, Treasurer
Facebook: www.facebook.com/clin
tonsampsonchamber
Instagram: www.instagram.com/explore/locations/968
418812/clinton-sampson-chamber-of-commerce
Description: Promotes business and community development in Clinton, NC area. **Publications:** *Clinton Area Chamber of Commerce* (Quarterly). **Geographic Preference:** Local.

43122 ■ Columbus Chamber of Commerce and Tourism (GWCC)
601 S Madison St.
Whiteville, NC 28472
Ph: (910)642-3171
Co. E-mail: info@thecolumbuschamber.com
URL: http://www.thecolumbuschamber.com
Contact: Jennifer Holcomb, President
Facebook: www.facebook.com/thecolumbuschamber
X (Twitter): x.com/DiscoverColumbu
YouTube: www.youtube.com/channel/UCmzhuUfdRC
tJy_NXE9Gflrw
Description: Promotes business and community development in the greater Whiteville, NC area. **Founded:** 1937. **Geographic Preference:** Local.

43123 ■ Davie County Chamber of Commerce - Davie County Public Library
135 S Salisbury St.
Mocksville, NC 27028
Ph: (336)751-3304
Fax: (336)751-5697
Co. E-mail: chamber@daviecounty.com
URL: http://www.daviechamber.com
Contact: Caroline Moser, President
E-mail: cmoser@daviecounty.com
Facebook: www.facebook.com/DavieChamber
Instagram: www.instagram.com/ishopdavie
YouTube: www.youtube.com/user/daviechamber
Description: Promotes business and community development in Davie County, NC. **Scope:** Genealogy; Local History. **Services:** Copying. **Founded:** 1945. **Holdings:** Books; eAudio; eMagazine; eBooks; journal. **Publications:** *Chamberlink* (Monthly). **Geographic Preference:** Local.

43124 ■ Dunn Area Chamber of Commerce (DACC)
109 S Ellis Ave.
Dunn, NC 28335
Ph: (910)892-4113
URL: http://dunnchamber.com
Contact: Wesley Johnson, President
Facebook: www.facebook.com/DunnChamber
Instagram: www.instagram.com/dunn_chamber
YouTube: www.youtube.com/channel/UCfY
25-cci9lPKWHrDOVK5_Q
Description: Represents business and industry. Seeks to work together to advance the economic growth, well-being and quality of life of its members and the community. **Founded:** 1887. **Publications:** *It's All Right Here!* (Monthly). **Geographic Preference:** Local.

43125 ■ E-Communicator
426 N 1st Ave.
Knightdale, NC 27545
Ph: (919)266-4603
URL: http://www.knightdalechamber.org
URL(s): www.knightdalechamber.org/membership
-application#MemberBenefits
Released: Weekly **Availability:** Online.

43126 ■ Eden Chamber of Commerce
678 S Van Buren Rd.
Eden, NC 27288
Ph: (336)623-3336
Fax: (336)623-8800
Co. E-mail: info@edenchamber.com
URL: http://www.edenchamber.com
Contact: Sandra Meadows, Executive Director
E-mail: director@edenchamber.com
Facebook: www.facebook.com/edenchamber
Description: Promotes business and community development in Eden, TX. Sponsors Fall Festival and Concho County Stampede. Conducts newcomer's program. **Founded:** 1955. **Publications:** *City of Eden* (Quarterly); *Business Directory*; *The Voice of Business* (Monthly). **Geographic Preference:** Local.

43127 ■ Edenton-Chowan Chamber of Commerce
101 W Water St.
Edenton, NC 27932
Ph: (252)482-3400
Co. E-mail: win.dale@edenton.nc.gov
URL: http://edentonchamber.org

Contact: Ted Haigler, President
E-mail: ted.haigler@ncfbins.com
Facebook: www.facebook.com/Eden
tonChowanChamber
YouTube: www.youtube.com/channel/UCYsnuFmXL
_mVBU_pRZrTkWQ
Description: Promotes business and community development in Chowan County, NC. **Publications:** *Membership Journal* (Quarterly). **Geographic Preference:** Local.

43128 ■ Elizabeth City Area Chamber of Commerce
502 E Ehringhaus St.
Elizabeth City, NC 27909
Ph: (252)335-4365
Fax: (252)335-5732
Co. E-mail: darlene@elizabethcitychamber.org
URL: http://www.elizabethcitychamber.org
Contact: Annalisa Morgan, Chairman of the Board
Facebook: www.facebook.com/
ECChamberCommerce
Instagram: www.instagram.com/ecchamber
Description: Works for the business community's growth and well-being. Offers networking opportunities throughout the year. **Geographic Preference:** Local.

43129 ■ Elizabethtown-White Lake Area Chamber of Commerce
207 E Broad St. Ste. B
Elizabethtown, NC 28337-9432
Ph: (910)862-4368
Fax: (910)862-3371
Co. E-mail: chamber@elizabethtownnc.org
URL: http://elizabethtownwhitelake.com
Contact: Anne Beyer, President
Facebook: www.facebook.com/EtownWhi
teLakeChamber
X (Twitter): x.com/EtownWLChamber
YouTube: www.youtube.com/channel/UCd-OtnDHdnp
d0F2pOceKBIQ
Description: Promotes business and community development in the Elizabethtown, NC area. **Geographic Preference:** Local.

43130 ■ Entrepreneurs' Organization - Raleigh Durham Chapter
801 Gilbert St., Ste. 201
Durham, NC 27701
Co. E-mail: admin@eoraleigh.com
URL: http://eoraleigh.com
Contact: Daniel Currin, Co-President
URL(s): www.eonetwork.org/raleighdurham
Facebook: www.facebook.com/eoraleighdurham
Linkedin: www.linkedin.com/company/eo-raleigh
-durham
X (Twitter): x.com/EORaleighDurham
Instagram: www.instagram.com/eoraleighdurham
Description: Provides local resources to members which includes networking events, mentorship, live forums, and leadership development. **Founded:** 1998.

43131 ■ Fuquay-Varina Chamber of Commerce (FVACC)
121 N Main St.
Fuquay Varina, NC 27526
Ph: (919)552-4947
Co. E-mail: info@fuquay-varina.com
URL: http://fuquay-varina.com
Contact: Kate Davis, Executive Director
E-mail: kate@fuquay-varina.com
Facebook: www.facebook.com/
FuquayVarinaChamberofCommerce
Linkedin: www.linkedin.com/company/943344
Instagram: www.instagram.com/fuquay_varina_coc
Description: Promotes business and community development in Fuquay-Varina, NC. **Founded:** 1947. **Publications:** *Chamber Connection* (Monthly). **Geographic Preference:** Local.

43132 ■ Garner Chamber of Commerce (GCC)
401 Cir., Dr.
Garner, NC 27529
Ph: (919)772-6440

STATE LISTINGS   North Carolina ■ 43145

Co. E-mail: info@garnerchamber.com
URL: http://www.garnerchamber.com
Contact: Matthew Coppedge, President
E-mail: matthew@garnerchamber.com
YouTube: www.youtube.com/channel/UCd-WCPP
33-bUAAOJioSL-hw
Description: Promotes business and community development in southeastern Wake County, NC. Conducts lobbying activities. Participates in charitable programs; sponsors Garner Celebration and golf outings. **Founded:** 1964. **Publications:** *Business Connection* (Periodic); *The Business Connection* (Monthly); *Newcomer's Guide* (Annual). **Geographic Preference:** Local.

43133 ■ Granville County Chamber of Commerce (GCCC)
124 Hillsboro St.
Oxford, NC 27565
Ph: (919)693-6125
Fax: (919)693-6126
Co. E-mail: cynthia@granville-chamber.com
URL: http://granville-chamber.com
Contact: Dan DiCarlo, President
E-mail: dan@creedmoorforest.com
Facebook: www.facebook.com/GranvilleChamberNC
Description: Promotes business and community development in Granville County, NC. Convention/Meeting: none. **Founded:** 1942. **Publications:** *Bright Leaf* (Monthly). **Geographic Preference:** Local.

43134 ■ Greater Durham Chamber of Commerce (DCC)
300 W Morgan St., Ste. 1400
Durham, NC 27701
Ph: (919)328-8700
Fax: (919)688-8351
Co. E-mail: chambermarketing@durhamchamber.org
URL: http://durhamchamber.org
Contact: Geoff Durham, President
E-mail: geoffdurham@durhamchamber.org
Facebook: www.facebook.com/DurhamChamber
Linkedin: www.linkedin.com/company/greater-durham-chamber-of-commerce
X (Twitter): x.com/durhamchamber
Instagram: www.instagram.com/durhamchamber
Description: Promotes business and community development in the Durham, NC area. **Founded:** 1906. **Publications:** *Action* (Monthly); *Chamber at a Glance*; *Clubs and Associations* (Annual). **Geographic Preference:** Local.

43135 ■ Greater Fayetteville Chamber
225 Ray Ave., Ste. 165
Fayetteville, NC 28301
Ph: (910)483-8133
Fax: (910)483-0263
Co. E-mail: info@faybiz.com
URL: http://faybiz.com
Contact: Tammy Thurman, Chairman of the Board
Linkedin: www.linkedin.com/company/greaterfayettevillechamber
X (Twitter): x.com/faync_chamber
Description: Promotes business and community development in the Fayetteville, NC area. **Founded:** 1899. **Publications:** *Fayetteville Business* (Monthly). **Educational Activities:** Business After Hours (Monthly). **Awards:** Fayetteville-Cumberland County Chamber of Commerce Athena Award (Annual). **Geographic Preference:** Local.

43136 ■ Greater Franklin County Chamber of Commerce
109 N Church St.
Louisburg, NC 27549
Ph: (919)496-3056
Fax: (919)496-0422
URL: http://www.franklin-chamber.org
Contact: Richard Veverka, Executive Director
E-mail: rveverka@franklin-chamber.org
Facebook: www.facebook.com/TheGreaterFranklinCountyChamber
Description: Promotes business and community development in the area. **Founded:** 1977. **Publications:** *Chamber Update*. **Geographic Preference:** Local.

43137 ■ Greater Mount Airy Chamber of Commerce
200 N Main St.
Mount Airy, NC 27030
Ph: (336)786-6116
URL: http://www.mtairyncchamber.org
Contact: Cristie Andrews, Director
E-mail: cristie@mtairyncchamber.org
Facebook: www.facebook.com/MountAiryChamber
Linkedin: www.linkedin.com/company/greater-mount-airy-chamber-of-commerce
X (Twitter): x.com/MtAiryChamber
Instagram: www.instagram.com/greatermtairychamber
YouTube: www.youtube.com/channel/UC5peehg3pW5ZJ_YG8NuGAVg
Description: Promotes business and community development in the greater Mt. Airy, NC area. Sponsors annual Autumn Leaves Festival. **Founded:** 1959. **Publications:** *Enterprise and Endeavor* (Bimonthly). **Awards:** Greater Mount Airy Chamber Citizen of the Year (Annual). **Geographic Preference:** Local.

43138 ■ Greater Raleigh Chamber of Commerce (GRCC)
800 S Salisbury St.
Raleigh, NC 27601
Ph: (919)664-7000
Co. E-mail: mail@raleighchamber.org
URL: http://www.raleighchamber.org
Contact: Adrienne Cole, President
Facebook: www.facebook.com/RaleighChamber
Linkedin: www.linkedin.com/company/raleighchamber
X (Twitter): x.com/raleighchamber
YouTube: www.youtube.com/user/RaleighChamber
Description: Promotes business and community development in Raleigh and Wake County, NC. **Founded:** 1888. **Publications:** *Greater Raleigh Chamber of Commerce--Membership Directory and Buyer's Guide*; *Greater Raleigh Chamber of Commerce--International Firms Directory*; *Triangle Business Journal's Book of Lists*; *Major Employers Directory*; *Greater Raleigh Chamber of Commerce--Major Employers Directory*; *Greater Raleigh Chamber of Commerce--Manufacturers Directory*. **Geographic Preference:** Local.

43139 ■ Greater Topsail Area Chamber of Commerce and Tourism
13775 NC Hwy. 50, Ste. 101
Surf City, NC 28445
Ph: (910)329-4446
Co. E-mail: info@topsailchamber.org
URL: http://www.topsailchamber.org
Contact: Kay Phelps, Coordinator
Facebook: www.facebook.com/topsailchamber
Linkedin: www.linkedin.com/company/greater-topsail-area-chamber-of-commerce
X (Twitter): x.com/TopsailC
Description: Promotes business and community development in Greater Topsail, NC area. **Founded:** 1983. **Publications:** *Membership Directory and Quality of Life Guide*; *Topsail Area Guide*. **Geographic Preference:** Local.

43140 ■ Greater Wilmington Chamber of Commerce
1 Estell Lee Pl.
Wilmington, NC 28401
Ph: (910)762-2611
Fax: (910)762-9765
Co. E-mail: info@wilmingtonchamber.org
URL: http://www.wilmingtonchamber.org
Contact: Natalie English, President
Facebook: www.facebook.com/WilmingtonNCChamber
Linkedin: www.linkedin.com/company/wilmington-chamber-of-commerce
X (Twitter): x.com/ilmchamber
YouTube: www.youtube.com/user/WilmingtonNCChamber
Description: Promotes business and community development in Wilmington, NC. Sponsors the Greater Wilmington Chamber Foundation. **Founded:** 1853. **Publications:** *Return On Investment* (Weekly); *Greater Wilmington's Best* (Annual). **Geographic Preference:** Local.

43141 ■ *Greensboro*
111 W February 1 Pl.
Greensboro, NC 27401
Ph: (336)387-8301
URL: http://greensboro.org
Contact: Brent Christensen, President
E-mail: bchristensen@greensboro.org
URL(s): chamber.greensboro.org/list/Details/our-state-magazine-1760549
Availability: Print.

43142 ■ Greensboro Area Chamber of Commerce
111 W February 1 Pl.
Greensboro, NC 27401
Ph: (336)387-8301
URL: http://greensboro.org
Contact: Brent Christensen, President
E-mail: bchristensen@greensboro.org
Facebook: www.facebook.com/GSOChamber
Linkedin: www.linkedin.com/company/greensboro-chamber-of-commerce
X (Twitter): x.com/gsochamber
Instagram: www.instagram.com/gsochamber
YouTube: www.youtube.com/channel/UCdfflAm0cl1QBSiJaGtKqfA
Description: Promotes business and community development in Greensboro, NC. **Founded:** 1877. **Publications:** *Directory of Manufacturers--Greensboro, North Carolina*; *Greensboro*; *Guilford County Major Employers* (Annual); *Guilford County Manufacturers Directory*. **Educational Activities:** Business After Hours and Super Smiley Project Launch Party. **Geographic Preference:** Local.

43143 ■ Greenville - Pitt County Chamber of Commerce (GPCCC)
302 S Greene St.
Greenville, NC 27834
Ph: (252)752-4101
Fax: (252)752-5934
Co. E-mail: chamber@greenvillenc.org
URL: http://www.greenvillenc.org/home
Contact: Trent McGee, President
Facebook: www.facebook.com/GPCChamber
X (Twitter): x.com/greenvillenccoc
YouTube: www.youtube.com/channel/UC503gF1ObimV2dLlrj4anEQ
Description: Promotes business and community development in Greenville, NC. **Founded:** 1907. **Publications:** *Chamber Business Update* (Monthly); *Club and Organizations Directory*; *Greenville-Pitt County Chamber of Commerce--Membership Directory*; *Greenville-Pitt County Chamber of Commerce--Manufacturers Directory*; *Manufacturer's Directory* (Annual); *Greenville-Pitt County Chamber of Commerce--Business Directory*; *Images of Greenville - Pitt County, NC*. **Geographic Preference:** Local.

43144 ■ Havelock Chamber of Commerce
201 Tourist Center Dr.
Havelock, NC 28532
Ph: (252)447-1101
URL: http://havelockchamber.org
Contact: Erin Knight, Executive Director
Facebook: www.facebook.com/havelockchamber
X (Twitter): x.com/havelockchamber
Instagram: www.instagram.com/havelockchamber
Description: Promotes business and community development in the Greater Havelock, NC area. **Founded:** 1971. **Geographic Preference:** Local.

43145 ■ Haywood County Chamber of Commerce
28 Walnut St.
Waynesville, NC 28786
Ph: (828)456-3021
Co. E-mail: info@haywoodchamber.com
URL: http://www.haywoodchamber.com/chamber-commerce
Contact: CeCe Hipps, President
E-mail: chipps@haywoodchamber.com
Facebook: www.facebook.com/HaywoodChamber

X (Twitter): x.com/Haywoodchamber
Instagram: www.instagram.com/haywoodchamber
Description: Promotes business and community development in Western North Carolina. Sponsors Elected Officials Reception, Melange of the Mountains-A Culinary Gala, Dust Off the Rust Golf Tournament, Home Business Expo, and Haywood County Apple Festival. Hold Issues & Eggs, Business After Hours, Annual Dinner and Holiday Cheer. **Publications:** *Business Directory* (Annual); *Vantage Point* (Quarterly). **Awards:** Haywood County Chamber Business of the Month (Monthly). **Geographic Preference:** Local.

43146 ■ Henderson-Vance County Chamber of Commerce
414 S Garnett St.
  Henderson, NC 27536
Ph: (252)438-8414
Fax: (252)492-8989
URL: http://hendersonvance.org
Contact: Sandra Wilkerson, Director
E-mail: sandra@hendersonvance.org
Description: Promotes business and community development in Henderson and Vance County, NC. **Geographic Preference:** Local.

43147 ■ The Hendersonville Information Guide
204 Kanuga Rd.
  Hendersonville, NC 28739
Ph: (828)692-1413
Fax: (828)693-8802
URL: http://www.hendersoncountychamber.org
Contact: Robert R. Williford, President
URL(s): www.hendersoncountychamber.org/visitors/things-to-do-attractions.htmldowntownhendersonville.org/virtual-tour/; www.hendersoncountychamber.org/newcw/cw_lst.htm
Released: Annual **Availability:** Print; Online.

43148 ■ Hickory Nut Gorge Chamber of Commerce
PO Box 32
  Chimney Rock, NC 28720
Ph: (828)625-2725
Co. E-mail: info@hickorynutchamber.org
URL: http://hickorynutchamber.org
Contact: Teri Coutu, President
E-mail: teri@tericenterprisesolutions.com
Facebook: www.facebook.com/TheChamberOfHickoryNutGorge
Description: Promotes business and community development in western Rutherford County, NC. Sponsors fundraising activities. **Founded:** 1984. **Publications:** *Gorge-US* (Monthly). **Geographic Preference:** Local.

43149 ■ High Point Chamber of Commerce (HPCC)
1634 N Main St.
  High Point, NC 27262
Ph: (336)882-5000
Co. E-mail: info@bhpchamber.org
URL: http://www.bhpchamber.org
Contact: Jewel Welborn, Director
Facebook: www.facebook.com/bhpchamber
Linkedin: www.linkedin.com/company/bhpchamber
Instagram: www.instagram.com/bhpchamber
YouTube: www.youtube.com/channel/UCoh3jbg35jKRQ8BrXlkQcoA
Description: Promotes business and community development in High Point, NC. **Founded:** 1919. **Publications:** *Business Advocate* (Monthly). **Geographic Preference:** Local.

43150 ■ Highlands Area Chamber of Commerce
108 Main St.
  Highlands, NC 28741
Ph: (828)526-5841
Fax: (828)526-2112
URL: http://www.highlandschamber.org
Contact: Kaye Mchan, Executive Director
Facebook: www.facebook.com/VisitHighlandsNC
X (Twitter): x.com/visit_highlands
Instagram: www.instagram.com/visithighlandsnc

Description: Promotes business and community development in Highlands, NC. **Founded:** 1931. **Publications:** *Highlands Happenings* (Annual). **Geographic Preference:** Local.

43151 ■ Hillsborough/Orange County Chamber of Commerce
200 N Churton St.
  Hillsborough, NC 27278
Ph: (919)732-8156
Co. E-mail: info@hillsboroughchamber.com
URL: http://www.hillsboroughchamber.com
Contact: Tom Struckmeyer, President
X (Twitter): x.com/hborochamber
Instagram: www.instagram.com/hborochamber
Description: Works to represent the business community in Hillsborough and Northern Orange County. Provides local access to information about members, businesses, and government agencies. **Founded:** 1966. **Publications:** *Business*; *Chapel Hill Herald/Herald Sun*. **Geographic Preference:** Local.

43152 ■ Holly Springs Chamber of Commerce
344 Raleigh St., Ste. 100
  Holly Springs, NC 27540
Ph: (919)567-1796
Co. E-mail: info@hollyspringschamber.org
URL: http://www.hollyspringschamber.org
Contact: Debra Kuffner, Executive Director
E-mail: debra@hollyspringschamber.org
Facebook: www.facebook.com/hollyspringschamber
Linkedin: www.linkedin.com/company/hollyspringschamber
X (Twitter): x.com/HollySprings_CC
Instagram: www.instagram.com/hollyspringschamber
YouTube: www.youtube.com/channel/UCxpfN-91Uk9a3yt31SS7JLA/feed
Description: Promotes business and community development in Holly Springs and Marshall County, MS. **Founded:** 1994. **Geographic Preference:** Local.

43153 ■ Jackson County Chamber of Commerce
773 W Main St.
  Sylva, NC 28779
Ph: (828)586-2155
Free: 800-962-1911
Co. E-mail: donotreply@mountainlovers.com
URL: http://www.mountainlovers.com
Contact: Julie Spiro Donaldson, Executive Director
E-mail: julie@nc-mountains.com
Facebook: www.facebook.com/mountainlovers
X (Twitter): x.com/mountainlovers
Instagram: www.instagram.com/mountainloversnc
YouTube: www.youtube.com/user/MountainsNC
Description: Promotes business and community development in Jackson County, NC. Sponsors fundraisers. **Publications:** *Images of Jackson County* (Annual); *Jackson County Report* (Monthly). **Geographic Preference:** Local.

43154 ■ Jacksonville - Onslow Chamber of Commerce
1099 Gum Branch Rd.
  Jacksonville, NC 28540
Ph: (910)347-3141
Co. E-mail: businessservices@jacksonvilleonline.org
URL: http://www.jacksonvilleonline.org
Contact: Laurette Leagon, President
E-mail: president@jacksonvilleonline.org
Facebook: www.facebook.com/JvilleOnslowCOC
X (Twitter): x.com/jvilleonslowcoc
Instagram: www.instagram.com/jaxncchamber
Description: Promotes business and community development in Jacksonville and Onslow County, NC. Sponsors annual Heritage Festival in May, Holiday Parade in November, and Business Expo in March. **Founded:** 1944. **Publications:** *Chamber Connection* (Monthly); *Images of Jacksonville-Onslow* (Monthly); *Welcome Guide* (Annual). **Geographic Preference:** Local.

43155 ■ Kernersville Chamber of Commerce (KCC)
136 E Mountain St.
  Kernersville, NC 27284
Ph: (336)993-4521
Co. E-mail: kchamber@kernersvillenc.com
URL: http://www.kernersvillenc.com
Contact: Chris Comer, President
Facebook: www.facebook.com/KernersvilleChamber
X (Twitter): x.com/kvillechamber21
Instagram: www.instagram.com/kernersvillechamber
Pinterest: www.pinterest.com/kvillechamber
Description: Promotes business and community development in Kernersville, NC. Sponsors Spring Folly Festival, Music at Twilight, Golf Tournament, Christmas Parade, and other events. **Founded:** 1968. **Publications:** *Heartbeat* (Periodic). **Geographic Preference:** Local.

43156 ■ King Chamber of Commerce (KCC)
124 S Main St.
  King, NC 27021
Ph: (336)983-9308
Co. E-mail: kingchamber14@gmail.com
URL: http://kingnc.com
Contact: Cathy L. Loveday, Executive Director
Facebook: www.facebook.com/KingNCChamber
Instagram: www.instagram.com/kingchamberofcommerce
Description: Promotes business and community development in King, NC. Sponsors KingFest Community Festival in May. **Founded:** 1988. **Publications:** *King Chamber of Commerce Newsletter* (Weekly). **Geographic Preference:** Local.

43157 ■ Kinston-Lenoir County Chamber of Commerce (KLCCC)
301 N Queen St.
  Kinston, NC 28501
Ph: (252)527-1131
Fax: (252)527-1914
Co. E-mail: info@kinstonchamber.com
URL: http://kinstonchamber.com
Contact: Vickie E. Jones, Chief Executive Officer
Facebook: www.facebook.com/kinstonchamber
Description: Promotes business and community development in Lenoir County, NC. **Founded:** 1910. **Publications:** *Business Update* (Bimonthly). **Geographic Preference:** Local.

43158 ■ Knightdale Chamber of Commerce
426 N 1st Ave.
  Knightdale, NC 27545
Ph: (919)266-4603
URL: http://www.knightdalechamber.org
Facebook: www.facebook.com/KnightdaleChamberofCommerce
Description: Committed to advancing civic, commercial, industrial, economic, and general welfare to the businesses and citizens of Knightdale, NC. **Publications:** *E-Communicator* (Weekly); *Official Knightdale Street MAP*; *Knightdale Chamber of Commerce Membership Directory/Economic Data Booklet*. **Geographic Preference:** Local.

43159 ■ Lake Gaston Regional Chamber of Commerce
2357 Eaton Ferry Rd.
  Littleton, NC 27850
Ph: (252)586-5711
Free: 866-730-5711
Fax: (252)586-3152
Co. E-mail: info@lakegastonchamber.com
URL: http://www.lakegastonchamber.com
Contact: Leanne Patrick, President
Facebook: www.facebook.com/lakegastonchamber
YouTube: www.youtube.com/channel/UCo2EY0v2-w79ImyloWbwi-Q
Pinterest: www.pinterest.com/lgchamber
Description: Serves the citizens and the community of the Lake Gaston area. **Founded:** 1953. **Geographic Preference:** Local.

43160 ■ Lake Norman Chamber and Convention and Visitors Bureau
19900 W Catawba Ave., Ste. 102
  Cornelius, NC 28031

Ph: (704)987-3300
Fax: (704)892-5313
Co. E-mail: visitorcenter@lakenorman.org
URL: http://www.visitlakenorman.org
Contact: Sally Ashworth, Executive Director
E-mail: ashworth@lakenorman.org
Facebook: www.facebook.com/VisitLakeNorman
X (Twitter): x.com/VisitLakeNorman
Instagram: www.instagram.com/visitlakenorman
YouTube: www.youtube.com/user/VisitLakeNorman
Pinterest: www.pinterest.com/VisitLakeNorman

Description: Provides programs, information, and outreach opportunities that enhance the community and support economic development. **Founded:** 2001. **Publications:** *The Lake Link* (Monthly). **Educational Activities:** Business After Hours (Annual). **Geographic Preference:** Local.

43161 ■ Laurinburg/Scotland County Area Chamber of Commerce (LSCC)
606 S Atkinson St.
Laurinburg, NC 28352
Ph: (910)276-7420
Fax: (910)277-8785
Co. E-mail: kbuie@laurinburgchamber.com
URL: http://www.laurinburgchamber.com
Contact: Chris English, Executive Director
E-mail: cenglish@laurinburgchamber.com
Facebook: www.facebook.com/LBGChamber
Instagram: www.instagram.com/lbgchamber

Description: Promotes business and community development in Laurinburg and Scotland County, NC. **Founded:** 1938. **Publications:** *The Scots Piper* (Monthly). **Educational Activities:** Laurinburg After Five Concert (Monthly). **Awards:** Dormagen/McLean Community Youth Service Award (Annual); Dunbar/McCoy Quality of Life Award (Annual). **Geographic Preference:** Local.

43162 ■ Lexington Area Chamber of Commerce
507 E Center St.
Lexington, NC 27292
Ph: (336)248-5929
Fax: (336)248-2161
Co. E-mail: chamber@lexingtonchamber.net
URL: http://www.lexingtonchamber.net
Contact: Joe Wallace, President
E-mail: jwallace@lexingtonchamber.net
Facebook: www.facebook.com/LexingtonNCChamber

Description: Promotes business and community development in the area. **Founded:** 1940. **Publications:** *Happenings* (Weekly); *Plum Creek Express* (Monthly). **Educational Activities:** The Great Plains Chautauqua. **Awards:** Lexington Area Chamber of Commerce Scholastic Awards (Periodic). **Geographic Preference:** Local.

43163 ■ Lillington Area Chamber of Commerce (LACC)
106 W Front St.
Lillington, NC 27546
Ph: (910)893-3751
Fax: (910)514-9797
Co. E-mail: contact@lillingtonchamber.org
URL: http://www.lillingtonchamber.org
Contact: Tara Fish, President
Facebook: www.facebook.com/people/Lillington-Chamber-of-Commerce/100063771413045
Instagram: www.instagram.com/lillingtonchamber

Description: Promotes business and community development in Lillington, NC. Conducts Lillington Fall Festival and other activities; bestows community service awards. **Founded:** 1948. **Geographic Preference:** Local.

43164 ■ Lincolnton-Lincoln County Chamber of Commerce
c/o Ken Kindley, President
101 E Main St.
Lincolnton, NC 28092
Ph: (704)735-3096
Co. E-mail: connect@lincolnchambernc.org
URL: http://lincolnchambernc.org
Contact: Ken Kindley, President
Facebook: www.facebook.com/LincolntonLincolnCountyChamberOfCommerce

Description: Promotes business and community development in Lincolnton and Lincoln County, NC. **Founded:** 1946. **Publications:** *The Linc* (Periodic). **Awards:** Lincolnton-Lincoln County Chamber New Member of the Year (Annual); Lincolnton-Lincoln County Chamber Small Business Person of the Year (Annual); Lincolnton-Lincoln County Chamber Volunteer of the Year (Annual). **Geographic Preference:** Local.

43165 ■ Lumberton NC Area Chamber of Commerce
800 N Chestnut St.
Lumberton, NC 28358
Ph: (910)739-4750
Fax: (910)671-9722
Co. E-mail: lumbertonchamber@bellsouth.net
URL: http://www.lumbertonchamber.com
Contact: Cindy Kern, Executive Director
X (Twitter): x.com/lumbertonchambr

Description: Promotes business and community development in Lumberton and Robeson County, NC. **Publications:** *Lumberton Area Chamber of Commerce Directory of Businesses and Services* (Annual). **Geographic Preference:** Local.

43166 ■ *Maggie Musings*
PO Box 279
Maggie Valley, NC 28751
Ph: (828)926-1686
Free: 800-624-4431
URL: http://www.maggievalley.org
URL(s): maggievalley.org/valley-views-3-28-2018-2-2-2-2-2-2-2-2-2-2-3-2-2
Released: Monthly **Availability:** Print.

43167 ■ Maggie Valley Area Chamber of Commerce and Visitors' Bureau (MVCC/VB)
PO Box 279
Maggie Valley, NC 28751
Ph: (828)926-1686
Free: 800-624-4431
URL: http://www.maggievalley.org

Description: Promotes tourism and business and community development in the Maggie Valley, NC area. Sponsors hospitality seminar and competitions. Operates the Maggie Valley Chamber of Commerce and Visitors Bureau. **Founded:** 1963. **Publications:** *The Gateway* (Periodic); *Maggie Musings* (Monthly); *Visitors Guide*. **Educational Activities:** Maggie Valley Arts and Crafts; Mountaineer Antique Auto Club. **Geographic Preference:** Regional.

43168 ■ Martin County Chamber of Commerce
415 E Blvd.
Williamston, NC 27892
Ph: (252)792-4131
Co. E-mail: admin@martincountync.com
URL: http://www.martincountync.com
Contact: David Whitley, Director
E-mail: director@martincountync.com

Description: Promotes business and community development in Martin County, NC. **Founded:** 1951. **Geographic Preference:** Local.

43169 ■ Matthews Chamber of Commerce (MCC)
210 Matthews Station St.
Matthews, NC 28105
Ph: (704)847-3649
Co. E-mail: info@matthewschamber.org
URL: http://matthewschamber.org
Contact: Sandtrica Elliott, President
Facebook: www.facebook.com/MatthewsChamber
Linkedin: www.linkedin.com/company/matthews-chamber-of-commerce
X (Twitter): x.com/MatthewsncCOC
Instagram: www.instagram.com/matthewschamber

Description: Promotes business and community development in the greater Matthews, North Carolina area. **Founded:** 1980. **Publications:** *Matthews Business News* (Monthly); *Newcomer's Guide and Business Directory* (Annual). **Geographic Preference:** Local.

43170 ■ McDowell Chamber of Commerce
1170 W Tate St.
Marion, NC 28752
Ph: (828)652-4240
Fax: (828)659-9620
Co. E-mail: mountains@mcdowellchamber.com
URL: http://www.mcdowellchamber.com
Contact: Kim Effler, Executive Director
E-mail: keffler@mcdowellchamber.com
Facebook: www.facebook.com/McDowell-Chamber-of-Commerce-370918672936
X (Twitter): x.com/ChamberMcdowell
YouTube: www.youtube.com/user/McDowellChamber

Description: Promotes business and community development in McDowell County, NC. **Founded:** 1957. **Publications:** *Business Directory*; *Manufacturing Directory*; *Chamber E-News* (Monthly); *McDowell Community Viewbook* (Biennial). **Educational Activities:** Chamber Dinner/Dance/Auction; Chamber Golf Tournament. **Geographic Preference:** Local.

43171 ■ Mitchell County Chamber of Commerce
11 Crystal St.
Spruce Pine, NC 28777
Ph: (828)765-9483
Co. E-mail: visitorinfo@mitchell-county.com
URL: http://mitchellcountychamber.org
Contact: David Wylie, Contact
Facebook: www.facebook.com/mitchellcountychamber

Description: Promotes business and community development in Mitchell County and western North Carolina. Sponsors festival. **Publications:** *Craft Your Adventure* (Periodic). **Geographic Preference:** Local.

43172 ■ Moore County Chamber of Commerce
160 W New York Ave. Unit 3
Southern Pines, NC 28387
Ph: (910)692-3926
Co. E-mail: info@moorecountychamber.com
URL: http://www.moorecountychamber.com
Contact: Linda M. Parsons, President
E-mail: lparsons@moorecountychamber.com
Facebook: www.facebook.com/MooreCountyChamber
X (Twitter): x.com/moorecountycham
Instagram: www.instagram.com/moorecountycoc

Description: Promotes business and community development in Moore County. **Founded:** 1967. **Geographic Preference:** Local.

43173 ■ Mooresville-South Iredell Chamber of Commerce
149 E Iredell Ave.
Mooresville, NC 28115
Ph: (704)664-3898
Co. E-mail: info@mooresvillenc.org
URL: http://www.mooresvillenc.org
Contact: Kirk Ballard, President
E-mail: kirk@mooresvillenc.org
Facebook: www.facebook.com/msichamber
X (Twitter): x.com/msichamber

Description: Promotes business and community development in Mooresville and South Iredell County, NC. **Founded:** 1916. **Geographic Preference:** Local.

43174 ■ Morrisville Chamber of Commerce
260 Town Hall Dr., Ste. A
Morrisville, NC 27560
Ph: (919)463-7150
Fax: (919)439-0212
Co. E-mail: chamber@morrisvillechamber.org
URL: http://www.morrisvillechamber.org
Contact: Linda Frenette, Co-President
E-mail: linda@morrisvillechamber.org
Facebook: www.facebook.com/morrisvillechamber
Linkedin: www.linkedin.com/company/morrisville-chamber-of-commerce
X (Twitter): x.com/MorrisvilleNC
YouTube: www.youtube.com/channel/UCT_fT4QHJ-Rn6pwCwDzsxBQ

Description: Promotes business and community development in Morrisville, NC. **Founded:** 1990. **Publications:** *Annual Directory and Economic Data Book* (Annual); *Morrisville Chamber Communicator* (Quarterly). **Geographic Preference:** Local.

43175 ■ Mount Olive Area Chamber of Commerce
123 N Center St.
  Mount Olive, NC 28365
Ph: (919)658-3113
URL: http://www.moachamber.com
Contact: Julie R. Beck, President
E-mail: president@mountolivechamber.com
Facebook: www.facebook.com/mountolivechambernc

Description: Promotes economic development in the Mt. Olive, NC area. Sponsors Annual North Carolina Pickle Festival. Conducts educational seminar. **Founded:** 1930. **Publications:** *The Architect* (Quarterly); *Mt. Olive Area Chamber of Commerce Membership Directory* (Annual). **Geographic Preference:** Local.

43176 ■ New Bern Area Chamber of Commerce
316 S Front St.
  New Bern, NC 28563
Ph: (252)637-3111
URL: http://www.newbernchamber.com
Contact: Kevin Roberts, President
Facebook: www.facebook.com/
  NewBernChamberofCommerce
X (Twitter): x.com/NewBernChamber
Instagram: www.instagram.com/newbernchamber
YouTube: www.youtube.com/channel/UCz-sx4JV
  2nGilsRhpnTJALA

Description: Promotes business and community development in Craven County, NC. **Founded:** 1991. **Publications:** *For Members Only* (Monthly); *New Bern Area Guide and Business* (Annual); *Business Wise* (Monthly). **Educational Activities:** Administrative Professionals' Day; New Bern Area Chamber of Commerce Flame Banquet Centre; Business Expo. **Geographic Preference:** Local.

43177 ■ *New Bern Area Guide and Business*
316 S Front St.
  New Bern, NC 28563
Ph: (252)637-3111
URL: http://www.newbernchamber.com
Contact: Kevin Roberts, President
URL(s): business.newbernchamber.com/list

Released: Annual **Description:** Covers businesses in New Bern/Craven County, NC. **Availability:** Online.

43178 ■ Northampton County Chamber of Commerce
127 W Jefferson St.
  Jackson, NC 27845
Ph: (252)534-1383
Fax: (252)534-1739
Co. E-mail: jcolliernhcoc@northamptonchamber.org
URL: http://www.northamptonchamber.org
Facebook: www.facebook.com/people/Northampton
  -County-Chamber-of-Commerce/100064633451707

Description: Promotes business and community development in Northampton County, VA area. **Publications:** *Country Sampler Calendar of Events* (Quarterly). **Educational Activities:** Cape Charles Fall Festival. **Geographic Preference:** Local.

43179 ■ Outer Banks Chamber of Commerce (OBCC)
101 Town Hall Dr.
  Kill Devil Hills, NC 27948
Ph: (252)441-8144
Co. E-mail: info@outerbankschamber.com
URL: http://www.outerbankschamber.com
Contact: Karen S. Brown, President
E-mail: kbrown@outerbankschamber.com

Description: Promotes business and community development in Currituck, Dare, and Hyde counties, NC. Sponsors seminars. **Founded:** 1949. **Publications:** *Chamber News*; *Outer Banks Relocation &*

Investors Guide. **Educational Activities:** Health and Fitness Expo; Legislative Breakfast. **Geographic Preference:** Local.

43180 ■ Perquimans County Chamber of Commerce (PECO)
118 W Market St.
  Hertford, NC 27944
Ph: (252)426-5657
URL: http://perqiumanschamber.com
Contact: LeAnna Lee, Executive Director
E-mail: director@perqiumanschamber.com

Description: Promotes business and community development in Perquimans County, NC. Sponsors Indian Summer Festival. **Founded:** 1961. **Publications:** *Promoting Perquimans* (Monthly). **Geographic Preference:** Local.

43181 ■ *Picture Perfect Guide*
4433 Long Beach Rd. SE
  Southport, NC 28461
Ph: (910)457-6964
Fax: (910)457-0598
Co. E-mail: info@southport-oakisland.com
URL: http://www.southport-oakisland.com
Contact: Ervin Etheridge, President
URL(s): www.southport-oakisland.com/blog/2024-pic
  ture-perfect-guide-arrives.html

Availability: Print.

43182 ■ Pleasure Island, Carolina Beach, and Kure Beach Chamber of Commerce
1121 N Lake Pk. Blvd.
  Carolina Beach, NC 28428
Ph: (910)458-8434
Co. E-mail: visitor@pleasureislandnc.org
URL: http://www.pleasureislandnc.org
Contact: Jim DeGilio, Executive Director
Facebook: www.facebook.com/PleasureIslandNC
Linkedin: www.linkedin.com/in/picc-chamber-a02aa
  420b
X (Twitter): x.com/PleasureIsland
Instagram: www.instagram.com/pleasureislandcham
  ber
YouTube: www.youtube.com/channel/UCSNUg
  1dGGaMzApNeyf6CleA

Description: Promotes business and community development in Carolina Beach and Kure Beach, NC. **Founded:** 1978. **Publications:** *Pleasure Island Newsletter*. **Geographic Preference:** Regional.

43183 ■ *Program of Work*
307 N Academy St.
  Cary, NC 27513
Ph: (919)467-1016
Free: 800-919-2279
Fax: (919)469-2375
Co. E-mail: info@carychamber.com
URL: http://www.carychamber.com
Contact: Mark Lawson, President
URL(s): www.carychamber.com/program-of-work
  .html

Released: Last Edition 2023-2024. **Availability:** Print; PDF; Download.

43184 ■ Raeford - Hoke Chamber of Commerce (RHCC)
101 N Main St.
  Raeford, NC 28376
Ph: (910)875-5929
Co. E-mail: info@raefordhokechamber.com
URL: http://www.rhchamber.com
Facebook: www.facebook.com/raefordhokechamber

Description: Promotes business and community development in Raeford, NC. **Publications:** *Chamber News*. **Geographic Preference:** Local.

43185 ■ Randleman Chamber of Commerce
102 W Naomi St.
  Randleman, NC 27317
Ph: (336)495-1100
Fax: (336)495-1133
Co. E-mail: chamber43@northstate.net
URL: http://randlemanchamber.com
Contact: Jeff Freeman, Executive Director
Facebook: www.facebook.com/ran
  dlemanchamberofcommerce

Description: Promotes business and community development in Randleman, NC. **Founded:** 1948. **Geographic Preference:** Local.

43186 ■ Richmond County Chamber of Commerce (RCCC)
505 Rockingham Rd.
  Rockingham, NC 28380
Ph: (910)895-9058
Co. E-mail: info@richmondcountychamber.com
URL: http://www.richmondcountychamber.com
Contact: Kristi R. King, President
E-mail: president@richmondcountychamber.com
Facebook: www.facebook.com/RichmondCoun
  tyChamber
X (Twitter): x.com/chamberatrock
Instagram: www.instagram.com/rcochamber

Description: Promotes business and community development in Richmond County, NC. **Founded:** 1983. **Publications:** *Images of Richmond County* (Annual); *Chamber Focus* (Monthly). **Geographic Preference:** Local.

43187 ■ Roanoke Valley Chamber of Commerce (RVCC)
730 Roanoke Ave., Ste. A1
  Roanoke Rapids, NC 27870
Ph: (252)537-3513
Fax: (252)541-2723
Co. E-mail: jmorgan@rvchamber.com
URL: http://www.rvchamber.com
Contact: Ginny Lewis, President

Description: Promotes business and community development in Roanoke Rapids, NC. **Publications:** *Impact*. **Educational Activities:** The Chair's Night Out. **Geographic Preference:** Local.

43188 ■ Rocky Mount Area Chamber of Commerce (RMACC)
100 Coastline St., No. 200
  Rocky Mount, NC 27804
Ph: (252)446-0323
Co. E-mail: rmacc@rockymountchamber.org
URL: http://www.rockymountchamber.org
Contact: David Farris, President
E-mail: dfarris@rockymountchamber.org
Facebook: www.facebook.com/rockymountchamber
Linkedin: www.linkedin.com/company/rocky-moun
  t-chamber-of-commerce
X (Twitter): x.com/rmchamber
Instagram: www.instagram.com/rockymountchamber

Description: Seeks to improve the overall business climate for its members through sponsorship of programs which stimulate economic growth, promote civic development and enhance political action. **Founded:** 1904. **Publications:** *Business Directory*; *Industrial Directory*; *Enterprise* (Quarterly). **Awards:** RMACC Volunteer of the Year Award (Annual). **Geographic Preference:** Local.

43189 ■ Rowan County Chamber of Commerce
204 E Innes St., Ste. 100
  Salisbury, NC 28145
Ph: (704)633-4221
Fax: (704)642-2011
Co. E-mail: info@rowanchamber.com
URL: http://www.rowanchamber.com
Contact: Elaine Spalding, President
E-mail: espalding@rowanchamber.com
Facebook: www.facebook.com/RowanChamber
X (Twitter): x.com/RowanCo_Chamber
Instagram: www.instagram.com/rowancounty
  _chamberofcommerce

Description: Promotes business and community development in Salisbury and Rowan County, NC. **Founded:** 1925. **Publications:** *At Work* (Monthly); *Elected Officials Directory*; *Manufacturers Directory*. **Geographic Preference:** Local.

43190 ■ Roxboro Area Chamber of Commerce (RACC)
211 N Main St.
  Roxboro, NC 27573
Ph: (336)599-8333
Co. E-mail: chamber@roxboronc.com
URL: http://roxboronc.com/index.html

STATE LISTINGS   North Carolina ■ 43204

Contact: Samantha Bagbey, Executive Director
Facebook: www.facebook.com/RoxChamber211
Linkedin: www.linkedin.com/in/roxboronccchamber
X (Twitter): x.com/RoxboroChamber
Instagram: www.instagram.com/roxborochamber
YouTube: www.youtube.com/channel/UCaDe8wh9S5y_mHW2SwFbekA
Description: Promotes business and community development in Person County, NC. Sponsors September Personality Festival. Maintains Business After Hours programs and numerous other programs. **Founded:** 1935. **Publications:** *Chamber Report* (Monthly). **Educational Activities:** Roxboro Area Chamber of Commerce Banquet. **Geographic Preference:** Local.

43191 ■ *Sources*
200 Nash St. NE
  Wilson, NC 27893
Ph: (252)237-0165
Fax: (252)243-7931
Co. E-mail: marketing@wilsonncchamber.com
URL: http://www.wilsonncchamber.com
Contact: Ryan W. Simons, President
URL(s): www.wilsonncchamber.com/sources
Availability: Print; Online.

43192 ■ Southport-Oak Island Chamber of Commerce
4433 Long Beach Rd. SE
  Southport, NC 28461
Ph: (910)457-6964
Fax: (910)457-0598
Co. E-mail: info@southport-oakisland.com
URL: http://www.southport-oakisland.com
Contact: Ervin Etheridge, President
Facebook: www.facebook.com/SouthportOakIslandChamber
Linkedin: www.linkedin.com/company/southport-oak-island-area-chamber-of-commerce
Instagram: www.instagram.com/southportoakislandchamber
Pinterest: www.pinterest.com/southportoa0341
Description: Promotes business and community development in the Southport and Oak Island, NC area. **Publications:** *Chamber E-News* (Bimonthly); *Picture Perfect Guide*. **Awards:** Southport-Oak Island Chamber of Commerce Small Business Person of the Year (Annual). **Geographic Preference:** Local.

43193 ■ Stanly County Chamber of Commerce (SCCoC)
1000 N 1st St., Ste. 11
  Albemarle, NC 28002
Ph: (704)982-8116
Co. E-mail: info@stanlychamber.org
URL: http://stanlychamber.org
Contact: Sandy Selvy-Mullis, President
Facebook: www.facebook.com/StanlyChamber
X (Twitter): x.com/StanlyChamber
Instagram: www.instagram.com/stanlychamber
Description: Promotes business and community development in Stanly County, NC. **Founded:** 1936. **Publications:** *Images of Stanley County*; *Linked* (Monthly). **Geographic Preference:** Local.

43194 ■ Swain County Chamber of Commerce
210 Main St.
  Bryson City, NC 28713
Ph: (828)488-3681
Free: 877-472-1681
Co. E-mail: chamber@greatsmokies.com
URL: http://www.greatsmokies.com
Contact: Karen Proctor Wilmot, Executive Director
URL(s): bryson-city-swain-county-chamber-of-business.site/?utm_source=gmb&utm_medium=referral
Description: Promotes business and community development in Swain County, NC. Encourages tourism. Sponsors event in the 4th of July. **Publications:** *Swain County Chamber News* (Weekly). **Educational Activities:** Chili Cook Off (Annual). **Geographic Preference:** Local.

43195 ■ TarboroEdgecombe Chamber of Commerce (TECC)
500 Main St.
  Tarboro, NC 27886
Ph: (252)823-7241
Co. E-mail: info@tarborochamber.com
URL: http://www.tarborochamber.com
Contact: Patrick Heins, Chief Executive Officer
E-mail: patrick.heins@ecuhealth.org
Facebook: www.facebook.com/tarboroedgecombe
Description: Promotes business and community development in Tarboro, NC. **Founded:** 1933. **Publications:** *TECC Update* (Monthly). **Awards:** Tarboro - Edgecombe Chamber Outstanding Citizen of the Year Award (Annual). **Geographic Preference:** Local.

43196 ■ *Topsail Area Guide*
13775 NC Hwy. 50, Ste. 101
  Surf City, NC 28445
Ph: (910)329-4446
Co. E-mail: info@topsailchamber.org
URL: http://www.topsailchamber.org
Contact: Kay Phelps, Coordinator
URL(s): www.topsailchamber.org/mail-me-an-area-guide
Description: Covers activities, annual events, maps and information about the greater Topsail area. **Availability:** Online.

43197 ■ Triangle East Chamber of Commerce
1115 Outlet Center Dr.
  Smithfield, NC 27577-0467
Ph: (919)934-9166
Fax: (919)934-1337
Co. E-mail: info@triangleeastchamber.com
URL: http://www.triangleeastchamber.com
Contact: Maureen McGuinness, President
Facebook: www.facebook.com/triangleeastchamber
Linkedin: www.linkedin.com/company/triangleeastchamber
X (Twitter): x.com/TriangleEastCOC
Instagram: www.instagram.com/triangleeastchamber
Description: Promotes business and community development in the Greater Smithfield-Selma and Johnston County, NC area. **Founded:** 1970. **Publications:** *Chamber E-Chats*. **Geographic Preference:** Local.

43198 ■ Union County Chamber of Commerce
903 Skyway Dr.
  Monroe, NC 28110
Ph: (704)289-4567
Fax: (704)282-0122
Co. E-mail: info@unioncountycoc.com
URL: http://www.unioncountycoc.com
Contact: Pat Kahle, President
E-mail: pat@unioncountycoc.com
Facebook: www.facebook.com/unioncountycoc
Linkedin: www.linkedin.com/company/union-county-chamber
X (Twitter): x.com/UnionCountyCOC
Instagram: www.instagram.com/unioncountycoc
Description: Leads in the promotion and advancement of Union County, NC's economic interests and improvement of the quality of life for its citizens. **Publications:** *Newcomers Guide*; *Union County Industrial Directory*; *Newcomers Guide*; *Union County Economic Development Resource Directory*. **Educational Activities:** Human Resources. **Awards:** Union County Chamber Business Leadership Hall of Fame (Annual); Union County Chamber Volunteer of the Year (Annual). **Geographic Preference:** Local.

43199 ■ *Visitors Guide*
2753 Lynn Rd., Ste. A
  Tryon, NC 28782
Ph: (828)859-6236
Co. E-mail: info@carolinafoothillschamber.com
URL: http://www.carolinafoothillschamber.com
Contact: Catina Gray, President
URL(s): carolinafoothillschamber.com/visit-the-carolina-foothills
Availability: Print.

43200 ■ Wake Forest Area Chamber of Commerce
350 S White St.
  Wake Forest, NC 27587
Ph: (919)556-1519
Co. E-mail: wfchamber@wakeforestchamber.org
URL: http://wakeforestchamber.org
Contact: Liz Simpers, President
X (Twitter): x.com/wf_chamber
Description: Serves as the voice of business in the Wake Forest Area. Encourages profitable enterprise and social progress for the benefit of the community. **Founded:** 1948. **Publications:** *Business Matters* (Monthly). **Geographic Preference:** Local.

43201 ■ Warren County Regional Chamber of Commerce
130 N Main St.
  Warrenton, NC 27589-1957
Ph: (252)257-2657
Co. E-mail: info@warrencountychamber.org
URL: http://www.warren-chamber.org/chamber_directors.shtml
Contact: Bill Miller, President
E-mail: bmiller912@gmail.com
Facebook: www.facebook.com/ChamberofCommerceofWarrenCounty
X (Twitter): twitter.com/WarrenChamber
Instagram: www.instagram.com/warrencochamber
Description: Promotes business and community development in the Hackettstown, NJ area. **Founded:** 1979. **Publications:** *Commentary* (Monthly). **Educational Activities:** Awards Banquet; Business Expo (Annual). **Geographic Preference:** Local.

43202 ■ Warsaw Chamber of Commerce (WCC)
121 S Front St.
  Warsaw, NC 28398
Ph: (910)293-7804
Fax: (910)293-6773
Co. E-mail: warsawchamber@townofwarsawnc.com
URL: http://www.warsawncchamber.com
Contact: Frank Rhodes, President
Facebook: www.facebook.com/Warsaw-Chamber-of-Commerce-181566088627075
Description: Promotes business and community development in Warsaw, NC. **Founded:** 1921. **Geographic Preference:** Local.

43203 ■ Washington - Beaufort County Chamber of Commerce (WBCCC)
102 Stewart Pky.
  Washington, NC 27889
Ph: (252)946-9168
Fax: (252)946-9169
Co. E-mail: cglover@wbcchamber.com
URL: http://www.wbcchamber.com
Contact: Pam Pippin, President
YouTube: www.youtube.com/channel/UCi21n2JVLUI8c_X6qyjSNAg
Description: Promotes business and community development in Washington, NC. **Founded:** 1904. **Geographic Preference:** Local.

43204 ■ Wayne County Chamber of Commerce
308 N William St.
  Goldsboro, NC 27533
Ph: (919)734-2241
Co. E-mail: laral@waynecountychamber.com
URL: http://www.waynecountychamber.com
Contact: Janet Brock, Director
E-mail: janetb@waynecountychamber.com
Facebook: www.facebook.com/WayneCountyChamberofCommerce
Linkedin: www.linkedin.com/company/wayne-county-chamber-of-commerce
X (Twitter): x.com/NCWayneChamber
Instagram: www.instagram.com/waynecountychamberofcommerce
Description: Promotes business and community development in Wayne County, NC. **Founded:** 1918. **Publications:** *Windows of Wayne* (Annual); *Visions* (Annual). **Educational Activities:** Farm City. **Geographic Preference:** Local.

43205 ■ Wendell Chamber of Commerce (WCC)
115 N Pine St.
Wendell, NC 27591
Ph: (919)365-6318
Co. E-mail: wcoc@wendellchamber.com
URL: http://www.wendellchamber.com
Contact: Peedie Edwards, President
Facebook: www.facebook.com/WendellChamberOfCommerce
Instagram: www.instagram.com/wendellchamberofcommerce
Description: Promotes business and community development in Wendell, NC. **Founded:** 1903. **Publications:** *Chamber Clips* (Semiannual). **Awards:** Wendell Chamber of Commerce Business of the Month (Monthly). **Geographic Preference:** Local.

43206 ■ Western Rockingham Chamber of Commerce (WRCC)
112 W Murphy St.
Madison, NC 27025
Ph: (336)548-6248
URL: http://wrcchamber.com
Contact: Mavis Dillon, Director
E-mail: director@wrcchamber.com
Facebook: www.facebook.com/WesternRockinghamChamberOfCommerce
Instagram: www.instagram.com/wrccyp
Description: Promotes business and community development in Madison, NC. **Publications:** *The Western Flyer* (Monthly). **Geographic Preference:** Local.

43207 ■ Wilkes Chamber of Commerce
717 Main St.
North Wilkesboro, NC 28659-4297
Ph: (336)838-8662
Fax: (336)838-3728
URL: http://www.wilkeschamber.com
Contact: Linda Cheek, President
E-mail: lcheek@wilkesnc.org
X (Twitter): x.com/WilkesChamber
YouTube: www.youtube.com/user/WilkesChamber
Pinterest: www.pinterest.com/wilkeschamber
Description: Strives to promote economic development and to enhance the quality of life in Wilkes County. **Founded:** 1946. **Publications:** *Images of Wilkes* (Annual). **Educational Activities:** Brushy Mountain Apple Festival (Annual). **Geographic Preference:** Local.

43208 ■ Wilson Chamber of Commerce (WCC)
200 Nash St. NE
Wilson, NC 27893
Ph: (252)237-0165
Fax: (252)243-7931
Co. E-mail: marketing@wilsonncchamber.com
URL: http://www.wilsonncchamber.com
Contact: Ryan W. Simons, President
Facebook: www.facebook.com/wilsonncchamber
Linkedin: www.linkedin.com/company/wilson-chamber-of-commerce
X (Twitter): x.com/WilsonChamber
YouTube: www.youtube.com/channel/UCgR_97426pMCbm8xBXIQcGQ
Description: Promotes business and community development in Wilson and Wilson County, NC. **Founded:** 1897. **Publications:** *Sources*; *The Chamber Focus* (Monthly). **Geographic Preference:** Local.

43209 ■ Windsor/Bertie County Chamber of Commerce
121 E Granville St.
Windsor, NC 27983
Ph: (252)794-4277
Co. E-mail: info@buconz.com
URL: http://windsorbertie.com
Contact: Jamie Harmon, Contact
E-mail: jamieharmon@embarqmail.com
Facebook: www.facebook.com/profile.php?id=100064468130558
Description: Membership is made up of area businesses, nonprofits, service and healthcare industries, manufacturers and individuals. Promotes business, tourism and community development. **Founded:** 1946. **Publications:** *Chamber News*. **Geographic Preference:** Local.

43210 ■ Winston-Salem Chamber of Commerce (WSCOC)
411 W 4th St., Ste. 211
Winston Salem, NC 27101
Ph: (336)728-9200
Co. E-mail: info@winstonsalem.com
URL: http://www.winstonsalem.com
Contact: Mark Owens, President
E-mail: markowens@winstonsalem.com
Facebook: www.facebook.com/greaterwinstonsaleminc
Linkedin: www.linkedin.com/company/greater-winston-salem-inc
X (Twitter): x.com/greater_ws
Instagram: www.instagram.com/greaterwinstonsaleminc
YouTube: www.youtube.com/channel/UCoExvVXjBnYd8mFPQISZWXQ
Description: Promotes business and community development in Winston-Salem, NC area. **Founded:** 1885. **Geographic Preference:** Local.

43211 ■ Yadkin County Chamber of Commerce
205 S Jackson St.
Yadkinville, NC 27055
Ph: (336)679-2200
Free: 877-492-3546
Fax: (336)579-0324
Co. E-mail: jamie@yadkinchamber.org
URL: http://yadkinchamber.org
Contact: Nolan Brown, Secretary Treasurer
E-mail: nbrown@yadtel.net
X (Twitter): x.com/yadkinchamber
Instagram: www.instagram.com/yadkinchamber
Description: Advocates for the business community and supports pro-business policies on the local, state, and federal level. Sponsors business seminars throughout the year. **Founded:** 1850. **Geographic Preference:** Local.

43212 ■ Yadkin Valley Chamber of Commerce
257 Standard St.
Elkin, NC 28621
Ph: (336)526-1111
Fax: (336)526-1879
URL: http://yadkinvalley.org
Contact: David Steelman, President
E-mail: president@yadkinvalley.org
Facebook: www.facebook.com/YadkinValleyChamberofCommerce
X (Twitter): x.com/YadkinValleyCOC
YouTube: www.youtube.com/user/yadkinvalleycoc
Description: Promotes business and community development in the Yadkin Valley Elkin, NC area. **Geographic Preference:** Local.

43213 ■ Yancey County/Burnsville Chamber of Commerce
106 W Main St.
Burnsville, NC 28714
Ph: (828)682-7413
Co. E-mail: info@yanceychamber.com
URL: http://www.yanceychamber.com
Contact: Lucy Doll, Member
Facebook: www.facebook.com/yanceychamber
Instagram: www.instagram.com/burnsvillechamber
Description: Promotes business and community development in Yancey County, NC. Conducts public forums and seminars. Sponsors annual crafts fair. **Founded:** 1834. **Publications:** *Yancey County Business Directory* (Periodic). **Educational Activities:** Old Timey Fall Festival (Annual). **Geographic Preference:** Local.

43214 ■ Zebulon Chamber of Commerce
815 N Arendell Ave.
Zebulon, NC 27597
Ph: (919)269-6320
Fax: (919)269-6350
Co. E-mail: reception@zebulonchamber.org
URL: http://www.zebulonchamber.org
Contact: John Saffold, Executive Director
E-mail: jsaffold@zebulonchamber.org
Facebook: www.facebook.com/zebulonchamber
X (Twitter): x.com/ZebulonChamber
Instagram: www.instagram.com/zebulon_chamber
Description: Business members and individual members of the community that join together for the common good of promoting businesses and the general welfare and prosperity of the Zebulon community. Provides benefits, programs, services, and a voice to the community and fellow member businesses. **Founded:** 1947. **Awards:** Zebulon Chamber of Commerce Citizen of the Year (Annual). **Geographic Preference:** Local.

MINORITY BUSINESS ASSISTANCE PROGRAMS

43215 ■ North Carolina Institute of Minority Economic Development - NC Minority Business Enterprise Center
114 W Parrish St.
Durham, NC 27701
Ph: (919)956-8889
Fax: (919)688-7668
Co. E-mail: info@ncimed.org
URL: http://theinstitutenc.org
Contact: Kevin J. Price, President
E-mail: kprice@theinstitutenc.org
Facebook: www.facebook.com/TheNCInstitute
X (Twitter): x.com/TheInstituteNC
YouTube: www.youtube.com/channel/UCbMmDDk-VR-FulTyiz0GJGw
Description: Provides finance management, access to capital, consulting, and procurement services to minority businesses in North Carolina. **Founded:** 1986.

43216 ■ Women's Business Center of Fayetteville (WBCFAY)
230 Hay St.
Fayetteville, NC 28301
Ph: (910)323-3377
Co. E-mail: wbc1@ncceed.org
URL: http://www.wbcfay.org
Contact: Danice Langdon, Director (Acting)
E-mail: danice@ncceed.org
Facebook: www.facebook.com/WBCFAY
Instagram: www.instagram.com/WBCFAYNC
YouTube: www.youtube.com/channel/UCER-Srvoe3OAI0PE1I6q5HA
Description: Works to promote the economic empowerment of women in North Carolina. Provides a variety of business ownership services. **Founded:** 1990.

FINANCING AND LOAN PROGRAMS

43217 ■ Carolina Angel Network (CAN)
137 E Rosemary St., Ste. 100
Chapel Hill, NC 27514
URL: http://www.carolinaangelnetwork.com
Contact: Ted Zoller, Executive Director
E-mail: ted@carolinaangel.net
Description: Connects the University of North Carolina community and alumni network to support early-stage new businesses with funding and advice. **Founded:** 2016.

43218 ■ Cherokee
310 S W St., Ste. 200
Raleigh, NC 27603
Ph: (919)743-2500
URL: http://cherokeefund.com
Contact: Tom Darden, Chief Executive Officer
Description: Investment firm offers private equity and venture capital. Blends creativity with capital to provide financial, social, and environmental returns.

43219 ■ Duke Capital Partners (DCP)
2812 Erwin Rd., Ste. 406
Durham, NC 27705
Co. E-mail: dukeangelnetwork@duke.edu
URL: http://dukecapitalpartners.duke.edu

STATE LISTINGS

North Carolina ■ 43237

Contact: Kurt Schmidt, Managing Director
Linkedin: www.linkedin.com/company/dukecapitalpartners
X (Twitter): x.com/DukeCapPartners
Description: Connects investors with innovative early-stage companies. Offers the Duke Innovation Fund. Supports the Duke University entrepreneurial community. **Founded:** 2015. **Investment Policies:** Founder, executive, board member, or major investor should be a current/former Duke student, employee, or parent; raising Seed or Series A capital of $500,000 or syndicating a later-stage equity financing with an existing or new institutional lead investor; solutions that add more value (over the long run) than what it cost; located in the United States.

43220 ■ Excelerate Health Ventures (EHV)
600 Pk. Offices Dr., Ste. 300
Durham, NC 27709-3965
Co. E-mail: info@exceleratehealth.com
URL: http://www.exceleratehealth.com
Contact: Bobby Bahram, Managing Partner
Description: Invests in groundbreaking healthcare companies. Also offers incubator and management consulting services. **Founded:** 2013.

43221 ■ Frontier Growth
525 N Tryon St., Ste. 1900
Charlotte, NC 28202
Ph: (704)414-2880
Co. E-mail: info@frontiercapital.com
URL: http://frontiergrowth.com
Contact: Whitney Lanier, Director
X (Twitter): x.com/thefrontierteam
Founded: 1999. **Preferred Investment Size:** $5,000,000 to $15,000,000. **Industry Preferences:** Internet specific, Communications, computer software, medical and health, financial services, and business service.

43222 ■ Hatteras Venture Partners
280 S Mangum St., Ste. 350
Durham, NC 27701
Ph: (919)484-0730
Fax: (919)484-0364
URL: http://www.hatterasvp.com
Contact: Ben Scruggs, Principal
Description: Venture partner firm with a risk-mitigated value-creation model. Focuses on a range of companies from those offering therapeutic or diagnostic benefits to those disrupting the status quo in healthcare and accelerating innovation. . **Founded:** 2000.

43223 ■ Intersouth Partners
4711 Hope Valley Rd., Ste. 4F - 632
Durham, NC 27707
Ph: (919)493-6640
URL: http://www.intersouth.com
Contact: Dennis Dougherty, Manager
E-mail: dennis@intersouth.com
Description: Investment firm provides private equity and venture capital investment services for life science and technology companies. **Founded:** 1985. **Preferred Investment Size:** $500,000 to $6,000,000. **Industry Preferences:** Medical and health, biotechnology, Internet specific, computer software and services, industrial and energy, semiconductors and other electronics, other products, computer hardware, communications and media, and consumer related.

43224 ■ MCNC Ventures L.L.C.
3021 E Cornwallis Rd.
Research Triangle Park, NC 27709-2889
Ph: (919)248-1900
Fax: (919)248-1101
URL: http://www.mcnc.org
Contact: Dr. Hope A. Williams, Chairman
Facebook: www.facebook.com/mcnc.ncren
Linkedin: www.linkedin.com/company/mcnc
X (Twitter): x.com/mcnc
YouTube: www.youtube.com/user/MCNCvideos
Description: Provider of broadband communications technology services and support services including data center, video conferencing, webcasting and more. **Investment Policies:** Seed and early stage. **Industry Preferences:** Communications.

43225 ■ Pappas Ventures
2520 Meridian Pky., Ste. 400
Durham, NC 27713
Ph: (919)998-3300
Fax: (919)998-3301
URL: http://www.pappas-capital.com
Contact: Matthew Boyer, Chief Financial Officer
X (Twitter): x.com/pappas_capital
Description: Firm providing Investments in life sciences. **Founded:** 1994. **Preferred Investment Size:** $100,000 to $6,000,000. **Investment Policies:** Balanced, first, early, later, and second stage, and mezzanine. **Industry Preferences:** Medical and health, biotechnology, computer software and services, and Internet specific.

43226 ■ Rex Health Ventures (RHV)
4420 Lake Boone Trl.
Raleigh, NC 27607
URL: http://rexhealthventures.com
Contact: Natasha Bonett DeLong, Manager
Linkedin: www.linkedin.com/company/rex-health-ventures
Description: Invests in and fosters healthcare companies. Established by UNC Rex Healthcare as part of their commitment to innovation. **Founded:** 2012.

43227 ■ RTP Capital Associates, Inc.
2 Davis Dr.
Research Triangle Park, NC 27709
Co. E-mail: info@rtpcapital.org
URL: http://www.rtpcapital.org
Contact: Mark Friedman, President
Description: Angel network provides capital, guidance, mentoring, and strategic resources for regionally-based early-stage companies.

43228 ■ SJF Ventures (SJF)
200 N Mangum St., Ste. 203
Durham, NC 27701
Ph: (919)530-1177
Fax: (919)530-1178
URL: http://sjfventures.com
Contact: Cody Nystrom, Managing Director
E-mail: cnystrom@sjfventures.com
Facebook: www.facebook.com/sjfventures
X (Twitter): x.com/sjfventures
Description: Venture capital firm investing in high-growth companies in resource efficiency, sustainability, and technology-enhances services. Also maintains offices in New York, San Francisco, and Seattle. **Founded:** 1999. **Industry Preferences:** Energy; mobility; asset recovery and logistics; food; education; health; consumer and enterprise software.

43229 ■ Southern Capitol Ventures
100 E Six Forks Rd., Ste. 200
Raleigh, NC 27609
Ph: (919)858-7580
URL: http://www.southcap.com
Contact: Ben Brooks, Founder
Linkedin: www.linkedin.com/company/southern-capitol-ventures
Description: Venture capital firm provides financial services. **Founded:** 2000. **Preferred Investment Size:** $500,000 to $1,500,000. **Industry Preferences:** Semiconductors and other electronics, computer software and services, Internet specific, communications and media.

43230 ■ The Sustainable Jobs Fund / SJF Ventures
200 N Mangum St., Ste. 203
Durham, NC 27701
Ph: (919)530-1177
Fax: (919)530-1178
URL: http://sjfventures.com
Contact: Julie Plowden, Chief Financial Officer
E-mail: jplowden@sjfventures.com
Facebook: www.facebook.com/sjfventures
Linkedin: www.linkedin.com/company/sjf-ventures
X (Twitter): x.com/sjfventures
Description: Provider of venture capital investment services for high-growth companies. **Founded:** 1999. **Preferred Investment Size:** $1,000,000 to $2,000,000. **Industry Preferences:** Computer software, semiconductors and other electronics, medical and health, consumer related, industrial and energy, business service, manufacturing, and utilities.

43231 ■ Syngenta Venutres
629 Davis Dr.
Research Triangle Park, NC 27709
URL: http://www.syngentagroupventures.com
Contact: Brian Watson, Manager
Description: Stage-agnostic venture capital firm for agriculture companies. Also operates out of Minnesota and Switzerland. **Founded:** 2009. **Industry Preferences:** Gene editing; synthetic biology; breeding technologies; natural products; farm management systems; aerial imagery; precision agriculture.

43232 ■ Triangle Angel Partners (TAP)
6002 Meadow Run Ct.
Chapel Hill, NC 27516
URL: http://www.triangleangelpartners.com
Description: Angel investment fund. **Founded:** 2011.

43233 ■ Truepilot L.L.C.
109 E Franklin St., Ste. 200
Chapel Hill, NC 27514-3564
Contact: Michael Brader-Araje, Manager
Founded: 2000. **Preferred Investment Size:** $50,000 to $500,000. **Industry Preferences:** Internet specific.

43234 ■ Wolfpack Investor Network (WIN)
1070 Partners Way, Ste. 5100
Raleigh, NC 27606
Ph: (919)513-3546
URL: http://research.ncsu.edu/win
Contact: Wade Fulghum, Chairman
X (Twitter): x.com/NCStateWIN
Description: Matches the North Carolina State alumni network with private companies to support growth. Offers and angel investing platform and a co-investment fund.

43235 ■ xElle Ventures
First Flight Venture Ctr.
2 Davis Dr.
Durham, NC 27709
Co. E-mail: info@xelleventures.com
URL: http://www.xelleventures.com
Facebook: www.facebook.com/xelleventures
Linkedin: www.linkedin.com/company/xelleventures
Description: Early-stage angel investment network created for--and by--women in North Carolina. Works to increase the percentage of women receiving venture financing. Operates on their 3M model (money, marketing, and mentoring). **Founded:** 2019.

PROCUREMENT ASSISTANCE PROGRAMS

43236 ■ North Carolina Small Business and Technology Development Center (NCSBTDC)
5 W Hargett St., Ste. 600
Raleigh, NC 27601
Ph: (919)715-7272
Free: 800-258-0862
Co. E-mail: info@sbtdc.org
URL: http://sbtdc.org
Contact: Byron Hicks, Director
E-mail: bhicks@sbtdc.org
Linkedin: www.linkedin.com/company/sbtdc
X (Twitter): x.com/ncsbtdc
Description: Goals are to increase job opportunities and capital investments; to assist in the creation or retention of jobs; to expand economic opportunities; to reduce the incidence of business failure; to assist in community development efforts; and to assist in the development, growth, and expansion of commercial, industrial, and business activities. **Founded:** 1984.

43237 ■ North Carolina Small Business and Technology Development Center (SBTDC) - SBTDC Regional Office
803 S College Rd., Ste. A
Wilmington, NC 28403-5977
Ph: (910)962-3744

Co. E-mail: uncw@sbtdc.org
URL: http://sbtdc.org/offices/uncw
Contact: Gloria Monroe, Director (Acting)
E-mail: gmonroe@sbtdc.org
Description: Helps businesses obtain contracts by providing comprehensive assistance in selling products and services to local, state and federal government entities.

INCUBATORS/RESEARCH AND TECHNOLOGY PARKS

43238 ■ Asheville-Buncombe Technical Community College - Small Business Center (SBC)
1465 Sand Hill Rd.
 Candler, NC 28715
Ph: (828)398-7950
Co. E-mail: sbcincubator@abtech.edu
URL: http://abtech.edu/programs/continuing-ed-work-force/business-incubation-and-small-business-center
Contact: Jill Sparks, Executive Director
E-mail: jillmsparks@abtech.edu
Description: Fosters and supports entrepreneurship, small business, and economic development with an emphasis on assisting startups, early stage, and at-risk enterprises.

43239 ■ Blue Ridge Food Ventures (BRFV)
1461 Sand Hill Rd.
 Candler, NC 28715
Ph: (828)348-0130
Co. E-mail: info@blueridgefoodventures.org
URL: http://blueridgefoodventures.org
Contact: Michael McDonald, Manager
Facebook: www.facebook.com/BlueRidgeFoodVentures
Instagram: www.instagram.com/blueridgefoodventures
YouTube: www.youtube.com/channel/UCyVYkL02gy79QBLHS8nklYw
Description: A shared-use food processing center providing services to those wishing to start or grow small businesses in the food industry. **Founded:** 2005.

43240 ■ The Cookery
1101 W Chapel Hill St.
 Durham, NC 27701
Ph: (919)908-8974
Co. E-mail: hello@durhamcookery.com
URL: http://www.durhamcookery.com
Contact: Rochelle Johnson, Owner
Facebook: www.facebook.com/DurhamCookery
Instagram: www.instagram.com/durhamcookery
Description: Culinary incubator providing the tools, both intellectual and practical, entrepreneurs need to launch a lasting and successful culinary venture.

43241 ■ Fayetteville Business Center
1200 Murchison Rd.
 Fayetteville, NC 28301
Ph: (910)672-1111
URL: http://www.uncfsu.edu/academics/colleges-schools-and-departments/broadwell-college-of-business-and-economics/outreach-centers
Contact: Wesley Fountain, Vice Chancellor
E-mail: wtfountain01@uncfsu.edu
Description: A small business incubator promoting economic development in the City of Fayetteville and the Murchison Road corridor by providing nurturing to entrepreneurs and business assistance in the growth and development of small business concerns and promoting a healthy entrepreneurial spirit for the growth and economic renewal of the community.

43242 ■ First Flight Venture Center (FFVC)
2 Davis Dr.
 Research Triangle Park, NC 27709
Ph: (919)473-9420
Co. E-mail: info@ffvcnc.org
URL: http://www.ffvcnc.org
Contact: Krista Covey, President
Facebook: www.facebook.com/ffvcnc
Linkedin: www.linkedin.com/company/first-flight-venture-center
X (Twitter): x.com/ffvcnc
Description: A technology incubator serving entrepreneurs and early-stage businesses in the Research Triangle Park area. **Founded:** 1991.

43243 ■ The Kitch Enterprises Inc.
120 Charing Pl.
 Mooresville, NC 28117
Contact: Jose Chalita Bruzual, President
Description: Fully equipped commercial kitchen available to rent for production, test kitchen, training center, or private events.

43244 ■ Launch Chapel Hill
306 West Franklin St., Ste. F
 Chapel Hill, NC 27516
Ph: (919)903-8462
Co. E-mail: info@launchchapelhill.com
URL: http://www.launchchapelhill.com
Contact: Chi Nwogu, Chief Executive Officer
E-mail: chijioge.nwogu@gmail.com
Facebook: www.facebook.com/LaunchChapelHill
Linkedin: www.linkedin.com/company/launch-chapel-hill
X (Twitter): twitter.com/launchch
Instagram: www.instagram.com/launchchapelhill
Description: A startup accelerator that provides co-working space and business resources. **Founded:** 2013.

43245 ■ MCNC Research and Development
3021 E Cornwallis Rd.
 Research Triangle Park, NC 27709-2889
Ph: (919)248-1900
Fax: (919)248-1101
URL: http://www.mcnc.org
Contact: Ray Carey, President
Facebook: www.facebook.com/mcnc.ncren
Linkedin: www.linkedin.com/company/mcnc
X (Twitter): x.com/mcnc
YouTube: www.youtube.com/user/MCNCvideos
Description: Promotes the use and development of electronic and information technologies by providing advanced research facilities in North Carolina's universities.

43246 ■ Nussbaum Center for Entrepreneurship (NCFE)
1451 S Elm Eugene St.
 Greensboro, NC 27406
Ph: (336)379-5001
Co. E-mail: lhazlett@nussbaumcfe.com
URL: http://nussbaumcfe.com
Contact: Sam Funchess, Contact
Facebook: www.facebook.com/NussbaumCFE
X (Twitter): x.com/NussbaumCenter
Instagram: www.instagram.com/nussbaumcfe
Description: A small business incubator designed to support non-retail, new or emerging businesses by providing modestly-priced office and light manufacturing space, along with shared support services such as business counseling, a receptionist, copier, fax, mail boxes, and data entry. **Founded:** 1987.

43247 ■ Piedmont Food Processing Center (PFPC)
500 Valley Forge Rd.
 Hillsborough, NC 27278
Ph: (919)241-4212
Co. E-mail: info@pfapnc.org
URL: http://www.pfapnc.org
Contact: Eric L. Hallman, Executive Director
Facebook: www.facebook.com/PFAPNC
Description: Shared-use commercial kitchen space to facilitate local food and agricultural entrepreneurship. Offers four kitchen spaces, along with dry, refrigerated, and frozen storage, and office space to rent. **Founded:** 2011.

43248 ■ Pitt County Development Commission - Technology Enterprise Center
111 S Washington St.
 Greenville, NC 27835-0837
URL: http://www.growpittcountync.com/entrepreneurship/resources/technology-enterprise-center
Contact: Crystal Melton, Contact
E-mail: crystal.melton@pittcountync.gov
Description: Provides space and resources for technology-based startups.

43249 ■ Raleigh Business & Technology Center (RBTC)
900 S Wilmington St.
 Raleigh, NC 27601
Description: Assists new and existing small businesses in areas critical to growth including management, marketing, and financial planning. Provides cost-effective office space and administrative services. **Founded:** 2000.

43250 ■ Research Triangle Regional Partnership (RTRP)
2626 Glenwood Ave., Durham-Chapel Hill
 Raleigh, NC 27608
URL: http://www.researchtriangle.org
Contact: Ryan Combs, Executive Director
E-mail: rcombs@researchtriangle.org
Linkedin: www.linkedin.com/company/research-triangle-regional-partnership
X (Twitter): x.com/triangleregion
YouTube: www.youtube.com/user/RTRPNC
Description: Economic development organization connects businesses and residents in the Triangle Region to U.S. markets. **Founded:** 1990.

43251 ■ Shaw University - Innovation and Entrepreneurship Center
118 E South St.
 Raleigh, NC 27601
Co. E-mail: iec@shawu.edu
URL: http://www.shawu.edu/InnovationCenter
Contact: Levi Beckwith, Chairman
E-mail: iec@shawu.edu
Description: Offers entrepreneurial training, business incubation, and financial resource services in partnership with Carolina Small Business Development fund.

43252 ■ tekMountain
1844 Sir Tyler Dr.
 Wilmington, NC 28405
Ph: (910)679-2766
Co. E-mail: info@tekmountain.com
URL: http://www.tekmountain.com
Contact: Joseph Finley, Manager
Linkedin: www.linkedin.com/company/tekmountain
Instagram: www.instagram.com/tekmtn
Description: A privately owned, community driven incubator and accelerator dedicating to attracting, hosting, and training tech-based companies.

43253 ■ The University of North Carolina at Charlotte - Charlotte Research Institute (CRI)
9201 University City Blvd.
 Charlotte, NC 28223-0001
URL: http://partnerships.charlotte.edu/about-cri/snapshot-cri/mission-vision
Description: Works with the community and the campus to accelerate technology commercialization, and champions the growth of entrepreneurial ventures.

43254 ■ Upper Coastal Plain Business Development Center
121 W Nash St.
 Wilson, NC 27893
Ph: (252)234-5952
Fax: (252)234-5971
URL: http://www.ucpcog.org/business_development_center/index.php
URL(s): www.ucpbdc.com/index.php
Description: An entrepreneurial business incubator serving startup and existing small businesses in the Upper Coastal Plain Region of Eastern North Carolina. Offers turnkey office space to startups. **Founded:** 1930.

STATE LISTINGS North Carolina ■ 43268

EDUCATIONAL PROGRAMS

43255 ■ Caldwell Community College and Technical Institute-Small Business Center
Caldwell Campus, 2855 Hickory Blvd.
 Hudson, NC 28638
Ph: (828)726-3065
URL: http://www.cccti.edu/SmallBusiness
Description: Seminars, workshops, and management consultation are available for small business owners. **Founded:** 1964.

43256 ■ Sandhills Community College (SCC)
3395 Airport Rd.
 Pinehurst, NC 28374
Ph: (910)692-6185
Free: 800-338-3944
URL: http://www.sandhills.edu
Contact: Dr. John R. Dempsey, President
Facebook: www.facebook.com/SandhillsCC
X (Twitter): x.com/SandhillsCC
Instagram: www.instagram.com/sandhillscc
YouTube: www.youtube.com/user/SandhillsCC
Description: Offers many business-related and personal enrichment classes, both at the college and at various off-campus sites. A Small Business Center has been established to attract, train, counsel, and provide educational services to small business owners or individuals interested in establishing small businesses in the area. **Founded:** 1963.

43257 ■ South College
140 Sweeten Creek Rd.
 Asheville, NC 28803
Ph: (828)398-2500
URL: http://www.south.edu
Linkedin: www.linkedin.com/school/southcollege
Description: Offers a program in small business administration. **Founded:** 1905.

43258 ■ Wilson Community College Small Business Center (WCCSBC)
Lee Technology Center Building R, Ste. R151 4815 Ward Blvd.
 Wilson, NC 27893
Ph: (252)246-1232
URL: http://www.wilsoncc.edu/continuing-education/small-business-center
Contact: Melissa Evans, Director
E-mail: msevans@wilsoncc.edu
Facebook: www.facebook.com/wcc.sbc
Description: Provides consultative services, resource information, and a variety of seminars, workshops, and courses to assist in the development of new businesses and the success of existing businesses.

CONSULTANTS

43259 ■ Out of the Box Advisors
Carnegie Blvd.
 Charlotte, NC 28209
Ph: (904)468-6268
Co. E-mail: info@outoftheboxadvisors.com
URL: http://www.outoftheboxadvisors.com
Contact: Ryan Pope, Founder
Facebook: www.facebook.com/unboxedthinking
Linkedin: www.linkedin.com/company/unboxedthinking
X (Twitter): x.com/UnboxedAdvisors
Instagram: www.instagram.com/unboxedthinking
Description: Offers business growth and coaching services, executive and marketing strategy, management consulting, and marketing and advertising advice. **Founded:** 2012.

PUBLICATIONS

43260 ■ *Business North Carolina (BNC)*
145 W Pennsylvania Ave.
 Southern Pines, NC 28388
Ph: (910)692-7271
Fax: (910)692-9382
Co. E-mail: feedback@thepilot.com
URL: http://www.thepilot.com
Contact: David Woronoff, Publisher
E-mail: david@thepilot.com
URL(s): businessnc.com
Facebook: www.facebook.com/businessnc
Linkedin: www.linkedin.com/company/business-north-carolina
X (Twitter): x.com/businessnc
YouTube: www.youtube.com/channel/UCZj5pjytlsyXj-JLHOu4baQ
Ed: David Mildenberg. **Released:** Monthly **Price:** $65, for 3 year 12 issue; $48, for 2 year 12 issue; $30, for annual subscription. **Description:** Regional business magazine covering North Carolina. **Availability:** Print; Online.

43261 ■ *Business Update*
301 N Queen St.
 Kinston, NC 28501
Ph: (252)527-1131
Fax: (252)527-1914
Co. E-mail: info@kinstonchamber.com
URL: http://kinstonchamber.com
Contact: Vickie E. Jones, Chief Executive Officer
URL(s): kinstonchamber.com/membership-benefits/presidents-club
Released: Bimonthly **Availability:** Print; Download.

43262 ■ *Charlotte Business Journal*
120 W Morehead St.
 Charlotte, NC 28202
Co. E-mail: circhelp@bizjournals.com
URL: http://www.acbj.com
Contact: Mike Olivieri, Executive Vice President
URL(s): www.bizjournals.com/charlotte
Linkedin: www.linkedin.com/company/charlotte-business-journal
X (Twitter): x.com/CBJnewsroom
Instagram: www.instagram.com/cbjnewsroom
Ed: Roberta Fuchs, Robert Morris. **Released:** Weekly **Price:** $70, for digital 52 week Annual Insights or Annual + Hardcopy; $4, for print + digital or digital 4 week; $220, for print + digital 52 week premium; $245, for Nationwide Access 40+ Cities; $950, for Nationwide + BOL 52 weeks; $210, for digital 52 week premium; $380, for nation wide 52 weeks. **Description:** Newspaper for the business community of Charlotte and the surrounding thirteen-county area. **Availability:** Print; Online. **Type:** Full-text.

43263 ■ *Charlotte Business Journal (CBJ)*
550 S Caldwell St., Ste. 910
 Charlotte, NC 28202
Ph: (704)973-1100
Fax: (704)973-1102
Co. E-mail: charlotte@bizjournals.com
URL: http://www.bizjournals.com/charlotte
Contact: Robert Morris, Editor
E-mail: rmorris@bizjournals.com
Facebook: www.facebook.com/charlottebizjournal
X (Twitter): x.com/CBJnewsroom
Instagram: www.instagram.com/cbjnewsroom
Description: Publication that covers business and economic development in North Carolina. **Founded:** 1986.

43264 ■ *Pacific Business News*
120 W Morehead St.
 Charlotte, NC 28202
Co. E-mail: circhelp@bizjournals.com
URL: http://www.acbj.com
Contact: Mike Olivieri, Executive Vice President
URL(s): www.bizjournals.com/pacific
Linkedin: www.linkedin.com/company/pacific-business-news
X (Twitter): x.com/Pacificbiznews
Instagram: www.instagram.com/pacificbusinessnews
Released: Weekly **Price:** $70, for digital only annual insights or print + digital annual + hardcopy; $950, for Nationwide + BOL Premium Unlimited; $4, for print + digital or digital 4 week; $220, for digital + print premium plus; $245, for Nationwide Access 40+ Cities; $380, for premium elite nation wide; $210, for digital only premium; $70, for print + digital. **Description:** Business tabloid. **Availability:** Print; Online.

PUBLISHERS

43265 ■ International Puzzle Features
4507 Panther Pl.
 Charlotte, NC 28269
Ph: (704)921-1818
Fax: (704)597-1331
Co. E-mail: drfun@cleverpuzzles.com
URL: http://cleverpuzzles.com
Contact: Pat Battaglia, Contact
Description: Publishes books of clever word games with surprising answers and amusing features for readers of all ages and also provides a weekly variety puzzle and game column to newspapers, accepts submissions of individual puzzles and games, not columns, send for writers guidelines with SASE and refer to website for samples and Reaches the market through reviews, listings, and distributors and wholesalers. **Founded:** 1990.

EARLY STAGE FINANCING

43266 ■ ABB Technology Ventures (ATV)
305 Gregson Dr.
 Cary, NC 27511
URL: http://global.abb/group/en
Contact: Kurt Kaltenegger, Head
Description: Venture capital unit of ABB Group. Partners with breakthrough technology companies to invest in industrial digitization. **Founded:** 2009. **Industry Preferences:** Robotics; drones; IoT; AI/machine learning; cybersecurity; distributed energy.

EXPANSION AND GROWTH FINANCING

43267 ■ Front Street Capital (FSC)
450 N Patterson Ave., Ste. 300
 Winston Salem, NC 27101
Ph: (336)243-2600
Co. E-mail: info@frontstreetcapital.com
URL: http://frontstreetcapitalnc.com
Contact: Claire Devon, Director
E-mail: claire@frontstreetcapital.com
Linkedin: www.linkedin.com/company/front-street-capital-llc
X (Twitter): x.com/FrontStreetCap
Instagram: www.instagram.com/frontstreetcapital
Description: Develops, acquires, and/or repositions Class-A assets focused on income production, maximizing value, and diversification in the southeastern United States. **Founded:** 2014.

VENTURE CAPITAL FIRM

43268 ■ IDEA Fund Partners
American Underground, 201 W Main St., Ste. 100, PMB B17
 Durham, NC 27701
URL: http://www.ideafundpartners.com
Contact: Lister Delgado, Managing Partner
Linkedin: www.linkedin.com/company/ideafundpartners
X (Twitter): twitter.com/ideafund
Description: Venture capital firm for seed and early-stage investors throughout the Southeast. **Founded:** 2007. **Preferred Investment Size:** $250,000 to $1,000,000. **Industry Preferences:** B2B software; tech-enabled services; materials technologies; medical devices and diagnostics; hardware/IoT.

North Dakota

ASSOCIATIONS AND OTHER ORGANIZATIONS

43269 ■ Associated General Contractors of North Dakota (AGCND) - Library
422 N 2nd St.
Bismarck, ND 58502
Ph: (701)223-2770
Fax: (701)223-6719
Co. E-mail: agc@agcnd.org
URL: http://www.agcnd.org
Contact: Carey N. Burke, Director
E-mail: cburke@agcnd.org
Facebook: www.facebook.com/Associated-General-Contractors-of-North-Dakota-120815938631167
X (Twitter): x.com/AGCofND

Description: Association of general contractors in North Dakota. **Scope:** General safety; cranes; derricks; health hazards; fall protection. **Services:** Interlibrary loan. **Founded:** 1950. **Holdings:** DVDs. **Publications:** *E-Scoop* (Monthly). **Geographic Preference:** State.

SMALL BUSINESS DEVELOPMENT CENTERS

43270 ■ North Dakota Small Business Development Center (NDSBDC)
1200 Memorial Hwy.
Bismarck, ND 58504
Ph: (701)777-3700
Co. E-mail: leadcenter@ndsbdc.org
URL: http://ndsbdc.org
Contact: Payton Tivis, Director
E-mail: payton.tivis@ndsbdc.org
Facebook: www.facebook.com/ndsbdc
Linkedin: www.linkedin.com/company/nd-small-business-development-centers
X (Twitter): x.com/ND_SBDC
YouTube: www.youtube.com/channel/UCOGuMzmhrUDIIyJNSNmb_Qg

Description: Committed to growing North Dakota's economy and is the collaborative resource for small business assistance. Provides one-on-one business advising services. **Founded:** 1986. **Geographic Preference:** State.

43271 ■ North Dakota Small Business Development Center Bismarck (ND SBDC)
1200 Memorial Hwy.
Bismarck, ND 58504
URL: http://ndsbdc.org
Contact: Tyler Demars, Director
E-mail: tyler@ndsbdc.org

Description: Represents and promotes the small business sector. Provides management assistance to current and prospective small business owners. Helps to improve management skills and expand the products and services of members. **Geographic Preference:** Local.

43272 ■ North Dakota Small Business Development Center Devils Lake (NDSBDC)
North Central Planning Council
417 NE 5th St.
Devils Lake, ND 58301
URL: http://ndsbdc.org
Contact: Sandy Shively, Director
E-mail: sandyncpc@gondtc.com
X (Twitter): x.com/ND_SBDC
YouTube: www.youtube.com/channel/UCOGuMzmhrUDIIyJNSNmb_Qg

Description: Represents and promotes the small business sector. Provides management assistance to current and prospective small business owners. Helps to improve management skills and expand the products and services of members. **Geographic Preference:** Local.

43273 ■ North Dakota Small Business Development Center Dickinson (ND SBDC)
103 1st Ave. W
Dickinson, ND 58601
Co. E-mail: leadcenter@ndsbdc.org
URL: http://ndsbdc.org/contact.html
Facebook: www.facebook.com/ndsbdc
X (Twitter): x.com/ND_SBDC
YouTube: www.youtube.com/channel/UCOGuMzmhrUDIIyJNSNmb_Qg

Description: Represents and promotes the small business sector. Provides management assistance to current and prospective small business owners. Helps to improve management skills and expand the products and services of members. **Geographic Preference:** Local.

43274 ■ North Dakota Small Business Development Center Fargo
1854 NDSU Research Cir. N, Ste. No. 7
Fargo, ND 58102
Ph: (701)499-5273
URL: http://ndsbdc.org/fargo.cfm

Description: Represents and promotes the small business sector. Provides management assistance to current and prospective small business owners. Helps to improve management skills and expand the products and services of members. **Geographic Preference:** Local.

43275 ■ North Dakota Small Business Development Center Grand Forks (ND SBDC)
140 Gamble Hall
Grand Forks, ND 58202
Ph: (701)777-3700
Fax: (701)777-1379
Co. E-mail: tiffany.ford@ndsbdc.org
URL: http://ndsbdc.org
Contact: Tiffany Ford, Director
E-mail: tiffany.ford@ndsbdc.org
Facebook: www.facebook.com/ndsbdc
Linkedin: www.linkedin.com/company/nd-small-business-development-centers
X (Twitter): x.com/ND_SBDC
YouTube: www.youtube.com/channel/UCOGuMzmhrUDIIyJNSNmb_Qg

Description: Represents and promotes the small business sector. Provides management assistance to current and prospective small business owners. Helps to improve management skills and expand the products and services of members. **Geographic Preference:** Local.

43276 ■ North Dakota Small Business Development Center Minot (NDSBDC)
1925 S Broadway, Ste. 2
Minot, ND 58703
URL: http://ndsbdc.org/contact.html

Description: Represents and promotes the small business sector. Provides management assistance to current and prospective small business owners. Helps to improve management skills and expand the products and services of members. **Geographic Preference:** Local.

SMALL BUSINESS ASSISTANCE PROGRAMS

43277 ■ North Dakota Department of Commerce - Economic Development & Finance Div. (EDF)
1600 E Century Ave., Ste. 6
Bismarck, ND 58502-2057
URL: http://www.commerce.nd.gov/economic-development-finance
Contact: Rich Garman, Director
E-mail: rgarman@nd.gov

Description: Encourages the establishment of new businesses and industries and assists new and expanding businesses with information and location decisions.

43278 ■ University of North Dakota - Center for Innovation (CFI)
4200 James Ray Dr.
Grand Forks, ND 58202
Ph: (701)777-3132
Fax: (701)777-2339
Co. E-mail: info@innovators.net
URL: http://www.innovators.net
Contact: Amy Whitney, Director
Facebook: www.facebook.com/centerforinnovation
Linkedin: www.linkedin.com/company/center-for-innovation
X (Twitter): x.com/ndinnovators
YouTube: www.youtube.com/channel/UC5dHMwGsDEBCW1Hwt3i-Z7g

Description: Provides technical and business support services to entrepreneurs, inventors, and small manufacturers. Assists specifically with the product evaluation process, the patenting process, and technology transfer. **Scope:** Offers market and demographic research, business plan development, financial forecasts, and manufacturing services to entrepreneurs, particularly manufacturing technology start-up enterprises. Provides assistance to innovators, entrepreneurs, and researchers to launch new ventures, commercialize new technologies, and secure access to capital from private and public

STATE LISTINGS   North Dakota ■ 43295

sources. **Founded:** 1984. **Publications:** The Business Plan: A State-Of-The-Art Guide; "The Marketing Plan: Step-By-Step"; "The Ultimate Business Planner"; "Campus Entrepreneurship: A Changing Curriculum for Changing Times"; "Financing Startup Ventures"; "The Business Plan: A State-of-the-Art Guide"; "The Marketing Plan: Step-by-Step". **Educational Activities:** Center for Innovation Conferences and workshops, Seed and Angel Capital, Entrepreneur Startups, Business Planning, Market Feasibility.

SCORE OFFICES

43279 ■ Grand Forks SCORE
4200 James Ray Dr., Ste. 202
Grand Forks, ND 58203
Ph: (701)746-5851
Co. E-mail: score@gra.midco.net
URL: http://grandforks.score.org
Contact: Liz Sara, President
Facebook: www.facebook.com/SCOREGrandForks
Linkedin: www.linkedin.com/company/score-mentors-grand-forks
X (Twitter): x.com/SCOREGrandForks
YouTube: www.youtube.com/channel/UCLTu2I2P4NhRJeAnkJGWPug/featured
Description: Unites active and retired business management professionals with men and women who are considering starting a small business, encountering problems with their business, or expanding their business. **Founded:** 1964.

43280 ■ SCORE - Bismarck-Mandan
1200 Memorial Hwy.
Bismarck, ND 58506
URL: http://www.score.org/westcentralnorthdakota
Description: Provides professional guidance and information to maximize the success of existing and emerging small businesses. Offers business counseling and workshops. **Founded:** 1964. **Geographic Preference:** Local.

43281 ■ SCORE - Dickinson
103 1st Ave. W, Ste. 101
Stark Development Corp.
Dickinson, ND 58601
Ph: (701)225-5997
URL: http://www.score.org/find-location
Description: Provides professional guidance and information to maximize the success of existing and emerging small businesses. Offers business counseling and workshops.

43282 ■ SCORE - Fargo
657 2nd Ave. N, Rm. 360
Fargo, ND 58108
Ph: (701)239-5677
Co. E-mail: help@score.org
URL: http://fargo.score.org
Contact: Alan Anderson, Contact
Linkedin: www.linkedin.com/company/score-mentors-fargo
Description: Provides professional guidance and information to maximize the success of existing and emerging small businesses. Offers business counseling and workshops. **Geographic Preference:** Local.

43283 ■ SCORE - Grand Forks
4200 James Ray Dr., Ste. 202
Grand Forks, ND 58203
Ph: (701)746-5851
Co. E-mail: score@gra.midco.net
URL: http://grandforks.score.org
Facebook: www.facebook.com/SCOREGrandForks
X (Twitter): x.com/SCOREGrandForks
Description: Provides professional guidance and information to maximize the success of existing and emerging small businesses. Offers business counseling and workshops.

43284 ■ SCORE - Jamestown
429 2nd St. SW, Ste. 208
Jamestown, ND 58401
URL: http://www.score.org/westcentralnorthdakota

Description: Provides professional guidance and information to maximize the success of existing and emerging small businesses. Offers business counseling and workshops.

43285 ■ SCORE - Minot
1200 Memorial Hwy.
Bismarck, ND 58506
Ph: (701)328-5861
Co. E-mail: bismarck@scorevolunteer.org
URL: http://www.score.org/westcentralnorthdakota
Linkedin: www.linkedin.com/company/score-mentors-minot
Description: Provides professional guidance and information to maximize the success of existing and emerging small businesses. Offers business counseling and workshops. **Founded:** 1964. **Geographic Preference:** Local.

CHAMBERS OF COMMERCE

43286 ■ Beulah Chamber of Commerce (BCC)
300 Hwy. 49 S
Beulah, ND 58523
Ph: (701)873-4585
Fax: (701)873-5361
Co. E-mail: chamber@westriv.com
URL: http://visitbeulah.com/about-the-chamber
Contact: Gloria Olheiser, Contact
Facebook: www.facebook.com/visitbeulah
Description: Promotes business and community development in Beulah, ND. **Founded:** 1954. **Publications:** Chamber Chatter (Periodic). **Geographic Preference:** Local.

43287 ■ Bismarck-Mandan Chamber of Commerce
1640 Burnt Boat Dr.
Bismarck, ND 58503
Ph: (701)223-5660
Co. E-mail: info@bmcedc.com
URL: http://www.bismarckmandan.com
Contact: Brian Ritter, President
E-mail: britter@bmcedc.com
Facebook: www.facebook.com/bismancedc
X (Twitter): x.com/bismancedc
Instagram: www.instagram.com/bismancedc
YouTube: www.youtube.com/user/BisManChamber
Description: Promotes business and community development in the Bismarck, ND Area. Participates in area Folkfest and Band Days Parade. **Founded:** 1990. **Publications:** Chamber Connection (Monthly). **Geographic Preference:** Local.

43288 ■ Bowman Area Chamber of Commerce
101 1st St. NE
Bowman, ND 58623
Ph: (701)523-5880
Free: 866-752-2691
Fax: (701)523-3322
Co. E-mail: chamber@bowmannd.com
URL: http://www.bowmannd.com/chamber
Contact: Emily Bostyan, President
E-mail: emily.turnquist@gmail.com
Facebook: www.facebook.com/GrowingBowmanCounty
X (Twitter): x.com/GrowingBowman
Instagram: www.instagram.com/growingbowmancounty
Description: Helps in the development of employment, industry, tourism and economic attributes within Bowman County. **Geographic Preference:** Local.

43289 ■ Carrington Area Chamber of Commerce
871 Main St.
Carrington, ND 58421-1257
Ph: (701)652-2524
URL: http://www.uschamber.com/co/chambers/north-dakota/carrington
Contact: Laurie Dietz, Officer
Description: Promotes business and community development in the city of Carrington, ND and surrounding area. Conducts charitable activities and competitions; sponsors Harvest Fest and Fourth of July celebration. **Founded:** 1962. **Publications:** The Carrington Connection (Monthly). **Geographic Preference:** Local.

43290 ■ Cavalier Area Chamber of Commerce
301 Division Ave., N
Cavalier, ND 58220
Ph: (701)265-8188
Co. E-mail: cacc@polarcomm.com
URL: http://www.cavaliernd.com
Contact: Kelsay Monson, President
Description: Promotes economic and community development in Cavalier and the surrounding area. **Founded:** 1878. **Geographic Preference:** Local.

43291 ■ Chamber Connection
1640 Burnt Boat Dr.
Bismarck, ND 58503
Ph: (701)223-5660
Co. E-mail: info@bmcedc.com
URL: http://www.bismarckmandan.com
Contact: Brian Ritter, President
E-mail: britter@bmcedc.com
URL(s): www.bismarckmandan.com/connection-magazine
Released: Monthly **Availability:** Online.

43292 ■ Devils Lake Area Chamber of Commerce
208 Hwy. 2 W
Devils Lake, ND 58301
Ph: (701)662-4903
Co. E-mail: chamber@gondtc.com
URL: http://chamber.devilslakend.com
Contact: Paula Vistad, Executive Director
E-mail: paula@devilslakend.com
Description: Promotes business and community development and tourism in the Devils Lake, ND area. Sponsors Fishing Tournament and Old Settlers Weekend. **Publications:** News-N-Views (Monthly). **Geographic Preference:** Local.

43293 ■ Dickinson Area Chamber of Commerce (DACC)
314 3rd Ave., W
Dickinson, ND 58601
Ph: (701)225-5115
Fax: (701)225-5116
Co. E-mail: team@dickinsonchamber.org
URL: http://www.dickinsonchamber.org
Contact: Carter Fong, Executive Director
E-mail: carter@dickinsonchamber.org
Facebook: www.facebook.com/DickinsonChamber
Linkedin: www.linkedin.com/company/dickinson-area-chamber-of-commerce
X (Twitter): x.com/DixNDChamber
Description: Promotes business, economic, and community development in Dickinson and Southwest North Dakota. **Founded:** 1906. **Publications:** Chamberline (Monthly); Quarterly Activities Report (Quarterly). **Awards:** Dickinson Area Chamber of Commerce - Community Volunteer Award; Dickinson Area Chamber of Commerce - Educator Business Awards (Annual); Dickinson Area Chamber of Commerce Educator of the Year Awards (Annual). **Geographic Preference:** Local.

43294 ■ Geographical Center of North America Chamber of Commerce (GCNACC)
102 Hwy 2 SE, Ste. B
Rugby, ND 58368
Ph: (701)776-5846
Co. E-mail: rugbychamber@gondtc.com
URL: http://www.rugbynorthdakota.com/pages/AboutUs
Contact: Leah Harper, President
Description: Promotes agricultural, business, and community development in the Rugby, ND area. **Founded:** 1931. **Geographic Preference:** Local.

43295 ■ Grafton Area Chamber of Commerce
432 Hill Ave.
Grafton, ND 58237
Ph: (701)352-0781
Co. E-mail: gracha@polarcomm.com

URL: http://www.graftonevents.com
Contact: Jason Nelson, President
Description: Promotes business and community development in Grafton, ND. Sponsors SummerFest, Charity Ball, and other events. Convention/Meeting: none. **Publications:** *Membership List* (Periodic). **Geographic Preference:** Local.

43296 ■ Grand Forks Chamber of Commerce (GFCC)
202 N 3rd St.
Grand Forks, ND 58203
Ph: (701)772-7271
Co. E-mail: info@gochamber.org
URL: http://www.gochamber.org
Contact: Barry Wilfahrt, President
E-mail: barry@gochamber.org
Facebook: www.facebook.com/THECHAMBERGFEGF
X (Twitter): x.com/thechambergfegf
Instagram: www.instagram.com/thechambergfegf
YouTube: www.youtube.com/user/TheChamberGFEGF
Description: Promotes business and community development in the Grand Forks, ND area. **Founded:** 1912. **Publications:** *The Voice* (Monthly). **Geographic Preference:** Local.

43297 ■ Greater Bottineau Area Chamber of Commerce (GBACC)
519 Main St., Ste. 1
Bottineau, ND 58318
Ph: (701)228-3849
Co. E-mail: bcc@utma.com
URL: http://bottineau.com
Contact: Kelly Beaver, Executive Director
Description: Promotes business and community development in Bottineau, ND. **Geographic Preference:** Local.

43298 ■ Greater North Dakota Chamber (GNDC)
PO Box 2639
Bismarck, ND 58502
Ph: (701)222-0929
Co. E-mail: ndchamber@ndchamber.com
URL: http://www.ndchamber.com
Contact: Arik Spencer, President
E-mail: arik@ndchamber.com
Facebook: www.facebook.com/NDChamber
Linkedin: www.linkedin.com/company/greater-north-dakota-chamber/about
X (Twitter): twitter.com/nodakchamber
Description: Strives to enhance North Dakota's business climate through efforts like the New Economy Initiative. Creates and fights for public policy initiatives and state and federal legislation that is pro-business. Supports and develops programs and services that help improve and strengthen North Dakota businesses. Creates economic development initiatives to create new jobs and new wealth in North Dakota. Promotes North Dakota's image as an outstanding place to live, work and do business. Unites the North Dakota business community on vital business issues. **Founded:** 1924. **Publications:** *North Dakota Horizons* (Quarterly). **Awards:** Greater North Dakota Community Leadership Award (Annual); Greater North Dakotan Award (Annual). **Geographic Preference:** Local.

43299 ■ Hazen Chamber of Commerce
146 E Main
Hazen, ND 58545
Ph: (701)748-6848
Free: 888-464-2936
Co. E-mail: hazenchamber@westriv.com
URL: http://www.visithazennd.com/chamber-cvb
Contact: Antoinette Heier, Executive Director
Facebook: www.facebook.com/hazenchambercvb
Description: Promotes business and community development in Hazen, ND area. **Geographic Preference:** Local.

43300 ■ Hettinger Area Chamber of Commerce
120 S Main St.
Hettinger, ND 58639
Ph: (701)567-2531
Co. E-mail: cpo@hettingernd.org
URL: http://www.hettingernd.com
Contact: Kat Weinert, President
Facebook: www.facebook.com/hettingernd
Instagram: www.instagram.com/hettingernd
Description: Promotes business and community development in the Hettinger, ND area. **Awards:** Hettinger Area Chamber Business Person of the Year (Annual); Hettinger Area Chamber Volunteer of the Year (Annual). **Geographic Preference:** Local.

43301 ■ Jamestown Area Chamber of Commerce
120 2nd St. SE
Jamestown, ND 58402
Ph: (701)252-4830
Fax: (701)952-4837
Co. E-mail: chamber@jamestownchamber.com
URL: http://www.jamestownchamber.com
Contact: Tonya Perkins, President
Facebook: www.facebook.com/JamestownAreaChamberofCommerce
X (Twitter): x.com/JtownND_Chamber
Instagram: www.instagram.com/jtownnd_chamber
Description: Promotes business and community development in Jamestown, ND. Sponsors Water and Buffalo Days. **Founded:** 1929. **Publications:** *Chamber News*. **Geographic Preference:** Local.

43302 ■ Kenmare Association of Commerce
53rd St. NE
Kenmare, ND 58746-0324
Ph: (701)385-4275
Fax: (701)385-4395
Co. E-mail: news@kenmarend.com
URL: http://www.kenmarend.com/association
Contact: Terry Froseth, President
Facebook: www.facebook.com/KenmareAssociation
Description: Serves businesses, professionals and individuals to help advance the economic status of Kenmare, North Dakota. **Geographic Preference:** Local.

43303 ■ Linton Industrial Development Corp. (LIDC)
c/o Sharon Jangula
101 NE 1st St.
Linton, ND 58552
Ph: (701)254-4460
URL: http://lintonnd.org/?page_id=128
Contact: Sharon Jangula, Administrator Auditor
Description: Aims to promote and assist existing businesses to prosper and expand. Assists clients in developing business ideas and business plans, in obtaining financing from local, state and federal agencies. Gives positive direction to the development of commerce in the City of Linton, the County of Emmons and the state of North Dakota. Carries out activities that will enhance the image and reputation of Linton as a place to live and invest. **Geographic Preference:** Local.

43304 ■ Oakes Area Chamber of Commerce
510 Main Ave.
Oakes, ND 58474
Ph: (701)742-3508
Co. E-mail: director@oakeschamber.com
URL: http://oakesnd.com/chamber
Contact: Heather Roney, President
E-mail: phroney@drtel.net
Facebook: www.facebook.com/oakeschamber
Description: Advances the commercial, industrial, professional, agricultural, educational and civic interests of the Oakes area. Stimulates and supports business creation and expansion. **Founded:** 1888. **Geographic Preference:** Local.

43305 ■ Valley City Area Chamber of Commerce
250 W Main St.
Valley City, ND 58072
Ph: (701)845-1891
Free: 888-288-1891
Fax: (701)845-1892
Co. E-mail: info@hellovalley.com
URL: http://valleycitynd.org
Contact: Kay Vinje, Executive Vice President
E-mail: chamber@valleycitychamber.com
Description: Promotes business and community development in the Valley City, ND area. Conducts Annual Chili Cook-Off, Community Days Festival, Ag Appreciation Days, Christmas Promotion and Parade, Crazy Day and Sheyenne Valley Fall Festival. **Founded:** 1904. **Publications:** *Chamber Advantage* (Monthly); *Weekly E-zine Newsletter* (Weekly). **Geographic Preference:** Local.

43306 ■ *The Voice*
202 N 3rd St.
Grand Forks, ND 58203
Ph: (701)772-7271
Co. E-mail: info@gochamber.org
URL: http://www.gochamber.org
Contact: Barry Wilfahrt, President
E-mail: barry@gochamber.org
URL(s): www.gochamber.org/newsletters.html
Released: Monthly **Availability:** PDF; Online.

43307 ■ Wahpeton Breckenridge Area Chamber of Commerce and Visitors Center
1505 11th St. N
Wahpeton, ND 58075
Ph: (701)642-8744
Free: 800-892-6673
Fax: (701)642-8745
Co. E-mail: info@wahpetonbreckenridgechamber.com
URL: http://www.wahpetonbreckenridgechamber.com
Contact: Jodi Hendrickson, President
Facebook: www.facebook.com/WahpetonBreckenridgeChamber
Linkedin: www.linkedin.com/company/wahpeton-breckenridge-area-chamber-of-commerce
Description: Promotes the businesses and community of Wahpeton, ND. **Founded:** 1899. **Awards:** Wahpeton Breckenridge Area Chamber of Commerce Extra Mile Award (Annual). **Geographic Preference:** Local.

43308 ■ Walhalla Area Chamber of Commerce
1103 Central Ave.
Walhalla, ND 58282
Ph: (701)549-2410
Co. E-mail: walcity@utma.com
URL: http://walhalland.org/chamber.php
Description: Promotes the region's natural resources, scenic overlooks, historic sites, Red River oxcart trails, Native American culture, and Paleo-Indian traditions. Conducts recreational activities and events. **Founded:** 1845. **Geographic Preference:** Local.

43309 ■ Watford City Area Chamber of Commerce
PO Box 458
Watford City, ND 58854
Ph: (701)570-5084
Co. E-mail: wcchamber@ruggedwest.com
URL: http://www.watfordcitychamber.com
Contact: Mary Gumke, Executive Director
X (Twitter): x.com/wcitychamber
YouTube: www.youtube.com/channel/UCY93GsrVclalhcTKdJ8FQzA/feed
Description: Promotes business and community development in the Watford City, ND area. **Publications:** *Chamber Newsletter* (Monthly). **Geographic Preference:** Local.

43310 ■ Williston Area Chamber of Commerce (WACC)
10 Main St.
Williston, ND 58801
Ph: (701)577-6000
Co. E-mail: wchamber@willistonchamber.com
URL: http://www.willistonchamber.com
Contact: Anna Nelson, President
Facebook: www.facebook.com/willistonchamber
Instagram: www.instagram.com/willistonchamber
Description: Seeks to promote the trade area and income potential of businesses, facilitate positive and proactive activities and encourage public/private

partnerships that benefit members and citizens. **Founded:** 1907. **Publications:** *Chamber Profile* (8/year). **Geographic Preference:** Local.

FINANCING AND LOAN PROGRAMS

43311 ■ 701 Ventures LLC
4200 James Ray Dr., GREG SYRUP
Grand Forks, ND 58202-6090
Contact: Gregory M. Syrup, Contact
Description: Angel investors for Midwest startups. **Founded:** 2015. **Industry Preferences:** Manufacturing and technologies (unmanned aerial systems); healthcare/medical devices; B2B software; cyber security; ag solutions/biotech.

43312 ■ North Dakota Development Fund (NDDF)
1600 E Century Ave., Ste. 6
Bismarck, ND 58503
URL: http://www.commerce.nd.gov/economic-development-finance/development-fund
Contact: Jim Albrecht-Wahpeton, President
Description: Offers flexible financing through loans and equity investments not available from most conventional lender. **Industry Preferences:** Investor-owned agriculture (livestock feeding, milking operations, or other value-added agriculture); manufacturers; food processors; export services; tourism.

PROCUREMENT ASSISTANCE PROGRAMS

43313 ■ Fargo Small Business Development Center - North Dakota State University (NDSU)
1854 NDSU Research Cir. N, Ste. No. 116
Fargo, ND 58102
URL: http://ndsbdc.org
Contact: Paul Smith, Director
E-mail: paul@ndsbdc.org

43314 ■ North Dakota Office of Management and Budget - State Procurement Office (SPO)
600 E Blvd., Ave., Dept. 110
Bismarck, ND 58505-0400
Ph: (701)328-2740
Co. E-mail: infospo@nd.gov
URL: http://www.omb.nd.gov/doing-business-state/procurement
Description: Helps businesses obtain federal, state, and local government contracts.

INCUBATORS/RESEARCH AND TECHNOLOGY PARKS

43315 ■ Center for Innovation - Ina Mae Rude Entrepreneur Center
4200 James Ray Dr.
Grand Forks, ND 58202
Ph: (701)777-3132
Fax: (701)777-2339
Co. E-mail: info@innovators.net
URL: http://www.innovators.net
Contact: Amy Whitney, Director
Facebook: www.facebook.com/centerforinnovation
Linkedin: www.linkedin.com/company/center-for-innovation
X (Twitter): x.com/NDInnovators
Instagram: www.instagram.com/center_for_innovation
YouTube: www.youtube.com/channel/UC5dHMwGsDEBCW1Hwt3i-Z7g/videos
Description: Provides assistance to innovators, entrepreneurs, and researchers to launch new ventures, commercialize new technologies, and secure access to capital from private and public sources. **Founded:** 1984.

43316 ■ Lake Agassiz Development Group Regional Small Business Center
417 Main Ave.
Fargo, ND 58103
URL: http://lakeagassiz.com/entrepreneurial-resources
Description: A non-profit business incubator operated by the Lake Agassiz Regional Development Corporation, Fargo, North Dakota whose purpose is to assist new and existing smaller businesses in critical areas such as management, marketing, manufacturing and finance. The Center provides attractive, cost-effective space and administrative support services to its tenants. **Founded:** 1975.

43317 ■ NDSU Research & Technology Park
1854 NDSU Research Cir. N
Fargo, ND 58102
Ph: (701)499-3600
Free: 800-366-6888
Fax: (701)499-3610
URL: http://ndsuresearchpark.com
Contact: Dr. David Cook, President
Facebook: www.facebook.com/ndsurtp
Description: Developer of new technologies, methods and systems for university and industry. **Founded:** 1993.

43318 ■ North Dakota State University - Upper Great Plains Transportation Institute - North Dakota Local Technical Assistance Program (NDLTAP)
608 E Blvd., Ave.
Bismarck, ND 58505
Ph: (701)328-9855
Co. E-mail: ndltap@ugpti.org
URL: http://www.ndltap.org
Contact: Matt Gardner, Executive Director
E-mail: matt@ndlc.org
Facebook: www.facebook.com/ndltap
Description: Enables North Dakota businesses to use the most advanced technologies available. **Founded:** 1984.

43319 ■ Square One Rental Kitchen & Events
1407 1st Ave. N
Fargo, ND 58102
Ph: (701)388-1137
Co. E-mail: info@squareonekitchens.com
URL: http://squareonekitchens.com
Facebook: www.facebook.com/SquareOneFM
X (Twitter): x.com/square1kitchens
Instagram: www.instagram.com/foodlovefargo
Description: Professional kitchen space available for culinary startups. Available to rent by the hour so small businesses can grow without the financial obligation and risk of starting a commercial kitchen. Also offers guidance on starting a food-based business.

43320 ■ University of North Dakota Center for Innovation (UND)
4200 James Ray Dr.
Grand Forks, ND 58202
Ph: (701)777-3132
Fax: (701)777-2339
Co. E-mail: info@innovators.net
URL: http://www.innovators.net
Contact: James Ray, Contact
Facebook: www.facebook.com/centerforinnovation
Linkedin: www.linkedin.com/company/center-for-innovation
X (Twitter): x.com/NDInnovators
Instagram: www.instagram.com/center_for_innovation
YouTube: www.youtube.com/channel/UC5dHMwGsDEBCW1Hwt3i-Z7g
Description: A small business incubator providing assistance to innovators, entrepreneurs, and researchers to launch new ventures, commercialize new technologies, and secure access to capital from private and public sources. **Founded:** 1984.

43321 ■ University of North Dakota - Center for Innovation (CFI)
4200 James Ray Dr.
Grand Forks, ND 58202
Ph: (701)777-3132
Fax: (701)777-2339
Co. E-mail: info@innovators.net
URL: http://www.innovators.net
Contact: Amy Whitney, Director
Facebook: www.facebook.com/centerforinnovation
Linkedin: www.linkedin.com/company/center-for-innovation
X (Twitter): x.com/ndinnovators
YouTube: www.youtube.com/channel/UC5dHMwGsDEBCW1Hwt3i-Z7g
Description: Provides technical and business support services to entrepreneurs, inventors, and small manufacturers. Assists specifically with the product evaluation process, the patenting process, and technology transfer. **Scope:** Offers market and demographic research, business plan development, financial forecasts, and manufacturing services to entrepreneurs, particularly manufacturing technology start-up enterprises. Provides assistance to innovators, entrepreneurs, and researchers to launch new ventures, commercialize new technologies, and secure access to capital from private and public sources. **Founded:** 1984. **Publications:** The Business Plan: A State-Of-The-Art Guide"; "The Marketing Plan: Step-By-Step"; "The Ultimate Business Planner"; "Campus Entrepreneurship: A Changing Curriculum for Changing Times"; "Financing Startup Ventures"; "The Business Plan: A State-of-the-Art Guide"; "The Marketing Plan: Step-by-Step". **Educational Activities:** Center for Innovation Conferences and workshops, Seed and Angel Capital, Entrepreneur Startups, Business Planning, Market Feasibility.

43322 ■ University of North Dakota Center for Innovation Foundation (UND)
4200 James Ray Dr.
Grand Forks, ND 58202
Ph: (701)777-3132
Fax: (701)777-2339
Co. E-mail: info@innovators.net
URL: http://www.innovators.net
Contact: Amy Whitney, Director
E-mail: amy.w@innovators.net
Facebook: www.facebook.com/centerforinnovation
Linkedin: www.linkedin.com/company/center-for-innovation
X (Twitter): x.com/ndinnovators
Instagram: www.instagram.com/center_for_innovation
YouTube: www.youtube.com/channel/UC5dHMwGsDEBCW1Hwt3i-Z7g
Description: Entrepreneurial outreach center that provides assistance to innovators, entrepreneurs, and researchers to launch new ventures, commercialize new technologies, and secure access to capital from private and public sources. **Founded:** 1984.

EDUCATIONAL PROGRAMS

43323 ■ Lake Region State College (LRSC)
1801 College Dr. N
Devils Lake, ND 58301
Ph: (701)662-1600
Free: 800-443-1313
Fax: (701)662-1570
Co. E-mail: lrsc.helpdesk@lrsc.edu
URL: http://www.lrsc.edu
Contact: Dr. Doug Darling, President
E-mail: doug.darling@lrsc.edu
Facebook: www.facebook.com/lakeregionstate
X (Twitter): x.com/lakeregionstate
Instagram: www.instagram.com/lakeregionstate
YouTube: www.youtube.com/channel/UCiOXSISkuy9Isak-AfFeY5Q
Description: Two-year college offering a program in accounting and business management. **Founded:** 1941.

43324 ■ University of North Dakota-Workforce Development
711 for Relay
Grand Forks, ND 58202-7131
Ph: (701)777-3000
Co. E-mail: und.info@und.edu
URL: http://und.edu
Contact: Andrew Armacost, President
E-mail: andrew.armacost@und.edu

Description: Offers a variety of business-related and professional enrichment courses, institutes, seminars, and workshops. The Department of Conferences and Institutes coordinates a large number of business skills and management development seminars and workshops geared for particular audiences, including small business owners/managers. **Founded:** 1968.

PUBLICATIONS

43325 ■ *Prairie Business Magazine (PB)*
101 5th St. N
  Fargo, ND 58102-4826
Ph: (701)235-7311
Co. E-mail: afredrickson@forumcomm.com
URL: http://www.forumcomm.com
URL(s): www.grandforksherald.com/prairie-business
X (Twitter): twitter.com/prairiebiz
Ed: Kris Bevill. **Released:** Monthly **Description:** Magazine featuring business people and companies from North Dakota, Minnesota and South Dakota. **Availability:** Online.

PUBLISHERS

43326 ■ **University of North Dakota - Center for Innovation (CFI)**
4200 James Ray Dr.
  Grand Forks, ND 58202
Ph: (701)777-3132
Fax: (701)777-2339
Co. E-mail: info@innovators.net
URL: http://www.innovators.net
Contact: Amy Whitney, Director
Facebook: www.facebook.com/centerforinnovation
Linkedin: www.linkedin.com/company/center-for
  -innovation
X (Twitter): x.com/ndinnovators
YouTube: www.youtube.com/channel/UC
  5dHMwGsDEBCW1Hwt3i-Z7g
Description: Provides technical and business support services to entrepreneurs, inventors, and small manufacturers. Assists specifically with the product evaluation process, the patenting process, and technology transfer. **Scope:** Offers market and demographic research, business plan development, financial forecasts, and manufacturing services to entrepreneurs, particularly manufacturing technology start-up enterprises. Provides assistance to innovators, entrepreneurs, and researchers to launch new ventures, commercialize new technologies, and secure access to capital from private and public sources. **Founded:** 1984. **Publications:** The Business Plan: A State-Of-The-Art Guide"; "The Marketing Plan: Step-By-Step"; "The Ultimate Business Planner"; "Campus Entrepreneurship: A Changing Curriculum for Changing Times"; "Financing Startup Ventures"; "The Business Plan: A State-of-the-Art Guide"; "The Marketing Plan: Step-by-Step". **Educational Activities:** Center for Innovation Conferences and workshops, Seed and Angel Capital, Entrepreneur Startups, Business Planning, Market Feasibility.

VENTURE CAPITAL FIRM

43327 ■ **Dakota Venture Group (DVG)**
Ctr. for Innovation, Ina Mae Rude Entrepreneur Ctr.,
  4200 Jame Ray Dr.
  Grand Forks, ND 58203
Co. E-mail: information@dakotaventuregroup.com
URL: http://www.dakotaventuregroup.com
Contact: Hunter Beck, Chairman
E-mail: hbeck@dakotaventuregroup.com
Facebook: www.facebook.com/DakotaVentureGroup
X (Twitter): x.com/DVGInc

Description: Venture capital firm. Run by students from the University of North Dakota, it's the first completely student-run venture capital investment fund in the United States. **Founded:** 2006.

Ohio

ASSOCIATIONS AND OTHER ORGANIZATIONS

43328 ■ **Association of Fundraising Professionals Greater Cincinnati Chapter**
PO Box 31206
   Cincinnati, OH 45231
Ph: (513)939-2652
Fax: (513)939-2653
Co. E-mail: admin@afpcincinnati.org
URL: http://www.afpcincinnati.org
Contact: Matthew Gellin, President
E-mail: matthew.gellin@americanlegacytheatre.org
Facebook: www.facebook.com/AFPCincinnati
X (Twitter): x.com/afpcincy
Instagram: www.instagram.com/afpcincinnati
YouTube: www.youtube.com/channel/UCxL-to9S 3L7Czg3oRraOkTww
Description: Supports fundraising professionals in southwestern Ohio and northern Kentucky. **Founded:** 1977. **Geographic Preference:** Local.

43329 ■ **Association of Fundraising Professionals Greater Cleveland Chapter (AFPGC)**
3053 Nationwide Pky.
   Brunswick, OH 44212
Ph: (216)696-1613
Co. E-mail: admin@afpcleveland.org
URL: http://afpcleveland.org
Contact: Fran Anderson, President
E-mail: fran-a@sbcglobal.net
Facebook: www.facebook.com/AFPCleveland
Linkedin: www.linkedin.com/company/association-of -fundraising-professionals-greater-clevelan d-chapter
X (Twitter): x.com/AFPCleveland
Instagram: www.instagram.com/afpcleveland
Description: Professional organization dedicated to elevating the fundraising profession, providing educational programming to members, and serving the community by promoting ethical and professional practices in philanthropy. **Founded:** 1960. **Geographic Preference:** Local.

43330 ■ **Association of Fundraising Professionals Northeast Ohio Chapter (AFPNEO)**
1967 E Maple St., Ste. 112
   North Canton, OH 44720
Ph: (330)323-8662
Co. E-mail: info@afpneo.org
URL: http://community.afpglobal.org/afpneo/home
Contact: Daniel Blakemore, President
Facebook: www.facebook.com/AFPNEO
Linkedin: www.linkedin.com/company/association-of -fundraising-professionals-northeast-ohio
Instagram: www.instagram.com/afpneo
YouTube: www.youtube.com/channel/UCOILtb tsLFbSZXtXugLxu8g
Geographic Preference: Local.

43331 ■ **Business Network International, Central Ohio/Greater Columbus Area**
3984 Russell Rd.
   Ostrander, OH 43061
Ph: (440)521-9090
Fax: (440)521-9090
URL: http://bnicentralohio.com/en-US/index
Contact: Wayne Horowitz, Executive Director
Description: Provides both men and women a structured environment for the development and exchange of quality business referrals. Offers members the opportunity to share ideas and contacts. **Geographic Preference:** Local.

43332 ■ **Business Network International, Eastern Ohio/Greater Akron Area**
26401 Emery Rd., Ste. 105
   Cleveland, OH 44128
Ph: (216)464-3336
URL: http://bnineo.com/en-US/index
Contact: Bob Willis, Executive Director
Description: Provides both men and women a structured environment for the development and exchange of quality business referrals. Offers members the opportunity to share ideas and contacts. **Geographic Preference:** Local.

43333 ■ **Business Network International, Northeast Ohio/Greater Cleveland Area**
c/o Bob Willis, Executive Director
   26401 Emery Rd., Ste. 105
   Cleveland, OH 44128
URL: http://bnineo.com/oh-northeast-greater-clevelan d-chapter-of-bni/en-US/index
Contact: Randa Hilal, President
Description: Provides both men and women a structured environment for the development and exchange of quality business referrals. Offers members the opportunity to share ideas and contacts. **Geographic Preference:** Local.

43334 ■ **Business Network International, Northwest Ohio**
1700 Woodlands Dr., Ste. 200
   Maumee, OH 43537
Ph: (419)537-9054
Co. E-mail: support@bninwo.com
URL: http://bninwo.com/en-US/index
Contact: Jason Madasz, Executive Director
Facebook: www.facebook.com/NorthwestOhioBNI
Linkedin: www.linkedin.com/company/bni-northwes t-ohio
X (Twitter): x.com/BNINWOhio
Instagram: www.instagram.com/bninwo
YouTube: www.youtube.com/channel/UCWZS3ms 3G07-t9YvtAkdutw
Description: Provides a structured environment for the development and exchange of quality business referrals. Offers members the opportunity to share ideas and contacts. **Geographic Preference:** Local.

43335 ■ **Business Network International Ohio [BNI Ohio]**
OH

URL: http://www.bni-ohio.com
Description: Provides both men and women a structured environment for the development and exchange of quality business referrals. Offers members the opportunity to share ideas and contacts. **Founded:** 2014. **Geographic Preference:** State.

43336 ■ **Entrepreneur's EDGE**
6801 Brecksville Rd., Ste. 160
   Independence, OH 44131
Ph: (216)346-6300
Co. E-mail: info@edgeneo.org
URL: http://edgeneo.org
Contact: Kirk Neiswander, President
E-mail: kirk@edgeneo.org
Facebook: www.facebook.com/EdgeNEOhio
Linkedin: www.linkedin.com/company/edgeneohio
X (Twitter): x.com/EntreEDGE
Description: Serves entrepreneurs and small businesses with strategic planning, process improvement, restructuring, and financial analysis. **Founded:** 2005.

43337 ■ **Entrepreneurs' Organization - Cincinnati Chapter (EO)**
Cincinnati, OH
Co. E-mail: info@eocincinnati.org
URL: http://www.eonetwork.org/cincinnati/about-our -chapter
URL(s): www.eocincinnati.org
Facebook: www.facebook.com/eocincy
Linkedin: www.linkedin.com/company/35540458/a dmin
Description: Provides local resources to members which includes networking events, mentorship, live forums, and leadership development. **Founded:** 1995.

43338 ■ **Entrepreneurs' Organization - Cleveland Chapter (EO)**
600 E Granger Rd., Ste., 200
   Cleveland, OH 44131
URL: http://www.eonetwork.org/cleveland
Contact: Joel Goldstein, Contact
Description: Provides local resources to members which includes networking events, mentorship, live forums, and leadership development. **Founded:** 1998.

43339 ■ **Entrepreneurs' Organization - Columbus Chapter (EO)**
Columbus, OH
Co. E-mail: sponsorship@eonetwork.org
URL: http://www.eonetwork.org/columbus
Description: Provides local resources to members which includes networking events, mentorship, live forums, and leadership development. **Founded:** 1999.

43340 ■ **International Association of Business Communicators Columbus**
PO Box 12528
   Columbus, OH 43212
URL: http://www.iabc.com/regions-chapters/us-heri tage-region/columbus

Small Business Sourcebook • 42nd Edition   2865

Description: Represents the interests of communication managers, public relations directors, writers, editors and audiovisual specialists. Encourages establishment of college-level programs in organizational communication. Conducts surveys on employee communication effectiveness and media trends. Conducts research in the field of communication. **Geographic Preference:** Local.

43341 ■ International Association of Women Cincinnati Chapter
Cincinnati, OH
URL: http://careers.iawomen.com/job/customer-service-associate-cincinnati-ohio-302792
Description: Serves as network of accomplished women united to achieve professional goals. Provides a forum for sharing ideas and experiences of professional women regarding career success. Promotes an active business and networking community from all industries. **Geographic Preference:** Local.

43342 ■ International Association of Women Cleveland Chapter
Cleveland, OH
URL: http://www.iawomen.com/chapters/cleveland-chapter
Contact: Jill Windelspecht, President
URL(s): community.iawomen.com/cleveland/home
Description: Serves as network of accomplished women united to achieve professional goals. Provides a forum for sharing ideas and experiences of professional women regarding career success. Promotes an active business and networking community from all industries. **Geographic Preference:** Local.

43343 ■ Mechanical Contractors Association of Akron (MCAA) - Library
2181 Akron Peninsula Rd.
Akron, OH 44313
Ph: (330)237-1880
URL: http://mca-akron.com
Contact: Aaron Hall, Executive Director
Description: Promotes the growth of the mechanical contracting industry. Provides educational opportunities to assist contractors and service providers to develop more efficient and professional business management practices. Discusses and addresses common concerns within the industry. **Scope:** Mechanical. **Holdings:** Books. **Geographic Preference:** Local.

43344 ■ National Association of Women Business Owners Columbus Ohio
1201 Dublin Rd., Ste. 153
Columbus, OH 43215
Ph: (614)636-2926
Co. E-mail: info@nawbocolumbusohio.com
URL: http://nawbocolumbusohio.com
Contact: Arien Lawless, Manager
E-mail: arien@nawbocolumbusohio.com
Facebook: www.facebook.com/NawboColumbus
Linkedin: www.linkedin.com/company/nawbo-columbus
X (Twitter): x.com/nawbocolumbus
Instagram: www.instagram.com/nawbocbus
YouTube: www.youtube.com/user/NAWBOColumbusOhio
Description: Represents and promotes women-owned businesses to shape economic and public policy. **Geographic Preference:** Local.

43345 ■ Ohio Valley Business Travel Association (OVBTA)
715 Shawan Falls
Dublin, OH 43017
Ph: (614)638-4337
Co. E-mail: communications@ovbta.org
URL: http://ovbta.org
Contact: Renee V. Huff, President
E-mail: president@ovbta.org
Facebook: www.facebook.com/OVBTA
Linkedin: www.linkedin.com/company/gbta-ohio-valley-ovbta
X (Twitter): x.com/Ohio_Valley_BTA
Description: Represents travel managers and providers. Promotes the value of the travel manager in meeting corporate travel needs and financial goals. Cultivates a positive public image of the corporate travel industry. Protects the interests of members and their corporations in legislative and regulatory matters. Promotes safety, security, efficiency and quality travel. Provides a forum for the exchange of information and ideas among members. **Founded:** 1969. **Geographic Preference:** Local.

43346 ■ Queen City Angels (QCA)
4555 Lake Forest Dr., Ste. 650
Cincinnati, OH 45242
Ph: (513)373-6972
Co. E-mail: sjacobs@qca.com
URL: http://www.qca.com
Contact: Scott Jacobs, Executive Director
E-mail: sjacobs@qca.com
Linkedin: www.linkedin.com/company/queen-city-angels
X (Twitter): x.com/QueenCityAngels
YouTube: www.youtube.com/channel/UCoedYOaDFNvNZieoSoaSa9A
Description: Offers capital, mentoring, educational programs, and counsel to disruptive startups. **Founded:** 2000.

SMALL BUSINESS DEVELOPMENT CENTERS

43347 ■ Akron Small Business Development Centers
526 S Main St., Ste. 601
Akron, OH 44311
Ph: (330)375-2111
Fax: (330)375-2175
Co. E-mail: info@akronsbdc.org
URL: http://akronsbdc.org
Contact: Mary Ann Jasionowski, Director
Facebook: www.facebook.com/AkronSBDC
Description: Represents and promotes the small business sector. Provides management assistance to current and prospective small business owners. Helps to improve management skills and expand the products and services of members. **Geographic Preference:** Local.

43348 ■ Ashland Small Business Development Center (SBDC AU)
401 College Ave.
Ashland, OH 44805
Ph: (419)207-6910
URL: http://midohiosbdc6.wordpress.com
Contact: Michalina Lacy, Director
E-mail: mlacy@sbdc6.com
Facebook: www.facebook.com/sbdc6
Description: Represents and promotes the small business sector. Provides management assistance to current and prospective small business owners. Helps to improve management skills and expand the products and services of members. **Geographic Preference:** Local.

43349 ■ Kent/Portage Small Business Development Center
211 E Summit St.
Kent, OH 44240
URL: http://www.sba.gov/local-assistance/find?type=Small%20Business%20Development%20Center&pageNumber=1&address=44240
X (Twitter): x.com/KentState
Description: Represents and promotes the small business sector. Provides management assistance to current and prospective small business owners. Helps to improve management skills and expand the products and services of members. **Geographic Preference:** Local.

43350 ■ Ohio Small Business Development Center
77 S High St., 28th Fl.
Columbus, OH 43216
Ph: (614)466-6581
Fax: (614)466-1789
Co. E-mail: sbdc@cscc.edu
URL: http://www.OhioSBDC.org
Contact: James Laipply, Director
E-mail: james.laipply@development.ohio.gov
Facebook: www.facebook.com/SBDC.Columbus
X (Twitter): x.com/Ohio_SBDC
YouTube: www.youtube.com/user/OhioSBDC
Description: Provide no-cost, confidential, in-depth, one-on-one counseling for businesses that will or currently employ under 500 employees. **Geographic Preference:** State.

43351 ■ Ohio Small Business Development Center for Butler County
BizTech Center Bldg.
20 High St.
Hamilton, OH 45011-2709
URL: http://www.miamioh.edu/regionals/sbdc/about/index.html
Contact: Greg Crawford, President
Description: Represents and promotes the small business sector. Provides management assistance to current and prospective small business owners. Helps to improve management skills and expand the products and services of members. **Geographic Preference:** Local.

43352 ■ Ohio Small Business Development Center at the Clermont Chamber of Commerce
4355 Ferguson Dr., Ste. 150
Cincinnati, OH 45245
Ph: (513)576-5000
Fax: (513)576-5001
Co. E-mail: chamber@clermontchamber.com
URL: http://clermontchamber.com/services/small-business-center
Contact: Joy Lytle, President
E-mail: joy.lytle@clermontchamber.com
Facebook: www.facebook.com/ClermontChamber
Linkedin: www.linkedin.com/company/clermont-chamber-of-commerce
X (Twitter): x.com/ClermontChamber
Instagram: www.instagram.com/ClermontChamber
Description: Represents and promotes the small business sector. Provides management assistance to current and prospective small business owners. Helps to improve management skills and expand the products and services of members. **Founded:** 1969. **Geographic Preference:** Local.

43353 ■ Ohio Small Business Development Center at Columbus State Community College
320 N Grant Ave., Ste. 1062
Columbus, OH 43215
Ph: (614)287-5294
Fax: (614)287-6311
URL: http://sbdccolumbus.com/events
Contact: Michael Bowers, Director
E-mail: mbowers3@cscc.edu
Facebook: www.facebook.com/SBDC.Columbus
X (Twitter): x.com/Ohio_SBDC
YouTube: www.youtube.com/user/OhioSBDC
Description: Represents and promotes the small business sector. Provides management assistance to current and prospective small business owners. Helps to improve management skills and expand the products and services of members. **Geographic Preference:** Local.

43354 ■ Ohio Small Business Development Center at James A. Rhodes State College
4240 Campus Dr.
Lima, OH 45804
URL: http://www.rhodesstate.edu/workforce-development-and-innovation/small-business-development-center/index.html
Contact: Kathleen Keller, Director
E-mail: keller.k@rhodesstate.edu
Description: Represents and promotes the small business sector. Provides management assistance to current and prospective small business owners. Helps to improve management skills and expand the products and services of members. **Geographic Preference:** Local.

43355 ■ Ohio Small Business Development Center at Kent State University Stark Campus
6000 Frank Ave. NW
Canton, OH 44720

URL: http://www.sba.gov/tools/local-assistance/map/filter/789cabca2cb03231313732b04ac92c2e49cc4b4eb53234300000516e06df
Description: Represents and promotes the small business sector. Provides management assistance to current and prospective small business owners. Helps to improve management skills and expand the products and services of members. **Geographic Preference:** Local.

43356 ■ **Ohio Small Business Development Center at Kent State University Tuscarawas Campus**
1776 Tech Pk. Dr. NE, Ste. 103
New Philadelphia, OH 44663
Ph: (330)308-7479
URL: http://www.kent.edu/kent/ohio-small-business-development-center-kent-state-tuscarawas-osbdc
Contact: Steve Schillig, Director
E-mail: sschil10@kent.edu
Description: Represents and promotes the small business sector. Provides management assistance to current and prospective small business owners. Helps to improve management skills and expand the products and services of members. **Geographic Preference:** Local.

43357 ■ **Ohio Small Business Development Center at Lorain County Community College**
151 Innovation Dr.
Elyria, OH 44035
URL: http://www.lorainccc.edu/business/sbdc
Contact: Marcia Ballinger, President
Description: Represents and promotes the small business sector. Provides management assistance to current and prospective small business owners. Helps to improve management skills and expand the products and services of members. **Geographic Preference:** Local.

43358 ■ **Ohio Small Business Development Center at Marietta (SBDC)**
2163 SR 821, Bldge 6-A
Marietta, OH 45750
Ph: (740)373-5150
Fax: (740)373-2984
URL: http://business.mariettachamber.com/list/member/ohio-small-business-development-center-2168
Contact: Pamela Lankford, Director
Description: Provides management assistance to current and prospective small business owners in Marietta. **Geographic Preference:** Local.

43359 ■ **Ohio Small Business Development Center at Ohio University**
The Ridges, Ste. 110
19 E Cir., Dr.
Athens, OH 45701
Ph: (740)593-1797
URL: http://sbdc.voinovichschool.ohio.edu
Contact: Lissa Jollick, Regional Director
E-mail: jollickl@ohio.edu
Facebook: www.facebook.com/sbdcohiouniversity
YouTube: www.youtube.com/channel/UC5dP47yM-kPglMmUeC0el6g
Description: Represents and promotes the small business sector. Provides management assistance to current and prospective small business owners. Helps to improve management skills and expand the products and services of members. **Founded:** 1988. **Geographic Preference:** Local.

43360 ■ **Ohio Small Business Development Center at Terra Community College**
2830 Napoleon Rd.
Fremont, OH 43420
URL: http://www.terra.edu/continuingeducation/smallbusinessdevelopment.html
Contact: Bill Auxter, Contact
E-mail: bauxter@terra.edu
Description: Represents and promotes the small business sector. Provides management assistance to current and prospective small business owners. Helps to improve management skills and expand the products and services of members. **Founded:** 1988. **Geographic Preference:** Local.

43361 ■ **Ohio Small Business Development Center at The OSU South Centers (SBDC)**
1864 Shyville Rd.
Piketon, OH 45661
Ph: (740)289-2071
Fax: (740)289-4591
URL: http://southcenters.osu.edu/small-business
Contact: Brad Bapst, Director
E-mail: bapst.4@osu.edu
Description: Represents and promotes the small business sector. Provides management assistance to current and prospective small business owners. Helps to improve management skills and expand the products and services of members. **Geographic Preference:** Local.

43362 ■ **Ohio Small Business Development Center at The Urban League of Greater Cleveland**
2930 Prospect Ave.
Cleveland, OH 44115-2608
Co. E-mail: sbdcinfo@ulcleveland.org
URL: http://clients.ohiosbdc.ohio.gov/center.aspx?center=17087&subloc=0
Description: Represents and promotes the small business sector. Provides management assistance to current and prospective small business owners. Helps to improve management skills and expand the products and services of members. **Geographic Preference:** Local.

43363 ■ **Ohio Small Business Development Center at Toledo Regional Chamber of Commerce**
300 Madison Ave., Ste. 200
Toledo, OH 43604
Ph: (419)243-8191
Co. E-mail: businesshelp@development.ohio.gov
URL: http://www.toledochamber.com/small-business-development-center.html
Contact: Jill Badger, Vice President
Description: Represents and promotes the small business sector. Provides management assistance to current and prospective small business owners. Helps to improve management skills and expand the products and services of members. **Geographic Preference:** Local.

43364 ■ **Ohio Small Business Development Center at Youngstown State University**
1 University Plz.
Youngstown, OH 44502
Ph: (330)941-2140
Co. E-mail: ohiosbdc@ysu.edu
URL: http://ysu.edu/academics/williamson-college-business-administration/centers/sbdc
Contact: Patricia Veisz, Director
E-mail: pkveisz@ysu.edu
Description: Provides management assistance to current and prospective small business owners in Youngstown. **Geographic Preference:** Local.

43365 ■ **Ohio Small Business Development Center at Zane State College (ZSC)**
1555 Newark Rd.
Zanesville, OH 43701
Ph: (740)588-5000
Co. E-mail: admissions@zanestate.edu
URL: http://www.zanestate.edu
Contact: Dr. Chad Brown, President
URL(s): sbdc.ohio.edu/events/locations/zane-state-college
Facebook: www.facebook.com/ZaneStateCollege
Linkedin: www.linkedin.com/school/zane-state-college
X (Twitter): x.com/ZaneStateC
Instagram: www.instagram.com/zanestatecollege
YouTube: www.youtube.com/channel/UC-7WTVJdLS_NoB7diAMknjA
Description: Represents and promotes the small business sector. Provides management assistance to current and prospective small business owners. Helps to improve management skills and expand the products and services of members. **Founded:** 1969. **Geographic Preference:** Local.

43366 ■ **Small Business Development Center at Edison Community College**
1973 Edison Dr.
Piqua, OH 45356
Ph: (937)778-8600
Co. E-mail: info@edisonohio.edu
URL: http://www.edisonohio.edu
Contact: Heather Lanham, Secretary
E-mail: hlanham@edisonohio.edu
URL(s): clients.ohiosbdc.ohio.gov/center.aspx?center=17041&subloc=0
Facebook: www.facebook.com/EdisonStateCC
X (Twitter): x.com/EdisonOhio
Instagram: www.instagram.com/edisonstatecc
Description: Provides management assistance to current and prospective small business owners in Edison. **Geographic Preference:** Local.

43367 ■ **Small Business Development Center at Lake County Economic Development Center**
105 Main St., Ste. B501
Painesville, OH 44077
Ph: (440)357-2290
URL: http://lcport.org/small-business-development-center
Contact: Art Lindrose, Chairman
Description: Provides management assistance to current and prospective small business owners in Lake County. **Geographic Preference:** Local.

43368 ■ **Small Business Development Center at Maumee Valley Planning Organization**
1300 E 2nd St., Ste. 200
Defiance, OH 43512
Ph: (419)784-3882
Fax: (419)784-2061
Co. E-mail: mvpo@mvpo.org
URL: http://www.mvpo.org
Contact: Mike Kauser, Treasurer Secretary
Facebook: www.facebook.com/maumeevalleyplanning
Linkedin: www.linkedin.com/company/mvpo
Description: Represents and promotes the small business sector. **Geographic Preference:** Local.

43369 ■ **Small Business Development Center at University of Cincinnati**
3458 Reading Rd.
Cincinnati, OH 45229
Ph: (513)487-1155
Co. E-mail: mhumphrey@ulgso.org
URL: http://clients.ohiosbdc.ohio.gov/center.aspx?center=17052&subloc=1
Contact: Wanda Walker-Smith, Director
Description: Represents and promotes the small business sector. Provides management assistance to current and prospective small business owners. Helps to improve management skills and expand the products and services of members. **Geographic Preference:** Local.

SMALL BUSINESS ASSISTANCE PROGRAMS

43370 ■ **National Institute for Occupational Safety and Health - Small Business Assistance and Outreach Cross-Sector Program**
4676 Columbia Pky., C-14
Cincinnati, OH 45226
URL: http://www.cdc.gov/niosh/programs/sbao/projects.html
Contact: Rick Niemeier, Contact
Description: Mission is to minimize and eliminate occupational illnesses, injuries, and hazardous exposures in small enterprises through a focused program of research, prevention efforts, and public health activities. **Scope:** Reductions in occupational illnesses, injuries and hazardous exposures in small businesses.

43371 ■ Ohio Department of Development - Office of Small Business and Entrepreneurship
77 S High St., 29th Fl.
Columbus, OH 43215
URL: http://development.ohio.gov/business/small-business-and-entrepreneurship
Description: Provides assistance to small businesses.

43372 ■ Ohio Development Services Agency (TID) - Technology and Innovation Div.
77 S High St., 25th Fl.
Columbus, OH 43215-6108
Free: 800-848-1300
URL: http://development.ohio.gov
Description: Stimulates working partnerships between business and academia in an effort to generate new technological ideas, new products and processes, and new companies. The three major components are: Edison Technology Centers, Edison Seed Development Fund, and Edison Incubators.

SCORE OFFICES

43373 ■ Canton Regional SCORE
Jackson Twp. Legal Office
5735 Wales Ave. NW
Massillon, OH 44646
Ph: (330)451-6509
Co. E-mail: ch.admin0580@scorevolunteer.org
URL: http://www.score.org/canton
Contact: Patricia Lance Ripple, Contact
Facebook: www.facebook.com/SCORECanton
Linkedin: www.linkedin.com/company/score-mentors-canton
X (Twitter): x.com/CantonSCORE

43374 ■ Columbus SCORE
65 E State St., Ste. 1350
Columbus, OH 43215
Ph: (614)664-7267
Co. E-mail: info@scorecolumbus.org
URL: http://columbusoh.score.org
Contact: Scott Harkins, Chairman of the Board
Facebook: www.facebook.com/SCOREColumbusOH
Linkedin: www.linkedin.com/company/score-counselors-to-america's-small-business
X (Twitter): x.com/SCOREColumbusOH
Description: Assists individuals with their decisions to begin or to operate small businesses. Provides educational seminars and business counseling. **Founded:** 1965. **Geographic Preference:** Local.

43375 ■ East Central Ohio SCORE
14 N Park Pl.
Newark, OH 43055
URL: http://www.score.org/columbusoh/content/about-us
Description: Seeks to educate entrepreneurs and help small businesses start, grow and succeed nationwide. Organizes volunteers who are working or retired business owners, executives and corporate leaders who wish to share their wisdom and lessons learned in business. **Geographic Preference:** Local.

43376 ■ North Central Ohio SCORE
55 N Mulberry St., Chamber Of Commerce
Mansfield, OH 44903
Ph: (419)522-3211
Fax: (419)526-6853
Co. E-mail: ncoscore@ncoscore.org
URL: http://www.score.org/northcentralohio
Contact: Neil Hamilton, Chief Executive Officer
Facebook: www.facebook.com/NCOSrichland.org

43377 ■ Northwest Ohio SCORE (SCORE)
2200 Jefferson Ave.
Mercy Healthcare Ctr., 1st Fl.
Toledo, OH 43604
Ph: (567)218-3494
Co. E-mail: office@nwoscore.org
URL: http://www.score.org/northwestohio
Linkedin: www.linkedin.com/company/northwest-ohio-score
X (Twitter): x.com/SCORENWOhio

Founded: 1964.

43378 ■ SCORE - Akron
175 S Main St., Ste. 204
Akron, OH 44308
Ph: (330)379-3163
Co. E-mail: help@score.org
URL: http://akron.score.org
Contact: Bridget Weston, Chief Executive Officer
Facebook: www.facebook.com/SCOREAkron
Linkedin: www.linkedin.com/company/akron-score
Description: Provides professional guidance and information to maximize the success of existing and emerging small businesses. Offers business counseling and workshops. **Founded:** 1965. **Geographic Preference:** Local.

43379 ■ SCORE - Ashtabula
3300 Lake Rd. W
Kent State University
Ashtabula, OH 44004-2316
Ph: (216)503-8168
URL: http://www.cleveland.score.org/branch/score-ashtabula-county
Description: Provides professional guidance and information to maximize the success of existing and emerging small businesses. Offers business counseling and workshops.

43380 ■ SCORE - Burton
1350 Euclid Ave., Ste. 216
Cleveland, OH 44115-1815
Ph: (216)503-8160
Fax: (216)522-4844
URL: http://cleveland.score.org
Description: Provides professional guidance and information to maximize the success of existing and emerging small businesses. Offers business counseling and workshops.

43381 ■ SCORE - Canton
6000 Frank Ave. NW
Canton, OH 44720
Ph: (330)244-3280
Fax: (330)244-3535
Co. E-mail: cantonscore@gmail.com
URL: http://canton.score.org
Facebook: www.facebook.com/SCORECanton
Linkedin: www.linkedin.com/company/score-mentors-canton
X (Twitter): x.com/CantonSCORE
Description: Provides professional guidance and information to maximize the success of existing and emerging small businesses. Offers business counseling and workshops.

43382 ■ SCORE - Cleveland
1350 Euclid Ave., Ste. 216
Cleveland, OH 44115
Ph: (216)503-8160
Fax: (216)522-4844
Co. E-mail: score.cleveland@scorevolunteer.org
URL: http://cleveland.score.org
Facebook: www.facebook.com/SCORECleveland
Linkedin: www.linkedin.com/company/score-cleveland
Description: Provides professional guidance and information to maximize the success of existing and emerging small businesses. Offers business counseling and workshops. **Founded:** 1965.

43383 ■ SCORE - Columbus, Ohio
65 E State St., Ste. 1350
Columbus, OH 43215
Ph: (614)664-7267
Co. E-mail: info@scorecolumbus.org
URL: http://columbusoh.score.org
Facebook: www.facebook.com/SCOREColumbusOH
Linkedin: www.linkedin.com/company/score-counselors-to-america's-small-business
X (Twitter): x.com/SCOREColumbusOH
Description: Provides professional guidance and information to maximize the success of existing and emerging small businesses. Offers business counseling and workshops.

43384 ■ SCORE - Dayton
5818 Wilmington Pke., Ste. 247
Dayton, OH 45459
Ph: (937)225-2887
Co. E-mail: score@daytonscore.org
URL: http://dayton.score.org
URL(s): www.daytonscore.org
Facebook: www.facebook.com/SCOREDayton
Linkedin: www.linkedin.com/company/score-mentors-dayton
X (Twitter): x.com/SCORE_Dayton
Description: Provides professional guidance and information to maximize the success of existing and emerging small businesses. Offers business counseling and workshops. **Founded:** 1970. **Geographic Preference:** Local.

43385 ■ SCORE - East Central Ohio
14 N Park Pl.
Newark, OH 43055
URL: http://eastcentralohio.score.org
Description: Provides professional guidance and information to maximize the success of existing and emerging small businesses. Offers business counseling and workshops.

43386 ■ SCORE - Greater Cincinnati
525 Vine St., Rm. 1030
Cincinnati, OH 45202
Ph: (513)954-5004
URL: http://greatercincinnati.score.org
URL(s): www.scoreworks.org
Facebook: www.facebook.com/SCORECincinnati
Linkedin: www.linkedin.com/company/score-cincinnati
X (Twitter): x.com/CincinnatiScore
YouTube: www.youtube.com/user/scorecincinnati
Pinterest: www.pinterest.com/cincinnatiscore
Description: Provides professional guidance and information to maximize the success of existing and emerging small businesses. Offers business counseling and workshops. **Founded:** 1964. **Geographic Preference:** Regional.

43387 ■ SCORE - Lorain
319 Black River Ln.
Lorain, OH 44052-3459
Ph: (216)407-2836
URL: http://cleveland.score.org
Description: Provides professional guidance and information to maximize the success of existing and emerging small businesses. Offers business counseling and workshops.

43388 ■ SCORE - North Central Ohio
55 N Mulberry St.
Mansfield, OH 44902
Ph: (419)522-3211
Fax: (419)526-6853
Co. E-mail: ncoscore@ncoscore.org
URL: http://northcentralohio.score.org
Contact: Shilpa Chawla, Co-President
Description: Seeks to educate entrepreneurs and help small businesses start, grow and succeed nationwide. Organizes volunteers who are working or retired business owners, executives and corporate leaders who wish to share their wisdom and lessons learned in business. **Geographic Preference:** Local.

43389 ■ SCORE - Northwest Ohio
Mercy Healthcare Ctr., 1st Fl.
2200 Jefferson Ave.
Toledo, OH 43604
Ph: (419)259-7598
Fax: (419)259-6460
Co. E-mail: office@nwoscore.org
URL: http://northwestohio.score.org
Contact: Bridget Weston, Chief Executive Officer
Facebook: www.facebook.com/SCORENWOhio
Linkedin: www.linkedin.com/company/northwest-ohio-score
X (Twitter): x.com/SCORENWOhio
Description: Provides professional guidance and information to maximize the success of existing and emerging small businesses. Offers business counseling and workshops.

STATE LISTINGS

Ohio ■ 43403

43390 ■ SCORE - Norwalk, Ohio
12 Benedict Ave.
Norwalk, OH 44857-2175
Ph: (216)503-8168
URL: http://cleveland.score.org
Description: Provides professional guidance and information to maximize the success of existing and emerging small businesses. Offers business counseling and workshops.

43391 ■ SCORE - Painesville
1 Victoria Pl., Ste. 265A
Painesville, OH 44077
Ph: (216)503-8168
Co. E-mail: appointments@chapter30.org
URL: http://cleveland.score.org
Description: Provides professional guidance and information to maximize the success of existing and emerging small businesses. Offers business counseling and workshops.

43392 ■ SCORE - Youngstown
101 W Rayen Ave.
Youngstown, OH 44555
Ph: (330)941-2948
Co. E-mail: help@score.org
URL: http://youngstown.score.org
Contact: Bridget Weston, Chief Executive Officer
Facebook: www.facebook.com/SCOREYoungstown
Linkedin: www.linkedin.com/company/score-mentors-youngstown
X (Twitter): x.com/ScoreYoungstown
Description: Provides professional guidance and information to maximize the success of existing and emerging small businesses. Offers business counseling and workshops.

43393 ■ Youngstown SCORE
101 W Rayen Ave.
Youngstown, OH 44555
Ph: (330)941-2948
Co. E-mail: help@score.org
URL: http://youngstown.score.org
Contact: Bridget Weston, Chief Executive Officer
Facebook: www.facebook.com/SCOREYoungstown
Linkedin: www.linkedin.com/company/score-mentors-youngstown
X (Twitter): x.com/ScoreYoungstown
Description: Promotes business and community development in Youngstown, OH area. Conducts business education seminars and workshops to those wanting to start a business. **Founded:** 1965. **Geographic Preference:** Local.

BETTER BUSINESS BUREAUS

43394 ■ Better Business Bureau of Akron
222 W Market St.
Akron, OH 44303
Ph: (330)253-4590
Fax: (330)253-6249
Co. E-mail: info@akronbbb.org
URL: http://www.bbb.org/local-bbb/bbb-of-akron
Facebook: www.facebook.com/BBBakron
Linkedin: www.linkedin.com/company/better-business-bureau-of-akron
X (Twitter): x.com/bbb_Akron
Description: Provides business reliability reports and complaint handling, including informal mediation, arbitration and alternative dispute resolution, business/consumer education resources and materials, national and local charitable information and the promotion of ethical business standards and voluntary self-regulation. **Founded:** 1920. **Publications:** *BBB Facts* (Semiannual). **Geographic Preference:** Local.

43395 ■ Better Business Bureau of Central Ohio
1169 Dublin Rd.
Columbus, OH 43215-1005
Ph: (614)486-6336
Fax: (614)486-6631
Co. E-mail: info@centralohio.bbb.org
URL: http://www.bbb.org/local-bbb/bbb-of-central-ohio
Contact: Judy Dollison, President
Facebook: www.facebook.com/bbbcentralohio
Linkedin: www.linkedin.com/company/better-business-bureau-of-central-ohio
X (Twitter): x.com/BBBCentralOhio
Instagram: www.instagram.com/bbbcentralohio
YouTube: www.youtube.com/user/CentralOhioBBB
Pinterest: www.pinterest.com/bbbcentralohio
Description: Seeks to promote and foster ethical relationship between businesses and the public through voluntary self-regulation, consumer and business education, and service excellence. Provides information to help consumers and businesses make informed purchasing decisions and avoid costly scams and frauds; settles consumer complaints through arbitration and other means. **Geographic Preference:** Local.

43396 ■ Better Business Bureau of Dayton/Miami Valley
15 W 4th St., Ste. 300
Dayton, OH 45402-1830
Ph: (937)222-5825
Fax: (937)222-3338
Co. E-mail: info@dayton.bbb.org
URL: http://www.bbb.org/local-bbb/bbb-of-dayton-and-miami-valley
Facebook: www.facebook.com/pages/Better-Business-Bureau-Dayton-OH/61539956175
Linkedin: www.linkedin.com/company/better-business-bureau---dayton-&-miami-valley
X (Twitter): x.com/bbb2day
YouTube: www.youtube.com/user/BBB2Day
Description: Seeks to promote and foster ethical relationship between businesses and the public through voluntary self-regulation, consumer and business education, and service excellence. Provides information to help consumers and businesses make informed purchasing decisions and avoid costly scams and frauds; settles consumer complaints through arbitration and other means. **Geographic Preference:** Local.

43397 ■ Better Business Bureau - Greater Cleveland
200 Treeworth Blvd.
Broadview Heights, OH 44147
Ph: (216)241-7678
Fax: (216)861-6365
Co. E-mail: info@cleveland.bbb.org
URL: http://www.bbb.org/local-bbb/bbb-serving-greater-cleveland
Contact: Sue McConnell, President
Facebook: www.facebook.com/BBBCleveland
Linkedin: www.linkedin.com/company/better-business-bureau-serving-greater-cleveland
X (Twitter): x.com/BBBCleveland
Instagram: www.instagram.com/bbbcleveland
YouTube: www.youtube.com/user/ClevelandBBB
Pinterest: www.pinterest.com/bbbcleveland
Description: Seeks to promote and foster ethical relationship between businesses and the public through voluntary self-regulation, consumer and business education, and service excellence. Provides information to help consumers and businesses make informed purchasing decisions and avoid costly scams and frauds; settles consumer complaints through arbitration and other means. **Founded:** 1913. **Geographic Preference:** Local.

43398 ■ Better Business Bureau of Mahoning Valley
201 E Commerce St. Ste. 137
Youngstown, OH 44503
Ph: (330)744-3111
Fax: (330)744-3336
Co. E-mail: info@youngstown.bbb.org
URL: http://www.bbb.org/local-bbb/bbb-of-mahoning-valley
Contact: Carol Potter, Contact
Facebook: www.facebook.com/bbbyoungstown
X (Twitter): x.com/BBB_Youngstown
Instagram: www.instagram.com/bbb_youngstown
Description: Seeks to promote and foster ethical relationship between businesses and the public through voluntary self-regulation, consumer and business education, and service excellence. Provides information to help consumers and businesses make informed purchasing decisions and avoid costly scams and frauds; settles consumer complaints through arbitration and other means. **Geographic Preference:** Local.

43399 ■ Better Business Bureau - Northwest and West Central Ohio and Southeast Michigan
7668 Kin's Pointe Rd.
Toledo, OH 43617
Ph: (419)531-3116
Free: 800-743-4222
Fax: (419)578-6001
URL: http://www.bbb.org/local-bbb/bbb-serving-northwest-and-west-central-ohio-and-southeast-michigan
X (Twitter): x.com/BBB_Toledo
Description: Seeks to promote and foster ethical relationship between businesses and the public through voluntary self-regulation, consumer and business education, and service excellence. Provides information to help consumers and businesses make informed purchasing decisions and avoid costly scams and frauds; settles consumer complaints through arbitration and other means. **Geographic Preference:** Regional; Local.

43400 ■ Cincinnati Better Business Bureau
1 E 4th St., Ste. 600
Cincinnati, OH 45202
Ph: (513)421-3015
Fax: (513)621-0907
Co. E-mail: info@cincinnati.bbb.org
URL: http://www.bbb.org/local-bbb/bbb-cincinnati
Contact: Jocile Ehrlich, Vice Chairman of the Board
Facebook: www.facebook.com/bbbcincinnati
X (Twitter): x.com/bbbcincinnati
Instagram: www.instagram.com/bbbcincinnati
YouTube: www.youtube.com/user/bbbcincinnati
Description: Seeks to promote and foster the highest ethical relationship between businesses and the public through voluntary self-regulation, consumer and business education, and service excellence. Provides information to help consumers and businesses make informed purchasing decisions and avoid costly scams and frauds; settles consumer complaints through arbitration and other means. **Founded:** 1926. **Geographic Preference:** Local.

CHAMBERS OF COMMERCE

43401 ■ African American Chamber of Commerce (AACC)
2303 Gilbert Ave.
Cincinnati, OH 45206
Ph: (513)751-9900
Co. E-mail: info@african-americanchamber.com
URL: http://www.african-americanchamber.com
Contact: Eric H. Kearney, President
Facebook: www.facebook.com/TheCincinnatiAAChamber
X (Twitter): x.com/CincyAAChamber
Instagram: www.instagram.com/thecincinnatiaachamber
Description: Provider of business development for the African American market. **Founded:** 1996.

43402 ■ *Allen County Business Directory*
144 S Main St., Ste. 100
Lima, OH 45801
Ph: (419)222-6045
Fax: (419)229-0266
URL: http://limachamber.com
Contact: Jed Metzger, President
E-mail: jmetzger@limachamber.com
URL(s): business.limachamber.com/list
Description: Contains lists of businesses from the public, private and not-for-profit sectors. **Availability:** Print; Online.

43403 ■ *Alliance*
225 S Detroit St.
Kenton, OH 43326
Ph: (419)673-4131
Co. E-mail: alliance@hccba.com

Small Business Sourcebook • 42nd Edition

2869

43404 ▪ Ohio

URL: http://hardincountyoh.org
Contact: Holli Underwood, President
E-mail: hunderwood@hccba.com
URL(s): www.hccba.com/chamber-of-commerce
Released: Weekly **Availability:** PDF; Online.

43404 ▪ Alliance Area Chamber of Commerce (AACC)
210 E Main St.
Alliance, OH 44601
Ph: (330)823-6260
Co. E-mail: info@allianceohiochamber.org
URL: http://www.allianceohiochamber.org
Contact: R. Mark Locke, President
E-mail: mark@allianceohiochamber.org
Linkedin: www.linkedin.com/company/allianceareachamberofcommerce
Description: Promotes business and community development in the Alliance, OH area. Sponsors Carnation City Festival. **Founded:** 1915. **Publications:** *Image Booklet* (Triennial); *MPRA Newsletter* (Monthly). **Geographic Preference:** Local.

43405 ▪ Anderson Area Chamber of Commerce (AACC)
7850 5 Mile Rd.
Cincinnati, OH 45230
Ph: (513)474-4802
Fax: (513)474-4857
Co. E-mail: info@andersonareachamber.org
URL: http://www.andersonareachamber.org
Contact: Kim Cunningham, Secretary
Facebook: www.facebook.com/AndersonAreaChamberofCommerce
X (Twitter): x.com/AndersonAreaCC
YouTube: www.youtube.com/channel/UCKIIdDlaS89hExdSzgCNRcw
Description: Supports the area business community. Creates partnerships with government and residents for the overall benefit of the Anderson area. **Founded:** 1970. **Publications:** *Chamber Notes*. **Awards:** Anderson Area Chamber Citizen of the Year (Annual). **Geographic Preference:** Local.

43406 ▪ Archbold Area Chamber of Commerce
300 N Defiance St.
Archbold, OH 43502
Ph: (419)445-2222
Co. E-mail: info@archboldchamber.com
URL: http://archboldchamber.com
Contact: Amy Cover, President
Facebook: www.facebook.com/archboldareachamber
Description: Promotes business and community development in Archbold, OH area. **Geographic Preference:** Local.

43407 ▪ Ashland Area Chamber of Commerce (AACC)
211 Claremont Ave.
Ashland, OH 44805
Ph: (419)281-4584
Co. E-mail: chamber@ashlandoh.com
URL: http://www.ashlandoh.com
Contact: Ginny Telego, Director
E-mail: leadershipashland@ashlandoh.com
Facebook: www.facebook.com/AshlandOHChamber
Description: Promotes and enhances the economic well-being of the Ashland area. **Founded:** 1909. **Geographic Preference:** Local.

43408 ▪ Ashtabula County Chamber of Commerce
4536 Main Ave.
Ashtabula, OH 44004
Ph: (440)998-6998
Fax: (440)992-8216
Co. E-mail: info@kollhoffinsurance.com
URL: http://www.ashtabulachamber.net
Contact: Greg Church, Executive Director
E-mail: gchurch@ashtabulachamber.com
Description: Promotes business and community development in the Ashtabula, OH area. **Founded:** 1887. **Publications:** *News and Views* (Monthly). **Geographic Preference:** Local.

43409 ▪ Aurora Chamber of Commerce
9 E Garfield Rd., Ste. 101
Aurora, OH 44202
Ph: (330)562-3355
URL: http://www.allaboutaurora.com
Contact: Kyle Hersh, President
Facebook: www.facebook.com/AllAboutAurora
X (Twitter): x.com/allaboutaurora
Instagram: www.instagram.com/auroraohiochamberofcommerce
Description: Promotes business and community development in Aurora, OH. **Founded:** 1799. **Publications:** *Community Profile and Map*. **Geographic Preference:** Local.

43410 ▪ Barnesville Area Chamber of Commerce
130 W Main St.
Barnesville, OH 43713
Ph: (740)425-4300
Co. E-mail: bacc@barnesvilleohiochamber.com
URL: http://www.barnesvilleohiochamber.com
Contact: Aaron Bruggeman, President
Facebook: www.facebook.com/barnesvilleohiochamber
Linkedin: www.linkedin.com/in/barnesville-chamber-of-commerce-3b618137
X (Twitter): x.com/bvillechamber1
Description: Promotes business and community development in Barnesville, OH. **Founded:** 1915. **Awards:** Barnesville Area Chamber of Commerce Citizen of the Year (Annual). **Geographic Preference:** Local.

43411 ▪ Beachwood Chamber of Commerce (BCC)
23355 Mercantile Rd.
Beachwood, OH 44122
Ph: (216)831-0003
Co. E-mail: chamber@beachwood.org
URL: http://www.beachwood.org
Contact: Brian Friedman, Co-President
Facebook: www.facebook.com/BeachwoodCOC
Linkedin: www.linkedin.com/company/beachwoodcoc
X (Twitter): x.com/beachwoodcoc
YouTube: www.youtube.com/channel/UCfh-X_wrKF3su1wBiXlNFsQ
Description: Firm works to assist local businesses and improve the economic base. **Founded:** 1995. **Publications:** *Purchase Directory*. **Geographic Preference:** Local.

43412 ▪ Bellbrook-Sugarcreek Area Chamber of Commerce (BSACoC)
2090 Ferry Rd.
Sugarcreek Township, OH 45305
Ph: (937)848-4930
Co. E-mail: info@bellbrooksugarcreekchamber.com
URL: http://bellbrooksugarcreekchamber.com
Contact: Dr. Tyler Lanning, President
Description: Promotes business and community development in Bellbrook-Sugarcreek area of Ohio. **Publications:** *Business / Community Directory*; *Newsgram* (Semiannual). **Geographic Preference:** Local.

43413 ▪ Bellevue Area Chamber of Commerce
1 Union Sq., Ste. A
Bellevue, OH 44811
Ph: (419)483-2182
URL: http://thechamberbellevue.com
Contact: Sarah Wilson, President
E-mail: sarah.eastman@willowsatbellevue.com
Description: Promotes business and community development in the Bellevue area. **Founded:** 1910. **Publications:** *Calendar of Events* (Annual). **Geographic Preference:** Local.

43414 ▪ Belpre Area Chamber of Commerce (BACC)
713 Pk. Dr.
Belpre, OH 45714
Ph: (740)423-8934
Co. E-mail: info@belprechamber.com
URL: http://belprechamber.com
Contact: Ashley Brown, President
Facebook: www.facebook.com/belpreareachamber
Description: Promotes business and community development in the Belpre, OH area. Conducts community social and promotional activities. **Publications:** *Chamberletter* (Monthly). **Geographic Preference:** Local.

43415 ▪ Berea, Ohio Chamber of Commerce
PO Box 774
Berea, OH 44017
Ph: (440)243-8415
Co. E-mail: director@bereachamber.org
URL: http://bereachamber.org
Contact: Dave Herwerden, President
Facebook: www.facebook.com/bereaohiochamberofcommerce
Description: Advances and develops the commercial, industrial, civic and general interest for the residents and the City of Berea. **Founded:** 1939. **Awards:** Berea Chamber of Commerce Grindstone Award (Annual). **Geographic Preference:** Local.

43416 ▪ Bexley Area Chamber of Commerce (BACC)
544 S Drexel Ave.
Bexley, OH 43209
Ph: (614)236-4500
Co. E-mail: info@bexleyareachamber.org
URL: http://www.bexleyareachamber.org
Contact: Tracie Baum, Executive Director
Facebook: www.facebook.com/BexleyAreaChamberCommerce
Linkedin: www.linkedin.com/company/bexley-chamber-of-commerce
X (Twitter): x.com/bexleychamber
YouTube: www.youtube.com/channel/UCUgEiWuKUC9Y6sPfpq0FbsQ
Description: Promotes business and community development in the Bexley area. **Founded:** 1986. **Geographic Preference:** Local.

43417 ▪ Brecksville Chamber of Commerce (BCC)
8803 Brecksville Rd., Ste. 7-267
Brecksville, OH 44141
Ph: (440)526-7350
Co. E-mail: chamber@brecksvillechamber.com
URL: http://brecksvillechamber.com
Contact: Kris Toth, President
Facebook: www.facebook.com/brecksvillechamber
Description: Promotes business and community development in Brecksville, OH. **Founded:** 1968. **Publications:** *The Voice* (Bimonthly). **Geographic Preference:** Local.

43418 ▪ Bremen Area Chamber of Commerce
PO Box 45
Bremen, OH 43107
URL: http://www.bremenareacoc.org
Contact: David W. Foltz, President
Description: Promotes business and community development in Bremen, OH. **Geographic Preference:** Local.

43419 ▪ Brimfield Area Chamber of Commerce (BACC)
PO Box 1613
Kent, OH 44240
Ph: (330)673-2170
Co. E-mail: info@brimfieldchamber.com
URL: http://www.brimfieldchamber.com
Contact: Tom Serle, President
E-mail: nrodd@brimfieldohio.gov
Facebook: www.facebook.com/BrimfieldChamber
Description: Promotes business and community development in the Brimfield, OH area. Organizes community donations for schools and police. **Founded:** 1960. **Publications:** *Monthly Minutes* (Monthly). **Geographic Preference:** Local.

43420 ▪ Bryan Area Chamber of Commerce
138 S Lynn St.
Bryan, OH 43506
Ph: (419)636-2247
Fax: (419)636-5556
Co. E-mail: info@bryanchamber.org
URL: http://www.bryanchamber.org

STATE LISTINGS

Contact: Daniel Yahraus, Executive Director
Facebook: www.facebook.com/Bryan-Area-Chamber-of-Commerce-99959687900
Description: Promotes Bryan and enhance the quality of life and economic stability of the community.
Founded: 1947. **Publications:** *Buzz* (Weekly).
Geographic Preference: Local.

43421 ■ Buckeye Lake Region Chamber of Commerce
PO Box 5
Buckeye Lake, OH 43008
Ph: (740)398-7205
Co. E-mail: buckeyelakeregioncc@gmail.com
URL: http://www.buckeyelakecc.com
Contact: Tim Ryan, President
Facebook: www.facebook.com/BuckeyeLakeChamber
Description: Promotes business and community development in Buckeye Lake, OH area. **Geographic Preference:** Local.

43422 ■ Bucyrus Area Chamber of Commerce (BACC)
117 E Mansfield St.
Bucyrus, OH 44820
Ph: (419)562-4811
Co. E-mail: bacc@bucyrusohio.com
URL: http://www.bucyrusohio.com
Contact: Brian Gernert, President
Facebook: www.facebook.com/bucyrusareachamberofcommerce
YouTube: www.youtube.com/channel/UCvgcZrr3A78ttGf-xLbq6FA
Description: Promotes business and community development in Crawford County, OH. **Founded:** 1925. **Publications:** *Chamber of Commerce News* (Weekly). **Geographic Preference:** Local.

43423 ■ *Business Barometer*
Released: Quarterly **Price:** free. **Availability:** Print.

43424 ■ *Business Broadcast*
501 S Main St.
Mount Vernon, OH 43050
Ph: (740)393-1111
Co. E-mail: chamber@knoxchamber.com
URL: http://www.knoxchamber.com
Contact: Carol Grubaugh, Executive Director
E-mail: carol@knoxchamber.com
URL(s): www.knoxchamber.com/marketing-opportunities
Released: Monthly **Availability:** Online.

43425 ■ *Business Bytes*
144 S Main St., Ste. 100
Lima, OH 45801
Ph: (419)222-6045
Fax: (419)229-0266
URL: http://limachamber.com
Contact: Jed Metzger, President
E-mail: jmetzger@limachamber.com
URL(s): limachamber.com/membership/discountprograms/chamber-publications
Released: Monthly **Availability:** Online.

43426 ■ *Business Directory*
130 Martz St., Ste. 5
Greenville, OH 45331
Ph: (937)548-2102
Co. E-mail: info@darkecountyohio.com
URL: http://www.darkecountyohio.com
Contact: Peggy Emerson, President
E-mail: peggye@darkecountyohio.com
URL(s): www.chamberdata.net/businesssearch.aspx?dbid2=ohdark
Availability: Print.

43427 ■ *Business Directory of Bedford*
Released: Biennial **Availability:** Print.

43428 ■ *Buyer's Guide and Membership Directory*
121 E Logan St.
Celina, OH 45822
Ph: (419)586-2219
Fax: (419)586-8645

Co. E-mail: info@celinamercer.com
URL: http://www.celinamercer.com
Contact: Stacy Beougher, Executive Director
URL(s): celinamercer.com/memberships/member-benefits
Released: Annual **Availability:** Print.

43429 ■ *Buzz*
138 S Lynn St.
Bryan, OH 43506
Ph: (419)636-2247
Fax: (419)636-5556
Co. E-mail: info@bryanchamber.org
URL: http://www.bryanchamber.org
Contact: Daniel Yahraus, Executive Director
URL(s): www.bryanchamber.org/chamber-buzz
Released: Weekly **Description:** Contains information, fun and interesting facts as well as upcoming events. **Availability:** Print.

43430 ■ Cambridge Area Chamber of Commerce (CCC)
607 Wheeling Ave.
Cambridge, OH 43725
Ph: (740)439-6688
Fax: (740)439-6689
Co. E-mail: info@cambridgeohiochamber.com
URL: http://cambridgeohiochamber.com
Contact: Jennifer Vincent, President
Facebook: www.facebook.com/CambAreaChamber
X (Twitter): x.com/CambAreaChamber
Description: Promotes business and community development in the Cambridge, OH area. **Founded:** 1947. **Geographic Preference:** Local.

43431 ■ Canal Winchester Area Chamber of Commerce (CWACC)
57 W Waterloo St.
Canal Winchester, OH 43110
Ph: (614)837-1556
Co. E-mail: cwchamber@canalwinchester.com
URL: http://www.canalwinchester.com
Contact: Denise Mathias, Advisor
Facebook: www.facebook.com/CWAChamber
Instagram: www.instagram.com/cwachamber
YouTube: www.youtube.com/channel/UCTRdzL7_DOhfbs19PA0uz0Q
Description: Represents businesses, individuals and organizations dedicated to the promotion of business and the community. Promotes and fosters the free enterprise system through economic development. Advocates for local business interests, and provides investor benefits. **Founded:** 1985. **Publications:** *Canal Winchester Area Chamber of Commerce Newsletter* (Monthly). **Geographic Preference:** Local.

43432 ■ *Canal Winchester Area Chamber of Commerce Newsletter*
57 W Waterloo St.
Canal Winchester, OH 43110
Ph: (614)837-1556
Co. E-mail: cwchamber@canalwinchester.com
URL: http://www.canalwinchester.com
Contact: Denise Mathias, Advisor
URL(s): www.canalwinchester.com/member-magazine-copy
Released: Monthly **Availability:** Print.

43433 ■ Canton Regional Chamber of Commerce (CRCC)
222 Market Ave., N
Canton, OH 44702
Ph: (330)456-7253
Free: 800-533-4302
Fax: (330)452-7786
URL: http://www.cantonchamber.org
Contact: Dennis P. Saunier, President
E-mail: dennys@cantonchamber.org
Facebook: www.facebook.com/CantonOhioChamber
X (Twitter): x.com/CantonChmbr
YouTube: www.youtube.com/user/CantonRegChamber
Description: Provides services to members and helps advance the economic growth of Canton and the Stark County region. **Founded:** 1914. **Geographic Preference:** Regional.

43434 ■ Carey Area Chamber of Commerce
132 E Findlay St.
Carey, OH 43316
Ph: (419)396-7856
Co. E-mail: director@careychamber.com
URL: http://careychamber.clubexpress.com
Contact: Deirdre Christy, Treasurer
Facebook: www.facebook.com/CareyChamber
Linkedin: www.linkedin.com/in/carey-chamber-529ba2140
X (Twitter): x.com/CareyChamber
Description: Promotes business and community development in Carey, OH. **Founded:** 1993. **Geographic Preference:** Local.

43435 ■ Celina-Mercer County Chamber of Commerce
121 E Logan St.
Celina, OH 45822
Ph: (419)586-2219
Fax: (419)586-8645
Co. E-mail: info@celinamercer.com
URL: http://www.celinamercer.com
Contact: Stacy Beougher, Executive Director
Facebook: www.facebook.com/celinachamber
Description: Promotes business and community development in the Mercer County, OH area. Sponsors area festival and operates Small Business Development Center. **Founded:** 1834. **Publications:** *Buyer's Guide and Membership Directory* (Annual). **Educational Activities:** Ambassador Committee Meeting (Monthly). **Geographic Preference:** Local.

43436 ■ Chagrin Valley Chamber of Commerce (CVCC)
83 N Main St.
Chagrin Falls, OH 44022
Ph: (440)247-6607
Co. E-mail: info@cvcc.org
URL: http://www.cvcc.org
Contact: Deby Lexow, President
Facebook: www.facebook.com/chagrinvalleychamber
Instagram: www.instagram.com/chagrinvalleychamber
Description: Serves as a powerful regional force, encouraging business to relocate to the Chagrin Valley. Presents the interests of business and industry before local and state governments. Supports the cultural and civic life of the communities and works to make the Valley a better place to live and do business. **Founded:** 1943. **Publications:** *Chagrin Valley Magazine* (Annual). **Geographic Preference:** Local.

43437 ■ Chamber of Commerce in Broadview Heights
PO Box 470211
Broadview Heights, OH 44147
Contact: Cheryle Costa, Contact
Facebook: www.facebook.com/BroadviewHeightsChamber
Description: Businesses, professionals, and government officials dedicated to advancing the prosperity of the Broadview Heights area, its residents, and business. Offers many free and low-cost promotional opportunities for members along with group benefits and discounts on products and services. **Founded:** 1943. **Geographic Preference:** Local.

43438 ■ *Chamber of Commerce News*
117 E Mansfield St.
Bucyrus, OH 44820
Ph: (419)562-4811
Co. E-mail: bacc@bucyrusohio.com
URL: http://www.bucyrusohio.com
Contact: Brian Gernert, President
URL(s): bucyrusohio.com/news
Released: Weekly **Availability:** Print.

43439 ■ *Chamber Directory*
4001 Old Salem Rd.
Englewood, OH 45322
Ph: (937)836-2550
Co. E-mail: angie@northmontchamber.com
URL: http://www.northmontchamber.com
Contact: Mike McKinniss, President
URL(s): www.northmontchamber.com/directory
Availability: Online.

43440 ■ Chamber Notes
32 S Sandusky St.
  Delaware, OH 43015
Ph: (740)369-6221
Fax: (740)369-4817
Co. E-mail: dachamber@delawareareachamber.com
URL: http://www.delawareareachamber.com
Contact: Holly Quaine, President
E-mail: hquaine@delawareareachamber.com
URL(s): www.delawareareachamber.com/newsletter
Released: Monthly **Availability:** PDF; Online.

43441 ■ Champaign County Chamber of Commerce
127 W Ct., St.
  Urbana, OH 43078
Ph: (937)653-5764
Co. E-mail: info@champaignohio.com
URL: http://www.champaignohio.com
Contact: Ty Henderson, President
Facebook: www.facebook.com/champaignohio
X (Twitter): x.com/champaignccc
Instagram: www.instagram.com/champaignohio
Description: Promotes business and community development in Champaign County, OH. Holds monthly board meeting. **Founded:** 1950. **Publications:** *The Chamber ADVANTAGE* (Monthly). **Geographic Preference:** Local.

43442 ■ Chardon Area Chamber of Commerce (CACC)
213 Main St., Ste. D
  Chardon, OH 44024
Ph: (440)285-9050
Co. E-mail: mricco@chardonchamber.com
URL: http://business.chardonchamber.com
Contact: Cathy Peters, President
Facebook: www.facebook.com/ChardonAreaChamberOfCommerce
Description: Promotes business and community development in the Chardon, OH area. **Founded:** 1927. **Publications:** *Chamber Chat* (Monthly). **Geographic Preference:** Local.

43443 ■ Chesterland Chamber of Commerce (CCC)
8228 Mayfield Rd., Ste. 4B
  Chesterland, OH 44026
Ph: (440)729-7297
Fax: (440)729-2690
URL: http://www.cvcc.org/list/member/chesterland-chamber-of-commerce-chesterland-252
Contact: Rose Pasternak, Office Manager
Description: Promotes business and community development in Chester Township, Ohio and surrounding areas, including Geauga County and adjacent Cuyahoga and Lake counties. Publishes the Chester telephone directory annually. **Founded:** 1962. **Publications:** *The Communicator* (Quarterly); *Telephone Directory* (Annual). **Geographic Preference:** Local.

43444 ■ Chillicothe Ross Chamber of Commerce (CRCC)
45 E Main St.
  Chillicothe, OH 45601
Ph: (740)702-2722
Fax: (740)702-2727
Co. E-mail: bkellough@chillicotheohio.com
URL: http://chillicotheohio.com
Contact: Bobbi Kellough, Member
E-mail: bkellough@chillicotheohio.com
Facebook: www.facebook.com/ChillRossChamber
Linkedin: www.linkedin.com/company/9274723
X (Twitter): x.com/ChamberChilli
YouTube: www.youtube.com/channel/UCj-OA00l_ClCvZCnWrR_Ndw
Description: Promotes business and community development in Ross County, OH. **Founded:** 1888. **Publications:** *Chillicothe Ross Chamber of Commerce--Membership Directory & Buyer's Guide* (Annual); *Directory of Members & Buyers Guide*. **Awards:** Chillicothe Ross Chamber of Commerce Entrepreneur of the Year (Annual). **Geographic Preference:** Local.

43445 ■ Cincinnati USA Regional Chamber - Library
3 E 4th St., Ste. 200
  Cincinnati, OH 45202
Ph: (513)579-3100
URL: http://www.cincinnatichamber.com
Contact: Chris Whittaker, President
Facebook: www.facebook.com/cincinnatichamber
Linkedin: www.linkedin.com/company/cincinnati-usa-regional-chamber
X (Twitter): x.com/CincyChamber
Description: Promotes business and community development in the Cincinnati, OH area. **Scope:** Business. **Founded:** 1839. **Holdings:** Figures not available. **Publications:** *Greater Cincinnati International Trade Directory* (Biennial); *Cincinnati USA Regional Chamber* (Annual); *Greater Cincinnati Chamber of Commerce--Clubs and Organizations Directory* (Annual); *Chamber Connect* (Monthly); *Chambervision* (Monthly); *Cincinnati U.S.A. Business Connections Directory* (Annual); *Greater Cincinnati Chamber of Commerce International Trade Directory* (Biennial); *Cincinnati USA Regional Chamber--Member Directory*; *Japanese Investment in the Midwest*; *Foreign Consulates*; *Building and Sites Guide*; *Major Employers* (Annual); *Fortune Firms Headquartered in Cincinnati and Ohio*; *Major Manufacturers*; *Headquartered Companies*; *Medium-Sized Companies*; *Foreign Firms* (Annual); *Industrial Pin-Pointer: Cincinnati* (Biennial). **Awards:** Cincinnati USA Regional Chamber Great Living Cincinnatians Award (Annual). **Geographic Preference:** Local.

43446 ■ Clermont Chamber of Commerce (CCC)
4355 Ferguson Dr., Ste. 150
  Cincinnati, OH 45245
Ph: (513)576-5000
Fax: (513)576-5001
Co. E-mail: chamber@clermontchamber.com
URL: http://clermontchamber.com
Contact: Joy Lytle, President
E-mail: joy.lytle@clermontchamber.com
Facebook: www.facebook.com/ClermontChamber
Linkedin: www.linkedin.com/company/clermont-chamber-of-commerce
X (Twitter): x.com/ClermontChamber
Instagram: www.instagram.com/clermontchamber
Description: Encourages businesses to relocate to Clermont, existing businesses to stay in Clermont, and new and growing businesses to establish their operations in the county. Provides economic development assistance to companies interested in Clermont County, including assistance with financing, expansion, relocation, site identification, and labor force development. **Founded:** 1969. **Publications:** *Images of Clermont County* (Annual); *Intercom* (Monthly). **Awards:** Excellence in Customer Focus Award (Annual); Clermont Chamber of Commerce Emerging Small Business Award (Annual); Clermont Chamber of Commerce Innovative Business Practice Award (Annual). **Geographic Preference:** Local.

43447 ■ Columbiana Area Chamber of Commerce (CACC)
c/o Erich Offenburg, Executive Director
333 N Main St.
  Columbiana, OH 44408
Ph: (330)482-3822
Co. E-mail: info@columbianachamber.com
URL: http://www.columbianachamber.com
Contact: Erich Offenburg, Executive Director
Facebook: www.facebook.com/columbiana.chamber.5
Linkedin: www.linkedin.com/company/columbus-area-chamber-of-commerce
Description: Represents business and community leaders committed to integrity and fair trade. Strives to promote business and commerce in the Columbiana area. Serves members by providing networking opportunities and promoting area businesses, industry and the community as a whole. Offers business involvement in: Safety Council; Human Resource Seminars; Quarterly Networking Opportunities; and Quarterly Educational Opportunities. **Publications:** *Chamber Connection* (Monthly). **Awards:** Columbiana Area Chamber of Commerce Business Person of the Year (Annual). **Geographic Preference:** Local.

43448 ■ Columbus Chamber of Commerce (CCC)
150 S Front St., Ste. 220
  Columbus, OH 43215
Ph: (614)221-1321
Co. E-mail: info@columbus.org
URL: http://columbus.org
Contact: Don DePerro, President
E-mail: dondeperro@columbus.org
Facebook: www.facebook.com/columbuschamberoh
Linkedin: www.linkedin.com/company/columbus-chamber
X (Twitter): x.com/ColumbusChamber
Instagram: www.instagram.com/columbuschamber
Description: Fosters economic growth and business development in Greater Columbus community. **Founded:** 1884. **Publications:** *Discovery* (Monthly); *Columbus Employment Resource Directory* (Biennial); *Member Connection* (Monthly). **Geographic Preference:** Local.

43449 ■ *The Communicator*
99 Commerce Pk. Dr., Ste. A
  Westerville, OH 43082
Ph: (614)882-8917
Fax: (614)882-2085
Co. E-mail: info@westervillechamber.com
URL: http://www.westervillechamber.com
Contact: Janet Tressler-Davis, President
E-mail: jdavis@westervillechamber.com
URL(s): www.westervillechamber.com/communicator-newsletter-2
Released: Monthly **Description:** Contains Chamber news, local events and important information about business in Westerville. **Availability:** Online.

43450 ■ *Compass*
Co. E-mail: contact@apf.org
URL: http://apf.org
Contact: Dr. Jay Gary, Chairman
URL(s): www.profuturists.org/pubs
Released: Bimonthly **Availability:** Print; Online.

43451 ■ Conneaut Area Chamber of Commerce
235 Main St.
  Conneaut, OH 44030
Ph: (440)593-2402
Co. E-mail: conneautchamber@gwcmail.net
URL: http://www.conneautareachamber.org
Contact: Wendy DuBey, Executive Director
Facebook: www.facebook.com/ConneautChamberOfCommerce
Description: Promotes business and community development in the Conneaut, OH area. Sponsors annual Community Appreciation Week in August, flag program in downtown area and harbor area, lights of love tree in November and December. **Founded:** 1906. **Geographic Preference:** Local.

43452 ■ Coshocton County Chamber of Commerce [Coshocton Area Chamber of Commerce; Coshocton Chamber of Commerce]
200 N Whitewoman St.
  Coshocton, OH 43812
Ph: (740)622-5411
URL: http://coshoctonchamber.com
Contact: Kirby Hasseman, President
X (Twitter): x.com/coshchamber
Description: Promotes business and community development in Coshocton County, OH. Sponsors annual Coshocton Canal Festival, Coshocton Hot Air Balloon Race, and T.V. Auction. **Founded:** 1973. **Geographic Preference:** Local.

43453 ■ Cuyahoga Falls Chamber of Commerce (CFCC)
151 Portage Trl., Ste. 1
  Cuyahoga Falls, OH 44221
Ph: (330)929-6756
Co. E-mail: info@cfchamber.com
URL: http://www.cfchamber.com

STATE LISTINGS

Contact: Kathy Romito, Vice President
Facebook: www.facebook.com/
 cuyahogafallschamber
Instagram: www.instagram.com/
 cuyahogafallschamber

Description: Promotes economic growth and development by encouraging programs designed to support, strengthen and expand the local businesses in Cuyahoga Falls. Supports activities of a civic, social and cultural nature which are designed to increase the functional and aesthetic values of the community. **Founded:** 1926. **Publications:** *Cuyahoga Falls Chamber of Commerce--Membership Directory.* **Geographic Preference:** Local.

43454 ■ Darke County Chamber of Commerce
130 Martz St., Ste. 5
 Greenville, OH 45331
Ph: (937)548-2102
Co. E-mail: info@darkecountyohio.com
URL: http://www.darkecountyohio.com
Contact: Peggy Emerson, President
E-mail: peggye@darkecountyohio.com
Facebook: www.facebook.com/darkecountychamber
X (Twitter): x.com/darkechamber

Description: Promotes business and community development in the Greenville, OH area. **Founded:** 1927. **Publications:** *Business Directory.* **Geographic Preference:** Local.

43455 ■ Dayton Area Chamber of Commerce (DACC)
8 N Main St., Ste. 100
 Dayton, OH 45402-1904
Ph: (937)226-1444
Fax: (937)226-8254
Co. E-mail: info@dacc.org
URL: http://daytonchamber.org
Contact: Chris Kershner, President
Linkedin: www.linkedin.com/company/day
 tonchamber
X (Twitter): x.com/DaytonChamber
YouTube: www.youtube.com/channel/UCE5v0mJOuF
 2CRs5Tlxh2lqQ

Description: Promotes business and community development in Dayton, OH area. **Founded:** 1907. **Publications:** *Dayton Area Chamber of Commerce--Membership Directory; ChamberWatch* (Bimonthly); *Focus.* **Geographic Preference:** Local.

43456 ■ Defiance Area Chamber of Commerce
400 Clinton St.
 Defiance, OH 43512
Ph: (419)782-7946
Co. E-mail: commerce@defiancechamber.com
URL: http://www.defiancechamber.com
Contact: Ray Meiers, Chairman of the Board
Facebook: www.facebook.com/DEFICHAMBER
Linkedin: www.linkedin.com/company/the-defiance
 -area-chamber-of-commerce
X (Twitter): x.com/DefianceChamber
Instagram: www.instagram.com/defiancechamber
YouTube: www.youtube.com/watch

Description: Office holders, business leaders, educators, youth professionals and small business owners. Acts as a respected voice of advocacy for business and education in Defiance County. **Publications:** *The Chamber Network* (Monthly). **Geographic Preference:** Local.

43457 ■ Delaware Area Chamber of Commerce
32 S Sandusky St.
 Delaware, OH 43015
Ph: (740)369-6221
Fax: (740)369-4817
Co. E-mail: dachamber@delawareareachamber.com
URL: http://www.delawareareachamber.com
Contact: Holly Quaine, President
E-mail: hquaine@delawareareachamber.com
Facebook: www.facebook.com/
 DelawareAreaChamber
X (Twitter): x.com/DelAreaChamber

Description: Promotes business and community development in Delaware County, OH. **Founded:** 1907. **Publications:** *Chamber Notes* (Monthly); *Delaware Area Chamber of Commerce Business Directory.* **Geographic Preference:** Local.

43458 ■ Delphos Area Chamber of Commerce
310 N Main St.
 Delphos, OH 45833
Ph: (419)695-1771
Co. E-mail: info@delphoschamber.com
URL: http://www.delphoschamber.com
Contact: Angie Gable, President
E-mail: agable@wlio.com
Facebook: www.facebook.com/delphoschamberwww
 .facebook.com/delphoschamber

Description: Promotes business and community development in the Delphos, OH area. Sponsors annual Canal Days Festival. **Geographic Preference:** Local.

43459 ■ Delta Chamber of Commerce
401 Main St.
 Delta, OH 43515
Ph: (419)822-3089
Co. E-mail: deltachambercommerce@gmail.com
URL: http://www.deltachamberofcommerce.org
Contact: Candy Baird, President
Facebook: www.facebook.com/Del
 taChamberCommerce

Description: Promotes business and community development in Delta, OH. **Geographic Preference:** Local.

43460 ■ Deshler Chamber of Commerce
PO Box 123
 Deshler, OH 43516
Ph: (419)601-2255
Co. E-mail: deshlerchamber@gmail.com
URL: http://deshlerohiochamber.com
Contact: Josh Biederstedt, President

Description: Promotes business and community development in Deshler, OH. **Geographic Preference:** Local.

43461 ■ *Discovery*
150 S Front St., Ste. 220
 Columbus, OH 43215
Ph: (614)221-1321
Co. E-mail: info@columbus.org
URL: http://columbus.org
Contact: Don DePerro, President
E-mail: dondeperro@columbus.org
URL(s): web.columbus.org/Social-Advocacy
 -Organizations/Capital-CrossroadsDiscovery-Distric
 t-4690

Released: Monthly **Availability:** Print.

43462 ■ Eastern Lake County Chamber of Commerce
77 N St. Clair, Ste. 103
 Painesville, OH 44077
Ph: (440)357-7572
Co. E-mail: info@mylakeoh.com
URL: http://www.easternlakecountychamber.org
Contact: Thomas Mitchell, President
Facebook: www.facebook.com/easternlakecounty
Linkedin: www.linkedin.com/company/eastern-lake
 -county-chamber-of-commerce
X (Twitter): x.com/easternlakecty
Instagram: www.instagram.com/easternlakecounty
YouTube: www.youtube.com/channel/UC
 4PYFTPTPhYwPde2BE6jAlw

Description: Promotes business and community development to enrich the economic, civic, social, cultural and environmental well being of Painesville area. **Awards:** Painesville Area Chamber of Commerce Citizen of the Year (Annual). **Geographic Preference:** Local.

43463 ■ Eastern Maumee Bay Chamber of Commerce
4350 Navarre Ave., Ste. C
 Oregon, OH 43616
Ph: (419)693-5580
Co. E-mail: director@embchamber.org

URL: http://www.embchamber.org
Contact: Richard Johnson, President
Facebook: www.facebook.com/EMBChamber
Linkedin: www.linkedin.com/company/eastern
 -maumee-bay-chamber-of-commerce
X (Twitter): x.com/EMBChamber

Description: Strives to improve the quality of life, general welfare and prosperity of Eastern Maumee Bay community. **Publications:** *Chamber Hi-Lites* (Monthly). **Geographic Preference:** Local.

43464 ■ Eaton - Preble County Chamber of Commerce (PCCC)
PO Box 303
 Eaton, OH 45320
Ph: (937)456-4949
Fax: (937)456-4949
Co. E-mail: chamberoffices@preblecountyohio.com
URL: http://www.preblecounty.com
Contact: Karen Moss, Executive Director
E-mail: karen.moss@preblecountyohio.com
Facebook: www.facebook.com/PrebleCoun
 tyChamberOfCommerce
YouTube: www.youtube.com/channel/
 UCUUynnfQwsWVjoWaPfYuNJw

Description: Promotes free enterprise and advances the business community in the Eaton and Preble County area. **Founded:** 1952. **Geographic Preference:** Local.

43465 ■ Edgerton Area Chamber of Commerce (EACC)
PO Box 682
 Edgerton, OH 43517
Ph: (567)210-1405
Co. E-mail: edgertonohiochamber@gmail.com
URL: http://edgertonohiochamber.com
Facebook: www.facebook.com/Edgerton-Area-Cham
 ber-of-Commerce-Official-606249369433729
X (Twitter): x.com/edgertonchamber

Description: Promotes business and community development in the Edgerton, WI area. **Geographic Preference:** Local.

43466 ■ *The Entrepreneur*
The Riverview Bldg.
 100 Front St.
 Marietta, OH 45750
Ph: (740)373-5176
Co. E-mail: info@mariettachamber.com
URL: http://www.mariettachamber.com
Contact: Kelsy Eaton, President
URL(s): www.mariettachamber.com/the-entrepreneur

Released: Monthly **Description:** Features current activities, legislation, and news items about the members. **Availability:** PDF; Online.

43467 ■ Euclid Chamber of Commerce (ECC)
22639 Euclid Ave.
 Euclid, OH 44117
Ph: (216)731-9322
Co. E-mail: info@euclidchamber.com
URL: http://www.euclidchamber.com
Contact: Dana Heil, Executive Director
X (Twitter): x.com/euclidchamber

Description: Individuals from business, industry, the professions, and the public sector interested in promoting business and community development in Euclid, OH. **Founded:** 1930. **Publications:** *Chamber News; Directory of Members & Buyers Guide.* **Geographic Preference:** Local.

43468 ■ Fairborn Area Chamber of Commerce (FACC)
12 N Central Ave.
 Fairborn, OH 45324
Ph: (937)878-3191
Fax: (937)878-3197
URL: http://fairbornchamber.com
Contact: Brenda Smith, Co-President
Facebook: www.facebook.com/fairbornchamber

Description: Promotes business and community development in the Fairborn, OH area. Participates in the annual Sweet Corn Festival and 4th of July parade. **Founded:** 1944. **Publications:** *Chamber Update.* **Educational Activities:** October Chamber

Chat (Monthly); Christmas Open House. **Awards:** Fairborn Area Chamber of Commerce President's Award (Annual). **Geographic Preference:** Local.

43469 ■ Fairfield Chamber of Commerce
670 Wessel Dr.
Fairfield, OH 45014
Ph: (513)881-5500
Fax: (513)881-5503
URL: http://fairfieldchamber.com
Contact: Kert Radel, President
E-mail: president@fairfieldchamber.com
Facebook: www.facebook.com/fairfiel
dchamberofcommerce
X (Twitter): x.com/FFC_of_Commerce
Description: Promotes business and community development in the Fairfield, OH area. Sponsors Indian Summer Days Festival. **Founded:** 1956. **Publications:** *The Fairfield Advantage* (Monthly). **Geographic Preference:** Local.

43470 ■ Fayette County Chamber of Commerce
206 E Ct. St.
Washington Court House, OH 43160
Ph: (740)335-0761
Co. E-mail: julie@fayettecountyohio.com
URL: http://fayettecountyohio.com
Contact: Kristy Bowers, President
E-mail: kristy@fayettecountyohio.com
Facebook: www.facebook.com/faycochamber
Linkedin: www.linkedin.com/company/fayette-co
-chamber-of-commerce
Description: Seeks to promote and enhance the business environment within the area. **Founded:** 1965. **Publications:** *Images Directory* (Annual); *The Voice of Business* (Monthly); *Fayette in Focus*. **Educational Activities:** Business After Hours. **Awards:** Fayette Chamber of Commerce Outstanding Partner of the Year Award (Annual). **Geographic Preference:** Local.

43471 ■ Findlay-Hancock County Chamber of Commerce
123 E Main Cross St.
Findlay, OH 45840
Ph: (419)422-3313
Fax: (419)422-9508
Co. E-mail: info@findlayhancockchamber.com
URL: http://findlayhancockchamber.com
Contact: Glenn Jost, President
Facebook: www.facebook.com/Fin
dlayHancockChamber
Linkedin: www.linkedin.com/company/fin
dlayhancockchamber
X (Twitter): x.com/FndlyHanChamber
Instagram: www.instagram.com/FndlyHanChamber
Description: Promotes the growth of the community by concentrating on the needs of businesses. Provides medical and business opportunities for the members and interested individuals. **Publications:** *Investor Report* (Bimonthly). **Geographic Preference:** Local.

43472 ■ Fostoria Area Chamber of Commerce
342 Perry St.
Fostoria, OH 44830
Ph: (419)435-0486
Co. E-mail: development@fostoriachamber.com
URL: http://www.fostoriaohio.org
Contact: Sarah Stephens Krupp, Director
E-mail: sarah@fostoriachamber.com
Description: Promotes business and community development in the Fostoria, OH area. **Geographic Preference:** Local.

43473 ■ Gahanna Area Chamber of Commerce (GACC)
81 Mill St., Ste. 300
Gahanna, OH 43230
Ph: (614)471-0451
Fax: (614)471-5122
Co. E-mail: info@gahannaareachamber.com
URL: http://gahannaareachamber.com
Contact: Brad Fisher, President
Facebook: www.facebook.com/gahannaareachamber

X (Twitter): x.com/GahannaChamber
YouTube: www.youtube.com/user/
gahannaareachamber
Description: Promotes business and community development in Gahanna, OH. **Founded:** 1981. **Geographic Preference:** Local.

43474 ■ Galion-Crestline Area Chamber of Commerce
312 N Seltzer St.
Crestline, OH 44827
Ph: (419)468-7737
Co. E-mail: ceo@galion-crestlinechamber.org
URL: http://galion-crestlinechamber.org
Contact: Miranda Jones, Executive Director
Facebook: www.facebook.com/galioncres
tlinechamberofcommerce
Linkedin: www.linkedin.com/company/galion-crestline
-area-chamber-of-commerce
X (Twitter): x.com/GCAreaChamber
Description: Promotes business and community development in Crestline, OH area. **Founded:** 1985. **Geographic Preference:** Local.

43475 ■ Gallia County Chamber of Commerce
16 State St.
Gallipolis, OH 45631
Ph: (740)446-0596
Co. E-mail: chamber@galliacounty.org
URL: http://galliacounty.org
Contact: Josh Wellington, Executive Director
E-mail: jwellington@galliacounty.org
Description: Promotes, supports and strengthens business and economic development throughout the county, and provides leadership through networking and education, to improve the overall business environment for Chamber members. **Publications:** *Bandstand* (Monthly); *Gallia County Chamber of Commerce Membership Directory & Community Profile* (Semiannual). **Awards:** The Bud and Donna McGhee Community Service Award (Annual). **Geographic Preference:** Local.

43476 ■ Garrettsville Area Chamber of Commerce
PO Box 1
Garrettsville, OH 44231
Ph: (330)527-2411
URL: http://www.garrettsvillearea.com
Contact: Ted Lysiak, President
E-mail: president@44231.org
Facebook: www.facebook.com/discover44231
X (Twitter): x.com/discover44231
Instagram: www.instagram.com/discover44231
Description: Promotes business and community development in Portage County, OH. Helps operate People Tree for the needy. Sponsors Silver Creek Turkey Daze Festival. **Founded:** 1804. **Publications:** *Garrettsville: New England Charm Today - We Have it All*. **Geographic Preference:** Local.

43477 ■ Geneva Area Chamber of Commerce (GACC)
866 E Main St.
Geneva, OH 44041
Ph: (440)466-8694
Fax: (440)466-0823
Co. E-mail: info@genevachamber.org
URL: http://www.genevachamber.org
Contact: Jamie Oritz, President
Facebook: www.facebook.com/GenevaOHChamber
Description: Promotes business and community development in the Geneva, OH area. **Geographic Preference:** Local.

43478 ■ Geneva on the Lake Chamber of Commerce
5540 Lake Rd. E
Geneva, OH 44041
Ph: (440)466-8600
Free: 800-862-9948
Co. E-mail: visitus@visitgenevaonthelake.com
URL: http://www.visitgenevaonthelake.com
Contact: Donald P. Woodward, Contact
Facebook: www.facebook.com/visitgotl
X (Twitter): x.com/visitgotl

Description: Geneva on the lake chamber of commerce is an independent non profit organization provides supporting services. **Geographic Preference:** Local.

43479 ■ Greater Akron Chamber (GAC)
388 S Main St., Ste. 205
Akron, OH 44311-1064
Ph: (330)376-5550
Co. E-mail: info@greaterakronchamber.org
URL: http://www.greaterakronchamber.org
Contact: Steve Millard, President
E-mail: smillard@greaterakronchamber.org
Facebook: www.facebook.com/Grea
terAkronChamber
Linkedin: www.linkedin.com/company/greater-akron
-chamber
X (Twitter): x.com/GrtAkronChamber
Instagram: www.instagram.com/grtakronchamber
YouTube: www.youtube.com/user/Grea
terAkronChamber
Description: Serves business organizations to improve the economic and social status of Greater Akron. **Founded:** 1907. **Publications:** *Akron--International Trade Directory* (Annual); *Greater Akron Chamber--Membership Directory & Buyer's Guide* (Annual); *Directions* (Bimonthly); *Directory of Metalworking Firms in the Greater Akron, Ohio Region* (Irregular). **Geographic Preference:** Regional.

43480 ■ Greater Cincinnati and Northern Kentucky African American Chamber of Commerce
2303 Gilbert Ave.
Cincinnati, OH 45206
Ph: (513)751-9900
Co. E-mail: info@african-americanchamber.com
URL: http://www.african-americanchamber.com
Contact: Eric H. Kearney, President
E-mail: kearney@african-americanchamber.com
Facebook: www.facebook.com/TheCincinna
tiAAChamber
X (Twitter): x.com/CincyAAChamber
Instagram: www.instagram.com/thecincinna
tiaachamber
YouTube: www.youtube.com/channel/UCPVtbb1QTJ
thekX-jJ-x7Qw
Description: Works to identify new market opportunities. Improves access to capital and economic growth for established and emerging African American businesses. **Founded:** 1996. **Geographic Preference:** Local.

43481 ■ Greater Hamilton Chamber of Commerce (GHCC)
201 Dayton St.
Hamilton, OH 45011
Ph: (513)844-1500
Co. E-mail: tiffany@hamilton-ohio.com
URL: http://www.hamilton-ohio.com
Contact: Dan Bates, Secretary
E-mail: dan@hamilton-ohio.com
Facebook: www.facebook.com/GreaterHamil
tonChamber
X (Twitter): x.com/hamchamberoh
Instagram: www.instagram.com/greaterhamil
tonchamberoh
YouTube: www.youtube.com/user/GrHamil
tonChamber
Description: Promotes business and community development in the Hamilton, OH area. **Founded:** 1910. **Publications:** *ChamberLetter* (Bimonthly). **Awards:** Greater Hamilton Chamber of Commerce Citizen of the Year (Annual). **Geographic Preference:** Local.

43482 ■ Greater Lawrence County Area Chamber of Commerce (GLCACC)
216 Collins Ave.
South Point, OH 45680
Ph: (740)377-4550
URL: http://lawrencecc.org/index.html
Contact: Katie McKnight, President
Facebook: www.facebook.com/lawrencecountycofc

Description: Promotes business and community development in Lawrence County, OH. Conducts seminars and workshops. **Founded:** 1983. **Geographic Preference:** Local.

43483 ■ Greater Medina Chamber of Commerce (GMCC)
211 S Ct., St.
  Medina, OH 44256
Ph: (330)723-8773
Co. E-mail: info@medinaohchamber.com
URL: http://www.medinaohchamber.com
Contact: Jaclyn Ringstmeier, Executive Director
E-mail: jaclyn@medinaohchamber.com
Facebook: www.facebook.com/medinachamber
Linkedin: www.linkedin.com/company/greaterme dinachamberofcommerce
X (Twitter): x.com/GrMedinaChamber
Instagram: www.instagram.com/medinachamber
YouTube: www.youtube.com/channel/UCS_V2kgS _GxkOFV1n8iuHSw
Description: Unites hundreds of businesses and professional firms and serves as the central agency that works to improve business and build a better community. **Founded:** 1938. **Publications:** *The Chamber Link* (Bimonthly). **Geographic Preference:** Local.

43484 ■ Greater Powell Area Chamber of Commerce
44 N Liberty St.
  Powell, OH 43065
Ph: (614)888-1090
Fax: (614)888-4803
Co. E-mail: admin@powellchamber.com
URL: http://www.powellchamber.com
Contact: Mark Goodwin, President
Facebook: www.facebook.com/PowellChamber
X (Twitter): x.com/PowellChamberC
YouTube: www.youtube.com/channel/UCbRu3L 5Cq8pikfDFOXsWSng
Description: Promotes business and community development in the greater Powell, OH area. **Founded:** 1991. **Publications:** *Greater Powell Area Chamber of Commerce Directory and Community Guide* (Annual). **Geographic Preference:** Local.

43485 ■ Green Chamber of Commerce
4735 Massillon Rd. No. 459
  Green, OH 44232
Ph: (330)896-3023
Co. E-mail: info@greenareachamber.org
URL: http://greenareachamber.org
Contact: Marco LaNave, Secretary
Facebook: www.facebook.com/greenareachamber
Instagram: www.instagram.com/greenareachamber
Description: Works to advance the interest of business and professional firms in the City of Green, Ohio and the surrounding communities. **Founded:** 2000. **Geographic Preference:** Local.

43486 ■ Grove City Area Chamber of Commerce (GCACC)
4069 Broadway
  Grove City, OH 43123
Ph: (614)875-9762
Fax: (614)875-1510
Co. E-mail: e.dir@gcchamber.org
URL: http://www.gcchamber.org
Contact: Shawn Conrad, Executive Director
E-mail: shawn@gcchamber.org
Facebook: www.facebook.com/gcchamber
X (Twitter): x.com/gcchamber
Instagram: www.instagram.com/gcchamber
Description: Business, industry, and professional persons interested in promoting business and community development in the southwestern Franklin County, OH area. Sponsors flea and farmer's markets. **Founded:** 1978. **Geographic Preference:** Local.

43487 ■ Hardin County Chamber and Business Alliance (HCCBA)
225 S Detroit St.
  Kenton, OH 43326
Ph: (419)673-4131
Co. E-mail: alliance@hccba.com
URL: http://hardincountyoh.org
Contact: Holli Underwood, President
E-mail: hunderwood@hccba.com
Facebook: www.facebook.com/HardinCoun tyChamberBusinessAlliance
X (Twitter): x.com/hccba
YouTube: www.youtube.com/channel/ UCRkrN0khjJZENDrdbt4yIAg
Description: Business, industry, and professional persons dedicated to business and community development in the Hardin County, OH area. **Founded:** 1921. **Publications:** *Alliance* (Weekly). **Awards:** Hardin County Chamber and Business Alliance Citizen of the Year (Annual); Hardin County Chamber and Business Alliance Community Service Awards (Annual). **Geographic Preference:** Local.

43488 ■ Heights-Hillcrest Regional Chamber of Commerce (HRCC)
4645 Mayfield Rd., Ste. 212
  South Euclid, OH 44121
Ph: (216)397-7322
Fax: (216)397-7353
Co. E-mail: info@hrcc.org
URL: http://www.hrcc.org
Contact: Kevin Smalley, President
Facebook: www.facebook.com/HRCC1948
Linkedin: www.linkedin.com/company/heights-hillcres t-regional-chamber-of-commerce
X (Twitter): x.com/HRCCEmpowers
Instagram: www.instagram.com/hrccempowers
Description: Represents the interests of businesses and professionals in the cities of Cleveland Heights, Lyndhurst, Richmond Heights, Shaker Heights, South Euclid and University Heights. **Founded:** 1948. **Geographic Preference:** Local.

43489 ■ Henry County Chamber of Commerce
611 N Perry St.
  Napoleon, OH 43545
Ph: (419)592-1786
Fax: (678)263-3979
Co. E-mail: hcncoc@henrycountychamber.org
URL: http://www.henrycountychamber.org
Contact: Joseph B. Henning, President
E-mail: jhenning@henrycounty.com
Facebook: www.facebook.com/HenryCoChamber
X (Twitter): x.com/HenryCoChamber
YouTube: www.youtube.com/channel/UC 4ilbDlCkpqoOb7q7qpfBRg
Description: Promotes business and community development in the area. Sponsors new teacher breakfast, tourism activities, and business after hours. **Founded:** 1967. **Geographic Preference:** Local.

43490 ■ Highland County Chamber of Commerce (HCCC)
338 W Main St.
  Hillsboro, OH 45133
Ph: (937)393-1111
Co. E-mail: info@thehighlandchamber.com
URL: http://www.thehighlandchamber.com
Contact: Jamie Wheeler, Executive Director
Facebook: www.facebook.com/TheHCCOC
Linkedin: www.linkedin.com/company/highland-coun ty-chamber-of-commerce
X (Twitter): x.com/TheHCCOC
Instagram: www.instagram.com/hccoc
Description: Promotes business and community development in the area. **Founded:** 1967. **Publications:** *Chamber Business Directory*. **Educational Activities:** Hands and Harvest Fall Foliage (Annual). **Geographic Preference:** Local.

43491 ■ Hilliard Area Chamber of Commerce (HACC)
4081 Main St.
  Hilliard, OH 43026
Ph: (614)876-7666
Co. E-mail: info@hilliardchamber.org
URL: http://www.hilliardchamber.org
Contact: Libby Gierach, President
Facebook: www.facebook.com/HilliardChamber
X (Twitter): x.com/HilliardChamber
Description: Businesses, organizations, and government officials organized to promote business and community development in northwestern Franklin County, OH. Sponsors seminars; holds luncheons and Business After Hours parties. Awards scholarships. Sponsors Hollyfest auction and art fair. **Founded:** 1973. **Publications:** *Hilliard Area Chamber of Commerce Professional Directory* (Annual); *News and Views* (Monthly). **Awards:** HACC Hollyfest Scholarship Foundation (Annual). **Geographic Preference:** Local.

43492 ■ Hispanic Chamber Cincinnati USA (HCCUSA)
2637 Erie Ave., Ste. 206
  Cincinnati, OH 45208
Ph: (513)979-6999
Fax: (513)979-6996
Co. E-mail: office@hispanicchambercincinnati.com
URL: http://www.hispanicchambercincinnati.com
Contact: Alfonso Cornejo, President
E-mail: acornejo999@gmail.com
Facebook: www.facebook.com/ HispanicChamberCincinnatiUSA
Linkedin: www.linkedin.com/company/hispanic-cham ber-cincinnati
X (Twitter): x.com/HCCCUSA
Instagram: www.instagram.com/hccusa
YouTube: www.youtube.com/channel/UCtF4oBdvw 6Fi_kgTD3KlFMw
Description: Promotes the continued growth and development of the Hispanic/Latino business community. Works to expand business opportunities, encourage mutually beneficial ties and promote trade community. **Founded:** 1996. **Geographic Preference:** Local.

43493 ■ Holland - Springfield Chamber of Commerce
7617 Angola Rd.
  Holland, OH 43528
Ph: (419)865-2110
URL: http://www.hschamber.com
Facebook: www.facebook.com/hollandspringfieldcoc
Description: Represents businesses. Provides business endorsements and referrals to members. **Founded:** 1990. **Geographic Preference:** Local.

43494 ■ Holmes County Chamber of Commerce
15454 State Rte. 39
  Loudonville, OH 44842
Ph: (330)763-0582
Co. E-mail: info@holmescountychamber.com
URL: http://www.holmescountychamber.com
Contact: Jason Hummel, President
Facebook: www.facebook.com/HolmesCoun tyChamber
YouTube: www.youtube.com/channel/UCiIqpgaaxazIz 4yrmd1-7Zg
Description: Promotes business and community development in the Millersburg, OH area. **Geographic Preference:** Local.

43495 ■ Huber Heights Chamber of Commerce
4707 Brandt Pke.
  Huber Heights, OH 45424
Ph: (937)233-5700
Fax: (937)233-5769
URL: http://huberheightschamber.com
Contact: Jaime Crooks, President
Facebook: www.facebook.com/HHChamber
Linkedin: www.linkedin.com/company/huber-heights -chamber-of-commerce
X (Twitter): x.com/HeightsCommerce
Instagram: www.instagram.com/huberheigh tscocommerce
Description: Promotes business and community development in Huber Heights, OH. **Founded:** 1980. **Geographic Preference:** Local.

43496 ■ Hudson Area Chamber of Commerce (HACC)
27 E Main St.
  Hudson, OH 44236
Ph: (330)650-0621

Co. E-mail: info@hudsoncoc.org
URL: http://www.explorehudson.com
Contact: Nicole Alverson, President
E-mail: nalverson@hudsoncoc.org
Facebook: www.facebook.com/ExploreHudson
Linkedin: www.linkedin.com/company/the-hudson
-area-chamber-of-commerce
Instagram: www.instagram.com/explorehudsonoh
Description: Promotes business and community development in the Hudson, OH area. Holds annual dinner. **Founded:** 1983. **Geographic Preference:** Local.

43497 ■ Huron Chamber of Commerce (HCC)
202 Cleveland Rd. W
Huron, OH 44839
Ph: (419)433-5700
Co. E-mail: chamber@huron.net
URL: http://www.huron.net
Contact: Dr. Heather Demos, President
Facebook: www.facebook.com/people/Huron-Chamber-of-Commerce/100064003964655
Linkedin: www.linkedin.com/in/huron-oh-chamber
-608b0139
Description: Promotes business and community development in Huron, OH. **Publications:** *The Wave* (Quarterly). **Geographic Preference:** Local.

43498 ■ Indian Lake Area Chamber of Commerce (ILACOC)
8200 State Rte. 366
Russells Point, OH 43348
Ph: (937)843-5392
Co. E-mail: office@indianlakechamber.org
URL: http://www.visitindianlakeohio.com
Contact: Kevin Campbell, Chairman
Facebook: www.facebook.com/IndianLakeChamber
Instagram: www.instagram.com/indianlakechamber
Description: Individuals, businesses, churches, and organizations united to promote business and community development in the Russells Point, OH area. **Founded:** 1957. **Publications:** *The Soundings* (Monthly). **Awards:** Indian Lake Area Chamber of Commerce Citizen of the Year (Annual). **Geographic Preference:** Local.

43499 ■ *Island Guide*
148 Delaware Ave.
Put in Bay, OH 43456
Ph: (419)285-2832
Co. E-mail: questions@visitputinbay.com
URL: http://www.visitputinbay.com
URL(s): www.visitputinbay.com/get-around/islan
d-guide
Released: Annual **Description:** Contains tourist information. **Availability:** PDF; Download; Online.

43500 ■ Jackson Area Chamber of Commerce (JACC)
Po Box 510
Jackson, OH 45640
Ph: (740)286-2722
Co. E-mail: jacksonareachamber@yahoo.com
URL: http://jacksonohiochamber.com
Contact: Robin Scaggs, President
Facebook: www.facebook.com/
JacksonOhioChamber
Linkedin: www.linkedin.com/company/jackson-area
-chamber-of-commerce-jackson-oh
X (Twitter): x.com/jacksonohio
Instagram: www.instagram.com/jacksonohiochamber
Pinterest: www.pinterest.com/jacksonchamber
Description: Promotes business and community development in Jackson, OH. **Founded:** 1911. **Publications:** *The Chamber Bulletin* (Monthly). **Awards:** Jackson Area Chamber of Commerce Entrepreneur of the Year (Annual). **Geographic Preference:** Local.

43501 ■ Jefferson Area Chamber of Commerce
PO Box 100
Jefferson, OH 44047
Ph: (440)576-0333
URL: http://jeffersonchamber.com
Contact: Patricia A. Fisher, President
Facebook: www.facebook.com/
JeffersonAreaChamber
Description: Aims to advance the commercial, industrial, professional, civic and general interests of the Jefferson trades areas. **Awards:** Jefferson Area Chamber of Commerce Citizen of the Year (Annual). **Geographic Preference:** Local.

43502 ■ Jefferson County Chamber of Commerce
630 Market St.
Steubenville, OH 43952
Ph: (740)282-6226
Fax: (740)282-6285
Co. E-mail: info@jeffersoncountychamber.com
URL: http://www.jeffersoncountychamber.com
Contact: Robert Naylor, Chairman
Facebook: www.facebook.com/JeffersonCoun
tyChamberofCommerce
X (Twitter): x.com/JeffCo_Chamber
Pinterest: www.pinterest.com/jeffcochamber
Description: To provide resources to maximize business performance through advocacy, education and networking. **Founded:** 1768. **Geographic Preference:** Local.

43503 ■ Kelleys Island Chamber of Commerce (KICC)
Kelleys Island, OH
Co. E-mail: info@kelleysislandchamber.com
URL: http://www.kelleysislandchamber.com
Contact: Gary Finger, President
Facebook: www.facebook.com/KelleysIslandChamber
YouTube: www.youtube.com/channel/UCJc2_K0c
1_ymLEp1-jPoajw
Description: Promotes tourism on Kelleys Island. Develops increased cooperation between the Kelleys Island Village Council and the business community. **Geographic Preference:** Local.

43504 ■ Kent Area Chamber of Commerce (KACC)
201B E Erie St.
Kent, OH 44240
Ph: (330)673-9855
Co. E-mail: kentchamber@kentbiz.com
URL: http://www.kentbiz.com
Contact: Anne E. Moneypenny, Officer
E-mail: kentchamber@kentbiz.com
Facebook: www.facebook.com/KentAreaChamber
X (Twitter): x.com/KentAreaChamber
Description: Promotes business and community development in the Kent, OH area. **Founded:** 1910. **Awards:** W. W. Reed Kent Medal for Public Service (Annual); Kent Area Small Business Person of the Year (Annual). **Geographic Preference:** Local.

43505 ■ Kettering-Moraine-Oakwood Chamber of Commerce (KMOCC)
1563 E Dorothy Ln., Ste. 111.
Kettering, OH 45429
Ph: (937)299-3852
Fax: (939)299-3851
Co. E-mail: annlisa@kmo-coc.org
URL: http://www.kmo-coc.org
Contact: Ann-Lisa Allen, President
E-mail: annlisa@kmo-coc.org
Facebook: www.facebook.com/KMOChamber
X (Twitter): x.com/kmococ
Instagram: www.instagram.com/kmochamber
Description: Promotes business and community development in Kettering, Moraine, and Oakwood, OH. **Founded:** 1957. **Educational Activities:** Kudos Milestones and Ovations Holiday Breakfast (Annual). **Geographic Preference:** Local.

43506 ■ Knox County Chamber of Commerce
501 S Main St.
Mount Vernon, OH 43050
Ph: (740)393-1111
Co. E-mail: chamber@knoxchamber.com
URL: http://www.knoxchamber.com
Contact: Carol Grubaugh, Executive Director
Facebook: www.facebook.com/KnoxCoun
tyOHChamberofCommerce
X (Twitter): x.com/KnoxChamberOHIO
Description: Promotes the businesses of Knox County, Ohio. **Founded:** 1943. **Geographic Preference:** Local.

43507 ■ Lake Township Chamber of Commerce (LTCC)
424 King Church Ave. SW Dr. 21
Uniontown, OH 44685
Ph: (330)877-5500
Co. E-mail: info@lakechamber.com
URL: http://www.lakechamber.com
Contact: Dr. Chip Weisel, President
Facebook: www.facebook.com/lakechamber
X (Twitter): x.com/lakechamber
YouTube: www.youtube.com/user/LakeChamber
Description: Promotes business and community development in the Hartville-Uniontown area in Ohio. **Founded:** 1988. **Geographic Preference:** Local.

43508 ■ Lakewood Chamber of Commerce (LCC)
16017 Detroit Ave.
Lakewood, OH 44107
Ph: (216)226-2900
Fax: (216)226-1340
Co. E-mail: info@lakewoodchamber.org
URL: http://www.lakewoodchamber.org
Contact: Mike DeStefano, Treasurer
Facebook: www.facebook.com/lakewoo
dchamberofcommerce
Linkedin: www.linkedin.com/company/lakewoo
d-chamber-of-commerce
X (Twitter): x.com/lccohio
Instagram: www.instagram.com/lakewoodchamber
YouTube: www.youtube.com/c/Lakewoo
dchamberOrgOH
Description: Promotes business and community development in Lakewood, OH. **Founded:** 1911. **Geographic Preference:** Local.

43509 ■ Lancaster Fairfield County Chamber of Commerce
109 N Broad St., Ste. 100
Lancaster, OH 43130
Ph: (740)653-8251
Co. E-mail: margie@lancoc.org
URL: http://www.lancoc.org
Contact: Travis Markwood, President
E-mail: travis@lancoc.org
Facebook: www.facebook.com/LANCOC
Linkedin: www.linkedin.com/company/lancaster
-fairfield-county-chamber-of-commerce
X (Twitter): x.com/LanFFCoChamber
Instagram: www.instagram.com/lancaster_chamber
_of_commerce
YouTube: www.youtube.com/user/lanfairchamber
Description: Promotes business and community development in the Lancaster, OH area. **Founded:** 1897. **Publications:** *Chamber Report* (Monthly); *Images of Fairfield County*. **Educational Activities:** Info Tech Meeting; Legislative Action Council Meeting. **Geographic Preference:** Local.

43510 ■ Lebanon Area Chamber of Commerce (LACC)
3 N Broadway St.
Lebanon, OH 45036
Ph: (513)932-1100
Co. E-mail: info@lebanonchamber.org
URL: http://www.lebanonchamber.org
Contact: Scott Brunka, President
Facebook: www.facebook.com/lebanonchamber
Linkedin: www.linkedin.com/company/lebanon-area
-chamber-of-commerce
X (Twitter): x.com/LebanonChamber
Instagram: www.instagram.com/lebanonchamber
YouTube: www.youtube.com/channel/
UCMfbJfSCSnjwHSrU8-n7SFg
Description: Promotes business and community development in the Lebanon, OH area. Sponsors Christmas Festival and Artstreet. **Publications:** *Lebanon Area Chamber of Commerce Directory*. **Geographic Preference:** Local.

STATE LISTINGS

43511 ■ Lebanon Area Chamber of Commerce Directory
3 N Broadway St.
 Lebanon, OH 45036
Ph: (513)932-1100
Co. E-mail: info@lebanonchamber.org
URL: http://www.lebanonchamber.org
Contact: Scott Brunka, President
URL(s): www.lebanonchamber.org/directory
Availability: Online.

43512 ■ Leipsic Area Chamber of Commerce
142 E Main St.
 Leipsic, OH 45856
Ph: (419)943-2009
URL: http://www.leipsicchamber.com
Contact: Melissa Maag, Co-President
Facebook: www.facebook.com/
 LeipsicAreaChamberOfCommerce
Description: Represents businesses in Leipsic, OH. **Geographic Preference:** Local.

43513 ■ Lima/Allen County Chamber of Commerce
144 S Main St., Ste. 100
 Lima, OH 45801
Ph: (419)222-6045
Fax: (419)229-0266
URL: http://limachamber.com
Contact: Jed Metzger, President
E-mail: jmetzger@limachamber.com
Facebook: www.facebook.com/LimaAllenCoun
 tyChamber
Linkedin: www.linkedin.com/company/lima-allen-coun
 ty-chamber-of-commerce
X (Twitter): x.com/TheLimaChamber
YouTube: www.youtube.com/user/TheLimaChamber
Description: Promotes business and community development in the Lima, OH area. **Founded:** 1887. **Publications:** *Minority Business/Professional Directory*; *Allen County Business Directory*; *Business Bytes* (Monthly). **Educational Activities:** Safety Council Meeting (Monthly); Wake, Rattle and Roll (Periodic). **Geographic Preference:** Local.

43514 ■ Lisbon Area Chamber of Commerce (LACC)
c/o Marilyn McCullough, Executive Director
120 N Market St.
 Lisbon, OH 44432
Ph: (330)424-1803
Fax: (330)424-9003
Co. E-mail: lacoc2@sbcglobal.net
URL: http://www.lisbonchamber.com
Contact: Susan Shank, President
Facebook: www.facebook.com/LisbonAreaChamber
X (Twitter): x.com/LisbonChamber
Description: Promotes business and community development in the Lisbon, OH area. Sponsors annual Johnny Appleseed Festival. **Founded:** 1964. **Publications:** *Chamber of Commerce Newsletter* (Quarterly). **Geographic Preference:** Local.

43515 ■ The Little Miami River Chamber Alliance
113 Karl Brown Way, 2nd Fl.
 Loveland, OH 45140
Ph: (513)683-1544
Co. E-mail: info@lmrchamberalliance.org
URL: http://lmrchamberalliance.org
Contact: Ceecee Collins, President
E-mail: ceecee@lmrchamberalliance.org
Facebook: www.facebook.com/LMRChamberAlliance
 .org
Linkedin: www.linkedin.com/company/loveland-area
 -chamber-of-commerce
Instagram: www.instagram.com/lmrchamberalliance
YouTube: www.youtube.com/channel/
 UCIO9SzP87wwdNvHEHFEKP5g
Description: Promotes business and community development in the Loveland, OH area. Sponsors Music in the Park concerts, valentine stamping program, and golf outing. **Founded:** 1969. **Geographic Preference:** Local.

43516 ■ Logan County Area Chamber of Commerce
100 S Main St.
 Bellefontaine, OH 43311
Ph: (937)599-5121
Fax: (937)599-2411
Co. E-mail: info@logancountyohio.com
URL: http://www.logancountyohio.com
Contact: Ben Vollrath, President
Facebook: www.facebook.com/logancountychamber
YouTube: www.youtube.com/channel/UCj9LLIB
 60QwYPaMqhNO1WnA
Description: Promotes business and community development in the Logan County, OH area. **Geographic Preference:** Local.

43517 ■ Logan - Hocking Chamber of Commerce
96 W Hunter St.
 Logan, OH 43138
Ph: (740)385-6836
Fax: (740)385-7259
Co. E-mail: bailey@hockinghillschamber.com
URL: http://hockinghillschamber.com
Contact: Rick Webb, President
Description: Aims to keep Logan area's economic condition at a level where businesses will risk their resources in the hope of making a profit. **Geographic Preference:** Local.

43518 ■ Lorain County Chamber of Commerce
226 Middle Ave., 5th Fl.
 Elyria, OH 44035
Ph: (440)328-2550
Fax: (440)328-2557
Co. E-mail: tcascio@loraincountychamber.com
URL: http://www.loraincountychamber.com
Contact: Anthony Gallo, President
Facebook: www.facebook.com/LorainCoun
 tyChamber
X (Twitter): x.com/LoCoChamber
Description: Businesses and individuals promoting economic and community development and social programs in Lorain County, OH. **Founded:** 1883. **Geographic Preference:** Local.

43519 ■ Louisville Area Chamber of Commerce
504 E Main St.
 Louisville, OH 44641
Ph: (330)875-7371
Co. E-mail: louisvilleohchamber@gmail.com
URL: http://www.louisvilleohchamber.org/home
Contact: Beth Campbell, Executive Director
Facebook: www.facebook.com/
 louisvilleohchamberofcommerce
Linkedin: www.linkedin.com/company/louisville-area
 -chamber-of-commerce
Description: Strives to develop and enhance the economic and business environment in the Louisville area through leadership, advocacy, and investor benefits. **Founded:** 1991. **Geographic Preference:** Local.

43520 ■ Marblehead Peninsula Chamber of Commerce
110 W Main St.
 Marblehead, OH 43440
Ph: (419)702-7492
Co. E-mail: info@themarbleheadpeninsula.com
URL: http://www.themarbleheadpeninsula.com
Contact: Steve Pitzer, President
Facebook: www.facebook.com/Marblehea
 dPeninsulaChamber
Instagram: www.instagram.com/marblehea
 dpeninsulachamber
Description: Promotes business and community development in the Marblehead, OH area. **Geographic Preference:** Local.

43521 ■ Marietta Area Chamber of Commerce (MACC)
The Riverview Bldg.
100 Front St.
 Marietta, OH 45750
Ph: (740)373-5176

Co. E-mail: info@mariettachamber.com
URL: http://www.mariettachamber.com
Contact: Kelsy Eaton, President
Facebook: www.facebook.com/MariettaChamber
Description: Promotes business and community development in the Marietta, OH area. **Founded:** 1788. **Publications:** *The Entrepreneur* (Monthly); *Industrial Guide*. **Geographic Preference:** Local.

43522 ■ Marion Area Chamber of Commerce
267 W Center St., Ste. 200
 Marion, OH 43302
Ph: (740)382-2181
Fax: (740)387-7722
Co. E-mail: chamberstaff@marionareachamber.org
URL: http://www.marionareachamber.org
Contact: Jacque Psyhogios, Vice Chairman of the Board
Facebook: www.facebook.com/MarionAreaChamber
YouTube: www.youtube.com/channel/UCOXu
 6zDnMMC_pLwJNRjkyUQ
Description: Represents businesses in Marion, OH. Provides leadership for improvement of the economic prosperity and quality of life in the local community. **Publications:** *Progressing Together* (Monthly). **Geographic Preference:** Local.

43523 ■ Massillon Area Chamber of Commerce (MACC)
The First N Bldg.
50 N Ave. NE
 Massillon, OH 44646
Ph: (330)833-3146
Co. E-mail: info@massillonohchamber.com
URL: http://www.massillonohchamber.com
Contact: Debbie Busby, President
Facebook: www.facebook.com/massillonchamber
Instagram: www.instagram.com/massillonchamber
Description: Promotes business and community development in the Massillon, OH area. **Founded:** 1915. **Publications:** *Community Guide* (Annual). **Geographic Preference:** Local.

43524 ■ Maumee Chamber of Commerce
605 Conant St.
 Maumee, OH 43537
Ph: (419)893-5805
Fax: (419)893-8699
Co. E-mail: info@maumeechamber.com
URL: http://maumeechamber.com
Contact: Debby Peters, President
Facebook: www.facebook.com/maumeechamber
Linkedin: www.linkedin.com/company/
 maumeechamber
X (Twitter): x.com/maumee_chamber
Instagram: www.instagram.com/
 maumeechamberofcommerce
YouTube: www.youtube.com/channel/UCtUStd_QIMi
 2cpBq---AwAA
Description: Promotes business and community development in Maumee, OH. **Founded:** 1955. **Publications:** *Members Bulletin* (8/year). **Geographic Preference:** Local.

43525 ■ Meigs County Chamber of Commerce (MCCC)
238 W Main St.
 Pomeroy, OH 45769
Contact: Susan White, Contact
Description: Promotes business and community development in Meigs County, OH. **Founded:** 1980. **Geographic Preference:** Local.

43526 ■ Mentor Area Chamber of Commerce (MACC)
6972 Spinach Dr.
 Mentor, OH 44060
Ph: (440)255-1616
Co. E-mail: info@mentorchamber.org
URL: http://mentorchamber.org
Contact: Christine Weber-Bresky, President
E-mail: cweber@mentorchamber.org
Facebook: www.facebook.com/mentorchamber
Linkedin: www.linkedin.com/company/mentor-area
 -chamber-of-commerce
X (Twitter): x.com/Mentor_Chamber
Instagram: www.instagram.com/mentor_chamber

43527 ■ Ohio

development in the Mentor, OH area. **Founded:** 1960. **Publications:** *Chamber News.* **Educational Activities:** Golf Outing (Annual). **Geographic Preference:** Local.

43527 ■ Middlefield Chamber of Commerce
16014 E High St.
 Middlefield, OH 44062
Ph: (440)632-5705
Co. E-mail: mccinfo@middlefieldcc.com
URL: http://middlefieldcc.com
Contact: Randy Kaser, President
E-mail: rkaser@acquirefireprotection.com
Facebook: www.facebook.com/middlefieldcc
Description: Promotes business and community development in Middlefield Township, OH. **Founded:** 1799. **Geographic Preference:** Local.

43528 ■ Milford Miami Township Chamber of Commerce (MMTCC)
220 Mill St.
 Milford, OH 45150
Ph: (513)831-2411
Co. E-mail: info@milfordmiamitownship.com
URL: http://milfordmiamitownship.com
Contact: Ron Swogger, President
E-mail: rswogger@rdicorp.com
Facebook: www.facebook.com/Milfor dMiamiTownshipChamber
Linkedin: www.linkedin.com/company/milford-miami -township-chamber-of-commerce
Instagram: www.instagram.com/milfordmiami townshipchamber
Founded: 1947. **Geographic Preference:** Local.

43529 ■ Minerva Area Chamber of Commerce (MACOC)
203 N Market St.
 Minerva, OH 44657
Ph: (330)868-7979
URL: http://www.minervachamber.org
Contact: Tom Dillie, President
Facebook: www.facebook.com/Minerva-Area-Chamber-of-Commerce-136972053116027
Description: Promotes the advancement of the industrial, retail, commercial, and professional environment in Minerva Area, OH. **Geographic Preference:** Local.

43530 ■ Mohican-Loudonville Convention & Visitors Bureau
544 N Union St.
 Loudonville, OH 44842
Ph: (419)994-2519
Co. E-mail: director@discovermohican.com
URL: http://discovermohican.com
Facebook: www.facebook.com/discovermohican
X (Twitter): x.com/DiscoverMohican
Instagram: www.instagram.com/discovermohican
Description: Promotes business and community development in the Loudonville, OH area. **Founded:** 1957. **Geographic Preference:** Local.

43531 ■ Montpelier Area Chamber of Commerce (MACC)
319 W Main
 Montpelier, OH 43543
Ph: (419)485-4416
URL: http://montpelierchamberofcommerce.com
Contact: Susan J. Gearhart, Officer
Facebook: www.facebook.com/Mon tpelierChamberofCommerce
Description: Promotes business and community development in the Montpelier, OH area. Sponsors annual Bean Days Festival and Blue Water train excursion. Maintains retail division. Holds bimonthly board meeting. Sponsors Bean Days Festival. **Founded:** 1845. **Publications:** *Directory of Members.* **Geographic Preference:** Local.

43532 ■ Morrow County Chamber of Commerce and Visitors' Bureau
169 W High St.
 Mount Gilead, OH 43338
Ph: (419)946-2821
Co. E-mail: morrowcountychamber@gmail.com

URL: http://morrowchamber.com
Contact: Erin Kelty, President
Facebook: www.facebook.com/MorrowCoun tyChamber
Linkedin: www.linkedin.com/company/morrow-county -chamber-of-commerce
Description: Promotes economic growth and community development in Morrow County, OH. **Geographic Preference:** Local.

43533 ■ Mount Vernon - Knox County Chamber of Commerce
501 S Main St.
 Mount Vernon, OH 43050
Ph: (740)393-1111
Co. E-mail: chamber@knoxchamber.com
URL: http://www.knoxchamber.com
Contact: Carol Grubaugh, Executive Director
E-mail: carol@knoxchamber.com
Facebook: www.facebook.com/KnoxCoun tyOHChamberofCommerce
Description: Represents businesses in Mount Vernon, OH. **Founded:** 1916. **Publications:** *Business Broadcast* (Monthly). **Awards:** Judy Klavins Ambassador of the Year Award (Annual); Mount Vernon - Knox County Chamber of Commerce Business of the Year Award (Annual); Mount Vernon - Knox County Chamber of Commerce Environmental Sustainability Award (Annual); Knox County Chamber of Commerce Lifetime Achievement Award (Annual); Knox County Heart Award (Annual); Knox County Investor in the Future Award (Annual); Paul Slaughter Volunteer of the Year Award (Annual); Knox County Quality of Life Award (Annual); Knox County Small Business of the Year Award (Annual); Knox County Women in Business Leadership Award (Annual). **Geographic Preference:** Local.

43534 ■ Nordonia Hills Chamber of Commerce (NHCC)
9821 Olde Eight Rd.
 Northfield, OH 44067
Contact: Kristine Bissler, Contact
Description: Promotes business and community development in the Northfield, OH area. **Founded:** 1985. **Geographic Preference:** Local.

43535 ■ North Canton Area Chamber of Commerce
121 S Main St.
 North Canton, OH 44720
Ph: (330)499-5100
Fax: (330)499-7181
Co. E-mail: info@northcantonchamber.org
URL: http://www.northcantonchamber.org
Contact: Keri Burick, President
E-mail: president@northcantonchamber.org
Description: Businesses, schools, churches, and individuals united to promote business in the North Canton, OH area. **Founded:** 1959. **Geographic Preference:** Local.

43536 ■ North Coast Chamber of Commerce
PO Box 275
 Avon Lake, OH 44012
Ph: (440)933-9311
Co. E-mail: memberservices@northcoastchamber .com
URL: http://www.northcoastchamber.com
Contact: Jerry Cline, President
E-mail: jcline@fisherphillips.com
Facebook: www.facebook.com/northcoastchamber
Description: Strives to improve the quality of life in and around the local community. **Founded:** 1989. **Geographic Preference:** Local.

43537 ■ North Olmsted Chamber of Commerce (NOCC)
PO Box 204
 North Olmsted, OH 44070
Ph: (440)777-3368
Co. E-mail: contact@powerofmorechambers.org
URL: http://www.nolmstedchamber.org
Contact: Cristina Bertero, President
Facebook: www.facebook.com/powerofmore

Description: Businesses, industries, and individuals. Promotes business and community development in North Olmsted, OH. **Founded:** 1954. **Publications:** *Chamber Insider.* **Geographic Preference:** Local.

43538 ■ Northern Cincinnati Chamber of Commerce (SCC)
2704 E Kemper Rd.
 Cincinnati, OH 45241
Ph: (513)554-1722
URL: http://www.northcincychamber.com
Contact: Lois Erven, President
Facebook: www.facebook.com/ sharonvillechamberofcommerce
Linkedin: www.linkedin.com/company/sharonville -chamber
YouTube: www.youtube.com/channel/UCEteihEjy -yaa0BEpqSQX-g
Description: Promotes member businesses by providing value through networking, benefits, education and marketing opportunities. **Founded:** 1988. **Geographic Preference:** Local.

43539 ■ Northmont Area Chamber of Commerce (NACC)
4001 Old Salem Rd.
 Englewood, OH 45322
Ph: (937)836-2550
Co. E-mail: angie@northmontchamber.com
URL: http://www.northmontchamber.com
Contact: Mike McKinniss, President
Description: Promotes business and economic growth in northern Montgomery County, OH. **Founded:** 1977. **Publications:** *Chamber Directory*; *The Informer* (Monthly); *The Outlook* (Monthly). **Geographic Preference:** Local.

43540 ■ Oak Harbor Area Chamber of Commerce (OHACC)
161 W Water St., Ste. A
 Oak Harbor, OH 43449
Ph: (419)898-0479
Co. E-mail: chamber@oakharborohio.net
URL: http://www.oakharborohio.net
Contact: Cherie Salazar, President
Facebook: www.facebook.com/Oak-Harbor-Area -Chamber-of-Commerce-10150126392870436
X (Twitter): x.com/oh_chamber
Description: Promotes business and community development in the Oak Harbor, OH area. **Founded:** 1970. **Geographic Preference:** Local.

43541 ■ Ohio Chamber of Commerce (OCC)
34 S Third St., Ste. 100
 Columbus, OH 43215
Ph: (614)228-4201
Co. E-mail: occ@ohiochamber.com
URL: http://ohiochamber.com
Contact: Steve Stiver, President
E-mail: sstivers@ohiochamber.com
Facebook: www.facebook.com/OhioChamber
Linkedin: www.linkedin.com/company/ohio-chamber -of-commerce
X (Twitter): x.com/OhioChamber
Instagram: www.instagram.com/ohiochamber
YouTube: www.youtube.com/channel/ UC0jT0ejDeFHfHlXvkluikCg
Description: Businesses organized to foster economic and industrial growth in Ohio. Serves as liaison between government and business. Keeps members informed of employment conditions, economic developments, and pertinent regulations. Conducts lobbying activities. **Founded:** 1893. **Publications:** *Ohio Matters* (Quarterly); *The Complete Wage and Hour Manual*; *Membership Notes* (Bimonthly); *Ohio Chamber of Commerce Legislative Directory* (Weekly (Mon.)); *Ohio Chamber of Commerce--Membership Directory and Buyers' Guide*; *Chambers of Commerce in Ohio* (Annual); *Environmental and Safety Directory* (Annual). **Geographic Preference:** State.

43542 ■ Ohio-Israel Chamber of Commerce (OICC)
25701 Science Park Dr.
 Cleveland, OH 44122
Ph: (216)965-4474
Co. E-mail: ohioisraelchamber@ameritech.net

URL: http://accessjewishcleveland.org/organizations/o/ohio-israel-chamber-of-commerce.aspx
Contact: Howard Gudell, President
Description: Promotes business between Ohio and Israeli companies by programming, matchmaking, and government contacts. **Founded:** 1996. **Geographic Preference:** State.

43543 ■ *Ohio Matters*
34 S Third St., Ste. 100
Columbus, OH 43215
Ph: (614)228-4201
Co. E-mail: occ@ohiochamber.com
URL: http://ohiochamber.com
Contact: Steve Stiver, President
E-mail: sstivers@ohiochamber.com
URL(s): ohiochamber.com/communications/ohio-matters
Released: Quarterly **Description:** Magazine containing information about business and legislative activities in Ohio. **Availability:** PDF; Online.

43544 ■ **Ohio Small Business Development Center at the Clermont Chamber of Commerce**
4355 Ferguson Dr., Ste. 150
Cincinnati, OH 45245
Ph: (513)576-5000
Fax: (513)576-5001
Co. E-mail: chamber@clermontchamber.com
URL: http://clermontchamber.com/services/small-business-center
Contact: Joy Lytle, President
E-mail: joy.lytle@clermontchamber.com
Facebook: www.facebook.com/ClermontChamber
Linkedin: www.linkedin.com/company/clermont-chamber-of-commerce
X (Twitter): x.com/ClermontChamber
Instagram: www.instagram.com/ClermontChamber
Description: Represents and promotes the small business sector. Provides management assistance to current and prospective small business owners. Helps to improve management skills and expand the products and services of members. **Founded:** 1969. **Geographic Preference:** Local.

43545 ■ **Ohio Small Business Development Center at Lorain County Community College**
151 Innovation Dr.
Elyria, OH 44035
URL: http://www.lorainccc.edu/business/sbdc
Contact: Marcia Ballinger, President
Description: Represents and promotes the small business sector. Provides management assistance to current and prospective small business owners. Helps to improve management skills and expand the products and services of members. **Geographic Preference:** Local.

43546 ■ **Ohio Small Business Development Center at Toledo Regional Chamber of Commerce**
300 Madison Ave., Ste. 200
Toledo, OH 43604
Ph: (419)243-8191
Co. E-mail: businesshelp@development.ohio.gov
URL: http://www.toledochamber.com/small-business-development-center.html
Contact: Jill Badger, Vice President
Description: Represents and promotes the small business sector. Provides management assistance to current and prospective small business owners. Helps to improve management skills and expand the products and services of members. **Geographic Preference:** Local.

43547 ■ **Ottawa Area Chamber of Commerce**
129 Ct. St.
Ottawa, OH 45875
Ph: (419)523-3141
Co. E-mail: ottawaareachamberofcommerce@gmail.com
URL: http://www.ottawachamber.org
Contact: Kendra Kuhlman, Contact
Facebook: www.facebook.com/OttawaareachamberofcommerceX (Twitter): x.com/OttawaOhChamber
Instagram: www.instagram.com/ottawaohchamber
Description: Promotes businesses in Ottawa, OH. Provides resources, referrals and promotional opportunities to members. **Founded:** 1921. **Geographic Preference:** Local.

43548 ■ **Over-The-Rhine Chamber of Commerce (OTRCC)**
1307 Walnut St.
Cincinnati, OH 45202
Ph: (513)512-5668
Co. E-mail: contact@otrchamber.com
URL: http://www.otrchamber.com
Contact: Kelly Adamson, Executive Director
Facebook: www.facebook.com/OTRChamber
Linkedin: www.linkedin.com/company/over-the-rhine-chamber-of-commerce
X (Twitter): x.com/otrchamber
Instagram: www.instagram.com/otrchamber
Description: Promotes business and community development in Over-the-Rhine, OH area. **Founded:** 1985. **Awards:** Over-The-Rhine Chamber Business of the Year (Annual); Over-The-Rhine Chamber Chairman's Award (Annual); Over-The-Rhine Chamber Entrepreneur of the Year (Annual); Over-The-Rhine Chamber New Business of the Year (Annual). **Geographic Preference:** Local.

43549 ■ **Oxford Chamber of Commerce (OCC)**
102 W High St.
Oxford, OH 45056
Ph: (513)523-5200
URL: http://oxfordchamber.org
Contact: Kelli Riggs, President
E-mail: president@oxfordchamber.org
Facebook: www.facebook.com/Oxfordohiochamberofcommerce
Linkedin: www.linkedin.com/in/oxford-chamber-78461280
X (Twitter): x.com/oxfordohchamber
YouTube: www.youtube.com/channel/UC1Vs8i6gtGtDTPO6n5HCM5w
Description: Businesspersons and professionals interested in promoting business and community development in Oxford, OH. **Founded:** 1979. **Geographic Preference:** Local.

43550 ■ **Parma Area Chamber of Commerce (PACC)**
5790 Ridge Rd.
Parma, OH 44129
Ph: (440)886-1700
Co. E-mail: chamber@parmaareachamber.org
URL: http://parmaareachamber.org
Contact: Rob Brill, Chairman of the Board
Facebook: www.facebook.com/Parma.Area.Chamber.Of.Commerce
X (Twitter): x.com/ParmaAreaCC
Description: Provides benefits and opportunities to over 500 business and organization members including networking referrals, sponsorships, advertising, direct marketing, discounts on insurance, payroll, timekeeping and credit card processing, workers' compensation group programs, member to member discounts and more. Supports community and member events, regional and local partnerships, legislative impact, leadership, and volunteer roles. **Founded:** 1955. **Publications:** *Insight*. **Geographic Preference:** Local.

43551 ■ **Perrysburg Area Chamber of Commerce**
105 W Indiana Ave.
Perrysburg, OH 43551
Ph: (419)874-9147
Co. E-mail: director@perrysburgchamber.com
URL: http://www.perrysburgchamber.com
Contact: Brody Walters, President
Facebook: www.facebook.com/PerrysburgChamber
X (Twitter): x.com/Pburg_Chamber
Instagram: www.instagram.com/perrysburgchamber
Description: Promotes business, community development and free enterprise system in the Perrysburg, OH area. **Publications:** *Chamber Connection* (Monthly). **Geographic Preference:** Local.

43552 ■ **Pickaway County Chamber of Commerce - Circleville**
325 W Main St.
Circleville, OH 43113
Ph: (740)474-4923
Co. E-mail: chamber@pickaway.com
URL: http://www.pickawaychamber.com
Contact: Jessica Calder, Chairman
Facebook: www.facebook.com/pickchamber
Description: Represents the interests of the business industry in Pickaway County. **Founded:** 1916. **Geographic Preference:** Local.

43553 ■ **Pickerington Area Chamber of Commerce (PACC)**
21 Lockville Rd.
Pickerington, OH 43147
Ph: (614)837-1958
Co. E-mail: info@pickeringtonchamber.com
URL: http://www.pickeringtonchamber.com
Contact: Andy Hardy, Chairman
Facebook: www.facebook.com/pickeringtoncoc
Linkedin: www.linkedin.com/company/pickerington-area-chamber
YouTube: www.youtube.com/channel/UCIM8Se_a-M2lgIdTLFLeSNw
Description: Promotes business and community development in Pickerington, OH. **Founded:** 1978. **Publications:** *Business in Motion* (Monthly); *Community Guide and Profile*; *Pickerington Area Map*. **Awards:** Doug Barr Safety Award (Annual). **Geographic Preference:** Local.

43554 ■ **Pike County Chamber of Commerce (PCCC)**
12455 State Rte. 104
Waverly, OH 45690
Ph: (740)947-7715
Co. E-mail: pikechamber@yahoo.com
URL: http://www.pikechamber.org
Contact: Shirley Bandy, Executive Director
Facebook: www.facebook.com/pikechamber
Description: Promotes business and community development in Pike County, OH. **Founded:** 1960. **Geographic Preference:** Local.

43555 ■ **Piqua Area Chamber of Commerce (PACC)**
326 N Main St.
Piqua, OH 45356
Ph: (937)773-2765
URL: http://piquaareachamber.com
Contact: Kathy Sherman, President
E-mail: ksherman@piquaareachamber.com
Facebook: www.facebook.com/PiquaAreaChamberofCommerce
X (Twitter): x.com/Piqua_Chamber
Instagram: www.instagram.com/piqua_chamber
Description: Promotes business and community development in the Piqua, OH area. **Geographic Preference:** Local.

43556 ■ *Progressing Together*
267 W Center St., Ste. 200
Marion, OH 43302
Ph: (740)382-2181
Fax: (740)387-7722
Co. E-mail: chamberstaff@marionareachamber.org
URL: http://www.marionareachamber.org
Contact: Jacque Psyhogios, Vice Chairman of the Board
URL(s): www.marionareachamber.org/memberbenefits
Released: Monthly **Availability:** Print; Online.

43557 ■ **Put-in-Bay Chamber of Commerce**
148 Delaware Ave.
Put in Bay, OH 43456
Ph: (419)285-2832
Co. E-mail: questions@visitputinbay.com
URL: http://www.visitputinbay.com
Facebook: www.facebook.com/VisitPutinBay
X (Twitter): x.com/visitputinbay
Instagram: www.instagram.com/visitputinbay
YouTube: www.youtube.com/channel/UCVZX6AKBjAszRv4OHYTBYDQ

Description: Seeks to attract business and tourism to the Put-in-Bay, OH area. **Publications:** *Island Guide* (Annual); *Island Guide* (Annual). **Geographic Preference:** Local.

43558 ■ Ravenna Area Chamber of Commerce
135 E Main St.
Ravenna, OH 44266
Ph: (330)296-3886
Co. E-mail: ryann@ravennaareachamber.com
URL: http://ravennaareachamber.com
Contact: Ryann Kuchenbecker, Executive Director
Facebook: www.facebook.com/people/Ravenna-Area-Chamber-of-Commerce/100069125353442
X (Twitter): x.com/RavennaChamber
YouTube: www.youtube.com/channel/UCOr1NS4QJTG0GUjYw8KvRyA

Description: Promotes business and community development in the area. **Founded:** 1886. **Awards:** Raven Awards (Annual). **Geographic Preference:** Local.

43559 ■ Reading Chamber of Commerce
PO Box 15164
Reading, OH 45215
Ph: (513)623-4145
URL: http://readingohiochamber.org
Contact: John Malot, President
E-mail: jensfurnitureandmore@yahoo.com

Description: Promotes business and community development in Reading, OH area. **Geographic Preference:** Local.

43560 ■ Reynoldsburg Area Chamber of Commerce (RACC)
1580 Brice Rd.
Reynoldsburg, OH 43068
Ph: (614)866-4753
Co. E-mail: admin@reynoldsburgchamber.com
URL: http://www.reynoldsburgchamber.com
Contact: Rick Wagner, Chairperson
E-mail: rickwagner@wagnerinsuranceagency.net
Facebook: www.facebook.com/Reynoldsburgchamber
X (Twitter): x.com/ReysChamber

Description: Promotes a strong business environment by being the collective voice in the Reynoldsburg area, enhances the general welfare of the community through economic prosperity. **Founded:** 1984. **Geographic Preference:** Local.

43561 ■ Richland Area Chamber of Commerce
55 N Mulberry St.
Mansfield, OH 44902
URL: http://richlandareachamber.com
Contact: Beth Delaney, President

Description: Promotes business and community development in the Richland County, OH area. **Founded:** 1899. **Publications:** *Chamber Business* (Semiannual). **Geographic Preference:** Local.

43562 ■ Rittman Area Chamber of Commerce
44 S Main St.
Rittman, OH 44270
Ph: (330)925-4828
Co. E-mail: rittmanchamber@ohio.net
URL: http://rittmanoh.org
Contact: Cali Reeves, President
Facebook: www.facebook.com/rittman.chamber.5

Description: Promotes businesses in Rittman, OH. **Geographic Preference:** Local.

43563 ■ *River Biz*
1236 Smith Ct.
Rocky River, OH 44116
Ph: (440)331-1140
Fax: (440)331-3485
Co. E-mail: info@rockyriverchamber.com
URL: http://www.rockyriverchamber.com
Contact: Angela Barth, Executive Director
E-mail: angela@rockyriverchamber.com
URL(s): www.rockyriverchamber.com/riverbiz-newsletters

Released: Biweekly **Description:** Includes news and reports concerning Rocky River Chamber of Commerce. **Availability:** Online.

43564 ■ Rocky River Chamber of Commerce (RRCC)
1236 Smith Ct.
Rocky River, OH 44116
Ph: (440)331-1140
Fax: (440)331-3485
Co. E-mail: info@rockyriverchamber.com
URL: http://www.rockyriverchamber.com
Contact: Angela Barth, Executive Director
E-mail: angela@rockyriverchamber.com
Facebook: www.facebook.com/RockyRiverCC
Linkedin: www.linkedin.com/company/rockyrivercc
X (Twitter): x.com/RockyRiverCC
Instagram: www.instagram.com/rockyrivercc
YouTube: www.youtube.com/channel/UCM5u6inkspOW0Lfr5s87Jdw

Description: Promotes business and community development in Rocky River, OH. Holds annual Christmas party to benefit Rocky River Assistance Program. **Founded:** 1922. **Publications:** *River Biz* (Biweekly); *Rocky River Residence Reference Guide* (Annual). **Educational Activities:** Business Mixers; Annual Business Expo (Annual). **Geographic Preference:** Local.

43565 ■ Rootstown Area Chamber of Commerce
PO Box 254
Rootstown, OH 44272
URL: http://www.rootstownchamber.org
Contact: Denese Schneckenburger, President
E-mail: president@rootstownchamber.org

Description: Promotes interest of its members and of business in general. **Geographic Preference:** Local.

43566 ■ Salem Area Chamber of Commerce (SACC)
210 E State St.
Salem, OH 44460
Ph: (330)337-3473
Fax: (330)337-3474
Co. E-mail: info@salemohiochamber.org
URL: http://salemchamber.org
Contact: Dr. Amanda Kenney, President
Facebook: www.facebook.com/SalemOHChamber
X (Twitter): x.com/SalemOhChamber

Description: Promotes business and community development in the Salem, OH area. Sponsors Salem Jubilee festival. **Publications:** *Salem Area Chamber of Commerce Directory*; *Salem Industrial Directory* (Biennial); *The Salem Chamber* (Weekly). **Geographic Preference:** Local.

43567 ■ *Salem Area Chamber of Commerce Directory*
210 E State St.
Salem, OH 44460
Ph: (330)337-3473
Fax: (330)337-3474
Co. E-mail: info@salemohiochamber.org
URL: http://salemchamber.org
Contact: Dr. Amanda Kenney, President
URL(s): members.salemohiochamber.org/memberdirectory

Availability: Print.

43568 ■ *The Salem Chamber*
210 E State St.
Salem, OH 44460
Ph: (330)337-3473
Fax: (330)337-3474
Co. E-mail: info@salemohiochamber.org
URL: http://salemchamber.org
Contact: Dr. Amanda Kenney, President
URL(s): www.salemohiochamber.org/newsletters

Released: Weekly **Description:** Contains the latest information on the activities of the chamber. **Availability:** PDF; Online.

43569 ■ Seneca Regional Chamber of Commerce and Visitor Services
19 W Market St., Ste. C
Tiffin, OH 44883
Ph: (419)447-4141
Co. E-mail: info@tiffinchamber.com
URL: http://tiffinchamber.com
Contact: Bryce Riggs, Director
Facebook: www.facebook.com/SenecaRegionalChamber
Linkedin: www.linkedin.com/company/senecaregionalchamber
X (Twitter): x.com/SenecaChamberOH

Description: Seeks to promote and support community enhancement activities that are beneficial to Tiffin area. **Publications:** *The Chamber* (Periodic). **Geographic Preference:** Local.

43570 ■ *The Solon Business Directory*
6240 SOM Center Rd., Ste. 211
Solon, OH 44139
Ph: (440)248-5080
Fax: (440)248-9121
URL: http://www.solonchamber.com
Contact: Tom Jackson, Chairman
URL(s): web.solonchamber.com/search

Description: Features listing of all industrial companies in Solon. **Availability:** Print.

43571 ■ Solon Chamber of Commerce
6240 SOM Center Rd., Ste. 211
Solon, OH 44139
Ph: (440)248-5080
Fax: (440)248-9121
URL: http://www.solonchamber.com
Contact: Tom Jackson, Chairman
Facebook: www.facebook.com/solonchamber
Linkedin: www.linkedin.com/company/solon-chamber-of-commerce
X (Twitter): x.com/solonchamberoh
Instagram: www.instagram.com/solonchamber

Description: Promotes business and community development in Solon, OH. **Founded:** 1927. **Publications:** *News and Views* (Monthly); *The Solon Connection*; *The Solon Business Directory*; *The Solon Industrial Guide*. **Educational Activities:** Coffee Connection. **Geographic Preference:** Local.

43572 ■ South Metro Regional Chamber of Commerce (SMRCOC)
332 Congress Pk. Dr., Ste. B
Dayton, OH 45459
Ph: (937)433-2032
Fax: (937)433-6881
Co. E-mail: info@smrcoc.org
URL: http://www.smrcoc.org
Contact: Julia Maxton, President
Facebook: www.facebook.com/South-Metro-Regional-Chamber-of-Commerce-119193701471639

Description: Promotes business and community development in the Southern Dayton, OH metropolitan area. Holds Business After Hours parties and monthly board of directors meeting. **Founded:** 1969. **Publications:** *The Business Advisor* (Monthly); *Comprehensive Guide to Members* (Annual); *South Metro Monthly Magazine* (Monthly). **Geographic Preference:** Local.

43573 ■ Southeastern Franklin County Chamber of Commerce
400 sheryl Dr.
Groveport, OH 43125
Contact: Terri Christensen, Contact

Description: Promotes business and community development in Southeastern Franklin County, OH. **Founded:** 1980. **Geographic Preference:** Local.

43574 ■ Southwestern Auglaize County Chamber of Commerce
22 S Water St.
New Bremen, OH 45869
Ph: (419)629-0313
Co. E-mail: info@auglaize.org
URL: http://www.auglaize.org
Contact: Sara Topp, Executive Director
E-mail: stopp@auglaize.org
Facebook: www.facebook.com/SWACChamber

X (Twitter): x.com/swacchamber
Instagram: www.instagram.com/swacchamber
YouTube: www.youtube.com/channel/UCwISX19RVJw6u9uLkFpTC2g

Description: Works to improve the economy and quality of life in Southwest Auglaize and the surrounding areas. **Founded:** 1998. **Geographic Preference:** Local.

43575 ■ Springboro Chamber of Commerce
115 Wright Station Way, Ste. 1
Springboro, OH 45066
Ph: (937)748-0074
Fax: (937)748-0525
Co. E-mail: chamber@springborooohio.org
URL: http://springboroohio.org
Contact: Marsha Kelley, Vice Chairman of the Board
Facebook: www.facebook.com/SpringboroChamber
Linkedin: www.linkedin.com/in/springboro-chamber-of-commerce-86784325
X (Twitter): x.com/BoroOhioChamber
Instagram: www.instagram.com/springborochamber

Description: Promotes and supports local business and community. **Founded:** 1975. **Geographic Preference:** Local.

43576 ■ Stow-Munroe Falls Chamber of Commerce (SMFCC)
PO Box 2714
Stow, OH 44224
Ph: (330)688-1579
Fax: (330)688-6234
Co. E-mail: smfcc@smfcc.com
URL: http://smfcc.com
Contact: Dave Segen, President
Facebook: www.facebook.com/Stow-Munroe-Falls-Chamber-Women2Women-342017552555940
Linkedin: www.linkedin.com/company/stow-munroe-falls-chamber
X (Twitter): x.com/smfcc
Instagram: www.instagram.com/stowmunroefallschamber
YouTube: www.youtube.com/channel/UC0n4dqozQ0ATg2SoMQTLq8Q

Description: Promotes business and community development in the Stow-Munroe Falls area. Sponsors annual Pride Week, golf outing and Community Showcase, Candidates and Issues Night, Public Officials Reception and more. Conducts charitable activities. **Founded:** 1965. **Publications:** *Moving a Business to Stow*; *Opening a Business in Stow*; *Stow-Munroe Falls Chamber of Commerce Member Business Directory*. **Awards:** Stow-Munroe Falls Chamber of Commerce Business Person of the Year (Annual); Stow-Munroe Falls Chamber of Commerce Friend of the Community Award (Annual). **Geographic Preference:** Local.

43577 ■ *Stow-Munroe Falls Chamber of Commerce Member Business Directory*
PO Box 2714
Stow, OH 44224
Ph: (330)688-1579
Fax: (330)688-6234
Co. E-mail: smfcc@smfcc.com
URL: http://smfcc.com
Contact: Dave Segen, President
URL(s): business.smfcc.com/list
Availability: Print; PDF.

43578 ■ Streetsboro Area Chamber of Commerce (SACC)
9205 State Rte. 43, Ste. 209
Streetsboro, OH 44241
Ph: (330)626-4769
Co. E-mail: sacc@streetsborochamber.org
URL: http://www.streetsborochamber.org
Contact: Deborah Covert, Executive Director
Facebook: www.facebook.com/StreetsboroAreaChamberOfCommerce
Linkedin: www.linkedin.com/company/streetsboro-area-chamber-of-commerce
Instagram: www.instagram.com/streetsborochamber

Description: Encourages the growth of Streetsboro business and tourism, and invests in programs that enhance and enrich the community. **Founded:** 1968. **Geographic Preference:** Local.

43579 ■ Strongsville Chamber of Commerce (SCC)
18829 Royalton Rd.
Strongsville, OH 44136
Ph: (440)238-3366
Fax: (440)238-7010
Co. E-mail: info@strongsvillechamber.com
URL: http://www.strongsvillechamber.com
Contact: Amy T. Ferree, Executive Director
Facebook: www.facebook.com/StrongsvilleChamberofCommerce

Description: Promotes business and community development in Strongsville, OH. Monitors legislation. Sponsors annual homecoming festival. **Founded:** 1941. **Publications:** *Strongsville Chamber of Commerce News* (3/year). **Geographic Preference:** Local.

43580 ■ *Strongsville Chamber of Commerce News*
18829 Royalton Rd.
Strongsville, OH 44136
Ph: (440)238-3366
Fax: (440)238-7010
Co. E-mail: info@strongsvillechamber.com
URL: http://www.strongsvillechamber.com
Contact: Amy T. Ferree, Executive Director
URL(s): www.strongsvillechamber.com/newsletters
Released: 3/year **Description:** Includes information, updates and other articles concerning Strongsville Chamber of Commerce. **Availability:** Online.

43581 ■ Sunbury - Big Walnut Area Chamber of Commerce
39 E Granville St.
Sunbury, OH 43074
Ph: (740)965-2860
Fax: (740)965-2860
Co. E-mail: info@sunburybigwalnutchamber.com
URL: http://www.sunburybigwalnutchamber.com
Contact: Maribeth Meluch, President
Facebook: www.facebook.com/SunburyBig-Walnut-Area-Chamber-of-Commerce-139958902697709
Linkedin: www.linkedin.com/company/sunbury-big-walnut-area-chamber-of-commerce
X (Twitter): x.com/SunburyChamber

Description: Encourages the development of a local infrastructure that will support existing and new businesses; organizes and supports civic activities for the benefit of community residents and enhances the relationship between the Sunbury/Big Walnut Area residents and business community. **Publications:** *News and Notes* (Quarterly). **Geographic Preference:** Local.

43582 ■ Swanton Area Chamber of Commerce (SACC)
100 Zeiter Way
Swanton, OH 43558
Ph: (419)826-1941
Co. E-mail: swantoncc@aol.com
URL: http://www.swantonareacoc.com
Contact: Neil Toeppe, Chief Executive Officer
Facebook: www.facebook.com/Swanton-Chamber-of-Commerce-227532140667956

Description: Businesses, factories, retail stores, wholesalers, professional and fraternal organizations, and individuals interested in promoting business and community development in eastern Fulton and western Lucas counties, OH. Conducts workshops. **Founded:** 1975. **Geographic Preference:** Local.

43583 ■ Swedish-American Chamber of Commerce Ohio
PO Box 81242
Cleveland, OH 44181
Ph: (216)403-8945
Co. E-mail: info@sacc-ohio.org
URL: http://sacc-ohio.org
Contact: Jim Hornyak, President
E-mail: jim.hornyak@sacc-ohio.org
Facebook: www.facebook.com/SACC-Ohio-101249438144883
Linkedin: www.linkedin.com/in/sacc-ohio-8324311a3
X (Twitter): x.com/SACC_OH

Description: Business organization that promotes trade, commerce, and investment between Sweden and the greater Ohio region, which includes western Pennsylvania, eastern Indiana, western New York, Kentucky, and West Virginia. **Geographic Preference:** State.

43584 ■ Sylvania Area Chamber of Commerce (SACC)
5632 N Main St.
Sylvania, OH 43560-1964
Ph: (419)882-2135
URL: http://www.sylvaniachamber.org
Contact: Tiffany Scott, Executive Director
E-mail: tscott@sylvaniachamber.org
Facebook: www.facebook.com/SylvaniaAreaChamberofCommerce
Linkedin: www.linkedin.com/company/sylvania-area-chamber-of-commerce
X (Twitter): x.com/sylvaniacofc
Instagram: www.instagram.com/sylvaniachamber
Pinterest: www.pinterest.com/sylvaniachamberandvisitorsbure

Description: Promotes business and community development in the Sylvania, OH area. Sponsors annual Arts and Crafts Festival. **Founded:** 1947. **Geographic Preference:** Local.

43585 ■ Tallmadge Chamber of Commerce (TCOC)
80 Community Rd.
Tallmadge, OH 44278
Ph: (330)633-5417
Fax: (330)633-5415
Co. E-mail: chamber@tallmadgechamber.com
URL: http://www.tallmadgechamber.com
Contact: Jim West, Co-President
Facebook: www.facebook.com/TallmadgeChamberofCommerce
Linkedin: www.linkedin.com/company/tallmadge-chamber-of-commerce

Description: Promotes business and community development in Tallmadge, OH. Sponsors arts and crafts festival. Conducts charitable activities. **Founded:** 1955. **Publications:** *Business Notes* (Bimonthly). **Educational Activities:** Tallmadge Chamber of Commerce Banquet (Annual). **Geographic Preference:** Local.

43586 ■ Toledo Regional Chamber of Commerce (TRCC)
300 Madison Ave., Ste. 200
Toledo, OH 43604
Ph: (419)243-8191
Co. E-mail: joinus@toledochamber.com
URL: http://www.toledochamber.com
Contact: Wendy Gramza, President
Facebook: www.facebook.com/toledochamber
Linkedin: www.linkedin.com/company/toledo-regional-chamber-of-commerce
X (Twitter): x.com/toledochamber
Instagram: www.instagram.com/toledo.chamber
YouTube: www.youtube.com/user/ToledoChamber

Description: Offers many business development resources to help entrepreneurs start a new venture or expand their existing one. **Founded:** 1894. **Publications:** *Insider* (Monthly); *Membership Reference Guide* (Annual); *Toledo Profile Series*. **Awards:** Toledo Regional Chamber of Commerce ATHENA Award (Annual). **Geographic Preference:** Local.

43587 ■ Troy Area Chamber of Commerce
405 SW Public Sq., Ste. 330
Troy, OH 45373
Ph: (937)339-8769
Co. E-mail: tacc@troyohiochamber.com
URL: http://www.troyohiochamber.com
Contact: Kathi Roetter, Executive Director
Facebook: www.facebook.com/TroyOhioChamberofCommerce
Linkedin: www.linkedin.com/company/troy-area-chamber-of-commerce
X (Twitter): x.com/TroyOhioChamber

Instagram: www.instagram.com/troyohiochamber
YouTube: www.youtube.com/channel/
UCxIcUQXFaGkSKJPp6YLyOsw
Description: Seeks to enhance the quality of life of Troy community through promotion of economic vitality and growth, stimulation of business environment and advancement of free enterprise system. **Founded:** 1934. **Publications:** *Troy Area Chamber News* (Monthly). **Awards:** A. Robert Davies MD Memorial Young Man of the Year Award (Annual); Troy Area Community Service Award (Annual); Troy Area Distinguished Citizen of the Year (Annual); Troy Area Outstanding Educator of the Year (Annual); Shirley Culp Davies Memorial Young Woman of the Year Award (Annual). **Geographic Preference:** Local.

43588 ■ Tuscarawas County Chamber of Commerce (TCCC)
1323 4th St. NW
New Philadelphia, OH 44663
Ph: (330)343-4474
Fax: (330)343-6526
Co. E-mail: info@tuschamber.com
URL: http://tuschamber.com
Contact: Scott Robinson, President
E-mail: scottr@tuschamber.com
Facebook: www.facebook.com/TuscarawasCoun tyChamberofCommerce
Linkedin: www.linkedin.com/company/tuscarawas -county-chamber-of-commerce
YouTube: www.youtube.com/channel/UC1wl1-XXZ 5ZQHUL3d3QGsvg
Description: Promotes business and community development in Tuscarawas County, OH. Operates safety council and export resource center. **Founded:** 1959. **Publications:** *Economic and Demographics of Tuscarawas County*; *Strictly Business* (Quarterly); *Images of Tuscarawas County* (Annual). **Geographic Preference:** Local.

43589 ■ Twin City Chamber of Commerce (TC)
210 E 3rd St.
Uhrichsville, OH 44683
Ph: (740)922-5623
Co. E-mail: info@twincitychamber.org
URL: http://twincitychamber.org
Facebook: www.facebook.com/twincitychamber
Linkedin: www.linkedin.com/company/twinci tychamber
Instagram: www.instagram.com/twincitychamber
Description: Manufacturers, retail store owners, and interested individuals organized to promote business and community development in the Dennison and Uhrichsville, OH area. Sponsors various community activities. **Founded:** 1960. **Geographic Preference:** Local.

43590 ■ Twinsburg Chamber of Commerce (TCC)
9044 Church St.
Twinsburg, OH 44087
Ph: (330)963-6249
Co. E-mail: atonozzi@twinsburgchamber.com
URL: http://www.twinsburgchamber.com
Description: Provides advocacy, education, cost savings benefits, and business promotion opportunities to businesses in the local area. **Founded:** 1921. **Publications:** *Chamber News*; *Twinsburg Quick Facts*; *Twinsburg Industrial and Commercial Directory* (Annual). **Educational Activities:** Chamber Golf Outing (Annual). **Geographic Preference:** Local.

43591 ■ Union County Chamber of Commerce (UCCC)
227 E Fifth St.
Marysville, OH 43040
Ph: (937)642-6279
Fax: (937)644-0422
Co. E-mail: chamber@unioncounty.org
URL: http://unioncounty.org
Contact: Tonya Woodruff, Director
E-mail: twoodruff@unioncounty.org
Facebook: www.facebook.com/UnionCountyOhio
X (Twitter): x.com/UCChamberChat
Instagram: www.instagram.com/unioncoun tychamberofcommerce
Description: Promotes business and community development in the area. Sponsors annual events and festivals. **Founded:** 1906. **Publications:** *Chamber Notes* (Quarterly); *Bridge Tour* (Annual); *Convention & Visitors Bureau* (Monthly); *Quality of Life Book & Membership Directory* (Annual). **Geographic Preference:** Local.

43592 ■ Van Wert Area County Chamber of Commerce (VWCCC)
118 N Washington St.
Van Wert, OH 45891
Ph: (419)238-4390
Co. E-mail: chamber@vanwertchamber.com
URL: http://www.vanwertchamber.com
Contact: Mark Verville, President
Facebook: www.facebook.com/vanwertchamber
Instagram: www.instagram.com/vanwertchamber
Description: Promotes business and community development in the Van Wert, OH area. Sponsors annual Home Show. **Founded:** 1926. **Publications:** *Chamber VieWpoint* (Monthly); *Membership Directory and Buyer's Guide* (Biennial); *Van Wert Community Guide* (Semiannual). **Geographic Preference:** Local.

43593 ■ Vermilion Chamber of Commerce (VCC)
5495 Liberty Ave.
Vermilion, OH 44089-1307
Ph: (440)967-4477
Co. E-mail: vermilionchamber1@gmail.com
URL: http://www.vermilionohio.com
Contact: Sandra Coe, Executive Director
Facebook: www.facebook.com/vermilionchamber
X (Twitter): x.com/vermilionchambe
Description: Promotes business and community development in Vermilion, OH. Sponsors annual dinner, Festival of Fish, Woollybear Festival, and awards luncheon. **Founded:** 1962. **Geographic Preference:** Local.

43594 ■ Vinton County Chamber of Commerce
104 W Main St.
McArthur, OH 45651
Ph: (740)596-5033
Co. E-mail: info@vintoncountytravel.com
URL: http://www.vintoncounty.com
Contact: Tim Eberts, President
Facebook: www.facebook.com/VintonCountyOhio
Description: Promotes business and community development in the McArthur, OH area. **Founded:** 1850. **Awards:** Vinton County Student of the Year Scholarship (Annual). **Geographic Preference:** Local.

43595 ■ The Voice
8803 Brecksville Rd., Ste. 7-267
Brecksville, OH 44141
Ph: (440)526-7350
Co. E-mail: chamber@brecksvillechamber.com
URL: http://brecksvillechamber.com
Contact: Kris Toth, President
URL(s): brecksvillechamber.com/about-us
Released: Bimonthly **Description:** Contains news and information for members of the organization and its industry partners. **Availability:** Print; PDF; Online.

43596 ■ Wadsworth Chamber of Commerce (WACC)
132 A Main St.
Wadsworth, OH 44281
Ph: (330)336-6150
URL: http://www.wadsworthchamber.com
Contact: Janie Parish, Executive Director
E-mail: exec@wadsworthchamber.com
Linkedin: www.linkedin.com/company/wadsworth -chamber-of-commerce-inc
Description: Promotes business and community development in the Wadsworth, OH area. Evaluates and responds to the needs of local businesses; provides programs and services to members. **Founded:** 1954. **Geographic Preference:** Local.

43597 ■ Wapakoneta Area Chamber of Commerce (WACC)
30 E Auglaize St.
Wapakoneta, OH 45895
Ph: (419)738-2911
Co. E-mail: chamber@wapakoneta.com
URL: http://www.wapakoneta.com
Contact: Stephanie Shutt, Contact
Facebook: www.facebook.com/wapakchamber
YouTube: www.youtube.com/channel/UCKfonX dIBqLYOhEv0cv2HTQ
Description: Promotes business and community development in the Wapakoneta, OH area. Sponsors the Indian Summer Festival. **Publications:** *Chamber Chat* (Monthly). **Geographic Preference:** Local.

43598 ■ Waterville Area Chamber of Commerce (WACC)
122 Farnsworth Rd.
Waterville, OH 43566
Ph: (419)878-5188
Fax: (419)878-5199
Co. E-mail: admin@watervillechamber.com
URL: http://watervillechamber.com
Contact: Carla Lammers, President
Facebook: www.facebook.com/Wa tervilleAreaChamber
Instagram: www.instagram.com/watervillechamber
Description: Businesspersons, professionals, retail and service merchants, manufacturer's representatives, and industry interested in promoting business and community development in the area. Assists new business and provides input for economic development. Sponsors annual events and festivals. **Founded:** 1970. **Publications:** *Business and Community Directory* (Quarterly). **Geographic Preference:** Local.

43599 ■ Wauseon Chamber of Commerce (WCC)
115 N Fulton St.
Wauseon, OH 43567
Ph: (419)335-9966
Fax: (419)335-7693
Co. E-mail: director@wauseonchamber.com
URL: http://www.wauseonchamber.com
Contact: Jeff Rupp, President
Facebook: www.facebook.com/Wauseon-Chamber-of -Commerce-147401702041866
Description: Promotes business and community development in the Wauseon, OH area. **Founded:** 1956. **Geographic Preference:** Local.

43600 ■ The Wave
202 Cleveland Rd. W
Huron, OH 44839
Ph: (419)433-5700
Co. E-mail: chamber@huron.net
URL: http://www.huron.net
Contact: Dr. Heather Demos, President
URL(s): huronchamber.com/about-us
Released: Quarterly **Description:** Includes information and articles concerning Huron Chamber of Commerce. **Availability:** Print; PDF.

43601 ■ Waynesville Area Chamber of Commerce
10B N Main St.
Waynesville, OH 45068-0281
Ph: (513)897-8855
URL: http://www.waynesvilleohio.com
Contact: Kelly Miller, Executive Director
E-mail: kelly@waynesvilleohio.com
Facebook: www.facebook.com/waynesvilleoh
X (Twitter): x.com/WaynesvilleOH
Instagram: www.instagram.com/waynesvilleoh
Pinterest: www.pinterest.com/ waynesvilleareachamberofcommer
Description: Works to advance, protect, and preserve the civic, economic, business, and individual interest of the Waynesville area. **Founded:** 1969. **Publications:** *Getting It Right The First Time: A Pocket Guide For New Business*. **Geographic Preference:** Local.

STATE LISTINGS

43602 ■ West Shore Chamber of Commerce
PO Box 45297
Westlake, OH 44145
Ph: (440)835-8787
Co. E-mail: contact@westshorechamber.org
URL: http://www.westshorechamber.org
Contact: Chris Stahurski, President

Description: Works as a voluntary organization of the business community. Unites hundreds of business and professional firms, thus creating a unique central agency working to improve business and build a better community. **Founded:** 1979. **Geographic Preference:** Local.

43603 ■ Westerville Area Chamber of Commerce
99 Commerce Pk. Dr., Ste. A
Westerville, OH 43082
Ph: (614)882-8917
Fax: (614)882-2085
Co. E-mail: info@westervillechamber.com
URL: http://www.westervillechamber.com
Contact: Janet Tressler-Davis, President
E-mail: jdavis@westervillechamber.com
Facebook: www.facebook.com/WAChamber
Linkedin: www.linkedin.com/company/westerville
 -area-chamber-of-commerce
X (Twitter): x.com/WAChamber

Description: Promotes business and community development in the Westerville, OH area. **Founded:** 1967. **Publications:** *The Communicator* (Monthly). **Educational Activities:** Westerville Music and Arts Festival (Annual). **Awards:** Westerville Area Chamber of Commerce Business Person of the Year (Annual). **Geographic Preference:** Local.

43604 ■ Whitehall Ohio Chamber of Commerce
360 S Yearling Rd.
Whitehall, OH 43213
Ph: (614)545-9702
Co. E-mail: whitehallohiochamber@gmail.com
URL: http://www.whitehallareachamber.org
Contact: Fred Everett, President

Description: Seeks to preserve and enhance the positive image of Whitehall community. **Publications:** *Chamber Chronicle* (Quarterly). **Geographic Preference:** Local.

43605 ■ Willoughby Western Lake County Chamber of Commerce (WWLC)
28 Public Sq.
Willoughby, OH 44094
Ph: (440)942-1632
Co. E-mail: info@wwlcchamber.com
URL: http://wwlcchamber.com
Contact: Liz Crosby, Secretary
E-mail: crosby@buckleyking.com
Facebook: www.facebook.com/WWLCchamber
Linkedin: www.linkedin.com/company/willoughby-wes
 tern-lake-county-chamber-of-commerce
X (Twitter): x.com/wwlcchamber
YouTube: www.youtube.com/c/wwlcchamber

Description: Promotes business and community development in the Willoughby, Willoughby Hills, and Kirtland, OH area. Offers Workers' Compensation and Health Insurance at greatly reduced premiums. **Publications:** *Directory of Members & Buyers Guide*. **Geographic Preference:** Local.

43606 ■ Wilmington-Clinton County Chamber of Commerce (WCCCC)
21 N S St.
Wilmington, OH 45177
Ph: (937)382-2737
Co. E-mail: info@wccchamber.com
URL: http://wccchamber.com
Contact: Dessie Rogers, Executive Director
E-mail: dbuchanan@wccchamber.com

Description: Promotes business and community development in the Clinton County, OH area. **Founded:** 1957. **Publications:** *Buyer's Guide* (Annual). **Geographic Preference:** Local.

43607 ■ Wooster Area Chamber of Commerce (WACC)
377 W Liberty St.
Wooster, OH 44691
Ph: (330)262-5735
URL: http://www.woosterchamber.com
Contact: Samira Zimmerly, President
E-mail: szimmerly@woosterchamber.com
Facebook: www.facebook.com/woosterchamber
Linkedin: www.linkedin.com/company/wooster-area
 -chamber-of-commerce
Instagram: www.instagram.com/woosterchamber
YouTube: www.youtube.com/channel/UC
 tSWgpRhSruXa14b3EphxIQ

Description: Promotes business and community development in Wayne County, OH. **Founded:** 1892. **Publications:** *Chamber Connection* (Monthly); *Wayne County Industrial* (Annual). **Educational Activities:** Wooster Area Chamber of Commerce Dinner (Annual); Annual Wayne County Home & Garden Show (Annual). **Awards:** Wooster Area Chamber of Commerce Business of the Year (Annual); Wooster Area Chamber of Commerce Small Business of the Year (Annual); Wooster Area Chamber of Commerce Wall of Fame Award (Annual). **Geographic Preference:** Local.

43608 ■ Wyandot Chamber of Commerce
108 E Wyandot Ave.
Upper Sandusky, OH 43351
Ph: (419)294-3349
URL: http://www.wyandotchamber.com
Contact: Ashley Snyder, Co-President
Facebook: www.facebook.com/WyandotChamber

Description: Promotes business and community development in Wyandot County, OH. **Founded:** 1947. **Publications:** *Industry Business* (Periodic); *Compass* (Bimonthly). **Geographic Preference:** Local.

43609 ■ Xenia Area Chamber of Commerce (XACC)
334 W Market St.
Xenia, OH 45385
Ph: (937)372-3591
Co. E-mail: admin@xacc.com
URL: http://www.xacc.com
Contact: Donna Saraga, President
Facebook: www.facebook.com/XeniaChamber
Linkedin: www.linkedin.com/in/xenia-chamber-of
 -commerce-a666521a
X (Twitter): x.com/xachamber

Description: Promotes business and community development in Xenia, OH. **Founded:** 1949. **Geographic Preference:** Local.

43610 ■ *Xenia Community Profile Book*
URL(s): www.xacc.com/article.php/20110728
 11152345
Released: Biennial **Availability:** Print; Online.

43611 ■ Yellow Springs Chamber of Commerce
101 Dayton St.
Yellow Springs, OH 45387
Ph: (937)767-2686
Co. E-mail: info@yschamber.org
URL: http://www.yellowspringsohio.org
Contact: Mark Heise, Chairman
Facebook: www.facebook.com/YellowSpringsOH
YouTube: www.youtube.com/results

Description: Promotes business and community development in Yellow Springs, OH area. **Publications:** *YSCHAMBER* (Monthly). **Geographic Preference:** Local.

43612 ■ Youngstown/Warren Regional Chamber of Commerce
City Center One, Ste. 500
100 E Federal St.
Youngstown, OH 44503
Ph: (330)744-2131
Co. E-mail: info@regionalchamber.com
URL: http://www.regionalchamber.com
Contact: Guy Coviello, President
E-mail: guy@regionalchamber.com
Facebook: www.facebook.com/ywregionalchamber
Linkedin: www.linkedin.com/company/youngstown
 -warren-regional-chamber_2
X (Twitter): x.com/ywchamber
Instagram: www.instagram.com/ywchamber
YouTube: www.youtube.com/user/RegionalChamber

Description: Promotes business and community development in Youngstown/Warren Region, OH area. **Geographic Preference:** Local.

43613 ■ *YSCHAMBER*
101 Dayton St.
Yellow Springs, OH 45387
Ph: (937)767-2686
Co. E-mail: info@yschamber.org
URL: http://www.yellowspringsohio.org
Contact: Mark Heise, Chairman
URL(s): www.yellowspringsohio.org/chamber-home/
 chamber-newsletters
Released: Monthly; latest edition 2018. **Availability:** Online.

43614 ■ Zanesville-Muskingum County Chamber of Commerce
205 N 5th St.
Zanesville, OH 43701
Ph: (740)455-8282
Co. E-mail: info@zmchamber.com
URL: http://www.zmchamber.com
Contact: Howard Stewart, Chairman
Facebook: www.facebook.com/zmchamber
Linkedin: www.linkedin.com/company/zanesville
 -muskingum-county-chamber-of-commerce
X (Twitter): x.com/zmchamber

Description: Promotes business and community development in the Muskingum County, OH area. **Founded:** 1905. **Publications:** *Commerce* (Annual); *Legislative Directory* (Annual); *Voice* (Monthly). **Geographic Preference:** Local.

MINORITY BUSINESS ASSISTANCE PROGRAMS

43615 ■ Cincinnati USA Regional Chamber - Minority Business Accelerator (MBA)
3 E 4th St.
Cincinnati, OH 45202
Ph: (513)579-3111
Co. E-mail: mbainfo@cincinnatichamber.com
URL: http://minoritybusinessaccelerator.com
Contact: Darrin Redus, Chief Executive Officer
E-mail: dredus@minoritybusinessaccelerator.com
Linkedin: www.linkedin.com/showcase/cincinnati
 -minority-business-accelerator

Description: Accelerates the growth and development of African-American and Hispanic owned businesses. Offers advisory support and coaching. **Investment Policies:** At least $1 millions; demonstrated growth potential; certification as a minority business enterprise; headquartered in the Cincinnati region.

43616 ■ City of Cleveland Office of Equal Opportunities (OEO)
c/o Tyson Mitchell, Director
601 LakeSide Ave., Rm. 335
Cleveland, OH 44114
Ph: (216)664-4152
Fax: (216)664-3870
URL: http://www.clevelandohio.gov/city-hall/depar
 tments/law/divisions/office-equal-opportunity
Contact: Tyson Mitchell, Director
E-mail: tmitchell4@clevelandohio.gov

Description: Managerial and technical assistance is provided to develop, support and promote business development for program participants in Cleveland.

43617 ■ Ohio Minority Supplier Development Council (OMSDC)
6956 E Broad St., Ste. 310
Columbus, OH 43213
Ph: (614)225-6959
Co. E-mail: marketing@ohiomsdc.org
URL: http://ohiomsdc.org
Contact: George R. Simms, President
E-mail: gsimms@ohiomsdc.org
Facebook: www.facebook.com/OhioMSDC

43618 ■ Ohio

X (Twitter): x.com/ohiomsdc
Instagram: www.instagram.com/ohiomsdc
Description: Aims to build a stronger society and to support business development. **Founded:** 1972. **Geographic Preference:** Local.

43618 ■ Women's Entrepreneurial Network (WEN)
OH
Ph: (419)536-6732
URL: http://www.wen-usa.com
Contact: Jennifer Alford, President
Facebook: www.facebook.com/WENOhio
Instagram: www.instagram.com/wen_toledo_oh
Description: Provides business development for female entrepreneurs. **Founded:** 1993. **Publications:** WEN Newsletter. **Geographic Preference:** Local.

FINANCING AND LOAN PROGRAMS

43619 ■ Blue Chip Venture Co.
425 Walnut St., No. 1800
Dayton, OH 45402
Contact: Gerald S. Greenberg, Contact
Description: Firm provides private equity and venture capital investment services. **Founded:** 1990. **Preferred Investment Size:** $4,000,000 to $6,000,000. **Industry Preferences:** Internet specific, computer software and services, medical and health, communications and media, semiconductors and other electronics, other products, consumer related, industrial and energy, biotechnology, and computer hardware.

43620 ■ Crystal Internet Venture Fund L.P.
Cleveland, OH
Co. E-mail: inquiries@crystalventures.com
URL: http://crystalventures.com
Contact: Joseph Tzeng, Managing Director
Co-Founder
Founded: 1997. **Preferred Investment Size:** $1,000,000 to $5,000,000. **Investment Policies:** Equity. **Industry Preferences:** Internet specific, computer software and services, communications and media, semiconductors and other electronics, and computer hardware.

43621 ■ Early Stage Partners (ESP)
1801 E Ninth St., Ste. 1700
Cleveland, OH 44114
Ph: (216)781-4600
Co. E-mail: inbox@esplp.com
URL: http://www.esplp.com
Contact: Charlie MacMillan, Chief Financial Officer
Description: Venture capital firm investing in early stage information technology and healthcare technology companies. **Founded:** 2001. **Investment Policies:** Early stage. **Industry Preferences:** Computer software, industrial and energy, and manufacturing.

43622 ■ Morgenthaler Ventures
50 Public Sq., Ste. 2700
Cleveland, OH 44113
Contact: Theodore A. Laufik, Contact
Description: Venture capital and private equity firm. **Preferred Investment Size:** $5,000,000 to $20,000,000. **Industry Preferences:** Semiconductors and other electronics, communications and media, medical and health, Internet specific, computer software and services, biotechnology, industrial and energy, other products, computer hardware, and consumer related.

43623 ■ NCT Ventures
One Marconi Pl., 274 Marconi Blvd., Ste. 400
Columbus, OH 43215
Co. E-mail: info@nctventures.com
URL: http://nctventures.com
Contact: Rich Langdale, Managing Partner
Facebook: www.facebook.com/NCTVentures
Linkedin: www.linkedin.com/company/nct-ventures
X (Twitter): x.com/nctventures

Description: Investment operator focused on the Midwest. Implements the Ideas- to-Business model created in conjunction with The Center for Entrepreneurship at Ohio State University. **Founded:** 2000. **Industry Preferences:** Marketing; logistics; disruptive platform technologies.

43624 ■ North Coast Ventures (NCV)
1 St. Clair Ave. No. 310
Cleveland, OH 44114
Co. E-mail: info@northcoast.vc
URL: http://northcoast.vc
Contact: Daniel Luketic, Director
Description: Invests in early-stage technology startups in Ohio. **Founded:** 2006.

43625 ■ Ohio Capital Fund (OCF)
303 Broadway, Ste. 1200
Cincinnati, OH 45202
Fax: (513)361-7685
URL: http://www.ohiocapitalfund.com
Contact: Stephen A. Baker, Managing Director Department Head
Description: Established by the State of Ohio to increase private investment in early- or seed-stage Ohio companies.

43626 ■ Ohio Innovation Fund (OIF)
629 N High St.
Columbus, OH 43215
Co. E-mail: info@ohioinnovationfund.com
URL: http://www.ohioinnovationfund.com
Contact: Bill Baumel, Managing Director
Linkedin: www.linkedin.com/ohio-innovation-fund
X (Twitter): x.com/ohioinnofund
Description: Venture capital firm for early-stage companies in Ohio. **Industry Preferences:** SaaS; cyber security; AI; medtech/pharma; advanced manufacturing; IoT.

43627 ■ Ohio TechAngels
1275 Kinnear Rd.
Columbus, OH 43212
URL: http://www.ohiotechangels.com
X (Twitter): x.com/OhioTechAngels
Description: Investment fund for Ohio-based technology companies. **Industry Preferences:** IT; advanced materials; life sciences.

43628 ■ PNC Erieview Capital
1900 E 9th St., 17th Fl.
Cleveland, OH 44114
Ph: (216)222-3763
URL: http://www.pnc.com/erieview/english/home.html
Contact: Edward S. Pentecost, President
E-mail: ed.pentecost@pncerieview.com
Founded: 1979. **Preferred Investment Size:** $5,000,000 to $35,000,000. **Industry Preferences:** Firm provides private equity services leveraged buyouts, management buyouts, recapitalizations, growth capital, middle market, mezzanine, acquisition capital and shareholder liquidity events transactions.

43629 ■ Primus Venture Partners Inc.
30100 Chagrin Blvd., Ste. 203
Pepper Pike, OH 44124
Ph: (440)684-7300
URL: http://primuscapital.com
Contact: Chris Welch, Director
E-mail: cwelch@primuscapital.com
Linkedin: www.linkedin.com/company/primus-capital-funds
Description: Private equity firm that offers investment solutions. **Founded:** 1984. **Preferred Investment Size:** $15,000,000 to $40,000,000. **Industry Preferences:** Communications and media, other products, Internet specific, consumer related, medical and health, biotechnology, business services, computer software and services, computer hardware, semiconductors and other electronics.

43630 ■ reLink Ventures
1755 Enterprise Pkwy., Ste. 400
Twinsburg, OH 44087
Ph: (216)762-0598
Co. E-mail: info@relinkventures.com
URL: http://relinkventures.com

Contact: Jeff Dalton, President
Description: Offers capital, consulting, strategy support, and development. **Founded:** 1996.

43631 ■ SunBridge Partners
3659 Green Rd., Ste. 100
Beachwood, OH 44122
Ph: (704)443-8369
URL: http://sunbridgepartners.com
Contact: Allen Miner, Co-Founder Partner
Description: Early-stage technology investor with operations in Japan and the US. **Founded:** 2004. **Industry Preferences:** Semiconductors; cloud computing; wireless communication; ecommerce; clean technology; enterprise software; digital media; business services; hardware; aerospace; energy.

PROCUREMENT ASSISTANCE PROGRAMS

43632 ■ Northeast Ohio Procurement Technical Assistance Center - Lake Erie College Campus
391 W Washington St.
Painesville, OH 44077
Ph: (440)375-7050
Co. E-mail: admission@lec.edu
URL: http://www.lec.edu
Contact: Donald Purtill, President
Facebook: www.facebook.com/lakeeriecollege
X (Twitter): x.com/lakeeriecollege
Instagram: www.instagram.com/lakeeriecollege
Description: Provides education, training, and consultation services as needed depending on the experience of the business. **Founded:** 1856.

43633 ■ Ohio Procurement Technical Assistance Center
77 S High St., 29th Fl.
Columbus, OH 43215
Ph: (614)644-1637
Co. E-mail: ohioptac@development.ohio.gov
URL: http://development.ohio.gov/business/manufacturing/procurement-technical-assistance-centers
Description: Offers many business development resources to help entrepreneurs start a new venture or expand their existing one.

43634 ■ Ohio Procurement Technical Assistance Center - Cincinnati Procurement Outreach Center
1776 Mentor Ave., Ste. 240
Cincinnati, OH 45212
URL: http://www.aptac-us.org/find-a-ptac/?state=OH
Description: Offers many business development resources to help entrepreneurs start a new venture or expand their existing one.

43635 ■ Ohio Procurement Technical Assistance Center - Lawrence Economic Development Corporation - Southern Ohio Procurement Outreach Center (SOPTAC) [Southern Ohio Procurement Outreach Center (SOPOC)]
216 Collins Ave.
South Point, OH 45680
Ph: (740)377-4550
Co. E-mail: info@sopoc.org
URL: http://sopoc.org/index.html
Contact: Jordan Lucas, Program Director
Facebook: www.facebook.com/soptacohio
Description: Identifies business firms that are qualified to sell their goods and services to the Department of Defense (DoD), other federal agencies, and state government programs serving Adams, Brown, Gallia, Highland, Jackson, Lawrence, Pike, Ross, Scioto and Vinton counties.

43636 ■ Ohio Procurement Technical Assistance Center - Mahoning Valley Technical Procurement Center - Mahoning Valley Economic Development Corporation (MVEDC)
4319 Belmont Ave.
Youngstown, OH 44505

STATE LISTINGS
Ohio ■ 43652

URL: http://www.valleyedp.com/getting-to-know-valley-partners
Description: Offers many business development resources to help entrepreneurs start a new venture or expand their existing one. **Founded:** 1978.

43637 ■ Ohio Procurement Technical Assistance Center - Procurement Technical Assistance Program (PTAC)
77 S High St.
  Columbus, OH 43215
URL: http://www.aptac-us.org
Description: Provides counseling, technical resources, historical contracting data, military specifications, financial guidance, and advocacy for federal procurement opportunities. **Founded:** 1985.

43638 ■ Ohio Procurement Technical Assistance Center - Procurement Technical Assistance Program
77 S High St.
  Columbus, OH 43215
Ph: (614)644-1637
Co. E-mail: ohioptac@development.ohio.gov
URL: http://development.ohio.gov/business/manufacturing/procurement-technical-assistance-centers
Contact: Joseph Scott, Program Manager
Description: Helps companies sell their products or service to local, state, or federal government agencies.

43639 ■ Ohio University Procurement Technical Assistance Center at Athens (PTAC)
Building 21, The Ridges 1 Ohio University
  Athens, OH 45701-2979
URL: http://www.ohio.edu/voinovich-school/news-resources/ohio-university-procurement-technical-assistance-center-has-another-record-breaking
Contact: Sharon Hopkins, Director
E-mail: hopkins1@ohio.edu
URL(s): www.aptac-us.org/find-a-ptac/?state=OH#
Description: Provides training, information, and technical assistance to businesses in Appalachia Ohio seeking government contracts.

43640 ■ Southern Ohio Procurement Technical Assistance Center (SOPTAC) - Lawrence Economic Development Corp.
216 Collins Ave.
  South Point, OH 45680-0488
Ph: (740)377-4550
Fax: (740)377-2091
URL: http://www.ledcorp.org
Contact: Dr. Bill Dingus, Executive Director
E-mail: dingus@ohio.edu
Facebook: www.facebook.com/LawrenceEconomicDevelopment
Founded: 1983.

43641 ■ Toledo Regional Chamber of Commerce (TRCC)
300 Madison Ave., Ste. 200
  Toledo, OH 43604
Ph: (419)243-8191
Co. E-mail: joinus@toledochamber.com
URL: http://www.toledochamber.com
Contact: Wendy Gramza, President
Facebook: www.facebook.com/toledochamber
Linkedin: www.linkedin.com/company/toledo-regional-chamber-of-commerce
X (Twitter): x.com/toledochamber
Instagram: www.instagram.com/toledo.chamber
YouTube: www.youtube.com/user/ToledoChamber
Description: Offers many business development resources to help entrepreneurs start a new venture or expand their existing one. **Founded:** 1894. **Publications:** *Insider* (Monthly); *Membership Reference Guide* (Annual); *Toledo Profile Series*. **Awards:** Toledo Regional Chamber of Commerce ATHENA Award (Annual). **Geographic Preference:** Local.

INCUBATORS/RESEARCH AND TECHNOLOGY PARKS

43642 ■ Akron Bar Association (ABA)
57 S Broadway St.
  Akron, OH 44308
Ph: (303)253-5007
URL: http://www.akronbar.org
Contact: C. Allen Nichols, Executive Director
E-mail: callen@akronbar.org
Facebook: www.facebook.com/AkronBarAssociation
X (Twitter): x.com/AkronBarAssoc
YouTube: www.youtube.com/channel/UCjMQOxo0eyBU-IOxNYNafbg
Description: Promotes the administration of law and justice by fostering community service, improving public understanding of the law and justice system, and promoting the integrity of the profession. **Founded:** 1875. **Awards:** Akron Bar Association Foundation Scholarships (Annual).

43643 ■ Allen Economic Development Group (AEDG)
144 S Main St., Ste. 200
  Lima, OH 45801
Ph: (419)222-7706
Co. E-mail: info@aedg.com
URL: http://www.aedg.org
Contact: Dave Stratton, President
E-mail: strattond@aedg.org
Facebook: www.facebook.com/AEDGLima
YouTube: www.youtube.com/channel/UCbtiG1dGjUWkFgBNAjbLjOg
Description: A small business incubator dedicated to supporting emerging firms through shared resources and other services. **Founded:** 1993.

43644 ■ Alloy Development Company (HCDC)
1776 Mentor Ave., Ste. 100
  Cincinnati, OH 45212
Ph: (513)631-8292
Fax: (513)631-4887
URL: http://alloydev.org
Contact: Patrick Longo, Chief Executive Officer
E-mail: plongo@alloydev.org
Facebook: www.facebook.com/theHCDC
Linkedin: www.linkedin.com/company/hamilton-county-development-company
X (Twitter): x.com/theHCDC
YouTube: www.youtube.com/user/HCDCvideos
Description: A nationally-recognized business incubation program helping Greater Cincinnati entrepreneurs launch and build successful companies. It is a mixed-use, technology-focused incubation program catering to those entrepreneurs who are starting up an innovative and growing business. **Founded:** 1989.

43645 ■ The Appalachian Center for Economic Networks, Inc. (ACEnet)
94 Columbus Rd.
  Athens, OH 45701
Ph: (740)592-3854
Co. E-mail: info@acenetworks.org
URL: http://acenetworks.org
Contact: Larry Fisher, Executive Director
E-mail: larryf@acenetworks.org
Facebook: www.facebook.com/acenetathens
X (Twitter): x.com/acenetathens
Instagram: www.instagram.com/acenetathens
Description: The ACEnet, located in rural, southeastern Ohio, is an incubator dedicated to improving the economy of the region. Offers business incubation, e-commerce, specialty food production, and venture loans. **Founded:** 1985.

43646 ■ Ariel Ventures L.L.C. (AV)
1163 E 40th St., Ste. 201
  Cleveland, OH 44114
Ph: (216)344-9441
Fax: (216)373-7356
URL: http://www.arielventures.com/ariel/aboutUs.html
Contact: Lynn Selzer, Partner
E-mail: ls@arielventures.com

Description: Provider of business incubation services to support startups. **Founded:** 2001.

43647 ■ Barberton Community Development Corporation (BCDC)
139 E Tuscarawas Ave.
  Barberton, OH 44203
Ph: (330)745-3070
URL: http://bcdcorp.org
Contact: Scott Wagner, Executive Director
E-mail: scottwagner@bcdc.org
Facebook: www.facebook.com/BarbertonCDC
Description: Provides business development services for the area. **Founded:** 1985.

43648 ■ Beachwood Chamber of Commerce (BCC)
23355 Mercantile Rd.
  Beachwood, OH 44122
Ph: (216)831-0003
Co. E-mail: chamber@beachwood.org
URL: http://www.beachwood.org
Contact: Brian Friedman, Co-President
Facebook: www.facebook.com/BeachwoodCOC
Linkedin: www.linkedin.com/company/beachwoodcoc
X (Twitter): x.com/beachwoodcoc
YouTube: www.youtube.com/channel/UCfh-X_wrKF3su1wBiXlNFsQ
Description: Firm works to assist local businesses and improve the economic base. **Founded:** 1995. **Publications:** *Purchase Directory*. **Geographic Preference:** Local.

43649 ■ BioEnterprise
11000 Cedar Ave., Ste. 100
  Cleveland, OH 44106-3052
Description: Helps bio science innovators crow their companies. **Founded:** 2002.

43650 ■ Bounce Innovation Hub
526 S Main St.
  Akron, OH 44311
Ph: (234)900-5961
Co. E-mail: info@bouncehub.org
URL: http://bouncehub.org
Contact: Doug Weintraub, Chief Executive Officer
E-mail: dweintraub@bouncehub.org
Facebook: www.facebook.com/BounceInnovationHub
Linkedin: www.linkedin.com/company/bounce-innovation-hub
X (Twitter): x.com/Bounce_Hub
Instagram: www.instagram.com/bounce_hub
Description: Innovation hub serving northeast Ohio's entrepreneurial and innovation community. **Founded:** 2018.

43651 ■ Braintree Business Development Center
201 E 5th St.
  Mansfield, OH 44902
Ph: (419)525-1614
Co. E-mail: info@braintreepartners.org
URL: http://braintreepartners.org
Contact: Barb Miller, President
X (Twitter): x.com/braintreebdc
Description: Firm provides advanced manufacturing, information technology, business development, agriculture, food sciences and many more. **Founded:** 1986.

43652 ■ The Brandery
1311 Vine St.
  Cincinnati, OH 45202
Co. E-mail: info@brandery.org
URL: http://www.mainstventures.org/brandery
Facebook: www.facebook.com/pg/Brandery
Linkedin: www.linkedin.com/company/the-brandery
X (Twitter): x.com/brandery
Instagram: www.instagram.com/gobrandery
Description: Business accelerator and incubator supporting startups by offering $50K in financing, mentorship, partnership, and introduction to seed stage investors. **Founded:** 2010.

Small Business Sourcebook • 42nd Edition

43653 ■ Cincinnati USA Regional Chamber - Minority Business Accelerator (MBA)
3 E 4th St.
  Cincinnati, OH 45202
Ph: (513)579-3111
Co. E-mail: mbainfo@cincinnatichamber.com
URL: http://minoritybusinessaccelerator.com
Contact: Darrin Redus, Chief Executive Officer
E-mail: dredus@minoritybusinessaccelerator.com
Linkedin: www.linkedin.com/showcase/cincinnati
  -minority-business-accelerator
Description: Accelerates the growth and development of African-American and Hispanic owned businesses. Offers advisory support and coaching. **Investment Policies:** At least $1 millions; demonstrated growth potential; certification as a minority business enterprise; headquartered in the Cincinnati region.

43654 ■ CincyTech
2900 Reading Rd., Ste. 410
  Cincinnati, OH 45206
Ph: (513)263-2720
Co. E-mail: contactus@cincytechusa.com
URL: http://www.cincytechusa.com
Contact: Mike Venerable, Chief Executive Officer
Facebook: www.facebook.com/CincyTech
X (Twitter): x.com/Cincy_Tech
Instagram: www.instagram.com/cincy_tech
Description: A public-private seed-stage investor helping to transform ideas from startups and entrepreneurs into high potential technology companies.

43655 ■ Cintrifuse
1311 Vine St.
  Cincinnati, OH 45202
Ph: (513)246-2700
Co. E-mail: info@cintrifuse.com
URL: http://cintrifuse.com
Contact: Pete Blackshaw, Chief Executive Officer
Facebook: www.facebook.com/Cintrifuse
X (Twitter): x.com/cintrifuse
Description: Provides high-growth tech entrepreneurs and startups with support through a network of talent, funding, and customers.

43656 ■ Cleveland Culinary Launch Kitchen [Central Kitchen]
2800 Euclid Ave.
  Cleveland, OH 44115
Free: 833-216-2525
Co. E-mail: hello@thecentral.kitchen
URL: http://thecentral.kitchen
Contact: Eric Diamond, Chief Executive Officer
Facebook: www.facebook.com/Centralkitcle
Linkedin: www.linkedin.com/company/central-kitchen
X (Twitter): x.com/centralkitcle
Instagram: www.instagram.com/centralkitcle
Description: Firm is a shared kitchen and food business incubator. **Founded:** 2000.

43657 ■ Cleveland-Marshall Solo Practice Incubator
2121 Euclid Ave., LB 138
  Cleveland, OH 44115
URL: http://www.law.csuohio.edu/career/solopracticeincubator
Contact: Sheronda Dobson, Member
Description: Incubator providing low-cost resources, including office space, conference rooms and a reception area, for recent graduates looking to start their career as legal entrepreneurs. **Founded:** 1897.

43658 ■ Columbus Bar Association (CBA)
175 S Third St., Ste. 1100
  Columbus, OH 43215
Ph: (614)221-4112
Fax: (614)221-4850
Co. E-mail: info@cbalaw.org
URL: http://www.cbalaw.org
Contact: Charles A. Schneider, Co-President
Facebook: www.facebook.com/ColumbusBar
Linkedin: www.linkedin.com/company/columbus-bar
  -association
X (Twitter): x.com/ColumbusBar
Instagram: www.instagram.com/cbalawyers
YouTube: www.youtube.com/user/ColumbusBarAssoc
Description: A program intended to accelerate the successful development of new lawyers in an environment that provides a range of business support resources. Provides an office facility, office equipment, access to attorney mentors, training on a variety of law practice management issues, and specially designed networking opportunities to help new lawyers build a successful practice based on sound business principles. **Founded:** 1869. **Publications:** *Columbus Bar Directory* (Annual); *Local Practice Handbook*.

43659 ■ Common Wealth Kitchen Incubator
907 Elm St.
  Youngstown, OH 44505
Ph: (330)746-9811
Co. E-mail: cwkiyoungstown@gmail.com
URL: http://www.cwkitchenincubator.org
Contact: Sean Dougherty, Manager
Description: Promotes economic development and food security in Youngstown, OH and the surrounding region. Provides local food entrepreneurs with a facility where they can launch their food enterprise or expand their current business. **Founded:** 2009.

43660 ■ Dublin Entrepreneurial Center (DEC)
565 Metro Pl. S, Ste. 300
  Dublin, OH 43017
Ph: (614)989-2429
URL: http://www.decindublin.com
Contact: Chaz Freutel, Manager
E-mail: chaz@get-u-connected.com
Facebook: www.facebook.com/decindublin
X (Twitter): x.com/decindublin
Description: Supports startups and entrepreneurs by offering collaborative work spaces. **Founded:** 2009.

43661 ■ Economic Community Development Institute (ECDI)
1655 Old Leonard Ave.
  Columbus, OH 43219
Ph: (614)559-0115
Free: 888-210-3039
Fax: (614)732-0986
Co. E-mail: info@ecdi.org
URL: http://www.ecdi.org
Contact: Steven Fireman, President
Description: Offers education, training, and funding to small business loans to entrepreneurs. **Founded:** 2004.

43662 ■ Endeavor Center
1862 Shyville Rd.
  Piketon, OH 45661
URL: http://southcenters.osu.edu/endeavor-center
Contact: Ryan Mapes, Program Manager Leader
E-mail: mapes.281@osu.edu
Description: A small business incubator that provides flexible lease space, management guidance, networking, and shared services to entrepreneurs in south central Ohio. **Founded:** 2005.

43663 ■ The Entrepreneurs Center (TEC)
31 S Main St.
  Dayton, OH 45402
Ph: (937)210-9473
Co. E-mail: info@ecinnovates.com
URL: http://ecinnovates.com
Contact: Kim Frazier, Director
Facebook: www.facebook.com/tecdayton
Linkedin: www.linkedin.com/company/the-entrepreneurs-center
X (Twitter): x.com/tecdayton
Description: Non-profit organization provides incubation, acceleration and technology development services for technology-oriented entrepreneurs. **Founded:** 2000.

43664 ■ FlashStarts
50 Public Sq., Ste. 200
  Cleveland, OH 44113
Ph: (216)220-0200
Co. E-mail: info@flashstarts.com
URL: http://www.flashstarts.com
Contact: Charles Stack, Chief Executive Officer
Facebook: www.facebook.com/Flashstarts
Linkedin: www.linkedin.com/in/charlesstack
X (Twitter): x.com/Flashstarts
Instagram: www.instagram.com/flashstarts
YouTube: www.youtube.com/user/flashstarts
Description: Unique startup accelerator providing teams with hands-on coaching through a 12-week summer program. **Founded:** 2012.

43665 ■ Global Cardiovascular Innovation Center (GCIC)
10000 Cedar Ave.
  Cleveland, OH 44195
Ph: (216)445-5610
URL: http://my.clevelandclinic.org/locations/directions/127-gcic-building-global-cardiovascular-innovations-center
Description: Houses start-up companies developing innovative solutions for the diagnosis and treatment of cardiovascular disease and contributing to Ohio's economic development. **Founded:** 2007.

43666 ■ Great Lakes Innovation and Development Enterprise (GLIDE)
151 Innovation Dr., Ste. 210
  Elyria, OH 44035
Ph: (440)366-4310
Fax: (440)366-4320
Co. E-mail: innovate@glideit.org
URL: http://www.glideit.org
Contact: Dennis Cocco, Director
Facebook: www.facebook.com/GLIDE-Incubator
  -121035349296765
X (Twitter): x.com/GLIDEincubator
Description: Helps Northeast Ohio entrepreneurs wrap sound business practices around great business ideas. Provides professional business assistance to companies at every stage of development and connects entrepreneurs with the tools and resources they need to succeed. **Founded:** 2001.

43667 ■ The Hamilton Mill (HM)
20 High St.
  Hamilton, OH 45011
Description: Business incubator specializing in attracting companies focused on green energy, advanced manufacturing, and technology.

43668 ■ Innovate New Albany
8000 Walton Pky., Ste. 200
  New Albany, OH 43054
Ph: (614)315-3357
Co. E-mail: info@newalbanybusiness.org
URL: http://innovatenewalbany.org
Facebook: www.facebook.com/InnovateNewAlbany
X (Twitter): x.com/InnovateNA
YouTube: www.youtube.com/channel/UCSGvkxsv3awZsFpSvEDr77Q
Description: A hub for startups and entrepreneurial activities with a wide range of services from a fiber optics network, office space and conference rooms, to workshops and seminars.

43669 ■ Jumpstart Inc.
6701 Carnegie Ave., Ste. 100
  Cleveland, OH 44103
Ph: (216)363-3400
Fax: (216)363-3401
URL: http://www.jumpstartinc.org
Contact: Jerry Frantz, President
Linkedin: www.linkedin.com/company/jumpstart-inc
X (Twitter): x.com/jumpstartinc
Instagram: www.instagram.com/jumpstartinc
Description: A nonprofit accelerating the success of diverse entrepreneurs. **Founded:** 1983.

43670 ■ LaunchHouse
675 Alpha Dr., Ste. E
  Highland Heights, OH 44143
Ph: (216)930-2453
Co. E-mail: info@launchhouse.com
URL: http://lhcowork.com
Contact: Todd Goldstein, Chief Executive Officer
E-mail: todd@launchhouse.com
Facebook: www.facebook.com/launchhouse
X (Twitter): x.com/launchhouse

STATE LISTINGS

Instagram: www.instagram.com/launchhouse
YouTube: www.youtube.com/channel/UC8aB_S
tBqquhnc321s9rZmg

Description: Firm provides hardware accelerator program that covers customer development, prototyping, sourcing, design, packaging, supply chain, strategy, marketing, distribution, fundraising, and financing.

43671 ■ Lightship Capital
2900 Reading Rd.
  Cincinnati, OH 45206
Co. E-mail: info@lightship.capital
URL: http://www.lightship.education
Contact: Dr. Kwane Watson, Chief Executive Officer
Facebook: www.facebook.com/lightship.cap
X (Twitter): x.com/lightshipcap
Instagram: www.instagram.com/lightship.capital

Description: Offers early-stage businesses mentorships, education, and (for selected companies) capital to underrepresented entrepreneurs. **Founded:** 2011.

43672 ■ MAGNET Incubation Center (MIC)
1768 E 25th St.
  Cleveland, OH 44114
Ph: (216)391-7002
Co. E-mail: info@magnetwork.org
URL: http://startupneo.org/resources/magnet
X (Twitter): x.com/magnetohio

Description: Provides a comprehensive package of business assistance services to support the growth of technology-oriented companies.

43673 ■ Manufacturing Advocacy & Growth Network (MAGNET) - Library
1768 E 25th St.
  Cleveland, OH 44114
Ph: (216)391-7002
Co. E-mail: info@magnetwork.org
URL: http://www.manufacturingsuccess.org
Contact: Dr. Ethan Karp, President
E-mail: ekarp@manufacturingsuccess.org
Linkedin: www.linkedin.com/company/manufac
turingsuccess
X (Twitter): x.com/magnetohio
Instagram: www.instagram.com/magnetohio
YouTube: www.youtube.com/user/TheMAGNETVideo

Description: Business incubation program provides a comprehensive package of business assistance services to support the growth of technology-oriented companies. **Scope:** Manufacturer of modernization projects, business management practices, information technology, human resource and work force development, and much more. **Founded:** 1984. **Holdings:** Figures not available. **Publications:** "NE Ohio manufacturers learn of options to diversify customer bases," Jun, 2009; "The manufacturing workforce of today and tomorrow needs the rights kills, training and certifications," Jul, 2009; "Invest in employees now," Jul, 2009; "Product design and engineering are manufacturing careers with a bright future," Jun, 2009. **Training:** Dream It. Do It, Ohio, Jan, 2007; Cuyahoga County New Product Development and Entrepreneurship Loan Fund; Manufacturer's Resource Link; Manufacturing Extension Program (MEP); Advanced manufacturing jobs in northeast Ohio require readily available high-tech training; Get Ready for the Rebound: Featuring Phillip Van Hooser.

43674 ■ The Mill
20 High St.
  Hamilton, OH 45011
Ph: (513)737-6543
Free: 866-540-4438
Co. E-mail: ideaswelcome@hamiltonmill.org
URL: http://hamiltonmill.org
Facebook: www.facebook.com/hamiltonmillohio
Linkedin: www.linkedin.com/company/hamiltonmill
X (Twitter): twitter.com/hamiltonmill_oh
Instagram: www.instagram.com/themill_ohio

Description: Firm provides small business counselling, office space rental, small business incubator, business training and coaching services and many more.

43675 ■ Northeast Ohio Medical University - Research, Entrepreneurship, Discovery and Innovation Zone (REDIzone)
4209 State Rte. 44
  Rootstown, OH 44272
Ph: (330)325-6800
URL: http://www.neomed.edu/redizone
Contact: Jordan Walker, Specialist
E-mail: jwalker3@neomed.edu

Description: Fosters innovation and technology commercialization. Offers physical space for early-state biomedical companies.

43676 ■ The Ohio State University Endeavor Center
1862 Shyville Rd.
  Piketon, OH 45661
Ph: (740)289-2071
URL: http://southcenters.osu.edu/endeavor-center
Facebook: www.facebook.com/southcenters
X (Twitter): x.com/southcenters

Description: Provides new and emerging businesses poised for rapid growth 4 tangible advantages--professional office space in flexible configurations, access to advanced technology they might not otherwise have, networking opportunities with other small business and access to expert business counseling on a free and timely basis.

43677 ■ Ohio University Innovation Center (OUIC)
1 Ohio University
  Athens, OH 45701
Ph: (740)593-1818
Co. E-mail: innovation@ohio.edu
URL: http://www.ohio.edu/research/innovation
Contact: Stacy Strauss, Director
E-mail: strauss@ohio.edu
Facebook: www.facebook.com/InnovationCntr
Linkedin: www.linkedin.com/company/ohio-university
 -innovation-center
X (Twitter): x.com/OUInnovationCtr
Instagram: www.instagram.com/ouinnovationcenter

Description: Provider of incubation resources to the local area. **Founded:** 1983.

43678 ■ Regional Incubator for Sustainability and Entrepreneurship (RISE)
247 Columbus Ave., Ste. 126
  Sandusky, OH 44870
Ph: (419)627-7791
Co. E-mail: office@eriecountyedc.org
URL: http://www.eriecountyedc.org/rise
Facebook: www.facebook.com/RISEingEn
trepreneurs
Instagram: www.instagram.com/rise_entrepreneurs

Description: A comprehensive resource hub that offers assistance across the entire business development continuum. Links business owners and aspiring entrepreneurs to regional service providers with expertise in business start-up, development and acceleration.

43679 ■ Rev1 Ventures
1275 Kinnear Rd.
  Columbus, OH 43212
Ph: (614)487-3700
Co. E-mail: info@rev1ventures.com
URL: http://www.rev1ventures.com
Contact: Tom Walker, President
Facebook: www.facebook.com/Rev1Ventures
Linkedin: www.linkedin.com/company/rev1ventures
X (Twitter): x.com/rev1ventures
Instagram: www.instagram.com/rev1ventures

Description: Provider of seed stage venture capital funding services. **Founded:** 2005.

43680 ■ Tollotly Technology Incubator
330 University Dr. NE
  New Philadelphia, OH 44663
Ph: (330)339-3391
Co. E-mail: locate@tusctechpark.com
URL: http://www.tusctechpark.com/business-incuba
tor.php
Facebook: www.facebook.com/TuscEDC
Linkedin: www.linkedin.com/company/tuscarawas
 -county-port-authority

X (Twitter): twitter.com/TuscEDC
Instagram: www.instagram.com/tuscedc
YouTube: www.youtube.com/channel/UCi7iT
2MH89NfuNQERpq28Kg

Description: Supports entrepreneurial efforts with dedicated business incubator space for start-up companies linked to high-tech research, development, and intellectual property enterprises. **Founded:** 2009.

43681 ■ The University of Toledo - LaunchPad Incubation Program (LPI)
2801 W Bancroft St.
  Toledo, OH 43606
Co. E-mail: incubation@utoledo.edu
URL: http://www.utoledo.edu/incubator

Description: Provides intensive entrepreneurial assistance, state-of-the-art facilities and other valuable resources to early-stage, technology-based start up companies. **Founded:** 1872.

43682 ■ The University of Toledo (UT) - Minority Business Development Center (MBDC)
1510 N Westwood Ave.
  Toledo, OH 43606
Ph: (419)530-3347
Co. E-mail: mbdc@utoledo.edu
URL: http://www.utoledo.edu/incubator/mbdc
Contact: Jeanine Bragg, Manager, Operations
Facebook: www.facebook.com/TheUToledoMBDC

Description: Fosters an environment that offers assistance for minority-owned, early-stage firms. Provides office space, training, mentoring, and a network of professional advisors.

43683 ■ Women's Small Business Accelerator
25 N St.
  Dublin, OH 43017
Ph: (614)414-2449
Co. E-mail: admin@wsbaohio.org
URL: http://www.wsbaohio.org
Contact: Mary McCarthy, President
Facebook: www.facebook.com/wsbaoh
Linkedin: www.linkedin.com/company/wsbaoh
X (Twitter): x.com/wsba_oh
Instagram: www.instagram.com/wsba_oh

Description: Accelerator founder by (and for) women business owners. Offers education, peer support, and mentoring.

43684 ■ Youngstown Business Incubator (YBI)
241 W Federal Plz.
  Youngstown, OH 44503
Ph: (330)746-5003
Co. E-mail: info@ybi.org
URL: http://ybi.org
Contact: Barb Ewing, Chief Executive Officer
Facebook: www.facebook.com/ybincubator
X (Twitter): x.com/ybitweets

Description: The YBI was established to nurture emerging technology and light manufacturing companies through shared resources, business assistance, and other services.

EDUCATIONAL PROGRAMS

43685 ■ Bryant & Stratton College - Parma Campus
12955 Snow Rd.
  Parma, OH 44130-1005
Ph: (216)265-3151
Co. E-mail: parcontactcampus@bryantstratton.edu
URL: http://www.bryantstratton.edu/location/clevelan
d-oh/parma

Description: Business college offering programs in business management and business operations. **Founded:** 1854.

43686 ■ Center for Entrepreneurship & Business Innovation (CEBI)
475 Ter., Dr.
  Kent, OH 44242

URL: http://www.kent.edu/business/center-entrepreneurship-and-business-innovation
Description: Advances the understanding of entrepreneurship for students, researchers, and policy makers in Northeast Ohio. Offers student venture funds, speaker series, and scholarships at Kent State University. Promotes franchising, social and global entrepreneurship, and tech commercialization.

43687 ■ Cuyahoga Community College (Tri-C)
700 Carnegie Ave.
Cleveland, OH 44115
Ph: (216)987-6000
Free: 800-954-8742
Co. E-mail: careerservices@tri-c.edu
URL: http://www.tri-c.edu
Contact: Alex Johnson, PhD, President
Facebook: www.facebook.com/TriC.edu
Linkedin: www.linkedin.com/school/cuyahoga-community-college
X (Twitter): x.com/tricedu
YouTube: www.youtube.com/user/CuyahogaCommCollege
Founded: 1963. **Publications:** *The High Point* (Monthly).

43688 ■ Hussian College
1160 Dublin Rd., Ste. 400
Columbus, OH 43215
Description: Business college offering classes in small business management. **Founded:** 1963.

43689 ■ University of Akron (UA)
302 Buchtel Common
Akron, OH 44325
Ph: (330)972-7111
Free: 800-621-3847
Fax: (330)972-6588
Co. E-mail: ask@uakron2.libanswers.com
URL: http://www.uakron.edu
Contact: Dr. Gary L. Miller, President
E-mail: president@uakron.edu
Facebook: www.facebook.com/UniversityofAkron
Linkedin: www.linkedin.com/school/the-university-of-akron
X (Twitter): x.com/uakron
Instagram: www.instagram.com/uakron
YouTube: www.youtube.com/uakron
Description: Two-year college offering a small business management program. **Founded:** 1870.

VIDEO/AUDIO MEDIA

43690 ■ *Columbus Top Startups*
URL(s): omny.fm/shows/startup-hustle/columbus-top-startups
Ed: Lauren Conway. **Released:** September 13, 2023. **Description:** Features the top startups of 2023 in Columbus, Ohio.

CONSULTANTS

43691 ■ Taivara
Columbus, OH
Ph: (614)300-7374
Co. E-mail: hello@taivara.com
URL: http://www.taivara.com
Contact: Brooke Paul, Chief Executive Officer
Facebook: www.facebook.com/taivara
X (Twitter): x.com/taivara
Description: Helps companies of all sizes turn their ideas into revenue generating new products. Using small investments, customer interactions, and experimentation, the company helps clients overcome innovation obstacles, make smarter investments, deliver quality new products on time and on budget, and achieve innovation ROI. **Founded:** 2011.

PUBLICATIONS

43692 ■ *Business Courier*
120 E 4th St., Ste. 230
Cincinnati, OH 45202
Ph: (513)621-6665
Fax: (513)621-2462
Co. E-mail: cincinnati@bizjournals.com
URL: http://www.bizjournals.com/cincinnati
Contact: Kelly Snyder, Director
E-mail: ktassos@bizjournals.com
URL(s): www.bizjournals.com/cincinnati
Ed: Rob Daumeyer. **Released:** Weekly **Description:** Newspaper (tabloid) serving business managers in greater Cincinnati. **Availability:** Print; Online.

43693 ■ *Cincinnati Business Courier*
120 W Morehead St.
Charlotte, NC 28202
Co. E-mail: circhelp@bizjournals.com
URL: http://www.acbj.com
Contact: Mike Olivieri, Executive Vice President
URL(s): www.bizjournals.com/cincinnati/newsletters
Linkedin: www.linkedin.com/company/business-courier
X (Twitter): x.com/BusinessCourier
Ed: Rob Daumeyer. **Released:** Weekly **Price:** $950, for nationwide premium unlimited; $380, for national wide access premium elite; $220, for print and online; $210, for digital Only. **Description:** Contains the full text of Cincinnati Business Courier, a business tabloid covering Cincinnati, Ohio. **Availability:** Print; Online. **Type:** Full-text.

43694 ■ *Columbus Business First*
120 W Morehead St.
Charlotte, NC 28202
Co. E-mail: circhelp@bizjournals.com
URL: http://www.acbj.com
Contact: Mike Olivieri, Executive Vice President
URL(s): www.bizjournals.com/columbus
X (Twitter): x.com/columbusbiz1st
Instagram: www.instagram.com/columbusbiz1st
Released: Weekly **Price:** $70, for premium elite 52 weeks; $70, for premium digital & print; $4, for premium intro digital only; $245, for premium elite nationwide access 52 weeks. **Description:** Contains the full text of Columbus Business First, a business tabloid covering Columbus, Ohio. **Availability:** Print; Online. **Type:** Full-text.

43695 ■ *Crain's Cleveland Business*
700 W St. Clair Ave., Ste. 310
Cleveland, OH 44113-1256
Ph: (216)522-1383
Co. E-mail: info@crain.com
URL: http://www.crain.com
Contact: K. C. Crain, President
URL(s): www.crainscleveland.com
Facebook: www.facebook.com/CrainsCleveland
Linkedin: www.linkedin.com/company/crain's-cleveland-business
X (Twitter): x.com/crainscleveland
Instagram: www.instagram.com/crainscleveland
Ed: Elizabeth Mcintyre, Elizabeth McIntyre. **Released:** Weekly **Price:** $499, for 12 months; $99, for print and digital or online 1 year; $10, for 4 weeks or online 4 weeks. **Description:** Metropolitan business newspaper serving seven counties. **Availability:** Print; Online. **Type:** Full-text.

43696 ■ *Dayton Business Journal*
120 W Morehead St.
Charlotte, NC 28202
Co. E-mail: circhelp@bizjournals.com
URL: http://www.acbj.com
Contact: Mike Olivieri, Executive Vice President
URL(s): www.bizjournals.com/dayton
Linkedin: www.linkedin.com/company/dayton-business-journal
X (Twitter): x.com/DBJnews
Instagram: www.instagram.com/dbjnews
Released: Weekly **Price:** $70, for 52 weeks lowest price; $380, for Nationwide Access; $950, for Nationwide + BOL; $220, for digital + print; $210, for digital.
Description: Contains the full text of Dayton Business Journal, a business tabloid covering Dayton, Ohio. **Availability:** Print; PDF; Download; Online. **Type:** Full-text.

PUBLISHERS

43697 ■ Betterway Books
4700 E Galbraith Rd.
Cincinnati, OH 45236-2726
Description: Publishes resource guides and handbooks on home building and remodelling, small business and finance, theater, woodworking, home decorating, parenting and genealogy. Accepts unsolicited manuscripts. Reaches market through commission representatives and wholesalers. **Founded:** 1980. **Publications:** *Complete Guide & Resource to In-Line Skating*; *The Doll Sourcebook*.

RESEARCH CENTERS

43698 ■ University of Dayton School of Business Administration - Business Research Group (BRG)
300 College Pk.
Dayton, OH 45469-2110
Ph: (937)229-2453
Fax: (937)229-2371
Co. E-mail: udlawreview@udayton.edu
URL: http://udayton.edu/business/experiential_learning/centers/business_research_group/index.php
Contact: Richard Stock, Director
E-mail: rstock1@udayton.edu
Description: Integral unit of School of Business Administration, University of Dayton. **Scope:** Economic analysis and forecasting, marketing, information systems development, management, human-computer interaction, socio-economic impact, and communications. Conducts survey research and usability testing of software; involved in television production and focus groups. **Founded:** 1986.

VENTURE CAPITAL FIRM

43699 ■ CoreNetwork Fund
31 N Summit, Ste. 200
Toledo, OH 43604
Ph: (419)697-9696
Fax: (888)696-1492
Co. E-mail: info@corenetworkfund.com
URL: http://corenetworkfund.com
Contact: Robert J. Savage, Contact
Description: Angel investors primarily interested in investment opportunities in Northeast Ohio and Southeast Michigan. .

43700 ■ Vine Street Ventures
Cincinnati, OH
Co. E-mail: info@vinestventures.com
URL: http://vinestventures.com
Contact: Dave Knox, Manager
Description: A venture capital investment firm dedicated to investing in internet and mobile businesses.

Oklahoma

ASSOCIATIONS AND OTHER ORGANIZATIONS

43701 ■ Business Network International Oklahoma-East [BNI OK East]
3430 Toringdon Way
 Charlotte, NC 28277
Free: 855-264-2673
URL: http://bniok.com/en-US/index
Contact: Tammy Lackey, Managing Director
E-mail: tammylackey@bni.com
Facebook: www.facebook.com/BNIOklahoma
X (Twitter): x.com/BNIOklahoma
Description: Provides both men and women a structured environment for the development and exchange of quality business referrals. Offers members the opportunity to share ideas and contacts. **Geographic Preference:** Local.

43702 ■ Entrepreneurs' Organization - Oklahoma City Chapter (EO)
Oklahoma City, OK
Co. E-mail: admin@eookc.org
URL: http://eookc.org
Contact: Deemah Ramadan, Membership Chairperson
E-mail: members@eookc.org
URL(s): www.eonetwork.org/oklahomacity
Facebook: www.facebook.com/EOOKC
Linkedin: www.linkedin.com/company/eookc
X (Twitter): x.com/EOOkc
Description: Provides local resources to members which includes networking events, mentorship, live forums, and leadership development. **Founded:** 2008.

43703 ■ Entrepreneurs' Organization - Tulsa Chapter (EO)
8139 E 74th Pl.
 Tulsa, OK 74133
URL: http://www.eonetwork.org/tulsa
Contact: Nathan Brim, Contact
Description: Provides local resources to members which includes networking events, mentorship, live forums, and leadership development. **Founded:** 2017.

43704 ■ International Association of Women Oklahoma City Chapter
Tulsa, OK
URL: http://www.iawomen.com/chapters
Description: Serves as network of accomplished women united to achieve professional goals. Provides a forum for sharing ideas and experiences of professional women regarding career success. Promotes an active business and networking community from all industries. **Geographic Preference:** Local.

43705 ■ International Association of Women Tulsa Chapter
Tulsa, OK
URL: http://www.iawomen.com/chapters/tulsa-chapter
Contact: Shohreh Woessner, President
E-mail: shohreh.woessner@gmail.com
Description: Serves as network of accomplished women united to achieve professional goals. Provides a forum for sharing ideas and experiences of professional women regarding career success. Promotes an active business and networking community from all industries. **Geographic Preference:** Local.

43706 ■ National Association of Women Business Owners Central Oklahoma
50 Penn Pl., No. 1420
 Oklahoma City, OK 73118
URL: http://www.nawbo.org/central-oklahoma/about
Contact: Ruthann Fairbairn, Contact
Geographic Preference: Local.

43707 ■ SeedStep Angels
840 Research Pkwy., Ste. 250
 Oklahoma City, OK 73104
Ph: (405)235-2305
URL: http://seedstepangels.com
Contact: Ryan Cargill, Director
E-mail: rcargill@i2e.org
Linkedin: www.linkedin.com/company/seedstep-angels
X (Twitter): x.com/seedstepangels
Description: Angel investor group for early-stage companies. **Founded:** 2009.

SMALL BUSINESS DEVELOPMENT CENTERS

43708 ■ East Central University Small Business Development Center
301 W University Blvd.
 Durant, OK 74701
URL: http://www.oksbdc.org/category/success-stories/page/2
Description: Represents and promotes the small business sector. Provides management assistance to current and prospective small business owners. Helps to improve management skills and expand the products and services of members. **Geographic Preference:** Local.

43709 ■ Langston University Small Business Development Center
c/o Della Dean, Director
 4205 N Lincoln Blvd., Ste. 112
 Oklahoma City, OK 73132
Ph: (405)530-7519
Co. E-mail: dmdean@langston.edu
URL: http://www.langston.edu/okc/programs-centers/oklahoma-small-business-development-center
Contact: Della Dean, Director
E-mail: dmdean@langston.edu
Description: Represents and promotes the small business sector. Provides management assistance to current and prospective small business owners. Helps to improve management skills and expand the products and services of members. **Geographic Preference:** Local.

43710 ■ Northeastern State University Small Business Development Center (NSUSBDC)
3100 E New Orleans St.
 Broken Arrow, OK 74014
Ph: (918)594-8673
URL: http://business.oksbdc.org/center.aspx?center=64020&subloc=7
Description: Represents and promotes the small business sector. Provides management assistance to current and prospective small business owners. Helps to improve management skills and expand the products and services of members. **Geographic Preference:** Local.

43711 ■ Northeastern State University Small Business Development Center
2400 W Shawnee St.
 Muskogee, OK 74401
URL: http://www.nsuok.edu
Description: Represents and promotes the small business sector. Provides management assistance to current and prospective small business owners. Helps to improve management skills and expand the products and services of members. **Geographic Preference:** Local.

43712 ■ Northwestern Oklahoma State University Small Business Development Center
108 Shockley Hall
 Alva, OK 73717
Ph: (580)327-8608
URL: http://www.nwosu.edu
Contact: Elizabeth Smith, Contact
E-mail: egsmith@nwosu.edu
Description: Represents and promotes the small business sector. Provides management assistance to current and prospective small business owners. Helps to improve management skills and expand the products and services of members. **Geographic Preference:** Local.

43713 ■ Northwestern Oklahoma State University Small Business Development Center
Northwestern - Alva
 Shockley Hall 108
 Enid, OK 73701
Ph: (580)327-8608
URL: http://www.nwosu.edu/employee-directory?filter=alva
Contact: Brown Tamara, Chairman Assistant Professor
E-mail: tlbrown@nwosu.edu
Description: Represents and promotes the small business sector. Provides management assistance to current and prospective small business owners. Helps to improve management skills and expand the products and services of members. **Geographic Preference:** Local.

43714 ■ Oklahoma Small Business Development Center (OKSBDC)
301 W University Blvd.
 Durant, OK 74701

Ph: (580)745-3326
Fax: (580)745-7471
Co. E-mail: info@oksbdc.org
URL: http://www.oksbdc.org
Contact: Michelle Hockersmith, Director
E-mail: mcampbell@se.edu
Facebook: www.facebook.com/
 OklahomaSmallBusinessDevelopmentCenter
Linkedin: www.linkedin.com/company/oklahoma
 -small-business-development-center
X (Twitter): x.com/OklahomaSBDC
YouTube: www.youtube.com/channel/UCaWDI
 6duPq0NctfnUuOhGLA

Description: Dedicated to providing business owners and aspiring entrepreneurs with the guidance they need to start, grow, and succeed in the business world. **Founded:** 1984. **Geographic Preference:** State; Local.

43715 ■ Rose State College - Oklahoma Small Business Development Center - Procurement Center
6420 SE 15th St.
 Midwest City, OK 73110
URL: http://www.rose.edu/content/business-communi
 ty/small-business-development
URL(s): www.rose.edu/content/news-events/events/
 event-details/?id=544

Description: Procurement center for all area small business development centers. **Founded:** 1983.

43716 ■ Rose State College Small Business Development Center (SBDC)
1720 Hudiburg Dr.
 Midwest City, OK 73110
URL: http://www.oksbdc.org/rose-state
X (Twitter): x.com/rosestate

Description: Represents and promotes the small business sector. Provides management assistance to current and prospective small business owners. Helps to improve management skills and expand the products and services of members. **Geographic Preference:** Local.

43717 ■ Southwestern Oklahoma State University Small Business Development Center Weatherford
100 Campus Dr.
 Weatherford, OK 73096
URL: http://www.swosu.edu

Description: Represents and promotes the small business sector. Provides management assistance to current and prospective small business owners. Helps to improve management skills and expand the products and services of members. **Geographic Preference:** Local.

SMALL BUSINESS ASSISTANCE PROGRAMS

43718 ■ Oklahoma Center for the Advancement of Science Technology Inventor's Assistance Service (IAS)
201 Advanced Technology Research Ctr., Oklahoma
 State University
 Stillwater, OK 74078
URL: http://ceat.okstate.edu/extension/npdc/ias.html
URL(s): oklahoma.gov/ocast/services/prototyping-an
 d-engineering.html

Description: Helps inventors navigate the invention process with information, educational and referrals.

43719 ■ Oklahoma Department of Agriculture, Food and Forestry - Market Development Div.
2800 N Lincoln Blvd.
 Oklahoma City, OK 73105
URL: http://ag.ok.gov/category/market-development
Contact: Meriruth Cohenour, Director
E-mail: meriruth.cohenour@ag.ok.gov

Description: Develops direct marketing outlets for farmers, including the promotion of direct retail sales, and the promotion of direct wholesaling through commercial systems. Offers the Made in Oklahoma/Grown in Oklahoma marketing program, featuring trademarked logos.

43720 ■ Oklahoma Department of Career and Technology Education - Library [CareerTech]
1500 W 7th Ave.
 Stillwater, OK 74074-4398
Ph: (405)377-2000
Free: 800-522-5810
Fax: (405)743-6809
Contact: Cori Gray, Deputy Director
E-mail: cori.gray@careertech.ok.gov
Facebook: www.facebook.com/OklahomaCareerTech
Linkedin: www.linkedin.com/company/oklahoma
 -department-of-career-and-technology-education
X (Twitter): x.com/okcareertech
Instagram: www.instagram.com/
 OklahomaCareerTech
YouTube: www.youtube.com/user/okcareertech

Description: Provides federal contracting at 21 offices, located at vo-tech schools statewide. **Scope:** Construction. **Founded:** 1917. **Holdings:** Figures not available. **Geographic Preference:** State.

43721 ■ Oklahoma Department of Commerce-Administration and Central Services
900 N Stiles Ave.
 Oklahoma City, OK 73104
Ph: (405)815-6552
Free: 800-879-6552
Co. E-mail: info@okcommerce.gov
URL: http://www.okcommerce.gov
Contact: Brent Kisling, Executive Director
Facebook: www.facebook.com/okcommerce
Linkedin: www.linkedin.com/company/okcommerce
X (Twitter): x.com/okcommerce
YouTube: www.youtube.com/okcommerce

Description: Provides assistance in developing business plans, financial packages, industry customized training, domestic and foreign market services, and small and minority business programs.

43722 ■ Oklahoma Department of Commerce Export Assistance Program
301 NW 63rd St., Ste. 420
 Oklahoma City, OK 73116
URL: http://2016.export.gov/oklahoma
Contact: Marcus Verner, Director
E-mail: marcus.verner@trade.gov

Description: Specializes in export programs to assist small Oklahoma companies.

43723 ■ University of Oklahoma Center for Business and Economic Development
660 Parrington Oval
 Norman, OK 73019-0390
Ph: (405)325-3136
Co. E-mail: admissions@ou.edu
URL: http://www.ou.edu/outreach/edi/online-courses
 .html
Contact: Joseph Harroz, Jr., President
E-mail: officeofthepresident@ou.edu
Facebook: www.facebook.com/uofoklahoma
Linkedin: www.linkedin.com/school/university-of
 -oklahoma
X (Twitter): twitter.com/uofoklahoma
Instagram: www.instagram.com/uofoklahoma
YouTube: www.youtube.com/user/Universi
 tyofOklahoma

Description: Assists small businesses throughout the state. **Founded:** 1890.

SCORE OFFICES

43724 ■ Enid/Northwest Oklahoma SCORE
301 NW 6th St., Ste. 116
 Oklahoma City, OK 73102
Ph: (405)233-3050
Fax: (405)609-8986
Co. E-mail: oklahomacity.score@scorevolunteer.org
URL: http://www.score.org
Facebook: www.facebook.com/SCOREOklahomaCity
Linkedin: www.linkedin.com/company/score-mentors
X (Twitter): twitter.com/SCOREMentors
Instagram: www.instagram.com/score_mentors
YouTube: www.youtube.com/user/
 SCORESmallBusiness
Pinterest: www.pinterest.com/scorementors

43725 ■ Oklahoma City SCORE
318 NW 13th St.
 Oklahoma City, OK 73103
Ph: (405)233-3050
Co. E-mail: oklahomacity.score@scorevolunteer.org
URL: http://www.score.org/oklahomacity
Facebook: www.facebook.com/SCOREOklahomaCity
Linkedin: www.linkedin.com/company/score-okla
 homa-city
YouTube: www.youtube.com/channel/UCSHiRvG
 5BPs5KpEmrwQHI9w

43726 ■ SCORE - Oklahoma City
301 NW 6th St., Ste. 116
 Oklahoma City, OK 73102
Ph: (405)609-8004
Fax: (405)609-8986
Co. E-mail: oklahomacity.score@scorevolunteer.org
URL: http://oklahomacity.score.org
Facebook: www.facebook.com/SCOREOklahomaCity
Linkedin: www.linkedin.com/company/score-okla
 homa-city
X (Twitter): x.com/SCOREChapter212
YouTube: www.youtube.com/channel/UCSHiRvG
 5BPs5KpEmrwQHI9w

Description: Seeks to educate entrepreneurs and help small businesses start, grow and succeed nationwide. Organizes volunteers who are working or retired business owners, executives and corporate leaders who wish to share their wisdom and lessons learned in business. **Founded:** 1964. **Geographic Preference:** Local.

43727 ■ SCORE - Tulsa
907 S Detroit Ave., Ste. 1001
 Tulsa, OK 74120
Ph: (918)212-6294
Fax: (918)212-6294
Co. E-mail: consult.tulsa@scorevolunteer.org
URL: http://tulsa.score.org
Contact: Bridget Weston, Chief Executive Officer
Linkedin: www.linkedin.com/company/tulsa-score
X (Twitter): x.com/TulsaScore

Description: Provides professional guidance and information to maximize the success of existing and emerging small businesses. Offers business counseling and workshops. **Founded:** 1964. **Geographic Preference:** Local.

BETTER BUSINESS BUREAUS

43728 ■ Better Business Bureau of Central Oklahoma
17 S Dewey Ave.
 Oklahoma City, OK 73102-2400
Ph: (405)239-6081
Fax: (405)235-5891
Co. E-mail: info@oklahomacity.bbb.org
URL: http://www.bbb.org/local-bbb/better-business
 -bureau-of-central-oklahoma
Contact: Kitt Letcher, President
E-mail: kitt@oklahomacity.bbb.org
Facebook: www.facebook.com/BBBCentralOk
Linkedin: www.linkedin.com/company/bbbcentralok
Instagram: www.instagram.com/bbbcentralok
YouTube: www.youtube.com/channel/UCmgAVzkZE
 5dqxpNx1Y3miFg

Description: Seeks to promote and foster ethical relationship between businesses and the public through voluntary self-regulation, consumer and business education, and service excellence. Provides information to help consumers and businesses make informed purchasing decisions and avoid costly scams and frauds; settles consumer complaints through arbitration and other means. **Geographic Preference:** Local.

43729 ■ Tulsa Better Business Bureau
4937 S 78th E Ave.
 Tulsa, OK 74145

STATE LISTINGS   Oklahoma ■ 43745

Ph: (918)492-1266
Fax: (918)492-1276
Co. E-mail: info@tulsabbb.org
URL: http://www.bbb.org/local-bbb/bbb-serving-eastern-oklahoma
Facebook: www.facebook.com/TulsaBBB
X (Twitter): x.com/tulsabbb
Instagram: www.instagram.com/tulsabbb
YouTube: www.youtube.com/user/BBBTulsa
Pinterest: www.pinterest.com/tulsabbb
Description: Members of the business community in eastern Oklahoma. Promotes the self-regulation of businesses. **Founded:** 1930. **Publications:** *The Member* (Bimonthly). **Geographic Preference:** Local.

CHAMBERS OF COMMERCE

43730 ■ Ada Area Chamber of Commerce
2025 Arlington St.
Ada, OK 74820
Ph: (580)332-2506
Co. E-mail: office@adachamber.com
URL: http://www.adachamber.com
Contact: Shana Wood, President
Facebook: www.facebook.com/AdaAreaChamber
X (Twitter): x.com/adachamber
Description: Promotes business and community development in Ada, OK. **Founded:** 1901. **Geographic Preference:** Local.

43731 ■ Altus Chamber of Commerce
301 W Commerce St.
Altus, OK 73521
Ph: (580)482-0210
Co. E-mail: info@altuschamber.com
URL: http://www.altuschamber.com
Contact: Rodger Kerr, President
E-mail: rkerr@altuschamber.com
Facebook: www.facebook.com/altuschamber
Linkedin: www.linkedin.com/company/altus-chamber-of-commerce
Description: Promotes business and community development in Altus, OK. **Founded:** 1908. **Publications:** *Infogram* (Monthly). **Geographic Preference:** Local.

43732 ■ Alva Chamber of Commerce
502 Oklahoma Blvd.
Alva, OK 73717
Ph: (580)327-1647
Co. E-mail: chamber@alvaok.net
URL: http:///alvaok.net
Contact: Melissa Graybill, President
Facebook: www.facebook.com/alvachamber
X (Twitter): x.com/alvachamber
Instagram: www.instagram.com/alvachamber
Description: Promotes business and community development in the Alva, OK area. **Publications:** *Chamber Newsletter* (Weekly). **Geographic Preference:** Local.

43733 ■ Ardmore Chamber of Commerce
410 W Main St.
Ardmore, OK 73401
Ph: (580)223-7765
URL: http://chamber.ardmore.org
Contact: Annilisa Peevy, Coordinator
E-mail: apeevy@ardmore.org
Facebook: www.facebook.com/pages/Ardmore-Chamber-of-Commerce/108617102988
X (Twitter): x.com/ArdmoreChamber
Instagram: www.instagram.com/ardmorechamberofcommerce
Description: Promotes business and community development in Ardmore, OK. **Founded:** 1914. **Publications:** *Ardmoreport* (Monthly); *Membership Directory and Information Guide* (Annual). **Geographic Preference:** Local.

43734 ■ Bartlesville Regional Chamber of Commerce (BRCC)
201 SW Keeler
Bartlesville, OK 74003
Ph: (918)336-8708
Fax: (918)337-0216

URL: http://www.bartlesville.com
Contact: Sherri Wilt, President
E-mail: swilt@bartlesville.com
Facebook: www.facebook.com/BartlesvilleChamber
Linkedin: www.linkedin.com/in/womeninbusiness
X (Twitter): x.com/mybville
Instagram: www.instagram.com/bartlesvillechamber
Description: Promotes business and community development in the Bartlesville, OK area. **Founded:** 1903. **Geographic Preference:** Local.

43735 ■ Bixby Metro Chamber of Commerce
12 W Dawes Ave.
Bixby, OK 74008
Ph: (918)366-9445
Fax: (918)366-9443
Co. E-mail: info@bixbychamber.com
URL: http://bixbychamber.com
Contact: Krystal Crocket, Co-President Co-Chief Executive Officer
Facebook: www.facebook.com/BixbyMetroChamber
Linkedin: www.linkedin.com/company/bixby-metro-chamber-of-commerce
X (Twitter): x.com/BixbyChamber
Instagram: www.instagram.com/bixbymetrochamber
YouTube: www.youtube.com/channel/UCK12HVz38RRfdv_2eMciZGQ
Description: Promotes business and community development in Bixby, OK. **Founded:** 1947. **Publications:** *Business Insurance Guide*; *Chamber Newsline* (Monthly); *Who's Who in Business* (Annual). **Geographic Preference:** Local.

43736 ■ Blackwell Area Chamber of Commerce
120 S Main St.
Blackwell, OK 74631
Ph: (580)363-4195
Co. E-mail: info@blackwellchamber.org
Facebook: www.facebook.com/blackwellchamber
Description: Promotes business and community development in Blackwell, OK. **Founded:** 1938. **Geographic Preference:** Local.

43737 ■ Broken Arrow Chamber of Commerce
210 N Main St., Ste. C
Broken Arrow, OK 74012
Ph: (918)893-2100
Co. E-mail: bachamber@bachamber.com
URL: http://brokenarrowchamber.com
Contact: Jennifer Conway, President
E-mail: jennifer.conway@bachamber.com
Facebook: www.facebook.com/BrokenArrowChamberandEDC
Linkedin: www.linkedin.com/company/broken-arrow-chamber-commerce
X (Twitter): x.com/bachamber
Instagram: www.instagram.com/bachamber
Description: Promotes business and community development in Broken Arrow, OK. **Founded:** 1903. **Publications:** *reDirection* (Bimonthly). **Geographic Preference:** Local.

43738 ■ Broken Bow Chamber of Commerce
113 W Martin Luther King Dr.
Broken Bow, OK 74728
Ph: (580)584-3393
Fax: (580)584-7698
Co. E-mail: bchamber@pine-net.com
URL: http://www.brokenbowchamber.com
Contact: April Roberts, President
Facebook: www.facebook.com/BrokenBowOKChamber
Description: Promotes business and community development in Broken Bow, OK. **Founded:** 1954. **Geographic Preference:** Local.

43739 ■ Chandler Area Chamber of Commerce (CACOC)
400 E Rte. 66
Chandler, OK 74834
Ph: (405)258-0673
Fax: (405)258-0008
Co. E-mail: chandlerchamber@gmail.com
URL: http://chandlerareachamberok.com
Contact: Marilyn Emde, Executive Director

Facebook: www.facebook.com/Chandler-Area-Chamber-of-Commerce-960751564070695
Description: Promotes business and community development in Chandler, OK. **Founded:** 1907. **Geographic Preference:** Local.

43740 ■ Checotah Chamber of Commerce
114 N Broadway St.
Checotah, OK 74426
Ph: (918)473-2070
Fax: (918)473-1453
Co. E-mail: checotahchamber@windstream.net
URL: http://checotah.com
Contact: David Prince, President
Instagram: www.instagram.com/checotahchamber
Description: Promotes business and community development in Checotah, OK. Sponsors Old Settlers Day. **Founded:** 1946. **Publications:** *Courier* (Periodic). **Geographic Preference:** Local.

43741 ■ Cheyenne - Roger Mills Chamber of Commerce and Tourism
101 So. L. L. Males Ave.
Cheyenne, OK 73628
Ph: (580)497-3318
Free: 877-497-3318
Co. E-mail: cheyennecoc@gmail.com
URL: http://www.cheyenneokchamberofcommerce.com
Contact: Penny Clift, President
Facebook: www.facebook.com/cheyenneokcoc
X (Twitter): twitter.com/Cheynnecoc
Description: Promotes business and community development in Cheyenne, OK and Roger Mills County. Sponsors arts and crafts show and Christmas Jubilee. Makes charitable donations for New Year Baby, food baskets, Harvest Queen, turkey giveaway, and Christmas treat giveaway. **Founded:** 1961. **Publications:** *Visit Roger Mills County and Cheyenne, Oklahoma*. **Awards:** Cheyenne - Roger Mills Chamber of Commerce and Tourism Volunteer of the Year (Annual). **Geographic Preference:** Local.

43742 ■ Chickasha Chamber of Commerce
221 W Chickasha Ave.
Chickasha, OK 73023
Ph: (405)224-0787
Co. E-mail: office@chickashachamber.com
URL: http://www.chickashachamber.com
Contact: Jim Cowan, President
E-mail: jim@chickashaedc.com
Description: Promotes business and community development in Chickasha, OK. Convention/Meeting availabilities. **Founded:** 1923. **Geographic Preference:** Local.

43743 ■ Choctaw Chamber of Commerce
2437 Main St.
Choctaw, OK 73020
Ph: (405)390-3303
Fax: (405)390-3330
Co. E-mail: office@choctawchamber.com
URL: http://choctawchamber.com
Facebook: www.facebook.com/ChoctawChamberOfCommerce
X (Twitter): x.com/choctaw_chamber
Instagram: www.instagram.com/choctawareachamber
YouTube: www.youtube.com/channel/UC8w5npxtbJw6IAHRciK0dyQ
Description: Works to promote business growth and development in Choctaw, OK. **Founded:** 1977. **Geographic Preference:** Local.

43744 ■ The City of Oilton
101 W Main St.
Oilton, OK 74052
Ph: (918)862-3202
Co. E-mail: utility@cityofoilton.com
URL: http://www.cityofoilton.com
Contact: Jerry Green, Chairman Counsel
Geographic Preference: Local.

43745 ■ Claremore Chamber of Commerce
419 W Will Rogers Blvd.
Claremore, OK 74017
Ph: (918)341-2818

Co. E-mail: chamber@claremore.org
URL: http://www.claremore.org
Contact: Barby Myers, President
E-mail: barby@claremore.org
Facebook: www.facebook.com/ClaremoreAreaChamber
Instagram: www.instagram.com/claremoreareachamber
Description: Promotes business and community development in Claremore, OK area. **Founded:** 1942. **Publications:** *Weekly Memo* (Weekly). **Geographic Preference:** Local.

43746 ■ Clinton Chamber of Commerce
101 S 4th St.
Clinton, OK 73601
Ph: (580)323-2222
Fax: (580)323-2931
Co. E-mail: office@clintonok.org
URL: http://www.clintonok.org
Contact: Valerie Miller, Treasurer
Description: Promotes business and community development in Clinton, OK. Sponsors activities including pageants, art festivals, and parades. Conducts charitable activities. **Founded:** 1899. **Publications:** *Clinton Connection* (Monthly). **Geographic Preference:** Local.

43747 ■ Collinsville Chamber of Commerce
1126 W Main St.
Collinsville, OK 74021
Ph: (918)371-4703
Co. E-mail: info@collinsvillechamber.org
URL: http://collinsvillechamber.org
Contact: Breann Audet, Owner
E-mail: president@collinsvillechamber.org
Facebook: www.facebook.com/collinsvilleokchamber
Pinterest: www.pinterest.com/collinsvillechamberok
Description: Promotes business and community development in Collinsville, OK. **Publications:** *Quest* (Monthly). **Geographic Preference:** Local.

43748 ■ Coweta Chamber of Commerce
115 S Broadway
Coweta, OK 74429
Ph: (918)486-2513
Co. E-mail: info@cowetachamber.com
URL: http://cowetachamber.com
Contact: Carrie Allamby, Executive Director
E-mail: coweta@cowetachamber.onmicrosoft.com
Facebook: www.facebook.com/cowetachamberofcommerce
X (Twitter): x.com/cowetaexecdir
Instagram: www.instagram.com/cowetachamber
YouTube: www.youtube.com/channel/UCQahYE5jmo-DCjKIDNXGZWQ
Pinterest: www.pinterest.com/cowetac
Description: Promotes business and community development in Coweta, OK area. **Geographic Preference:** Local.

43749 ■ Cushing Chamber of Commerce and Industry
1301 E Main St.
Cushing, OK 74023
Ph: (918)225-2400
Co. E-mail: tracy@cushingchamber.org
URL: http://cushingchamberofcommerce.org
Contact: Tracy Caulfield, President
E-mail: tracy@cushingchamber.org
Facebook: www.facebook.com/CushingChamberOfCommerce
YouTube: www.youtube.com/channel/UCFpZsGshX19F9H43-P0V0KQ
Description: Promotes business and community development in Cushing, OK. **Publications:** *Chamber Challenger* (Monthly). **Geographic Preference:** Local.

43750 ■ Davenport Chamber of Commerce
PO Box 66
Davenport, OK 74026
Ph: (918)377-2241
Fax: (918)377-2506
Co. E-mail: davenportcoc@cotc.net
URL: http://www.davenportok.org
Description: Promotes business and community development in Davenport, OK. **Founded:** 1891. **Geographic Preference:** Local.

43751 ■ Drumright Chamber of Commerce
103 E Broadway St.
Drumright, OK 74030
Ph: (918)352-8013
Co. E-mail: drumrightchamber@gmail.com
Facebook: www.facebook.com/DrumrightChamber
Description: Promotes business and community development in Drumright, OK. **Geographic Preference:** Local.

43752 ■ Duncan Chamber of Commerce and Industry
1600 US-81 2nd Fl.
Duncan, OK 73534
Ph: (580)255-3644
Fax: (580)255-6482
URL: http://www.duncanchamber.com
Contact: Rex Outhier, Chairman
Description: Promotes business and community development in Duncan, OK. **Geographic Preference:** Local.

43753 ■ Edmond Area Chamber of Commerce
825 E 2nd St.
Edmond, OK 73034
Ph: (405)341-2808
Co. E-mail: info@edmondchamber.com
URL: http://www.edmondchamber.com
Contact: Sherry Jordan, President
E-mail: sjordan@edmondchamber.com
Facebook: www.facebook.com/EdmondChamberOfCommerce
X (Twitter): x.com/edmondchamber
Description: Promotes business and community development in the Edmond, OK area. **Founded:** 1954. **Publications:** *The Chamber e-Voice* (Semiannual); *Directory and Buyer's Guide* (Annual); *Edmond Living Magazine*; *Edmond Area Chamber of Commerce Community Profile and Business Directory*. **Educational Activities:** Business After Hours (Monthly). **Geographic Preference:** Local.

43754 ■ El Reno Chamber of Commerce and Development Corp.
206 N Bickford Ave.
El Reno, OK 73036
Ph: (405)262-1188
Co. E-mail: elrenococ@coxinet.net
URL: http://www.elrenochamber.com
Facebook: www.facebook.com/elrenochamber
Description: Promotes business and community development in El Reno, OK. **Founded:** 1911. **Geographic Preference:** Local.

43755 ■ Elk City Chamber of Commerce
102 S Main St.
Elk City, OK 73648
Ph: (580)225-0207
Fax: (580)225-2639
Co. E-mail: elkcitychamber@itlnet.net
URL: http://www.elkcitychamber.com/main.aspx
Contact: Susie Cupp, Executive Director
E-mail: scupp@elkcitychamber.com
Facebook: www.facebook.com/elkcitychamber
X (Twitter): x.com/elkcitychamber
Description: Promotes business and community development in Elk City, OK. **Geographic Preference:** Local.

43756 ■ Erick Chamber of Commerce
PO Box 1232
Erick, OK 73645-1232
Ph: (580)526-3505
Fax: (580)526-3275
URL: http://www.chamber-commerce.net/dir/6482/Erick-Chamber-of-Commerce-in-Erick
Description: Promotes business and community development in Erick, OK. **Geographic Preference:** Local.

43757 ■ Eufaula Area Chamber of Commerce
301 N Main St.
Eufaula, OK 74432
Ph: (918)689-2791
Co. E-mail: chamber@eufaulachamberofcommerce.com
URL: http://chambereufaulachamberofcommerce.com
Contact: Jay Hunn, President
Facebook: www.facebook.com/Eufaula-Area-Chamber-975514155823222
YouTube: www.youtube.com/channel/UCdWeYsujF6eNQKiD0RL5jwA
Description: Promotes business and community development in the Eufaula, OK area. **Founded:** 1924. **Geographic Preference:** Local.

43758 ■ Fairview Chamber of Commerce
206 E Broadway
Fairview, OK 73737
Ph: (580)227-2527
Co. E-mail: fairviewchamber@att.net
URL: http://fairviewokchamber.com
Facebook: www.facebook.com/fairviewokchamberofcommerce
Description: Promotes business and community development in Fairview, OK. Sponsors festivals including Fairview Follies, Wrangler Rodeo weekend, national John Deere Two-cylinder Show, Gloss Mt. cruisers car show/cruise-in, major county fair/farm and ranch expo, old time threshing bee, Boot Scoot'n 5k run, oldest free fly-in and air show, Fairview quilt festival and Christmas on Main, Easter Egg Hunt, and Business Seminars. Acts as Tourism Headquarters for major county. **Publications:** *Chamber News*. **Geographic Preference:** Local.

43759 ■ Fort Gibson Chamber of Commerce
108 W Poplar St.
Fort Gibson, OK 74434
Ph: (918)478-4780
Co. E-mail: fortgibson@sbcglobal.net
URL: http://fortgibson.com
Contact: Kimberly Martin, Executive Director
Facebook: www.facebook.com/FortGibsonChamberOfCommerce
Description: Promotes business and community development in Ft. Gibson, OK. **Geographic Preference:** Local.

43760 ■ Frederick Chamber of Commerce and Industry
100 S Main St.
Frederick, OK 73542
Ph: (580)335-2126
Co. E-mail: frederickcc@pldi.net
URL: http://www.frederickokchamber.org
Contact: Felisha Crawford, Co-Chairman of the Board
Facebook: www.facebook.com/frederickcc
X (Twitter): x.com/FrederickOKcc
Instagram: www.instagram.com/frederickoklahoma
Pinterest: www.pinterest.com/frederickok
Description: Promotes agriculture business, industry, and community development in Tillman County, OK. Involves in economic development, tourism promotion, and improving the quality of life. **Publications:** *What's Happening in Frederick* (Monthly). **Geographic Preference:** Local.

43761 ■ Freedom Chamber of Commerce
941 Eagle Pass
Freedom, OK 73842
Ph: (816)541-9629
URL: http://www.freedomchamber.com
Facebook: www.facebook.com/FreedomChamber
Description: Promotes business and community development in Freedom, OK. **Founded:** 1969. **Geographic Preference:** Local.

43762 ■ Greater Enid Chamber of Commerce
210 Kenwood Blvd.
Enid, OK 73702
Ph: (580)237-2494
URL: http://www.enidchamber.com
Contact: Jon Blankenship, President
E-mail: jon@enidchamber.com

STATE LISTINGS

Facebook: www.facebook.com/enidchamber
X (Twitter): x.com/EnidChamber
Description: Promotes business and community development in the Enid, OK area. **Publications:** Update (Monthly). **Educational Activities:** Camp Tomahawk (Annual). **Awards:** Greater Enid Chamber of Commerce Academic Achievement Awards (Annual); Greater Enid Chamber of Commerce Teacher of the Year (Annual). **Geographic Preference:** Local.

43763 ■ Greater Muskogee Area Chamber of Commerce (GMCC)
310 W Broadway St.
Muskogee, OK 74402
Ph: (918)682-2401
Fax: (918)682-2403
Co. E-mail: info@muskogeechamber.org
URL: http://www.muskogeechamber.org
Contact: Angela Wilson, President
E-mail: angela@muskogeechamber.org
Facebook: www.facebook.com/muskogee.chamber
Linkedin: www.linkedin.com/company/muskogeechamber
Instagram: www.instagram.com/muskogeechamber
Description: Promotes business and community development in the greater Muskogee area. **Founded:** 1922. **Publications:** Chamber Directory (Biennial); The Muskogee Chamber Connection (Monthly); Chamber Directory (Biennial); Greater Muskogee Area Chamber of Commerce--Chamber Directory (Biennial). **Geographic Preference:** Local.

43764 ■ Greater Oklahoma City Chamber of Commerce
123 Pk. Ave.
Oklahoma City, OK 73102
Ph: (405)297-8900
Co. E-mail: membership@okcchamber.com
URL: http://www.okcchamber.com
Contact: Christy Gillenwater, Co-President Co-Chief Executive Officer
Facebook: www.facebook.com/okcchamber
X (Twitter): x.com/okcchamber
YouTube: www.youtube.com/c/okcchamber
Description: Promotes business and community development in Oklahoma City, OK. **Founded:** 1889. **Publications:** The Point; OKC Action (Biweekly). **Geographic Preference:** Local.

43765 ■ Greater Oklahoma City Hispanic Chamber of Commerce
3321 S W Ave.
Oklahoma City, OK 73109
Ph: (405)616-5031
Co. E-mail: info@okchispanicchamber.org
URL: http://www.okchispanicchamber.org
Contact: David Castillo, President
E-mail: david.castillo@okchispanicchamber.org
Facebook: www.facebook.com/Greater-Oklahoma-City-Hispanic-Chamber-of-Commerce-291539706176
X (Twitter): x.com/okchisp_chamber
Description: Promotes the advancement of the commercial and economic interests of Hispanic-owned businesses, Hispanic-managed businesses, and Hispanic-oriented businesses, trades, and professionals in central Oklahoma. **Founded:** 2000. **Geographic Preference:** Local.

43766 ■ Grove Area Chamber of Commerce (GACC)
111 W 3rd St.
Grove, OK 74344
URL: http://www.groveok.org
Contact: Donnie Crain, President
E-mail: donniecrain.gacc@gmail.com
Facebook: www.facebook.com/GroveAreaChamberOfCommerce
Instagram: www.instagram.com/groveokchamber
YouTube: www.youtube.com/channel/UCbE0PjpLy0Y4cldwPG9idSQ
Description: Promotes business, community development, and tourism in the Grove, OK area. Markets Grove as a retirement and recreation center. Sponsors Grovefest and annual Christmas parade. **Founded:** 1962. **Geographic Preference:** Local.

43767 ■ Guthrie Chamber of Commerce
113 W Oklahoma Ave.
Guthrie, OK 73044
Ph: (405)282-1947
Co. E-mail: info@guthriechamber.com
URL: http://guthriechamber.com
Contact: Brittany Timmons, President
Facebook: www.facebook.com/GuthrieOK
X (Twitter): x.com/GuthrieCoolness
Instagram: www.instagram.com/guthriechamber
YouTube: www.youtube.com/channel/UCOxAvtZRLK6YLKblfeBJB8A
Description: Promotes business and community development in Guthrie, OK. Sponsors annual Christmas Celebration. **Founded:** 1889. **Geographic Preference:** Local.

43768 ■ Hartshorne Chamber of Commerce
1011 Pennsylvania Ave.
Hartshorne, OK 74547
Ph: (918)297-3651
URL: http://cityofhartshorne.com/chamber-of-commerce
Contact: Jerry Earp, President
Facebook: www.facebook.com/HartshorneChamber
Description: Promotes business and community development in Hartshorne, OK. **Geographic Preference:** Local.

43769 ■ Heart of Oklahoma Chamber of Commerce
220 W Main St.
Purcell, OK 73080
Ph: (405)527-3093
Co. E-mail: chamberoffice@theheartofok.com
URL: http://www.theheartofok.com
Contact: Elisabeth Baker, Director
Facebook: www.facebook.com/heartofokchamber
Linkedin: www.linkedin.com/company/heart-of-oklahoma-chamber-of-commerce
Instagram: www.instagram.com/heartofokchamber
Description: Promotes business and community development in Purcell, OK. **Founded:** 1944. **Publications:** The Heart of Oklahoma Chamber (Monthly). **Geographic Preference:** Local.

43770 ■ Henryetta Chamber of Commerce
415 W Main
Henryetta, OK 74437
Ph: (918)652-3331
Co. E-mail: henryettachamber@att.net
URL: http://henryetta.org
Contact: Shawn Okerson, President
Description: Promotes business and community development in Henryetta, OK. **Geographic Preference:** Local.

43771 ■ Holdenville Chamber of Commerce (HCC)
102 N Broadway St.
Holdenville, OK 74848
Ph: (405)379-3675
Co. E-mail: chamber@holdenvillechamber.com
URL: http://holdenvillechamber.com
Contact: Jim Davis, Vice President
E-mail: jim@rainbowautosalvage.com
X (Twitter): x.com/HoldenvilleC
Description: Promotes business and community development in Holdenville, OK. **Geographic Preference:** Local.

43772 ■ Hominy Area Chamber of Commerce
City Hall
Hominy, OK 74035
Contact: T. F. Dukes, Contact
Description: Promotes business and community development in Hominy, OK. **Founded:** 1960. **Geographic Preference:** Local.

43773 ■ Idabel Chamber of Commerce and Agriculture
7 SW Texas St.
Idabel, OK 74745
Ph: (580)286-3305
Fax: (580)286-6708
Co. E-mail: idabelchamber@yahoo.com
URL: http://www.theidabelchamber.com

Contact: Jerry Speck, Co-President
Facebook: www.facebook.com/TheIdabelChamber
X (Twitter): x.com/IdabelChamber
Instagram: www.instagram.com/theidabelchamber
Description: Promotes business and community development in McCurtain County, OK. Sponsors community events. **Founded:** 1945. **Geographic Preference:** Local.

43774 ■ Jenks Chamber of Commerce (JCC)
115 S First St.
Jenks, OK 74037
Ph: (918)299-5005
Co. E-mail: info@jenkschamber.com
URL: http://jenkschamber.com
Contact: Josh Driskell, President
Facebook: www.facebook.com/jenkschamber
X (Twitter): x.com/jenkschamber
YouTube: www.youtube.com/user/TheJenksChamber
Description: Promotes business and community development in Jenks, OK. **Founded:** 1966. **Geographic Preference:** Local.

43775 ■ Kingfisher Chamber of Commerce
110 E Broadway
Kingfisher, OK 73750
Ph: (405)375-4445
Co. E-mail: chamber@kingfisherchamber.com
URL: http://www.kingfisher.org
Contact: Shauna L. Rupp, Executive Director
Description: Works to promote economic and cultural development through business and individual participation. **Geographic Preference:** Local.

43776 ■ Lawton - Fort Sill Chamber of Commerce and Industry
302 W Gore Blvd.
Lawton, OK 73501
Ph: (580)355-3541
URL: http://www.lawtonfortsillchamber.com
Contact: Krista Smith-Ratliff, President
E-mail: kratliff@lawtonfortsillchamber.com
Facebook: www.facebook.com/lawtonfortsillchamber
Linkedin: www.linkedin.com/company/lawton-fort-sill-chamber-of-commerce
X (Twitter): x.com/LFSChamber
Instagram: www.instagram.com/lawtonfortsillchamber
Description: Promotes business and community development in Lawton, OK. **Geographic Preference:** Local.

43777 ■ Love County Chamber of Commerce
PO Box 422
Marietta, OK 73448
Ph: (580)276-3102
Co. E-mail: lovecountychamber@yahoo.com
URL: http://www.lovecountyokla.org
Contact: Kenneth L. Delashaw, Jr., Contact
Facebook: www.facebook.com/Love-County-Chamber-of-Commerce-148552981866805
Description: Promotes business and community development in Love County, OK. **Geographic Preference:** Local.

43778 ■ McAlester Area Chamber of Commerce and Agriculture (MACCA)
216 E Choctaw
McAlester, OK 74502
URL: http://mcalester.org
Contact: Caroline Russell, President
Description: Promotes agriculture, business, and community development in McAlester, OK. **Founded:** 1932. **Geographic Preference:** Local.

43779 ■ Membership Directory and Information Guide
410 W Main St.
Ardmore, OK 73401
Ph: (580)223-7765
URL: http://chamber.ardmore.org
Contact: Annilisa Peevy, Coordinator
E-mail: apeevy@ardmore.org
URL(s): chamber.ardmore.org/membership/benefits
Released: Annual **Description:** Contains information on community and business with advertising opportunities for Chamber members. **Availability:** Print; PDF.

43780 ■ Miami Area Chamber of Commerce
11 S Main St.
Miami, OK 74354
Ph: (918)542-4481
Co. E-mail: tmestes@miamiokchamber.com
URL: http://miamiokchamber.com
Facebook: www.facebook.com/MiamiRegionalChamberofCommerce
Instagram: www.instagram.com/miamiregionalchamber
Description: Promotes business and community development in Miami, OK. **Geographic Preference:** Local.

43781 ■ Midwest City Chamber of Commerce
5905 Prosper Blvd.
Midwest City, OK 73140
Ph: (405)733-3801
Fax: (405)733-5633
Co. E-mail: information@midwestcityok.com
URL: http://www.midwestcityok.com
Contact: Mike Kloiber, Member
Facebook: www.facebook.com/MidwestCityChamberOfCommerce
Linkedin: www.linkedin.com/company/midwest-city-chamber-of-commerce
X (Twitter): x.com/MWCChamber
YouTube: www.youtube.com/channel/UC2U6OUZibEisIZ9N58sdDNA
Description: Strives to create and maintain a favorable business climate in the community. Provides leadership necessary to advance the civic, commercial, industrial, and general interests of the business and professional community in the Midwest City trade area. **Founded:** 1947. **Publications:** *Mainstream*. **Geographic Preference:** Local.

43782 ■ Moore Chamber of Commerce
305 W Main Moore.
Moore, OK 73160
Ph: (405)794-3400
Co. E-mail: info@moorechamber.com
URL: http://www.moorechamber.com
Contact: Kim Brown, President
E-mail: kbrown@moorechamber.com
Facebook: www.facebook.com/moorechamberofcommerce
Linkedin: www.linkedin.com/company/moore-chamber-of-commerce
X (Twitter): x.com/MooreChamber
Instagram: www.instagram.com/moorechamber
YouTube: www.youtube.com/channel/UCCsHP1WYu3DetgDVFNxDW7g
Description: Promotes business and community development in Moore, OK. **Founded:** 1946. **Publications:** *Moore Business Network* (Monthly). **Geographic Preference:** Local.

43783 ■ Mustang Chamber of Commerce
1125 W Hwy. 152, Ste. 103
Mustang, OK 73064
Ph: (405)376-2758
Co. E-mail: director@mustangchamber.com
URL: http://www.mustangchamber.com
Contact: Renee Peerman, President
E-mail: director@mustangchamber.com
Facebook: www.facebook.com/themustangchamber
X (Twitter): x.com/mustangchamber
Description: Promotes business and community development in the Mustang, OK area. **Geographic Preference:** Local.

43784 ■ Norman Chamber of Commerce
424 W Main St.
Norman, OK 73069-7203
Ph: (405)321-7260
Co. E-mail: normanchamber@normanchamber.com
URL: http://business.normanchamber.com
Contact: Scott Martin, President
Facebook: www.facebook.com/normanchamber
Linkedin: www.linkedin.com/company/normanchamber
X (Twitter): x.com/NORMANCHAMBER
Instagram: www.instagram.com/normanchamber
YouTube: www.youtube.com/user/NormanChamber

Description: Promotes business and community development in Norman, OK. Sponsors Leadership Norman and Tomorrow's Leaders programs. **Founded:** 1889. **Publications:** *Norman Business Journal* (Monthly); *Relocation Guide*; *Visitors Guide* (Periodic). **Educational Activities:** Business After Hours (Monthly); Business Before Hours (Monthly). **Geographic Preference:** Local.

43785 ■ Northwest Chamber of Commerce
6644 NW 39th Expy.
Bethany, OK 73008
Ph: (405)789-1256
Fax: (405)789-2478
Co. E-mail: info@nwokc.com
URL: http://www.nwokc.com
Contact: Jill McCartney, President
E-mail: jmc@nwokc.com
Facebook: www.facebook.com/NWOKC
Linkedin: www.linkedin.com/company/nwokc
X (Twitter): x.com/nwokc
Instagram: www.instagram.com/nwokc
YouTube: www.youtube.com/c/nwokc
Pinterest: www.pinterest.com/NWOKC
Description: Promotes business and community development in Bethany, OK area. **Founded:** 1939. **Publications:** *Northwest Network* (Monthly). **Geographic Preference:** Local.

43786 ■ Okemah Chamber of Commerce
411 W Broadway St.
Okemah, OK 74859
Ph: (918)600-2023
Co. E-mail: info@visitokemah.com
URL: http://www.visitokemah.com
Contact: Alan Oatsvall, President (Acting)
Facebook: www.facebook.com/pg/OkemahChamberOfCommerce
Description: Promotes business and community development in Okemah, OK. **Geographic Preference:** Local.

43787 ■ Oklahoma City Black Chamber of Commerce (OKCBCC)
PO Box 36127
Oklahoma City, OK 73111
Ph: (405)595-4874
Co. E-mail: info@okcblackchamber.com
URL: http://okcblackchamber.com
Facebook: www.facebook.com/okcblackchamberofcommerce
X (Twitter): x.com/okcblackchamber
Instagram: www.instagram.com/okcblackchamber
Description: Represents Black owned businesses. Seeks to empower and sustain African American communities through entrepreneurship and capitalistic activity. Provides advocacy, training and education to Black communities. **Founded:** 1989. **Geographic Preference:** Local.

43788 ■ Oklahoma State Chamber
330 NE 10th St.
Oklahoma City, OK 73104
Ph: (405)235-3669
Fax: (405)235-3670
URL: http://www.okstatechamber.com
Contact: Chad Warmington, President
Description: Promotes business and community development in Oklahoma. **Founded:** 1926. **Publications:** *The Advocate* (Periodic). **Geographic Preference:** State.

43789 ■ Oologah Area Chamber of Commerce
120 W Sequoyah
Oologah, OK 74053
Co. E-mail: oologahareachamberofcommerce@gmail.com
Contact: Larry Burchett, Contact
Facebook: www.facebook.com/p/Oologah-Area-Chamber-of-Commerce-100083571960239
Description: Promotes business and economic development in Oologah, OK area. Serves as a civic organization and an advocate for the community. **Geographic Preference:** Local.

43790 ■ Owasso Chamber of Commerce
315 S Cedar St.
Owasso, OK 74055
Ph: (918)272-2141
Co. E-mail: chelsea@owassochamber.com
URL: http://www.owassochamber.com
Contact: Fayren Akin, Office Manager
E-mail: fayrene@owassochamber.com
Facebook: www.facebook.com/owassochamber
Linkedin: www.linkedin.com/company/owasso-chamber-of-commerce
X (Twitter): x.com/owassochamber
Description: Promotes business and community development in Owasso, OK. **Founded:** 1953. **Publications:** *Owasso News Line* (Monthly). **Educational Activities:** Owasso Chamber of Commerce Luncheon. **Geographic Preference:** Local.

43791 ■ Pauls Valley Chamber of Commerce
112 E Paul Ave.
Pauls Valley, OK 73075
Ph: (405)238-6491
Co. E-mail: businessservices@paulsvalleychamber.com
URL: http://www.paulsvalleychamber.com
Contact: Nancy Runge, President
Linkedin: www.linkedin.com/company/pauls-valley-chamber-of-commerce
Description: Promotes business, economic and community development in the Pauls Valley, OK service area. **Founded:** 1921. **Geographic Preference:** Local.

43792 ■ Pawhuska Chamber of Commerce
210 W Main St.
Pawhuska, OK 74056
Ph: (918)287-1208
URL: http://pawhuskachamber.com
Contact: Joey Lee, Officer
Linkedin: www.linkedin.com/company/pawhuska-chamber-of-commerce
X (Twitter): x.com/PawhuskaChamber
Description: Promotes business and community development in Pawhuska, OK. **Geographic Preference:** Local.

43793 ■ Pawnee Community Chamber of Commerce
c/o Joyce Freeman, 613 Harrison St.
Pawnee, OK 74058
Ph: (918)762-2108
Co. E-mail: pawneeok@att.net
URL: http://www.pawneechamberofcommerce.org
Contact: Joyce Freeman, Manager
Facebook: www.facebook.com/Pawnee2015
Description: Promotes business and tourism in Pawnee, OK area. Sponsors variety of events and activities throughout the year. **Geographic Preference:** Local.

43794 ■ Perkins Community Chamber of Commerce
730 N Main
Perkins, OK 74059
Ph: (405)747-6809
Co. E-mail: perkinschamber@gmail.com
URL: http://perkinschamber.org
Contact: Ashton Johns, President
Facebook: www.facebook.com/PerkinsCommunityChamber
Description: Promotes business and community development in Perkins, OK. **Geographic Preference:** Local.

43795 ■ Perry Chamber of Commerce
327 N 7th St.
Perry, OK 73077
Ph: (580)336-4684
Co. E-mail: info@perrychamber.net
URL: http://www.perryokchamber.com
Contact: Kali Hughey, President
Facebook: www.facebook.com/PerryOKChamber

Description: Promotes business and community development in Perry, OK. Sponsors Cherokee Strip Celebration, Springfest home, Sales Expo, Holidayfest, and Crazy Days. **Founded:** 1893. **Publications:** *The Communicator* (Quarterly). **Geographic Preference:** Local.

43796 ■ Piedmont Chamber of Commerce
12 Monroe Ave., NW
Piedmont, OK 73078
Ph: (405)883-6162
Fax: (405)373-2234
Co. E-mail: piedmontokchamber@gmail.com
URL: http://piedmontokchamber.org
Contact: Darren Owens, Member
X (Twitter): x.com/piedmontokcoc

Description: Promotes business and community development in Piedmont, OK. **Geographic Preference:** Local.

43797 ■ Ponca City Area Chamber of Commerce (PCACC)
420 E Grand Ave.
Ponca City, OK 74601
Ph: (580)765-4400
Fax: (580)765-2798
Co. E-mail: info@poncacitychamber.com
URL: http://www.poncacitychamber.com
Contact: Rich Cantillon, President
E-mail: rich@poncacitychamber.com
Facebook: www.facebook.com/poncacitychamber

Description: Promotes business, community tourism and economic development in the Ponca City, OK area. **Founded:** 1894. **Geographic Preference:** Local.

43798 ■ *Positively Anadarko*
516 W Kentucky Ave.
Anadarko, OK 73005
Ph: (405)247-6651
Fax: (405)247-6652
Co. E-mail: coc@anadarko.org
Contact: Carla Hall, Executive Director
Released: Monthly **Price:** Included in membership. **Availability:** Print.

43799 ■ Poteau Chamber of Commerce
501 S Broadway St.
Poteau, OK 74953
Ph: (918)647-9178
Fax: (918)647-4099
Co. E-mail: info@poteauchamber.com
URL: http://www.poteauchamber.com
Contact: Karen Wages, Executive Director
Facebook: www.facebook.com/PoteauChamber

Description: Promotes business and community development in Poteau, OK. **Founded:** 1917. **Geographic Preference:** Local.

43800 ■ Prague Chamber of Commerce
820 Jim Thorpe Blvd.
Prague, OK 74864
Ph: (405)567-2616
Co. E-mail: office@praguechamber.org
URL: http://praguechamber.org
Contact: Debbie Grissom, Secretary

Description: Promotes business and community development in Prague, OK. **Founded:** 1891. **Geographic Preference:** Local.

43801 ■ Pryor Area Chamber of Commerce (PACC)
100 E Graham Ave.
Pryor, OK 74361
Ph: (918)825-0157
Co. E-mail: info@pryorchamber.com
URL: http://www.pryorchamber.com
Contact: Katie Thibodeaux, Director, Communications
E-mail: katie@pryorchamber.com
YouTube: www.youtube.com/channel/UC5uhAiaSDrKpZb7juwvb5Gw

Description: Promotes business and community development in Mayes County, OK. Sponsors Leadership Pryor, business seminars and workshops, FunFest, DAM J.A.M. Bicycle Tour of N.E. Oklahoma's Lakes and Dams and Lighted Christmas Parade. **Founded:** 1943. **Geographic Preference:** Local.

43802 ■ Sallisaw Chamber of Commerce
101N Wheeler Ave.
Sallisaw, OK 74955
Ph: (918)775-2558
Co. E-mail: director@sallisawchamber.com
URL: http://sallisawchamber.com
Contact: Roye Frye, Jr., Contact
Facebook: www.facebook.com/sallisawchamberofcommerce

Description: Promotes business and community development in Sallisaw, OK. **Founded:** 1886. **Geographic Preference:** Local.

43803 ■ Sand Springs Area Chamber of Commerce
109 N Garfield Ave.
Sand Springs, OK 74063
Ph: (918)245-3221
Co. E-mail: info@sandspringschamber.com
URL: http://www.sandspringschamber.com
Facebook: www.facebook.com/Sand-Springs-Chamber-of-Commerce-314545058580657

Description: Aims to advance the business community and improve the quality of life for the Sand Springs area citizens. **Founded:** 1946. **Publications:** *Chamber Comments*. **Educational Activities:** City of Sand Springs/City Council Meeting (Monthly). **Geographic Preference:** Local.

43804 ■ Sapulpa Area Chamber of Commerce
101 E Dewey Ave.
Sapulpa, OK 74066
Ph: (918)224-0170
Fax: (918)224-0172
Co. E-mail: info@sapulpachamber.com
URL: http://www.sapulpachamber.com
Facebook: www.facebook.com/SapulpaChamber

Description: Promotes business and community development in the Sapulpa, OK area. **Geographic Preference:** Local.

43805 ■ Seminole Chamber of Commerce
326 Evans St.
Seminole, OK 74868
Ph: (405)382-3640
Co. E-mail: info@seminoleokchamber.org
URL: http://seminoleokchamber.org
Facebook: www.facebook.com/SeminoleChamberofCommerce

Description: Promotes business and community development in Seminole, Oklahoma. **Founded:** 1928. **Publications:** *Seminole Chamber of Commerce Member Directory* (Annual). **Educational Activities:** Gusher Days. **Awards:** Seminole Chamber of Commerce Citizen of the Year (Annual). **Geographic Preference:** Local.

43806 ■ Shattuck Chamber of Commerce
115 Main St.
Shattuck, OK 73858
Ph: (580)938-2818
Co. E-mail: shattuckchamber@gmail.com
URL: http://shattuckchamber.com
Contact: Jeni Hinkle, President
Facebook: www.facebook.com/shattuck.chamber

Description: Promotes business and community development in Shattuck, OK. **Founded:** 1949. **Geographic Preference:** Local.

43807 ■ Skiatook Chamber of Commerce
304 E Rogers Blvd.
Skiatook, OK 74070
Ph: (918)396-3702
Co. E-mail: admin@skiatookchamber.com
URL: http://www.skiatookchamber.com
Contact: Hannah Park, Contact
Facebook: www.facebook.com/Skiatookchamberofcommerce
Instagram: www.instagram.com/skiatookchamber

Description: Promotes business and community development in Skiatook, OK. **Founded:** 1918. **Publications:** *ChamberNews* (Monthly). **Geographic Preference:** Local.

43808 ■ South Oklahoma City Chamber of Commerce (SOKC)
701 SW 74th St.
Oklahoma City, OK 73139
Ph: (405)634-1436
Co. E-mail: info@southokc.com
URL: http://southokc.com
Contact: Elaine Lyons, President
Facebook: www.facebook.com/southokcchamber
X (Twitter): x.com/SouthOKCChamber
YouTube: www.youtube.com/user/SouthOKCChamber

Description: Promotes business and community development in southern Oklahoma City, OK. **Founded:** 1905. **Educational Activities:** After 5 Mixers. **Geographic Preference:** Local.

43809 ■ Stillwater Chamber of Commerce (SCC)
409 S Main St.
Stillwater, OK 74074
Ph: (405)372-5573
Co. E-mail: info@stillwaterchamber.org
URL: http://www.stillwaterchamber.org
Contact: Justin Minges, President
E-mail: justin@stillwaterchamber.org
Facebook: www.facebook.com/StillwaterChamber
Linkedin: www.linkedin.com/pub/stillwater-chamber-of-commerce/7b/bb1/a70
X (Twitter): x.com/StwChamber
Instagram: www.instagram.com/stillwaterchamber

Description: Promotes business and community development in Stillwater, OK. **Founded:** 1892. **Publications:** *Stillwater Commerce* (Quarterly); *Stillwater Connection* (Weekly). **Educational Activities:** Stillwater Chamber of Commerce Breakfast; Business Showcase and Mixer. **Geographic Preference:** Local.

43810 ■ *Stillwater Commerce*
409 S Main St.
Stillwater, OK 74074
Ph: (405)372-5573
Co. E-mail: info@stillwaterchamber.org
URL: http://www.stillwaterchamber.org
Contact: Justin Minges, President
E-mail: justin@stillwaterchamber.org
URL(s): stillwaterchamber.org/join-or-renew-membership

Released: Quarterly **Availability:** Print.

43811 ■ Stroud Chamber of Commerce
216 W Main St.
Stroud, OK 74079
Ph: (918)968-3321
Co. E-mail: stroudch@cotc.net
URL: http://www.stroudchamber.com
Contact: Kyle Anderson, President
Facebook: www.facebook.com/stroudchamber

Description: Aims to advance the economic, civic, educational and cultural growth of Stroud and to enhance the quality of life in the community. Fosters continuous improvement of the Stroud area as a place to conduct business and enjoy life. **Geographic Preference:** Local.

43812 ■ Sulphur Chamber of Commerce
717 W Broadway
Sulphur, OK 73086
Ph: (580)622-2824
Co. E-mail: sulphur@brightok.net
URL: http://sulphurchamber.com
Contact: Misty Treptow, Executive Director
Facebook: www.facebook.com/Sulphurchamber
Instagram: www.instagram.com/sulphurchamberok

Description: Promotes business and community development in Sulphur, OK. Sponsors 5k Run and Racewalk, annual Sulphur Days Festival, Hills of Oklahoma Tour (bicycle race), Christmas parade, and Arbuckle County Christmas Festivities. **Geographic Preference:** Local.

43813 ■ Tahlequah Area Chamber of Commerce and Tourism Council (TACC)
123 E Delaware St.
Tahlequah, OK 74464
Ph: (918)456-3742
Fax: (918)456-3751
Co. E-mail: info@tahlequahchamber.com
URL: http://www.tahlequahchamber.com
Contact: Jim Berry, Chairman
Facebook: www.facebook.com/tahlequahareachamber
Instagram: www.instagram.com/tahlequahchamber
Description: Promotes business and community development in Tahlequah, OK. Sponsors 4-H Livestock Show, Moonlight Classic golf tournament, Christmas Parade, Festival of Lights, Cherokee Square Arts and Crafts Festival. **Founded:** 1898. **Publications:** *Chamber Voice* (Monthly). **Geographic Preference:** Local.

43814 ■ Talihina Chamber of Commerce
201 1st. St.
Talihina, OK 74571
Ph: (918)567-3434
Co. E-mail: contact@talihinacc.com
URL: http://talihinacc.com
Contact: Vera Nelson, Contact
Facebook: www.facebook.com/talihina.chamber
Description: Promotes business and community development in Talihina, Oklahoma. **Geographic Preference:** Local.

43815 ■ Tecumseh Chamber of Commerce
114 N Broadway St.
Tecumseh, OK 74873
Ph: (405)598-8666
URL: http://www.tecumsehchamber.org
Contact: Kellie Clay, Treasurer
Description: Promotes business and community development in Tecumseh, OK. **Publications:** *Chamber Chimes* (Quarterly). **Geographic Preference:** Local.

43816 ■ Tulsa Regional Chamber
1 W 3rd St., Ste. 100
Tulsa, OK 74103
Ph: (918)585-1201
Co. E-mail: info@tulsachamber.com
URL: http://tulsachamber.com
Contact: Michael S. Neal, Chief Executive Officer
E-mail: mikeneal@tulsachamber.com
Facebook: www.facebook.com/TulsaChamber
Linkedin: www.linkedin.com/company/tulsaregionalchamber
X (Twitter): x.com/tulsachamber
YouTube: www.youtube.com/channel/UCAJZQGIWUGHIJNWUYTPz4dg
Description: Promotes business and community development in the Tulsa and Northeastern Oklahoma areas. Convention/Meeting: none. **Founded:** 1903. **Publications:** *Tulsa Newcomer Prospect List* (Bimonthly); *Tulsa Area Large Employers* (Annual). **Geographic Preference:** Regional.

43817 ■ Vinita Area Chamber of Commerce (VACC)
332 N Scraper
Vinita, OK 74301
Ph: (918)256-7133
Co. E-mail: vinitachamber@gmail.com
URL: http://www.vinitachamber.com
Contact: Bruce Sooter, President
Facebook: www.facebook.com/vinitachamber
Linkedin: www.linkedin.com/company/vinita-area-chamber-of-commerce
X (Twitter): x.com/vinitachamber
Description: Promotes business and community development in Vinita, OK. Sponsors competitions and festivals. **Founded:** 1898. **Publications:** *Chamber News* (Semimonthly). **Educational Activities:** Vinita Area Chamber of Commerce Meeting. **Geographic Preference:** Local.

43818 ■ Watonga Chamber of Commerce
103 S NOBLE
Watonga, OK 73772
Contact: Joyce Lucas, Contact
Description: Promotes business and community development in Watonga, OK. **Founded:** 1941. **Awards:** Watonga Business Beautification Award (Annual); Watonga Business of the Year (Annual); Watonga New Business of the Year (Annual); Watonga Volunteer of the Year (Annual). **Geographic Preference:** Local.

43819 ■ Weatherford Area Chamber of Commerce (WACC)
210 W Main St.
Weatherford, OK 73096
Ph: (580)772-7744
Co. E-mail: welcome@weatherfordchamber.com
URL: http://weatherfordchamber.com
Contact: Karen Magill, President
Facebook: www.facebook.com/weatherfordokchamber
X (Twitter): x.com/ok_weatherford
Description: Promotes business and community development in Weatherford, OK. Sponsors Southwest Festival of the Arts, Heartland/Route 66 Cruise, and IPRA Rodeo. **Founded:** 1907. **Publications:** *Guide to Doing Business in Waterford* (Annual). **Geographic Preference:** Local.

43820 ■ Wewoka Chamber of Commerce
PO Box 719
Wewoka, OK 74884
Ph: (405)257-5485
Fax: (405)257-2662
Co. E-mail: wewokachamber@sbcglobal.net
URL: http://wewokachamber.wordpress.com
Description: Promotes business and community development in Wewoka, OK. **Geographic Preference:** Local.

43821 ■ *What's Happening in Frederick*
100 S Main St.
Frederick, OK 73542
Ph: (580)335-2126
Co. E-mail: frederickcc@pldi.net
URL: http://www.frederickokchamber.org
Contact: Felisha Crawford, Co-Chairman of the Board
URL(s): www.frederickokchamber.org/membership.html
Released: Monthly **Description:** Keeps members informed about Chamber activities. **Availability:** Print; Online.

43822 ■ Wilburton Chamber of Commerce
302 W Main St.
Wilburton, OK 74578
Ph: (918)465-2759
Fax: (918)465-2759
Co. E-mail: wilburtonchamber@sbcglobal.net
URL: http://wilburtonareachamber.com
Contact: Lindsay Ward, Contact
Description: Promotes business and community development in Wilburton, OK. **Geographic Preference:** Local.

43823 ■ Woodward Chamber of Commerce (WCC)
1006 Oklahoma Ave.
Woodward, OK 73801
Ph: (580)256-7411
Fax: (580)254-3585
Co. E-mail: wwchamber@sbcglobal.net
URL: http://www.woodwardchamber.com
Contact: C. J. Montgomery, President
E-mail: cjmontgomery@sbcglobal.net
Description: Promotes business and community development in Woodward, OK. Monitors issues such as minimum wage, educational funding, and worker's compensation. Lobbies for favorable legislation. Holds area festivals and other activities. **Geographic Preference:** Local.

43824 ■ Wynnewood Chamber of Commerce
102 E Robert S Kerr Blvd.
Wynnewood, OK 73098
Contact: Sandy Garrett, Contact
Facebook: www.facebook.com/WynnewoodChamberOfCommerce
Description: Promotes business and community development in Wynnewood, OK. **Founded:** 1951. **Geographic Preference:** Local.

43825 ■ Yukon Chamber of Commerce
10 W Main St., Ste. 130
Yukon, OK 73099
Ph: (405)354-3567
Co. E-mail: chamber@yukoncc.com
URL: http://yukoncc.com
Contact: Pam Shelton, Chief Executive Officer
E-mail: pshelton@yukoncc.com
Facebook: www.facebook.com/yukonchamber
Instagram: www.instagram.com/yukonokchamberofcommerce
Description: Promotes business and community development in Yukon, OK. **Geographic Preference:** Local.

MINORITY BUSINESS ASSISTANCE PROGRAMS

43826 ■ Oklahoma Department of Commerce - Business Services & Start-up Guide - Women & Minority Business Certifications - Minority-Owned Businesses
900 N Stiles Ave.
Oklahoma City, OK 73104
URL: http://www.okcommerce.gov/doing-business/business-services/minority-owned-business-information
Contact: Ken Talley, Specialist Coordinator
E-mail: ken.talley@okcommerce.gov
Description: Specializes in finance export programs to assist small Oklahoma companies.

43827 ■ Oklahoma Native American Business Enterprise Center
3902 E 51st St., Ste. 208-210
Tulsa, OK 74135
URL: http://www.okcu.edu/business/professional-education/programs/native-american-business
URL(s): reimbc.org
Description: Provider of business assistance to Native American and other minority-owned companies in Oklahoma.

FINANCING AND LOAN PROGRAMS

43828 ■ Cimarron Capital Partners LLC
1833 S Morgan Rd.
Oklahoma City, OK 73128
URL: http://www.cimarroncapital.com
Contact: Philip B. Heard, Manager
Description: Private equity and venture capital asset management .

43829 ■ Cowboy Technology Investors
Oklahoma City, OK
URL: http://www.cowboytechnologyangels.com
Description: Alumni and affiliates of Oklahoma State University working as an angel investor group.

43830 ■ Davis, Tuttle Venture Partners (DTVP)
110 W 7th St., Ste. 1000
Tulsa, OK 74119
Contact: Lee Frost, Officer
Description: Provides financial services for food, construction and engineering and apparel and textile mill products. **Founded:** 1990. **Preferred Investment Size:** $500,000 to $5,000,000. **Industry Preferences:** Other products, consumer related, medical and health, industrial and energy, computer software and services, semiconductors and other electronics, Internet specific, communications and media.

43831 ■ Spur Capital Partners
2370 Nowata Pl.
Bartlesville, OK 74006
Ph: (918)331-3800
Co. E-mail: spur@spurcap.com
URL: http://www.spurcapital.com

Contact: Joan Heidorn, Co-Founder Managing Director
X (Twitter): x.com/spurventures
Description: Early-stage venture capital firm for technology companies. **Founded:** 2001.

PROCUREMENT ASSISTANCE PROGRAMS

43832 ■ **Autry Technology Center**
1201 W Willow
  Enid, OK 73703
Ph: (580)242-2750
URL: http://autrytech.edu
Contact: Jesse Ashlock, Contact
Facebook: www.facebook.com/AutryTechnology
X (Twitter): x.com/AutryTechnology
Instagram: www.instagram.com/autrytechnology
YouTube: www.youtube.com/user/AutryTechnology
Description: Provides programs and services that enhance skill development and job opportunities. **Founded:** 1967.

43833 ■ **Great Plains Technology Center (GPTC)**
4500 W Lee Blvd.
  Lawton, OK 73505
Ph: (580)355-6371
URL: http://www.greatplains.edu
Contact: Justin McNeil, Executive Director
E-mail: jmcneil@greatplains.edu
Facebook: www.facebook.com/greatplains technologycenter
X (Twitter): x.com/greatplainstech
Instagram: www.instagram.com/greatplainstech
YouTube: www.youtube.com/user/GPTCLawton
Description: Business college offering a small business management program. **Founded:** 1971.

43834 ■ **Mid-America Technology Center**
27438 State Hwy. 59
  Wayne, OK 73095-0210
Ph: (405)449-3391
Description: Center focuses on economic education and training programs. **Founded:** 1968.

43835 ■ **Moore Norman Technology Center (MNTC) - Business Development Center**
13301 S Pennsylvania
  Oklahoma City, OK 73170
Ph: (580)745-2877
URL: http://business.oksbdc.org/center.aspx?center=64030&subloc=18
Description: The center serves the businesses and individuals in MNTC's district of Moore, Norman, and south Oklahoma City. Services offered include: bid notification registration, bid matching, access to specifications, standards and drawings as well as introductions to a networks of procurement specialists. **Founded:** 1972.

43836 ■ **Oklahoma APEX Accelerator (OkAPEX)**
Okla. Dept. of CareerTech
1500 W 7th Ave.
  Stillwater, OK 74074-4398
Ph: (405)743-5122
URL: http://oklahoma.gov/careertech/business-and-industry/okapex.html
Contact: Lana Knott, Program Manager
Description: Helps client firms find potential government customers, register in government systems such as the Central Contractor Registration System, and market themselves to both government agencies and prime contractors.

43837 ■ **Oklahoma Department of Career and Technology Education - Library [CareerTech]**
1500 W 7th Ave.
  Stillwater, OK 74074-4398
Ph: (405)377-2000
Free: 800-522-5810
Fax: (405)743-6809
URL: http://oklahoma.gov/careertech.html
Contact: Cori Gray, Deputy Director
E-mail: cori.gray@careertech.ok.gov

Facebook: www.facebook.com/OklahomaCareerTech
Linkedin: www.linkedin.com/company/oklahoma-department-of-career-and-technology-education
X (Twitter): x.com/okcareertech
Instagram: www.instagram.com/OklahomaCareerTech
YouTube: www.youtube.com/user/okcareertech
Description: Provides federal contracting at 21 offices, located at vo-tech schools statewide. **Scope:** Construction. **Founded:** 1917. **Holdings:** Figures not available. **Geographic Preference:** State.

43838 ■ **Oklahoma Procurement Technical Assistance Center - Eastern Oklahoma County Technology Center**
4601 N Choctaw Rd.
  Choctaw, OK 73020
Ph: (405)390-5350
URL: http://www.aptac-us.org/find-a-ptac/?state=OK
Contact: David Hoffmeier, Director
E-mail: dhoffmeier@eoctech.edu
Description: Provides individuals with life-long career/technical training and personal development through quality programs, services and activities serving the school districts of Choctaw, Harrah, Jones and Luther.

43839 ■ **Oklahoma Procurement Technical Assistance Center-Gordon Cooper Technology Center (GCTC)**
1 John C. Bruton Blvd.
  Shawnee, OK 74804
Ph: (405)273-7493
Co. E-mail: info@gctech.edu
URL: http://www.gctech.edu
Contact: Dean Evans, President
Facebook: www.facebook.com/gctech
X (Twitter): x.com/gctechok
YouTube: www.youtube.com/channel/UC_fnQne0aRtk2nvcUCqw20w
Description: Provides timely information and training for businesses interested in government markets.

43840 ■ **Oklahoma Procurement Technical Assistance Center - Kiamichi Technology Center**
1004 Hwy 2 N
  Wilburton, OK 74578-0548
Ph: (918)465-2323
URL: http://www.aptac-us.org/find-a-ptac/?state=OK
Contact: Ronald DeGiacomo, Director
E-mail: rdegiacomo@ktc.edu
Description: Provides training and assistance in locating and competing for government contracts.

43841 ■ **Oklahoma Procurement Technical Assistance Center (OkPTAC) - Oklahoma Bid Assistance Network (OBA) - Southwest Technology Center (SWTC)**
711 W Tamarack
  Altus, OK 73521
Ph: (580)477-2250
URL: http://www.aptac-us.org/find-a-ptac/?state=OK
Contact: Leslie Snapp, Contact
E-mail: lsnapp@swtech.edu
Facebook: www.facebook.com/Southwest.Technology.Center
X (Twitter): x.com/southwest_tech
YouTube: www.youtube.com/user/SWTechnologyCenter
Description: Assists area businesses obtain government contracts. Help is available to cut through red tape, find what contracts are out for bid, how to request an opportunity to bid, and how to complete and submit a bid package. **Founded:** 1986.

43842 ■ **Oklahoma Procurement Technical Assistance Center - Oklahoma Bid Assistance Network (OBA) - Tri-County Technology Center**
6101 Nowata Rd.
  Bartlesville, OK 74006
Ph: (918)331-3333
Co. E-mail: enrichinglives@tricountytech.edu
URL: http://tricountytech.edu
Contact: George Halkiades, President

URL(s): oklahoma.gov/careertech/technology-centers/profiles.html
Facebook: www.facebook.com/tricountytech
Linkedin: www.linkedin.com/school/tricountytech/about
X (Twitter): x.com/tricountytech
Instagram: www.instagram.com/tricountytech
Description: Assists in competing for government contracts and will help you develop a pro-active marketing strategy identifying bid opportunities from all levels of government covering Washington, Nowata, Craig, Ottawa, Mayes, Rogers, and Tulsa Counties. **Founded:** 1967.

43843 ■ **Pioneer Technology Center (PTC)**
2101 N Ash
  Ponca City, OK 74601
Ph: (580)762-8336
Free: 866-612-4782
Co. E-mail: info@pioneertech.edu
URL: http://www.pioneertech.edu
Contact: Kahle Goff, Executive Director
E-mail: kahleg@pioneertech.edu
Facebook: www.facebook.com/PioneerTech
Linkedin: www.linkedin.com/school/pioneer-technology-center
X (Twitter): x.com/PIONEERTECHCTR
YouTube: www.youtube.com/user/PioneerTechEdu
Pinterest: www.pinterest.com/pioneertech
Description: Business college offering a small business management program. **Founded:** 1973.

43844 ■ **Procurement Technical Assistance Center Indian Capital Technology Center (PTAC)**
2403 N 41st St. E
  Muskogee, OK 74403
Ph: (918)348-7940
URL: http://www.aptac-us.org/find-a-ptac/?state=OK
Contact: Darla Bennett, Coordinator
E-mail: darla.bennett@ictech.edu
Description: Goal is to present potential contractors with a clear understanding of the bidding process as well as providing the most up-to-date information required for contract bidding.

43845 ■ **Red River Technology Center**
3300 W Bois D'Arc
  Duncan, OK 73534
Ph: (580)255-2903
URL: http://www.rrtc.edu
Contact: Lisa Williams, Coordinator
E-mail: lgwilliams@rrtc.edu
Facebook: www.facebook.com/redrivertechcenter
Description: Business college offering a small business management program. **Founded:** 1975. **Geographic Preference:** Local.

43846 ■ **Tribal Government Institute (TGI)**
111 N Peters Ste. 450
  Norman, OK 73069
Ph: (405)329-5542
Fax: (405)329-5543
Co. E-mail: tgi@coxinet.net
URL: http://tgiok.com
Facebook: www.facebook.com/tgiptac
Linkedin: www.linkedin.com/company/tgi-ptac
YouTube: www.youtube.com/channel/UCFcZkWNm7C0AzQCk0OGZ4RQ
Description: Provides management training, consulting, technical assistance, program and project applications, and tribal government assistance in the fields of drafting housing codes, constitutional law, policies and procedures, coordinating housing bond issues, grant proposals, public health and safety codes, law and order codes and many types of legislative requirements of tribal governments and their agencies. **Scope:** Issues impacting Native Americans and their tribal governments. **Founded:** 1990.

43847 ■ **Tulsa Technology Center Procurement Technical Assistance Center**
3638 S Memorial
  Tulsa, OK 74145
Ph: (918)828-5438
URL: http://www.aptac-us.org/find-a-ptac/?state=OK

Contact: Cindy Jackson, Counselor
E-mail: cindy.jackson@tulsatech.edu
Description: Assist in competing for government contracts.

INCUBATORS/RESEARCH AND TECHNOLOGY PARKS

43848 ■ Artist Incubation Inc.
421 N Main
Guymon, OK 73942
Description: Supports artists as a business incubator.

43849 ■ Autry Technology Center Business Incubator
1201 W Willow
Enid, OK 73703
Ph: (580)242-2750
URL: http://autrytech.edu
Contact: Shelby Cottrill, Director, Marketing
Facebook: www.facebook.com/AutryTechnology
X (Twitter): x.com/AutryTechnology
Instagram: www.instagram.com/autrytechnology
YouTube: www.youtube.com/AutryTechnology
Description: Business incubator that aids start-ups.

43850 ■ Cameron University - Center for Emerging Technology and Entrepreneurial Studies (CU)
2800 W Gore Blvd.
Lawton, OK 73505
Ph: (580)581-5447
URL: http://www.cameron.edu/administrative-offices
Contact: Jari Askins, President
E-mail: president@cameron.edu
Description: Offers entrepreneurs and startup businesses office space in its business incubator, and a host of business services to support their success and growth. **Founded:** 2005.

43851 ■ The Catbird Seat
101 N EK Gaylord Blvd., Ste. 1
Oklahoma City, OK 73102
Ph: (405)974-3030
URL: http://www.thecatbirdseat.org
Contact: Dawna Terrell, Director
E-mail: dterrell@uco.edu
Facebook: www.facebook.com/UCOCE
Linkedin: www.linkedin.com/company/uco-customized-education
Description: A small business incubator located in downtown Oklahoma City at the University of Central Oklahoma's Santa Fe location.

43852 ■ Center for Emerging Technology and Entrepreneurial Studies at Cameron University (CETES CU)
2800 W Gore Blvd.
Lawton, OK 73505
Ph: (580)581-5447
URL: http://www.cameron.edu/administrative-offices
Contact: Jari Askins, President
E-mail: president@cameron.edu
Description: Offers entrepreneurs and startup businesses office space in its business incubator, and a host of business services to support their success and growth.

43853 ■ Central Oklahoma Business And Job Development Corp.
420 E Broadway
Drumright, OK 74030
Contact: Clayton L. Badger, Contact
Description: A non-profit program providing a supportive environment for small business start-up, survival, and growth.

43854 ■ Duncan Center for Business Development
941 W Peach Ave.
Duncan, OK 73533
URL: http://ok-duncan.com/site-selection/business-incubator
Contact: Lyle Roggow, President
E-mail: lyle@ok-duncan.com
Description: Helps startups to get established and to become self-sufficient enough to afford renting space in non-incubator facilities.

43855 ■ Earth Elements Entrepreneurs' Kitchen (E3K)
1408 N Portland Ave.
Oklahoma City, OK 73107
Ph: (405)673-7945
Co. E-mail: 405okck@gmail.com
URL: http://www.earthelementskitchen.com
Description: Commercial kitchen incubator providing resources for food startups including business startup assistance, peer networking, resource collaboration, and business and regulation support. **Founded:** 2011.

43856 ■ Eastern Oklahoma County Technology Center (EOCTC)
4601 N Choctaw Rd.
Choctaw, OK 73020
Ph: (405)390-9591
Co. E-mail: communications@eoctech.edu
URL: http://www.eoctech.edu
Contact: Bill McCully, Treasurer
E-mail: bmccully@eoctech.edu
Facebook: www.facebook.com/eoctech
Linkedin: www.linkedin.com/school/eoctech
X (Twitter): x.com/eoctech
Instagram: www.instagram.com/eoctech
YouTube: www.youtube.com/channel/UCxdyxTdA_JrN8mg2BvR87Qg
Description: Business incubator working with start-ups to ensure success. **Founded:** 1982.

43857 ■ The Forge
125 W 3rd St.
Tulsa, OK 74103
URL: http://tedcnet.com/leading
Description: Accelerates the development and success of start-ups and existing businesses in Tulsa by offering a place where raw ideas and passionate people are shaped into entrepreneurial success stories. **Founded:** 2009.

43858 ■ Great Plains Technology Center Business Incubator
1601 SW Pk. Ridge Blvd.
Lawton, OK 73505
URL: http://www.greatplains.edu/business-services
Contact: Cody Holt, Coordinator
E-mail: cholt@greatplains.edu
Description: Economic development organization.

43859 ■ Great Plains Technology Center - Economic Development Center
4500 SW Lee Blvd.
Lawton, OK 73505
Co. E-mail: edc@greatplains.edu
URL: http://www.greatplains.edu
Contact: Morgan Gould, Director
E-mail: mgould@greatplains.edu
Facebook: www.facebook.com/greatplainsedc
Description: A comprehensive business assistance program that helps start-up and early stage firms with the goal of improving their chances to grow into healthy, sustainable, and self-sufficient companies. **Founded:** 1971.

43860 ■ i2E Inc.
840 Research Pky., Ste. 250
Oklahoma City, OK 73104
Ph: (405)235-2305
Co. E-mail: i2e_comments@i2e.org
URL: http://i2e.org
Contact: Rex Smitherman, President
E-mail: rsmitherman@i2e.org
Facebook: www.facebook.com/i2EInc
Linkedin: www.linkedin.com/company/i2e-inc.
X (Twitter): x.com/i2E_Inc
Instagram: www.instagram.com/i2e_inc
Description: Focused on growing innovative small businesses in Oklahoma and making a positive impact on the state's economy. Provides venture advisory services, access to capital, and entrepreneurial development.

43861 ■ Kiamichi Technology Centers
1410 Old Military Rd.
Stigler, OK 74462
Ph: (918)967-2801
URL: http://www.ktc.edu
Contact: April Williams, Director
Facebook: www.facebook.com/kiamichitechstigler
Description: Education technology centers provides education process, training, short-term classes, education and obtaining important job skills for adults.

43862 ■ Kiamichi Technology Centers
1509 S McKenna St.
Poteau, OK 74953
Ph: (918)647-4525
URL: http://www.ktc.edu
Contact: Michael Culwell, Director
Facebook: www.facebook.com/kiamichitech
X (Twitter): x.com/kiamichitech
Description: Education technology centers provides education process, training, short-term classes, education and obtaining important job skills for adults.

43863 ■ Launch Pad FT
2824 Progressive Dr.
Edmond, OK 73034
Ph: (405)717-7777
URL: http://launchpadft.wordpress.com
Contact: Fred Green, Director
Description: Provides the starting point for a small business to grow, mature, and become a sustainable business.

43864 ■ Major County Economic Development Incubator (MCEDC)
2004 Commerce St.
Fairview, OK 73737
Facebook: www.facebook.com/fairviewoklife
Description: Embraces business support services tailored to new and emerging companies with the intent to to create sustainable businesses which contribute to local and regional economic growth.

43865 ■ Meridian Technology Center - Center for Business Development
1312 S Sangre Rd.
Stillwater, OK 74074
URL: http://www.meridiantech.edu/bes/our-team
Contact: Erica Pereira, Specialist
E-mail: ericap@meridiantech.edu
Description: A business incubator that fosters the development of new and emerging businesses. The Center offers office and manufacturing space, conference rooms, and other resources.

43866 ■ Moore Norman Technology Center Business (MNTC)
13101 S Pennsylvania
Oklahoma City, OK 73170
Ph: (405)801-5000
Fax: (405)809-3548
Co. E-mail: customer.inquiry@mntc.edu
URL: http://www.mntc.edu
Contact: Stephania Cordova, Executive Director, Human Resources
Facebook: www.facebook.com/MooreNormanTech
Linkedin: www.linkedin.com/school/moore-norman-technology-center
X (Twitter): x.com/MooreNormanTech
Instagram: www.instagram.com/moorenormantech
YouTube: www.youtube.com/user/MooreNorman
Description: Education, business and community work together to create an elevated economy. **Founded:** 1972.

43867 ■ Moore Norman Technology Center's Business Development Center
13301 S Pennsylvania
Oklahoma City, OK 73170
URL: http://www.mntc.edu/workforce-development
Description: An innovative business facility designed to help you investigate and clarify your business plan and build your business.

STATE LISTINGS

43868 ■ Northwest Technology Center Small Business Incubator
1801 11th St.
Alva, OK 73717
URL: http://www.nwtech.info/bis-incubator.htm
Contact: Allan Poe, Contact
E-mail: apoe@nwtech.edu
Description: Business incubator offering services to start-ups.

43869 ■ Oklahoma Business Incubator Association (OkBIA)
c/o Brad Rickelman, Secretary
Treasurer1414 S Sangre Rd., Meridian Technology Ctr. for Business Development
Stillwater, OK 74074
Co. E-mail: okbialeadership@gmail.com
URL: http://www.okbia.org
Contact: Brad Rickelman, Treasurer Secretary
Facebook: www.facebook.com/OklahomaBusinessIncubatorAssociation
Description: Seeks to advance business incubation and entrepreneurship. Educates businesses and investors on incubator benefits. Provides information, research and networking resources to help members develop and manage successful business incubation programs. **Geographic Preference:** State.

43870 ■ Pioneer Technology Center Business Incubator
2101 N Ash
Ponca City, OK 74601
URL: http://pioneertech.edu/business-incubator?category=business
Contact: Janet Schwabe, Manager
E-mail: janets@pioneertech.edu
Description: A certified business incubator for new businesses. Offers space for service, light manufacturing, or wholesale companies.

43871 ■ Pontotoc Technology Center Business Incubator (PTC)
601 W 33rd St.
Ada, OK 74820
URL: http://www.pontotoctech.edu/aboutpages/about
Description: Business incubator aids start-ups in finding success.

43872 ■ REI Oklahoma (REI)
2912 Enterprise Blvd.
Durant, OK 74701
Free: 800-658-2823
Fax: (580)920-2745
Co. E-mail: info@reiok.org
URL: http://www.reiok.org
Contact: Scott Dewald, President
Description: Distributor of Hydronic plumbing, heating equipment and supplies. **Founded:** 1964.

43873 ■ Sallisaw Improvement Corporation Business Incubator
101 N Wheeler
Sallisaw, OK 74955
Ph: (918)775-2558
Co. E-mail: director@sallisawchamber-2.megaphoneps.com
URL: http://sallisawchamber.com
Facebook: www.facebook.com/sallisawchamberofcommerce
Description: Business incubator offering aid to start-ups.

43874 ■ Southwest Technology Center Business Incubator (SWTC)
711 W Tamarack Rd.
Altus, OK 73521
Ph: (580)477-2250
Fax: (580)477-0138
URL: http://www.swtech.edu/?p=businessandindustry
Contact: Dale Latham, Chief Executive Officer
E-mail: dlatham@swtech.edu
Description: Business incubator helping seed and early stage companies.

43875 ■ Startup 405
424 W Main St.
Norman, OK 73069

URL: http://www.selectnorman.com/entrepreneurs/startup-405
Description: Offers support, tools, resources, and technical assistance to Oklahoma businesses less than five years old.

43876 ■ The Strategy Center (TSC)
6101 Nowata Rd.
Bartlesville, OK 74006
Free: 833-661-0512
URL: http://tricountytech.edu/services/campus-the-strategy-center
Description: A certified business incubator which provides start-up businesses with the assistance they need to move forward. **Founded:** 1988.

43877 ■ Synergy Enterprise Development
7300 NW 23rd St.
Bethany, OK 73008
Ph: (405)495-0100
URL: http://www.myincubator.net
Contact: Daniel Meek, Board Member
Description: Certified business incubator committed to helping businesses succeed.

43878 ■ Wes Watkins Technology Center Business Incubator (WWTC)
RT 2 BOX 159-1
Wetumka, OK 74883
Contact: James Moore, Contact
Description: Center provides programs, evening courses, business and industry programs, student services and many more. **Founded:** 1987.

EDUCATIONAL PROGRAMS

43879 ■ Canadian Valley Technology Center (CVTECH)
6505 E Hwy. 66
El Reno, OK 73036
Ph: (405)262-2629
Co. E-mail: info@cvtech.edu
URL: http://cvtech.edu
Contact: Jimmie Vickrey, President
Facebook: www.facebook.com/CanadianValleyTech
X (Twitter): x.com/cv_tech
YouTube: www.youtube.com/channel/UC1GmIImKRzkvEPV9GA6904Q
Description: Trade and technical college offering a small business management program. **Founded:** 1970.

43880 ■ Central Oklahoma Business And Job Development Corp.
420 E Broadway
Drumright, OK 74030
Contact: Clayton L. Badger, Contact
Description: A non-profit program providing a supportive environment for small business start-up, survival, and growth.

43881 ■ Central Technology Center
1720 S Main St.
Sapulpa, OK 74066
Ph: (918)224-9300
URL: http://centraltech.edu
Contact: Joe Naifeh, President
Instagram: www.instagram.com/centraltechedu
YouTube: www.youtube.com/channel/UCa8_YS9syQLbJjSb9trFF1Q
Description: Trade and technical college offering a small business management program. **Founded:** 1990.

43882 ■ EOC Technology Center (EOCTC)
4601 N Choctaw Rd.
Choctaw, OK 73020
Ph: (405)390-9591
Fax: (405)390-9598
Co. E-mail: communications@eoctech.edu
URL: http://www.eoctech.edu
Contact: Bill McCully, Treasurer
E-mail: bmccully@eoctech.edu
Facebook: www.facebook.com/eoctech
Linkedin: www.linkedin.com/school/eoctech
X (Twitter): x.com/eoctech

Instagram: www.instagram.com/eoctech
YouTube: www.youtube.com/channel/UCxdyxTdA_JrN8mg2BvR87Qg
Description: Business college offering a small business management program. **Founded:** 1982.

43883 ■ Francis Tuttle Technology Center (Rockwell Campus)
12777 N Rockwell Ave.
Oklahoma City, OK 73142
Ph: (405)717-7799
URL: http://www.francistuttle.edu/about/our-locations/rockwell/rockwell-campus-map
Contact: Sherry Adrian, Director, Information Technology Director, Programs
E-mail: sherry.adrian@francistuttle.edu
Facebook: www.facebook.com/francistuttle
Linkedin: www.linkedin.com/school/francis-tuttle-technology-center
X (Twitter): x.com/FrancisTuttle
YouTube: www.youtube.com/user/francistuttletech
Description: Business college offering a small business management program. **Founded:** 1979.

43884 ■ Great Plains Technology Center (GPTC)
4500 W Lee Blvd.
Lawton, OK 73505
Ph: (580)355-6371
URL: http://www.greatplains.edu
Contact: Justin McNeil, Executive Director
E-mail: jmcneil@greatplains.edu
Facebook: www.facebook.com/greatplainstechnologycenter
X (Twitter): x.com/greatplainstech
Instagram: www.instagram.com/greatplainstech
YouTube: www.youtube.com/user/GPTCLawton
Description: Business college offering a small business management program. **Founded:** 1971.

43885 ■ High Plains Technology Center (HPTC)
3921 34th St.
Woodward, OK 73801
Ph: (580)256-6618
Free: 800-725-1492
URL: http://hptc.edu
Contact: Barclay Holt, Chief Executive Officer
Facebook: www.facebook.com/HighPlainsTechCenter
X (Twitter): x.com/highplainstech
Instagram: www.instagram.com/highplainstechcenter
Description: Business college offering a small business management program. **Founded:** 2001.

43886 ■ Kiamichi Area Vo-Tech - Atoka [Kiamichi Technology Centers - Atoka]
1763 W Liberty Rd.
Atoka, OK 74525
Ph: (580)889-7321
URL: http://www.ktc.edu/466259_3
Contact: Greg Davidson, Director
Description: Business college offering a small business management program.

43887 ■ Kiamichi Technology Center (KTC)
301 Kiamichi Dr.
McAlester, OK 74501
Ph: (918)426-0940
Fax: (918)426-1626
URL: http://www.ktc.edu
Contact: Raymond Wilson, Director
Facebook: www.facebook.com/kiamichitech
X (Twitter): x.com/kiamichitech
Description: Business college offering a small business management program. **Founded:** 1970.

43888 ■ Kiamichi Technology Center - Stigler (KTC)
1410 Old Military Rd.
Stigler, OK 74462
Ph: (918)967-2801
URL: http://www.ktc.edu
Contact: April Williams, Director
Facebook: www.facebook.com/ktcstigler
Description: Business college offering a small business management program.

43889 ■ Meridian Technology Center (MTC)
1312 S Sangre Rd.
Stillwater, OK 74074
Ph: (405)377-3333
Free: 888-607-2509
Co. E-mail: info@meridiantech.edu
URL: http://www.meridiantech.edu
Contact: Dr. Doug Major, Chief Executive Officer
E-mail: dougm@meridiantech.edu
Facebook: www.facebook.com/meridiantech.edu
Linkedin: www.linkedin.com/school/meridian-technology-center
X (Twitter): x.com/MeridianTech
Instagram: www.instagram.com/meridiantech
YouTube: www.youtube.com/user/meridiantechcenter
Description: Business college offering a small business management program. **Founded:** 1973.

43890 ■ Metro Technology Centers (MTC)
1900 Springlake Dr.
Oklahoma City, OK 73111-5238
Ph: (405)424-8324
Co. E-mail: purchasing@metrotech.edu
URL: http://www.metrotech.edu
Contact: Aaron Collins, Chief Executive Officer
Facebook: www.facebook.com/MetroTechOKC
Linkedin: www.linkedin.com/school/metro-technology-centers
X (Twitter): x.com/MetroTechOK
Instagram: www.instagram.com/metrotechokc
YouTube: www.youtube.com/metrotechokc
Description: Business college offering a small business management program. **Founded:** 1979.

43891 ■ Mid-America Technology Center
27438 State Hwy. 59
Wayne, OK 73095-0210
Ph: (405)449-3391
Description: Center focuses on economic education and training programs. **Founded:** 1968.

43892 ■ Moore Norman Technology Center (MNTC)
4701 12th Ave. NW
Norman, OK 73069
Ph: (405)801-5000
Fax: (405)561-4167
Co. E-mail: customer.inquiry@mntc.edu
URL: http://www.mntc.edu
Contact: Brian Ruttman, Chief Executive Officer
E-mail: brian.ruttman@mntc.edu
Facebook: www.facebook.com/MooreNormanTech
Linkedin: www.linkedin.com/school/moore-norman-technology-center
X (Twitter): x.com/MooreNormanTech
Instagram: www.instagram.com/moorenormantech
YouTube: www.youtube.com/user/MooreNorman
Description: Trade and technical college offering a small business management program. **Founded:** 1972.

43893 ■ National Technical Honor Society Gordon Cooper Technology Center (GCTC)
1 John C. Bruton Blvd.
Shawnee, OK 74804
Ph: (405)273-7493
Co. E-mail: info@gctech.org
URL: http://www.gctech.edu
Contact: Dr. Dean Evans, President
URL(s): www.nths.org/chapter/directory?filler=1&state=OK
Facebook: www.facebook.com/gctech
X (Twitter): x.com/gctechok
YouTube: www.youtube.com/channel/UC_fnQne0aRtk2nvcUCqw20w
Description: Business college offering a small business management program. **Founded:** 1970. **Geographic Preference:** Local.

43894 ■ Northeast Technology Center - Pryor, Oklahoma
6195 W Hwy. 20
Pryor, OK 74361
Ph: (918)825-5555
Fax: (918)825-5513
URL: http://www.netech.edu
Contact: Paul Hocutt, Director
E-mail: paul.hocutt@netech.edu
Description: Business college offering a small business management program. **Founded:** 1973.

43895 ■ Pioneer Technology Center (PTC)
2101 N Ash
Ponca City, OK 74601
Ph: (580)762-8336
Free: 866-612-4782
Co. E-mail: info@pioneertech.edu
URL: http://www.pioneertech.edu
Contact: Kahle Goff, Executive Director
E-mail: kahleg@pioneertech.edu
Facebook: www.facebook.com/PioneerTech
Linkedin: www.linkedin.com/school/pioneer-technology-center
X (Twitter): x.com/PIONEERTECHCTR
YouTube: www.youtube.com/user/PioneerTechEdu
Pinterest: www.pinterest.com/pioneertech
Description: Business college offering a small business management program. **Founded:** 1973.

43896 ■ Red River Technology Center
3300 W Bois D'Arc
Duncan, OK 73534
Ph: (580)255-2903
URL: http://www.rrtc.edu
Contact: Lisa Williams, Coordinator
E-mail: lgwilliams@rrtc.edu
Facebook: www.facebook.com/redrivertechcenter
Description: Business college offering a small business management program. **Founded:** 1975. **Geographic Preference:** Local.

43897 ■ Tri County Technology Center (TCTC)
6101 Nowata Rd.
Bartlesville, OK 74006
Ph: (918)331-3333
URL: http://tricountytech.edu
Contact: George Halkiades, President
Facebook: www.facebook.com/tricountytech
Linkedin: www.linkedin.com/school/tricountytech
X (Twitter): x.com/tricountytech
Instagram: www.instagram.com/tricountytech
Description: Business college offering a small business management program.

43898 ■ Tulsa Community College (TCC)
6111 E Skelly Dr., Ste. 415
Tulsa, OK 74135
Ph: (918)595-8000
Co. E-mail: records@tulsacc.edu
URL: http://www.tulsacc.edu
Contact: Leigh B. Goodson, President
E-mail: leigh.goodson@tulsacc.edu
Facebook: www.facebook.com/TulsaCC
X (Twitter): x.com/tulsacc
Instagram: www.instagram.com/tulsacc
YouTube: www.youtube.com/channel/UCC83LNbMq68uhGSSJnCXDuw
Description: Two-year college offering a small business management program. **Founded:** 1970.

43899 ■ Western Technology Center - Burns Flat Campus
621 Sooner Dr.
Burns Flat, OK 73624
Ph: (580)562-3181
Fax: (580)562-4476
URL: http://www.westtech.edu/about-district/campuses/burns-flat
Contact: Jeff Lewallen, Director, Student Services
E-mail: jlewallen@westtech.edu
Description: Business college offering a small business management program.

CONSULTANTS

43900 ■ BioSource Consulting
755 Research Pkwy., Ste. 410
Oklahoma City, OK 73104
Ph: (405)850-5066
URL: http://biosourceconsulting.com
Contact: Craig Shimasaki, Contact
Description: Solves problems that impact biotech businesses. Offers services from strategy through execution for start-ups and growing companies, including market assessment and scientific development strategies and management and leadership programs for workflow efficiencies.

Oregon

ASSOCIATIONS AND OTHER ORGANIZATIONS

43901 ■ Association of Fundraising Professionals Oregon & SW Washington Chapter
PO Box 55512
  Portland, OR 97238
Ph: (503)715-3100
Co. E-mail: afp-oregon@comcast.net
URL: http://community.afpglobal.org/afporswwa/home
Contact: Lauren Cox, President
Facebook: www.facebook.com/AFPOregonSWWashington
Linkedin: www.linkedin.com/company/afp-oregon-sw-washington
YouTube: www.youtube.com/channel/UCygfNGMg-wW8du-FXrpzjog
Description: Seeks to advance philanthropy in Oregon and southwest Washington through education, training and advocacy. **Founded:** 1984. **Geographic Preference:** State.

43902 ■ Business Network International - Eugene Metro
2525 Martin Luther King Blvd.
  Eugene, OR 97401
URL: http://bniorgon.com/eugenemetro/en-US/index
Contact: Candice Hook, President
Description: Provides both men and women a structured environment for the development and exchange of quality business referrals. Offers members the opportunity to share ideas and contacts. **Geographic Preference:** Local.

43903 ■ International Association of Women Portland Chapter
Portland, OR
URL: http://www.iawomen.com/chapters/portland-chapter
Description: Serves as a network for businesswomen to promote their product or service.

43904 ■ National Federation of Independent Business Oregon (NFIB-OR)
1149 Ct., St. NE
  Salem, OR 97302
Ph: (503)364-4450
URL: http://www.nfib.com/oregon
Contact: Anthony K. Smith, Director
E-mail: anthony.smith@nfib.org
Description: Represents small and independent businesses. Aims to promote and protect the rights of members to own, operate and grow their businesses. **Geographic Preference:** State.

43905 ■ Northeast Oregon Economic Development District (NEO EDD)
101 NE 1st St. Ste. 100
  Enterprise, OR 97828
Ph: (541)426-3598
URL: http://www.neoedd.org
Contact: Lisa Dawson, Executive Director
E-mail: lisadawson@neoedd.org
Facebook: www.facebook.com/neoedd
X (Twitter): x.com/neoedd
Description: Offers financial, technical, and educational assistance to entrepreneurs, nonprofits, and municipalities in Northeast Oregon. **Founded:** 1985.

43906 ■ Oregon-Columbia Chapter of the International Association of Business Communicators (OCIABC) [IABC Oregon-Columbia]
PO Box 9206
  Portland, OR 97204
URL: http://www.iabc.com/Connect/Chapters-Regions/US-Pacific-Plains-Region/Oregon-Columbia
Contact: Theresa Staples, President
X (Twitter): x.com/iabc_oregon
Description: Commits to improve the effectiveness of organizations through strategic, interactive and integrated business communication management. Provides products, services, and networking activities to help people and organizations excel in public relations, employee communication, marketing communication, public affairs and other forms of communication. **Founded:** 1970. **Geographic Preference:** Local.

SMALL BUSINESS DEVELOPMENT CENTERS

43907 ■ Blue Mountain Community College Small Business Development Center (SBDC)
2411 NW Carden Ave.
  Pendleton, OR 97801
Ph: (541)278-5833
Co. E-mail: blue-mountain@oregonsbdc.org
URL: http://oregonsbdc.org/center/blue-mountain-sbdc
Contact: Eric DeLary, Director
Facebook: www.facebook.com/bluemountainsbdc
Linkedin: www.linkedin.com/company/blue-mountain-small-business-development-center
X (Twitter): x.com/BlueMtnSBDC
YouTube: www.youtube.com/channel/UCO37oGyVBJ5x2oG2hcJcf1w
Description: Represents and promotes the small business sector. Provides management assistance to current and prospective small business owners. Helps to improve management skills and expand the products and services of members. **Founded:** 1983. **Geographic Preference:** Local.

43908 ■ Chemeketa Community College Small Business Development Center (SBDC)
Chemeketa Center for Business & Industry
  626 High St. NE
  Salem, OR 97301
Ph: (503)399-5088
Co. E-mail: sbdc@chemeketa.edu
URL: http://www.chemeketa.edu/alumni-community/business-opportunities/business-support
Contact: Tara Kramer, Owner
Facebook: www.facebook.com/SBDCSalem
Instagram: www.instagram.com/chemeketa_sbdc
Description: Represents and promotes the small business sector. Provides management assistance to current and prospective small business owners. Helps to improve management skills and expand the products and services of members. **Geographic Preference:** Local.

43909 ■ Clackamas Community College Small Business Development Center
Harmony Community Campus, Ste. 160
  Milwaukie, OR 97222
Ph: (503)594-0738
Co. E-mail: bizcenter@clackamas.edu
URL: http://www.clackamas.edu/academics/skills-development-training/connections-with-business-and-industry-(cbi)/small-business-development-center
Contact: Rob Campbell, Contact
Description: Provides management assistance to current and prospective small business owners in Clackamas. **Geographic Preference:** Local.

43910 ■ Columbia Gorge Community College Small Business Development Center
400 E Scenic Dr.
  The Dalles, OR 97058
Ph: (541)506-6121
URL: http://www.cgcc.edu/sbdc
Contact: Gregory Price, Director
URL(s): oregonsbdc.org/centers/columbia-gorge-sbdc
Description: Represents and promotes the small business sector. Provides management assistance to current and prospective small business owners. Helps to improve management skills and expand the products and services of members. **Geographic Preference:** Local.

43911 ■ Hermiston Small Business Development Center
975 SE Columbia Dr.
  Hermiston, OR 97838
Ph: (541)278-5833
URL: http://oregonsbdc.org/centers/blue-mountain-sbdc
Contact: Eric DeLary, Director
Description: Represents and promotes the small business sector. Provides management assistance to current and prospective small business owners. Helps to improve management skills and expand the products and services of members. **Geographic Preference:** Local.

43912 ■ Mt. Hood Community College Small Business Development Center (MHCC SBDC)
c/o Gerri Raisanen, Administrative Coordinator
  26000 SE Stark St., GE201 Near the aquatics Ctr.
  Gresham, OR 97030
Ph: (503)491-7658
Co. E-mail: oregonsbdc@mhcc.edu
URL: http://www.mhcc.edu/sbdc
Contact: Gerri Raisanen, Coordinator

Description: Represents and promotes the small business sector. Provides management assistance to current and prospective small business owners. Helps to improve management skills and expand the products and services of members. **Geographic Preference:** Local.

43913 ■ Oregon Coast Community College Small Business Development Center
3788 SE High School Dr.
Lincoln City, OR 97367
Ph: (541)994-4166
Co. E-mail: occc@oregoncoast.edu
URL: http://oregoncoast.edu/sbdc
Contact: Dave Price, Director
E-mail: dave.price@oregoncoastcc.org
Description: Represents and promotes the small business sector. Provides management assistance to current and prospective small business owners. Helps to improve management skills and expand the products and services of members. **Geographic Preference:** Local.

43914 ■ Oregon Small Business Development Center - Lead Office (OSBDC)
1445 Willamette St., Ste. 5
Eugene, OR 97401
Ph: (541)463-5250
Fax: (541)345-6006
Co. E-mail: gregorym@lanecc.edu
URL: http://www.bizcenter.org
Contact: Mark Gregory, Director
E-mail: gregorym@lanecc.edu
Description: Provides advising, training, online courses, and resources for businesses in Oregon. **Geographic Preference:** State.

43915 ■ Rogue Community College Small Business Development Center (RCCSBDC)
3345 Redwood Hwy., Bldg. B
Grants Pass, OR 97527
Ph: (541)956-7494
Co. E-mail: sbdc@roguecc.edu
URL: http://sbdc.roguecc.edu
Contact: Ruth Swain, Director
E-mail: rswain@roguecc.edu
Facebook: www.facebook.com/RCCSBDC
Description: Represents and promotes the small business sector. Provides management assistance to current and prospective small business owners. Helps to improve management skills and expand the products and services of members. **Founded:** 1984. **Geographic Preference:** Local.

43916 ■ Southern Oregon University Small Business Development Center
101 S Bartlett St., Ste. 130
Medford, OR 97501
Ph: (541)552-8300
Co. E-mail: sbdc@sou.edu
URL: http://sbdc.sou.edu
Contact: Marshall Doak, Director
E-mail: doakm@sou.edu
URL(s): inside.sou.edu
Description: Represents and promotes the small business sector. Provides management assistance to current and prospective small business owners. Helps to improve management skills and expand the products and services of members. **Geographic Preference:** Local.

43917 ■ Tillamook Bay Community College Small Business Development Center
4301 3rd St.
Tillamook, OR 97141
Ph: (503)842-8222
Co. E-mail: tillamooksbdc@bizcenter.org
URL: http://oregonsbdc.org/centers/tillamook-bay-sbdc
Contact: Arlene Soto, Contact
Description: Provides management assistance to current and prospective small business owners in Tillamook. **Geographic Preference:** Local.

43918 ■ Treasure Valley Community College Small Business Development Center (TVCC SDDC)
650 College Blvd.
Ontario, OR 97914
Ph: (541)881-5772
URL: http://oregonsbdc.org/centers/treasure-valley-sbdc
Contact: Andrea Testi, Director
Description: Represents and promotes the small business sector. Provides management assistance to current and prospective small business owners. Helps to improve management skills and expand the products and services of members. **Founded:** 1962. **Geographic Preference:** Local.

SMALL BUSINESS ASSISTANCE PROGRAMS

43919 ■ Business Oregon - Global Strategy Section
775 Summer St., NE
Ste. 200
Salem, OR 97301
URL: http://www.oregon.gov/biz/Pages/default.aspx
Description: Provides assistance through one-to-one consultation, trade shows and exhibitions, export seminars, a Personalized Export Panel session, participation in an overseas trade mission, and student international market research program.

43920 ■ Float Small Business
Portland, OR
Co. E-mail: floatsmallbiz@gmail.com
URL: http://www.floatsmallbusiness.com
Facebook: www.facebook.com/floatsmallbiz
Instagram: www.instagram.com/floatsmallbiz
Description: A collaborative effort to build and maintain a list of local businesses within the Portland, OR area who need community support to stay open during and after the Covid-19 pandemic.

43921 ■ Micro Enterprise Services of Oregon (MESO)
4008 NE MLK Jr., Blvd.
Portland, OR 97212
Ph: (503)841-3351
Co. E-mail: meso@mesopdx.org
URL: http://www.mesopdx.org
Contact: Cam Turner, Chairman of the Board
Facebook: www.facebook.com/MESOPDX
Linkedin: www.linkedin.com/company/micro-enterprise-services-of-oregon
X (Twitter): x.com/mesopdx
Instagram: www.instagram.com/mesopdx
Description: Assists small businesses that experienced challenges in the wake of gentrification, new development, and increased rents in Portland. Works as an SBA microlender, IDA fiduciary, USDA RMAP lender, and a CDFI. **Founded:** 2005.

43922 ■ Oregon Department of Agriculture (ODA) - Agricultural Development and Marketing Div.
635 Capitol St. NE
Salem, OR 97301
Ph: (541)656-8951
Fax: (503)986-4737
Co. E-mail: agmarket@oda.state.or.us
URL: http://www.oregon.gov/ODA/programs/MarketAccess/DevelopmentMarketing/Pages/AboutDevelopmentMarketing.aspx
Description: Operates a marketing program that assists in the development of new markets or in the expansion of existing markets for agricultural commodities produced or processed in the state.

43923 ■ Oregon Department of Business Development - Business Development Div.
775 Summer St. NE, Ste. 200
Salem, OR 97301-1280
URL: http://www.oregon.gov/biz/Pages/default.aspx

Description: Helps to coordinate state programs with local community efforts in business expansion, recruitment, retention, and start-up efforts. **Founded:** 1859.

43924 ■ Oregon Department of Business Development - Business Development Division - Eastern Regional Business Development Office
775 Summer St. NE, Ste. 200
Salem, OR 97301-1280
Ph: (503)986-0123
Fax: (503)581-5115
Co. E-mail: biz.info@state.or.us
URL: http://www.oregon4biz.com
X (Twitter): x.com/BusinessOregon
YouTube: www.youtube.com/user/BusinessOregon#p
Description: Helps to coordinate state programs with local community efforts in business expansion, recruitment, retention, and start-up efforts.

43925 ■ Oregon Economic and Community Development Department
775 Summer St. NE, Ste. 200
Salem, OR 97301
Ph: (503)986-0123
URL: http://www.oregon.gov/Pages/index.aspx
Description: A government agency for the state of Oregon, focused on administering programs that foster economic growth and community development. Maintains a clearinghouse database to provide information to businesses, industry, government agencies, and the general public. Coordinates business, financial, job training, and community development resources for individuals, businesses, and local jurisdictions. **Founded:** 1973. **Publications:** *Directory of Oregon Manufacturers* (Biennial).

43926 ■ Southern Oregon Regional Economic Development, Inc. (SOREDI)
1311 E Barnett Rd., Ste. 301
Medford, OR 97504
Ph: (541)773-8946
Fax: (541)779-0953
Co. E-mail: info@soredi.org
URL: http://soredi.org
Contact: Terri Coppersmith, President
Facebook: www.facebook.com/SOREDI.OR
Linkedin: www.linkedin.com/company/soredi-or
Instagram: www.instagram.com/soredi_oregon
YouTube: www.youtube.com/channel/UCoEMkhT-fa2aRFOGAAfdd_w
Description: Helps to coordinate state programs with local community efforts in business expansion, recruitment, retention, and start-up efforts. **Founded:** 1987.

SCORE OFFICES

43927 ■ Central Oregon SCORE
NE Thurston Ave.
Bend, OR 97708
Ph: (541)316-0662
Co. E-mail: info.centraloregon@scorevolunteer.org
URL: http://www.score.org/centraloregon
Facebook: www.facebook.com/SCOREcentraloregon
Linkedin: www.linkedin.com/company/score-central-oregon
Instagram: www.instagram.com/scorecentraloregon
Founded: 1964.

43928 ■ SCORE - Central Oregon
Northeast Thurston Ave.
Bend, OR 97708
Ph: (541)316-0662
Co. E-mail: help@score.org
URL: http://www.score.org/centraloregon
Facebook: www.facebook.com/SCOREcentraloregon
Linkedin: www.linkedin.com/company/score-central-oregon
Description: Seeks to educate entrepreneurs and help small businesses start, grow and succeed nationwide. Organizes volunteers who are working or retired business owners, executives and corporate leaders who wish to share their wisdom and lessons learned in business. **Geographic Preference:** Local.

STATE LISTINGS

Oregon ■ 43943

43929 ■ SCORE - Hood River
PO Box 1396
Hood River, OR 97031
Ph: (503)326-5211
Co. E-mail: scorepdx@scorevolunteer.org
URL: http://portlandor.score.org
Contact: Steve Patterson, Contact
Facebook: www.facebook.com/SCOREPortland
Linkedin: www.linkedin.com/company/score-mentors-portland
X (Twitter): x.com/scorepdx
YouTube: www.youtube.com/user/scorepdx
Description: Provides professional guidance and information to maximize the success of existing and emerging small businesses. Offers business counseling and workshops.

43930 ■ SCORE - Portland
620 SW Main, Ste. 314
Portland, OR 97205
Ph: (503)326-5211
Co. E-mail: scorepdx@scorevolunteer.org
URL: http://portlandor.score.org
Contact: Jeff Iwasaki, Treasurer
E-mail: treasurer0011@scorevolunteer.org
Facebook: www.facebook.com/scoreportland
Linkedin: www.linkedin.com/company/score-mentors-portland
X (Twitter): x.com/scorepdx
YouTube: www.youtube.com/user/scorepdx
Description: Provides professional guidance and information to maximize the success of existing and emerging small businesses. Offers business counseling and workshops. **Founded:** 1964. **Geographic Preference:** Local.

43931 ■ SCORE - Salem, Oregon
922 NW Cir., Blvd., Ste. 160, No. 327
Corvallis, OR 97330
Ph: (503)370-2896
URL: http://salem.score.org
Contact: W. Kenneth Yancey, Jr., Chief Executive Officer
Facebook: www.facebook.com/SCORESalem
X (Twitter): x.com/SCORE_Salem
Description: Seeks to educate entrepreneurs and help small businesses start, grow and succeed nationwide. Organizes volunteers who are working or retired business owners, executives and corporate leaders who wish to share their wisdom and lessons learned in business. **Geographic Preference:** Local.

43932 ■ SCORE - Willamette
1401 Willamette St.
Eugene, OR 97401
Ph: (541)465-6600
Co. E-mail: help@score.org
URL: http://willamette.score.org
Linkedin: www.linkedin.com/company/score-mentors-willamette
Description: Seeks to educate entrepreneurs and help small businesses start, grow and succeed nationwide. Organizes volunteers who are working or retired business owners, executives and corporate leaders who wish to share their wisdom and lessons learned in business. **Founded:** 1964. **Geographic Preference:** Local.

43933 ■ Willamette SCORE
1401 Willamette St.
Eugene, OR 97401
Ph: (541)465-6600
URL: http://www.score.org/find-location?state=OR
Contact: Scott Harkins, Chairman of the Board
URL(s): www.score.org/search/site/find%20l
Facebook: www.facebook.com/SCOREWillamette
YouTube: www.youtube.com/channel/UCcomR7FDCodK-43Kc9o-nag

BETTER BUSINESS BUREAUS

43934 ■ Better Business Bureau Great West + Pacific [BBB Great West + Pacific]
PO Box 191279
Boise, ID 83719
Ph: (208)342-4649

URL: http://www.bbb.org/local-bbb/bbb-great-west-pacific
Linkedin: www.linkedin.com/company/bbbgwp
Instagram: www.instagram.com/bbbgwp
YouTube: www.youtube.com/bbbgwp
Description: Seeks to promote and foster the highest ethical relationship between businesses and the public through voluntary self-regulation, consumer and business education, and service excellence. Provides information to help consumers and businesses make informed purchasing decisions and avoid costly scams and frauds; settles consumer complaints through arbitration and other means. **Geographic Preference:** State.

CHAMBERS OF COMMERCE

43935 ■ Albany Area Chamber of Commerce (AACC)
435 1st Ave. W
Albany, OR 97321
Ph: (503)926-1517
Fax: (503)926-7064
Co. E-mail: info@albanychamber.com
URL: http://www.albanychamber.com
Contact: Janet Steele, President
E-mail: jsteele@albanychamber.com
Facebook: www.facebook.com/albanyorchamber
Linkedin: www.linkedin.com/company/albanyorchamber
X (Twitter): x.com/albanyorchamber
Instagram: www.instagram.com/albanyorchamber
YouTube: www.youtube.com/channel/UCrGd1OeSKprEmw6d4dSMHYg
Description: Promotes business and community development in the Albany, OR area. Sponsors appreciation breakfasts, tradeshows, Albany and youth leadership, high school scholarships, distinguished services awards, and youth job fairs. **Founded:** 1904. **Publications:** The Chamber Network (Monthly); Membership and Buyers Guide (Periodic). **Geographic Preference:** Local.

43936 ■ Albany Chamber of Commerce
435 1st Ave., W
Albany, OR 97321
Ph: (541)926-1517
Fax: (541)926-7064
Co. E-mail: info@albanychamber.com
URL: http://www.albanychamber.com
Contact: Janet Steele, President
E-mail: jsteele@albanychamber.com
Facebook: www.facebook.com/albanyorchamber
Linkedin: www.linkedin.com/company/albanyorchamber
X (Twitter): x.com/albanyorchamber
Instagram: www.instagram.com/albanyorchamber
YouTube: www.youtube.com/channel/UCrGd1OeSKprEmw6d4dSMHYg
Description: Works to maintain a terrific business climate in Albany, to represent and assist members, and help build a better community for everyone. **Founded:** 1920. **Geographic Preference:** Local.

43937 ■ Ashland Chamber of Commerce
110 E Main St.
Ashland, OR 97520
Ph: (541)482-3486
Co. E-mail: members@ashlandchamber.com
URL: http://www.ashlandchamber.com
Contact: Katharine Cato, Director, Sales and Marketing
Description: Promotes business and community development in Ashland, OR. Sponsors Winter Wine, Food, and Arts festival and Cultural Heritage Month. **Founded:** 1889. **Publications:** Ashland Chamber News (Monthly). **Geographic Preference:** Local.

43938 ■ *Ashland Chamber News*
110 E Main St.
Ashland, OR 97520
Ph: (541)482-3486
Co. E-mail: members@ashlandchamber.com
URL: http://www.ashlandchamber.com
Contact: Katharine Cato, Director, Sales and Marketing

URL(s): www.ashlandchamber.com/page.asp?navid=793
Released: Monthly **Description:** Includes informational articles, the latest news within the society and updated list of members. **Availability:** Print; Online.

43939 ■ Astoria-Warrenton Area Chamber of Commerce (AWACC)
111 W Marine Dr.
Astoria, OR 97103
Ph: (503)325-6311
Co. E-mail: info@oldoregon.com
URL: http://www.oldoregon.com
Contact: Lois Perdue, President
Facebook: www.facebook.com/AstoriaWarrentonChamber
X (Twitter): x.com/oldoregon
Instagram: www.instagram.com/travelastoriawarrenton
YouTube: www.youtube.com/channel/UCMeQYFqyz11-YJnvTwj0Avw
Description: Promotes business and community development in Astoria, Warrenton, and the lower Columbia region. Sponsors Crab and Seafood Festival in April and Oktoberfish, a microbrew and seafood festival in October. **Founded:** 1873. **Publications:** ChamberWorks (Monthly); Visitor Information Guide (Annual). **Educational Activities:** Great Columbia Crossing (Annual). **Awards:** George Award (Annual). **Geographic Preference:** Local.

43940 ■ Aurora Colony Visitors Association (ACVA)
21611 Main St. NE
Aurora, OR 97002-0086
Ph: (503)939-0312
Co. E-mail: info@auroracolony.com
URL: http://auroracolony.com
Facebook: www.facebook.com/auroracolony
Description: Promotes business and community development in Aurora, OR. **Founded:** 1856. **Geographic Preference:** Local.

43941 ■ Baker County Unlimited Chamber of Commerce (BCCC)
490 Campbell St.
Baker City, OR 97814
Ph: (541)523-5855
Fax: (541)523-9187
Co. E-mail: info@visitbaker.com
URL: http://www.visitbaker.com
Contact: Jerry Peacock, President
Facebook: www.facebook.com/Visitbaker
X (Twitter): x.com/Visitbaker
Instagram: www.instagram.com/visitbaker
YouTube: www.youtube.com/user/BaseCampBaker
Pinterest: www.pinterest.com/bcccvb
Description: Promotes business and community development in Baker County, OR. Sponsors community events, including Miner's Jubilee and community beautification program. Provides business referral service and visitor information; offers small business consultation services. Bestows Man, Woman and Business of the Year awards. **Publications:** Business, Club, and Organizations (Periodic); The Chamber Charge (Monthly). **Geographic Preference:** Local.

43942 ■ Bandon Chamber of Commerce (BCC)
300 2nd St. SE
Bandon, OR 97411
Ph: (541)347-9616
URL: http://bandon.com
Contact: Margaret Pounder, President
Facebook: www.facebook.com/BandonOregon
Instagram: www.instagram.com/bandonoregon
Description: Promotes business and community development in Bandon, OR. **Geographic Preference:** Local.

43943 ■ *Basin Business*
205 Riverside Dr., Ste. A
Klamath Falls, OR 97601
Ph: (541)884-5193
Co. E-mail: reception@klamath.org
URL: http://klamath.org

Small Business Sourcebook • 42nd Edition

Contact: Jason Aarstad, Officer
URL(s): klamath.org/benefit-spotlight-basin-business-reaching-40000-people
Released: Monthly; 3rd Thursday of Every Month. **Availability:** Print.

43944 ■ Bay Area Chamber of Commerce (BACC)
145 Central Ave.
Coos Bay, OR 97420
Ph: (541)266-0868
Co. E-mail: info@oregonsbayarea.org
URL: http://coosbaynorthbendcharlestonchamber.com
Contact: Timm Slater, Executive Director
E-mail: timmslater@oregonsbayarea.org
Facebook: www.facebook.com/BayAreaChamber
X (Twitter): x.com/OregonsBACC

Description: Promotes business and community development in the Coos Bay/North Bend, OR area. **Founded:** 1980. **Publications:** *Economic Profile* (Annual); *Your Bay Area Business Connection* (Monthly). **Awards:** Bay Area Chamber Business of the Year (Annual); Bay Area Chamber Citizen of the Year (Annual); Bay Area Chamber 4 Star Customer Service Award (Quarterly). **Geographic Preference:** Local.

43945 ■ Beaverton Area Chamber of Commerce (BACC)
12600 SW Cres., St., Ste. 160
Beaverton, OR 97005
Ph: (503)644-0123
Co. E-mail: info@beaverton.org
URL: http://www.beaverton.org
Contact: Alicia Bermes, President
E-mail: alicia@beaverton.org
Facebook: www.facebook.com/BeavertonChamber
Linkedin: www.linkedin.com/company/beaverton-chamber-of-commerce
X (Twitter): x.com/BeavtonChamber
Instagram: www.instagram.com/beavertonchamber
YouTube: www.youtube.com/user/BeavertonChamber
Pinterest: www.pinterest.com/beavertonchambe

Description: Promotes business development and retention, advocate sound public policy. Provides innovative member services to sustain and enhances vibrant and diverse community. **Founded:** 1953. **Publications:** *Business Beat* (Weekly (Thurs.)); *Visitors Guide and Business Directory* (Annual). **Educational Activities:** Beaverton Area Chamber of Commerce Luncheon. **Geographic Preference:** Local.

43946 ■ *Bend Chamber Business*
1567 SW Chandler Ave., Ste. 204
Bend, OR 97702
Ph: (542)323-8826
Fax: (542)385-9929
URL: http://bendchamber.org
Contact: Garrett Jaenicke, Director
URL(s): bendchamber.org/category/business
Released: Monthly **Availability:** Print; Online.

43947 ■ Bend Chamber of Commerce (BCC)
1567 SW Chandler Ave., Ste. 204
Bend, OR 97702
Ph: (542)323-8826
Fax: (542)385-9929
URL: http://bendchamber.org
Contact: Garrett Jaenicke, Director
Facebook: www.facebook.com/bendchamber
X (Twitter): x.com/BendChamber
YouTube: www.youtube.com/user/bendchamber

Description: Promotes business and community development in the Bend, OR area. **Founded:** 1926. **Publications:** *Bend Chamber Business* (Monthly). **Educational Activities:** City Club Forum. **Awards:** Citizen of the Year Award for SAGE Business Awards (Annual); Bend Chamber of Commerce Distinguished Business of the Year (Annual); Bend Chamber Large Distinguished Business of the Year (Annual); Bend Chamber Small Distinguished Business of the Year (Annual). **Geographic Preference:** Local.

43948 ■ Brookings-Harbor Chamber of Commerce
703 Chetco Ave.
Brookings, OR 97415
Ph: (541)469-3181
Co. E-mail: chamber@brookingsor.com
URL: http://brookingsharborchamber.com
Contact: Judy May-Lopez, Office Manager
E-mail: judyml@brookingsharborchamber.com

Description: Seeks to help create and maintain a viable economy that provides all citizens with a high quality of life. Promotes business and community development in the Brookings, OR area. Sponsors the Azalea Festival. **Founded:** 1951. **Publications:** *Brookings Harbor Light* (Monthly); *Business Review* (Monthly); *Calendar of Events* (Annual); *Restaurant and Dining Guide* (Periodic). **Geographic Preference:** Local.

43949 ■ *Business Directory*
1055 S Hwy. 395, Ste. 111
Hermiston, OR 97838
Ph: (541)567-6151
Co. E-mail: info@hermistonchamber.com
URL: http://hermistonchamber.com
Contact: Kris Bennett, Chairman of the Board
E-mail: kris@krisanthemums.com
URL(s): cca.hermistonchamber.com/businesssearch.aspx
Availability: Online.

43950 ■ *Business News*
446 SW 7th St.
Redmond, OR 97756
Ph: (541)923-5191
Co. E-mail: info@visitredmondoregon.com
URL: http://www.visitredmondoregon.com
Contact: Eric Sande, Executive Director
E-mail: eric@visitredmondoregon.com
URL(s): www.visitredmondoregon.com/chamber-of-commerce/join-the-chamber/#join
Released: Monthly **Availability:** Print; Online.

43951 ■ *Business Review*
101 E 8th St.
Medford, OR 97501
Ph: (541)779-4847
Fax: (541)776-4808
Co. E-mail: business@medfordchamber.com
URL: http://www.medfordchamber.com
Contact: Eli Matthews, President
URL(s): www.medfordchamber.com/the-business-review
Released: Monthly **Availability:** Download; PDF; Online.

43952 ■ Canby Area Chamber of Commerce
191 SE 2nd Ave.
Canby, OR 97013
Ph: (503)266-4600
Co. E-mail: chamber@canbyareachamber.org
URL: http://canbyareachamber.com
Contact: Jim Davis, President
X (Twitter): x.com/TravelCanby

Description: Promotes business and community development in the Canby, OR area. Sponsors annual holiday lighting competition, golf tournament and produces annual collectible Christmas ornament Monthly luncheon. **Founded:** 1911. **Publications:** *Business Informer* (Monthly); *Canby Area Chamber Directory and Buyer's Guide* (Periodic). **Geographic Preference:** Local.

43953 ■ Cannon Beach Chamber of Commerce (CBCC)
207 N Spruce
Cannon Beach, OR 97110
Ph: (503)436-2623
Free: 800-745-1546
Fax: (503)436-1047
Co. E-mail: cbcc@cbcc.net
URL: http://www.cannonbeach.org
Contact: James Paino, Executive Director
URL(s): www.cbcc.net

Description: Promotes business and community development in Cannon Beach, OR. **Founded:** 1945. **Publications:** *Shore Lines* (Monthly). **Geographic Preference:** Local.

43954 ■ Central Point Area Chamber of Commerce
650 E Pine St., No. 104 C
Central Point, OR 97502
Ph: (541)664-5301
Fax: (541)664-3667
Co. E-mail: steph@centralpointchamber.org
URL: http://centralpointchamber.org
Contact: Chris Richey, President
Facebook: www.facebook.com/CentralPointChamber
X (Twitter): x.com/cp_chamber

Description: Promotes business and community development in Central Point, OR. **Geographic Preference:** Local.

43955 ■ *The Chamber Charge*
490 Campbell St.
Baker City, OR 97814
Ph: (541)523-5855
Fax: (541)523-9187
Co. E-mail: info@visitbaker.com
URL: http://www.visitbaker.com
Contact: Jerry Peacock, President
URL(s): www.visitbaker.com/membership-benefits
Released: Monthly **Description:** Contains up to date Chamber news. **Availability:** Online.

43956 ■ Chamber of Medford - Jackson County
101 E 8th St.
Medford, OR 97501
Ph: (541)779-4847
Fax: (541)776-4808
Co. E-mail: business@medfordchamber.com
URL: http://www.medfordchamber.com
Contact: Eli Matthews, President
Facebook: www.facebook.com/MedfordChamber
Linkedin: www.linkedin.com/company/the-chamber-of-medford-jackson-county
X (Twitter): x.com/MedfordChamber

Description: Promotes business and community development in the Medford, OR area. Sponsors Pear Blossom Golf Tournament. **Founded:** 1895. **Publications:** *Business Review* (Monthly); *BusinessALERT* (Quarterly); *Community Profile and Membership Directory*. **Geographic Preference:** Local.

43957 ■ *The Chamber Network*
435 1st Ave. W
Albany, OR 97321
Ph: (503)926-1517
Fax: (503)926-7064
Co. E-mail: info@albanychamber.com
URL: http://www.albanychamber.com
Contact: Janet Steele, President
E-mail: jsteele@albanychamber.com
URL(s): www.albanychamber.com/unique-services
Released: Monthly **Availability:** Print; Download; PDF; Online.

43958 ■ *Chamber News*
PO Box 1275
Sandy, OR 97055
Ph: (503)668-4006
Co. E-mail: info@sandyoregonchamber.org
URL: http://sandyoregonchamber.org
Contact: Paula Siverly, President
E-mail: paula.siverly@htlenders.com
URL(s): sandyoregonchamber.org/membership/member-benefits
Released: Weekly **Availability:** Online.

43959 ■ *Chamber's Profile*
1995 NW Vine St.
Grants Pass, OR 97526
Ph: (541)476-7717
Fax: (541)476-9574
Co. E-mail: gpcoc@grantspasschamber.org
URL: http://www.grantspasschamber.org
Contact: Josie Molloy, President
E-mail: jmolloy@grantspasschamber.org

URL(s): www.grantspasschamber.org/chamber-maps-profile-brochures
Released: Annual **Availability:** PDF; Online.

43960 ■ *ChamberWorks*
111 W Marine Dr.
Astoria, OR 97103
Ph: (503)325-6311
Co. E-mail: info@oldoregon.com
URL: http://www.oldoregon.com
Contact: Lois Perdue, President
URL(s): www.oldoregon.com/marketing-sponsorship-opportunities
Released: Monthly **Availability:** PDF; Online.

43961 ■ **Chehalem Valley Chamber of Commerce**
112 N Garfield St.
Newberg, OR 97132
Ph: (503)538-2014
Co. E-mail: office@chehalemvalley.org
URL: http://www.chehalemvalley.org
Contact: Tonna Faxon, President
Facebook: www.facebook.com/chehalemvalleychamber
Linkedin: www.linkedin.com/company/chehalem-valley-chamber-of-commerce
X (Twitter): x.com/ChehalemChamber
YouTube: www.youtube.com/channel/UCK6y3vwT595m8JGF15nlYCQ
Pinterest: www.pinterest.com/chehalemvalley
Description: Promotes business and community development in the Newberg, Dundee, and St. Paul, OR area. **Founded:** 1941. **Publications:** *Chamber Notes* (Monthly). **Geographic Preference:** Local.

43962 ■ **Clatskanie Chamber of Commerce**
PO Box 635
Clatskanie, OR 97016
Ph: (503)728-2502
Co. E-mail: info@clatskaniechamber.com
URL: http://www.clatskaniechamber.com
Contact: Sarah Johnson, President
E-mail: sjohnson@clatskaniepud.com
Facebook: www.facebook.com/ClatskanieChamber
Description: Promotes business and community development in Clatskanie, OR. **Publications:** *Clatskanie Chamber Newsletter* (Monthly). **Geographic Preference:** Local.

43963 ■ **Coquille Chamber of Commerce and Visitor Information Center**
119 N Birch
Coquille, OR 97423
Ph: (541)396-3414
Co. E-mail: coquillechamber@mycomspan.com
URL: http://coquillechamber.net
Facebook: www.facebook.com/pg/Coquille-Chamber-of-Commerce-419862778081189
Description: Works to promote and foster a healthy economy in the Coquille area by supporting citizens and the business community. Places an emphasis on quality in business and life in the community, as well as willingness to invest in the area's future. **Founded:** 1885. **Geographic Preference:** Local.

43964 ■ **Corvallis Chamber of Commerce**
420 NW 2nd St.
Corvallis, OR 97330
Ph: (541)757-1505
URL: http://www.corvallischamber.com
Contact: Simon Date, President
E-mail: simon@corvallischamber.com
Facebook: www.facebook.com/CorvallisChamberofCommerce
Linkedin: www.linkedin.com/company/corvallis-chamber-of-commerce
X (Twitter): x.com/corvallisbiz
YouTube: www.youtube.com/channel/UCFa6xr3eeFQoveBZZ4ybnXw
Description: Promotes business and community development in the Corvallis, OR area. **Founded:** 1930. **Geographic Preference:** Local.

43965 ■ **Cottage Grove Area Chamber of Commerce**
836 E Main St.
Cottage Grove, OR 97424
Ph: (541)942-2411
Co. E-mail: info@cgchamber.com
URL: http://www.cgchamber.com
Contact: Dale Smith, President
Facebook: www.facebook.com/CottageGroveChamber
X (Twitter): x.com/CottageGrovers
YouTube: www.youtube.com/channel/UCYuKhO9QfsbGO7u8jpag0IQ
Description: Promotes business and community development in Cottage Grove, OR. **Publications:** *Chamber News*. **Awards:** Cottage Grove Area Chamber of Commerce First Citizen of the Year. **Geographic Preference:** Local.

43966 ■ **Creswell Chamber of Commerce**
95 W Oregon Ave.
Creswell, OR 97426
Ph: (541)895-4398
Co. E-mail: creswellchamber@gmail.com
URL: http://www.creswellchamber.com
Contact: Jason Stubbs, President
Facebook: www.facebook.com/creswellchamber97426
Description: Promotes business and community activities in Creswell such as the July 4th Celebration and the Annual Banquet. **Founded:** 1909. **Geographic Preference:** Local.

43967 ■ **Dallas Area Chamber of Commerce (DACC)**
168 SW Ct., St.
Dallas, OR 97338
Ph: (503)623-2564
Co. E-mail: info@dallasoregon.org
URL: http://www.dallasoregon.org
Contact: Sam Dufner, President
Description: Promotes the Dallas Area as an excellent place to live, work, play and do business. **Founded:** 1937. **Awards:** DACC Business of the Year (Annual); DACC Exceptional Family (Annual); DACC First Citizen (Annual); DACC Good Samaritan (Annual); DACC Junior First Citizen (Annual); DACC Most Improved Business of the Year (Annual); DACC Outstanding Organization (Annual); DACC Small Business of the Year (Annual). **Geographic Preference:** Local.

43968 ■ **Estacada Chamber of Commerce**
475 SE Main St.
Estacada, OR 97023
Ph: (503)630-3483
Co. E-mail: info@estacadachamber.com
URL: http://estacadachamber.com
Contact: Connie Redmond, Co-President
Facebook: www.facebook.com/EstacadaChamber
X (Twitter): x.com/EstacadaChamber
Description: Promotes business and community development in the Estacada, OR area. Sponsors local celebrations and competitions. Operates the Visitor Information Services Complex. **Founded:** 1956. **Publications:** *Community & Business Directory*; *Historical Estacada Walking Tour*. **Geographic Preference:** Local.

43969 ■ **Eugene Area Chamber of Commerce**
1401 Willamette St.
Eugene, OR 97401
Ph: (541)484-1314
Fax: (541)484-4942
Co. E-mail: info@eugenechamber.com
URL: http://www.eugenechamber.com
Contact: Brittany Quick-Warner, Chief Executive Officer
E-mail: brittanyw@eugenechamber.com
Facebook: www.facebook.com/EugeneChamber
Linkedin: www.linkedin.com/company/eugene-area-chamber-of-commerce
X (Twitter): x.com/EugeneChamber
Description: Promotes a healthy local economy within the Eugene community by influencing business success, public policy and community development. **Founded:** 1903. **Publications:** *Chamber Update*. **Geographic Preference:** State.

43970 ■ **Florence Area Chamber of Commerce (FACC)**
290 Hwy. 101
Florence, OR 97439
Ph: (541)997-3128
Fax: (541)997-4101
Co. E-mail: info@florencechamber.com
URL: http://florencechamber.com
Contact: Bettina Hannigan, President
Facebook: www.facebook.com/florenceoregon
X (Twitter): x.com/FlorenceOrCoast
Description: Promotes business and community development in the Florence, OR area. **Publications:** *Business Beat* (Monthly). **Geographic Preference:** Local.

43971 ■ **Forest Grove/Cornelius Chamber of Commerce**
2417 Pacific Ave.
Forest Grove, OR 97116
Ph: (503)357-3006
Co. E-mail: info@fgcchamber.org
URL: http://visitforestgrove.com
Contact: Chris Barron, President
Facebook: www.facebook.com/fgchamber
X (Twitter): x.com/FGCChamber
Instagram: www.instagram.com/fgcchamber
Description: Promotes business and community development in Cornelius, OR. **Founded:** 1917. **Geographic Preference:** Local.

43972 ■ **Gold Beach Chamber of Commerce**
703 Chetco Ave., Ste. 14
Brookings, OR 97415
Co. E-mail: info@goldbeachchamber.com
URL: http://goldbeachchamber.com
Contact: Marie Curtis, Contact
Description: Promotes business and community development in the Gold Beach, OR area. Sponsors America's Wild Rivers Coast Art, fireworks display, and seafood and wine festivals. Holds annual business conference. **Publications:** *Gold Beach Chamber of Commerce Annual Business Directory* (Annual). **Awards:** Gold Beach Chamber of Commerce Business of the Year (Annual); Gold Beach Chamber of Commerce Citizen of the Year (Annual); Gold Beach Chamber of Commerce Volunteer of the Year (Annual). **Geographic Preference:** Local.

43973 ■ *Gold Beach Chamber of Commerce Annual Business Directory*
703 Chetco Ave., Ste. 14
Brookings, OR 97415
Co. E-mail: info@goldbeachchamber.com
URL: http://goldbeachchamber.com
Contact: Marie Curtis, Contact
URL(s): goldbeachchamber.com/about-us
Released: Annual **Description:** Covers businesses in the Gold Beach, OR area. **Availability:** Print.

43974 ■ **Grant County Chamber of Commerce (GCCC)**
301 W Main St.
John Day, OR 97845
Ph: (541)575-0547
Co. E-mail: gcadmin@gcoregonlive.com
URL: http://www.gcoregonlive.com
Contact: Taci Philbrook, President
Description: Promotes business and community development in Grant County, OR. **Founded:** 1864. **Geographic Preference:** Local.

43975 ■ **Grants Pass - Josephine County Chamber of Commerce**
1995 NW Vine St.
Grants Pass, OR 97526
Ph: (541)476-7717
Fax: (541)476-9574
Co. E-mail: gpcoc@grantspasschamber.org
URL: http://www.grantspasschamber.org
Contact: Josie Molloy, President

E-mail: jmolloy@grantspasschamber.org
Facebook: www.facebook.com/GrantsPassJosephineCountyChamber
Description: Encourages, assists, and promotes the business community in the Josephine County, OR area through programs and services. Sponsors concerts in the park. **Founded:** 1924. **Publications:** *Chamber's Profile* (Annual); *Chamber Update*. **Geographic Preference:** Local.

43976 ■ **Greater Hermiston Chamber of Commerce (GHCC)**
1055 S Hwy. 395, Ste. 111
Hermiston, OR 97838
Ph: (541)567-6151
Co. E-mail: info@hermistonchamber.com
URL: http://hermistonchamber.com
Contact: Kris Bennett, Chairman of the Board
E-mail: kris@krisanthemums.com
Facebook: www.facebook.com/hermistonchamberofcommerce
X (Twitter): x.com/hermchamber
Description: Promotes business growth, economic diversification, and livability in the Greater Hermiston, OR area. Sponsors Wine and Cheese Festival. **Founded:** 1933. **Publications:** *Business Directory*; *Chamber Connection* (Monthly); *Greater Hermiston Chamber of Commerce--Member Business Directory*. **Geographic Preference:** Local.

43977 ■ **Greater Newport Chamber of Commerce (GNCC)**
555 SW Coast Hwy.
Newport, OR 97365-4934
Ph: (541)265-8801
Free: 800-COA-ST44
Fax: (541)265-5589
Co. E-mail: info@newportchamber.org
URL: http://www.newportchamber.org
Contact: Jessica Steenkolk, President
Facebook: www.facebook.com/NewportChamberofCommerce
Instagram: www.instagram.com/newportchamberofcommerce
Description: Promotes business and community development in Newport, OR. Sponsors competitions and annual festival. **Founded:** 1939. **Publications:** *Communique* (Monthly); *Pocket Guide* (Annual). **Geographic Preference:** Local.

43978 ■ **Gresham Area Chamber of Commerce (GACC)**
1312 E Powell Blvd.
Gresham, OR 97030
Ph: (503)665-1131
Co. E-mail: gacc@greshamchamber.org
URL: http://www.greshamchamber.org
Contact: Leslie Parker, President
Facebook: www.facebook.com/GreshamAreaChamberofCommerce
YouTube: www.youtube.com/channel/UCuUYNyJweUNcaSliGhK8u7A
Description: Promotes business and community development in eastern Multnomah County, OR. Participates in charitable activities, including Business Education Partnership, and Excellence in Business. Sponsors Windjam Music Festival, Mt. Hood Jazz Festival, annual children's week, and Christmas Festival. **Founded:** 1931. **Geographic Preference:** Local.

43979 ■ **Harney County Chamber of Commerce (HCCC)**
484 N Broadway Ave.
Burns, OR 97720
Ph: (541)573-2636
Co. E-mail: info@harneycounty.com
URL: http://harneycounty.com
Contact: Mike Haines, President
Description: Promotes economic well being through leadership and advocacy for business, industry, education and tourism. **Publications:** *Chamber News* (Monthly). **Geographic Preference:** Local.

43980 ■ **Heppner Chamber of Commerce**
133 N Main St.
Heppner, OR 97836
Ph: (541)676-5536
Co. E-mail: heppnerchamber@gmail.com
URL: http://www.heppnerchamber.com
Contact: Andy Fletcher, President
Description: Promotes business and community development in the Heppner, Oregon area. **Founded:** 1954. **Geographic Preference:** Local.

43981 ■ **Hispanic Metropolitan Chamber (HMC)**
1618 SW 1st Ave., Ste. 250
Portland, OR 97201
Ph: (503)222-0280
Co. E-mail: info@hmccoregon.com
URL: http://hmccoregon.com
Contact: Nicole Davison León, Executive Director
E-mail: nleon@hmccoregon.com
Facebook: www.facebook.com/hmccoregon
Instagram: www.instagram.com/hmccoregon
Description: Works with all the members of the community to achieve the economic advancement of Hispanic-owned businesses in OR and Southwest WA. **Founded:** 1994. **Awards:** Oregon Latino Scholarship Fund (Annual); Oregon Latino Scholarship Program (Annual). **Geographic Preference:** Regional.

43982 ■ **Hood River County Chamber of Commerce (HRCCC)**
PO Box 1842
Hood River, OR 97031
Co. E-mail: info@visithoodriver.com
URL: http://visithoodriver.com
Contact: Corina Farrar, Chairman
Description: Promotes business and community development in the Hood River County, OR area. Sponsors Harvestfest and Blossom Festival, and Cross Channel Swim. **Founded:** 1924. **Geographic Preference:** Local.

43983 ■ **Jacksonville Chamber of Commerce and Visitor Center**
185 N Oregon St.
Jacksonville, OR 97530
Ph: (541)899-8118
Co. E-mail: chamber@jacksonvilleoregon.org
URL: http://jacksonvilleoregon.org
Facebook: www.facebook.com/JacksonvilleOregon
Description: Promotes business and community development in Jacksonville, OR. Sponsors annual Whole Town Garage Sale, Victorian Christmas Celebration, Chinese New Year, Block Party, Fritillaria Festival, Harvest Auction, and Harvest-Halloween Parade. **Geographic Preference:** Local.

43984 ■ **Junction City-Harrisburg Chamber of Commerce**
341 W 6th St.
Junction City, OR 97448
Ph: (541)998-6154
URL: http://www.tri-countychamber.com/communities/junction-city
Contact: Dave Zech, President
Facebook: www.facebook.com/TriCountyChamberOregon
Instagram: www.instagram.com/tricounty_chamber
Description: Promotes business and community development in the Junction City-Harrisburg, OR area. **Founded:** 1872. **Geographic Preference:** Local.

43985 ■ **Keizer Chamber of Commerce**
4118 River Rd. N
Keizer, OR 97303
Ph: (503)393-9111
Co. E-mail: info@keizerchamber.com
URL: http://keizerchamber.com
Contact: Corri Falardeau, Executive Director
Facebook: www.facebook.com/keizerchamber
Linkedin: www.linkedin.com/company/keizer-chamber-of-commerce
X (Twitter): x.com/keizerEVENTS
Instagram: www.instagram.com/keizerchamber
YouTube: www.youtube.com/user/TheKeizerChamber
Description: Promotes business and community development in Keizer, OR area. **Founded:** 1959. **Geographic Preference:** Local.

43986 ■ **Klamath County Chamber of Commerce (KCCC)**
205 Riverside Dr., Ste. A
Klamath Falls, OR 97601
Ph: (541)884-5193
Co. E-mail: reception@klamath.org
URL: http://klamath.org
Contact: Jason Aarstad, Officer
Facebook: www.facebook.com/KlamathChamber
Linkedin: www.linkedin.com/company/klamath-county-chamber-of-commerce
Instagram: www.instagram.com/klamathchamber
YouTube: www.youtube.com/user/KlamathCoChamber/videos
Description: Promotes business and community development in Klamath County, OR. **Founded:** 1905. **Publications:** *Basin Business* (Monthly). **Geographic Preference:** Local.

43987 ■ **La Pine Chamber of Commerce**
51429 Huntington Rd.
La Pine, OR 97739
Ph: (541)536-9771
URL: http://lapine.org
Contact: Jeremy Johnson, President
Facebook: www.facebook.com/lapine.chamber
Description: Promotes business and community development in La Pine, OR area. **Geographic Preference:** Local.

43988 ■ **Lake County Chamber of Commerce**
126 N E St.
Lakeview, OR 97630
Ph: (541)947-6040
Co. E-mail: shelley@allaboutlakecounty.com
URL: http://www.allaboutlakecounty.com
Contact: Alan Palmer, President
Facebook: www.facebook.com/allaboutlakecounty
Instagram: www.instagram.com/allaboutlakecounty
Description: Promotes business and community development in Lake County, OR. **Geographic Preference:** Local.

43989 ■ **Lincoln City Chamber of Commerce**
4039 NW Logan Rd.
Lincoln City, OR 97367
Ph: (541)994-3070
Co. E-mail: info@lcchamber.com
URL: http://lcchamber.com
Facebook: www.facebook.com/lcchamber
YouTube: www.youtube.com/channel/UC8Ka6I3OEm5Xcv_aFqUe4Gw
Description: Promotes business and community development in Lincoln City, OR. Sponsors Community Days Banquet, Holiday Gala, a weekly forum, Business Trade Show, "A Bite at the Beach" event and "Radio Days". **Founded:** 1855. **Publications:** *Dining and Shopping Guide* (Annual); *Lincoln City Business Resource Guide and Membership Directory* (Annual); *$5 Friday Flyers* (Weekly). **Geographic Preference:** Local.

43990 ■ **Madras-Jefferson County Chamber of Commerce and Visitors Center**
274 SW 4th St.
Madras, OR 97741
Ph: (541)475-2350
Co. E-mail: office@madraschamber.com
URL: http://www.madraschamber.com
Contact: Joe Krenowicz, Executive Director
E-mail: director@madraschamber.com
Facebook: www.facebook.com/MadrasJeffersonCountyChamber
Description: Promotes business and community development in Jefferson County, OR area. **Publications:** *Chamber News*. **Geographic Preference:** Local.

43991 ■ **McMinnville Area Chamber of Commerce (GMCC)**
417 NW Adams St.
McMinnville, OR 97128
Ph: (503)472-6196

Co. E-mail: chamberinfo@mcminnville.org
URL: http://www.mcminnville.org
Contact: Gioia Goodrum, President
Facebook: www.facebook.com/macchamber
X (Twitter): x.com/MacChamber
Description: Promotes business and community development in the greater McMinnville, OR area. Sponsors annual Turkey Rama Festival in July. **Founded:** 1915. **Publications:** *Area Business Directory* (Annual). **Geographic Preference:** Local.

43992 ■ Molalla Area Chamber of Commerce (MACC)
109 E Main St.
 Molalla, OR 97038
Ph: (503)829-6941
Co. E-mail: macc@molalla.net
URL: http://www.molallachamber.com
Contact: Darrel Sandquist, President
Description: Promotes business and community development in Molalla, OR. **Founded:** 1983. **Geographic Preference:** Local.

43993 ■ Monmouth-Independence Area Chamber of Commerce & Visitors Center (MICC)
355 Pacific N Ave., Ste. A
 Monmouth, OR 97361
Ph: (503)838-4268
Co. E-mail: micc@micc-or.org
URL: http://micc-or.org
Contact: Nicki Marazzani, President
Facebook: www.facebook.com/MIChamber
Instagram: www.instagram.com/miccoregon
Description: Promotes business and community development in Monmouth and Independence, OR. Sponsors charitable events and festivals. Holds community clean-up day. **Founded:** 1964. **Geographic Preference:** Local.

43994 ■ Mount Angel Chamber of Commerce
PO Box 221
 Mount Angel, OR 97362
Ph: (503)845-9291
Co. E-mail: mtangelchamber@gmail.com
URL: http://www.mtangelchamber.com
Contact: Sarah Belleque, President
E-mail: sarahbauman84@gmail.com
Facebook: www.facebook.com/pg/mtangelchamber
Description: Promotes business and community development in Mount Angel, OR. **Geographic Preference:** Local.

43995 ■ North Clackamas County Chamber of Commerce
8305 SE Monterey Ave., Ste. 104
 Happy Valley, OR 97086
Ph: (503)654-7777
Co. E-mail: reception@yourchamber.com
URL: http://yourchamber.com
Contact: Donna Baten, President
X (Twitter): x.com/YourChamberOR
YouTube: www.youtube.com/c/yourchamber
Description: Promotes business and community development in Clackamas County, OR. Sponsors harvest festival. **Founded:** 1955. **Publications:** *Business and Professional Directory* (Annual); *Business News* (Monthly). **Educational Activities:** Greeters; Business Forum. **Awards:** North Clackamas County Chamber of Commerce Business Person of the Year (Annual); Irwin Adams Memorial Lifetime Achievement Award (Annual); Rohn Bly Memorial Volunteer of the Year (Annual). **Geographic Preference:** Local.

43996 ■ North Santiam Chamber of Commerce (NSCC)
PO Box 222
 Mill City, OR 97360
Ph: (503)897-5000
Co. E-mail: director@nschamber.org
URL: http://northsantiamchamber.org
Contact: Rex Mittelstaedt, President
E-mail: rex@reximages.com
Facebook: www.facebook.com/northsantiamchamber
Description: Promotes business and community development in several communities of the Santiam Canyon. **Geographic Preference:** Local.

43997 ■ Nyssa Chamber of Commerce & Agriculture
105 Main St.
 Nyssa, OR 97913
Ph: (541)372-3091
Co. E-mail: nyssachamberofcommerce@gmail.com
URL: http://www.nyssachamberofcommerce.com
Facebook: www.facebook.com/NyssaChamberCommerce
Description: Works to advance the commercial, industrial, farming, civic and general interests of the City of Nyssa and its business area. **Geographic Preference:** Local.

43998 ■ Oakridge - Westfir Chamber of Commerce
PO Box 217
 Oakridge, OR 97463
Ph: (541)313-6758
Co. E-mail: oakridgewestfirchamber@gmail.com
URL: http://oakridgechamber.com
Contact: Lynda Kamerrer, Member
Facebook: www.facebook.com/oakridgewestfir.chamber
Description: Promotes business, community development, and tourism in the Oakridge/Westfir, OR area. Sponsors tree-planting and covered bridge Christmas lighting. **Publications:** *Food, Lodging and Service Guide.* **Geographic Preference:** Local.

43999 ■ Ontario Area Chamber of Commerce
251 SW 9th St.
 Ontario, OR 97914
Ph: (541)889-8012
Free: 866-989-8012
Fax: (541)889-8331
Co. E-mail: info@ontariochamber.com
URL: http://ontariochamber.com
Contact: John Breidenbach, President
Facebook: www.facebook.com/Ontario-Chamber-of-Commerce-129496620440977
Description: Promotes business and community development in Ontario, OR. Participates in local charitable activities. Sponsors America's Global Village and Festival. **Founded:** 1912. **Publications:** *Meeting and Tour Planner Guide.* **Geographic Preference:** Local.

44000 ■ Oregon City Chamber of Commerce
2895 S Beavercreek Rd., Ste. 103
 Oregon City, OR 97045
Ph: (503)656-1619
Fax: (503)656-2274
Co. E-mail: victoria@oregoncity.org
URL: http://oregoncity.org
Contact: Ray Stobie, Chairman
Linkedin: www.linkedin.com/company/oregoncitychamber/about
Description: Works to promote the economic vitality and quality of life in the community of Oregon City. **Founded:** 1909. **Publications:** *ChamberWire* (Monthly). **Geographic Preference:** Local.

44001 ■ Pendleton Business
501 S Main St.
 Pendleton, OR 97801
Ph: (541)276-7411
Fax: (800)547-8911
Co. E-mail: info@pendletonchamber.com
URL: http://www.pendletonchamber.com
Contact: Velda Arnaud, President
E-mail: veldaa@gmail.com
URL(s): pendletonchamber.com/business-plus
Released: Monthly **Availability:** Print; Online.

44002 ■ Pendleton Chamber of Commerce
501 S Main St.
 Pendleton, OR 97801
Ph: (541)276-7411
Fax: (800)547-8911
Co. E-mail: info@pendletonchamber.com
URL: http://www.pendletonchamber.com
Contact: Velda Arnaud, President
E-mail: veldaa@gmail.com
Facebook: www.facebook.com/PendletonChamber
Linkedin: www.linkedin.com/company/pendleton-chamber-of-commerce

X (Twitter): x.com/PendletonCC
Pinterest: www.pinterest.com/pendletoncoc
Description: Promotes business and community development in Pendleton, OR. Operates visitors and convention bureau. **Founded:** 1893. **Publications:** *Pendleton Business* (Monthly); *Pendleton Chamber of Commerce Directory* (Periodic). **Geographic Preference:** Local.

44003 ■ Pendleton Chamber of Commerce Directory
501 S Main St.
 Pendleton, OR 97801
Ph: (541)276-7411
Fax: (800)547-8911
Co. E-mail: info@pendletonchamber.com
URL: http://www.pendletonchamber.com
Contact: Velda Arnaud, President
E-mail: veldaa@gmail.com
URL(s): members.pendletonchamber.com/atb/search
Released: Periodic **Availability:** Online.

44004 ■ Philomath Area Chamber of Commerce (PACC)
1427 M St.
 Philomath, OR 97370
Ph: (541)929-2454
Co. E-mail: director@philomathchamber.org
URL: http://www.philomathchamber.org
Contact: Lisa Watkins, Executive Director
Facebook: www.facebook.com/PhilomathAreaChamberofCommerce
X (Twitter): x.com/PhilomathAreaCC
Description: Promotes business and community development in Philomath, OR. **Founded:** 1963. **Awards:** Philomath Samaritan Awards (Annual). **Geographic Preference:** Local.

44005 ■ Portland Business Alliance (PBA)
121 SW Salmon St., Ste. 1440
 Portland, OR 97204
Ph: (503)224-8684
Fax: (503)323-9186
Co. E-mail: membership@portlandalliance.com
URL: http://portlandalliance.com
Contact: Mike Golub, President
Facebook: www.facebook.com/portlandbusiness
Linkedin: www.linkedin.com/company/portland-business-alliance
X (Twitter): x.com/PDX_BizAlliance
Instagram: www.instagram.com/pdx_bizalliance
YouTube: www.youtube.com/channel/UCzNaHflwqG7e3dyn0k2-5AQ
Description: Works to ensure economic prosperity in the Portland region by providing strong leadership, partnership and programs that encourage business growth and vitality. **Founded:** 1870. **Publications:** *Portland's Top Stocks and Major Employers*; *Alliance E-Newsletter* (Monthly); *Alliance News* (Monthly); *Membership Directory and Resource Guide*; *Manufacturers of the Portland Metropolitan Area* (Annual); *The Top 25*; *Largest Employers of the Portland/Vancouver Metropolitan Area* (Annual); *Oregon International Trade Directory* (Irregular); *Taking Stocks: A Snapshot of Portland Metro-Area Public Companies* (Annual); *Portland Metropolitan Chamber of Commerce--Membership Directory* (Annual). **Geographic Preference:** Local.

44006 ■ Prineville-Crook County Chamber of Commerce (PCCCC)
185 NW 10th St.
 Prineville, OR 97754
Ph: (541)447-6304
Fax: (541)447-6537
Co. E-mail: info@prinevillechamber.com
URL: http://www.prinevillechamber.com
Contact: Sheena York, President
Facebook: www.facebook.com/PrinevilleChamber
Linkedin: www.linkedin.com/company/prineville-crook-county-chamber-of-commerce
X (Twitter): x.com/pccchamber
Description: Promotes business and community development in Prineville, OR area. Holds weekly legislative committee meeting. **Founded:** 1919.

Awards: Prineville-Crook County Chamber of Commerce Business of the Year (Annual). **Geographic Preference:** Local.

44007 ■ *RACC Business Perspectives*
410 SE Spruce St.
 Roseburg, OR 97470
Ph: (541)672-2648
Fax: (541)673-7868
Co. E-mail: info@roseburgareachamber.org
URL: http://roseburgchamber.com
Contact: Debbie Fromdahl, President
URL(s): roseburgchamber.com/news/monthly-newsletter
Released: Bimonthly **Availability:** PDF.

44008 ■ Redmond Chamber of Commerce
446 SW 7th St.
 Redmond, OR 97756
Ph: (541)923-5191
Co. E-mail: info@visitredmondoregon.com
URL: http://www.visitredmondoregon.com
Contact: Eric Sande, Executive Director
E-mail: eric@visitredmondoregon.com
Facebook: www.facebook.com/RedmondOregon
X (Twitter): x.com/visitrdm
Instagram: www.instagram.com/visitrdm
Description: Promotes business and community development in Redmond, OR. Sponsors events. **Publications:** *Business News* (Monthly). **Geographic Preference:** Local.

44009 ■ Reedsport - Winchester Bay Chamber of Commerce
2741 Frontage Rd.
 Reedsport, OR 97467
Ph: (541)271-3495
Co. E-mail: reedsportchamberofcommerce@gmail.com
URL: http://reedsportcc.org
Contact: Bill Hendrickson, Co-Chairman of the Board
Facebook: www.facebook.com/reedsportcc
Description: Promotes business and community development in Reedsport, OR. Seeks to establish the area as a tourist destination. Holds Ocean Festival. **Founded:** 1968. **Geographic Preference:** Local.

44010 ■ Rogue River Area Chamber of Commerce
8898 Rogue River Hwy.
 Grants Pass, OR 97527
Ph: (541)582-0242
URL: http://www.rogueriverchamber.com
Contact: Tim Shreeve, President
E-mail: timshreeve@gmail.com
Facebook: www.facebook.com/rogueriverchamber
Instagram: www.instagram.com/rogueriverchamberofcommerce
Description: Promotes business and community development in the Rogue River, OR area. **Founded:** 1912. **Geographic Preference:** Local.

44011 ■ Roseburg Area Chamber of Commerce and Visitors Center
410 SE Spruce St.
 Roseburg, OR 97470
Ph: (541)672-2648
Fax: (541)673-7868
Co. E-mail: info@roseburgareachamber.org
URL: http://roseburgchamber.com
Contact: Debbie Fromdahl, President
Facebook: www.facebook.com/roseburgareachamber
YouTube: www.youtube.com/channel/UCJZNhveaPwzYavNjlZ5mNEQ
Description: Promotes business and community development in Roseburg and central Douglas County, OR. **Founded:** 1920. **Publications:** *RACC Business Perspectives* (Bimonthly). **Educational Activities:** Business Fair. **Awards:** RACC First Citizens Awards (Annual). **Geographic Preference:** Local.

44012 ■ Salem Area Chamber of Commerce (SACC)
1110 Commercial St. NE
 Salem, OR 97301
Ph: (503)581-1466
Fax: (503)581-1466
Co. E-mail: info@salemchamber.org
URL: http://salemchamber.org
Contact: Alan Rasmussen, President
Facebook: www.facebook.com/salemchamber
X (Twitter): x.com/salemchamber
Instagram: www.instagram.com/Salem_Chamber
YouTube: www.youtube.com/user/salemchamber
Description: Promotes business and community development in the area. **Founded:** 1922. **Publications:** *Salem Area Chamber of Commerce Business Directory and Resource Guide* (Annual); *Community & Business Directory*; *Business News* (Monthly). **Awards:** Salem Area Chamber of Commerce Agri-Business of the Year (Annual); Salem Area Chamber of Commerce Business of the Year (Annual); Salem Area Chamber of Commerce Crystal Apple Awards (Irregular); Salem Area Chamber of Commerce Employer of the Year (Annual); Salem Area Chamber of Commerce First Citizen Awards (Annual); Salem Area Chamber of Commerce New Business of the Year (Annual); Salem Area Chamber of Commerce Small Business of the Year (Annual). **Geographic Preference:** Local.

44013 ■ Sandy Area Chamber of Commerce (SACC)
PO Box 1275
 Sandy, OR 97055
Ph: (503)668-4006
Co. E-mail: info@sandyoregonchamber.org
URL: http://sandyoregonchamber.org
Contact: Paula Siverly, President
E-mail: paula.siverly@htlenders.com
Facebook: www.facebook.com/sandyoregonchamber
YouTube: www.youtube.com/channel/UCPcbXdsUlb_9JefDwoKEgpg
Pinterest: www.pinterest.it/pin/319263061056450006
Description: Promotes business and community development in the area. **Founded:** 1978. **Publications:** *Chamber News* (Weekly); *Progress Business Journal* (Bimonthly); *Sandy Area Metro Guide* (Annual); *Chamber Progress* (Bimonthly); *Chamber Business Directory*. **Educational Activities:** Ambassadors Meeting (Annual); Education Committee Meeting (Monthly). **Awards:** Sandy Area Chamber of Commerce Titan Award (Annual). **Geographic Preference:** Local.

44014 ■ Sherwood Chamber of Commerce (SCC)
16273 SW Railroad St.
 Sherwood, OR 97140
Ph: (503)625-7800
URL: http://sherwoodchamber.org
Contact: Bill Sikkens, President
Facebook: www.facebook.com/SherwoodChamber
Instagram: www.instagram.com/sherwoodchamberofcommerce
Description: Promotes business and community development in the Sherwood, OR area. Sponsors the Sherwood Cruising in June and The Great Onion Festival in October. **Publications:** *Sherwood Chamber of Commerce Newsletter* (Bimonthly). **Geographic Preference:** Local.

44015 ■ *Shore Lines*
207 N Spruce
 Cannon Beach, OR 97110
Ph: (503)436-2623
Free: 800-745-1546
Fax: (503)436-1047
Co. E-mail: cbcc@cbcc.net
URL: http://www.cannonbeach.org
Contact: James Paino, Executive Director
URL(s): www.cannonbeach.org/things-to-do/outdoors-and-wildlife/tide-pools-and-tide-charts
Released: Monthly **Description:** Contains informational articles, announcements and latest news to keep the member up-to-date. **Availability:** Online.

44016 ■ Silverton Area Chamber of Commerce (SACC)
426 S Water St.
 Silverton, OR 97381
Ph: (503)873-5615
Fax: (503)873-7144
Co. E-mail: info@silvertonchamber.org
URL: http://www.silvertonchamber.org
Contact: Tim Punzel, President
E-mail: tim@kingofscents.com
Facebook: www.facebook.com/SilvertonChamberOR
X (Twitter): x.com/SilvChamber
YouTube: www.youtube.com/channel/UCNzG3vwkriyQE2-Q5bwi4eA
Description: Promotes business, community development, and tourism in the Silverton, OR area. Sponsors First Citizen banquet, farm and industrial tours, hanging flower basket program, and Christmas decorating contest. **Founded:** 1952. **Publications:** *Visitor's Guide and Business Directory*. **Geographic Preference:** Local.

44017 ■ Sisters Area Chamber of Commerce
291 E Main Ave.
 Sisters, OR 97759
Ph: (541)549-0251
Free: 800-549-0252
Fax: (541)549-4253
Co. E-mail: accounting@sisterscountry.com
URL: http://www.sisterscountry.com
Contact: Judy Trego, Contact
E-mail: judy@sisterscountry.com
Facebook: www.facebook.com/SistersCountry
Description: Strives to promote the civic, industrial, commercial, agricultural, environmental and general welfare of the city of Sisters, Oregon and its economic area. **Founded:** 1974. **Geographic Preference:** Local.

44018 ■ South County Chamber of Commerce (SCCC)
2194 Columbia Blvd.
 Saint Helens, OR 97051
Ph: (503)397-0685
Co. E-mail: mgr@sccchamber.org
URL: http://sccchamber.org
Contact: Alex Tardif, President
Facebook: www.facebook.com/southcolumbiacountychamber
Description: Promotes business and community development in St. Helens, Scappoose, Warren, Columbia City, and Deer Island, OR. **Founded:** 1947. **Publications:** *Chamber Update*. **Awards:** San Luis Obispo Citizen of the Year (Annual). **Geographic Preference:** Local.

44019 ■ Springfield Area Chamber of Commerce
101 S A St.
 Springfield, OR 97477
Ph: (541)746-1651
Fax: (541)726-4727
Co. E-mail: info@springfield-chamber.org
URL: http://www.springfield-chamber.org
Contact: Mike Eyster, President
Facebook: www.facebook.com/springfieldchamberofcommerce
X (Twitter): x.com/SpfldChamber
Instagram: www.instagram.com/explore/locations/35665982/springfield-chamber-of-commerce
YouTube: www.youtube.com/channel/UCeRPUOvY2tvy_WNVWqf4eBA
Description: Promotes business and community development in the Springfield, OR area. **Founded:** 1949. **Geographic Preference:** Local.

44020 ■ Stayton - Sublimity Chamber of Commerce (SSCC)
175 E High St.
 Stayton, OR 97383
Ph: (503)769-3464
Co. E-mail: info@staytonsublimitychamber.org
URL: http://www.staytonsublimitychamber.org
Contact: Carmélle Bielenberg, Chief Executive Officer
E-mail: carmelle@staytonsublimitychamber.org
Facebook: www.facebook.com/StaytonSublimityChamber
Instagram: www.instagram.com/sscoc
Pinterest: www.pinterest.com/sscoc

STATE LISTINGS

Description: Promotes business and community development in the Stayton/Sublimity, OR area. Sponsors area festivals and Christmas activities. **Founded:** 1891. **Geographic Preference:** Local.

44021 ■ Sunriver Area Chamber of Commerce
56825 Venture Ln., Ste. 110
Sunriver, OR 97707
Ph: (541)593-8149
Co. E-mail: exec@sunriverchamber.com
URL: http://www.sunriverchamber.com
Contact: Aaron Schofield, Treasurer
Facebook: www.facebook.com/Sunriverchamber
Instagram: www.instagram.com/sunriverareachamberofcommerce
Description: Promotes business and community development in Sunriver, OR area. **Founded:** 1987. **Geographic Preference:** Local.

44022 ■ Sutherlin Area Chamber of Commerce
1310 W Central Ave.
Sutherlin, OR 97479
Ph: (541)459-3280
Co. E-mail: info@visitsutherlin.com
URL: http://www.visitsutherlin.com
Contact: Emily Blakely, President
Facebook: www.facebook.com/SutherlinAreaChamber
Description: Promotes business and community development in the Sutherlin, OR area. Sponsors festivals. Assists in boy scouting activities. **Founded:** 2010. **Geographic Preference:** Local.

44023 ■ Sweet Home Chamber of Commerce
1575 Main St.
Sweet Home, OR 97386
Ph: (541)367-6186
Co. E-mail: sweethomecoc@gmail.com
URL: http://www.sweethomechamber.com
Contact: Christy Duncan, President
Description: Promotes business and community development in Sweet Home, OR. Sponsors festival. **Founded:** 1962. **Publications:** *Hot Deals* (Monthly). **Geographic Preference:** Local.

44024 ■ Tigard Area Chamber of Commerce (TACC)
12345 SW Main St.
Tigard, OR 97223
Ph: (503)639-1656
URL: http://tigardchamber.org
Contact: Yi Kang Hu, President
Facebook: www.facebook.com/TigardChamber
X (Twitter): x.com/tigardchamber
Instagram: www.instagram.com/tigardchamber
YouTube: www.youtube.com/user/tigardchamber
Description: Promotes business and community development in the Tigard, OR area. **Publications:** *Hotline* (Monthly). **Educational Activities:** Tigard Area Chamber of Commerce Luncheon. **Awards:** Tigard Chamber of Commerce & Visitor Center Tigard's First Citizen Award (Annual). **Geographic Preference:** Local.

44025 ■ Tillamook Area Chamber of Commerce
208 Main Ave.
Tillamook, OR 97141
Ph: (503)842-7525
Co. E-mail: info@tillamookchamber.org
URL: http://tillamookchamber.org
Contact: Justin Aufdermauer, President
E-mail: justin@tillamookchamber.org
Description: Promotes business and community development in Tillamook, OR. Participates in area festivals. **Founded:** 1931. **Publications:** *Business / Community Directory*; *Focus on Business* (Monthly). **Geographic Preference:** Local.

44026 ■ *Tualatin Business and Community Guide*
8101 SW Nyberg St., Ste. No. 102
Tualatin, OR 97062
Ph: (503)692-0780
Fax: (503)692-6955
Co. E-mail: chamber@tualatinchamber.com
URL: http://tualatinchamber.com
Contact: Susan Noack, Chairman of the Board
URL(s): tualatinchamber.com/city-of-tualatin/economic-development-resources
Availability: Print.

44027 ■ Tualatin Chamber of Commerce (TCC)
8101 SW Nyberg St., Ste. No. 102
Tualatin, OR 97062
Ph: (503)692-0780
Fax: (503)692-6955
Co. E-mail: chamber@tualatinchamber.com
URL: http://tualatinchamber.com
Contact: Susan Noack, Chairman of the Board
Facebook: www.facebook.com/tualatin.chamber.of.commerce
Linkedin: www.linkedin.com/company/4014416
X (Twitter): x.com/tualatinchamb3r
Instagram: www.instagram.com/tualatinchamber
YouTube: www.youtube.com/channel/UCUSLaiubu0zy8x4zDdlvphw
Description: Promotes business and community development in Tualatin, OR. Sponsors trade show. Conducts Tualatin Crawfish Festival, Membership luncheon, weekly Networking AMs, Golf Tournament, and Holiday Tree Lighting. **Founded:** 1980. **Publications:** *Tualatin Business and Community Guide*; *Tualatin Business Connection* (Bimonthly). **Geographic Preference:** Local.

44028 ■ Umatilla Chamber of Commerce
100 Cline Ave.
Umatilla, OR 97882
Ph: (541)922-4825
Co. E-mail: info@umatillaorchamber.org
URL: http://umatillaorchamber.org
Facebook: www.facebook.com/umatillaoregonchamber
Description: Promotes business and community development in Umatilla, OR. Hosts the Oregon Governor's Cup Walleye Tournament each Labor Day weekend. **Founded:** 1947. **Publications:** *Chamber News*. **Educational Activities:** Business-to-Business Luncheon. **Awards:** Umatilla Chamber of Commerce Distinguished Citizens Awards (Annual). **Geographic Preference:** Local.

44029 ■ Union County Chamber of Commerce
207 Depot St.
La Grande, OR 97850
Ph: (541)963-8588
Co. E-mail: memebrship@visitunioncounty.org
URL: http://visitunioncounty.org
Contact: Scott Newman, Executive Director
Facebook: www.facebook.com/TravelUnionCounty
X (Twitter): x.com/UCChamber
Instagram: www.instagram.com/travelunioncounty
Description: Promotes business and community development in Union County, OR. **Founded:** 1932. **Publications:** *Chamber Times* (Monthly); *Slick Magazine* (Annual). **Geographic Preference:** Local.

44030 ■ Vale Chamber of Commerce
PO Box 661
Vale, OR 97918
Ph: (208)615-9399
Co. E-mail: vale.chamber.or@gmail.com
URL: http://www.valechamber.com
Contact: Cathy Zacharias, President
Facebook: www.facebook.com/valechamber20
Description: Promotes business and community development in Vale, OR. **Geographic Preference:** Local.

44031 ■ *Visitor's Guide and Business Directory*
426 S Water St.
Silverton, OR 97381
Ph: (503)873-5615
Fax: (503)873-7144
Co. E-mail: info@silvertonchamber.org
URL: http://www.silvertonchamber.org
Contact: Tim Punzel, President
E-mail: tim@kingofscents.com
URL(s): www.silvertonchamber.org/about-us
Availability: Print.

44032 ■ Waldport Chamber of Commerce
320 NW Hwy. 101
Waldport, OR 97394-0669
Ph: (541)563-3500
Co. E-mail: director@waldportchamber.org
URL: http://findyourselfinwaldport.com
Contact: Kevin Battles, President
Facebook: www.facebook.com/chamberwaldport
Description: Promotes business and community development in Waldport, OR. **Founded:** 1959. **Geographic Preference:** Local.

44033 ■ Wallowa County Chamber of Commerce
309 S River St.
Enterprise, OR 97828
Ph: (541)426-4622
Fax: (541)426-2032
Co. E-mail: info@wallowacounty.org
URL: http://www.wallowacountychamber.com
Contact: Jenni Word, President
Facebook: www.facebook.com/WallowaCountyChamber
Linkedin: www.linkedin.com/company/wallowa-county-chamber-of-commerce
YouTube: www.youtube.com/channel/UCbo4AyiWBgEvl3eWjEMeHTg
Description: Promotes agricultural, business, and community development in the Wallowa County, OR area. Conducts annual Old Time Fiddlers Contest. Publications: none. **Awards:** WC Chamber Citizens Award (Annual). **Geographic Preference:** Local.

44034 ■ Wilsonville Chamber of Commerce (WACC)
8565 SW Salish Ln., Ste. 150
Wilsonville, OR 97070
Ph: (503)682-0411
Co. E-mail: info@wilsonvillechamber.com
URL: http://wilsonvillechamber.com
Contact: Jaimy Beltran, Chairman
E-mail: jaimy@beltranproperties.com
Linkedin: www.linkedin.com/company/wilsonville-area-chamber-of-commerce
Description: Promotes business and community development in Wilsonville, OR area. **Founded:** 1973. **Publications:** *Catalyst* (Monthly); *Wilsonville Community and Business Directory*. **Geographic Preference:** Local.

44035 ■ *Wilsonville Community and Business Directory*
8565 SW Salish Ln., Ste. 150
Wilsonville, OR 97070
Ph: (503)682-0411
Co. E-mail: info@wilsonvillechamber.com
URL: http://wilsonvillechamber.com
Contact: Jaimy Beltran, Chairman
E-mail: jaimy@beltranproperties.com
URL(s): wilsonvillechamber.com/business-directory
Description: Contains listing of community and business resources for Wilsonville. **Availability:** Print.

44036 ■ Winston-Dillard Area Chamber of Commerce
PO Box 68
Winston, OR 97496-0068
Ph: (541)679-0118
Co. E-mail: info@winstonchamber.org
URL: http://www.uschamber.com/co/chambers/oregon/winston
Facebook: www.facebook.com/winstonchamber.org
Description: Works for the advancement of commercial, industrial, civic, and general interests of the Winston-Dillard area. **Founded:** 1960. **Publications:** *W-D Area Chamber News* (Monthly). **Geographic Preference:** Local.

44037 ■ Woodburn Area Chamber of Commerce (WACC)
270 Montgomery st.
Woodburn, OR 97071
Ph: (503)982-8221
Co. E-mail: welcome@woodburnchamber.org

URL: http://woodburnchamber.org
Contact: Jenne Marquez, President
Facebook: www.facebook.com/WoodburnAreaChamberofCommerce

Description: Promotes business and community development in the Woodburn, OR area. Sponsors Woodburn Business Showcase. **Founded:** 1938. **Publications:** *Woodburn Chamber News* (Monthly). **Awards:** Woodburn Area Chamber of Commerce Crystal Apple Awards (Annual); Woodburn Area Chamber of Commerce Distinguished Service Awards (Annual). **Geographic Preference:** Local.

44038 ■ *Woodburn Chamber News*
270 Montgomery st.
Woodburn, OR 97071
Ph: (503)982-8221
Co. E-mail: welcome@woodburnchamber.org
URL: http://woodburnchamber.org
Contact: Jenne Marquez, President
URL(s): woodburnchamber.org/join
Released: Monthly **Availability:** Print.

44039 ■ Yachats Area Chamber of Commerce (YACC)
241 Hwy. 101
Yachats, OR 97498-0728
Ph: (541)547-2345
Free: 800-929-0477
URL: http://www.yachats.org
X (Twitter): x.com/VisitYachats
Pinterest: www.pinterest.com/VisitYachats

Description: Promotes business and community development in south Lincoln County, OR. Sponsors Arts and Crafts Fair, Smelt Fry, and Kite Festival. **Publications:** *The Gem*. **Geographic Preference:** Local.

MINORITY BUSINESS ASSISTANCE PROGRAMS

44040 ■ Oregon Association of Minority Entrepreneurs (OAME)
731 N Hayden Meadows Dr.
Portland, OR 97217
Ph: (503)249-7744
Co. E-mail: oame@oame.org
URL: http://oame.org
Contact: Jorge Guerra, President
E-mail: jorge@oame.org

Description: A non-profit organization formed to promote and develop entrepreneurship and economic development for ethnic minorities in the state of Oregon and southwest Washington. **Founded:** 1987.

44041 ■ Oregon Office of Minority, Women, & Emerging Small Businesses New Certifications
North Mall Office Building 725 Summer St. NE, Ste. B
Salem, OR 97301-1266
Ph: (503)378-3104
Fax: (503)373-7643
URL: http://www.oregon.gov/ohcs/development/Pages/mwesb-sdvbe-rental-housing.aspx

Description: Advocates for disadvantaged and emerging small businesses, allowing their participation in the state's targeted purchasing programs. Also identifies and seeks to remove barriers that prevent these businesses from entering the mainstream of commercial activity.

44042 ■ Portland Minority Business Development Center
10260 SW Greenburg Rd.
Tigard, OR 97223
Free: 800-334-8725
Co. E-mail: info@mdcreserach.com.com
URL: http://mdcresearch.com
Contact: Dima Sokolov, President
Linkedin: www.linkedin.com/company/mdc-research

FINANCING AND LOAN PROGRAMS

44043 ■ Cambridge Samsung Partners L.L.C. (CSP)
7175 NW Evergreen Pky, Bldg 100
Hillsboro, OR 97124
URL: http://pseps.com/company/Cambridge-Samsung-Partners-LLC
Contact: Linda Skinner, Vice President, Human Resources

Description: Firm provides independent venture capital services.

44044 ■ Cascade Seed Fund
Bend, OR
Co. E-mail: hello@cascadeseedfund.com
URL: http://cascadeseedfund.com
Contact: Julie Harrelson, Managing Director
X (Twitter): x.com/CascadeFund

Description: Offers early-stage capital. **Founded:** 2014. **Investment Policies:** Extends priority to overlooked entrepreneurs: market disruptors, minorities, and those located outside major metropolitan areas. **Industry Preferences:** Enterprise/B2B; cloud-first businesses built on the internet; elevated consumer experiences; delivering healthcare, education, or financial services using new approaches or models.

44045 ■ Craft3
409 Maynard Ave. S, Ste. 200
Seattle, WA 98104-2959
Free: 888-231-2170
Fax: (360)455-4879
Co. E-mail: info@craft3.org
URL: http://www.craft3.org
Contact: Sonya Lynn, Chief Operating Officer
Facebook: www.facebook.com/Craft3Org
Linkedin: www.linkedin.com/company/craft3
X (Twitter): x.com/Craft3Org

Description: CFDI provides loans to established nonprofits as well as growing and start-up businesses in Oregon and Washington.

44046 ■ Oregon Entrepreneurs Network (OEN)
PO Box 6452
Portland, OR 97228
Ph: (503)222-2270
Co. E-mail: info@oen.org
URL: http://www.oen.org
Contact: Amanda Oborne, President
E-mail: amanda@oen.org
Facebook: www.facebook.com/oenorg
Linkedin: www.linkedin.com/company/244877
X (Twitter): x.com/oenorg
Instagram: www.instagram.com/oenorg
YouTube: www.youtube.com/user/orentrepreneurs

Description: Assists entrepreneurs and scalable startups in Oregon by offering funding opportunities, networking, and training. **Founded:** 1991.

44047 ■ Oregon Sports Angels (OSA)
805 SW Broadway
Portland, OR 97205
URL: http://oregonsportsangels.org
Contact: Kate Delhagen, President
Linkedin: www.linkedin.com/company/oregon-sports-angels
X (Twitter): x.com/orsportsangels

Description: Identifies and invests in early-stage sports and fitness product, experience, technology, and service companies. Also mentors and connects entrepreneurs to resources needed for business development. **Founded:** 2017.

44048 ■ Rogue Venture Partners
Portland, OR
URL: http://roguewmn.com
Contact: Adam Stoll, Partner

Description: Invests in disruptive entrepreneurs and makes undercapitalized regions relevant. **Founded:** 2010.

44049 ■ Women's VC Fund II
311 NW 12th Ave., Ste. 1003
Portland, OR 97209
Co. E-mail: deals@womensvcfund.com
URL: http://www.womensvcfund.com
Contact: Susan Namkung, Director
Linkedin: www.linkedin.com/company/womensvcfund

Description: Early stage venture capital firm interested in female-led startups. Also maintains an office in California. **Founded:** 2017. **Investment Policies:** Revenue-generating, high-growth companies let by gender-inclusive management teams. **Industry Preferences:** Enterprise SaaS; consumer internet; education technology.

PROCUREMENT ASSISTANCE PROGRAMS

44050 ■ Northwest Environmental Business Council (NEBC)
Six Centerpointe Dr., Ste. 340
Lake Oswego, OR 97035
Ph: (503)227-6361
Fax: (503)227-1007
Co. E-mail: info@nebc.org
URL: http://www.nebc.org
Contact: Jeff Jordan, Contact
E-mail: jeff@nebc.org
Linkedin: www.linkedin.com/company/northwest-environmental-business-council-nebc
X (Twitter): x.com/nebcorg

Description: Trade association representing the interests of its members, while promoting the health of the industry and the environment as a whole. The organization engages in a range of activities and services designed to connect members to customers, regulators and legislators, knowledge, resources, and each other. **Founded:** 1996. **Geographic Preference:** Regional.

44051 ■ Oregon Procurement Technical Assistance Center (OR-PTAC) [Government Contract Assistance Program (GCAP)]
1144 Gateway Loop, Ste. 203
Springfield, OR 97477
Ph: (541)736-1088
Free: 800-497-7551
URL: http://www.gcap.org
Contact: Dee Edwards, Program Manager

Description: Supports state and local government by providing leadership, training, oversight and a vehicle for public contracting. **Founded:** 1986.

44052 ■ Oregon Procurement Technical Assistance Center - Government Contract Assistance Program (GCAP)
1144 Gateway Loop, Ste. 203
Springfield, OR 97477
Ph: (541)736-1088
Free: 800-497-7551
Co. E-mail: gcapdee@gcap.org
URL: http://www.gcap.org
Contact: Rick Evans, Executive Director
E-mail: revans@gcap.org
Facebook: www.facebook.com/gcaporegonptac

Description: Supports state and local government by providing leadership, training, oversight and a vehicle for public contracting. **Founded:** 1986.

44053 ■ Oregon Procurement Technical Assistance Center - Government Contract Assistance Program - Pacific Northwest Defense Coalition (PNDC)
7650 SW Beveland St., Ste. 170
Portland, OR 97223
Ph: (503)344-6618
Free: 888-701-7632
Fax: (503)517-8095
Co. E-mail: info@pndc.us
URL: http://www.pndc.us
Contact: Denise Ryser, Executive Director
E-mail: denise@pndc.us
URL(s): www.aptac-us.org/find-a-ptac/?state=OR#
Facebook: www.facebook.com/nwdefense
Linkedin: www.linkedin.com/company/732374

X (Twitter): x.com/nwdefense
Instagram: www.instagram.com/nwdefense
YouTube: www.youtube.com/channel/UCFITF_lr9Y9QmmoGp-jSqFQ
Description: Provides educational programs, business-to-business networking, and outreach to government decision makers ensuring success.
Founded: 2005.

44054 ■ Oregon Procurement Technical Assistance Center (OEI) - Organization for Economic Initiatives, Inc.
1144 Gateway Loop., Ste. 203
Springfield, OR 97477
URL: http://www.gcap.org/home/gca/cpage_12/organization_for_economic_initiatives_inc.html
Contact: Michael Lainoff, President
Founded: 1993.

44055 ■ Oregon's Procurement Technical Assistance Center - Disadvantaged Business Enterprise (GCAP)
1144 Gateway Loop., Ste. 203
Springfield, OR 97477
URL: http://www.gcap.org/the-office-for-business-inclusion-and-diversity-co
Description: Ensures nondiscrimination in the award and administration of Federal contracts. The program creates a level playing field for small companies that are Black, Hispanic, Native Americans, Asian-Pacific Islanders, Subcontinent Asians, or women owned.

INCUBATORS/RESEARCH AND TECHNOLOGY PARKS

44056 ■ The Barrow
150 Shelton McMurphey Blvd.
Eugene, OR 97401
Ph: (541)632-4288
Co. E-mail: info@backtothebarrow.com
URL: http://www.backtothebarrow.com
Facebook: www.facebook.com/BackToTheBarrow
Instagram: www.instagram.com/thebarroweugene
Description: Rental space for small businesses focused on health and sustainability.

44057 ■ The Collective Kitchen
173 NE 3rd Ave., Ste. 105, 106, Historic Downtown
Hillsboro, OR 97124
URL: http://www.collectivekitchen.net
Facebook: www.facebook.com/collectivekitchenpdx
X (Twitter): x.com/collectivekitch
Instagram: www.instagram.com/collectivekitchenpdx
Description: Commissary kitchen and cooking classroom. Incubates small craft businesses and preserves handmade traditions for future generations.

44058 ■ The Commons Law Center
PO Box 16520
Portland, OR 97292
Ph: (503)850-0811
Co. E-mail: hello@thecommonslawcenter.org
URL: http://thecommonslawcenter.org
Contact: John E. Grant, President
Facebook: www.facebook.com/thecommonslawcenter
Linkedin: www.linkedin.com/company/thecommonslawcenter
X (Twitter): x.com/commons_law
YouTube: www.youtube.com/channel/UC99wHhLbh-3vkVZ3CUmCJVQ
Description: Incubator offering three-year fellowships for recent law school graduates to provide them with the experience they need to leverage their education.

44059 ■ Hummingbird's Incubator Kitchen
150 Shelton McMurphey Blvd.
Eugene, OR 97401
Ph: (541)632-4288
Co. E-mail: info@backtothebarrow.com
URL: http://www.backtothebarrow.com
Facebook: www.facebook.com/BackToTheBarrow
Linkedin: www.linkedin.com/company/the-barrow
Instagram: www.instagram.com/thebarroweugene

Description: Allows small-scale food producers to offer a product to the marketplace without the investing in a commercial kitchen in the initial stages of growth. Focused on businesses with local, organic, and nutritionally valuable foods.

44060 ■ Oregon Innovation Center (OIC)
The Innovation Bldg.
Bend, OR 97702
Ph: (541)362-1229
Co. E-mail: info@innovationcenter.org
URL: http://www.innovationcenter.org
Description: The OIC is a small business incubator for emerging technology firms and entrepreneurs. In addition to affordable space, the Center offers tenants capital sourcing, economic facilities and other services. **Founded:** 1990.

44061 ■ Oregon Technology Business Center (OTBC)
3800 SW Cedar Hills Blvd., Ste. 260
Beaverton, OR 97005
Ph: (971)223-4660
URL: http://otbc.org
Contact: Steve Morris, Executive Director
Facebook: www.facebook.com/OregonStartupCenter
Linkedin: www.linkedin.com/company/oregon-technology-business-center
Description: A small business incubator devoted to supporting the growth of technology startups in Oregon by taking a company's technology and helping turn it into a growth business through individualized coaching programs and commercialization assistance that accelerate each company's progress.

44062 ■ OTRADI Bioscience Incubator (OBI)
4640 S Macadam Ave., Ste. 240
Portland, OR 97239
Ph: (503)227-1814
URL: http://www.otradi.org
Contact: Heather Ellis, Executive Director
X (Twitter): x.com/OTRADIBio
Description: Business incubator for bio science startup companies, providing lab and office space.

44063 ■ Portland Incubator Experiment (PIE)
221 SE Ankeny St.
Portland, OR 97214
Co. E-mail: info@piepdx.com
URL: http://www.piepdx.com
Facebook: www.facebook.com/piepdx
X (Twitter): x.com/piepdx
Description: Mentors, nurtures, and accelerates startups from around the world in Portland, Oregon.

44064 ■ Portland Seed Fund (PSF)
805 SW Broadway, Ste. 2440
Portland, OR 97205
Ph: (503)419-3007
Co. E-mail: info@portlandseedfund.com
URL: http://portlandseedfund.com
Contact: Jim Huston, Manager Director
Facebook: www.facebook.com/PortlandSeedFund
Linkedin: www.linkedin.com/company/portland-seed-fund
X (Twitter): x.com/pdxseedfund
Description: A privately managed fund and non-resident accelerator focused on providing emerging companies the capital, mentoring, and connections to propel them to the next level. **Founded:** 2011.

44065 ■ Portland State Business Accelerator (PSU)
2828 SW Corbett Ave.
Portland, OR 97201
Ph: (503)725-2312
Co. E-mail: accelerator@pdx.edu
URL: http://www.pdx.edu/accelerator
Contact: Arsh Haque, Director
Facebook: www.facebook.com/PSUAccelerator
X (Twitter): x.com/PSUAccelerator
Description: Business accelerator that is home to over 30 startup companies in technology, bio science, and cleantech.

44066 ■ Portland State University Business Accelerator (PSU)
2828 SW Corbett Ave.
Portland, OR 97201
Ph: (503)725-2312
Co. E-mail: accelerator@pdx.edu
URL: http://www.pdx.edu/accelerator
Contact: Christelle Sheldon, Program Manager
E-mail: christelle.sheldon@pdx.edu
Facebook: www.facebook.com/PSUAccelerator
Linkedin: www.linkedin.com/organization-guest/company/psuaccelerator
X (Twitter): x.com/PSUAccelerator
Description: Business accelerator that is home to 30+ startup companies in technology, bio science, and cleantech. Works to speed the success of high-tech growth companies by providing resources and connections. **Founded:** 2011.

44067 ■ Portland State University Business School Business Accelerator (PSBA)
2828 SW Corbett Ave.
Portland, OR 97201
Ph: (503)725-2312
Co. E-mail: accelerator@pdx.edu
URL: http://www.pdx.edu/accelerator
Contact: Arsh Haque, Director
Facebook: www.facebook.com/PSUAccelerator
X (Twitter): x.com/PSUAccelerator
Description: Accelerator that speeds the success of these high-growth companies by providing resources, connections, expertise, University support, and control of high-impact costs, all within a growth-focused entrepreneurial community. **Founded:** 1946.

44068 ■ Stellaria Community Incubator Kitchen
150 Shelton McMurphey Blvd.
Eugene, OR 97401
Ph: (541)632-4288
Co. E-mail: info@backtothebarrow.com
URL: http://www.backtothebarrow.com
Description: Culinary incubator designed to support small scale food producers in offering a product to the marketplace without having to invest in the required commercial kitchen setting at start-up or as they are growing larger. The emphasis of this incubator is on food businesses that emphasize local, organic and nutritionally valuable foods. **Founded:** 1923.

44069 ■ TiE Orgeon
PO Box 25627
Portland, OR 97298
Ph: (971)303-9063
URL: http://oregon.tie.org
Contact: Nitin Rai, President
E-mail: nitin@elevate.vc
Facebook: www.facebook.com/tieoregon
X (Twitter): x.com/TiEoregon
YouTube: www.youtube.com/channel/UCnMY2lHn2JB3SgVH5sshWNQ
Description: Generates and nurtures entrepreneurs through mentoring, networking, education, funding, and incubation. Promotes giving back to the community. .

44070 ■ Umpqua Business Center (UBC)
522 SE Washington Ave.
Roseburg, OR 97470
Ph: (541)440-0995
Co. E-mail: brandy.gardener@uidcorp.com
URL: http://umpquabusiness.com
Description: Business incubator that offers low-cost office space, workshops, classes, and one-on-one counseling to help with business growth.

44071 ■ VertueLab
PO Box 212
Portland, OR 97207
Ph: (971)770-2378
Co. E-mail: info@vertuelab.org
URL: http://vertuelab.org
Contact: David Kenney, President
E-mail: david.kenney@vertuelab.org
X (Twitter): x.com/vertuelab

Description: Helps connect Oregon start-ups with the resources needed to move their products to market. **Founded:** 2007.

EDUCATIONAL PROGRAMS

44072 ■ Mt. Hood Community College (MHCC)
26000 SE Stark St.
 Gresham, OR 97030
Ph: (503)491-6422
Co. E-mail: collegenow@mhcc.edu
URL: http://www.mhcc.edu
Contact: Dr. Lisa Skari, President
Facebook: www.facebook.com/MtHoodCommuni
 tyCollege
Linkedin: www.linkedin.com/school/mt.-hoo
 d-community-college
X (Twitter): x.com/MtHoodCommunity
Instagram: www.instagram.com/mthoodcommuni
 tycollege
Description: Two-year college offering a small business management program. **Founded:** 1966. **Educational Activities:** Stronger Together conference.

44073 ■ Southwestern Oregon Community College (SWOCC)
1988 Newmark Ave.
 Coos Bay, OR 97420
Ph: (541)888-2525
Free: 800-962-2838
Co. E-mail: swoccathletics@socc.edu
URL: http://www.socc.edu
Contact: Dr. Patty M. Scott, President
E-mail: pscott@socc.edu
Facebook: www.facebook.com/swocc
Linkedin: www.linkedin.com/school/southwestern
 -oregon-community-college
X (Twitter): x.com/swocc
Instagram: www.instagram.com/swocc_oregon
Description: Two-year college offering a small business management program. **Founded:** 1961.

44074 ■ Umpqua Community College (UCC)
1140 Umpqua College Rd.
 Roseburg, OR 97470
Ph: (541)440-4600
Free: 800-820-5161
Co. E-mail: marketing@umpqua.edu
URL: http://www.umpqua.edu
Contact: Dr. Rachel Pokrandt, President
Facebook: www.facebook.com/umpquacc
Linkedin: www.linkedin.com/school/umpqua-communi
 ty-college
X (Twitter): x.com/umpquacc
YouTube: www.youtube.com/c/umpquacc

Description: Two-year college offering a small business management program. **Founded:** 1964.

TRADE PERIODICALS

44075 ■ *Portland Business Journal*
Pub: American City Business Journals, Inc.
Contact: Mike Olivieri, Executive Vice President
URL(s): www.bizjournals.com/portland
Facebook: www.facebook.com/PortlandBizJournal
Linkedin: www.linkedin.com/company/portlan
 d-business-journal
X (Twitter): x.com/PDXBizJournal
Ed: Suzanne Stevens. **Released:** Weekly **Price:** $380, for Nationwide Access 52 weeks; $950, for Nationwide + BOL 52 weeks; $220, for print and online 52 week; $210, for digital 52 week. **Description:** Business newspaper for the Portland area. **Availability:** Print; PDF; Download; Online. **Type:** Full-text.

VIDEO/AUDIO MEDIA

44076 ■ *Portland Top Startups*
URL(s): omny.fm/shows/startup-hustle/portland-top-s
 tartups
Ed: Matt DeCoursey, Lauren Conaway. **Released:** August 23, 2023. **Description:** Podcast highlights 12 of Portland, Oregon's top startups.

CONSULTANTS

44077 ■ Illumination Consulting
818 SW 3rd Ave., Ste. 161
 Portland, OR 97204
Free: 800-619-3734
Fax: (619)599-1950
Co. E-mail: contact@illuminationconsulting.com
URL: http://illuminationconsulting.com
Facebook: www.facebook.com/IlluminationConsulting
Linkedin: www.linkedin.com/company/illumination
 -consulting
X (Twitter): x.com/Illumination_Co
YouTube: www.youtube.com/user/consultingbusiness
Pinterest: www.pinterest.com/illuminationco
Description: Offers start-up, marketing, design, and development consulting services.

PUBLICATIONS

44078 ■ Oregon Business
12570 SW 69th Ave., Ste. 102
 Portland, OR 97223
Ph: (503)445-8811
URL: http://www.oregonbusiness.com

Contact: Craig Peebles, Manager
E-mail: craigp@oregonbusiness.com
Facebook: www.facebook.com/OregonBusiness
Linkedin: www.linkedin.com/company/oregon
 -business-magazine
X (Twitter): x.com/OregonBusiness
Instagram: www.instagram.com/oregonbusiness
YouTube: www.youtube.com/channel/UCkCSDdhm
 4Ut0Fg8QM2hwM2w
Description: Firm that publish magazines and newspaper. **Founded:** 1981. **Publications:** *Oregon Business Magazine* (Monthly).

44079 ■ *Oregon Business Magazine*
12570 SW 69th Ave., Ste. 102
 Portland, OR 97223
Ph: (503)445-8811
URL: http://www.oregonbusiness.com
Contact: Craig Peebles, Manager
E-mail: craigp@oregonbusiness.com
URL(s): oregonbusiness.com
Facebook: www.facebook.com/OregonBusiness
Linkedin: www.linkedin.com/company/oregon
 -business-magazine
X (Twitter): x.com/OregonBusiness
Instagram: www.instagram.com/oregonbusiness
YouTube: www.youtube.com/channel/UCkCSDdhm
 4Ut0Fg8QM2hwM2w
Ed: Linda Baker. **Released:** Monthly; 8 times per year, Mar/Apr, Jul/Aug and Oct/Nov/Dec. **Price:** $2.08, for month; $24.95, Single issue for print per year. **Description:** Business in the state of Oregon. **Availability:** Print; PDF; Download; Online.

44080 ■ Portland Business Journal (PBJ)
851 SW 6th Ave., Ste. 500
 Portland, OR 97204
Ph: (503)274-8733
Fax: (503)219-3450
Co. E-mail: portland@bizjournals.com
URL: http://www.bizjournals.com/portland
Contact: Andy Giegerich, Managing Editor
E-mail: agiegerich@bizjournals.com
Facebook: www.facebook.com/PortlandBizJournal
X (Twitter): x.com/PDXBizJournal
Description: Publisher of journal covering breaking news, industry analysis, business tools, market leads. **Founded:** 1985.

PUBLISHERS

44081 ■ L&R Publishing, LLC
PO Box 3531
 Ashland, OR 97520
Free: 800-795-4059
Co. E-mail: sales@hellgatepress.com
URL: http://www.hellgatepress.com
Description: Publishes military history/memoirs, adventure travel, and historical fiction under the imprint Hellgate Press. Manuscript queries welcomed. **Founded:** 1997.

Pennsylvania

ASSOCIATIONS AND OTHER ORGANIZATIONS

44082 ■ Association of Fundraising Professionals Berks Regional Chapter - Lending Library
PO Box 331
 Shillington, PA 19607
Co. E-mail: afpberks@gmail.com
URL: http://community.afpglobal.org/afppaberksregionalchapter/home
Contact: Brett Mayer, President
Facebook: www.facebook.com/AFPBerks
Scope: Philanthropy. **Holdings:** Books; magazines. **Geographic Preference:** Local.

44083 ■ Association of Fundraising Professionals Greater Philadelphia Chapter
PO Box 37635 No. 88658
 Philadelphia, PA 19101
Ph: (267)665-2700
Co. E-mail: chapter@afpgpc.org
URL: http://afpgpc.org
Contact: Doris Parent, Vice President
Facebook: www.facebook.com/AFPGPC
X (Twitter): x.com/afpgpc
Description: Provides professional development and educational opportunities to individuals involved in fundraising in the Philadelphia area. **Founded:** 1968. **Geographic Preference:** Regional.

44084 ■ Business Network International Western Pennsylvania (BNI-WPA) [BNI Western Pennsylvania]
PA
Ph: (724)941-0101
URL: http://bni-westernpa.com/en-US/index
Description: Provides both men and women a structured environment for the development and exchange of quality business referrals. Offers members the opportunity to share ideas and contacts. **Geographic Preference:** Local.

44085 ■ Entrepreneurs Forum of Greater Philadelphia (EFGP)
PO Box 1155
 Havertown, PA 19083
URL: http://www.philly100.org
Contact: Emily Biscardi, President
Description: Acts as a platform for CEOs and like-minded leaders from Philadelphia to meet, connect and learn new opportunities. **Geographic Preference:** Local.

44086 ■ Entrepreneurs' Organization - Pittsburgh Chapter (EO)
Pittsburgh, PA
URL: http://www.eonetwork.org/pittsburgh
Description: Seeks to help entrepreneurs achieve their full potential in their business and personal lives through networking, shared experiences, and collaborative learning. **Founded:** 1993.

44087 ■ The Indus Entrepreneurs Pittsburgh
PO Box 82
 Bridgeville, PA 15017
Ph: (412)334-8855
Co. E-mail: ed@tiepgh.org
URL: http://pittsburgh.tie.org
Contact: Robin Prasad, President
Linkedin: www.linkedin.com/company/tie-pittsburgh
X (Twitter): x.com/TiEPittsburgh
Description: Advocates for the advancement of entrepreneurship and exchange of ideas. Works in fostering entrepreneurship and nurturing entrepreneurs, providing a networking platform for members and helping members integrate with the mainstream community. **Founded:** 2000. **Geographic Preference:** Local.

44088 ■ International Association of Business Communicators Harrisburg (IABC)
Harrisburg, PA
Co. E-mail: info@iabcharrisburg.com
URL: http://iabcharrisburg.com
Facebook: www.facebook.com/iabcharrisburg
Description: Represents the interests of public relations and communication professionals. Aims to improve the effectiveness of organizations through strategic, interactive and integrated business communication management. Provides products, services, and networking activities to help people and organizations excel in public relations, employee communication, marketing communication, public affairs and other forms of communication. **Geographic Preference:** Local.

44089 ■ International Association of Women Philadelphia Chapter
Philadelphia, PA
URL: http://thewisefund.org/who-we-are
Description: Serves as network of accomplished women united to achieve professional goals. Provides a forum for sharing ideas and experiences of professional women regarding career success. Promotes an active business and networking community from all industries. **Geographic Preference:** Local.

44090 ■ International Association of Women Pittsburgh Chapter
Pittsburgh, PA
URL: http://community.iawomen.com/pittsburgh/home
Contact: Sarah Maynard, President
Facebook: www.facebook.com/IAWomenPittsburgh
Description: Serves as network of accomplished women united to achieve professional goals. Provides a forum for sharing ideas and experiences of professional women regarding career success. Promotes an active business and networking community from all industries. **Geographic Preference:** Local.

44091 ■ Pittsburgh Venture Capital Association (PVCA)
700 Bursca Dr., Ste. 706
 Bridgeville, PA 15017
Ph: (412)228-5826
Fax: (412)228-5879
Co. E-mail: information@thepvca.org
URL: http://thepvca.org
Contact: Kelly Szejko, President
Facebook: www.facebook.com/ThePVCA
Linkedin: www.linkedin.com/company/986616
X (Twitter): x.com/ThePVCA
YouTube: www.youtube.com/channel/UCFCJ_gNg87IIVtY5SnHcqDA
Description: Offers venture investment and encourages entrepreneurialism in Western Pennsylvania. Facilitates deal flow, encourages investor collaboration, and fosters relationships with key service providers. **Founded:** 1982.

SMALL BUSINESS DEVELOPMENT CENTERS

44092 ■ Bucknell University Small Business Development Center (SBDC)
229 Dana Engineering Bldg.
 Lewisburg, PA 17837
Ph: (570)577-1249
Co. E-mail: sbdc@bucknell.edu
URL: http://www.bucknell.edu/azdirectory/small-business-development-center
Facebook: www.facebook.com/BucknellSBDC
X (Twitter): x.com/bucknellsbdc
Instagram: www.instagram.com/bucknellsbdc
YouTube: www.youtube.com/channel/UChIDJos2OGgmoCzAeUIVX8Q
Description: Represents and promotes the small business sector. Provides management assistance to current and prospective small business owners. Helps to improve management skills and expand the products and services of members. **Founded:** 1846. **Geographic Preference:** Local.

44093 ■ Clarion University Small Business Development Center (SBDC)
909 E Wood St.
 Clarion, PA 16214
Ph: (814)393-2060
Co. E-mail: sbdc@clarion.edu
URL: http://www.pennwest.edu/community/clarion
Contact: Cindy Nellis, Director
E-mail: cnellis@clarion.edu
Facebook: www.facebook.com/sbdcclarion
Linkedin: www.linkedin.com/company/clarion-university-sbdc
X (Twitter): x.com/ClarionSBDC
Description: Small Business Development Center (SBDC) that supports the growth of the economy of western Pennsylvania by providing entrepreneurs with the education, information and tools necessary to build successful businesses. **Founded:** 1980. **Geographic Preference:** Local.

44094 ■ Duquesne University Small Business Development Center
108 Rockwell Hall
 600 Forbes Ave.
 Pittsburgh, PA 15282-0103
Ph: (412)396-1633

Small Business Sourcebook • 42nd Edition

Fax: (412)396-5884
Co. E-mail: duqsbdc@duq.edu
URL: http://www.sbdc.duq.edu
Contact: Rich Longo, Director
X (Twitter): x.com/duquesnesbdc
YouTube: www.youtube.com/user/DuquesneSBDC
Description: Represents and promotes the small business sector. Provides management assistance to current and prospective small business owners. Helps to improve management skills and expand the products and services of members. **Founded:** 1986. **Geographic Preference:** Local.

44095 ■ Gannon University Small Business Development Center (GUSBDC)
900 State St., Ste. 100
Erie, PA 16501
Ph: (814)871-7232
Fax: (814)871-7383
Co. E-mail: gannonsbdc@gannon.edu
URL: http://www.sbdcgannon.org
Contact: Maggie Horne, Director
Facebook: www.facebook.com/GannonSBDC
Linkedin: www.linkedin.com/company/sbdc-gannon
Description: Represents and promotes the small business sector. Provides management assistance to current and prospective small business owners. Helps to improve management skills and expand the products and services of members. **Founded:** 1981. **Geographic Preference:** Local.

44096 ■ Indiana University of Pennsylvania Small Business Development Center (SBDC)
Eberly College of Business Rm., 108 664 Pratt Dr.
Indiana, PA 15705
Ph: (724)357-5729
Co. E-mail: eswift@innovation.pitt.edu
URL: http://www.iup.edu/business/centers/sbdc/index.html
Description: Represents and promotes the small business sector. Provides management assistance to current and prospective small business owners. Helps to improve management skills and expand the products and services of members. **Scope:** Business management and technical assistance, including studies that benefit the small business community. **Founded:** 2003. **Educational Activities:** SBDC Workshops. **Geographic Preference:** Local.

44097 ■ Kutztown University Small Business Development Center (KUSBDC)
Old Main - E Wing - Rm. 24, 15219 Kutztown Rd.
Kutztown, PA 19530
Ph: (610)683-4000
Free: 877-472-7232
Co. E-mail: sbdc@kutztown.edu
URL: http://www.kutztown.edu/about-ku/administrative-offices/small-business-development-center.html
Contact: Ernie Post, Director
E-mail: post@kutztown.edu
Linkedin: www.linkedin.com/company/kutztown-university-small-business-development-center
X (Twitter): x.com/KutztownSBDC
YouTube: www.youtube.com/user/KUSBDCtv
Pinterest: www.pinterest.com/kutztownsbdc
Description: Represents and promotes the small business sector. Provides management assistance to current and prospective small business owners. Helps to improve management skills and expand the products and services of members. **Founded:** 1993. **Geographic Preference:** Local.

44098 ■ Lehigh University Small Business Development Center (LUSBDC) - Library
416 E 5th St.
Bethlehem, PA 18015
Ph: (610)758-3980
Fax: (610)758-5205
Co. E-mail: insbdc@lehigh.edu
URL: http://sbdc.lehigh.edu
Contact: Brett Smith, Director
E-mail: bds206@lehigh.edu
Linkedin: www.linkedin.com/in/lehighsbdc
X (Twitter): x.com/lehighsbdc
Description: Represents and promotes the small business sector. Provides management assistance to current and prospective small business owners. Helps to improve management skills and expand the products and services of members. **Scope:** Problems faced by small businesses, the impact of the general economy on the formation and operation of small business, and characteristics on entrepreneurs. **Services:** Library open to the public on a limited schedule. **Founded:** 1978. **Holdings:** Books. **Publications:** *Export Planning Guide*; *Financing Guide for Northampton*; *Financing Your Business*; *Lehigh and Berks County*; *Lehigh Valley Business Support Services*; *Market Planning Guide*. **Educational Activities:** First Step Seminar. **Geographic Preference:** Local.

44099 ■ Lock Haven University Small Business Development Center (SBDC)
301 W Church St.
Lock Haven, PA 17745
Ph: (814)863-4293
Co. E-mail: sbdc@psu.edu
URL: http://sbdc.psu.edu
Facebook: www.facebook.com/PennStateSBDC
X (Twitter): x.com/PennStateSBDC
Description: Represents and promotes the small business sector. Provides management assistance to current and prospective small business owners. Helps to improve management skills and expand the products and services of members. **Founded:** 1992. **Geographic Preference:** Local.

44100 ■ Penn State Small Business Development Center
155 Technology Ctr.
200 Innovation Blvd.
University Park, PA 16802
Ph: (814)863-4293
Co. E-mail: sbdc@psu.edu
URL: http://sbdc.psu.edu
Contact: Tim Keohane, Director
E-mail: tjk272@psu.edu
Facebook: www.facebook.com/pennstatesbdc
Linkedin: www.linkedin.com/company/penn-state-small-business-development-center
X (Twitter): x.com/PennStateSBDC
Instagram: www.instagram.com/pennstatesbdc
Description: Represents and promotes the small business sector. Provides management assistance to current and prospective small business owners. Helps to improve management skills and expand the products and services of members. **Founded:** 1997. **Publications:** *Advisor Newsletter* (3/year); *SBDC News* (Semiannual). **Geographic Preference:** Local.

44101 ■ Pennsylvania Small Business Development Centers (SBDC)
Kutztown University of Pennsylvania
15200 Kutztown Rd., E-Wing, Ste. 24
Kutztown, PA 19530
Free: 877-472-7232
Co. E-mail: sbdc@kutztown.edu
URL: http://www.pasbdc.org
Contact: Ernie Post, Director
E-mail: post@kutztown.edu
Facebook: www.facebook.com/PennsylvaniaSBDC
Linkedin: www.linkedin.com/company/pennsylvania-small-business-development-centers
X (Twitter): x.com/PASmallBusiness
Description: The Pennsylvania SBDC State Director's office is hosted by the Wharton School at the University of Pennsylvania. The State Director's office is responsible for the administration and oversight of the Pennsylvania system of 18 centers. **Scope:** Helps small businesses improve profitability and increase employment through programs of procurement, international trade, product development, and business law. **Founded:** 1980. **Geographic Preference:** State.

44102 ■ Saint Francis University Small Business Development Center (SBDC)
132 Franciscan Way
Loretto, PA 15940
Ph: (814)472-3200
Co. E-mail: sbdc@francis.edu
URL: http://www.francis.edu/about-us/community-resources/small-business-development-center
Contact: Jeffrey A. Boldizar, Director
E-mail: jboldizar@francis.edu
Facebook: www.facebook.com/SaintFrancisSBDC
Description: Represents and promotes the small business sector. Provides management assistance to current and prospective small business owners. Helps to improve management skills and expand the products and services of members. **Founded:** 1980. **Geographic Preference:** Local.

44103 ■ Saint Vincent College Small Business Development Center (SVC)
300 Fraser Purchase Rd.Aurelius Hall - First Fl.
Latrobe, PA 15650
Ph: (724)537-4572
Co. E-mail: sbdc@stvincent.edu
URL: http://www.stvincent.edu/academics/academic-centers/small-business-development-center.html
Contact: James H. Kunkel, Executive Director
E-mail: james.kunkel@email.stvincent.edu
Description: Represents and promotes the small business sector. Provides management assistance to current and prospective small business owners. Helps to improve management skills and expand the products and services of members. **Founded:** 1984. **Geographic Preference:** Local.

44104 ■ Shippensburg University Small Business Development Center (SBDC)
405 Grove Hall
1871 Old Main Dr.
Shippensburg, PA 17257
Ph: (717)477-1935
Fax: (717)477-4010
Co. E-mail: sbdc@ship.edu
URL: http://www.pasbdc.org/shippensburg
Contact: Robin Burtner, Director
E-mail: reburtner@ship.edu
Description: Represents and promotes the small business sector. Provides management assistance to current and prospective small business owners. Helps to improve management skills and expand the products and services of members. **Founded:** 2007. **Geographic Preference:** Local.

44105 ■ Temple University Small Business Development Center (SBDC)
1515 Market St., Ste. 525
Philadelphia, PA 19102
Ph: (215)204-7282
Fax: (215)204-4554
Co. E-mail: sbdc@temple.edu
URL: http://www.fox.temple.edu/institutes-centers/small-business-development-center
Contact: Jamie Shanker, Director
Facebook: www.facebook.com/temple.sbdc
Linkedin: www.linkedin.com/in/temple-small-business-development-ctr-a2630914
X (Twitter): x.com/TU_SBDC
Description: Helps small business grow and succeed. We provide high quality business management consulting and training for aspiring entrepreneurs and small emerging growth companies in Southeastern Pennsylvania. **Scope:** Small business operations, entrepreneurship, and the success and failure of small businesses. **Founded:** 1983. **Geographic Preference:** Local.

44106 ■ University of Pittsburgh Small Business Development Center
3520 Forbes Ave.
Pittsburgh, PA 15261
URL: http://entrepreneur.pitt.edu/centers/small-business-development-center-sbdc
Contact: Bob Stein, Executive Director
Facebook: www.facebook.com/Pghentrepreneur
X (Twitter): x.com/pghentrepreneur
Description: Represents and promotes the small business sector. Provides management assistance to current and prospective small business owners. Helps to improve management skills and expand the products and services of members. **Founded:** 1980. **Geographic Preference:** Local.

44107 ■ University of Scranton Small Business Development Center (SBDC)
600 Linden St.
Scranton, PA 18510-4639
Ph: (570)941-7588
Co. E-mail: sbdc@scranton.edu
URL: http://www.scrantonsbdc.com
Contact: Lisa Hall Zielinski, Director
E-mail: lisa.hall@scranton.edu
Facebook: www.facebook.com/sbdcscranton
X (Twitter): x.com/scrantonsbdc
Instagram: www.instagram.com/scrantonsbdc
YouTube: www.youtube.com/c/ScrantonSBDC
Pinterest: www.pinterest.com/scrantonsbdc
Description: Represents and promotes the small business sector. Provides management assistance to current and prospective small business owners. Helps to improve management skills and expand the products and services of members. **Founded:** 1980. **Geographic Preference:** Local.

44108 ■ Widener University Small Business Development Center
School of Business - Quick Ctr., 1304 Walnut St.
Chester, PA 19013
Ph: (610)499-4109
Co. E-mail: wdsbdc@widener.edu
URL: http://www.widenersbdc.org
Contact: Lenin Agudo, Director
E-mail: lpagudo@widener.edu
Facebook: www.facebook.com/widenerSBDC
X (Twitter): x.com/widenersbdc
Description: Represents and promotes the small business sector. Provides management assistance to current and prospective small business owners. Helps to improve management skills and expand the products and services of members. **Founded:** 2007. **Geographic Preference:** Local.

44109 ■ Wilkes University Small Business Development Center
85 S Main St.
Wilkes Barre, PA 18701
Ph: (570)408-4340
Co. E-mail: sbdc@wilkes.edu
URL: http://www.wilkes.edu/sbdc
Contact: Dorothy Lane, Director
E-mail: dorothy.lane@wilkes.edu
Facebook: www.facebook.com/wilkessbdc
X (Twitter): x.com/wilkessbdc
Description: Represents and promotes the small business sector. Provides management assistance to current and prospective small business owners. Helps to improve management skills and expand the products and services of members. **Founded:** 1980. **Geographic Preference:** Local.

SMALL BUSINESS ASSISTANCE PROGRAMS

44110 ■ Pennsylvania Department of Community and Economic Development (OIBD) - Office of International Business Development
Commonwealth Keystone Bldg.
400 N St., 4th Fl.
Harrisburg, PA 17120-0225
Ph: (717)787-7190
Fax: (717)772-5106
URL: http://dced.pa.gov/business-assistance/international/trade/office-of-international-business-development
Contact: Jen Black, Executive Director
E-mail: jblack@pa.gov
Description: Provides assistance to companies seeking the latest information on potential foreign markets for their products, and regional economic development organizations and companies with information about all facets of international trade. Responds to inquiries from foreign importers in search of new suppliers.

44111 ■ Pennsylvania Department of Community and Economic Development - Pennsylvania Industrial Development Authority (PIDA)
Commonwealth Keystone Bldg., 400 N St., 4th Fl.
Harrisburg, PA 17120-0225
URL: http://dced.pa.gov/programs/pennsylvania-industrial-development-authority-pida
Contact: Jared Lucas, Contact
E-mail: jarlucas@pa.gov
Description: Established in 1956 to make long-term, low-interest business loans to firms engaged in manufacturing or industrial enterprises. **Founded:** 1956.

44112 ■ Pennsylvania Department of Community & Economic Development - Site Development Div.
Commonwealth Keystone Bldg., 400 N St., 4th Fl.
Harrisburg, PA 17120-0225
URL: http://dced.pa.gov/programs/tax-increment-financing-tif-guarantee-program
Description: Provides financing for infrastructure improvements such as sewer and water systems, waste disposal facilities, transportation facilities, and fire and safety facilities.

44113 ■ Pennsylvania Department of Community and Economic Development, Technology Innovation - Ben Franklin Technology Partners
116 Research Dr., Plz. Level
Bethlehem, PA 18015
Ph: (610)758-5200
Fax: (610)861-5918
Co. E-mail: info@nep.benfranklin.org
URL: http://nep.benfranklin.org
Contact: Angelo J. Valletta, President
Facebook: www.facebook.com/BenFranklinNortheast
Linkedin: www.linkedin.com/company/ben-franklin-technology-partners-of-northeastern-pennsylvania
YouTube: www.youtube.com/user/BFTechVentures/featured
Description: Programs promote advanced technology in an effort to make traditional industry more competitive in the international marketplace. BFP's Advanced Technology Centers represent consortia of businesses that provide joint applied research and development efforts, assistance to higher education institutions and entrepreneurial assistance services. **Founded:** 1983.

44114 ■ Pennsylvania State University Technical Assistance Program (TAP)
200 Innovation Blvd., Ste. 117
University Park, PA 16802
Ph: (814)865-0427
Co. E-mail: penntap@psu.edu
URL: http://penntap.psu.edu
Contact: Tanna Pugh, Director
E-mail: tannapugh@psu.edu
Facebook: www.facebook.com/penntap.psu
Linkedin: www.linkedin.com/company/pennsylvania-technical-assistance-program-penntap
X (Twitter): x.com/penntap
YouTube: www.youtube.com/channel/UCL2vHSt1GrPiDaxsnItVkJw
Description: Provides technical information and assistance in problem-solving, business start-up, and increasing productivity. **Founded:** 1965.

SCORE OFFICES

44115 ■ Pittsburgh SCORE
3 Pky., Ctr., Dr. S, Ste. 375
Pittsburgh, PA 15220
Ph: (412)395-6560
Co. E-mail: info.pittsburgh@scorevolunteer.org
URL: http://www.score.org/pittsburgh
Facebook: www.facebook.com/SCOREPittsburgh
Linkedin: www.linkedin.com/company/score-pittsburgh
Instagram: www.instagram.com/score_mentors_pittsburgh
Description: Aims to help small businesses in Southwestern Pennsylvania to grow and prosper by providing workshops and one-on-one counseling by members that have many years of experience in managing businesses. **Founded:** 1965. **Geographic Preference:** Local.

44116 ■ SCORE - Altoona
Devorris Ctr.
3900 Industrial Pk. Dr.
Altoona, PA 16602
URL: http://westmoreland.score.org
Description: Provides professional guidance and information to maximize the success of existing and emerging small businesses. Offers business counseling and workshops.

44117 ■ SCORE - Berks and Schuylkill County
401 Penn St.
Reading, PA 19601
Ph: (610)376-3497
Fax: (610)376-4135
URL: http://www.score.org/berksschuylkill
Linkedin: www.linkedin.com/company/score-mentors-berks-and-schuylkill-cty
X (Twitter): x.com/SCOREBerkSchlkl
Description: Provides professional guidance and information to maximize the success of existing and emerging small businesses. Offers business counseling and workshops. **Founded:** 1964.

44118 ■ SCORE - Blue Bell
Parkhouse Hall, 340 Dekalb Pike
Rm. 55
Blue Bell, PA 19422
URL: http://montgomerycountypa.score.org/blue-bell-location
Description: Provides professional guidance and information to maximize the success of existing and emerging small businesses. Offers business counseling and workshops.

44119 ■ SCORE - Boyertown
3 E Philadelphia Ave.
Boyertown, PA 19512
Ph: (610)327-2673
Co. E-mail: tricounty@scorevolunteer.org
URL: http://tricounty.score.org/branch/boyertown-branch-office
Description: Provides professional guidance and information to maximize the success of existing and emerging small businesses. Offers business counseling and workshops.

44120 ■ SCORE - Bucks County
11 Welden Dr., Ste.100
Doylestown, PA 18901
Ph: (215)943-8850
Co. E-mail: buckscounty@scorevolunteer.org
URL: http://www.score.org/buckscounty
Contact: Linda Zangrilli, Contact
Facebook: www.facebook.com/SCOREBucksCountyPA
Linkedin: www.linkedin.com/company/score-mentors-bucks-county
X (Twitter): x.com/scorebcpa
Description: Provides professional guidance and information to maximize the success of existing and emerging small businesses. Offers business counseling and workshops. **Founded:** 1964.

44121 ■ SCORE - Carlisle
212 N Hanover St.
Carlisle, PA 17013
URL: http://susquehanna.score.org/contact-susquehanna-score
Contact: David Riggs, Contact
Description: Provides professional guidance and information to maximize the success of existing and emerging small businesses. Offers business counseling and workshops.

44122 ■ SCORE - CCP Northeast
105 N 22nd St.
Philadelphia, PA 19103
Ph: (215)231-9880

URL: http://philadelphia.score.org/branch/ccp-northeast
Contact: Mary Livingston, President
Description: Provides professional guidance and information to maximize the success of existing and emerging small businesses. Offers business counseling and workshops.

44123 ■ SCORE - CCP Northwest
1300 W Godfrey Ave.
Philadelphia, PA 19141
Ph: (215)231-9880
Fax: (215)231-9881
Co. E-mail: contact.scorephiladelphia@gmail.com
URL: http://www.score.org/find-location
Description: Provides professional guidance and information to maximize the success of existing and emerging small businesses. Offers business counseling and workshops.

44124 ■ SCORE - CCP West Philadelphia
632 N 2nd St., Unit 786
Philadelphia, PA 19123
Ph: (215)231-9880
Co. E-mail: philadelphia@scorevolunteer.org
URL: http://www.score.org/philadelphia
Contact: Jack Musgrove, Chairman
Facebook: www.facebook.com/SCOREPhiladelphia
Linkedin: www.linkedin.com/company/score-philadelphia
X (Twitter): x.com/SCOREPhila
Instagram: www.instagram.com/scorephila
Description: Provides professional guidance and information to maximize the success of existing and emerging small businesses. Offers business counseling and workshops.

44125 ■ SCORE - Central Pennsylvania
2820 E College Ave., Ste. E
State College, PA 16801
Ph: (814)234-9415
Co. E-mail: help@score.org
URL: http://centralpa.score.org
Facebook: www.facebook.com/SCORECentralPA
Linkedin: www.linkedin.com/company/score-central-pa
X (Twitter): x.com/SCORECentralPA
Description: Provides professional guidance and information to maximize the success of existing and emerging small businesses. Offers business counseling and workshops. **Founded:** 1991. **Geographic Preference:** Local.

44126 ■ SCORE - Chester County Economic Development Council (CCEDC)
737 Constitution Dr., Eagleview Corporate Ctr.
Exton, PA 19341
Ph: (610)344-6910
URL: http://chesterdelco.score.org/content/about-us-40
Contact: John M. Davis, Contact
URL(s): www.score.org/find-location
Description: Provides professional guidance and information to maximize the success of existing and emerging small businesses. Offers business counseling and workshops.

44127 ■ SCORE - Chester and Delaware Counties
601 Westtown Rd., No. 281
West Chester, PA 19380
Ph: (610)344-6910
Co. E-mail: contact.0544@scorevolunteer.org
URL: http://chesterdelco.score.org
Facebook: www.facebook.com/SCOREChesterandDelawareCounties
Linkedin: www.linkedin.com/company/score-chester-&-delaware-county
X (Twitter): x.com/SCOREChesDelco
Instagram: www.instagram.com/score_chester_delaware
Description: Provides professional guidance and information to maximize the success of existing and emerging small businesses. Offers business counseling and workshops. **Geographic Preference:** Local.

44128 ■ SCORE - City of Philadelphia
632 N 2nd St., Unit 786
Philadelphia, PA 19123
Ph: (215)231-9880
Co. E-mail: philadelphia@scorevolunteer.org
URL: http://www.score.org/philadelphia
Contact: Daniel Garlen, Contact
Facebook: www.facebook.com/SCOREPhiladelphia
Linkedin: www.linkedin.com/company/score-philadelphia
Description: Provides professional guidance and information to maximize the success of existing and emerging small businesses. Offers business counseling and workshops.

44129 ■ SCORE - Coatesville
Lincoln University satellite campus
351 Kersey St.
Coatesville, PA 19320
URL: http://chesterdelco.score.org
Description: Provides professional guidance and information to maximize the success of existing and emerging small businesses. Offers business counseling and workshops.

44130 ■ SCORE - Collegeville
601 E Main St.
Kaleidoscope Hall, Rm. 207
Collegeville, PA 19426
URL: http://montgomerycountypa.score.org/collegeville-location
Description: Provides professional guidance and information to maximize the success of existing and emerging small businesses. Offers business counseling and workshops.

44131 ■ SCORE - Devon
800 E Lancaster Ave.
Devon, PA 19333
URL: http://chesterdelco.score.org
URL(s): www.score.org/find-location
Description: Provides professional guidance and information to maximize the success of existing and emerging small businesses. Offers business counseling and workshops.

44132 ■ SCORE - Doylestown
11 Weldon Dr., Ste., 100
Doylestown, PA 18901
Ph: (215)943-8850
Co. E-mail: buckscounty@scorevolunteer.org
URL: http://buckscounty.score.org
Contact: Linda Zangrilli, Chairperson
Linkedin: www.linkedin.com/company/score-mentors-bucks-county
X (Twitter): x.com/scorebcpa
YouTube: www.youtube.com/channel/UC8_A2Fnn4HGqA5kMgrlsRrw
Description: Provides professional guidance and information to maximize the success of existing and emerging small businesses. Offers business counseling and workshops. **Founded:** 1964.

44133 ■ SCORE - Fairless Hills
409 Hood Blvd.
Fairless Hills, PA 19030
URL: http://buckscounty.score.org/about-us-33
Description: Provides professional guidance and information to maximize the success of existing and emerging small businesses. Offers business counseling and workshops.

44134 ■ SCORE - Glen Mills
395 Wilmington -west chester Pke.
Glen Mills, PA 19342
URL: http://chesterdelco.score.org/content/about-us-40
Description: Provides professional guidance and information to maximize the success of existing and emerging small businesses. Offers business counseling and workshops.

44135 ■ SCORE - Harrisburg
3211 N Front St., Ste. 201
Harrisburg, PA 17110
Ph: (717)845-8830

URL: http://susquehanna.score.org/contact-susquehanna-score
URL(s): www.score.org/find-location
Description: Provides professional guidance and information to maximize the success of existing and emerging small businesses. Offers business counseling and workshops.

44136 ■ SCORE - Horsham
300 Welsh Rd., Bldg.
Horsham, PA 19044
Co. E-mail: counselor@score513.org
URL: http://www.score.org/content/horsham
Description: Provides professional guidance and information to maximize the success of existing and emerging small businesses. Offers business counseling and workshops.

44137 ■ SCORE - Jenkintown
1653 The Fairway, Ste. 204
Jenkintown, PA 19046
Co. E-mail: counselor@score513.org
URL: http://montgomerycountypa.score.org/jenkintown-location
Description: Provides professional guidance and information to maximize the success of existing and emerging small businesses. Offers business counseling and workshops.

44138 ■ SCORE - Kennett Square
Bayard Taylor Memorial Library
216 E State St.
Kennett Square, PA 19348
URL: http://chesterdelco.score.org/content/about-us-40
Description: Provides professional guidance and information to maximize the success of existing and emerging small businesses. Offers business counseling and workshops.

44139 ■ SCORE - Lancaster-Lebanon
313 W Liberty St.
Lancaster, PA 17603
Ph: (717)397-3092
Co. E-mail: help@score.org
URL: http://lancaster.score.org
Contact: Peter Barber, Contact
Facebook: www.facebook.com/SCORE.LancasterPA
Linkedin: www.linkedin.com/company/score-lancaster
Instagram: www.instagram.com/scorelancaster
YouTube: www.youtube.com/user/scorelancaster
Description: Strives for the formation, growth, and success of small businesses. Promotes entrepreneur education throughout Lancaster County. **Founded:** 1965. **Geographic Preference:** Local.

44140 ■ SCORE - Lehigh Valley (LV SCORE)
4525 Education Pk. Dr.
Schnecksville, PA 18078
Ph: (610)266-3000
Co. E-mail: admin.0074@scorevolunteer.org
URL: http://www.lehighvalley.score.org
Contact: Catherine Bailey, President
Facebook: www.facebook.com/SCORELehighValleyPA
Linkedin: www.linkedin.com/company/lehigh-valley-score
Description: Provides professional guidance and information to maximize the success of existing and emerging small businesses. Offers business counseling and workshops. **Founded:** 1964. **Geographic Preference:** Local.

44141 ■ SCORE - Media
1617 John F. Kennedy Blvd., Ste., 860
Philadelphia, PA 19103
URL: http://file.dos.pa.gov/search/business
Description: Provides professional guidance and information to maximize the success of existing and emerging small businesses. Offers business counseling and workshops.

44142 ■ SCORE - Montgomery County, PA
1150 1st Ave., Ste. 1001
King of Prussia, PA 19406
Ph: (215)943-8850
Co. E-mail: help@score.org

STATE LISTINGS Pennsylvania ■ 44160

URL: http://montgomerycountypa.score.org
Contact: Bridget Weston, Chief Executive Officer
Description: Provides professional guidance and information to maximize the success of existing and emerging small businesses. Offers business counseling and workshops. **Geographic Preference:** Local.

44143 ■ SCORE - Mount Airy
6700 Germantown Ave.
Philadelphia, PA 19119
URL: http://philadelphia.score.org
Description: Provides professional guidance and information to maximize the success of existing and emerging small businesses. Offers business counseling and workshops.

44144 ■ SCORE - Northeast Pennsylvania
Stegmaier Bldg., Ste. 400M
Wilkes Barre, PA 18702-5241
Ph: (570)826-6502
Co. E-mail: help@score.org
URL: http://nepa.score.org
Contact: Bridget Weston, Chief Executive Officer
Facebook: www.facebook.com/NortheastPaScore
X (Twitter): x.com/SCORE_NEPenn
Description: Seeks to educate entrepreneurs and help small businesses start, grow and succeed nationwide. Organizes volunteers who are working or retired business owners, executives and corporate leaders who wish to share their wisdom and lessons learned in business. **Geographic Preference:** Local.

44145 ■ SCORE - Northwest Pennsylvania
120 W 9th St.
Erie, PA 16501
Ph: (814)871-5650
Fax: (814)871-7997
URL: http://erie.score.org
Contact: Markie Sessamen, Vice Chairman of the Board
Description: Provides professional guidance and information to maximize the success of existing and emerging small businesses. Offers business counseling and workshops. **Geographic Preference:** Local.

44146 ■ SCORE - Oil City
217 Elm St.
Oil City, PA 16301
URL: http://www.score.org/westmoreland/about
Description: Provides professional guidance and information to maximize the success of existing and emerging small businesses. Offers business counseling and workshops.

44147 ■ SCORE - Philadelphia
632 N 2nd St., Unit 786
Philadelphia, PA 19123
Ph: (215)231-9880
Co. E-mail: philadelphia@scorevolunteer.org
URL: http://www.score.org/philadelphia
Contact: Mary Livingston, Chairman
Facebook: www.facebook.com/SCOREPhiladelphia
Linkedin: www.linkedin.com/company/score-philadelphia
X (Twitter): x.com/SCOREPhila
Instagram: www.instagram.com/scorephila
Description: Provides professional guidance and information to maximize the success of existing and emerging small businesses. Offers business counseling and workshops. **Founded:** 1964.

44148 ■ SCORE - Philadelphia Free Library (Lovett Branch)
105 N 22nd St.
Philadelphia, PA 19103
Ph: (215)231-9880
Fax: (215)231-9881
Co. E-mail: contact.scorephiladelphia@gmail.com
URL: http://philadelphia.score.org
Contact: Mary Livingston, President
Linkedin: www.linkedin.com/company/score-philadelphia
X (Twitter): twitter.com/SCOREPhila
YouTube: www.youtube.com/channel/UC6u3wJUh5C66XQfG7khXF3w

Description: Provides professional guidance and information to maximize the success of existing and emerging small businesses. Offers business counseling and workshops.

44149 ■ SCORE - Philadelphia Free Library (Parkway)
1901 Vine St., Ground Fl., BRIC, Ground Fl.
Philadelphia, PA 19103
Ph: (215)686-5423
Co. E-mail: nonprofit@freelibrary.org
URL: http://www.freelibrary.org
Contact: Joe Benford, Project Manager
Facebook: www.facebook.com/freelibrary
X (Twitter): twitter.com/FreeLibrary
Instagram: www.instagram.com/freelibrary
YouTube: www.youtube.com/user/freelibraryofphilly
Description: Provides professional guidance and information to maximize the success of existing and emerging small businesses. Offers business counseling and workshops.

44150 ■ SCORE - Phoenixville
171 E Bridge St.
Phoenixville Regional Chamber of Commerce
Phoenixville, PA 19460
Ph: (610)344-6910
URL: http://www.score.org/find-location?state=PA
Description: Provides professional guidance and information to maximize the success of existing and emerging small businesses. Offers business counseling and workshops.

44151 ■ SCORE - Pittsburgh
411 7th Ave., Ste. 1450
Pittsburgh, PA 15219
Ph: (412)353-3577
Fax: (412)395-6562
Co. E-mail: info.pittsburgh@scorevolunteer.org
URL: http://pittsburgh.score.org
Facebook: www.facebook.com/SCOREPittsburgh
Linkedin: www.linkedin.com/company/score-pittsburgh
Instagram: www.instagram.com/score_mentors_pittsburgh
Pinterest: www.pinterest.com/scorepittsburgh
Description: Provides professional guidance and information to maximize the success of existing and emerging small businesses. Offers business counseling and workshops. **Founded:** 1965.

44152 ■ SCORE - Quakertown
21 N Main St.
Quakertown, PA 18951
Ph: (215)536-3211
Fax: (215)536-7767
URL: http://buckscounty.score.org/about-us-33
Description: Provides professional guidance and information to maximize the success of existing and emerging small businesses. Offers business counseling and workshops.

44153 ■ SCORE - St. Joseph University
105 N 22nd St.
Philadelphia, PA 19103
Ph: (215)231-9881
URL: http://philadelphia.score.org
Contact: Mary Livingston, President
Facebook: www.facebook.com/SCOREPhiladelphia
Linkedin: www.linkedin.com/company/score-philadelphia
X (Twitter): twitter.com/SCOREPhila
Instagram: www.instagram.com/scorephila
Description: Provides professional guidance and information to maximize the success of existing and emerging small businesses. Offers business counseling and workshops.

44154 ■ SCORE - Springfield, Pennsylvania
537 Baltimore Pke.
Springfield, PA 19064
Ph: (610)344-6910
URL: http://chesterdelco.score.org/mentoring-services-offered-following-locations

Description: Provides professional guidance and information to maximize the success of existing and emerging small businesses. Offers business counseling and workshops.

44155 ■ SCORE - Susquehanna
2101 Pennsylvania Ave.
York, PA 17404
Ph: (717)845-8830
Co. E-mail: susquehanna@scorevolunteer.org
URL: http://susquehanna.score.org
Contact: Joe Cervenak, Vice Chairman of the Board
Facebook: www.facebook.com/SusquehannaScore
Linkedin: www.linkedin.com/in/susquehanna-score-392a919b
X (Twitter): x.com/YorkSCORE
Instagram: www.instagram.com/susquehannascore
YouTube: www.youtube.com/channel/UCXCUm5hB1UDV-PeGbHPXYRQ
Description: Provides professional guidance and information to maximize the success of existing and emerging small businesses. Offers business counseling and workshops. **Founded:** 1979. **Geographic Preference:** Local.

44156 ■ SCORE - Telford
741 N County Line Rd.
Harleysville Savings Bank
Telford, PA 18969
URL: http://www.score.org/content/our-souderton-location
Description: Provides professional guidance and information to maximize the success of existing and emerging small businesses. Offers business counseling and workshops.

44157 ■ SCORE - Tricounty [SCORE - Pottstown]
343 E High St.
Pottstown, PA 19464
Ph: (610)327-2673
Co. E-mail: tricounty@scorevolunteer.org
URL: http://www.score.org/tricounty
Contact: Ralph A. Clemmer, Contact
Facebook: www.facebook.com/SCORETriCounty
Linkedin: www.linkedin.com/company/scoretricounty
X (Twitter): x.com/SCORETriCounty
Description: Provides professional guidance and information to maximize the success of existing and emerging small businesses. Offers business counseling and workshops. **Founded:** 1991. **Geographic Preference:** Local.

44158 ■ SCORE - Villanova
Villanova Idea Accelerator Center, Falvey Library
800 E Lancaster Ave.
Villanova, PA 19085
URL: http://chesterdelco.score.org
Description: Provides professional guidance and information to maximize the success of existing and emerging small businesses. Offers business counseling and workshops.

44159 ■ SCORE - Wayne
230 Sugartown Rd., Ste. 20
Wayne, PA 19087
Ph: (610)548-5278
URL: http://chesterdelco.score.org/mentoring-services-offered-following-locations
Description: Provides professional guidance and information to maximize the success of existing and emerging small businesses. Offers business counseling and workshops.

44160 ■ SCORE - West Chester
601 Westtown Rd., Ste.,281
West Chester, PA 19382
Ph: (484)356-8624
Co. E-mail: contact.0544@scorevolunteer.org
URL: http://chesterdelco.score.org
Linkedin: www.linkedin.com/company/score-chester-&-delaware-county
Description: Provides professional guidance and information to maximize the success of existing and emerging small businesses. Offers business counseling and workshops.

44161 ■ Pennsylvania STATE LISTINGS

44161 ■ SCORE - West Grove
8 Federal Rd., Ste. 1
West Grove, PA 19390
Ph: (610)444-0774
URL: http://www.score.org/find-location?state=PA
Description: Provides professional guidance and information to maximize the success of existing and emerging small businesses. Offers business counseling and workshops.

44162 ■ SCORE - West Shore
4211 Trindle Rd.
Camp Hill, PA 17011
Ph: (717)845-8830
URL: http://susquehanna.score.org
Description: Provides professional guidance and information to maximize the success of existing and emerging small businesses. Offers business counseling and workshops.

44163 ■ SCORE - Westmoreland County
St. Vincent College
300 Fraser Purchase Rd.
Latrobe, PA 15650
Ph: (724)539-7505
Co. E-mail: score@email.stvincent.edu
URL: http://westmoreland.score.org
Facebook: www.facebook.com/westmorelandscore
Linkedin: www.linkedin.com/company/score-mentors-westmoreland
X (Twitter): x.com/SCOREWstmorelnd
Description: Provides professional guidance and information to maximize the success of existing and emerging small businesses. Offers business counseling and workshops. **Geographic Preference:** Local.

44164 ■ SCORE - Wilkes-Barre
7 N Wilkes-Barre Blvd., Ste. 400M
Stegmaier Bldg.
Wilkes Barre, PA 18702-5241
Ph: (570)826-6502
Co. E-mail: wjevans@ptd.net
URL: http://nepa.score.org
Description: Provides professional guidance and information to maximize the success of existing and emerging small businesses. Offers business counseling and workshops. **Geographic Preference:** Local.

44165 ■ Tri-County SCORE
244 High St., Ste. 102
Pottstown, PA 19464
Ph: (610)327-2673
Co. E-mail: tricounty@scorevolunteer.org
URL: http://www.score.org/tricounty
Contact: Bridget Weston, Chief Executive Officer
Facebook: www.facebook.com/SCORETriCounty
Linkedin: www.linkedin.com/company/scoretricounty
X (Twitter): x.com/SCORETriCounty
Founded: 1991.

BETTER BUSINESS BUREAUS

44166 ■ Better Business Bureau of Western Pennsylvania (BBB)
520 E Main St., Ste. 100
Carnegie, PA 15106
Free: 877-267-5222
Fax: (412)922-8656
Co. E-mail: info@pittsburgh.bbb.org
URL: http://www.bbb.org/local-bbb/bbb-of-western-pennsylvania
Contact: Matthew Klingensmith, Member
Facebook: www.facebook.com/bbbwesternpa
Linkedin: www.linkedin.com/company/bbb-of-western-pa
X (Twitter): x.com/BBB_WesternPA
Instagram: www.instagram.com/bbb_westernpa
YouTube: www.youtube.com/user/WesternPABBB
Pinterest: www.pinterest.com/bbbwesternpa
Description: Seeks to promote and foster ethical relationship between businesses and the public through voluntary self-regulation, consumer and business education, and service excellence. Provides information to help consumers and businesses make informed purchasing decisions and avoid costly scams and frauds; settles consumer complaints through arbitration and other means. **Geographic Preference:** Local.

CHAMBERS OF COMMERCE

44167 ■ African-American Chamber of Commerce of Pennsylvania, New Jersey and Delaware (AACC)
1 Penn Ctr., Ste. 889
1617 John F. Kennedy Blvd.
Philadelphia, PA 19103
Ph: (215)751-9501
Co. E-mail: membership@aachamber.org
URL: http://aachamber.com
Contact: Lowell Thomas, Officer
Facebook: www.facebook.com/AAChamber
Linkedin: www.linkedin.com/company/aachamber
X (Twitter): x.com/official_AACC
Instagram: www.instagram.com/official_aacc
Description: Promotes business and community development in Philadelphia, PA. **Founded:** 1993. **Publications:** *Chamber News* (Monthly). **Geographic Preference:** State.

44168 ■ Alle Kiski Strong Chamber of Commerce
1525 Freeport Rd.
Natrona Heights, PA 15065
Ph: (724)224-3400
Fax: (724)224-3442
Co. E-mail: staff@akstrong.com
URL: http://allekiskistrong.com
Contact: Mary E. Bowlin, President
Facebook: www.facebook.com/allekiskistrong
Linkedin: www.linkedin.com/company/alle-kiski-strong-chamber
X (Twitter): x.com/akstrongchamber
Description: Promotes business and community development in northern Westmoreland and Southern Armstrong counties, PA. Operates Kiski Valley Enterprises; sponsors cycling race. **Founded:** 1985. **Publications:** *Chamber Climate* (Bimonthly); *Quickletter* (Monthly). **Educational Activities:** Homexpo (Annual). **Geographic Preference:** Regional; Local.

44169 ■ Ambridge Area Chamber of Commerce (AACC) [Ambridge Regional Chamber of Commerce]
562 Merchant St.
Ambridge, PA 15003
Ph: (724)266-3040
URL: http://www.ambridgeregionalchamber.org
Contact: Valerie Pedigo, President
Facebook: www.facebook.com/AmbridgeRegionalChamber
X (Twitter): x.com/ambridgercc
Instagram: www.instagram.com/ambridgeregionalchamber
Description: Promotes business and community development in the Ambridge, PA area. Sponsors Nationality Days. **Founded:** 1916. **Publications:** *Chamber Membership Roster* (Annual). **Geographic Preference:** Local.

44170 ■ Beaver County Chamber of Commerce (BCCC)
525 Third St., 2nd Fl.
Beaver, PA 15009
Ph: (724)775-3944
Co. E-mail: info@bcchamber.com
URL: http://www.beavercountychamber.com
Contact: Donna Lee Siple, President
E-mail: president@bcchamber.com
Facebook: www.facebook.com/BeaverCountyChamber
Linkedin: www.linkedin.com/company/beaver-county-chamber-of-commerce
Instagram: www.instagram.com/beavercountychamber
Description: Advances the economic, industrial, physical, professional, cultural and civic welfare of Beaver County through its membership. Encourages and protects the trade and commerce of the area and promotes its orderly growth and development. **Founded:** 1972. **Publications:** *Connections* (Monthly). **Awards:** Beaver County Chamber of Commerce Business of the Year Awards (Annual). **Geographic Preference:** Local.

44171 ■ Bedford County Chamber of Commerce
203 S Juliana St.
Bedford, PA 15522
Ph: (814)623-2233
Fax: (814)623-6089
Co. E-mail: director@bedfordcountychamber.org
URL: http://www.bedfordcountychamber.com
Contact: Kellie Goodman Shaffer, President
Description: Promotes business and community development in the Bedford County, PA area. **Founded:** 1986. **Publications:** *Chamber News*. **Geographic Preference:** Local.

44172 ■ Bellefonte Intervalley Area Chamber of Commerce (BIACC)
320 W High St., Train Sta.
Bellefonte, PA 16823
Ph: (814)355-2917
Co. E-mail: contact@bellefontechamber.org
URL: http://bellefontechamber.org
Contact: Tamara Schuster, President
E-mail: ofl.schuster@gmail.com
Facebook: www.facebook.com/bellefontechamber
Description: Promotes business and community development in the Bellefonte, PA area. **Founded:** 1938. **Geographic Preference:** Local.

44173 ■ *Blair Business Mirror*
3900 Industrial Pk. Dr., Ste. 12
Altoona, PA 16602
Ph: (814)943-8151
Fax: (814)943-5239
Co. E-mail: chamber@blairchamber.com
URL: http://www.blairchamber.com
Contact: Joe Hurd, President
E-mail: jhurd@blairchamber.com
URL(s): www.blairchamber.com/publications.html
Released: Monthly **Description:** Newspaper featuring Blair County Chamber of Commerce news, stories of chamber members and notices of upcoming programs and events. **Availability:** Print; Online.

44174 ■ Blair County Chamber of Commerce
3900 Industrial Pk. Dr., Ste. 12
Altoona, PA 16602
Ph: (814)943-8151
Fax: (814)943-5239
Co. E-mail: chamber@blairchamber.com
URL: http://www.blairchamber.com
Contact: Joe Hurd, President
E-mail: jhurd@blairchamber.com
Facebook: www.facebook.com/TheBlairCountyChamber
Linkedin: www.linkedin.com/company/blair-county-chamber
X (Twitter): x.com/Blair_Chamber
Instagram: www.instagram.com/blaircountychamberofcommerce
YouTube: www.youtube.com/channel/UCa1z5isopzJroMS1YDFHTjg
Description: Promotes business and community development in Blair County, PA. **Founded:** 1887. **Publications:** *Blair Business Mirror* (Monthly); *Chamber Extra* (Monthly). **Geographic Preference:** Local.

44175 ■ Bradford Area Chamber of Commerce (BACC)
121 Main St.
Bradford, PA 16701
Ph: (814)368-7115
Co. E-mail: chambercare@bradfordchamber.com
URL: http://www.bradfordareachamber.com
Contact: Sarah Lonzi, President
Facebook: www.facebook.com/BradfordPAChamber
Instagram: www.instagram.com/bacc_bradford
YouTube: www.youtube.com/channel/UCiwKXmkwbr2ZqiaG9iH4YZw
Description: Promotes business and community development in the Bradford, PA area. **Founded:** 1882. **Publications:** *Small Street Journal* (Monthly). **Geographic Preference:** Local.

STATE LISTINGS

44176 ■ Brentwood-Baldwin-Whitehall Chamber of Commerce (BBWCC)
3501 Brownsville Rd.
Pittsburgh, PA 15227
Co. E-mail: info@bbwchamber.com
URL: http://www.bbwchamber.com
Contact: Chris Crompton, President
Facebook: www.facebook.com/Brentwood-Baldwin-Whitehall-Chamber-of-Commerce-551238931585651
X (Twitter): x.com/BBWChamber
Description: Promotes business and community development in Brentwood, Baldwin, and Whitehall, PA. Sponsors annual trade fair and seminars. **Founded:** 1959. **Publications:** *In the Spotlight* (Monthly). **Geographic Preference:** Local.

44177 ■ Brookville Area Chamber of Commerce (BACC)
100 Franklin Ave.
Brookville, PA 15825
Ph: (814)849-8448
URL: http://brookvillechamber.com
Contact: Jolene Hartle, Executive Director
E-mail: director@brookvillechamber.com
Facebook: www.facebook.com/BrookvilleAreaChamber
Instagram: www.instagram.com/brookvillepachamberofcommerce
Description: Promotes business and community development in the Brookville, PA area. **Founded:** 1925. **Geographic Preference:** Local.

44178 ■ *Brush Valley Buyer's Guide*
URL(s): brushvalleychamber.com/page/online_directory
Released: Annual **Price:** Included in membership. **Availability:** Print; Online.

44179 ■ *Business and Industry*
65 W Main St.
Uniontown, PA 15401
Ph: (724)437-4571
Fax: (724)438-3304
Co. E-mail: info@fayettechamber.com
URL: http://www.fayettechamber.com
Contact: Devan White, President
URL(s): web.fayettechamber.com/cwt/external/wcpages/chamber/member_benefits.aspx
Released: Annual **Description:** Contains list of Fayette County businesses and their products. **Availability:** Print; Online.

44180 ■ Butler Area Chamber of Commerce
130 S Main St.
Butler, PA 16001
Ph: (724)283-2222
Co. E-mail: info@butlercountychamber.com
URL: http://butlercountychamber.com/contact
Contact: Jordon Grady, Executive Director
Facebook: www.facebook.com/BCChamber1896
Linkedin: www.linkedin.com/company/butler-county-chamber-of-commerce-1896
Instagram: www.instagram.com/butlercountychamber
Description: Promotes business and community development in the Butler, WI area. Offers special health insurance program for small businesses and real estate and employment referrals. **Founded:** 1896. **Publications:** *Butler Area Chamber of Commerce Newsletter* (Monthly). **Geographic Preference:** Local.

44181 ■ Butler County Chamber of Commerce (BCCC)
110 E Diamond St., Ste. 202
Butler, PA 16001
Ph: (724)283-2222
Co. E-mail: info@butlercountychamber.com
URL: http://butlercountychamber.com
Contact: Joseph Saeler, Executive Director
Facebook: www.facebook.com/BCChamber1896
Linkedin: www.linkedin.com/company/butler-county-chamber-of-commerce-1896
Description: Promotes business and community development in Butler County, NE. **Founded:** 1920. **Geographic Preference:** Local.

44182 ■ *Buyer's Guide*
8 W Broad St., Mezzanine, Ste. 1490
Hazleton, PA 18201
Ph: (570)455-1509
Fax: (570)450-2013
Co. E-mail: info@hazletonchamber.org
URL: http://www.hazletonchamber.org
Contact: Mary Malone, President
E-mail: mmalone@hazletonchamber.org
URL(s): www.hazletonchamber.org/business-directory/16-about-greater-hazleton.html
Description: Contains categorical listing of Chamber member firms. **Availability:** PDF; Online.

44183 ■ *Calendar of Events*
Released: Semiannual; Spring/Summer & Fall/Winter. **Availability:** Print.

44184 ■ Central Bradford County Chamber of Commerce (CBCCC)
304 Main St., 3rd Fl.
Towanda, PA 18848
Ph: (570)637-5053
Co. E-mail: rhonnda@towandawysox.com
URL: http://www.towandawysox.com
Contact: John Secor, President
Facebook: www.facebook.com/centralbradfordcountychamberofcommerce
Description: Serves members and the community with networking opportunities, business seminars, promotion and referrals. **Founded:** 1925. **Geographic Preference:** Local.

44185 ■ Central Bucks Chamber of Commerce (CBCC)
252 W Swamp Rd., Ste. 23
Doylestown, PA 18901
Ph: (215)348-3913
Fax: (215)348-7154
Co. E-mail: info@centralbuckschamber.com
URL: http://www.centralbuckschamber.com
Contact: Theresa M. Fera, Co-President Co-Chief Executive Officer
Facebook: www.facebook.com/buckschamber
X (Twitter): x.com/BucksChamber
Description: Promotes business and community development in central Bucks County, PA. **Founded:** 1946. **Publications:** *The Business & Arts Journal*. **Geographic Preference:** Local.

44186 ■ Central Pennsylvania Chamber of Commerce
30 Lawton Ln.
Milton, PA 17847
Ph: (570)742-7341
URL: http://centralpachamber.com
Contact: Tea Jay Aikey, President
E-mail: tjaikey@centralpachamber.com
Facebook: www.facebook.com/centralpachamberofcommerce
YouTube: www.youtube.com/channel/UCSkSp1Pzd84G97nfLot1qtQ
Description: Promotes business and community development in upper Northumberland and eastern Union counties, PA. **Founded:** 1905. **Awards:** Central Pennsylvania Chamber Business and Education Awards (Annual). **Geographic Preference:** Local.

44187 ■ Chamber of Business and Industry of Centre County (CBICC)
131 S Fraser St., Ste. 1
State College, PA 16801
Ph: (814)234-1829
URL: http://www.cbicc.org
Contact: Vern Squier, President
Facebook: www.facebook.com/CBICC
Linkedin: www.linkedin.com/company/cbicc
X (Twitter): x.com/CBICC
Instagram: www.instagram.com/cbicc
YouTube: www.youtube.com/channel/UCB6q387jL0Z9sXmycSAn_Hw
Description: Promotes commerce, business, and industry in Centre County. **Publications:** *ChamberNet* (Quarterly); *Chamber of Business and Industry of Centre County--Membership Directory*. **Geographic Preference:** Local.

44188 ■ *Chamber Chatter*
3157 Mt. Morris Rd. No. 103
Waynesburg, PA 15370
Ph: (724)627-5926
Co. E-mail: info@greenechamber.org
URL: http://greenechamber.org
Contact: Casey Durdines, President
E-mail: cdurdines@eqt.com
URL(s): greenechamber.org/newsletters
Released: Monthly **Price:** $20, Members; $25, Nonmembers. **Description:** Includes information for Waynesburg Chamber of Commerce members. **Availability:** PDF.

44189 ■ Chamber of Commerce of Greater West Chester (CCGWC)
137 N High St.
West Chester, PA 19380
Ph: (610)696-4046
Co. E-mail: info@gwcc.org
URL: http://www.greaterwestchester.com
Contact: Katie L. Walker, President
E-mail: katie@gwcc.org
Facebook: www.facebook.com/GreaterWestChester
Linkedin: www.linkedin.com/company/the-greater-west-chester-chamber-of-commerce
X (Twitter): x.com/GWCC_PA
Instagram: www.instagram.com/greaterwestchester
YouTube: www.youtube.com/channel/UCA-8hDUlCAlqLpQRY4vFbiA
Description: Promotes business and community development in Greater West Chester. Conducts educational and networking opportunities. **Founded:** 1888. **Publications:** *Images of Greater West Chester* (Annual); *Membership & Resource Directory* (Annual). **Awards:** Greater West Chester Chamber of Commerce Business of the Year (Annual); J. Dewees Mosteller Community Service Award (Annual); Greater West Chester Chamber of Commerce Outstanding Citizen of the Year (Annual); Greater West Chester Chamber of Commerce Volunteer of the Year (Annual). **Geographic Preference:** Local.

44190 ■ *Chamber E-Central*
241 Tollgate Hill Rd.
Greensburg, PA 15601
Ph: (724)834-2900
Fax: (724)837-7635
Co. E-mail: info@westmorelandchamber.com
URL: http://www.westmorelandchamber.com
Contact: Dan DeBone, President
E-mail: dan@westmorelandchamber.com
URL(s): www.westmorelandchamber.com/newsletter
Released: Monthly **Description:** Provides detailed information on upcoming events, includes photos and event reviews, advertising space, member news and more. **Availability:** PDF; Online.

44191 ■ *Chamberline*
68 W King St.
Shippensburg, PA 17257
Ph: (717)532-5509
Fax: (717)532-7501
Co. E-mail: chamber@shippensburg.org
URL: http://www.shippensburg.org
Contact: Scott Brown, President
URL(s): www.shippensburg.org/membership-application
Released: Monthly **Availability:** Print; PDF; Online.

44192 ■ Chester County Chamber of Business and Industry (CCCBI)
1600 Paoli Pke.
Malvern, PA 19355
Ph: (610)725-9100
Fax: (610)725-8479
Co. E-mail: info@chescochamber.org
URL: http://www.chescochamber.org
Contact: Caitlin Ganley, Secretary
Facebook: www.facebook.com/chescochamber
Linkedin: www.linkedin.com/company/chescochamber
X (Twitter): x.com/chescochamber
Instagram: www.instagram.com/chescochamber
YouTube: www.youtube.com/channel/UCaA_6JUW5FO0zMlrSf5JNMg

44193 ■ Pennsylvania

Description: Serves as the voice of business in Chester County to positively influence the business climate through developing effective relationships with government, media and the public. Provides effective, results-oriented training, networking information, resources and other services. **Founded:** 1992. **Publications:** *The Voice*. **Geographic Preference:** Local.

44193 ■ Chilean and American Chamber of Commerce of Greater Philadelphia (CACCGP)
200 S Broad St., Ste. 700
  Philadelphia, PA 19102-3813
Ph: (215)790-3627
Co. E-mail: cacc@chamberphl.com
URL: http://caccgp.com
Contact: Robert W. Palaima, President
E-mail: rpalaima@d-r-s.com
Facebook: www.facebook.com/CACCGP
YouTube: www.youtube.com/user/CACCPhiladelphia
Description: Fosters increased and improved commercial and trade relations between the Republic of Chile and the Greater Philadelphia Region. Participates in a variety of activities and programs. **Founded:** 1988. **Geographic Preference:** Regional.

44194 ■ Clarion Area Chamber of Business and Industry
650 Main St.
  Clarion, PA 16214
Ph: (814)226-9161
Fax: (814)226-4903
Co. E-mail: info@clarionpa.com
URL: http://www.clarionpa.com
Contact: Kim Titley, President
E-mail: titleykimber44@gmail.com
Facebook: www.facebook.com/ClarionAreaChamber
X (Twitter): x.com/cacbi
Description: Promotes business and community development in Clarion County, PA. Monitors legislation; holds special events, seminars, and shop talks. Sponsors Autumn Leaf Festival, Clarion Summer Fun Fest and Fishing Derby. **Founded:** 1954. **Publications:** *In Touch* (Bimonthly); *Buyer's Guide*; *Demographic Packet*. **Awards:** Clarion Area Business of the Year (Annual); Clarion Area Citizen of the Year (Annual). **Geographic Preference:** Local.

44195 ■ Clearfield Chamber of Commerce
c/o Kim M. Bloom, Executive Director?
  218 S Second St.
  Clearfield, PA 16830
Ph: (814)765-7567
Fax: (814)765-6948
Co. E-mail: info@clearfieldchamber.com
URL: http://www.clearfieldchamber.com
Contact: Josh Kunkle, Secretary
Facebook: www.facebook.com/ClearfieldChamber
Description: Promotes business and community development in the Clearfield and Curwensville, PA area. **Founded:** 1877. **Geographic Preference:** Local.

44196 ■ Clinton County Economic Partnership (CCEP)
212 N Jay St.
  Lock Haven, PA 17745
Ph: (570)748-5782
Fax: (570)893-0433
Co. E-mail: info@cenconinc.com
URL: http://www.clintoncountyinfo.com
Contact: Michael Flanagan, President
E-mail: ceo@clintoncountyinfo.com
Description: Promotes business and community development in Clinton County, PA. Provides promotional materials. Holds Business After Hours party. **Founded:** 1989. **Publications:** *Chamber Update* (Monthly); *Partnership Press* (Monthly). **Geographic Preference:** Local.

44197 ■ Columbia Montour Chamber of Commerce
238 Market St.
  Bloomsburg, PA 17815
Ph: (570)784-2522
Co. E-mail: chamber@columbiamontourchamber.com

URL: http://columbiamontourchamber.com
Contact: Chris Berleth, Co-President
E-mail: cberleth@columbiamontourchamber.com
Facebook: www.facebook.com/cmchambercommerce
Description: Promotes business and community development in the Bloomsburg, PA area. **Founded:** 1941. **Publications:** *E-biz* (Weekly). **Geographic Preference:** Local.

44198 ■ Corry Area Chamber of Commerce
221 N Center St.
  Corry, PA 16407
Ph: (814)665-9925
URL: http://www.corrychamber.com
Contact: Cherie Brookman-Dickey, President
Facebook: www.facebook.com/corrychamber
Instagram: www.instagram.com/corrychamber
Description: Promotes its members and the Corry Area Community. **Founded:** 1921. **Publications:** *Chamber Report* (Quarterly); *Industrial & Membership Directory* (Periodic). **Geographic Preference:** Local.

44199 ■ Coudersport Area Chamber of Commerce
PO Box 261
  Coudersport, PA 16915
Facebook: www.facebook.com/CoudersportAreaChamberOfCommerce
Description: Promotes business and community development in Coudersport, PA. **Geographic Preference:** Local.

44200 ■ Delaware County Chamber of Commerce
1001 Baltimore Pke., Ste. 9 LL
  Springfield, PA 19064
Ph: (610)565-3677
Co. E-mail: info@delcochamber.org
URL: http://www.delcochamber.org
Contact: Trish McFarland, President
E-mail: trishm@delcochamber.org
Facebook: www.facebook.com/DelcoChamber
X (Twitter): x.com/DelcoChamber
Instagram: www.instagram.com/delcochamber
YouTube: www.youtube.com/channel/UCGSs47MyAF5TWwhJ6QXRX-w
Pinterest: www.pinterest.com/delcochamber
Description: Promotes business and community development in Delaware County, PA. **Founded:** 1913. **Publications:** *Delco Chamber of Commerce Membership Directory* (Annual); *Chambergram* (Quarterly); *Member Update* (Quarterly). **Educational Activities:** Hermes Expo. **Geographic Preference:** Local.

44201 ■ Downingtown-Thorndale Regional Chamber of Commerce (DTRCC)
216 E Lancaster Ave.
  Downingtown, PA 19335
URL: http://www.dtrcc.com
Description: Promotes business and community development in the Downingtown, PA area. **Founded:** 1945. **Publications:** *Your Chamber Matters* (Monthly). **Geographic Preference:** Local.

44202 ■ E-biz
238 Market St.
  Bloomsburg, PA 17815
Ph: (570)784-2522
Co. E-mail: chamber@columbiamontourchamber.com
URL: http://columbiamontourchamber.com
Contact: Chris Berleth, Co-President
E-mail: cberleth@columbiamontourchamber.com
Released: Weekly **Description:** Contains chamber information, business news and events. **Availability:** Online.

44203 ■ East Liberty Quarter Chamber of Commerce (ELQCC)
5907 Penn Ave., Ste. 314
  Pittsburgh, PA 15206
Ph: (412)661-9660
Co. E-mail: director@eastlibertychamber.org
URL: http://www.eastlibertychamber.org

Contact: Lori L. Moran, President
E-mail: lmoran@ballymoneyrealestate.com
Description: Promotes business and community development in the East Liberty Quarter area of Pittsburgh, PA. **Founded:** 1927. **Geographic Preference:** Local.

44204 ■ Eastern Cambria County Chamber of Commerce
PO Box 113
  Cresson, PA 16630
Facebook: www.facebook.com/p/Eastern-Cambria-County-Chamber-of-Commerce-100046788763998
Description: Promotes business and economic development in the Cresson, PA area. Supports local business and community interest. **Geographic Preference:** Local.

44205 ■ Eastern Montgomery County Chamber of Commerce (EMCCC)
436 Old York Rd.
  Jenkintown, PA 19046
Ph: (215)887-5122
Co. E-mail: info@emccc.org
URL: http://www.emccc.org
Contact: Wendy Klinghoffer, Executive Director
E-mail: wendy@emccc.org
Linkedin: www.linkedin.com/company/eastern-montgomery-county-chamber-of-commerce
X (Twitter): x.com/EMontcoChamber
Instagram: www.instagram.com/emccc_pa
Description: Promotes business and community development in southeastern Montgomery County. Sponsors business card exchanges. **Founded:** 1918. **Publications:** *Commerce Comments* (Quarterly); *Membership Directory and Buyer's Guide* (Annual). **Awards:** Eastern Montgomery County Humanitarian Organization of the Year (Annual); Eastern Montgomery County Small Business of the Year (Annual); Eastern Montgomery County Business of the Year (Annual). **Geographic Preference:** Regional.

44206 ■ Ellwood City Area Chamber of Commerce
806 Lawrence Ave.
  Ellwood City, PA 16117
Ph: (724)758-5501
Co. E-mail: info@ellwoodchamber.org
URL: http://ellwoodchamber.org
Contact: Kristin Swab, President
Facebook: www.facebook.com/EllwoodCityChamber
Linkedin: www.linkedin.com/company/ellwood-city-chamber-of-commerce
X (Twitter): x.com/ec_chamber
Instagram: www.instagram.com/ellwoodcitychamber
Description: Serves as the information center for Ellwood City area businesses and the community. Provides business information, business counseling, tourism brochures, maps, and referrals to a wide network of agencies, businesses and government offices. **Founded:** 1933. **Publications:** *The Business Brief* (Bimonthly). **Geographic Preference:** Local.

44207 ■ Erie Regional Chamber and Growth Partnership (ERCGP)
1128 State St., Ste. 300
  Erie, PA 16501
Ph: (814)454-7191
Fax: (814)240-6207
Co. E-mail: communications@eriepa.com
URL: http://www.eriepa.com
Contact: James Grunke, President
E-mail: jgrunke@eriepa.com
Facebook: www.facebook.com/erieregionalchamber
Linkedin: www.linkedin.com/company/erie-regional-chamber-&-growth-partnership
X (Twitter): x.com/eriepachamber
YouTube: www.youtube.com/user/ErieRegionalChamber
Description: Promotes business and community development in Erie County, PA. Promotes tourism. Provides assistance and information. Maintains Economic/Business Resource Center and Videoconference Center. **Founded:** 2002. **Publications:** *Erie* (Bimonthly); *Erie Business and Community Resource Guide*; *Erie City/County Map*; *Erie County Fact*

Packet; *Erie Extra* (Biweekly); *ERIE Industrial Directory* (Periodic); *Tourist/Motorcoach* (Periodic). **Awards:** ATHENA PowerLink Award (Annual); Louis J. Tullio Community Service Award (Annual). **Geographic Preference:** Local.

44208 ■ Exton Region Chamber of Commerce (ERCC)
310 Exton Sq. Pky.
 Exton, PA 19341
Ph: (610)363-7746
Co. E-mail: chamber@ercc.net
URL: http://extonregionchamber.com
Contact: Laurie Ryan, President
Facebook: www.facebook.com/ExtonRegionChamber
Linkedin: www.linkedin.com/company/exton-region
 -chamber-commerce
X (Twitter): x.com/ExtonChamber
YouTube: www.youtube.com/channel/
 UCMrub0BScWW6P0qdVFKIkEg/featured
Description: Promotes business and community development in Exton and surrounding Central Chester County, PA area. Works on regional issues such as the environment, legislation, and road improvements. Conducts scholarship fundraisers and silent/live auction. Sponsors annual golf outing. **Founded:** 1972. **Publications:** *Membership and Resource Directory* (Annual). **Awards:** ERCC Chairman's Award (Annual); Harold Martin Business Leadership Award (Annual). **Geographic Preference:** Local.

44209 ■ Fayette Chamber of Commerce
65 W Main St.
 Uniontown, PA 15401
Ph: (724)437-4571
Fax: (724)438-3304
Co. E-mail: info@fayettechamber.com
URL: http://www.fayettechamber.com
Contact: Devan White, President
Facebook: www.facebook.com/FayCham
X (Twitter): x.com/fay65cham
Instagram: www.instagram.com/faye
 ttechamberofcommerce
Description: Promotes business and community development in Fayette County, PA. **Founded:** 1925. **Publications:** *Business and Industry* (Annual). **Geographic Preference:** Local.

44210 ■ Fayette County Chamber of Commerce
65 W Main St., Ste. 107
 Uniontown, PA 15401
Ph: (724)437-4571
Fax: (724)438-3304
Co. E-mail: info@fayettechamber.com
URL: http://www.fayettechamber.com
Contact: Devan White, President
X (Twitter): x.com/fay65cham
Description: Promotes business and community development in Fayette County, TN. **Founded:** 1925. **Geographic Preference:** Local.

44211 ■ Franklin Area Chamber of Commerce (FACC)
1255 Liberty St.
 Franklin, PA 16323
Ph: (814)432-5823
Co. E-mail: administrator@franklinareachamber.org
URL: http://www.franklinareachamber.org
Contact: Jodi Lewis, Executive Director
E-mail: jodi@franklinareachamber.org
Facebook: www.facebook.com/FranklinAreaChamber
Instagram: www.instagram.com/franklinareachamber
YouTube: www.youtube.com/channel/UCilTsJ2jDQ
 ttiuBgO3UxqXg/featured
Description: Provides economic, educational, and legislative information and assistance which can be used by members to achieve profit, progress, and prosperity. Unites hundreds of business and professional firms, thus creating a unique central agency working to improve business and build a better community. **Founded:** 1913. **Publications:** *Images of the Franklin Area*; *Chamber News* (Bimonthly). **Educational Activities:** Business After Hours (Monthly). **Awards:** Franklin Area Chamber Gold Shovel Awards (Annual); Franklin Area Chamber Man and Woman of the Year Awards (Annual). **Geographic Preference:** Local.

44212 ■ French-American Chamber of Commerce (FACC)
c/o Welcoming Ctr.
 211 N 13th St., 4th Fl.
 Philadelphia, PA 19107
Co. E-mail: info@faccphila.org
URL: http://www.faccphila.org
Contact: Jeremy Heep, President
Facebook: www.facebook.com/FACCphila
Linkedin: www.linkedin.com/company/faccphila
X (Twitter): x.com/faccphila
Instagram: www.instagram.com/faccphila
Description: Seeks to contribute, through the efforts of the chapters and members, to the development and improvement of economic, commercial, and financial relations between France and the United States. **Founded:** 1989. **Geographic Preference:** Regional.

44213 ■ Fulton County Chamber of Commerce and Tourism
101 Lincoln Way W
 McConnellsburg, PA 17233
Ph: (717)485-4064
Fax: (717)325-0023
URL: http://www.fultoncountypa.com
Description: Helps to promote business and stimulate the economic successes of Fulton County as a whole. **Founded:** 1951. **Geographic Preference:** Local.

44214 ■ German American Chamber of Commerce - Philadelphia (GACC)
1635 Market St., Ste. 1600
 Philadelphia, PA 19103
Ph: (215)501-7102
Co. E-mail: info@gaccphiladelphia.com
URL: http://gaccphiladelphia.com
Contact: Susanne Johnson, Executive Director
X (Twitter): x.com/gaccphilly
Description: Promotes development of trade and investment opportunities between the United States and Germany. **Founded:** 1989. **Geographic Preference:** Local.

44215 ■ Gettysburg Adams Chamber of Commerce
1382 Biglerville Rd.
 Gettysburg, PA 17325
Ph: (717)334-8151
Co. E-mail: info@gettysburg-chamber.org
URL: http://www.gettysburg-chamber.org
Contact: Carrie Stuart, President
Description: Promotes business and community development in Adams County, PA. **Founded:** 1919. **Publications:** *Major Employers of Adams County*; *Major Manufacturers of Adams County*; *Relocation Packet*. **Awards:** Gettysburg-Adams County Area Outstanding Citizen of the Year (Annual); Gettysburg-Adams County Area Small Business Person of the Year (Annual); Gettysburg-Adams County Area Volunteer of the Year (Annual). **Geographic Preference:** Local.

44216 ■ Great Valley Regional Chamber of Commerce (GVRCC)
65 Valley Stream Pkwy Great Valley Corpo, Rate Ctr.
 Malvern, PA 19355
Description: Supports and promotes business and economic development which ensures that Great Valley Region remains an ideal area to live, work, and invest. **Founded:** 1989. **Geographic Preference:** Local.

44217 ■ Greater BucksMont Chamber of Commerce (GBMCC)
PO Box 3014
 Warminster, PA 18974
Ph: (215)672-6633
Co. E-mail: admin@bucksmontchamber.com
URL: http://www.bucksmontchamber.com
Contact: Patricia Hueber-Bodor, Vice President
Facebook: www.facebook.com/BucksMontChamber
Description: Supports the business community of the Greater BucksMont region. Advocates for services and policies to stimulate economic growth through business development within our communities. **Founded:** 1963. **Geographic Preference:** Local.

44218 ■ Greater Carbondale Chamber of Commerce
27 N Main St.
 Carbondale, PA 18407
Ph: (570)282-1690
Fax: (570)282-1206
URL: http://www.carbondalechamber.org
Contact: Michele Bannon, President
Description: Promotes business and community development in the Carbondale, PA area. **Geographic Preference:** Local.

44219 ■ Greater Carlisle Area Chamber of Commerce
801 S Hanover St.
 Carlisle, PA 17013
Ph: (717)243-4515
Fax: (717)243-4446
Co. E-mail: info@carlislechamber.org
URL: http://www.carlislechamber.org
Contact: Jennifer Germain, Director
E-mail: jgermain@carlislechamber.org
Facebook: www.facebook.com/CarlisleAreaChamber
Linkedin: www.linkedin.com/company/carlisle-area
 -chamber-of-commerce
Instagram: www.instagram.com/carlisleareachamber
Description: Promotes business and community development in the Carlisle, PA area. Conducts trade fairs, seminars, and social activities. **Founded:** 1913. **Publications:** *Business and Industry* (Quarterly); *Quality of Life*. **Geographic Preference:** Local.

44220 ■ Greater Chambersburg Chamber of Commerce (GCCC)
100 Lincoln Way E, Ste. A
 Chambersburg, PA 17201
Ph: (717)264-7101
Fax: (717)267-0399
Co. E-mail: chamber@chambersburg.org
URL: http://www.chambersburg.org
Contact: Stephen Christian, President
Facebook: www.facebook.com/cburgchamber
Linkedin: www.linkedin.com/company/greater
 -chambersburg-chamber-of-commerce
X (Twitter): x.com/CburgChamber
Instagram: www.instagram.com/cburgchamber
Pinterest: www.pinterest.com/cburgchamber
Description: Advocates and promotes economic growth through the free enterprise system, helps members prosper, promotes planned community growth and enhances the quality of life in the Chambersburg area. **Founded:** 1911. **Publications:** *Chamber Outlook* (Weekly (Mon.)). **Geographic Preference:** Local.

44221 ■ Greater Connellsville Chamber of Commerce
100 S Arch St.
 Connellsville, PA 15425
Ph: (724)628-5500
Co. E-mail: cvchamber@zoominternet.net
URL: http://connellsvillechamber.com
Contact: Max House, President
Facebook: www.facebook.com/greaterccc
X (Twitter): x.com/greaterccc
Instagram: www.instagram.com/greaterccc
Description: Promotes business and community development in Connellsville, PA area. **Geographic Preference:** Local.

44222 ■ Greater DuBois Chamber of Commerce (DCC)
103 Beaver Dr.
 Dubois, PA 15801
Ph: (814)371-5010
Fax: (814)371-5005
Co. E-mail: dacc@duboispachamber.com
URL: http://www.duboispachamber.com
Contact: Jodi K. August, Executive Director

Facebook: www.facebook.com/
duboischamberofcommerce
Linkedin: www.linkedin.com/company/greater-dubois
-chamber-of-commerce

Description: Promotes business and community development in the Du Bois, PA area. Holds monthly breakfast, annual dinner, ribbon cuttings, and business expo. **Founded:** 1945. **Publications:** *Chamber Chatter* (Monthly). **Geographic Preference:** Local.

44223 ■ **Greater Glenside Chamber of Commerce**
452 N Easton Rd.
Glenside, PA 19038

Description: Promotes business and community development in the Glenside, PA area. Sponsors craft show and car show. **Founded:** 1963. **Publications:** *Chamber Chat* (Monthly). **Geographic Preference:** Local.

44224 ■ **Greater Hatboro Chamber of Commerce (GHCC)**
Red Barn Mall
120 S York Rd., Ste. 6
Hatboro, PA 19040
Ph: (215)956-9540
Co. E-mail: hatborochamber@gmail.com
URL: http://hatborochamber.org
Contact: Timothy Schultz, President
Facebook: www.facebook.com/Hatborochamber

Description: Promotes business and community development in Hatboro, PA. Sponsors Christmas parade, Little Miss. and Mr. Hatboro Contest, County Music Festival, sidewalk sale festival, car show, Halloween and Christmas stroll. **Founded:** 1968. **Publications:** *Chamber Voice* (Quarterly); *Hatboro Online Business Directory*. **Geographic Preference:** Local.

44225 ■ **Greater Hazleton Chamber of Commerce**
8 W Broad St., Mezzanine, Ste. 1490
Hazleton, PA 18201
Ph: (570)455-1509
Fax: (570)450-2013
Co. E-mail: info@hazletonchamber.org
URL: http://www.hazletonchamber.org
Contact: Mary Malone, President
E-mail: mmalone@hazletonchamber.org
Facebook: www.facebook.com/greaterhazle
tonchamber
X (Twitter): x.com/hazletonchamber

Description: Promotes business and community development in the Hazleton, PA area. **Founded:** 1892. **Publications:** *Buyer's Guide*; *Clubs and Organizations Directory*; *Hazleton Area Image*; *Greater Hazleton Chamber of Commerce--Clubs and Organization Directory*; *Greater Hazleton Chamber of Commerce--Industrial Directory*; *Greater Hazleton Chamber of Commerce--Membership Directory/Buyer's Guide*; *Hazleton Industrial Directory*; *Greater Hazleton Image*. **Geographic Preference:** Local.

44226 ■ **Greater Johnstown/Cambria County Chamber of Commerce**
416 Main St., Ste. 201
Johnstown, PA 15901
Ph: (814)536-5107
Fax: (814)539-5800
Co. E-mail: contact@crchamber.com
URL: http://www.crchamber.com
Contact: Amy Bradley, President
E-mail: amy@crchamber.com
Facebook: www.facebook.com/
CambriaRegionalChamber
Linkedin: www.linkedin.com/company/crchamber
X (Twitter): x.com/JSTChamber

Description: Stimulates and encourage an informed membership, to be the advocate of business and to form private/public partnerships to promote the health and growth of area business and the community. **Founded:** 1910. **Publications:** *Chamber Ink* (Biweekly). **Educational Activities:** Showcase for Commerce (Annual). **Geographic Preference:** Local.

44227 ■ **Greater Latrobe-Laurel Valley Regional Chamber of Commerce**
PO Box 463
Latrobe, PA 15650
Ph: (724)537-2671
Fax: (724)537-2671
Co. E-mail: info@gllv.org
URL: http://www.latrobelaurelvalley.org
Contact: Briana Tomack, President
Facebook: www.facebook.com/GLLVChamber
Instagram: www.instagram.com/gllvchamber
YouTube: www.youtube.com/user/gllvchamber

Description: Promotes business and community development in the Latrobe, PA area. **Founded:** 1945. **Publications:** *Chamber X-Change* (Monthly); *Industrial Directory*; *Welcome to Latrobe Area Neighborhood*. **Geographic Preference:** Local.

44228 ■ **Greater Lehigh Valley Chamber of Commerce**
840 Hamilton St., Ste. 205
Allentown, PA 18101
Co. E-mail: info@lehighvalleychamber.org
URL: http://www.lehighvalleychamber.org
Contact: Tony Iannelli, President
E-mail: tonyi@lehighvalleychamber.org
Facebook: www.facebook.com/TheChambe
Linkedin: www.linkedin.com/company/
lehighvalleychamber
Instagram: www.instagram.com/lehighvalleychamber
YouTube: www.youtube.com/channel/
UCLuiZcMHNaweVxJSScjJu7Q

Description: Seeks to improve the economy and quality of life in the Lehigh Valley, PA area. **Publications:** *Clubs and Organizations*; *Connections* (Monthly); *Relocation Guide*. **Awards:** Lehigh Valley Excellence in Business Awards (Annual). **Geographic Preference:** Local.

44229 ■ **Greater Northeast Philadelphia Chamber of Commerce (GNPCC)**
8025 Roosevelt Blvd., Ste. 200
Philadelphia, PA 19152
Ph: (215)332-3400
Co. E-mail: info@nephilachamber.com
URL: http://www.nephilachamber.com
Contact: Pam Henshall, President
E-mail: phenshall@nephilachamber.com
Facebook: www.facebook.com/GNPCC
Linkedin: www.linkedin.com/groups/2102762
X (Twitter): x.com/gnpcc
Instagram: www.instagram.com/gnpcc

Description: Represents business and professional interests. Serves as a catalyst for growth and promotes the area's residential and commercial assets. **Founded:** 1922. **Geographic Preference:** Local.

44230 ■ **Greater Philadelphia Chamber of Commerce (GPCC)**
200 S Broad St., Ste. 700
Philadelphia, PA 19102
Ph: (215)545-1234
Fax: (215)790-3600
Co. E-mail: join@chamberphl.com
URL: http://chamberphl.com
Contact: Robert C. Wonderling, President
E-mail: rwonderling@chamberphl.com
Facebook: www.facebook.com/ChamberPHL
Linkedin: www.linkedin.com/company/chamberphl
X (Twitter): x.com/ChamberPHL
Instagram: www.instagram.com/chamberphl
YouTube: www.youtube.com/user/Grea
terPhilaChamber

Description: Seeks to facilitate and promote quality and excellence in business, governmental, and educational organizations in the Delaware Valley area of Delaware, New Jersey, and Pennsylvania. Offers custom designed and project team training and consultant referral. Provides print and video resources. Sponsors 20 seminars per year and PACE Network. **Founded:** 1800. **Publications:** *Business Relocation Package--Greater Philadelphia Region*; *Construction Forecast Kit--Philadelphia*; *Franklin's Finance Finder*; *Individual Relocation Package--Philadelphia*; *Media Listing--Philadelphia*; *Non-Profit Start-Up Guide--Philadelphia*; *Select Demographics of the Region--Philadelphia*; *Zip Code and Neighborhood Directory--Philadelphia*; *Greater Philadelphia Chamber of Commerce Job Fair Employer Handbook*; *Greater Philadelphia Chamber of Commerce--Membership Directory* (Annual); *Colleges and Universities*; *Hospital Directory*; *Major Employers of the Greater Philadelphia Region*; *Non-Profit Council Directory*; *Industrial PinPointer: Philadelphia*; *The Greater Philadelphia Pocket Atlas*; *Greater Philadelphia Chamber of Commerce Job Fair Job Seekers Guide: 2004 Edition*; *Greater Philadelphia Chamber of Commerce Colleges and Universities/Hospital Directory*; *Associations of the Delaware Valley* (Biennial); *Associations of the Greater Philadelphia Region*. **Geographic Preference:** Local.

44231 ■ **Greater Pittsburgh Chamber of Commerce**
11 Stanwix St., 17th Fl.
Pittsburgh, PA 15222-1312
Ph: (412)281-1890
Co. E-mail: info@alleghenyconference.org
URL: http://www.greaterpi
ttsburghchamberofcommerce.com
Contact: Daniel S. Wilson, Secretary Treasurer
Linkedin: www.linkedin.com/company/
alleghenyconference
X (Twitter): x.com/gpghcc

Description: Promotes business and community development in Greater Pittsburgh, PA. **Founded:** 1876. **Publications:** *Major Firms in the Pittsburgh Metro Area* (Annual); *Greater Pittsburgh Chamber of Commerce--Membership Directory and Economic Profile* (Annual). **Geographic Preference:** Local.

44232 ■ **Greater Pittston Chamber of Commerce (GP)**
104 Kennedy Blvd.
Pittston, PA 18640
Ph: (570)655-1424
Fax: (570)655-0336
Co. E-mail: info@pittstonchamber.org
URL: http://www.pittstonchamber.org
Contact: Michelle Mikitish, President
E-mail: mmikitish@pittstonchamber.org
Facebook: www.facebook.com/greater.p.chamber
X (Twitter): x.com/Pittstonchamber
Instagram: www.instagram.com/pittstonchamber

Description: Promotes business and community development in the Pittston, PA area. **Founded:** 1920. **Publications:** *Great Pittston Life*. **Geographic Preference:** Local.

44233 ■ **Greater Pocono Chamber of Commerce (GPCC)**
1004 W Main St.
Stroudsburg, PA 18360
Ph: (570)421-4433
Fax: (570)424-7281
Co. E-mail: mmoreno@poconochamber.org
URL: http://www.greaterpoconochamber.com
Contact: Sarah Wallace, Chairman
E-mail: swallace@essabank.com
Facebook: www.facebook.com/GPChamber
Linkedin: www.linkedin.com/company/
poconochamber
X (Twitter): x.com/ChamberPocono
YouTube: www.youtube.com/channel/ucgki2r8hk
60wmitgru-ia

Description: Promotes business and community development in the Monroe County, PA area. **Founded:** 1910. **Publications:** *Impact* (Bimonthly). **Awards:** Greater Pocono Chamber Athena Award; Greater Pocono Chamber Citizen of the Year; Greater Pocono Chamber Humanitarian of the Year. **Geographic Preference:** Local.

44234 ■ **Greater Scranton Chamber of Commerce**
222 Mulberry St.
Scranton, PA 18501
Ph: (570)342-7711
Fax: (570)347-6262
Co. E-mail: information@scrantonchamber.com
URL: http://www.scrantonchamber.com
Contact: Bob Durkin, President

E-mail: rdurkin@scrantonchamber.com
Facebook: www.facebook.com/scrantonchamber
Linkedin: www.linkedin.com/company/the-greater-scranton-chamber-of-commerce
X (Twitter): x.com/ScrantonChamber
Instagram: www.instagram.com/scrantonchamber
YouTube: www.youtube.com/user/ScrantonChamber1
Description: Provides members with the opportunity to forge bonds that serve as the foundations for the growth of Greater Scranton. **Founded:** 1867. **Publications:** *Momentum* (Monthly); *Leadership Lackawanna News*; *The Scranton Plan News*; *Greater Scranton Chamber of Commerce Business & Buyers' Guide.* **Geographic Preference:** Local.

44235 ■ Greater Susquehanna Valley Chamber of Commerce (GSVCC)
Routes 11 and 15
2859 N Susquehanna Trl.
Shamokin Dam, PA 17876
Ph: (570)743-4100
Free: 800-410-2880
Fax: (570)743-1221
Co. E-mail: info@gsvcc.org
URL: http://www.gsvcc.org
Contact: Bob Garrett, President
E-mail: rgarrett@gsvcc.org
Linkedin: www.linkedin.com/company/greater-susquehanna-valley-chamber-of-commerce
X (Twitter): x.com/gsvcc
YouTube: www.youtube.com/channel/UC9ojeFY1zNEJczWf8TB_87g
Description: Businesses in Snyder, Union, Northumberland, and Montour Counties. Strives to advance business environment and quality of life by providing programs and services which promote civic, social, business and economic growth and development. **Publications:** *The Voice of the Valley* (Daily). **Awards:** Greater Susquehanna Valley Business of the Year (Annual); Karen L. Hackman Star of Excellence Award (Annual); Greater Susquehanna Valley Small Business of the Year (Annual). **Geographic Preference:** Local.

44236 ■ Greater Waynesboro Chamber of Commerce
118 Walnut St.
Waynesboro, PA 17268
Ph: (717)762-7123
Fax: (717)762-7124
Co. E-mail: admin@waynesboro.org
URL: http://www.waynesboro.org
Contact: Lesley Quesada, President
YouTube: www.youtube.com/channel/UCjGkyEkH-GLN1jlHkrgEV5g/featured
Description: Promotes business and community development in the Waynesboro, PA area. Convention/Meeting: none. **Publications:** *Member Directory and Buyers Guide* (Annual). **Geographic Preference:** Local.

44237 ■ Greencastle-Antrim Chamber of Commerce
217 E Baltimore St.
Greencastle, PA 17225
Ph: (717)597-4610
Co. E-mail: info@greencastlepachamber.org
URL: http://www.greencastlepachamber.org
Contact: Brad Kearns, Treasurer
Description: Promotes business and community development in Antrim Township and Greencastle, PA. **Publications:** *Castle Views* (Bimonthly). **Geographic Preference:** Local.

44238 ■ Greene County Chamber of Commerce
3157 Mt. Morris Rd. No. 103
Waynesburg, PA 15370
Ph: (724)627-5926
Co. E-mail: info@greenechamber.org
URL: http://greenechamber.org
Contact: Casey Durdines, President
E-mail: cdurdines@eqt.com
Facebook: www.facebook.com/greenecountypachamber
Description: Provides services and programs that will increase the success of member businesses and organizations and enhance the economy and quality of life in the Waynesburg area. **Founded:** 1949. **Publications:** *Chamber Chatter* (Monthly). **Awards:** Waynesburg Area Chamber of Commerce Distinguished Service Award (Annual). **Geographic Preference:** Local.

44239 ■ Greenville Area Chamber of Commerce (GACC)
182 Main St.
Greenville, PA 16125
Ph: (724)588-7150
Co. E-mail: info@greenvillechamber-pa.com
URL: http://www.greenvillechamber-pa.com
Contact: Amanda Banic, President
Linkedin: www.linkedin.com/company/greenville-area-chamber-of-commerce
X (Twitter): x.com/GreenvilleCham1
Description: Promotes business and community development in the Greenville area. **Founded:** 1948. **Publications:** *Chamber Notes* (Monthly). **Geographic Preference:** Local.

44240 ■ Grove City Area Chamber of Commerce
119 S Broad St.
Grove City, PA 16127
Ph: (724)458-6410
Fax: (724)458-6841
Co. E-mail: gcchamber@shopgrovecity.com
URL: http://grovecityareachamber.com
Contact: Micaela May, President
Linkedin: www.linkedin.com/company/grove-city-pa-area-chamber-of-commerce
X (Twitter): x.com/gcchamberpa
Description: Promotes business and community development in the Grove City, PA area. **Founded:** 1952. **Geographic Preference:** Local.

44241 ■ *Guide to Somerset County*
601 N Center Ave.
Somerset, PA 15501
Ph: (814)445-6431
Fax: (814)443-4313
Co. E-mail: info@somersetcountychamber.com
URL: http://somersetcountychamber.com
Contact: Lisa Bittner, President
URL(s): somersetcountychamber.com/membership
Availability: Print.

44242 ■ Hanover Area Chamber of Commerce (HACC)
40 York St., Ste. 2
Hanover, PA 17331
Ph: (717)637-6130
Co. E-mail: office@hanoverchamber.com
URL: http://www.hanoverchamber.com
Contact: Gary Laird, President
E-mail: glaird@hanoverchamber.com
Facebook: www.facebook.com/HanoverAreaChamberCommerce
Linkedin: www.linkedin.com/company/hanoverareachambercommerce
X (Twitter): x.com/hanoverchamber
Instagram: www.instagram.com/hanoverareachamberofcommerce
Description: Promotes business and community development in Hanover, Littlestown, McSherrystown, New Oxford, Spring Grove, Abbottstown, East Berlin, and Codrus, PA. **Founded:** 1923. **Publications:** *Chamber Connections* (Monthly); *Chamber Report* (Monthly); *Hanover Area Church Directory* (Annual); *Quality of Life Directory* (Biennial); *Relocation Packet* (Semiannual). **Geographic Preference:** Local.

44243 ■ Harrisburg Regional Chamber of Commerce & CREDC (HACC)
3211 N Front St., Ste. 201
Harrisburg, PA 17110-1342
Ph: (717)232-4099
Free: 877-883-8339
Co. E-mail: info@hbgrc.org
URL: http://www.harrisburgregionalchamber.org
Contact: Ryan Unger, President
Facebook: www.facebook.com/hrccredc
Linkedin: www.linkedin.com/company/harrisburg-regional-chamber-&-credc
X (Twitter): x.com/hrccredc
Instagram: www.instagram.com/hrccredc
YouTube: www.youtube.com/user/HRCandCREDC
Description: Promotes business and community development in the area. **Founded:** 1884. **Geographic Preference:** Local.

44244 ■ Harrisburg Regional Chamber & CREDC
3211 N Front St., Ste. 201
Harrisburg, PA 17110-1342
Ph: (717)232-4099
Free: 877-883-8339
Fax: (717)232-5184
Co. E-mail: info@hbgrc.org
URL: http://www.harrisburgregionalchamber.org
Contact: Ryan Unger, President
E-mail: dblack@hbgrc.org
Facebook: www.facebook.com/hrccredc
X (Twitter): x.com/hrccredc
YouTube: www.youtube.com/user/HRCandCREDC
Description: Promotes business and community development in the Harrisburg, PA area. **Founded:** 1912. **Publications:** *Government Officials Guide*; *Harrisburg Regional Industrial Directory*; *The Harrisburg Regional News* (Quarterly); *Membership Directory and Regional Profile* (Annual); *Who's Who in the Capital Region* (Annual). **Awards:** Harrisburg Regional Chamber of Commerce Athena Award (Annual); Harrisburg Regional Chamber of Commerce Small Business of the Year (Annual). **Geographic Preference:** Local.

44245 ■ Hatfield Chamber of Commerce
PO Box 445
Hatfield, PA 19440-0445
Ph: (215)855-3335
URL: http://www.hatfieldchamber.com
Facebook: www.facebook.com/HatfieldCC
Description: Organized to advance the economic, industrial, professional, cultural and civic welfare of Hatfield Borough and Hatfield Township. **Founded:** 1927. **Publications:** *Business Spotlight.* **Geographic Preference:** Local.

44246 ■ Indian Valley Chamber of Commerce (IVCC)
121 E Chestnut St., Ste. 201
Souderton, PA 18964
Ph: (215)723-9472
Co. E-mail: ivchamber@indianvalleychamber.com
URL: http://www.indianvalleychamber.com
Contact: Steven P. Hunsberger, President
Facebook: www.facebook.com/ivchamber
Linkedin: www.linkedin.com/in/indian-valley-chamber-86590410
X (Twitter): x.com/IVChamber
Instagram: www.instagram.com/ivchamber
YouTube: www.youtube.com/channel/UCxh6KU3T0NxD_dBjizo5ZFw
Description: Promotes business and community development in the area. Sponsors programs and activities. **Founded:** 1970. **Publications:** *The Participant* (Bimonthly). **Geographic Preference:** Local; Regional.

44247 ■ Indiana County Chamber of Commerce
1019 Philadelphia St.
Indiana, PA 15701
Ph: (724)465-2511
Free: 866-866-5545
Fax: (724)465-3706
Co. E-mail: jmountain@indianacountychamber.com
URL: http://indianacountychamber.com
Contact: Mark Hilliard, President
E-mail: mhilliard@indianacountychamber.com
Facebook: www.facebook.com/IndianaCountyChamber
Linkedin: www.linkedin.com/company/indiana-county-chamber-of-commerce
X (Twitter): x.com/IndianaCoCOC
Instagram: www.instagram.com/indianacountychamber

YouTube: www.youtube.com/channel/UCFTNm8
67aVWPIH3IbQOXvoQ
Description: Promotes business and community development in Indiana County, PA. Provides New Business Assistance Kits and Newcomers Kits. Maintains liaison with government agencies. Operates Indiana County Development Corp. **Founded:** 1912. **Publications:** *Business Directory*; *Clubs and Organizations Directory* (Periodic); *Industrial Directory*; *Update* (Periodic). **Geographic Preference:** Local.

44248 ■ Jim Thorpe Chamber of Commerce
Route 209
Jim Thorpe, PA 18229
Co. E-mail: info@jimthorpe.org
URL: http://www.poconomountains.com/jim-thorpe
Contact: Chris Barrett, President
E-mail: cbarrett@poconos.org
Facebook: www.facebook.com/VisitJimThorpe
Description: Promotes business and tourism. Activities include Jim Thorpe Birthday weekend, Fall Foliage Festival, Renaissance Festival and Old Time Christmas Celebration. **Founded:** 1982. **Publications:** *Jim Thorpe' Visitor's Guide* (Annual). **Geographic Preference:** Local.

44249 ■ Juniata River Valley Chamber of Commerce and Visitors Bureau (JVACC)
Historic Courthouse
1 W Market St.
Lewistown, PA 17044
Ph: (717)248-6713
Fax: (717)248-6714
Co. E-mail: info@juniatarivervalley.org
URL: http://jrvchamber.com
Contact: Rhonda S. Kelley, Director
E-mail: rhondak@juniatarivervalley.org
Facebook: www.facebook.com/JRVVB
Pinterest: www.pinterest.com/jaybeeyell
Description: Offers low-cost insurance and phone service to members and offers information on the community to people from the area and from other areas. Holds programs to inform the public about happenings in the community. **Geographic Preference:** Local.

44250 ■ Lancaster Chamber of Commerce (LCC)
115 E King St.
Lancaster, PA 17602
Ph: (717)397-3531
Co. E-mail: info@lancasterchamber.com
URL: http://www.lancasterchamber.com
Contact: Heather Valudes, Co-President Co-Chief Executive Officer
E-mail: hvaludes@lancasterchamber.com
Facebook: www.facebook.com/LancasterChamberPA
Linkedin: www.linkedin.com/company/the-lancaster
-chamber-of-commerce-&-industry
X (Twitter): x.com/Lanc_Chamber
Instagram: www.instagram.com/lancchamber
Description: Promotes business and economic development in the area. **Founded:** 1872. **Publications:** *Business Development News* (Monthly); *Buyer's Guide* (Periodic); *Chamber News* (Bimonthly); *Import/Export Guide* (Annual); *Industrial Directory Labels* (Annual); *Industrial Parks Guide* (Periodic); *Lancaster Marketplace*; *Legislative Update*; *Major Employers Directory* (Annual); *Sample Employee Handbook*; *Lancaster Chamber of Commerce & Industry/The Lancaster County Industrial Directory & Locator* (Biennial); *Lancaster Chamber of Commerce & Industry--Major Employers Directory* (Annual). **Geographic Preference:** Local.

44251 ■ Lawrence County Chamber of Commerce
325 E Washington St.
New Castle, PA 16101
Ph: (724)658-1488
Co. E-mail: info@lawrencecounty.com
URL: http://www.lawrencecounty.com
Contact: Alex McCoy, Chief Executive Officer
E-mail: amccoy@lawrencecountychamber.org
Facebook: www.facebook.com/LawrenceCoRegCC
Instagram: www.instagram.com/lawrencecoregcc

Description: Strives to recruit and enhance business, as well as foster community development in Lawrence County, Mississippi. **Founded:** 1849. **Geographic Preference:** Local.

44252 ■ *Leadership Lackawanna News*
222 Mulberry St.
Scranton, PA 18501
Ph: (570)342-7711
Fax: (570)347-6262
Co. E-mail: information@scrantonchamber.com
URL: http://www.scrantonchamber.com
Contact: Bob Durkin, President
E-mail: rdurkin@scrantonchamber.com
URL(s): www.leadershiplackawanna.com/news
Released: Latest Issue: Winter 2023. **Availability:** Print; Online; PDF.

44253 ■ Lebanon Valley Chamber of Commerce
989 Quentin Rd., Ste. 1
Lebanon, PA 17042-5272
Ph: (717)273-3727
Co. E-mail: info@lvchamber.org
URL: http://www.lvchamber.org
Contact: Karen Groh, President
E-mail: kgroh@lvchamber.org
Facebook: www.facebook.com/
lebanonvalleychamber
Linkedin: www.linkedin.com/company/lebanon-valley
-chamber-of-commerce
X (Twitter): x.com/LV_Chamber
Description: Promotes business and community development in the Lebanon County, PA area. Convention/Meeting: none. **Founded:** 1917. **Publications:** *Images Magazine* (Annual); *Manufacturers & Processors Directory* (Annual); *Memberandum* (Monthly). **Geographic Preference:** Local.

44254 ■ Lower Bucks County Chamber of Commerce (LBCCC)
409 Hood Blvd.
Fairless Hills, PA 19030
Ph: (215)943-7400
Fax: (215)943-7404
Co. E-mail: info@lbccc.org
URL: http://lbccc.org
Contact: Minesh V. Pathak, Executive Director
E-mail: mpathak@lbccc.org
Facebook: www.facebook.com/LowerBucksChamber
Linkedin: www.linkedin.com/company/
lowerbuckschamber
X (Twitter): x.com/LowerBksChamber
Instagram: www.instagram.com/lowerbuckschamber
Pinterest: www.pinterest.com/lowerbkschamber
Description: Promotes business and community development in Bucks County, PA. Holds annual Expo and job fairs. Sponsors semi-annual seminars. **Founded:** 1958. **Publications:** *Outlook* (Bimonthly); *Outlook* (Monthly). **Geographic Preference:** Local.

44255 ■ Main Line Chamber of Commerce (MLCC)
175 Strafford Ave., Ste. 130
Wayne, PA 19087
Ph: (610)687-6232
Fax: (610)687-8085
URL: http://www.mlcc.org
Contact: Bernard Dagenais, President
E-mail: bdagenais@mlcc.org
X (Twitter): x.com/mainlinechamber
Description: Promotes business and community development in Chester, Delaware, and Montgomery counties, PA. Conducts business card exchanges and Main Line Week activities. **Founded:** 1921. **Publications:** *Main Line Chamber of Commerce-- Membership Directory and Business Resource Guide*; *Main Line Chamber of Commerce Membership Directory* (Annual); *NewsLine* (Bimonthly). **Educational Activities:** Business Exposition; Inspirational Breakfast (Annual). **Geographic Preference:** Local.

44256 ■ *Main Line Chamber of Commerce Membership Directory*
175 Strafford Ave., Ste. 130
Wayne, PA 19087
Ph: (610)687-6232

Fax: (610)687-8085
URL: http://www.mlcc.org
Contact: Bernard Dagenais, President
E-mail: bdagenais@mlcc.org
URL(s): www.mlcc.org/index.php?submenu=member
_directory&src=sba&srctype=businesssearch_lister
Released: Annual **Description:** Contains member listing alphabetically and by category. **Availability:** Print; Online.

44257 ■ *Major Employers of Adams County*
1382 Biglerville Rd.
Gettysburg, PA 17325
Ph: (717)334-8151
Co. E-mail: info@gettysburg-chamber.org
URL: http://www.gettysburg-chamber.org
Contact: Carrie Stuart, President
URL(s): www.gettysburg-chamber.org/business
-resources
Availability: PDF; Online.

44258 ■ Manheim Area Chamber of Commerce
15 Market Sq.
Manheim, PA 17545
Ph: (717)665-6330
Co. E-mail: info@manheimchamber.com
URL: http://www.manheimchamber.com
Contact: Katelyn Haldeman, Team Leader
Facebook: www.facebook.com/manheimchamber
Instagram: www.instagram.com/manheim_chamber
Description: Promotes business and community development in the Manheim, PA area. **Founded:** 1967. **Publications:** *Business Directory*. **Geographic Preference:** Local.

44259 ■ Mansfield Chamber of Commerce (MCC)
8 S Main St. Rear Unit 1
Mansfield, PA 16933
Ph: (570)662-3442
Co. E-mail: info@mansfield.org
URL: http://www.mansfield.org
Facebook: www.facebook.com/mansfieldchamberpa
Description: Promotes business and community development in the Mansfield, PA area. Sponsors annual Home for the Holidays Christmas Celebration and 1890s celebration. **Founded:** 1985. **Publications:** *Chamber Update*. **Geographic Preference:** Local.

44260 ■ Meadville - Western Crawford County Chamber of Commerce
908 Diamond Pk.
Meadville, PA 16335
Ph: (814)337-8030
Fax: (814)337-8022
Co. E-mail: kstaudt@meadvillechamber.com
URL: http://www.meadvillechamber.com
Contact: Adam Prenatt, President
Facebook: www.facebook.com/meadvillechamber
Description: Promotes business and community development in western Crawford County, PA. Promotes tourism; provides educational programs. **Founded:** 1807. **Publications:** *Chamber Media Network* (Monthly); *Community Audit* (Periodic); *Industrial Directory*. **Geographic Preference:** Local.

44261 ■ Mercersburg Area Chamber of Commerce (MACC)
113 S Main St.
Mercersburg, PA 17236
Ph: (717)328-5827
Co. E-mail: cardinger@tachamber.org
URL: http://tachamber.org
Contact: Chris Ardinger, Executive Director
Description: Promotes business and community development in the Mercersburg, PA area. Conducts charitable activities. Sponsors festival. **Founded:** 1975. **Publications:** *Mercersburg Area Chamber of Commerce Business Directory* (Annual). **Awards:** Tuscarora Area Chamber of Commerce Business Person of the Year (Annual). **Geographic Preference:** Regional.

STATE LISTINGS

44262 ■ *Momentum*
222 Mulberry St.
Scranton, PA 18501
Ph: (570)342-7711
Fax: (570)347-6262
Co. E-mail: information@scrantonchamber.com
URL: http://www.scrantonchamber.com
Contact: Bob Durkin, President
E-mail: rdurkin@scrantonchamber.com
URL(s): www.scrantonchamber.com/momentum
Released: Monthly **Availability:** Online.

44263 ■ Mon Valley Regional Chamber of Commerce
1 Chamber Plz.
Charleroi, PA 15022
Ph: (724)483-3507
Fax: (724)489-1045
Co. E-mail: members@mvrchamber.org
URL: http://mvrchamber.org
Contact: Armand Ferrara, President
X (Twitter): x.com/mvrof
Description: Promotes business and community development in the Mid Mon Valley Region of Southwestern Pennsylvania. Encourages networking, educational, and economic development. **Founded:** 1921. **Publications:** *Regional Reporter* (Quarterly). **Awards:** MVR Chamber Excellence in Business Awards (Annual). **Geographic Preference:** Local.

44264 ■ Mon Yough Area Chamber of Commerce
4304 Walnut St.
McKeesport, PA 15132
Ph: (412)678-2450
Fax: (412)678-2451
URL: http://www.monyoughchamber.com
Contact: Maury Burgwin, President
Facebook: www.facebook.com/MYAChamber
X (Twitter): x.com/MYAChamber
Description: Promotes business and community development in southeastern Allegheny County, PA. Provides business goods and services and industrial referrals. Holds small business seminars. Sponsors Mon-Yough Science Fair. **Founded:** 1906. **Publications:** *Action!* (Monthly); *Mon-Yough Membership Directory*. **Geographic Preference:** Local.

44265 ■ *Mon-Yough Membership Directory*
4304 Walnut St.
McKeesport, PA 15132
Ph: (412)678-2450
Fax: (412)678-2451
URL: http://www.monyoughchamber.com
Contact: Maury Burgwin, President
URL(s): www.monyoughchamber.com/members-area
Availability: Print.

44266 ■ *Monroeville Area Business Directory*
2790 Mosside Blvd., Ste. 150
Monroeville, PA 15146
Ph: (412)856-0622
Co. E-mail: macc@monroevillechamber.com
URL: http://www.monroevillechamber.com
Contact: Sean Logan, President
URL(s): www.monroevillechamber.com/business-directory/#/cid/1955/id/401
Availability: Print.

44267 ■ Monroeville Area Chamber of Commerce (MACC)
2790 Mosside Blvd., Ste. 150
Monroeville, PA 15146
Ph: (412)856-0622
Co. E-mail: macc@monroevillechamber.com
URL: http://www.monroevillechamber.com
Contact: Sean Logan, President
Facebook: www.facebook.com/MonroevilleAreaChamber
Linkedin: www.linkedin.com/in/monroevilleareachamber
X (Twitter): x.com/MonroevilleArea
Pinterest: www.pinterest.com/monroevillearea
Description: Promotes business and community development in the Monroeville, PA area. Sponsors "Chamber Challenge" and annual Golf Invitational among other major events. **Founded:** 1953. **Publications:** *Monroeville Area Business Directory*; *Industrial Directory*; *MACConnections* (Monthly). **Geographic Preference:** Local.

44268 ■ Nazareth-Bath Area Chamber of Commerce
201 N Main St.
Nazareth, PA 18064
Ph: (610)759-9188
Co. E-mail: jessicao@lehighvalleychamber.org
URL: http://www.discoverlehighvalley.com/listing/nazareth-bath-area-chamber-of-commerce/2880
Contact: Alex Michaels, President
E-mail: alex@discoverlehighvalley.com
X (Twitter): x.com/NazarethChamber
Description: Preserves and enhances the interests of the members and the business community by improving the general welfare and prosperity of the region. **Founded:** 1939. **Publications:** *Nazareth Chamber News* (Monthly). **Geographic Preference:** Local.

44269 ■ North East Area Chamber of Commerce (NEACC)
44 W Main St.
North East, PA 16428
Ph: (814)725-4262
Co. E-mail: info@nechamber.org
URL: http://www.nechamber.org
Contact: Lori Ion, Director
Facebook: www.facebook.com/TheNorthEastChamber
X (Twitter): x.com/NEPAChamber
YouTube: www.youtube.com/channel/UC4BiP7aFn67SFiY_bl_ppgw
Description: Promotes business and community development in the North East, PA area. Promotes educational and recreational activities. Sponsors annual Wine Country Harvest Festival on last weekend of September. **Publications:** *From the Chamber...* (Biweekly); *Welcome to Wine County* (Annual). **Educational Activities:** Wine Fest (Annual). **Geographic Preference:** Local.

44270 ■ The Northern Lancaster County Chamber of Commerce (EACC)
PO Box 723
Ephrata, PA 17522
Ph: (717)738-9010
Co. E-mail: info@northernlancasterchamber.org
URL: http://www.northernlancasterchamber.org
Contact: Mark Thompson, Co-President
Facebook: www.facebook.com/NorthernLancasterChamber
Linkedin: www.linkedin.com/company/northernlancasterchamber
X (Twitter): x.com/NLCChamber
Instagram: www.instagram.com/northernlancasterchamber
Description: Promotes business and community development in the Ephrata, PA area. **Founded:** 1922. **Publications:** *Down to Business* (Weekly). **Geographic Preference:** Local.

44271 ■ Norwin Chamber of Commerce
321 Main St.
Irwin, PA 15642
Ph: (724)863-0888
Co. E-mail: info@norwinchamber.com
URL: http://norwinchamber.com
Contact: Rosanne Barry Novotnak, President
E-mail: rnovotnak@norwinchamber.com
Description: Promotes business and community development in Irwin, North Huntingdon, and North Irwin, PA. **Founded:** 1942. **Publications:** *Vocal Point* (Monthly). **Educational Activities:** Norwin Chamber of Commerce Luncheon. **Geographic Preference:** Local.

44272 ■ Oxford Area Chamber of Commerce (OACC)
59 S 3rd St., Ste. 5
Oxford, PA 19363
Ph: (610)932-0740
Co. E-mail: oxfordchamber@zoominternet.net
URL: http://oxfordpa.org
Contact: Rich Hannum, Chairman
Facebook: www.facebook.com/OxfordChamber
X (Twitter): x.com/OxfordPAChamber
Description: Promotes business and community development in southern Chester County, PA. **Publications:** *Oxfordian* (Semiannual). **Geographic Preference:** Local.

44273 ■ *Oxfordian*
59 S 3rd St., Ste. 5
Oxford, PA 19363
Ph: (610)932-0740
Co. E-mail: oxfordchamber@zoominternet.net
URL: http://oxfordpa.org
Contact: Rich Hannum, Chairman
URL(s): oxfordpa.org/oxfordian
Released: Semiannual; fall and spring. **Price:** $1.50, Single issue. **Availability:** PDF; Online.

44274 ■ Palmerton Area Chamber of Commerce
418 Princeton Ave.
Palmerton, PA 18071
Ph: (610)826-5777
URL: http://business.carboncountychamber.org/list/member/palmerton-area-chamber-of-commerce-2963
Description: Promotes business and community development in Palmerton, PA. **Geographic Preference:** Local.

44275 ■ Penn Hills Chamber of Commerce (PHCC)
12 Federal Dr., Ste.,106
Penn Hills, PA 15235
Description: Promotes the interests of the business community. Supports and encourages cultural and civic activities beneficial to the business community, and endorses those activities which will improve or expand the general quality of life in Penn Hills. **Publications:** *The Changing Times* (Monthly). **Geographic Preference:** Local.

44276 ■ Pennridge Chamber of Commerce (PCC)
524 W Market St.
Perkasie, PA 18944
URL: http://www.pennridge.com
Description: Represents business in the Pennridge community. Works with business and the community in striving to make the Pennridge area a better place to work and live. **Founded:** 1963. **Publications:** *The Communicator* (Monthly). **Geographic Preference:** Local.

44277 ■ PennSuburban Chamber of Commerce
325 Madison St.
Lansdale, PA 19446
Ph: (215)362-9200
Fax: (267)613-8865
Co. E-mail: info@chambergmc.org
URL: http://www.chambergmc.org
Contact: David Onorato, Chairman
Facebook: www.facebook.com/ChamberGMC
X (Twitter): x.com/chambergmc
Instagram: www.instagram.com/thechambergmc
Description: Preserves and enhances the interests of the members and the business community by improving the general welfare and prosperity of the region. **Founded:** 1913. **Publications:** *The Chamber of Commerce for Greater Montgomery County-Membership Directory*; *Prospector* (Monthly). **Geographic Preference:** Local.

44278 ■ Pennsylvania Chamber of Business and Industry
417 Walnut St.
Harrisburg, PA 17101
Ph: (717)255-3252
Free: 800-225-7224
Fax: (717)255-3298
Co. E-mail: info@pachamber.org
URL: http://www.pachamber.org
Contact: Gene Barr, President
E-mail: gbarr@pachamber.org
Facebook: www.facebook.com/PAChamber

44279 ■ Pennsylvania

Linkedin: www.linkedin.com/company/pa-chamber-of-business-and-industry
X (Twitter): x.com/pachamber
Instagram: www.instagram.com/pachamber
Description: Seeks to advocate business by influencing legislative, regulatory, and judicial branches of state government. **Founded:** 1916. **Publications:** *Catalyst* (Quarterly). **Geographic Preference:** State.

44279 ■ Perkiomen Valley Chamber of Commerce (PVCC)
521 W Main St., Ste. 103
Trappe, PA 19426
Ph: (610)489-6660
Fax: (610)454-1270
Co. E-mail: info@pvchamber.net
URL: http://perkiomenvalleychamber.org
Contact: Matthew Baker, Treasurer
Facebook: www.facebook.com/PerkValleyChamber
Description: Seeks to preserve, protect and promote members and their businesses. Programs include monthly meetings, educational seminars, legislative forums, social functions and business mixers. Serves boroughs of Collegeville, Schwenksville and Trappe and the townships of Limerick, Lower Frederick, Lower Providence, Perkiomen, Skippack and Upper Providence in Western Montgomery County, PA. **Founded:** 1957. **Geographic Preference:** Local.

44280 ■ Perry County Chamber of Commerce (PCCC)
9 W Main St.
New Bloomfield, PA 17068
Ph: (717)582-4523
Co. E-mail: pccc@perrycountychamber.org
URL: http://www.perrycountychamber.org
Contact: Clay Merris, President
Facebook: www.facebook.com/perrycoChamber
Linkedin: www.linkedin.com/in/perry-county-chamber-20947063
X (Twitter): x.com/PerryCntyChmbr
Description: Promotes local business and community development in the area. **Founded:** 2009. **Publications:** *Perry County Community Profile Magazine* (Triennial); *Chamber Business* (Monthly). **Geographic Preference:** Local.

44281 ■ Peters Township Chamber of Commerce
1061 Waterdam Plz. Dr.
McMurray, PA 15317
Ph: (724)941-6345
Co. E-mail: info@ptcoc.org
URL: http://www.peterstownshipchamber.com
Contact: Brian Schill, Executive Director
Facebook: www.facebook.com/PetersTownshipCC
Linkedin: www.linkedin.com/company/peters-township-chamber-of-commerce
Description: Promotes business and community development in the Peters Township, PA area. Conducts community service projects. Recognizes graduating high school seniors and honors new teachers. **Founded:** 1954. **Publications:** *Business Guide and Community Directory* (Annual); *Chamber News and Notes* (Quarterly). **Geographic Preference:** Local.

44282 ■ Philadelphia-Israel Chamber of Commerce (PICC)
100 E Penn Sq.
Philadelphia, PA 19107
Ph: (215)515-9544
Co. E-mail: picc@phillyisraelchamber.com
URL: http://www.phillyisraelchamber.org
Contact: Tiffany S. S. McKever, President
Facebook: www.facebook.com/PICofC
Linkedin: www.linkedin.com/company/philadelphia-israel-chamber-of-commerce
X (Twitter): x.com/PICofC
Description: Promotes the interests of the U.S.-Israel business community. **Founded:** 1987. **Geographic Preference:** Regional.

44283 ■ Phoenixville Area Chamber of Commerce
171 E Bridge St.
Phoenixville, PA 19460
Ph: (610)933-3070
Fax: (610)917-0503
Co. E-mail: info@phoenixvillechamber.org
URL: http://www.phoenixvillechamber.org
Contact: Jessica Capistrant, President
E-mail: jcapistrant@phoenixvillechamber.org
Facebook: www.facebook.com/PXVChamber
Linkedin: www.linkedin.com/company/phoenixville-regional-chamber-of-commerce
X (Twitter): x.com/PXVChamber
Description: Promotes business and community development in the Phoenixville, PA and the Valley Forge region. Conducts entrepreneurial education. Sponsors annual Summer Music Festival. **Founded:** 1928. **Publications:** *The Rising Phoenix* (Quarterly). **Educational Activities:** Phoenixville Area Chamber of Commerce Dinner (Annual). **Geographic Preference:** Regional.

44284 ■ Pike County Chamber of Commerce
201 Broad St., Ste. 2
Milford, PA 18337
Ph: (570)296-8700
Co. E-mail: info@pikechamber.com
URL: http://www.pikechamber.com
Contact: Katrina Mancini, Vice President
Facebook: www.facebook.com/pikechamberpa
X (Twitter): x.com/pikechamberpa
Description: Promotes business and community development in Pike County, PA. Assists new businesses and homeowners. Provides legislative representation and group insurance. Bestows Community Achievement Award. **Founded:** 1962. **Publications:** *NewsFlash* (Monthly); *Pike County Pennsylvania*. **Geographic Preference:** Local.

44285 ■ Pittsburgh Airport Area Chamber of Commerce (PAACC)
850 Beaver Grade Rd., Ste. 101
Moon Township, PA 15108
Ph: (412)264-6270
Fax: (412)264-1575
Co. E-mail: info@paacc.com
URL: http://www.paacc.com
Contact: Chris Heck, President
E-mail: bpuzzuole@paacc.com
Facebook: www.facebook.com/paacc
Linkedin: www.linkedin.com/in/pittsburghairportchamber
X (Twitter): x.com/AirportChamber
Description: Promotes business and community development in the Pittsburgh, PA airport area. Sponsors scholarship programs and educational seminars. **Founded:** 1949. **Publications:** *News Bulletin* (Monthly). **Educational Activities:** Business Expo (Annual). **Geographic Preference:** Local.

44286 ■ *Quality of Life*
801 S Hanover St.
Carlisle, PA 17013
Ph: (717)243-4515
Fax: (717)243-4446
Co. E-mail: info@carlislechamber.org
URL: http://www.carlislechamber.org
Contact: Jennifer Germain, Director
E-mail: jgermain@carlislechamber.org
URL(s): www.carlislechamber.org/the-chamber
Availability: Print.

44287 ■ *Regional Reporter*
1 Chamber Plz.
Charleroi, PA 15022
Ph: (724)483-3507
Fax: (724)489-1045
Co. E-mail: members@mvrchamber.org
URL: http://mvrchamber.org
Contact: Armand Ferrara, President
URL(s): mvrchamber.org/membership/newsletters
Released: Quarterly **Availability:** Print; PDF.

44288 ■ *Ridgway Area Business Directory*
300 Main St.
Ridgway, PA 15853
Ph: (814)776-1424
Co. E-mail: info@ridgwaychamber.com
URL: http://www.ridgwaychamber.com
Contact: Kylee Mader, Treasurer

STATE LISTINGS

URL(s): www.ridgwaychamber.com/members
Released: Annual **Availability:** Print; Online.

44289 ■ Ridgway-Elk County Chamber of Commerce
300 Main St.
Ridgway, PA 15853
Ph: (814)776-1424
Co. E-mail: info@ridgwaychamber.com
URL: http://www.ridgwaychamber.com
Contact: Kylee Mader, Treasurer
Facebook: www.facebook.com/Ridgway-Elk-County-Chamber-Of-Commerce-146225898842778
Description: Promotes business and community development in Ridgway and Elk County, PA. Holds educational seminars. **Founded:** 1892. **Publications:** *Historical Walking Tour of Ridgway*; *Industrial Directory*; *Ridgway Area Business Directory* (Annual). **Educational Activities:** Community Service Awards Dinner. **Geographic Preference:** Local.

44290 ■ *The Rising Phoenix*
171 E Bridge St.
Phoenixville, PA 19460
Ph: (610)933-3070
Fax: (610)917-0503
Co. E-mail: info@phoenixvillechamber.org
URL: http://www.phoenixvillechamber.org
Contact: Jessica Capistrant, President
E-mail: jcapistrant@phoenixvillechamber.org
URL(s): phoenixvillechamber.org/news-events/publications
Released: Quarterly **Availability:** PDF.

44291 ■ *Route 422 Business Advisor*
152 High St., Ste. 360
Pottstown, PA 19464
Ph: (610)326-2900
Co. E-mail: eileen@tricountyareachamber.com
URL: http://www.tricountyareachamber.com
Contact: April Barkasi, President
URL(s): www.422business.com
Released: Monthly **Description:** Magazine containing topics of interest to the business community of the Pottstown, PA area. **Availability:** Print; Online.

44292 ■ St. Marys Area Chamber of Commerce (SMACC)
53 S Saint Marys St.
Saint Marys, PA 15857
Ph: (814)781-3804
Co. E-mail: info@stmaryschamber.org
URL: http://stmaryschamber.org
Contact: Andrew Mohney, President
Facebook: www.facebook.com/StMarysChamber
Description: Promotes business and community development in St. Marys, PA. **Founded:** 1984. **Publications:** *Business Directory* (Monthly); *Industrial Directory*. **Educational Activities:** Business Expo. **Geographic Preference:** Local.

44293 ■ *Sample Employee Handbook*
115 E King St.
Lancaster, PA 17602
Ph: (717)397-3531
Co. E-mail: info@lancasterchamber.com
URL: http://www.lancasterchamber.com
Contact: Heather Valudes, Co-President Co-Chief Executive Officer
E-mail: hvaludes@lancasterchamber.com
URL(s): connect.lancasterchamber.com/LCCRedesign/iCore/Store/StoreLayouts/Item_Detail.aspx?iProductCode=HNDBK&Category=PUB
Price: $75, Single issue. **Description:** Provides model policies and practices in ready to be adopted language. **Availability:** Print.

44294 ■ Schuylkill Chamber of Commerce (SCC)
Union Station., 1 Progress Cir., Ste. 201
Pottsville, PA 17901
Ph: (570)622-1942
Free: 800-755-1942
Co. E-mail: memberservices@schuylkillchamber.com
URL: http://www.schuylkillchamber.com
Contact: Robert S. Carl, Jr., President
E-mail: rcarl@schuylkillchamber.com

Facebook: www.facebook.com/SchuylkillChamber
Linkedin: www.linkedin.com/company/schuylkill-chamber-of-commerce
Instagram: www.instagram.com/schuylkillchamber
Description: Serves members and affiliates with value-added programs and services and improves the quality of life and economic vitality of Schuylkill County. **Founded:** 1918. **Publications:** *Communicator* (Bimonthly); *Schuylkill Chamber of Commerce--Business Directory.* **Geographic Preference:** Local.

44295 ■ **Scottdale Area Chamber of Commerce**
PO Box 534
Scottdale, PA 15683
Ph: (724)887-3611
Co. E-mail: scottdalechamber@gmail.com
URL: http://www.scottdale.com
Contact: David Mardis, President
Facebook: www.facebook.com/Scottdale-Area-Chamber-of-Commerce-250127211723329
Description: Promotes business and community development in the Scottdale, PA area. Sponsors festival and contests; participates in charitable activities. Publications: none. **Founded:** 1878. **Geographic Preference:** Local.

44296 ■ *The Scranton Plan News*
222 Mulberry St.
Scranton, PA 18501
Ph: (570)342-7711
Fax: (570)347-6262
Co. E-mail: information@scrantonchamber.com
URL: http://www.scrantonchamber.com
Contact: Bob Durkin, President
E-mail: rdurkin@scrantonchamber.com
URL(s): www.scrantonchamber.com/news/chamber-news
Availability: Print.

44297 ■ **Shenango Valley Chamber of Commerce**
41 Chestnut Ave.
Sharon, PA 16146
Ph: (724)981-5880
Fax: (724)981-5480
Co. E-mail: info@svchamber.com
URL: http://www.svchamber.com
Contact: David Grande, President
Facebook: www.facebook.com/shenangovalleychamber
X (Twitter): x.com/SVChamberPA
Instagram: www.instagram.com/shenangovalleychamber
Description: Promotes business and community development in northwestern Pennsylvania and Brookfield and Masury, OH. Provides business assistance, educational programs, and government liaison. Holds breakfast and luncheon meetings with local, state and federal legislators. Sponsors Business and Industry Golf Classic, Business After Hours networking events, annual Business Expo, and other professional development and networking events. **Founded:** 1956. **Publications:** *Images* (Bimonthly); *Shenango Valley Chamber of Commerce Membership Directory and Buyer's Guide* (Annual). **Awards:** Shenango Valley Chamber Person of the Year (Annual); Shenango Valley Chamber Phoenix Award (Annual). **Geographic Preference:** Local.

44298 ■ **Shippensburg Area Chamber of Commerce (SACOC)**
68 W King St.
Shippensburg, PA 17257
Ph: (717)532-5509
Fax: (717)532-7501
Co. E-mail: chamber@shippensburg.org
URL: http://www.shippensburg.org
Contact: Scott Brown, President
Description: Promotes business and community development in Franklin and Cumberland counties, PA. **Founded:** 1938. **Publications:** *Chamberline* (Monthly). **Geographic Preference:** Local.

44299 ■ **Somerset County Chamber of Commerce**
601 N Center Ave.
Somerset, PA 15501
Ph: (814)445-6431
Fax: (814)443-4313
Co. E-mail: info@somersetcountychamber.com
URL: http://somersetcountychamber.com
Contact: Lisa Bittner, President
Facebook: www.facebook.com/SomersetCountyChamber
Linkedin: www.linkedin.com/company/somerset-county-chamber-of-commerce
X (Twitter): x.com/somersetchamber
YouTube: www.youtube.com/channel/UCVhwlzP__Kl_VP7z8HaRdXA
Pinterest: www.pinterest.com/somersetcochmbr
Description: Established to network with businesses to enhance economic opportunities. **Founded:** 1912. **Publications:** *Somerset County Chamber of Commerce--Member Directory*; *Chamber Progress* (Bimonthly); *Business Directory*; *Guide to Somerset County.* **Educational Activities:** Annual Somerset Antique Show (Annual). **Geographic Preference:** Local.

44300 ■ **South Hills Chamber of Commerce (SHCC)**
61 McMurray Rd., Ste. 105
Pittsburgh, PA 15241
Ph: (412)306-8090
Co. E-mail: office@shchamber.org
URL: http://south-hills-chamber-of-commerce.square.site
Contact: John A. A. Biedrzycki, Owner
Description: Promotes business and community development in the South Hills area of Pittsburgh, PA. **Founded:** 1981. **Publications:** *The Pacesetter* (Monthly). **Geographic Preference:** Local.

44301 ■ **South West Communities Chamber of Commerce (SWCCOC)**
990 Washington Pke.
Bridgeville, PA 15017
Ph: (412)221-4100
Co. E-mail: info@swccoc.org
URL: http://southwestcommunitieschamber.org
Contact: Stacie Riley, President
Facebook: www.facebook.com/SWCCOC
Description: Promotes business and community development in Upper St. Clair, PA. **Geographic Preference:** Local.

44302 ■ **Southern Chester County Chamber of Commerce (SCCCC)**
8 Federal Rd., Ste. 1
West Grove, PA 19390
Ph: (610)444-0774
Co. E-mail: info@sccccc.com
URL: http://www.sccccc.com
Contact: Cheryl B. Kuhn, President
E-mail: ckuhn@sccccc.com
Facebook: www.facebook.com/southernchestercountychamber
Linkedin: www.linkedin.com/company/southern-chester-county-chamber-of-commerce
X (Twitter): x.com/SCCCC1930
Description: Promotes business and community development in Southern Chester County, PA. **Founded:** 1929. **Awards:** SCCCC Outstanding Citizen of the Year Award (Annual). **Geographic Preference:** Regional.

44303 ■ *Southern Wayne Regional Chamber*
569 Easton Tpke.
Lake Ariel, PA 18436
Ph: (570)689-4199
Free: 877-228-7941
Fax: (570)689-4391
Co. E-mail: swrchamber@swrchamber.org
Contact: Patty Blaum, Executive Director
URL(s): swcrc.com
Released: Quarterly **Description:** Contains information on what is going on in the area, chamber news, and upcoming events. **Availability:** Print.

44304 ■ **Sullivan County Chamber of Commerce, Pennsylvania**
202 S Tpke., St.
Dushore, PA 18614
Ph: (272)202-0123
URL: http://sullivancountypachamber.com
Description: Promotes business and community development in Sullivan County, PA. **Founded:** 1986. **Geographic Preference:** Local.

44305 ■ *Susquehanna Style*
144 Roosevelt Ave.
York, PA 17401
Ph: (717)848-4000
Fax: (717)843-8837
Co. E-mail: marketing@ycea-pa.org
URL: http://www.yceapa.org
Contact: Kevin Schreiber, President
E-mail: kevin@ycea-pa.org
URL(s): www.yceapa.org/membership/benefitssusquehannastyle.com
Facebook: www.facebook.com/susquehannastyle
X (Twitter): x.com/SusquehannaStyl
Instagram: www.instagram.com/susquehannastyle
Pinterest: www.pinterest.com/SusquehannaStyl
Released: Monthly **Availability:** Print; Download; Online.

44306 ■ **Susquehanna Valley Chamber of Commerce and Visitors Center (SVCC)**
2859 N Susquehanna Trl.
Shamokin Dam, PA 17876
Ph: (570)743-4100
Free: 800-410-2880
Co. E-mail: info@gsvcc.org
URL: http://www.gsvcc.org
Contact: Bob Garrett, President
Linkedin: www.linkedin.com/company/gsvchamber
X (Twitter): x.com/gsvcc
Instagram: www.instagram.com/gsvchamber
YouTube: www.youtube.com/channel/UC9ojeFY1zNEJczWf8TB_87g
Description: Promotes business and community development in Columbia, Marietta, Mountville, and Wrightsville, PA. Sponsors annual Antique and Craft Fair. Operates Susquehanna Heritage Tourist and Information Center and Susquehanna Tri-Bourough Development Company. **Founded:** 1928. **Publications:** *Calendar of Events - Information Directory* (Periodic). **Geographic Preference:** Local.

44307 ■ **Swedish-American Chamber of Commerce Philadelphia**
2929 Arch St., Ste. 1700
Philadelphia, PA 19104
Ph: (267)360-2128
Co. E-mail: info@sacc-philadelphia.org
URL: http://www.sacc-philadelphia.org
Contact: Anders Näsman, President
Facebook: www.facebook.com/SACCphiladelphia
Linkedin: www.linkedin.com/company/sacc-phl
Instagram: www.instagram.com/saccphiladelphia
Description: Encourages and promotes the exchange of technology, trade, and culture between Sweden and the Greater Philadelphia region. **Founded:** 1999. **Geographic Preference:** Local.

44308 ■ **Titusville Area Chamber of Commerce (TACC)**
202 W Central Ave.
Titusville, PA 16354
Ph: (814)827-2941
Co. E-mail: info@victoriantitusvillepa.com
URL: http://victoriantitusvillepa.com
Facebook: www.facebook.com/TitusvilleChamberofCommerce
X (Twitter): x.com/TitusvlChamber
Description: Promotes business, community development, and downtown revitalization in the Titusville, PA area. Conducts business advocacy through the legislative, transportation, and education committee programs. Sponsors leadership programs, golf outing, Chamber Week activities, community surveys, active tourism programs, $30,000 per year gift certificate program, and member insurance program. Maintains small business development and outreach center.

Founded: 1889. **Publications:** *Historic Brochure* (Periodic); *Industrial Directory*. **Educational Activities:** Oil Festival (Annual). **Geographic Preference:** Local.

44309 ■ **Township of Richland Chamber of Commerce**
4019 Dickey Rd.
Gibsonia, PA 15044
Ph: (724)443-5921
Fax: (724)443-8860
Co. E-mail: info@richland.pa.us
URL: http://richland.pa.us
Contact: Raymond Kendrick, Chairman
Description: Promotes bueiness in Richland. **Geographic Preference:** Local.

44310 ■ **TriCounty Area Chamber of Commerce (TCACC)**
152 High St., Ste. 360
Pottstown, PA 19464
Ph: (610)326-2900
Co. E-mail: eileen@tricountyareachamber.com
URL: http://www.tricountyareachamber.com
Contact: April Barkasi, President
Facebook: www.facebook.com/TriCoun tyAreaChamber
Linkedin: www.linkedin.com/company/tricounty-area -chamber-of-commerce
X (Twitter): x.com/TcaccTri
Instagram: www.instagram.com/tricoun tyareachamber
YouTube: www.youtube.com/channel/UCHwCxgl6AZ -1VudddTiEutw
Description: Promotes business and community development in the Pottstown, PA area. **Founded:** 1927. **Publications:** *Connection* (Monthly); *Route 422 Business Advisor* (Monthly). **Educational Activities:** Chamber 101. **Geographic Preference:** Local.

44311 ■ **Tyrone Area Chamber of Commerce**
1004 Logan Ave.
Tyrone, PA 16686
Ph: (814)684-0736
Co. E-mail: rose@tyronechamber.com
URL: http://tyronechamber.com
Contact: Janet Pearson, President
E-mail: alleghenychorale@gmail.com
Facebook: www.facebook.com/tyroneeventsan dpromotionspa
Description: Promotes business and community development in the Tyrone, PA area. **Founded:** 1916. **Publications:** *Tyrone Chamber Tab* (Monthly). **Educational Activities:** Business After Hours (Monthly). **Geographic Preference:** Local.

44312 ■ **Upper Bucks Chamber of Commerce (UBCC)**
21 N Main St.
Quakertown, PA 18951
Ph: (215)536-3211
Fax: (215)536-7767
Co. E-mail: info@ubcc.org
URL: http://www.ubcc.org
Contact: Vickie McClatchy, President
X (Twitter): x.com/upperbucks
Description: Promotes business and community development in Upper Bucks County, PA. **Founded:** 1954. **Publications:** *Bridges to Business* (Bimonthly). **Geographic Preference:** Local.

44313 ■ **Venango Area Chamber of Commerce (VACC)**
24 Seneca St.
Oil City, PA 16301
Ph: (814)676-8521
Fax: (814)676-8185
Co. E-mail: chamber@venangochamber.org
URL: http://venangochamber.org
Contact: Susan Williams, President
E-mail: swilliams@venangochamber.org
Facebook: www.facebook.com/ VenangoAreaChamberOfCommerce
Linkedin: www.linkedin.com/company/venango-area -chamber-of-commerce
X (Twitter): x.com/venangochamber
Instagram: www.instagram.com/venangochamber

YouTube: www.youtube.com/user/VenangoChamber
Description: Provides services that promote successful business growth by coordinating activities and forums that address community issues. **Founded:** 2005. **Geographic Preference:** Local.

44314 ■ *Vocal Point*
321 Main St.
Irwin, PA 15642
Ph: (724)863-0888
Co. E-mail: info@norwinchamber.com
URL: http://norwinchamber.com
Contact: Rosanne Barry Novotnak, President
E-mail: rnovotnak@norwinchamber.com
URL(s): norwinchamber.com/newsletters
Released: Monthly; latest issue august-2023. **Description:** Contains Business information, calendar events, and Chamber developments. **Availability:** PDF; Download; Online.

44315 ■ *The Voice*
1600 Paoli Pke.
Malvern, PA 19355
Ph: (610)725-9100
Fax: (610)725-8479
Co. E-mail: info@chescochamber.org
URL: http://www.chescochamber.org
Contact: Caitlin Ganley, Secretary
URL(s): www.chescochamber.com/about-us
Availability: Print.

44316 ■ *The Voice of the Valley*
Routes 11 and 15
2859 N Susquehanna Trl.
Shamokin Dam, PA 17876
Ph: (570)743-4100
Free: 800-410-2880
Fax: (570)743-1221
Co. E-mail: info@gsvcc.org
URL: http://www.gsvcc.org
Contact: Bob Garrett, President
E-mail: rgarrett@gsvcc.org
URL(s): www.gsvcc.org/about/publications
Released: Daily **Availability:** PDF; Online.

44317 ■ **Warren County Chamber of Business and Industry (WCCBI)**
308 Market St.
Warren, PA 16365
Ph: (814)723-3050
Co. E-mail: chamberofbusinesswarrencounty@gmail .com
URL: http://www.wccbi.org
Contact: James Decker, President
E-mail: jdecker@wccbi.org
Facebook: www.facebook.com/warrenpa
Description: Promotes business and community development in Warren County, PA. Sponsors business seminars, programs, and workshops. Maintains consulting service. Holds annual golf outing. **Founded:** 2003. **Publications:** *Business Directory* (Annual); *Directory of Members & Buyers Guide*. **Geographic Preference:** Local.

44318 ■ **Washington County Chamber of Commerce (WCCOC)**
375 Southpointe Blvd., Ste. 240
Canonsburg, PA 15317
Ph: (724)225-3010
Fax: (724)228-7337
Co. E-mail: info@washcochamber.com
URL: http://www.washcochamber.com
Contact: Jeff M. Kotula, President
E-mail: jeff@washcochamber.com
Facebook: www.facebook.com/washcochamber
Linkedin: www.linkedin.com/in/washington-county -chamber-of-commerce-56881836
X (Twitter): x.com/WashCoChamberPA
Description: Promotes business and community development in the Washington, PA area. **Founded:** 1881. **Geographic Preference:** Local.

44319 ■ **Wellsboro Area Chamber of Commerce (WACC)**
114 Main St., No. 1
Wellsboro, PA 16901
Ph: (570)724-1926

Fax: (570)724-5084
Co. E-mail: info@wellsboropa.com
URL: http://www.wellsboropa.com
Contact: Kevin Thomas, President
E-mail: kc101fm@gmail.com
Facebook: www.facebook.com/Wellsboro-Area -Chamber-of-Commerce-193891613981765
X (Twitter): x.com/WellsboroCC
YouTube: www.youtube.com/channel/UCu 13XFSYBqVfMbg4Xc2kNYg
Description: Promotes business and community development in the Wellsboro, PA area. **Founded:** 1806. **Geographic Preference:** Local.

44320 ■ **West Shore Chamber of Commerce**
4211 Trindle Rd.
Camp Hill, PA 17011
Ph: (717)761-0702
Fax: (717)761-4315
Co. E-mail: wschamber@wschamber.org
URL: http://wschamber.org
Contact: George M. Book, Jr., President
E-mail: george@wschamber.org
Facebook: www.facebook.com/wschamber
Linkedin: www.linkedin.com/company/west-shore -chamber-of-commerce
X (Twitter): x.com/WS_Chamber
Instagram: www.instagram.com/ws_chamber
Description: Promotes business and community development in the Camp Hill, PA area. **Founded:** 1948. **Publications:** *Connections* (Monthly); *Membership Directory and Business Resource Guide* (Annual). **Educational Activities:** Spotlight Breakfast; Business and Industry Night (Annual). **Awards:** George C. Hoopy Award (Annual); Les Ginanni Business and Community Connection Award (Annual). **Geographic Preference:** Local.

44321 ■ **Western Chester County Chamber of Commerce (WCCCC)**
50 S 1st Ave.
Coatesville, PA 19320
Ph: (610)384-9550
Co. E-mail: chamber@westernchestercounty.com
URL: http://www.westernchestercounty.com
Contact: Justin Chan, President
Facebook: www.facebook.com/WCCChamber
X (Twitter): x.com/chescowest
Description: Promotes business and community development in Western Chester County, PA. Maintains hall of fame. **Founded:** 1916. **Publications:** *Western View* (Quarterly). **Geographic Preference:** Local.

44322 ■ *Western View*
50 S 1st Ave.
Coatesville, PA 19320
Ph: (610)384-9550
Co. E-mail: chamber@westernchestercounty.com
URL: http://www.westernchestercounty.com
Contact: Justin Chan, President
URL(s): www.westernchestercounty.com/western -view-newsletter
Released: Quarterly **Availability:** Download; PDF.

44323 ■ **Westmoreland Chamber of Commerce**
241 Tollgate Hill Rd.
Greensburg, PA 15601
Ph: (724)834-2900
Fax: (724)837-7635
Co. E-mail: info@westmorelandchamber.com
URL: http://www.westmorelandchamber.com
Contact: Dan DeBone, President
E-mail: dan@westmorelandchamber.com
Facebook: www.facebook.com/westmorelandcham ber
X (Twitter): x.com/westmocochamber
Instagram: www.instagram.com/westmorelandcham ber
YouTube: www.youtube.com/channel/ UCXsJ7gXYznsgy4A_PkSla4g
Description: Provides leadership to facilitate, maintain, and advance an environment conducive to the economic well being and superior quality of life for Westmoreland County through leadership, growth,

STATE LISTINGS

and vision. **Founded:** 1976. **Publications:** *Westmoreland Chamber of Commerce--Business Directory*; *Chamber E-Central* (Monthly). **Geographic Preference:** Local.

44324 ■ Wilkinsburg Chamber of Commerce (WCC)
900 Wood St.
Wilkinsburg, PA 15221
Ph: (412)999-2688
Co. E-mail: info@wilkinsburgchamber.com
URL: http://wilkinsburgchamber.com
Contact: John Irwin, President
Facebook: www.facebook.com/WilkChamber
X (Twitter): x.com/wilkinsburgcc
Description: Promotes the improvement of the business community, being cognizant of the social and economic changes that have occurred in the borough over the past century. **Founded:** 1893. **Geographic Preference:** Local.

44325 ■ Williamsport-Lycoming Chamber of Commerce (WLCC)
102 W 4th St.
Williamsport, PA 17701
Ph: (570)326-1971
Co. E-mail: chamber@williamsport.org
URL: http://williamsport.org
Contact: Jason C. Fink, Chief Executive Officer
E-mail: jfink@williamsport.org
Facebook: www.facebook.com/WilliamsportLycomingChamberofCommerce
YouTube: www.youtube.com/user/WilliamsportChamber
Description: Promotes business and community development in the Williamsport, PA area. **Founded:** 1885. **Publications:** *Chamber Connection* (Monthly); *Industrial Directory* (Semiannual). **Geographic Preference:** Local.

44326 ■ York County Economic Alliance (YCEA)
144 Roosevelt Ave.
York, PA 17401
Ph: (717)848-4000
Fax: (717)843-8837
Co. E-mail: marketing@ycea-pa.org
URL: http://www.yceapa.org
Contact: Kevin Schreiber, President
E-mail: kevin@ycea-pa.org
URL(s): business.ycea-pa.org/list/member/york-county-convention-visitors-bureau-york-3911
Facebook: www.facebook.com/YCEAPA
Linkedin: www.linkedin.com/company/york-county-economic-alliance
X (Twitter): x.com/yceapa
Instagram: www.instagram.com/yceapa
YouTube: www.youtube.com/user/YCEAPA
Description: Promotes business and community development in the York, PA area. Offers advocacy service. **Founded:** 1898. **Publications:** *York County Economic Alliance Business Directory*; *Business Voice* (Monthly); *Community and Economic Profile*; *Import/Export Directory* (Annual); *Map of York Area* (Annual); *Susquehanna Style* (Monthly); *Treasures*; *York Economic Outlook* (Quarterly). **Geographic Preference:** Local.

MINORITY BUSINESS ASSISTANCE PROGRAMS

44327 ■ Minority Supplier Development Council of PA-NJ-DE (MSDC PA-NJ-DE)
Rodin Pl.
2000 Hamilton St., Ste. 308
Philadelphia, PA 19130
Co. E-mail: info@emsdc.org
URL: http://emsdc.org/about-us
Description: Provides a direct link between corporate America and minority-owned businesses. Increases procurement and business opportunities for minority businesses of all sizes. **Geographic Preference:** Regional.

44328 ■ Pennsylvania Department of General Services - Bureau of Small Business Opportunities (BSBO)
603 N Office Bldg.
Harrisburg, PA 17125
URL: http://www.dgs.pa.gov/About/Pages/Contact.aspx
Description: Actively pursues contracting and subcontracting opportunities in state government and the private sector for minority and women business enterprises. **Founded:** 1975.

44329 ■ Pennsylvania Minority Business Development Authority (PMBDA)
Commonwealth Keystone Bldg., 400 N St., 4th Fl.
Harrisburg, PA 17120-0225
Free: 833-722-6778
URL: http://dced.pa.gov
Description: Provider of low-interest, long-term loans and equity guarantees to assist in the start-up or expansion of minority-owned businesses. **Founded:** 1998.

44330 ■ Pennsylvania Minority Business Enterprise Center
4548 Market St.
Philadelphia, PA 19139
URL: http://www.theenterprisecenter.com
Description: Firm provides business consulting services. **Founded:** 1989.

FINANCING AND LOAN PROGRAMS

44331 ■ Adams Capital Management Inc. (ACM)
500 Blackburn Ave.
Sewickley, PA 15143
Ph: (412)749-9454
Fax: (412)749-9459
URL: http://www.acm.com
Contact: Jennifer E. Parulo, Chief Financial Officer
E-mail: jep@acm.com
Description: Private equity and venture capital firm provider of business valuation, asset valuation and financial advisory services. **Founded:** 1994. **Preferred Investment Size:** $5,000,000 to $30,000,000. **Industry Preferences:** Internet specific, semiconductors and other electronics, computer software and services, medical and health, biotechnology, computer hardware, communications and media.

44332 ■ Ben Franklin Technology Partners (BFTP)
4801 S Broad St., Ste. 200 The Navy Yard
Philadelphia, PA 19112
Ph: (215)972-6700
Fax: (215)972-5588
Co. E-mail: info@cnp.benfranklin.org
URL: http://benfranklin.org
Contact: Scott D. Nissenbaum, President
Facebook: www.facebook.com/bftp.sep
Founded: 1983. **Preferred Investment Size:** $50,000 to $150,000. **Industry Preferences:** Biotechnology, Internet specific, medical and health, computer software and services, other products, industrial and energy, computer hardware, consumer related, semiconductors and other electronics, communications and media.

44333 ■ BioAdvance
101 W Elm St., Ste. 330
Conshohocken, PA 19428
Ph: (610)230-0544
URL: http://www.bioadvance.com
Contact: Dr. Shahram Hejazi, Chief Executive Officer
Description: Early-stage investment in life sciences companies. **Founded:** 2002. **Preferred Investment Size:** $500,000 to $1,000,000. **Investment Policies:** Seed and early stage. **Industry Preferences:** Biotechnology, and medical and health.

44334 ■ Birchmere Ventures
Pittsburgh, PA 15222
Co. E-mail: info@birchmerevc.com
URL: http://birchmerevc.com
Contact: Ned Renzi, Partner
E-mail: ned@birchmerevc.com
X (Twitter): x.com/BirchmereVC
Founded: 1996. **Preferred Investment Size:** $1,000,000 to $2,500,000. **Industry Preferences:** Computer software and services, biotechnology, Internet specific, computer hardware, industrial and energy, medical and health, semiconductors and other electronics.

44335 ■ BlueTree Allied Angels
PO Box 1323
Wexford, PA 15090
Ph: (724)475-4538
Fax: (888)550-3093
Co. E-mail: info@bluetreecapital.com
URL: http://www.bluetreealliedangels.com
Contact: Catherine Mott, President
Description: Angel investor group for regional early-stage companies in Western Pennsylvania. **Founded:** 2003. **Investment Policies:** Experienced management team; beta product preferred; proof-of-concept via customer sales commitments; clear path to break-even cash flow; clear exit strategy; minimum of 10x return within 3-5 years; pre-money valuation of less than $5,000,000. **Industry Preferences:** $200,000 to $3,000,000.

44336 ■ Draper Triangle Ventures
2 Gateway Ctr., Ste. 2000
Pittsburgh, PA 15222
Ph: (412)288-9800
Fax: (412)288-9799
URL: http://drapertriangle.com
Contact: Tom Jones, Managing Director
E-mail: tom@dtvc.com
Linkedin: www.linkedin.com/company/draper-triangle-ventures
X (Twitter): x.com/drapertriangle
Description: Provider of early venture capital investments for dynamic entrepreneurs and technology companies. **Founded:** 1999. **Preferred Investment Size:** $250,000 to $2,000,000. **Industry Preferences:** Communications, Internet specific, semiconductors and other electronics, medical and health, computer software, industrial and energy, and consumer related.

44337 ■ Element Partners
565 E Swedesford Rd., Ste. 207
Wayne, PA 19087
Fax: (610)964-8005
Co. E-mail: patti@elementpartners.com
URL: http://www.elementpartners.com
Contact: David Lincoln, Partner Founder
E-mail: david@elementpartners.com
Description: Growth equity investment firm. **Investment Policies:** Companies offering sustainable solutions for large industrial markets. **Industry Preferences:** Energy, industrial, and resource markets.

44338 ■ Enertech Capital /Enertech Capital Partners L.P.
One Tower Bridge 100 Front St., Ste. 1225
Conshohocken, PA 19428
Contact: Anne-Marie Bourgeois, Vice President
E-mail: ambourgeois@enertechcapital.com
Description: Firm offers investment for companies in the energy sector. **Founded:** 1996. **Preferred Investment Size:** $1,000,000 to $7,000,000. **Industry Preferences:** Internet specific, computer software and services, industrial and energy, semiconductors and other electronics, consumer related, computer hardware, other products, communications and media.

44339 ■ First Round Capital
2400 Market St., Ste. 237
Philadelphia, PA 19103
URL: http://firstround.com
Contact: Ryan Donnon, Director
Facebook: www.facebook.com/firstroundcapital
X (Twitter): x.com/firstround
Description: Early stage venture capital firm and angel investor. Also maintains offices in New York and San Francisco. **Founded:** 2004.

44340 ■ Gamma Investors LLC
555 Croton Rd., Ste. 111
  King of Prussia, PA 19406
Contact: Alec H. Petro, President
Preferred Investment Size: $250,000 to $3,000,000.
Industry Preferences: Internet specific.

44341 ■ Innovation Works, Inc.
Nova Tower 2 Two Allegheny Ctr., Ste. 100
  Pittsburgh, PA 15212
Ph: (412)681-1520
Co. E-mail: info@innovationworks.org
URL: http://www.innovationworks.org
Contact: Deborah Walker, Legal Counsel
Facebook: www.facebook.com/iwpgh
X (Twitter): x.com/iwpgh
Description: Provider of investment services to early-stage companies. Founded: 1999. Preferred Investment Size: $100,000 to $500,000. Industry Preferences: Communications and media, computer hardware and software, Internet specific, semiconductors and other electronics, biotechnology, medical and health, industrial and energy.

44342 ■ LaunchCyte L.L.C.
2403 Sidney St., Ste. 207
  Pittsburgh, PA 15203
Ph: (412)481-2200
Co. E-mail: patty@launchcyte.com
URL: http://launchcyte.com
Contact: Thomas Petzinger, Jr., Chief Executive Officer
Description: Provider of venture capital for incubation, seed and early stage investments. Founded: 2000. Investment Policies: Start-up. Industry Preferences: Biotechnology.

44343 ■ Liberty Venture Partners Inc.
2001 Market St.
  Philadelphia, PA 19103
Preferred Investment Size: $1,000,000 to $3,000,000. Industry Preferences: Medical and health, computer software and services, communications and media, and Internet specific, medical and health, industrial and energy, and biotechnology.

44344 ■ MVP Capital Partners
259 N Radnor-Chester Rd., Ste. 130
  Radnor, PA 19087
Ph: (610)254-2999
Co. E-mail: info@mvpcap.com
URL: http://www.mvpcap.com
Contact: Becky Broderick, Director
Description: Investment firm provides investment advisory services, equity investments and financial services for acquisitions and recapitalizations including aviation, publishing, media, specialty retailing, manufacturing, healthcare and business services. Founded: 1987. Preferred Investment Size: $2,000,000 to $8,000,000. Industry Preferences: Consumer related, Internet specific, computer software and services, medical and health, industrial and energy, other products, communications and media, biotechnology, and computer hardware.

44345 ■ NewSpring Ventures [NewSpring Capital]
NewSpring Ventures
  Radnor Financial Ctr.
  555 E Lancaster Ave., 3rd Fl.
  Radnor, PA 19087
Ph: (610)567-2380
Fax: (610)567-2388
URL: http://newspringcapital.com
Contact: Jon Schwartz, President
E-mail: jschwartz@newspringcapital.com
Linkedin: www.linkedin.com/company/newspring-capital
X (Twitter): x.com/NewSpring_PE
Description: Provider of financial services specializing in growth capital, expansion, recapitalization and more. Founded: 1999. Preferred Investment Size: $2,000,000 to $5,000,000. Industry Preferences: Communications and media, computer software, computer related, semiconductors and other electronics, Internet specific, medical and health, financial services, business service, and manufacturing.

44346 ■ Next Act Fund (NAF)
5850 Ctr. Ave., Ste. 411
  Pittsburgh, PA 15206
Co. E-mail: info@nextactfund.com
URL: http://www.nextactfund.com
Contact: Yvonne Campos, President
Facebook: www.facebook.com/NextActFund
Linkedin: www.linkedin.com/company/nextactfund
X (Twitter): x.com/nextactfund
Description: Invests in early-stage, women-owned/led companies to positively impact women, the region, and the nation. Founded: 2016.

44347 ■ Originate Ventures
205 Webster St.
  Bethlehem, PA 18015
Description: Venture capital firm interested in product/service companies in the Mid-Atlantic region of the United States. Founded: 2007.

44348 ■ Osage Venture Partners (OVP)
50 Monument Rd., Ste. 201
  Bala Cynwyd, PA 19004
Ph: (484)434-2255
Co. E-mail: ovp@osagepartners.com
URL: http://osageventurepartners.com
Contact: Jennifer Usas Peranteau, Director
E-mail: jperanteau@osagepartners.com
Linkedin: www.linkedin.com/company/osage-partners
X (Twitter): x.com/OsageVP
Description: Venture capital firm for early-stage enterprise and technology-enabled service companies in the Mid-Atlantic region of the Untied States. Founded: 2005. Industry Preferences: B2B software; data; technology-enabled service companies.

44349 ■ Pittsburgh Equity Partners (PEP)
700 Bursca Dr., Ste. 706
  Bridgeville, PA 15017
Ph: (412)265-1325
Co. E-mail: info@pghpep.com
URL: http://www.pghpep.com
Contact: Edward Engler, Managing Partner
E-mail: ed@pghpep.com
Description: Venture capital fund for early-stage companies in Western Pennsylvania. Industry Preferences: Life sciences; information technology.

44350 ■ Pittsburgh Life Sciences Greenhouse (PLSG)
2730 Sidney St., Ste. 300
  Pittsburgh, PA 15203
Ph: (412)201-7370
Co. E-mail: info@plsg.com
URL: http://www.plsg.com
Contact: Diana Cugliari, President
Facebook: www.facebook.com/pghlifesciencesgreenhouse
Linkedin: www.linkedin.com/company/pittsburgh-life-sciences-greenhouse
X (Twitter): x.com/PghLifeSciences
Description: Provider of capital investment to early stage life science enterprises in Western Pennsylvania. Founded: 2002. Industry Preferences: Biotechnology; diagnostics; healthcare technology; medical devices; therapeutics.

44351 ■ Quaker Partners Management LP
150 Monument Rd., Ste. 207
  Bala Cynwyd, PA 19004
Ph: (215)988-6800
URL: http://www.quakerpartners.com
Contact: Adele C. Oliva, Partner
Description: Healthcare investment firm for East Coast healthcare companies. Founded: 2002. Industry Preferences: Pharmaceuticals; biotechnology; healthcare; medical technologies.

44352 ■ RAF Netventures/RAF Ventures
50 Monument Rd., Ste. 303
  Bala Cynwyd, PA 19004
Ph: (215)572-0738
Co. E-mail: acquisitions@rafequity.com
URL: http://www.rafequity.com
Contact: Richard M. Horowitz, Chief Executive Officer
Linkedin: www.linkedin.com/company/rafequity
Description: Provider of investment and financial services. Founded: 1979. Preferred Investment Size: $20,000,000 to $200,000,000. Industry Preferences: Internet specific, medical and health, computer software and services, and biotechnology.

44353 ■ The Reinvestment Fund (TRF)
1700 Market St., 19th Fl.
  Philadelphia, PA 19103-3904
Ph: (215)574-5800
Co. E-mail: info@reinvestment.com
URL: http://www.reinvestment.com
Contact: Donald Hinkle-Brown, Chief Executive Officer
Facebook: www.facebook.com/ReinvestFund
Linkedin: www.linkedin.com/company/the-reinvestment-fund
X (Twitter): x.com/ReinvestFund
YouTube: www.youtube.com/c/reinvestmentfund
Description: Firm provides financial services. Founded: 1985. Preferred Investment Size: $1,000,000 to $5,000,000. Industry Preferences: Firm provides financial services.

44354 ■ Rock Hill Ventures, Inc.
1059 Indian Creek Rd.
  Wynnewood, PA 19096-3424
Contact: Dr. Hal Broderson, President
Preferred Investment Size: $1,000,000 to $2,000,000. Industry Preferences: Medical and health, and biotechnology.

44355 ■ S.R. One Ltd.
985 Old Eagle School Rd., Ste. 511
  Wayne, PA 19087
URL: http://www.srone.com
Contact: Simeon J. George, Chief Executive Officer
Description: Provides investment management services. Founded: 1985. Preferred Investment Size: $500,000 to $5,000,000. Industry Preferences: Biotechnology, medical and health, computer software and services, Internet specific, and consumer related.

44356 ■ TL Ventures, Inc.
435 Devon Pk., Dr., Bldg. 700
  Wayne, PA 19087
Contact: Pamela A. Strisofsky, President
Description: Finance: Investment in venture capital companies in the software, information technology and business service sectors. Founded: 1988. Preferred Investment Size: $3,000,000 to $20,000,000. Industry Preferences: Internet specific, computer software and services, communications and media, biotechnology, semiconductors and other electronics, medical and health, other products, computer hardware, and consumer related.

44357 ■ Wharton Alumni Angels
Fort Washington, PA 19034
Free: 888-236-8477
URL: http://www.whartonalumniangels.com
Contact: John Braze, President
Description: Angel investor group. Primarily invests in technology companies at the seed and Series A stages. Founded: 2016.

PROCUREMENT ASSISTANCE PROGRAMS

44358 ■ Indiana University of Pennsylvania Government Contracting Assistance Program (GCAP)
1011 S Dr.
  Indiana, PA 15705
URL: http://www.iup.edu
Description: Provides procurement technical assistance to firms interested in selling their goods or services to the local, state, and/or federal government.

STATE LISTINGS

44359 ■ Johnstown Area Regional Industries (JARI)
245 Market St., Ste. 200
Johnstown, PA 15901-2910
Ph: (814)535-8675
Fax: (814)535-8677
Co. E-mail: info@jari.com
URL: http://www.jari.com
Contact: Linda Thompson, President
Facebook: www.facebook.com/JARI.Johnstown
X (Twitter): x.com/JARI_Johnstown
Description: Works to retain and create jobs in order to provide opportunities for the development of Cambria and Somerset counties. **Founded:** 1974. **Geographic Preference:** Local.

44360 ■ Kutztown University Procurement Technical Assistance Center (PTAC)
24 Old Main
Kutztown, PA 19530
Ph: (484)646-5937
Co. E-mail: ptac@kutztown.edu
URL: http://www.kutztown.edu/about-ku/administrative-offices/small-business-development-center/established-business/government-marketing-services.html
Description: To grow the economy of Pennsylvania by providing entrepreneurs with the education, information and tools necessary to build successful businesses. **Geographic Preference:** Local.

44361 ■ Lehigh University Procurement Technical Assistance Center
201 E Packer Ave.
Bethlehem, PA 18015
URL: http://business.lehigh.edu/centers/small-business-development-center
Description: To grow the economy of Pennsylvania by providing entrepreneurs with the education, information and tools necessary to build successful businesses. **Geographic Preference:** Local.

44362 ■ North Central Pennsylvania Regional Planning and Development Commission (NCPRPDC)
49 Ridgmont Dr.
Ridgway, PA 15853
Ph: (814)773-3162
Co. E-mail: ncprpdc@ncentral.com
URL: http://www.ncentral.com
Contact: Jim Chorney, Executive Director
E-mail: jchorney@ncentral.com
Facebook: www.facebook.com/NCPRPDC
Linkedin: www.linkedin.com/company/ncprpdc
X (Twitter): x.com/NCPCommission
Description: Designed to increase the number of area companies receiving government contracts by educating management on how to market their products to the government. **Founded:** 2010.

44363 ■ Pennsylvania Procurement Technical Assistance Center - California University of Pennsylvania - Government Agency Coordination Office (GACO)
250 University Ave.
California, PA 15419-1394
Ph: (724)938-5881
Fax: (724)938-4575
Co. E-mail: gacocalu@pennwest.edu
URL: http://www.calu.edu/community/business-careers/gaco/index.aspx
Contact: Kate Lacey Glodek, Director
E-mail: glodek@pennwest.edu
Facebook: www.facebook.com/gaco.gcac.ptac
Description: Provides services to companies interested in pursuing federal, state and local contracting, subcontracting and export opportunities. **Founded:** 1985.

44364 ■ Pennsylvania Procurement Technical Assistance Center (GACO) - California University of Pennsylvania - Government Agency Coordination Office
700 River Ave., Ste. 220
Pittsburgh, PA 15212
Ph: (724)938-5881
Fax: (724)938-4575
Co. E-mail: gacocalu@pennwest.edu
URL: http://www.calu.edu/community/business-careers/gaco/index.aspx
Contact: Dr. Pricilla A. Robertson, Specialist
E-mail: robertson@pennwest.edu
Facebook: www.facebook.com/gaco.gcac.ptac
Description: Provides services to companies interested in pursuing federal, state and local contracting, subcontracting and export opportunities.

44365 ■ Pennsylvania Procurement Technical Assistance Center (EDD) - Economic Development Council of Northeast Pennsylvania - The Northeastern Pennsylvania Alliance - Enterprise Development District
1151 Oak St.
Pittston, PA 18640-3726
URL: http://www.nepa-alliance.org
Description: Helps businesses expand into new markets and get the financial assistance they need to grow.

44366 ■ Pennsylvania Procurement Technical Assistance Center (NEPA) - Northeastern Pennsylvania Alliance
1151 Oak St.
Pittston, PA 18640-3726
Ph: (570)655-5581
Free: 866-758-1929
Fax: (570)654-5137
Co. E-mail: info@nepa-alliance.org
URL: http://ptac.nepa-alliance.org
Facebook: www.facebook.com/NEPAAlliance
Linkedin: www.linkedin.com/company/nepa
X (Twitter): x.com/NEPA_Alliance
Instagram: www.instagram.com/nepa_alliance
YouTube: www.youtube.com/channel/UCItMFO-wZ0cWG7d1OqXm2TQ
Description: Serves as a liaison to help local companies, usually small businesses (suppliers) and local government contractors (buyers/procurers) increase sales and growth for our regional economy. **Founded:** 1964.

44367 ■ Pennsylvania Procurement Technical Assistance Center (NTRPDC) - Northern Tier Regional Planning and Development Commission
312 Main St.
Towanda, PA 18848
Ph: (570)265-9103
Free: 888-868-8800
Fax: (570)265-7585
Co. E-mail: info@northerntier.org
URL: http://www.northerntier.org
Contact: Amy Benjamin, Director, Finance
E-mail: benjamin@northerntier.org
Description: Providing resources to help businesses and entrepreneurs, local governments, and non-profit organizations.

44368 ■ Pennsylvania Procurement Technical Assistance Center - Northwest Pennsylvania Regional Planning and Development Commission
395 Seneca St.
Oil City, PA 16301
URL: http://www.aptac-us.org/find-a-ptac/?state=PA
Description: Local development district serving Clarion, Crawford, Erie, Forest, Lawrence, Mercer, Venango, and Warren Counties. **Founded:** 1967.

44369 ■ Pennsylvania Procurement Technical Assistance Center (SEDA-COG) - SEDA Council of Governments
201 Furnace Rd.
Lewisburg, PA 17837
Ph: (570)524-4491
Free: 800-332-6701
Fax: (570)524-9190
Co. E-mail: information@seda-cog.org
URL: http://seda-cog.org
Contact: Kim Wheeler, Executive Director
E-mail: kwheeler@seda-cog.org
Facebook: www.facebook.com/sedacog
Linkedin: www.linkedin.com/company/seda-council-of-governments
X (Twitter): x.com/SEDA_COG
Description: Assist companies in either entering the government market place or expanding their current market share. **Founded:** 1957.

44370 ■ Pennsylvania Procurement Technical Assistance Center (SPC) - Southwestern Pennsylvania Commission
42 21st St., Ste. 101
Pittsburgh, PA 15222
Ph: (412)391-5590
Fax: (412)391-9160
Co. E-mail: input@spcregion.org
URL: http://www.spcregion.org
Contact: Vincent Valdes, President
Facebook: www.facebook.com/spcregion
Linkedin: www.linkedin.com/company/southwestern-pennsylvania-commission
X (Twitter): x.com/spcregion
Instagram: www.instagram.com/spcregion
YouTube: www.youtube.com/channel/UCC8ONjuFksmnLyxhYOHCf7Q
Description: Helps companies to enter and succeed in the world of government contracting.

44371 ■ Pennsylvania Small Business Development Centers (SBDC)
Kutztown University of Pennsylvania
15200 Kutztown Rd., E-Wing, Ste. 24
Kutztown, PA 19530
Free: 877-472-7232
Co. E-mail: sbdc@kutztown.edu
URL: http://www.pasbdc.org
Contact: Ernie Post, Director
E-mail: post@kutztown.edu
Facebook: www.facebook.com/PennsylvaniaSBDC
Linkedin: www.linkedin.com/company/pennsylvania-small-business-development-centers
X (Twitter): x.com/PASmallBusiness
Description: The Pennsylvania SBDC State Director's office is hosted by the Wharton School at the University of Pennsylvania. The State Director's office is responsible for the administration and oversight of the Pennsylvania system of 18 centers. **Scope:** Helps small businesses improve profitability and increase employment through programs of procurement, international trade, product development, and business law. **Founded:** 1980. **Geographic Preference:** State.

44372 ■ Private Industry Council of Westmoreland/Fayette, Inc. (PIC)
219 Donohoe Rd.
Greensburg, PA 15601
Ph: (724)836-2600
Fax: (724)836-4588
Co. E-mail: info@privateindustrycouncil.com
URL: http://privateindustrycouncil.com
Contact: Shujuane Martin, President
E-mail: ssingosky@privateindustrycouncil.com
Facebook: www.facebook.com/privateindustrycouncil
Linkedin: www.linkedin.com/company/the-private-industry-council-of-westmoreland-fayette-inc-
Instagram: www.instagram.com/pic.westfay
Founded: 1983.

44373 ■ Southeast Pennsylvania Procurement Technical Assistance Center (SE PTAC)
3711 Market Str., Ste. 8.
Philadelphia, PA 19104
Ph: (610)683-1397
Co. E-mail: ptac@kutztown.edu
URL: http://www.ptac-southeastpa.org
Contact: Natasa Borcanin, Program Manager
E-mail: borcanin@kutztown.edu
X (Twitter): twitter.com/SEPA_PTAC
YouTube: www.youtube.com/channel/UCK1kxBplisxp1r45uAurbOQ

44374 ■ Southern Alleghenies Planning and Development Commission (SAP&DC)
3 Sheraton Dr.
Altoona, PA 16601-9343

Ph: (814)949-6500
Fax: (814)949-6505
Co. E-mail: sapdc@sapdc.org
URL: http://www.sapdc.org
Contact: Gerald Walker, President

Description: A non-profit regional economic and community development organization. **Geographic Preference:** Local.

44375 ■ Temple University Small Business Development Center (SBDC)
1515 Market St., Ste. 525
 Philadelphia, PA 19102
Ph: (215)204-7282
Fax: (215)204-4554
Co. E-mail: sbdc@temple.edu
URL: http://www.fox.temple.edu/institutes-centers/
 small-business-development-center
Contact: Jamie Shanker, Director
Facebook: www.facebook.com/temple.sbdc
Linkedin: www.linkedin.com/in/temple-small-business
 -development-ctr-a2630914
X (Twitter): x.com/TU_SBDC

Description: Helps small business grow and succeed. We provide high quality business management consulting and training for aspiring entrepreneurs and small emerging growth companies in Southeastern Pennsylvania. **Scope:** Small business operations, entrepreneurship, and the success and failure of small businesses. **Founded:** 1983. **Geographic Preference:** Local.

44376 ■ U.S. Department of Defense - Defense Logistics Agency - Defense Supply Center Philadelphia (DSCP)
700 Robbins Ave.
 Philadelphia, PA 19111-5092
Ph: (215)737-7209
Co. E-mail: dscc.partssupport@dla.mil
URL: http://www.dla.mil/Land-and-Maritime/Offers/
 Technical-Support/Document-Standards/Parts
 -Management

Description: Covers activities for GSA, Public Building Services (Philadelphia, PA), Army Corps of Engineers (Philadelphia, PA), Defense Personnel Support Center-Clothing & Textile (Philadelphia, PA), Defense Personnel Support Center-Medical (Philadelphia, PA), Defense Personnel Support Center-Subsistence (Philadelphia, PA). **Founded:** 1952.

44377 ■ Widener University Procurement Technical Assistance Center (PTAC)
One University Pl.
 Chester, PA 19013
URL: http://www.widener.edu/about/campus
 -community-resources/clinics-centers/small-busi-
 ness-development-center

Description: To grow the economy of Pennsylvania by providing entrepreneurs with the education, information and tools necessary to build successful businesses. **Geographic Preference:** Local.

INCUBATORS/RESEARCH AND TECHNOLOGY PARKS

44378 ■ 76FWD
3401 Grays Ferry Ave.
 Philadelphia, PA 19146
Free: 833-247-7282
Co. E-mail: info@1776.vc
URL: http://www.76forward.com
Facebook: www.facebook.com/76Forward
Linkedin: www.linkedin.com/company/76forward

Description: A global incubator and seed fund that helps engineer the success of the world's most promising startups tackling important challenges in areas like education, health, energy & sustainability, and transportation & smart cities. **Founded:** 2013.

44379 ■ AlphaLab Gear
2000 Technology Dr., Ste. 250
 Pittsburgh, PA 15219
URL: http://www.alphalabgear.org
Linkedin: www.linkedin.com/showcase/alphalabpa

Description: Guides early-stage physical product companies through a 24-week customer discovery module and a 14-week manufacturing module, with up to $75,000 in funding.

44380 ■ Altoona Blair County Development Corporation (ABCD Corp.)
3900 Industrial Pk. Dr.
 Altoona, PA 16602
Ph: (814)944-6113
Co. E-mail: abcd@abcdcorp.org
URL: http://abcdcorp.org
Contact: Stephen McKnight, President
E-mail: stevem@abcdcorp.org

Description: Provides business development and entrepreneurial assistance. **Founded:** 1946.

44381 ■ Anna's Commercial Kitchen
931 Hamilton St.
 Allentown, PA 18101
Ph: (610)730-5345
Co. E-mail: cplace200@aol.com
URL: http://www.thecaringplace.org
Contact: Mary Griffin, Executive Director
Facebook: www.facebook.com/annaskitchenpa

Description: Kitchen incubator offering an affordable, shared kitchen, assistance of experts, and a community of entrepreneurs who provide valuable advice. **Founded:** 1996.

44382 ■ Artisan Exchange (AE)
208 Carter Dr., Ste. 13B
 West Chester, PA 19382
Ph: (610)719-0282
Co. E-mail: info@artisanexchange.net
URL: http://www.artisanexchange.com
Contact: Frank J. Baldassarre, Owner Principal
Facebook: www.facebook.com/Ar
 tisanExchangeWCPa
Instagram: www.instagram.com/ar
 tisanexchangewcpa

Description: Incubator that provides an affordable environment that supports entrepreneurs committed to producing hand-crafted, sustainable foods while sharing sound business practices that have a positive social impact. **Founded:** 2012.

44383 ■ Ben Franklin TechVentures (BFTV)
116 Research Dr.
 Bethlehem, PA 18015
Ph: (610)758-5200
Fax: (610)861-5918
Co. E-mail: info@nep.benfranklin.org
URL: http://nep.benfranklin.org/venture-idol
Contact: Doug Engler, Regional Manager
E-mail: dengler@nep.benfranklin.org

Description: High-tech workspace and community for early-stage companies. **Founded:** 2007.

44384 ■ Bridgeworks Enterprise Center (BEC)
Allentown Economic Development Corp.
 905 Harrison St.
 Allentown, PA 18103
URL: http://www.allentownedc.com
Contact: R. Scott Unger, Executive Director
E-mail: sunger@allentownedc.com

Description: A small business incubator providing a building and a program where new businesses receive special benefits and reduced costs in order to increase their likelihood of success. **Founded:** 1989.

44385 ■ Bucknell University Entrepreneurs Incubator (BUEI)
One Dent Dr.
 Lewisburg, PA 17837
URL: http://www.bucknell.edu/azdirectory/small
 -business-development-center/sbdc-services

Description: Member entrepreneurs and early stage companies have access to consulting services, broadband internet service, and exclusive networking opportunities in the Bucknell community.

44386 ■ The Business Center (TBC)
7500 Germantown Ave.
 Elders Hall, Ste. 113
 Philadelphia, PA 19119
Ph: (215)247-2473
Co. E-mail: education@thebizctr.com
URL: http://www.thebizctr.com
Contact: Pamela J. Rich-Wheeler, Executive Director
E-mail: prichwheeler@thebizctr.com
Facebook: www.facebook.com/thebizctr
X (Twitter): x.com/thebizctr

Description: Provides office space, consulting, workshops, and technical resources. **Founded:** 1999.

44387 ■ Carbondale Technology Transfer Center (CTTC)
10 Enterprise Dr.
 Carbondale, PA 18407
Ph: (570)282-1255
URL: http://www.4cttc.org
Contact: Paul Browne, Executive Director
E-mail: paul@cttc.org
Facebook: www.facebook.com/CdaleTTC
Linkedin: www.linkedin.com/company/cttc-carbondale
 -technology-transfer-center

Description: A small business incubator providing technical support, business assistance, financial resources and appropriate facilities to entrepreneurs, small businesses, and light industry/light assembly manufacturers working with technology applications or innovative products or processes. **Founded:** 1996.

44388 ■ Carnegie Mellon University - Tepper School of Business - Donald H. Jones Center for Entrepreneurship
Tepper Quad, 3rd Fl., 4765 Forbes Ave.
 Pittsburgh, PA 15213
URL: http://www.cmu.edu/swartz-center-for-en
 trepreneurship/about/index.html
Contact: Dave Mawhinney, Executive Director
E-mail: dmawhin@andrew.cmu.edu

Description: Provides formal entrepreneurship training. **Founded:** 1989.

44389 ■ Catalyst Connection
4501 Lytle St., Ste. 301
 Pittsburgh, PA 15207
Ph: (412)918-4300
Fax: (412)687-2791
Co. E-mail: info@catalystconnection.org
URL: http://www.catalystconnection.org
Contact: Petra Mitchell, President
E-mail: pmitchell@catalystconnection.org
Facebook: www.facebook.com/CatalystConnection
Linkedin: www.linkedin.com/company/catalys
 t-connection
X (Twitter): x.com/madeinswpa
YouTube: www.youtube.com/user/CatalystConnec
 tion

Description: Provider of consulting and training services. **Founded:** 1988.

44390 ■ Centre County Industrial Development Corp. (CCIDC)
131 S Fraser St.
 State College, PA 16801
URL: http://centrecountypa.gov/601/Industrial
 -Development-Authority

Description: Offers space at two business incubators where Pennsylvania firms can obtain start-up assistance including the use of offices and specialized laboratory facilities.

44391 ■ Chamber of Business and Industry of Centre County (CBICC)
131 S Fraser St., Ste. 1
 State College, PA 16801
Ph: (814)234-1829
URL: http://www.cbicc.org
Contact: Vern Squier, President
Facebook: www.facebook.com/CBICC
Linkedin: www.linkedin.com/company/cbicc
X (Twitter): x.com/CBICC
Instagram: www.instagram.com/cbicc
YouTube: www.youtube.com/channel/UCB6q
 387jL0Z9sXmycSAn_Hw

STATE LISTINGS   Pennsylvania ■ 44410

Description: Promotes commerce, business, and industry in Centre County. **Publications:** *Chamber-Net* (Quarterly); *Chamber of Business and Industry of Centre County--Membership Directory*. **Geographic Preference:** Local.

44392 ■ Community Association for New Business Entrepreneurship (CAN BE) [CAN BE Innovation Center]
103 Rotary Dr.
  West Hazleton, PA 18202
Ph: (570)455-1508
Fax: (570)455-9881
URL: http://www.canbe.biz
Contact: Jocelyn Sterenchock, Director, Economics
E-mail: jsterenchock@canbe.biz
Facebook: www.facebook.com/CANBEinnovationcenter
X (Twitter): x.com/canbeinnovation
YouTube: www.youtube.com/channel/UCWfSVGvzcKspStTU7tL_q2w
Description: Fosters entrepreneurship and new venture development in the Hazleton area. Offers facilities, business mentoring and development, and legal assistance.

44393 ■ Corry Redevelopment Authority
9 N Ctr.
  Corry, PA 16407
Ph: (814)664-3884
URL: http://corryidc.org
Description: A full service development team that provides low interest financing, grant assistance, tax credit preparation, leasable facilities, fully infrastructured industrial sites, and an abundance of business support services.

44394 ■ East Stroudsburg University Business Accelerator (ESU)
562 Independence Rd.
  East Stroudsburg, PA 18301-2999
Ph: (570)422-7956
URL: http://www.esu.edu/entrepreneurship/startup/business-accelerator/index.cfm
Description: Provides an entrepreneurial environment that supports business start-ups, encourages innovation, and enhances the economic vitality of the region. **Founded:** 1893.

44395 ■ eCenter@LindenPointe
3580 Innovation Way
  Hermitage, PA 16148
Ph: (724)981-1829
Co. E-mail: ecenter@lindenpointe.com
URL: http://ecenterlindenpointe.com
Contact: Jeff Meier, Executive Director
Facebook: www.facebook.com/eCenterLindenPointe
Instagram: www.instagram.com/ecenterlindenpointe
YouTube: www.youtube.com/channel/UCHdW3Z62Y6r9zpdzo-noCpg
Description: Promotes innovation and entrepreneurship by providing a supportive environment, including infrastructure, education, training, mentorship and a network of service providers. **Founded:** 2011.

44396 ■ Erie Technology Incubator (ETI)
900 State St.
  Erie, PA 16501
Ph: (814)459-6068
URL: http://www.erietech.org
Contact: Jim Bahm, President
Description: Business incubator that nurtures and mentors startup companies via strategic guidance, mentor teams, coaching, and networking. **Founded:** 2008.

44397 ■ Executive Office Link
5 Great Valley Pky., Ste. 210
  Malvern, PA 19355
Ph: (610)251-6850
Co. E-mail: info@execofficelink.com
URL: http://www.execofficelink.com
Contact: D. Blair Kalemjian, President
E-mail: bkalemjian@execofficelink.com
Facebook: www.facebook.com/ExecOfficeLink
Linkedin: www.linkedin.com/company/executive-office-link
X (Twitter): x.com/ExecOfficeLink
Description: Firm provides real estate and commercial property management services. **Founded:** 1984.

44398 ■ Fair Shake Environmental Legal Services
6425 Living Pl.
  Pittsburgh, PA 15206
Ph: (412)664-5546
Co. E-mail: info@fairshake-els.org
URL: http://www.fairshake-els.org
Contact: Bala Kumar, President
Facebook: www.facebook.com/FairShakeELS
Linkedin: www.linkedin.com/company/fair-shake-environmental-legal-services
X (Twitter): x.com/FairShakeELS
Instagram: www.instagram.com/fairshakeels
Description: Provides legal services to moderate income individuals and non-profits on environmental and land use matters, through a 2 year residency program designed to incubate small start-up firms. **Founded:** 2013.

44399 ■ Girard Area Industrial Development Corp. - Model Works Industrial Commons
Girard, PA
Description: Firm provides incubation facilities and a multi-tenant facility for incubator graduates.

44400 ■ GoodCompany Ventures
601 Walnut St., Ste. 1200
  Philadelphia, PA 19106
Description: Helps launch entrepreneurs with businesses modeled on the conviction that global challenges are the raw materials for transformative solutions. Works with seed-stage entrepreneurs and guides them through a 12-week curriculum designed to test assumptions, expose and remediate business vulnerabilities, and provide a platform for rapid scale.

44401 ■ Greater Hazleton Business and Innovation Center
103 Rotary Dr.
  West Hazleton, PA 18202
URL: http://www.canbe.biz
Contact: Jocelyn Sterenchock, Director, Economics
E-mail: jsterenchock@hazletoncando.com
Description: Firm offers business incubator helping entrepreneurs grow new ventures in the community.

44402 ■ Greater Hazleton Business Innovation Center
103 Rotary Dr.
  West Hazleton, PA 18202
URL: http://www.canbe.biz
Description: Incubator that helps entrepreneurs grow during the startup period. Provides hands-on management assistance, access to financing, and technical support services. **Founded:** 2005.

44403 ■ Greater Susquehanna Keystone Innovation Zone (GSKIZ)
240 Market St.
  Bloomsburg, PA 17815
URL: http://driveindustry.com/gskiz
Description: Fosters local job growth by aiding entrepreneurs, newly formed startup companies, and mature companies in identifying and capitalizing on new ideas and opportunities.

44404 ■ Greenville Area Economic Development Corporation - McNeilly Business Center
301 Arlington Dr.
  Greenville, PA 16125
URL: http://www.gaedc.org/mcneilly.asp
Description: An incubator offering small business office space and financing assistance. **Geographic Preference:** Local.

44405 ■ Jump Start Incubator (JSI)
237 Ct. St.
  Reading, PA 19601
URL: http://bccf.org
Facebook: www.facebook.com/JumpStartIncubator
Linkedin: www.linkedin.com/company/jump-start-incubator
Description: Works with start-up and early-stage businesses to provide support and mentoring services as they work on growing and advancing their businesses. Professional office space is provided at a low cost and consulting services are furnished to all participants in the program. **Founded:** 2012.

44406 ■ Kitchen Incubator @ CTTC
10 Enterprise Dr.
  Carbondale, PA 18407
URL: http://www.4cttc.org
Description: A commercial kitchen housed within a small business incubator. Offers business and technical assistance, guided access to low interest capital and hourly rental of kitchen equipment. **Founded:** 1996.

44407 ■ La Salle Center for Entrepreneurship (LCE)
1900 W Olney Ave.
  Philadelphia, PA 19141
URL: http://www.lasalle.edu/school-of-business/centers-and-facilities/center-for-entrepreneurship
Contact: Steve Melick, Executive Director
E-mail: melick@lasalle.edu
Description: Provides mentoring, networking, and experiential learning to business startups and entrepreneurs.

44408 ■ Lehigh University Baker Institute for Entrepreneurship
Whitaker Lab 318 5 E Packer Ave.
  Bethlehem, PA 18015
Ph: (610)758-5626
Co. E-mail: bakerinfo@lehigh.edu
URL: http://www.lehighbakerinstitute.com
Contact: Lisa Getzler, Executive Director
E-mail: lig4@lehigh.edu
Facebook: www.facebook.com/BakerLehigh
X (Twitter): x.com/bakerlehigh
Instagram: www.instagram.com/bakerlehigh
Description: Dedicated to inspiring and educating the next generation of entrepreneurial thinkers. Provides authentic opportunities for Lehigh students from every discipline to deeply engage in the entrepreneurial process.

44409 ■ Mifflin County Industrial Development Corp. (MCIDC)
Bldg. 58 Ste. 300., 6395 SR 103 N
  Lewistown, PA 17044
Ph: (717)242-0393
Fax: (717)242-1842
Co. E-mail: mcidc@mcidc.org
URL: http://mcidc.org
Contact: Nick Felice, President
Facebook: www.facebook.com/Mifflin-County-Industrial-Development-Corporation-177741042245883
Description: Promotes economic development by redeveloping and financing Brownfield Parcels and industrial buildings in Mifflin County. **Scope:** Specialists in business planning of start up. Also offers aid in financial applications for variety of manufacturers. Serves private industries as well as government agencies. **Founded:** 1953. **Geographic Preference:** Local.

44410 ■ NextFab
2025 Washington Ave.
  Philadelphia, PA 19146
Ph: (215)921-3649
Co. E-mail: info@nextfab.com
URL: http://nextfab.com
Contact: Evan Malone, President
Facebook: www.facebook.com/NextFabStudio
X (Twitter): x.com/NextFab_PHL
Instagram: www.instagram.com/nextfab_phl
Description: Works closely with technology-based economic development programs and other funding institutions in order to provide easy access to grants and loans to the companies in its business incubator. **Founded:** 2009.

Small Business Sourcebook • 42nd Edition

44411 ■ Pennsylvania | STATE LISTINGS

44411 ■ North Central Pennsylvania Regional Planning and Development Commission Enterprise Development
49 Ridgmont Dr.
 Ridgway, PA 15853
URL: http://www.ncentral.com/enterprise
Contact: Christine Perneski, Director
E-mail: ncexport@ncentral.com
Description: Works to foster the economic vitality of the county. Programs include: Export Marketing; Procurement Technical Assistance; Loan Assistance; Entrepreneurial Network; Keystone Opportunity Zones; and North Central Enterprises Inc.

44412 ■ Pennsylvania Biotechnology Center of Bucks County (PB)
3805 Old Easton Rd.
 Doylestown, PA 18902
Ph: (215)589-6300
Fax: (215)489-4920
Co. E-mail: info@pabiotechbc.org
URL: http://www.pabiotechbc.org
Contact: Timothy M. Block, President
Facebook: www.facebook.com/PennsylvaniaBio
 technologyCenter
Linkedin: www.linkedin.com/company/pabio
 techcenter
X (Twitter): x.com/BiotechnologyPa
Instagram: www.instagram.com/pabiotech
Description: Business incubator that supports biotechnology startups and entrepreneurs.

44413 ■ Pennsylvania Department of Community and Economic Development, Technology Innovation - Ben Franklin Technology Partners
116 Research Dr., Plz. Level
 Bethlehem, PA 18015
Ph: (610)758-5200
Fax: (610)861-5918
Co. E-mail: info@nep.benfranklin.org
URL: http://nep.benfranklin.org
Contact: Angelo J. Valletta, President
Facebook: www.facebook.com/BenFranklinNortheast
Linkedin: www.linkedin.com/company/ben-franklin
 -technology-partners-of-northeastern-pennsylvania
YouTube: www.youtube.com/user/BFTechVentures/
 featured
Description: Programs promote advanced technology in an effort to make traditional industry more competitive in the international marketplace. BFP's Advanced Technology Centers represent consortia of businesses that provide joint applied research and development efforts, assistance to higher education institutions and entrepreneurial assistance services. **Founded:** 1983.

44414 ■ Philadelphia Fashion Incubator (PFI)
706 S 4th St.
 Philadelphia, PA 19147
Ph: (215)241-9000
URL: http://philadelphiafashionincubator.com
Contact: Elissa Bloom, Executive Director
E-mail: elissa@philadelphiafashionincubator.com
Facebook: www.facebook.com/phila
 delphiafashionincubator
Instagram: www.instagram.com/philaincubator
Description: Business incubator supporting the fashion industry.

44415 ■ Port Business Incubator
3675 Market St., Ste. 400
 Philadelphia, PA 19104
URL: http://sciencecenter.org/news/science-center
 -port-business-incubator-opens-co-working-space
Description: Business incubator that supports startups. Offers office space with full amenities as well as individual laboratory suites.

44416 ■ Redevelopment Authority of the City of Meadville
415 Chestnut St.
 Meadville, PA 16335
Description: Works to revitalize the city of Meadville through economic community growth. **Founded:** 1956.

44417 ■ Riverside Center for Innovation (RCI)
700 River Ave.
 Pittsburgh, PA 15212
Co. E-mail: info@riversidecenterforinnovation.com
URL: http://www.riversidecenterforinnovation.com
Contact: Juan Garrett, Executive Director
Facebook: www.facebook.com/RiversideCen
 terforInnovation
X (Twitter): x.com/rcipittsburgh
YouTube: www.youtube.com/channel/UCURYI5iqRR
 3PTTCrQMt1w-w
Description: Business incubator that helps entrepreneurs start their businesses by providing office space, consulting services, educational seminars, and various programs that help startups become established businesses. **Founded:** 1983.

44418 ■ Sayre Enterprise Center
703 S Elm Ave.
 Sayre, PA 18840
Ph: (570)882-9324
Co. E-mail: sayreenterprise@gmail.com
URL: http://www.sayreenterprisecenter.com
Contact: Tim Phinney, Executive Director
Facebook: www.facebook.com/EnterpriseCen
 terSayre
YouTube: www.youtube.com/channel/UCNq4SBvSdq
 42wZZ8mmD16uQ
Description: Dedicated to creating new jobs by facilitating start-ups. **Founded:** 1994.

44419 ■ The Scranton Enterprise Center (SEC)
222 Mulberry St.
 Scranton, PA 18501-0431
URL: http://www.scrantonplan.com/real-estate/scran
 ton-enterprise-center
Contact: Aaron W. Whitney, Director
E-mail: awhitney@scrantonchamber.com
Description: Nurtures young firms, helping them to grow during the startup phase. Provides hands-on management assistance, access to financing, intensive mentoring programs, and netowrking opportunities. **Founded:** 2003.

44420 ■ Sill Business Incubator (SBI)
419 14th St.
 Huntingdon, PA 16652
URL: http://www.juniata.edu/offices/sbi
Contact: Jim Watt, Director
E-mail: wattj@juniata.edu
Description: Business incubator that helps start and grow businesses. Provides office space as well as coaches and mentors. **Founded:** 2004.

44421 ■ Sterling Business & Technology Park
20 Easton Tpke.
 Lake Ariel, PA 18436
Ph: (646)236-3400
Co. E-mail: troy@sterlingbusinesspark.com
URL: http://www.sterlingbusinesspark.com
Facebook: www.facebook.com/S
 terlingBusinessTechnologyPark
Linkedin: www.linkedin.com/in/sterlingbiztechpark
X (Twitter): x.com/SterlingBizTech
Pinterest: www.pinterest.com/sterlingbizpark
Description: Technology park supporting startups and entrepreneurs.

44422 ■ University City Science Center (UCSC)
3675 Market St., Ste. 400
 Philadelphia, PA 19104
Ph: (215)966-6000
Co. E-mail: info@sciencecenter.org
URL: http://sciencecenter.org
Facebook: www.facebook.com/UcScienceCenter
Linkedin: www.linkedin.com/company/
 ucsciencecenter
X (Twitter): x.com/ucsciencecenter
Instagram: www.instagram.com/ucsciencecenter
YouTube: www.youtube.com/channel/
 UCQcrgmIc0V0iFl5NVOBgJYw
Description: The UCSC is dedicated to fostering science and technology-based economic development. The incubator offers tenants office and laboratory space, business services, and research management assistance. **Scope:** Manages research and development programs and provides facilities and service to support Research Park tenants. **Founded:** 1963.

44423 ■ Volunteers of America of Pennsylvania - Working Order Incubator
1650 Main St.
 Pittsburgh, PA 15215
URL: http://www.voapa.org/what-we-do
Description: Small business incubator for entrepreneurs with disadvantages and/or disabilities to create a bridge to traditional employment.

44424 ■ Warren-Forest Counties Economic Opportunity Council (WFEOC)
1209 Pennsylvannia Ave.
 Warren, PA 16365
Ph: (814)726-2400
URL: http://www.wfeoc.org
Contact: Misty Roos, Contact
E-mail: mroos@wfeoc.org
Facebook: www.facebook.com/WarrenForestEOC
Founded: 1965.

44425 ■ Welcoming Center for New Pennsylvanians
211 N 13th St. 4th Fl.
 Philadelphia, PA 19107
URL: http://welcomingcenter.org/publications
Description: Offers numerous practical tools to assist new and emerging small business owners succeed. **Founded:** 2003.

44426 ■ Women Empowered for Entrepreneurial Excellence (WEEE)
1413 Marlboro Ave.
 Pittsburgh, PA 15221
Co. E-mail: weee.incubator@gmail.com
URL: http://www.weeeincubator.org
Contact: Alice Williams, Executive Director
Description: Incubator for microenterprise and small business growth whose purpose is to reinforce a collaborative business culture and develop entrepreneurial skills among women. Provides an environment of opportunity for peer support, shared learning experiences and business growth. **Founded:** 2009.

44427 ■ YorKitchen
144 Roosevelt Ave., Ste. 100
 York, PA 17401
Description: A shared commercial kitchen incubator available for rent by the hour to food producers, 24 hours a day, 7 days a week.

EDUCATIONAL PROGRAMS

44428 ■ Central Pennsylvania College (CPC)
600 Valley Rd.
 Summerdale, PA 17093-0309
Ph: (717)732-0702
Free: 800-759-2727
Co. E-mail: admissions@centralpenn.edu
URL: http://www.centralpenn.edu
Contact: Dr. Linda Fedrizzi-Williams, President
E-mail: officeofthepresident@centralpenn.edu
Facebook: www.facebook.com/centralpenn
X (Twitter): x.com/centralpenn
YouTube: www.youtube.com/user/centralpennknight
Description: Two-year college offering a program in entrepreneurship and small business management. **Founded:** 1881.

44429 ■ Community College of Allegheny County - North Campus (CCAC)
8701 Perry Hwy.
 Pittsburgh, PA 15237-5353
URL: http://www.ccac.edu/campus-life/maps-an
 d-directions.php
Description: Two-year college offering a small business management program. **Founded:** 1966.

44430 ■ Delaware County Community College (DCCC) - Library
901 S Media Line Rd.
 Media, PA 19063

STATE LISTINGS   Pennsylvania ■ 44444

Ph: (610)359-5000
URL: http://www.dccc.edu
Contact: Dr. Joy L. Gates Black, President
Facebook: www.facebook.com/DelawareCoun
  tyCommunityCollege
Linkedin: www.linkedin.com/school/delaware-county
  -community-college
X (Twitter): x.com/delawareCCC
Instagram: www.instagram.com/delawareCCC
YouTube: www.youtube.com/user/DelawareC
  tyCommCol
Description: Conducts small business courses, including financial management for small business; choosing microcomputer software; how to cash in on your crafts; how to start a consulting business; marketing for your small business; develop your own typing/word processing business; how to develop a business plan; fundamentals of small business management; start-up financing; record keeping and taxes for small business; and microcomputer awareness. Also offers consulting and technical assistance. Works with Community Accountants of Media to provide free accounting and financial assistance to eligible small business owners. **Scope:** Allied health-nursing; arts and humanities; business education; history, political science and law; literature; psychology; social work and sociology; science, technology, engineering and mathematics. **Services:** Interlibrary loan; circulation. **Founded:** 1967. **Holdings:** Books; articles; newspapers; journals.

44431 ■ Northampton Community College (NCC)
3835 Green Pond Rd.
  Bethlehem, PA 18020
Ph: (610)861-5300
Co. E-mail: helpdesk@northampton.edu
URL: http://www.northampton.edu
Contact: Dr. David A. Ruth, President
Facebook: www.facebook.com/northamptoncomm
X (Twitter): x.com/NorthamptonComm
YouTube: www.youtube.com/user/samspartanncc
Description: Two-year college offering a small business management program. **Founded:** 1967.

44432 ■ Penn Foster Career School
925 Oak St.
  Scranton, PA 18515
Ph: (570)961-4033
Free: 800-275-4410
Fax: (570)702-8380
Co. E-mail: infoims@pennfoster.com
URL: http://www.pennfoster.edu
URL(s): penn-foster.com
Description: Home-study school offering a small business management program. **Founded:** 1958.

CONSULTANTS

44433 ■ BioBM Consulting Inc.
216 Market St., Side Entrance
  Philadelphia, PA 19106
Ph: (313)312-4626
Co. E-mail: info@biobm.com
URL: http://biobm.com
Contact: Edgard Sayegh, Director
Facebook: www.facebook.com/BioBM
X (Twitter): x.com/biobm
Description: Offers marketing and operations management services to start-ups and small companies.

44434 ■ Core Money Engine
188 Bruceton Rd.
  Pittsburgh, PA 15236
Ph: (724)968-6277
URL: http://www.coremoneyengine.com
Contact: Wayde Nelson, Contact
Description: Offers growth services to companies by targeting customers with high value products and systemic processes.

44435 ■ NuCoPro
114 Scarborough Ln.
  McMurray, PA 15317
Ph: (412)491-7747
Co. E-mail: info@nucopro.com

URL: http://www.nucopro.com
Contact: Gary Rosensteel, Founder
Description: Works with entrepreneurs to transition from start-up to emerging company.

PUBLICATIONS

44436 ■ Crain's Philadelphia
1155 Gratiot Ave.
  Detroit, MI 48207-2732
Ph: (313)446-6000
Co. E-mail: info@crain.com
URL: http://www.crain.com
Contact: Barry Asin, President
URL(s): www.crain.com/jobs/regional-freelance-editor
  -philadelphia-2
Description: Covers business in the Philadelphia area. **Availability:** Print.

44437 ■ Lehigh Valley Business (LVB)
7025 Albert Pick Rd.
  Greensboro, NC 27409
Ph: (612)317-9420
Free: 877-615-9536
Co. E-mail: customerservice@bridgetowermedia.com
URL: http://www.bridgetowermedia.com
Contact: Adam Reinebach, President
URL(s): www.lvb.com
Facebook: www.facebook.com/LehighValleyBusiness
Linkedin: www.linkedin.com/company/lehigh-valley
  -business
X (Twitter): x.com/lvb_com
Instagram: www.instagram.com/lehighvalley_business
Released: Monthly **Price:** $399, for leads and data + print; $369, for leads and data; $8, for monthly; $99, for annual. **Description:** Magazine devoted to small- and medium-sized businesses in Lehigh Valley. **Availability:** Print; Online.

44438 ■ Philadelphia Business Journal
400 Market St., Ste. 1200
  Philadelphia, PA 19106
Ph: (215)238-1450
Fax: (215)238-9489
Co. E-mail: philadelphia@bizjournals.com
URL: http://www.bizjournals.com/philadelphia
Contact: Sierra Quinn, Director
E-mail: squinn@bizjournals.com
URL(s): www.bizjournals.com/philadelphia
Linkedin: www.linkedin.com/company/philadelphia
  -business-journal
X (Twitter): x.com/PHLBizJournal
Released: Weekly **Price:** $70, for online; $70, for print and digital; $245, for 52 week; $4, for digital trial 4 weeks or digital only (premium) or digital + print (premium plus); $950, for nationwide + bol premium unlimited 52 weeks; $220, for digital + print premium plus 52 weeks; $380, for nationwide access premium elite; $9, for 4 weeks nationwide access; $210, for digital only 52 weeks. **Description:** Regional and general business newspaper. **Availability:** Print; Online.

PUBLISHERS

44439 ■ Bookhaven Press L.L.C.
302 Scenic Ct.
  Moon Township, PA 15108
Ph: (412)494-6926
Co. E-mail: support@bookhavenpress.com
URL: http://www.bookhavenpress.com
Contact: Dennis V. Damp, Owner
Description: Publisher of books for general audience on business and employment. **Founded:** 1985. **Publications:** The Book of U.S. Government Jobs: Where They Are, What's Available, and How to Get One.

44440 ■ The Danielle Adams Publishing Co.
PO Box 100
  Merion Station, PA 19066
Ph: (610)642-1000
URL: http://www.danielleadams.com
Contact: Jeffrey Dobkin, Contact

Description: Publishes books and articles of interest to small business owners, Investors, Marketers and Entrepreneurs. Does not accept unsolicited manuscripts. Reaches market through commission representatives, direct mail and wholesalers. **Scope:** Provider of marketing and direct marketing services and consulting. Offers a full range of services: Analysis, action plans, benchmarking, testing and reviews of marketing campaigns, advertising, copy writing and direct sell catalogs analysis. Assists clients in any industry worldwide. **Founded:** 1986. **Publications:** "A 15-Point Check List for Your Ads"; "12 Places to Buy a Mailing List"; "Forget Theory Here's What Works Best in Direct Marketing"; "How to Market a Product for Under 500"; "Uncommon Marketing Techniques"; "Direct Marketing Strategies"; "Successful Low Cost Direct Marketing Methods"; "Vital Signs.". **Training:** Marketing and Direct Marketing.

EARLY STAGE FINANCING

44441 ■ Delaware Crossing Investor Group (DCIG)
2700 Kelly Rd., Ste.
  Warrington, PA 18976
URL: http://www.delawarecrossing.org
Contact: Elizabeth Sigety, Managing Director
Linkedin: www.linkedin.com/company/delaware
  -crossing-investor-group
Description: Network of former and current entrepreneurs and executives who offer counsel and capital to early-stage and other growth-oriented companies. **Founded:** 2005. **Preferred Investment Size:** $250,000 to $1,000,000. **Investment Policies:** Potential to create at least $10 million in annual revenues within three to five years; within a three-hour drive of Philadelphia, Pennsylvania, or Princeton, New Jersey. **Industry Preferences:** Technology and life sciences.

44442 ■ iNetworks Advisors
820 Evergreen Ave., Ste. 202
  Pittsburgh, PA 15209
Ph: (412)904-1014
Co. E-mail: info@inetworkspe.com
URL: http://inetworksllc.com
Contact: Anthony Lacenere, President
Linkedin: www.linkedin.com/company/inetworks-a
  dvisors-inc
Description: Invests in disruptive healthcare, life sciences, and IT companies at various stages. **Founded:** 1999.

44443 ■ Robin Hood Ventures
2526 Naudain St.
  Philadelphia, PA 19146
Ph: (215)839-6256
Fax: (484)214-0114
Co. E-mail: info@robinhoodventures.com
URL: http://www.robinhoodventures.com
Contact: Scott Fishman, President
Facebook: www.facebook.com/robinhoodventures
Linkedin: www.linkedin.com/company/2333369
X (Twitter): x.com/RobinHoodVent
Instagram: www.instagram.com/robinhoodventures
Description: Early stage investment group. **Preferred Investment Size:** $250,000 to $500,000. **Investment Policies:** Sustainable and scalable business model with potential for high return; proprietary technology or product; within a three-hour drive of Philadelphia.

EXPANSION AND GROWTH FINANCING

44444 ■ iNetworks Advisors
820 Evergreen Ave., Ste. 202
  Pittsburgh, PA 15209
Ph: (412)904-1014
Co. E-mail: info@inetworkspe.com
URL: http://inetworksllc.com
Contact: Anthony Lacenere, President
Linkedin: www.linkedin.com/company/inetworks-a
  dvisors-inc

Small Business Sourcebook • 42nd Edition   2935

Description: Invests in disruptive healthcare, life sciences, and IT companies at various stages. **Founded:** 1999.

44445 ■ Mentor Capital Partners Ltd.
PO Box 560
  Yardley, PA 19067
Ph: (215)736-8882
Fax: (215)736-8882
URL: http://mentorcapitalpartners.com
Contact: Edward F. Sager, Jr., Founder
E-mail: sager@mentorcapitalpartners.com

Description: Offers investment capital opportunities for public and private companies. **Founded:** 1994. **Industry Preferences:** Business and financial services; consumer, distribution and logistics; healthcare and life sciences; industrial technology; information and media technology.

44446 ■ Stonewood Capital Management, Inc.
209 4th Ave.
  Pittsburgh, PA 15222
Ph: (412)391-0300
Fax: (412)391-0500
Co. E-mail: info@stonewoodcapital.com
URL: http://stonewoodcapital.com
Contact: J. Kenneth Moritz, President

Description: Private equity group specializing in management-led buyouts. **Founded:** 1993. **Industry Preferences:** Manufacturing; assembly; distributing.

VENTURE CAPITAL FIRM

44447 ■ Life Sciences Greenhouse of Central Pennsylvania (LSGPA)
225 Market St., Ste. 500
  Harrisburg, PA 17101
Ph: (717)635-2100
URL: http://www.lsgpa.com
Contact: Billingsley Mel, President

Description: Venture capital firm for early-stage life science technology companies. **Founded:** 2002. **Investment Policies:** Innovative life science technology companies with strong market potential, skilled management team, sound financial plan, strong probability of raising matching fund or follow-on funding, and a demonstrated long-term commitment to Pennsylvania.

44448 ■ Rittenhouse Ventures, LLC (RV)
The Navy Yard Bldg., 100 Innovation Ctr., 4801 S Broad St., Ste. 340
  Philadelphia, PA 19112
Ph: (215)972-1502
Co. E-mail: bizplans@rittenhouse.vc
URL: http://rittenhouseventures.com
Contact: Steve Holstad, Chief Financial Officer

Description: Emerging-growth venture capital firm focused on innovative software solutions across the Mid-Atlantic region. **Preferred Investment Size:** $1,000,000. **Investment Policies:** Capital efficient; B2B software; recurring revenue. **Industry Preferences:** Healthcare; life sciences; financial services; human resources; general business services.

Rhode Island

ASSOCIATIONS AND OTHER ORGANIZATIONS

44449 ■ Association of Fundraising Professionals Rhode Island Chapter (AFP-RI)
PO Box 1857
Asheville, NC 28802
Ph: (401)267-8086
Co. E-mail: info@afpri.org
URL: http://community.afpglobal.org/afprhodeisland/home
Contact: Edward McPherson, President
Linkedin: www.linkedin.com/in/afp-rhode-island-a8013313

Description: Seeks to empower individuals and organizations to practice ethical fundraising through professional education, networking, research and advocacy. **Founded:** 1987. **Geographic Preference:** State.

44450 ■ International Association of Women Providence Chapter
Providence, RI
URL: http://www.iawomen.com/chapters/providence-chapter

Description: Serves as network of accomplished women united to achieve professional goals. Provides a forum for sharing ideas and experiences of professional women regarding career success. Promotes an active business and networking community from all industries. **Geographic Preference:** Local.

44451 ■ National Federation of Independent Business Rhode Island
c/o Christopher Carlozzi, Director
1800 Mineral Spring Ave., Ste. 271
North Providence, RI 02904
Free: 877-262-7662
Co. E-mail: christopher.carlozzi@nfib.org
URL: http://www.nfib.com/rhode-island
Contact: Christopher Carlozzi, Director
E-mail: christopher.carlozzi@nfib.org
X (Twitter): x.com/nfib_ri

Description: Represents small and independent businesses. Aims to promote and protect the rights of members to own, operate and grow their businesses. **Geographic Preference:** State.

SMALL BUSINESS DEVELOPMENT CENTERS

44452 ■ Rhode Island Small Business Development Center
315 Iron Horse Way
Providence, RI 02908
Ph: (401)490-0378
URL: http://web.uri.edu/risbdc
Contact: Manuel Batlle, Director
E-mail: mjbatlle@uri.edu
Facebook: www.facebook.com/SBDCRhodeIsland

Description: Provides local small business owners with counseling, relevant training, and access to important resources to help their businesses succeed from start-up to maturity. **Scope:** Provider of assistance; advice; information and free consulting services to owners of small businesses. Also offers low-cost training programs and numerous specialty programs and assistance with loan packaging. **Founded:** 1982. **Training:** Exploring Self Employment: Pre-Venture Clinic, Jul, 2012; Opening the Doors to Your Business: Start-up Clinic, Jun, 2012; Business Development Programs and Software Training.

44453 ■ Rhode Island Small Business Development Center (RISBDC)
75 Lower College Rd.
Kingston, RI 02881
Ph: (401)874-7232
URL: http://web.uri.edu/risbdc

Description: Provides local small business owners with the services and expertise they need to succeed: no-cost expert counseling, relevant training and access to important resources.

44454 ■ Rhode Island Small Business Development Center - Northern Rhode Island/Central Falls (RISBDC)
650 George Washington Hwy., Ste. 206
Lincoln, RI 02865
Ph: (401)874-7232
URL: http://www.risbdc.org
Contact: Dennis McCarthy, Director

Description: Provides local small business owners with the services and expertise they need to succeed: no-cost expert counseling, relevant training and access to important resources.

44455 ■ Rhode Island Small Business Development Center - State Office (RISBDC)
Carlotti Administration Bldg.
University of Rhode Island
75 Lower College Rd.
Kingston, RI 02881
Ph: (401)874-7232
URL: http://web.uri.edu/risbdc
Contact: Diane Fournaris, Director
Geographic Preference: State.

SMALL BUSINESS ASSISTANCE PROGRAMS

44456 ■ Brown Forum for Enterprise
Brown University
Providence, RI 02912
URL: http://brownenterpriseforum.org
Contact: William Jackson, President

Description: Brings together entrepreneurs, venture capitalists, executives, and others to discuss the problems of starting and expanding a business. Sponsors start-up workshops. **Founded:** 1984.

44457 ■ Rhode Island Commerce Corp. (RIC)
315 Iron Horse Way, Ste. 101
Providence, RI 02908
Ph: (401)278-9100
Fax: (401)273-8270
Co. E-mail: info@commerceri.com
URL: http://commerceri.com
Contact: Hilary Fagan, President
Facebook: www.facebook.com/CommerceRI
Linkedin: www.linkedin.com/company/commerce-ri
X (Twitter): x.com/CommerceRI
Instagram: www.instagram.com/ricommerce

Description: Provides site and building information to businesses expanding or relocating within the state. Also provides employee relocation assistance for out-of-state companies moving to Rhode Island. **Founded:** 1974. **Publications:** *Directory of Rhode Island Manufacturers* (Annual).

44458 ■ Rhode Island Department of Environmental Management - Division of Agriculture and Resource Marketing
235 Promenade St.
Providence, RI 02908
URL: http://dem.ri.gov/natural-resources-bureau/agriculture-and-forest-environment/agriculture/regulatory-services/organic-certification

Description: Provides information on markets for agriculture, seafood, and aquaculture products.

SCORE OFFICES

44459 ■ SCORE - Lincoln, Rhode Island
6 Blackstone Valley Pl., Ste. 402
Lincoln, RI 02865
Ph: (401)334-1000
URL: http://ri.score.org
Facebook: www.facebook.com/SCORERhodeIsland
Linkedin: www.linkedin.com/company/score-rhode-island
X (Twitter): x.com/SCORE_RI

Description: Provides professional guidance and information to maximize the success of existing and emerging small businesses. Offers business counseling and workshops.

44460 ■ SCORE - Middletown, Rhode Island
35 Valley Rd.
Middletown, RI 02842
Ph: (401)847-1600
URL: http://ri.score.org
Facebook: www.facebook.com/SCORERhodeIsland
Linkedin: www.linkedin.com/company/score-rhode-island
X (Twitter): x.com/SCORE_RI

Description: Provides professional guidance and information to maximize the success of existing and emerging small businesses. Offers business counseling and workshops.

44461 ■ SCORE - North Kingstown
8045 Post Rd.
North Kingstown, RI 02852
Ph: (401)295-5566

URL: http://ri.score.org
Description: Provides professional guidance and information to maximize the success of existing and emerging small businesses. Offers business counseling and workshops.

44462 ■ SCORE - Providence
315 Iron Horse Way, Ste. 101
Providence, RI 02908
Ph: (401)278-9174
URL: http://www.score.org/ri
Description: Provides professional guidance and information to maximize the success of existing and emerging small businesses. Offers business counseling and workshops.

44463 ■ SCORE - Providence Secretary of State
148 W River St.
Providence, RI 02904
Ph: (401)222-3040
URL: http://ri.score.org/find-location?state=RI
Contact: Jack Newman, Contact
Description: Provides professional guidance and information to maximize the success of existing and emerging small businesses. Offers business counseling and workshops.

44464 ■ SCORE - Rhode Island
380 Westminster St., Ste. 511
Providence, RI 02903
Ph: (401)226-0077
Co. E-mail: info@riscore.org
URL: http://ri.score.org
Contact: Jack Newman, Contact
Facebook: www.facebook.com/SCORERhodeIsland
X (Twitter): x.com/SCORE_RI
Description: Provides professional guidance and information to maximize the success of existing and emerging small businesses. Offers business counseling and workshops. **Geographic Preference:** Local.

44465 ■ SCORE - Warren, Rhode Island
380 Westminster St., Ste. 511
Providence, RI 02903
Ph: (401)245-0750
URL: http://ri.score.org
Contact: Jack Newman, President
Facebook: www.facebook.com/SCORERhodeIsland
Linkedin: www.linkedin.com/company/score-rhode-island
X (Twitter): x.com/SCORE_RI
Description: Provides professional guidance and information to maximize the success of existing and emerging small businesses. Offers business counseling and workshops.

44466 ■ SCORE - Warwick
3288 Post Rd.
Warwick, RI 02886
Ph: (401)732-1100
URL: http://ri.score.org
Description: Provides professional guidance and information to maximize the success of existing and emerging small businesses. Offers business counseling and workshops.

CHAMBERS OF COMMERCE

44467 ■ Central Rhode Island Chamber of Commerce
3288 Post Rd.
Warwick, RI 02886
Ph: (401)732-1100
Fax: (401)732-1107
Co. E-mail: info@centralrichamber.com
URL: http://www.centralrichamber.com
Contact: Lauren E. I. Slocum, President
Facebook: www.facebook.com/CentralRIchamber
X (Twitter): x.com/CentralRI
Description: Promotes business and community development in Kent County, RI. Sponsors Management Assistance Team, Legislative Action Organization, and Commercial and Sales Leads programs. Provides health insurance program. Holds monthly luncheon and trade show series. **Founded:** 1980. **Publications:** *ChamberWorks*. **Geographic Preference:** Local.

44468 ■ Charlestown Chamber of Commerce
4945 Old Post Rd.
Charlestown, RI 02813
Ph: (401)364-3878
Co. E-mail: info@charlestownrichamber.com
URL: http://www.charlestownrichamber.com
Contact: Heather Paliotta, Director
E-mail: heatherpaliotta@earhlink.net
Facebook: www.facebook.com/charlestownchamber.in
Linkedin: www.linkedin.com/company/charlestown-chamber-of-commerce
Instagram: www.instagram.com/charlestown.chamber
YouTube: www.youtube.com/channel/UChyp2BWUA1TcpeVkbfTJbSw
Description: Serves members and the community with networking opportunities, business seminars, and referrals. **Publications:** *Annual Area Resource Guide and Directory* (Annual). **Geographic Preference:** Local.

44469 ■ East Bay Chamber of Commerce (EBCC)
16 Cutler St.
Warren, RI 02885
Ph: (401)245-0750
Fax: (401)245-0110
Co. E-mail: info@eastbaychamberri.org
URL: http://www.eastbaychamberri.org
Contact: Michelle Hughes, Chairman
Facebook: www.facebook.com/eastbaychamberri
X (Twitter): x.com/eastbaychamber
Pinterest: www.pinterest.com/eastbaychamber
Description: Strives to promote economic development and improve the quality of life for the East Bay, RI community. **Founded:** 1958. **Publications:** *East Bay Community and Buyers' Guide* (Annual); *Moving Forward* (Monthly); *East Bay Chamber of Commerce Directory* (Annual). **Awards:** East Bay Chamber of Commerce – Outstanding Citizen of the Year Award (Annual). **Geographic Preference:** Local.

44470 ■ East Greenwich Chamber of Commerce (EGCC)
580 Main St.
East Greenwich, RI 02818
Ph: (401)885-0020
Fax: (401)885-0048
Co. E-mail: steve@eastgreenwichchamber.com
URL: http://www.eastgreenwichchamber.com
Contact: Stephen M. Lombardi, Executive Director
E-mail: steve@eastgreenwichchamber.com
Facebook: www.facebook.com/EGCCRI
X (Twitter): x.com/EGChamberC
YouTube: www.youtube.com/channel/UCHS8T6CRaduJSOHSn7Ayh-g
Description: Promotes business and community development in East Greenwich, RI. **Founded:** 1929. **Publications:** *Messenger* (Monthly). **Geographic Preference:** Local.

44471 ■ East Providence Area Chamber of Commerce (EPACC)
1011 Waterman Ave.
East Providence, RI 02914
Ph: (401)438-1212
Co. E-mail: office@eastprovidenceareachamber.com
URL: http://www.eastprovidenceareachamber.com
Contact: Laura A. McNamara, Executive Director
Description: Promotes business and community development in East Providence, Barrington, Rhode Island and Seekonk and Rehoboth, Massachusetts and surrounding areas. **Founded:** 1897. **Publications:** *Chamber News: A Focus on Business* (Quarterly). **Awards:** East Providence Area Chamber of Commerce Business of the Year (Annual). **Geographic Preference:** Local.

44472 ■ *Go Westerly*
1 Chamber Way
Westerly, RI 02891
Ph: (401)596-7761
Fax: (401)596-2190
Co. E-mail: info@oceanchamber.org
URL: http://www.oceanchamber.org
Contact: Lisa Konicki, President
E-mail: lkonicki@oceanchamber.org
URL(s): www.oceanchamber.org/info
Availability: Online.

44473 ■ Greater Cranston Chamber of Commerce (GCCC)
150 Midway Rd., Ste. 178
Cranston, RI 02920
Ph: (401)785-3780
Co. E-mail: sboyle@cranstonchamber.com
URL: http://cranstonchamber.com
Contact: Randy Wyrofsky, Vice Chairman of the Board
E-mail: rwyro@yahoo.com
Description: Promotes business and community development in Cranston, RI. Sponsors Adopt-A-School program. Holds business seminars. **Founded:** 1929. **Publications:** *Cranston Chamber News* (Monthly); *Who's Who in Greater Cranston*. **Educational Activities:** Business Expansion Network (Monthly). **Geographic Preference:** Local.

44474 ■ Greater Newport Chamber of Commerce (NCCC)
513 Broadway, Ste. 218
Newport, RI 02840
Ph: (401)847-1608
Co. E-mail: info@newportchamber.com
URL: http://www.newportchamber.com
Contact: Erin Donovan Boyle, President
Facebook: www.facebook.com/NewportChamberCC
Linkedin: www.linkedin.com/company/newport-county-chamber-of-commerce
X (Twitter): x.com/Newport_Chamber
Instagram: www.instagram.com/newport_chamber
Description: Promotes business and community development in Newport County, RI. **Founded:** 1927. **Geographic Preference:** Local.

44475 ■ Greater Providence Chamber of Commerce (GPCC)
30 Exchange Ter.
Providence, RI 02903
Ph: (401)521-5000
Fax: (401)621-6109
Co. E-mail: chamber@provchamber.com
URL: http://www.providencechamber.com
Contact: Laurie White, President
E-mail: lwhite@provchamber.com
Facebook: www.facebook.com/GreaterProvChamber
Linkedin: www.linkedin.com/company/greater-provi-dence-chamber-of-commerce
X (Twitter): x.com/provchamber
Instagram: www.instagram.com/provchamber
YouTube: www.youtube.com/channel/UCuTWF1dnheTJNa5FDuxQPsQ
Description: Strives to develop a positive and productive business climate for the community through economic development, political action and civic endeavor. Helps member to grow and prosper in Rhode Island. Promotes program of a civic, social and cultural nature. Provides leadership, ideas, energy and finances to help address major community challenges. **Founded:** 1868. **Geographic Preference:** State.

44476 ■ Narragansett Chamber of Commerce (NCC)
36 Ocean Rd.
Narragansett, RI 02882
Ph: (401)783-7121
URL: http://narragansettcoc.com
Contact: Peg Fradette, Executive Director
E-mail: pfradette@narragansettcoc.com
Description: Businesses. Promotes business and community development in Narragansett, RI. Sponsors annual Heritage Days, Festival of Lights, and parades. **Publications:** *Chamber News*. **Geographic Preference:** Local.

44477 ■ North Kingstown Chamber of Commerce (NKCC)
8045 Post Rd.
North Kingstown, RI 02852
Ph: (401)295-5566
Co. E-mail: info@northkingstown.com
URL: http://northkingstown.com
Contact: Kristin Urbach, Executive Director
E-mail: kurbach@northkingstown.com
Facebook: www.facebook.com/NKchamberRI
X (Twitter): x.com/NKchamberRI
Instagram: www.instagram.com/NKchamberRI
Description: Individuals, businesses, and manufacturers. Promotes business, tourism, and community development in North Kingstown, RI area. **Founded:** 1929. **Publications:** *Connections* (Monthly). **Geographic Preference:** Local.

44478 ■ Northern Rhode Island Chamber of Commerce (NRICC)
6 Blackstone Valley Pl., Ste. 402
Lincoln, RI 02865
Ph: (401)334-1000
Co. E-mail: general@nrichamber.com
URL: http://www.nrichamber.com
Contact: Liz Catucci, President
E-mail: lcatucci@nrichamber.com
X (Twitter): x.com/NRI_Chamber
Description: Strives to strengthen the economic climate of Northern Rhode Island, through business leadership that fosters member and community prosperity. **Founded:** 1991. **Publications:** *Business and Community Resource Guide* (Annual); *Business Pulse* (Monthly). **Educational Activities:** Golf Tournament (Annual); Table Top Expo. **Geographic Preference:** Local.

44479 ■ Ocean Community Chamber of Commerce
1 Chamber Way
Westerly, RI 02891
Ph: (401)596-7761
Fax: (401)596-2190
Co. E-mail: info@oceanchamber.org
URL: http://www.oceanchamber.org
Contact: Lisa Konicki, President
E-mail: lkonicki@oceanchamber.org
Facebook: www.facebook.com/OceanChamber
YouTube: www.youtube.com/channel/UCO65X-j46FzVeaYc3UtvK9g
Description: Business owners. Promotes business and community development in the greater Westerly, RI and Pawcatuck, CT areas. **Publications:** *Go Westerly*. **Awards:** Ocean Community Chamber of Commerce Community Service/Citizen of the Year Award (Annual). **Geographic Preference:** Local.

44480 ■ South Kingstown Chamber of Commerce (SKCC)
230 Old Tower Hill Rd.
Wakefield, RI 02879
Ph: (401)783-2801
Fax: (401)789-3120
Co. E-mail: info@srichamber.com
URL: http://web.srichamber.com/chamber/index.aspx
Description: Banks, small businesses, lawyers, doctors, utilities, and hospitals. Promotes business and community development in the South Kingstown, RI area. Co-sponsors community holiday decorations; conducts annual Business Expo. **Founded:** 1933. **Publications:** *Business Matters* (Semimonthly). **Geographic Preference:** Local.

MINORITY BUSINESS ASSISTANCE PROGRAMS

44481 ■ Rhode Island Black Business Association (RIBBA)
3 Regency Plz., Ste. 3 E
Providence, RI 02903
Ph: (401)383-1179
Fax: (401)383-5366
Co. E-mail: info@ri-bba.org
URL: http://ri-bba.org
Contact: Lisa Ranglin, President
X (Twitter): x.com/RIBBABIZ
Description: Seeks to enhance the growth and economic empowerment of Black-owned businesses, entrepreneurs, and professionals in the state of Rhode Island. **Founded:** 2011.

44482 ■ Rhode Island Minority Business Enterprise (RI MBE)
One Capitol Hill
Providence, RI 02908
URL: http://dedi.ri.gov
Description: Promotes the development of certified minority, women and disadvantaged businesses in Rhode Island. Offers advocacy, business assistance and certification.

FINANCING AND LOAN PROGRAMS

44483 ■ Providence Equity Partners L.L.C.
Providence Equity Partners L.L.C.
50 Kennedy Plz. 18th Fl.
Providence, RI 02903
Ph: (401)751-1700
Fax: (401)751-1790
Co. E-mail: info@provequity.com
URL: http://www.provequity.com
Contact: Benjamin Zampello, Director
Linkedin: www.linkedin.com/company/providence-equity-partners
YouTube: www.youtube.com/c/ProvidenceEquityPartners/about
Description: Provides investment service for media, communications, and education. **Founded:** 1989.

44484 ■ RevUp Capital
91 Clemence St.
Providence, RI 02903
URL: http://www.revupfund.com
Contact: Allan Tear, II, Contact
Linkedin: www.linkedin.com/company/revupcapital
Description: Invests in rapidly growing B2B and B2C companies. Works on a science-driven process to accelerate growth. Also operates OperationAthena, a program for women-led companies. **Founded:** 2016. **Preferred Investment Size:** $100,000-$250,000.

44485 ■ Slater Technology Fund
225 Dyer St.
Providence, RI 02903
Ph: (401)831-6633
URL: http://slaterfund.com
Contact: Thorne Sparkman, Managing Director
Linkedin: www.linkedin.com/company/slater-technology-fund
X (Twitter): x.com/slatertech_fund
Description: Evergreen not-for-profit seed fund for early-stage technology ventures. **Founded:** 1997. **Investment Policies:** Prefers transformative technologies to solve the world's biggest problems; companies committed to building and basing locally. **Industry Preferences:** Software; life science; energy.

PROCUREMENT ASSISTANCE PROGRAMS

44486 ■ Rhode Island Economic Development Corporation (RIPTAC) - Rhode Island Procurement Technical Assistance Center
315 Iron Horse Way, Ste. 101
Providence, RI 02908
Ph: (401)278-9100
Fax: (401)273-8270
Co. E-mail: ptac@riptac.org
URL: http://riptac.org
Contact: Melody Weeks, Program Manager
E-mail: melody.weeks@commerceri.com
Description: Provides specialized and professional assistance to individuals and businesses seeking to sell, or currently selling, their goods or services to the Department of Defense, other federal agencies, state, and local governments.

INCUBATORS/RESEARCH AND TECHNOLOGY PARKS

44487 ■ Hope & Main
691 Main St.
Warren, RI 02885
Ph: (401)245-7400
Co. E-mail: info@makefoodyourbusiness.org
URL: http://makefoodyourbusiness.org
Contact: Lisa Raiola, President
E-mail: lisa@makefoodyourbusiness.org
Facebook: www.facebook.com/HopeandMain
Linkedin: www.linkedin.com/company/hope-&-main
X (Twitter): x.com/HopeandMain
Instagram: www.instagram.com/hopemain
Description: Culinary business incubator. Helps local entrepreneurs jump-start early-stage food companies and food related businesses by providing low cost, low risk access to shared-use commercial kitchens and other industry-specific technical resources. **Founded:** 2014.

44488 ■ Urban Ventures
807 Broad St., Office 246
Providence, RI 02907
Contact: Solange Lopes, President
Description: A small business incubator that assists entrepreneurs in the business start-up process and gives aid to new businesses to help ensure their survival. Also know as the Rhode Island Urban Business Incubator. **Founded:** 1999.

EDUCATIONAL PROGRAMS

44489 ■ Johnson & Wales University (JWU)
8 Abbot Pk. Pl.
Providence, RI 02903
Free: 800-342-5598
Fax: (401)598-2948
Co. E-mail: onlineadmissions@jwu.edu
URL: http://www.jwu.edu
Contact: Mim L. Runey, Chancellor
Facebook: www.facebook.com/johnsonandwales
X (Twitter): x.com/johnsonandwales
Instagram: www.instagram.com/johnsonandwales
YouTube: www.youtube.com/user/JWUmedia
Description: Business college offering classes in small business management. **Founded:** 1914.

REFERENCE WORKS

44490 ■ *"Food Trucks Savor Rebirth in City" in Providence Business News (Vol. 27, April 16, 2012, No. 2, pp. 1)*
Description: Providence, Rhode Island has been experiencing the growth of the food truck business as the trucks and their devoted followers become regular fixtures in the city. Food trucks have a strong presence in the West Coast and have proliferated across the U.S. in recent years. Insights into Providence's food truck community are also given. **Availability:** Online.

PUBLICATIONS

44491 ■ *Providence Business News*
400 Westminster St., Ste. 600
Providence, RI 02903
Ph: (401)273-2201
Fax: (401)274-6580
Co. E-mail: production@pbn.com
URL: http://www.pbn.com
Contact: Donna Rofino, Manager
E-mail: rofino@pbn.com
URL(s): pbn.com
Released: Biweekly **Price:** $459, for all access one year; $145, for print + digital or digital only annual; $15, for print and online month; $15, for online month. **Description:** Publisher of weekly business newspaper. **Availability:** Print; Online.

44492 ■ Providence Business News Inc. (PBN)
400 Westminster St., Ste. 600
  Providence, RI 02903
Ph: (401)273-2201
Fax: (401)274-6580
Co. E-mail: production@pbn.com
URL: http://www.pbn.com
Contact: Donna Rofino, Manager
E-mail: rofino@pbn.com
Facebook: www.facebook.com/Providence BusinessNews
Linkedin: www.linkedin.com/company/providence-business-news
X (Twitter): x.com/ProvBusNews
Instagram: www.instagram.com/providencebusinessnews
YouTube: www.youtube.com/channel/UCaDfVbqO_3joLkzJ6Q-34Rg
Description: A weekly business newspaper focusing on the economy in Rhode Island and Bristol County, Massachusetts. **Founded:** 1986. **Publications:** *Providence Business News* (Biweekly).

EARLY STAGE FINANCING

44493 ■ Cherrystone Angel Group
50 S Main St. .No.301
  Providence, RI 02903
Ph: (401)519-4311
Co. E-mail: info@cherrystoneangelgroup.com
URL: http://www.cherrystoneangelgroup.com
Contact: Stephen Schweich, Chairman
Founded: 2004.

South Carolina

ASSOCIATIONS AND OTHER ORGANIZATIONS

44494 ■ Association of Fundraising Professionals South Carolina Lowcountry Chapter
PO Box 22094
Charleston, SC 29413
Co. E-mail: afplowcountry@gmail.com
URL: http://community.afpglobal.org/afpsclowcountrychapter/home
Contact: Sam Shirley, President
E-mail: samanthas@virtuous.org

Description: Fosters the development and growth of fundraising professionals. Promotes high ethical standards in the fundraising profession. Provides training opportunities for fundraising professionals. **Geographic Preference:** Local.

44495 ■ Business Network International, Columbia Area
Columbia, SC
URL: http://bniofmidlands.com/en-US/chapterlist?chapterName=&chapterCity=Columbia&chapterArea=&chapterMeetingDay=&chapterMeetingTime=&chapterMeetingType=&regionIds=14080

Description: Provides both men and women a structured environment for the development and exchange of quality business referrals. Offers members the opportunity to share ideas and contacts. **Geographic Preference:** Local.

44496 ■ Entrepreneurs' Organization - Charleston Chapter (EO)
3 Broad St., 4th Fl.
Charleston, SC 29401
Co. E-mail: info@eocharleston.org
URL: http://www.eonetwork.org/charleston

44497 ■ National Federation of Independent Business South Carolina
PO Box 8881
Columbia, SC 29202
Ph: (404)522-1290
URL: http://www.nfib.com/south-carolina

Description: Represents small and independent businesses. Aims to promote and protect the rights of members to own, operate and grow their businesses. **Geographic Preference:** State.

44498 ■ South Carolina Young Farmer and Agribusiness Association (SCYFAA)
c/o Jennifer Lyda
PO Box 1746
Clemson, SC 29633
Ph: (864)656-8668
Co. E-mail: jrlyda@clemson.edu
URL: http://www.clemson.edu/extension/scaged/SC-Farmer-Agribusiness-Association/membership-application.html
Contact: Jennifer Lyda, Administrative Assistant
E-mail: jrlyda@clemson.edu

Description: Young farmers in South Carolina over 16 years of age who are out of school and enrolled in an Adult Agricultural Education class. Aims to assist young farmers through educational programs to become satisfactorily established in farming or agribusiness occupations. **Founded:** 1947. **Publications:** South Carolina Young Farmer and Agribusiness Association (Bimonthly).

SMALL BUSINESS DEVELOPMENT CENTERS

44499 ■ Aiken Area Small Business Development Center [Aiken Area SBDC]
471 University Pky.
Aiken, SC 29801
Ph: (803)641-3646
Co. E-mail: sbdc@usca.edu
URL: http://www.scsbdc.com/locations
Contact: Brent Hoover, Consultant

Description: Represents and promotes the small business sector. Provides management assistance to current and prospective small business owners. Helps to improve management skills and expand the products and services of members. **Founded:** 1961. **Geographic Preference:** Local.

44500 ■ Beaufort Area Small Business Development Center [Beaufort Area SBDC]
USCB Historic Beaufort Campus
801 Carteret St.
Beaufort, SC 29902
Ph: (843)521-4143
Co. E-mail: goodman@uscb.edu
URL: http://www.scsbdc.com/locations
Contact: Martin Goodman, Manager
E-mail: goodman@uscb.edu

Description: Represents and promotes the small business sector. Provides management assistance to current and prospective small business owners. Helps to improve management skills and expand the products and services of members. **Geographic Preference:** Local.

44501 ■ Charleston Small Business Development Center
6296 Rivers Ave., Ste. 300
North Charleston, SC 29406
Ph: (843)740-6160
URL: http://charlestonsbdc.com
Contact: Paul Featheringill, Director

Description: Provides management assistance to current and prospective small business owners in Charleston. **Geographic Preference:** Local.

44502 ■ Clemson Area Small Business Development Center [Clemson Area SBDC]
Wilbur O. and Ann Powers College of Business
Clemson, SC 29634
Ph: (864)710-4717
Fax: (864)656-4770
Co. E-mail: ithelp@clemson.edu
URL: http://www.clemson.edu/centers-institutes/sbdc

Contact: Ben Smith, Manager
E-mail: bennys@clemson.edu

Description: Represents and promotes the small business sector. Provides management assistance to current and prospective small business owners. Helps to improve management skills and expand the products and services of members. **Geographic Preference:** Local.

44503 ■ Clemson Regional Small Business Development Center (SBDC)
225 S Pleasantburg Dr., Ste. C-12
Greenville, SC 29607
Ph: (864)370-1545
Co. E-mail: clemsonsbdc@clemson.edu
URL: http://www.clemson.edu/centers-institutes/sbdc
Contact: Ben Smith, Regional Director
URL(s): www.scsbdc.com/locations
Facebook: www.facebook.com/clemsonregionsbdc

Description: Mission is to advance South Carolina's economic development by helping entrepreneurs grow successful businesses. **Scope:** Conducts research, continuing education, and consulting for persons in small business, addressing basic needs of small business such as accounting and payroll procedures, inventory control, cost reduction, computer management, marketing, business start-ups, record keeping processes, and general management. **Founded:** 2006.

44504 ■ Clemson Small Business Development Center
413 Sirrine Hall
Clemson University
Clemson, SC 29634
Ph: (864)710-4717
Fax: (864)656-4770
URL: http://www.clemson.edu/centers-institutes/sbdc/contact.html
Contact: Ben Smith, Manager
E-mail: bennys@clemson.edu

Description: Offer a variety of services and management training courses tailored to meet the needs of small and medium sized businesses, including managerial and technical assistance to those wishing to start or expand and enterprise. **Geographic Preference:** Local.

44505 ■ Florence Area Small Business Development Center (SBDC)
2715 W Lucas St., Bldg. 110, Rm. 115
Florence, SC 29501-1242
Ph: (843)661-8256
URL: http://www.winthropregionalsbdc.org/florence-sc-sbdc
Contact: Charles Page, Manager
E-mail: charles.page@fdtc.edu
URL(s): www.scsbdc.com/locations

Description: Represents and promotes the small business sector. Provides management assistance to current and prospective small business owners. Helps to improve management skills and expand the products and services of members. **Geographic Preference:** Local.

44506 ■ Greenwood Area Small Business Development Center
c/o Ben Calhoun
430 Helix Rd.
Greenwood, SC 29646
Ph: (864)941-8092
Co. E-mail: bncalho@clemson.edu
URL: http://www.scsbdc.com/locations
Contact: Ben Calhoun, Manager
E-mail: bncalho@clemson.edu

Description: Provides management assistance to current and prospective small business owners in Greenwood. **Geographic Preference:** Local.

44507 ■ Hilton Head Area Small Business Development Center
USCB Hilton Head Campus
1 Sand Shark Dr., Rm. 238
Hilton Head Island, SC 29928
Ph: (843)208-8259
URL: http://www.scsbdc.com/locations
Contact: Pat Cameron, Manager
E-mail: pcameron@uscb.edu

Description: Represents and promotes the small business sector. Provides management assistance to current and prospective small business owners. Helps to improve management skills and expand the products and services of members. **Geographic Preference:** Local.

44508 ■ Myrtle Beach Area Small Business Development Center
PO Box 261954
Conway, SC 29528-6054
Ph: (843)349-4010
URL: http://www.coastal.edu/sbdc
Contact: Janet Graham, Manager
E-mail: jpgraham@coastal.edu

Description: Represents and promotes the small business sector. Provides management assistance to current and prospective small business owners. Helps to improve management skills and expand the products and services of members. **Geographic Preference:** Local.

44509 ■ Rock Hill Area Small Business Development Center
118 Thurmond Bldg.
Winthrop University
Rock Hill, SC 29733
Ph: (803)323-2283
URL: http://www.winthropregionalsbdc.org
Contact: Tom George, Regional Director
E-mail: georget@winthrop.edu
URL(s): www.scsbdc.com/locations

Description: Represents and promotes the small business sector. Provides management assistance to current and prospective small business owners. Helps to improve management skills and expand the products and services of members. **Geographic Preference:** Local.

44510 ■ South Carolina Small Business Development Centers (SC SBDC)
UofSC Moore School of Business
1014 Greene St.
Columbia, SC 29208
Ph: (803)777-0749
Co. E-mail: scsbdc@sc.edu
URL: http://www.scsbdc.com
Contact: Steve Bailey, Contact
E-mail: sbailey@merusinc.com
Facebook: www.facebook.com/SCSBDC
Linkedin: www.linkedin.com/company/sc-sbdc
X (Twitter): x.com/scsbdc

Description: Offers a variety of services and management training courses tailored to meet the needs of small and medium sized businesses, including managerial and technical assistance. **Founded:** 1979. **Geographic Preference:** Local.

44511 ■ South Carolina Small Business Development Centers Orangeburg Area (SC SBDC)
South Carolina State University
Algernon S Belcher Hall
300 College St. Campus
Orangeburg, SC 29117
Ph: (803)536-8445
Co. E-mail: scstatesbdc@scsu.edu
URL: http://www.scsbdc.com/locations#orangeburg
Facebook: www.facebook.com/OrangeburgSBDC

Description: Offers a variety of services and management training courses tailored to meet the needs of small and medium-sized businesses, including managerial and technical assistance. **Geographic Preference:** Local.

44512 ■ Spartanburg Small Business Development Center
Tyger River Campus
1875 E Main St., Ste. 4
Duncan, SC 29334
Ph: (864)592-6318
URL: http://www.scsbdc.com/locations
Contact: Katrina Meeks, Manager
E-mail: meeks5@clemson.edu

Description: Represents and promotes the small business sector. Provides management assistance to current and prospective small business owners. Helps to improve management skills and expand the products and services of members. **Geographic Preference:** Local.

44513 ■ Sumter Area SBDC
200 Miller Rd., Rm. 216
Sumter, SC 29150
Ph: (803)938-3833
Co. E-mail: fls@mailbox.sc.edu
URL: http://www.scsbdc.com/locations

Description: Provides management assistance to current and prospective small business owners in Sumter. **Geographic Preference:** Local.

44514 ■ University of South Carolina Small Business Development Center (SC SBDC)
1014 Greene St.
Columbia, SC 29208
Ph: (803)777-0749
Co. E-mail: scsbdc@sc.edu
URL: http://www.scsbdc.com
Contact: Jim Rohrer, Chairman
Facebook: www.facebook.com/scsbdc
X (Twitter): x.com/scsbdc

Description: Represents and promotes the small business sector. Provides management assistance to current and prospective small business owners. Helps to improve management skills and expand the products and services of members. **Founded:** 2006. **Geographic Preference:** Local.

SMALL BUSINESS ASSISTANCE PROGRAMS

44515 ■ South Carolina Department of Commerce
1201 Main St., Ste. 1600
Columbia, SC 29201-3200
Ph: (803)737-0400
Free: 800-868-7232
Co. E-mail: info@sccommerce.com
URL: http://sccommerce.com
Contact: Robert M. Hitt, III, Secretary
Facebook: www.facebook.com/sccommerce
Linkedin: www.linkedin.com/company/sccommerce
X (Twitter): x.com/SCCommerce
Instagram: www.instagram.com/sccommerce
YouTube: www.youtube.com/user/SCDofC

Description: Offers a range of innovative services to assist entrepreneurs and expanding industries. Services include: Buyer/Supplier Match; Financing Assistance; International Trade Opportunities; Research Park System; Location, Training, and Labor Assistance; Market Research; and Entrepreneurial Support Services. **Founded:** 1905. **Publications:** *International Companies in South Carolina* (Annual); *South Carolina Industrial Directory* (Annual). **Educational Activities:** Fall IAMC Professional Forum (Annual).

44516 ■ South Carolina Division of Small and Minority Business Contracting and Certification (SMBCC)
1205 Pendleton St., Ste. 372A
Columbia, SC 29201
Ph: (803)734-5010
Free: 855-723-7283
Fax: (803)734-4061
Co. E-mail: oig@oig.sc.gov
URL: http://smbcc.sc.gov
Contact: Johnny Burch, Contact
E-mail: johnny.burch@admin.sc.gov

Description: Provides advocacy and referral services, training and other educational activities for small and minority businesses. **Founded:** 1979.

44517 ■ South Carolina Jobs-Economic Development Authority
Capitol Ctr.
1201 Main St., Ste. 1600
Columbia, SC 29201
Ph: (803)737-0268
Fax: (803)737-0628
Co. E-mail: generalinfo@scjeda.com
URL: http://scjeda.com
Contact: Harry Huntley, Executive Director
E-mail: hhuntley@scjeda.com
Linkedin: www.linkedin.com/company/scjeda

Description: Raises capital and provides technical assistance to small businesses in creating jobs; sells general and industrial revenue bonds. **Founded:** 1983.

SCORE OFFICES

44518 ■ SCORE - Chapin
302 Columbia Ave.
Chapin, SC 29036
Ph: (803)345-1100
URL: http://midlands.score.org
Facebook: www.facebook.com/SCOREMidlandsSC
Linkedin: www.linkedin.com/company/score-mentors-midlands

Description: Provides professional guidance and information to maximize the success of existing and emerging small businesses. Offers business counseling and workshops.

44519 ■ SCORE - Charleston, South Carolina
4045 Bridge View Dr., B151
North Charleston, SC 29405
Ph: (843)727-4778
Co. E-mail: info.charlestonsc@scorevolunteer.org
URL: http://charlestonsc.score.org
Linkedin: www.linkedin.com/company/charleston-sc-score
Instagram: www.instagram.com/score_mentors
YouTube: www.youtube.com/user/SCORESmallBusiness
Pinterest: www.pinterest.com/scorementors

Description: Provides professional guidance and information to maximize the success of existing and emerging small businesses. Offers business counseling and workshops.

44520 ■ SCORE - Columbia, South Carolina
930 Richland St.
Columbia, SC 29201
Ph: (803)765-5131
URL: http://midlands.score.org
Facebook: www.facebook.com/SCOREMidlandsSC
Linkedin: www.linkedin.com/company/score-mentors-midlands

Description: Provides professional guidance and information to maximize the success of existing and emerging small businesses. Offers business counseling and workshops.

44521 ■ SCORE - Grand Strand
605 10th Ave. N
Myrtle Beach, SC 29577

Ph: (843)918-1079
Fax: (843)918-1080
Co. E-mail: admin.0381@scorevolunteer.org
URL: http://grandstrand.score.org
Contact: Chet Herman, Officer
Facebook: www.facebook.com/SCOREGrandStrand
Linkedin: www.linkedin.com/company/score-mentors
-grand-strand
X (Twitter): x.com/SCOREGrandStrnd

Description: Provides professional guidance and information to maximize the success of existing and emerging small businesses. Offers business counseling and workshops. **Founded:** 1984. **Geographic Preference:** Local.

44522 ■ SCORE - Greater Aiken
121 Richland Ave. E, Ste. A
Aiken, SC 29801
Ph: (803)641-1111
Fax: (803)641-4174
Co. E-mail: help@score.org
URL: http://greateraiken.score.org
Contact: John Gregg, Contact
Linkedin: www.linkedin.com/company/greater-aiken
-score
YouTube: www.youtube.com/channel/UC1cqxpULjt8
-hfOt_3P5xtw

Description: Provides professional guidance and information to maximize the success of existing and emerging small businesses. Offers business counseling and workshops.

44523 ■ SCORE - Hartsville
214 N Fifth St.
Hartsville, SC 29550
Ph: (843)332-6401
URL: http://midlands.score.org
Facebook: www.facebook.com/scoremidlands
Linkedin: www.linkedin.com/company/score-mentors
-midlands

Description: Provides professional guidance and information to maximize the success of existing and emerging small businesses. Offers business counseling and workshops.

44524 ■ SCORE - Lady's Island
135 Sea Island Pky.
Beaufort, SC 29907
Ph: (843)470-0800
URL: http://sclowcountry.score.org
Facebook: www.facebook.com/
SCORESCLowcountry
X (Twitter): x.com/SCORELowcountry

Description: Provides professional guidance and information to maximize the success of existing and emerging small businesses. Offers business counseling and workshops.

44525 ■ SCORE - Lexington, South Carolina
Lexington, SC 29072
Ph: (803)765-5131
URL: http://midlands.score.org
Facebook: www.facebook.com/SCOREMentors
Linkedin: www.linkedin.com/company/score-mentors
X (Twitter): x.com/SCOREMentors
Instagram: www.instagram.com/score_mentors
YouTube: www.youtube.com/user/
SCORESmallBusiness/featured
Pinterest: www.pinterest.com/scorementors

Description: Provides professional guidance and information to maximize the success of existing and emerging small businesses. Offers business counseling and workshops.

44526 ■ SCORE - Midlands
1225 Laurel St., Ste. 410
Columbia, SC 29201
Ph: (803)851-3100
Fax: (803)545-3826
Co. E-mail: help@score.org
URL: http://midlands.score.org
Linkedin: www.linkedin.com/company/score-mentors
-midlands

Description: Provides professional guidance and information to maximize the success of existing and emerging small businesses. Offers business counseling and workshops. **Founded:** 1970. **Geographic Preference:** Local.

44527 ■ SCORE - North Augusta
406 W Ave.
North Augusta, SC 29841
Ph: (803)641-1111
URL: http://greateraiken.score.org
URL(s): www.score.org/find-location
Facebook: www.facebook.com/SCOREGreaterAiken

Description: Provides professional guidance and information to maximize the success of existing and emerging small businesses. Offers business counseling and workshops.

44528 ■ SCORE - Orangeburg
1225 Laurel St., Ste. 410
Columbia, SC 29201
Ph: (803)851-3100
URL: http://midlands.score.org
Facebook: www.facebook.com/scoremidlands

Description: Provides professional guidance and information to maximize the success of existing and emerging small businesses. Offers business counseling and workshops.

44529 ■ SCORE - Piedmont
31 Boland Ct., Ste. 150
Greenville, SC 29615
Ph: (864)271-3638
Co. E-mail: info@piedmontscore.org
URL: http://piedmont.score.org
Contact: Terrence P. McKenney, President
Facebook: www.facebook.com/SCOREPiedmont
Linkedin: www.linkedin.com/company/score-mentors
-piedmont
X (Twitter): x.com/PiedmontSCORE
YouTube: www.youtube.com/channel/UCO3Q
248eO8FahEWPSqqBq8g
Pinterest: www.pinterest.com/piedmontscore

Description: Provides professional guidance and information to maximize the success of existing and emerging small businesses. Offers business counseling and workshops. **Geographic Preference:** Local.

44530 ■ SCORE - South Carolina Lowcountry
1 Chamber of Commerce Dr.
Hilton Head Island, SC 29938
Ph: (843)785-7107
Co. E-mail: sclowcountry@scorevolunteer.org
URL: http://www.score.org/sclowcountry
Contact: Denine M. Pezone, Contact
Facebook: www.facebook.com/
SCORESCLowcountry
Linkedin: www.linkedin.com/company/score-mentors
-sc-lowcountry
X (Twitter): x.com/SCORELowcountry
Instagram: www.instagram.com/scoresclowcountry
YouTube: www.youtube.com/channel/UC7Yt1qgAYI
dWCKCQ1q_Qq5w

Description: Provides professional guidance and information to maximize the success of existing and emerging small businesses. Offers business counseling and workshops. **Founded:** 1964. **Geographic Preference:** Local.

44531 ■ SCORE - Sumter
32 E Calhoun St.
Sumter, SC 29150
URL: http://midflorida.score.org

Description: Provides professional guidance and information to maximize the success of existing and emerging small businesses. Offers business counseling and workshops.

BETTER BUSINESS BUREAUS

44532 ■ Better Business Bureau of Coastal Carolina
1121 3rd Ave.
Conway, SC 29526
Ph: (843)488-2227
Fax: (843)488-0998
Co. E-mail: bbbinfo@coastalcarolina.bbb.org
URL: http://www.bbb.org/local-bbb/bbb-of-coastal
-carolina
Facebook: www.facebook.com/BBB.CoastalCarolina
X (Twitter): x.com/BBBCoastal
Instagram: www.instagram.com/bbb_coastalcarolina

Description: Seeks to promote and foster ethical relationship between businesses and the public through voluntary self-regulation, consumer and business education, and service excellence. Provides information to help consumers and businesses make informed purchasing decisions and avoid costly scams and frauds; settles consumer complaints through arbitration and other means. **Publications:** *BBB Broadcaster* (Monthly). **Geographic Preference:** Local.

44533 ■ Better Business Bureau Serving Central South Carolina and Charleston Area
2442 Devine St.
Columbia, SC 29205
Ph: (803)254-2525
Fax: (803)779-3117
Co. E-mail: info@columbia.bbb.org
URL: http://www.bbb.org/bbb-directory/us/sc
Contact: Chris Hadley, President
E-mail: chadley@columbia.bbb.org
X (Twitter): x.com/BBBColaChas

Description: Works to promote public confidence in business and stimulate fair competition between local businesses through effective self-regulation of local advertising and selling practices; conducts standardized evaluations of local charitable organizations; protects businesses, investors and consumers from fraudulent and unfair practices; provides programs for the resolution of disputes, including mediation and arbitration; promotes reliable and secure e-commerce through the BBB Online Reliability and Privacy Seal programs; and educates consumers and the business community. **Founded:** 1912. **Geographic Preference:** Local.

44534 ■ Better Business Bureau of Upstate South Carolina
408 N Church St., Ste. C
Greenville, SC 29601-2164
Ph: (864)242-5052
Fax: (864)271-9802
URL: http://www.bbb.org/local-bbb/bbb-of-upstate
-south-carolina
Contact: Vee Daniel, President
Facebook: www.facebook.com/bbbupstatesc
Linkedin: www.linkedin.com/organization-guest/company/bbbupstatesc
X (Twitter): x.com/bbbupstatesc
Instagram: www.instagram.com/bbbupstatesc
YouTube: www.youtube.com/channel/
UCpJ7NOTgrfGUbCVibj3eQKw

Description: Seeks to promote and foster the highest ethical relationship between businesses and the public through voluntary self-regulation, consumer and business education, and service excellence. **Founded:** 1982. **Publications:** *BBB Business and Consumer Brochures* (Periodic). **Awards:** BBB Upstate South Carolina Student of Integrity (Annual). **Geographic Preference:** Regional.

CHAMBERS OF COMMERCE

44535 ■ Anderson Area Chamber of Commerce
129 N Main St., Ste. 200
Anderson, SC 29621
Ph: (864)226-3454
Fax: (864)226-3300
Co. E-mail: jgagnon@andersonscchamber.com
URL: http://www.andersonscchamber.com
Contact: Pamela L. Christopher, President
E-mail: pchristopher@andersonscchamber.com
Facebook: www.facebook.com/An
dersonAreaChamber
X (Twitter): x.com/AndersonChamber
Instagram: www.instagram.com/an
dersonareachamber

Description: Promotes business and community development in the Anderson, SC area. **Founded:** 1903. **Publications:** *New Horizons*. **Geographic Preference:** Local.

44536 ■ Beaufort Regional Chamber of Commerce
1106 Carteret St.
 Beaufort, SC 29902
Ph: (843)525-8525
Co. E-mail: hello@beaufortchamber.org
URL: http://beaufortchamber.org
Contact: Ian Scott, President
E-mail: ian@beaufortchamber.org
Facebook: www.facebook.com/beaufortsc.chamber
X (Twitter): x.com/BeaufortRegCoC
YouTube: www.youtube.com/channel/UCnqlhs0uv-nt0mDsBDYB8NA/videos
Description: Advocates for and supports a positive business climate and leads the enhancement, expansion and diversification of the business community throughout Beaufort County, SC. **Founded:** 1892. **Publications:** *On The Move* (Monthly). **Geographic Preference:** Regional.

44537 ■ Carolinas Association of Chamber of Commerce Executives (CACCE)
1622 Tarklin Valley
 Knoxville, TN 37920
Ph: (404)312-0524
Co. E-mail: tfulmer@tlfexecutiveservices.com
URL: http://www.cacce.org
Contact: Pamela Christopher, President
Facebook: www.facebook.com/Carolinas-Association-of-Chamber-of-Commerce-Executives-CACCE-115043361908258
X (Twitter): x.com/CACCExecs
Description: Strives to advance comprehensive leadership and professional development for Chambers of Commerce through the efforts of the members of the association and their resources. **Founded:** 1994. **Geographic Preference:** Regional.

44538 ■ Charleston Metro Chamber of Commerce (CMCC)
4922 O'Hear Ave., Ste. 101
 North Charleston, SC 29405
Ph: (843)577-2510
Co. E-mail: mail@charlestonchamber.org
URL: http://www.charlestonchamber.org
Contact: Bryan Derreberry, President
E-mail: bderreberry@charlestonchamber.org
Facebook: www.facebook.com/ChasChamber
Linkedin: www.linkedin.com/company/charleston-metro-chamber-of-commerce
X (Twitter): x.com/ChasChamber
Description: Promotes business and community development in Charleston, SC. **Founded:** 1773. **Publications:** *Visitors Guide*; *Industrial & Technology-Based Firms Directory*; *Charleston Metro Chamber of Commerce--Major Employers Directory* (Annual); *Major Employers Directory* (Annual); *Manufacturers Directory* (Annual); *Membership Directory and Buyers Guide* (Annual). **Geographic Preference:** Regional.

44539 ■ Chester County Chamber of Commerce (CCCC)
109 Gadsden St.
 Chester, SC 29706
Ph: (803)581-4142
Co. E-mail: chestercountychamber@gmail.com
URL: http://www.chesterchamber.com
Contact: Lisa Burrel, Chairman
Facebook: www.facebook.com/Chester-County-Chamber-of-Commerce-178250019845
X (Twitter): x.com/co_chamber
Instagram: www.instagram.com/chestercountychamber
YouTube: www.youtube.com/channel/UC3UbiSADXUcugPBqdnzcl3A
Description: Promotes business and community development in Chester County, SC. **Founded:** 1790. **Publications:** *Chamber Connection* (Weekly). **Geographic Preference:** Local.

44540 ■ Clarendon County Chamber of Commerce (CCCC)
19 N Brooks St.
 Manning, SC 29102
Ph: (803)435-4405
Free: 800-731-LAKE
Co. E-mail: chamber@clarendoncounty.com
URL: http://www.clarendoncounty.com
Contact: Jason Montgomery, President
Facebook: www.facebook.com/ClarendonSCChamber
Instagram: www.instagram.com/clarendonscchamber
Description: Promotes business and community development in Clarendon County, SC. Supports United Way. Conducts litter control program. Sponsors April Striped Bass Festival and Murah Program Education. **Founded:** 1986. **Publications:** *County Business Directory* (Annual). **Geographic Preference:** Local.

44541 ■ Clemson Area Chamber of Commerce (CACC)
1105 Tiger Blvd.
 Clemson, SC 29631
Ph: (864)654-1200
Fax: (864)654-5096
Co. E-mail: info@clemsonareachamber.org
URL: http://www.clemsonareachamber.org
Contact: Merritt Rechichar, President
E-mail: merritt@clemsonareachamber.org
Facebook: www.facebook.com/clemsonareachamber
Linkedin: www.linkedin.com/company/clemsonareachamberofcommerce
Instagram: www.instagram.com/clemsonareachamber
Description: Promotes business and community development in the greater Clemson, SC area. Sponsors Clemson Bicycle Race. **Founded:** 1956. **Geographic Preference:** Local.

44542 ■ Conway Area Chamber of Commerce (CACC)
203 Main St.
 Conway, SC 29526-0831
Ph: (843)248-2273
Fax: (843)248-0003
Co. E-mail: info@conwayscchamber.com
URL: http://www.conwayscchamber.com
Contact: Jill Marshall, President
Facebook: www.facebook.com/conwaychamber
X (Twitter): x.com/conwaychamber
Description: Promotes business and community development in Conway, SC. **Founded:** 1732. **Publications:** *The Chamber Quill* (Quarterly). **Geographic Preference:** Local.

44543 ■ *Demographics*
550 S Main St., Ste. 550
 Greenville, SC 29601
Ph: (864)242-1050
Free: 866-485-5262
Co. E-mail: mcampbell@greenvillechamber.org
URL: http://www.greenvillechamber.org
Contact: Carlos Phillips, President
E-mail: cphillips@greenvillechamber.org
URL(s): www.greenvillechamber.org/greenville/data-demographics
Availability: Print.

44544 ■ Fairfield County Chamber of Commerce (FCCC)
100 Congress St.
 Winnsboro, SC 29180
Ph: (803)635-4242
Co. E-mail: fchamber02@truvista.net
URL: http://www.fairfieldchambersc.com
YouTube: www.youtube.com/channel/UCexKViEf2SJPMISO82_AWAQ
Description: Promotes business, community development and tourism in Fairfield County, SC. **Founded:** 1945. **Geographic Preference:** Local.

44545 ■ Georgetown County Chamber of Commerce (GCCC)
531 Front St.
 Georgetown, SC 29440
Ph: (843)546-8436
Co. E-mail: bstedman@visitgeorge.com
URL: http://www.visitgeorge.com
Contact: Beth Stedman, President
E-mail: bstedman@visitgeorge.com
Facebook: www.facebook.com/GeorgetownCountyChamber
Linkedin: www.linkedin.com/company/georgetown-county-chamber-of-commerce
X (Twitter): x.com/GeorgetownCCOC
YouTube: www.youtube.com/user/GtownCountyChamber
Description: Promotes business and community development in Georgetown County, SC. **Founded:** 1917. **Publications:** *Georgetown County Chamber of Commerce Quarterly* (Quarterly). **Geographic Preference:** Local.

44546 ■ *The Grand Strander*
1200 N Oak St.
 Myrtle Beach, SC 29577
Ph: (843)626-7444
Free: 800-356-3016
Fax: (843)448-3010
Co. E-mail: info@visitmyrtlebeach.com
URL: http://www.myrtlebeachareachamber.com
Contact: Karen Riordan, President
E-mail: karen.riordan@visitmyrtlebeach.com
URL(s): www.myrtlebeachareachamber.com/news/category/grand-strander
Availability: Print.

44547 ■ Greater Aiken Chamber of Commerce
121 Richland Ave., E
 Aiken, SC 29801
Ph: (803)641-1111
Co. E-mail: chamber@aikenchamber.net
URL: http://www.aikenchamber.net
Contact: J. David Jameson, President
E-mail: djameson@aikenchamber.net
Facebook: www.facebook.com/AikenChamber
Linkedin: www.linkedin.com/in/aiken-chamber-of-commerce-379b931b
Instagram: www.instagram.com/aiken.chamber
YouTube: www.youtube.com/user/AikenChamber
Description: Promotes business and community development in Aiken, SC. **Geographic Preference:** Local.

44548 ■ Greater Cayce West Columbia Chamber of Commerce
1006 12th St.
 Cayce, SC 29033
Ph: (803)794-6504
Co. E-mail: info@cwcchamber.com
URL: http://www.cwcchamber.com
Contact: Margaret Causey, Secretary
Facebook: www.facebook.com/cwcchamber
X (Twitter): x.com/CWCChamber
Instagram: www.instagram.com/caycewestcolumbiachamber
Pinterest: www.pinterest.com/meucci123/cayce-west-columbia-sc-outdoor-vacation-ideas
Description: Promotes business and community development in Cayce, Pine Ridge, South Congaree, Springdale, and West Columbia, SC. Sponsors fishing rodeo, Congaree Carnival river events, Christmas parade, and golf tournament. **Founded:** 1982. **Publications:** *Just One Minute* (Bimonthly). **Geographic Preference:** Local.

44549 ■ Greater Cheraw Chamber of Commerce (GCCC)
221 Market St.
 Cheraw, SC 29520
Ph: (843)537-7681
Fax: (843)537-5886
Co. E-mail: cherawchamber@cherawchamber.com
URL: http://www.cherawchamber.com
Contact: Rebecca Prevatte, Co-President
Description: Promotes business and community development in the Greater Cheraw, SC area. **Founded:** 1945. **Geographic Preference:** Local.

STATE LISTINGS

South Carolina ■ 44563

44550 ■ Greater Chesterfield Chamber of Commerce, Inc.
PO Box 708
Chesterfield, SC 29709
Ph: (843)623-2343
Co. E-mail: chesterfieldscchamber@gmail.com
URL: http://www.chesterfieldscchamberofcommerce.com
Contact: Betty Barrett, Member
Facebook: www.facebook.com/chesterfieldchamber
Description: Promotes business and community development in Chesterfield, SC. **Geographic Preference:** Local.

44551 ■ Greater Columbia Chamber of Commerce (GCCC)
1225 Lady St., No. 100
Columbia, SC 29201
Ph: (803)733-1110
Co. E-mail: info@columbiachamber.com
URL: http://www.columbiachamber.com
Contact: Carl Blackstone, President
E-mail: cblackstone@columbiachamber.com
Facebook: www.facebook.com/ColumbiaChamber
X (Twitter): x.com/colachamber
Instagram: www.instagram.com/columbiachamber
YouTube: www.youtube.com/user/TheColumbiaChamber
Description: Promotes convention business and tourism in Columbia, SC. **Founded:** 1902. **Publications:** *Major Employers Directory*; *Chamber E-Gram* (Weekly); *Focal Points* (Monthly). **Awards:** Greater Columbia Chamber of Commerce Ambassador of the Year (Annual). **Geographic Preference:** Local.

44552 ■ Greater Easley Chamber of Commerce (GECC)
2001 E Main St.
Easley, SC 29641
Ph: (864)859-2693
Fax: (864)859-1941
Co. E-mail: ecc@easleychamber.org
URL: http://easleychamber.net
Contact: Cindy B. Hopkins, President
E-mail: chopkins@easleychamber.org
Facebook: www.facebook.com/greatereasleychamber
YouTube: www.youtube.com/user/easleychamber
Description: Promotes business and community development in Easley, SC and the surrounding area. Maintains economic development and tourism center. **Founded:** 1935. **Publications:** *Foothills Focus* (Weekly). **Geographic Preference:** Local.

44553 ■ Greater Florence Chamber of Commerce
100 W Evans St.
Florence, SC 29501
Ph: (843)665-0515
Fax: (843)662-2010
Co. E-mail: info@flochamber.com
URL: http://www.flochamber.com
Contact: Michael Miller, President
E-mail: mmiller@flochamber.com
Facebook: www.facebook.com/florencechamber
X (Twitter): x.com/florencechamber
YouTube: www.youtube.com/user/FlorenceChamber
Description: Provides leadership to promote and enhance a favorable business climate and improve the quality of life in Florence and the Pee Dee Area. **Publications:** *Chamber Link* (Monthly). **Awards:** Greater Florence Chamber of Commerce Business Person of the Year (Annual); Greater Florence Chamber of Commerce Small Business Person of the Year (Annual). **Geographic Preference:** Local.

44554 ■ Greater Greenville Chamber of Commerce (GCC)
550 S Main St., Ste. 550
Greenville, SC 29601
Ph: (864)242-1050
Free: 866-485-5262
Co. E-mail: mcampbell@greenvillechamber.org
URL: http://www.greenvillechamber.org
Contact: Carlos Phillips, President
E-mail: cphillips@greenvillechamber.org
Facebook: www.facebook.com/GreenvilleSCChamber
Linkedin: www.linkedin.com/company/greenvillechamber
X (Twitter): x.com/gvillechamber
Instagram: www.instagram.com/greenvillechamber
YouTube: www.youtube.com/user/greenvillescchamber
Description: Promotes business and community development in the Greenville County, SC area. **Founded:** 1889. **Publications:** *Demographics*; *Employer's Desk Manual* (Biennial); *International Business Directory* (Annual); *Market Facts*; *Outlook* (Monthly); *Real Estate Report* (Semiannual); *Wage and Benefit Survey* (Annual). **Geographic Preference:** Local.

44555 ■ Greater Greer Chamber of Commerce
111 Trade St.
Greer, SC 29651
Ph: (864)877-3131
Fax: (864)877-0961
Co. E-mail: info@greerchamber.com
URL: http://www.greerchamber.com
Contact: David Merhib, President
E-mail: david@greerchamber.com
Facebook: www.facebook.com/GreerChamber
Linkedin: www.linkedin.com/company/greater-greer-chamber-of-commerce
X (Twitter): x.com/GreerChamber
Instagram: www.instagram.com/GreerChamber
YouTube: www.youtube.com/user/greerchamber
Description: Promotes business and community development in Greer, SC. **Founded:** 1937. **Publications:** *Chamber Times* (Quarterly). **Geographic Preference:** Local.

44556 ■ Greater Hartsville Chamber of Commerce
214 N 5th St.
Hartsville, SC 29550
Ph: (843)332-6401
Fax: (843)332-8017
Co. E-mail: admin@hartsvillechamber.org
URL: http://www.hartsvillechamber.org
Contact: Murphy Monk, President
E-mail: president@hartsvillechamber.org
Facebook: www.facebook.com/hartsvillechamber
Description: Provides business and community development in Hartsville, SC area. **Founded:** 1910. **Publications:** *Chamber Heart Beat* (Quarterly). **Geographic Preference:** Local.

44557 ■ Greater Lake City Chamber of Commerce
144 S Acline St.
Lake City, SC 29560
Ph: (843)374-8611
Fax: (843)374-7938
Co. E-mail: lccoc1@ftc-i.net
URL: http://www.lakecitysc.org
Contact: Timmy Lynch, President
Facebook: www.facebook.com/GLCChamber
Description: Promotes Lake City, South Carolina's business and community. **Founded:** 1913. **Geographic Preference:** Local.

44558 ■ Greater Mauldin Chamber of Commerce
101 E Butler Rd.
Mauldin, SC 29662
Ph: (864)297-1323
Fax: (864)297-5645
Co. E-mail: info@mauldinchamber.org
URL: http://www.mauldinchamber.org
Contact: Pat Pomeroy, President
E-mail: pat.pomeroy@mauldinchamber.org
Description: Works to provide an environment for business growth and development in the Mauldin area. **Founded:** 1982. **Geographic Preference:** Local.

44559 ■ Greater Pickens Chamber of Commerce (GPCC)
222 W Main St.
Pickens, SC 29671
Ph: (864)878-3258
Co. E-mail: greaterpickenschamber@gmail.com
URL: http://www.explorepickens.com
Contact: Debbie Gravely, President
Facebook: www.facebook.com/GREATERPICKENSCHAMBER
Description: Promotes business and community development in the greater Pickens, SC area. Sponsors Azalea Festival. **Publications:** *The Communicator* (Quarterly); *Pickens Directory* (Periodic). **Geographic Preference:** Local.

44560 ■ Greater Summerville/Dorchester County Chamber of Commerce
402 N Main St.
Summerville, SC 29483
Ph: (843)873-2931
Co. E-mail: membership@greatersummerville.org
URL: http://www.greatersummerville.org
Contact: Rita C. Berry, President
E-mail: rberry@greatersummerville.org
Facebook: www.facebook.com/summervillesc
Linkedin: www.linkedin.com/in/the-greater-summerville-dorchester-county-chamber-of-commerce
Instagram: www.instagram.com/summervillechamber
YouTube: www.youtube.com/user/summervillesc
Description: Promotes business and community development in the Summerville, SC area. Sponsors Tour de Bloom Bike Race. Holds periodic board meeting. **Founded:** 1911. **Geographic Preference:** Local.

44561 ■ Greater Sumter Chamber of Commerce
32 E Calhoun St.
Sumter, SC 29150
Ph: (803)775-1231
Fax: (803)775-0915
Co. E-mail: chamber@sumterchamber.com
URL: http://www.sumterchamber.com
Contact: Chris Hardy, President
E-mail: chris.hardy@sumterchamber.com
Facebook: www.facebook.com/SumterSCChamber
X (Twitter): x.com/SumterSCChamber
Instagram: www.instagram.com/SumterSCChamber
Description: Promotes business and community development in the greater Sumter, SC area. **Founded:** 1910. **Publications:** *The Connector* (Quarterly); *Who's Who in the Sumter Chamber* (Annual). **Awards:** Greater Sumter Chamber of Commerce Business Person of the Year (Annual); Greater Sumter Chamber of Commerce Military Citizen of the Year (Annual); Greater Sumter Chamber of Commerce Minority Business Person of the Year (Annual); Greater Sumter Chamber of Commerce Outstanding Achievement Award (Annual). **Geographic Preference:** Local.

44562 ■ Greenwood Area Chamber of Commerce
110 Phoenix St.
Greenwood, SC 29646
Ph: (864)223-8431
Co. E-mail: info@greenwoodscchamber.org
URL: http://www.greenwoodscchamber.org
Facebook: www.facebook.com/GreenwoodSCChamber
Linkedin: www.linkedin.com/groups/1294817/profile
X (Twitter): x.com/gwdchamber
Instagram: www.instagram.com/greenwoodscchamber
YouTube: www.youtube.com/channel/UCl5GuJvhnV4JxnK9VasOHPQ
Description: Promotes business and community development in Greenwood, SC. **Publications:** *Chamber News*. **Geographic Preference:** Local.

44563 ■ Hampton County Chamber of Commerce
200 Jackson Ave., E
Hampton, SC 29924
Ph: (803)914-2143
Co. E-mail: info@hamptoncountychamber.org
URL: http://hamptoncountychamber.org
Contact: Susanne Peeples, President

44564 ■ South Carolina

Description: Promotes business and commerce in Hampton County, SC. **Founded:** 1986. **Geographic Preference:** Local.

44564 ■ Hilton Head Island-Bluffton Chamber of Commerce
1 Chamber of Commerce Dr.
Hilton Head Island, SC 29928
Ph: (843)785-3673
Co. E-mail: info@hiltonheadisland.org
URL: http://www.hiltonheadchamber.org
Contact: Bill Miles, President
E-mail: bmiles@hiltonheadisland.org
Facebook: www.facebook.com/hhibchamber
Linkedin: www.linkedin.com/company/hilton-head-island-bluffton-chamber-of-commerce
X (Twitter): x.com/HHIBChamber
Instagram: www.instagram.com/hhibchamber
YouTube: www.youtube.com/user/hiltonheadislandvcb
Description: Advance the common interest of our membership, stimulate the expanding regional economy and enhance the quality of life for all. **Founded:** 1957. **Publications:** Hilton Head Island-Bluffton Chamber of Commerce--Membership Directory (Annual). **Geographic Preference:** Local.

44565 ■ Industrial Guide
Released: Annual **Availability:** Print.

44566 ■ Jasper County Chamber of Commerce (JCCC)
403 Russell St.
Ridgeland, SC 29936
Ph: (843)726-8126
Co. E-mail: jasperchamber@jaspersc.org
URL: http://jaspersc.org
Contact: Kendall Malphrus, Executive Director
E-mail: kendall@jaspersc.org
Facebook: www.facebook.com/Jasper-County-Chamber-of-Commerce-128437243879126
Instagram: www.instagram.com/jaspercountychamber
Description: Promotes business and community development in the area. Sponsors local festivals. **Founded:** 1961. **Geographic Preference:** Local.

44567 ■ Kershaw County Chamber of Commerce
80 Campus Dr.
Camden, SC 29020
Ph: (803)432-2525
Free: 800-968-4037
URL: http://www.kershawcountychamber.org
Contact: Amy Kinard, Executive Director
E-mail: director@kershawcountychamber.org
Facebook: www.facebook.com/kershawcountychamber
Linkedin: www.linkedin.com/company/kershaw-county-chamber-of-commerce
Instagram: www.instagram.com/kershawcountychamber
Description: Promotes business and community development in Kershaw County, SC. **Founded:** 1910. **Geographic Preference:** Local.

44568 ■ Lake Wylie Chamber of Commerce
264 Latitude Ln., Ste. 101
Lake Wylie, SC 29710
Ph: (803)831-2827
Co. E-mail: lakewyliechamber@yahoo.com
URL: http://lakewyliechambersc.com
Contact: Susan Bromfield, President
Facebook: www.facebook.com/lkwchamber
Linkedin: www.linkedin.com/company/lake-wylie-chamber-of-commerce
YouTube: www.youtube.com/channel/UCE-GkDarZFEKGTTiM3Ti3kg
Description: Promotes business and community development in Lake Wylie, SC area. **Founded:** 1979. **Geographic Preference:** Local.

44569 ■ Lancaster County Chamber of Commerce
453 Colonial Ave.
Lancaster, SC 29721
Ph: (803)283-4105
Co. E-mail: info@lancasterchambersc.com
URL: http://www.lancasterchambersc.org
Contact: John Mccain, President
E-mail: john@lancasterchambersc.com
Facebook: www.facebook.com/LancasterCountyChamberOfCommerce
Linkedin: www.linkedin.com/in/lancaster-county-chamber-of-commerce-181045183
Description: Promotes business and community development in the area. **Founded:** 1996. **Publications:** Lancaster Life (Monthly); The Bridge. **Geographic Preference:** Local.

44570 ■ Little River Chamber of Commerce (LRCC)
440 Hwy. 90 E, Ste. 1
Little River, SC 29566
Ph: (843)249-6604
Co. E-mail: info@littleriverchamber.org
URL: http://www.littleriverchamber.org
Contact: Jennifer Walters, President
E-mail: jennifer@littleriverchamber.org
Facebook: www.facebook.com/littleriverchamber
X (Twitter): x.com/littlerivercc
Instagram: www.instagram.com/littleriversc
YouTube: www.youtube.com/user/littleriverchamber
Pinterest: www.pinterest.com/littleriversc
Description: Promotes business and community development in Little River County. **Founded:** 2004. **Publications:** Making Waves (Quarterly). **Awards:** Little River Chamber of Commerce Citizen of the Year (Annual). **Geographic Preference:** Local.

44571 ■ Loris Chamber of Commerce
4242 Main St.
Loris, SC 29569
Ph: (843)756-6030
Co. E-mail: loriscoc@sccoast.net
URL: http://lorischamber.com
Contact: Samantha Norris, Executive Director
Description: Promotes conventions and tourism in Loris, SC area. **Geographic Preference:** Local.

44572 ■ Making Waves
440 Hwy. 90 E, Ste. 1
Little River, SC 29566
Ph: (843)249-6604
Co. E-mail: info@littleriverchamber.org
URL: http://www.littleriverchamber.org
Contact: Jennifer Walters, President
E-mail: jennifer@littleriverchamber.org
URL(s): www.littleriverchamber.org/chamber/newsletters
Released: Quarterly **Availability:** Print; PDF; Online.

44573 ■ McCormick County Chamber of Commerce
100 S Main St.
McCormick, SC 29835
Ph: (864)852-2835
Fax: (864)852-2837
Co. E-mail: info@mccormickscchamber.org
URL: http://mccormickscchamber.org
Contact: Shaaron Kohl, President
Facebook: www.facebook.com/mcscc
Linkedin: www.linkedin.com/company/mccormick-sc-chamber
Instagram: www.instagram.com/mccormickscchamber
Description: Promotes business and community development in McCormick, SC. Promotes tourism. **Founded:** 1988. **Geographic Preference:** Local.

44574 ■ Myrtle Beach Area Chamber of Commerce
1200 N Oak St.
Myrtle Beach, SC 29577
Ph: (843)626-7444
Free: 800-356-3016
Fax: (843)448-3010
Co. E-mail: info@visitmyrtlebeach.com
URL: http://www.myrtlebeachareachamber.com
Contact: Karen Riordan, President
E-mail: karen.riordan@visitmyrtlebeach.com
Facebook: www.facebook.com/MyrtleBeachAreaChamber
Linkedin: www.linkedin.com/company/mbacc

STATE LISTINGS

X (Twitter): x.com/MBAChamber
Instagram: www.instagram.com/mbachamber
YouTube: www.youtube.com/user/MyrtleBeachCOC
Description: Promotes business and community development in the Myrtle Beach, SC area. **Founded:** 1938. **Publications:** The Grand Strander; Progress Report (Annual); Sand and Surf Beach Safety. **Educational Activities:** Membership Programs and Services Committee. **Awards:** Ann DeBock Leadership Award (Annual); Myrtle Beach Area Chamber of Commerce Leadership Grand Strand Scholarship (Annual). **Geographic Preference:** Local.

44575 ■ North Augusta Chamber of Commerce
406 W Ave.
North Augusta, SC 29841
Ph: (803)279-2323
Co. E-mail: info@northaugustachamber.org
URL: http://www.northaugustachamber.org
Contact: Terra Carroll, President
E-mail: terra@northaugustachamber.org
Facebook: www.facebook.com/GNACOC
Linkedin: www.linkedin.com/company/north-augusta-chamber-of-commerce
X (Twitter): x.com/NAChamber
Instagram: www.instagram.com/nachamber
YouTube: www.youtube.com/channel/UCH5pH9YPYQg_DE53zOKSmFw
Description: Promotes business and community development in the greater North Augusta, SC area. **Founded:** 1951. **Publications:** Chamber Connection (Monthly); North Augusta Lifestyle Guide. **Geographic Preference:** Local.

44576 ■ North Myrtle Beach Chamber of Commerce Convention and Visitors Bureau (NMBCOC)
1521 Hwy. 17 S
North Myrtle Beach, SC 29582
Ph: (843)281-2662
Co. E-mail: info@northmyrtlebeachchamber.com
URL: http://www.explorenorthmyrtlebeach.com/chamber
Contact: Brandon Cox, Chairman
Facebook: www.facebook.com/ExploreNorthMyrtleBeach
X (Twitter): x.com/explorenorthmyr
Instagram: www.instagram.com/explorenorthmyrtlebeach
YouTube: www.youtube.com/channel/UC5jlmejczl9TQrk2Petu7-g
Pinterest: www.pinterest.com/northmyrbeach
Description: Promotes North Myrtle Beach area and its businesses by providing strong leadership and supports economic, tourism and community development. **Founded:** 1985. **Publications:** Chamber Connection. **Geographic Preference:** Local.

44577 ■ Oconee County Chamber of Commerce (OCCC)
2 Leas Courtyard Dr.
Seneca, SC 29672
Ph: (864)882-2097
Co. E-mail: director@oconeechambersc.com
URL: http://oconeechambersc.com
Contact: Darryl Broome, Chairman
E-mail: darrylbroome1977@gmail.com
Facebook: www.facebook.com/oconeechambersc
Description: Promotes business and community development in the greater Seneca, SC area. **Geographic Preference:** Local.

44578 ■ Onward Orangeburg
155 Riverside Dr., SW
Orangeburg, SC 29116-0328
Ph: (803)534-6821
Free: 800-545-6153
Fax: (803)531-9435
Co. E-mail: chamber@orangeburgsc.net
URL: http://www.orangeburgchamber.com
Contact: James McQuilla, President
E-mail: jmcquilla@orangeburgsc.net
URL(s): www.orangeburgchamber.com/news-events
Released: Monthly **Availability:** Print.

STATE LISTINGS

44579 ■ Orangeburg County Chamber of Commerce (OCCC)
155 Riverside Dr., SW
Orangeburg, SC 29116-0328
Ph: (803)534-6821
Free: 800-545-6153
Fax: (803)531-9435
Co. E-mail: chamber@orangeburgsc.net
URL: http://www.orangeburgchamber.com
Contact: James McQuilla, President
E-mail: jmcquilla@orangeburgsc.net
Facebook: www.facebook.com/OrangeburgChamber
Linkedin: www.linkedin.com/company/orangeburg-co-chamber-of-commerce
X (Twitter): x.com/OburgCoChamber
Description: Promotes business and community development in Orangeburg County, SC. Conducts local festivals; makes available scholarships. **Founded:** 1904. **Publications:** *Orangeburg County Chamber of Commerce--Membership Directory* (Semiannual); *Membership Guide* (Semiannual); *Onward Orangeburg* (Monthly); *Orangeburg County Visitors Information Guide.* **Geographic Preference:** Local.

44580 ■ Partnership for Tomorrow (PFT)
c/o Greer Development Corporation
111-B S Main St., Ste. B
Greer, SC 29650
Ph: (864)416-0125
URL: http://greerdevelopment.com/pft
Description: Business initiative focuses on improving community's economic well-being. **Founded:** 1998. **Geographic Preference:** Local.

44581 ■ *Progress Report*
1200 N Oak St.
Myrtle Beach, SC 29577
Ph: (843)626-7444
Free: 800-356-3016
Fax: (843)448-3010
Co. E-mail: info@visitmyrtlebeach.com
URL: http://www.myrtlebeachareachamber.com
Contact: Karen Riordan, President
E-mail: karen.riordan@visitmyrtlebeach.com
URL(s): www.myrtlebeachareachamber.com/annualreport
Released: Annual **Availability:** Online; PDF.

44582 ■ Simpsonville Area Chamber of Commerce
105 W Curtis St., Ste. A
Simpsonville, SC 29681
Ph: (864)963-3781
Fax: (864)228-0003
Co. E-mail: info@simpsonvillechamber.com
URL: http://www.simpsonvillechamber.com
Contact: Allison McGarity, President
E-mail: amcgarity@simpsonvillechamber.com
Facebook: www.facebook.com/simpsonvillechamber
Linkedin: www.linkedin.com/company/simpsonville-area-chamber-of-commerce
X (Twitter): x.com/SvilleChamberSC
Instagram: www.instagram.com/simpsonvillechamber
Pinterest: www.pinterest.com/simpsonvilleare
Description: Promotes business and community development in the Simpsonville, SC area. Provides volunteering opportunities for members. **Publications:** *ChamberChat Newsletters* (Bimonthly); *Industrial Guide* (Annual); *Industrial Guide* (Annual); *Simpsonville Membership Directory* (Annual); *Simpsonville Membership Directory* (Annual). **Geographic Preference:** Local.

44583 ■ South Carolina Chamber of Commerce (SCCC)
1301 Gervais St., Ste. 1100
Columbia, SC 29201
Ph: (803)799-4601
URL: http://www.scchamber.net
Contact: Bob Morgan, President
E-mail: bob.morgan@scchamber.net
X (Twitter): x.com/scchamber
YouTube: www.youtube.com/user/sccoc
Description: Promotes business and community development in South Carolina. **Founded:** 1984. **Publications:** *South Carolina Business Journal* (Bimonthly); *The Competitiveness Update*; *SC Business Journal* (Monthly); *SC Business Magazine*; *South Carolina Chamber of Commerce Business Directory & Resource Guide* (Annual); *South Carolina Chamber of Commerce Business Directory & Resource Guide.* **Educational Activities:** Summit (Annual). **Awards:** South Carolina Chamber of Commerce Small Business Person of the Year (Annual); South Carolina Chamber of Commerce HR Professional of the Year (Annual); South Carolina Chamber of Commerce Public Servant of the Year (Annual). **Geographic Preference:** State.

44584 ■ Tri-County Regional Chamber of Commerce
225 N Parler Ave.
Saint George, SC 29477
Ph: (843)563-8187
Fax: (843)563-9091
Co. E-mail: tricounty@tri-crcc.com
URL: http://www.tri-crcc.com
Contact: David Little, Jr., President
Facebook: www.facebook.com/TriCountyRCC
Linkedin: www.linkedin.com/company/tri-county-regional-chamber-of-commerce-st-george
Instagram: www.instagram.com/tricountyrcc
Description: Promotes business and community development in Berkeley, Dorchester, and Orangeburg counties. **Geographic Preference:** Local.

44585 ■ Union County Chamber of Commerce (UCCC)
135 W Main St.
Union, SC 29379
Ph: (864)427-9039
Fax: (864)427-9030
Co. E-mail: chamber@unionsc.com
URL: http://unionsc.chambermaster.com
Contact: Jami D. Trammell, Contact
E-mail: jtrammell@unionsc.com
Facebook: www.facebook.com/UnionCountyChamberofCommerce
X (Twitter): x.com/unionchamber_sc
Description: Promotes business and community development in Union County, SC as well as industrial and economic development. Develops grants and loan packages for economic development. Conducts preliminary engineering studies, site design, and environmental analysis on sites. **Founded:** 1966. **Awards:** Union County Chamber of Commerce Volunteer of the Year (Annual). **Geographic Preference:** Local.

44586 ■ Walterboro-Colleton Chamber of Commerce (WCCC)
209 E Washington St.
Walterboro, SC 29488
Ph: (843)549-9595
Fax: (843)549-5775
Co. E-mail: chamberadmin@lowcountry.com
URL: http://www.walterboro.org
Facebook: www.facebook.com/walterborocolletonchamber
Description: Citizens from all segments of the community, dedicated to promoting the business environment in Walterboro and Colleton Counties. **Founded:** 1951. **Publications:** *Chamber Chain* (Monthly); *Chamber Membership Directory.* **Geographic Preference:** Local.

44587 ■ Williamsburg HomeTown Chamber of Commerce
131 N Academy St.
Kingstree, SC 29556
Ph: (843)355-6431
Fax: (843)355-3343
Co. E-mail: whtc@williamsburgsc.org
URL: http://www.williamsburgsc.org
Facebook: www.facebook.com/williamsburghometown.chamber
Description: Promotes business development and community involvement in Williamsbury County, SC. **Founded:** 1945. **Geographic Preference:** Local.

44588 ■ York County Regional Chamber of Commerce (YCRC)
116 E Main St.
Rock Hill, SC 29730
Ph: (803)324-7500
Co. E-mail: info@yorkcountychamber.com
URL: http://www.yorkcountychamber.com
Contact: Dean Faile, President
E-mail: dean.faile@yorkcountychamber.com
Facebook: www.facebook.com/yorkcochamber
X (Twitter): x.com/ycrchamber
Description: Promotes business and community development in the Rock Hill, Fort Mill and Tega Cay, SC areas. **Publications:** *York County Regional Chamber of Commerce--Business Directory* (Annual); *Industrial Directory*; *Business Resource Guide* (Annual). **Awards:** York County Regional Chamber of Commerce Business Person of the Year (Annual); York County Regional Chamber of Commerce Small Business of the Year (Annual). **Geographic Preference:** Local.

MINORITY BUSINESS ASSISTANCE PROGRAMS

44589 ■ Greenville Chamber of Commerce - Minority Business Accelerator (MBA)
550 S Main St., Ste. 550
Greenville, SC 29601
URL: http://www.greenvillechamber.org/mba
Contact: James Bennett, Coach
Description: Prepares minority-owned firms for growth and expansion through business development services, mentoring, technical assistance, and access to large companies for partnership opportunities.

FINANCING AND LOAN PROGRAMS

44590 ■ Charleston Angel Partners (CA)
75 Port City Landing, Ste. 110
Mount Pleasant, SC 29464
URL: http://www.chapsc.com
Contact: Will Cruz, Executive Director
Linkedin: www.linkedin.com/company/charleston-angel-partners
Description: Angel investment group for early-stage companies in the Southeast offering innovative solutions to large market problems. **Founded:** 2004. **Industry Preferences:** Medical devices; technology.

44591 ■ Fuse Capital
PO Box 22501
Hilton Head, SC 29925
Ph: (650)325-9600
URL: http://fusecapital.com
Description: Venture capital firm. **Industry Preferences:** Digital media and communications.

44592 ■ SC Launch, Inc.
1000 Catawba St.
Columbia, SC 29201
URL: http://scra.org
Contact: Andrea Marshall, Chairman of the Board
Description: Offers loan and investments to South Carolina-based companies. **Founded:** 2006.

44593 ■ Upstate Carolina Angel Network (UCAN)
225 S Pleasantburg Dr., Ste. C-15
Greenville, SC 29607
Contact: Matt Dunbar, Contact
Description: Investor group for early-stage, high-growth businesses in the Southeast. **Founded:** 2008.

44594 ■ VentureSouth
319 Garlington Rd., Ste. A2
Greenville, SC 29615
Co. E-mail: charlie@venturesouth.vc
URL: http://www.venturesouth.vc
Contact: Alex Biermann, Principal
Facebook: www.facebook.com/VentureSouthVC
Linkedin: www.linkedin.com/company/venturesouth-vc
X (Twitter): x.com/VentureSouth_VC

Description: Early-stage venture capital firm. Develops and manages angel groups and funds across the Southeast United States. **Founded:** 2014.

PROCUREMENT ASSISTANCE PROGRAMS

44595 ■ Clemson Small Business Development Center
413 Sirrine Hall
  Clemson University
  Clemson, SC 29634
Ph: (864)710-4717
Fax: (864)656-4770
URL: http://www.clemson.edu/centers-institutes/sbdc/contact.html
Contact: Ben Smith, Manager
E-mail: bennys@clemson.edu
Description: Offer a variety of services and management training courses tailored to meet the needs of small and medium sized businesses, including managerial and technical assistance to those wishing to start or expand and enterprise. **Geographic Preference:** Local.

44596 ■ South Carolina Procurement Technical Assistance Center - The Frank L. Roddey Small Business Development Center - University of South Carolina - Moore School of Business
1014 Greene St.
  Columbia, SC 29208
URL: http://www.scsbdc.com/government
Description: Established to aid small business start-up ventures and to assist in the continued growth of small businesses across the country. The program is supported with federal, state and private funds and is open to any present or prospective small business owner generally fee free.

44597 ■ South Carolina Small Business Development Centers (SC SBDC)
UofSC Moore School of Business
  1014 Greene St.
  Columbia, SC 29208
Ph: (803)777-0749
Co. E-mail: scsbdc@sc.edu
URL: http://www.scsbdc.com
Contact: Steve Bailey, Contact
E-mail: sbailey@merusinc.com
Facebook: www.facebook.com/SCSBDC
Linkedin: www.linkedin.com/company/sc-sbdc
X (Twitter): x.com/scsbdc
Description: Offers a variety of services and management training courses tailored to meet the needs of small and medium sized businesses, including managerial and technical assistance. **Founded:** 1979. **Geographic Preference:** Local.

44598 ■ South Carolina Small Business Development Centers Orangeburg Area (SC SBDC)
South Carolina State University
  Algernon S Belcher Hall
  300 College St. Campus
  Orangeburg, SC 29117
Ph: (803)536-8445
Co. E-mail: scstatesbdc@scsu.edu
URL: http://www.scsbdc.com/locations#orangeburg
Facebook: www.facebook.com/OrangeburgSBDC
Description: Offers a variety of services and management training courses tailored to meet the needs of small and medium-sized businesses, including managerial and technical assistance. **Geographic Preference:** Local.

INCUBATORS/RESEARCH AND TECHNOLOGY PARKS

44599 ■ Charles W. Gould Business Incubator (GBI)
1951 Pisgah Rd.
  Florence, SC 29501
Ph: (843)413-2755
URL: http://gouldincubator.sc.gov
Facebook: www.facebook.com/GouldIncubator
X (Twitter): x.com/GouldIncubator
Instagram: www.instagram.com/gouldincubator
Description: Business incubator that offers a clean and modern environment for office-based and manufacturing ventures with affordable work spaces, free phone and internet service and the most modern shared support amenities. **Founded:** 2012.

44600 ■ Columbia Technology Incubator
1225 Laurel St.
  Columbia, SC 29201
Ph: (803)545-4423
URL: http://www.usccolainc.org
Contact: Chad Hardaway, Executive Director
Facebook: www.facebook.com/usccolainc
Linkedin: www.linkedin.com/company/usccolainc
X (Twitter): x.com/usccola_inc
Instagram: www.instagram.com/usccola_inc
Description: Provides opportunities for entrepreneurs to commercialize their ideas. Produces successful, financially viable and freestanding businesses all while creating hundreds of additional jobs in the community. **Founded:** 1999.

44601 ■ DER Kitchen
2501 Main St.
  Columbia, SC 29201
Ph: (803)779-3003
Co. E-mail: info@derkitchen.com
URL: http://www.derkitchen.com
Contact: Dave Roberts, Contact
Facebook: www.facebook.com/DERKitchen
Description: Kitchen incubator providing bakers, food truck operators and caterers a pay-by-the-hour base of operations without the need to build and equip a commercial kitchen.

44602 ■ Don Ryan Center for Innovation (DRCI)
7 Venture Dr., No. 100
  Bluffton, SC 29910
Ph: (843)540-0405
Co. E-mail: donryaninfo@townofbluffton.com
URL: http://www.donryancenter.com
Contact: Matt Green, Vice Chairman of the Board
Facebook: www.facebook.com/DonRyanCenter
Linkedin: www.linkedin.com/company/donryancenter
Description: Supports new innovative/technology company formation and development in Bluffton, SC. The program blends the attributes of hands-on consulting support, resource identification and availability, and long distance learning to help increase the probability entrepreneurs, who we call innovators, will be successful. **Founded:** 2012.

44603 ■ Florence Area Small Business Development Center (SBDC)
2715 W Lucas St., Bldg. 110, Rm. 115
  Florence, SC 29501-1242
Ph: (843)661-8256
URL: http://www.winthropregionalsbdc.org/florence-sc-sbdc
Contact: Charles Page, Manager
E-mail: charles.page@fdtc.edu
URL(s): www.scsbdc.com/locations
Description: Represents and promotes the small business sector. Provides management assistance to current and prospective small business owners. Helps to improve management skills and expand the products and services of members. **Geographic Preference:** Local.

44604 ■ GreenHouse
160 E St. John St., Ste. 374
  Spartanburg, SC 29306
Ph: (864)503-7623
URL: http://ww.uscupstate.edu/academics/george-dean-johnson-jr.-college-of-business-and-economics/greenhouse-business-incubator
Contact: Brian Brady, Director
E-mail: bbrady3@uscupstate.edu
Description: Nurtures startups in their early stages as they grow and thrive. Helps to build leadership capabilities and provide functional area support and directed peer interaction as they build their business.

44605 ■ Greenville Chamber of Commerce - Minority Business Accelerator (MBA)
550 S Main St., Ste. 550
  Greenville, SC 29601
URL: http://www.greenvillechamber.org/mba
Contact: James Bennett, Coach
Description: Prepares minority-owned firms for growth and expansion through business development services, mentoring, technical assistance, and access to large companies for partnership opportunities.

44606 ■ The Harbor Entrepreneur Center
2070 Sam Rittenberg Blvd., B 272
  Charleston, SC 29407
Ph: (843)972-4070
Co. E-mail: harborec@gmail.com
URL: http://harborec.com
Contact: Grady Johnson, Executive Director
E-mail: grady@harborec.com
Facebook: www.facebook.com/theharborec
Linkedin: www.linkedin.com/company/the-harbor-accelerator
X (Twitter): x.com/harborec
Instagram: www.instagram.com/theharborec
Description: Accelerator supports the growth of scalable businesses in the Charleston region. Creates collision in the community to grow the economy. Also offers shared workspace and a coding school. **Investment Policies:** Looks for innovation, scalability, and the ability to execute. **Industry Preferences:** Digital; advanced security; aerospace; healthcare; food/tourism.

44607 ■ Imagine Kitchen
420P The Pky.
  Greer, SC 29650
Ph: (864)663-2466
Co. E-mail: jh@imaginekitchen.com
URL: http://www.imaginekitchen.com
Contact: Jef Heuerman, Owner Founder
Facebook: www.facebook.com/imaginekitchen
Linkedin: www.linkedin.com/company/imagine-kitchen-llc
Description: Culinary incubator providing a professional kitchen facility and services for chefs and food artisans who need a great space to start and grow their food businesses. food prep space, cooking equipment, cooking tools, food storage, and meeting space. **Founded:** 2015.

44608 ■ Midlands Technical College Business Accelerator
PO Box 2408
  Columbia, SC 29202
URL: http://www.midlandstech.edu/about/enterprise-campus
Description: Accommodates emerging businesses to ramp up for the next phase of production and delivery. **Founded:** 1974.

44609 ■ SCBIO
1140 Woodruff Rd., Ste. 106
  Greenville, SC 29607
Ph: (864)397-5101
Co. E-mail: info@scbio.org
URL: http://www.scbio.org
Contact: James Chappell, President
Facebook: www.facebook.com/SCarBIO
X (Twitter): x.com/SCBiotech
YouTube: www.youtube.com/channel/UCeCUjLnLUidcSWeuwR5Lt3w
Description: Supports South Carolina's business environment for start-up and existing life science companies by advocating for public policy enhancements and infrastructure expansions that support the growth of the industry. Helps startups through collaboration, access to capital, workforce development, business opportunities and support. **Founded:** 2004.

44610 ■ Spartanburg Community College - The Center for Business & Entrepreneurial Development
1875 E Main St. (Hwy. 290)
  Duncan, SC 29334
Ph: (864)592-4600
Free: 800-922-3679
Co. E-mail: infoscc@sccsc.edu

URL: http://www.sccsc.edu/Center

Description: Helps entrepreneurs and businesses launch, build, expand, and reorganize. One of the business offerings is space...which allows for flexibility in design to suit the needs of the individual client. In exchange for services provided, business clients consent to locate their permanent facility. **Founded:** 2006.

EDUCATIONAL PROGRAMS

44611 ■ Florence-Darlington Technical College (FDTC)
2715 W Lucas St.
 Florence, SC 29502-0548
Ph: (843)661-8324
Free: 800-228-5745
Fax: (843)661-8208
Co. E-mail: admissions@fdtc.edu
URL: http://www.fdtc.edu
Contact: Dr. Jermaine Ford, President
Facebook: www.facebook.com/FlorenceDarlingtonTechnicalCollege
X (Twitter): x.com/flodar_tech

Description: Two-year college offering a small business management program. **Founded:** 1964.

44612 ■ Greenville Technical College - Northwest Campus (GTC)
738 S Pleasantburg Dr.
 Greenville, SC 29607
Ph: (864)250-3650
URL: http://www.gvltec.edu/about_greenvilletech/campus_locations/northwest_campus/index.html

Description: Offers a variety of business-oriented courses, seminars, workshops, and weekend courses for credit or noncredit status. Some courses offer continuing education units. Special emphasis is placed on small business start up, management, and computer and employee training.

44613 ■ Piedmont Technical College Continuing Ed
620 N Emerald Rd.
 Greenwood, SC 29648
Ph: (864)941-8400
URL: http://www.ptc.edu/continuing-ed
Contact: Carroll Sams, Director, Development
E-mail: sams.c@ptc.edu

Description: Offer program/classes in small business/small business management. **Founded:** 1966.

CONSULTANTS

44614 ■ TransDomo LLC
460 King St., Ste. 200
 Charleston, SC 29403
Ph: (864)908-0690
Co. E-mail: info@transdomo.com
URL: http://transdomo.com
Facebook: www.facebook.com/TransDomo

Description: Offers transcontinental market entry and start-up services, new business development and marketing, real estate consulting and scouting services in the US and German-speaking countries. **Founded:** 2005.

PUBLICATIONS

44615 ■ *Charleston Regional Business Journal*
7025 Albert Pick Rd.
 Greensboro, NC 27409
Ph: (612)317-9420
Free: 877-615-9536
Co. E-mail: customerservice@bridgetowermedia.com
URL: http://www.bridgetowermedia.com
Contact: Adam Reinebach, President
URL(s): charlestonbusiness.com
X (Twitter): twitter.com/CRBJ

Released: Biweekly **Price:** $295, for print and online; $67, for one year; $97, for 2 years; $57, for online; $97, for 2 year online. **Description:** Local business journal. **Availability:** Print; Online.

44616 ■ *Columbia Regional Business Report*
7025 Albert Pick Rd.
 Greensboro, NC 27409
Ph: (612)317-9420
Free: 877-615-9536
Co. E-mail: customerservice@bridgetowermedia.com
URL: http://www.bridgetowermedia.com
Contact: Adam Reinebach, President
URL(s): columbiabusinessreport.com
Facebook: www.facebook.com/ColumbiaBusinessReport
Linkedin: www.linkedin.com/company/columbia-regional-business-report
X (Twitter): x.com/CRBR

Released: Daily **Price:** $295, for annual subscription + premium access; $57, for online access 1 year; $97, for online access 2 year. **Description:** Business publication serving senior-level decision-makers in Columbia, South Carolina. **Availability:** Print; Online.

44617 ■ *Greenville Business Magazine (GBM)*
303 Haywood Rd.
 Greenville, SC 29607
Ph: (864)271-1105
URL: http://www.integratedmediapublishing.com
Contact: Jordan R. Finn, Contact
URL(s): www.greenvillebusinessmag.com
Facebook: www.facebook.com/GreenvilleBusinessMagazine

Ed: John McCurry. **Released:** Monthly **Price:** $35, For print 1 years subscription.; $60, for print 2 years subscription.; $75, For print 3 years subscription.; $4.95, Single issue. **Description:** Magazine featuring Greenville businesses and communities. **Availability:** Print; Online.

44618 ■ *GSA Business*
35 Cessna Ct., Ste. A
 Greenville, SC 29607
Ph: (864)235-5677
URL: http://gsabusiness.com
Contact: Kim McManus, Manager
E-mail: kmcmanus@scbiznews.com
URL(s): gsabusiness.com
Facebook: www.facebook.com/GSABusiness
Linkedin: www.linkedin.com/company/gsabusinessreport
X (Twitter): x.com/gsabusiness

Ed: Matt Clark, Chuck Crumbo, Andy Owens. **Released:** Daily **Price:** $295, for print and digital business lists 1 year; $57, for 1 year digital; $97, Two years for digital. **Description:** Local business newspaper. **Availability:** Print; Online.

44619 ■ *GSA Business Report*
7025 Albert Pick Rd.
 Greensboro, NC 27409
Ph: (612)317-9420
Free: 877-615-9536
Co. E-mail: customerservice@bridgetowermedia.com
URL: http://www.bridgetowermedia.com
Contact: Adam Reinebach, President
URL(s): gsabusiness.com
Facebook: www.facebook.com/GSABusiness
Linkedin: www.linkedin.com/company/gsabusinessreport
X (Twitter): x.com/gsabusiness

Released: Annual **Price:** $67, for print and online 1 year; $97, for print and online 2 year; $57, for online only 1 year; $97, for online only 2 year; $295, for leads & data per year. **Description:** Provides business news and information pertaining to upstate South Carolina, encompassing the cities of Greenville, Spartanburg, and Anderson and the 10 surrounding counties. **Availability:** Print; Online.

EARLY STAGE FINANCING

44620 ■ Coast Capital Partners
1567 Meeting St., Rd., No. 130
 Charleston, SC 29405
Ph: (843)790-5544
Co. E-mail: info@coast-capital.com
URL: http://www.coast-capital.com
Contact: Nicolas Boccabella, Co-Founder Partner

Description: Alternative investment and asset management firm. Specialized in private real estate financing solutions in the Southeast. Generates attractive risk-adjusted returns while providing funding alternatives for sponsors and developers. Looks for less accessible underserved markets. **Founded:** 2016.

www.ingramcontent.com/pod-product-compliance
Lightning Source LLC
Jackson TN
JSHW060748100425
82367JS00003B/58